Chemistry of
Organic Compounds

CARL R. NOLLER

Professor of Chemistry, Stanford University

SECOND EDITION

W. B. SAUNDERS COMPANY

Philadelphia   *London*

PREFACE TO THE SECOND EDITION

The six years that have passed since the publication in 1951 of the first edition of *Chemistry of Organic Compounds* have witnessed remarkable advances in all aspects of organic chemistry. In this second edition much old material has been revised and new material added. Conformation, transannular reactions, inclusion compounds, telomerization, oxidation mechanisms, ansa compounds and cyclophanes, ferrocene, tropolones, ylides, sigma complexes, insulin and oxytocin, tetracyclines, reserpine, aldosterone, lanosterol, natural acetylenic compounds, polyisoprene and urethan rubbers, epoxy and polyester resins, and syntheses from acrolein are only a few of the new topics and compounds presented. To keep the size of the book in reasonable bounds, no detailed discussions of the chemistry of biological processes have been included, despite the tremendous amount of pure organic chemical work that has been done in following, by means of isotopic tracers, the course of biosynthesis and metabolism of organic compounds.

The rapid application of infrared and nuclear magnetic resonance absorption spectra to the determination of structure has made it desirable to acquaint the beginning student with the basic principles involved. This material has been combined with that on absorption in the ultraviolet and visible regions in a new chapter dealing with the absorption of electromagnetic radiation in general.

Now that the mechanism of organic reactions has become a part of almost every elementary course in organic chemistry, deferring its discussion until after that of alkyl halides no longer seems desirable. Hence the material previously included in a separate chapter on mechanism now is distributed through the earlier chapters. Omission of any reference to the phenomenon of hyperconjugation is intentional. The author is of the opinion that this concept has been used promiscuously and that it is unnecessary for most qualitative treatments of mechanism. An introduction to cyclic hydrocarbons has been advanced to Chapter 3 to permit a better understanding of the products of petroleum.

In response to numerous requests from instructors, a greater number and wider variety of problems are provided. They have been separated from the review questions to facilitate assignment. In certain problems the sections labeled *A*, *B*, *C*, or *D* cover the same principles or types of reactions but differ in specific examples. Thus an instructor may assign problems to several classes without repeating. Parts labeled (*a*), (*b*), (*c*), and so on, illustrate different principles or reactions.

It has been a source of satisfaction that so many instructors and students have been sufficiently interested in the first edition of this textbook to take the time to report errors and to make suggestions for improvement. Their help is gratefully acknowledged. It is hoped that this revision will justify their efforts and that readers will continue to show their interest by reporting errors and expressing their views.

CARL R. NOLLER

Stanford University

PREFACE TO THE FIRST EDITION

Since 1860 the integrating theory behind the enormous mass of data that has been accumulated concerning organic compounds has been the theory of gross structure, that is, the theory correlating the reactions and physical properties of organic molecules with the kind of atoms present and with the order in which the atoms are bonded to each other in the molecule. This theory has been exceptionally fruitful and has led to the determination of the constitution of very complicated molecules and to the synthesis in the laboratory of hundreds of thousands of new compounds, many of which have important practical uses. It is these aspects of organic chemistry that are emphasized in this text.

Nevertheless the development of the theory of the electronic structure of atoms and molecules by mathematicians, physicists, and physical chemists has provided a more detailed picture of the nature of the forces holding atoms together, with the result that now it often is possible to give a reasonably consistent interpretation of the behavior of organic molecules. Consequently organic chemists are concerning themselves more and more with how organic reactions take place, that is, with the mechanism of the reactions. The introduction of this material into basic organic textbooks, however, has been very slow. The essential facts regarding the mechanism of the addition of hydrogen cyanide to aldehydes, for example, were reported by Lapworth in 1903, and the manner in which many other organic reactions take place is known now with reasonable certainty. Yet most texts still pay little attention to current views on mechanism.

As to bonding and electronic structure, textbooks now usually go beyond the ideas introduced by G. N. Lewis in 1916, to the extent that resonance is mentioned, but the discussion of resonance is based on the valence-bond treatment developed by Heitler and London, Pauling, and others since 1927. This approach does not provide the nonmathematical mind with a physical picture of the phenomenon and frequently leads to a misconception of the nature of resonance. In contrast, the molecular orbital treatment developed since 1928 by Hund, Mulliken, Coulson, and others is particularly helpful for interpreting the source of bond energies, the nature of multiple bonds, and resonance. Once a physical picture has been obtained, Pauling's convenient symbolism for resonance may be used with understanding. Hence the present trend among organic chemists is to combine the molecular orbital picture of bonding and resonance with the valence-bond symbolism.

It is appropriate that current ideas concerning the mechanism of organic reactions and the forces which determine the chemical and physical properties of organic compounds be incorporated in an elementary textbook. Too often the student's criticism that the elementary course in organic chemistry merely is memory work is justified. Although "memory is necessary for all the operations

v

of reason," it also is true that theories which correlate facts are an aid to memory. Moreover it is desirable that students majoring in chemistry and allied sciences become acquainted with the current ideas and language of chemistry. Therefore in this text considerable emphasis is placed on the explanation of physical properties and on the mechanism of organic reactions. Where such material is given, an effort has been made to keep the discussion as simple as possible even at the risk of being quantitatively inaccurate, for "except ye utter by the tongue words easy to be understood, how shall it be known what is spoken?"

In the earlier chapters the student is introduced to the subject matter gradually. No compound is used in the methods of preparation or in the reactions unless its structure has been discussed previously. For example, when alkanes and alkenes first are considered, no methods of synthesis are given. Instead, discussion of these procedures is delayed until the student is familiar with the methods of preparation and with the reactions of alcohols and alkyl halides. Reactions which are pedagogically bad, such as the halogenation of saturated hydrocarbons, are not presented until the student is able to see them in their proper perspective. Brief descriptions of experiments are given to make the reactions seem more real to the student who has not progressed very far in laboratory work. In equations illustrating the factual part of the text, the full formula for the usual reagent is given: for example $NaOH$ or $Ca(OH)_2$ and not OH^-; HCl or H_2SO_4 and not H^+ or H_3O^+; $Na_2Cr_2O_7$ or $KMnO_4$ and not $Cr_2O_7^=$ or MnO_4^-. In this way the practical aspects of the subject are kept separate from the theoretical aspects, and the student who thinks in terms of the materials with which he works rather than in terms of more abstract ideas is not handicapped.

The uses of organic compounds are of great importance. It is a source of pride to most organic chemists that the results of their investigations have led to practical applications and that the organic chemical industry is important to the economic life and well-being of the individual and his nation. Moreover most of the students majoring in chemistry are preparing themselves for industrial positions. Hence the practical applications and economic aspects of organic chemistry frequently are discussed in some detail.

For some years textbooks have been published which present aliphatic and aromatic compounds simultaneously. There is some advantage in discussing as a single unit all compounds having like functional groups. However, this treatment requires consideration of the effect of the rest of the molecule on the properties of the functional group and overloads the new student of organic chemistry with more detail than he can assimilate readily. It is the author's opinion that it is better first to cover all of the monofunctional aliphatic compounds, next to consider both monofunctional and polyfunctional aromatic compounds, and finally to return to polyfunctional aliphatic compounds. In the last portion, aromatic compounds may be included wherever desired, because the student is familiar with their behavior. This progression also permits the requirements of different students to be met by the same course. Those students who do not need a full year course can stop at the end of a term and still have a good introduction to organic chemistry.

This book is designed for those who desire a text that is comprehensive at the basic level, thus providing the better student with ample opportunity to acquire as much knowledge as he is able to assimilate. It is realized that if too much material is presented and if everything is given equal emphasis, the average student may be overwhelmed. Hence only the physical properties, methods of preparation, nomenclature, chemical reactions, and uses of organic compounds are printed in the standard-sized type. Portions which deal with mechanism or which are considered to be of a supplementary nature are printed in smaller type. Since instructors will not be able to hold their students responsible for everything presented in the text, the material has been arranged and cross-indexed in such a way that sections or whole chapters may be omitted, or the sequence of chapters may be altered considerably without impairing the readability of the text. For those teachers who wish to use a text containing an amount of material that can be covered in ninety to one hundred lectures, attention is called to the author's *Textbook of Organic Chemistry.*

Several time-honored reactions have been omitted because they were considered not sufficiently general in their application, or not important enough to be included. The author hopes that he has been able also to correct a few misconceptions that have been handed down over the years, although he is certain that he himself has committed many to print of which he is not aware. Furthermore it is likely that in his efforts to generalize or to explain reactions, he has made statements contrary to fact. Readers are urged to bring these errors to his attention and to submit other suggestions or comments for improving the text.

Many persons have contributed directly or indirectly to the preparation of this text, and the author gratefully acknowledges their assistance. He is indebted especially to Richard H. Eastman and Charles D. Hurd, who have read the entire manuscript; to Arthur L. Fox, Bernard S. Greensfelder, George W. Hearne, J. Murray Luck, Harry S. Mosher, Richard A. Ogg, W. A. Peterson, William T. Simpson, and William E. Vaughn, who have read one or more chapters; to Mildred J. Hall, who typed the manuscript; to Anadel Smith Brown, who prepared the illustrations; and to Edna Rasmussen Noller, his wife, who has helped in the preparation of the manuscript and in the reading of proof.

CARL R. NOLLER

Stanford University

CONTENTS

PREFACE TO THE SECOND EDITION.............................. iii

PREFACE TO THE FIRST EDITION.............................. v

1. INTRODUCTION 1

2. ALKANES.. 28

3. ALKENES. CYCLIC HYDROCARBONS............................. 49

4. NATURAL GAS, PETROLEUM, AND DERIVED PRODUCTS............ 69

5. ALCOHOLS. ESTERS OF INORGANIC ACIDS...................... 84

6. ALKYL HALIDES. GRIGNARD REAGENTS......................... 113

7. SYNTHESIS OF ALKANES AND ALKENES. ALKYNES (ACETYLENES)...... 126

8. ETHERS 136

9. CARBOXYLIC ACIDS AND THEIR DERIVATIVES. ORTHO ESTERS........ 143

10. WAXES, FATS, AND OILS...................................... 178

11. ALDEHYDES AND KETONES..................................... 194

12. ALIPHATIC NITROGEN COMPOUNDS............................. 228

13. ALIPHATIC SULFUR COMPOUNDS............................... 272

14. PROTEINS, AMINO ACIDS, AND PEPTIDES....................... 293

15. DERIVATIVES OF CARBONIC ACID AND THIOCARBONIC ACID......... 308

16. STEREOISOMERISM 329

17. CARBOHYDRATES 359

18. BENZENE AND ITS HOMOLOGS. SOURCES OF AROMATIC COMPOUNDS.. 416

19. HALOGEN DERIVATIVES OF AROMATIC HYDROCARBONS............. 432

20. AROMATIC NITRO COMPOUNDS. MECHANISM OF AROMATIC
    SUBSTITUTION.. 439

21. AROMATIC SULFONIC ACIDS AND THEIR DERIVATIVES.............. 466

22. AROMATIC AMINES.. 475

23. DIAZONIUM SALTS AND DIAZO COMPOUNDS...................... 492

24. PHENOLS, AMINOPHENOLS, AND QUINONES...................... 502

25. AROMATIC ALCOHOLS, ARALKYLAMINES, ALDEHYDES AND KETONES.
    STEREOCHEMISTRY OF THE OXIMES........................... 525

26. AROMATIC CARBOXYLIC ACIDS AND DERIVATIVES................. 547

27. ARYLALKANES. FREE GROUPS. ARYLALKENES AND ARYLALKYNES.
    BIPHENYL AND ITS DERIVATIVES............................ 565

28. CONDENSED NUCLEAR HYDROCARBONS AND THEIR DERIVATIVES.... 582

29. HETEROCYCLIC COMPOUNDS. ALKALOIDS........................ 606

30. VIBRATIONAL AND ELECTRONIC ABSORPTION SPECTRA. NUCLEAR-
    AND ELECTRON-SPIN RESONANCE............................. 657

31. COLOR. DYES AND DYEING. ORGANIC PIGMENTS................. 670

32. DIENES. RUBBER AND SYNTHETIC RUBBERS..................... 706

33. CHLORINATED AND FLUORINATED ALIPHATIC HYDROCARBONS...... 722

34. UNSATURATED ALCOHOLS, POLYHYDRIC ALCOHOLS, AND THEIR
    DERIVATIVES. AMINO ALCOHOLS AND POLYAMINES............. 736

35. HYDROXY, UNSATURATED, HALOGENATED, AND AMINO CARBONYL
    COMPOUNDS. DICARBONYL COMPOUNDS........................ 759

36. HALOGENATED, HYDROXY, AMINO, AND UNSATURATED ACIDS...... 778

37. POLYCARBOXYLIC ACIDS..................................... 791

38. KETO ACIDS.. 812

39. ALICYCLIC COMPOUNDS. TERPENES AND STEROIDS............... 828

40. ORGANIC PEROXIDES. AUTOXIDATION AND ANTIOXIDANTS.......... 873

41. ORGANOMETALLIC COMPOUNDS................................. 889

42. PHOSPHORUS AND SILICON COMPOUNDS........................ 907

INDEX 917

Chapter 1

INTRODUCTION

Most students beginning the study of organic chemistry already have some idea of the material with which it deals, because courses in general chemistry usually include a brief introduction to the subject. Not everyone, however, may be aware of the extent to which organic chemistry touches on everyday life. Man's chief requirements are food, fuel, and clothing. Food consists mainly of organic compounds, namely the fats, proteins, and carbohydrates. The digestion and assimilation of food takes place by organic chemical reactions, and the proper functioning of the animal organism requires other organic compounds such as the vitamins and hormones. Fuel is chiefly coal, wood, natural gas, and petroleum. Clothing is made from cotton, wool, silk, and synthetic fibers. Organic chemistry is concerned with all of these substances.

The study of the chemical behavior of these products of biological origin has enabled the organic chemist to convert them by chemical reactions into a host of other accessory substances. Soaps, perfumes, flavors, dyestuffs, protective coatings for wood and metal, plastics, photographic films and developers, explosives, synthetic rubber, artificial leather, synthetic fibers, and many medicinals, disinfectants, and insecticides add to man's comfort and pleasure. Hence it readily can be understood that the investigation of the chemistry of organic compounds has not merely extended chemical knowledge. It has influenced profoundly the health of man, his daily life, and the development of civilization. The study of organic chemistry may be considered to be a part of cultural training, as well as necessary background for certain scientific professions.

Beginnings of Organic Chemistry

Organic chemistry, as a separate branch of science, dates from the early part of the nineteenth century. Many compounds now referred to as organic must have existed on earth before life began, but only in very recent times has much progress been made in their study. The investigation of organic compounds lagged considerably behind that of inorganic compounds, because the naturally occurring organic compounds were more complex, their reactions were more difficult to understand, and they usually occurred as mixtures that were more difficult to separate than the mixtures of inorganic compounds.

Specific properties of a few organic compounds were known to the ancients. Noah was familiar with the effect of fermented grape juice on the human system. Acetic acid in the form of sour wine was well known; one of the proverbs of Solomon refers to the action of vinegar on chalk. Acetic acid was, in fact, the only acid known to the ancients. Indigo and alizarin have been identified as dyestuffs used on Egyptian mummy cloth, and royal purple was extracted from a Mediterranean mollusk by the Phoenicians.

The assignment of specific properties to individual compounds required the development of methods for isolating the compounds in a pure state. The process of distillation first was described in detail by the Alexandrians in the beginning of the fifth century A.D., and was developed and used by their successors, the Arabians, during the eighth century to concentrate acetic acid and alcohol. However it remained for Lowitz[1] to prepare acetic acid sufficiently pure to obtain it in crystalline form in 1789, and to obtain alcohol free of water in 1796. Cane sugar had been obtained in crystalline form in northeastern India about 300 A.D., but it did not become known until about 640 to the Arabians, who introduced the growing of cane into Egypt and southern Europe. Tartar from wine was known at an early date, and the older alchemists experimented with it. Benzoic acid and succinic acid were prepared in the sixteenth century, and methyl alcohol, grape sugar, and milk sugar were isolated during the seventeenth century. Persistent **attempts to isolate pure organic compounds** came only with the rise of chemistry during the latter half of the eighteenth century. Scheele[2] was the first to isolate uric, oxalic, tartaric, lactic, citric, and malic acids, acetaldehyde, and glycerol. As late as the beginning of the nineteenth century, however, the view was held that acetic acid was the only vegetable acid, and that all others consisted of some combined form of acetic acid.

Along with the work on isolation, some **chemical transformations** were discovered. It was known as early as the thirteenth century that sulfuric acid reacts with ethyl alcohol, and later a mixture of ether and alcohol prepared by this reaction was used in medicine. It was not until 1730 that the properties of a relatively pure ether, incompletely miscible with water, were described, and not until 1800 that the absence of sulfur was proved, thus showing that the sulfuric acid was not incorporated into the ether molecule. Acetone was prepared by the thermal decomposition of lead acetate, and ethyl chloride was prepared from ethyl alcohol and hydrochloric acid during the seventeenth century. Ethyl acetate, formate, oxalate, and benzoate were prepared during the latter half of the eighteenth century. Scheele obtained oxalic acid by the oxidation of cane sugar, and mucic acid by the oxidation of milk sugar.

Much less was known about **compounds present in animal organisms.** At the end of the eighteenth century, the only accomplishments of importance were the isolation of urea from urine in 1773, and of uric acid from urinary calculi in 1776. It generally was assumed that there was a fundamental difference between animal and vegetable matter since distillation of the former always yielded ammonia.

Of greatest importance for the advance of organic chemistry was the **development of methods for qualitative and quantitative analysis.** Lavoisier,[3] who was

---

[1] Johann Tobias Lowitz (1757–1804), German-born Court Apothecary at St. Petersburg, who made several outstanding contributions to basic laboratory technique. He discovered the absorptive property of activated charcoal and used it in the purification of organic compounds. He also discovered the phenomenon of supersaturation, used ice and various salts to make freezing mixtures, and was the first to use calcium chloride to remove water from organic liquids.

[2] Carl Wilhelm Scheele (1742–1786), Swedish apothecary. Besides being the first to isolate and prepare many organic compounds, he was the first to prepare molybdic, tungstic, and arsenic acids, to show that graphite is a form of carbon, to characterize manganese and barium, and to note the insolubility of barium sulfate. He also discovered oxygen (independently and prior to Priestley) and chlorine.

[3] Antoine Lavoisier (1743–1794), French scientist and public servant, who was condemned to death by a judge of the Revolutionary Tribunal with the remark, "The Republic has no need for savants."

one of the earliest investigators to analyze organic compounds, showed that they contain carbon and hydrogen and usually oxygen. He showed also that products derived from animal sources frequently contained nitrogen. Berzelius,[4] Liebig,[5] and Dumas[6] made further improvements in organic analysis particularly from the quantitative standpoint.

Originally no distinction was made between the chemistry of mineral compounds and the chemistry of those of biological origin. However, after a representative group of compounds had been isolated from natural sources, the differences became so apparent that a division soon was made. Bergman[7] in 1780 was the first to differentiate between organic compounds and nonorganic compounds. Berzelius first used the term *organic chemistry* in 1808 and published the first independent treatment of organic chemistry in his textbook of 1827.

The slowness in the advance of organic chemistry before the nineteenth century has been ascribed to the belief that compounds produced by living organisms could not be synthesized without the intervention of a *vital force*. The rapid advance during the nineteenth century has been attributed to the renunciation of this theory after Woehler[8] reported in 1828 the synthesis of urea from ammonium cyanate. Actually this event had little immediate effect in combating the vitalistic theory, which persisted in one form or another for at least another twenty years.

During this period, arguments for and against the vitalistic theory continued but did not deter chemists from trying to synthesize organic compounds. Their work, however, was leading them into chaos because of the confusion that existed concerning **atomic and molecular weights.** Although Avogadro's law provided the basis for atomic and molecular weight determinations in 1811, order did not begin to appear until after Cannizzaro[9] clearly showed in 1858

---

[4] Joens Jacob Berzelius (1779–1848), Swedish chemist, known chiefly for his accurate work on the combining weights of the elements and for his support of the dualistic theory, which held that elements were either electrically positive or negative in character and that only elements oppositely charged were capable of combining with each other.

[5] Justus Liebig (1803–1873), German professor who first introduced laboratory work into general instruction in chemistry. He perfected the combustion method of organic analysis, established the theory of radicals, laid the foundations of agricultural chemistry, and was the forceful editor who built up the prestige of the *Annalen der Chemie und Pharmacie*. The present title, *Justus Liebig's Annalen der Chemie*, was given to this publication after his death.

[6] Jean Baptiste André Dumas (1800–1884), French chemist, teacher, and public servant. He was noted for the accuracy of his experimental work and for his clear thinking. His name is associated chiefly with his analytical methods and with the phenomenon of substitution in organic compounds.

[7] Torbern Olof Bergman (1735–1784), professor of mathematics and later of chemistry at the University of Upsala, Sweden.

[8] Friedrich Woehler (1800–1882), professor at the University of Goettingen and friend of Berzelius and Liebig. Besides his work in organic chemistry, he discovered aluminum when he was only 27 years old and did important work on boron, aluminum, and titanium.

[9] Stanislao Cannizzaro (1826–1910), Sicilian revolutionist and politician, professor of chemistry at the Universities of Genoa, Palermo, and Rome. His *Summary of a Course of Chemical Philosophy*, which he wrote for his students, was published in 1858. An international congress of the most eminent chemists was called by Wurtz and Kekulé and presided over by Weltzien, Kopp, and Dumas at Karlsruhe in 1860 to try to bring order out of the confusion of atomic weights and chemical notation. At the close of the congress, which had failed to reach agreement, Cannizzaro's pamphlet was distributed to those present by his friend, Pavesi. Lothar Meyer was convinced by the exposition, and, largely through his influence, Cannizzaro's views soon were accepted.

how the application of the hypothesis would resolve many of the difficulties. At about the same time, the **theories of valence and structure** expounded by Kekulé[10] and others paved the way for the extremely rapid advances of the next fifty years.

During the first half of the nineteenth century, it gradually was realized that *the essential difference between inorganic and organic compounds is that the latter always contain carbon.* Gmelin[11] was the first to state this fact in 1848. At the present time, the number of carbon compounds synthesized in the laboratory far exceeds number isolated from organic products, and the phrase *chemistry of the compounds of carbon* would be more accurate than organic chemistry. The latter term, however, is less cumbersome and is used almost universally. The study of the chemical reactions taking place in living organisms now is termed *biochemistry*.

Differences Between Inorganic and Organic Compounds

Actually there are more cogent reasons for considering the chemistry of carbon compounds as a separate branch of chemistry than their derivation from organic sources or the presence of carbon. First the physical properties of nonsalts, which include most organic compounds, differ sharply from the physical properties of salts, the most numerous class of inorganic compounds (Table 1). Then the reactions of most salts in solution are almost instantaneous

TABLE 1

USUAL PHYSICAL PROPERTIES OF SALTS AND NONSALTS

SALTS	NONSALTS
High melting point (above 700°)	Low melting point (under 300°)
Nonvolatile	Distill readily
Insoluble in nonaqueous liquids	Soluble in nonaqueous liquids
Soluble in water	Insoluble in water
Conduct electric current in molten state and in solution	Solutions and melts are nonconducting

whereas those of nonsalts usually are slow. Also the number of known compounds that contain carbon is about ten times the number that do not contain carbon. Finally the concept of structure or the way in which the atoms are bound together is essential for an understanding of organic chemistry.

---

[10] Friedrich August Kekulé (1829–1896), professor at the Universities of Ghent and Bonn. He extended the type theory and laid the foundations of structural theory in organic chemistry. It seems significant that before becoming interested in chemistry, he was a student of architecture.

[11] Leopold Gmelin (1788–1853), professor of medicine and chemistry at the University of Heidelberg, originator of *Gmelin's Handbuch der Chemie*, now in its eighth edition, and member of a family noted for the large number and long line of prominent chemists it contained, beginning with Johann Georg Gmelin, born in 1674.

Bond Types. The explanation for these differences can be found in the different types of bonds in the two groups of compounds,[12] and a brief review of the qualitative aspects of the electron theory of bond formation may be of value. Since organic chemistry is concerned chiefly with the elements in the first three periods of the periodic table, the discussion is limited to these elements. According to the electronic theory, atoms consist of positive nuclei surrounded by a number of negative electrons equal to the positive charge on the nucleus (the *atomic number*). These electrons group themselves in a first shell with a maximum of two electrons (K shell), a second shell with a maximum of eight electrons (L shell), and a third shell with a maximum of eighteen electrons (M shell).

A somewhat more detailed picture represents the electrons as distributed in a definite way in orbitals and groups of orbitals. Strictly speaking, an **orbital** is the mathematical expression describing the behavior of an electron moving in the vicinity of a positively charged nucleus. For a qualitative pictorial discussion of bonding, it is sufficient to think of orbitals as *preexisting regions in space about atomic nuclei in which electrons, if present, are most likely to be found;* that is, the system electron-nuclei will be most stable when the electrons are in these regions (cf. p. 9). The groups of orbitals are known as **shells,** and within a shell there are **subshells.** The K shell consists of a single orbital, the $1s$ orbital. The L shell consists of four orbitals: a subshell known as the $2s$ orbital, and a subshell of three orbitals known as the $2p_x$, $2p_y$, and $2p_z$ orbitals. The numerals 1, 2, 3, 4, 5, 6, and 7, called the *principal quantum numbers*, designate the shell or principal energy levels of the electrons just as do the letters $K, L, M, N, O, P,$ and Q. They indicate more, however, in that the number of subshells in a shell is equal to the principal quantum number, and the total number of orbitals in a shell is equal to the square of the principal quantum number. Thus the M shell with the principal quantum number 3 contains three subshells and nine orbitals—one $3s$, three $3p$, and five $3d$ orbitals. The N shell contains four subshells and sixteen orbitals—one $4s$, three $4p$, five $4d$, and seven $4f$ orbitals.

Because of the attraction of the positive charge on the nucleus, electrons occupy an orbital as close to the nucleus as possible. Hence there is a greater tendency to occupy a $1s$ orbital than a $2s$ orbital, and a $2s$ orbital than a $2p$ orbital. However, no more than two electrons can occupy a given orbital, and even this condition is possible only if the electrons have opposite spin, that is, if they are affected in opposite ways by a magnetic field. If more than one electron is available for a given set of p orbitals which are equidistant from the nucleus, the electrons usually do not pair but occupy separate orbitals until each of the three p orbitals has at least one electron. Hence the pairing of electrons does not contribute to the stability of the atom but merely is permissive if the electrons have opposite spins. This behavior may be summarized by two important rules for the distribution of electrons in orbitals: (*1*) no orbital can contain more than two electrons and these electrons must have opposite spin (Pauli exclusion principle); (*2*) two electrons usually do not occupy a given orbital in a subshell until all of the orbitals of the subshell have at least one electron (Hund rule).

The distribution of the electrons for the elements in the first three periods is given in Table 2. In accordance with the Hund rule, the carbon atom has two unpaired electrons in two p orbitals, and nitrogen has three unpaired electrons in the three p orbitals. Pairing of electrons in the p orbitals does not begin until oxygen, which has one pair in one p orbital and an unpaired electron in each of the two remaining p orbitals. The number of unpaired electrons decreases to one for fluorine and none for neon. The elements of the third period have no electrons in the $3d$ orbitals although these orbitals are available for bonding purposes and may be used in complex ion formation, or electrons may be promoted into them in excited states. There are no $1p$ orbitals corresponding to the $2p$ and $3p$ orbitals, and no $1d$ or $2d$ orbitals corresponding to the $3d$ orbitals.

It is known that *atoms with filled electron shells,* such as helium and neon, *are extremely inert.* If the outside shell is incompletely filled, it is conceivable that an atom could acquire one or more electrons from another atom or atoms,

---

[12] The differences in physical properties do not depend so much on bond type as on the atomic arrangement and the distribution of the bonds. However there is some correlation between bond type and type of atomic arrangement.

TABLE 2

DISTRIBUTION OF ELECTRONS FOR THE GROUND STATE OF ELEMENTS OF THE
FIRST THREE PERIODS OF THE PERIODIC TABLE

SHELL	ORBITALS	FIRST PERIOD		SECOND PERIOD						
		H	He	Li	Be	B	C	N	O	F	Ne
K	$1s$	1	2	2	2	2	2	2	2	2	2
L	$2s$			1	2	2	2	2	2	2	2
	$2p_x$					1	1	1	2	2	2
	$2p_y$						1	1	1	2	2
	$2p_z$							1	1	1	2

SHELL	ORBITALS	THIRD PERIOD							
		Na	Mg	Al	Si	P	S	Cl	A
K	$1s$	2	2	2	2	2	2	2	2
L	$2s$	2	2	2	2	2	2	2	2
	$2p_{x,y,z}$	6	6	6	6	6	6	6	6
M	$3s$	1	2	2	2	2	2	2	2
	$3p_{x,y,z}$			1	2	3	4	5	6
	$3d$								

provided that the transfer would lead to an energetically more stable arrangement. The tendency of atoms to fill incomplete shells varies with the ability to attract electrons. This tendency is called the *electronegativity* of the atom or better its *electron-affinity* (cf. p. 117). In a given *period* the electron-affinity of atoms increases from left to right because the increasing nuclear charge pulls all of the electrons closer to the nucleus, the attraction being greater the closer the electron shells are to the nucleus. Thus a nitrogen nucleus with a charge of $+7$ pulls the K shell of electrons closer to it than does a carbon nucleus with a charge of $+6$. Hence the electrons in the periphery of a nitrogen atom also will be able to come in closer to the nucleus and be held more strongly than those of a carbon atom. However, the electron-affinity decreases from top to bottom of a given *column* of the periodic table. Although the nuclear charge increases greatly with each succeeding atom, the effective charge operating on the peripheral electrons remains the same while the electrons are removed one shell away from the nucleus. For example, one may consider that the charge operating on the four electrons in the outer shell of carbon is $+4$, because two of the nuclear charges are neutralized by the two electrons in the K shell. For silicon, ten of the nuclear charges are neutralized by the ten electrons in the K and L shells, again leaving an effective charge of $+4$ for the four electrons in the M shell. Since the M shell of silicon is much farther from the nucleus than the L shell of carbon, the attraction of the nucleus for electrons in the outer shell is much less for silicon than for carbon. Therefore *the ease of filling electron shells by acquiring electrons from other atoms increases from left to right and decreases from top to bottom of the periodic table.*

In the extreme case of two elements at opposite sides of the periodic table, such as sodium and chlorine, the attraction of the chlorine atom for electrons is much greater than that of the sodium atom; that is, the energy liberated when the last orbital of chlorine is filled is much greater than the energy required to remove an electron from the sodium atom. The result is that *the sodium atom transfers its electron to the chlorine atom* to give a chloride ion with a negative charge and a sodium ion with a positive charge (Fig. 1). In a mixture of sodium ions and chloride ions, the positive ions would exhibit a strong attraction for negative ions and the negative ions for positive ions. The attraction obeys Coulomb's law, varying inversely with the square of the distance; hence as the ions approach each other closely, the attractive forces become very large. In solid sodium chloride, the size of the ions permits them to group themselves so that each sodium ion is surrounded by six chloride ions and each chloride ion by six sodium ions to give solid sodium chloride. This type of bond is known as an **electrovalence,** or as an **ionic bond.**

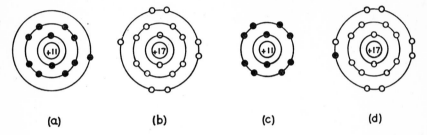

(a)   (b)   (c)   (d)

Fig. 1. Electronic representation of (*a*) the sodium atom, (*b*) the chlorine atom, (*c*) the sodium ion, and (*d*) the chloride ion.

When there is less difference between the attractions of two atoms for electrons, insufficient energy is liberated when an electron is transferred from one atom to the other to make the new arrangement more stable than the old one. In the extreme case of two like atoms, such as two chlorine atoms, any energy gained by one atom acquiring an electron from the other would be offset by the energy necessary to remove the electron from the other atom. Yet it is known from experiment that chlorine is a diatomic molecule. Therefore there must be a second way in which bonds can be formed. Apparently *a considerable amount of energy is liberated when the unpaired electrons of two chlorine atoms occupy the shells of both chlorine atoms*. This process has been called a *sharing of electrons* and is illustrated diagrammatically in Fig. 2. In the alternative simplified formula, the symbol for the element represents the nucleus with the inner full shells of electrons, and only the electrons in the outermost shell, the so-called *valence electrons*, are indicated. Since each atom has gained as much charge as it has lost, the molecule as a whole is electrically neutral. This type of bond is known as a **covalence,** or as a **covalent** or **electron-pair bond,** and occurs for the most part between atoms containing four or more electrons in the valence shell.

Just as a chlorine molecule consists of two chlorine atoms sharing one pair of electrons, the water molecule consists of two hydrogen atoms, each pairing one electron with one of the two unpaired electrons of an oxygen atom (Fig. 3). Since the K shell is filled when it contains two electrons, the hydrogen atoms have stable electronic arrangements, as does the oxygen atom with eight electrons in its L shell. Similarly in the ammonia molecule, three hydrogen atoms are joined by covalent bonds to a nitrogen atom, and in carbon tetra-chloride, four chlorine atoms to a carbon atom.

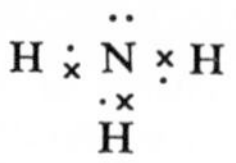

$$
\begin{array}{cc}
\overset{\cdot\cdot}{\text{H} \overset{\times}{} \text{N} \overset{\times}{} \text{H}} &
\overset{\text{Cl}}{\overset{\times\cdot}{\text{Cl} \overset{\times}{} \text{C} \overset{\times}{} \text{Cl}}} \\
\overset{\cdot\times}{\text{H}} & \overset{\cdot\times}{\text{Cl}} \\
\text{Ammonia, NH}_3 & \text{Carbon tetrachloride, CCl}_4
\end{array}
$$

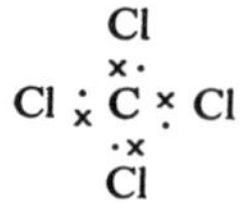

In the above formulas, and occasionally throughout the text, different marks are used to differentiate between the sources of the electrons forming the bonds.

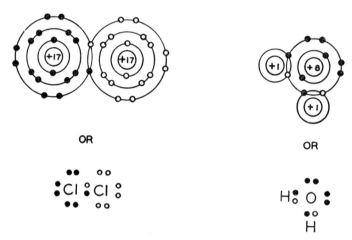

OR

:Cl:Cl:°

Fig. 2. Electronic representation of the chlorine molecule.

OR

H:O:
H

Fig. 3. Electronic representation of the water molecule

For example, in the ammonia molecule the dots represent the valence electrons which belonged originally to the nitrogen atom and the crosses those which belonged to the hydrogen atoms. Since electrons are all alike and constantly are interchanging (*electronic interaction*), there is no distinction between them once the bond is formed. The above representation is justified only in that it simplifies the procedure in keeping track of electrons when writing formulas representing electronic structures.

The difference in properties between the typical salt, sodium chloride, and the typical nonsalt, carbon tetrachloride, now can be explained. In solid sodium chloride there are no individual NaCl molecules. The crystal is composed of positive sodium ions each surrounded by six negatively charged chloride ions, and negative chloride ions each surrounded by six positively charged sodium ions. Strong electrostatic forces hold the ions together, and high temperatures are required to cause melting or volatilization. In carbon tetrachloride, however, the CCl$_4$ molecule is a distinct entity which is electrically neutral. The bonds between the carbon and the chlorine atoms are strong, but only relatively weak attractive forces exist between the individual molecules. Since only a small amount of energy is required to separate the molecules, carbon tetrachloride is a liquid at room temperature and is vaporized easily.

Molecular Orbitals and Covalent Bonds. The covalent or electron-pair bond, when first considered, seems to be definitely anomalous. Electrons can only repel each other, and the pairing of electrons cannot account for the liberation of energy when a covalent bond is formed. Yet the hydrogen molecule is more stable than two hydrogen atoms by 103 kcal. per mole. The explanation appears to be that the two positive nuclei of the hydrogen atoms can act as a combined nucleus having a charge of $+2$. An electron encompassing both nuclei will be held more strongly than if it encompassed a nucleus with a charge of $+1$. Hence the electron occupies a new orbital encompassing both nuclei and energy is liberated. Since orbitals of this type are responsible for the formation of molecules, they are called **molecular orbitals**. Like the atomic orbitals, they obey the Pauli exclusion principle in that a second electron can occupy the same molecular orbital and increase the bond strength provided the two electrons have opposite spins, but a third electron must occupy an orbital of higher energy.

Direction of Bond Orbitals. Atomic orbitals are considered as the regions in space where an electron is most likely to be (p. 5). This region also is one of high probability when an electron occupies a molecular orbital. Therefore the more nearly the individual atomic orbitals can coincide or overlap with each other, the greater the tendency for an electron to occupy a molecular orbital and the stronger the bond.

The atomic orbitals have a definite distribution in space. The *s* orbitals are spherically symmetrical about the nucleus as illustrated in perspective in Fig. 4*a*, and in cross section through the nucleus in Fig. 4*b*. The ability to overlap other atomic orbitals is the same in all

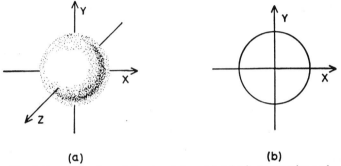

(a)   (b)

Fig. 4. Representation of the atomic 1*s* orbital (*a*) in perspective and (*b*) in cross section through the nucleus.

directions. In these figures no attempt is made to indicate the radial distribution of the electron within the orbital but only the relatively small region in space which the electron occupies most of the time. Several methods may be used to illustrate the distribution of the electron about the nucleus. Visually one may think of the electron as moving randomly in all directions but being more frequently in some places than in others. Suppose one could locate the electron at a particular moment and place a dot at that point in space and could do this repeatedly after equal intervals of time. Then after many such operations, the relative density of the dots would represent the probability of finding the electron in space. This relative density is called the *charge distribution* or *charge cloud* of the electron. Fig. 5*a* represents the cross section of such

(a)   (b)   *r* in Å

Fig. 5. Representations of the distribution of an electron about a hydrogen nucleus.

a cloud formed by an electron in the 1*s* orbital of the hydrogen atom. The charge density is distributed spherically about the nucleus but decreases with increasing distance from the nucleus. This picture does not indicate *how much* of the charge is at a particular distance from the nucleus. Thus although the charge density is greatest close to the nucleus, the volume occupied by a thin shell is very small, and only a small fraction of the total charge is present. Similarly at great distances from the nucleus, a shell of equal thickness has a large volume, but the density is so small that again a negligible fraction of the charge is present. Figure 5*b* illustrates the variation in the amount of charge, *e*, on a uniformly charged shell with increasing distance, *r*, from the nucleus. The maximum of the curve is at 0.529 Å, the radius of the old Bohr orbit. For most purposes it is sufficient to represent the orbital by a boundary surface or by a cross section of the surface. This surface is chosen to enclose the space in which the charge density is greatest and in which most of the charge is contained.

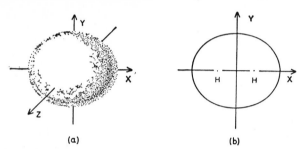

(a) (b)

Fig. 6. Representation of the σ-type molecular orbital of the hydrogen molecule (*a*) in perspective and (*b*) in cross section through the nuclei.

When two hydrogen atoms bond to form the hydrogen molecule, their *s* orbitals overlap, and the pair of electrons encompasses both nuclei as indicated in Fig. 6. This new orbital which describes the time-average position of the bonding pair of electrons is the new **molecular orbital.** Since it is symmetrical about the line joining the two nuclei, it resembles an *s* orbital and is called a σ (*sigma*)-*type orbital.* The bond formed when a pair of electrons occupies a molecular orbital that results from the overlapping of two *s* orbitals is called an *s—s* bond.

For elements in the second period the 1*s* orbital shrinks to a size proportional to the size of the 1*s* orbital of hydrogen divided by the atomic number. Thus the 1*s* orbital of oxygen is about one eighth the size of that of hydrogen. The 1*s* orbital is surrounded by the 2*s* orbital, which also is spherically symmetrical about the nucleus and bonds equally well in any direction.

The electrons of the 2*p* orbitals are most likely to be in regions resembling a dumb-bell as illustrated in Fig. 7. These orbitals possess a *nodal plane*, that is, a plane in which the probability of finding the electron is zero. The three dumb-bells representing the three 2*p* orbitals

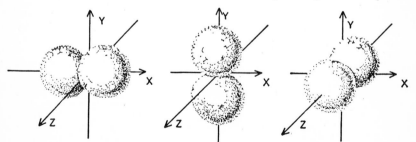

Fig. 7. Perspective representation of the p_x, p_y, and p_z atomic orbitals.

are oriented perpendicularly to each other in the *x*, *y*, and *z* directions. Hence elements using *p* orbitals, such as oxygen and nitrogen, tend to form bonds making angles of 90 degrees with each other. The *p* orbitals form stronger bonds than *s* orbitals because their projection away from the nucleus permits greater overlap with other atomic orbitals. The bonding of two hydrogen atoms with an oxygen atom to form a water molecule is shown in cross section in

Fig. 8. The third *p* orbital of oxygen, containing a pair of electrons and extending above and below the plane of the paper, is indicated by the inner circle about the nucleus of the oxygen atom. Thus when oxygen is linked to two other atoms, two of its six valence electrons are in σ-type orbitals, two are in the 2*s* atomic orbital, and two are in the 2*p* atomic orbital. Although the *p* orbitals make angles of 90 degrees with each other in the oxygen atom, the hydrogen-oxygen bonds in the water molecule actually make an angle of 105 degrees with each other as shown by spectroscopic data. Similarly the nitrogen-hydrogen bonds in ammonia make angles

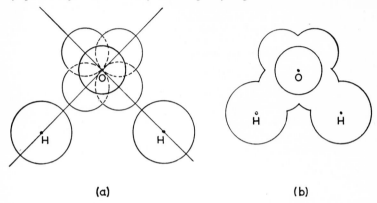

(a)   (b)

Fig. 8. (*a*) Atomic orbitals of hydrogen and oxygen. (*b*) Overlapping of atomic orbitals to give two σ-type molecular orbitals in the water molecule.

of 107 degrees with each other. The widening of the angle may be caused by the mutual repulsion of the electrons in the bonds (steric effect) or of the induced like charges on the hydrogen atoms resulting from the polarization of the bond (p. 197), or by the partial *sp³* hybridization of the bonds (see below). The electrostatic repulsions would seem to be most important, because in hydrogen sulfide and phosphine, where the hydrogen atoms are farther away from the nucleus and hence farther apart, the bond angles are found to be 92 degrees and 99 degrees.

Hybridization of Atomic Orbitals. From the distribution of the electrons in the ground state of the atom as given in Table 2, p. 6, it might be expected that beryllium and other elements of Group II would be inert or could form only ionic bonds, because both valence electrons are paired in the 2*s* orbital. As far as the members of the IIa group are concerned, they do form compounds which are largely ionic. The elements zinc, cadmium, and mercury of the IIb

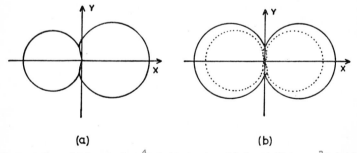

(a)   (b)

Fig. 9. Cross section of (*a*) a single *sp* hybrid atomic orbital and (*b*) two *sp* hybrid orbitals.

group, however, form compounds in which the atom is largely dicovalent. The explanation is that the 2*s* orbital can combine with one 2*p* orbital to give two *sp hybrid orbitals* (Fig. 9), each of which can accommodate two electrons. These *sp* hybrid orbitals make an angle of 180 degrees with each other and can overlap other atomic orbitals better than can *p* orbitals. The result is that the energy liberated during bond formation exceeds that necessary to promote the electrons to the hybrid orbitals. Electron diffraction data have shown that the halides of zinc, cadmium, and mercury are linear in the vapor phase. Hybridization of two atomic orbitals is called *digonal hybridization*.

Referring again to Table 2, p. 6, one might expect that boron would be monovalent and carbon divalent. However, the 2*s* orbital and two 2*p* orbitals can undergo *trigonal hybridization* for the purposes of bond formation to give three new orbitals designated as sp^2 orbitals. The superscript indicates that two *p* orbitals are involved. These three hybrid orbitals make angles of 120 degrees with each other and hence lie in a plane (Fig. 10). Boron forms tricovalent compounds, and the boron halides have been shown to be planar with 120 degree bond angles.

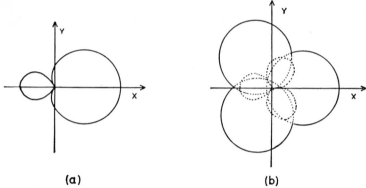

(a)   (b)

Fig. 10. Cross section of (*a*) a single sp^2 hybrid atomic orbital and
(*b*) three sp^2 hybrid orbitals.

Finally the 2*s* orbital can hybridize with three *p* orbitals to give four sp^3 hybrid orbitals which are tetrahedrally distributed, making angles of 109°28' with each other (Fig. 11). It is these orbitals that are used by carbon when it is united to four other atoms.

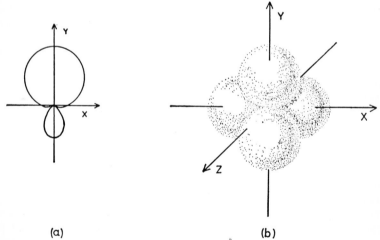

(a)   (b)

Fig. 11. (*a*) Cross section of a single sp^3 hybrid atomic orbital;
(*b*) perspective of four sp^3 hybrid orbitals.

Solubility. The difference in bond type also explains the difference in solubility behavior. Water is a polar compound; that is, when water molecules are placed in an electric field, they tend to be oriented with the hydrogen atoms toward the negative pole and the oxygen atom toward the positive pole. Because of this orientation, the molecule appears to have a positive and a negative end and is called a *dipole*. The dipole is believed to arise from several factors, but primarily from the unshared electrons on the oxygen atom. When sodium chloride is placed in contact with water, there is an *attraction between the positive sodium ion and the negative ends of water molecules*, thus forming the hydrated sodium ion. Similarly *the negative chloride ion attracts the positive ends of the water molecules* (Fig. 12). Actually each water molecule is associated with other water molecules (p. 87), and a considerable quantity of water is affixed to each ion.

Water has a *high dielectric constant*, and when the water molecules come between the sodium ions and the chloride ions, they decrease the electrostatic attractions between the ions with the result that the ions separate, and the salt

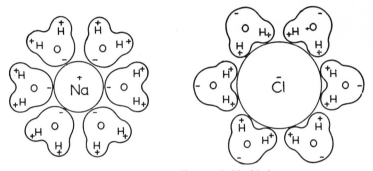

Fig. 12. Hydrated sodium and chloride ions.

dissolves in the water. This solution conducts the electric current because the ions are free to move, being insulated from each other by the water molecules. Salts are insoluble in most organic liquids because the latter either are not sufficiently polar, or do not possess a sufficiently high dielectric constant, or the geometry may be such that the atoms giving rise to the dipole cannot get sufficiently close to the ions for the forces to be effective.

Carbon tetrachloride is insoluble in water because there is no charge on the molecule and no tendency for the carbon atom and the chlorine atoms to separate as ions. Hence there is no strong attraction for water molecules. Moreover water molecules have a relatively strong attraction for each other (see *association*, p. 87) which prevents simple mixing or intermingling of the water and carbon tetrachloride molecules. On the other hand, the carbon tetrachloride molecules have no difficulty in mixing with the molecules of other organic compounds, such as the molecules in gasoline, that likewise have little attraction for each other.

Number of Organic Compounds. The large number of organic compounds also can be explained by the electronic structure of the carbon atom, which places it in the center of the second period. With four valence electrons, it is capable of uniting with the maximum number of monovalent atoms or groups,[13] and *it is able to form four strong covalent bonds not only with other kinds of atoms but also with other carbon atoms indefinitely*. Polyethylene, and many other high

---

[13] This statement applies to atoms with a coordination number of four, that is, those having a maximum covalence of four. Atoms in the third and higher periods can make use of *d* orbitals (Table 2) and can combine with larger numbers of groups. They do not, however, bond with themselves to the extent that carbon does.

molecular weight plastics, have a thousand or more carbon atoms linked to each other chain-wise. Moreover the bonds formed by the carbon atom are directed to the corners of a tetrahedron (pp. 12, 30), and *three-dimensional molecules and molecules having atoms joined in polygons are possible.* Carbon is unique because the other elements having four valence electrons, such as silicon, germanium, and tin, have a decreasing attraction for their valence electrons because of the increasing distance from the nucleus, and hence they are less likely to form covalent bonds; that is, they become more like a metal. Moreover, because of their larger size, the space relationships may be such that many types of compounds known for carbon are unknown for the other elements.

It may be stated, then, that organic chemistry is based on *two fundamental principles*: (*1*) **carbon has a valence of four;** that is, it is able to combine covalently with four univalent atoms or groups of atoms; (*2*) **carbon can unite with itself indefinitely.** These principles were discussed independently and almost simultaneously by Kekulé and by Couper[14] in 1858, and formed the basis for the development of structural organic chemistry. They were enunciated long before chemists had any conception of the electronic nature of valence and were developed purely from observations of the composition and chemical behavior of organic compounds.

Isolation and Purification of Organic Compounds

Before any study can be made of an unknown compound, it first must be isolated in a pure state. A number of processes are available for this purpose.

Distillation. Because of the small attractive forces between most individual organic molecules, many organic compounds can be converted into the gaseous state, without decomposition, by heating to a temperature at which the vapor pressure becomes equal to the external pressure. This temperature is known as the **boiling point** of the liquid. The vapors may be forced into a cooling device where they condense to the original liquid. The process is called **distillation.**

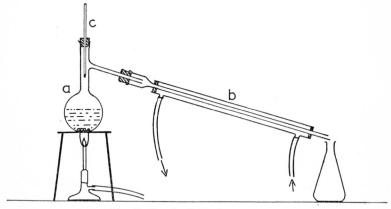

Fig. 13. Simple distillation apparatus.

[14] Archibald Scott Couper (1831–1892), brilliant young Scottish chemist whose career was cut short by illness in 1859. He was the first to publish formulas for organic compounds comparable to present-day structural formulas.

A simple distillation apparatus is shown in Fig. 13. The substance to be distilled is placed in a distilling flask *a* and connected to a water-cooled condenser *b*. A thermometer *c* is placed in the neck of the flask to record the temperature at which the vapors distill.

Because the attraction between the molecules of one compound differs from that between the molecules of another, different organic compounds usually distill at different temperatures. Hence distillation can be used not only to separate volatile organic compounds from nonvolatile materials but also mixtures of organic compounds having different boiling points. To separate substances whose boiling points are not far apart, it may be necessary to use fractional distillation or an efficient fractionating column.

In **fractional distillation,** the mixture is distilled into a number of fractions. These fractions usually differ in composition from the original material, the lower-boiling fractions containing a higher percentage of the lower-boiling substance (cf. p. 93). By a systematic redistillation of the fractions a further separation takes place, and the process is repeated until the desired degree of separation has been achieved. A **fractionating column** is a device for bringing about a more efficient separation than can be obtained in an ordinary distilling flask. It consists of a tall column through which the vapors rise and a certain amount of liquid, known as *reflux*, descends. As the hot vapors from the still come into contact with the cooler descending liquid, a heat interchange takes place. The vapors are cooled slightly and some of the higher-boiling constituents condense. The heat of condensation given up to the reflux vaporizes a small

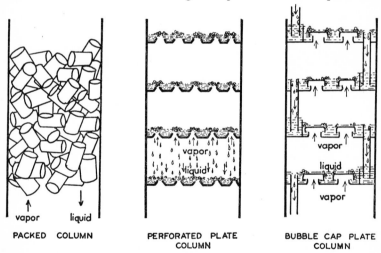

PACKED COLUMN   PERFORATED PLATE   BUBBLE CAP PLATE
                        COLUMN   COLUMN

Fig. 14. Sections through three types of fractionating columns.

amount of its lower-boiling constituents. Hence there is a gradual enrichment of the lower-boiling constituent in the vapors as they rise in the column, and an enrichment of the higher-boiling constituent in the reflux as it descends.

The operation of a fractionating column depends on intimate contact of the distilling vapors and the reflux, and many types of columns have been devised to achieve this. There are two main classes of columns, the **packed columns** and the **plate columns,** sections of which are illustrated in Fig. 14 Theoretically it is not possible to separate two liquids completely by distillation. Even when the difference in their boiling points is large, the higher-boiling constituent always exerts its vapor pressure at the boiling point of the other constituent and some molecules of the higher-boiling constituent distill. For all practical purposes, however, it is possible to separate by means of efficient fractionation, liquids boiling as little as 3° apart.

If a mixture of equal amounts of ethyl alcohol, a colorless liquid boiling at 78°, and of azobenzene, an orange solid boiling at 297°, is distilled from an ordinary distilling flask, even the first distillate will be colored yellow by the azobenzene molecules that have come over with the alcohol, despite the difference in boiling points of over 200°.

Distillation under reduced pressure, which frequently is called **vacuum distillation,** is used for high-boiling compounds to avoid the decomposition that might take place at the high temperatures necessary to produce distillation at atmospheric pressure. Since substances distill as soon as their vapor pressures exceed the pressure at the surface of the liquid, reducing the pressure enables the substance to distill at a lower temperature. **Steam distillation,** consisting of passing steam through the substance or distilling in the presence of water, accomplishes the same purpose. Distillation takes place when the sum of the vapor pressures of the compound and of water exceeds the pressure in the distillation apparatus. This condition occurs at a lower temperature than for either component alone.

Crystallization. This procedure is useful for the purification of organic solids, just as it is an important method for salts. The solubilities of organic compounds usually increase greatly with increasing temperature. Hence the usual method of crystallization consists in making a saturated solution at the boiling point of the solvent and then cooling to room temperature or below. The pure compound crystallizes, and the more soluble or less abundant impurities remain in solution. A large variety of solvents is available, and the one most suitable for the material being purified can be chosen.

Extraction. Extraction with solvents also is an important method for isolating and purifying organic compounds. Solid mixtures are extracted with volatile solvents that will extract the desired constituents and leave the undesired constituents behind. Organic compounds can be separated from aqueous solutions by shaking with a water-immiscible solvent which will dissolve more of the desired material than will water. The organic compound passes into the organic solvent, from which the compound can be recovered by evaporating or distilling the solvent. Organic or inorganic salts can be separated from nonsalts by shaking the mixture with water and an organic solvent, the salt dissolving in the water and the nonsalt in the organic solvent.

Adsorption. Selective adsorption at the surfaces of solids is important for removing impurities and for separating mixtures of compounds having similar physical properties. Activated charcoal (decolorizing carbon) is used widely to remove colored impurities of high molecular weight from liquids or solutions. In another procedure a solution of the mixture of compounds is passed through a column of activated aluminum oxide or one of numerous other solid adsorbents, and the column is eluted with suitable solvents. The components of the mixture usually pass down the column at different rates, dependent on their relative adsorbability, and are separated. This process first was applied to a mixture of leaf pigments (p. 863) which separated as colored bands on the white alumina.

Hence the procedure was called *chromatography*, a term now used for all types of separations using a column of a solid adsorbent. Separations of mixtures of ions in aqueous solution can be made using ion-exchange resins (p. 513) as the adsorbent.

Since 1952 a process called *gas-liquid partition chromatography* has been used to separate complex mixtures of volatile compounds. The mixture in an inert carrier gas such as nitrogen or helium is passed through a column of diatomaceous earth coated with a thin film of a nonvolatile liquid. The components of the mixture are carried through the column at rates dependent on their relative solubility in the stationary liquid. Surprisingly sharp separations can be obtained using very small samples. A 4-foot column can be as effective as a 1200-plate fractionating column.

Criteria of Purity. Pure substances distill at a constant temperature; hence *constancy of boiling point* is a good criterion of purity. Pure solid compounds usually *melt over a very narrow range of temperature* which is characteristic of the compound. Since these melting points are relatively low, they may be determined easily and form a second criterion of purity. Other useful criteria are *density, refractive index, solubilities in various solvents,* and *absorption spectra* (pp. 38 and 657).

Analysis of Organic Compounds for the Elements

Qualitative Tests. After a compound has been isolated in a pure state, any investigation of it must begin with the identification of the elements present. Qualitative tests for the elements depend almost exclusively on reactions of ions. Since the elements in organic compounds usually are not present in ions, other types of tests must be devised, or the organic compounds must be converted into ionizable salts. Both methods of attack are used. **Carbon** and **hydrogen** may be detected readily by heating the unknown in a test tube with dry copper oxide powder and passing the evolved gases into a solution of barium hydroxide. The hydrogen is burned to water, which collects in droplets on the cooler portion of the test tube and may be observed visually. The carbon is burned to carbon dioxide, which reacts with the barium hydroxide solution to give a precipitate of barium carbonate.

Several methods are available for converting other elements into detectable ions, but the procedure most commonly used is to heat the compound with molten sodium. This process is known as *sodium fusion.* **Sulfur** is converted to sodium sulfide, **halogen** to sodium halide, and **nitrogen,** in the presence of carbon, to sodium cyanide.

$$\text{Organic compound containing} \atop \text{C, H, N, S, X}^{15} \quad \xrightarrow{\text{Na fusion}} \quad {\text{NaCN} \atop \text{Na}_2\text{S} \atop \text{NaX}}$$

An aqueous solution of the ions is obtained by decomposing with water. The *cyanide ion* may be converted to insoluble ferric ferrocyanide (Prussian blue) by heating a portion of the aqueous solution with ferrous and ferric

---

[15] The symbol X is used to indicate chlorine, bromine, or iodine.

sulfate in alkaline solution. Addition of hydrochloric acid dissolves the iron hydroxides and leaves the blue precipitate.

$$18 \text{ NaCN} + 3 \text{ FeSO}_4 + 2 \text{ Fe}_2(\text{SO}_4)_3 \longrightarrow \text{Fe}_4[\text{Fe(CN)}_6]_3 + 9 \text{ Na}_2\text{SO}_4$$

Sulfide ion is detected readily by acidifying the solution with acetic acid, heating to drive off hydrogen sulfide, and allowing the vapors to come in contact with a solution of lead acetate on filter paper. A dark, lustrous spot of lead sulfide will form if sulfide ion is present.

$$\text{Na}_2\text{S} + 2 \text{ HC}_2\text{H}_3\text{O}_2 \longrightarrow \text{H}_2\text{S} + 2 \text{ NaC}_2\text{H}_3\text{O}_2$$

$$\text{Pb(C}_2\text{H}_3\text{O}_2)_2 + \text{H}_2\text{S} \longrightarrow \text{PbS} + 2 \text{ HC}_2\text{H}_3\text{O}_2$$

To test for *halide ion*, the solution is boiled with nitric acid to remove cyanide ion and sulfide ion, and then aqueous silver nitrate is added. If halogen is present, a white, pale yellow, or deep yellow precipitate will be formed depending on whether chlorine, bromine, or iodine is present.

$$\text{NaX} + \text{AgNO}_3 \longrightarrow \text{AgX} + \text{NaNO}_3$$

Quantitative Analysis. The determination of the *kind* of elements present in a new compound under investigation is followed by the determination of the *relative amounts* of the elements. **Carbon** and **hydrogen** are estimated by a procedure perfected by Liebig, which is based on the same principle used for qualitative detection, namely combustion to carbon dioxide and water. The apparatus and the functions of the various parts are given in Fig. 15.

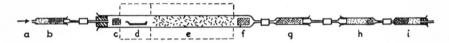

Fig. 15. Apparatus for the determination of carbon and hydrogen: *a*, source of air or oxygen; *b*, tube packed with solid absorbent containing sodium hydroxide for removing carbon dioxide, and a second solid absorbent such as anhydrous magnesium perchlorate or activated alumina for removing water; *c*, copper oxide gauze to oxidize vapor diffusing backward; *d*, porcelain or platinum boat containing weighed sample and heated by sectional combustion furnace (dotted lines); *e*, packing of copper oxide wire heated to 600°–800°; *f*, clean copper gauze to reduce oxides of nitrogen to nitrogen; *g*, weighed tube containing water absorbent; *h*, weighed tube containing carbon dioxide absorbent backed by water absorbent; *i*, safety tube packed with water absorbent and carbon dioxide absorbent to prevent diffusion of atmospheric moisture and carbon dioxide into *h*.

The combustion is carried out in a glass tube packed with copper oxide, which is maintained at 600°–800° by means of an electrically- or gas-heated furnace to insure complete oxidation of the organic matter. The tube first is swept out with purified air to remove moisture and carbon dioxide, and then the weighed sample is burned completely to carbon dioxide and water. The gases from the combustion tube are passed through an absorption train, which consists of a tube containing a water absorbent, a tube containing a carbon dioxide absorbent, and a safety tube containing an additional quantity of the water and carbon dioxide absorbents. After the initial decomposition, a slow stream of purified air or oxygen is passed through the tube to complete the combustion. At the end of the combustion the apparatus is swept out with purified air to drive all the carbon dioxide and water into the absorption tubes.

The increases in weight of the first and second absorption tubes *g* and *h* of Fig. 15 give the weights of water and carbon dioxide respectively. From these data and the weight of the original substance, the per cent of hydrogen and of carbon can be calculated.

The *Dumas method* is the most important for the determination of **nitrogen** because it can be used for any type of nitrogen compound. The apparatus is illustrated in Fig. 16. The weighed sample mixed with powdered copper oxide is placed in a tube which can be swept out with pure carbon dioxide. When the section containing the sample and copper oxide is heated, the sample is burned to carbon dioxide, water, and nitrogen, and the gases passed over more hot

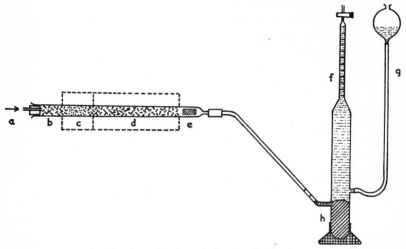

Fig. 16. Apparatus for the determination of nitrogen (Dumas): *a*, source of pure carbon dioxide; *b*, copper oxide wire; *c*, weighed sample mixed with copper oxide powder and heated by sectional combustion furnace (dotted lines); *d*, copper oxide wire heated to 600°–800°; *e*, clean copper gauze to reduce oxides of nitrogen to nitrogen; *f*, nitrometer containing 50 per cent aqueous potassium hydroxide solution; *g*, leveling bulb and potassium hydroxide reservoir; *h*, mercury valve.

copper oxide to insure complete combustion. Any oxides of nitrogen that form are reduced to nitrogen by passing the gases over clean copper gauze. At the end of the combustion, the tube is swept out again with carbon dioxide. The gases are passed into a nitrometer tube filled with 50 per cent potassium hydroxide solution,[16] which absorbs the carbon dioxide and leaves the nitrogen. The volume of nitrogen is measured and the temperature and barometric pressure noted. The vapor pressure of the potassium hydroxide solution is obtained from a table and subtracted from the barometric pressure. From these data the weight of nitrogen and the per cent in the sample can be calculated.

In the *Kjeldahl method* a weighed sample is heated with concentrated sulfuric acid and an oxidizing catalyst such as mercuric oxide, or copper sulfate and selenium. The nitrogen in the sample is converted to ammonium sulfate. At the end of the digestion, sodium hydroxide is added to liberate ammonia, which

---

[16] Potassium hydroxide is used instead of sodium hydroxide because potassium carbonate is soluble in concentrated potassium hydroxide solution, whereas sodium carbonate is insoluble in concentrated sodium hydroxide solution and would precipitate.

is distilled into a measured volume of standard acid. Back titration with standard alkali, using methyl red as an indicator, gives the amount of ammonia formed. The procedure lends itself to routine analyses of large numbers of samples and is very useful for those types of compounds for which it gives accurate results. However, some compounds evolve nitrogen or do not decompose completely during the digestion, and the results are low.

The only special feature in the quantitative determination of **other elements** is the necessity of converting them into ionized compounds. In the determination of **sulfur, halogen,** or **phosphorus,** for example, the compound may be fused in a Parr bomb with sodium peroxide, which burns the carbon and hydrogen to carbon dioxide and water, and converts halogen, sulfur, and phosphorus into the alkali halide, sulfate, and phosphate. Alternatively the compound may be oxidized with nitric acid in a sealed tube at elevated temperature (*Carius method*). When the conversion to the inorganic salts has been effected, the usual quantitative methods, gravimetric or volumetric, may be employed. No method for the direct estimation of **oxygen** is in general use. As a result this element is determined as the difference between 100 per cent and the sum of the per cents of the other elements.

The *quantity of material* needed for an analysis depends on the experience of the operator, on the apparatus, and on the sensitivity of the balance available. **Macroanalyses** use from 0.1 to 0.2 g. of substance, **semimicroanalyses** use from 0.01 to 0.02 g., and **microanalyses** use from 0.003 to 0.005 g. In each case a balance must be used that is accurate to four significant figures.

Empirical Formulas. From the analyses the relative proportion by weight of the various elements present may be calculated, but for convenience the results are expressed as an *empirical formula* which shows the relative number of different atoms in the molecule. To calculate the empirical formula, the per cent of each element is divided by its atomic weight. The result usually is in the form of fractions, and it is customary to convert these fractions into ratios of whole numbers.

The following example illustrates the general method for determining an empirical formula from analyses.

A sample weighing 0.1824 g. gave on combustion 0.2681 g. of carbon dioxide and 0.1090 g. of water.

Weight of carbon in sample $= 0.2681 \times \dfrac{12}{44} = 0.07312$ g.

Weight of hydrogen in sample $= 0.1090 \times \dfrac{2}{18} = 0.01211$ g.

Per cent carbon in sample $= \dfrac{0.07312}{0.1824} \times 100 = 40.09$

Per cent hydrogen in sample $= \dfrac{0.01211}{0.1824} \times 100 = 6.64$

Per cent oxygen in sample $= 100 - (40.09 + 6.64) = 53.27$

Element	Per cent by weight		Atomic weight		Atomic ratio				Atomic ratio in integers
C	40.09	÷	12	=	3.36	÷	3.33	=	1
H	6.64	÷	1	=	6.64	÷	3.33	=	2
O	53.27	÷	16	=	3.33	÷	3.33	=	1

The empirical formula therefore is CH_2O.

Molecular Formulas. Usually a determination of the empirical formula identifies an inorganic compound. For most organic compounds, however, the empirical formula is less definitive. One reason for this difference is that several organic compounds may have the same empirical formula but differ in molecular weight. Thus formaldehyde, acetic acid, lactic acid, and glucose all have the empirical formula CH_2O, but their molecular formulas, that is, formulas indicating not only the ratio but also the number of atoms in the molecule, are respectively CH_2O, $C_2H_4O_2$, $C_3H_6O_3$, and $C_6H_{12}O_6$. Molecular formulas represent the *composition* of the compound. The importance of determining molecular weights was brought to the attention of chemists by Cannizzaro in 1860, although the basis for their determination had been provided by Avogadro in 1811 (p. 3).

Several methods for determining molecular weights are available. The *Dumas method*, which still is one of the most accurate, is suitable only for gases and low-boiling liquids. A glass bulb of known volume is weighed when it is completely evacuated, and when it is filled with gas. From the weight of the known volume of gas at the observed temperature and pressure, the weight of 22.4 liters at 0° and 760 mm. can be calculated.

In the *Victor Meyer*[17] *method*, which is suitable for easily volatilized substances, a known weight of the compound is vaporized in a closed system and the volume of air displaced is measured. The apparatus is illustrated in Fig. 17.

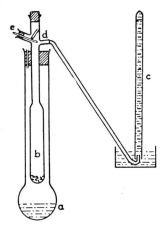

Fig. 17. Victor Meyer apparatus for the determination of molecular weights.

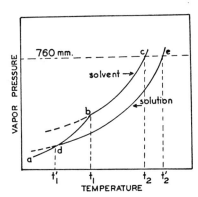

Fig. 18. Variation of the vapor pressure of solvent and solution with temperature.

A liquid boiling higher than the sample is placed in the jacket *a* and boiled uniformly until bubbles no longer are emitted from the outlet of the inner chamber *b*, indicating that temperature equilibrium has been reached. The eudiometer tube *c* is placed over the outlet, the sample *d* introduced through a device *e* into the chamber *b*, and heating continued until equilibrium again is

[17] Victor Meyer (1848–1897), professor of chemistry at the University of Heidelberg. He is remembered not only for the apparatus which bears his name but also for his work on steric hindrance (p. 549), aliphatic nitro compounds (p. 258), oximes (p. 210), thiophene (p. 606), and iodoso compounds (p. 436).

reached. The volume of air collected is that which the substance would occupy if it were a gas at the same temperature and pressure at which the volume of the displaced air was measured.

Two methods which are more generally applicable than those given above are known as the *cryoscopic* or *freezing point method*, and the *ebullioscopic* or *boiling point method*. They depend on the effect of a nonvolatile solute on the vapor pressure of the solvent. This effect may be illustrated by the curves in Fig. 18. Curve *bc* represents the vapor pressure of the pure solvent in the liquid phase and curve *ab* that of the solid phase. The vapor pressure of a solid is lower than that of the liquid at the same temperature because the attractive forces between molecules are greater in the closely packed crystal lattice than in the liquid. It is this greater attraction that gives rise to the heat of fusion of a solid. Since the vapor pressure is lowered by dissolved molecules of a substance having negligible vapor pressure, the vapor pressure of the solution may be represented by the curve *de*. The freezing point *b* of the pure liquid will be lowered to *d* for the solution, the difference being Δt_1. The boiling point *c* for the pure liquid will be increased to *e* for the solution, the difference being Δt_2. Since the lowering of the vapor pressure depends on the number of molecules dissolved, one gram molecular weight of any nondissociating substance dissolved in 1000 grams of a solvent will lower the melting point $K_{f.p.}$ degrees, called the *molal lowering of the freezing point* of the solvent, or raise the boiling point $K_{b.p.}$ degrees, the *molal elevation of the boiling point*. If W grams of a substance of molecular weight M is dissolved in G grams of solvent,

$$\Delta = K \frac{W}{M} \times \frac{1000}{G}$$

$$\text{or } M = \frac{KW}{\Delta t} \times \frac{1000}{G}$$

The experimentally determined values of K for a few of the common solvents are given in Table 3.

TABLE 3

CRYOSCOPIC AND EBULLIOSCOPIC CONSTANTS

SOLVENT	$K_{f.p.}$	$K_{b.p.}$ (760 mm.)
Water	1.86	0.51
Acetic acid	3.86	3.07
Benzene	5.12	2.53
Exaltone	21.3	
Camphor	39.7	

In determining the molecular weights of unknown compounds, the boiling point or freezing point is determined in a special apparatus (Figs. 19a and b), first on the pure solvent and then on a solution of known concentration. Knowing K, W, G, and Δt, the molecular weight M can be calculated. Because the changes in the boiling point or melting point usually are small, a special differential thermometer which measures small differences in temperature, such as the *Beckmann thermometer*, or the *Menzies-Wright thermometer*, is used, and relatively large amounts of material are needed. The molecular lowering of the freezing point of camphor, however, is large, and since it is a solid, the melting

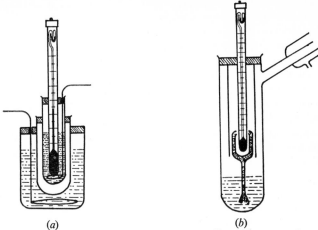

(a)   (b)

Fig. 19. (*a*), Freezing point apparatus. (*b*), Boiling point apparatus.

point lowering may be determined in a capillary tube using an ordinary thermometer (Fig. 20). This procedure is known as the *Rast camphor method* for determining molecular weights.

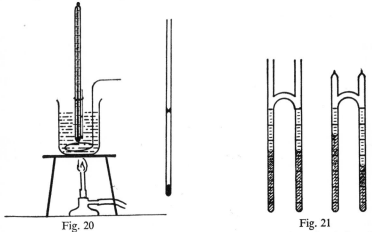

Fig. 20   Fig. 21

Fig. 20. Capillary tube melting point apparatus with enlarged view of sealed capillary melting point tube.

Fig. 21. Signer molecular weight apparatus.

Another useful method for determining the molecular weights of compounds having a low vapor pressure is known as the *Signer method*. It depends on the fact that equimolar solutions of different nonvolatile substances in the same solvent have the same vapor pressure. A weighed amount of a pure substance of known molecular weight is dissolved in a solvent having a high vapor pressure and placed in one leg of an inverted **U**-tube having legs of the same diameter (Fig. 21). A weighed amount of the unknown compound dissolved in the same solvent is placed in the other leg. The system is evacuated, sealed, and allowed to stand at a uniform temperature.

Solvent distills from the solution of higher vapor pressure to that of lower vapor pressure, and when equilibrium is reached, the molar concentrations of the two solutions is identical. From the relative volumes of the two solutions, obtained by measuring the heights of the columns of liquid, the molecular weight of the unknown can be calculated. A modification of the apparatus using a ground glass joint (1954) permits a more rapid attainment of equilibrium and avoids the necessity of sealing the tubes.

The relative error of molecular weight determinations rarely is less than ± 5 per cent, and the result of a combustion analysis usually is considered acceptable if the absolute error is less than ± 0.5 per cent.[18] Hence it is difficult to determine by analyses alone the exact molecular formulas of saturated hydrocarbons (compounds containing carbon and the maximum amount of hydrogen) having molecular weights greater than about 150. If other elements are present, the differences in the per cent composition of compounds differing by one carbon atom are considerably greater. Thus if a compound contains carbon and hydrogen and one oxygen atom per molecule, empirical formulas can be determined for compounds having molecular weights up to about 400 Analyses for the elements usually are more accurate than ordinary molecular weight determinations, and the latter are used merely to determine whether the molecular formula is a multiple of the empirical formula

Classification of Organic Compounds

The number of organic compounds known in 1948 has been estimated to be around 1,000,000. The reasons for this large number have been given, namely that a carbon atom is able to combine with four other atoms or groups of atoms, and that carbon atoms are able to combine with each other indefinitely to produce stable compounds. The possible number of compounds of carbon is infinite. Because of this large number of compounds, it might seem that the study of organic chemistry would be hopeless, but fortunately it is possible to divide these compounds into a comparatively small number of groups or *families of compounds*. Most members of each family may be prepared by similar methods, and most members exhibit similar chemical behavior. Moreover the individual members of each family differ from each other more or less regularly in their physical properties. The families, on the other hand, usually differ from each other markedly in their chemical properties and are prepared by different types of chemical reactions. Accordingly it is possible to concentrate on the methods of preparation and reactions of the families of compounds, and it is not necessary to discuss each member of a family. Special methods of preparation and special reactions of individual compounds then can be considered as additions or exceptions to the generalizations.

The numerous families may be grouped according to similarities in structure. The three main classifications are (*1*) *acyclic* compounds, which contain no ring

[18] Accuracy is expressed in terms of absolute error or relative error. The error of a measurement is the deviation from what is thought to be the true value. The *absolute error* is the difference between the numerical value observed and the true value and is expressed in the units used to express the numerical value. The *relative error* usually is expressed as the per cent deviation and is the absolute error divided by the true value and multiplied by 100. For example if a compound has a molecular weight of 200 g. and the observed value is 210 g., the absolute error is 10 g. and the relative error is 5 per cent. If a compound contains 5.5 per cent hydrogen and the value found is 5.3 per cent, the absolute error is 0.2 per cent and the relative error is 3.6 per cent

structures of the atoms, (2) *carbocyclic* compounds, which contain rings made up solely of carbon atoms, and (3) *heterocyclic* compounds, which contain rings made up of more than one kind of atom. The acyclic compounds more commonly are called *aliphatic* compounds from the Greek word *aleiphatos* meaning *fat*, because the fats have this type of structure.

REVIEW QUESTIONS

1. Define the term *organic chemistry.*
2. What date usually is considered as the time when the modern science of organic chemistry began and why? When did it begin to be placed on a rational basis?
3. Give one significant contribution of each of the following men to the early development of organic chemistry: Scheele, Lavoisier, Liebig, Cannizzaro, Victor Meyer, Berzelius, Dumas, Woehler.
4. Discuss and give examples of the two common modes of bond formation between atoms.
5. List the important differences in the physical and chemical properties of most salts and most nonsalts, give the primary reason for these differences, and tell how it explains them.
6. How does the number and complexity of the compounds of carbon compare with the number and complexity of the compounds of other elements? Why is carbon unique in this respect?
7. Discuss the solubility of sodium chloride in water, carbon tetrachloride, and gasoline, and the mutual solubility relationships of the last three substances. Give an explanation of the facts.
8. List the more important processes used to purify organic compounds.
9. What is the usual procedure for the purification of organic solids by crystallization?
10. What physical properties are most commonly used as criteria of purity for organic compounds? Why are these criteria of little importance for inorganic salts?
11. Give a sketch of the apparatus and a brief description of the usual method for determining the per cent of carbon and of hydrogen in an organic compound.
12. Give a brief description of the Dumas method for determining nitrogen in an organic compound.
13. Describe the Kjeldahl method for determining nitrogen in organic compounds. What are its limitations?
14. Why is it necessary to determine the molecular weights of organic compounds? What is the difference between an empirical formula and a molecular formula?
15. Give the formula relating molecular weight to the lowering of the freezing point of a solvent, together with the meaning of the symbols. How can the elevation of the boiling point be used to determine molecular weights?
16. Given a new organic compound mixed with other substances, outline briefly the experimental steps necessary for determining the molecular formula of the compound.

PROBLEMS

17. Calculate the per cent composition of the compounds having the following molecular formulas: (a) C_3H_8; (b) C_2H_6O; (c) C_2H_3ClO; (d) C_3H_7NO; (e) $C_2H_8N_2$; (f) $C_2H_5NO_2$; (g) C_3H_5BrO; (h) $C_3H_9O_4P$; (i) CH_4S; (j) $C_4H_8Cl_2S$; (k) CH_6BrN; (l) C_4H_9Br; (m) C_2H_6Hg; (n) C_3H_9SiCl; (o) $C_2H_2O_4$.
18. Calculate the differences in the per cent of carbon and hydrogen for the following pairs of compounds:

    A. (a) $C_{17}H_{36}$ and $C_{18}H_{38}$; (b) $C_{17}H_{36}O$ and $C_{18}H_{38}O$; (c) $C_{30}H_{48}O$ and $C_{31}H_{50}O$.

    B. (a) $C_{16}H_{32}$ and $C_{17}H_{34}$; (b) $C_{16}H_{32}O$ and $C_{17}H_{34}O$; (c) $C_{27}H_{46}O$ and $C_{28}H_{48}O$.

    C. (a) $C_{15}H_{32}$ and $C_{16}H_{34}$; (b) $C_{15}H_{32}O$ and $C_{16}H_{34}O$; (c) $C_{30}H_{62}O$ and $C_{31}H_{64}O$.

    D. (a) $C_{14}H_{12}$ and $C_{15}H_{14}$; (b) $C_{14}H_{12}O$ and $C_{15}H_{14}O$; (c) $C_{30}H_{50}O$ and $C_{30}H_{52}O$.

19. Calculate the volume of nitrogen that would be obtained at S.T.P.* when the stated weight of the given compound is burned in a Dumas apparatus: (a) 0.044 g. of C_2H_7N; (b) 0.072 g. of C_2H_5NO; (c) 0.104 g. of C_6H_7N; (d) 0.035 g. of $C_2H_6N_2$; (e) 0.065 g. of CH_4N_2S.

---

* Standard temperature and pressure; that is, 0° and 760 mm. of mercury.

20. Calculate the empirical formulas for the following compounds which contain X per cent carbon, Y per cent hydrogen, Z per cent sulfur, and possibly oxygen:

	A	B	C	D
X	38.65	47.29	53.32	57.65
Y	9.68	10.50	11.05	11.49
Z	51.62	42.15	35.60	30.78

21. For the following compounds which contain X per cent carbon, Y per cent hydrogen, and possibly oxygen, and have the approximate molecular weight Z, calculate the molecular formula of the compound and the exact molecular weight:

	A	B	C	D
X	54.55	62.05	66.72	69.75
Y	9.02	10.34	11.05	11.62
Z	84	164	148	88

22. Calculate the approximate molecular weight of the compounds that gave the following freezing point depressions when 0.310 g. was dissolved in 15 g. of benzene: (a) 1.582°; (b) 1.196°; (c) 0.719°; (d) 0.384°.

23. Calculate the approximate molecular weight of the following compounds, X g. of which in a Victor Meyer apparatus displaced Y cc. of air collected at 747 mm. pressure and 20° over water (vapor pressure 17 mm. of mercury):

	A	B	C	D
X	0.202	0.152	0.175	0.168
Y	60.5	55.8	72.7	49.8

24. What is the minimum molecular weight of a compound that contains (a) 59.2 per cent chlorine; (b) 35.6 per cent sulfur; (c) 11.6 per cent nitrogen; (d) 4.24 per cent copper?

25. An ether solution of 9.82 mg. of a pure compound having a molecular weight of 154 was placed in one leg of the Signer apparatus, and in the other leg was placed an ether solution of the unknown compound. After reaching equilibrium, the heights of the liquids in the two legs were measured. If X was the weight of the unknown in milligrams, Y the height of the liquid in the leg containing the known compound and Z the height of the liquid in the leg containing the unknown compound, calculate the molecular weight of the following compounds:

	A	B	C	D
X	10.09	9.04	8.16	10.91
Y	5.32	7.31	8.45	6.35
Z	6.56	5.98	5.65	7.83

26. The following compounds contain carbon, hydrogen, and possibly oxygen. Combustion of X g. gave Y g. of carbon dioxide and Z g. of water. Calculate the per cent composition and the empirical formulas. When M g. was vaporized in a Victor Meyer apparatus, the volume of displaced air corrected to S.T.P. was N cc. What are the molecular formulas of the compounds?

	A	B	C	D
X	0.1562	0.1234	0.1085	0.1356
Y	0.4904	0.2359	0.3411	0.1863
Z	0.2020	0.1458	0.1394	0.1535
M	0.130	0.321	0.169	0.052
N	34.2	16.6	39.2	35.2

27. The following compounds contain carbon, hydrogen, bromine, and possibly oxygen. Combustion of X g. gave Y g. of carbon dioxide and Z g. of water. Fusion of M g. with sodium peroxide, acidification with nitric acid, and precipitation with silver nitrate gave N g. of silver bromide. Calculate the empirical formulas of the compounds.

	A	B	C	D
X	0.2001	0.1763	0.1523	0.1835
Y	0.1902	0.2822	0.1753	0.2675
Z	0.0907	0.1259	0.0812	0.1213
M	0.1523	0.1836	0.1682	0.1783
N	0.2058	0.2088	0.2064	0.2217

28. Combustion of X g. of a substance gave Y g. of carbon dioxide and Z g. of water. Combustion of M g. in a Dumas apparatus gave N cc. of nitrogen measured over 50 per cent aqueous potassium hydroxide solution at 25° (vapor pressure of solution = 9 mm. of mercury) and at 735 mm. atmospheric pressure. When U g. was dissolved in 25 g. of benzene, the freezing point of the benzene was lowered V degrees. Calculate the molecular formula of the compound.

	A	*B*	*C*	*D*
X	0.1908	0.1853	0.2350	0.2031
Y	0.2895	0.2763	0.3692	0.1986
Z	0.1192	0.1418	0.0756	0.1226
M	0.1825	0.1932	0.1792	0.1520
N	40.2	41.9	43.2	40.9
U	1.082	0.523	1.310	0.752
V	1.72	1.99	1.25	1.81

Chapter 2

ALKANES

Several families of organic compounds exist which contain only hydrogen and carbon in the molecule. They are known as *hydrocarbons*. The simplest family of this group is known as the *alkanes*. For reasons which will become apparent, they are known also as *saturated hydrocarbons* or *paraffin hydrocarbons*, or the *methane series* of hydrocarbons. All other families of the acyclic or aliphatic series can be considered as derived from the alkanes, and hence a knowledge of their properties and constitution is the best preparation for further study.

The simplest member of this family of hydrocarbons contains only one carbon atom and is called *methane*. It is a gas that liquefies at $-161°$ and has the composition and molecular weight corresponding to the molecular formula CH_4. The next member boils at $-89°$, has the molecular formula C_2H_6, and is called *ethane*. The third member, *propane*, C_3H_8, boils at $-42°$. It is apparent already that this family is a series of compounds having the general formula C_nH_{2n+2}, in which one member differs from each adjacent member by one carbon atom and two hydrogen atoms, that is, by CH_2. Such a series is known as a *homologous series*, and the members of the series are known as *homologs* (Gr. *homos*, same, and *logos*, speech; i.e., related or similar).

Structural Formulas

The electronic structure of the carbon atom explains the composition of these compounds and the existence of a homologous series. The carbon atom has four electrons which it can pair with four electrons of other atoms. Since only compounds of carbon and hydrogen are being considered, the simplest compound would be that in which a single carbon atom had paired its four electrons with the electrons of four hydrogen atoms to give the molecule

$$\begin{array}{c} H \\ \overset{\times}{\underset{\cdot\times}{H \overset{\cdot}{\underset{}{\times}} C \overset{\times}{\underset{}{\times}} H}} \\ H \end{array}$$

or CH_4. If two carbon atoms are in the molecule, they must be united to each other by a mutual sharing of electrons, $\cdot\, \overset{\cdot}{\underset{\cdot}{C}} \overset{\circ}{\underset{\circ}{\overset{}{}}} \overset{\circ}{C} \circ$, because the hydrogen atom with only one valence electron cannot combine with more than one carbon atom. Six electrons remain to be paired by combination with six hydrogen atoms to give the molecule

$$H \overset{\times\cdot}{\underset{\cdot\times}{C}} \overset{\times\circ}{\underset{\circ\times}{C}} H$$

with H H above and H H below, or C_2H_6. This process amounts to introducing a CH_2 group between one of the hydrogen atoms and the carbon atom in the methane molecule, or replacing a hydrogen atom by a

28

CH_3 group. If three atoms of carbon are in the molecule, the formula would be

$$\begin{array}{ccc} H & H & H \\ \cdot\cdot & \cdot\cdot & \cdot\cdot \\ H:C:C:C:H, & & or \quad C_3H_8. \\ \cdot\cdot & \cdot\cdot & \cdot\cdot \\ H & H & H \end{array}$$

In the last electronic formula no distinction has been made between the electrons supplied by different atoms. This representation is less artificial than the previous ones, since all electrons are identical. The important points to observe when writing electronic formulas are that the total number of valence electrons is correct, that all are paired, and that the valence shells of the atoms are filled (two electrons for hydrogen and usually eight electrons for all elements in the next two periods).

The operation of building hydrocarbons by applying the rules for valence can be carried on indefinitely. Hence compounds should exist with the molecular formulas C_4H_{10}, C_6H_{14}, or in fact any compound with the general formula C_nH_{2n+2}; that is, n CH_2 groups plus two hydrogen atoms to satisfy the remaining two unshared electrons. For alkanes having four or more carbon atoms, however, the situation becomes somewhat more complicated because two compounds are known having the same molecular formula C_4H_{10}. One boils at $-0.5°$, and the other boils at $-12°$. Two or more compounds having the same molecular formula but differing in at least one chemical or physical property are known as **isomers** (Gr. *isos*, equal and *meros*, part; that is, having equal or like parts), and the phenomenon is known as **isomerism.** It can be explained readily on the basis of electronic formulas. As soon as more than three carbon atoms are present, they can be arranged in more than one way. Four carbon atoms, for example, can be joined consecutively to each other, or one carbon atom can be united to the central atom of a chain of three atoms.

$$\begin{array}{cc} & \cdot \quad \cdot \quad \cdot \\ & \cdot C:C:C \cdot \\ \cdot C:C:C:C \cdot \quad \text{or} & \cdot\cdot \quad \cdot\cdot \\ & \cdot C \cdot \\ & \cdot \end{array}$$

Pairing the remaining unpaired electrons with those of hydrogen atoms gives the formulas

$$\begin{array}{cc} \begin{array}{cccc} H & H & H & H \\ \cdot\cdot & \cdot\cdot & \cdot\cdot & \cdot\cdot \\ H:C:C:C:C:H \\ \cdot\cdot & \cdot\cdot & \cdot\cdot & \cdot\cdot \\ H & H & H & H \end{array} \quad \text{and} & \begin{array}{ccc} H & H & H \\ \cdot\cdot & \cdot\cdot & \cdot\cdot \\ H:C & : & C & : C:H \\ \cdot\cdot & & \cdot\cdot \\ H & H:C:H & H \\ & \cdot\cdot \\ & H \end{array} \end{array}$$

Ordinarily the electron pair bond is represented by a dash, and the above formulas may be written

$$\begin{array}{cc} \begin{array}{cccc} H & H & H & H \\ | & | & | & | \\ H-C-C-C-C-H \\ | & | & | & | \\ H & H & H & H \end{array} \quad \text{and} & \begin{array}{ccc} H & H & H \\ | & | & | \\ H-C & C & C-H \\ | & | & | \\ H & & H \\ & H-C-H \\ & | \\ & H \end{array} \end{array}$$

Since the atoms are arranged differently in the two molecules, they should have different chemical and physical properties. The above two compounds are known as *butanes*. The compound with the carbon atoms linked consecutively in a chain is known as *normal butane*, and its isomer is called *isobutane*. Hydrocarbons having the carbon atoms linked in a continuous chain are called *normal* or *straight-chain* hydrocarbons. If *side chains* or *branches* are present, as in isobutane, they are known as *branched-chain* hydrocarbons. Formulas which show not only the number of atoms in the molecule but also the way in which they are united to each other are known as *structural* or *graphic formulas*. The arrangement of the atoms in the molecule is referred to as the *constitution* of the compound as distinguished from its *composition* as represented by its molecular formula (p. 21).

If the formulas are written in a plane with the carbon bonds directed to the corners of a square, more than one propane should be possible also; that is,

$$H_3C\overset{\displaystyle \overset{H}{|}}{\underset{\displaystyle \underset{CH_3}{|}}{C}}H \quad \text{might be expected as well as} \quad H_3C\overset{\displaystyle \overset{H}{|}}{\underset{\displaystyle \underset{H}{|}}{C}}CH_3. \quad \text{Similarly a consider-}$$

ably larger number of butanes should exist. Additional isomers, however, are not known, and the existence of optical isomers, which can be explained only by different arrangements in three dimensions (p. 335), led to the postulation that the bonds of a carbon atom are directed to the corners of a regular tetrahedron, as shown by the formula for methane (Fig. 22*a*) (cf. p. 12). Stuart or

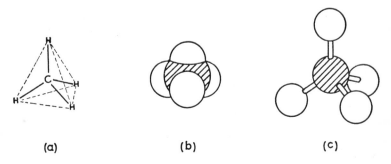

(a)   (b)   (c)

Fig. 22. Space representations of methane: (*a*) tetrahedral; (*b*) Stuart model; (*c*) ball and stick model.

Hirschfelder models (Fig. 22*b*) give the correct interatomic distances and the distances of closest approach of different molecules as determined by X-ray diffraction studies. It is difficult, however, to see the mode of linkage of atoms in complicated molecules with this type of model, and the ball and stick type (Fig. 22*c*) more commonly is used. On paper or on the lecture board the plane formulas, which show only the order in which the atoms are linked to each other, are most convenient.

With a tetrahedral arrangement of the carbon valences, all of the hydrogen atoms in the ethane molecule are alike; that is, each bears exactly the same space relationship to all the other atoms in the molecule (Fig. 23*a*). Hence replacement of any hydrogen atom by another atom or group of atoms gives only one new compound, and the two plane formulas for propane become identical in the space formula (Fig. 23b).

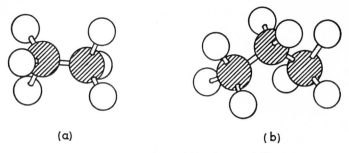

(a)   (b)

Fig. 23. Space representations of (a) ethane and (b) propane.

For compounds of more than three carbon atoms, the tetrahedral distribution of the valences might be thought capable of giving isomeric compounds even for normal hydrocarbons. A five-carbon chain might be expected to exist in numerous arrangements. In the examples illustrated in Fig. 24, only the carbon

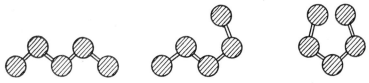

Fig. 24. Possible arrangements of carbon atoms in a five-carbon chain.

skeleton is indicated. Actually no isomers corresponding to these different arrangements have been detected. It is believed that all of the above arrangements and an infinite number of others exist in gases and liquids, but that, because of essentially free rotation about a single bond, the various forms interconvert at room temperature. The actual relative positions of the atoms at any instant is referred to as the *conformation* of the molecule. Thus the same molecule may have an infinite number of conformations, and a gas or liquid of the same molecular species consists of a mixture of molecules of different and continually changing conformations. However, the molecules do have preferred conformations in which they exist most of the time. Gaseous ethane, for example, is believed to prefer the staggered position (Fig. 23a) because the electron concentrations in the carbon-hydrogen bonds repel each other. It has been calculated that the barrier to free rotation about the carbon-carbon bond in the ethane molecule is about 3 kcal. per mole. This so-called *energy barrier* is the energy required to rotate the methyl groups with respect to each other sufficiently to bring the hydrogen atoms from the staggered position to the opposed position. Once the hydrogen atoms reach this position, further rotation of the methyl groups in the same or in the reverse direction returns the hydrogen atoms to a more stable position with the liberation of the same amount of energy. An energy barrier of 3 kcal. per mole is sufficient to ensure that most of the molecules at any instant have the most stable conformation. However, an energy barrier of at least 20 kcal. per mole is required to prevent thermal interconversions, that is, to permit the independent existence of isomers, at room temperature.

In the solid state the molecules are held in more or less fixed positions. Thus X-ray diffraction has shown that in crystals of long-chain paraffin hydrocarbons the molecules have the extended zigzag conformation (p. 40).

Besides the square and tetrahedral arrangements for carbon bonds, a pyramidal form could be considered in which the carbon atom occupies the apex of a square pyramid, and the valences are directed to the corners of the base (Fig. 25a). This structure has the same defect as the plane

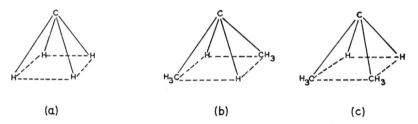

(a)   (b)   (c)

Fig. 25. (*a*) Pyramidal structure for methane; (*b*) and (*c*) predicted isomeric pyramidal structures for propane.

square in that the hydrogen atoms of methane could be replaced by two CH_3 groups in two different ways giving rise to two propanes (Fig. 25*b* and *c*), whereas only one propane is known.

With these facts available, it is possible to predict the number of isomeric alkanes having five carbon atoms. Three arrangements of the carbon atoms, called *carbon skeletons*, are possible,

$$C\text{—}C\text{—}C\text{—}C\text{—}C, \qquad C\text{—}C\underset{\overset{|}{C}}{\text{—}}C\text{—}C, \qquad \text{and} \qquad C\text{—}\underset{\overset{|}{C}}{\overset{\overset{C}{|}}{C}}\text{—}C.$$

They give rise to the three hydrocarbons

$$H\text{—}\underset{\overset{|}{H}}{\overset{\overset{H}{|}}{C}}\text{—}\underset{\overset{|}{H}}{\overset{\overset{H}{|}}{C}}\text{—}\underset{\overset{|}{H}}{\overset{\overset{H}{|}}{C}}\text{—}\underset{\overset{|}{H}}{\overset{\overset{H}{|}}{C}}\text{—}\underset{\overset{|}{H}}{\overset{\overset{H}{|}}{C}}\text{—}H, \quad \ldots, \quad \text{and} \quad \ldots$$

Actually three and only three compounds having the molecular formula C_5H_{12} are known. The compound to which the first structure has been assigned boils at 36° and is called *normal pentane*, that having the second structure boils at 28° and is called *isopentane*, and that having the third structure boils at 9.5° and is called *neopentane* (Gr. *neos*, new).

The above formulas are known as *extended structural formulas*. In order to conserve space and time in writing, they usually are replaced by *condensed structural formulas*, for example, $CH_3(CH_2)_3CH_3$, $CH_3CH_2CH(CH_3)_2$ or $C_2H_5CH(CH_3)_2$, and $C(CH_3)_4$.

Nomenclature

Obviously each organic compound must have a name. The development of nomenclature in organic chemistry always has followed the same pattern. When only a few compounds of a particular type are known and before their structures have been determined, they are given names usually indicative of their source. These names are called *trivial* or *common* names. As more compounds of a series become known, an attempt is made to develop a more systematic nomenclature which shows the relation of the new compounds to the older ones. Finally an attempt is made to develop a truly rational system. In the meantime, however, the older names have become established, and it is difficult to replace them by new ones, with the result that the simpler compounds usually have two or three names. Since all of these names are in more or less general use and appear in the literature, it is necessary to become familiar with them and to be able to use them interchangeably.

Common Names. In all systems names of the members of the alkane series end in *ane*. The names of hydrocarbons having four carbon atoms or less may be called common names because they are derived from the common names of the alcohols having the same number of carbon atoms. Above C_4 the names become a little more systematic by using the Greek (or Latin)[1] prefix to indicate the number of carbon atoms in the molecule.

C_5	pentanes	C_{16}–C_{19}	etc.
C_6	hexanes	C_{20}	eicosanes
C_7	heptanes	C_{21}	heneicosanes
C_8	octanes	C_{22}	docosanes
C_9	nonanes	C_{23}	tricosanes
C_{10}	decanes	C_{24}–C_{29}	etc.
C_{11}	undecanes	C_{30}	triacontanes
C_{12}	dodecanes	C_{31}	hentriacontanes
C_{13}	tridecanes	C_{32}–C_{39}	etc.
C_{14}	tetradecanes	C_{40}	tetracontanes
C_{15}	pentadecanes		etc.

These names do not indicate the structures of the many isomers existing in each case. When a second butane was found it was called *isobutane*, and the third pentane became *neopentane*, but new prefixes, if coined indefinitely, would become difficult to remember. The term *iso* still is retained for all compounds having a single carbon atom branch at the end of a straight chain. Thus isohexane is $(CH_3)_2CH(CH_2)_2CH_3$ and isononane is $(CH_3)_2CH(CH_2)_5CH_3$. The term *neo* is used in this series only for neopentane and neohexane.

As Derivatives of Methane. The necessity for devising a system that could be used for a larger number of isomers led to naming compounds as derivatives of a simple compound. Thus any alkane can be considered as derived from methane by replacing the hydrogen atoms by other groups of atoms. In isobutane three hydrogens of methane have been replaced by three CH_3 groups, and in isopentane by two CH_3 groups and one C_2H_5 group. In neopentane four

---

[1] Most of the names are of Greek derivation, but the Latin combining form *nona* is used almost universally instead of the Greek *ennea*. Similarly *undecane* is used more frequently than *hendecane*. Purists object to these inconsistencies as they do to the use of terms such as *mono-, di-, tri-,* and *tetravalent*, where prefixes of Greek origin are used with a word of Latin origin. Once a word becomes a part of a language, however, it is impractical, even if it were desirable, to try to bring about changes in terminology merely to be consistent.

TABLE 4

ALKYL GROUPS CONTAINING UP TO FOUR CARBON ATOMS

STRUCTURE OF GROUP	COMMON NAME	GENEVA NAME*
CH_3-	methyl	methyl
CH_3CH_2- or C_2H_5-	ethyl	ethyl
$CH_3CH_2CH_2-$	*n*-propyl	propyl
CH_3CHCH_3, CH_3 $\diagdown$ $CH-$, CH_3 $\diagup$ or $(CH_3)_2CH-$	*i*-propyl	(methylethyl)
$CH_3CH_2CH_2CH_2-$	*n*-butyl	butyl
$CH_3CH_2CHCH_3$, CH_3CH_2CH-, CH_3 or C_2H_5CH- CH_3	*s*-butyl	(1-methylpropyl)
CH_3CHCH_2- or CH_3 $(CH_3)_2CHCH_2-$	*i*-butyl	(2-methylpropyl)
CH_3 CH_3C- or $(CH_3)_3C-$ CH_3	*t*-butyl	(dimethylethyl)

* All isoalkyl names and also *s*-butyl, *t*-butyl, and neopentyl may be used as alternates for the systematic names of alkyl groups.

hydrogens have been replaced by four CH_3 groups. If these groups are given names, the compounds can be named as derivatives of methane. The groups themselves are hydrocarbons less one hydrogen atom and are called *alkyl* groups. They are named by dropping the *ane* of the alkane having the same number of carbon atoms and adding *yl*. CH_3 is *methyl* and C_2H_5 is *ethyl*. Isobutane then becomes trimethylmethane, isopentane becomes dimethyl-ethylmethane, and neopentane is tetramethylmethane. The prefix always is attached directly to the name to give one word.

It is customary to make use also of groups containing three and four carbon atoms in order to name more complicated compounds. Since there are *two kinds of hydrogen*[2] in propane, there are two propyl groups, $CH_3CH_2CH_2$— and $CH_3\overset{|}{C}HCH_3$. In order to indicate more clearly the carbon atom which lacks a hydrogen atom, it is customary to attach a long dash. In a molecule the group must be bonded to some other atom or group of atoms at this point.[3] To distinguish between the two propyl groups by name, they are called *normal propyl* or *n-propyl*, and *isopropyl* or *i-propyl*, respectively. Two groups each can be derived from *n*-butane and isobutane. *n*-Butane gives rise to the *n-butyl* group, $CH_3(CH_2)_2CH_2$—, and a group $CH_3CH_2\overset{|}{C}HCH_3$ which is called

secondary butyl (s-butyl) because the carbon atom which lacks a hydrogen atom is united directly to two other carbon atoms. Such a carbon atom is known as a *secondary carbon atom*. Isobutane gives rise to the *isobutyl* (*i-butyl*) group, $(CH_3)_2CHCH_2$—, and to the group $(CH_3)_3C$—. The latter is known as *tertiary butyl* (*t-butyl*), because the carbon atom lacking a hydrogen atom is a *tertiary carbon atom*; that is, it is united to three other carbon atoms. These eight groups form the basis for the systematic naming of a large number of compounds. Their names and their structures must be memorized. Once this has been done the nomenclature of most organic compounds will be remarkably simple. For convenience these groups and their names are collected in Table 4.

It is customary to name only branched alkanes as derivatives of methane. In general the most highly branched carbon atom is considered to be the methane carbon unless a less highly branched atom permits naming a smaller group. Thus compound (*a*) would be called trimethyl-*i*-propylmethane rather than

$$
\begin{array}{ccc}
& \overset{\displaystyle CH_3}{|} & \\
CH_3-CH-\overset{\displaystyle |}{C}-CH_3 \\
& \overset{\displaystyle |}{CH_3}\ \ \overset{\displaystyle |}{CH_3}
\end{array}
\qquad
\begin{array}{ccc}
& \overset{\displaystyle CH_3}{|} & \\
CH_3-CH-\overset{\displaystyle |}{C}-CH_3 \\
CH_3-\overset{\displaystyle |}{C}H\ \ \overset{\displaystyle |}{CH_3} \\
& \overset{\displaystyle |}{CH_3}
\end{array}
$$

(*a*)   (*b*)

---

[2] This expression arises from the fact that the properties of an atom in a molecule depend not only on the atom itself but also on the atom or atoms to which it is bonded. Thus it is possible to distinguish a hydrogen atom bonded to carbon from one bonded to oxygen or nitrogen. Likewise a hydrogen atom bonded to a carbon atom that in turn is joined to one carbon atom and two other hydrogen atoms is different from a hydrogen atom bonded to a carbon atom joined to two carbon atoms and one other hydrogen atom.

[3] In the past it has been customary to refer to these groups as *radicals*. The term *radical*, however, has taken on the connotation of a *free* group such as a *free radical*, which has an unpaired electron. Hence it is considered better to refer to the portions of a stable molecule as *groups*.

dimethyl-*t*-butylmethane. On the other hand compound (*b*) could be named methyl-*i*-propyl-*t*-butylmethane if the less highly branched carbon atom were considered to be the methane carbon atom but would require a name for a five-carbon group if the more highly branched carbon atom were chosen to represent methane.

Geneva, I.U.C., or I.U.P.A.C. System. The system which names compounds as derivatives of methane has the disadvantage that the eight groups given in Table 4 still are not sufficient for naming the more complicated compounds. This disadvantage is overcome to a considerable extent in the system adopted by the International Congress held at Geneva, Switzerland, in 1892, which has come to be known as the *Geneva system*. This system, as extended by the meeting of the International Union of Chemistry at Liège in 1930 and of the International Union of Pure and Applied Chemistry at Amsterdam in 1949 and subsequently, attempts to cover all the more important phases of the nomenclature of organic chemistry.[4] A summary of the rules for alkanes follows:[5]

(*1*) The ending for alkanes is *ane*.

(*2*) The common names for the normal (straight-chain) hydrocarbons are used.

(*3*) Branched-chain hydrocarbons are regarded as derivatives of normal hydrocarbons, the longest normal chain in the molecule being considered as the parent hydrocarbon. If there are two or more chains of equal length, that chain is selected which has the most branches, that is, the one which is the most highly substituted.

(*4*) The carbon atoms of the parent hydrocarbon are numbered from the end which gives the branched atoms the smaller numbers.

(*5*) The names of the branches or side chains are attached as prefixes directly to the parent name. Their position is indicated by the number of the atom to which they are attached. If two branches are on the same carbon atom, the number is repeated. The numbers precede the groups and are separated from the groups by hyphens. Consecutive numbers are separated from each other by commas.

(*6*) Alkyl groups containing more than four carbon atoms are named in the same way as the alkanes except that the ending is *yl*, and the point of attachment is numbered 1. The full name of the group is enclosed in parentheses (cf. Table 4, p. 34).

These rules and the other methods of nomenclature are illustrated in Table 5 by the names for the five isomeric hexanes and for a still more complicated compound. The advantages of naming compounds as derivatives of parent hydrocarbons are that it is easy to assign a name to every compound and to write the formula from the name. Thus the structure for 2,2,5-trimethyl-3-ethyl-hexane is written by joining six carbon atoms in a row, numbering them from 1 to 6, attaching three methyl groups and an ethyl group at the proper positions, and satisfying the remaining valences of the carbon atoms with hydrogen atoms.

---

[4] After the revisions the system has been referred to by some as the *I.U.C. system* and then the *I.U.P.A.C. system*, but most chemists still call the modified system the *Geneva system*.

[5] The rules laid down by the International Union are not without ambiguity, and a certain amount of flexibility has been allowed. What may be the best system for indexing may not be the most suitable for general use. The rules given are considered to be those most widely followed by chemists in the United States.

TABLE 5

NOMENCLATURE OF ALKANES

STRUCTURE	COMMON NAME	AS A DERIVATIVE OF METHANE	BY GENEVA SYSTEM
$CH_3(CH_2)_4CH_3$	normal hexane	not used	hexane

$CH_3CH(CH_2)_2CH_3$
     |
     CH_3
	isohexane	dimethyl-*n*-propylmethane	2-methylpentane

$CH_3CH_2CHCH_2CH_3$
        |
       CH_3
	none	methyldiethylmethane	3-methylpentane

$CH_3CH{-}CHCH_3$
    | |
   CH_3 CH_3
	(diisopropyl*)	dimethyl-*i*-propylmethane	2,3-dimethylbutane

CH_3
     |
 $CH_3{-}C{-}CH_2CH_3$
     |
     CH_3
	neohexane	trimethylethylmethane	2,2-dimethylbutane

$\overset{9}{C}H_3(CH_2)_3\overset{5}{C}H(CH_2)_3CH_3$
      |&overset{4}{}
    $CH_3{-}\overset{4}{C}H$
      | &overset{3}{} &overset{2}{} &overset{1}{}
       $\overset{3}{C}H_2{-}\overset{2}{C}H\overset{1}{C}H_3$
          |
         CH_3
	none	not possible using the first eight groups	2,4-dimethyl-5-butylnonane

* Occasionally a hydrocarbon is given a common name which indicates that it may be divided into two like groups.

A useful check on the correctness of a one-word name is that the sum of the carbon atoms in the various groups and in the parent hydrocarbon must equal the total number of carbon atoms in the molecule. In the last example of Table 5 each methyl group has one carbon atom, the butyl group has four, and the parent name nine, making a total of fifteen carbon atoms. This number checks with the number of carbon atoms in the formula. It should be noted also in this example that there are two different nine-carbon chains, but that by choosing the most highly substituted chain the necessity for naming a complicated six-carbon group is avoided. If it had been necessary to name this group, it would have been called the (1,3-dimethylbutyl) group. The parentheses are necessary to prevent confusion concerning the portion of the molecule to which the numbers refer. The compound

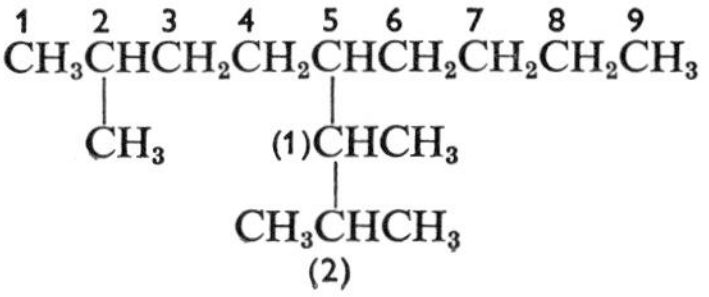

$$\overset{1}{C}H_3\overset{2}{C}H\overset{3}{C}H_2\overset{4}{C}H_2\overset{5}{C}H\overset{6}{C}H_2\overset{7}{C}H_2\overset{8}{C}H_2\overset{9}{C}H_3$$
$$\;\;\;\;\;\;| \;\;\;\;\;\;\;\;\;\;\;\;\;\; |$$
$$\;\;\;\;\;CH_3 \;\;\;\;\;\;\; (1)CHCH_3$$
$$\;\;\;\;\;\;\;\;\;\;\;\;\;\;\; CH_3CHCH_3$$
$$\;\;\;\;\;\;\;\;\;\;\;\;\;\;\;\; (2)$$

for example, would be called 2-methyl-5-(1,2-dimethylpropyl)nonane. The first five compounds in Table 5 are all hexanes because they have six carbon atoms, regardless of the fact that they are named as derivatives of methane, butane, and pentane. The last compound of the list is a pentadecane even though it is named as a derivative of nonane.

In the naming of compounds as derivatives of another compound, it is conventional to consider the name as one word rather than to write the names of groups and parent compound as separate words or to use an unnecessary number of hyphens. It is preferable to limit the use of hyphens to the attachment of position numbers and symbols.

As the number of carbon atoms increases, the number of structural isomers possible soon reaches astronomical proportions as shown by the following figures which were arrived at by rather complicated mathematical formulas.

C_7 —9	C_{15}—4347
C_8 —18	C_{20}—366,319
C_9 —35	C_{30}—4,111,846,763
C_{10}—75	C_{40}—6.25 × 10^{13}

By 1947 all of the predicted alkanes through the nonanes, and over half of the decanes were known. Only a few isomers of each of the higher groups of compounds are known, chiefly because there has not been a sufficiently good reason for organic chemists to attempt to synthesize them or because those who are interested in them have not yet had time to do so. The largest alkane of known structure and molecular weight synthesized so far has the molecular formula $C_{100}H_{202}$.

Physical Properties

The physical properties of organic compounds depend in general on the number and kind of atoms in the molecule and on the way in which the atoms are linked together. At 25° and 760 mm., the normal hydrocarbons are gases from C_1 to C_4, liquids from C_5 to C_{17}, and solids for C_{18} and above.

Boiling Points. The boiling points of the normal hydrocarbons increase with increasing molecular weight. When plotted against the number of carbon atoms, they fall on a smooth curve as shown in Fig. 26. The rise in boiling point is due to the increased attraction between molecules as the number of atoms increases. This attraction is known as the *van der Waals force*[6] and comes into play when molecules are close to each other.

Branching of the chain always results in a lowering of the boiling point, the van der Waals force being smaller for a more compact molecule than for a longer molecule. Thus *n*-pentane boils at 36°, isopentane at 28°, and neopentane at 9.5°.

---

[6] So-called because it is the cause of the *a* term in the van der Waals equation, $\left(P + \dfrac{a}{V^2}\right)(V - b) = RT$ for one mole of gas. The law for a perfect gas, $PV = RT$, holds only if the molecules of a gas have no attraction for each other and occupy no volume. By introducing a constant *a* to take care of the attraction between molecules and a constant *b* to offset the volume occupied by the molecules, the equation fits more closely the experimental data. Constants *a* and *b* are characteristic for each compound.

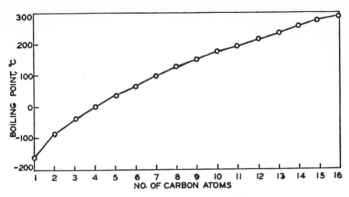

Fig. 26. Boiling points of normal alkanes.

The boiling point of a compound at a given pressure may be taken as a rough measure of the attractive forces between molecules, since the boiling point is merely the temperature at which the thermal agitation of the molecules is sufficient to overcome the attractive forces between them. All attractive forces are electrical and vary continuously with the structure of the molecule. For the alkanes these forces arise because of the *polarizability* of the molecule. Although the negative charges of the electrons in a neutral molecule are balanced by the positive charges on the nuclei, the electrons are in motion, and the center of density of the negative charges of the electrons does not coincide continuously with the center of density of the positive charges of the nuclei. This condition gives rise to a transient slight separation of charge in the molecule, or an *electrical dipole*, which is called the *polarization* of the molecule. As a result of this dipole, molecules which approach each other closely enough and with the proper orientation tend to adhere, the ends of unlike charge attracting each other. Once the attractive force comes into play, the polarization of the molecule is increased. Therefore even simple molecules such as helium and hydrogen have some tendency to adhere. The ease of polarizability and hence the strength of the attractive force increases as the number of electrons increases and hence as the number and complexity of the atoms in the molecule increases. For normal alkanes the force amounts to about 1.0 kcal. per carbon atom per mole and accounts for the regular increase in boiling point with increasing molecular weight within a homologous series. It is not possible to distill without decomposition hydrocarbons having more than around 80 carbon atoms, no matter how perfect the vacuum, because the energy of about 80 kcal. per mole required to separate the molecules is approximately the same as that necessary to break a carbon-carbon bond (pp. 45, 46). These forces vary inversely as the seventh power of the distance between the molecules and hence are operative only when molecules approach each other very closely. Branching of a molecule tends to decrease the magnitude of the transient dipole and prevents the optimum proximity of the molecules to each other, thus accounting for the lower boiling points of branched compounds. Attractive forces that are due to transient polarizability usually are called *London forces*.

Melting Points. The melting points of normal alkanes do not fall on a smooth curve but show alternation (Fig. 27). With the exception of methane they fall on two curves, an upper one for the hydrocarbons having an even number of carbon atoms and a lower one for those with an odd number of carbon atoms. X-ray investigations of solid hydrocarbons have shown that the chains of the saturated hydrocarbons are extended, the carbon atoms taking a zigzag arrangement. With compounds having an even number of carbon atoms the end carbon atoms are on opposite sides of the molecule, whereas for those having an odd number they are on the same side (Fig. 28). Apparently the molecules having an odd number of carbon atoms do not fit together so well as those having an even number, and the van der Waals force is not so effective.

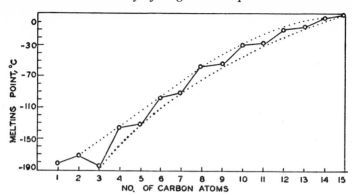

Fig. 27. Melting points of normal alkanes.

Unlike the variation in boiling points, there is no regularity in the change in melting point with branching, because the effectiveness of the attractive forces depends on how well the molecule fits into the crystal lattice. Thus *n*-pentane melts at $-129.7°$, isopentane at $-160°$, and neopentane at $-20°$. In general, however, the more symmetrical and compact the molecule, the higher its melting point. Hexamethylethane, $(CH_3)_3CC(CH_3)_3$, is interesting in that it melts at $100.7°$ and boils at $106.3°$.

Fig. 28. Extended chains having an even and an odd number of carbon atoms.

Other Properties. The *density* of the normal alkanes gradually increases from 0.626 g. per cc. at $20°$ for pentane to 0.769 for pentadecane. This behavior is to be expected if the attraction between the molecules increases as indicated by the rise in boiling points. Similarly the density decreases with branching of the chain. The *viscosity* of the normal alkanes increases with increasing chain length, because the greater attraction between the molecules and the increased possibility for entanglement increases the difficulty for the molecules to slip past one another. The alkanes are almost completely *insoluble in water*, because they have little attraction for water molecules whereas water molecules have considerable attraction for each other (pp. 87, 88). They are miscible with many other organic compounds because the attractions between like molecules and unlike molecules are of the same order of magnitude.[7]

Sources of the Alkanes

The commercial sources of the saturated hydrocarbons are *natural gas* and *petroleum*. Paraffin hydrocarbons are present also in the *products of the destructive distillation of coal*. Natural gas usually is composed chiefly of **methane** and

---

[7] The outstanding investigator of the relation of physical properties to chemical constitution was Herman Kopp (1817–1892), professor of chemistry at Heidelberg. He is well known also for his History of Chemistry, a four-volume work, the first volume of which was published in 1843, when Kopp was twenty-six years old, and the last in 1847. It still is the outstanding work in its field for the period covered.

smaller amounts of **ethane, propane** and the **butanes** (p. 69). Petroleum contains a large number of the liquid hydrocarbons (p. 71). Methane also is a product of the action of anaerobic organisms on cellulose and other organic matter. For example it is formed during the decomposition of vegetable matter under water in marshes, whence the common name *marsh gas*. Large amounts are formed during the treatment of sewage by the activated sludge process. It also is present in coal mines and, because it is one of the causes of explosions, it is known as *fire damp*. **n-Heptane** is present in the volatile oil of the fruit of *Pittosporum resiniferum*, and in the turpentine of the digger pine (*Pinus sabiniana*) and the Jeffrey pine (*Pinus jeffreyi*) of the Sierras. It readily can be obtained pure in quantity from the last source. The normal hydrocarbons having an odd number of carbon atoms from C_{25} to C_{37} occur in many plant and insect waxes. For example the waxes from leaves of members of the cabbage family (*Brassica*) contain the C_{29} and C_{31} normal hydrocarbons, and spinach wax contains the C_{33}, C_{35}, and C_{37} hydrocarbons.

Individual alkanes of known structure usually are obtained by synthesis, that is, by making them from certain other compounds. These methods of synthesis are given in Chapter 7.

Chemical Properties

1. **Inertness to Most Reagents.** The alkanes are not affected by aqueous solutions of acids, alkalies, oxidizing agents, or most other reagents at room temperature and frequently resist reaction under more drastic conditions. This inertness gave rise to the name paraffin (L. *parum* little; *affinis* akin) for a saturated hydrocarbon.[8]

Two factors are important to chemists in their use of chemical reactions: (*1*) the position of equilibrium for the reaction, and (*2*) the rate at which equilibrium is established. The first factor determines the maximum yield of products under the conditions of the experiment, and the second factor determines how fast the reaction goes. The chemist is interested in the latter aspect, not only because a reaction must go at an appreciable rate to be useful, but also because if two or more competing reactions are taking place, as usually is the case in organic reactions, the relative rates of the reactions may be more important in determining the yield of desired product than the relative positions of equilibrium of the competing reactions.

The position of equilibrium depends only on the free energy change of the reaction; that is, it is governed only by energy relationships or thermodynamics, and is not concerned with the path by which the reactants are converted into the products. Relative rates of reactions, however, are intimately concerned with the process by which the molecules react.

In order to explain the inertness of alkanes, it is necessary to consider in detail the way in which reactions that involve covalent bonds take place. Such reactions usually result from a series of steps known as the *mechanism* of the reaction. Covalent bonds are strong bonds and must be broken before or during the reaction in order that recombination of the parts of the reactants can take place. It is conceivable that the covalent bond may break in two ways: either one electron goes to each atom joined by the bond as in (*a*), or the pair of electrons stays with one or the other of the two atoms as in (*b*) or (*c*). The first way is called *homolysis*, and the second *heterolysis* (Gr. *homos*, same; *hetero*, other; and *lysis*, loosing).

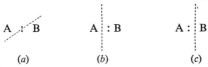

$$A \cdot \cdot B \qquad\qquad A : B \qquad\qquad A : B$$

$$(a) \qquad\qquad\quad (b) \qquad\qquad\quad (c)$$

---

[8] The term *paraffin* first was used by Karl Reichenbach (1788–1869), an Austrian, for a wax which he isolated from the tar obtained by the destructive distillation of beechwood.

If the fragments $[A \cdot]$ and $[B \cdot]$ could exist with an unpaired electron, they would be known as *free radicals* (p. 567); hence mechanisms in which bonds break by process (*a*) are known as **free-radical mechanisms.** Reactions in the gas phase and reactions catalyzed by free radicals in the liquid phase usually are explainable by this type of mechanism. If the fragments resulting from process (*b*) or (*c*) could exist as such, they would be the ions $[A^+]$ and $[: B^-]$, or $[A : ^-]$ and $[B^+]$. Positive groups containing a carbon atom that lacks a pair of electrons in its valence shell are called **carbonium ions.** Negative groups containing a carbon atom that has an unshared pair of electrons are called **carbanions.** Mechanisms in which the bonds are assumed to break by process (*b*) or (*c*) during reaction are known as **ionic mechanisms.** Reactions involving polar molecules or ions in the liquid phase are believed to take place usually by way of ionic mechanisms.

It should be emphasized that this theory does not postulate that the formation of free radicals or ions is necessary as an intermediate step in the reaction or that the free radicals or ions represented by $[A \cdot], [B \cdot], [A^+], [: B^-], [A : ^-],$ or $[B^+]$ are capable of independent existence. There is good evidence that under certain conditions some groups of this type do have an appreciable life span or can exist in appreciable equilibrium concentration, but under the usual conditions for reactions the energies required for complete dissociation into free radicals or ions are too great for dissociation to take place prior to reaction. The transition from one covalently bound state to another takes place continuously without the formation of a really free radical or free ion at any time. The arrangement of maximum energy content through which the reacting molecules must pass before the products can be formed is known as the **transition state** or the **activated complex.** The energy that must be supplied to the reacting molecules before they can attain the transition state is called the **activation energy** for the reaction. **Catalysts** are substances that can cause the formation of a transition state having a lower activation energy than one that must be formed in the absence of a catalyst.

High reactivity is associated with conditions in the molecule which favor the making or breaking of a covalent bond. Such conditions are the presence in the molecule of (*1*) an incomplete valence shell, (*2*) an unshared pair of electrons, or (*3*) a partially polarized covalent bond. Thus boron fluoride lacks a pair of electrons in its valence shell and hydrogen fluoride has unshared pairs of electrons on the fluorine atom. Moreover the strongly electron-attracting fluorine atom pulls the bonding pair of electrons away from the hydrogen atom, leaving the latter deficient in electrons. Hence the activation energy for the reaction between hydrogen fluoride and boron fluoride is very low and reaction takes place spontaneously at well below room temperature.

$$H : \overset{\cdot\cdot}{\underset{\cdot\cdot}{F}} : + B : \overset{\cdot\cdot}{\underset{\cdot\cdot}{\overset{\textstyle : \overset{\cdot\cdot}{F} :}{\underset{\textstyle : \overset{\cdot\cdot}{F} :}{F}}}} : \longrightarrow \left[H : \overset{\cdot\cdot}{\underset{\cdot\cdot}{F}} : \overset{\textstyle : \overset{\cdot\cdot}{F} :}{\underset{\textstyle : \overset{\cdot\cdot}{F} :}{B}} : \overset{\cdot\cdot}{\underset{\cdot\cdot}{F}} : \right] \longrightarrow [H^+] [BF_4^-]$$

None of these conditions exists in the alkanes. All valence shells are filled and all electron pairs are shared. The carbon-carbon bonds of alkanes are nonpolar and the carbon-hydrogen bonds only slightly so. Hence it is not surprising that the saturated hydrocarbons are relatively unreactive.

2. Oxidation at High Temperature. Hydrocarbons in the presence of oxygen or strong oxidizing agents at high temperatures burn to carbon dioxide and water.

$$CH_4 + 2 O_2 \longrightarrow CO_2 + 2 H_2O$$

$$C_2H_6 + 3\tfrac{1}{2} O_2 \longrightarrow 2 CO_2 + 3 H_2O$$

$$C_3H_8 + 5 O_2 \longrightarrow 3 CO_2 + 4 H_2O$$

$$C_nH_{2n+2} + \frac{3n+1}{2} O_2 \longrightarrow n CO_2 + (n + 1) H_2O$$

For the gaseous hydrocarbons, the difference between the total volume of gases before combustion and the total volume after combustion changes from one homolog to the next. At room temperature, the water formed is condensed to a liquid. Hence one volume of methane and two volumes of oxygen, a total of three volumes, give one volume of carbon dioxide, a contraction in volume of twice the volume of methane. Similarly 4.5 volumes of ethane give rise to 2 volumes, a contraction of 2.5 times the volume of ethane, and 6 volumes of propane give 3 volumes, a contraction of 3 volumes. Therefore a pure hydrocarbon gas can be identified by mixing a known volume with an excess of oxygen or air, burning in a closed system, and measuring the volume after combustion.

The equations indicate also that the volume of carbon dioxide produced per volume of hydrocarbon is different for different hydrocarbons. Thus one volume of methane gives one volume of carbon dioxide, one volume of ethane gives two of carbon dioxide, and one volume of propane gives three of carbon dioxide. The volume of carbon dioxide produced can be determined readily by noting the decrease in volume on shaking with a solution of potassium hydroxide. Hence it is possible to identify pure unknown hydrocarbons by measuring either the contraction on combustion or the volume of carbon dioxide produced. Moreover the composition of a mixture of two pure known hydrocarbons can be determined by either measurement. The composition of a mixture of two known hydrocarbons with a third nonoxidizable gas can be determined by measuring both the contraction and the volume of carbon dioxide, and setting up and solving algebraic equations.

The oxidation or combustion of hydrocarbons to carbon dioxide and water takes place with the evolution of heat. The amount of energy liberated per mole of compound is known as the *heat of combustion* of the compound. The data in Table 6 show that the heat of combustion per mole increases with increasing

TABLE 6

HEATS OF COMBUSTION OF PARAFFIN HYDROCARBONS

	COMPOUND	KCAL. PER MOLE	KCAL. PER GRAM
Gaseous	Methane	212.8	13.3
	Ethane	372.8	12.4
	Propane	530.6	12.2
	n-Butane	688.0	11.9
	i-Butane	686.3	11.8
	n-Pentane	845.2	11.8
	i-Pentane	843.2	11.7
	Neopentane	840.5	11.7
Liquid	n-Pentane	838.8	11.6
	n-Hexane	995.0	11.6
	n-Heptane	1151.3	11.5
	n-Octane	1307.5	11.5
	n-Nonane	1463.8	11.4
	n-Decane	1620.1	11.4
	n-Pentadecane	2401.4	11.3
	n-Eicosane	3182.7	11.3

number of carbon atoms. Most of the heat arises from the difference between the sum of the bond energies of the reactants and that of the products. Therefore the greater the number of bonds broken and reformed to more stable structures, the greater the heat evolved. For any homologous series the increment per CH_2 group is constant at approximately 156 kcal. The data show further that the heat of combustion of the liquid form is less than that of the gaseous form by the heat of vaporization of the compound, and that isomers do not have identical heats of combustion.

Although the energy relationships (thermodynamics) for the oxidation of alkanes are highly favorable, the activation energy is high. Thermal energy equal to the activation energy must be supplied to start the reaction. Once the reaction starts, sufficient energy is liberated to permit the reaction to continue. Catalysts, such as finely divided platinum, may greatly lower the activation energy and hence the temperature at which ignition takes place.

The fact that the combustion of hydrocarbons is exothermic is the basis for their use as fuels. The flammability depends on the volatility of the hydrocarbon. Mixtures of air and hydrocarbon vapors in the proper proportions explode on ignition, which gives rise to their use in the internal combustion engine. In a deficient oxygen supply, carbon monoxide, or elementary carbon in the form of carbon black, may be produced.

The term **flammability** is a very loose one. For example it may refer merely to the relative ability of the material to burn in the presence of oxygen with the evolution of heat. From this viewpoint hydrocarbons are more flammable than compounds containing a high per cent of oxygen, which in turn are more flammable than those containing a large amount of halogen. On the other hand flammability may refer to the volatility of the compound such as the greater flammability of gasoline over lubricating oil. This factor is measured by the **flash point** of the material, that is, the temperature to which it must be heated before the vapors will ignite by a free flame in the presence of air. The flash point of gasoline is $-45°$ whereas that of motor lubricating oil is $232°$. The flammability also may be influenced by the **explosion limits** of mixtures of air and combustible vapors. Thus mixtures of n-pentane vapors and air will explode only when the per cent by volume of pentane is between 1.5 and 7.5. With higher or lower pentane content no explosion will take place on application of a spark or flame. At the other extreme, hydrogen is explosive in the range of 4 to 74 per cent. Finally the **ignition temperature,** that is, the temperature at which a combustible mixture with air will ignite in the absence of a flame, is important. Hydrogen will not ignite until a temperature of $582°$ is reached, n-pentane vapor ignites at $309°$, whereas carbon disulfide vapors will ignite at $100°$, the temperature of boiling water.

From the hazard standpoint, one other factor should be mentioned. Most vapors have a density greater than that of air and may create a hazard by accumulating in low spots such as along the floor, in sinks, and in sewers.

3. **Decomposition at High Temperature.** At sufficiently high temperatures hydrocarbons decompose in the absence of oxygen, a phenomenon known as **cracking** or **pyrolysis** (Gr. *pyr*, fire, and *lysis*, loosing). Methane yields carbon and hydrogen as final products.

$$CH_4 \longrightarrow C + 2 H_2$$

For the reaction to proceed rapidly with methane, temperatures above $1200°$ are required.[9] Other hydrocarbons decompose rapidly at considerably lower temperatures. In the decomposition of ethane at $600°$ a new hydrocarbon is formed by the loss of one molecule of hydrogen from a molecule of ethane.

$$C_2H_6 \longrightarrow C_2H_4 + H_2$$
Ethylene

The new compound, ethylene, belongs to another homologous series, C_nH_{2n}, known as the alkenes, olefins, or unsaturated hydrocarbons (Chapter 3).

---

[9] When subjected to higher temperatures for very short periods, other products such as ethylene, acetylene, and benzene also are formed (p. 133).

Propane at 600° decomposes to give four products which arise from the following reactions.

$$CH_3CH_2CH_3 \longrightarrow C_3H_6 + H_2$$

Propylene

$$CH_3CH_2CH_3 \longrightarrow C_2H_4 + CH_4$$

Ethylene   Methane

Actually ethylene and methane are the principal products (p. 52). Higher alkanes on cracking give hydrogen and mixtures of alkanes and alkenes having varying numbers of carbon atoms. This cracking process is of great importance to the petroleum industry (p. 74), because it provides a means for making smaller, more volatile hydrocarbon molecules from the larger, less volatile molecules that predominate in most natural petroleum.

The energy required for the heterolytic dissociation of hydrocarbons into two free ions is about three times that required for homolytic dissociation into two free radicals or into a free radical and a hydrogen atom. Hence thermal cracking takes place by a free radical mechanism (cf. p. 41). Thus methane decomposes into carbon atoms and hydrogen atoms.

$$
\begin{array}{c}
\text{H} \\
\overset{\cdot\cdot}{} \\
\text{H} : \text{C} : \text{H} \longrightarrow 4\text{H} \cdot + \cdot \text{C} \cdot \\
\overset{\cdot\cdot}{} \\
\text{H}
\end{array}
$$

The hydrogen atoms combine to form molecular hydrogen and the carbon atoms to give amorphous carbon.

For ethane two primary reactions are possible, dissociation of the carbon-carbon bond to give two methyl radicals, or dissociation of the carbon-hydrogen bond to give an ethyl radical and a hydrogen atom.

$$CH_3CH_3 \longrightarrow 2\,CH_3 \cdot \tag{1}$$

$$CH_3CH_3 \longrightarrow C_2H_5 \cdot + H \cdot \tag{2}$$

Energetically the first reaction is easier, the homolytic bond dissociation energy of a carbon-carbon bond in ethane being 84.4 kcal. per mole compared with 97.5 kcal. per mole for a carbon-hydrogen bond.[10]

Once free methyl radicals are formed, several other reactions can take place readily because their activation energy is relatively small (5 to 10 kcal. per mole).

$$CH_3 \cdot + CH_3CH_3 \longrightarrow CH_4 + C_2H_5 \cdot \tag{3}$$

$$C_2H_5 \cdot \longrightarrow C_2H_4 + H \cdot \tag{4}$$

$$H \cdot + C_2H_6 \longrightarrow C_2H_5 \cdot + H_2 \tag{5}$$

Reaction (1) initiates the process. Reactions (3) and especially (4) and (5) are the propagating steps in the conversion of ethane into ethylene and hydrogen. Because each time a free radical

---

[10] Two methods of expressing bond energies are used. One assumes that the bond energy between two given kinds of atoms is the same regardless of the rest of the structure of the molecule. Although widely referred to simply as "bond energy," it should be called the *average* or *mean bond energy*. Its chief use has been to calculate the energy liberated or adsorbed during a reaction, but it is of no value in predicting the relative rates of different reactions. The second method recognizes that the energy required to break a bond between two given kinds of elements depends on. the structure of the rest of the molecule. This energy is called the *bond dissociation energy* and refers to the energy necessary to break a specific bond.

is destroyed a new one is formed, this type of reaction is called a **chain reaction**. The chain may be terminated by combination of any pair of free radicals. In the decomposition of ethane, it is thought that the chief chain-breaking reactions are the combination of two ethyl radicals and the combination of an ethyl radical and a hydrogen atom. The three phases *initiation*, *propagation*, and *termination* are characteristic of chain reactions.

The possible primary homolytic dissociations for propane are

$$CH_3CH_2CH_3 \longrightarrow CH_3CH_2 \cdot + CH_3 \cdot \tag{1}$$

$$CH_3CH_2CH_3 \longrightarrow CH_3CH_2CH_2 \cdot + H \cdot \tag{2}$$

$$CH_3CH_2CH_3 \longrightarrow CH_3\overset{\cdot}{C}HCH_3 + H \cdot \tag{3}$$

with bond dissociation energies of 82.2, 95.5, and 90.8 kcal. per mole respectively. Here again reaction (1) chiefly is responsible for initiating the decomposition. Possible propagating reactions are

$$CH_3 \cdot + CH_3CH_2CH_3 \longrightarrow CH_4 + CH_3CH_2CH_2 \cdot \tag{4}$$

$$\longrightarrow CH_4 + CH_3\overset{\cdot}{C}HCH_3 \tag{5}$$

$$C_2H_5 \cdot + CH_3CH_2CH_3 \longrightarrow C_2H_6 + CH_3CH_2CH_2 \cdot \tag{6}$$

$$\longrightarrow C_2H_6 + CH_3\overset{\cdot}{C}HCH_3 \tag{7}$$

$$C_2H_5 \cdot \longrightarrow C_2H_4 + H \cdot \tag{8}$$

$$CH_3CH_2CH_2 \cdot \longrightarrow C_3H_6 + H \cdot \tag{9}$$

$$CH_3\overset{\cdot}{C}HCH_3 \longrightarrow C_3H_6 + H \cdot \tag{10}$$

$$H \cdot + CH_3CH_2CH_3 \longrightarrow H_2 + CH_3CH_2CH_2 \cdot \tag{11}$$

$$\longrightarrow H_2 + CH_3\overset{\cdot}{C}HCH_3 \tag{12}$$

$$CH_3CH_2CH_2 \longrightarrow C_2H_4 + CH_3 \cdot \tag{13}$$

Energetically the easiest reaction should be (13). Although reaction (5) would be expected to require less energy than (4), the chance for colliding with a secondary hydrogen atom is only one third of that for colliding with a primary hydrogen. Hence it is not surprising that reactions (4) and (13) predominate over reactions (5), (9), and (10). Termination of chains again can take place by the combination of two free radicals.

4. **Isomerization.** Although alkanes show a marked resistance to structural change, a phenomenon which is characteristic of carbon bonds and which van't Hoff (p. 335) termed "the inertia of the carbon system," they undergo certain reactions readily in the presence of suitable catalysts. Thus when either *n*-butane or *i*-butane is placed in contact with a catalyst of aluminum bromide and hydrogen bromide, an equilibrium mixture of 20 per cent *n*-butane and 80 per cent *i*-butane is formed at 27°.

$$CH_3CH_2CH_2CH_3 \underset{\longleftarrow}{\overset{AlBr_3,\ HBr}{\rightleftarrows}} \underset{\underset{CH_3}{|}}{CH_3CHCH_3}$$

The conversion of one isomer into another is known as **isomerization.** The isomerization of hydrocarbons plays an important part in the production of modern gasolines (p. 78). The mechanism of isomerization is discussed on p. 79.

The alkanes also undergo other reactions such as alkylation (p. 77), controlled oxidation (p. 220), halogenation (p. 119), and nitration (p. 259).

REVIEW QUESTIONS

1. What is meant by the term *isomers?* How is the existence of isomers explained?
2. How does a structural formula differ from a molecular formula and why are structural formulas necessary for organic compounds? What are the fundamental assumptions on which structural theory is based?
3. What is meant by the term *homologous series?* Compare the physical and chemical properties of the members of a homologous series. Compare the chemical properties of the members of one homologous series with those of another series.
4. Give condensed structural formulas and names for all alkyl groups containing four carbon atoms and less.
5. What is meant by the terms *primary, secondary, tertiary,* and *quaternary* as applied to carbon atoms?

PROBLEMS

6. Write condensed structural formulas for all of the isomers that meet the following descriptions, name each isomer by the Geneva system, and name branched chain compounds also as derivatives of methane: (*a*) all of the heptanes; (*b*) all of the octanes having a chain of five carbon atoms; (*c*) all of the octanes having a chain of six carbon atoms; (*d*) all of the decanes having a chain of five carbon atoms.
7. Give the Geneva name and one other name for the following compounds:
   (*a*) $CH_3(CH_2)_7CH_3$; (*b*) $(CH_3)_2CH(CH_2)_7CH_3$; (*c*) $(CH_3)_2CHCH_2CH(CH_3)_2$;
   (*d*) $C_2H_5CH(CH_3)CH_2CH_3$; (*e*) $(CH_3)_3CCH(CH_3)C_2H_5$; (*f*) $(CH_3)_3CC(CH_2)_3CH_3$;
   (*g*) $(CH_3)_2CHCH_2C(CH_3)_3$; (*h*) $C_2H_5CH(CH_3)CH(CH_3)_2$; (*i*) $(C_2H_5)_2C(CH_3)CH(CH_3)_2$;
   (*j*) $(CH_3)_3CCH(CH_3)C_2H_5$.
8. Give a suitable name for each of the following compounds:

   (*a*) $(CH_3)_3C$ $CH(CH_3)_2$ (*b*) $(CH_3)_2CHCH_2$ (*c*) CH_3CHCH_3

        CH_3CH—CH $(CH_3)_3CCCH_3$ $CH_3CHCHCH_3$

        $C_2H_5CHCH_3$ C_2H_5 $CH_3CH_2CHCH_3$

   (*d*) CH_3CH_2 (*e*) CH_3CHCH_3 (*f*) $C_2H_5CHCH(CH_3)_2$

       $(CH_3)_3CCC(CH_3)_3$ $C_2H_5CCH_2CH(CH_3)_2$ $CHCH_3$

        CH_3CHCH_3 $CH_3CHCH(CH_3)_2$ $CH_3(CH_2)_3CH(CH_2)_3CH_3$

9. Write condensed structural formulas for the following compounds: (*a*) undecane; (*b*) isodecane; (*c*) methyldiethyl-*i*-butylmethane; (*d*) 6-(1,2-dimethylpropyl)dodecane; (*e*) hexadecane; (*f*) 2,3,4-trimethylpentane; (*g*) 5-(2,2-dimethylpropyl)nonane; (*h*) 4-*i*-propyl-5-*t*-butyloctane; (*i*) 5-(2,2-dimethylpropyl)-7-(1-methyl-2-ethylbutyl)dodecane; (*j*) 2-methyl-3-ethyl-3-*i*-propylheptane.
10. Tell why the following names are objectionable and give a suitable name to each: (*a*) 3-propylhexane; (*b*) 4-methylpentane; (*c*) methyl-3-pentane; (*d*) methyl-*i*-propylmethane; (*e*) 3-*i*-propylhexane; (*f*) 4-(1,2-dimethylethyl)heptane; (*g*) dimethyl-*t*-butylmethane.
11. Write structural formulas and give the Geneva names for all of the alkyl groups that can be derived from the following compounds and indicate whether the alkyl group is primary, secondary, or tertiary: (*a*) 2-methylpentane; (*b*) 3-methylpentane; (*c*) neohexane; (*d*) isoheptane; (*e*) isopentane; (*f*) 2,3-dimethylpentane; (*g*) methyldiethyl-*i*-propylmethane.
12. Write balanced equations for the combustion of the following gases in an excess of oxygen and give the contraction in volume and the volume of carbon dioxide produced compared to the original volume of hydrocarbon: (*a*) ethane; (*b*) propane; (*c*) butane; (*d*) neopentane.

13. Identify the alkane and write the equation for the reaction in each of the following combustions: (a) The volume of carbon dioxide formed was twice the volume of hydrocarbon used; (b) the contraction in volume was four fifths of the volume of carbon dioxide produced; (c) the volume of carbon dioxide produced was one half of the contraction in volume; (d) the contraction was equal to the volume of carbon dioxide formed.

14. (a) When 100 cc. of a mixture of ethane and air was burned with an excess of oxygen, 32 cc. of carbon dioxide was formed. How much ethane was in the mixture?

   (b) When 100 cc. of a mixture of butane and nitrogen was mixed with an excess of oxygen and burned, a contraction in volume of 70 cc. took place. How much butane was in the mixture?

   (c) When 50 cc. of a mixture containing only ethane and propane was burned with an excess of oxygen, the volume of carbon dioxide formed was 130 cc. How much ethane was in the mixture?

   (d) When 10 cc. of a mixture containing only propane and pentane was burned with an excess of oxygen, the contraction in volume was 36 cc. How much propane was in the mixture?

   (e) Ten cubic centimeters of a mixture of methane, ethane, and air was burned completely with an excess of oxygen in a closed system. The contraction in volume on burning was 13 cc. and a further contraction of 8 cc. was observed on washing the products of combustion with a solution of potassium hydroxide. All volumes were measured at the same temperature and pressure. What was the per cent composition of the original mixture? (Hint: let x equal the volume of methane and y equal the volume of ethane, and from the data set up two simultaneous equations and solve.)

Chapter 3

ALKENES.   CYCLIC HYDROCARBONS

ALKENES

Like the alkanes, the second family or homologous series of organic compounds also are hydrocarbons. They are known as the *alkenes*. They also are
called *ethylenes* from the name of the first member of the series, or *olefins* from
olefiant gas, an old name for ethylene (p. 53). The members of this second
series have the general formula C_nH_{2n}; that is, each member has two less
hydrogen atoms than the corresponding alkane. Because they do not contain
the maximum number of hydrogen atoms, they frequently are called *unsaturated*
hydrocarbons in contrast to the alkanes which are called *saturated* hydrocarbons.

Structure

The simplest member of this homologous series, ethylene, has the molecular
formula C_2H_4. No stable compound having a single carbon atom is known for
this series. Three electronic formulas suggest themselves. Either one carbon
atom has two unshared electrons (I), each has one unshared electron (II), or
the carbon atoms are joined by two pairs of electrons (III).

$$
\begin{array}{ccc}
\text{H} \quad \text{H} & \text{H} \quad \text{H} & \text{H} \qquad \text{H} \\
\cdot\text{x} \quad \text{x}\circ & \cdot\text{x} \quad \text{x}\circ & \text{x} \qquad \circ \\
\text{H}\,{}^{\text{x}}\text{C}\,{}^{\circ}_{\circ}\text{C}\,\circ & \text{H}\,{}^{\text{x}}\text{C}\,{}^{\circ}_{\circ}\text{C}\,{}^{\text{x}}\text{H} & \text{C}\,{}^{\circ}_{\circ}\text{C} \\
\text{x}\cdot \qquad \circ & \cdot \qquad \circ & \text{x} \qquad \text{x} \\
\text{H} & & \text{H} \qquad \text{H} \\
\text{I} & \text{II} & \text{III}
\end{array}
$$

If I or II were capable of existence, $\text{H}\,{}^{\text{x}}_{\cdot}\text{C}\cdot$ or $\text{H}\,{}^{\text{x}}_{\text{x}\cdot}\text{C}\cdot$ with H groups above and below, should be stable also,

but these groups have been detected only as highly reactive, short-lived *free
radicals* (p. 568). Formula I is ruled out also on chemical grounds because its
reactions would involve only one carbon atom, whereas all known reactions of
the olefins involve both carbon atoms. Formula III satisfies all requirements.
Atoms sharing two pairs of electrons are said to be joined by a **double bond.**

The exact nature of the covalent bond has not been described completely as yet for systems
more complex than the hydrogen molecule, although by making certain reasonable assumptions a qualitatively satisfactory picture is obtained (p. 9). The detailed description of the
multiple bond is still more difficult. A current theory which is proving useful to organic
chemists and spectroscopists postulates that when a carbon atom is united to only three other
atoms, it makes use of sp^2 hybrid orbitals, the three bonds being planar and making angles of
120 degrees with each other (p. 12). The remaining unpaired electron is in a p orbital (p. 10)
perpendicular to the plane of the three bonds. In ethylene, for example, overlapping of one sp^2
orbital from each carbon atom forms a single sp^2—sp^2 bond between the carbon atoms. The
remaining four sp^2 orbitals overlap with the s orbitals of four hydrogen atoms to form four s—sp^2
bonds. All of these bonds result from the formation of σ-type molecular orbitals (p. 10) and

make angles of 120 degrees with each other. These molecular orbitals accommodate three of the valence electrons of each carbon atom, leaving one electron in a *p* orbital on each carbon atom. This orbital is perpendicular to the plane of the carbon-hydrogen bonds. Figure 29*a* represents a cross section through this plane and Fig. 29*b* represents a cross section through the carbon

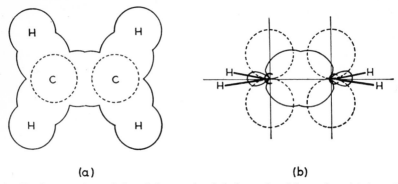

(a)   (b)

Fig. 29. Cross sections of the ethylene molecule before π bond formation: (*a*) through the carbon and hydrogen atoms; (*b*) through the carbon atoms and perpendicular to the plane of the hydrogen atoms.

atoms and perpendicular to this plane. The molecule represented by Fig. 29 would acquire added stability if the two electrons which are occupying monocentric *p* orbitals (electrons encompassing a single nucleus) could occupy a dicentric molecular orbital (encompass two nuclei). The formation of a molecular orbital could result if the *p* orbitals overlapped sufficiently. Since the *p* orbitals are perpendicular to the planes of the CH_2 groups, these orbitals can overlap best when the planes of the two CH_2 groups are coincident. In this position the two *p* orbitals coalesce to form a molecular orbital which resembles two fat sausages above and below the plane of the molecule and can accommodate two electrons. Figure 30*a* is the same cross section as Fig. 29*b* but after the formation of the molecular orbital. Figure 30*b* is a perspective representation, and Fig. 30*c* is a convenient schematic representation in which the figure eights indicate the *p* orbitals and the light lines joining them indicate the overlapping to form the molecular

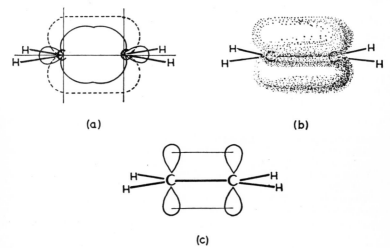

(a)   (b)

(c)

Fig. 30. The ethylene molecule after π bond formation: (*a*) cross section through the carbon atoms and perpendicular to the plane of the hydrogen atoms; (*b*) perspective representation of the π bond; (*c*) schematic representation of the π bond.

orbital. The presence of a nodal plane (p. 10) makes this molecular orbital resemble a *p* orbital. Hence the type of bond that it represents is called a π *(pi) bond*, and the electrons forming the bond are called π *electrons*.

Because the overlapping of the two *p* orbitals is relatively poor, the π-type molecular orbital is not as stable as a σ-type molecular orbital. The energy associated with a carbon-carbon σ bond is about 80 kcal. per mole, whereas that associated with a carbon-carbon π bond is about 60 kcal. per mole. The lower stability of the π bond (higher energy content of the electrons) accounts for the greater reactivity of the π bond, that is, the tendency to form the more stable σ bonds with other atoms. Hence the π electrons also are called *unsaturation electrons*.

Another observable effect of the π bond is the decrease in the distance between the carbon atoms. The interatomic distance of a carbon-carbon single bond is 1.54 Å, but that of a carbon-carbon double bond is 1.34 Å; that is, the nuclei are bound together more strongly when encompassed by an additional pair of electrons.

This theory amounts to a reinterpretation of the much older partial valence theory proposed by Thiele.[1] He assumed that the valence forces, the nature of which was unknown, were only partially satisfied at the carbon atoms of a double bond. The second bond was represented by a dotted line to indicate that it was more reactive than the single bond. Thiele's theory lost adherents because it could not be explained by the Lewis electron-pair bond theory.

Formulas for the homologs of ethylene can be constructed in the same way as formulas for the homologs of methane, that is, by inserting CH_2 groups (*methylene groups*) between hydrogen and carbon atoms or by replacing hydrogen atoms by alkyl groups. For example, the next member of the series, propylene, C_3H_6, would have the formula $CH_3CH{=}CH_2$. Since the propylene molecule has three kinds of hydrogen atoms, there should be three isomeric butylenes, all of which are known.

$$CH_3CH_2CH{=}CH_2 \qquad CH_3CH{=}CHCH_3 \qquad CH_3C{=}CH_2$$
$$\overset{\displaystyle\qquad\qquad\qquad\qquad\qquad\qquad\qquad\qquad\quad|}{\qquad\qquad\qquad\qquad\qquad\qquad\qquad\qquad\quad CH_3}$$

The same formulas would have been obtained if the double bond had been put in all possible positions in normal butane and in isobutane.

Nomenclature

Common Names. The common names are derived by replacing the *ane* of the common name for the saturated hydrocarbon by *ylene*, but *n*-(normal) is omitted for straight chain compounds. Greek letters sometimes are used to distinguish between isomers (Table 7, p. 52).

As Derivatives of Ethylene. The alkyl groups replacing the hydrogen atoms of ethylene are named and the word *ethylene* added. Since ethylene has two hydrogens on each of two carbon atoms, the replacement of two hydrogens by two groups would give rise to two isomers depending on whether the new groups were on different carbon atoms or both on the same carbon atom. In order to distinguish between these two isomers the one with the two groups on different carbon atoms is called *symmetrical* (prefix sym-); that is, the groups are placed symmetrically with respect to the double bond. The isomer with both groups on the same carbon atom is called *unsymmetrical* (prefix unsym-). These designations apply only to the distribution of the two groups which give rise to the isomerism and have nothing to do with the symmetry of the molecule as a whole. In the last two examples given in Table 7, the molecules as a whole

---

[1] Johannes Thiele (1865–1918), professor at the University of Strassburg. He is noted chiefly for his work on the addition reactions of unsaturated compounds (p. 707).

are unsymmetrical, but the methyl and ethyl groups in the first and the two methyl groups in the second are symmetrically placed with respect to the double bond. Hence they are called sym-methylethylethylene and sym-dimethyl-*s*-butylethylene.

TABLE 7

NOMENCLATURE OF ALKENES

FORMULA	COMMON NAME	AS DERIVATIVE OF ETHYLENE	BY GENEVA SYSTEM
$CH_2{=}CH_2$	ethylene	none	ethene
$CH_3CH{=}CH_2$	propylene	methylethylene	propene
$CH_3CH_2CH{=}CH_2$	α-butylene	ethylethylene	1-butene
$CH_3CH{=}CHCH_3$	β-butylene	sym-dimethylethylene	2-butene
$CH_3C{=}CH_2$ $\quad\vert$ $\quad CH_3$	isobutylene*	unsym-dimethylethylene	methylpropene
$C_2H_5CH{=}CHCH_3$	β-amylene†	sym-methylethylethylene	2-pentene
$\overset{6}{C}H_3\overset{5}{C}H_2\overset{4}{C}HCH_3$ $\qquad\vert$ $\quad \overset{}{C}H_3\overset{}{\underset{3}{C}}{=}\overset{}{\underset{2}{C}}H\overset{}{\underset{1}{C}}H_3$	none	sym-dimethyl-*s*-butylethylene	3,4-dimethyl-2-hexene

  * The name isobutene, which frequently is used, is undesirable because it mixes two systems.
  † Olefins having five carbon atoms are known as *amylenes* instead of *pentylenes* (see *fusel oil*, p. 91).

Geneva System. The Geneva rules for naming alkenes resemble the rules for naming alkanes (p. 36): (*1*) the ending *ane* of the corresponding saturated hydrocarbon is replaced by the ending *ene*; (*2*) the parent compound is considered to be the longest chain *containing the double bond*; (*3*) the chains are numbered from the end nearest the double bond, and the position of the double bond is indicated by the number of the lower-numbered carbon atom to which it is attached; (*4*) side chains are named and their position indicated by a number.

Sources and Uses of the Alkenes

Alkenes are produced commercially by the cracking of natural gas and petroleum hydrocarbons (p. 44). **Ethylene** is by far the most important olefin as a raw material for the synthesis of other chemicals. Production in 1954 was over 3 billion pounds, and the contract price less than 5 cents a pound. About 50 per cent was produced by cracking propane, 40 per cent from ethane, and 10 per cent from petroleum refinery gas (p. 72). About 25 per cent each was used for the synthesis of ethyl alcohol (p. 92) and ethylene oxide (p. 743), and 10 per cent each for styrene (p. 573), ethyl chloride (p. 118), and polyethylene (p. 61).

Propylene and the **butylenes** find some use for the production of chemicals, but are used chiefly for the production of gasoline (pp. 76, 77) and synthetic rubber (p. 716). Methods of synthesis for individual olefins, for example from alcohols or compounds containing halogen, are given in Chapter 8.

Physical Properties

The general physical properties of the alkenes are much the same as those of the corresponding saturated hydrocarbons. The solubility of the lower alkenes in water, though slight, is considerably greater than that of the alkanes, because the higher concentration of electrons in the double bond leads to a greater attraction for the positive end of the water dipole (p. 12).

General Chemical Properties

In contrast to the saturated hydrocarbons, the unsaturated hydrocarbons are very reactive. Many reagents will add to the two carbon atoms joined by the double bond. In this process the reagent itself is decomposed, one part combining with one carbon atom and the other part with the other carbon atom. Such reactions are known as **addition reactions.** The bonding properties of one pair of electrons in the double bond are not fully satisfied, and in the presence of a suitable reagent one pair reacts with the reagent to give a new bond system that is more stable. The reagent is said to have *added* to the double bond. The reactions may be divided into two groups, depending on whether the addenda are identical or nonidentical.

Addition to the double bond results in the net replacement of one π bond by one σ bond. Because the overlap of the atomic orbitals to form a π bond is poorer than the overlap of atomic orbitals to form a σ bond, the σ bonds are stronger (p. 51). Hence the addition to a double bond usually results in the liberation of considerable energy and the reaction goes to completion. In the isomerization of butane (p. 46), there is little change in bond strengths, and the equilibrium mixture contains appreciable quantities of both isomers.

IDENTICAL ADDENDA

1. **Halogen.** The most characteristic reaction of the double bond is the rapid addition, in the liquid phase or in solution, of chlorine or bromine to those alkenes in which each of the doubly bound carbon atoms is united to at least one hydrogen atom.

$$CH_2{=}CH_2 + Cl_2 \longrightarrow ClCH_2CH_2Cl$$

Ethylene chloride [2]
(1,2-dichloroethane)

$$CH_3CH{=}CH_2 + Br_2 \longrightarrow CH_2CHBrCH_2Br$$

Propylene bromide
(1,2-dibromopropane)

The reaction in general may be expressed by the equation

$$RCH{=}CHR + X_2 \longrightarrow RCHXCHXR$$

---

[2] It is this reaction that gave rise to the old name for ethylene, namely *olefiant gas* (meaning *oil-making gas*), because the reaction of gaseous ethylene with gaseous chlorine gave liquid ethylene chloride.

where R is any alkyl group or a hydrogen atom, and X is any halogen atom. In practice the reaction is limited to chlorine and bromine, because fluorine reacts too violently to be controllable, and iodine does not give stable 1,2-diiodo derivatives except with a few simple olefins. If both hydrogen atoms on the same carbon atom of ethylene are replaced by alkyl groups as in isobutylene, addition of chlorine does not take place as readily as another reaction, *substitution*, in which a hydrogen atom is replaced by a chlorine atom (p. 727). Bromine, however, adds regularly, forming isobutylene bromide.

The simplest picture of the reaction of halogen with a double bond would be the simultaneous addition of both halogen atoms from the same molecule. From a number of experimental facts, however, it is quite certain that this type of reaction does not take place. Instead, a stepwise reaction occurs by an ionic mechanism (p. 42) in which the unsaturated hydrocarbon uses the π electrons of the double bond to remove from the halogen molecule a halogen particle having only six electrons. The resulting carbonium ion then adds a negative halide ion from the solution.

$$\text{RCH—CHR} \; + \; :\!\overset{\cdot\cdot}{\underset{\cdot\cdot}{X}}\!:\!\overset{\cdot\cdot}{\underset{\cdot\cdot}{X}}\!: \; \longrightarrow \; \left[\begin{array}{c} \text{RCH—CHR} \\ {\scriptstyle +} \quad {\overset{\cdot\cdot}{}} \\ :\!\underset{\cdot\cdot}{X}\!: \end{array}\right] \; + \; \left[:\!\overset{\cdot\cdot}{\underset{\cdot\cdot}{X}}\!:\right]^{-}$$

$$:\!\overset{\cdot\cdot}{\underset{\cdot\cdot}{X}}\!:^{-} \; + \; \left[\begin{array}{c} \text{RCH—CHR} \\ {\scriptstyle +} \quad {\overset{\cdot\cdot}{}} \\ :\!\underset{\cdot\cdot}{X}\!: \end{array}\right] \; \longrightarrow \; \begin{array}{c} \text{RCH—CHR} \\ {\scriptstyle |} \quad {\scriptstyle |} \\ \text{X} \quad \text{X} \end{array}$$

The halide ion removed from the solution need not be, and from a statistical viewpoint probably is not, the same halide ion liberated in the first step of the reaction. The intermediate positive ion may abstract a halide ion from molecular halogen, especially when the concentration of halogen is relatively high.

$$\left[\begin{array}{c} \text{RCH—CHR} \\ {\scriptstyle +} \quad {\overset{\cdot\cdot}{}} \\ :\!\underset{\cdot\cdot}{X}\!: \end{array}\right] \; + \; :\!\overset{\cdot\cdot}{\underset{\cdot\cdot}{X}}\!:\!\overset{\cdot\cdot}{\underset{\cdot\cdot}{X}}\!: \; \longrightarrow \; \begin{array}{c} \text{RCH—CHR} \\ {\scriptstyle |} \quad {\scriptstyle |} \\ \text{X} \quad \text{X} \end{array} \; + \; \left[\overset{\cdot\cdot}{\underset{\cdot\cdot}{X}}\!:\right]^{+}$$

The positive halogen ion liberated can react with an olefin molecule to continue the chain, or with a negative halide ion to give a halogen molecule.

These halogen derivatives are colorless liquids. Hence decolorization of a solution of bromine in water, or better in a mutual solvent such as carbon tetrachloride or acetic acid, may be used as a *test for unsaturation*, provided that no other group is present which reacts with bromine. To determine the amount of a known olefin in a mixture with other substances, the mixture can be titrated with a standardized solution of bromine. A similar titration of a pure unknown olefin would give the equivalent weight of the compound, that is, the weight associated with one double bond. The number of double bonds would be equal to the molecular weight divided by the equivalent weight.

2. **Hydrogen.** In the presence of a suitable catalyst such as finely divided platinum, palladium, or nickel, hydrogen adds to a double bond with the

evolution of about 30 kcal. of energy per mole. The process is called *catalytic hydrogenation*.[3]

$$CH_2{=}CH_2 + H_2 \xrightarrow{\text{Pt, Pd, or Ni}} CH_3CH_3$$

$$R_2C{=}CR_2 + H_2 \xrightarrow{\text{Pt, Pd, or Ni}} R_2CHCHR_2$$

If the olefin is a gas, a mixture with hydrogen may be passed over the catalyst. Liquid olefins, or solid olefins dissolved in an inert solvent, may be shaken with hydrogen in the presence of a suspension of the finely divided catalyst. The reaction can be used for analytical as well as for preparative purposes. From the volume of hydrogen absorbed, the amount of an unsaturated compound of known structure in a mixture with saturated compounds, or the number of double bonds in an unknown compound whose molecular weight has been determined, can be calculated.

Although hydrogenation is an exothermic process, the reaction does not take place spontaneously because the amount of energy required to break a π bond in the olefin or a σ bond in hydrogen and thus initiate the reaction is too large. The function of the metal catalyst is to lower this activation energy by permitting a series of steps, the activation energy for each of which is much lower than that required for thermal breaking of a π or σ bond.

Metals such as platinum, palladium, nickel, and copper strongly adsorb hydrogen and unsaturated molecules. The atoms in the metal surface have unpaired electrons which can interact with the electrons in the relatively exposed σ orbital of the hydrogen molecule and the π orbital of the double bond. The resulting formation of weak bonds with the metal atoms causes adsorption. As indicated in the schematic representation, the hydrogen molecule can be dissociated to give adsorbed hydrogen atoms and the olefin to give an adsorbed free biradical. Reaction of the atom and free biradical leaves an adsorbed hydrogen atom and an adsorbed free radical. Further reaction gives the saturated hydrocarbon which is desorbed.

Because the various steps in the reaction involve unpaired electrons and weak bonds, none has a high activation energy.

Although the illustration indicates that both hydrogen atoms that add to the double bond come from the same hydrogen molecule, this is not necessary. The adsorbed ethyl radical is surrounded by several adsorbed hydrogen atoms and can react with any of them. When ethylene is reduced catalytically with a mixture of hydrogen and its isotope, deuterium (D_2), ethane (CH_3CH_3), monodeuteroethane (CH_3CH_2D), and dideuteroethane (CH_2DCH_2D) are produced.

---

[3] The first reference to the use of catalytic hydrogenation appears to be that by Debus in 1863. He found hydrogen added to hydrogen cyanide in the presence of platinum to give methylamine (p. 228). Scattered references to similar reactions were made during the next thirty-four years. In 1897 Paul Sabatier (1854–1941) and Jean Baptiste Senderens (1856–1937) at the University of Toulouse found that ethylene and hydrogen when passed over cobalt, iron, copper, or platinum at 300° gave ethane, and that benzene and hydrogen over nickel gave cyclohexane (p. 830). Sabatier pursued the subject until his retirement in 1930. He was awarded the Nobel Prize in Chemistry, jointly with Victor Grignard (p. 120), in 1912. Senderens entered industry and introduced contact catalysis into technical organic chemistry. He was a very religious man and became an abbé and later a canon in the Roman Catholic Church.

In order that reaction may take place between the adsorbed molecules, they must approach each other closely and be properly oriented. Not only the size and structure of the reactants but also the crystal structure of the surface of the catalyst determines these space relationships. It is evident that the optimum conditions and type of catalyst will vary for every different pair of molecules reacting, and that the choice of such conditions and catalyst still must be largely empirical. Fortunately hydrogenation catalysts have been developed which show high activity for a wide variety of compounds; hence catalytic hydrogenation is an eminently practical process.

3. **Ozone.** If a stream of ozonized air or ozonized oxygen is passed through a liquid olefin or a nonaqueous solution of an unsaturated compound, the ozone is removed rapidly and quantitatively with the formation of an ozonide.

$$RCH{=}CHR' + O_3 \longrightarrow RCH\underset{\underset{O\!-\!O}{\diagdown\quad\diagup}}{\overset{\overset{O}{\diagup\quad\diagdown}}{}}CHR'$$

$$CH_3CH_2CH{=}CHCH_3 + O_3 \longrightarrow CH_3CH_2CH\underset{\underset{O\!-\!O}{\diagdown\quad\diagup}}{\overset{\overset{O}{\diagup\quad\diagdown}}{}}CHCH_3$$

2-Pentene ozonide

The evidence concerning the structure of ozonides formed from simple olefins indicates that both bonds of the double bond are broken with the formation of a five-membered ring containing three oxygen atoms (p. 880). The olefin is said to be *ozonized*, and the process is known as *ozonation* or *ozonization*. The former term seems preferable because it is analogous to the term *oxidation*.

The ozonides would not be of importance were it not for the fact that they react readily with water with the formation of aldehydes or ketones (Chapter 11).

$$RCH\underset{\underset{O\!-\!O}{\diagdown\quad\diagup}}{\overset{\overset{O}{\diagup\quad\diagdown}}{}}CHR' + H_2O \longrightarrow RCHO + OCHR' + H_2O_2$$

$$CH_3CH_2CH\underset{\underset{O\!-\!O}{\diagdown\quad\diagup}}{\overset{\overset{O}{\diagup\quad\diagdown}}{}}CHCH_3 + H_2O \longrightarrow CH_3CH_2CHO + OCHCH_3 + H_2O_2$$

Propionalde- Acetalde-
hyde   hyde

Ketones result from more highly substituted ethylenes.

$$R_2C{=}CR_2 \overset{O_3}{\longrightarrow} R_2C\underset{\underset{O\!-\!O}{\diagdown\quad\diagup}}{\overset{\overset{O}{\diagup\quad\diagdown}}{}}CR_2 \overset{H_2O}{\longrightarrow} 2\,R_2CO + H_2O_2$$

Ozonation of an unsaturated compound followed by decomposition with water therefore becomes a useful method for synthesizing aldehydes and ketones. Moreover since the aldehydes and ketones can be isolated and analyzed, the reaction can be used to locate the position of double bonds in unknown compounds. For example, the formation of a three-carbon aldehyde and a two-carbon aldehyde from an olefin proves that it is 2-pentene. If it had been 1-pentene, a four-carbon aldehyde and a one-carbon aldehyde would have been formed.

The process of ozonation followed by hydrolysis is known as *ozonolysis*. The hydrolysis is somewhat more complicated than is indicated above, a mixture of organic peroxides and aldehydes or ketones being formed rather than hydrogen peroxide. Usually the decomposition is carried out in the presence of a reducing agent, such as zinc dust and acetic acid or hydrogen and platinum, to destroy the peroxides and prevent the oxidation of the aldehydes to organic acids (p. 212).

4. **Aqueous Permanganate.** Reaction of alkenes with dilute aqueous permanganate solutions gives rise to the addition of two hydroxyl (OH) groups to the doubly-bound carbon atoms. Little is known about the mechanism of this reaction, but for the purpose of writing the equation it may be assumed that the permanganate supplies an oxygen atom which with a water molecule gives two hydroxyl groups, and that the latter add to the double bond.

$$R_2C{=}CR_2 + [O](KMnO_4) + H_2O \longrightarrow R_2COHCOHR_2$$

The symbol [O] does not indicate atomic oxygen, but some reagent capable of supplying oxygen in an oxidation reaction. Here the reagent is given in parentheses. This device avoids the necessity for writing balanced equations, but does not excuse the student from being able to write a balanced equation when required to do so. In neutral or alkaline solution the permanganate is reduced to manganese dioxide, and three atoms of oxygen are available for oxidation from each two molecules of potassium permanganate. Hence the balanced equation for the reaction is

$$3\,R_2C{=}CR_2 + 2\,KMnO_4 + 4\,H_2O \longrightarrow 3\,R_2COHCOHR_2 + 2\,MnO_2 + 2\,KOH$$

Methods for balancing oxidation-reduction reactions of organic compounds are considered on page 145.

Evidence of reaction with permanganate is the change in color from the purple of the permanganate ion to the brown of the precipitate of manganese dioxide. In the absence of sufficient reducing agent the permanganate ion may be reduced only as far as the green manganate ion, $MnO_4^=$. The change from purple to green should not be considered a positive test, however, since this change can take place in a strongly alkaline solution in the absence of reducing agent. The reaction with permanganate usually is referred to as *Baeyer's test for a double bond*. It should be pointed out, however, that like the reaction with bromine and with hydrogen, *this test is* **not specific** *for a double bond*. Reaction with permanganate indicates a double bond only in the absence of other easily oxidized groups.

NONIDENTICAL ADDENDA

Numerous reagents add unlike groups to a double bond. For example, sulfuric acid adds H and OSO_3H, and halogen acids add H and X. If the molecule is symmetrical, that is, if identical groups are on both of the doubly-bound carbon atoms, only one compound can be obtained on addition even if the addenda are not alike. However *if the olefin molecule is unsymmetrical, two isomers should be possible*. Actually *one isomer is formed in predominant amount, namely that in which the hydrogen of sulfuric acid, or of the halogen acid adds to the carbon atom having the larger number of hydrogen atoms.* This generalization is known as the **Markovnikov rule.**[4]

1. **Sulfuric Acid.** Olefins add sulfuric acid to give *alkyl hydrogen sulfates.*

$$CH_3CH_2CH{=}CH_2 + HOSO_3H \longrightarrow CH_3CH_2\underset{\underset{OSO_3H}{|}}{C}HCH_3$$

1-Butene

s-Butyl hydrogen
sulfate

$$RCH{=}CR_2 + HOSO_3H \longrightarrow RCH_2\underset{\underset{OSO_3H}{|}}{C}R_2$$

2-Butene can give only one product which is the same as that from 1-butene.

$$CH_3CH{=}CHCH_3 + HOSO_3H \longrightarrow CH_3CH_2\underset{\underset{OSO_3H}{|}}{C}HCH_3$$

2-Butene

The ease of addition of sulfuric acid depends on the number of alkyl substituents at the double bond. For example, ethylene reacts slowly at room temperature with concentrated sulfuric acid, requiring a catalyst such as silver sulfate for rapid addition; propylene reacts with 85 per cent sulfuric acid in the absence of a catalyst; isobutylene reacts with 65 per cent sulfuric acid at room temperature. Use is made of these differences in reactivity to analyze and to separate mixtures of olefins.

If the air in a 100-cc. cylindrical separatory funnel containing 10 cc. of 20 per cent fuming sulfuric acid is swept out with ethylene and the funnel stoppered and shaken, a vacuum is created because of the reaction of the ethylene with the sulfuric acid to give the nonvolatile ethyl hydrogen sulfate, together with ethionic acid, $HO_3SCH_2CH_2OSO_2OH$. The presence of the vacuum can be demonstrated by dipping the end of the funnel beneath the surface of about 150 cc. of concentrated sulfuric acid and opening the stopcock. The sulfuric acid rushes into the separatory funnel and nearly fills it.

It is difficult to separate the free alkyl hydrogen sulfates from the excess sulfuric acid because neither compound is volatile and both have about the same solubility characteristics. The mixture can be neutralized, however, for example with potassium hydroxide, and the potassium alkyl sulfate separated from potassium sulfate by crystallization. The calcium and barium alkyl sulfates can be isolated even more readily because they are soluble in water, whereas calcium or barium sulfate is insoluble in water. A mixture of the sodium salts of *s*-alkyl hydrogen sulfates having from eight to eighteen carbon atoms is used in Europe as a detergent (p. 191). The mixture of olefins from which it is made is produced by cracking the wax distillate from petroleum (p. 74).

---

[4] Vladimir Vasil'evich Markovnikov (1838–1904), director of the Chemical Institute of the University of Moscow. Although his ideas concerning the effect of structure on the course of chemical reactions were published in Russian in 1869, they went unnoticed in Europe until 1899, because he refused to publish them in a foreign language. After 1881 he did important work on the chemistry of petroleum hydrocarbons.

In the presence of an excess of olefin, a second molecule can add to the alkyl hydrogen sulfate to give an alkyl sulfate.

$$CH_3CH_2OSO_2OH + CH_2{=}CH_2 \longrightarrow CH_3CH_2OSO_2OCH_2CH_3$$
Ethyl hydrogen sulfate   Ethyl sulfate

2. Halogen Acids. Olefins add halogen acids to give *alkyl halides*.

$$CH_3CH{=}CH_2 + HBr \longrightarrow CH_3\underset{\underset{Br}{|}}{C}HCH_3$$

i-Propyl bromide
(2-bromopropane)

$$RCH{=}CR_2 + HX \longrightarrow RCH_2\underset{\underset{X}{|}}{C}R_2$$

Halogen acids also add more readily the greater the amount of alkyl substitution at the double bond. For example, the order of ease of addition of hydrogen chloride is isobutylene > propylene > ethylene. The ease of addition varies also with the halogen acid, the order from concentrated aqueous solutions being hydrogen iodide > hydrogen bromide > hydrogen chloride > hydrogen fluoride.

The organic chemist recognizes that such qualitative statements are not exact. What does the statement mean that one reagent reacts more readily than another? Usually it means that the reaction (*1*) goes more rapidly under the same conditions, (*2*) proceeds at the same speed at lower temperatures, or (*3*) proceeds at lower pressures if the reaction takes place in the gas phase with a decrease in volume. It may mean, however, that the position of equilibrium is more favorable in one case than in another. More often than not it is not known whether the generalizations are based on relative rates or on relative positions of equilibria. Only the relative yields of desired products under the conditions of the reactions may be known.

Too often generalizations are made from comparisons under widely different conditions without consideration of the effect of solvent and of heterogeneous or homogeneous catalysts. For example, although neither gaseous nor aqueous hydrogen chloride adds to ethylene at an appreciable rate, anhydrous hydrogen chloride adds readily in the liquid phase at low temperature in the presence of anhydrous aluminum chloride. Here the question merely is one of providing a catalyst to enable the reaction to go at a practical rate. The product, ethyl chloride, is perfectly stable at room temperature. Although hydrogen fluoride in aqueous solution is less reactive than hydrogen chloride, anhydrous hydrogen fluoride adds rapidly to olefins to give yields of monofluoroalkanes up to 80 per cent, [5] even in the absence of a catalyst, provided that the reaction is carried out at −45° in the presence of a large excess of hydrogen fluoride. If the monofluoroalkanes are allowed to warm to room temperature, however, they spontaneously decompose into olefin and hydrogen fluoride. Here the nonaddition at room temperature is not a matter of rate of addition but of position of equilibrium.

The general lack of knowledge concerning the fundamentals of even simple reactions is not surprising, because organic reactions are exceedingly numerous and complex. It is safe to say that organic chemistry has reached its present state of development because it has been handled not only as a science but as an art as well. Until future chemists reduce the qualitative statements to quantitative measurements, the former must continue to serve.

---

[5] Organic compounds rarely are produced in the amount expected from a particular equation. Frequently the reaction is reversible and does not go to completion, and still more frequently several simultaneous or consecutive reactions take place starting with a given set of reactants. Moreover, mechanical losses usually occur during isolation of the product. For these reasons, organic chemists always are concerned with yield. The yield of the desired product usually is expressed as the per cent of the amount expected if the reaction took place quantitatively according to the equation.

The behavior of hydrogen bromide is anomalous if peroxides are present. Under these conditions the mode of addition for the most part is contrary to the Markovnikov rule. For example when propylene reacts with hydrogen bromide in the presence of peroxides, *n*-propyl bromide is formed instead of *i*-propyl bromide.

$$CH_3CH{=}CH_2 + HBr \xrightarrow{\text{(Peroxides)}} CH_3CH_2CH_2Br$$

The mode of addition of hydrogen chloride or hydrogen iodide is not affected by the presence of peroxides.

In the addition of sulfuric acid and in the uncatalyzed addition of halogen acids to alkenes, it is believed that the first step is the combination of the π electrons of the double bond with a proton derived from the nonionized but polarized acid to give what is known as a π complex.

$$RCH{-}CHR + H : \ddot{X} : \longrightarrow \left[RCH\overset{H}{\underset{+}{-}}CHR \right] \left[: \ddot{X} : \right]$$

Attack of the intermediate positive ion by a negative ion or abstraction of a negative ion from a neutral molecule gives the final product.

$$\left[RCH\overset{H}{\underset{+}{-}}CHR \right] + \left[: \ddot{X} : \right]^- \longrightarrow RCH\overset{H}{\underset{X}{-}}CHR$$

$$\left[RCH\overset{H}{\underset{+}{-}}CHR \right] + : X : H \longrightarrow RCH\overset{H}{\underset{X}{-}}CHR + [H^+]$$

If the alkene is symmetrical, the molecule is nonpolar; that is, the electrons on a time average are symmetrically distributed about the center of the molecule. If the alkene is unsymmetrical, the electrons are shifted with respect to the positive nuclei and the molecule is polarized. This polarization is believed to be due to two factors. First, the unsaturated carbon atoms make use of sp^2 hybrid orbitals in bonding to other atoms instead of sp^3 orbitals used by saturated carbon atoms. The sp^2 orbitals have a higher proportion of s orbital (more s character) than sp^3 orbitals. Because electrons in an s orbital are closer to the nucleus than those in a p orbital, an sp^2 orbital pulls electrons closer to the nucleus than an sp^3 orbital. Hence a multiple bond pulls electrons away from a single bond. Second, an alkyl group with its larger number of electrons is more highly polarizable than hydrogen and releases electrons to an unsaturated carbon atom more readily than hydrogen. The resulting increase in electron density about the carbon atom to which the alkyl group is attached causes a shift of the less strongly held π electrons away from the methyl group to give a polarized molecule.

$$R \rightarrow \overset{}{\underset{H}{C}}{-}\overset{}{\underset{H}{C}}{-}H \qquad \text{or} \qquad \underset{\delta+}{RCH}{-}\underset{\delta-}{CH_2}$$

For the same reason, the hydrogen bonded to the π electrons in the π complex with acids is closer to the carbon atom with the smaller number of alkyl groups. Accordingly, attack by a negative ion occurs at the carbon atom having the greater number of alkyl groups, thus explaining the Markovnikov rule.

$$\left[RCH\overset{H}{\underset{+}{-}}CH_2 \right] + \left[: \ddot{X} : \right]^- \longrightarrow RCH\overset{H}{\underset{X}{-}}CH_2$$

The abnormal addition of hydrogen bromide to terminal double bonds in the presence of peroxides is explained by a free-radical mechanism rather than an ionic mechanism (p. 42). The peroxide reacts with the hydrogen bromide and gives bromine *atoms*, which initiate the reaction. The addition then proceeds by a free-radical chain mechanism.

$$\text{Peroxide} + \text{HBr} \longrightarrow \text{Reduced peroxide} + H_2O + [\cdot Br]$$

$$RCH{=\!=}CH_2 + [\cdot Br] \longrightarrow [RCHCH_2Br]$$

$$[RCHCH_2Br] + HBr \longrightarrow RCH_2CH_2Br + [\cdot Br]$$

Of the halogen acids only hydrogen bromide shows this effect, because hydrogen chloride is not oxidized readily enough for peroxides to produce chlorine atoms; although hydrogen iodide readily gives iodine atoms, they are too unreactive to add to a double bond and give molecular iodine instead. No really satisfactory explanation of the orientation of the abnormal addition has been given. Of the two possible intermediates [RCHCH_2Br] and [RCHBrCH_2], it is reasonable that only the first would be affected by a substituent R. It has been assumed that R stabilizes the first intermediate by interaction with the unpaired electron.

3. **Polymerization.** A *polymer* is a compound of high molecular weight whose structure can be considered as being made up of many smaller identical parts (Gr. *polys*, many, and *meros*, part). The process by which polymers are formed is called *polymerization*. It consists of a series of stepwise reactions. Two molecules of the simple compound, known as the *monomer*, react to give a *dimer*, the dimer reacts with a third molecule to give a *trimer*, and the process continues until all of the monomer is consumed.

Under the influence of various catalysts olefins undergo a self-addition known as *addition polymerization*, with the formation of compounds having many times the molecular weight of the original compound. For example when ethylene is heated above 100° and under pressures above 15,000 p.s.i. in the presence of 0.01 per cent of oxygen, it is converted into a high molecular weight saturated hydrocarbon.

$$x\,CH_2{=\!=}CH_2 \longrightarrow (-CH_2CH_2-)_x$$

Polymerization takes place also at nearly atmospheric pressure when special catalysts are used (p. 898). The product consists of long chains with x being from 100 to 1000 or more. In the equation, the formula for the polymer does not indicate what is at the ends of the chains, because the chains may have terminal groups of several types such as a double bond, a hydrogen atom, or a hydroxyl (OH) group. However, the number of these groups is so small compared to the molecular weight that the polymers are almost as inert as paraffin hydrocarbons. Neither does the formula show that the molecules are somewhat branched. It is estimated that one methyl group is present for each 8 to 10 methylene (CH_2) groups.

Polymers of ethylene are called *polyethylenes*. They may be waxlike, or tough and flexible, or hard. They soften and flow on heating, because the molecules can slip past each other. After being extruded into the desired shape, irradiation with electrons or neutrons causes bonds to form between chains (cross-linking) and leads to a material that has greater rigidity and a higher melting point. Polyethylene is used chiefly in the manufacture of thin sheets, wire and cable insulation, and plastic pipe. Production in the United States was 400 million pounds in 1955.

Polymerizations catalyzed by oxygen take place by a free-radical mechanism. The oxygen molecule is unusual in that it contains two unpaired electrons of like spin as evidenced by the fact that it is paramagnetic. Having unpaired electrons, the oxygen molecule behaves to some extent like a free radical. It is thought that in oxygen-catalyzed polymerizations the oxygen molecule combines with one carbon atom of the unsaturated compound by taking one electron from the π bond (p. 51) and leaving a free electron on the other carbon atom.

$$\cdot \overset{..}{\underset{..}{O}} : \overset{..}{\underset{..}{O}} \cdot + CH_2 \!\!-\!\! CH_2 \longrightarrow \left[\cdot \overset{..}{\underset{..}{O}} : \overset{..}{\underset{..}{O}} : CH_2 \!\!-\!\! CH_2 \cdot \right]$$

This intermediate can combine with another molecule of olefin.

$$[\cdot O \!\!-\!\! O \!\!-\!\! CH_2 \!\!-\!\! CH_2 \cdot] + CH_2 \!\!-\!\! CH_2 \longrightarrow [\cdot O \!\!-\!\! O \!\!-\!\! CH_2 \!\!-\!\! CH_2 \!\!-\!\! CH_2 \!\!-\!\! CH_2 \cdot]$$

The process repeats itself until the chain is broken by the union of two free radicals or by taking a hydrogen atom from another molecule. In the latter case a new chain is started. The greater the amount of oxygen used as a catalyst the lower the molecular weight of the polymer, because the larger the number of chains that are started, the less the amount of monomer that will be available for each chain, and the more likely that a chain will be stopped by colliding with another oxygen molecule or chain. If too large an amount of oxygen is used, polymerization does not take place because the chains are stopped as fast as they are started.

When propylene is passed over a granular "solid" phosphoric acid catalyst (a calcined mixture of phosphoric acid and diatomaceous earth) at about 200° and 150 p.s.i., a mixture of higher alkenes is produced.

$$x \, CH_3CH\!\!=\!\!CH_2 \xrightarrow{\;H_3PO_4\;} CH_3\underset{CH_3}{\underset{|}{CH}} \left[\underset{CH_3}{\underset{|}{CH_2CH}} \right]_{x-2} CH\!\!=\!\!CHCH_3$$

and

$$CH_3\underset{CH_3}{\underset{|}{CH}} \left[\underset{CH_3}{\underset{|}{CH_2CH}} \right]_{x-2} CH_2CH\!\!=\!\!CH_2$$

The tetramer ($x = 4$) is manufactured commercially as an intermediate for one of the widely used synthetic detergents (p. 469). Recently catalysts have been developed that convert propylene into polypropylene plastics analogous to the polyethylene plastics.

If isobutylene is passed into cold 60 per cent sulfuric acid and the solution heated to 100°, a mixture of dimers and trimers (about 4 : 1), together with smaller amounts of higher polymers, is formed. The mixture of dimers is known as *diisobutylene* and consists of four parts of 2,4,4-trimethyl-1-pentene and one part of 2,4,4-trimethyl-2-pentene.

$$2 \, (CH_3)_2C\!\!=\!\!CH_2 \underset{}{\overset{H_2SO_4}{\rightleftarrows}} \underset{\text{20 per cent}}{(CH_3)_3CCH\!\!=\!\!C(CH_3)_2} \text{ and } \underset{\text{80 per cent}}{(CH_3)_3CCH_2C(CH_3)\!\!=\!\!CH_2}$$

The trimers and higher polymers are formed by reaction of the dimers with more isobutylene. If boron fluoride or anhydrous aluminum chloride is used as a catalyst at −100°, high molecular weight polyisobutylenes having from 400 to 8000 C_4H_8 units and varying from sticky viscous resins to elastic rubber-like solids are obtained.

$$x \, (CH_3)_2C\!\!=\!\!CH_2 \underset{-100°}{\overset{BF_3}{\rightleftarrows}} [\!-\!C(CH_3)_2CH_2\!-\!]_x$$

The acid-catalyzed polymerizations take place by an ionic mechanism and follow the Markovnikov rule. In the polymerization of propylene, a proton from the acid catalyst adds to the double bond at the terminal carbon atom, giving a carbonium ion with a positive charge. The carbonium ion adds in the same way to a terminal carbon atom of a second molecule of propylene to give a new carbonium ion. This process is repeated until the chain is terminated.

Any of the carbonium ions can be stabilized and the chain terminated by loss of a proton from either carbon adjacent to the carbonium ion. Hence the product always contains one double bond per molecule and consists of a mixture of isomers in which, barring further isomerization, the double bond is in either the 1,2 or 2,3 position.

$$CH_3CH{=}CH_2 \xrightarrow{[H^+]} \left[\underset{\underset{CH_3}{|}}{CH_3CH^+}\right] \xrightarrow{CH_2{=}CHCH_3} \left[\underset{\underset{CH_3}{|}}{CH_3CHCH_2}\underset{\underset{CH_3}{|}}{CH^+}\right] \xrightarrow{xCH_2{=}CHCH_3}$$

$$\left[\underset{\underset{CH_3}{|}}{CH_3CH}\left(\underset{\underset{CH_3}{|}}{CH_2CH}\right)_x \underset{\underset{CH_3}{|}}{CH_2CH^+}\right] \xrightarrow{\text{Loss of }[H^+]} \underset{\underset{CH_3}{|}}{CH_3CH}\left[\underset{\underset{CH_3}{|}}{CH_2CH}\right]_x CH_2CH{=}CH_2 \text{ and}$$

$$\underset{\underset{CH_3}{|}}{CH_3CH}\left[\underset{\underset{CH_3}{|}}{CH_2CH}\right]_x CH{=}CHCH_3$$

A similar series of steps accounts for the formation of the mixture of dimers, 2,4,4-trimethyl-1-pentene and 2,4,4-trimethyl-2-pentene, and for the structure of the polymers formed by the polymerization of isobutylene.

The alkenes undergo numerous other addition reactions. Some of these are considered from time to time in subsequent chapters.

All of the reactions of the alkenes that have been considered are dependent on the presence of the double bond. The rest of the molecule is inert like the paraffin hydrocarbons. *A reactive group such as the double bond is called a* **function** *or a* **functional group.** Most of the homologous series have their characteristic functional groups. The methods of introducing this group are the methods of preparation for members of the series, and the effects of other agents on this group are the general reactions of the series. The number of functional groups is small in comparison to the number of organic compounds. By emphasizing the functional groups of each homologous series, the facts of organic chemistry are systematized and made easier to remember.

CYCLIC HYDROCARBONS

In addition to the alkenes, a second series of hydrocarbons having the general formula C_nH_{2n} is known. The lowest member of the series has three carbon atoms. In contrast to the alkenes, most of the members of this isomeric series are as unreactive as the alkanes. The only way in which three carbon atoms could be joined other than in a linear fashion would be in the form of a closed triangle as in (*a*). Each of the six unshared electrons on the carbon atoms could

(*a*) (*b*) (*c*)

bond with a hydrogen atom to give structure (*b*), or as usually written (*c*). This molecule has the molecular formula C_3H_6 and is isomeric with propylene. However, no double bond is present, which is consistent with the fact that the compound does not decolorize alkaline permanganate solution or react with ozone.

If four, five, six, or *n* carbon atoms were joined in similar fashion, the homologous series C_4H_8, C_5H_{10}, C_6H_{12}, C_nH_{2n} would result. Carbon atoms joined in this way are thought of as forming a closed ring and compounds having this feature are called *cyclic compounds*. Because the members of this series are saturated and hence resemble the alkanes, they are called *cyclanes*. Another name is *alicyclic hydrocarbons*, that is, cyclic compounds having aliphatic properties. Petroleum chemists frequently call them *naphthenes*, because they occur in the naphtha fraction of petroleum and are isomeric with the alkenes. Names for the individual compounds are formed by adding the prefix *cyclo* to the name of the saturated hydrocarbon having the same number of hydrocarbons. Thus C_3H_6 is cyclopropane; C_4H_8, cyclobutane; C_5H_{10}, cyclopentane; C_6H_{12}, cyclohexane; and C_7H_{14}, cycloheptane.

Each of the cyclanes can give rise to a separate homologous series if hydrogen atoms are replaced by alkyl groups. Thus methylcyclopropane, ethylcyclo-propane and several dimethylcyclopropanes and higher homologs exist. The cyclic atoms are numbered consecutively around the ring to distinguish among the various possible isomers.

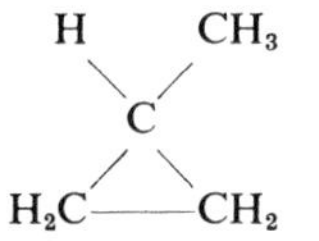

Methylcyclopropane 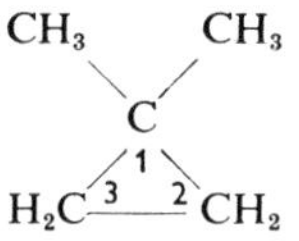   1,1-Dimethylcyclopropane 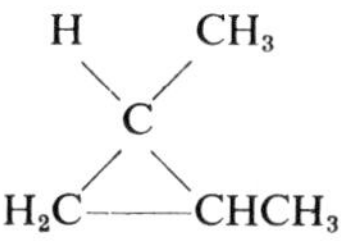   1,2-Dimethylcyclopropane

Of the various types of cyclanes, only those having five and six carbon atoms in the rings are abundant. Consideration of those having fewer or more carbon atoms and of the derivatives of cyclanes is deferred until Chapter 39.

The cyclopentane ring is less stable at room temperature than the cyclohexane ring, and isomerization of the cyclopentane ring to the cyclohexane ring can take place. Thus methylcyclopentane isomerizes in the presence of anhydrous aluminum chloride to an equilibrium mixture containing 80 per cent of cyclo-hexane. 1,2-Dimethylcyclopentane isomerizes to a mixture containing 97 per cent of methylcyclohexane.

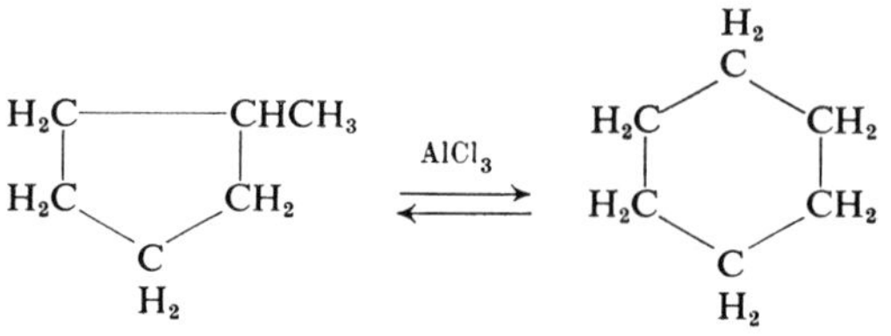

Methylcyclopentane   Cyclohexane

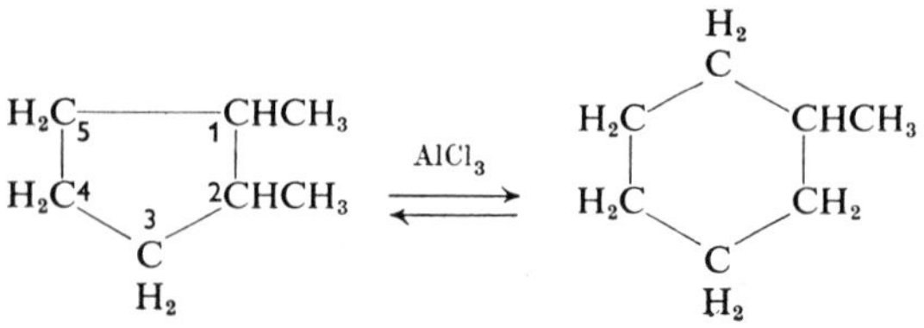

1,2-Dimethyl-cyclopentane   Methylcyclohexane

Alicyclic hydrocarbons having double bonds in the ring also are known. The compound with one double bond in a six-membered ring is called cyclo-hexene. Those with two double bonds are called 1,3-cyclohexadiene and 1,4-cyclohexadiene.

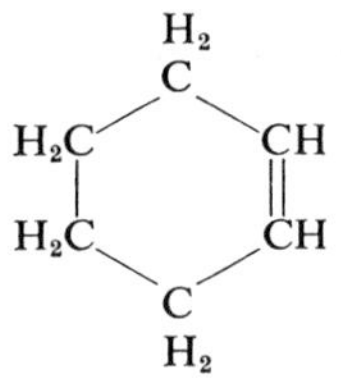

Cyclohexene 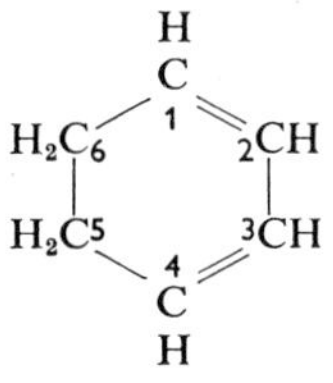   1,3-Cyclohexadiene 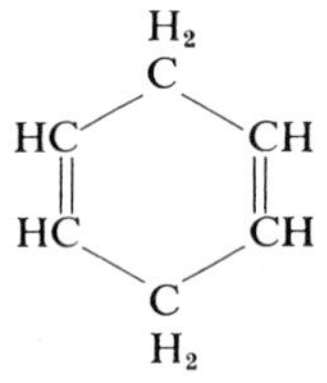   1,4-Cyclohexadiene

These compounds are typical unsaturated compounds and undergo all of the addition reactions of the alkenes (p. 53).

When a third double bond is present in a six-membered ring, the properties differ radically from those of either the cyclanes or the cyclenes. The members of this series are called *aromatic hydrocarbons*. The parent compound is benzene, C_6H_6. The lower homologs are toluene, $C_6H_5CH_3$, ethylbenzene, $C_6H_5C_2H_5$, and three dimethylbenzenes, known as the xylenes.

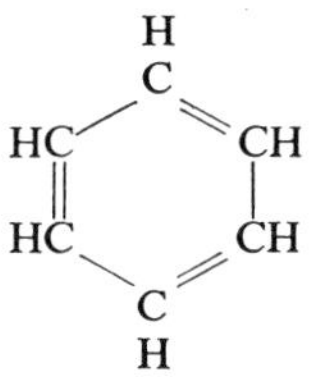

Benzene 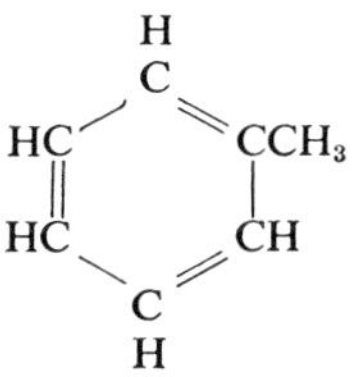   Toluene 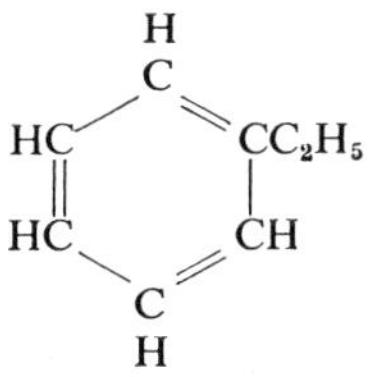   Ethylbenzene

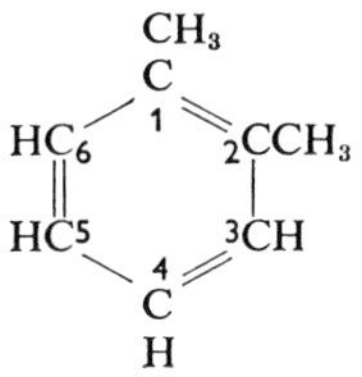

1,2-Dimethylbenzene (*ortho*xylene) 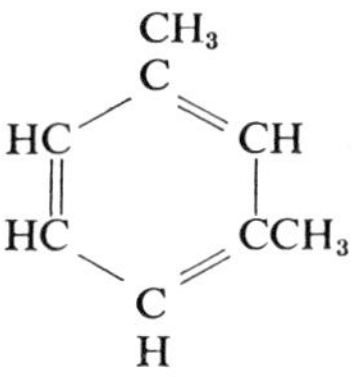   1,3-Dimethylbenzene (*meta*xylene) 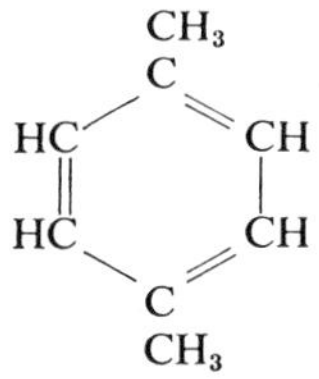   1,4-Dimethylbenzene (*para*xylene)

The special properties of the aromatic hydrocarbons are discussed in Chapter 18. It is sufficient here to state that when three double bonds alternate with three single bonds in a six-membered ring, the unsaturation electrons are almost as unreactive as the electrons in single bonds. For example, benzene does not decolorize a solution of bromine and does not react with aqueous permanganate solution.

Aromatic hydrocarbons occur in coal tar (p. 427) and petroleum (p. 71). They can be prepared by dehydrogenating cyclohexanes over a platinum catalyst or by cyclization of alkanes to cyclanes, followed by dehydrogenation.

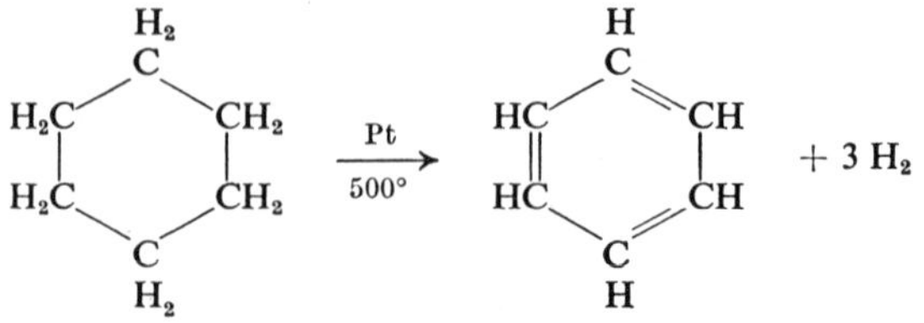

Cyclohexane → Benzene

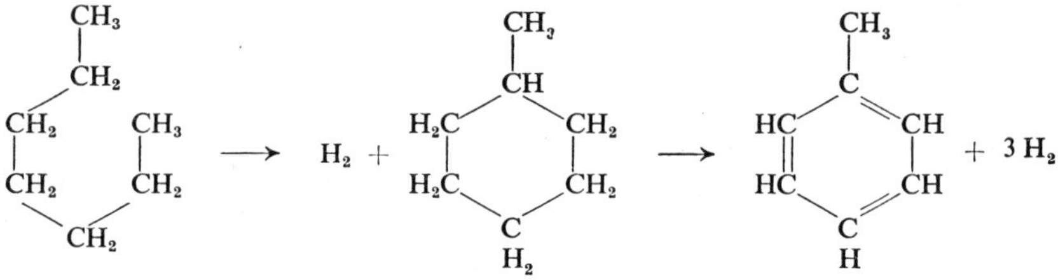

Heptane   Methylcyclohexane   Toluene

REVIEW QUESTIONS

1. Give the evidence for the commonly accepted structure of ethylene.
2. Compare the alkenes with the alkanes in respect to their physical and chemical properties.
3. State the Markovnikov rule and give an equation illustrating its application. Discuss the exceptions to the Markovnikov rule.
4. Tell what is meant by the following terms and illustrate by an example or equation: (*a*) double bond; (*b*) addition reaction; (*c*) hydrogenation; (*d*) ozonolysis; (*e*) polymerization; (*f*) functional group; (*g*) cyclic hydrocarbon; (*h*) a cyclane; (*i*) an aromatic hydrocarbon.

PROBLEMS

5. Write condensed structural formulas and give a suitable name to the members of the following groups of compounds: (*a*) all of the isomeric pentenes; (*b*) all of the hexenes with a terminal double bond; (*c*) all of the octenes with a central double bond; (*d*) all of the heptenes with six carbon atoms in a chain; (*e*) all of the octenes that contain a branching ethyl group.

6. Write structural formulas for the following compounds:

   A. (*a*) 2-2-Dimethyl-3-hexene; (*b*) *s*-butylethylene; (*c*) *sym*-ethyl-*t*-butylethylene; (*d*) 3-(1-methylpropyl)-2-heptene; (*e*) (*sym*-dimethyl)ethylethylene.

   B. (*a*) 2-Methyl-3-ethyl-1-pentene; (*b*) *sym*-methyl-*i*-propylethylene; (*c*) 6,6-dimethyl-4-(2,2-dimethylpropyl)-3-octene; (*d*) *i*-butylethylene; (*e*) *unsym*-di-*n*-propylethylene.

   C. (*a*) Tetramethylethylene; (*b*) (*unsym*-methylethyl)-*n*-propyl-*i*-propylethylene; (*c*) *sym*-*i*-butyl-*n*-amylethylene; (*d*) 3-(2-methylpropyl)-2-heptene; (*e*) 3-methyl-4-ethyl-3-hexene.

7. Name the following compounds by the Geneva system and as derivatives of ethylene:

A. (a) $(CH_3)_3CCH{=}CHCH_3$ (b) $CH_3CH_2CH(CH_3)CH{=}CHC_2H_5$

(c) $(CH_3)_2CHC{=}C(CH_3)_2$ (d) $CH_3CH_2C{=}C(CH_2)_4CH_3$
    | | |
    C_2H_5 CH_3 CH_3

B. (a) $(CH_3)_2CHCH{=}CH(CH_2)_5CH_3$ (b) $(CH_3)_2CHCH_2CH{=}CHC_2H_5$

(c) $CH_3CH_2CH{=}CCH_3$ (d) $C_2H_5C{=}C(CH_3)_2$
       | |
   $CH_3(CH_2)_3CH_2$ CH_3

C. (a) $(CH_3CH_2CH_2)_2C{=}CHCH_3$ (b) $(CH_3)_3CCH{=}CHC_2H_5$

(c) $CH_3C{=}CHCH_2CH(CH_3)_2$ (d) $C_2H_5C{=}CHCHCH_3$
  | | |
 $CH_2(CH_2)_4CH_3$ CH_3 CH_3

8. Indicate the objections to the following names and give suitable ones:
   A. (a) 2-Ethyl-3-hexene; (b) 3-methyl-4-heptene; (c) methyl-*t*-butylethylene; (d) 2,3-di-methylpentene-2; (e) (1-methylethyl)ethylene.
   B. (a) Ethyl-*i*-propylethylene; (b) 3,3-dimethylpentene-1; (c) 5-ethyl-2-hexene; (d) *sym*-methyl-(2-methylpropyl)ethylene; (e) 2,2-dimethyl-3-butene.
   C. (a) 3,5-Dimethylheptene-1; (b) 2,3-dimethyl-3-pentene; (c) *n*-butyl-*i*-butylethylene; (d) 3-ethyl-4-*s*-butyl-1-hexene; (e) *unsym*-ethyl(dimethylethyl)ethylene.
9. Write equations for the following reactions and give a suitable name to the organic product:
   A. (a) Chlorine and 2-pentene; (b) sulfuric acid and 1-hexene; (c) hydrogen chloride and 2-methyl-1-pentene; (d) dilute permanganate and *t*-butylethylene; (e) hydrogen, platinum, and 3-ethyl-1-pentene; (f) hydrogen bromide, peroxides, and isobutylethylene.
   B. (a) Bromine and trimethylethylene; (b) sulfuric acid and *sym*-dimethylpropylethylene; (c) hydrogen bromide and 3-methyl-2-pentene; (d) dilute permanganate and 2,3-di-methyl-1-pentene; (e) hydrogen, platinum, and 4-methyl-2-pentene; (f) hydrogen bromide, peroxides, and isopropylethylene.
   C. (a) Chlorine and 3-heptene; (b) sulfuric acid and 2-methyl-2-pentene; (c) hydrogen bromide, peroxides, and 2,3,3-trimethyl-1-butene; (d) hydrogen bromide and 2,4-dimethyl-2-pentene; (e) dilute permanganate and 2,3-dimethyl-2-butene; (f) hydrogen, platinum, and *sym*-methyl-*t*-butylethylene.
10. Give reactions illustrating the preparation of the following compounds from the proper alkene:
   A. (a) 2,3-Dimethylpentane; (b) 2-chloro-2-methylbutane; (c) 1,1,2-trimethylpropyl hydrogen sulfate; (d) 2,3-dibromo-2-methylhexane; (e) 2-methylpentyl bromide.
   B. (a) Neohexane; (b) 3-bromo-3-methylhexane; (c) 1,1-dimethylpentyl hydrogen sulfate; (d) 1,2-dichloro-2-ethylpentane; (e) 2,3-dihydroxy-2,3-dimethylbutane.
   C. (a) Isoheptane; (b) 1-methylpropyl hydrogen sulfate; (c) 2-methyl-2-chlorohexane; (d) 2,3-dimethyl-2,3-dibromopentane; (e) 2-methylhexyl bromide.
11. Deduce the structure of the olefin which gives the following products on ozonolysis: (a) a one-carbon aldehyde and a three-carbon ketone; (b) a two-carbon aldehyde and a four-carbon ketone; (c) two moles of a four-carbon ketone; (d) a two-carbon aldehyde and a four-carbon aldehyde having an isopropyl group; (e) a three-carbon ketone and a four-carbon ketone.
12. If one gram of an olefin decolorized the indicated number of cubic centimeters of a standard solution of bromine in carbon tetrachloride containing 20 g. of bromine per 100 cc. of solution, calculate the equivalent weight of the compound: (a) 14.3 cc.; (b) 8.2 cc.; (c) 19.1 cc.; (d) 11.4 cc.
13. If X is the weight of a pure olefin having one double bond which decolorized Y grams of bromine, calculate the molecular formulas of the following olefins:

	A	B	C	D	E
X	5.6	8.9	11.7	2.2	9.3
Y	16.0	14.5	26.7	3.2	17.8

14. When X grams of a pure hydrocarbon having one or more double bonds was shaken with hydrogen in the presence of a platinum catalyst, Y cc. of hydrogen (S.T.P.) was absorbed. If Z was the molecular weight as determined by the Victor Meyer method, calculate the number of double bonds and the molecular formula of the following compounds:

	A	B	C	D	E
X	0.235	0.192	0.117	0.133	0.151
Y	168	89.6	74.7	112	72
Z	90 ± 8	94 ± 6	73 ± 5	81 ± 8	101 ± 7

15. When X grams of a mixture of pentenes and pentanes was titrated with a standard bromine solution, Y grams of bromine was absorbed. Calculate the per cent of pentenes in the following mixtures:

	A	B	C	D	E
X	4.2	3.9	5.5	2.6	8.4
Y	5.76	2.23	0.44	5.05	1.92

16. A sample of a mixture of air, ethane, propane, and propylene measuring W cc. was washed with concentrated sulfuric acid. It then had a volume of X cc. After mixing this residue with a known volume of oxygen and burning completely to carbon dioxide and water in a slow combustion pipette, there was a contraction of Y cc. When the combustion products were washed with 30 per cent aqueous potassium hydroxide, a further contraction of Z cc. took place. Calculate the per cent composition by volume of the following original mixtures:

	A	B	C	D
W	28.9	26.6	27.3	30.2
X	12.6	6.5	10.5	5.5
Y	16.3	20.1	16.8	24.7
Z	20.6	27.8	20.6	23.7

Chapter 4

NATURAL GAS, PETROLEUM, AND
DERIVED PRODUCTS

Natural gas and petroleum are important natural resources. Their chief use is as fuel for generating mechanical and electrical energy and for space heating. The world production of petroleum in 1955 was estimated to be 5.6 billion barrels of 42 gallons. Although the United States possessed less than 16 per cent of the known world reserves, and because of the much more thorough exploration in the United States certainly much less of the actual reserves, it produced over 2.4 billion barrels or 43 per cent of the total production. In other words the petroleum resources of the United States are being depleted much more rapidly than the average rate for the rest of the world. The Middle East was responsible for 21 per cent of world production, Venezuela for 14 per cent and the U.S.S.R. for 9 per cent. The remainder was widely distributed throughout the world.

Origin

Natural gas and petroleum were formed by the decomposition of vast quantities of organic material, undoubtedly of marine origin, buried in sediment. The view that petroleum is of biological origin, rather than that it was formed from inorganic carbides, or from carbon monoxide or carbon dioxide and hydrogen, is supported by the presence of organic nitrogen and sulfur compounds, optically active compounds (p. 331), and complex organic compounds known as porphyrins, which are produced only by plants and animals. The exact processes which converted organic matter into hydrocarbons, the principal components of petroleum, are not known. It is believed, however, that they took place for the most part at ordinary temperatures, because porphyrins would have been decomposed if elevated temperatures had been involved. Oil at depths of 10,000 to 15,000 feet has, of course, been subjected to temperatures of at least 150° to 200°. Hence heat has played a part in determining the composition of oils found or formed at these or lower depths.

Both natural gas and petroleum accumulate in porous formations capped by dome-shaped impervious layers of rock or in other stratigraphic traps. When a well is bored through the impervious cap, hydrostatic pressure forces the gas or oil to the surface. After the pressure has been entirely released and oil no longer flows from the well, the oil is pumped out mechanically.

NATURAL GAS

Natural gas varies greatly in composition. Most unprocessed gases contain 60 to 80 per cent methane, 5 to 9 per cent ethane, 3 to 18 per cent propane, and 2 to 14 per cent higher hydrocarbons. However, one Pennsylvania well delivers natural gas containing 98.8 per cent methane, and gas from a well in

Kentucky contains only 23 per cent methane. Varying amounts of nonhydro-carbon gases also are present, including nitrogen, carbon dioxide, and hydrogen sulfide. Gas from some wells contains up to 98 per cent carbon dioxide and from others up to 40 per cent hydrogen sulfide. Natural gas, after the removal of propane and butanes by liquefaction, is used chiefly as fuel. After processing, the composition is in the range 70 to 90 per cent methane, 6 to 24 per cent ethane, and 1 to 8 per cent propane. Natural gas pipe lines serve practically every section of the United States and extend from Texas to New York and to California.

Large quantities of natural gas are converted by incomplete combustion into a finely divided form of carbon known as lamp black, carbon black, or gas black.

$$CH_4 + O_2 \text{ (air)} \longrightarrow C + 2 H_2O$$

In the older process the sooty methane flames impinge on moving steel channels. The deposited carbon, known as *channel black*, is scraped continuously into conveyors. The newer *furnace blacks* are prepared by the partial combustion of methane, or of a petroleum fraction low in hydrogen, in a furnace. The carbon is carried out of the furnace by the gas stream, cooled, and collected by passing through fabric bags.

Carbon blacks are used chiefly to confer abrasion resistance to tread stocks of automobile tires, and account for about one third of the weight of the tread. Channel blacks once were used exclusively and still are best for natural rubber, but the furnace blacks are superior for GRS synthetic rubber. As a result the production of channel black in the United States decreased from about 600 to 500 million pounds per year between 1948 and 1954, while that of furnace blacks has increased from practically nothing to over one billion pounds per year.

Carbon black and hydrogen are produced by the thermal decomposition of methane.

$$CH_4 \xrightarrow{1200°} C + 2 H_2$$

Hydrogen and carbon monoxide may be prepared from methane or other hydrocarbons and steam,

$$CH_4 + H_2O \xrightarrow[800°-900°]{Ni} CO + 3 H_2$$

or by the partial oxidation of methane with oxygen prepared from liquid air.

$$2 CH_4 + O_2 \longrightarrow 2 CO + 4 H_2$$

Both reactions may be combined using a mixture of methane, oxygen, and steam. The second exothermic reaction (heat evolved) provides the energy required by the first reaction, which is endothermic (heat absorbed). The carbon monoxide may be converted to carbon dioxide and more hydrogen by another endothermic process.

$$CO + H_2O \xrightarrow[450°-500°]{Fe_2O_3 + promoters} CO_2 + H_2$$

The carbon dioxide is removed by scrubbing with water under pressure or with alkaline reagents such as solutions of sodium carbonate or ethanolamine (p. 752). About two thirds of the hydrogen used to make synthetic ammonia is produced by these reactions. The mixture of carbon monoxide and hydrogen can be used for the synthesis of methyl alcohol (p. 90) and ketones (p. 223). Processes for the conversion of natural gas into acetylene (p. 133), halogenated hydrocarbons (p. 118), alcohols (Chapter 5), acids (Chapter 9), and aldehydes and ketones (Chapter 11) have been developed.

PETROLEUM

Petroleum is the liquid mixture of organic compounds obtained at certain points from the upper strata of the earth. Its composition varies widely depending on the area from which it is obtained. The chief components of this very complex mixture are hydrocarbons, which may be paraffinic, alicyclic (p. 64), or aromatic (p. 65) in varying proportions, depending on the source of the petroleum. The examples given in Table 8 were chosen to illustrate the maximum variations observed.

TABLE 8

COMPOSITION OF STRAIGHT-RUN PETROLEUM FRACTIONS

BOILING RANGE °C	ORIGIN	PER CENT BY VOLUME		
		PARAFFINIC	ALICYCLIC	AROMATIC
40–200	Michigan	74	18	8
	Hastings, Tex	27	67	6
	Conroe, Tex.	35	39	26
200–300	Michigan	48	40	12
	Hastings, Tex.	0	75	25
	Conroe, Tex.	32	47	21
350–500	Pennsylvania	30	50	20
	East Texas	20	55	25
	California	0	60	40

The separation of the individual components is very difficult, but between 1927 and 1952, at the U.S. Bureau of Standards and at the Carnegie Institute of Technology, 130 pure hydrocarbons were isolated from the gas, gasoline, and kerosene fractions of a midcontinent petroleum. Of the 130 hydrocarbons, 54 were paraffinic, 39 were alicyclic, 33 were aromatic, and 4 were aromatic-alicyclic. It is estimated that the portion of petroleum boiling up to 200° contains at least 500 compounds.

In addition to carbon and hydrogen, petroleum contains 1 to 6 per cent of sulfur, nitrogen, and oxygen. The per cent of sulfur, nitrogen, and oxygen compounds, however, is much higher. Thus if a fraction has a sulfur content of 1 per cent, and the sulfur compound has a molecular weight of 300 and one atom of sulfur to the molecule, the sulfur compound constitutes approximately 10 per cent of the fraction by weight.

Refining

Petroleum is *refined*, that is, separated into useful products, near the oil field, or it is shipped by pipe line or tanker to refineries located near centers of high population or readily available transportation. Refining consists essentially of distilling the petroleum into fractions of different boiling ranges, converting the less desirable components into more valuable products, and special treatments of the fractions to remove undesirable components. Originally distillation was a batch operation using horizontal cylindrical direct-fired stills. The fractions were cut according to density, the lighter fractions having the lower boiling point. When all of the volatile components had been removed, the still was cooled, and men entered through a manhole and dug the coke out with a pick and shovel. This type of still has been displaced by the tubular furnace with fractionating column illustrated in Fig. 31. Oil is pumped continuously

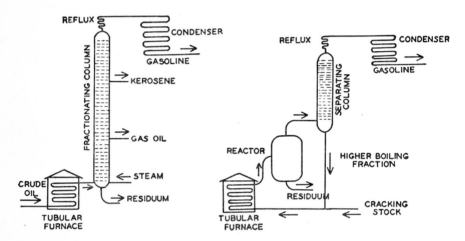

Fig. 31. Straight-run distillation unit.   Fig. 32. Dubbs cracking unit.

through heated pipes and flashed into a fractionating column from which the various fractions can be withdrawn. The main fractions are gas, gasoline, kerosene, gas oil, and high-boiling residue. The residue can be distilled under reduced pressure for the recovery of lubricating oils and wax, or it can be cracked to gasoline (p. 75) or used directly as fuel. The relative amounts of the different fractions vary widely with the source of the crude oil. Thus one yellow crude from California yields 2 per cent gas, 80 per cent gasoline, 10 per cent kerosene, and 8 per cent gas oil; a green crude from Texas yields 1 per cent gas, 39 per cent gasoline, 11 per cent kerosene, 22 per cent gas oil, and 27 per cent residuum; a black crude from California yields 1 per cent gas, 28 per cent gasoline, 8 per cent kerosene, 18 per cent gas oil, and 45 per cent residuum.

Gas. The gas fractions are obtained during the first distillation of petroleum and also result from cracking operations (p. 74). They consist chiefly of hydrocarbons having from one to five carbon atoms, which are both saturated and unsaturated. They are separated into their various components by chemical methods and by efficient fractionating columns. The methane and ethane usually are burned as fuel. The olefins may be removed by conversion into alcohols (pp. 92, 97), or by polymerization or alkylation reactions (pp. 76, 77). The butenes are particularly valuable for the manufacture of high-octane gasoline and synthetic rubber (p. 716). The propane and butanes may be liquefied and distributed in high-pressure tanks and cylinders or used for the synthesis of other organic compounds. A total of 7 billion gallons of liquefied petroleum gas was used in the United States in 1956. Large amounts of the butanes and most of the pentanes are blended into gasoline.

Gasoline. With the rapid increase in the use of motor vehicles since 1910, gasoline has become the most important product derived from petroleum. The composition of gasoline varies widely, but motor gasoline may be defined as a complex mixture of hydrocarbons boiling between 0° and 200°. Aviation gasoline boils between 30° and 150°. Initially the gasoline fraction obtained from the first distillation of petroleum, referred to as *straight-run gasoline*, was more than enough to supply the demands for motor fuel, but the increase in the number of automobiles soon made this source insufficient and recourse was had to the thermal decomposition of higher hydrocarbons into lower molecular weight molecules (p. 44). The manufacture of gas from oil was discussed in England as early as 1792, and in 1865 Young distilled shale oil under pressure to raise the boiling point of the oil and cause partial pyrolysis (thermal decomposition) during distillation. Large-scale commercial cracking was developed in the United States in 1912 by Burton [1] who carried out distillations under pressure in horizontal stills as a batch operation. Numerous continuous processes have been developed since then.

Qualities other than the proper volatility are important in gasoline, especially the *octane number*. Everyone is familiar with *knocking* in a gasoline automobile engine, the *ping* that develops when pulling up a long grade or attempting to accelerate a car too rapidly. In the operation of an engine the down stroke of the piston draws air through the carburetor where the air becomes laden with vapor and fine droplets of gasoline. This air-fuel mixture is next compressed by the piston to a small volume, the ratio of the initial and final volumes being known as the *compression-ratio* of the engine. When the piston reaches the top of the stroke, the ignition system produces a spark at the spark-plug, which ignites the air-fuel mixture. As the gases ignite and expand, the piston is forced down providing power to the crankshaft. During proper combustion the wave-front travels from the point of ignition through the fuel mixture at a rate of 25 to 250 feet per second. In *knocking*, the wave-front is normal during the first three-fourths of the combustion but then suddenly begins to travel at 1000 feet per second. This sudden increase in rate is accompanied by an increased rate of pressure increase which sets off shock waves of the same frequency as the sound of knocking. Knocking decreases power and increases wear on the engine. Engine efficiency increases with the compression ratio of the engine but so does knocking. Nevertheless the compression ratio of gasoline engines, which was around 4 to 1 in 1920, was 7.5—10 to 1 in 1956. This increase has been possible because of the development of anti-knock fuels. It has been found that the knocking characteristic of a fuel depends on the structures of the hydrocarbon molecules and that knocking can be increased or decreased by the addition of relatively small amounts of other chemicals (p. 80).

As a means of measuring the knocking properties of a fuel, two pure hydro-carbons were selected as standards. One is *n*-heptane, which was worse in its tendency to cause knocking than any ordinary gasoline, and the other is

---

[1] William Meriam Burton (1865–1954) began his career as the first chemist employed by the Standard Oil Company at its Whiting, Indiana, refinery and became president of the Standard Oil Company of Indiana in 1918. He is regarded as the founder of modern petroleum technology.

2,2,4-trimethylpentane [2] which was better than any gasoline known at the time. Blends of these two pure hydrocarbons could be made to match the knocking characteristics of any known fuel. The knocking property of the fuel then could be described by its **octane number,** the per cent of 2,2,4-trimethylpentane in the synthetic blend that matched the gasoline in knocking properties. Investigation of a large number of pure hydrocarbons has shown that in general the octane number increases with increase in branching, and that olefins and aromatic hydrocarbons (pp. 65, 429) are better than saturated hydrocarbons. The trend in gasoline production has been to develop methods for producing gasoline with higher and higher octane numbers. It is possible to design gasoline engines using special fuels, for example trimethylbutane (triptane), that will operate at compression ratios between 12 and 16 to 1 and have an efficiency equal to that of a Diesel engine (p. 81). In 1955 the octane numbers of regular and premium gasoline in the United States were about 87 and 95.

Thermal Cracking. Thermal decomposition of hydrocarbons results not only in smaller molecules of higher volatility but also in the production of olefins and aromatic hydrocarbons. Hence the cracking process gives a higher yield of gasoline and a product with higher octane number. The products formed depend on their relative thermodynamic stability and on the relative rates of the reactions taking place, both factors being dependent on temperature and pressure. Between 400° and 500° gaseous and liquid hydrocarbons of lower boiling range are formed. Above 500° gas production becomes more important. The commercial production of oil-gas (gas from oil) normally is carried out at about 700°. Around 900° the maximum yield of aromatic hydrocarbons (p. 429) is obtained, and above 1000°, methane, hydrogen, and carbon are the chief products.

The **basic cracking equipment** consists of a *heating coil* and a *reactor*. All the various possible reactions require time for the reaction to take place. Preheated oil is pumped through the coil and heated to the cracking temperature of 450°–500° so rapidly (contact time one-half to three minutes) that undesirable phases of decomposition, especially coke formation, do not have time to take place in the coil. On passing into the reactor, which is simply an insulated cylindrical tank, the rate of flow is decreased sufficiently to give time for the completion of the reaction. The operation thus far takes place at pressures of 175–250 p.s.i., to increase the amount of material in the liquid phase. On leaving the reactor the oil is flashed into a fractionating column, where it is separated into the desired products. Figure 32, page 72, shows diagrammatically the *Dubbs process* which may be operated to yield only gas, gasoline, and residual fuel oil or coke from any type of stock.

If clean recycle stocks are used which deposit practically no coke, it is possible to dispense with the reactor. A higher cracking temperature is used (500°–600°) and the cracking is permitted to take place in soaking tubes, an extension of the tubular furnace. Whereas the octane number of a straight-run gasoline will be 50–55, that of a thermally cracked gasoline will be 70–72. Few new thermal cracking units have been built since 1945 because of the rapid change to catalytic cracking.

---

[2] Unfortunately designated *isooctane* by petroleum technologists. The prefix *iso* should be reserved for compounds having two methyl groups at the end of a straight chain (p. 33).

Catalytic Cracking. Since the products formed during the cracking operation depend not only on their relative stability but on the relative rates at which the different reactions take place, the aim has been to find catalysts which will accelerate the rates of reactions leading to desirable products over those leading to undesirable products. As a result **catalytic cracking** has become of prime importance. By these processes gasolines with octane numbers of 77 to 81 are obtained. The catalysts used are natural clays or synthetic alumina-silica mixtures, and the operation is carried out at 450°–500° and relatively low pressures of 10–50 p.s.i. In all catalytic processes the catalyst becomes deactivated by the deposition of coke, which must be burned off periodically to regenerate

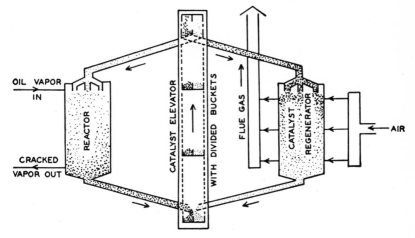

Fig. 33. Moving-bed catalytic cracking unit.

the catalyst. The more recent processes are continuous. In the *moving-bed* type the catalyst in the form of beads is carried through the reaction, purging, and regenerating zones by mechanical conveyors and gravity (Fig. 33). In later modifications the reactor is above the regenerator, and the spent catalyst moves to the regenerator by gravity. The regenerated catalyst is carried to a hopper above the reactor by an air lift. Processes using fluidized catalyst are similar except that the catalyst is in the form of a fine powder which behaves as a fluid and is transported through the various zones by the gas streams. The catalyst is removed centrifugally from the cracked gases or from the flue gases by means of cyclone separators.

Economically, catalytic cracking has another advantage over thermal cracking. In the former the heat necessary for cracking comes from the burning of coke whereas in the latter, the heat is supplied by burning the more valuable refinery gases or liquid fuels.

Coking. In the refining operations, large quantities of residual oils are obtained. Cracking of these residual oils can yield more gasoline, but when carried out as a batch process, the coke is obtained in a massive form which is difficult to remove from the stills. As a result, distillation and thermal cracking were carried only to the point where the residual oils were sufficiently fluid to be burned as fuel. New coking processes have been described in which the residual oil is brought in contact with hot coke particles previously heated by partial combustion. The particles grow in size during the cracking process and are removed continuously and replaced by freshly heated particles. As in catalytic cracking, either a moving bed or fluidized bed may be used.

Reforming. Most aromatic hydrocarbons in the boiling range of gasoline have octane numbers above 100. Because of the demand for gasoline of higher and higher octane number, catalytic processes for the conversion of the cyclohexanes, cyclopentanes, and alkanes into aromatic hydrocarbons have been developed (pp. 64, 65).

During World War II, a catalyst of molybdenum oxide supported on alumina was used to convert methylcyclohexane to toluene (p. 66). Since 1949, much more active catalysts containing less than 1 per cent of platinum supported on alumina have been used. Dehydrogenation of cyclohexanes (p. 66) is the easiest operation, isomerization of methylcyclopentanes to cyclohexanes (p. 64) is harder, and cyclization of alkanes to cyclohexanes is the most difficult. All of the reactions are favored by high temperatures and low pressures. These factors, however, increase the deposition of coke on the catalyst, which then must be regenerated by burning. The various commercial processes are all compromises. If the process is operated at 470° and 600 p.s.i., the catalyst may be active for years without regeneration, but the yield of aromatics comes chiefly from the cyclohexanes. If operated at 480° and 500 p.s.i., more methylcyclopentanes are isomerized to cyclohexanes, but the catalyst needs occasional regeneration. Processes operated at 510° and 300 p.s.i. give more cyclization of alkanes, but the catalyst needs periodic regeneration. Because dehydrogenation is an endothermic process, heat must be supplied for the reaction and the vapors must be preheated in furnaces before being passed over the catalyst. By combining an extraction process with a reforming process, the low octane components can be recycled and the feed converted entirely into fuel having an octane number of 100 or better.

In any reforming operation, the conversion to aromatic compounds is not complete. When pure benzene, toluene, or xylenes are desired, the aromatics are separated by extraction with an appropriate solvent such as diethylene glycol (p. 744) or by extractive distillation. In the latter operation a higher boiling solvent, such as phenol (p. 502), is added near the top of the fractionating column. The solvent is chosen to increase the difference in volatility of the materials being separated.

Large quantities of hydrogen have become available from the reforming operations. Some of it is being used to improve various petroleum fractions and to remove sulfur by hydrogenation. Most of it probably will be used to hydrogenate low quality crude oils and residual oils, which then would yield more gasoline and less coke on cracking.

Polymerization. The availability of large quantities of gases from the cracking operations has made it desirable to convert them into more useful products. One such procedure for the utilization of olefins is **polymerization** to liquid fuels. The polymerization of propylene to dodecylenes and of isobutylene to diisobutylenes has been discussed on page 62. If mixtures of propylene and the butylenes are used, an interpolymerization, called *copolymerization*, takes place. The products have octane numbers of 80 to 85 and, as the equation for the polymerization of propylene shows (p. 62), still contain a double bond. Because of the unsaturation, the polymers on exposure to air are slowly oxidized and further polymerized to undesirable compounds of high molecular weight known as *gums*. The rate of oxidation and polymerization can be decreased greatly by the addition of small amounts of substances known as *antioxidants* (p. 886). When used for this purpose they are called *gum inhibitors*. Gum formation can be completely eliminated by hydrogenating to a mixture of saturated hydrocarbons. Hydrogenation of the diisobutylenes with hydrogen and a nickel catalyst (p. 55) gives 2,2,4-trimethylpentane, the standard 100 octane fuel. These saturated, high-octane alkanes are blended with aromatic hydrocarbons for aviation gasolines (p. 430).

Alkylation. Since 1938, branched alkanes have been added to the double bond of olefins to give high-octane gasoline, a process known as **alkylation.** At atmospheric pressure this process is thermodynamically possible only at relatively low temperatures, and a catalyst is necessary to make the reaction take place at a practical rate. Using 85 to 100 per cent sulfuric acid or anhydrous hydrogen fluoride as a catalyst at temperatures below 20°, isobutane reacts with the mixed butylenes to give a mixture of octanes having an octane number of 92 to 94.

$$CH_3CHCH_2C(CH_3)_3,$$
$$CH_3$$

$$(CH_3)_3CH \; + \quad \begin{array}{c} CH_3CH_2CH{=}CH_2 \\ \\ and \\ \\ CH_3CH{=}CHCH_3 \end{array} \quad \longrightarrow \quad \begin{array}{c} CH_3CH_2CHC(CH_3)_3, \; and \\ CH_3 \\ \\ CH_3CH{-}CHCH(CH_3)_2 \\ CH_3 \quad CH_3 \end{array}$$

The advantages of the alkylation process over polymerization are that the branched alkanes are used as well as the olefins, and that the product is saturated, thus avoiding the necessity for hydrogenation or the use of gum inhibitors.

The alkylation reaction is believed to take place by an ionic mechanism. The initial step is the transfer of a proton from the proton-donating catalyst to a molecule of olefin to give a carbonium ion, followed by addition of the carbonium ion to a second molecule of olefin to give a dimeric carbonium ion as in the polymerization of olefins (p. 63).

$$CH_3C{=}CH_2 \quad \xrightarrow{H_2SO_4} \quad HSO_4^- \; + \; CH_3\overset{+}{C}CH_3 \quad \xrightarrow{CH_3CH{=}CHCH_3} \quad CH_3\overset{+}{C}HCH{-}\overset{CH_3}{\underset{CH_3 \; CH_3}{C}}CH_3$$
$$CH_3 \qquad\qquad\qquad\qquad CH_3$$

However, instead of stabilization of the dimeric ion by loss of a proton to give an unsaturated dimer or of further polymerization, the presence of isobutane permits transfer of a hydride ion, [H:⁻], to give a saturated molecule with regeneration of a *t*-butyl carbonium ion.

$$\overset{+}{CH_3}CHCH{-}\underset{CH_3 \; CH_3}{\overset{CH_3}{C}}CH_3 + (CH_3)_3CH \quad \longrightarrow \quad CH_3CH_2CH{-}\underset{CH_3 \; CH_3}{\overset{CH_3}{C}}CH_3 + (CH_3)_3C^+$$

2,2,3-Trimethylpentane

The reason that isobutane is necessary in the alkylation reaction is that only the *t*-butyl carbonium ion is sufficiently stabilized by the electron-donating properties of the methyl groups (p. 60) to permit transfer of hydrogen with a pair of electrons from an alkane to a carbonium ion under the conditions of the reaction.

To account for the formation of 2,2,4-trimethylpentane and 2,3,4-trimethylpentane, it is necessary to assume rearrangement of the intermediate carbonium ion with migration to the carbonium atom of a methide ion, [CH₃:⁻], from an adjacent carbon atom, followed by hydride ion transfer from isobutane.

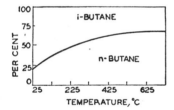

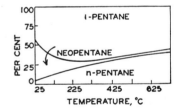

2,2,4-Trimethylpentane   2,3,4-Trimethylpentane

Although the initial formation of the *t*-butyl carbonium ion is indicated as coming from isobutylene, it can arise also by hydride ion transfer from isobutane to a carbonium ion formed from 1-butene or 2-butene. Moreover, since 1-butene and 2-butene are in equilibrium in the presence of sulfuric acid (p. 105), both can give rise to the same products. Other compounds may be formed by numerous other paths involving similar steps. The final composition of the product depends on the relative rates of the various steps and the extent to which thermodynamic equilibrium is attained.

Isomerization. Of the lower-boiling saturated hydrocarbons the least useful are methane, ethane, propane, and *n*-butane, because they do not enter into alkylation reactions, and *n*-pentane and *n*-hexane because of their low octane numbers. Although *n*-butane and isobutane are stable indefinitely in the absence of catalysts, Fig. 34 indicates that at room temperature they should exist in

Fig. 34. Variation of the equilibrium composition of the butanes with temperature.

Fig. 35. Variation of the equilibrium composition of the pentanes with temperature.

equilibrium in the ratio of 1 : 4. Commercially catalysts consisting of a liquid complex of anhydrous aluminum chloride, dry hydrogen chloride, and hydrocarbon, or a solid catalyst of aluminum chloride on alumina is used to cause this equilibrium to be established rapidly at room temperature. The isobutane produced is used in the alkylation reactions. According to Fig. 35 the equilibrium mixture of the pentanes should contain large amounts of neopentane. No neopentane ever has been obtained, although either *n*-pentane or isopentane readily isomerizes to the equilibrium composition of the two isomers calculated from their relative thermodynamic stabilities. Isopentane and the branched hexanes formed by isomerization of *n*-pentane and *n*-hexane are valuable blending stocks for gasoline.

Isomerization, like alkylation, is believed to take place by a carbonium ion mechanism. Aluminum halides in the absence of hydrogen halides are not effective catalysts, and the isomerization is greatly accelerated by the presence of olefins. Accordingly it is assumed that the first step is the addition of a proton to an olefin molecule present as an impurity.

$$R_2C{=}CR_2 + HX + AlX_3 \longrightarrow [R_2\overset{+}{C}CHR_2] + [^-AlX_4]$$

The carbonium ion, [R^+], thus formed can remove a hydride ion from a secondary or tertiary carbon atom to give another carbonium ion.

$$CH_3CH_2CH_2CH_3 + [R^+] \longrightarrow [CH_3CH_2\overset{+}{C}HCH_3] + RH$$

Shift of a methide ion gives a rearranged carbonium ion which can undergo a hydride ion shift to give an intermediate able to remove a hydride ion from a secondary carbon atom.

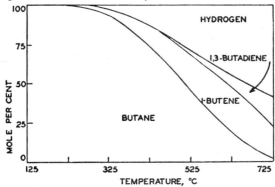

It is neccessary to assume that a primary carbonium ion, in this case the isobutyl carbonium ion, cannot abstract a proton directly from a butane molecule. Otherwise it should be possible to isomerize isopentane to neopentane by a similar mechanism.

Likewise it is assumed that a carbonium ion cannot abstract a hydride ion from a primary carbon atom.

Dehydrogenation. Another use that can be made of ethane, propane, and the butanes is conversion into the more valuable olefins by thermal cracking, partial oxidation, or by dehydrogenation using chromic oxide on alumina as the catalyst. Figure 36 illustrates the equilibrium concentrations of *n*-butane,

Fig. 36. Variation of equilibrium composition of butane, 1-butene,
1,3-butadiene, and hydrogen with temperature.

1-butene, 1,3-butadiene, and hydrogen at one atmosphere from 100°–800°. Butenes may be used in the polymerization and alkylation processes, and butadiene is the basis for the large volume production of synthetic rubber (p. 716).

Knock Inhibitors. Numerous substances when added to gasoline increase its octane number. Iodine and aniline were recognized first as knock-reducing agents, but the metal alkyls are the most effective. Tetraethyllead, $Pb(C_2H_5)_4$ (p. 899), is by far the best and is the only compound now used commercially.[3] One of the disadvantages of tetraethyllead when used alone is that the product of combustion is lead oxide which is reduced to lead and causes pitting of the cylinder walls. If ethylene bromide is added with the tetraethyllead, lead bromide if formed which is more resistant to reduction. The commercial *Ethyl Fluid*, which is added to gasoline, consists of approximately 65 per cent tetraethyllead, 25 per cent ethylene bromide, and 10 per cent ethylene chloride. It is of interest that the increased use of bromine in Ethyl Fluid and other tetraethyllead mixtures led to the development of processes for the extraction of bromine from sea water. The extent of improvement in octane number on addition of tetraethyllead varies with the hydrocarbon, and the increase in octane number per unit of addition of tetraethyllead is known as the **lead susceptibility.** The paraffin hydrocarbons have a better lead susceptibility than olefins or more highly unsaturated compounds. Hence although a straight-run gasoline may have a low octane number, it may be more desirable than certain types of cracked gasoline because of the small amount of tetraethyllead necessary to bring the octane number to a desired value. Gasolines having octane numbers above 100 are rated according to the number of cubic centimeters of tetraethyllead that must be added to one gallon of 2,2,4-trimethylpentane to produce a fuel equivalent to the gasoline being tested, 6 cc. being defined as 120.3 octane number.

Kerosene. Previous to 1910, kerosene was the most important product derived from petroleum because of its use in lamps for lighting purposes. Considerable quantities still are used for domestic heating with small heaters. The kerosene fraction distills at 175°–275°, and all of the olefins and most of the aromatics must be removed to enable it to burn from a wick with a white flame and leave no residue. Refining is accomplished by washing with concentrated sulfuric acid or with liquid sulfur dioxide (*Edeleanu process*). Although aromatics burn with a smoky flame, it is not necessary to remove them completely. The burning qualities of the kerosene actually are improved when up to 20 per cent is present. The demand for the kerosene fraction is increasing again, since it is being used as the fuel for gas turbines and jet engines. The specifications for jet engine fuel require that it flow at −60°. Hence the higher-melting normal alkanes must be removed to prevent them from crystallizing at this low temperature.

Gas Oil, Fuel Oil, and Diesel Oil. Hydrocarbons distilling above kerosene and below lubricating oils (250°–400°) may be used in a variety of ways. They

---

[3] The story behind the development of tetraethyllead as an anti-knock agent is instructive. Thomas Midgley, Jr. (1889–1944) thought that knocking was caused by the presence of droplets of incompletely vaporized fuel. The suggestion was made that if a red dye were added to gasoline, the droplets might absorb more heat and be vaporized. Midgley could not find a red dye in the stockroom, and because it was Saturday afternoon, the supply houses were closed. Iodine came to mind as a possible substitute, and on trying it Midgley found that it decreased knock. On Monday he obtained all of the oil-soluble dyes that he could find in Dayton, but not one reduced knocking. Although the theory was wrong, he had found that knocking could be reduced by adding a chemical. Further exhaustive search led to one that was more effective than iodine and not corrosive.

may be cracked to gasoline or more drastically to oil gas, they may be burned as such for the generation of heat, or they may be used in internal combustion engines of the *Diesel* type. These engines differ from the gasoline engine in that the combustible mixture of air and fuel is not ignited by a spark but by the high temperature generated during the compression of the air. Air is drawn into the cylinder on the downward stroke of the piston and highly compressed on the upward stroke. At the moment of maximum compression, oil is sprayed into the hot air by injectors. In order that the temperature will be high enough for ignition to take place, the compression ratio must be at least 12 to 1 and usually is 14–17 to 1. At the compression ratio of 16 to 1 the theoretical thermodynamic efficiency is about 50 per cent, compared with an efficiency of 40 per cent for a gasoline engine having a compression ratio of 6 to 1. The fuel must have a low spontaneous ignition temperature and be clean to avoid clogging of the jets. For the purposes of Diesel fuel, straight chain paraffin hydrocarbons are superior to branched chain hydrocarbons and aromatics. Cetane (*n*-hexadecane), which ignites rapidly, is rated as 100 and α-methylnaphthalene (p. 588), which ignites slowly, is rated as zero. The **cetane number** of a fuel is the per cent of cetane in a cetane-α-methylnaphthalene mixture which has the same ignition qualities as the fuel. In addition to somewhat better efficiency than the gasoline engine, the Diesel engine has the advantage of being able to use less expensive fuel. A more recent development is the *gas turbine* in which, presumably, any type of combustible liquid or powdered fuel may be used.

Lubricating Oils. Friction is due to rough surfaces and molecular attraction. Before a journal starts to rotate in a bearing lubricated by some liquid, the journal and the bearing are in close contact, and the friction is at a maximum. As the journal picks up speed, the friction decreases rapidly until the journal is floating in a layer of lubricant. During this period of decreasing friction the journal is said to be in a region of *unstable lubrication*. As the speed of the journal continues to increase, the coefficient of friction again rises slowly because of increasing molecular friction in the lubricant. This period is called the region of *stable lubrication*. In the region of stable lubrication when the journal is floating in a complete layer of lubricant, any liquid of the proper viscosity should be satisfactory. On starting or stopping, however, the system is in the region of unstable lubrication, where the behavior of the lubricant depends on the composition of the lubricant and the nature of the surfaces.

The resinous and asphaltic constituents of oil are not lubricants. Moreover the higher polycyclic and aromatic hydrocarbons are undesirable. At low temperatures, paraffin waxes would crystallize out in the oil line. Hence refining of lubricating oils aims at removal of the resinous, asphaltic, higher polycyclic, and wax constituents. The crude higher-boiling oil fractions or still residues are distilled at reduced pressure to obtain fractions of different viscosities and then extracted with suitable solvents such as liquid sulfur dioxide, furfural (p. 620), β-chloroethyl ether (Chlorex, p. 141), phenol (p. 502), or mixtures of liquid propane and cresylic acid (p. 502) (Duosol process), which remove the undesirable nonparaffinic constituents. Dewaxing is brought about by solution in a mixture of methyl ethyl ketone (p. 225) and toluene (p. 420), chilling, filtering the wax, and removing the solvent. Small amounts of additives such as esters of acids of phosphorus (p. 515) and sulfur compounds usually are added to improve the lubricating properties of the oil and to produce the present-day "extreme pressure" lubricants. Polyisobutylene (p. 62) may be added to improve the viscosity index, that is, the change in viscosity with change in temperature.

Miscellaneous Products. Numerous fractions of petroleum are used as solvents. **Petroleum ether** is a fraction consisting chiefly of pentanes and hexanes boiling at 30°–60°. Fractions boiling at 60°–90° and 90°–100° usually are referred to as **ligroin. Solvent naphthas** and **paint thinners** boil at 140°–200°. Even though the boiling point range may be the same, the composition of these products may vary widely depending on the source of the petroleum and the refining process (cf. Table 8, p. 71). The naphthas are used as fat solvents, dry cleaning agents, and paint and synthetic enamel thinners. Gasoline never should be substituted for naphtha or mixed with it for any of these purposes, because gasoline contains low-boiling components whose vapors are ignited readily by a flame or spark. Moreover practically all commercial gasoline contains the highly toxic tetraethyllead. **White mineral oils** or **paraffin oils** are polycyclic high-boiling fractions that have been decolorized by activated Fuller's earth (a diatomaceous clay) or bauxite (crude aluminum oxide). **Paraffin wax**[4] is a refined grade of the solid hydrocarbon fraction. The *ordinary paraffin wax* crystallizes from the wax distillate. It is removed by filtration and is purified by crystallization from methyl ethyl ketone (p. 225). The better grades melt at 52°–57° and consist for the most part of normal alkanes having from 20 to 30 carbon atoms. The *microcrystalline waxes* are obtained by crystallization of the still residues and consist of molecules having 30 to 50 carbon atoms. Because of the high molecular weight of the molecules, these waxes melt as high as 88°–90° and hence are more valuable for many purposes. Some are hard and brittle, and others are fairly tough and flexible. **Petrolatum (petroleum jelly** or **Vaseline)** is a semisolid fraction used chiefly for pharmaceutical purposes. **Greases** are made by dissolving metallic soaps (p. 192) in hot lubricating oils. On cooling, the solution sets to a semisolid mass. **Pitch** and **asphalt** are residual products used as protective coatings and as binding agents for fibers and crushed rock. If these residues are distilled to dryness, **petroleum coke** is obtained which can be calcined to a practically pure carbon valuable for the manufacture of carbon electrodes.

Destructive Hydrogenation and Synthetic Fuels

In the cracking process, the formation of olefins, coke, and cyclic compounds takes place because of a lack of hydrogen and can be prevented if an excess of hydrogen is supplied in the presence or absence of a catalyst. A low cracking temperature is used at pressures around 3000 p.s.i. During the process, which is known as **destructive hydrogenation,** nitrogen, sulfur, and oxygen are removed completely as their hydrides, and the gasolines and kerosenes obtained are saturated and do not require further refining. Moreover each barrel of oil yields over a barrel of liquid products.[5] Because of the availability of hydrogen

---

[4] cf. Footnote 8, p. 41.

[5] The increase in volume is not due to the amount of hydrogen absorbed but to the fact that the hydrocarbons of lower molecular weight have a lower density than the original hydrocarbons. Ordinary cracking also would result in increased volume were it not for the gases and coke produced.

from the newer reforming processes (p. 76), the hydrogenation of low grade crudes and residual oils undoubtedly will come into wider use.

A similar process has been used for the conversion of coal and other solid fuels to liquid fuel in countries which do not have petroleum resources. Germany was the pioneer in this development, but other countries have built experimental plants as a safeguard against the day when petroleum supplies have become exhausted.[6] The *Bergius process* is carried out in two stages. In the liquid phase treatment, powdered coal is mixed with heavy oil residues and a small amount of catalyst, presumably iron oxide, and converted to heavy and middle oils at 450° and hydrogen pressures of 10,000 p.s.i. In the second stage, the middle oils are vaporized and passed with hydrogen over a fixed catalyst. The products are separated by distillation.

More recently, processes based on the *Fischer-Tropsch synthesis* of liquid fuels have been investigated extensively. Coal or other carbonaceous material is converted into carbon monoxide and hydrogen by the water-gas reaction.

$$C + H_2O \longrightarrow CO + H_2$$

The mixture of carbon monoxide and hydrogen is enriched with hydrogen (p. 70) and passed over a cobalt-thoria catalyst on a suitable support at 200°–250° and atmospheric pressure.

$$n\,CO + (2n + 1)H_2 \longrightarrow C_nH_{2n+2} + n\,H_2O$$

The gasoline fraction must be reformed to improve the octane number. An obvious advantage over the Bergius process is that equipment capable of withstanding high pressure and temperature is not necessary. Nevertheless most of the German synthetic fuels were made by the Bergius process.

REVIEW QUESTIONS

1. Discuss the source and composition of petroleum. What are the current theories concerning its origin and the conditions under which it was produced?

2. What is meant by the following terms: liquefied petroleum gas; petroleum ether; ligroin; straight-run gasoline; cracked gasoline; naphtha; kerosene; gas oil; Diesel fuel; lubricating oil; white mineral oil; petroleum jelly?

3. Give a brief discussion of knocking, octane number, anti-knock gasoline, Ethyl Fluid, and cetane number.

4. Discuss briefly the Burton, Dubbs, Thermofor, and Fluid Catalyst processes for cracking petroleum, giving the advantages and disadvantages of each.

5. Describe the following processes as used by the petroleum industry: polymerization, alkylation; isomerization; reforming; dehydrogenation.

6. Give a brief description of the Fischer-Tropsch process and the Bergius process for the production of hydrocarbon oil from natural gas, lignite, or coal.

---

[6] The proved reserves of petroleum in the United States at the end of 1955 were 30 billion barrels. Production during the same year was 2.4 billion barrels. Newer geophysical methods for locating oil pools are increasing reserves somewhat but cannot do so indefinitely. Before the exhaustion of reserves, other sources of liquid fuel such as coal and oil shale must be developed if the United States wishes to remain independent of foreign sources.

Chapter 5

ALCOHOLS. ESTERS OF INORGANIC ACIDS

ALCOHOLS

The simplest alcohols contain oxygen and have the general empirical formula $C_nH_{2n+2}O$. The first member, methyl alcohol, has the molecular formula CH_4O. Since oxygen has six valence electrons, it requires two more to complete its valence shell. It does this by pairing two of its electrons· with two electrons from one or two other atoms or groups, thus forming two covalent bonds. In the alcohol molecule, CH_4O, the oxygen atom must be joined to both carbon and hydrogen because if it shared both of the electrons with carbon, carbon would have only two valence electrons left to share with hydrogen and the formula would be CH_2O. If both electrons of oxygen were shared with hydrogen, a water molecule would result. Hence only one structural formula is possible,

$$\text{H} \atop | $$

namely H—C—O—H or CH_3OH. This formula is in accord with the general

$$| \atop \text{H}$$

methods of preparation and the reactions of methyl alcohol.

The number of possible structures for the other members of this homologous series can be predicted in much the same way as was done for the olefins, namely from a consideration of the possible positions which the functional group, in this case the *hydroxyl group* (OH), can occupy in the carbon skeletons of the alkanes. The procedure leads to one C_2 alcohol, two C_3 alcohols, four C_4 alcohols, and eight C_5 alcohols.

Nomenclature

The word *alcohol* has been applied to the active principle of intoxicating beverages since the eighteenth century. The usually accepted derivation is from *al-kuhl*, the Arabic word for finely powdered antimony sulfide used as a cosmetic to darken eyelids. Later the term was applied to any finely divided substance and then during the sixteenth century in the sense of "essence". Thus *alcool vini* was the essence or spirit of wine. Gradually *vini* was dropped, but it was not until the early part of the nineteenth century that the term *alcohol* came to be used generally for wine spirits. It now is used also as a family name for the homologous series.

Three systems of nomenclature are in general use. In the first the alkyl group attached to the hydroxyl group is named and the separate word *alcohol* is added. In the second system the higher alcohols are considered as derivatives of the first member of the series, which is called *carbinol*. The third method is the modified Geneva system in which (*1*) the longest carbon chain containing the hydroxyl group determines the surname, (*2*) the ending *e* of the corresponding saturated hydrocarbon is replaced by *ol*, (*3*) the carbon chain is numbered

84

from the end that gives the hydroxyl group the smaller number, and (4) the side chains are named and their positions indicated by the proper number. The following examples illustrate these various systems.

CH_3OH	methyl alcohol carbinol methanol
C_2H_5OH	ethyl alcohol [1] methylcarbinol [1] ethanol
$CH_3CH_2CH_2OH$	normal propyl alcohol (*n*-propyl alcohol) ethylcarbinol 1-propanol

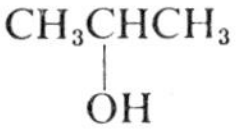

$$CH_3CHCH_3$$
$$|$$
$$OH$$

isopropyl alcohol (*i*-propyl alcohol)
dimethylcarbinol
2-propanol

$CH_3CH_2CH_2CH_2OH$ normal butyl alcohol (*n*-butyl alcohol)
n-propylcarbinol
1-butanol

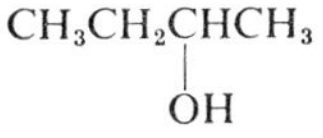

$$CH_3CH_2CHCH_3$$
$$|$$
$$OH$$

secondary butyl alcohol (*s*-butyl alcohol)
methylethylcarbinol
2-butanol

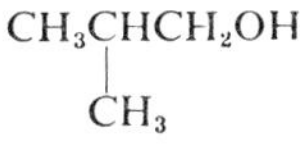

$$CH_3CHCH_2OH$$
$$|$$
$$CH_3$$

isobutyl alcohol (*i*-butyl alcohol)
i-propylcarbinol
2-methyl-1-propanol

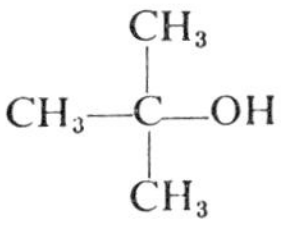

$$CH_3{-}\overset{\displaystyle CH_3}{\underset{\displaystyle CH_3}{\overset{|}{\underset{|}{C}}}}{-}OH$$

tertiary butyl alcohol (*t*-butyl alcohol)
trimethylcarbinol
2-methyl-2-propanol

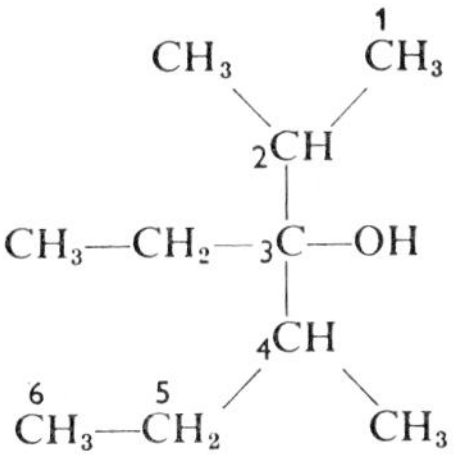

ethyl-*i*-propyl-*s*-butylcarbinol
2,4-dimethyl-3-ethyl-3-hexanol

Alcohols in general are divided into three classes. In *primary* alcohols the hydroxyl group is united to a primary carbon atom, that is, a carbon atom united directly to only one other carbon atom. *Secondary* alcohols have the hydroxyl group united to a secondary carbon atom, that is, one united to two

---

[1] Whether a chemical name for an organic compound is written as one word or more than one depends on whether the compound is being named as a derivative of a chemical entity. Thus *carbinol* is a definite compound, CH_3OH, and names for compounds considered to be derivatives of it are written as one word, for example *methylcarbinol*. On the other hand *alcohol* is not the name of any compound but is the name of a class of compounds. Hence *ethyl alcohol* is written as two words.

other carbon atoms. *Tertiary* alcohols have the hydroxyl group united to a tertiary carbon atom, that is, one joined directly to three other carbon atoms. The three classes can be represented by the general formulas RCH_2OH, R_2CHOH, and R_3COH. In the above list ethyl, *n*-propyl, *n*-butyl, and *i*-butyl alcohols are primary alcohols, *i*-propyl and *s*-butyl alcohols are secondary alcohols, and *t*-butyl alcohol and ethyl-*i*-propyl-*s*-butylcarbinol are tertiary alcohols. Ordinarily methyl alcohol is grouped with the primary alcohols, although really it is unique in that it is the only alcohol having only hydrogen atoms attached to the carbon atom that bears the hydroxyl group.

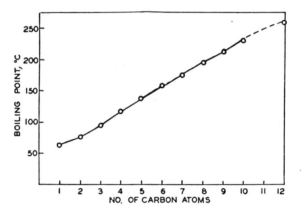

Fig. 37. Boiling points of normal alcohols.

Physical Properties

Methyl alcohol, the first member of the series, is a liquid boiling at 65°, in contrast to methane which boils at −161°. Even ethane, which has almost the same molecular weight as methyl alcohol, boils at −88°. The alcohols in general boil at a considerably higher temperature than the saturated hydrocarbons of the same molecular weight. The rise in boiling point of the straight chain primary alcohols with increasing molecular weight is about 18° for each additional CH_2 group, as shown by Fig. 37. For a given molecular weight, branching of the carbon chain lowers the boiling point just as it does in hydrocarbons. The boiling points of *n*-, *i*-, and *t*-butyl alcohols are respectively 117°, 107°, and 83°. The boiling point of *s*-butyl alcohol is 100° indicating that the hydroxyl group acts like a branch as might be expected.

The much higher boiling point of water and of alcohols as compared with alkanes of the same molecular weight means that an attractive force, in addition to the transient dipole caused by polarizability (p. 39), must be operating. This second type of van der Waals force appears between molecules having hydrogen bound to oxygen or nitrogen and molecules containing an unshared pair of electrons on oxygen or nitrogen, and in a few other isolated instances.

The hydrogen atom is unique in that it has a single electron surrounding the nucleus. When it is bonded to other elements, the hydrogen nucleus, that is, the proton, is less protected by a cover of electrons than the nuclei of other elements, and it can approach the electron shells of other molecules more closely. The result is that an attractive force can appear between the proton and any concentration of negative charge in another molecule.

If the other molecule contains an atom having an unshared pair of electrons and if this atom will share this pair of electrons more nearly equally with the proton than does the atom to which the proton is attached, that is, form a more nearly covalent bond, transfer of the proton from one atom to the other takes place. The usual acid-base reactions are of this type.

$$H_3N \, . \, + \, H:Cl \longrightarrow \left[H_3\overset{+}{N}:H \right] [Cl^-]$$

If the new bond were less covalent than the original bond, no transfer would take place. Thus there is no tendency for an alkane to transfer a proton to other elements, because hydrogen forms a more nearly covalent bond with carbon than with any other element except another hydrogen

Conceivably an intermediate condition should be possible in which the relative electrical forces are such that the tendency of hydrogen to form covalent bonds with two atoms is equal or nearly so. Then if the molecules approach each other closely enough and in the right orientation for transfer of a proton to take place, there will be a stage where the proton is attracted equally or almost equally by the atoms of two molecules. Under such conditions the proton may or may not transfer from one molecule to the other, and if transfer does take place, it will be reversible. Nevertheless during the time when the molecules are close enough for the transfer to take place, there will be a strong attraction of the proton for both molecules and hence an increased attraction between the molecules. This type of attraction is called *proton bonding* or *hydrogen bonding*. The former term is more descriptive of the process and avoids confusion with the normal covalent hydrogen bond. The phenomenon also is known as *association*, and compounds exhibiting proton bonding are said to be associated.

On this basis the high boiling point of water as compared with methane is due to the association of water molecules by proton bonding. The high boiling point of the alcohols as compared with the boiling point of alkanes of similar molecular weight may be explained in the same way

Liquid water   Liquid methyl alcohol

However, the attractive forces between alcohol molecules are not so great as those between water molecules, because the hydrogen atoms of the alkyl groups do not form proton bonds, and the bulk of the alkyl groups decreases the chance that collision of two alcohol molecules will form a proton bond between two hydroxyl groups

In proton bonding, a single proton cannot attract more than two other atoms. Because of the small size of the proton, two water molecules or two alcohol molecules approach each other so closely that a third molecule cannot approach the proton closely enough to be attracted appreciably. However, a proton of a third molecule can bond to one of the oxygen atoms, and this process can be repeated until the attractive forces balance the disruptive forces caused by thermal agitation.

The reason that proton bonding occurs most frequently between molecules having hydrogen on oxygen or on nitrogen and those having an unshared pair of electrons on oxygen or nitrogen is simply that then the balance of electrical forces is such that proton bonding is possible. The proton is held neither too strongly nor too loosely by oxygen and nitrogen and the negative charge resulting from the unshared pair on oxygen or nitrogen is sufficiently concentrated to be effective. Fundamentally the attraction is not concerned with an unshared pair of electrons. However only when an atom has an unshared pair is the negative charge sufficiently exposed for a proton attached to another oxygen or nitrogen atom in another molecule to get close enough to the electrons for an attractive force to operate.

Dodecyl alcohol is the first straight chain alcohol which is solid at room temperature, although the more nearly spherical branched alcohols with fewer carbon atoms, for example *t*-butyl alcohol, also may be solids at room temperature. There is no evidence for alternation in melting point (Fig. 38) as is exhibited by saturated hydrocarbons (Fig. 27, p. 40).

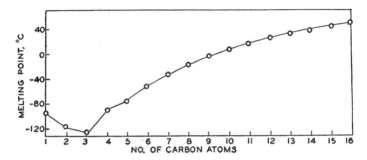

Fig. 38. Melting points of normal alcohols.

The alcohols containing three carbon atoms or less and *t*-butyl alcohol are miscible with water at 20°, but *n*-butyl alcohol is soluble to the extent of only about 8 per cent, and primary alcohols with more than five carbon atoms are less than 1 per cent soluble in water.

Solubility has been mentioned previously on page 12 and page 40. Solution is nothing more than the intermingling of molecules. Two liquids will not mix if the attractive forces of like molecules for each other are much greater than the attractive forces between unlike molecules. Moreover the more closely molecules are related in composition and structure, the more similar will be the attractive and repulsive forces between them. These statements explain the very approximate rule that *like dissolves like.*

It is desirable to have a somewhat clearer picture of the factors producing solubility and insolubility. From the differences in boiling points, it was concluded that the attraction between water molecules is considerably greater than between alcohol molecules, and it might be predicted that water and methyl alcohol would not mix. However alcohol molecules can form proton bonds with water molecules and vice versa with the result that the differences in attractive forces are decreased and intermingling takes place.

As the length of the hydrocarbon chain increases, the attractive forces resulting from the polarizability of the molecule (p. 39) increase until a point is reached at which the association with water molecules is no longer sufficient to prevent alcohol molecules from being attracted more strongly to each other than to water complexes, and two phases result. The separation is not complete, however. Some alcohol-water complexes remain in the water layer, and some remain in the alcohol layer. Thus 100 g. of *n*-butyl alcohol dissolves 37 g. of water, and 100 g. of water dissolves 7.3 g. of *n*-butyl alcohol at 15°. The fact that *t*-butyl alcohol is miscible with water agrees with the fact that it boils lower than *n*-butyl alcohol, since the higher solubility and lower boiling point are both dependent on the lower attractive forces between *t*-butyl alcohol molecules.

Alcohols of Commercial Importance

Methyl Alcohol. The word *methyl*, first used by Dumas and Peligot in 1834, was derived from the Greek word *methy* meaning wine and *yle* meaning wood or material, and refers to the fact that it is the chief alcohol formed by the destructive distillation of wood. Previous to 1919 it commonly was called *wood alcohol* or *Columbian spirits* in the United States. With the introduction of national prohibition of alcoholic beverages and the advent of the "speak-easy" over which the authorities had no supervisory control, anything called alcohol was used for intoxicating drinks. Since methyl alcohol is highly toxic, the result was an alarming number of deaths and cases of blindness. As one combative measure the use of the Geneva name *methanol* was urged, and it now largely has displaced the older term.

Methyl alcohol now is obtained both by wood distillation and by a synthetic process. In the **wood distillation** process dried hardwood such as beech, birch, hickory, maple, or oak is decomposed in an oven or retort at a temperature increasing from about 160° to 450°. If the wood is dry when placed in the retort, the reaction is exothermic, and heat is supplied only to start the reaction. The products are gases, which are burned as fuel, a liquid condensate, and a residue of charcoal. The liquid condensate separates into an aqueous layer called *pyroligneous acid*, and a tarry layer. The pyroligneous acid, of which 200 to 250 gallons per cord of wood is obtained, is mostly water but contains 1 to 6 per cent of methyl alcohol, 4 to 10 per cent acetic acid, 0.1 to 0.5 per cent of acetone, and smaller amounts of methyl acetate and a number of other organic compounds.

In the oldest process for the separation of the components, the acetic acid is neutralized with lime to produce the nonvolatile calcium acetate, and the mixture is distilled to give a liquid containing 8 to 10 per cent of methyl alcohol and the other volatile constituents. Fractional distillation gives the so-called "82 per cent methyl alcohol" containing 82 per cent organic compounds or 60–65 per cent methyl alcohol, 11–14 per cent acetone, and 6–8 per cent methyl acetate. Further fractionation removes the methyl acetate and acetone as low constant-boiling mixtures with methyl alcohol. This mixture is known as "methyl acetone" and is sold as a solvent[2] without further separation. The next fraction contains 92–95 per cent methyl alcohol. The higher-boiling fractions contain allyl alcohol (p. 738), *n*-propyl alcohol, and methyl ethyl ketone (p. 225). Pure methyl alcohol was obtained through the calcium chloride complex (p. 97).

During the year 1924 the total importation of methyl alcohol by the United States was 48 gallons. This material was of high purity, the import duty of 12 cents per gallon being sufficient to prevent importation of the commercial grade of foreign wood alcohol. During the first five months of 1925, the Badische Company of Germany shipped into the United States almost a quarter of a million gallons of methyl alcohol. Wood alcohol was selling for 88 cents per

---

[2] The term *solvent* refers to the use of organic liquids for the purpose of dissolving other organic substances. Solvents may be used as reaction media, or for extraction of organic compounds from solids or from aqueous solutions. Following the operation the solvent is removed by distillation or evaporation. Hence they usually are low-boiling liquids. Solvents may be used also to dissolve solid organic materials in order to form the latter into sheets or fibers or to coat other materials with them.

gallon, but the imported material was being made by a synthetic process perfected in 1923 which could produce methanol at a cost of around 20 cents per gallon. Even raising the import duty to 18 cents per gallon, the maximum permitted by law, was of little help to the wood distillers. Not enough methanol was shipped into the country to drive the price below 57 cents per gallon in 1925, and for some reason the price rose again to 82 cents per gallon in February 1927. However with the advent of synthetic production in the United States, the price became stabilized in 1930 at about 40 cents per gallon. Many of the wood distillation plants survived because of more efficient operation and revision of their procedures, particularly the development of new methods for separating acetic acid by extraction or by special distillation processes (p. 158).

The **synthetic process** starts with carbon monoxide and hydrogen which combine over a zinc oxide catalyst containing other promoter oxides, for example 10 per cent chromium oxide, at a temperature of 300°–400° and at pressures of 200 to 300 atmospheres.

$$CO + 2\,H_2 \xrightarrow{\text{ZnO–Cr}_2\text{O}_3} CH_3OH$$

The synthesis frequently is carried out in conjunction with some other operation such as the synthesis of ammonia, acetylene (p. 133) or hydrogen cyanide (p. 255). By-product hydrogen from other processes, such as the anaerobic fermentation of carbohydrates (p. 96), or the electrolytic production of chlorine, may be used, but most of the carbon monoxide and hydrogen is produced from natural gas (p. 70).

Some higher alcohols also are produced in the synthetic process. The amount can be increased by modifying the catalyst, for example by adding alkalies or by using an iron base-alkali catalyst, and by raising the temperature to 350°–475°.

Methyl alcohol is obtained also as one of the products of the controlled air oxidation of natural gas (p. 220). Other alcohols also are formed, as well as aldehydes, ketones, and organic acids.

The total production of synthetic methanol in the United States in 1955 was 1.3 billion pounds, or 204 million gallons, exceeding the production of any other synthetic organic chemical. About 45 per cent was used for the manufacture of formaldehyde (p. 220), 25 per cent for the synthesis of other chemicals, 15 per cent as radiator antifreeze, and 15 per cent as solvent and denaturant for ethyl alcohol. Production of wood alcohol was 2.3 million gallons. Practically all of it was used to denature ethyl alcohol. When pure synthetic methanol sold for 30 cents per gallon, impure wood alcohol sold for 70 cents per gallon, because by law it is a required ingredient of certain formulas for denatured ethyl alcohol (p. 95).

Ethyl Alcohol. Although the suffix *yl* was used in 1834 by Dumas and Peligot in the word *methyl* to indicate its derivation from wood, Liebig and Woehler had used the same suffix in 1832 in the term *benzoyl* in the sense of stuff or material. It is in the latter sense that it ordinarily is used. *Ethyl* means the material which gives rise to ether (p. 136).

One important source of ethyl alcohol is the *fermentation of sugars*. **Fermentation** is the decomposition of organic compounds into simpler compounds through the agency of enzymes. **Enzymes** are complex organic compounds secreted by living cells. The name *enzyme* means *in yeast* and was given because the earliest known enzymes were those secreted by yeast cells. Pasteur,[3] who discovered the nature of fermentation, thought that the living cell was necessary, but this view was disproven by Buchner in 1897. He showed that the juice expressed from yeast cells which had been completely destroyed still was capable of bringing about fermentation.

The chief sources of sugars for fermentation are the various starches and the molasses residue from sugar refining. Corn (maize) is the chief source of starch in the United States, and ethyl alcohol made from corn commonly.is known as *grain alcohol*. Potatoes are the chief source of starch in Europe, and rice in Asia. In preparing alcohol from corn the germ first is removed, and the remainder ground and cooked to give the mash. Malt (sprouted barley), or a mold such as *Aspergillus oryzae*, containing the enzyme *diastase* is added, and the mixture kept at 40° until all of the starch has been converted into the sugar maltose. This solution is known as the *wort*.

$$2 (C_6H_{10}O_5)_n + n\, H_2O \xrightarrow[\text{in malt}]{\text{Diastase}} n\, C_{12}H_{22}O_{11}$$

$$\text{Starch} \qquad\qquad\qquad\qquad\qquad\qquad \text{Maltose}$$

The wort is cooled to 20°, diluted to 10 per cent maltose, and a pure yeast culture added, usually a strain of *Saccharomyces cerevisiae* (or *ellipsoidus*). The yeast cells secrete two enzymes, *maltase*, which converts the maltose into glucose, and *zymase*, which converts the glucose into carbon dioxide and alcohol.

$$C_{12}H_{22}O_{11} + H_2O \xrightarrow{\text{Maltase}} 2\, C_6H_{12}O_6$$

$$\text{Maltose} \qquad\qquad\qquad\qquad\qquad \text{Glucose}$$

$$C_6H_{12}O_6 \xrightarrow{\text{Zymase}} 2\, CO_2 + 2\, C_2H_5OH + 26\,\text{kcal.}$$

Heat is liberated, and the temperature must be kept below 32° by cooling. After 40 to 60 hours, fermentation is complete, and the product is run through beer stills (perforated plate type, Fig. 14, p. 15) to remove the alcohol from solid matter. The distillate is fractionated by means of an efficient column of the bubble cap type. A small amount of acetaldehyde (b.p. 21°) distills first and is followed by 95 per cent alcohol. **Fusel oil** is withdrawn from the center of the column. The fusel oil .consists of a mixture of higher alcohols, chiefly *n*-propyl, *i*-butyl, *i*-amyl (3-methyl-1-butanol), and active amyl[4] (2-methyl-1-butanol). The exact composition of fusel oil varies considerably, being dependent particularly on the type of raw material that is fermented. These higher alcohols are not formed by fermentation of glucose but arise from certain amino acids (p. 293) derived from the proteins present in the raw material and in the yeast.

---

[3] Louis Pasteur (1822–1895), French chemist and microbiologist whose studies of fermentation led to the germ theory of disease and to immunization by inoculation with attenuated organisms and viruses. The "Life of Pasteur" written by his son-in-law, Vallery-Radot, is a most interesting account of the life and work of an outstanding scientist.

[4] The five-carbon alcohols commonly are referred to as *amyl alcohols*, because they first were obtained from the products of fermentation (L. *amylum*, starch). The use of *pentyl* instead of *amyl* is being advocated. The term *active* refers to the effect of the compound on plane-polarized light (p. 331). The higher alcohols are toxic even in small amounts. The term *fusel oil* comes from the German word *fusel* meaning *bad liquor*.

Industrial alcohol is ethyl alcohol used for nonbeverage purposes and usually is not produced from starch. Previous to the development of efficient synthetic processes, the chief source of industrial alcohol was the fermentation of blackstrap molasses, the noncrystallizable residue from the refining of sucrose (cane sugar). It contains about 50 per cent of sucrose. Malt is unnecessary in the fermentation, since yeast contains an enzyme, *sucrase* (*invertase*), capable of converting sucrose into glucose and fructose, both of which are fermentable by zymase.

$$C_{12}H_{22}O_{11} + H_2O \xrightarrow{\text{Sucrase}} C_6H_{12}O_6 + C_6H_{12}O_6$$
$$\text{Sucrose} \qquad\qquad\qquad \text{Glucose} \quad \text{Fructose}$$

$$C_6H_{12}O_6 \xrightarrow{\text{Zymase}} 2\,CO_2 + 2\,C_2H_5OH$$
$$\text{Glucose} \\ \text{or} \\ \text{fructose}$$

The black-strap molasses is shipped from the islands of the Caribbean Sea by tankers to plants located on the Atlantic and Gulf coasts. It is diluted with water to give a sucrose concentration of 14 to 18 per cent, and the solution is weakly acidified with sulfuric acid to prevent the growth of harmful organisms. After the addition of yeast, the process is the same as for the production of alcohol from starch. Plants may have fermenters of a half million gallons capacity, which are enclosed to collect the carbon dioxide for recovery of alcohol vapors and for the condensation of the carbon dioxide to the liquid or solid form. Storage capacity for molasses may be as high as 6,000,000 gallons.

The waste liquors from the production of wood pulp by the sulfite process (p. 400) contain a low concentration of fermentable sugars and can yield about 20 gallons of alcohol per ton of wood pulp produced. Numerous plants utilizing waste sulfite liquors are operated in the Scandinavian countries and in Germany, and in 1954 two plants were operating in Canada and one in the United States. Glucose formed by the hydrolysis of wood cellulose (pp. 360, 399) also is a possible source of carbohydrate for fermentation which has been utilized in Germany. Experimental plants have been built in the United States, but they have not been able to compete with other processes under normal economic conditions. The flowers of *Bassia latifolia* and other species have a high content of glucose and fructose and are used extensively for the production of alcohol in India.

Several processes for the **synthesis of ethyl alcohol** are possible. The first synthesis was reported by Hennel[5] in 1828, the same year in which Woehler reported the synthesis of urea (p. 311). In 1826 Hennel had reported the isolation of potassium ethyl sulfate (p. 58) from a sample of sulfuric acid which had absorbed 80 volumes of ethylene, and which had been given to him by Faraday[6]

---

[5] Henry Hennel, English apothecary and contemporary of Michael Faraday. He was killed in 1842 by the explosion of a large quantity of mercury fulminate which he had prepared for the East India Company for military purposes.

[6] Michael Faraday (1791–1867). Although best known for his work on electricity and magnetism, he made outstanding contributions to chemistry as well. He was the first to liquefy a number of gases and was the discoverer of benzene (p. 416). He established the laws of electrolysis and discovered the phenomenon of magnetic optical rotation.

for investigation. In 1828 Hennel reported the hydrolysis of potassium ethyl sulfate to ethyl alcohol. Hennel's discovery was overlooked, however, and the synthesis was rediscovered in 1855 by Berthelot,[7] who absorbed the ethylene from coal gas in concentrated sulfuric acid, and diluted and distilled the solution.

$$CH_2{=}CH_2 + H_2SO_4 \longrightarrow CH_3CH_2OSO_3H$$

$$CH_3CH_2OSO_3H + H_2O \longrightarrow CH_3CH_2OH + H_2SO_4$$

Although the possibility of industrial synthesis by this process was discussed in the following year and a claim made in France in 1862 that the cost of synthetic alcohol was about one-third that of fermentation alcohol, the first continuously successful process was not operated until 1930 in the United States. The ethylene used as the raw material is produced by the cracking of hydrocarbons. It is absorbed in concentrated sulfuric acid at 100° to give a mixture of ethyl hydrogen sulfate and ethyl sulfate (p. 103). Dilution with water brings about hydrolysis to ethyl alcohol, which is removed by distillation. The dilute sulfuric acid is concentrated for reuse. Since 1949 ethyl alcohol has been manufactured also by direct hydration of ethylene in the vapor phase. The conditions reported are a large excess of water, high temperature (300°) and pressure (1000–4000 p.s.i.), and a solid catalyst such as phosphoric acid on a carrier, hydrogen fluoride-treated clays, or promoted tungsten oxide. By 1940, the synthetic process accounted for 25 per cent of the total U.S. production of industrial alcohol and in 1955 for 80 per cent. Ethyl alcohol also is one of the products of the butyl alcohol fermentation of starch (p. 96), of the Fischer-Tropsch synthesis of liquid hydrocarbon fuels (p. 83) and of the controlled oxidation of natural gas (p. 220).

Various grades of ethyl alcohol are produced. **Ordinary alcohol** is 92–95 per cent ethyl alcohol by weight, the remainder being chiefly water. Anhydrous alcohol cannot be obtained by simple distillation because a constant-boiling mixture (also called an *azeotrope*) containing 95.6 per cent alcohol by weight boils lower (78.15°) than pure alcohol (78.3°).

A general discussion of distillation and fractionation was given on page 14. In distillation three types of binary mixtures are recognized. In type I, the boiling point of all compositions lies between those of the two components. In type II, there is some particular composition at which the boiling point is lower than that of either component. In type III, there is a particular composition at which the boiling point is higher than that of either component. Figure 39 gives typical boiling point diagrams for the three types. With reference to the diagram for type I, curve *L* represents the boiling point of the liquid for different mixtures of components *A* and *B*. Curve *V* represents the composition of the vapor phase when it is in equilibrium with the liquid. If a mixture has the composition *x*, the instantaneous boiling point of the liquid will be *t*, and the composition of the vapor in equilibrium with the liquid at this temperature will be *x'*. In other words the vapor phase contains a higher concentration of the lower-boiling constituent than the liquid phase from which it distilled. If this vapor is condensed and redistilled, the new vapor phase will have the composition *x''*. Hence it is possible by fractional distillation or by the use of a fractionating column, which is a device for providing continuous fractional distillation (p. 15), to separate the mixture into its pure components.

---

[7] Marcellin Pierre Eugene Berthelot (1827–1907), French chemist and statesman. He is noted especially for his high temperature syntheses of organic compounds, for his study of esterification, and for his work in thermochemistry.

In types II and III the vapor and liquid curves touch at some particular composition. In other words, at this composition of the liquid the vapor coming from it has the same composition as the liquid. Hence no separation can occur on distillation, the liquid phase retains a constant composition, and the mixture boils at a constant temperature. In these types the mixture behaves like a binary mixture of type I, consisting of the constant-boiling mixture and one of the pure components. For example referring to the diagram for type II, if the mixture has composition x, distillation will concentrate the constant-boiling mixture C in the distillate, and component B in the still; if the mixture has composition y, the constant-boiling mixture again will concentrate in the distillate, and component A will concentrate in the still. For mixtures of type III, either component A or B will concentrate in the distillate and the constant-boiling mixture, which boils higher than either component, remains in the still.

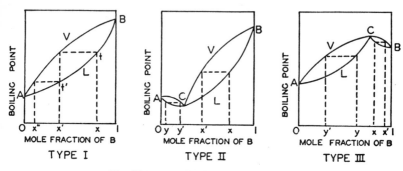

Fig. 39. Types of boiling point diagrams.

The deviations from ideality arise when different molecules exert an attraction for each other which differs from the attractive forces between like molecules. Maxima and minima in physical phenomena occur when more than one factor influences a property and when these factors vary in opposite directions with change of a third factor. The various attractive forces between molecules play an important part in determining the extent of deviation from ideality and whether maxima or minima will arise in the distillation curves as the composition of the liquid changes.

Absolute alcohol (anhydrous, 99.9+ per cent) usually is prepared in the laboratory by removing the water by chemical means, for example by heating with calcium oxide, which reacts with the water, and distilling the dried alcohol from the calcium hydroxide. The 5 per cent water in ordinary alcohol has a marked effect on its solvent properties, and there is a considerable large-scale demand for the anhydrous product. One commercial method of dehydration makes use of the fact that a ternary mixture consisting of 18.5 per cent alcohol, 74.1 per cent benzene (C_6H_6, p. 65), and 7.4 per cent water by weight boils at 64.85°. Since the ratio of water to alcohol in the ternary mixture is 1 : 2.5, enough benzene can be added to remove all of the water in the low-boiling distillate, and anhydrous alcohol can be withdrawn from the still pot. A binary mixture containing 80.2 per cent of benzene and 19.8 per cent of ethyl alcohol, and boiling at 68.2°, permits complete removal of any excess benzene. The ternary distillate separates into two layers. The upper layer comprises 84.7 per cent of the total and consists of 11.6 per cent alcohol, 85.6 per cent benzene, and 2.8 per cent water. The lower layer amounts to 15.3 per cent and consists of 51.3 per cent alcohol, 8.1 per cent benzene, and 40.6 per cent water. Redistillation of the upper layer removes all of its water as the ternary mixture, and the residue is returned to the main still. Redistillation of the lower layer removes all of its benzene as the ternary mixture and leaves a dilute alcohol which is rectified to 95 per cent alcohol and returned to the main still. By the use of four stills the process can be made continuous, with 95 per cent ethyl alcohol entering the system and absolute alcohol and water being withdrawn. Other substances such as 2,2,4-trimethylpentane (p. 77), trichloroethylene (p. 723), or ethyl ether (p. 136) may be used as entrainers instead of benzene.

Since all countries have derived a sizeable portion of their revenue by taxing alcohol for beverage purposes, ethyl alcohol for industrial use first must be converted into **denatured alcohol** if the payment of tax is to be avoided. Denaturing is the addition of substances which render the alcohol unfit to drink. Many formulas are available to the manufacturer in order that he may choose one suitable for his purpose. Only denatured alcohols containing obnoxious mixtures that are difficult to remove may be sold to the general public without payment of tax. On January 1, 1940, the price of tax-free denatured alcohol was 31 cents per gallon, compared with $4.55 per gallon for taxed grain alcohol; on January 1, 1956, the prices were 40 cents and $20.35 respectively. The difference in each case is approximately the tax per gallon. The United States tax is based on "100 U. S. proof" alcohol, which contains half of its volume of absolute alcohol. Since there is a contraction in volume on mixing alcohol and water, one volume of proof spirits contains 0.537 volumes of water. Proof spirits is 42.5 per cent alcohol by weight. Ordinary so-called 95 per cent alcohol is 190 proof. One volume contains 0.95 volume of alcohol and 0.062 volume of water and is 92.4 per cent alcohol by weight. The term **proof spirit** has its origin in an old method of testing whiskey by pouring it on some gunpowder and lighting it. Ignition of the gunpowder after the alcohol burned away was considered proof that the whiskey did not contain too much water.

The **economics of industrial alcohol** has changed often and markedly since 1930. Previous to 1931 the price of industrial alcohol was governed by the price of molasses. In 1929 with molasses at 12 cents per gallon, alcohol sold at 48 cents per gallon. In 1931 with molasses at 7 cents, alcohol sold at 27 cents. Since 1931, synthetic alcohol has been made in the United States from ethylene and has controlled the price of alcohol. After a slight rise to 30 cents in 1932, the price of alcohol dropped regularly due to improvements and expansion in synthesis until it reached 20 cents in 1939. Since molasses is a by-product of sugar manufacture, it had to be sold at a price permitting competition of fermentation with synthetic alcohol, and in spite of general economic recovery, its price dropped to 5 cents per gallon in 1939. Then a demand developed for black-strap molasses for animal feeds, and it no longer needed to be sold at distress prices. At the end of 1947 molasses sold for 31 cents per gallon, and since 2.5 gallons are required to make one gallon of alcohol, it no longer was a low-cost raw material.

With the increase in requirements during World War II and the decrease in the importation of molasses because of submarine warfare, it became necessary to revert to the use of grain (corn and wheat) as a source of industrial alcohol with resulting increase in cost. While price controls were in effect, alcohol sold for around 60 cents per gallon. After the removal of controls it rose to over $1.00 per gallon in 1947 despite the low cost of making synthetic alcohol, simply because the supply was not able to meet the demand. Failure of the manufacturers of synthetic alcohol to expand sufficiently to bring the price back in line with their costs undoubtedly was due to several factors. Probably the most important ones were the high cost of building new plants and the shortage of materials, and the uncertainty concerning the future because of the possibility that alcohol formed as a by-product in the synthesis of gasoline would become more than sufficient to meet the entire needs of the country. This last threat has not materialized and synthetic manufacture expanded sufficiently to bring the price down to 30 cents per gallon in 1954.

Production in 1940 was 128 million gallons but rose to 606 million gallons in 1944. In 1955 it was 217 million gallons, of which 80 per cent was made by synthesis from ethylene and only 20 per cent by fermentation of carbohydrates. The sharp rise during World War II was due to its use for the synthesis of butadiene for the manufacture of synthetic rubber (p. 716). This use required about 55 per cent of the total production. In 1954 about 45 per cent was used for the synthesis of acetaldehyde (p. 222) and 26 per cent for solvent purposes. The remainder was used for the synthesis of other chemicals and for miscellaneous purposes.

Higher Alcohols. Previous to World War I the chief source of higher alcohols was fusel oil from which *n*-propyl, *i*-butyl, *i*-amyl, and active amyl alcohols were separated by distillation (p. 91). Since then many other alcohols have become available. *n*-**Butyl alcohol** is made by a special bacterial fermentation process. Corn mash or black-strap molasses is inoculated with a pure culture of one of several strains of *Clostridium acetobutylicum* in closed tanks under anaerobic conditions. The products of fermentation are *n*-butyl alcohol, acetone, and ethyl alcohol in proportions varying from 60 : 30 : 10 to 74 : 24 : 2. The evolved gas contains hydrogen and carbon dioxide in the ratio of 1 volume : 2 volumes. The process was developed during World War I as a source of acetone when the supply from the decomposition of calcium acetate from pyroligneous acid was insufficient to meet the requirements of the British for the production of cordite (p. 401). At that time there was no large-scale use for *n*-butyl alcohol, and huge stocks accumulated. Since then uses for *n*-butyl alcohol have been developed, and now it is the most valuable product, and acetone has become the by-product. *n*-Butyl alcohol is manufactured also by a synthetic process starting with acetaldehyde (p. 222). Since acetone also is made by synthesis (p. 224), the ability of the fermentation process to compete economically depends on the price of corn and molasses. In 1955 the total U.S. production of *n*-butyl alcohol was 225 million pounds of which about one third was produced by fermentation and two thirds by synthesis. The chief uses of *n*-butyl alcohol are as a solvent, for the manufacture of esters (p. 173), and for the synthesis of *n*-butyraldehyde (p. 223) and *n*-butyric acid (p. 159).

Higher branched chain primary alcohols result when normal primary alcohols are heated with the sodium alkoxide in the presence of a nickel catalyst (**Guerbet reaction**).

$$RCH_2CH_2OH + RCH_2CH_2OH \xrightarrow[200°-250°]{NaOCH_2CH_2R, \ Ni} RCH_2CH_2\underset{\underset{R}{|}}{CH}CH_2OH + H_2O$$

2-Methyl-1-pentanol is made commercially in this way from *n*-propyl alcohol and **2-ethyl-1-hexanol** from *n*-butyl alcohol. The reaction has not been used much in the laboratory because complex mixtures frequently are obtained.

Secondary and tertiary alcohols are manufactured on a large scale from the lower olefins obtained by the cracking of saturated hydrocarbons.

$$CH_3CH{=}CH_2 \xrightarrow{H_2SO_4} CH_3CHCH_3 \xrightarrow{H_2O} CH_3CHCH_3$$

Propylene　　　　　　　　　$\underset{OSO_3H}{|}$　　　　　　$\underset{OH}{|}$

i-Propyl alcohol

$$CH_3CH{=}CHCH_3$$
2-Butene
and
$$CH_3CH_2CH{=}CH_2$$
1-Butene

$$\xrightarrow{H_2SO_4} CH_3CH_2CHCH_3 \xrightarrow{H_2O} CH_3CH_2CHCH_3$$

$\underset{OSO_3H}{|}$　　　　　　$\underset{OH}{|}$

s-Butyl alcohol

$$(CH_3)_2C{=}CH_2 \xrightarrow{H_2SO_4} (CH_3)_2CCH_3 \xrightarrow{H_2O} (CH_3)_3COH$$

Isobutylene　　　　　　　$\underset{OSO_3H}{|}$

t-Butyl alcohol

Similarly amylenes (pentenes) are converted into secondary and tertiary amyl alcohols.

Some of the higher alcohols are obtained also as co-products of methanol synthesis (p. 90), the Fischer-Tropsch synthesis (p. 83), and the controlled air oxidation of natural gas (p. 220). Other methods for synthesizing alcohols are considered after the structures of the compounds from which they are derived have been discussed (pp. 113, 162, 172, 198, 199).

Chemical Properties

From a structural viewpoint an alcohol may be considered as derived from a water molecule by replacement of a hydrogen atom by an alkyl group. Since both water and alcohols contain a hydroxyl group, alcohols would be expected to undergo reactions analogous to those of water, and in many respects this is true.

1. **Formation of Complexes with Metallic Salts.** Alcohols resemble water in that they associate readily, as evidenced by their abnormally high boiling points. Just as water forms hydrates of inorganic salts, alcohols form complexes which might be called *alcoholates*. Corresponding to $MgCl_2 \cdot 6\ H_2O$ there exist the molecular complexes, $MgCl_2 \cdot 6\ CH_3OH$ and $MgCl_2 \cdot 6\ C_2H_5OH$. Although calcium chloride forms a hexahydrate, the reported complexes with methyl and ethyl alcohols have the composition, $CaCl_2 \cdot 4\ CH_3OH$ and $CaCl_2 \cdot 3\ C_2H_5OH$. Some salts which form hydrates, for example anhydrous calcium sulfate, do not form complexes with alcohols.

If to an aqueous solution of ammonium hexanitratocerate or perchloratoceric acid is added about 5 per cent of an alcohol, the color changes from orange to red. This color change may be used as a *test for the alcoholic hydroxyl group*. The reaction undoubtedly depends on the replacement of nitrate or perchlorate groups in the complex ion by alcohol molecules.

$$(NH_4^+)_2[Ce(NO_3)_6]^- + 2\ ROH \longrightarrow Ce(NO_3)_4(ROH)_2 + 2\ NH_4NO_3$$

$$(H^+)_2[Ce(ClO_4)_6]^- + 2\ ROH \longrightarrow Ce(ClO_4)_4(ROH)_2 + 2\ HClO_4$$

Hydrates have been classified into three types: (*1*) the water molecules merely occupy holes in the crystal lattice (inclusion or clathrate compounds, L. *clathri*, lattice), the number of water molecules associated with one mole of substance depending on the number of voids in the crystal which can hold a water molecule; (2) the water molecules are combined with a specific ion, an unshared pair of electrons of each water molecule occupying an orbital of the

metallic ion as in [Cu(H₂O)₄]⁺⁺ or

$$\begin{bmatrix} & & H & & \\ & & \overset{..}{\underset{..}{}} & & \\ & H : & O & : H & \\ & & \overset{..}{\underset{..}{}} & & \\ H : & O : & Cu & : O : & H \\ & & \overset{..}{\underset{..}{}} & & \\ & H : & O & : H & \\ & & \overset{..}{\underset{..}{}} & & \\ & & H & & \end{bmatrix}^{++}$$

; (3) the crystal resembles ice in

which the ions are dissolved, the water molecules being associated with the ions because of ion-dipole attraction (p. 13). Since alcohols have permanent dipoles and unshared pairs of electrons, the same possibilities might be expected for combination between salts and alcohols. The size and shape of the molecule would be expected to play a part in the formation of such complexes, and it is not surprising that the number of alcohol molecules associated with a given salt is not always the same but varies with different alcohols.

In general, salts are not as soluble in alcohols as in water because alcohols have a much lower dielectric constant (methyl alcohol = 34, water = 81) (p. 13). If a salt, such as calcium chloride, forms a definite coordination complex with the alcohol, the complex may be highly soluble.

2. Oxonium Salt Formation. It is well known that when a strong acid is dissolved in water, there is practically complete transfer of the proton from the acid radical to the water molecule as illustrated by the following equation.

$$H : \overset{..}{\underset{..}{O}} : \; + \; H : \overset{..}{\underset{..}{Cl}} : \quad \longrightarrow \quad \begin{bmatrix} H \\ \overset{..}{\underset{+}{O}} \\ H : O : H \end{bmatrix} \begin{bmatrix} : \overset{..}{\underset{..}{Cl}} : \end{bmatrix}^{-}$$

The product from hydrogen chloride is called *hydronium chloride*, and the [H₃O⁺] ion is the *hydronium ion*. The explanation of this reaction is that the negative charge on the larger chlorine atom is more diffuse than that on the oxygen atom. Hence the proton can form a more nearly covalent bond with the water molecule than with a chloride ion. The relative ability to combine with a proton or an electron-deficient molecule is called the *basicity* of a group, and the proton is transferred to a water molecule because the water molecule is a stronger base than the chloride ion.

Alcohols also are stronger bases than the anions of strong acids. Hence alcohols dissolve in strong acids with the formation of alkonium salts.

$$R : \overset{..}{\underset{..}{O}} : \; + \; H : \overset{..}{\underset{..}{Cl}} : \quad \longrightarrow \quad \begin{bmatrix} H \\ \overset{..}{\underset{+}{O}} \\ R : O : H \end{bmatrix} \begin{bmatrix} : \overset{..}{\underset{..}{Cl}} : \end{bmatrix}^{-}$$

The general term for this type of compound is *oxonium salt*. Concentrated sulfuric acid will dissolve practically all organic compounds containing oxygen, frequently without chemical change other than salt formation. This fact is used in qualitative organic analysis *to distinguish oxygen-containing compounds from saturated hydrocarbons.*

Alcohols and all other oxygen-containing compounds are more soluble in aqueous solutions of strong acids than in water because of the competition of alcohol and water molecules for the proton.

$$R : \overset{\cdot\cdot}{\underset{\cdot\cdot}{O}} : H \;+\; \left[H : \overset{\cdot\cdot}{\underset{\underset{+}{\cdot\cdot}}{O}} : H \right] \;\rightleftarrows\; \left[R : \overset{\cdot\cdot}{\underset{\underset{+}{\cdot\cdot}}{O}} : H \right] + H_2O$$

n-Butyl alcohol is miscible with concentrated aqueous hydrochloric acid although it is soluble only to the extent of 8 per cent in water.

Oxonium salt formation differs from proton bonding, since in the latter the proton bonds two molecules together by electrostatic attraction, whereas in the former a proton is transferred completely from one molecule to another. The proton is completely engulfed in the electron shell of the new molecule and carries a positive charge with it. Alcohols are more soluble in aqueous acids than in water because the charged oxonium ions are considerably more heavily hydrated than the alcohol molecule, which is dependent primarily on proton bonding for hydration.

3. **Reaction with Metals.** Just as water reacts with metallic sodium to give hydrogen and sodium hydroxide, the alcohols react with sodium to give hydrogen and sodium alkoxide.

$$HOH + Na \longrightarrow HO^{-+}Na \quad + \tfrac{1}{2} H_2$$
Sodium hydroxide

$$CH_3OH + Na \longrightarrow CH_3O^{-+}Na \quad + \tfrac{1}{2} H_2$$
Sodium methoxide

$$ROH + Na \longrightarrow RO^{-+} Na \quad + \tfrac{1}{2} H_2$$
Sodium alkoxide

In these equations the ionic bond between the sodium atom and the hydroxyl, methoxyl, and alkoxyl groups is indicated by (+) and (−) signs. Usually ionic bonds will not be indicated for inorganic salts, because it is assumed that the reader understands that inorganic salts are completely ionized and that although the formula is written NaOH, for example, two types of bonds are involved, the ionic bond between sodium and the hydroxyl group and the covalent bond between the hydrogen atom and the oxygen atom. Also it is assumed that the reader understands that the molecule represented by the formula CH_3OH involves only covalent bonds. However when an organic molecule contains both ionic and covalent bonds, the presence of the ionic bond frequently will be emphasized by indicating the ionic bond with (+) and (−) charges.

Proton transfer reactions frequently will be indicated merely by the symbol [H$^+$] without designating the base with which the proton is associated. Thus the formation of an oxonium salt may be written

$$R : \overset{\cdot\cdot}{\underset{\cdot\cdot}{O}} : \;+\; [H^+] \;\longrightarrow\; \left[R : \overset{\cdot\cdot}{\underset{\underset{+}{\cdot\cdot}}{O}} : H \right]$$

If anhydrous hydrogen chloride is used, [H$^+$] stands for [HCl]; if an aqueous solution of hydrogen chloride is used, [H$^+$] stands for [H_3O^+]. If a stronger base than an alcohol is being neutralized with an alcoholic solution of hydrogen chloride, [H$^+$] stands for [ROH_2^+]. An objection to the use of the symbol [H$^+$] is that it represents a proton, and free protons under ordinary conditions are nonexistent. In organic reactions, however, where a number of bases may be involved, there usually is no point in trying to indicate the base with which the proton is associated.

The reaction with alcohols is slower than with water and decreases with increasing molecular weight of the alcohol.

If a small piece of sodium is dropped into a beaker containing water at room temperature, the reaction is so vigorous that the hydrogen formed bursts into flame; if dropped into methyl alcohol, the reaction is vigorous, but no ignition takes place; if dropped into *n*-butyl alcohol, only a slow evolution of hydrogen is observed. The decrease in rate probably is caused more by the decrease in solubility of the alkoxide in the alcohol and by the slower rate of diffusion of the ions away from the metal surface in the more viscous medium with resultant coating of the surface of the sodium, than by a decrease in the chemical reactivity of the alcohol.

The reaction product of methyl alcohol with sodium is known as *sodium methoxide*. The term *sodium methylate* also is used but is less satisfactory, since the term *alcoholate* frequently is used for complexes with inorganic salts analogous to the hydrates (p. 97).

Other active metals also react at elevated temperatures. For example, anhydrous methyl alcohol reacts with magnesium to give hydrogen and magnesium methoxide, $Mg(OCH_3)_2$, and amalgamated aluminum reacts with ethyl alcohol, *i*-propyl alcohol, or *t*-butyl alcohol, to give respectively aluminum ethoxide, $Al(OC_2H_5)_3$, *i*-propoxide, $Al(OC_3H_7\text{-}i)_3$, or *t*-butoxide, $Al(OC_4H_9\text{-}t)_3$. Since in all cases only one hydrogen atom per mole of alcohol is liberated, these reactions indicate that one hydrogen is different from all the rest and is linked to oxygen.

The reason that hydrogen united to carbon ordinarily is not displaced by metallic sodium is the same as the reason that hydrogen united to carbon does not form proton bonds, namely that the carbon-hydrogen bond is almost completely covalent. The rate of displacement of hydrogen may be greatly increased by the presence of other groups which make the carbon-hydrogen bond less covalent (pp. 131, 213, 260).

Metallic alkoxides are hydrolyzed extensively by water because the acidity of water and of alcohols is about the same.

$$RONa + H_2O \rightleftarrows ROH + NaOH$$

This equilibrium is reversible, and sodium ethoxide is made commercially from ethyl alcohol and sodium hydroxide by removing the water by azeotropic distillation with benzene (p. 94). Magnesium and aluminum alkoxides may be used to remove small amounts of water from alcohols, because the extreme insolubility of magnesium or aluminum hydroxide in alcohols shifts the equilibrium to the right.

4. **Reaction with Inorganic Acid Halides.** Another typical reaction of water is with inorganic acid halides to give halogen acid and a second inorganic acid.

$$3 HOH + PCl_3 \longrightarrow 3 HCl + P(OH)_3 \qquad (1)$$

The alcohols not only behave similarly but react in two different ways. In the above equation the water molecule may split between the oxygen atom and either hydrogen atom. Hydrogen and hydroxyl result in both cases. With alcohol molecules, however, hydrogen and alkoxyl would be obtained in one case and hydroxyl and alkyl in the other. Hence two different reactions may occur.

$$3 ROH + PCl_3 \longrightarrow 3 HCl + P(OR)_3 \qquad (2)$$

$$3 ROH + PCl_3 \longrightarrow 3 RCl + P(OH)_3 \qquad (3)$$

The relative proportion of reactions *2* and *3* depends on the conditions and the reagent. Phosphorus trichloride with primary alcohols at room temperature gives mostly reaction *2*, but phosphorus tribromide at 0° gives mostly reaction *3*.

Tertiary alcohols invariably give reaction *3*, whereas secondary alcohols undergo both reactions simultaneously.

Compounds of the type $P(OR)_3$ are *alkyl esters of phosphorous acid* and are named like salts. For example $P(OC_2H_5)_3$ is *ethyl phosphite*. Compounds of the type RCl are called *alkyl chlorides*, the terminology being carried over from that of salts. They may be considered also as derivatives of hydrocarbons. Thus $CH_3CHClCH_3$ is called either *i*-propyl chloride or 2-chloropropane.

The reactions with phosphorus halides are a further chemical proof that the alcohols contain a hydroxyl group, because it appears in phosphorous acid in reaction *3*. The production of one mole of hydrogen chloride from one mole of alcohol in reaction *2* is another indication that one hydrogen atom in an alcohol is linked differently than all the rest.

Although these reactions indicate that phosphorous acid has the structure : $P(OH)_3$, it is a dibasic acid and has reducing properties. Hence its stable form undoubtedly has the isomeric structure : $O : \overset{..}{P}H(OH)_2$. On the other hand $P(OR)_3$, which has no ionizable hydrogen, cannot isomerize and has the structure : $\overset{..}{P}(OR)_3$. The great mobility of hydrogen, that is, its ease of transfer from one electron-attracting element to another or to an element with less attraction for electrons, compared to the nonmobility of alkyl groups, can be accounted for by its very small size and its lack of a shielding shell of electrons. These conditions permit sufficiently close approach to another molecule for reaction to take place without requiring a high energy of activation.

Other inorganic acid chlorides, for example thionyl chloride, react like phosphorus trichloride.

$$HOH + SOCl_2 \longrightarrow 2\,HCl + SO_2 \tag{4}$$

$$2\,ROH + SOCl_2 \longrightarrow 2\,HCl + SO(OR)_2 \tag{5}$$

$$ROH + SOCl_2 \longrightarrow HCl + RCl + SO_2 \tag{6}$$

Here also primary alcohols give chiefly esters (alkyl sulfites, reaction *5*), whereas tertiary alcohols give alkyl chlorides (reaction *6*).

Most reactions involving more than two molecules take place stepwise in such a way that only two molecules are involved in each step. The reason is that the chance that more than two molecules will approach each other with the proper energies and in just the right orientation with respect to each other for all to react simultaneously is very small. In reaction *5* the two steps are

$$ROH + SOCl_2 \longrightarrow ROSOCl + HCl \tag{7}$$

$$ROSOCl + HOR \longrightarrow ROSOOR + HCl \tag{8}$$

Even a reaction such as *6* which appears to be bimolecular takes place in at least two steps. The first is the same as reaction *7*, and the second is

$$ROSOCl \longrightarrow RCl + SO_2 \tag{9}$$

Tertiary amine hydrochlorides, such as pyridine hydrochloride (p. 620), catalyze the decomposition of alkyl thionyl chlorides (reaction *9*), and hence a good yield of alkyl chloride can be obtained even from a primary alcohol and thionyl chloride in the presence of pyridine, if the mole ratio is 1 : 1 : 1. If an excess of pyridine is present, the yield of chloride is reduced with the formation of other by-products. If two moles of alcohol, one of thionyl chloride, and two of pyridine react, an excellent yield of the alkyl sulfite is produced (reaction *8*).

Reasoning by analogy may not always lead to a correct interpretation of the way in which an organic reaction takes place. For example, since the acid chlorides of monoalkyl sulfites (ROSOCl) decompose in the presence of pyridine hydrochloride to give alkyl chlorides, the formation of chlorides from phosphorus trichloride and a primary alcohol might be expected to result from the decomposition of the acid chlorides of alkyl phosphites. Actually these compounds are very stable in the presence of pyridine. The formation of chlorides in the absence of pyridine is caused by the reaction of the ester with the hydrogen chloride formed in reaction 2.

$$(RO)_3P + 3\ HCl \longrightarrow 3\ RCl + (HO)_3P \tag{10}$$

If pyridine is present during reaction 2, the yield of phosphite is increased and that of chloride is decreased, because the pyridine combines with the hydrogen chloride and prevents reaction 10. With tertiary alcohols it seems likely that the hydroxyl group is replaced directly by halogen (reaction 3).

5. **Reaction with Halogen Acids.** Inorganic acids in general react with alcohols with the elimination of water. The products of reaction with halogen acids are alkyl halides.

$$ROH + HX \longrightarrow RX + H_2O$$

The rate of this reaction varies with the acid and with the type of alcohol. The order for halogen acids is hydrogen iodide > hydrogen bromide > hydrogen chloride > hydrogen fluoride. The order for the alcohols is tertiary > secondary > primary.

Methyl and *i*-butyl alcohols, and neopentyl alcohol, $(CH_3)_3CCH_2OH$, are exceptions to this rule. With aqueous hydrogen bromide methyl alcohol reacts as rapidly as *s*-butyl alcohol and more rapidly than *i*-propyl alcohol. It is known that in general methyl derivatives are much more reactive than ethyl and higher alkyl derivatives. *i*-Butyl alcohol reacts at about one tenth of the rate for normal primary alcohols. Not only is the reaction of neopentyl alcohol slow, but the chief product is *t*-amyl bromide (cf. p. 169).

In practice conditions are chosen suitable for the particular compound being prepared. Primary alcohols will react even with aqueous solutions of hydrogen iodide but usually require anhydrous hydrogen bromide or aqueous hydrogen bromide and sulfuric acid. They react with hydrochloric acid at a practical rate only with hot concentrated solutions and zinc chloride as a catalyst. Tertiary alcohols on the other hand react with concentrated aqueous solutions of hydrochloric acid at room temperature.

The *Lucas test* for **distinguishing between primary, secondary, and tertiary alcohols** is based on their relative rates of reaction with hydrogen chloride. The reagent is a solution of zinc chloride in concentrated hydrochloric acid. The lower alcohols all dissolve in this reagent because of oxonium salt formation (p. 98), but the alkyl chlorides are insoluble. Tertiary alcohols react so rapidly that it is difficult to detect solution, the chloride separating immediately. Secondary alcohols give a clear solution at first which becomes cloudy within five minutes with eventual separation into two layers. Primary alcohols dissolve, and the solution remains clear for several hours.

The reaction of alcohols with halogen acids belongs to the class known as displacement reactions (p. 116). The initial step is merely the formation of the oxonium salt (p. 98).

$$
\begin{array}{c}
R : \overset{\cdot\cdot}{\underset{\underset{H}{|}}{O}} : +\ H : X : \ \rightleftharpoons \ \left[R : \overset{\cdot\cdot}{\underset{\underset{H}{|}}{\overset{+}{O}}} : H \right] + \left[: \overset{\cdot\cdot}{\underset{\cdot\cdot}{X}} : \right]^{-}
\end{array}
$$

The addition of a proton to the hydroxyl group causes the pair of electrons between the alkyl group and oxygen to shift toward the oxygen atom and makes it easier for the hydroxyl group to leave with the proton as a water molecule. The halide ion then attacks the oxonium ion with displacement of a water molecule.

$$[\,:\overset{..}{\underset{..}{X}}:\,]^- + \left[\, R:\overset{..}{O}:\overset{+}{H}\, \right] \longrightarrow \;\; :\overset{..}{\underset{..}{X}}:R + \;:\overset{..}{O}:H$$
$$\qquad\qquad\qquad\quad H \qquad\qquad\qquad\qquad\quad H$$

6. **Reaction with Inorganic Oxygen Acids.** Some oxygen-containing inorganic acids react with alcohols to form alkyl esters in which the alkyl group is linked to the acid radical through oxygen.

$$ROH + HONO \;\rightleftarrows\; RONO \; + H_2O$$
Alkyl nitrite

$$ROH + HONO_2 \;\rightleftarrows\; RONO_2 \; + H_2O$$
Alkyl nitrate

$$ROH + H_2SO_4 \;\rightleftarrows\; ROSO_3H \; + H_2O$$
Alkyl hydrogen
sulfate

$$ROH + HOSO_2OR \;\rightleftarrows\; ROSO_2OR \; + H_2O$$
Alkyl sulfate

$$3\,ROH + H_3BO_3 \;\rightleftarrows\; (RO)_3B \; + 3H_2O$$
Alkyl borate

Sulfuric acid esters from tertiary alcohols capable of dehydration have not been isolated, probably because of easy decomposition to the olefin.

Insofar as is known, the reaction of alcohols with inorganic oxygen acids follows a different course than the reaction with halogen acids. The oxygen acids are capable of self-ionization with the formation of positive ions other than protons. For example the following equilibria exist in concentrated sulfuric acid.

$$H:\overset{..}{\underset{..}{O}}:SO_3H + H:\overset{..}{\underset{..}{O}}:SO_3H \;\rightleftarrows\; \left[H:\overset{..}{\overset{+}{O}}:SO_3H \right] + \left[\overset{..}{\underset{..}{:O}}:SO_3H \right]^-$$
$$\qquad\qquad\qquad\qquad\qquad\qquad\qquad\qquad H$$

$$\left[H:\overset{+}{\overset{..}{O}}:SO_3H \right] \;\rightleftarrows\; H:\overset{..}{\underset{..}{O}}: + \left[\overset{+}{S}O_3H \right]$$
$$\quad H \qquad\qquad\qquad\qquad H$$

$$H:\overset{..}{\underset{..}{O}}: + H:\overset{..}{\underset{..}{O}}:SO_3H \;\rightleftarrows\; \left[H:\overset{+}{\overset{..}{O}}:H \right] + \left[\overset{..}{\underset{..}{:O}}:SO_3H \right]^-$$
$$\; H \qquad\qquad\qquad\qquad\qquad\qquad H$$

The $\left[\overset{+}{S}O_3H\right]$ ion, which lacks a pair of electrons on the sulfur atom, attaches to an unshared pair of electrons on the oxygen atom of the alcohol.

$$R:\overset{..}{\underset{..}{O}}: + \left[\overset{+}{S}O_3H\right] \;\rightleftarrows\; \left[R:\overset{+}{\overset{..}{O}}:SO_3H \right]$$
$$\quad H \qquad\qquad\qquad\qquad\qquad H$$

Loss of proton to a bisulfate ion gives the ester.

$$\left[R:\overset{+}{\overset{..}{O}}:SO_3H \right] + \left[\overset{..}{\underset{..}{:O}}:SO_3H \right]^- \;\rightleftarrows\; R:\overset{..}{\underset{..}{O}}:SO_3H + H_2SO_4$$
$$\quad H$$

It will be noted that in this mechanism the oxygen atom in the water molecule which is eliminated in the over-all reaction comes from the acid and not from the alcohol.

7. Dehydration to Olefins. If the alcohol is volatile, it can be dehydrated most conveniently by passing the vapors through a hot tube packed with activated alumina.[8]

$$\text{RCHOHCH}_2\text{R} \xrightarrow[350°-450°]{\text{Al}_2\text{O}_3} \text{RCH=CHR} + \text{H}_2\text{O}$$

By using pure alumina, molecular rearrangements which frequently take place when acid catalysts are used are largely avoided.

When sulfuric acid is used as a catalyst, it usually is assumed that the alkyl hydrogen sulfate is an intermediate in the reaction.

$$\text{RCHOHCH}_2\text{R} + \text{H}_2\text{SO}_4 \longrightarrow \underset{\underset{\text{OSO}_3\text{H}}{|}}{\text{RCHCH}_2\text{R}} \xrightarrow{\text{Heat}} \text{RCH=CHR} + \text{H}_2\text{SO}_4$$

If the boiling point of the alcohol is lower than the temperature of decomposition, it is necessary to use sufficient acid to convert all of the alcohol into the non-volatile alkyl hydrogen sulfate or the oxonium salt. The process may be made catalytic and continuous by passing the alcohol vapors over pumice impregnated with sulfuric or phosphoric acid and heated to the required temperature.

The relative ease of dehydration of alcohols is tertiary > secondary > primary. Tertiary alcohols dehydrate so readily that olefin is the chief product when attempts are made to carry out other reactions in the presence of strong acids. The order of removal of hydrogen atoms, when alternate paths exist, is tertiary in preference to secondary, and secondary in preference to primary (**Saytzev rule**). Thus the dehydration of *s*-butyl alcohol gives almost exclusively 2-butene.

Although the dehydration of alcohols to olefins in the presence of sulfuric acid usually is indicated as proceeding by way of an intermediate alkyl hydrogen sulfate, and although the formation of alkyl hydrogen sulfates takes place on heating alcohols with sulfuric acid, other acids such as sulfonic acids that do not esterify readily and nonesterifiable electron-seeking reagents such as zinc chloride also catalyze the dehydration. These acid-catalyzed dehydrations of alcohols belong to the class known as **elimination reactions**. The initial step is the reaction of the alcohol with the acid, HB, to form the oxonium salt, just as in the reaction of alcohols with halogen acids (p. 102).

$$\underset{\underset{\text{R R H}}{|\quad|\;\;}}{\overset{\overset{\text{R R}}{|\quad|\;\;}}{\text{H}:\text{C}-\text{C}:\text{O}:}} + \text{H}:\text{B} \longrightarrow \left[\underset{\underset{\text{R R H}}{|\quad|\;\;}}{\overset{\overset{\text{R R}\;\;+}{|\quad|\;\;}}{\text{H}:\text{C}-\text{C}:\text{O}:\text{H}}}\right] + [\,:\text{B}^-]$$

Subsequently a base, which may be another alcohol molecule or the anion [: B⁻], removes a hydrogen as proton from the second carbon atom with simultaneous loss of a water molecule.

$$\underset{\overset{|}{\text{H}}}{\overset{\overset{\cdot\cdot}{\cdot\cdot}}{\text{R}:\text{O}:}} + \underset{\underset{\text{R R H}}{|\quad|\;\;}}{\overset{\overset{\text{R R}}{|\quad|\;\;}}{\text{H}:\text{C}-\text{C}:\text{O}:\text{H}}} \longrightarrow \left[\underset{\overset{|}{\text{H}}}{\overset{\overset{+}{\cdot\cdot}}{\text{R}:\text{O}:\text{H}}}\right] + \underset{\underset{\text{R R}}{|\quad|}}{\overset{\overset{\text{R R}}{|\quad|}}{\text{C}=\text{C}}} + \underset{\overset{\cdot\cdot}{\text{H}}}{\overset{\cdot\cdot}{:\text{O}:\text{H}}}$$

or [B⁻]   or H : B

Frequently in acid-catalyzed dehydrations, the product does not have the structure expected. For example, the dehydration of *n*-butyl alcohol gives chiefly 2-butene instead of 1-butene. If

---

[8] Some forms of solid catalysts are more effective than others. When prepared in such a way that they have the maximum activity, they are called *activated* catalysts. Activated alumina has an optimum porosity or surface structure, and an optimum amount of adsorbed water or water of constitution.

the oxonium salt loses a water molecule to give the *n*-butyl carbonium ion, a hydride ion shift would lead to an *s*-butyl carbonium ion which can give rise by loss of a proton to either 1-butene or 2-butene.

$$\left[CH_3CH_2CH_2CH_2 : \overset{..}{\underset{..}{O}} : H \atop H \right]^{+} \rightleftharpoons \left[CH_3CH_2CH_2\overset{+}{C}H_2 \right] + H_2O$$

$$\updownarrow$$

$$[H^+] + CH_3CH_2CH{=}CH_2 \rightleftharpoons \left[CH_3CH_2\overset{+}{C}HCH_3 \right] \rightleftharpoons CH_3CH{=}CHCH_3 + [H^+]$$

Olefins are more highly stable thermodynamically the more highly substituted the doubly-bound carbon atoms. Hence the above equilibria are shifted in favor of 2-butene rather than 1-butene. The last steps also account for the isomerization of 1-butene to 2-butene in the presence of strong acids.

Sometimes dehydration involves also the migration of alkyl groups. For example, if methyl-*t*-butylcarbinol is dehydrated in the presence of acids, very little of the expected *t*-butylethylene is formed, the chief products being the result of methide ion shifts (cf. p. 78).

$$(CH_3)_2C{=}C(CH_3)_2 \qquad \text{61 per cent}$$

$$(CH_3)_3CCHCH_3 \underset{\text{heat}}{\overset{H_2SO_4}{\longrightarrow}} (CH_3)_2CHC{=}CH_2 \qquad \text{31 per cent}$$
$$\underset{OH}{|} \qquad\qquad\qquad \underset{CH_3}{|}$$

$$(CH_3)_3CCH{=}CH_2 \qquad \text{3 per cent}$$

Some alcohols whose structure does not appear to permit loss of water can be dehydrated to form olefins by rearrangement of the carbon skeleton.

$$\overset{CH_3}{\underset{CH_3}{\overset{|}{\underset{|}{CH_3CCH_2OH}}}} \underset{\text{heat}}{\overset{H_2SO_4}{\longrightarrow}} \underset{CH_3}{\overset{|}{CH_3C{=}CHCH_3}} + H_2O$$

A change in structure during a reaction frequently is called a **molecular rearrangement**. It is nothing more than an isomerization that takes place during the course of another reaction. Because of the possibility of molecular rearrangements, proof of structure should be based on degradative as well as synthetic reactions. The structures of the above olefins can be determined by ozonation, decomposition of the ozonides, and identification of the products (p. 56).

8. **Dehydrogenation or Oxidation to Aldehydes and Ketones.** Primary and secondary alcohols may be dehydrogenated to aldehydes and ketones respectively by passing the vapors over activated copper, copper-chromium, or copper-nickel catalyst at 300°–325°.

$$RCH_2OH \underset{325°}{\overset{Cu}{\rightleftharpoons}} \overset{H}{\underset{\text{An aldehyde}}{\overset{|}{RC{=}O}}} + H_2$$

$$R_2CHOH \underset{325°}{\overset{Cu}{\rightleftharpoons}} \underset{\text{A ketone}}{R_2C{=}O} + H_2$$

If air is used along with the alcohol, the hydrogen is converted into water and the reaction goes to completion.

$$RCH_2OH + O_2 \underset{600°}{\overset{Cu \text{ or } Ag}{\longrightarrow}} RCHO + H_2O$$

$$R_2CHOH + O_2 \underset{600°}{\overset{Cu \text{ or } Ag}{\longrightarrow}} R_2CO + H_2O$$

Tertiary alcohols, which do not have a hydrogen atom on the carbon atom united to the hydroxyl group, do not undergo these reactions but may dehydrate if the temperature is sufficiently high.

The same type of dehydrogenation can be brought about by chemical oxidizing agents. The reagent most commonly employed is dichromic acid in aqueous sulfuric acid (sodium dichromate and sulfuric acid), or chromic anhydride (chromium trioxide) dissolved in glacial acetic acid.

$$3 RCH_2OH + Na_2Cr_2O_7 + 4 H_2SO_4 \longrightarrow 3 RCHO + Na_2SO_4 + Cr_2(SO_4)_3 + 7 H_2O$$

$$3 R_2CHOH + 2 CrO_3 + 6 HC_2H_3O_2 \longrightarrow 3 R_2CO + 2 Cr(C_2H_3O_2)_3 + 6 H_2O$$

The formation of aldehydes by this method is successful only if the aldehyde is removed rapidly from the oxidizing mixture by distillation; otherwise it is oxidized further to an organic acid (p. 212).

$$RCHO + [O] \longrightarrow RCOOH$$

Strong oxidizing agents such as hot dichromic acid or potassium permanganate may oxidize tertiary alcohols by breaking the carbon chain. The products always have fewer carbon atoms than the original alcohol.

$$\underset{\overset{|}{CH_3}}{\overset{CH_3}{\underset{|}{CH_3COH}}} + 2 [O] \longrightarrow \underset{\text{Acetone}}{CH_3COCH_3} + \underset{\text{Formaldehyde}}{H_2CO} + H_2O$$

Under such vigorous conditions these products undergo further oxidation.

$$CH_3COCH_3 + 2 [O] \longrightarrow \underset{\text{Acetic acid}}{CH_3COOH} + H_2CO$$

$$H_2CO + [O] \longrightarrow \underset{\text{Formic acid}}{HCOOH}$$

$$HCOOH + [O] \longrightarrow CO_2 + H_2O$$

The mechanism of the oxidation of primary and secondary alcohols to aldehydes and ketones in acidic solution appears to follow the same course for most oxidizing agents. The active oxidizing agent is an electron-deficient species which may be a positive ion or a molecule with an electron-deficient atom. For example, dichromic acid oxidizes by way of the [$^+$CrO$_3$H] ion which is present because of the following series of equilibria.

$$H_2Cr_2O_7 + H_2O \rightleftharpoons 2 H_2CrO_4$$

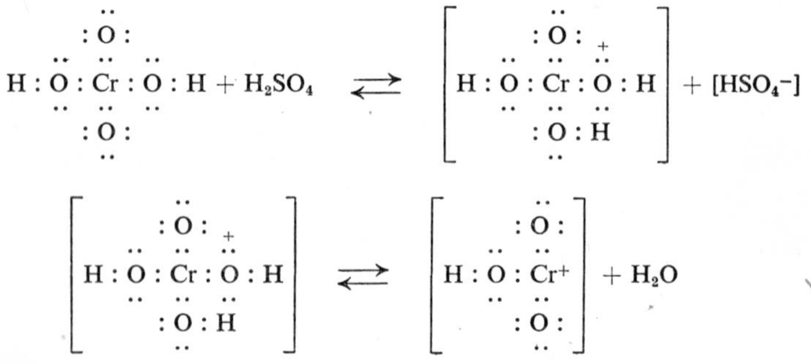

$$H:\overset{\overset{\displaystyle :O:}{}}{\underset{\underset{\displaystyle :O:}{}}{O}}:Cr:O:H + H_2SO_4 \rightleftharpoons \left[H:\overset{\overset{\displaystyle :O:}{}}{\underset{\underset{\displaystyle :O:H}{}}{O}}:Cr:O:H \right]^+ + [HSO_4{}^-]$$

$$\left[H:\overset{\overset{\displaystyle :O:}{}}{\underset{\underset{\displaystyle :O:H}{}}{O}}:Cr:O:H \right]^+ \rightleftharpoons \left[H:\overset{\overset{\displaystyle :O:}{}}{\underset{\underset{\displaystyle :O:}{}}{O}}:Cr^+ \right] + H_2O$$

$$H_2O + H_2SO_4 \rightleftharpoons [H_3O^+] + [HSO_4{}^-]$$

The over-all effect may be written as

$$H_2Cr_2O_7 + 3\ H_2SO_4 \longrightarrow 2\ [^+CrO_3H] + 3\ [HSO_4^-] + [H_3O^+]$$

In the oxidation the positively charged atom of the active agent first attacks a free electron pair on the oxygen atom of the alcohol.

$$RCH_2 : \overset{..}{\underset{H}{O}} : + \left[\begin{array}{c} \overset{..}{:O:} \\ ^+Cr : \overset{..}{O} : H \\ :\overset{..}{O}: \end{array} \right] \rightleftarrows \left[\begin{array}{c} \underset{+}{}\overset{..}{:O:} \\ RCH_2 : \overset{..}{O} : Cr : \overset{..}{O} : H \\ H : \overset{..}{O} : \end{array} \right] \quad \checkmark$$

Loss of a proton to some base gives a neutral intermediate, which is an ester (p. 103) of chromic acid.

$$\left[\begin{array}{c} \underset{+}{}\overset{..}{:O:} \\ RCH_2 : \overset{..}{O} : Cr : \overset{..}{O} : H \\ H : \overset{..}{O} : \end{array} \right] + [HSO_4^-] \rightleftarrows RCH_2 : \overset{..}{\underset{:O:}{O}} : Cr : \overset{..}{O} : H + H_2SO_4 \quad \checkmark$$

The esters from primary or secondary alcohols and inorganic acids that are strong oxidizing agents are unstable, and the alkyl chromate decomposes with loss of a proton and loss of the acid chromite ion to give the aldehyde and chromous acid. The curved arrows indicate the electron transfers taking place.

$$RCH : \overset{..}{\underset{H}{O}} : \overset{..}{\underset{:O:}{Cr}} : \overset{..}{O} : H \longrightarrow RCH{=}O + [HCrO_3^-] + [H^+] \quad \checkmark$$

$$\phantom{RCH : O : Cr : O : H \longrightarrow RCH{=}O +} \downarrow$$

$$\phantom{RCH : O : Cr : O : H \longrightarrow RCH{=}O +} H_2CrO_3 \quad \checkmark$$

A similar series of steps can reduce chromous acid to hypochromous acid, H_2CrO_2. Reaction of hypochromous acid and chromous acid can yield chromic oxide, which with sulfuric acid yields chromic sulfate.

$$H : \overset{..}{\underset{:O:}{O}} : Cr + : \overset{..}{\underset{:O:}{O}} : Cr : \overset{..}{\underset{H}{O}} : H \longrightarrow H : \overset{..}{\underset{H}{O}} : Cr : \overset{..}{\underset{:O:}{O}} : Cr : \overset{..}{\underset{H}{O}} : H \longrightarrow Cr_2O_3 + 2\ H_2O$$

$$Cr_2O_3 + 3\ H_2SO_4 \longrightarrow Cr_2(SO_4)_3 + 3\ H_2O$$

Secondary alcohols are oxidized to ketones by the same mechanism, but the esters of tertiary alcohols with chromic acid cannot decompose by the mechanism indicated and are fairly stable compounds. When the esters of tertiary alcohols are forced to decompose, a carbonium ion must be expelled, a more difficult process than losing a proton.

$$CH_3{-}\overset{\displaystyle CH_3 \quad :\overset{..}{O}:}{\underset{\displaystyle CH_3 \quad :\overset{..}{O}:}{C{-}O}} : \overset{..}{Cr} : \overset{..}{O} : H \rightleftarrows CH_3COCH_3 + [HCrO_3^-] + [CH_3^+]$$

$$[CH_3^+] + H_2O \longrightarrow CH_3 : \overset{..}{\underset{H}{O}} \overset{+}{:} H \rightleftarrows CH_3OH + [H^+]$$

The primary alcohol produced is oxidized to aldehyde and further oxidation products by the usual mechanism.

Other oxidizing agents behave similarly in acid solution, the active electron-deficient agent being formed as indicated by the following condensed equilibria.

$$HOCl + 2\ HCl \rightleftarrows [H_3O^+] + 2\left[\ :\ddot{\underset{\cdot\cdot}{Cl}}:^-\right] + \left[\ :\ddot{\underset{\cdot\cdot}{Cl}}{}^+\right]$$

$$HO{-\!}OH + 2\ H_2SO_4 \rightleftarrows [H_3O^+] + 2\ [HSO_4{}^-] + \left[H:\ddot{\underset{\cdot\cdot}{O}}{}^+\right]$$

$$3\ HONO_2 \rightleftarrows [H_3O^+] + 2\ [NO_3{}^-] + \left[\ :\ddot{\underset{\cdot\cdot}{O}}:\ddot{\underset{:O:}{N}}{}^+\right]$$

ESTERS OF INORGANIC ACIDS

Preparation

Esters of inorganic acids are produced by the reaction of alcohols with inorganic acid halides (reactions *2* and *5*, pp. 100, 101), or with inorganic acids (p. 103). **Sulfites, phosphites, phosphates, arsenites, titanates,** and **silicates** usually are prepared by the first method. Sometimes the sodium alkoxide is used in place of the alcohol to avoid the formation of hydrogen chloride.

$$3\ RONa + POCl_3 \longrightarrow (RO)_3PO + 3\ NaCl$$

More frequently the alcohol is used together with the calculated amount of a tertiary amine such as pyridine (p. 620) to combine with the halogen acid that is liberated.

Nitrites, nitrates, methyl and **ethyl sulfates,** and **borates** are prepared directly from the alcohol and acid (p. 103). The alkyl nitrites are formed by passing oxides of nitrogen ($NO + NO_2 + N_2O_3$) into the alcohol, or by adding sulfuric acid to a mixture of the alcohol and an aqueous solution of sodium nitrite.

When nitric acid reacts with alcohols some reduction takes place to form nitrous acid. The nitrous acid catalyzes the oxidation of the alcohol and violent explosions may result. This autocatalytic reaction can be decreased by the addition of urea, which destroys the nitrous acid as it is formed (p. 312).

Methyl and ethyl sulfates are isolated by the distillation of a mixture of sulfuric acid and the alcohol under reduced pressure. The esters of the higher alcohols boil at too high a temperature and their acid esters decompose to give olefins at too low a temperature (p. 104) to permit their preparation by this method. Instead they are made by the reaction of the alkyl sulfite with the chlorosulfonic ester.

$$\underset{\substack{\text{Butyl}\\\text{chlorosulfonate}}}{C_4H_9OSO_2Cl} + \underset{\text{Butyl sulfite}}{(C_4H_9O)_2SO} \longrightarrow \underset{\text{Butyl sulfate}}{(C_4H_9O)_2SO_2} + C_4H_9Cl + SO_2$$

The alkyl chlorosulfonate may be prepared by the reaction of sulfuryl chloride with either the alcohol or the sulfite.

$$C_4H_9OH + SO_2Cl_2 \longrightarrow C_4H_9OSO_2Cl + HCl$$

$$(C_4H_9O)_2SO + SO_2Cl_2 \longrightarrow C_4H_9OSO_2Cl + C_4H_9Cl + SO_2$$

Borates are prepared by heating a mixture of the alcohol with either boric acid (p. 103) or boric anhydride, B_2O_3.

Only the tertiary alkyl hypochlorites are stable (p. 107). They may be prepared by passing chlorine into an alkaline solution of the alcohol.

$$(CH_3)_3COH + NaOH + Cl_2 \longrightarrow (CH_3)_3COCl + NaCl + H_2O$$
$$\text{\textit{t}-Butyl}$$
$$\text{hypochlorite}$$

Properties

In esters of oxygen acids the hydrocarbon group always is linked to the acid group through oxygen. Although the esters are named like salts, they are covalent compounds. The lower molecular weight esters are volatile liquids, whereas the higher esters can be distilled under reduced pressure. They are insoluble in water and soluble in organic solvents.

The esters are hydrolyzed by water with varying degrees of ease. Ethyl borate and ethyl silicate, for example, are hydrolyzed readily by water at room temperature.

$$(C_2H_5O)_3B + 3 H_2O \longrightarrow 3 C_2H_5OH + B(OH)_3$$

$$(C_2H_5O)_4Si + 4 H_2O \longrightarrow 4 C_2H_5OH + Si(OH)_4$$

One alkyl group of sulfates and phosphates is hydrolyzed much more readily than a second group. For example, at 95° and low concentration the first methyl group of methyl sulfate is completely removed in 3 minutes, whereas only 25 per cent of the second methyl group is removed after 3 hours.

Ethyl nitrate and ethyl perchlorate are hydrolyzed only very slowly by water even at elevated temperatures. Care should be exercised in handling these compounds as they decompose explosively. It is stated that ethyl perchlorate in the anhydrous condition explodes on pouring from one vessel to another.

In contrast to the hydrolysis of esters of organic (carboxylic) acids (p. 170), the hydrolysis of esters of inorganic acids does not appear to be catalyzed by hydrogen ion. Although alkali appears to accelerate the hydrolysis, the effect is not very marked.

Esters react with halogen acids under anhydrous conditions to give the alkyl halide and inorganic acid.

$$RONO + HX \longrightarrow RX + HONO$$

The esters of boric acid differ from the others in that they combine with one mole of an alcohol to give a monobasic acid. This behavior can be explained by the fact that the boron atom lacks a pair of electrons and can form a complex with a molecule of alcohol by taking an unshared pair of electrons from the oxygen atom into its valence shell. The electron pair is held so strongly that the proton can be removed readily.

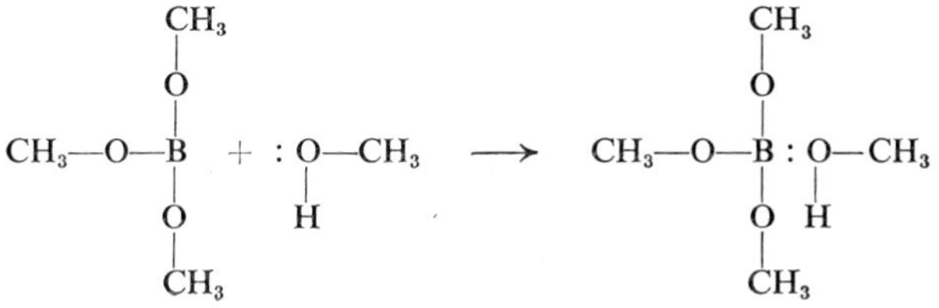

The complex can be titrated in methyl alcohol solution with a solution of sodium methoxide in alcohol with the consumption of one equivalent of base.

$$CH_3-O-B:O-CH_3 + Na^+{}^-OCH_3 \longrightarrow \left[CH_3-O-\overset{-}{B}-O-CH_3 \right] Na^+ + HOCH_3$$

Aluminum alkoxides behave similarly.

Uses

Nitrites relax the smooth muscles of the body and produce a rapid lowering of the blood pressure. **i-Amyl nitrite** is used for the relief of pain in acute angina pectoris although the normal brevity of the attacks in the absence of medication makes it difficult to determine whether amyl nitrite actually assists in the relief of pain. **Ethyl, butyl,** and **i-amyl nitrites** are used extensively as a source of nitrous acid in organic reactions when it is necessary or desirable to carry the reaction out in an anhydrous solvent (p. 493). The **sulfites, sulfates,** and **phosphates** find important use as alkylating agents, that is, as reagents for the introduction of alkyl groups (pp. 137, 504). **Methyl sulfate,** which is used extensively as a methylating agent, is highly toxic and care must be exercised to avoid exposure to its vapors.

When ethyl phosphate reacts with phosphorus oxychloride, a product is obtained which is an effective insecticide, particularly against plant aphids and mites. This material, commonly called tetraethylpyrophosphate (*TEPP*), is a mixture of substances of which the active constituent appears to be **ethyl pyrophosphate,** $(C_2H_5O)_4P_2O_3$. Although highly toxic to animals, it hydrolyzes rapidly to harmless phosphoric acid and ethyl alcohol when exposed to moist air. The ready hydrolysis of **ethyl silicate** finds use for the preparation of colloidal solutions of silicic acid and for depositing on porous material films of silicic acid which subsequently dehydrate to silica. Again this chemical must be handled with care, since the vapors cause opacity of the cornea. Similarly **i-propyl** and **n-butyl titanates,** $(RO)_4Ti$, hydrolyze easily to titanium oxide, TiO_2, and are used in the formulation of protective coatings.

REVIEW QUESTIONS

1. What steps are necessary to establish the molecular formula of methyl alcohol? What are the arguments based on the theory of chemical bonding for assigning the structure, CH_3OH? What chemical evidence shows that one hydrogen atom is different from the other three and that a hydroxyl group is present?
2. State the conditions necessary for proton bond (hydrogen bond) formation and give an example.
3. Why might methane and water be expected to have nearly the same boiling points? Give and explain the actual facts.
4. Compare the boiling points of alcohols with those of the saturated hydrocarbons having approximately the same molecular weight and explain the differences.
5. Discuss and explain the solubility behavior of hydrocarbons and of alcohols in water.
6. What is the relative order of reactivity of primary, secondary, and tertiary alcohols (a) with hydrochloric acid and zinc chloride, (b) with phosphorus trichloride to give phosphorous esters, (c) with phosphorus trichloride to give alkyl chlorides, and (d) when dehydrated?

7. What is the relative reactivity of hydrochloric, hydrobromic, and hydroiodic acid with primary alcohols?
8. Describe the Lucas test for distinguishing between primary, secondary, and tertiary alcohols.
9. Discuss briefly (a) the destructive distillation of wood, (b) synthetic methanol, (c) production of ethyl alcohol by fermentation, and (d) the anaerobic fermentation of starch with *Clostridium acetobutylicum*.
10. What is fusel oil and what are its chief components?
11. What is absolute alcohol and how is it prepared? Why is it not possible to prepare it by simple distillation?

PROBLEMS

12. For each of the following groups, write condensed structural formulas for all of the isomeric alcohols that meet the given specifications, name by the Geneva system, and indicate by Roman numerals I, II, or III, whether the alcohols are primary, secondary, or tertiary: (a) molecular formula $C_5H_{12}O$; (b) a chain of five carbon atoms and a single methyl branch; (c) a chain of five carbon atoms and two methyl branches on a single carbon atom; (d) a chain of five carbon atoms and two methyl branches on different carbon atoms.
13. Write structural formulas for the following alcohols:
    A. (a) *n*-Amyl alcohol; (b) dimethylethylcarbinol; (c) 2,2-dimethyl-3-pentanol; (d) *i*-hexyl alcohol; (e) diethyl-*s*-butylcarbinol; (f) 3-ethyl-2-hexanol; (g) neopentyl alcohol; (h) di-*i*-propylcarbinol; (i) 4-methyl-2-*i*-propyl-1-pentanol; (j) active amyl alcohol.
    B. (a) *n*-Butyl alcohol; (b) methyldiethylcarbinol; (c) 2,3-dimethyl-2-pentanol; (d) *i*-octyl alcohol; (e) dimethyl-*i*-propylcarbinol; (f) 3-methyl-3-hexanol; (g) neohexyl alcohol; (h) di-*s*-butylcarbinol; (i) 4-methyl-3-*i*-propyl-2-hexanol; (j) *t*-amyl alcohol.
    C. (a) Ethyl-*t*-butylcarbinol; (b) 2,2,3-trimethyl-1-butanol; (c) *i*-amyl alcohol; (d) *n*-decyl alcohol; (e) diethyl-*n*-propylcarbinol; (f) *t*-butyl alcohol; (g) lauryl alcohol; (h) methyl-di-*i*-butylcarbinol; (i) 2,2-diethyl-1-pentanol; (j) triethylcarbinol.
14. Tell why each of the following names is unsatisfactory and give an acceptable name:
    A. (a) Isopropanol; (b) 3-*i*-propyl-1-pentanol; (c) methyl ethyl carbinol; (d) dimethyl-(2-methylbutyl)carbinol; (e) 2-methyl-hexanol-1; (f) *s*-amyl alcohol; (g) *i*-amylalcohol; (h) *s*-butanol; (i) 4,4-dimethyl-3-pentanol; (j) 3-ethyl-2-butanol.
    B. (a) *t*-Hexyl alcohol; (b) *n*-propylalcohol; (c) neopentanol; (d) (1-methylpropyl)-ethyl-carbinol; (e) 3-*i*-butyl-2-hexanol; (f) 2-methyl-3-butanol; (g) 2-ethyl-2-propanol; (h) diethyl carbinol; (i) 3-ethylpentanol-3; (j) 3-*s*-butyl-1-hexanol.
    C. (a) Isobutanol; (b) 2-methylpentanol-2; (c) *s*-butylalcohol; (d) 3-*s*-butyl-1-hexanol; (e) 3-methyl-4-hexanol; (f) *s*-octyl alcohol; (g) methyl diethyl carbinol; (h) 2-propyl-1-butanol; (i) (1-methylbutyl)-*n*-propylcarbinol; (j) 2-(1-methylpropyl)-1-butanol.
15. Give reactions illustrating the preparation of the following alcohols from suitable olefins:
    A. (a) 2-Pentanol; (b) dimethyl-*n*-propylcarbinol; (c) *t*-amyl alcohol; (d) triethylcarbinol.
    B. (a) 3,3-Dimethyl-2-pentanol; (b) methylethyl-*n*-propylcarbinol; (c) methylneopentyl-carbinol; (d) 2,3-dimethyl-2-butanol.
    C. (a) Dimethyl-*t*-butylcarbinol; (b) 3-methyl-2-pentanol; (c) methylethyl-*i*-propyl-carbinol; (d) 3,3-dimethyl-2-butanol.
16. Give balanced equations for two reactions suitable for the following conversions:
    A. (a) 2-Methyl-1-butanol to 1-chloro-2-methylbutane; (b) *i*-hexyl alcohol to *i*-hexyl iodide; (c) tridecanol to 1-bromotridecane.
    B. (a) Diethylcarbinol to 3-chloropentane; (b) 4-methyl-3-pentanol to 3-bromo-4-methylpentane; (c) 2,4-dimethyl-2-pentanol to 2-iodo-2,4-dimethylpentane.
    C. (a) *n*-Hexadecyl alcohol to *n*-hexadecyl bromide; (b) ethyl-*n*-propylcarbinol to 3-chlorohexane; (c) 3,3-dimethyl-2-pentanol to 2-iodo-3,3-dimethylpentane.
17. Give balanced equations for the preparation of an alkoxide, an alkene, and an inorganic ester from the following alcohols, and name the organic product of the reaction:
    A. (a) Octadecanol; (b) 2-methyl-1-pentanol; (c) 2,3-dimethyl-1-butanol.
    B. (a) *n*-Nonyl alcohol; (b) methyl-*i*-butylcarbinol; (c) 2,3-dimethyl-1-pentanol.
    C. (a) *i*-Heptyl alcohol; (b) 2,4-dimethyl-3-pentanol; (c) methyl-*n*-butylcarbinol.
18. Give a series of reactions for the following conversions:
    A. (a) *n*-Butyl alcohol to *s*-butyl alcohol; (b) 2-methyl-1-butene to 2-methyl-2-butene; (c) ethyl-*i*-propylcarbinol to 2-methyl-2-chloropentane.
    B. (a) 1-Pentene to 2-pentene; (b) 1-propanol to 2-propanol; (c) di-*i*-propylcarbinol to dimethyl-*i*-butyl-bromomethane.

    C. (*a*) Methyl-*i*-propylcarbinol to *t*-amyl alcohol; (*b*) *i*-butyl alcohol to *t*-butyl chloride; (*c*) *i*-amyl alcohol to 2-methyl-2-butene.

19. Give equations for the following reactions and name the organic product:

    A. (*a*) Sodium *n*-butoxide and phosphorus oxychloride; (*b*) ethyl nitrite and dry hydrogen chloride; (*c*) methyl borate and water.

    B. (*a*) *i*-Amyl alcohol and nitrous acid; (*b*) *n*-propyl phosphate and aqueous sodium hydroxide; (*c*) *n*-butyl nitrite and dry hydrogen chloride.

    C. (*a*) Methyl alcohol and boric anhydride; (*b*) ethyl silicate and water; (*c*) *n*-undecyl alcohol and nitric acid.

20. Give and explain a chemical test that could be used to distinguish between the members of each of the following pairs of compounds:

    A. (*a*) *n*-Propyl alcohol and *i*-propyl alcohol; (*b*) ethyl nitrite and ethyl nitrate; (*c*) sodium *n*-butoxide and aluminum *n*-butoxide; (*d*) methanol and hexane; (*e*) *n*-propyl sulfate and *n*-undecane; (*f*) *i*-amyl alcohol and 1-octene; (*g*) 2-methyl-1-propanol and ethyl phosphate; (*h*) 1-tridecene and ethyl silicate.

    B. (*a*) Methyl sulfate and methyl borate; (*b*) 2-methylbutanol and 1-octadecene; (*c*) neohexane and ethyl sulfite; (*d*) magnesium methoxide and potassium methoxide; (*e*) *n*-butyl alcohol and *n*-butyl nitrite; (*f*) 1-butanol and 2-butanol; (*g*) *i*-propyl titanate and 2-octene.

    C. (*a*) Sodium ethoxide and sodium hydroxide; (*b*) *n*-hexyl alcohol and ethyl silicate; (*c*) 2-methyl-2-propanol and 2-methyl-1-propanol; (*d*) 2,4,4-trimethyl-2-pentene and ethyl phosphate; (*e*) ethyl sulfate and ethyl sulfite; (*f*) neohexane and *n*-butyl nitrite; (*g*) *s*-butyl alcohol and *i*-octane; (*h*) 4-methyl-2-pentene and methanol.

Chapter 6

ALKYL HALIDES. GRIGNARD REAGENTS

ALKYL HALIDES

Alkyl halides are important intermediates for the synthesis of other compounds. Not only do they undergo a variety of reactions, but they are prepared readily in good yields.

Preparation

Alkyl halides are formed when alcohols react with either inorganic acid halides or with hydrogen halides under appropriate conditions (pp. 100, 102). These two procedures are the most satisfactory general methods of preparation, although the addition of hydrogen halides to olefins (p. 59) and the direct halogenation of saturated hydrocarbons (p. 119) also may be used. Primary alkyl iodides may be made from primary alkyl chlorides and bromides by the reaction of sodium iodide in acetone solution (*Finckelstein reaction*).

$$RCH_2Cl + NaI \longrightarrow RCH_2I + NaCl$$

This reaction takes place because sodium chloride and sodium bromide, in contrast to sodium iodide, are insoluble in acetone, and the equilibrium is shifted to the right. The reaction of secondary and tertiary chlorides and bromides is too slow to be practical.

Structure and Nomenclature

The methods of formation from alcohols leave no question as to the structure of the alkyl halides. They usually are named as if they were salts of halogen acids. They may be considered also as halogen derivatives of saturated hydrocarbons and often are so named. Thus ethyl chloride may be called chloroethane, and isobutyl bromide may be called 1-bromo-2-methylpropane.

Physical Properties

In physical properties the alkyl halides resemble the saturated hydrocarbons. They are insoluble in water and are good solvents for most organic compounds. The boiling points of the chlorides are of the same order of magnitude as those of hydrocarbons of the same molecular weight, whereas bromides boil about 60° lower than chlorides, and iodides 70° lower than bromides, again comparing compounds of the same molecular weight (Table 9, p. 114).

The reason for the decrease in boiling points of bromides compared with chlorides, and of iodides compared with bromides, probably is the same as the reason for the lowering of boiling point with branching of the hydrocarbon chain. The increase in size of the atom from chlorine to bromine to iodine would be expected to have much the same effect as branching in decreasing the van der Waals forces between the molecules.

Alkyl halides are more dense than hydrocarbons. The densities of the compounds considered so far increase in the order hydrocarbons < alcohols < alkyl chlorides < bromides < iodides, if compounds with the same number of

TABLE 9

COMPARISON OF THE BOILING POINTS OF *n*-ALKANES WITH THOSE OF *n*-ALKYL CHLORIDES, BROMIDES, IODIDES, AND ALCOHOLS OF SIMILAR MOLECULAR WEIGHT

ALKANES Mol. wt.	B.p.	CHLORIDES Mol. wt.	B.p.	BROMIDES Mol. wt.	B.p.	IODIDES Mol. wt.	B.p.	ALCOHOLS Mol. wt.	B.p.
C_3 44	−45	C_1 51	−24					C_2 46	78
C_4 58	+0.6	C_2 65	+13					C_3 60	97
C_5 72	36	C_3 78	46					C_4 74	118
C_6 86	69	C_4 93	78	C_1 94	5			C_5 88	138
C_7 100	98	C_5 107	108	C_2 108	38			C_6 102	157
C_8 114	126	C_6 121	133	C_3 123	71			C_7 116	177
C_9 128	150	C_7 135	157	C_4 137	102			C_8 130	195
C_{10} 142	174	C_8 149	183	C_5 151	130	C_1 142	42	C_9 144	213
C_{11} 156	194	C_9 163	190	C_6 165	156	C_2 156	75	C_{10} 158	231
C_{12} 170	214	C_{10} 177	223	C_7 179	178	C_3 170	103	C_{11} 172	248

carbon atoms are compared. The density of hydrocarbons increases with increasing length of chain because of the increasing van der Waals forces, but because carbon atoms are less dense than elements of higher atomic number, increasing the size of the alkyl group in alkyl halides causes a decrease in density.

Reactions

The importance of the alkyl halides lies in the great variety of reactions which they undergo. In all of these reactions, the halogen is removed or replaced by another group. Some of the more important reactions for primary and secondary halides are illustrated by the following equations.

$$RX + AgOH \longrightarrow ROH + AgX \qquad (1)$$
$$\text{(or aqueous NaOH)} \quad \text{An alcohol (or NaX)}$$

$$RX + NaOR \longrightarrow ROR + NaX \qquad (2)$$
$$\text{An ether}$$

$$RX + NaSH \longrightarrow RSH + NaX \qquad (3)$$
$$\text{A mercaptan,}$$
$$\text{thio alcohol,}$$
$$\text{or alkanethiol}$$

$$2 RX + Na_2S \longrightarrow R_2S + 2 NaX \qquad (4)$$
$$\text{An alkyl}$$
$$\text{sulfide}$$

$$RX + NaCN \longrightarrow RCN + NaX \qquad (5)$$
$$\text{An alkyl}$$
$$\text{cyanide}$$

$$RX + NH_3 \longrightarrow RNH_3^+X^- \tag{6}$$

An alkylammonium halide
(amine hydrohalide)

$$RX + Mg \longrightarrow RMgX \tag{7}$$

An alkylmagnesium halide
(Grignard reagent, p. 120)

$$RX + Zn\text{-}Cu \text{ couple} \longrightarrow RZnX \ (+ Cu) \tag{8}$$

An alkylzinc
halide

$$2\,RX + 2\,Zn\text{-}Cu \text{ couple} \longrightarrow R_2Zn + ZnX_2\,(+ Cu) \tag{9}$$

A dialkylzinc

$$2\,RX + 2\,Na \longrightarrow RR + 2\,NaX \text{ (Wurtz synthesis, p. 126)} \tag{10}$$

An alkane

$$RX + Zn + HX \longrightarrow RH + ZnX_2 \tag{11}$$

(in alcohol)   An alkane

The reagents that react with an alkyl halide are metals or salts of weak acids. These same reagents react with halogen acids. The reactions for the most part are identical in both cases except that a hydrogen atom of the acid takes the part of an alkyl group in the alkyl halide. For example, silver hydroxide and halogen acid give water and silver halide, sodium sulfide gives hydrogen sulfide, sodium cyanide gives hydrogen cyanide, ammonia gives ammonium halide, and sodium gives hydrogen. The principal difference is that the reactions with alkyl halides are slow, whereas those with halogen acids are rapid.

Alkyl iodides react more rapidly than bromides, and bromides than chlorides. Since bromides are cheaper than iodides and usually are sufficiently reactive, they are used most frequently in the laboratory. The specific conditions for carrying out the above reactions and the limitations of the reactions are considered later where the methods for preparing the various compounds formed in the reactions are discussed.

One additional reaction of alkyl halides should be discussed, namely the removal of halogen acids by alkaline reagents to give olefins.

$$R_2CHCR_2 + KOH \text{ (in alcohol)} \longrightarrow R_2C{=}CR_2 + KX + H_2O$$
$$\overset{|}{X}$$

This reaction usually is not suitable for the removal of halogen acid from primary halides because another reaction leading to the formation of ethers may predominate (p. 137).

$$C_2H_5OH + KOH \rightleftharpoons C_2H_5OK + H_2O$$

$$C_2H_5OK + RX \longrightarrow C_2H_5OR + KX$$

For reactions *1* to *10* the relative rates for the alkyl halides are primary > secondary > tertiary. The ease of olefin formation, however, is tertiary > secondary > primary. Hence primary halides give the best yields in reactions *1* to *10*. Elimination of halogen acid from tertiary halides takes place so much more readily than replacement of halogen by another group that most reagents that can combine with halogen acid give the olefin. Tertiary butyl chloride, for example, reacts with sodium cyanide to give isobutylene, hydrogen cyanide and sodium chloride. An exception to this generalization is the reaction with magnesium to give Grignard reagents, but even here special conditions are necessary to obtain good yields with tertiary halides (p. 121). As in the dehydration of alcohols, the direction of elimination of halogen acid follows the Saytzev rule (p. 104).

Like dehydrohalogenation, the ease of hydrolysis of alkyl halides also follows the order tertiary $>$ secondary $>$ primary. Tertiary halides hydrolyze with water alone, the rate not being affected by either acids or bases.

$$R_3CX + H_2O \longrightarrow R_3COH + HX$$

The difference between the rate of hydrolysis of *i*-butyl bromide and *t*-butyl bromide is so great that the composition of mixtures of the two can be estimated by shaking with water, separating the unreacted *i*-butyl bromide, and determining the bromide ion in the aqueous layer by precipitation with silver nitrate.

The reactions of alkyl halides with the salts of weak acids take place by the simplest form of the displacement reaction (p. 102). The reactive agent is the basic or electron-donating negative ion, for example $\left[\overset{..}{\underset{..}{:}} \overset{..}{O} H \right]^{-}$, $\left[\overset{..}{\underset{..}{:}} S H \right]^{-}$, or $\left[\overset{..}{\underset{..}{:}} C N \right]^{-}$, which can be symbolized as $[^{-} : B]$. Molecules having an unshared pair of electrons, such as water or ammonia, behave in the same way. Collision of the negative ion with the alkyl halide molecule causes loss of a halide ion and formation of a new molecule.

$$[B : ^{-}] + R : \overset{..}{\underset{..}{X}} : \longrightarrow B : R + \left[: \overset{..}{\underset{..}{X}} : \right]^{-}$$

For effective collision, the attacking ion must approach from the rear, in line with the carbon atom and the ion which is leaving.

$$[B : ^{-}] + H \overset{H}{\underset{R}{-}} C - X \rightleftarrows \left[B : \overset{H \quad H}{\underset{R}{C}} : X \right]^{-} \rightleftarrows B - \overset{H}{\underset{R}{C}} - H + [: X^{-}]$$

One reason that this approach is more effective is that a portion of the orbital or "tail" from the carbon-halogen bond extends in this direction (Fig. 11*a*, p. 12). Moreover, the configuration of the half-reacted stage is the reasonably stable one of a trigonal bipyramid found in the phosphorus pentahalides.

As the negative ion approaches closely enough, bonding with the carbon atom begins, and the halide ion starts to leave the molecule, assisted by hydration with solvent molecules. At the mid-stage of the reaction, the carbon atom and the three groups that remain bound to the carbon atom lie in a plane which is perpendicular to the line passing through the two halogen atoms and the carbon atom. This half-reacted condition, together with the associated solvent molecules, is the transition state (p. 42) for the reaction. As the halide ion leaves, the carbon moves through the plane to bond with the entering group. Hence at the end of the reaction, the tetrahedral arrangement of bonds again exists. This process resembles an umbrella being turned inside out and is known as a **Walden inversion** (p. 346).

The rates of reactions that follow this mechanism are proportional to the concentration of both the entering ion and the alkyl halide. They are called bimolecular and are said to take place by an S_N2 **mechanism**. This symbol stands for substitution by a nucleophilic (nucleus seeking, i.e., electron-donating) reagent, the rate of reaction being governed by a bimolecular step.[1] Displacement reactions of compounds having a functional group attached to a primary alkyl group usually take place by this mechanism.

It has been found experimentally that the rates of displacement reactions of compounds having a functional group attached to secondary or tertiary alkyl groups or to certain other types of groups (p. 437) may be dependent only on the concentration of the compound and independent of the concentration of the nucleophilic reagent. Such kinetically first order reactions are said to take place by an S_N1 **mechanism.** Reactions of this type may occur with or without Walden inversion. Despite the extensive investigations of these reactions, their detailed mechanism still is a matter of controversy. In view of the fact that S_N1 reactions occur when factors are present that can increase the stability of a carbonium ion, the least complicated explanation is that the rate-controlling step is the dissociation of the alkyl halide into a carbonium ion and a halide ion. The dissociation is followed by a rapid combination of the carbonium ion with the nucleophilic reagent.

$$R : X \xrightarrow{\text{Slow}} [R^+] + [: X^-]$$

$$[R^+] + [: B^-] \xrightarrow{\text{Fast}} R : B$$

Thus the over-all rate is dependent only on bond-breaking and hence on the concentration of the alkyl halide. If the base attacks the carbonium ion before it becomes planar, no Walden inversion occurs. If the carbonium ion becomes planar, inversion may or may not take place, depending on which side the base approaches.

The fact that tertiary halides react by an S_N1 mechanism whereas primary halides react by an S_N2 mechanism may be explained by the greater polarizability of the alkyl groups compared to hydrogen atoms, which permits the alkyl groups to supply electrons to the tertiary carbon atom, thus making it easier for the halogen to leave as a solvated negative ion. For other compounds that react by the S_N1 mechanism, stabilization of the intermediate carbonium ion may be brought about in other ways (p. 463). It has been proposed also that a tertiary carbonium ion forms more readily than a primary carbonium ion because the alkyl groups occupy more space than hydrogen and the resulting crowding is relieved in the planar carbonium ion.

For reactions that take place by an S_N2 mechanism the order of reactivity of alkyl halides is primary > secondary > tertiary. Alkyl groups are larger than hydrogen and block the approach of the nucleophilic reagent to the back side of the molecule. This space effect is called **steric hindrance.** For reactions that take place by an S_N1 mechanism, the order is tertiary > secondary > primary because this is the order of ease of formation of the carbonium ion. These statements do not imply that a particular order signifies a specific mechanism. Both S_N1

---

[1] Numerous coined terms and symbols have come into general use, the meaning of which is not always immediately clear to the uninitiated, and the appropriateness or necessity of which may be questionable. Nevertheless they have become established in chemical language, and it is important that their meaning be understood. The more common terms are defined here for reference purposes.

As already indicated, *nucleophilic* literally means nucleus-loving (Gr. *philos*, loving), but even the translation is not immediately clear. The group is not necessarily interested in a nucleus but only in an empty orbital or a point of low electron density. The synonymous term *anionoid reagent* refers to the presence of an unshared pair of electrons characteristic of an anion and *electrodotic* to the ability of the reagent to supply a pair of electrons. *Electron-donating* and *electron-sharing* are self-explanatory.

The term *electrophilic* literally means electron-loving. It is applied to a group deficient in electrons, such as a proton. *Cationoid* is used to mean the same thing because positive cations are deficient in electrons. The terms *electron-deficient* or *electron-accepting* are more descriptive. The very confusing term *electronegative* is used to mean *electron-attracting*; that is, an electro negative group is *positive* with respect to the group to which it is attached. Originally it was used to designate groups that enhanced the acidity of acids and hence referred to the state of the atom or group after electrons had been acquired. The term *electropositive*, except as applied to elements, has been almost wholly replaced by the term *electron-repelling* or *electron-donating*.

The use of the letter S in the symbol S_N1 and S_N2 does not permit one to refer to displacement reactions as nucleophilic substitution. The term *substitution* should be limited to reactions in which hydrogen attached to carbon is replaced by another group (p. 120).

and S_N2 reactions may be taking place simultaneously, and various stages between pure S_N1 and pure S_N2 seem likely. Moreover solvation of the molecules and ions (p. 13), including intermediate carbonium ions, and the nature of the nucleophilic reagent play a part in the reactions. The rate of any particular reaction is dependent on all of these factors.

Olefin formation takes place by removal of a proton and some other group from adjacent carbon atoms (p. 115). In the reaction of alkyl halides with bases, the negative hydroxide ion removes a proton, and the halogen leaves as halide ion.

$$[HO:^-] + H:\underset{\underset{R}{|}}{\overset{\overset{R}{|}}{C}}\!-\!\underset{\underset{R}{|}}{\overset{\overset{R}{|}}{C}}:X \longrightarrow H_2O + \underset{\underset{R}{|}}{\overset{\overset{R}{|}}{C}}\!=\!\underset{\underset{R}{|}}{\overset{\overset{R}{|}}{C}} + [:X^-]$$

The elimination reaction may be bimolecular, the rate depending on the concentrations of both the base and the alkyl halide (**E2 mechanism**), or the rate determining step may be dependent only on the concentration of the alkyl halide, when it is said to follow a unimolecular mechanism (**E1 mechanism**).

Alkyl Halides of Commercial Importance

It is evident from the variety of compounds obtainable from them that the alkyl halides are extremely important to the organic chemist. Only a few of the simple halides are of industrial importance, however, because only a very small fraction of the known organic compounds are manufactured in large quantities. In the laboratory the chemist usually uses bromides or iodides because of their greater reactivity, but industrially the chlorides are used because of their lower cost. Many of the polyhalogen compounds are industrially important, and they are discussed in Chapter 33. **Methyl chloride**, b.p. —24°, is made by heating methyl alcohol with hydrochloric acid. It is formed also as one product of the reaction of chlorine with methane (p. 722). Its principal uses are as a refrigerant in mechanical refrigerators, as a solvent at low temperatures, and as a methylating agent in the preparation of methylcellulose (p. 404), silicones (p. 914), and other organic compounds. **Methyl bromide**, b.p. 4.5°, is made from methyl alcohol and hydrogen bromide. It is highly toxic and is used as a poison gas for rodent control. It is toxic to other forms of life also and is used as a soil and grain fumigant. Its use in fire extinguishers probably depends on dissociation into free radicals (p. 568) which act as chain breakers and inhibit the propagation of flame. Because of its high toxicity to human beings, it should be used for this purpose only with proper precautions to prevent inhalation of the vapors. The same precautions should be taken when using methyl bromide in chemical reactions. **Ethyl chloride**, b.p. 13°, is made either from ethyl alcohol and hydrochloric acid in the presence of zinc chloride, by passing an equimolar mixture of ethylene and hydrogen chloride into a solution of anhydrous aluminum chloride in liquid ethyl chloride, or by the reaction of a mixture of ethane and ethylene with chlorine whereby the hydrogen chloride formed by the substitution of ethane is added to the ethylene.

$$C_2H_6 + Cl_2 \longrightarrow C_2H_5Cl + HCl$$

$$C_2H_4 + HCl \longrightarrow C_2H_5Cl$$

It is used for the manufacture of tetraethyllead (p. 899) and of ethylcellulose (p. 404), and as a quick acting general anesthetic (footnote, p. 141) for minor operations.

The **amyl chlorides** are made by the direct substitution of the hydrogen atoms of *n*-pentane and *i*-pentane by halogen, a process known as *halogenation*.

$$C_5H_{12} + Cl_2 \longrightarrow C_5H_{11}Cl + HCl$$

This reaction of the hydrocarbons is of limited usefulness and hence was not discussed in Chapter 2. Fluorine reacts with the alkanes spontaneously and so rapidly that the reaction may be explosive. Most combustible compounds will burst into flame when a stream of fluorine is allowed to impinge upon them. Chlorine, bromine, and iodine do not react with alkanes in the dark at room temperature. Chlorine and bromine react with hydrocarbons photochemically under the influence of light of short wavelength (250–500 mμ[2]) or thermally at high temperatures. The usefulness of the reaction is limited by the fact that it is not very selective. All types of hydrogen are attacked with almost equal ease, and the introduction of one halogen atom does not appreciably affect the replacement of a second hydrogen atom. The result is that a mixture of almost all of the possible monosubstitution products is obtained, and some poly-substitution products as well.

In the commercial chlorination of pentanes the reaction is carried out in the gas phase at 250°–300° using a volume ratio of pentane to chlorine of 15 to 1 in order to form chiefly monosubstitution products. Even at this ratio about 5 per cent of disubstitution products are formed. The rate of flow of the gases is about 60 miles per hour. This rate is faster than the rate of propagation of the chlorine-hydrocarbon flame, and the unreacted material behind the flame cannot explode. The relative amounts of the monosubstitution products formed from *n*-pentane at 300° are 24 per cent 1-chloropentane, 49 per cent 2-chloropentane, and 27 per cent 3 chloropentane. From *i*-pentane there is obtained 33 per cent 1-chloro-2-methylbutane, 22 per cent 2-chloro-2-methylbutane, 17 per cent 1-chloro-3-methylbutane, and 28 per cent 2-chloro-3-methylbutane. Commercially the mixed monochlorides are hydrolyzed to mixed amyl alcohols (Pentasol). Reaction with ammonia gives amylamines, and with sodium hydrosulfide gives amyl mercaptans and amyl sulfides. It is possible to separate the mixtures by distillation, but for most uses separation is unnecessary.

Substitution Reactions

The direct replacement of hydrogen by a halogen atom or other monovalent group is known as **substitution** and is of considerable importance for other compounds as well as for the saturated hydrocarbons. Substitution of hydrogen by halogen was investigated first by Dumas after an episode at the Tuileries. On the occasion of a ball during the reign of Charles X of France, the guests were driven from the ballroom by choking fumes given off by the burning candles. Brongiart, the chemical advisor to the king, called in his son-in-law Dumas, who found that the candles had been bleached by a new process using chlorine. The bleaching had given rise to chlorinated fat acids, which on burning gave off hydrogen chloride. Dumas then made an extensive investigation of the substitution reaction. One of the *fundamental concepts of substitution and of all replacement reactions* is

---

[2] The abbreviation mμ is used for millimicron, which is equal to 10^{-7} centimeter or 10 Ångstrom units.

that the new atom or group takes the position formerly occupied by the replaced atom or group of atoms.

Substitution, chlorination, halogenation, and other terms for analogous reactions should be used only for the direct replacement of hydrogen. For example, the reaction of an alcohol with hydrogen bromide should not be spoken of as the bromination of an alcohol or as a substitution reaction, but as the replacement of hydroxyl by bromine.[3] Similarly the reaction of 2-butene and chlorine to give 2,3-dichlorobutane should not be called chlorination, but the addition of chlorine to 2-butene. Although these conventions may seem somewhat arbitrary, they should be observed if chemists are to understand each other without confusion.

GRIGNARD REAGENTS

Zinc or magnesium reacts with alkyl halides to give compounds in which the alkyl group is united to the metal. Such compounds are known as *organometallic compounds* (p. 899). The organozinc compounds found use in early synthetic work but have the disadvantage that only methyl and ethyl iodides give good yields, and that even methylzinc and ethylzinc are difficult to use because they are spontaneously flammable in air. In 1899 Barbier[4] announced that in many cases the alkylzincs could be replaced by a mixture of alkyl halide and magnesium in ether (p. 136) in the presence of the compound with which the reaction was to take place. This reaction was improved by Grignard,[5] a student of Barbier's, who reported in 1900 the separate preparation of alkylmagnesium halide solutions and their reaction with a variety of compounds. Subsequent work by Grignard and a large number of other investigators has shown that the use of alkylmagnesium halide solutions, now commonly known as *Grignard reagents*, is of more practical importance for the laboratory synthesis of organic compounds than is any other single synthetic method. By the time of Grignard's death, the literature contained about 6000 articles dealing with this reagent. The reaction has few commercial applications.

Preparation

Grignard reagents are made by the direct action of alkyl halides on magnesium turnings. Reaction takes place in the absence of a solvent but soon stops because the alkylmagnesium halide is a solid that is insoluble in alkyl halide and coats over the surface of the magnesium. In the presence of a solvent for the alkylmagnesium halide, the reaction goes to completion. Ether is the solvent most commonly used, although tetrahydrofuran (p. 620) has many advantages. Sometimes the reaction is slow to start. The drier the reagents and apparatus and

---

[3] To avoid such phrases it has been suggested that displacement reactions be designated by the name of the entering group followed by *de*, the name of the departing group, and the suffix *ation*. Thus the replacement of hydroxyl by bromine would be called *bromodehydroxylation*.

[4] Francois Philippe Antoine Barbier (1848–1922), professor at the University of Lyon, France, who is known not only for his discovery of the usefulness of magnesium in organic synthesis but also for his work on the constitution of the terpenes. In his later years he was interested in mineralogy and the analysis of minerals.

[5] Victor Grignard (1871–1935), professor at the University of Nancy and later successor to Barbier at Lyon. In 1912 he was awarded the Nobel Prize in chemistry jointly with Paul Sabatier (p. 55).

the less oxide film on the surface of the magnesium, the easier the reaction starts. Usually a small crystal of iodine is added to initiate the reaction. Alkyl iodides react more readily than bromides, and bromides than chlorides, but the yields are in the reverse order, namely chlorides > bromides > iodides. The higher the dilution and the greater the purity and state of subdivision of the magnesium, the higher the yields.

Several **side reactions** account for decreased yield.
1. The halide may react at the surface of the magnesium in a manner analogous to the Wurtz reaction (p. 126).

$$2\ RX + Mg \longrightarrow RR + MgX_2$$

2. If the halogen is replaced readily, as with tertiary halides, excess halide may react with the Grignard reagent.

$$RMgX + RX \longrightarrow RR + MgX_2$$

3. Halogen acid may be removed, especially from tertiary halides, with the formation of alkene.

$$2\ R_2CHCXR_2 + Mg \longrightarrow 2\ R_2C{=}CR_2 + H_2 + MgX_2$$

4. Alkyl halides which can lose halogen acid may react with magnesium in the presence of metallic impurities, especially copper, with the formation of alkene and alkane.

$$2\ RCH_2CHXR + Mg \longrightarrow RCH{=}CHR + RCH_2CH_2R + MgX_2$$

Reactions

1. **With Reactive Hydrogen.** Grignard reagents react with all compounds that evolve hydrogen with alkali metals. The organic product is an alkane.

$$RMgX \begin{cases} + HOH \longrightarrow \\ + HOR \longrightarrow \\ + HNH_2 \longrightarrow \\ + HX \longrightarrow \end{cases} RH \begin{cases} + Mg(OH)X \\ + Mg(OR)X \\ + Mg(NH_2)X \\ + MgX_2 \end{cases}$$

For simplicity in balancing the equations, the inorganic products usually are written as the mixed compounds $Mg(OH)X$, $Mg(OR)X$, and $Mg(NH_2)X$. Since the molecules are ionic, it is more likely that the solid salts are mixtures of the various possible crystal species, including MgX_2 and $Mg(OH)_2$, $Mg(OR)_2$, or $Mg(NH_2)_2$. The reactivity of Grignard reagents with hydroxyl groups accounts for the necessity of having all materials and apparatus dry and free of alcohol during the preparation of the reagent.

The formation of the alkane is an acid-base reaction, that is, a proton-transfer reaction. Hydrogen united to oxygen is lost more readily as proton than hydrogen united to carbon, and hence the weaker acid, the alkane, is liberated. In other words the reaction of a Grignard reagent with water to give alkane and magnesium hydroxide is analogous to the reaction of sodium cyanide with hydrochloric acid to give hydrogen cyanide and sodium chloride.

This type of reaction is valuable for the estimation of groups containing replaceable hydrogen, for example hydroxyl groups. The procedure was proposed first by Chugaev[6] and further

---

[6] Leo A. Chugaev (1872–1922), professor at the University of St. Petersburg, Russia.

developed by his student Zerevitinov and by others. It commonly is referred to as the *Zerevitinov determination.* A simple form of the apparatus is shown in Fig. 40. A solution of methylmagnesium iodide in a high-boiling ether, such as *i*-amyl ether (p. 141), is placed in one leg of the bifurcated tube, and a weighed amount of the compound dissolved in a suitable solvent is placed in the other leg. The apparatus is brought to temperature equilibrium with the stopcock open, the cock then is closed, and the height of the mercury column read. The two solutions are mixed, and after again reaching temperature equilibrium, the volume of methane formed in the reaction is determined. From these data and the molecular weight of the compound, the number of active hydrogen atoms in the molecule can be calculated. Various refinements in the above procedure have been introduced to increase the accuracy of the determination.

The concentration of Grignard solutions can be determined by adding water to a known volume of the reagent and titrating the magnesium hydroxide formed. The method is inaccurate to the extent that the reagent has reacted with air, since magnesium alkoxides also react with water to give magnesium hydroxide (p. 100).

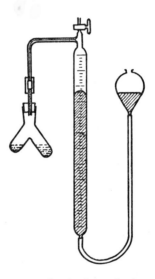

Fig. 40. Zerevitinov apparatus for the determination of reactive hydrogen.

2. **With Halogen.** Halogens react with alkylmagnesium halide to give alkyl halide and magnesium halide.

$$RMgX + X_2 \longrightarrow RX + MgX_2$$

This reaction can be used to determine the concentration of Grignard solutions by titrating with standard iodine solution.

3. **With Oxygen.** Grignard reagents absorb oxygen with the formation of alkoxides, from which the alcohol can be liberated by the addition of water.

$$2\,RMgX + O_2 \longrightarrow 2\,ROMgX$$

$$ROMgX + HOH \longrightarrow ROH + Mg(OH)X$$

Hence it is necessary to exclude air from the reagents to obtain optimum yields. At low temperatures the product is the salt of the alkyl hydroperoxide (p. 874).

$$RMgX + O_2 \longrightarrow RO{-}O^{-+}MgX$$

4. **With Inorganic Halides.** Grignard reagents react with the halides of all elements below magnesium in the electromotive series, usually by replacing the halogen with alkyl groups.

$$HgCl_2 + 2\,RMgX \longrightarrow HgR_2 + 2\,MgX_2$$

$$AlCl_3 + 3\,RMgX \longrightarrow AlR_3 + 3\,MgX_2$$

$$SnCl_4 + 4\,RMgX \longrightarrow SnR_4 + 4\,MgX_2$$

$$PCl_3 + 3\,RMgX \longrightarrow PR_3 + 3\,MgX_2$$

$$SiCl_4 + 4\,RMgX \longrightarrow SiR_4 + 4\,MgX_2$$

If less reagent is used than is required to react with all of the halogen, intermediate reaction products are obtained. For example, silicon tetrachloride and methylmagnesium chloride can give rise to methylsilicon trichloride, CH_3SiCl_3, dimethylsilicon dichloride, $(CH_3)_2SiCl_2$, trimethylsilicon chloride, $(CH_3)_3SiCl$, and tetramethylsilicon, $(CH_3)_4Si$. Mercurous chloride and the chlorides of iron, copper, silver, and gold cause chiefly coupling of the alkyl groups.

$$2\,RMgX + CuCl_2 \longrightarrow RR + 2\,MgX_2 + Cu$$

5. **With Carbon Dioxide.** Grignard reagents add to the carbon-oxygen double bond of carbon dioxide with the formation of the halomagnesium salt of a carboxylic acid.

$$RMgX + O{=}C{=}O \longrightarrow \underset{\underset{R}{|}}{O{=}C{-}OMgX}$$

Addition of a mineral acid liberates the free carboxylic acid (p. 143).

$$RCOOMgX + HCl \longrightarrow RCOOH + MgX_2$$

In the organometallic compounds, the carbon-metal bond undoubtedly is highly polarized with the metal the positive end of the dipole (*a*).

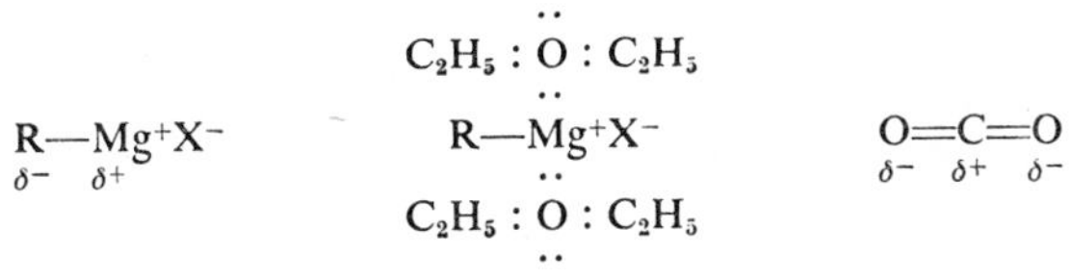

$$C_2H_5 : \overset{..}{\underset{..}{O}} : C_2H_5$$

$$\underset{\delta^- \quad \delta^+}{R{-}Mg^+X^-} \qquad \underset{}{R{-}Mg^+X^-} \qquad \underset{\delta^- \quad \delta^+ \quad \delta^-}{O{=}C{=}O}$$

$$C_2H_5 : \overset{..}{\underset{..}{O}} : C_2H_5$$

$$(a) \qquad\qquad (b) \qquad\qquad (c)$$

Therefore in reactions in which the carbon-metal bond is cleaved, it is to be expected that the alkyl group will leave with the pair of electrons. This type of cleavage for organomagnesium compounds is assisted by the solvation of the reagent with ether molecules (*b*) which supplies electrons to the magnesium atom and permits the alkyl group to leave more readily. In compounds such as carbon dioxide, aldehydes, and ketones (p. 197), the carbonyl group is polarized with the carbon atom at the positive end of the dipole because the oxygen nucleus is more strongly electron-attracting than the carbon nucleus (*c*). Hence in the addition of Grignard reagents and other reactive organometallic compounds (p. 891) to a carbonyl group, the alkyl group adds to carbon and the metal to oxygen.

$$\underset{\delta^- \ \ \delta^+ \ \ \delta^-}{O{=}C{=}O} + \underset{\delta^- \ \ \delta^+}{R{-}Mg^+X^-} \longrightarrow \underset{\underset{R}{|}}{O{=}C{-}O^{-+}Mg^+{-}X}$$

Often the reaction of the Grignard reagent with carbonyl compounds is preceded by complex formation in which the carbonyl compound displaces ether molecules from the solvated magnesium atom. Although such preliminary complex formation may determine the course of certain Grignard reactions (p. 438), it does not appear to be necessary for reaction, since solvates of Grignard reagents with tertiary amines such as pyridine (p. 620) still react with carbonyl compounds. These solvates are so stable that it seems unlikely that the tertiary amine is displaced by the carbonyl compound, a much weaker base, prior to the addition reaction.

6. With Other Compounds. The many important reactions of Grignard reagents with other organic compounds are considered as new functional groups are discussed.

REVIEW QUESTIONS

1. Discuss the physical properties of the alkyl halides.
2. Summarize the general methods for the preparation of alkyl halides.
3. Discuss the differences in conditions necessary for the preparation of alkyl chlorides, bromides, and iodides from primary, secondary, and tertiary alcohols using (*a*) halogen acids, and (*b*) phosphorus trihalides.
4. Discuss the direct substitution of hydrogen in a saturated hydrocarbon by halogen. Why is the reaction usually not satisfactory from a preparative standpoint?
5. How may primary alkyl chlorides be converted into alkyl iodides?
6. Compare primary, secondary, and tertiary halides in regard to ease of hydrolysis and ease of removal of halogen acid.
7. Compare the ease of displacement of halogen from primary, secondary, and tertiary halides by another group (excluding hydrolysis).
8. Discuss the action of aqueous solutions of hydroxides, and of alcoholic potassium hydroxide, on alkyl halides.
9. Give the reasons for and against considering the alkyl halides as belonging to the class of compounds known as esters.
10. What are the differences in the chemical and physical properties of alkali halides and alkyl halides?

PROBLEMS

11. Give a condensed structural formula and a suitable name for each member of the following groups: (*a*) the monobromopentanes; (*b*) the dichlorobutanes; (*c*) those dibromopentanes that can be prepared readily from olefins; (*d*) all of the secondary iodohexanes; (*e*) all of the primary bromohexanes.
12. Give reactions for three methods, each using a different reagent, for preparing each of the following compounds: (*a*) *i*-propyl bromide; (*b*) *t*-butyl chloride; (*c*) *s*-butyl iodide; (*d*) *n*-butyl chloride; (*e*) *t*-amyl bromide; (*f*) 2-chloropentane; (*g*) *n*-propyl chloride; (*h*) *i*-octyl iodide.
13. Write equations for the following reactions:
    A. (*a*) *s*-Butyl bromide with silver hydroxide; (*b*) *i*-amyl chloride with sodium ethoxide; (*c*) 1-iodobutane with sodium sulfide; (*d*) *t*-amyl bromide with magnesium in ether; (*e*) *i*-propyl iodide with sodium cyanide; (*f*) *n*-amyl chloride with sodium iodide; (*g*) *t*-butyl chloride with water; (*h*) *n*-butyl bromide with sodium; (*i*) 2-bromopentane with sodium hydrosulfide.
    B. (*a*) 2-Bromooctane with sodium cyanide; (*b*) *t*-butyl chloride and magnesium; (*c*) *i*-propyl iodide with silver hydroxide; (*d*) *i*-amyl chloride and sodium iodide; (*e*) lauryl bromide and sodium hydrosulfide; (*f*) *n*-butyl bromide and sodium *i*-propoxide; (*g*) ethyl iodide and sodium sulfide; (*h*) *t*-amyl bromide and water; (*i*) 1-bromohexane and sodium.
    C. (*a*) Ethyl bromide and sodium hydrosulfide; (*b*) *n*-heptyl iodide and sodium cyanide; (*c*) *i*-octyl bromide and sodium; (*d*) *t*-butyl iodide and water; (*e*) *n*-amyl iodide and sodium *t*-butoxide; (*f*) *s*-butyl bromide and sodium sulfide; (*g*) 3-methyl-3-bromopentane; (*h*) *n*-propyl chloride and sodium iodide; (*i*) 2-chloropentane with silver hydroxide.

14. Give equations for the following reactions:

    A. (*a*) Ethylmagnesium bromide with mercuric chloride; (*b*) *t*-butylmagnesium chloride with carbon dioxide; (*c*) *n*-hexylmagnesium iodide with water; (*d*) methylmagnesium chloride with silicon tetrachloride; (*e*) 1-methylbutylmagnesium bromide with phosphorus trichloride; (*f*) *n*-nonylmagnesium iodide with methanol; (*g*) *i*-octylmagnesium bromide with cupric chloride.

    B. (*a*) Methylmagnesium iodide with aluminum chloride; (*b*) laurylmagnesium bromide with water; (*c*) *n*-butylmagnesium chloride with zinc chloride; (*d*) *s*-butylmagnesium chloride with ethanol; (*e*) *i*-amylmagnesium iodide with silver chloride; (*f*) *n*-tetradecyl-magnesium bromide with carbon dioxide; (*g*) ethylmagnesium iodide with stannic chloride.

    C. (*a*) *i*-Butylmagnesium bromide with mercurous chloride; (*b*) *n*-propylmagnesium chloride with arsenic chloride; (*c*) 1-methylheptylmagnesium iodide with 2-propanol; (*d*) *i*-propylmagnesium bromide with cadmium chloride; (*e*) *n*-heptylmagnesium bromide with carbon dioxide; (*f*) methylmagnesium iodide with germanium chloride; (*g*) *i*-amylmagnesium bromide with water.

15. If a 20 per cent excess of sodium bromide and sulfuric acid is used and if the yield is 90 per cent, calculate the amount of alcohol and sodium bromide that must be used to prepare the following amounts of the indicated alkyl bromide: (*a*) 100 g. of *i*-propyl bromide; (*b*) 150 g. of *n*-butyl bromide; (*c*) 180 g. of *i*-amyl bromide; (*d*) 50 g. of ethyl bromide.

16. Calculate the volume (S.T.P.) of methane that would be evolved when an excess of methyl-magnesium iodide reacts with 0.1 g. of the following compounds: (*a*) butanol; (*b*) 3-methyl-1-pentanol; (*c*) 2,3-dihydroxybutane; (*d*) octanol; (*e*) 1,2,3-trihydroxypropane.

17. If 0.1 g. of the unknown compound having a molecular weight of *X* g. reacts with an excess of methylmagnesium iodide in the Zerevitinov apparatus to give *Y* cc. of methane (S.T.P.), calculate the number of hydroxyl groups that are in the following compounds:

	A	*B*	*C*	*D*
X	62 ± 5	86 ± 4	100 ± 7	120 ± 8
Y	72.0	50.0	63.5	56.3

18. What are the possible structures for the compounds in Problem 17 if they are hydroxy- or polyhydroxyalkanes?

Chapter 7

SYNTHESIS OF ALKANES AND ALKENES.
ALKYNES (ACETYLENES)

ALKANE AND ALKENE SYNTHESIS

As indicated in Chapters 5 and 6, some of the reactions of alcohols and alkyl halides lead to the production of paraffin and olefin hydrocarbons. It now is possible to summarize some of the general methods for the synthesis of the paraffin hydrocarbons and olefins having a desired structure.

Syntheses of Alkanes

1. **Reduction of an Alkyl Halide.** The direct reduction of alkyl halides may be brought about by a variety of reagents such as zinc and hydrochloric acid in alcoholic solution, sodium and alcohol, sodium amalgam and water, hydrogen iodide, or hydrogen and a catalyst such as platinum. The reaction may be represented by the equation

$$RX + 2[H] \longrightarrow RH + HX$$

where [H] represents any of the above reducing agents. If hydrogen iodide is used the reaction is

$$RI + HI \longrightarrow RH + I_2$$

In this reaction red phosphorus frequently is used along with aqueous hydrogen iodide. The phosphorus reacts with the iodine to form phosphorus triiodide, which is hydrolyzed by the water, regenerating hydrogen iodide. In this way the concentration of hydrogen iodide does not decrease, and only red phosphorus is consumed in the reduction. Because the position of equilibrium favors the formation of hydrocarbon and iodine, the substitution of iodine into a molecule by direct iodination is not possible unless some other reagent is present which will destroy the hydrogen iodide. This reducing action of hydrogen iodide also limits the usefulness of its reaction with alcohols to form alkyl iodides (p. 102).

One of the best methods for preparing pure alkanes is the indirect reduction of halides through the Grignard reagents (p. 121).

$$RX + Mg \longrightarrow RMgX$$
$$RMgX + HOH \longrightarrow RH + Mg(OH)X$$

2. **Wurtz[1] Reaction.** The reaction of an alkyl halide with an alkali metal gives a hydrocarbon in which the two alkyl groups have combined (p. 115).

$$2RX + 2Na \longrightarrow RR + 2NaX$$

---

[1] Charles Adolphe Wurtz (1817–1894), successor to Dumas on the latter's resignation from the faculty of the École de Médecine in 1853, and first occupant of the chair of organic chemistry established at the Sorbonne in 1875. He was the first to synthesize amines in 1849. His synthesis of alkanes was published in 1855. Among his many other contributions are the synthesis of ethylene glycol and ethylene oxide in 1859, the reduction of aldehydes to alcohols in 1866, and the synthesis of aldol in 1872. In a work on the history of chemical principles, he antagonized many chemists of other nations with his opening statement, "Chemistry is a French science. It was founded by Lavoisier of immortal memory."

The reaction is carried out in an ordinary flask to which a reflux condenser having a wide bore is attached. The metallic sodium is cut into small pieces and placed in the flask, and dry alkyl bromide added through the condenser at such a rate that the reaction always is under control. The surface of the sodium first turns blue and then white with the formation of sodium bromide. When the reaction is complete, the liquid is free of halogen and is distilled. The best yields are obtained with primary halides. Tertiary halides yield almost exclusively olefin.

It should be possible to prepare unsymmetrical hydrocarbons by the reaction of sodium with a mixture of two alkyl halides.

$$RX + 2\,Na + R'X \longrightarrow RR' + 2\,NaX$$

This mixed coupling does take place readily if the reactivities of the two halides are approximately the same. However, since the other two possible hydrocarbons, RR and R'R', also are formed, the yield of the desired product is small. Mixed coupling takes place to some extent even when there is a marked difference in reactivity, but the greater this difference, the greater are the amounts of symmetrical hydrocarbons produced.

3. **Reduction of Olefins.** The double bond of an olefin adds hydrogen quantitatively in the presence of finely divided platinum, nickel, palladium, or other hydrogenation catalysts, with the formation of alkanes (p. 55).

$$RCH{=}CHR + H_2 \xrightarrow[\text{or Pd}]{\text{Pt, Ni,}} RCH_2CH_2R$$

If the unsaturated hydrocarbon is available, for example, by the dehydration of an alcohol, this method is an excellent one for alkane synthesis. To convert an alcohol to an alkane, it is easier in general to use the series of reactions alcohol $\longrightarrow$ alkene $\longrightarrow$ alkane, rather than the series alcohol $\longrightarrow$ alkyl halide $\longrightarrow$ alkane.

Syntheses of Alkenes

1. **Pyrolysis of Saturated Hydrocarbons.** Refinery gases from the industrial cracking of petroleum (p. 72) and the gases formed by the cracking of propane or the dehydrogenation of butane (p. 79) are the chief source of the lower alkenes. Cracking of alkanes is not a useful laboratory procedure, however, because the reaction cannot be controlled to give a single product, and the separation of pure products from the complex mixture that is formed is too difficult in small scale operations.

2. **Dehydration of Alcohols.** Generally the best procedure for converting alcohols to olefins consists of passing them in the vapor state over hot activated alumina (p. 104).

$$RCH_2CHOHR \xrightarrow[350°-450°]{Al_2O_3} RCH{=}CHR + H_2O$$

This method is least likely to give rearranged products. For example if highly purified alumina is used, *n*-butyl alcohol will give largely 1-butene with only small amounts of 2-butene.

When acid catalysts are used, molecular rearrangement frequently takes place (p. 105). When rearrangement does not take place, or when the constitution of the rearranged product is known, heating the alcohol to a sufficiently high temperature in the presence of a strong acid such as sulfuric, phosphoric, or *p*-toluenesulfonic acid (p. 470) may be a satisfactory procedure. The last two acids have the advantage that they are relatively nonoxidizing. If the alcohol boils above the temperature required for decomposition, a trace of the acid may be sufficient; otherwise enough acid must be present to keep the alcohol in the form of the nonvolatile oxonium salt. Alternatively, the alcohol vapor may be passed over hot pumice impregnated with phosphoric acid. Some alcohols such as diacetone alcohol (p. 206) dehydrate so easily that a trace of iodine is sufficient to catalyze the decomposition.

3. **Removal of Halogen Acid from Alkyl Halides.** The order of ease of removal of halogen acid from alkyl halides is tertiary > secondary > primary for both the halogen atom and the hydrogen atom. The usual reagent is an alcoholic solution of potassium hydroxide.

$$RCH_2CHXR + KOH \text{ (alcoholic)} \longrightarrow RCH{=}CHR + KX + H_2O$$

Alcohol is used as a mutual solvent for the base and the alkyl halide, thus permitting the reaction to take place in a single phase. Potassium hydroxide is preferred to sodium hydroxide because the former dissolves in alcohol much more easily than does sodium hydroxide. Tertiary alkyl halides lose halogen acid so readily that a higher-boiling organic base such as pyridine (p. 620) or quinoline (p. 628) may be used. Primary halides lose halogen acid so slowly that ether formation becomes the dominant reaction.

$$C_2H_5OH + KOH \rightleftharpoons C_2H_5OK + H_2O$$

$$RCH_2X + KOC_2H_5 \longrightarrow RCH_2OC_2H_5 + KX$$

4. **Removal of Two Halogen Atoms from Adjacent Carbon Atoms.** If a compound contains two halogen atoms on adjacent carbon atoms, the halogen may be removed readily by heating with zinc dust in alcohol, leaving a double bond in the molecule.

$$\underset{\underset{X}{|}\quad\underset{X}{|}}{RCHCHR} + Zn \text{ (in alcohol)} \longrightarrow RCH{=}CHR + ZnX_2$$

This reaction is not of much use as a preparative method since the best way to obtain 1,2-dihalides is by adding halogen to an olefin. It occasionally is valuable for the purification of unsaturated compounds if the dihalide can be purified more readily than the olefin itself. The olefin is converted to the dihalide, the dihalide purified, and the olefin regenerated by means of zinc dust.

ALKYNES (ACETYLENES)

In addition to the olefins, a second homologous series of unsaturated hydrocarbons exists, called **acetylenes** from the first member of the series, or the **alkynes.** Acetylene has the molecular formula C_2H_2. The acetylenes add two moles of halogen whereby two halogen atoms are united to each of two adjacent carbon atoms. Using the same arguments advanced for the structure of the olefins, the only logical structure for the acetylenes would be one in which two carbon atoms are joined by a triple bond. Acetylene would have the structure $HC{\equiv}CH$, and acetylenes in general the structure $RC{\equiv}CR$.

The description of the triple bond follows the same reasoning as that for the double bond (p. 49). In acetylene each carbon atom is joined to only two other atoms. Hence *sp* hybridization takes place on bonding, and the bond directions are in a straight line (p. 11). The primary carbon-carbon bond results from *sp—sp* overlapping of orbitals, and the carbon-hydrogen bonds result from *sp—s* overlapping, giving rise to a linear molecule. Both carbon atoms still have two *p* orbitals perpendicular to each other, each containing one electron. Overlapping of the four *p* orbitals gives two π molecular orbitals, both having cylindrical symmetry. Figure 41*a* illustrates a cross section through the σ orbitals and the π orbitals. Figure 41*b* gives a perspective view of the π orbitals and Fig. 41*c* is a schematic representation of the overlapping of *p* orbitals.

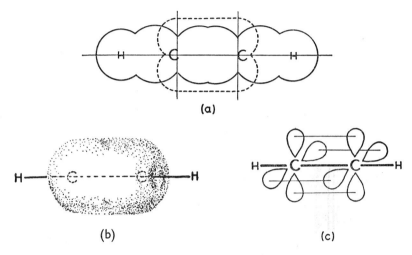

(a)

(b)   (c)

Fig. 41. The acetylene molecule: (*a*) cross section through the molecular orbitals; (*b*) perspective representation of the π bonds; (*c*) schematic representation of the π bonds.

Physical Properties and Nomenclature

The physical properties of the alkynes closely resemble those of the alkanes and the alkenes, although the boiling points are somewhat higher and the solubility in water is greater. The systems of nomenclature are analogous to those for olefins. Alkynes may be named (*1*) as derivates of acetylene, and (*2*) by the Geneva system. In the latter the ending is *yne*. These methods are illustrated by the following examples.

$(CH_3)_2CHC{\equiv}CH$ $CH_3CH_2CHC{\equiv}CC_2H_5$
$\qquad\qquad\qquad\qquad\qquad\qquad\qquad |$
$\qquad\qquad\qquad\qquad\qquad\qquad\ CH_3$

i-Propylacetylene   Ethyl-*s*-butylacetylene
(methylbutyne)   (5-methyl-3-heptyne)

Preparation

Acetylenes in general may be prepared by two procedures analogous to the preparation of olefins, and by a third that cannot be used for olefins.

1. **Removal of Two Moles of Hydrogen Halide from Dihalides.** If a dihalide has the halogen atoms on the same or adjacent carbon atoms, boiling with an

alcoholic solution of potassium hydroxide removes two moles of halogen acid with the introduction of a triple bond.

$$RCH_2CX_2R + 2\ KOH\ \text{(alcoholic)} \longrightarrow RC\!\equiv\!CR + 2\ KX + 2\ H_2O$$

$$\underset{\overset{|}{X}\ \overset{|}{X}}{RCHCHR} + 2\ KOH\ \text{(alcoholic)} \longrightarrow RC\!\equiv\!CR + 2\ KX + 2\ H_2O$$

Since 1,2-dihalides can be prepared easily from olefins, this method can be used to convert olefins into acetylenes.

2. **Removal of Four Halogen Atoms from Adjacent Carbon Atoms.** If a tetrahalide has two halogen atoms on each of two adjacent carbon atoms, boiling with zinc dust in alcoholic solution removes the halogen, and an alkyne is formed.

$$RCX_2CX_2R + 2\ Zn\ \text{(in alcohol)} \longrightarrow RC\!\equiv\!CR + 2\ ZnX_2$$

This reaction has the same limitations as the similar one used for the preparation of olefins, namely that the halides required are best made by adding halogen to the unsaturated compound.

3. **From Other Acetylenes.** This procedure does not produce a triple bond but depends on the fact that hydrogen united to a triply bonded carbon atom is much more acidic than hydrogen united to a singly or doubly bonded carbon atom. Acetylenes of this type form metallic derivatives in which hydrogen is replaced by a metal.

$$RC\!\equiv\!CH + Na\ \text{(in liquid NH}_3\text{)} \longrightarrow [RC\!\equiv\!C^-]Na^+ + \tfrac{1}{2}\ H_2$$

The sodium-carbon bond in acetylides is ionic; that is, these metallic derivatives are salts.

The sodium acetylides react with alkyl halides or alkyl sulfates to give higher homologs of the acetylenes.

$$RC\!\equiv\!CNa + R'X \longrightarrow RC\!\equiv\!CR' + NaX$$

$$\underset{\substack{\text{Sodium}\\\text{methyl-}\\\text{acetylide}}}{CH_3C\!\equiv\!CNa} + C_2H_5Br \longrightarrow \underset{\substack{\text{Methylethyl-}\\\text{acetylene}\\\text{(2-pentyne)}}}{CH_3C\!\equiv\!CC_2H_5} + NaBr$$

Reactions

The acetylenes undergo addition reactions analogous to those of the olefins and are capable of adding two moles of reagent instead of one. Unlike hydrogen united to a doubly bonded carbon atom, however, hydrogen united to a triply bonded carbon is replaced readily by metals.

1. **Addition to the Triple Bond.** Hydrogen can be added to the triple bond in the presence of a suitable catalyst.

$$RC\!\equiv\!CR + 2\ H_2 \xrightarrow{Pt} RCH_2CH_2R$$

If finely divided palladium or iron is used as catalyst, it is possible to stop the reaction when one mole of hydrogen has been added.

$$RC\!\equiv\!CR + H_2 \xrightarrow{\text{Pd or Fe}} RCH\!=\!CHR$$

One or two moles of halogen or halogen acid can be added to the triple bond.

$$RC\equiv CH \begin{cases} + \ X_2 & \longrightarrow \quad RCX\!\!=\!\!CHX \\ + \ 2X_2 & \longrightarrow \quad RCX_2CHX_2 \\ + \ HX & \longrightarrow \quad RCX\!\!=\!\!CH_2 \\ + \ 2HX & \longrightarrow \quad RCX_2CH_3 \end{cases}$$

The addition of nonidentical addenda follows the Markovnikov rule.

Although water does not add directly to the triple bond, the acetylenes react with water in the presence of sulfuric acid and mercurous sulfate (mercury-mercuric sulfate mixture). However instead of forming hydroxy compounds, as occurs in the reactions of olefins with water and sulfuric acid, acetylene yields acetaldehyde.

$$HC\equiv CH + H_2O \xrightarrow[\text{Hg—HgSO}_4]{\text{H}_2\text{SO}_4} [H_2C\!\!=\!\!CHOH]^{[2]} \longrightarrow \underset{\text{Acetaldehyde}}{CH_3\overset{\text{H}}{\underset{}{C}}\!\!=\!\!O}$$

The initial mercury salt complex probably yields a hydroxyolefin having a hydroxyl group on a carbon atom united to another carbon atom by a double bond. Such structures are known as *enols*. The simple enols are unstable[2] and rearrange to give the more stable isomer having the double bond between the carbon atom and the oxygen atom rather than between the two carbon atoms. Alkynes other than acetylene yield ketones because addition takes place according to the Markovnikov rule.

$$RC\equiv CH + HOH \xrightarrow[\text{Hg—HgSO}_4]{\text{H}_2\text{SO}_4} \left[\underset{\text{OH}}{RC}\!\!=\!\!CH_2\right]^{[2]} \longrightarrow \underset{\text{O}}{RCCH_3}$$

A ketone

Alcohols add to acetylene in the presence of alkali to give vinyl ethers (p. 737).

$$HC\equiv CH + ROH \xrightarrow[150°-180°]{\text{KOH}} H_2C\!\!=\!\!CHOR$$

2. Reactions of Hydrogen. If one of the acetylenic carbon atoms bears a hydrogen atom, this hydrogen is replaceable by metals. Acetylene reacts with molten sodium to form a monosodium derivative (sodium acetylide) at 110°.

$$HC\equiv CH + Na \,(\text{molten at } 110°) \longrightarrow [HC\equiv C^-][Na^+] + \tfrac{1}{2} H_2$$

Sodium acetylide can be formed also by passing acetylene into a dilute solution of sodium in liquid ammonia or into a solution of sodium amide in liquid ammonia.

$$HC\equiv CH + NaNH_2 \longrightarrow [HC\equiv C^-]Na^+ + NH_3$$

If acetylene is passed into sodium at 190°–220°, or if sodium acetylide is heated at this temperature, sodium carbide is formed.

$$HC\equiv CH + 2Na \,(\text{at } 190°-220°) \longrightarrow Na^+[^-C\equiv C^-]Na^+ + H_2$$

$$2\,[HC\equiv C^-]Na^+ \xrightarrow{\text{Heat at } 200°} Na_2C_2 + C_2H_2$$

---

[2] To indicate that a structure is unstable and that a compound having this structure cannot be isolated, the formula is enclosed in brackets.

Acetylene reacts readily with aqueous ammoniacal silver nitrate or aqueous ammoniacal cuprous chloride solutions to give water-insoluble carbides.

$$HC\equiv CH + 2\, Ag(NH_3)_2NO_3 \longrightarrow Ag_2C_2 + 2\, NH_4NO_3 + 2\, NH_3$$

$$HC\equiv CH + 2\, Cu(NH_3)_2Cl \longrightarrow Cu_2C_2 + 2\, NH_4Cl + 2\, NH_3$$

Compounds of the type $RC\equiv CH$ yield acetylides, $[RC\equiv C^-]Ag^+$ and $[RC\equiv C^-]Cu^+$, whereas compounds of the type $RC\equiv CR$ do not react. These reactions are useful to distinguish acetylene and monosubstituted acetylenes from olefins and disubstituted acetylenes.

The heavy metal carbides are thermodynamically unstable and may be exploded when dry by heat or shock with the formation of the metal and carbon. Silver carbide, for example, explodes at $140°$–$150°$. Sodium carbide, on the other hand, is stable up to $400°$, and calcium carbide, which is made in the electric furnace, melts without decomposition at $2300°$.

The acetylides and carbides are salts of the very weak acid, acetylene, and hence are hydrolyzed by water.

$$[HC\equiv \bar{C}]\, Na^+ + H_2O \longrightarrow NaOH + C_2H_2$$

$$Ca^{++}[\bar{C}\equiv \bar{C}] + 2\, H_2O \longrightarrow Ca(OH)_2 + C_2H_2$$

A mineral acid is required to decompose the heavy metal salts.

$$Ag_2C_2 + 2\, HNO_3 \longrightarrow 2\, AgNO_3 + C_2H_2$$

Acetylenic hydrogen (the hydrogen in $HC\equiv CH$ or $RC\equiv CH$) is sufficiently more acidic than alkane hydrogen (the hydrogen in RCH_3) to liberate alkanes from alkyl Grignard reagents with the formation of acetylenic Grignard reagents.

$$RC\equiv CH + R'MgX \longrightarrow RC\equiv CMgX + R'H$$

Since Grignard reagents undergo a great variety of reactions, the acetylenic Grignard reagents are valuable for the preparation of other compounds containing the triple bond.

The acidity of ethylene is between that of acetylene and ethane, although the difference between ethylene and ethane is less than that between acetylene and ethylene. It is of interest that the increased acidity coincides with a change in bond type from sp^3—s to sp^2—s to sp—s (p. 11). Although this correlation merely is another way of saying that ethylene is more acidic than ethane, and acetylene than ethylene, it permits a generalization that includes the hydrogen-nitrogen bond and the hydrogen-oxygen bond (p. 252). Quantum mechanical calculations indicate that an atom joined to another by a triple bond tends to localize a fourth pair of electrons about the atom and hence forms a covalent bond with a second atom less readily than an atom joined to others by only single or double bonds. In other words the sp hybrid orbital available for bonding with hydrogen has more s character than an sp^3 or sp^2 orbital, and the pair of electrons of the sp—s bond is held closer to the carbon nucleus than that in an sp^3—s or sp^2—s bond.

Industrial Preparation and Use of Acetylene

Acetylene is the only commercially important compound of the series. Although it can be made by any of the general methods, it is made much more cheaply from coke by way of calcium carbide, or from natural gas.

$$3\ C + CaO \xrightarrow[\text{(2000°)}]{\text{Electric furnace}} CaC_2 + CO$$

$$\text{Coke}\quad\text{Lime}\qquad\qquad\qquad\qquad \underset{\substack{\text{Calcium}\\\text{carbide}}}{}$$

$$CaC_2 + 2\ H_2O \longrightarrow HC\!\equiv\!CH + Ca(OH)_2$$

When methane is heated to a very high temperature, acetylene is one of the products.

$$2\ CH_4 \rightleftharpoons C_2H_2 + 3\ H_2 - 95.5\ \text{kcal.}$$

If the time of exposure to the high temperature (1400°–1600°) is short enough (.1 to 0.01 second) and the products are cooled quickly enough, a reasonably high yield of acetylene can be obtained. Numerous processes for attaining these conditions are being tried such as passing the methane through an electric arc or over a refractory heated to a high temperature. The process operated most successfully in the United States in 1955 was developed in Germany. The necessary heat is supplied by partial combustion of methane with oxygen. Natural gas and 95 per cent oxygen are preheated separately to 600°, mixed, ignited in a special burner, and the products immediately cooled by a water spray. The cooled gases are compressed and the acetylene is absorbed in the water from which it can be recovered in 99.8 per cent purity. The off gases consist of carbon monoxide and hydrogen in the ratio of 7 to 15, a satisfactory composition for the synthesis of methanol (p. 90).

The initial step in the decomposition of methane is the formation of methyl radicals and hydrogen atoms. The methyl radicals can give rise to ethane, ethylene, and acetylene. Combination of hydrogen atoms gives molecular hydrogen.

$$CH_4 \rightleftharpoons CH_3 \cdot + H \cdot$$

$$2\ CH_3 \cdot \rightleftharpoons CH_3CH_3$$

$$CH_3CH_3 \rightleftharpoons CH_3CH_2 \cdot + H \cdot$$

$$CH_3CH_2 \cdot \rightleftharpoons CH_2\!=\!CH_2 + H \cdot$$

$$CH_2\!=\!CH_2 \rightleftharpoons CH_2\!=\!CH \cdot + H \cdot$$

$$CH_2\!=\!CH \cdot \rightleftharpoons CH\!\equiv\!CH + H \cdot$$

$$2\ H \cdot \rightleftharpoons H_2$$

Whereas the order of stability at 25° is ethane > ethylene > acetylene, at 1000° they are about equally stable and at higher temperatures the order is reversed.

Acetylene is a colorless gas which boils at −84°. The crude product from calcium carbide and water has a garlic odor because of the presence of phosphine. Acetylene cannot be liquefied safely, since it is thermodynamically unstable and explodes from shock with the formation of the elements.

$$C_2H_2 \longrightarrow 2\ C + H_2 + 56\ \text{kcal.}$$

Procedures have been developed for handling acetylene safely at pressures up to 30 atmospheres (450 p.s.i.). Contact with all copper and copper alloys is avoided, and the free space kept to a minimum. No pipes for carrying the gas under pressure are over 35 mm. in diameter, all larger pipes being filled with small pipes. Higher pressures can be used without explosion by adding an inert gas such as water vapor or nitrogen.

At atmospheric pressure acetylene is soluble to the extent of one volume of the gas in one volume of water, four volumes in one of benzene (p. 65), six volumes in one of ethyl alcohol, twenty-five volumes in one of acetone (p. 224), and 33 volumes in one of methyl sulfoxide (p. 284). At twelve atmospheres 300 volumes dissolve in one volume of acetone. Since this solution is stable, acetylene is transported under pressure in tanks filled with a porous material saturated with acetone.

One of the earlier **uses for acetylene** was as an illuminant. When special tips are used which mix it with the proper amount of air, it burns with an intense white flame. Decomposition of the gas gives carbon particles which, because of the high temperature of the flame, are heated to a white incandescence. For the same reason acetylene was mixed with coal gas used for lighting to increase the luminosity of the flame. In 1954 about 45 per cent of the 600 million pounds consumed in the United States was used for the welding, cutting, and cleaning of iron and steel by means of the oxyacetylene flame, which has a temperature in the neighborhood of 2800°.

From the heats of combustion of ethane, ethylene, and acetylene, it might be expected that ethane would give the highest temperature.

$$C_2H_6 + 3\tfrac{1}{2} O_2 \longrightarrow 2 CO_2 + 3 H_2O + 373 \text{ kcal.}$$

$$C_2H_4 + 3 O_2 \longrightarrow 2 CO_2 + 2 H_2O + 337 \text{ kcal.}$$

$$C_2H_2 + 2\tfrac{1}{2} O_2 \longrightarrow 2 CO_2 + H_2O + 317 \text{ kcal.}$$

Actually acetylene gives the hottest flame because the least amount of oxygen is required to burn a given volume of hydrocarbon, and hence less heat is required to raise the gases from room temperature to the temperature of the flame. The temperatures of these flames would be much higher if the reactions went to completion. At 2800° water is dissociated to hydrogen and oxygen and carbon dioxide to carbon monoxide and oxygen, probably to the extent of 20 to 25 per cent.

About 55 per cent of the acetylene produced was used for the preparation of other organic chemicals. Acetylene dichloride and tetrachloride are made by the addition of chlorine to acetylene and are used as solvents and for the preparation of other compounds (p. 723). Catalytic addition of water gives acetaldehyde from which acetic acid and a large number of other organic compounds can be made (p. 222). Catalytic addition of acetic acid yields vinyl acetate (p. 736), and addition of alcohols yields vinyl ethers (p. 737), which are used in the preparation of plastics and other useful products. Addition of hydrogen cyanide gives acrylonitrile (p. 787) used for the production of synthetic fibers (p. 788) and synthetic rubber (p. 718). Vinylacetylene (p. 719) and 1,3-butadiene (p. 716), which are starting points for synthetic rubbers, are synthesized from acetylene.

During World War II Germany prepared ethylene by the catalytic reduction of acetylene at the rate of 3000 tons per month. The extent to which the German chemical industry was based on acetylene can be appreciated by comparing the scheduled production of 450,000 tons in Germany in 1943 with the production of 186,000 tons in the United States in 1944.

REVIEW QUESTIONS

1. Summarize the general methods discussed thus far for the synthesis of alkanes.
2. Summarize the general methods discussed thus far for the synthesis of alkenes.
3. Compare the general methods for preparing olefins with those for preparing acetylenes.
4. Compare the reactions of alkynes, alkenes, and alkanes.
5. Discuss the commercial methods for preparing acetylene and the industrial uses for acetylene.

PROBLEMS

6. Write structural formulas for the members of the following groups of compounds and give a name to each: (a) alkynes having the molecular formula C_6H_{10}; (b) dialkylacetylenes having the molecular formula C_7H_{12}; (c) ethylacetylenes and propylacetylenes having the molecular formula C_8H_{14}.
7. Give reactions for the following preparations:
   A. (a) 2,3-Dimethylbutane from a three-carbon alkyl halide; (b) 3-methyl-1-pentene from a dihalide; (c) n-heptane from an alkyl halide; (d) i-butylene from an alcohol.
   B. (a) i-Pentane from an alkyl halide; (b) 3,4-dimethylhexane from a four-carbon alkyl halide; (c) 4-methyl-2-pentene from a dihalide; (d) neohexane from an olefin.
   C. (a) n-Octane from a four-carbon alkyl halide; (b) hexadecane from an alkyl halide; (c) tetramethylethylene from a dihalide; (d) trimethylethylene from an alcohol.
8. Give reactions for the following syntheses:
   A. (a) 1-Pentyne from n-propyl bromide; (b) 2,2-dibromobutane from ethylacetylene; (c) 3-hexene from 3-hexyne; (d) 2-butyne from acetylene.
   B. (a) 1-Butyne from acetylene; (b) 3,3-dibromohexane from 3-hexyne; (c) 3-hexyne from ethyl iodide; (d) 3-methyl-1-butene from i-propylacetylene.
   C. (a) Methylethylacetylene from propyne; (b) 2,5-dimethyl-2,2-dibromohexane from isopropylacetylene; (c) 4-octyne from acetylene; (d) i-pentane from 3-methyl-1-butyne.
9. Give a series of reactions for carrying out the following conversions:
   A. (a) 1-Pentene to 2-pentene; (b) ethyl-s-butylcarbinol to 3-methylhexane; (c) n-hexyl bromide to 1-hexyne; (d) i-butyl alcohol to 2,4-dimethylhexane; (e) 2,3-dibromobutane to 2,2-dibromobutane.
   B. (a) t-Amyl chloride to dimethylethylmethane; (b) s-butyl alcohol to 2-butyne; (c) ethylacetylene to s-butyl bromide; (d) 3-methyl-1-butene to trimethylethylene; (e) 1-pentene to 4,5-dimethyloctane.
   C. (a) Propylene to 3-methyl-1-butyne; (b) 2,3-dimethyl-1-butene to 2,3-dimethyl-2-butene; (c) n-hexyl alcohol to n-dodecane; (d) 1,2-dibromopentane to 2-bromopentane; (e) 2-octanol to n-octane.
10. Without resorting to quantitative determinations, how may one distinguish by chemical tests between the members of the following groups of gases: (a) ethyl chloride, butane, or 2-butyne; (b) propane, propene, or propyne; (c) ethylacetylene, i-butane, or dimethylacetylene.
11. Making use of chemical reactions, describe a procedure for obtaining in a relatively pure form the components of the following mixtures: (a) ethane, ethylene, and acetylene; (b) methyl chloride, 2-butyne, and 1-butyne; (c) 1-pentyne, 2-pentyne, and pentane; (d) ethylacetylene, diethylacetylene, and 3-hexene.

Chapter 8

ETHERS

The simplest ethers have the general molecular formula $C_nH_{2n+2}O$, and hence are isomeric with the alcohols. Unlike the alcohols, no ether is known containing only one carbon atom, the first member of the series having the molecular formula C_2H_6O. If the formula CH_3CH_2OH is assigned to ethyl alcohol, the only other structural formula possible for an isomer would be that in which the oxygen atom joins two carbon atoms. Hence the first ether should contain the structure C—O—C. By placing the hydrogen atoms on the two carbon atoms to give the compound CH_3OCH_3, all of the rules of valence are satisfied. The general formula for the ethers would be ROR. The methods of preparation and chemical properties of the ethers confirm this structure.

Nomenclature

The word *ether* (Gr. *aither*, applied to the material filling heavenly space) was given to ethyl ether because of its volatility. The ethers commonly are divided into two groups, the simple ethers, ROR, in which both R groups are alike, and the mixed ethers, ROR', in which the R groups are different. They generally are designated by naming the alkyl groups and adding the word *ether*. For the simple ethers no indication need be given that two alkyl groups are present in the molecule; $(CH_3)_2O$ is methyl ether, $CH_3OC_2H_5$ is methyl ethyl ether, and $(C_2H_5)_2O$ is ethyl ether.[1]

The group RO is known as an *alkoxyl group*, although as a substituent it is called *alkoxy*. In the Geneva system the ethers are named as alkoxy derivatives of hydrocarbons. Methyl ether is methoxymethane, and methyl ethyl ether is methoxyethane. This system usually is used only when other functional groups are present. For example $CH_3OCH_2CH_2CH_2OH$ may be called 3-methoxy-1-propanol.

Physical Properties

Since the ethers do not contain hydrogen united to the oxygen atom, there is no tendency for molecules to associate with each other by proton bonding, and the boiling points are nearly normal. Methyl ether boils at $-24°$ and propane at $-42°$, methyl ethyl ether boils at $6°$ and *n*-butane at $-0.5°$, and ethyl ether boils at $35°$ and *n*-pentane at $36°$.

Ethers have, however, unshared pairs of electrons on oxygen and can form

---

[1] Since there is no ambiguity in the term methyl ether, it is redundant to call it dimethyl ether. The situation is comparable to naming Na_2SO_4 sodium sulfate rather than disodium sulfate. Similarly the addition product of chlorine to ethylene was called ethylene chloride rather than ethylene dichloride (p. 53), just as $MgCl_2$ is called magnesium chloride rather than magnesium dichloride. This same principle will be followed later in naming derivatives of other polyvalent compounds such as the ketones (p. 197), sulfides (p. 278), sulfoxides and sulfones (p. 286), esters of polycarboxylic acids (p. 792) and alkyl peroxides (p. 875).

proton bonds with water molecules. As would be expected, the solubilities in water are roughly the same as those of alcohols having the same number of carbon atoms. A saturated solution of ethyl ether in water at 25° contains 6 per cent by weight of the ether, and a saturated solution of *n*-butyl alcohol at 25° contains 7.5 per cent by weight of the alcohol. Water is soluble in both but only to the extent of 1.5 per cent in ether at 25° compared with 26 per cent in *n*-butyl alcohol.

Preparation

Ethers usually are made by one of two processes.

1. **The Williamson[2] Synthesis.** This method involves the reaction of a metallic alkoxide with an alkyl halide.

$$RONa + XR' \longrightarrow ROR' + NaX$$

The reaction may be used to prepare mixed ethers as well as simple ethers, because it is not reversible. The reaction is important also because it affords synthetic proof of the structure of the ethers. Since an alkyl group has replaced the sodium of an alkoxide made by replacing the hydrogen of the hydroxyl group of an alcohol by sodium, an ether must have two alkyl groups combined with oxygen. Alkyl sulfates resemble alkyl halides in displacement reactions and also may be used to prepare ethers.

$$RONa + (R'O)_2SO_2 \longrightarrow ROR' + NaSO_3OR'$$

2. **The Sulfuric Acid Process.** Alkyl hydrogen sulfates react with alcohols to give ethers. Hence ethers can be made from alcohols by reaction with sulfuric acid.

$$ROH + H_2SO_4 \rightleftharpoons ROSO_3H + H_2O$$

$$ROSO_3H + HOR \rightleftharpoons ROR + H_2SO_4$$

This reaction is carried out by mixing equal moles of alcohol and concentrated sulfuric acid, and heating to a temperature sufficiently high to cause rapid reaction with alcohol but below the temperature for appreciable decomposition of the alkyl hydrogen sulfate to alkene (p. 104). On adding more alcohol to the mixture the ether distills. Yields of ethers are best with primary alcohols because the latter are the least readily dehydrated to olefins. The more volatile the ether, the more readily it is removed from the reaction mixture. If the ether boils above the temperature at which the alkyl hydrogen sulfate decomposes to olefin, the ether must be removed under reduced pressure. It is not possible to prepare ditertiary alkyl ethers by either process, because sodium alkoxides remove hydrogen halide from *t*-alkyl halides, and mineral acids dehydrate tertiary alcohols to give the olefin.

The equations indicate that the sulfuric acid procedure could be used for the preparation of mixed ethers by making the alkyl hydrogen sulfate from one alcohol and allowing the product to react with a second alcohol. Although the

---

[2] Alexander William Williamson (1824–1904), professor at the University College, London. His synthesis of ethyl ether in 1850 cleared up the confusion existing then concerning the constitution of the alcohols and ethers. He also was the first to synthesize ortho esters (p. 174), and to assign the correct structure to acetone (p. 197).

second alcohol does react, and some mixed ether is formed, the mixed ether always is accompanied by large amounts of both simple ethers because of the easy reversibility of the reactions involved.

It is not necessary that the alkyl hydrogen sulfate be formed as an intermediate for ether formation to take place. As in the dehydration of alcohols, it has been shown that any strong acid such as hydrochloric acid or the sulfonic acids (p. 468), or in fact any strongly electron-accepting reagent such as zinc chloride or boron fluoride, will catalyze ether formation. It has been shown also that hydrogen chloride catalyzes ether formation under conditions which do not lead to the formation of ether from ethyl chloride and ethyl alcohol. In general the mechanism undoubtedly is one of acid catalysis and displacement.

$$\overset{H}{\underset{\cdot\cdot}{R : \overset{\cdot\cdot}{O} :}} \underset{[B^-]}{\overset{HB}{\rightleftarrows}} \left[\overset{H}{\underset{+}{R : \overset{\cdot\cdot}{O} : H}} \right] \underset{H_2O}{\overset{ROH}{\rightleftarrows}} \left[\underset{H}{\overset{+}{R : \overset{\cdot\cdot}{O} : R}} \right] \underset{HB}{\overset{[B^-]}{\rightleftarrows}} R : \overset{\cdot\cdot}{\underset{\cdot\cdot}{O}} : R$$

In the above series and in subsequent equilibrium reactions illustrating stepwise mechanisms, it is convenient to adopt a convention which eliminates the necessity of rewriting formulas. The reagent is placed above the double arrow and the minor product which is eliminated is placed below the double arrow. According to the above series of reactions an alcohol molecule picks up a proton from the acid HB eliminating the base [B$^-$]. The alkoxonium ion intermediate on collision with another alcohol molecule loses water with the formation of the ether oxonium ion which reacts with the base [B$^-$] to regenerate the acid and produce the ether. In the reverse reaction the reagent is the substance below the arrows and the minor product eliminated is above the arrows. For example, in the acid-catalyzed hydrolysis of ethers, an acid molecule, HB, transfers a proton to the ether molecule forming an ether oxonium ion and eliminating the base [B$^-$]. The ether oxonium ion reacts with a water molecule forming the alcohol oxonium ion and eliminating a molecule of alcohol. The alcohol oxonium ion transfers a proton to the base [B$^-$] forming a molecule of alcohol and regenerating the acid, HB. It will be observed that the intermediates in brackets disappear and reagents and intermediates that appear both above and below the arrows cancel each other. Hence the over-all reaction is

$$ROH + ROH \rightleftarrows ROR + H_2O$$

In the sulfuric acid process it is possible that ether formation results from two different reactions that take place simultaneously. The more direct route would be that postulated for acids in general. The second route would involve the alkyl hydrogen sulfate as an intermediate (p. 103).

$$R : OSO_3H \underset{[\bar{O}SO_3H]}{\overset{ROH}{\rightleftarrows}} \left[\underset{H}{\overset{+}{R : \overset{\cdot\cdot}{O} : R}} \right] \underset{H_2SO_4}{\overset{[\bar{O}SO_3H]}{\rightleftarrows}} R : \overset{\cdot\cdot}{O} : R$$

Ethers are obtained as co-products in the manufacture of alcohols from olefins (p. 97). Since the reactions by which ethers are formed from alcohols in the presence of acids are reversible (p. 140), what cannot be sold profitably is recycled. The direct preparation of ethers from olefins is useful especially for the preparation of ethers in which one of the alkyl groups is tertiary. Here the olefin reacts with a primary alcohol in the presence of sulfuric acid.

$$\underset{\overset{|}{CH_3}}{CH_3C{=}CH_2} + HOC_2H_5 \overset{H_2SO_4}{\rightleftarrows} (CH_3)_3COC_2H_5$$

Ethyl *t*-butyl
ether

Tertiary butyl ether is the only ditertiary-alkyl ether known. It was made by the reaction of *t*-butyl chloride with dry silver carbonate.

$$2 (CH_3)_3CCl + Ag_2CO_3 \longrightarrow (CH_3)_3C{-}O{-}C(CH_3)_3 + 2 AgCl + CO_2$$

The reaction of sulfuric acid with an alcohol is a good example of the way in which the course of an organic reaction may be modified by conditions. At room temperature the chief reaction is the formation of the oxonium salt.

$$C_2H_5OH + H_2SO_4 \rightleftharpoons \left[C_2H_5\overset{+}{O}H_2\right]\left[\overset{-}{S}O_4H\right]$$

If ethyl alcohol is warmed with an excess of sulfuric acid, ethyl hydrogen sulfate is formed.

$$C_2H_5OH + H_2SO_4 \rightleftharpoons C_2H_5OSO_3H + H_2O$$

If ethyl hydrogen sulfate is heated to the point where it decomposes (above 150°), ethylene is formed.

$$C_2H_5OSO_3H \rightleftharpoons CH_2{=}CH_2 + H_2SO_4$$

If sulfuric acid is allowed to react with an excess of alcohol and the mixture heated under reduced pressure, ethyl sulfate (p. 108) distills.

$$C_2H_5OSO_3H + C_2H_5OH \rightleftharpoons (C_2H_5)_2SO_4 + H_2O$$

If ethyl hydrogen sulfate is heated to 140°–150° and alcohol added below the surface, ethyl ether distills.

$$C_2H_5OSO_3H + C_2H_5OH \rightleftharpoons (C_2H_5)_2O + H_2SO_4$$

Since all of these reactions are reversible, all of the reactants and products are in equilibrium with each other. To prepare any particular compound, the optimum conditions must be chosen for obtaining it rather than the unwanted compounds.

Reactions

Ethers are relatively inert. Because the oxygen atom contains unshared electrons, ethers are capable of forming oxonium salts with any strong acid, HB, and addition complexes with any molecule having an atom that lacks a pair of electrons in its valence shell.

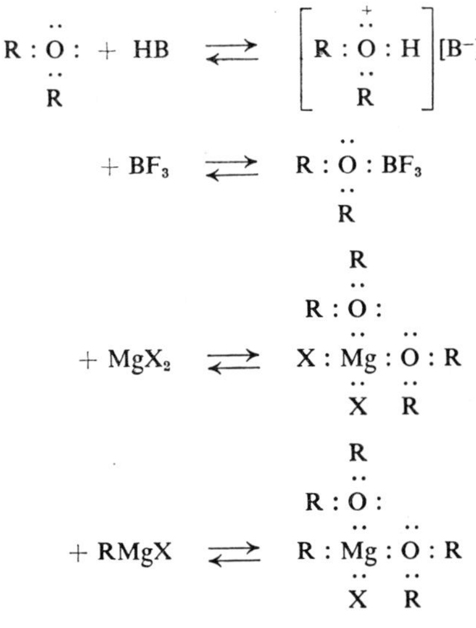

$$R:\overset{..}{\underset{..}{O}}: + HB \rightleftharpoons \left[R:\overset{+}{\overset{..}{\underset{..}{O}}}:H\right][B^-]$$
$$\quad R \qquad\qquad\qquad\quad R$$

$$+ BF_3 \rightleftharpoons R:\overset{..}{\underset{..}{O}}:BF_3$$
$$\qquad\qquad\qquad R$$

$$\qquad\qquad\qquad\qquad R$$
$$\qquad\qquad\qquad R:\overset{..}{\underset{..}{O}}:$$
$$+ MgX_2 \rightleftharpoons X:Mg:\overset{..}{\underset{..}{O}}:R$$
$$\qquad\qquad\qquad X \quad R$$

$$\qquad\qquad\qquad\qquad R$$
$$\qquad\qquad\qquad R:\overset{..}{\underset{..}{O}}:$$
$$+ RMgX \rightleftharpoons R:Mg:\overset{..}{\underset{..}{O}}:R$$
$$\qquad\qquad\qquad X \quad R$$

It is because of the last reaction that ether dissolves alkylmagnesium halides and is used as a solvent in preparing Grignard reagents. Not all ethers are suitable solvents, since the complexes in some cases, for example with *i*-propyl ether and dioxane (p. 642), are insoluble in an excess of the solvent.

All other reactions of the ethers must involve a scission of the carbon-oxygen bond. Because reagents which can split the carbon-oxygen bond in ethers can split the carbon-oxygen bond in alcohols as well, the initial reaction may be followed by a second to give the final product.

$$\text{ROR} \xrightleftharpoons{\text{H}_2\text{SO}_4} \text{ROSO}_3\text{H} + \text{ROH} \xrightleftharpoons{\text{H}_2\text{SO}_4} 2\,\text{ROSO}_3\text{H} + \text{H}_2\text{O}$$

$$\text{ROR} \xrightleftharpoons{\text{HBr}} \text{RBr} + \text{ROH} \xrightleftharpoons{\text{HBr}} 2\,\text{RBr} + \text{H}_2\text{O}$$

$$\text{ROR} + \text{AlCl}_3 \longrightarrow \text{ROAlCl}_2 + \text{RCl}$$

The reaction of ethers and of other compounds containing alkoxyl groups with hydrogen iodide is important, chiefly because it is the basis of the *Zeisel procedure for the estimation of methoxyl and ethoxyl*. Methyl or ethyl groups linked to oxygen are converted to the volatile methyl or ethyl iodides, which are distilled. The amount of alkyl iodide in the distillate is determined by allowing it to react with alcoholic silver nitrate solution and collecting and weighing the precipitate of silver iodide. In the *Vieboeck and Schwappach modification* the accuracy of the estimation is greatly increased. The alkyl iodide is absorbed in a solution of bromine and potassium acetate in glacial acetic acid, which converts the iodide to iodate.

$$\text{RI} + \text{Br}_2 \longrightarrow \text{RBr} + \text{IBr}$$

$$\text{IBr} + 2\,\text{Br}_2 + 3\,\text{H}_2\text{O} \longrightarrow \text{HIO}_3 + \text{HBr}$$

The excess bromine is destroyed by adding formic acid. On adding potassium iodide and acidifying, six atoms of iodine are liberated for each atom originally present in the alkyl iodide; that is, six iodine atoms are obtained for each alkoxyl group.

$$\text{HIO}_3 + 5\,\text{HI} \longrightarrow 3\,\text{I}_2 + 3\,\text{H}_2\text{O}$$

The iodine is titrated by standard thiosulfate solution.

A reaction of ethers which has not found a use but which always should be kept in mind because of its potential danger is the absorption of atmospheric oxygen to form peroxides (p. 884).

$$\text{R}_2\text{O} + \text{O}_2 \longrightarrow \text{R}_2\text{O}_3$$

These peroxides are unstable and decompose violently on heating. An instance has been reported in which a can containing *i*-propyl ether that had been exposed to air for some time exploded on being moved. Hence ethers should not be exposed to air unnecessarily and always should be tested for peroxides before use and especially before distillation (cf. p. 884).

Uses of Ethers

Methyl ether boils at $-24°$ and can be used as a solvent and extracting agent at low temperatures and as a propellant for aerosol sprays. The preparation of impure **ethyl ether** first was recorded in the sixteenth century. Since it was made by the sulfuric acid process, it usually contained sulfur as an impurity, and it was not until 1800 that it was proved that sulfur was not part of the ether molecule. Since 1846 ethyl ether has been used as a general anesthetic[3] and still is the most widely used substance for this purpose. It is used also as a solvent for fats. It frequently is used in the laboratory as a solvent for extracting organic compounds from aqueous solutions, although it is not always the best solvent for this purpose. Ether is highly flammable and it is very soluble in strongly acid solutions. Moreover it emulsifies readily making separation of the ether and water layers difficult. Finally it usually contains peroxides, which should be removed both for safety and because the peroxides may oxidize the product being extracted. One of the lower boiling chlorinated hydrocarbons, such as methylene chloride (p. 722) or ethylene chloride (p. 723), may be preferable. One advantage of ether is that the equilibrium distribution of a compound between the water and the ether is attained rapidly because ether and water are appreciably soluble in each other.

Ordinary ether contains some water and alcohol which are detrimental for some purposes such as the preparation of Grignard reagents. Both impurities can be removed by allowing the ether to stand over metallic sodium, since sodium hydroxide and sodium ethoxide are insoluble in ether. The pure product is known as **absolute ether.**

Methyl propyl ether (*metopryl*) has been reported to be more potent and less irritant than ethyl ether as a general anesthetic. *i*-**Propyl ether** is a co-product of the manufacture of *i*-propyl alcohol from propylene. *n*-**Butyl ether** (b.p. 142°) and *i*-**amyl ether** (b.p. 173°) are made from the alcohols and are used as higher boiling solvents. β-**Chloroethyl ether** (Chlorex), $(ClCH_2CH_2)_2O$, is made by the action of sulfuric acid on ethylene chlorohydrin, $ClCH_2CH_2OH$ (p. 743). It is used as a soil 'fumigant and as a solvent for refining lubricating oils (p. 81). Like other β-chloroethers, the halogen is very unreactive. For example it does not react with sodium cyanide to give the cyano ether or with magnesium to give a Grignard reagent.

REVIEW QUESTIONS

1. Explain the advantages and disadvantages of the Williamson synthesis and the sulfuric acid process for making ethers.
2. Give the probable mechanism for the acid-catalyzed formation of ethers from alcohols. What facts support this view?
3. Why are di-*t*-alkyl ethers difficult to prepare? How may the mixed primary-tertiary alkyl ethers be prepared (*a*) from olefins; (*b*) by the Williamson synthesis?
4. Give equations and conditions for preparing each of the following compounds from the two reagents, ethyl alcohol and sulfuric acid: ethyl hydrogen sulfate; ethylene; ethyl ether; ethyl sulfate.
5. Why does ethyl ether have about the same solubility in water as *n*-butyl alcohol but a boiling point 82° lower? What normal alkane would be expected to boil approximately where ether boils?
6. Why is ether only slightly soluble in water but miscible with concentrated aqueous hydrochloric acid? Why is dry hydrogen chloride very soluble in both ether and water but not in hexane or carbon tetrachloride?
7. Why does the Grignard reagent dissolve in ether but not in hydrocarbons? Name some inorganic compounds that dissolve in ether.

---

[3] A general anesthetic is one that acts on the brain and produces unconsciousness as well as insensitivity to pain. In local anesthesia and spinal anesthesia, only portions of the body are rendered insensitive to pain, and the patient retains consciousness.

8. What is absolute ether and how may it be prepared? What are some of the common uses of ether?
9. Why is it dangerous to distill ethers that have been exposed to air? What disadvantage may arise if an ether that has been exposed to air is used as a solvent for extraction or for a reaction? What reactions can be used to determine whether an ether is safe to use?

PROBLEMS

10. Write structural formulas for all of the isomeric ethers in each of the following groups that meet the given specifications, and give a name to each compound: (a) all ethers having the molecular formula $C_5H_{12}O$; (b) methyl alkyl ethers having the molecular formula $C_6H_{14}O$; (c) ethers other than methyl alkyl ethers having the molecular formula $C_6H_{14}O$.
11. Give reactions for all of the possible ways by which the following ethers can be prepared by the Williamson synthesis making use of alcohols and alkyl chlorides, bromides and iodides: (a) methyl i-butyl ether; (b) methyl n-amyl ether; (c) ethyl n-propyl ether; (d) ethyl i-amyl ether.
12. Using a handbook, find the boiling points of each of the alcohols and alkyl halides used in the reactions of Problem 11 and determine which reaction would permit the easiest separation of the product by distillation.
13. Give equations for the following conversions:
    A. (a) n-Butyl ether into n-butyl iodide; (b) i-propyl ether into propylene; (c) s-butyl ether into s-butyl alcohol; (d) isobutylene into ethyl t-butyl ether.
    B. (a) i-Propyl ether into i-propyl bromide; (b) s-butyl ether into 2-butene; (c) n-amyl ether into n-amyl alcohol; (d) 2-methyl-2-butene into methyl t-amyl ether.
    C. (a) i-Amyl ether into i-amyl alcohol; (b) 1-methylbutyl ether into 2-pentene; (c) n-propyl ether into 1-iodopropane; (d) 2-butene into s-butyl ether.
14. What simple chemical tests could be used to distinguish between the members of the following groups of compounds: (a) ethanol, i-propyl alcohol, and i-propyl ether; (b) 2-hexene, ethyl ether, and n-hexane; (c) s-butyl alcohol, n-butylacetylene, and n-propyl ether; (d) i-amyl ether, i-amyl chloride, and 3-hexyne.
15. Describe a procedure for distinguishing between the members of the following groups of compounds: (a) compounds having the molecular formula C_3H_8O; (b) ethers having the molecular formula $C_4H_{10}O$; (c) ethers having the molecular formula $C_5H_{12}O$.
16. If X g. of a compound gave Y g. of silver iodide in a Zeisel determination, calculate the per cent methoxyl and the equivalent weight for the following compounds:

	A	B	C	D
X	0.1178	0.0604	0.1121	0.1532
Y	0.3137	0.2540	0.3604	0.3341

17. If X g. of a compound required Y cc. of 0.1 N thiosulfate solution in a methoxyl determination by the method of Vieboeck and Schwappach, calculate the per cent methoxyl and the equivalent weight for the following compounds:

	A	B	C	D
X	0.0511	0.0302	0.0589	0.0560
Y	28.42	35.68	40.11	46.81

Chapter 9

CARBOXYLIC ACIDS AND THEIR DERIVATIVES.
ORTHO ESTERS

CARBOXYLIC ACIDS

Numerous types of organic compounds transfer protons to bases more readily than does the water molecule. These compounds are referred to as organic acids or acidic compounds. The carboxylic acids constitute one of the most important groups of compounds having this property.

Structure

The simplest carboxylic acids have the general formula $C_nH_{2n}O_2$, and since a carboxylic acid having only one carbon atom is known, namely formic acid, CH_2O_2, the number of possible structures is limited. If unlikely structures containing unpaired electrons are omitted, only two formulas, I and II, are reasonable from the theory of electronic structure.

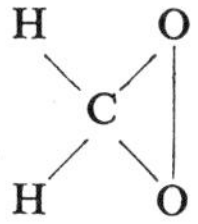

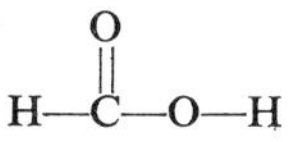

Formula I has two oxygen atoms joined to each other; that is, it contains a peroxide structure. Carboxylic acids, however, do not show any of the properties of peroxides, such as the liberation of iodine from hydrogen iodide solutions. Moreover all monocarboxylic acids contain only one ionizable hydrogen atom. If the hydrogen atoms in formula I ionized, both would be expected to do so. Formula II in which one hydrogen is joined to oxygen and one to carbon accounts for the difference in behavior of the hydrogen atoms. Formula III is the general formula for the homologous series. The methods of synthesis and the reactions of carboxylic acids confirm the view that both the doubly bound oxygen atom and the hydroxyl group are combined with a single carbon atom to give the group —COOH, which is known as the *carboxyl group*.

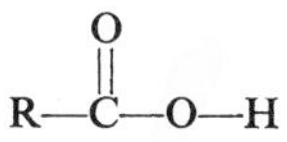

General Methods of Preparation

1. **From the Grignard Reagent and Carbon Dioxide** (p. 123).

$$RMgX + O{=}C{=}O \longrightarrow R-\overset{O}{\underset{\|}{C}}-OMgX \overset{HX}{\longrightarrow} R-\overset{O}{\underset{\|}{C}}-OH + MgX_2$$

This reaction is not only one of the best general methods for synthesizing carboxylic acids, but it proves that both oxygen atoms are united to the same carbon atom.

143

2. By the Hydrolysis of Alkyl Cyanides (Nitriles).

$$RC\equiv N + 2\,H_2O \; \underset{[H^+]}{\rightleftharpoons} \; \left[\begin{array}{c} OH \\ | \\ R-C-OH \\ | \\ NH_2 \end{array} \right] \; \xrightarrow{HCl} \; RCOOH + NH_4Cl$$

$$RC\equiv N + 2\,H_2O \; \underset{[\bar{O}H]}{\rightleftharpoons} \; \left[\begin{array}{c} OH \\ | \\ R-C-OH \\ | \\ NH_2 \end{array} \right] \; \xrightarrow{NaOH} \; RCOONa + H_2O + NH_3$$

Both of these reactions are the result of the addition of water to the cyano group, followed by loss of ammonia. The addition is catalyzed both by protons and by hydroxide ions and is a reversible reaction, but the secondary reactions, that is, the formation of ammonium chloride or of ammonia, are irreversible and the reactions go to completion. The mechanism of hydrolysis of alkyl cyanides is discussed on pages 253 and 246. The formation of carboxylic acids by the hydrolysis of nitriles proves that the alkyl group and both oxygen atoms must be united to a single carbon atom.

3. **By the Oxidation of Primary Alcohols.** When primary alcohols are oxidized by an excess of a strong oxidizing agent such as sodium dichromate and sulfuric acid, chromium trioxide in glacial acetic acid, potassium permanganate, or nitric acid, carboxylic acids are produced without loss of carbon.

$$RCH_2OH + 2\,[O] \; \longrightarrow \; RCOOH + H_2O$$

An aldehyde is an intermediate in this reaction (p. 194). The symbol [O] merely means any suitable oxidizing agent. The oxidizing agents suitable for the reaction must be remembered. Moreover it is assumed that the student has learned how to balance oxidation and reduction reactions and is able to write balanced equations when necessary (p. 145). For example, when sodium dichromate and sulfuric acid is used as the oxidizing agent, the balanced equation is

$$3\,RCH_2OH + 2\,Na_2Cr_2O_7 + 8\,H_2SO_4 \; \longrightarrow \; 3\,RCOOH + 2\,Cr_2(SO_4)_3 + 2\,Na_2SO_4 + 11\,H_2O$$

The mechanism of the oxidation of alcohols to aldehydes and ketones is discussed on p. 106. The oxidation of aldehydes to acids is discussed on p. 212.

If organic compounds containing methyl groups attached to methylidyne (CH) groups are subjected to extremely vigorous oxidizing conditions (hot chromium trioxide in concentrated sulfuric acid), each $CH_3CH<$ group is oxidized to acetic acid. The acetic acid can be distilled and determined quantitatively. Thus a method is available for determining the number of methyl branches in a molecule (*C-methyl determination*).

4. **By the Oxidation of Unsaturated Compounds.** Controlled oxidation of alkenes with a dilute solution of potassium permanganate yields the dihydroxy derivative (p. 57). The presence of oxygen on two adjacent carbon atoms makes the carbon-carbon bond more susceptible to oxidation, and under the more vigorous conditions of higher temperature, longer time of reaction, and higher concentration of oxidizing agent, the dihydroxyalkane is oxidized to two

molecules of carboxylic acid. Since potassium hydroxide is one of the products of oxidation, the salt of the acid is the actual product.

$$3\,RCH{=}CHR' + 2\,KMnO_4 + 4\,H_2O \longrightarrow 3\,RCH{-}CHR' + 2\,MnO_2 + 2\,KOH$$
$$\underset{\displaystyle OH \quad OH}{\phantom{3\,RCH{-}CHR'}}$$

$$3\,RCH{-}CHR' + 6\,KMnO_4 \longrightarrow 3\,RCOOK + 3\,KOOCR' + 6\,MnO_2 + 6\,H_2O$$
$$\underset{\displaystyle OH \quad OH}{\phantom{3\,RCH{-}CHR'}}$$

Adding these two equations gives

$$3\,RCH{=}CHR' + 8\,KMnO_4 \longrightarrow 3\,RCOOK + 3\,KOOCR' + 8\,MnO_2 + 2\,H_2O + 2\,KOH$$

If one or both of the doubly bound carbon atoms lacks a hydrogen atom, the reaction gives one or two molecules of ketone.

$$R_2C{=}CHR' + 2\,KMnO_4 \longrightarrow R_2C{=}O + KOOCR' + 2\,MnO_2 + KOH$$

Unsaturated compounds having a terminal methylene group give potassium carbonate, since the formic acid produced is oxidized further to carbon dioxide and water (p. 158).

$$3\,RCH{=}CH_2 + 10\,KMnO_4 \longrightarrow 3\,RCOOK + 3\,K_2CO_3 + 10\,MnO_2 + 4\,H_2O + KOH$$

Balancing Oxidation-Reduction Equations

By Inspection. When sodium dichromate is reduced to chromic sulfate, three oxygen atoms are available for oxidation. When a primary alcohol is oxidized to an acid, two atoms of oxygen are required.

$$Na_2Cr_2O_7 + 4\,H_2SO_4 \longrightarrow Na_2SO_4 + Cr_2(SO_4)_3 + 4\,H_2O + 3\,[O]$$

$$RCH_2OH + 2\,[O] \longrightarrow RCOOH + H_2O$$

Therefore if the first equation is multiplied by two and the second by three and these equations added, a balanced equation results.

Potassium permanganate in neutral or alkaline solution is reduced to manganese dioxide. For each two moles of permanganate, three atoms of oxygen are available for oxidation.

$$2\,KMnO_4 + H_2O \longrightarrow 2\,KOH + 2\,MnO_2 + 3\,[O]$$

In acid solution the reduction product is a manganous salt, and five atoms of oxygen are available from two moles of permanganate.

$$2\,KMnO_4 + 3\,H_2SO_4 \longrightarrow K_2SO_4 + 2\,MnSO_4 + 3\,H_2O + 5\,[O]$$

When nitric acid is used as an oxidizing agent, the reduction product ordinarily is considered to be nitrogen dioxide and each two moles of nitric acid provide one atom of oxygen.

$$2\,HNO_3 \longrightarrow 2\,NO_2 + H_2O + [O]$$

If the reduction product is nitrogen trioxide, each mole of nitric acid provides one atom of oxygen.

$$2\,HNO_3 \longrightarrow N_2O_3 + H_2O + 2\,[O]$$

If the reduction product is nitric oxide, two moles of nitric acid provide three atoms of oxygen.

$$2\,HNO_3 \longrightarrow 2\,NO + H_2O + 3\,[O]$$

By Change in Polar Number (Oxidation Number). Since oxidation is the loss of electrons and reduction the gain of electrons, balancing the loss and gain of electrons will lead to the balancing of oxidation and reduction equations. Here certain atoms of the molecules involved are considered to be oxidized or reduced in the reaction. The degree of oxidation or reduction of an atom in a molecule or ion is considered to be proportional to the electron concentration about the atom compared with that of the free atom. Each bond to the atom is assigned a unit polarity, the direction of polarity depending on which atom has the greater attraction for electrons. Hydrogen always is considered positive with respect to other atoms. For other elements the attraction for electrons increases from left to right in a given period and decreases from top to bottom in a given column of the periodic table. Thus in a primary alcohol the R—C bond is between two carbon atoms and is assigned zero polarity. Each C—H bond and the O—H bond are assigned polarities with the negative end at carbon or oxygen and the positive end at hydrogen. The C—O bond is assigned a polarity with the positive end at carbon and the negative end at oxygen. The same is true for each bond of the double bond in the carboxyl group of the acid.

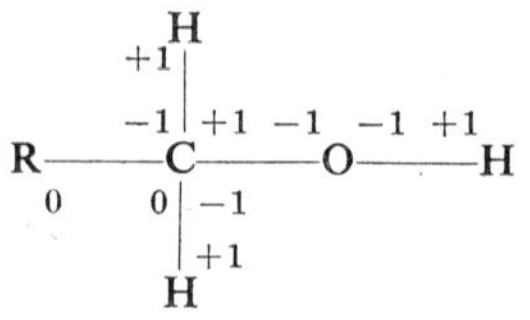

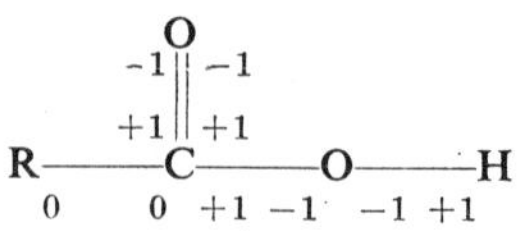

$$
\begin{array}{ccccc}
& \overset{+1}{\underset{-1}{H}} & & & \\
R\!-\!\!\!-\!\!\!-\!\!\!\overset{+1\ -1\ -1\ +1}{\underset{0\ \ -1}{C}}\!\!\!-\!\!\!-\!\!\!O\!\!\!-\!\!\!-\!\!\!H & & & &
\end{array}
\qquad
\begin{array}{ccc}
& \overset{-1\,\|\,-1}{\underset{+1\,\|\,+1}{O}} & \\
R\!-\!\!\!-\!\!\!\overset{}{\underset{0\ +1\ -1\ \ -1\ +1}{C}}\!\!\!-\!\!\!-\!\!\!O\!\!\!-\!\!\!-\!\!\!H &
\end{array}
$$

The algebraic sum of the charges on any atom is its **polar number** or **oxidation number**. Thus the polar number of carbon in a primary alcohol group is $0 - 1 + 1 - 1 = -1$, and that in a carboxyl group is $0 + 1 + 1 + 1 = +3$. If the polar number becomes more positive in a reaction, indicating a decrease in electron density, the atom is oxidized, and if it becomes less positive, indicating an increase in electron density, it is reduced. The change in polar number of an atom in an oxidizing agent must balance the change in the polar number of an atom in the molecule being oxidized.

In the unbalanced reaction

$$RCH_2OH + Na_2Cr_2O_7 + H_2SO_4 \longrightarrow RCOOH + Cr_2(SO_4)_3 + Na_2SO_4 + H_2O$$

the atoms undergoing a change in polar number are the carbon atom in the primary alcohol, which changes from -1 to $+3$ or a change of $+4$, and the chromium atoms in the dichromate which change from $+6$ to $+3$ or a change of -3 for each chromium atom, a total change for the two atoms of -6. To balance $+4$ against -6, $+4$ may be multiplied by 6 and -6 by 4, or more simply $+4$ by 3 and -6 by 2. Hence three molecules of alcohol will be oxidized by two molecules of dichromate. The moles of sulfuric acid required and the moles of water formed follow from the number of sulfate ions required and the amount of hydrogen available.

It is unfortunate that the expression *change in valence* sometimes is used in balancing oxidation-reduction reactions when *change in polar number* is meant. The term *valence* should be reserved for the number of covalent bonds by which an atom is united to other atoms or for the number of charges which an ion bears. It is obvious in this example that the valence of carbon has not changed on being oxidized from a CH_2 group to a C=O group but remains four throughout, whereas the polar number has changed from -1 to $+3$.

By Means of Half-Reactions. Oxidation and reduction equations may be balanced by the method of half-reactions. In the present example one half of the reaction is the oxidation of alcohol molecules to acid molecules, and the other half is the reduction of dichromate ion to chromic ion. The source of oxygen for the oxidation half may be considered to be water molecules.

$$RCH_2OH + H_2O \longrightarrow RCOOH + 4\,[H^+] + 4\,[e^-]$$

$$[Cr_2O_7^-] + 14\,[H^+] + 6\,[e^-] \longrightarrow 2\,[Cr^{+++}] + 7\,H_2O$$

Since the first half-reaction must supply as many electrons as are used by the second half-reaction, the first half-reaction must be multiplied by 3 and the second by 2. Addition then gives

$$3\,RCH_2OH + 2\,[Cr_2O_7^-] + 16\,[H^+] \longrightarrow 3\,RCOOH + 4\,[Cr^{+++}] + 11\,H_2O$$

All of the above schemes for balancing oxidation and reduction equations are empirical and arbitrary and none is more scientific than the others. In the first method oxygen is assumed to be available from the oxidizing agent; in the second method the atoms are assumed to differ in polarity by unit charges; in the third method the reaction is assumed to take place by the elimination of electrons and the consumption of electrons. These assumptions merely are devices for arriving at the desired result, and that method should be used which seems preferable to the individual. The oxidation of organic compounds usually is limited to the addition of oxygen or the removal of hydrogen, and reduction to the addition of hydrogen or the removal of oxygen. Since the oxygen or hydrogen requirement in organic oxidations and reductions can be determined at a glance, the first method given for balancing oxidation-reduction equations is the simplest. Whatever method is used, it should be practiced sufficiently to be carried out correctly and with facility.

Nomenclature

Common Names. Normal carboxylic acids were isolated first from natural sources, particularly from the fats (Chapter 10). Hence they frequently are called *fatty acids*. Since nothing was known about their structure, they were given common names indicating their source. These names and the derivations of the names together with some physical properties are given in Table 10.

TABLE 10

COMMON NAMES OF NORMAL CARBOXYLIC ACIDS

NO. OF CARBON ATOMS	NAME OF ACID	DERIVATION OF NAME	BOILING POINT	MELTING POINT	DENSITY 20°/4°
			°	°	
1	Formic	L. *formica*, ant	100.7	8.4	1.220
2	Acetic	L. *acetum*, vinegar	118.2	16.6	1.049
3	Propionic	Gr. *proto*, first; *pion*, fat	141.4	−20.8	0.993
4	Butyric	L. *butyrum*, butter	164.1	−5.5	0.958
5	Valeric	valerian root (L. *valere*, to be strong)	186.4	−34.5	0.939
6	Caproic	L. *caper*, goat	205.4	−3.9	0.936
7	Enanthic	Gr. *oenanthe*, vine blossom	223.0	−7.5	0.918
8	Caprylic	L. *caper*, goat	239.3	16.3	0.909
9	Pelargonic	Pelargonium	253.0	12.0	
10	Capric	L. *caper*, goat	268.7	31.3	
11	Undecanoic		280	28.5	
12	Lauric	laurel		43.2	
13	Tridecanoic			41.6	
14	Myristic	Myristica (nutmeg)		54.4	
15	Pentadecanoic			52.3	
16	Palmitic	palm oil		62.8	
17	Margaric	Gr. *margaron*, pearl		61.2	
18	Stearic	Gr. *stear*, tallow		69.6	
19	Nonadecanoic			68.7	
20	Arachidic	Arachis (peanut)		75.4	
21	Heneicosanoic			74.3	
22	Behenic	behen oil		79.9	
23	Tricosanoic			79.1	
24	Tetracosanoic			84.2	
25	Pentacosanoic			83.5	
26	Cerotic	L. *cera*, wax		87.7	

Geneva names are given for the odd-carbon acids above C_{10} rather than common names. The reason is that only acids with an even number of carbon atoms had been found in fats,[1] the odd-carbon acids having been prepared

---

[1] The presence of small amounts of normal odd-carbon acids in natural fats has been reported recently. Thus tri-, penta-, and heptadecanoic acids have been obtained from butter fat. Heptadecanoic acid has been isolated also from mutton fat and from shark liver oil.

synthetically by hydrolysis of the nitriles. The name *margaric* appears to be an exception. However it has been shown that the material isolated from fats and thought to be a C_{17} acid actually is a mixture of palmitic and stearic acids. When the true C_{17} normal acid was synthesized, the common name was retained.

As with other homologous series, those compounds having an isopropyl group at the end of a normal hydrocarbon chain may be named by adding the prefix *iso* to the common name, for example $(CH_3)_2CHCOOH$, isobutyric acid, or $(CH_3)_2CHCH_2CH_2CH_2CH_2CH_2CH_2COOH$, isocapric acid. If the methyl branch occurs at any other portion of the chain, the designation *iso* may not be used.

As Derivatives of Normal Acids. Acetic acid frequently is chosen as the parent compound, and derivatives are named as compounds in which the hydrogen atoms of the methyl group are replaced by other groups.

$$\overset{\underset{\delta}{5}}{CH_3}\overset{\underset{\gamma}{4}}{CH_2}\overset{\underset{\beta}{3}}{CH}-\overset{\underset{\alpha}{2}}{CH}\overset{1}{COOH}$$
$$\qquad\quad | \qquad |$$
$$\qquad\quad CH_3 \quad CH_3$$

This compound may be called methyl-*s*-butylacetic acid. It also may be considered to be derived from valeric acid and called α,β-dimethylvaleric acid or 2,3-dimethylvaleric acid. When Greek letters are used to designate the positions of the substituents, the α carbon atom of the chain is the carbon atom adjacent to the carboxyl group. When numerals are used, the carbon atom of the carboxyl group is numbered 1.

Geneva System. The final *e* is dropped from the name of the hydrocarbon having the same number of carbon atoms as the longest chain containing the carboxyl group, and *oic acid* is added. The carbon atom of the carboxyl group always is numbered 1 when numbering the atoms of the longest chain. For example $CH_3CH_2CH(CH_3)CH(CH_3)COOH$ is called 2,3-dimethylpentanoic acid.

Physical Properties

The **boiling points** of carboxylic acids (Table 10) rise more or less uniformly with increase in molecular weight. The increase for those listed averages about 18° per additional methylene group, the same as for the alcohols. The magnitude of the boiling points, however, is even more abnormal than for the alcohols. Ethyl alcohol boils at 78°, but formic acid having the same molecular weight boils at 101°; *n*-propyl alcohol boils at 98°, but acetic acid boils at 118°. The explanation of the abnormal boiling points of the acids is the same as that for the alcohols, namely association by proton bonds, but the acids are able to form double molecules which are more stable than the association complexes formed by the alcohols.

$$R-C\overset{\displaystyle O:H-O}{\underset{\displaystyle O-H:O}{\Big\langle\qquad\Big\rangle}}C-R$$

It has been shown by vapor density measurements that the double molecules of acetic acid persist even in the vapor state. Hence it is not surprising that the boiling point of acetic acid (118°, mol. wt. $= 60 \times 2 = 120$) is of the same order of magnitude as *n*-octane (126°, mol. wt. 114).

An interesting characteristic of the normal carboxylic acids is the alternation in **melting points.** Acids with an even number of carbon atoms always melt at a higher temperature than the next higher member of the series (Fig. 42). X-ray diffraction has shown that in the solid state the carbon atoms of the hydrocarbon chain assume an extended zigzag arrangement in which the carboxyl groups of the odd carbon acids are on the same side of the chain as the terminal methyl groups, whereas those of the even carbon acids are on the

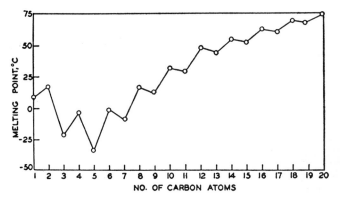

Fig. 42. Melting points of normal carboxylic acids.

opposite side of the chain (see p. 40). Although all of the acids are double molecules, the arrangement of those with an even number of carbon atoms gives a more symmetrical molecule and a more stable crystal lattice.

Other homologous compounds may show oscillation in melting points. Thus the first four normal paraffin hydrocarbons exhibit complete alternation in melting points, but the remainder show incomplete alternation; that is, in passing from an even number of carbon atoms to an odd number there is not a decrease in melting point, but the increase is less than in passing from an odd number to an even number (Fig. 27, p. 40). For the normal alcohols (Fig. 38, p. 88) no alternation in melting point is observable. Other physical properties such as heats of crystallization, solubility, and viscosity also may oscillate with successive members of a homologous series.

Because of partial ionization in water, carboxylic acids are somewhat more heavily hydrated than alcohols and hence show somewhat greater **solubility** in water. In general they have about the same solubility in water as the alcohol with one less carbon atom. For example *n*-butyric acid is miscible with water as is *n*-propyl alcohol, whereas *n*-butyl alcohol dissolves only to the extent of about 1 volume in 11 volumes of water. Monocarboxylic acids usually are soluble in other organic solvents.

The marked attraction of carboxylic acids for water molecules is indicated by the behavior of the lower acids on distillation of an aqueous solution. It would be expected that the lower the boiling point of the acid, the more readily the acid would distill with water. If a dilute solution of an acid is distilled and 10 per cent of the original volume collected, the mole per cent of the total amount of acid that appears in the first 10 per cent of distillate is as given in Table 11. These results show that the volatility increases rather than decreases with increasing boiling point. This behavior must mean that the attractive forces between water and the carboxylic acids decrease with increasing molecular weight, which is in accordance with the solubility behavior of the acids in water. The numerical results given in Table 11 are known as the *Duclaux values* for the acids and are sufficiently characteristic of the pure acids to be used for identification purposes.

TABLE 11

DUCLAUX VALUES FOR SOME VOLATILE CARBOXYLIC ACIDS

ACID	MOLE PER CENT OF ACID IN FIRST 10 PER CENT OF DISTILLATE
Formic	3.9
Acetic	6.8
Propionic	11.9
Butyric	17.9
Valeric	24.5
Caproic	33.0

Odor and Taste

The carboxylic acids which are sufficiently soluble in water to give an appreciable hydrogen ion concentration have a sour taste. The lower members have a sharp acrid odor, and the acids from butyric through caprylic have a disagreeable odor. The odor of rancid butter and strong cheese is due to volatile acids, and caproic acid gets its name from the fact that it is present in the skin secretions of goats. The higher acids are practically odorless because of their low volatility.

General Reactions of Free Acids

1. **Salt Formation.** The acidity of alcohols is of the same order of magnitude as that of water, whereas carboxylic acids are stronger than carbonic acid but weaker than mineral acids. The strength of acids, that is the degree of ionization in water, usually is expressed in terms of the ionization constant, which is related to the equilibrium constant for the reversible reaction

$$HB + H_2O \rightleftharpoons [H_3O^+] + [B^-]$$

The equilibrium constant for this reaction is

$$K = \frac{[H_3O^+][B^-]}{[HB][H_2O]}$$

where the symbols in brackets now indicate the concentration in moles per liter. Since the concentration of the water is so large that it may be considered to be constant, the above expression may be written

$$K_a = \frac{[H_3O^+][B^-]}{[HB]}$$

K_a is called the ionization constant for the acid and is proportional to the extent of ionization. The ionization constants for most simple carboxylic acids vary between 10^{-4} and 10^{-5}, whereas the first ionization constant of carbonic acid is 4.3×10^{-7}. The acid ionization constant of water is 1.8×10^{-16}. Hence carboxylic acids react with bicarbonates, carbonates, or hydroxides to form salts that are not hydrolyzed appreciably by water.

$$RCOOH + NaHCO_3 \longrightarrow RCOO^{-+}Na + CO_2 + H_2O$$

$$2\,RCOOH + Na_2CO_3 \longrightarrow 2\,RCOO^{-+}Na + CO_2 + H_2O$$

$$RCOOH + NaOH \longrightarrow RCOO^{-+}Na + H_2O$$

However, carboxylic acids are displaced from their salts by mineral acids $(K_a > 10^{-1})$.

$$RCOO^{-+}Na + HCl \longrightarrow RCOOH + NaCl$$

The neutralization of an acid by a standard solution of a base is the customary procedure for estimating acids. When a weak acid is neutralized by a strong base, the equivalence point will be on the alkaline side because of hydrolysis of the salt. Therefore an indicator changing color at the proper acidity is necessary. For carboxylic acids, phenolphthalein usually is satisfactory. The equivalent weight of an acid as determined by neutralization with a standard base is known as the *neutralization equivalent* of the acid.

Since salts are completely ionized, and ions are more heavily hydrated than neutral molecules, the alkali metal salts of carboxylic acids are much more soluble than the acids themselves. For example, whereas water solubility of the free normal acids approaches that of the saturated hydrocarbons above C_5, the sodium salts are very soluble up to C_{10} and form colloidal solutions from C_{10} to C_{18}. This fact is used to separate acids from water-insoluble compounds such as alcohols or hydrocarbons. Extraction of the mixture with dilute alkali causes the acid to go into the aqueous layer as the salt. The aqueous layer then can be separated and the free acid liberated from its salt by the addition of a mineral acid. It is necessary to add at least the calculated amount of mineral acid, or if the amount of salt present is unknown, to add mineral acid until a universal indicator, such as Hydrion paper, shows that a pH of 1 or 2 has been reached. Merely making the solution acid to litmus will not completely free the carboxylic acid from its salt because a mixture of the salt and organic acid will be acid to litmus.

Another result of the ionic nature of salts is that they are nonvolatile. The nonvolatility of salts permits volatile acids to be recovered from aqueous solutions or separated from other volatile substances by converting into salts and evaporating to dryness.

2. **Replacement of Hydroxyl by Halogen.** Since the hydroxyl group of alcohols can be replaced by halogen (p. 100), the hydroxyl group of carboxylic acids likewise might be expected to be replaceable. Replacement cannot be brought about with reagents such as the hydrogen halides, however, because the position of equilibrium lies far on the side of the carboxylic and halogen acid. Inorganic acid halides on the other hand react readily, the products being an organic acid halide (acyl halide) and an inorganic acid.

$$3\,RCOOH + PX_3 \longrightarrow 3\,R\overset{\displaystyle O}{\underset{\displaystyle \text{An acyl}}{\overset{\displaystyle \|}{C}}}{-}X + P(OH)_3$$

An acyl
halide

The reactions of other inorganic acid halides are discussed under the preparation of acyl halides (p. 160).

3. Esterification. Carboxylic acids react with alcohols to give esters and water. The reaction is catalyzed by hydrogen ion (p. 166).

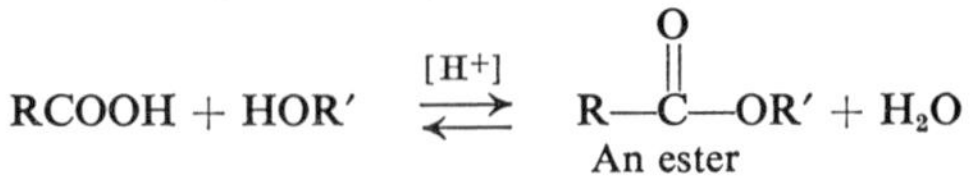

$$RCOOH + HOR' \underset{}{\overset{[H^+]}{\rightleftharpoons}} R-\overset{\overset{\displaystyle O}{\|}}{C}-OR' + H_2O$$
An ester

Methyl esters may be prepared easily by the reaction of acids with diazo methane (p. 266).

$$RCOOH + CH_2N_2 \longrightarrow RCOOCH_3 + N_2$$

4. Decomposition to Ketones. Ketones are formed when carboxylic acids are heated in the presence of thoria or manganous oxide to the point where decomposition takes place, or when salts of polyvalent metals such as calcium, lead, or thorium are pyrolyzed.

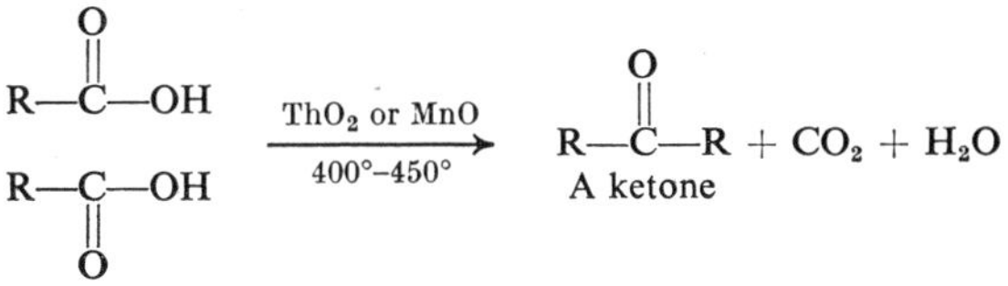

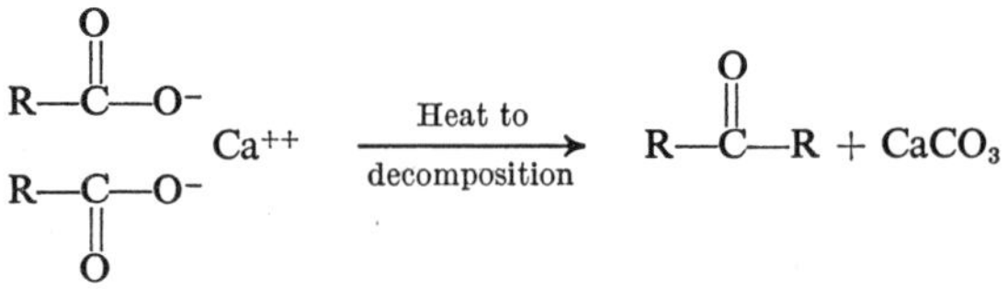

In general the vapor-phase decomposition over thoria is the preferred method.

When the vapor of the free acid is passed over a weakly basic oxide, the salt need not be formed as an intermediate. The oxygen atoms of the thoria may act simply as a basic surface which can assist the transfer of a proton from one acid molecule to the other.

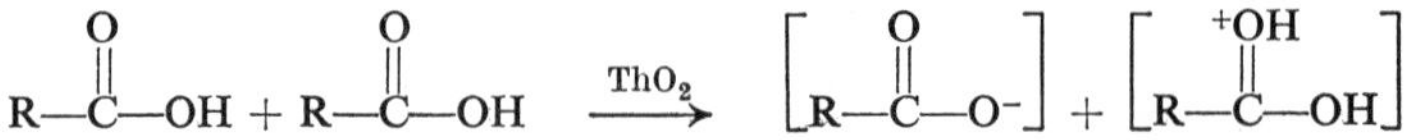

Decomposition of the negative ion can give a carbanion which may react with the second positive ion to give the ketone.

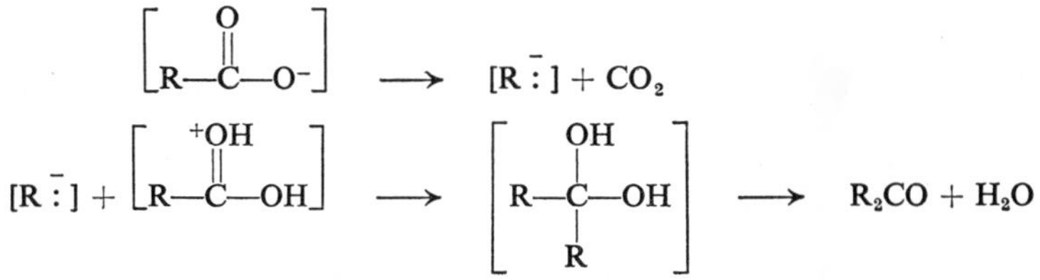

Another possibility is that the hydrated ketone arises directly from the reaction of the oxonium ion with the carboxylate ion.

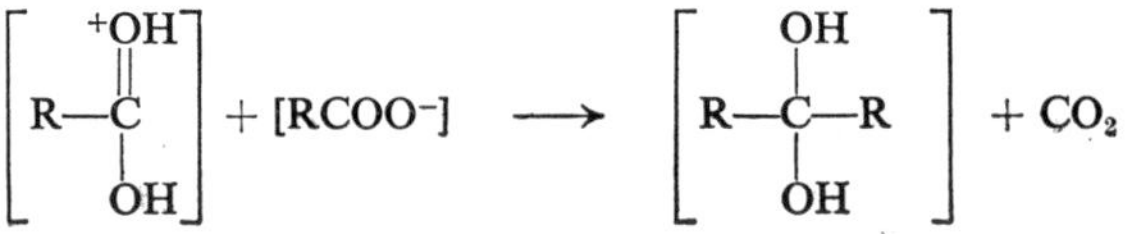

5. **Reaction with Hydrogen Peroxide.** When carboxylic acids are mixed with 90 per cent hydrogen peroxide in the presence of sulfuric acid, peroxy acids (per acids) are formed (p. 875). The process undoubtedly is analogous to esterification.

$$RCOOH + HO\!-\!OH \xrightarrow{H_2SO_4} RC\!-\!O\!-\!OH + H_2O$$
$$\hspace{4.5cm}\underset{O}{\|}$$

Peroxy acids readily add oxygen to unsaturated compounds to give the three-membered *oxirane* ring. These compounds commonly are called *epoxides* (p. 744), and the process is known as *epoxidation*.

$$RCH\!=\!CHR + CH_3C\!-\!O\!-\!OH \longrightarrow RCH\!-\!CHR + CH_3COOH$$
$$\hspace{2.7cm}\underset{O}{\|} \hspace{4cm}\underset{O}{\diagdown\diagup}$$

In the presence of strong acids, the ring opens with the formation of esters of the dihydroxy compound.

Acidity of Carboxylic Acids and Resonance in the Carboxylate Ion

The question arises as to why the replacement of one hydrogen atom of the water molecule by the acyl group markedly increases the acidity. It is assumed that during ionization a proton leaves the acid; that is, the pair of electrons binding the hydrogen and oxygen atoms remains with the oxygen atom. Hence any factors which tend to withdraw the electrons from the hydrogen should facilitate its removal as a proton. An acyl group is an electron-attracting group because the oxygen atom with its greater nuclear charge pulls the electrons away from the carbon atom and makes it deficient in electrons (p. 6). Hence the acyl group facilitates the loss of a proton from a hydroxyl group. This effect of the acyl group is called the *electrostatic* or *inductive* effect.

Another factor which makes carboxylic acids lose a proton more readily than water is the interaction of π electrons with the nuclei of the carbon atom and both oxygen atoms, a phenomenon called **resonance**. In the carboxylate ion the primary bonds between the carbon atom and the three groups to which it is attached are formed by the presence of two electrons in each of three σ-type orbitals (p. 10). Because of the sp^2 hybridization of the atomic orbitals of the carbon atom, the molecular orbitals make angles of approximately 120 degrees with each other and lie in a plane (p. 12). These bonds, which are indicated in Fig. 43 by the usual dash, utilize three of the four valence electrons of the carbon atom. Each oxygen atom contributes one of its six valence electrons to these bonds. Two more of the valence electrons of each oxygen atom are in a $2s$ orbital and two are in a p orbital, leaving one unassigned electron for each oxygen atom. Since one electron is acquired in the ionization of the proton, a total of four electrons have not been assigned. Three p orbitals remain, one at each of the oxygen atoms and one at the carbon atom. Their axes can become parallel to each other and perpendicular to the plane of the σ orbitals. If the p orbital of carbon overlaps that of one of the oxygen atoms to form a molecular π orbital, the latter could hold two electrons. The remaining pair could occupy the empty p orbital of the second oxygen atom. This type of overlapping is indicated by Fig. 43a or by the conventional valence bond structure (b). Alternatively the p orbital of carbon could overlap with that of the other oxygen atom as indicated by (c) or (d). Either structure (a) or structure (c) would be more stable than that with an unpaired electron occupying each of two p orbitals, because in either case the electrons can encompass two positive nuclei (p. 9). However, since the p orbital of carbon can overlap the p orbital of either oxygen atom equally well, a molecular orbital can be formed encompassing all three nuclei as indicated in (e) in which the electrons would have a still lower energy than in either (a) or (c) because now the electrons encompass three nuclei. Two such tricentric molecular orbitals are possible, one having a single nodal plane (f) and the other having two nodal planes perpendicular to each other (g). Hence two pairs of electrons can be accommodated. Although the orbital (g) with two nodal planes has a higher energy than that with a single nodal plane (f), the total energy of two electrons in (g) and two in (f) is less than the total energy of two electrons in a dicentric orbital and two electrons in a p orbital as in (a) or (c). This ability to utilize molecular orbitals involving more than two positive nuclei is the phenomenon which is called *resonance*. The difference in energy

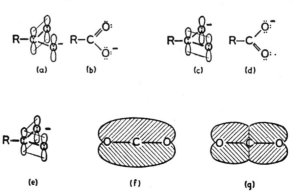

(a)   (b)   (c)   (d)

(e)   (f)   (g)

Fig. 43. Resonance in the carboxylate ion.

between the tricentric and the dicentric states is called the *resonance energy* of the molecule. This type of interaction may be indicated by placing a double-headed arrow between the conventional valence structures and enclosing the whole in braces.

$$
\left\{
\begin{array}{ccc}
\overset{\cdot\cdot}{O} : & & \overset{\cdot\cdot}{O} : \\
\parallel & & | \\
R{-}C & \longleftrightarrow & R{-}C \\
\backslash & & \parallel \\
\overset{\cdot\cdot}{O} : & & \overset{\cdot\cdot}{O} :
\end{array}
\right\}
$$

It should be clear from the above discussion that these separate valence structures do not exist in the ground state of the molecule. It usually is said that the actual molecule is a *resonance hybrid* of the two structures. The hybrid concept is a convenient alternate symbolism for resonance.

The **source of resonance energy** is the same as that of any other type of bonding energy. Thus the energy of a single bond or of a double bond arises from the ability of an electron to encompass two positive nuclei in a molecule instead of one in an atom (p. 9). Resonance energy is merely the additional stabilization resulting from the ability of an electron to encompass three or more nuclei instead of two. Electrons encompassing more than two nuclei frequently are called *mobile electrons*, and are said to be *delocalized* in contrast to the localized electrons in the σ bonds. Hence resonance energy is referred to also as *delocalization energy*. Another term for resonance is *mesomerism* (Gr. *mesos*, middle) because the state of the molecule is intermediate between that of the possible classical valence-bond structures.

Two physical properties by which the extent of resonance can be observed are heats of reaction and interatomic distances. Thus the heat of combustion of a resonance hybrid should be less, by an amount equal to the resonance energy, than the heat of combustion of an isomeric compound containing the same functional groups in isolated positions where no resonance is possible. This effect is observed, although resonance energies as determined by differences in heats of combustion are not very accurate. The numerical values of the latter are large compared with the magnitude of the resonance energies, and small percentage errors in the heats of combustion may cause considerable error in the calculated value of the resonance energy.

Interatomic distances in molecules can be determined with high precision from X-ray diffraction data on crystals, from electron diffraction data on gases, or from spectroscopic data. The double bond shortens the distance between two atoms (p. 51). Thus the distance between a carbon and oxygen atom linked by a single bond is 1.43 Å, whereas that between doubly linked carbon and oxygen is 1.24 Å. In the resonance hybrid, however, there is neither a single nor a double bond but a bond uniformly encompassing all three atoms. Therefore the distances between the carbon and either oxygen should be identical. Moreover this distance might be expected to be less than the average of the distance for a double and a single bond, since the resonance energy would cause the atoms to be bound more strongly. The measured distance in the formate ion is 1.27 Å.

To account for the fact that carboxylic acids ionize more readily than water or alcohols, it is necessary only to consider that for a proton to combine with a carboxylate ion, energy equivalent to the resonance energy of the ion must be supplied. Since a hydroxide or alkoxide ion is not stabilized by resonance, more energy is evolved on combination with a proton. Conversely a proton can leave the carboxyl group of an acid more readily than the hydroxyl group of water or an alcohol. Both the electrostatic (inductive) effect and the resonance effect operate to increase the ease of ionization of the proton from a carboxyl group. It is not known which effect is the more important.

The resonance energy of the undissociated carboxyl group is much less than that of the carboxylate ion, although the opportunity for overlapping of *p* orbitals might appear to be identical (Fig. 44). Actually, however, in the undissociated carboxyl group (*a*) the *p* orbital of

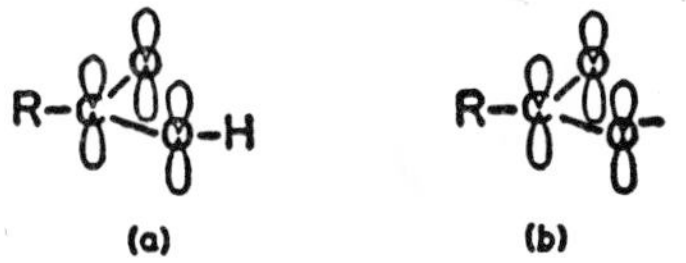

(a)   (b)

Fig. 44. *p* Orbitals available for π bond formation (*a*) in the undissociated carb- oxyl group and (*b*) in the carboxylate ion.

the hydroxyl oxygen overlaps that of the carbon atom much less than does the *p* orbital of the other oxygen atom, because bond formation with the additional positive nucleus causes a deficiency of electrons about the hydroxyl oxygen. In other words because the hydroxyl oxygen has one less unshared pair of electrons, it is less able than the other oxygen atom to contribute electrons to a π orbital. Therefore there is a greater tendency to form a dicentric orbital, that is, an ordinary double bond, than to form a tricentric orbital. If the molecule is considered as a resonance hybrid of the ordinary electronic valence structures, the second structure involving

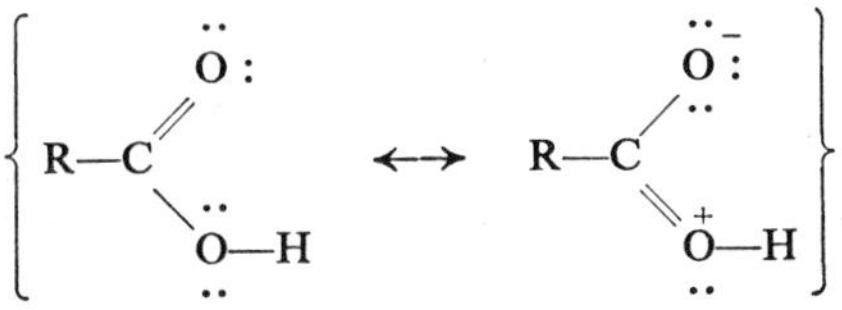

a separation of charge within the molecule is much less stable than the first.[2] Hence there is less

---

[2] The charges in these structures sometimes are called *formal charges*. They are arrived at by assuming that each atom possesses all of the unshared electrons placed about it and half of those in each shared pair. The difference between this number and the number of valence electrons in the normal state of the atom is the formal charge. Thus the hydroxyl oxygen possesses two electrons in the unshared pair and half of the three shared pairs or a total of five electrons. Since the oxygen atom has six valence electrons, the hydroxyl oxygen has a deficiency of one electron and bears a formal charge of +1. The carboxyl carbon has half of four shared pairs of electrons, which is the same as the number of valence electrons of the carbon atom, and the formal charge is 0. The second oxygen atom has three unshared pairs and half of a shared pair or a total of seven electrons. Therefore it possesses an excess of one electron and carries a formal charge of −1.

tendency for a hybrid to be formed, and the resonance energy for such a system is small. The structure

$$R—\overset{\overset{\displaystyle ..}{\displaystyle :\overset{..}{O}:^-}}{\underset{+}{C}}—OH$$

is still less stable than that having both charges on the oxygen atoms, because the p orbital of carbon is not being used at all. Consequently hybridization of this structure with

$$R—\overset{\overset{\displaystyle O}{\|}}{C}—OH$$

is still less. These views are confirmed by electron-diffraction data which show two carbon-oxygen distances in monomeric formic acid or acetic acid, one of 1.43 Å and the other of 1.24 Å, identical within experimental error with the single and double bond interatomic distances.

General Reactions of Salts of Carboxylic Acids

1. **Electrolysis (Kolbe Hydrocarbon Synthesis).** If an aqueous solution of a water-soluble salt of a carboxylic acid is electrolyzed, alkane and carbon dioxide are formed at the positive electrode (anode) and hydroxide ion and hydrogen at the negative electrode (cathode).

$$2\,RCOO^{-\,+}Na + 2\,H_2O \longrightarrow R—R + CO_2 + NaOH + H_2$$

The carboxylate ions migrate to the anode and are discharged to give carbon dioxide and hydrocarbon.

$$2\,[RCOO^-] \longrightarrow 2e + 2\,[RCOO \cdot] \longrightarrow R:R + 2\,CO_2$$

Hydroxide ion and hydrogen are formed at the cathode.

$$2\,H_2O + 2e \longrightarrow 2\,[^-OH] + 2\,[H \cdot]$$

$$2\,[H \cdot] \longrightarrow H_2$$

2. **Reaction with Alkyl Halides.** Reaction of a metallic salt with an alkyl halide produces an ester and metallic halide.

$$RCOO^{-\,+}M + XR' \longrightarrow RCOOR' + MX$$

This reaction follows the same course as other displacement reactions of alkyl halides (p. 116).

Although sodium salts frequently give satisfactory yields, the use of the salt of a metal such as silver or mercury which forms a nonionized halide usually will improve the yield.

3. **Decomposition of Ammonium Salts.** When ammonium carboxylates are heated, two reactions take place: dissociation into the acid and ammonia,

$$RCOO^{-\,+}NH_4 \rightleftharpoons RCOOH + NH_3$$

and decomposition with the formation of an *amide* and water.

$$R—\overset{\overset{\displaystyle O}{\|}}{C}—O^{-\,+}NH_4 \rightleftharpoons R—\overset{\overset{\displaystyle O}{\|}}{C}—NH_2 + H_2O$$
$$\text{An amide}$$

If the ammonium salt is heated with an excess of the free acid or in the presence of ammonia, the dissociation is repressed. Removal of the water by distillation gives good yields of the amide.

4. **Reaction of Silver Salts with Bromine (Hunsdiecker Reaction).** When silver salts react under anhydrous conditions with a solution of bromine in carbon tetrachloride, decarboxylation with the formation of an alkyl bromide takes place.

$$RCOOAg + Br_2 \longrightarrow RBr + CO_2 + AgBr$$

Iodine gives an alkyl iodide. Since one carbon atom is lost, this reaction is useful for decreasing the length of a carbon chain.

These reactions are accelerated by light and appear to take place by a free-radical mechanism.

$$Br_2 \longrightarrow 2[Br \cdot]$$

$$RCOOAg + [Br \cdot] \longrightarrow AgBr + [RCOO \cdot] \longrightarrow [R \cdot] + CO_2$$

$$[R \cdot] + Br_2 \longrightarrow RBr + [Br \cdot]$$

Industrially Important Acids

Compounds of commercial importance frequently are made by special reactions which are not applicable to other members of the homologous series. The reason for this situation is that industry tries to use low-cost raw materials and to find new ways of reducing the cost of indispensable materials. Hence a compound may be of commercial importance because a special method has been discovered by which it can be made cheaply. On the other hand the intrinsic value of a compound may be such that a great deal of effort and money have been spent to discover new ways of making it more cheaply than by the general procedures.

Formic Acid. Sodium formate is made by a special process from carbon monoxide and caustic soda.

$$CO + NaOH \xrightarrow[\text{6--10 atm.}]{200°} HCOO^{-+}Na$$

This reaction was one of the earliest used commercially for the synthesis of an organic compound from carbon and salt as the raw materials. **Formic acid** can be liberated from the sodium salt by adding a mineral acid. With the increased uses for pentaerythritol, more than enough formic acid is available as a co-product than is needed to meet the demand (p. 752).

Because the carboxyl group is united to a hydrogen atom, rather than to a carbon atom as in all subsequent members of the series, formic acid undergoes a number of *special reactions*. When heated with dehydrating agents it decomposes into carbon monoxide and water.

$$HCOOH \xrightarrow[\text{H}_2\text{SO}_4]{\text{Conc.}} CO + H_2O$$

Reaction with phosphorus trichloride gives carbon monoxide and hydrogen chloride because formyl chloride is unstable at ordinary temperatures.

$$3 \; H{-}\overset{\overset{\displaystyle O}{\|}}{C}{-}OH + PCl_3 \longrightarrow P(OH)_3 + 3\left[H{-}\overset{\overset{\displaystyle O}{\|}}{C}{-}Cl\right] \rightleftharpoons 3 \; CO + 3 \; HCl$$

The latter reaction is reversible and formyl chloride may be obtained from carbon monoxide and hydrogen chloride at the temperature of liquid air. When sodium formate is heated, hydrogen is evolved and sodium oxalate remains.

$$HCOO^{-+}Na \atop HCOO^{-+}Na \longrightarrow H_2 + {COO^{-+}Na \atop COO^{-+}Na}$$

Like other compounds containing the H—C=O group (p. 212), formic acid is a mild reducing agent.

$$HCOOH + [O] \longrightarrow [HOCOOH] \longrightarrow CO_2 + H_2O$$

Because formic acid is approximately ten times as strong an acid as its homologs, it is used when an acid stronger than acetic acid, but not so strong as a mineral acid, is desired. It is used also for the manufacture of its esters and salts. Sodium formate is used to make formic acid and oxalic acid, and as a reducing agent.

Acetic Acid. This organic acid is by far the most important from the standpoint of quantity used. Production was 185 million pounds in 1940 and 524 million pounds in 1955, exclusive of the amount produced in the form of vinegar. The unit value was 8 cents per pound. It appears in the market largely as *glacial acetic acid* of about 99.5 per cent purity, so-called because on cold days it freezes to an ice-like solid. The melting point of pure acetic acid is 16.7°.

Several methods for the preparation of acetic acid are in use.

1. ENZYME-CATALYZED OXIDATION OF ETHYL ALCOHOL. Acetic acid is the chief component of **vinegar.** The alcohol in fermented fruit juices or fermented malt (beer) in the presence of various species of *Acetobacter* and air is oxidized to acetic acid.

$$CH_3CH_2OH + O_2 \text{ (air)} \xrightarrow{\text{\textit{Acetobacter}}} CH_3COOH + H_2O$$

In the *barrel process* the fruit juice is contained in barrels exposed to air, and the bacteria form a slimy film on the surface known as *mother of vinegar*. Since the alcohol must come in contact with the oxygen and bacteria by diffusion processes, oxidation is slow, and an acetic acid content of 4–5 per cent is reached only after several months. In the *quick process* a vat is filled with shavings or other porous material which is inoculated with the microorganism. A 12–15 per cent alcohol solution containing nutrient salts for the growth of the bacteria is allowed to trickle over the shavings while a controlled amount of warm air is forced up through the shavings. In this way a vinegar with an acetic acid content of 8–10 per cent may be obtained, which is diluted to 4–5 per cent for use. Vinegar produced by fermentation is used almost exclusively as a preservative and condiment, its value for this purpose being enhanced by flavors present in the cider, wine, or malt.

2. FROM PYROLIGNEOUS LIQUOR. Pyroligneous liquor from the destructive distillation of wood (p. 89) contains 4–10 per cent of acetic acid which may be recovered by neutralizing with lime and distilling to dryness. The **gray acetate of lime** so obtained may be converted to glacial acetic acid by concentrated sulfuric acid. In recent years acetic acid has been recovered from dilute aqueous solutions by extraction from the vapor state with tar oil (*Suida process*), and by azeotropic distillation (p. 93) using ethylene chloride, propyl

acetate, or butyl acetate to form a constant-boiling mixture with the water (*Clarke-Othmer process*). It may be recovered as ethyl acetate by esterifying with ethyl alcohol.

3. FROM ACETALDEHYDE. In the United States, prior to 1952, most of the synthetic acetic acid was made by the oxidation of acetaldehyde, which may be produced either by the hydration of acetylene (p. 131), by the catalytic dehydrogenation or air oxidation of ethyl alcohol (p. 105), or by the partial oxidation with air of propane and butane (p. 220). Acetaldehyde absorbs oxygen from the air rapidly to form peroxyacetic acid, a peroxide (p. 875), which in the presence of manganous or cobalt acetate reacts with the acetaldehyde to give acetic acid.

$$CH_3\overset{\overset{O}{\|}}{C}H + O_2 \longrightarrow CH_3\overset{\overset{O}{\|}}{C}\!-\!O\!-\!OH$$
$$\text{Peroxyacetic acid}$$

$$CH_3\overset{\overset{O}{\|}}{C}\!-\!O\!-\!OH + CH_3CHO \xrightarrow[\text{Co(OCOCH}_3)_2]{\text{Mn(OCOCH}_3)_2 \text{ or}} 2\ CH_3COOH$$

Using 99–99.8 per cent acetaldehyde, 96 per cent acetic acid is obtained, which may be rectified readily to 99.5 per cent.

4. FROM BUTANE. Since 1952 increasing amounts of acetic acid have been made by the air oxidation of butane in the liquid phase. A mixture of air and a large excess of butane is passed into acetic acid containing dissolved manganese and cobalt acetates maintained at 165° under 300 p.s.i. The rate of flow of gases is such that the nitrogen and unreacted butane carry off the products as fast as they are formed. The oxygenated products, chiefly acetic acid and methyl ethyl ketone (p. 225), are washed out with water and separated by fractional distillation. Methyl ethyl ketone in excess of demand is recycled.

$$CH_3CH_2CH_2CH_3 + O_2 \longrightarrow CH_3CH_2COCH_3 + H_2O$$
$$\text{Methyl ethyl ketone}$$

$$2\ CH_3CH_2COCH_3 + 3\ O_2 \longrightarrow 4\ CH_3COOH$$

Acetic acid is used where a cheap organic acid is required; for the preparation of metallic salts, acetic anhydride (p. 164), and esters (p. 173); in the manufacture of cellulose acetate (p. 403) and white lead; as a precipitating agent for casein from milk, and for rubber or synthetic rubber from their aqueous emulsions (p. 709); and for numerous other purposes. **Sodium acetate** is used to reduce the acidity of mineral acids. **Lead acetate,** known as **sugar of lead,** and **basic lead acetate,** $Pb(OH)(OCOCH_3)$, are used to prepare other lead salts. **Verdigris** is the basic copper acetate, $Cu(OH)_2 \cdot 2\ Cu(OCOCH_3)_2$, and **Paris green** is a mixed cupric acetate-arsenite. **Aluminum acetate** is used to impregnate cotton cloth or fibers with aluminum hydroxide prior to dyeing, a process known as *mordanting* (p. 674).

Other Acids. Propionic acid and **butyric acid** may be made by the oxidation of the corresponding alcohols or aldehydes, or by special fermentation processes from starch. They are used in the manufacture of cellulose acetate-propionates and acetate-butyrates (p. 404). **Calcium propionate** is used in bread to prevent molding and ropiness.

The **higher normal acids** having an even number of carbon atoms are obtained by the hydrolysis of fats (p. 183). A few branched-chain fatty acids have been isolated from microorganisms. Hydrolysis of the antibiotic from *Bacillus polymyxa* gives 6-methyloctanoic acid. **Tuberculostearic acid,** from the fatty capsule of the tuberculosis bacillus, *Mycobacterium tuberculosis*, is 10-methyl-stearic acid. In Germany during World War II, paraffin from the Fischer-Tropsch synthesis (p. 83) was oxidized by air at 115°–125° in the presence of manganese salts to give a complex mixture of higher acids which served as a substitute for acids derived from natural fats.

ACYL HALIDES

Preparation

Since acyl halides result from the replacement of the hydroxyl group by a halogen atom, their structure is represented by the general formula $R-\overset{\overset{\displaystyle O}{\|}}{C}-X$. An inorganic acid halide such as phosphorus trichloride, phosphorus penta-chloride, thionyl chloride, or sulfuryl chloride must be used to effect this replacement. These compounds are the acid chlorides of phosphorous, phos-phoric, sulfurous, and sulfuric acids, respectively. Their reactions with organic acids take place according to the following equations.

$$3\ RCOOH + PCl_3 \longrightarrow 3\ RCOCl + P(OH)_3$$

$$RCOOH + PCl_5 \longrightarrow RCOCl + POCl_3 + HCl$$

$$RCOOH + SOCl_2 \longrightarrow RCOCl + SO_2 + HCl$$

$$2\ RCOOH + SO_2Cl_2 \longrightarrow 2\ RCOCl + H_2SO_4$$

If the sodium salt of the organic acid is used, phosphorus oxychloride also will react.

$$2\ RCOONa + POCl_3 \longrightarrow 2\ RCOCl + NaCl + NaPO_3$$

Hence when the sodium salt reacts with phosphorus pentachloride, three fifths of the total chlorine is available instead of only one fifth.

$$3\ RCOONa + PCl_5 \longrightarrow 3\ RCOCl + 2\ NaCl + NaPO_3$$

Thionyl chloride, $SOCl_2$, has an advantage over other reagents in that the acyl chloride is obtained in good yield and can be purified readily, the other products of the reaction being gases. For these reasons thionyl chloride is used for small scale preparations even though it is somewhat more expensive than the other reagents.

The **acyl bromides** may be made from organic acids and inorganic acid bromides analogous to the preparation of acyl chlorides. **Acyl iodides** are made ordinarily from the acyl chloride and calcium iodide or dry hydrogen iodide.

$$2\ RCOCl + CaI_2 \longrightarrow 2\ RCOI + CaCl_2$$

$$RCOCl + HI \longrightarrow RCOI + HCl$$

Similarly **acyl fluorides** are made from acyl chlorides and antimony fluoride or hydrogen fluoride.

Nomenclature

Acyl halides are named by dropping the ending *ic acid* from the name of the corresponding acid and adding *yl halide*; for example CH_3COCl is acetyl chloride or ethanoyl chloride, and $(CH_3)_2CHCOBr$ is *i*-butyryl bromide or 2-methylpropanoyl bromide. If common names are used for acyl halides having more than five carbon atoms in the chain, the ending is *oyl*. Thus lauric acid gives rise to lauroyl chloride. Where confusion may arise between common names systematic names should be used.

Physical Properties

Since the acyl halides do not contain hydrogen united to oxygen, no proton bonding can occur; hence they have normal boiling points. For example, acetic acid with a molecular weight of 60 boils at 118°, but acetyl chloride of molecular weight 78.5 boils at 51°. This value is between the boiling points of pentane (mol. wt. 72, b.p. 36°) and hexane (mol. wt. 86, b.p. 69°). Acyl halides are insoluble in water, the covalently-bound halogen atom having the effect of about two or three methylene groups in reducing the water solubility due to the carbonyl group. The acyl halides have a sharp odor and an irritating action on the mucous membranes.

Reactions

1. **With Water, Alcohols, and Ammonia.** The acyl halides may be considered as mixed anhydrides of a carboxylic acid and hydrogen halide and as such react like anhydrides in general with water, alcohols, and ammonia, giving acids, esters, and amides.

$$RCOCl \begin{cases} + \ HOH & \longrightarrow \quad RCOOH + HCl \\ + \ HOR' & \longrightarrow \quad RCOOR' + HCl \\ & \qquad\qquad \text{An ester} \\ + \ HNH_2 & \longrightarrow \quad RCONH_2 + HCl \xrightarrow{NH_3} NH_4Cl \\ & \qquad\qquad \text{An amide} \end{cases}$$

In the last reaction two moles of ammonia are required, since its rate of reaction with hydrogen chloride is greater than its rate of reaction with acyl chloride.

The greater ease of hydrolysis, alcoholysis, and ammonolysis of acyl halides when compared with alkyl halides may be ascribed to the inductive effect of the doubly bound oxygen atom (p. 153), which causes a lower electron density on the carbonyl carbon atom. The rate of reaction with electron-donating reagents is faster for acyl halides than for alkyl halides, even though the same inductive effect decreases the tendency of the chlorine to leave as a chloride ion.

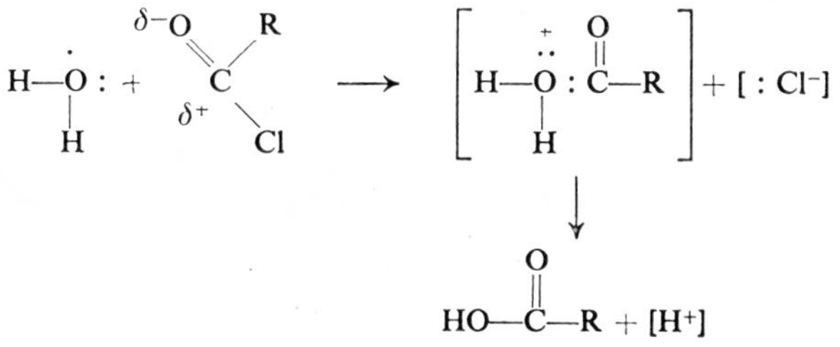

The inductive effect of the oxygen also accounts for the greater ease of substitution of the α hydrogen by halogen, since the positive charge on the carbonyl carbon atom facilitates the loss of a proton from the α carbon atom (Sec. 3 below).

2. **With Salts of Carboxylic Acids.** Acyl halides react with metallic salts of organic acids to give *carboxylic acid anhydrides.*

$$RCOCl + NaO\overset{O}{\overset{\|}{C}}\!-\!R' \longrightarrow R\overset{O}{\overset{\|}{C}}\!-\!O\!-\!\overset{O}{\overset{\|}{C}}R' + NaCl$$

3. **With Halogen.** Acyl halides halogenate more readily than hydrocarbons and free acids. Moreover only an α hydrogen atom, that is, one on the first carbon atom adjoining the carbonyl group, is replaced readily.

$$RCH_2COX + X_2 \longrightarrow RCHXCOX + HX$$

In actual practice free acids are used, the halogenation being carried out in the presence of a small amount of phosphorus trihalide. The reactions then are

$$3\,RCH_2COOH + PX_3 \longrightarrow 3\,RCH_2COX + P(OH)_3$$

$$RCH_2COX + X_2 \longrightarrow RCHXCOX + HX$$

$$RCHXCOX + RCH_2COOH \rightleftarrows RCHXCOOH + RCH_2COX$$

Because of the last reaction a small amount of acid halide is sufficient to permit the direct halogenation of a large amount of acid. This procedure for making halogen acids is known as the *Hell-Volhard-Zelinsky reaction.*

4. **Reduction.** (*a*) CATALYTIC REDUCTION TO ALDEHYDES (*Rosenmund reduction*). Acyl chlorides can be reduced catalytically to aldehydes using a palladium catalyst. The catalyst usually is partially poisoned by the addition of sulfur compounds which renders it inactive for the catalysis of the further reduction of aldehydes to alcohols.

$$RCOCl + H_2 \overset{Pd}{\longrightarrow} RCHO + HCl$$

(*b*) LITHIUM ALUMINUM HYDRIDE REDUCTION TO ALCOHOLS. When an ether solution of lithium aluminum hydride is added to an acyl halide, reduction to the alcohol takes place. The product is the lithium aluminum salt of the alcohol, from which the alcohol is liberated by adding hydrochloric acid.

$$4\,RCOCl + 2\,LiAlH_4 \longrightarrow (RCH_2O)_4LiAl + LiAlCl_4$$

$$(RCH_2O)_4LiAl + 4\,HCl \longrightarrow 4\,RCH_2OH + LiAlCl_4$$

ACID ANHYDRIDES

Preparation

Two general methods for the preparation of acid anhydrides may be used, the first of which, from an acid halide and a salt, clearly defines the structure of carboxylic acid anhydrides.

$$R\overset{O}{\overset{\|}{C}}Cl + Na^+\!\!{}^-O\overset{O}{\overset{\|}{C}}R' \longrightarrow R\overset{O}{\overset{\|}{C}}\!-\!O\!-\!\overset{O}{\overset{\|}{C}}R' + NaCl$$

The second method depends on the fact that an equilibrium exists between carboxylic acids and acid anhydrides.

$$2\,RCOOH + CH_3\overset{O}{\overset{\|}{C}}\!-\!O\!-\!\overset{O}{\overset{\|}{C}}CH_3 \rightleftarrows R\overset{O}{\overset{\|}{C}}\!-\!O\!-\!\overset{O}{\overset{\|}{C}}R + 2\,CH_3COOH$$

Since acetic acid boils at a lower temperature than any other component in the system, it can be removed by careful distillation and the reaction forced to completion. The first reaction may be used for preparing anhydrides in which the R groups are either alike or different. Although the second method is suitable only for the preparation of anhydrides in which both R groups are the same, it is preferred for this purpose because of the availability and low cost of acetic anhydride and the excellent yields.

Nomenclature

A member of this class of compounds is named by adding the word *anhydride* to the name of the acid or acids from which it is derived. For example $(CH_3CO)_2O$ is acetic anhydride or ethanoic anhydride, and $(CH_3CO)O(COCH_2CH_2CH_3)$ is acetic butyric anhydride or ethanoic butanoic anhydride. Those anhydrides having both R groups alike are called *simple anhydrides* whereas those with different R groups are known as *mixed anhydrides*. The former are the more important.

Physical Properties

Anhydrides have higher boiling points than hydrocarbons but lower than alcohols of comparable molecular weight. Acetic anhydride and its higher homologs are insoluble in water. Like the acid halides, the volatile anhydrides are irritating to the mucous membranes.

Acetic anhydride might be expected to be soluble in water because of the relatively large amount of oxygen present. However the resonance energy arising from the interaction of the *p* orbitals of the oxygen and carbon atoms is high (40 kcal.). Consequently there is little tendency for the oxygen atoms to form proton bonds with water molecules.

Reactions

The reactions of carboxylic acid anhydrides with water, alcohols, and ammonia are identical with those of acyl halides except that an organic acid replaces halogen acid as a product of the reactions.

$$
R—\overset{O}{\overset{\|}{C}}—O—\overset{O}{\overset{\|}{C}}—R
\begin{cases}
+\ HOH & \longrightarrow & RCOOH + RCOOH \\
+\ HOR' & \longrightarrow & RCOOR' + RCOOH \\
& & \text{An ester} \\
+\ HNH_2 & \longrightarrow & RCONH_2 + RCOOH \xrightarrow{NH_3} RCOONH_4 \\
& & \text{An amide}
\end{cases}
$$

The reaction of anhydrides with sodium peroxide in aqueous solution gives the **acyl peroxides** (p. 877).

$$2\,(RCO)_2O + Na_2O_2 \longrightarrow R\overset{O}{\overset{\|}{C}}—O—O—\overset{O}{\overset{\|}{C}}R + 2\,NaOCOR$$

Acetyl peroxide is useful as a source of free acetate and methyl radicals.

$$CH_3CO—O—O—COCH_3 \longrightarrow 2\,[CH_3COO\cdot] \longrightarrow 2\,[CH_3\cdot] + CO_2$$

It should be used with care and only in small amounts, because it explodes when heated.

Acetic Anhydride

Acetic anhydride is the only important member of the series. When the chief source of acetic acid was pyroligneous acid, from which it was recovered as calcium or sodium acetate, the anhydride was prepared by the reaction of sodium acetate with one half of the amount of sulfuryl chloride, or of sulfur chloride and chlorine, necessary to form acetyl chloride. The acetyl chloride thus formed reacted with the remainder of the salt to give the anhydride. With the advent of synthetic acetic acid and other methods of recovery from aqueous solutions, new methods of preparation of the anhydride were developed. In one procedure acetic acid is added to acetylene in the presence of mercury salts to give ethylidene acetate, which then is decomposed by heating with acid catalysts such as sulfuric acid or zinc chloride to give acetaldehyde and acetic anhydride.

$$
HC{\equiv}CH + 2\ CH_3COOH \xrightarrow{\text{Hg salts}} H_3C{-}\underset{\underset{OCOCH_3}{|}}{\overset{\overset{OCOCH_3}{|}}{CH}} \xrightarrow[\text{or ZnCl}_2]{H_2SO_4} CH_3CHO + (CH_3CO)_2O
$$

Ethylidene acetate

In a second process the anhydride is formed by the controlled air oxidation of acetaldehyde. Some anhydride always is formed in the synthesis of acetic acid from acetaldehyde, the intermediate peroxyacetic acid (p. 159) apparently reacting with acetaldehyde to give anhydride and water.

$$
CH_3{-}\overset{\overset{O}{\|}}{C}{-}O{-}OH + CH_3CHO \longrightarrow (CH_3CO)_2O + H_2O
$$

By using a cobalt acetate-copper acetate catalyst at 50°, increasing the speed of oxidation, and using an entrainer such as ethyl acetate, it is possible to convert two thirds of the acetaldehyde to acetic anhydride while one third is converted to acetic acid. By distillation at reduced pressure the temperature is kept low enough to permit removal of the aqueous azeotrope without hydrolysis of the anhydride.

A third process of importance at present is the addition of acetic acid to ketene (p. 760). Ketene is a gas prepared by the decomposition of acetic acid or acetone. Acetic acid vapor containing ethyl phosphate is heated to 700°–720°, or acetic acid vapor is passed over aluminum phosphate at 600°–700°.

$$
CH_3COOH \longrightarrow \underset{\text{Ketene}}{CH_2{=}C{=}O} + H_2O
$$

The mixture of ketene, water, and acetic acid vapor is cooled quickly to condense the water and unreacted acetic acid. The ketene then is absorbed in acetic acid in a scrubbing tower, giving acetic anhydride.

$$
CH_2{=}C{=}O + HOOCCH_3 \longrightarrow \underset{\overset{\|}{O}\quad\overset{\|}{O}}{CH_3C{-}O{-}CCH_3}
$$

In the alternate procedure for the manufacture of ketene, acetone is decomposed noncatalytically at 700°.

$$
CH_3COCH_3 \longrightarrow CH_2{=}C{=}O + CH_4
$$

Acetic anhydride is used chiefly to make esters that cannot be made by direct esterification of alcohols with acetic acid. The most important of these is cellulose acetate. Production of acetic anhydride in the United States rose from 250 million pounds in 1940 to 842 million pounds in 1955, when it was valued at 15 cents per pound.

ESTERS

Preparation

Most of the procedures for making esters have been described, namely direct esterification between an acid and an alcohol (p. 160), the reaction of a metallic salt with an alkyl halide (p. 153), the reaction of an acyl halide with an alcohol (p. 161), and the reaction of an acid anhydride with an alcohol (p. 163). A few generalizations should be made about these reactions. In the first place all except direct esterification proceed practically to completion. However, side reactions may take place, particularly with tertiary alcohols and tertiary alkyl halides, which make the reactions useless unless special conditions can be found that will produce satisfactory yields. In general the ease of loss of water from alcohols or of halogen acid from alkyl halides is tertiary > secondary > primary (pp. 104, 115). Therefore when a tertiary alcohol reacts with an acid anhydride, which is a dehydrating agent, or when a tertiary alkyl halide reacts with a sodium salt, which acts as a base, the rate of olefin formation is much greater than the rate of ester formation and only olefin results.

The constitution of the carboxylic acid affects the rate of esterification. Thus the rate of esterification of aliphatic carboxylic acids with methyl alcohol decreases with increasing substitution by alkyl groups on the α and β carbon atoms of the acid.

The effect bears a rough relationship to the sum of the number of substituents on the α and β carbon atoms. For each of the following compounds, the first number in the parentheses is the sum of the number of α and β substituents, and the second is the relative rate compared to acetic acid: dimethylacetic acid (2, 0.33); trimethylacetic acid (3, 0.037); di-*n*-butylacetic acid (4, 0.008); methyl-*t*-butylacetic acid (5, 0.0006); dimethyl-*t*-butylacetic acid (6, 0.0001). For those compounds studied, the right order of magnitude is obtained if one assumes that beyond two substituents, the rate is decreased to one seventh of the previous value for each additional substituent on a γ or β carbon atom. If there are at least three substituents on γ carbon atoms, a further decrease in rate is observed. Groups on the α and β carbon atoms block the approach of an alcohol molecule, which must attack the carbon atom of the carboxyl group (p. 168). This blocking effect of substituents is another example of steric hindrance (cf. p. 117).

When acetic acid is esterified with various alcohols, little decrease in rate is observed with increasing substitution in the alcohol. Such an effect might become noticeable, however, if a more highly substituted acid were used.

Tertiary alkyl esters are cleaved very readily by hydrogen halides. Hence the action of an acyl halide on a tertiary alcohol usually results in the formation of the alkyl halide and the organic acid. A good method for preparing *t*-butyl bromide is by the reaction of *t*-butyl alcohol and acetyl bromide.

$$(CH_3)_3COH + BrCOCH_3 \longrightarrow (CH_3)_3C—O—COCH_3 + HBr$$

$$\downarrow$$

$$(CH_3)_3CBr + HOCOCH_3$$

If the halogen acid is removed as fast as it is formed, fair yields of tertiary esters may be obtained. For example when acetyl chloride reacts with *t*-butyl alcohol in the presence of magnesium, the yield of *t*-butyl acetate is 50 per cent.

$$(CH_3)_3COH + ClCOCH_3 + \tfrac{1}{2} Mg \longrightarrow (CH_3)_3C—O—COCH_3 + \tfrac{1}{2} MgCl_2 + \tfrac{1}{2} H_2$$

Similarly a 65 per cent yield can be obtained using an organic tertiary amine base such as dimethylaniline (p. 488) in place of magnesium.

$$(CH_3)_3COH + ClCOCH_3 + C_6H_5N(CH_3)_2 \longrightarrow (CH_3)_3C—O—COCH_3 + [C_6H_5\overset{+}{N}(CH_3)_2H]Cl^-$$

Just as tertiary alkyl ethers can be made by the addition of alcohols to olefins (p. 138), so tertiary alkyl esters can be made by the addition of carboxylic acids to olefins.

$$CH_3COOH + CH_2{=}CCH_3 \quad \xrightarrow[\text{or HBF}_4]{H_2SO_4} \quad CH_3COOC(CH_3)_3$$
$$\underset{CH_3}{} \qquad \qquad \text{\textit{t}-Butyl acetate}$$

Methyl esters can be made readily by the reaction of carboxylic acids with diazomethane (p. 266).

Direct esterification is a good example of a reversible reaction. The term *reversible reaction* ordinarily is used to mean either that appreciable quantities of the original reactants still are present when equilibrium between the forward and reverse reactions is reached, or that the rate of attaining equilibrium, that is, the mobility of the reaction, is so great that the reaction can be reversed readily by altering concentrations.

The esterification reaction has been studied extensively to determine the quantitative laws of reversible reactions, because no by-products are formed in the reaction, the analytical procedures are simple and accurate, the reaction takes place at a convenient rate for measurements, and the position of equilibrium is such that it can be determined accurately. The reaction may be written

$$RCOOH + HOR' \underset{V_2}{\overset{V_1}{\rightleftarrows}} RCOOR' + H_2O$$

The velocities V_1 of the forward reaction and V_2 of the reverse reaction are proportional to the mole fractions of the reacting substances.

$$V_1 = k_1[RCOOH][R'OH]$$

$$V_2 = k_2[RCOOR'][H_2O]$$

At the start of the reaction the concentrations of alcohol and acid are at a maximum and those of the products are zero. Consequently V_1 is at its maximum and V_2 is zero. As the reactants are used and the products are formed, V_1 decreases and V_2 increases. A point eventually will be reached where $V_1 = V_2$, which is the condition for chemical equilibrium. Therefore at equilibrium

$$k_1[RCOOH][R'OH] = k_2[RCOOR'][H_2O]$$

$$\frac{k_1}{k_2} = \frac{[RCOOR'][H_2O]}{[RCOOH][R'OH]} = K_E$$

K_E is known as the *equilibrium constant* for the reaction.

When one mole of ethyl alcohol and one mole of acetic acid are allowed to react until equilibrium is reached, two thirds of a mole of ethyl acetate and two thirds of a mole of water are present in equilibrium with one third mole of ethyl acetate and one third mole of acetic acid. Exactly the same equilibrium composition is reached starting with one mole of water and one mole of ethyl acetate. Since there is no change in the total number of moles during this reaction, one may substitute moles for mole fraction in the equation and calculate the equilibrium constant.

$$K_E = \frac{2/3 \times 2/3}{1/3 \times 1/3} = 4$$

Knowing the equilibrium constant, it is possible to calculate the equilibrium composition starting with any mole ratio of ethyl alcohol and acetic acid.

The position of equilibrium is not affected by catalysts, since at this stage catalysts affect the rates of the forward and reverse reactions to exactly the same extent. Catalysts merely change the mobility of the system, that is, the time required to attain equilibrium.

Although the mass law holds very well for the esterification reaction, the good agreement probably is fortuitous because the solution is not ideal, a condition necessary for strict adherence to the mass law. Nonideality also may account for the fact that the position of equilibrium is not always independent of the presence of catalysts. Thus when the number of moles of hydrogen chloride for one mole of ethyl alcohol and one mole of acetic acid is increased from about 0.005 to 0.33, the apparent equilibrium constant changes from 4.3 to 8.8 because of the change in the environment of the reaction.

The effect of temperature on the position of equilibrium is governed by the principle of Le Chatelier. If heat is evolved in a reaction (*exothermic reaction*), the position of equilibrium will shift to the left as the temperature is increased, whereas if heat is absorbed (*endothermic reaction*), the reaction will go more nearly to completion as the temperature is raised. The esterification reaction is only slightly exothermic (ΔH = ca. -1 kcal.), and hence temperature has practically no effect on the position of equilibrium.

Temperature, like catalysts, has a marked effect on the mobility of the system. Roughly speaking, the rate of a chemical reaction increases from two to three times for each rise of ten degrees in temperature. Pressure affects the position of equilibrium only if a change in volume results during the course of the reaction. Marked changes in volume occur only when one or more of the reactants is a gas under the conditions of the experiment. Where gases are involved, pressure also will affect the rate of attaining equilibrium, since increase in pressure results in an increase in the concentration of the reactants.

The equation for the equilibrium constant indicates that the reaction may be forced in the direction of forming more product by increasing the concentration of either the alcohol or the acid. If the value of the denominator is increased and K_E remains constant, the value of the numerator also must increase. When one reactant is very cheap and the other relatively costly, a large excess of the cheaper compound may be used advantageously to force more complete utilization of the more expensive one. Another way to force complete utilization of the reactants is to remove one or both of the products, since a decrease in the value of the numerator forces a decrease in that of the denominator. The second procedure is the better, when it can be employed, because the reactants can be used in stoichiometric proportions and complete conversion can be obtained. When water is one of the products, it often may be removed readily by azeotropic distillation (p. 93).

Superficially the reaction of an alcohol and an acid appears to resemble neutralization of a base by an acid, but nothing could be further from the truth. Neutralization is a reaction between ions, is almost instantaneous at room temperature in the absence of a catalyst, and goes to completion. Esterification is a reaction between molecules, is slow even at elevated temperatures, requiring a catalyst to attain a practical rate, and does not go to completion.

The mechanism of acid-catalyzed esterification is not thoroughly understood, but the following series of equilibria give a picture of the complexity of the reactions taking place in the esterification of a primary or secondary alcohol by a weak acid, and of the function of the catalysts. In the equilibria the convention has been adopted that the reagent is placed above a double arrow and the minor product below the double arrow (p. 138). If reagents are given both above and below the same pair of arrows, the step is one of direct displacement with or without Walden inversion (p. 116), or is one of proton transfer. Using this convention, it is possible to avoid writing each step as a separate equilibrium.

It frequently is argued that in writing intermediates of this sort the (+) charge should be indicated outside of the bracket, since the intermediate is a resonance hybrid and the charge is not on one oxygen atom any more than on the other but is distributed over the group as a whole. Although the latter statement is true, in the structure as it is written the charge is certainly on one oxygen atom and not on the other. If the charge is to be placed outside of the bracket, the group should be represented by the symbolism for a resonance hybrid (p. 154). The simple electronic valence structure is less cumbersome, however, and is satisfactory for most purposes.

Although a strong acid such as sulfuric acid is the actual material added, an equilibrium at once is established in which all the bases present—sulfate ions, carboxylic acid molecules, water, ester, and alcohol molecules—compete for the available proton. Accordingly the catalyst is indicated as HB, where B is any base and may be a neutral molecule or a negatively charged ion depending on whether HB is a positively charged group such as the ammonium ion, $[NH_4^+]$, or a neutral molecule such as hydrogen chloride, HCl.

The catalysis involves the transfer of the proton from one base to another, an hence the point of attack will be an electron-dense portion of the molecule. The first effective step is the transfer of the proton to the carbonyl group of the acid (I) with elimination of another base. Next the available electrons on an alcohol molecule satisfy the electron-deficient carbon atom of II to give III. A base removes a proton from III to give an intermediate IV, which accepts a proton from a proton donor to give V. Loss of water gives VI, which loses a proton to a base to give the ester VII. The acid-catalyzed hydrolysis of an ester is the exact reverse of this series going from VII to I. From this series of reactions the over-all equation may be obtained by cancelling reagents appearing both above and below the double arrows. The reactants are the initial compound and the reagents remaining above the arrows, and the products are the final compound and the reagents remaining below the arrows. The series of equilibria then reduces to

$$RCOOH + HOR' \rightleftarrows RCOOR' + H_2O$$

Besides the equilibria indicated, numerous other proton transfer reactions are taking place simultaneously which do not lead to new products. Moreover since all steps are reversible, not every molecule which reaches an intermediate stage completes the series and ends up as product. The final composition is dependent on the relative thermodynamic stability of the reactants and the products.

This mechanism accounts for the fact that, in the esterification of primary and secondary alcohols by weak acids, the oxygen atom in the eliminated water molecule comes not from the alcohol but from the acid (acyl-oxygen scission). Experimental evidence for this type of scission was obtained first from the esterification of carboxylic acids with mercaptans, the sulfur analogs of alcohols (p. 278). A rigid proof that alcohols behave in the same way results from the esterification of an acid containing ordinary oxygen with an alcohol containing a high percentage of the O^{18} isotope. The labeled oxygen becomes a part of the ester molecule and not of the water molecule.

$$RCOOH + HO^{18}R' \rightleftarrows RCOO^{18}R' + H_2O$$

Moreover alcohols such as neopentyl alcohol which normally rearrange if a hydroxide ion becomes detached from the hydrocarbon radical (p. 105) esterify without rearrangement. Indications are that the esterification of tertiary alcohols takes place by a different mechanism in which the oxygen atom eliminated as water comes from the alcohol (alkyl-oxygen scission, p. 171). In fact four distinct types of acid-catalyzed esterification and hydrolysis have been proposed.

Nomenclature

Esters are named as if they were alkyl salts of the organic acids, because the early investigators assumed that esterification is analogous to neutralization. Thus $CH_3COOC_2H_5$ is ethyl acetate or ethyl ethanoate. It is necessary to be careful to recognize the portion of the molecule derived from the acid and that from the alcohol, particularly in condensed structural formulas. For example both $(CH_3)_2CHOCOCH_2CH_3$ and $CH_3CH_2COOCH(CH_3)_2$ are *i*-propyl propionate and not ethyl *i*-butyrate. No difficulty will be encountered if it is remembered that the oxygen of a carbonyl group usually immediately follows the carbon atom to which it is attached and that the alkyl group from the alcohol portion of the ester is joined to an oxygen atom. If it is necessary to name esters as substitution products, the ester group is called an *alkoxycarbonyl* group. For example $COOCH_3$ is the methoxycarbonyl group.

Physical Properties

The esters have normal boiling points, but their solubility in water is less than would be expected from the amount of oxygen present. Ethyl acetate with four carbon atoms and two oxygen atoms dissolves to about the same extent as *n*-butyl alcohol, which has four carbon atoms and one oxygen atom (cf. acid anhydrides, p. 163). The volatile esters have pleasant odors which usually are described as fruity.

Reactions

The reactions of the esters depend for the most part on the scission of the linkage between the carbonyl group and the alkoxy group (*acyl-oxygen scission*), or between the alkyl group and the oxygen atom (*alkyl-oxygen scission*). The ease of scission of a carbon-oxygen bond and the type of catalysis which is possible depend on the groups attached to the carbon atoms joined by the oxygen atom. Ethers, R—O—R, having two alkyl groups joined by oxygen are hydrolyzed least readily, and the hydrolysis is subject only to acid catalysis. Esters, RCO—O—R, in which one acyl and one alkyl group are linked through oxygen are hydrolyzed more readily, and both acids and bases catalyze the reaction. Anhydrides, RCO—O—COR, having two acyl groups joined by oxygen are most easily hydrolyzed, water alone bringing about the reaction.

1. **Hydrolysis or Saponification.** Esters may be split by water (hydrolysis) in the presence of either acidic or basic catalysts.

$$RCOOR' + HOH \quad \overset{[H^+]}{\underset{}{\rightleftarrows}} \quad RCOOH + HOR'$$

$$RCOOR' + HOH \quad \overset{[OH^-]}{\underset{}{\rightleftarrows}} \quad RCOOH + HOR'$$
$$\downarrow [OH^-]$$
$$[RCOO^-] + HOH$$

Alkaline hydrolysis frequently is referred to as **saponification,** because it is the type of reaction used in the preparation of soaps (p. 188). The acid-catalyzed reaction is exactly the reverse of acid-catalyzed esterification and either results in the same equilibrium. The base-catalyzed hydrolysis goes to completion and requires one equivalent of alkali for each equivalent of ester, because the acid formed in the base-catalyzed equilibrium reacts irreversibly with the catalyst to form a salt and water. The over-all reaction becomes

$$RCOOR' + NaOH \quad \longrightarrow \quad [RCOO^-]Na^+ + R'OH$$

Because this reaction goes to completion, alkaline saponification is used as a quantitative procedure for the estimation of esters. A weighed sample of the unknown is refluxed with an excess of a standardized aqueous or alcoholic solution of alkali, and the excess base at the end of the reaction is titrated with standard acid using a suitable indicator, usually phenolphthalein (p. 700). The equivalent weight as determined by saponification is called the **saponification equivalent** of the ester.

Since in the acid-catalyzed hydrolysis the same position of equilibrium is attained as in esterification, the effect of the constitution of the alcohol and of the acid on the rate of hydrolysis is the same as their effect on the rate of esterification (p. 165). In alkaline hydrolysis the substitution of hydrogen atoms of both acetic acid and methyl alcohol by alkyl groups greatly decreases the rate of reaction. Thus the rate of saponification for ethyl trimethylacetate is about one hundredth of that for ethyl acetate, and the rate for *t*-butyl acetate one hundredth of that for methyl acetate.

2. **Alcoholysis.** The alkoxy group of an ester of a primary or secondary alcohol and a weak acid may be exchanged readily for that of another alcohol using an acidic or basic catalyst.

$$RCOOR' + HOR'' \quad \overset{[H^+] \text{ or } [R'O]^-}{\underset{}{\rightleftarrows}} \quad RCOOR'' + HOR'$$

Both types of catalysis lead to the same equilibrium, since an acid is not one of the products of reaction. Alkoxide ion, formed by the reaction of an active metal, for example sodium, with the alcohol involved, is used as the basic catalyst rather than hydroxide ion, because the latter would cause saponification of the ester.

Acid-catalyzed hydrolysis of an ester is merely the reverse of esterification (p. 168), and acid-catalyzed alcoholysis is identical except that a second alcohol replaces water. It has been mentioned several times that acyl-oxygen scission takes place during the esterification of primary or secondary alcohols with weak acids. For esters of strong acids such as sulfuric or sulfonic acids, or esters or tertiary alcohols, reaction with alcohols leads to ether formation and not to transesterification. These reactions probably result from a displacement by the alcohol on carbon, and if so, would be expected to proceed with alkyl-oxygen scission.

$$C_2H_5 : O : + CH_3 : O : \longrightarrow \left[C_2H_5 : \overset{+}{O} : CH_3 \right]\left[\overset{-}{:} O : SO_3CH_3 \right]$$
$$\quad H \qquad\qquad SO_3CH_3 \qquad\qquad\qquad H$$

$$CH_3 : O : + (CH_3)_3C : O : CR \longrightarrow \left[CH_3 : \overset{+}{O} : C(CH_3)_3 \right]\left[\overset{-}{:} O : CR \right]$$
$$\quad H \qquad\qquad\quad O \qquad\qquad\qquad\quad H \qquad\qquad\qquad O$$

Loss of proton from the oxonium ion would yield the ether.

Basic catalysis differs from acid catalysis in that the catalyst is an electron-rich group, and the point of attack will be the carbon atom of the carbonyl group, which is deficient in electrons because of the greater electron-attracting power of the oxygen atom. It has been shown that the same intermediate is formed in alkaline saponification as in acid-catalyzed hydrolysis (IV, p. 168).

$$R'O-\overset{\overset{O}{\|}}{\underset{R}{C}} \rightleftharpoons \overset{[-OH]}{\longrightarrow} \left[R'O-\overset{\overset{O^-}{}}{\underset{R}{C}}-OH \right] \overset{H_2O}{\underset{[-OH]}{\rightleftharpoons}} \left[R'O-\overset{\overset{OH}{}}{\underset{R}{C}}-OH \right] \underset{HOR'}{\rightleftharpoons} \overset{\overset{O}{\|}}{\underset{R}{C}}-OH$$

The acid reacts irreversibly with hydroxide ion to form the salt.

$$RCOOH + [^-OH] \longrightarrow [RCOO^-] + H_2O$$

These mechanisms agree with the fact that when either the alkaline saponification or the acid-catalyzed hydrolysis of an ester is carried out in water rich in O^{18}, the O^{18} isotope enters the acid molecule but not the alcohol molecule formed on hydrolysis.

$$\left[H : \overset{-}{O} : \right] + H : \overset{18}{\overset{..}{O}} : H \rightleftharpoons H : \overset{..}{O} : H + \left[\overset{-}{:} \overset{18}{\overset{..}{O}} : H \right]$$

$$\overset{\overset{O}{\|}}{RC}-OR' + \left[\overset{-}{:} \overset{18}{\overset{..}{O}} : H \right] \longrightarrow \left[R-\overset{\overset{O}{\|}}{C}-O^{18-} \right] + HOR'$$

$$\overset{\overset{O}{\|}}{RCOR'} + H_2O^{18} \overset{[H^+]}{\rightleftharpoons} RCO^{18}H + HOR'$$

3. **Ammonolysis.** Ammonia splits esters with the formation of amides.

$$\overset{\overset{O}{\|}}{RC}-OR' + : NH_3 \rightleftharpoons \overset{\overset{O}{\|}}{RC}-NH_2 + R'OH$$

The mechanism of ammonolysis probably is identical with base-catalyzed hydrolysis or alcoholysis, the ammonia molecule taking the place of the hydroxide or alkoxide ion.

4. **Scission by Acids.** Dry hydrogen bromide, hydrogen iodide, and concentrated sulfuric acid split esters just as they do ethers (p. 140), the products being the organic acid and the alkyl halide or alkyl hydrogen sulfate.

$$RCOOR' + HBr \rightleftharpoons RCOOH + R'Br$$

The reaction is important principally in the determination of methoxyl and ethoxyl by the Zeisel procedure (p. 140).

5. **Reduction.** The ester group, and thus indirectly the carboxyl group, can be converted into a primary alcohol group by reduction either with sodium and an alcohol, or catalytically. These reactions involve addition of hydrogen to the carbonyl group and elimination of the alkoxyl group.

$$RCOOR' + 4\,Na + 2\,R'OH \longrightarrow RCH_2ONa + 3\,NaOR'$$

Addition of water liberates the alcohol from its salt. Ordinarily in the *sodium-alcohol reduction* the methyl, ethyl, or *n*-butyl esters are used along with an excess of the corresponding alcohol as solvent and source of hydrogen. Improved yields are obtained if an equivalent amount of a higher boiling secondary alcohol, such as the secondary hexyl alcohols or methylcyclohexanols (p. 841), is used as the source of hydrogen in an inert solvent such as toluene or xylene (p. 65). *Lithium aluminum hydride*, LiAlH$_4$, in ether solution may be used as a reducing agent instead of sodium.

$$4\,RCOOR' + 2\,LiAlH_4 \longrightarrow LiAl(OCH_2R)_4 + LiAl(OR')_4$$

One half mole or 19 g. of lithium aluminum hydride is equivalent in reducing power to four atoms or 92 g. of sodium. The former is, however, a considerably more expensive reagent, since it is made from lithium hydride.

$$4\,LiH + AlCl_3 \longrightarrow LiAlH_4 + 3\,LiCl$$

In the *catalytic reduction* of esters, a copper oxide-chromium oxide catalyst is used with hydrogen in the absence of a solvent at 200° and 200 atmospheres.

$$RCOOR' + 2\,H_2 \xrightarrow[200°,\ 200\ at.]{CuO-Cr_2O_3} RCH_2OH + HOR'$$

Catalytic reduction of esters is preferred to sodium-alcohol reduction for large-scale laboratory preparations if suitable apparatus is available.

Acids may be reduced catalytically to alcohols at 350°–400° using a copper-zinc-cadmium oxide-chromium oxide catalyst. The process has had some commercial application but is not generally used in the laboratory. Likewise it is possible to reduce acids with lithium aluminum hydride, but three moles of reagent is required for each mole of acid, because the first stage is the formation of the salt of the acid with liberation of hydrogen.

$$4\,RCOOH + 3\,LiAlH_4 \longrightarrow (RCH_2O)_4LiAl + 2\,LiAlO_2 + 2\,H_2$$

The reduction of esters to alcohols is important for preparing higher alcohols from natural fat acids. Thus octyl, decyl, dodecyl (lauryl), tetradecyl (myristyl), hexadecyl (cetyl), and octadecyl (stearyl) alcohols can be made readily from the corresponding fat acids. The mixed alcohols formed by the reduction of coconut oil are used in the manufacture of synthetic detergents

(p. 191). The reaction is important also because it is the last step in a series of reactions which permits the continuous increase in length of a hydrocarbon chain one carbon atom at a time.

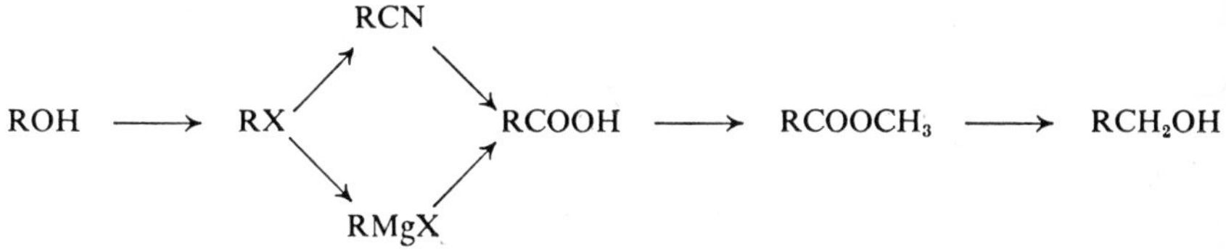

$$ROH \longrightarrow RX \begin{array}{c} \nearrow \quad RCN \quad \searrow \\ \\ \searrow \quad RMgX \quad \nearrow \end{array} RCOOH \longrightarrow RCOOCH_3 \longrightarrow RCH_2OH$$

Repetition of the above series of reactions gives the higher homologs.

6. Reaction with Grignard Reagents. Grignard reagents add to a carbonyl group (p. 123). When they react with an ester, the initial addition product loses magnesium alkoxide to give a ketone which adds a second mole of Grignard reagent. Therefore the final product of the reaction of an ester with a Grignard reagent is the magnesium salt of a tertiary alcohol, which yields the alcohol on decomposition with water.

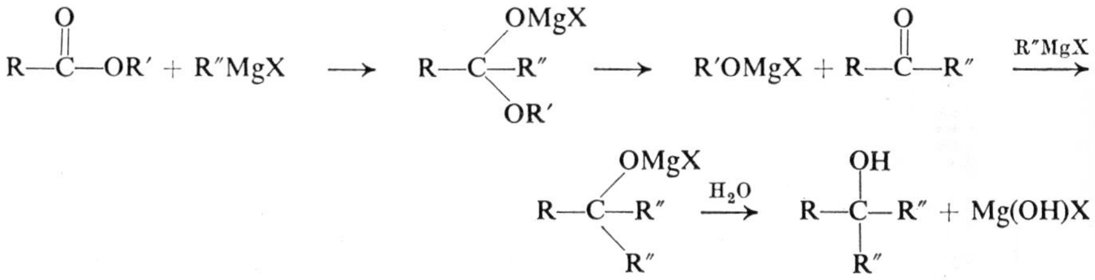

$$R-\overset{O}{\underset{||}{C}}-OR' + R''MgX \longrightarrow R-\overset{OMgX}{\underset{OR'}{\overset{|}{C}}}-R'' \longrightarrow R'OMgX + R-\overset{O}{\underset{||}{C}}-R'' \xrightarrow{R''MgX}$$

$$R-\overset{OMgX}{\underset{R''}{\overset{|}{C}}}-R'' \xrightarrow{H_2O} R-\overset{OH}{\underset{R''}{\overset{|}{C}}}-R'' + Mg(OH)X$$

7. Acyloin Formation. When an ester in ether solution reacts with sodium, condensation of two moles of the ester takes place with the formation of the sodium salt of the enol form (p. 131) of a hydroxy ketone. Addition of water gives the hydroxy ketone which is known as an **acyloin.**

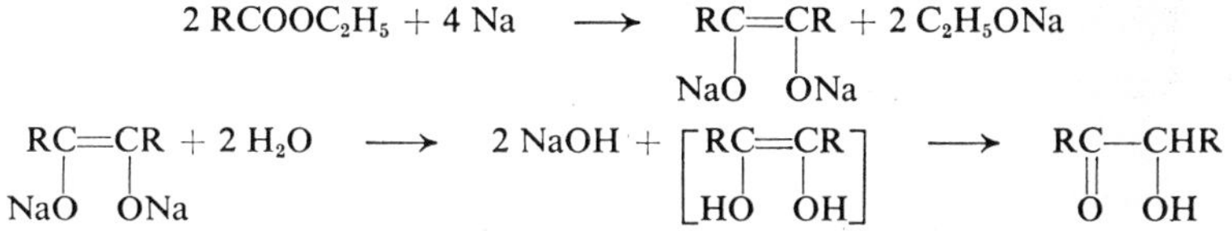

$$2\,RCOOC_2H_5 + 4\,Na \longrightarrow \underset{NaO\quad ONa}{RC{=}CR} + 2\,C_2H_5ONa$$

$$\underset{NaO\quad ONa}{RC{=}CR} + 2\,H_2O \longrightarrow 2\,NaOH + \left[\underset{HO\quad OH}{RC{=}CR}\right] \longrightarrow \underset{O\quad OH}{RC{-}CHR}$$

An acyloin

8. Pyrolysis to Olefins. When esters having hydrogen on the β carbon atom of the alkoxy group are heated to 500°, a molecule of acid is lost with the formation of an olefin. Esters of primary alcohols give 1-alkenes.

$$RCOOCH_2CH_2R' \xrightarrow{500°} RCOOH + CH_2{=}CHR'$$

When esters of secondary or tertiary alcohols are decomposed, a primary β hydrogen is removed in preference to secondary and secondary in preference to tertiary. This order is the opposite of that for the dehydration of alcohols (p. 104).

Uses

By far the most important general use for esters is as solvents, especially for cellulose nitrate in the formulation of lacquers (p. 402). For this purpose ethyl acetate and butyl acetate are used to the greatest extent. Production of these two esters in the United States in 1955 was 77 and 67 million pounds valued at 10 and 13 cents per pound respectively. Ethyl formate is used as a fumigant and larvicide for grains and food products. Higher boiling esters are used as softening agents (plasticizers) for resins and plastics (p. 552), and a number of the resins and plastics are themselves esters, such as polymethyl methacrylate (p. 788), polyvinyl acetate (p. 736), cellulose acetate (p. 403), Dacron (p. 555), and alkyd resins (p. 552).

Some of the volatile esters have specific fruit odors. For example, the odors of *i*-amyl acetate, *i*-amyl valerate, butyl butyrate and *i*-butyl propionate resemble the odors of banana, apple, pineapple, and rum respectively. Hence they are used to a limited extent in synthetic flavors or perfumes. Natural odors and flavors are the result of complex mixtures of organic compounds. Very careful blending of synthetic compounds is necessary to imitate the natural product. Table 12 summarizes the results of a careful analysis of the substances responsible

TABLE 12

COMPOSITION OF THE VOLATILE OIL OF THE PINEAPPLE

WINTER FRUIT		SUMMER FRUIT	
Constituent	Mg. per kg.	Constituent	Mg. per kg.
Total volatile oil	15.6	Total volatile oil	190.0
Ethyl acetate	2.91	Ethyl acetate	119.6
Ethyl alcohol	0.0	Ethyl alcohol	60.5
Acetaldehyde	0.61	Acetaldehyde	1.35
Methyl *n*-valerate	0.49	Ethyl acrylate	0.77
Methyl *i*-valerate	0.60	Ethyl *i*-valerate	0.39
Methyl *i*-caproate	1.40	Ethyl *n*-caproate	0.77
Methyl caprylate	0.75		

for the odor and flavor of the pineapple. Both the amount of volatile oil and its components vary with the time of the year at which the fruit is harvested. The bouquet of fine wines has been ascribed to esters produced by the slow esterification of organic acids during the ageing process.

ORTHO ESTERS

Ortho acids are acids in the highest state of hydration; that is, they contain the maximum number of hydroxyl groups. For example, orthoformic acid should have the formula $HC(OH)_3$. However, compounds having more than one hydroxyl group on the same carbon atom usually are unstable and lose water.

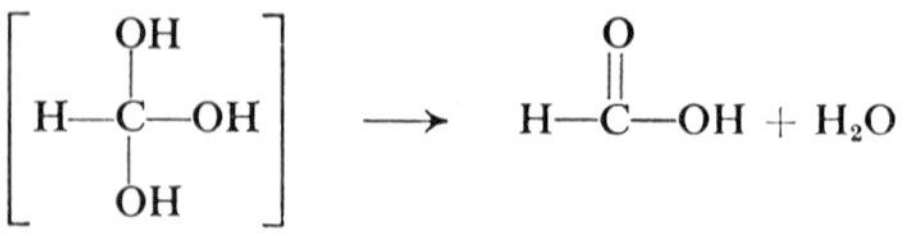

$$\left[\begin{array}{c} OH \\ | \\ H{-}C{-}OH \\ | \\ OH \end{array} \right] \longrightarrow \begin{array}{c} O \\ || \\ H{-}C{-}OH \end{array} + H_2O$$

If orthoformic acid exists at all, it exists only in aqueous solutions. When more than one alkoxy group occurs on a single carbon atom, however, the compounds are perfectly stable. The oxygen-alkyl derivatives of the ortho acids are known as ortho esters.

Two methods commonly are used for the synthesis of ortho esters. The first was discovered by Williamson (p. 137) and is the reaction of a trihalide with sodium alkoxide analogous to his synthesis of ethers. For example, **ethyl orthoformate** usually is prepared by the reaction of chloroform with sodium ethoxide.

$$HCCl_3 + 3\ NaOC_2H_5 \longrightarrow HC(OC_2H_5)_3 + 3\ NaCl$$

Although formally this reaction is analogous to the reaction of alkyl halides with sodium ethoxide, chloroform is about 1000 times more reactive than either carbon tetrachloride or methylene chloride. It has been proposed that reactions involving chloroform and a strongly alkaline reagent take place through the intermediate formation of the dichloromethylene radical (dichlorocarbene).

$$CHCl_3 + [C_2H_5O^-] \longrightarrow [^-CCl_3] + C_2H_5OH$$

$$[^-CCl_3] \longrightarrow [:CCl_2] + [Cl^-]$$

$$[:CCl_2] + 3\ [C_2H_5O^-] \longrightarrow [(C_2H_5O)_3C\bar{:}] + 2\ [Cl^-]$$

$$[(C_2H_5O)_3C\bar{:}] + C_2H_5OH \longrightarrow (C_2H_5O)_3CH + [C_2H_5O^-]$$

The second method was developed by Pinner. When an alkyl cyanide reacts with an alcohol and hydrogen chloride under anhydrous conditions, the hydrochloride of the product of addition of one mole of alcohol to the cyanide is obtained. The product is known as an *imidoester hydrochloride* (p. 248). Methyl cyanide, for example, reacts with ethyl alcohol and hydrogen chloride to give ethyl imidoacetate hydrochloride.

$$CH_3C{\equiv}N + HOC_2H_5 + HCl \longrightarrow \left[\overset{\overset{+NH_2}{\|}}{CH_3C-OC_2H_5}\right][Cl^-]$$

On warming the imidoester hydrochlorides with an excess of alcohol, ortho esters are produced.

$$\left[\overset{\overset{+NH_2}{\|}}{CH_3C-OC_2H_5}\right][Cl^-] + 2\ HOC_2H_5 \longrightarrow CH_3C(OC_2H_5)_3 + NH_4Cl$$
$$\text{Ethyl orthoacetate}$$

These reactions of alcoholysis are analogous to the hydrolysis of nitriles to amides and acids (pp. 253, 252).

The lack of a carbonyl group makes the ortho esters resemble ethers rather than carboxylic esters in some of their chemical properties. Thus they are very stable to aqueous alkali but are hydrolyzed readily and irreversibly by dilute acid solutions.

$$RC(OC_2H_5)_3 + H_2O \xrightarrow{[H^+]} RCOOC_2H_5 + 2\ C_2H_5OH$$

The carboxylic ester goes to reversible equilibrium with the alcohol and the free acid. Grignard reagents replace one of the alkoxy groups by an alkyl group.

$$\underset{\underset{OC_2H_5}{|}}{\overset{\overset{OC_2H_5}{|}}{H-C-OC_2H_5}} + RMgX \longrightarrow \underset{\underset{OC_2H_5}{|}}{\overset{\overset{R}{|}}{H-C-OC_2H_5}} + C_2H_5OMgX$$

Use is made of this reaction for the synthesis of aldehydes (p. 196).

REVIEW QUESTIONS

1. What are the most commonly used names for the normal carboxylic acids having from one to eighteen carbon atoms?
2. How does the boiling point of acetic acid compare with that of alcohols and hydrocarbons of approximately the same molecular weight? Explain.
3. Discuss the solubility of carboxylic acids in water and organic solvents; in dilute potassium hydroxide.
4. Discuss commercial methods for the preparation of formic, acetic, propionic, and butyric acids. What is the chief source of the higher normal carboxylic acids?
5. What is the chief difference in the preparation of esters by direct esterification and by the use of acyl halides or anhydrides?
6. Compare the reaction of neutralization with that of esterification, and explain the difference.
7. What is meant by the terms *reversible reaction* and *chemical equilibrium?* What factors markedly influence the rate of a chemical reaction? How may the position of equilibrium be shifted?
8. Discuss the relative ease of hydrolysis of ethers, esters, and anhydrides.

PROBLEMS

9. Write condensed structural formulas for members of the following groups of isomeric carboxylic acids and name each as a derivative of acetic acid and by the Geneva system: (*a*) those having six carbon atoms; (*b*) dialkylacetic acids having seven carbon atoms or less; (*c*) trialkylacetic acids having eight carbon atoms or less; (*d*) dialkylacetic acids having two four-carbon alkyl groups.
10. Using accepted structural theory, write formulas for all the possible compounds having the molecular formula $C_2H_4O_2$.
11. Give balanced equations for the oxidation of the following compounds to carboxylic acids:
    A. (*a*) *n*-Propyl alcohol with dichromate and sulfuric acid; (*b*) *i*-butyl alcohol with alkaline permanganate; (*c*) 2-butene with acid permanganate; (*d*) 1-octanol with nitric acid.
    B. (*a*) 1-Butanol with acid permanganate; (*b*) *i*-amyl alcohol with chromium trioxide in acetic acid; (*c*) 3-hexene with alkaline permanganate; (*d*) 1-hexanol with nitric acid.
    C. (*a*) 4-Octene with dichromate and sulfuric acid; (*b*) 2-methyl-1-butanol with nitric acid; (*c*) *n*-amyl alcohol with alkaline permanganate; (*d*) *i*-hexyl alcohol with acid permanganate.
12. Write reactions for the preparation of the following compounds from any other organic compound:
    A. (*a*) Heptanoyl bromide; (*b*) *n*-butyric anhydride; (*c*) *i*-caproic acid; (*d*) *n*-valeramide; (*e*) *s*-butyl propionate; (*f*) calcium acetate.
    B. (*a*) *i*-Butyramide; (*b*) undecanoic acid; (*c*) acetic butyric anhydride; (*d*) barium heptanoate; (*e*) *i*-amyl propionate; (*f*) propionyl chloride.
    C. (*a*) Pentanoamide; (*b*) *n*-valeric acid; (*c*) *i*-propyl *i*-butyrate; (*d*) *i*-butyryl chloride; (*e*) zinc stearate; (*f*) propionic anhydride.
    D. (*a*) 2-Methylbutyl acetate; (*b*) butanoic anhydride; (*c*) aluminum formate; (*d*) lauric acid; (*e*) propionamide; (*f*) *n*-valeryl bromide.
13. Give equations for the reaction of water, of ethyl alcohol, and of ammonia with each of the following compounds, assuming, where necessary, that the reaction with water or alcohol is acid-catalyzed:
    A. (*a*) *n*-Butyryl chloride; (*b*) propionic anhydride; (*c*) ethyl palmitate.
    B. (*a*) *n*-Butyl stearate; (*b*) heptanoyl bromide; (*c*) butanoic anhydride.
    C. (*a*) *i*-Propyl valerate; (*b*) lauric anhydride; (*c*) 2-methylbutanoyl bromide.
    D. (*a*) 2-Methylpentanoic anhydride; (*b*) *i*-valeryl chloride; (*c*) *s*-butyl propionate.
14. Devise a simple chemical procedure for distinguishing between the members of the following groups of compounds:
    A. (*a*) *n*-Butyl ether, ethyl butyrate, and acetic anhydride; (*b*) palmityl chloride, palmitoyl chloride, and palmitic anhydride; (*c*) water, *n*-propyl alcohol, and acetic acid; (*d*) aluminum hydroxide, aluminum acetate, and aluminum ethoxide.
    B. (*a*) Formic acid, water, and methyl alcohol; (*b*) methyl palmitate, butyric anhydride, and *i*-amyl ether; (*c*) lauroyl bromide, lauryl bromide, and lauric anhydride; (*d*) sodium ethoxide, sodium hydroxide, and sodium acetate.

C. (*a*) Magnesium formate, magnesium methoxide, and magnesium hydroxide; (*b*) *i*-propyl alcohol, water, and propionic acid; (*c*) caproic anhydride, *n*-butyl caproate, and *n*-hexyl ether; (*d*) propionic anhydride, *n*-hexyl chloride, and hexanoyl chloride.

15. Give a series of reactions for each of the following conversions: (*a*) *n*-hexyl bromide to heptanoic acid; (*b*) *i*-amyl alcohol to ethyl *i*-valerate; (*c*) methyl caprate to *n*-decyl bromide; (*d*) 1-dodecanol to *n*-docosane; (*e*) stearic acid to 1-octadecanol; (*f*) ethyl myristate to 1-tetradecene; (*g*) *n*-hexadecyl alcohol to *n*-pentadecyl bromide; (*h*) lauroyl chloride to *n*-dodecyl iodide; (*i*) propionic acid to triethylcarbinol; (*j*) 2-butene to 2-methylbutanoic acid.

16. If *X* g. of a carboxylic acid required *Y* cc. of 0.1 *N* sodium hydroxide when titrated to the phenolphthalein end-point, calculate the equivalent weight of the following acids:

	A	B	C	D
X	0.2410	0.1356	0.1824	0.1065
Y	23.61	18.35	20.72	17.75

17. For each of the following esters, calculate the equivalent weight of the alcohol with which the acid was esterified if *X* is the saponification equivalent of the ester and *Y* is the neutralization equivalent of the acid:

	A	B	C	D
X	116	130	116	102
Y	74	102	60	88

18. If in Problem 17 the acid is monobasic and the alcohol monohydric, what are the possible structures for the ester?

Chapter 10

WAXES, FATS, AND OILS

Waxes, fats, and oils are naturally occurring esters of higher straight chain carboxylic acids. They usually are classified on a mixed basis including source, physical properties, and chemical properties.

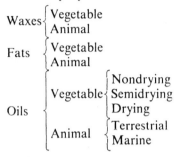

A practical definition of a wax might be that it is anything with a waxy feel and a melting point above body temperature and below the boiling point of water. Thus the term paraffin wax is used for a mixture of solid hydrocarbons, beeswax for a mixture of esters, and Carbowax for a synthetic polyether. Chemically, however, waxes are defined as *esters of high molecular weight monohydric* (one hydroxyl group) *alcohols with the common higher fat acids* (Table 10, p. 147). Hence they have the general formula of a simple ester, RCOOR′. Actually the natural waxes are mixtures of esters and frequently contain hydrocarbons as well.

Carnauba wax is the most valuable of the vegetable waxes. It occurs as a coating on the leaves of a Brazilian palm, *Corypha cerifera*, from which it is removed by shredding and beating of the leaves. It consists of a mixture of esters of the normal alcohols and fat acids having even numbers of carbon atoms from 24 to 34, the C_{32} and C_{34} compounds predominating. Hydrocarbons having odd numbers of carbon atoms from C_{25} to C_{31} also are present. Because of its high melting point of 80°–87°, its hardness, and its imperviousness to water, carnauba wax is a valuable ingredient of automobile and floor polishes and carbon paper coatings. **Ouricuri wax** from the leaves of the Brazilian palm, *Scheelia martiana*, has about the same composition and properties as carnauba wax. **Beeswax** is the material from which the bee builds the cells of the honeycomb. Its composition resembles that of carnauba wax except that the esters on hydrolysis yield chiefly C_{26} and C_{28} acids and alcohols, and hence it has the lower melting point of 60°–82°. **Spermaceti** is obtained from the head of the sperm whale (*Cetaceae*). It is chiefly cetyl palmitate, $C_{15}H_{31}COOC_{16}H_{33}$, and melts at 42°–47°. **Degras** or **wool grease** is a complex mixture of waxes, alcohols, and free fat acids recovered from the scouring of wool. Some of the acids obtained by the hydrolysis of the waxes are unusual in that they have a methyl branch and contain both odd and even numbers of carbon atoms from C_9 to C_{27}. Wool grease has the unusual property of forming a stable semisolid emulsion containing up to 80 per cent water. A purified product known as **lanolin** or **lanum** finds use as a base for salves and ointments in which it is desired to incorporate both water-soluble and fat-soluble substances.

FATS AND OILS

The constitution of fats and oils was investigated systematically first by Chevreul.[1] They are *esters of higher fat acids and a trihydric alcohol, glycerol,* $HOCH_2CHOHCH_2OH$. Esters of glycerol frequently are called *glycerides*. They have the general formula $RCOOCH_2CHCH_2OCOR'$ and are differentiated

$$\overset{|}{OCOR''}$$

solely by the fact that fats are solid or semisolid at room temperature, whereas oils are liquids. Vegetable fats and oils usually occur in the fruits and seeds of plants and are extracted (*1*) by cold pressing in hydraulic presses or continuous expellers, (*2*) by hot pressing, and (*3*) by solvent extraction. Cold pressing gives the blandest product and is used for producing the highest grade food oils such as olive, cottonseed, and peanut oils. Hot pressing gives a higher yield, but larger quantities of undesirable constituents are expressed, and the oil has a stronger odor and flavor. Solvent extraction gives the highest recovery, and in recent years the process has been so improved that even food oils may be prepared which are free from undesirable odors and flavors. Animal fats are recovered by heating fatty tissue to a high temperature (dry-rendering) or by treating with steam or hot water and separating the liberated fat.

Fat Acids

Since all fats and oils are esters of glycerol, their differences must be due to the acids with which the glycerol is esterified. These acids are both saturated and unsaturated. Of the saturated acids the most important are **lauric acid,** $CH_3(CH_2)_{10}COOH$, **palmitic acid,** $CH_3(CH_2)_{14}COOH$, and **stearic acid,** $CH_3(CH_2)_{16}COOH$. The most important unsaturated acids have eighteen carbon atoms, and one double bond usually is at the middle of the chain. If other double bonds are present they lie further removed from the carboxyl group. **Oleic acid,** $CH_3(CH_2)_7CH{=}CH(CH_2)_7COOH$, has only one double bond; **linoleic acid (linolic acid),** $CH_3(CH_2)_4CH{=}CHCH_2CH{=}CH(CH_2)_7COOH$, has two double bonds separated by one methylene group; **linolenic acid,** $CH_3CH_2CH{=}CHCH_2CH{=}CHCH_2CH{=}CH(CH_2)_7COOH$, has three double bonds each separated by methylene groups; **eleostearic acid,** $CH_3(CH_2)_3{-}CH{=}CH{-}CH{=}CH{-}CH{=}CH(CH_2)_7COOH$, also has three double bonds,

---

[1] Michael Eugene Chevreul (1786–1889), professor of chemistry at Paris. He was among the first to study the chemistry of complex natural products and isolated the glycoside quercitrin (p. 698) in 1810. He is noted chiefly for his work on fats begun in 1811. He was the first to show the nature of saponification, and from the hydrolysis products of fats he isolated caproic, capric, palmitic, stearic, and oleic acids. In 1818 he discovered cetyl alcohol in the unsaponifiable fraction of spermaceti and in 1834 isolated creatine (p. 322) from urine. He was an active investigator until his death at the age of 102 years and 7 months.

but they are conjugated;[2] **licanic acid** is 4-ketoeleostearic acid, $CH_3(CH_2)_3$-$CH{=}CH{-}CH{=}CH{-}CH{=}CH(CH_2)_4CO(CH_2)_2COOH$; **parinaric acid,** $CH_3CH_2CH{=}CH{-}CH{=}CH{-}CH{=}CH{-}CH{=}CH(CH_2)_7COOH$, has four conjugated double bonds.

Several other unsaturated acids are of interest. **Ricinoleic acid,** $CH_3(CH_2)_5$-$CHOHCH_2CH{=}CH(CH_2)_7COOH$, is 12-hydroxyoleic acid. In **palmitoleic acid,** $CH_3(CH_2)_5CH{=}CH(CH_2)_7COOH$, **petroselenic acid,** $CH_3(CH_2)_{10}$-$CH{=}CH(CH_2)_4COOH$, **vaccenic acid,** $CH_3(CH_2)_5CH{=}CH(CH_2)_9COOH$, and **erucic acid,** $CH_3(CH_2)_7CH{=}CH(CH_2)_{11}COOH$, the double bond is not at the middle of the chain. **Tariric acid,** $CH_3(CH_2)_{10}C{\equiv}C(CH_2)_4COOH$, and **erythrogenic (isanic) acid,** $CH_2{=}CH(CH_2)_4C{\equiv}C{-}C{\equiv}C(CH_2)_7COOH$, contain triple bonds. Of all the fat acids palmitic acid is the most abundant, and oleic acid is the most widely distributed.

Fats and oils are chiefly mixed glycerides and not a mixture of simple glycerides. The different fat acids are not wholly randomly distributed but are divided as widely as possible among the glycerol molecules. Simple glycerides occur in quantity only if more than two thirds of the acyl groups are of one kind. The approximate relative amounts of the different acids obtained by the hydrolysis of fats are given in Table 13.

In the acids obtained from fats, saturated acids predominate, but in those from oils, unsaturated acids predominate. In other words unsaturation lowers the melting point. Another factor which lowers the melting point is molecular weight. The acids from low-melting fats such as coconut oil, palm oil, and butter contain relatively small amounts of unsaturated acids but considerable amounts of lower fat acids. Although classified as fats because they are solid in temperate zones, coconut oil and palm oil were called oils because they are liquids in the tropics where they are produced.

Individual Fats and Oils

Palm oil is obtained from the fruit of a species of palm, *Elaeis guineensis*, native to Nigeria and the west coast of Africa and grown on plantations in Sumatra. It is yellow to red in color and possesses a characteristic odor. Hydrolysis yields chiefly palmitic and oleic acids. Palm trees on plantations yield more fat per acre than any other agricultural crop. Average yields are 2500 pounds, whereas coconut yields 730 pounds, peanuts yield 360 pounds, and soybeans yield 190 pounds. **Coconut oil** is expressed from copra, the dried meat of the nut from the coconut palm, *Cocos nucifera*. It is imported into the United States chiefly from the Philippines. The fat acids obtained on hydrolysis contain for the most part less than sixteen carbon atoms. World production is greater than that of any other vegetable fat or oil. **Babassu oil** from the seed kernel of a Brazilian palm, *Orbignya oleifera*, closely resembles coconut oil. Production could be greatly increased were it not for the difficulty of cracking the hard shells, which is done entirely by hand. It has been estimated that 75,000 persons were engaged in the production of babassu oil before World War II. **Butter** from milk is characterized by the liberation of appreciable

---

[2] If double bonds and single bonds alternate successively in a molecule, the double bonds are said to be *conjugated*.

TABLE 13

SAPONIFICATION AND IODINE VALUES OF FATS AND OILS AND THE COMPOSITION OF THE FAT ACIDS OBTAINED BY HYDROLYSIS

	FAT OR OIL	Saponification value	Iodine value	COMPOSITION OF FAT ACIDS (PERCENT)						
				Myristic	Palmitic	Stearic	Palmitoleic	Oleic	Linoleic	Other components
Vegetable fats	Coconut	250–60	8–10	17–20	4–10	1–5		2–10	0–2	a
	Babassu	245–55	10–18	15–20	6–9	3–6		12–18	1–3	b
	Palm	196–210	48–58	1–3	34–43	3–6		38–40	5–11	
Animal fats	Butter	216–35	26–45	7–9	23–26	10–13	5	30–40	4–5	c
	Lard	193–200	46–66	1–2	28–30	12–18	1–3	41–48	6–7	d
	Tallow	190–200	31–47	2–3	24–32	14–32	1–3	35–48	2–4	
Vegetable oils — Nondrying	Castor	176–87	81–90		0–1			0–9	3–7	e
	Olive	185–200	74–94	0–1	5–15	1–4	0–1	69–84	4–12	
	Peanut	185–95	83–98		6–9	2–6	0–1	50–70	13–26	f
	Rape	172–5	94–106	0–2	0–1	0–2		20–38	10–15	g
Vegetable oils — Semi-drying	Corn	188–93	116–30	0–2	7–11	3–4	0–2	43–49	34–42	
	Sesame	187–93	104–16		8	4	1	45	41	h
	Cottonseed	191–6	103–15	0–2	19–24	1–2	0–2	23–33	40–48	
Vegetable oils — Drying	Soybean	189–94	124–36	0–1	6–10	2–4		21–29	50–59	i
	Sunflower	190–2	122–36			10–13		21–39	51–68	
	Hemp	190–3	149–67			4–10		13	53	j
	Linseed	189–96	170–204		4–7	2–5		9–38	3–43	k
	Tung	189–95	160–80			2–6		4–16	0–1	l
	Oiticica	186–94	139–55			11		6		m
Animal oils — Terrestrial	Lard oil	190–95	46–70		22–26	15–17		45–55	8–10	
	Neat's-foot	192–7	67–73		17–18	2–3		74–77		
Animal oils — Marine	Whale	188–94	110–50	4–6	11–18	2–4	13–18	33–38		n
	Fish	185–95	120–90	6–8	10–16	1–2	6–15			o

(a) 5–10 caprylic, 5–11 capric, and 45–51 lauric acids.

(b) 4–7 caprylic, 3–8 capric, 44–46 lauric acids.

(c) 3–4 butyric, 1–2 caproic, 1 caprylic, 2–3 capric, and 2–3 lauric acids.

(d) 2 of C_{20} and C_{22} unsaturated fat acids.

(e) 80–92 ricinoleic acid.

(f) 2–5 arachidic and 1–5 tetracosanoic acids.

(g) 1–2 tetracosanoic, 1–4 linolenic, and 43–57 erucic acid.

(h) 1 arachidic acid.

(i) 4–8 linolenic acid.

(j) 24 linolenic acid.

(k) 25–58 linolenic acid.

(l) 4–5 saturated acids and 74–91 eleostearic acid.

(m) 70–78 licanic acid.

(n) 11–20 C_{20} and 6–11 C_{22} unsaturated acids.

(o) 24–30 C_{18}, 19–26 C_{20}, and 12–19 C_{22} unsaturated acids.

quantities of butyric acid on hydrolysis. **Lard** from hogs and **tallow** from cattle and sheep differ chiefly in the amount of combined oleic acid. When lard is chilled and pressed in hydraulic presses, the lower melting fractions are removed and constitute **lard oil.** The press-cake has a higher melting point than the original material and is known as *summer lard.* The composition of animal fats varies greatly with the diet. For example, hogs fed on corn give a lard of higher melting point than do those fed on peanuts. **Neat's-foot oil,** obtained by boiling the feet and shin bones of cattle, resembles lard oil in composition. **Whale oil** acids are characterized by the high percentage of unsaturated acids containing twenty to twenty-four carbon atoms, as well as by a considerable amount of palmitoleic acid. The chief fish oils are **menhaden** and **pilchard oils** derived from several species of sardine. *Clupea pilchardus* is the European sardine or pilchard, whereas *Clupea menhaden* is taken off the Atlantic coast of North America. *Clupea caerulea* from the waters of the Pacific coast and Japan closely resembles the European pilchard. The oils yield a complex mixture of highly unsaturated acids, some containing up to four double bonds.

The classification of oils into nondrying, semidrying, and drying oils depends on the ease of autoxidation and polymerization, which increases with increasing unsaturation. The chief unsaturated fat acids from the nondrying oils (Table 13) contain only one double bond; those from semidrying oils contain a higher percentage of the doubly unsaturated acid, linoleic acid; the acids from drying oils contain very little oleic acid but chiefly linoleic and the triply unsaturated linolenic, eleostearic, and licanic acids. However there is no distinct line of demarcation between the various types of oils. **Olive oil,** which is pressed from the ripe fruit of the olive tree, *Oleo europea*, is characterized chiefly by the high percentage of oleic acid in the acids formed on hydrolysis. **Peanut oil** from the seeds of the legume, *Arachis hypogaea*, yields acids which consist of less oleic and more linoleic acid. The world production of peanut oil approaches that of coconut oil.

Corn oil from the seed germ of corn, *Zea mays*, cottonseed oil from the seed of different varieties of *Gossypium*, and sesame oil from the seed of *Sesamum indicum* have similar properties and contain larger amounts of linoleic acid than peanut oil. Although world production of sesame oil approaches that of olive oil, very little is imported into the United States. Most of it is consumed as food in India and China where the plant has been cultivated probably as long as rice. Sunflower seed oil from *Helianthus annuus*, and hemp seed oil from *Cannabis sativa* yield somewhat larger amounts of linoleic acid, and soybean oil from the seed of the legume *Glycine max* gives a small amount of the triply unsaturated linolenic acid. This acid becomes an important component of the fat acids from **linseed oil,** the oil pressed from the seed of flax, *Linum usitatissimum.* Thus there is a gradual increase from olive oil to linseed oil in the components giving rise to drying properties, and the classification into nondrying, semidrying, and drying is purely arbitrary. For example soybean oil originally was classed as a semidrying oil but now is classed as a drying oil.

Frequently some unusual fat acid will be characteristic of an oil. **Castor oil** from the seed of the castor bean plant, *Ricinus communis*, yields fat acids characterized by the high concentration of the hydroxy unsaturated acid, ricinoleic acid. The purgative action of castor oil is caused by the irritation of the walls of the intestines by the ricinoleic acid portion of the molecule. **Rapeseed** or **colza oil** from the seed of *Brassica rapa* and related species yields large amounts of erucic acid. **Peanut oil** acids are characterized by the presence of arachidic acid. **Tung** or **China wood oil** from the seed of the tung tree, *Aleurites fordii,* yields the triply unsaturated eleostearic acid. **Oiticica oil** from the seed kernels of the Brazilian tree *Licania rigida* yields licanic acid.

TABLE 14

APPARENT CONSUMPTION OF FATS AND OILS IN
THE UNITED STATES IN 1954

PRODUCT	AMOUNT IN MILLIONS OF POUNDS
Soybean oil	2336
Cottonseed oil	1880
Lard	1662
Butter	1564
Tallow	1393
Coconut oil	555
Linseed oil	484
Corn oil	260
Fish oils	98
Peanut oil	65
Castor oil	56
Tung oil	47
Whale and sperm oils	37

Reactions of Fats and Oils

The characteristic chemical features of the fats are the ester linkages and the unsaturation. As esters they may be hydrolyzed in the presence of acids, enzymes, or alkali to free fat acids, or their salts, and glycerol.

$$
\begin{array}{l}
RCOOCH_2 \\
| \\
R'COOCH + 3\ H_2O \xrightarrow[\text{enzymes}]{[H^+]\ or} \\
| \\
R''COOCH_2
\end{array}
\quad
\begin{array}{ll}
RCOOH & CH_2OH \\
 & | \\
R'COOH + & CHOH \\
 & | \\
R''COOH & CH_2OH \\
 & \text{Glycerol}
\end{array}
$$

$$
+ 3\ M^+OH^- \longrightarrow
\begin{array}{ll}
[RCOO^-]M^+ & CH_2OH \\
 & | \\
[R'COO^-]M^+ + & CHOH \\
 & | \\
[R''COO^-]M^+ & CH_2OH
\end{array}
$$

Since the fat acids differ in molecular weight, and since substances which do not react with alkali, such as high molecular weight alcohols and hydrocarbons, may be present, different fats will require different amounts of alkali for saponification. Hence the amount of alkali required to saponify a given weight of fat may be used as a characteristic of the particular fat. An arbitrary unit known technically as the **saponification value** is used, which is the *number of milligrams of potassium hydroxide required to saponify one gram of fat.* Table 13 shows that the fats containing chiefly C_{18} acids have almost identical saponification values and the determination is useful only to identify or detect the presence of coconut oil and butter fat, or to determine whether these fats have been adulterated with others having a lower saponification value, or with mineral oils or greases.

The extent of unsaturation likewise is characteristic of a fat and may be determined by the amount of halogen which the double bonds will add. Iodine does not ordinarily form stable addition products with the double bond (p. 54), and chlorine or bromine substitute as well as add. In practice standardized solutions of iodine monochloride (*Wijs solution*) or of iodine monobromide (*Hanus solution*) in glacial acetic acid are used. However, the Wijs or Hanus solution is standardized by adding potassium iodide and titrating the liberated iodine with standard thiosulfate solution. The amount of reagent remaining after reaction with a fat is determined in the same way. *The difference expressed in terms of grams of iodine* (as if iodine had added) *per 100 grams of fat* is known as the **iodine value** of the fat. The increase in iodine value with increasing amounts of unsaturated acids is apparent in Table 13.

Thiocyanogen, $(SCN)_2$ (p. 326), shows many of the properties of halogens. It liberates iodine from potassium iodide, and also adds to double bonds. It has been found, however, that whereas one mole adds to monoethylenic acids such as oleic acid, only slightly more than one mole adds to the diethylenic linoleic acid, and somewhat less than two moles to the triply unsaturated linolenic acid. Solutions of thiocyanogen in glacial acetic acid are prepared by adding bromine to lead thiocyanate and are standardized and used like Wijs and Hanus solutions. *The amount of thiocyanogen added expressed in terms of grams of iodine per gram of fat* is known as the **thiocyanogen value.** Since Wijs or Hanus solution saturates all double bonds, it is possible to estimate the composition of mixtures of oleic, linoleic, and saturated acids from the iodine and thiocyanogen values or the amounts of oleic, linoleic, and linolenic acids if the amount of saturated acids is known.

The **hydrogenation of oils** is carried out technically on a large scale by bubbling hydrogen through the oil containing a suspension of finely divided nickel. In this process the double bonds of oleic, linoleic, linolenic, and eleostearic glycerides are hydrogenated and the oils converted into the hard waxy tristearin. By controlling the amount of hydrogen added, any consistency desired may be obtained. Since people of temperate zones prefer fat to oil for cooking purposes, and since fats are more useful than oils as soap stocks, hydrogenation greatly increases the value of an oil.

Rancidity of oils is caused chiefly by air oxidation of the unsaturated acids, which gives a complex mixture of volatile aldehydes, ketones, and acids. In some cases rancidity may be caused by microorganisms. Fats which have been freed of odor and undesirable tastes are now stabilized by the addition of substances which inhibit oxidation (antioxidants, p. 886).

Waste or rags containing unsaturated oils is subject to **spontaneous combustion** if air is not excluded, or if not enough ventilation is possible to prevent a rise in temperature as the oil oxidizes. Any rise in temperature increases the rate of oxidation, and the process is accelerated until the material bursts into flame.

Castor oil is characterized by the high percentage of ricinoleic acid, which contains a hydroxyl group. The hydroxyl group may be acetylated and the *number of milligrams of potassium hydroxide that is needed to neutralize the acetic acid liberated from one gram of acetylated product* is known as the **acetyl**

value. Castor oil has an acetyl value of 142 to 150, but other common fats and oils range from 2 to 20. Substances other than ricinoleic acid, for example, high molecular weight alcohols and partially hydrolyzed glycerides, also acetylate and may account for all or part of the acetyl value.

A second double bond may be introduced into the ricinoleic portion of castor oil by **dehydration,** giving rise to a mixture of linoleic acid and the 9,11-diunsaturated acid in which the double bonds are conjugated, thus changing it from a nondrying to a drying oil. Moreover the high percentage of conjugation that results makes the dehydrated oil resemble tung oil in its properties.

Transesterification is important technically for modifying the properties of a fat. It is carried out under anhydrous conditions using sodium methoxide as a catalyst. In the presence of methoxide ion the various fat acids randomly exchange very rapidly with the hydroxyl groups of the glycerol molecules. Since the fat acids in the natural fat are evenly distributed among the glycerol molecules, treatment with methoxide ion gives random distribution and changes the properties of the fat. Lard for example is unsatisfactory for making cake because it tends to crystallize in large crystals. It is greatly improved by redistribution of the fat acids among the glycerol molecules.

The equilibrium is so mobile that transesterification can be carried out at a temperature such that the higher-melting saturated triglycerides crystallize from the mixture. As they crystallize, the equilibrium shifts until most of the saturated acids are removed from the liquid portion. After separation of the crystallized material, the oil remaining is much more highly unsaturated. In this way the drying properties of the oils are improved.

If the transesterification is carried out in the presence of glycerol, alcoholysis occurs (p. 170). The triglycerides are thus converted to mono- and diglycerides, useful as emulsifying agents (p. 188).

Reduction of fats **to primary alcohols** and glycerol can be carried out using sodium and a secondary alcohol (p. 172). Alternatively the free acids may be reduced catalytically to alcohols (p. 172).

For the laboratory **isolation of individual fat acids** for use as such or as a means of estimating the relative amounts composing the fat, the methyl or ethyl esters are prepared by alcoholysis (p. 170) and are fractionally distilled under reduced pressure. This procedure is useful only in separating acids differing appreciably in molecular weight, and cannot be used to separate different unsaturated acids having the same number of carbon atoms. The esters are distilled rather than the free acids because the latter form mixed double molecules which tend to smooth out the differences in boiling points between the individual acids. Commercially the free fat acids are separated by distillation or by solvent extraction processes. Saturated fat acids may be separated from unsaturated acids by converting the mixture to the **lead salts** and extracting with ether. The lead salts of unsaturated fat acids are much more soluble in ether than those of the saturated fat acids.

Linoleic acid forms a tetrabromide, m.p. 115°–116°, and linolenic acid a hexabromide, m.p. 185°–186°, which can be isolated and purified readily. The linoleic and linolenic acids can be regenerated from their bromides by debromination with zinc dust in alcoholic solution (p. 128).

Oxidation of unsaturated acids with dilute permanganate solutions yields solid polyhydroxy acids, two hydroxyl groups being introduced per double bond (p. 57). These polyhydroxy acids are useful derivatives for identification of the individual unsaturated acids.

Oxides of nitrogen from mercury and nitric acid (*Poutet's reagent*) convert liquid unsaturated acids into solid isomers (p. 356). Oleic acid is converted into *elaidic acid* and the process is known as **elaidinization.** Oils may be partially solidified by the same reaction.

Uses of Fats and Oils

Food. From 25 to 50 per cent of the caloric intake of man consists of fats. On combustion in animals, fats produce about 9.5 kcal. of energy per gram compared to 4 kcal. per gram for carbohydrates or proteins. Fats in their ordinary form cannot be absorbed through the walls of the intestine because of their insolubility in water and their large particle size. In the small intestine they are partially hydrolyzed in the presence of the enzyme catalyst, **steapsin,** to di- and monoglycerides which, together with the bile salts (p. 869), can bring about emulsification. Sufficient reduction in particle size takes place to permit passage through the intestinal walls into the lymph ducts which discharge the fats into the blood stream as a highly dispersed emulsion. The blood stream transports them to the tissues where they are burned for energy or stored as fat deposits for future use. From the standpoint of digestion one fat is as useful as another unless its melting point is so high that when mixed with other fats it does not melt or emulsify with the bile at body temperature, in which case it passes into the feces unchanged. However, either linoleic or linolenic acid must be supplied by the ingested fats to insure a healthy condition of the skin.

Although some of the fat consumed is mixed with the other foodstuffs, the proteins and carbohydrates, a considerable portion first is isolated in a relatively pure state and consumed as such in bread spreads or used for frying or as salad oils and salad dressings such as mayonnaise. The relatively high cost of butter has led to the development of a substitute generally referred to as **oleomargarine.** Selected vegetable or animal fats and oils, which have been highly refined and properly hydrogenated to give the desired melting point and consistency, are emulsified with about 17 per cent by weight of milk which has been cultured with certain microorganisms to give it flavor. An emulsifying agent such as a monoglyceride (p. 192) or a vegetable lecithin (p. 753) usually is added as well. Butter consists of droplets of water suspended in oil (water-in-oil type emulsion). Oleomargarines may be either water-in-oil or oil-in-water types of emulsions depending on the method of manufacture. Diacetyl, $CH_3COCOCH_3$ (p. 771), and methylacetylcarbinol, $CH_3CHOHCOCH_3$, which account for the characteristic taste of butter, also may be added along with vitamins A and D. For many years oleomargarine manufacturers were not permitted to add color to their product unless an additional Federal tax of ten cents per pound was paid. This law was repealed in 1950, and by 1953, the production of oleomargarine exceeded that of butter. In 1953 six states still prohibited the sale of colored oleomargarine, and coloring matter was packaged separately.

Protective Coatings. Glycerides of fat acids containing two or more double bonds absorb oxygen on exposure to air to give peroxides, which catalyze the polymerization of the unsaturated portions. As a result the oils become solid or semisolid and are known as *drying oils*. If exposed in thin layers, tough elastic waterproof films are formed. **Paint** is a mixture of drying oil, pigment, thinner, and drier. The pigment is an opaque material having a refractive index different from that of the oil film. It provides color and covering power, and protects the oil film from the destructive action of light. The thinner is a volatile solvent, either turpentine (p. 855) or a petroleum fraction called mineral paint spirits (p. 82). It permits spreading and on evaporation leaves a thin even film of oil and pigment that does not run. The drier is a solution of cobalt, manganese, or lead salts of organic acids, usually naphthenic acids from petroleum (p. 839), which catalyzes the oxidation and polymerization of the oil. The drying oil is known as the *vehicle* because after polymerization it holds or carries the pigment. Linseed oil is the most widely used drying oil, although a certain amount of tung oil in a paint gives it superior properties which seem to be due to the conjugation of the unsaturation. Tung oil has been imported chiefly from China, but the tree can grow in a rather limited belt extending across southern United States, and plantations are in production. Dehydrated castor oil (p. 185) has properties resembling tung oil and is used to replace tung oil to a certain extent, especially when supplies from China are not available. The amount of conjugation of the double bonds can be determined from the ultraviolet absorption spectrum of the oil (p. 707).

Although soybean oil has in recent years been classed as a drying oil, it formerly was classed as a semidrying oil, and as indicated by Table 13 its composition is such that its properties would be expected to be intermediate between those of cottonseed oil and linseed oil. Its drying properties can be enhanced, a procedure known as *up-grading*, by extraction with solvents which separate the oil into fractions having varying degrees of unsaturation, or by transesterification (p. 185). Another method of up-grading an oil consists of liberating the mixed acids by hydrolysis and re-esterifying with alcohols having a larger number of hydroxyl groups such as pentaerythritol, $C(CH_2OH)_4$ (p. 752), or sorbitol, $CH_2OH(CHOH)_4CH_2OH$ (p. 412). In this way molecules having higher molecular weights than the glycerides are formed and less polymerization is necessary to give a solid film. Such "synthetic" vehicles "dry" much faster and may give superior films. In still another process the saturated acids and oleic acid are removed as inclusion compounds with urea (p. 311), and the remaining highly unsaturated acids are re-esterified with a polyhydric alcohol. Many of the synthetic resins used for baking enamels contain unsaturated acid residues in the molecule and depend on polymerization for the solidification of the film (p. 553).

Varnish is a mixture of drying oil, rosin (p. 861), and thinner. The rosin imparts hardness and high gloss to the dried film and may be replaced by other natural or synthetic resins. **Oil cloth** is made by coating cotton cloth with a mixture of partially oxidized oil and a pigment, and drying in warm chambers. If the oil is more highly oxidized to a thick viscous mass, mixed with rosin and ground cork or other filler, and rolled into a continuous sheet, **linoleum** is produced. The sheet travels slowly through warm chambers to permit complete polymerization.

Wetting Agents, Emulsifying Agents, and Detergents. If the attractive force between water molecules and some surface is not sufficient to overcome the surface tension of water, water will not wet the surface. If some third substance is added which is adsorbed on the surface more strongly than water and which provides a new surface which strongly adsorbs water, the surface will be wet by water. Such substances are known as **wetting agents.**

Oil and water do not mix because there is a greater attraction of water molecules for each other and of oil molecules for each other than of water molecules for oil molecules. If the molecules of a third substance have a portion which has a strong attraction for oil molecules and a portion which has a strong attraction for water molecules, the substance can disperse in water to give a colloidal solution, if the effect of the water-attracting portion of its molecules is sufficiently great. The dispersed substance, however, has an attraction for oil molecules also, and if an oil is shaken with the colloidal solution, the oil will be dispersed into tiny droplets and an oil-in-water type of emulsion results. On the other hand, if the effect of the oil-soluble portion of the molecule having mixed properties is sufficiently great, the substance can dissolve in oil. The water-solubilizing group, however, has an attraction for water, and if the solution is shaken with water, the latter will be dispersed in the oil to give a water-in-oil type of emulsion. Substances having the property of facilitating the production of emulsions are called **emulsifying agents.** If a substance lowers the surface tension of water, the solution foams readily. It has been shown that oils concentrate in thin lines at the junctures of the film surfaces. Hence lowering of the surface tension may facilitate emulsification on agitation by spreading out the oils into thin lines.

Dirt adheres to fabric and other surfaces chiefly by means of films of oil, and **detergent action** is largely the result of wetting and emulsification. The adsorption of the detergent at the solid surface permits wetting of the surface by the water and allows the oil film to roll up into small droplets. Agitation of the oil droplets with the detergent solution causes emulsification of the oil, which permits the oil and adhering dirt to be washed away from the surface. If the detergent foams, the oil may be emulsified more readily, because it is spread out into thin lines. It should be noted, however, that detergent action is not dependent on the formation of foam, and that numerous nonfoaming detergents are available and have distinct advantages over foaming detergents in equipment such as automatic dishwashers.

The alkali metal salts of fat acids having from ten to eighteen carbon atoms are known as **soaps.** They have a long oil-soluble hydrocarbon chain attached to a water-soluble carboxylate ion, and hence act as wetting agents, emulsifying agents, and detergents. Strictly speaking, only such salts should be referred to as soaps. If the hydrocarbon chain of the alkali metal salts is less than ten carbon atoms long, it does not cause emulsification of oil. If more than eighteen carbon atoms are present, the salt is too insoluble in water to form a sufficiently concentrated colloidal solution. The alkaline earth and heavy metal salts are water-insoluble and hence useless as detergents. Hard water, containing calcium, magnesium, and iron ions, precipitates insoluble salts when soap solutions are added, and lathering does not take place until these ions are completely removed. Moreover the scum of insoluble salts produced from the soap and inorganic salts may be difficult to remove from the article being washed. The insoluble salts have other uses, however (p. 192), and frequently are called soaps.

Ordinary soaps usually are sodium salts. Stocks containing mostly saturated fats give hard soaps, whereas highly unsaturated fats give soft soaps. Low molecular weight soaps, for example from coconut oil, are most soluble in water and give a loose lather consisting of large unstable bubbles, whereas higher molecular weight soaps, such as those from tallow, give a close lather consisting of fine stable bubbles. Potassium soaps are more soluble than sodium soaps but more costly. The fats and hydrogenated oils used in soap manufacture are blended carefully for the particular type of soap desired.

About three-fourths of the hard soap is manufactured by the *full-boiled* or *settled process*. Three basic operations are involved, saponification, washing, and "fitting." The caustic soda solution (about 14 per cent sodium hydroxide) and melted fat are run simultaneously into a large tank with a conical bottom and boiled by steam in both open and closed coils in the bottom of the tank. When the saponification is complete as indicated by control tests, the soap is *grained*, that is, precipitated by the addition of salt. Soap is insoluble in strong salt or sodium hydroxide solutions, probably because the carboxylate ion is less heavily hydrated. After settling, the brine solution is drawn from the bottom and the soap is boiled with water and again precipitated with salt and settled. Next the soap is boiled with a 6.5 per cent caustic solution to insure complete saponification. The lye is strong enough to prevent solution of the soap and is drawn off to be strengthened and used on a new lot of fat. Finally the soap is boiled with water to give a smooth mixture, a process known as *fitting*. On settling, three layers are formed: an upper layer called *neat soap* containing 30–35 per cent of water; a middle layer called *nigre*, containing soap, soap solution and some impurities; and a small lower layer of alkali. The alkali is drawn from the bottom, and the melted soap is pumped from the top. The remaining nigre may be worked into the next batch. The tendency has been to make soap in larger and larger batches because of the smaller labor requirement per pound of soap and because the settling operations proceed better. Soap kettles holding a million pounds of liquid and producing a half million pounds of soap are in use. The brine solutions are evaporated to recover the glycerol and salt. More recently the washing of the soap has been carried out counter-currently to increase the recovery of glycerol and also to increase the concentration of glycerol in the spent lye. In the counter-current process as many as ten washings may be used giving a recovery of 95 per cent of the calculated amount of glycerol and a concentration of 10–15 per cent.

In the *cold process* the fats and lye are mixed in a mechanical mixer, known as a crutcher, at 30°–40° until a homogeneous emulsion is formed, which then is run into molds where completion of the saponification takes place. Either a slight excess over the necessary amount of alkali is used to give a hard white soap, or a 5–10 per cent excess of fat is used to give a smooth, translucent soap. In either case all of the water, glycerol, and excess lye or fat remain in the soap. Soap is easier to make by this process, but it requires better fat stocks, and if an excess of lye is present, the product may be more irritating to the skin. Castile and coconut castile soaps are made in this way, and also potassium soaps, which cannot be salted out efficiently by potassium chloride because of their greater solubility.

In the *direct neutralization* or *carbonate process* free fat acids are neutralized with the calculated amount of either sodium hydroxide or sodium carbonate. The latter is cheaper but the neutralization cannot be carried out as smoothly because of the large volume of carbon dioxide liberated. The chief advantage of this process is that neutralization of the free fat acids is more rapid than saponification of the fat, and salting out and settling are avoided. A batch of soap can be made in three to four hours compared to several days to a week for the settled process. The free fat acids are obtained by the hydrolysis of fats with or without acid or alkaline catalysts. In the *Twitchell process*, 30 per cent sulfuric acid is used, along with 0.5–1 per cent of sulfonic acids which aid emulsification of the fat and water. With two treatments 95 per cent hydrolysis or better can be obtained. The free fat acids are washed and purified by vacuum distillation. The water layer is neutralized with lime to precipitate calcium sulfate, which is removed by filtration, and the glycerol is recovered by concentration of the filtrate. Not only does the filtrate contain from 15–20 per cent glycerol, compared with 3–5 per cent in spent lye from batch washing or 10–15 per cent from counter-current washing, but no salt is present to complicate the recovery. In the more modern *continuous processes*, fat and water without catalyst are heated in coils at 260°. Operated counter-currently the process is very efficient and recovery of glycerol greatly simplified. Because the fat acids are distilled before use, lower grade fats may be used. In the past the production of free fat acids has been largely for the manufacture of commercial stearic acid. With the advent of continuous processes and better methods of purification of the fat acids, direct neutralization may largely replace saponification of fats for the manufacture of soap.

Laundry soap is produced in largest amount. The yellow bar soap usually is made from two parts of grease and one part of rosin, added as sodium resinate (p. 862). The rosin increases the solubility of the soap and its lathering properties, and has some detergent action. White laundry soaps may contain sodium silicate up to 12 per cent, sodium carbonate up to 5 per cent, or trisodium phosphate up to 5 per cent. After mixing with the additives in the crutcher, the soap is poured into molds, allowed to solidify by cooling, and cut or pressed into slabs or bars. The finished product contains about 30 per cent water. If it is dried and chipped to give **soap chips,** or spray-dried to form **powdered soap,** the water content is 10–15 per cent. **Soap powder** is a spray-dried mixture containing about 20 per cent soap, 40 per cent sodium carbonate, and 40 per cent water. It is dry because most of the water is combined with the sodium carbonate as the decahydrate, $Na_2CO_3 \cdot 10 H_2O$. The consumer should be aware of the difference between powdered soap which contains 85–90 per cent soap, and soap powder which contains 20 per cent soap. **Toilet soap** is next in volume. Better grade fats are used, and the desired solubility and lathering properties are obtained by using about three fourths tallow or palm oil and one fourth coconut oil. The kettle soap is shredded and dried to a water content of 10–15 per cent, mixed by milling and plodding with perfumes and dyes, and possibly whitening agents such as titanium oxide, and pressed into cakes. This process produces a hard bar which is known as *milled soap*. **Floating soaps** are made by blending in sufficient air in the crutcher to make the soap less dense than water. The incorporation of air requires that the soap be semiliquid and hence the finished product may contain 30–35 per cent water. In recent years the water content has been reduced to below 25 per cent. **Salt water soaps** are made by the cold process from coconut oil, because the sodium salts of the lower fat acids are less readily salted out and the magnesium salts are more soluble. Such soaps may contain up to 50–55 per cent water. They have an irritating action on the skin, however, which is caused by the coconut oil, and it is for this reason that the coconut oil content of toilet soaps is kept to a minimum. **Liquid soaps** contain 70–85 per cent water and are the potassium salts of coconut oil acids. **Shaving soaps** are potassium soaps chiefly of palmitic and stearic acid. The higher saturated fat acid soaps give a close stable lather, and potassium soaps are used to obtain sufficient solubility.

Synthetic Detergents and Emulsifying Agents. In recent years numerous synthetic compounds have become available which meet the general structural requirements for a detergent or emulsifying agent, namely a water-soluble portion and an oil-soluble portion. The earliest of these were the *sulfated fats and oils* (formerly called sulfonated), which have been in commercial use for over one hundred years. When an unsaturated fat is treated with sulfuric acid, the double bonds add sulfuric acid to give the hydrogen sulfate of the hydroxy acid. For example, the oleic acid portion reacts according to the equation

$$
\begin{array}{l}
CH_2OCO(CH_2)_7CH{=}CH(CH_2)_7CH_3 \\
| \\
CHOCOR \qquad\qquad\qquad + H_2SO_4 \longrightarrow \\
| \\
CH_2OCOR'
\end{array}
\qquad
\begin{array}{l}
CH_2OCO(CH_2)_7CH_2CH(CH_2)_7CH_3 \\
| \qquad\qquad\qquad\quad | \\
CHOCOR \qquad\quad OSO_3H \\
| \\
CH_2OCOR'
\end{array}
$$

Neutralization gives the sodium salt, which provides the water-solubilizing portion of the molecule. In the sulfation of *castor oil*, the hydroxyl group of the ricinoleic acid portion of the molecule reacts more readily than the double bond. If sulfation is carried out at a sufficiently low temperature, the double bond is largely unaffected.

$$
C_3H_5\left[OCO(CH_2)_7CH{=}CHCH_2\underset{\underset{OH}{|}}{CH}(CH_2)_5CH_3\right]_3 + 3\,H_2SO_4 \longrightarrow
$$

$$
C_3H_5\left[OCO(CH_2)_7CH{=}CHCH_2\underset{\underset{OSO_3H}{|}}{CH}(CH_2)_5CH_3\right]_3
$$

Sulfated castor oil is known as *Turkey Red oil* because it was used in the application of the dye alizarin to an aluminum mordanted cloth to give the color known as Turkey Red (p. 688). Turkey Red oil should not be confused with *red oil*, which is the technical name given to commercial oleic acid. During 1955 over 53 million pounds of sulfated oils were produced in the United States, of which approximately 10 million pounds were from fish oils, 11 million pounds from tallow, and 9 million pounds from castor oil.

In Europe a mixture of the sodium salts of secondary alkyl hydrogen sulfates having from eight to eighteen carbon atoms is used as a detergent under the name of *Teepol*. It is made by sulfating an olefin fraction obtained by cracking the wax distillate of petroleum (p. 58).

Since 1930 the catalytic reduction of fat acids or the sodium-alcohol reduction of fats (p. 172), especially coconut oil, has been used to produce mixtures of higher alcohols which can be sulfated to produce detergents.

$$
RCH_2OH + H_2SO_4 \longrightarrow RCH_2OSO_3H \longrightarrow RCH_2OSO_3Na
$$

The number of synthetic surface-active agents has increased enormously in recent years. Between 500 and 600 are available commercially. The most widely used synthetic detergents in 1955 were the sodium salts of alkylated aromatic sulfonic acids (p. 469), production of which amounted to 591 million pounds. The use of products containing synthetic detergents has increased rapidly. By 1954 the sale of synthetic detergents in the United States exceeded that of soaps.

In contrast to the triglycerides, monoglycerides have free hydroxyl groups which act as water-solubilizing groups, and hence they become emulsifying agents. They have found extensive use particularly in the manufacture of oleomargarine and in other food industries, and in the preparation of cosmetic creams. They are mixtures prepared either by the partial esterification of glycerol with free fat acids or by the glycerolysis of fats (p. 170). Almost 12 million pounds of glycerylmonostearate alone was produced in 1955. Acetylation of the monostearate gives a product that shows promise as a flexible, nongreasy, edible coating for foods.

Other Uses for Fat Acids. Free fat acids are used as softening agents for rubber. Commercial stearic acid is a mixture of stearic and palmitic acids used in the manufacture of candles, cosmetics, and shaving soaps. The aluminum, calcium, lead, and other metallic soaps when heated with petroleum oils form a gel and are used to thicken oils in the manufacture of lubricating greases. Magnesium and zinc stearates are used in face powders and dusting powders, and as lubricants to prevent sticking in the molding of plastics. Fat acid chains are incorporated into the molecules of antiseptics, drugs, dyes, resins, and plastics to modify their solubility and setting characteristics. Lately, fat acids have been converted on an industrial scale into esters, amides, nitriles, and amines, the last being particularly valuable as a starting point for the synthesis of one type of antiseptic (p. 243).

REVIEW QUESTIONS

1. Define the terms wax, fat, and oil.
2. Give a classification of waxes, fats, and oils and list under each class and subclass the more common representatives.
3. Discuss the composition of fats and oils. Give the names and structures of the more important acids formed on the hydrolysis of carnauba wax, butter, lard, tallow, coconut oil, olive oil, tung oil, and linseed oil. What is unusual about the naturally occurring fat acids?
4. What is meant by the terms saponification value; iodine value; acetyl value? How could cottonseed oil be distinguished readily from lubricating oil; castor oil from olive oil; coconut oil from lard; olive oil from linseed oil; spermaceti from tallow?
5. Discuss the manufacture of soap.
6. Give the principle and the method for converting oils into fats.
7. What so-called synthetic detergents are derived from fat acids and how are they made?

PROBLEMS

8. Calculate the volume (S.T.P.) of hydrogen that would be required to convert 500 g. of an oil having the given iodine value into the completely saturated fat: (a) 90; (b) 105; (c) 130; (d) 180.

9. The acids *A*, *B*, *C*, and *D* were isolated from the saponification products of natural fats and their neutralization equivalents were determined by titration. The acids then were oxidized vigorously with alkaline permanganate. Each gave two new acidic products which were isolated and their neutralization equivalents determined. From the following data give a likely structure for the original compounds:

	A	*B*	*C*	*D*
Neutralization equivalent of original acid	254	282	282	338
Neutralization equivalent of oxidation products	94 and 130	73 and 200	94 and 158	122 and 158

10. How many pounds of sodium hydroxide would be required to saponify 10 pounds of a fat having the given saponification value: (*a*) 250; (*b*) 210; (*c*) 175; (*d*) 190?
11. What would be the maximum yield of glycerol obtainable in each of the saponifications indicated in Problem 10?
12. Calculate the weight of metallic sodium required to reduce 100 g. of a fat having the given saponification value: (*a*) 260; (*b*) 205; (*c*) 185; (*d*) 195.
13. What would be the maximum amount of anhydrous sodium alkyl sulfate that could be obtained from the reductions indicated in Problem 12?

Chapter 11

ALDEHYDES AND KETONES

Both alcohols and ethers have the general formula $C_nH_{2n+2}O$. A less saturated group of compounds is known having the formula $C_nH_{2n}O$. Since the first member of the series, CH_2O, has only one carbon atom, the unsaturation cannot be due to a carbon-carbon double bond. Therefore the only logical structure satisfying the rules of valence is one in which the carbon atom is united to the oxygen atom by a double bond. This functional group, $C{=}O$, which is known as a *carbonyl group*, was present in the carboxyl group of carboxylic acids, but its properties were masked by the presence on the same carbon atom of a hydroxyl group. If only hydrogen or carbon atoms are united to the carbonyl group, the group is characteristic of the compounds known as *aldehydes* and *ketones*. The **aldehydes** have at least one hydrogen atom united to the carbonyl group and are represented by the general formula RCHO. The **ketones** have two carbon atoms united to the carbonyl group and are represented by the formula RCOR. The methods of preparation and reactions are in agreement with these structures.

Preparation

1. **Oxidation or Dehydrogenation of Alcohols.** Aldehydes and ketones are formed by the oxidation or dehydrogenation of primary and secondary alcohols respectively (p. 104).

$$RCH_2OH + [O] \longrightarrow R{-}\overset{\overset{\displaystyle O}{\|}}{C}{-}H + H_2O$$

$$R_2CHOH + [O] \longrightarrow R{-}\overset{\overset{\displaystyle O}{\|}}{C}{-}R + H_2O$$

The oxidizing agent may be air in the presence of a copper or silver catalyst at 550°–600°, or a chemical oxidizing agent such as sodium dichromate and sulfuric acid (dichromic acid). The latter reagent is useful for the preparation of the lower aldehydes only, because their low boiling points permit them to be distilled from the reaction mixture as fast as they are formed. Otherwise the aldehyde is retained and oxidized rapidly to acid (p. 212). The ketones undergo further oxidation less readily, and the reaction is more generally applicable for their preparation. The calculated amount of chromium trioxide, CrO_3, in glacial acetic acid also may be used for the conversion of secondary alcohol groups to ketone groups. For the oxidation of the higher primary alcohols to aldehydes, *t*-butyl chromate, prepared from *t*-butyl alcohol and chromium trioxide, is a good reagent.

Catalytic dehydrogenation is a convenient process for the preparation of aldehydes and ketones.

$$\begin{array}{c} RCH_2OH \\ (or\ R_2CHOH) \end{array} \underset{325°}{\overset{Cu\text{-}Zn}{\rightleftarrows}} \begin{array}{c} RCHO + H_2 \\ (or\ R_2CO) \end{array}$$

Because of the equilibrium the reaction does not go to completion, but the product can be separated by distillation and the alcohol recycled. Copper chromite, silver, or alloys of copper and silver, or copper and nickel, also have been recommended as catalysts. It is from this first method of preparation that the name aldehyde is derived (*alcohol dehydrogenatum*).

Heat is absorbed in dehydrogenation (endothermic reaction) but evolved in the oxidation with oxygen (exothermic reaction). Technically the two processes may be combined by using just enough air to supply the heat required for dehydrogenation. In this way the operation may be carried out without the necessity of adding or removing heat externally in order to maintain the optimum temperature for the reaction.

2. **Ozonolysis of Unsaturated Compounds.** Addition of ozone to the carbon-carbon double bond, followed by hydrolysis, yields aldehydes or ketones or both (p. 56).

$$RCH{=}CR_2 \xrightarrow{O_3} \underset{\underset{O-O}{\diagdown \diagup}}{RCH \overset{O}{\diagup \diagdown} CR_2} \xrightarrow{H_2O} RCHO + H_2O_2 + OCR_2$$

To obtain maximum yields of aldehydes and ketones the decomposition is carried out in the presence of a reducing agent such as zinc dust and acetic acid, or hydrogen and platinum, to destroy the peroxides (p. 880) and prevent the formation of organic acids. Whether aldehydes, ketones, or both are obtained depends on the structure of the olefin from which the ozonide was prepared.

3. **Pyrolysis of Carboxylic Acids.** Pyrolysis of carboxylic acids over thoria gives ketones (p. 152). The catalyst is deposited on a porous material such as pumice and packed into a tube which is heated to the proper temperature. The organic acid is run into the tube where it vaporizes and passes over the catalyst. The exit gases are condensed and the product separated by distillation.

$$2\,RCOOH \xrightarrow[400°-450°]{ThO_2} R_2CO + CO_2 + H_2O$$

By using a mixture of organic acids, mixed ketones can be obtained; or if a mixture of formic acid with another organic acid is used, aldehydes may be produced.

$$\begin{matrix} RCOOH \\ + \\ R'COOH \end{matrix} \xrightarrow[400°-450°]{ThO_2} RCOR' + CO_2 + H_2O$$

$$\begin{matrix} RCOOH \\ + \\ HCOOH \end{matrix} \xrightarrow[400°-450°]{ThO_2} RCHO + CO_2 + H_2O$$

The yields of mixed ketones and aldehydes are likely to be poor, because simple ketones and formaldehyde also are produced, and formic acid decomposes into carbon monoxide and water.

4. **Addition of Water to Alkynes.** The addition of water to acetylene leads to the formation of acetaldehyde (p. 131). All other alkynes add water in accordance with the Markovnikov rule and give ketones.

$$RC{\equiv}CH + H_2O \xrightarrow[Hg-HgSO_4]{H_2SO_4} \left[\underset{OH}{R-C{=}CH_2} \right] \longrightarrow \underset{O}{R-C-CH_3}$$

5. Hydrolysis of Acetals. One of the best laboratory procedures for the synthesis of aldehydes consists of the reaction of ethyl orthoformate (p. 175) with a Grignard reagent to give an acetal (p. 203), which can be hydrolyzed by aqueous acids to give the aldehyde.

$$HC(OC_2H_5)_3 + RMgX \longrightarrow \underset{\text{An acetal}}{RCH(OC_2H_5)_2} + C_2H_5OMgX$$

$$RCH(OC_2H_5)_2 + 2 H_2O \xrightarrow{[H^+]} [RCH(OH)_2] + 2 C_2H_5OH$$

$$\downarrow$$

$$RCHO + H_2O$$

6. Addition of Grignard Reagents to Organic Cyanides. Grignard reagents add to the triple bond of cyanides in the same way that they add to a carbonyl group (p. 199), although much more slowly (p. 892). The product hydrolyzes readily in acid solution to a ketone.

$$RC{\equiv}N + R'MgX \longrightarrow \underset{R'}{RC{=}NMgX} \xrightarrow{H_2O + 2 HX} \underset{R'}{RC{=}O} + NH_4X + MgX_2$$

If the α carbon atom of the nitrile carries a hydrogen atom, the chief product may be the salt of the nitrile (cf. p. 200).

$$RCH_2C{\equiv}N + R'MgX \longrightarrow [R\overset{-}{C}HC{\equiv}N]\overset{+}{M}gX + R'H$$

7. Reaction of Grignard Reagents or Alkylcadmiums with Acyl Chlorides. Grignard reagents react with acyl chlorides at low temperature in the presence of ferric chloride to give good yields of ketones.

$$RCOCl + R'MgCl \xrightarrow[-65°]{FeCl_3} RCOR' + MgCl_2$$

If the reaction is carried out at room temperature, the ketone reacts further to give a tertiary alcohol (p. 199). Methyl ketones have been obtained in good yields from Grignard reagents and acetic anhydride at low temperatures.

$$(CH_3CO)_2O + RMgX \xrightarrow{-70°} CH_3COR + CH_3COOMgX$$

Alkylcadmiums (p. 893) also replace the halogen of acyl halides by alkyl, but react less readily with the carbonyl group. The alkylcadmium solutions are prepared from the Grignard reagents and cadmium chloride.

$$2 RMgCl + CdCl_2 \longrightarrow CdR_2 + 2 MgCl_2$$

$$2 R'COCl + CdR_2 \longrightarrow 2 R'COR + CdCl_2$$

Alkyl cadmium compounds having primary alkyl groups are obtained in better yield than those having secondary or tertiary alkyl groups.

Nomenclature

Aldehydes. The **common names** of aldehydes are derived from the acids which would be formed on oxidation, that is, the acids having the same number of carbon atoms. In general the *ic acid* is dropped and *aldehyde* added, for example formaldehyde, acetaldehyde, and *i*-butyraldehyde corresponding to the fact that they yield formic, acetic, and *i*-butyric acids on oxidation. Just as more complex acids may be named as derivatives of acetic acid, aldehydes may be named **as derivatives of acetaldehyde;** thus $C_2H_5CH(CH_3)CHO$ may be called methylethylacetaldehyde. In the **Geneva system** the aldehydes are named by dropping the *e* of the hydrocarbon corresponding to the longest chain containing the aldehyde group and adding *al.* The compound having the above formula would be called 2-methylbutanal. The position of the aldehyde group is not indicated because it always is at the end of the chain, and its carbon atom is numbered one.

Ketones. The **common names** of ketones are derived from the acid which on pyrolysis would yield the ketone. For example acetone, CH_3COCH_3, may be derived from two molecules of acetic acid, and *i*-butyrone, $(CH_3)_2CHCOCH(CH_3)_2$, from *i*-butyric acid. A second method, especially useful for naming **mixed ketones,** simply names the alkyl groups and adds the word *ketone.* For example $CH_3COC_2H_5$ is methyl ethyl ketone. The name is written as three separate words since the compound is not a substitution product of a substance *ketone.* In the **Geneva system** the ending is *one* and the position of the carbonyl group must be indicated by a number, unless the name is unambiguous without the number. Thus methyl ethyl ketone may be called simply butanone, but ethyl ketone, $CH_3CH_2COCH_2CH_3$, must be called 3-pentanone to distinguish it from methyl *n*-propyl ketone, $CH_3COCH_2CH_2CH_3$, which is 2-pentanone. Side chains are named and numbered as usual.

If it is necessary to designate a carbonyl function when another functional group is present, the doubly bound oxygen is called *oxo.* Thus $CH_3COCH_2CH_2$-COOH is 4-oxopentanoic acid. Generically, however, it is called a keto acid rather than an oxo acid.

Physical Properties

The aldehydes and ketones resemble the ethers in their solubility characteristics and volatility, although aldehydes and ketones boil somewhat higher than ethers having the same number of carbon atoms. For example methyl ether boils at $-24°$ and acetaldehyde at $+20°$; methyl ethyl ether boils at 6°, whereas propionaldehyde boils at 49° and acetone at 56°.

Thus far two sources of van der Waals forces have been considered, the London forces resulting from the polarizability of the molecule (p. 39), and proton bonding (p. 87). Neither of these attractive forces can account for the fact that aldehydes and ketones boil higher than ethers of approximately the same molecular weight, because the polarizabilities should be nearly the same, and proton bonding is not possible. Hence a third attractive force must be present which either does not exist between ether molecules or is greater for aldehydes and ketones than for ethers. This third attractive force is that caused by the presence of **permanent dipoles** in the molecules.

In atoms the center of positive charge and the center of negative charge coincide; that is, the probability of finding an electron at any point about the nucleus is the same as that of finding it at the same distance away from the nucleus on the opposite side. The same situation exists in diatomic molecules made up of like atoms, for example hydrogen or chlorine molecules, or in symmetrical polyatomic molecules such as methane and carbon tetrachloride. However, when unlike atoms are bonded to give an unsymmetrical molecule, the centers of positive and negative charge in the molecule ordinarily do not coincide, and the molecule has a positive and a negative end; that is, it is an electrical dipole. This dipole is a permanent one, in contrast to the dipoles resulting from the transient polarizability of the molecule. Whenever such an unequal distribution of charge occurs, an electrical moment, known as the *dipole moment*, exists. This moment, which is the product of the charge at either end of the dipole by the distance between the centers of charge, can be measured. These dipoles have a tendency to line up in an electric field, and a gas with a permanent dipole will change the capacity of a condenser. The alignment is opposed by the thermal agitation of the molecules, and the effect on the capacity of the condenser varies with the temperature. From the variation in the dielectric constant of the compound with temperature, it is possible to calculate the dipole moment, which is designated by the symbol μ. The usual magnitude of the moment is of the order of 10^{-18} electrostatic units, and this quantity is known as a *debye unit*, or simply a *debye* (after P. Debye, who first measured electric moments), and is given the symbol D. Thus methyl ether has a moment of 1.3 D and methyl ethyl ether one of 1.2 D. The moments of acetaldehyde, propionaldehyde, and acetone are respectively 2.7 D, 2.7 D, and 2.8 D. These permanent dipoles add to those caused by the polarizability of the molecule and increase the attractive forces between the molecules. Thus the higher dipole moments of the carbonyl compounds as compared to those for ethers can account for the higher boiling points of the carbonyl compounds. The attractive forces caused by dipoles are proportional to the square of the dipole moment rather than directly proportional (p. 251). Hence their effect rapidly increases with increasing magnitude.

At one time it was assumed that the origin of the dipoles lay in the relative attraction of different nuclei for the bonding pair of electrons, which in turn was related to the relative charges on the nuclei and the relative distances of the valence electrons from the nuclei. Bond moments were assigned to individual bonds and these bond moments were considered to be additive vectorially. It now is believed that this view is an oversimplification and that at least three other factors contribute to the origin of dipole moments. The older view not only may lead to a discrepancy in the calculated magnitude of the moment of a molecule but to an erroneous prediction of the direction of the moment. Thus, based on the relative electronegativities of carbon and hydrogen, it was believed that the dipole of the carbon-hydrogen bond always had its positive end at hydrogen. It now is believed that in alkanes, the negative end is at hydrogen, but that electron-withdrawing groups can reverse the polarity of the carbon-hydrogen bond. For these reasons it seems advisable, at least for the present, not to assign bond moments to individual bonds, but to deal only with the experimentally determined dipole moments of molecules. There are times, however, when certain bond moments obviously may be considered as the main source of the moment of a group or of the molecule as a whole, and where the additivity of group moments may be applied (cf. p. 451).

Reactions

In the carbonyl group, the carbon and oxygen atom are linked by a double bond, and most of the reactions of aldehydes and ketones take place by addition. Because the nuclear charge on oxygen is larger than that on carbon and because the oxygen atom has unshared pairs of electrons, the carbon-oxygen double bond is more highly polarized than a carbon-carbon double bond. Hence the carbonyl group reacts with a greater variety of reagents. In general aldehydes differ from ketones only in the relative rate of reaction and in the position of equilibrium. Aldehydes usually react faster, and the reaction goes more nearly to completion. The large variety of reactions makes it desirable to group them into several divisions.

SIMPLE ADDITION

1. **Hydrogen.** Aldehydes on reduction yield primary alcohols, and ketones yield secondary alcohols.

$$
\begin{array}{l}
\overset{\text{H}}{\underset{|}{\text{R}}}\text{C}{=}\text{O} + 2\,[\text{H}] \longrightarrow \text{RCH}_2\text{OH} \\
\text{R}_2\text{C}{=}\text{O} + 2\,[\text{H}] \longrightarrow \text{R}_2\text{CHOH}
\end{array}
$$

The reduction may be brought about catalytically with hydrogen and a platinum, palladium, or nickel catalyst, or by chemical reducing agents in neutral or alkaline solution, for example sodium and absolute alcohol, sodium amalgam and water, lithium aluminum hydride (p. 172) in ether solution, or sodium borohydride ($NaBH_4$) in aqueous solution. Another method known as the *Meerwein-Ponndorf reduction* depends on the equilibrium that exists between alcohols and carbonyl compounds in the presence of aluminum alkoxides.

$$R'CHO + R_2CHOH \quad \underset{\longleftarrow}{\overset{Al(OR)_3}{\longrightarrow}} \quad R'CH_2OH + R_2CO$$
$$\text{or} \qquad\qquad\qquad\qquad\qquad \text{or}$$
$$R'_2CO \qquad\qquad\qquad\qquad\qquad R'_2CHOH$$

If the alcohol used as the reducing agent is so chosen that the aldehyde or ketone formed boils at a lower temperature than any of the other reactants, it may be removed by slow distillation, and the reaction forced to completion. For example, if ethyl alcohol and aluminum ethoxide, or *i*-propyl alcohol and aluminum *i*-propoxide, are used, the low-boiling acetaldehyde or acetone is removed. Ketones as well as aldehydes may be reduced. If the reaction is carried out in such a way that it is used to oxidize an alcohol by means of a ketone, it is called an *Oppenauer oxidation*.

Coordination of an unshared pair of electrons from the carbonyl group of the aldehyde or ketone with the metal facilitates the transfer of a hydride ion from the primary or secondary alkoxide group to the carbonyl group by means of a cyclic mechanism.

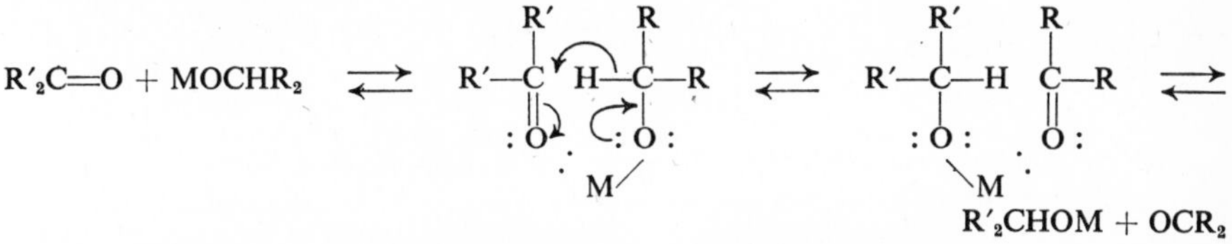

$$R'_2CHOM + OCR_2$$

Only a small amount of metal alkoxide is necessary because of the equilibration of the alkoxides with the alcohols.

$$R'_2CHOM + R_2CHOH \quad \rightleftarrows \quad R'_2CHOH + R_2CHOM$$

2. **Grignard Reagents.** Addition of Grignard reagents takes place as with the carbonyl group of carbon dioxide (p. 123), that is, R to carbon and MgX to oxygen. Formaldehyde yields primary alcohols, all other aldehydes yield secondary alcohols, and ketones yield tertiary alcohols. This procedure is one of the most important for the synthesis of complex alcohols, since by choosing the proper R groups in the aldehyde or ketone and in the Grignard reagent almost any desired alcohol may be synthesized, provided the R groups are not too highly branched to cause steric hindrance and prevent addition.

---

[1] Cf. page 121.

Although the above reactions take place readily to give good yields of the products when simple aldehydes or ketones or simple Grignard reagents are involved, branching of the alkyl groups in either the carbonyl compound or the Grignard reagent or both may permit side reactions to predominate. Other reactions that have been observed are as follows:

(*a*) REDUCTION. In this reaction the halomagnesium salt of the primary or secondary alcohol is formed, and the alkyl group of the Grignard reagent forms an alkene.

$$R_2C{=}O + R'_2CHCH_2MgX \longrightarrow R_2CHOMgX + R'_2C{=}CH_2$$

Under certain conditions a Meerwein-Ponndorf type of reduction (p. 199) or pinacol reduction (p. 217) may take place.

(*b*) SALT FORMATION. The Grignard reagent may remove a proton from an α carbon atom with the formation of the halomagnesium salt of the ketone (cf. p. 213).

$$R_2CHCOR + R'MgX \longrightarrow \left[R_2\overset{\cdot\cdot}{\bar{C}}COR \right] \overset{+}{MgX} + R'H$$

Addition of water regenerates the ketone.

$$\left[R_2\overset{\cdot\cdot}{\bar{C}}COR \right] \overset{+}{MgX} + H_2O \longrightarrow R_2CHCOR + HOMgX$$

Salt formation with ketones frequently is referred to as the *enolizing action* of the Grignard reagent, because at one time it was believed that only in the enol form of the ketone would the hydrogen be sufficiently acidic to produce hydrocarbons from Grignard reagents (cf. p. 213).

(*c*) CONDENSATION. Halomagnesium alkoxide formed by reduction (*a*) or oxidation (p. 122) may catalyze an aldol-type addition (p. 205).

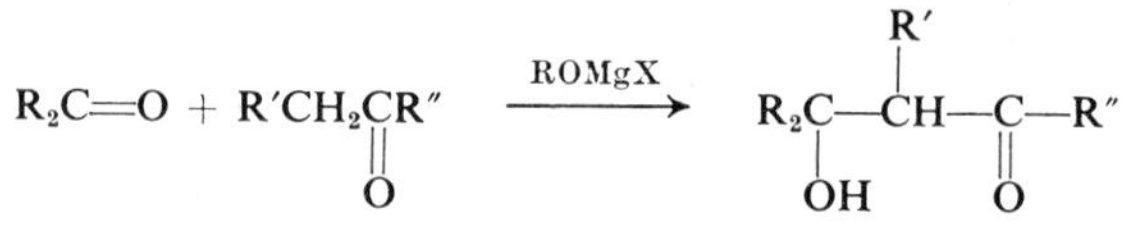

$$R_2C{=}O + R'CH_2CR'' \ (\overset{ROMgX}{\longrightarrow})\ R_2C\overset{\overset{\textstyle R'}{|}}{-}CH-C-R''$$

$$\underset{O}{\|} \qquad\qquad \underset{OH}{|}\ \ \underset{O}{\|}$$

These side reactions become so important with branched aldehydes, ketones, and Grignard reagents that it is not possible to synthesize many alcohols by the reaction of a Grignard reagent with an aldehyde or ketone. For example the reaction of trimethylacetaldehyde with *t*-butylmagnesium bromide gives almost exclusively neopentyl alcohol, and the reaction of di-*t*-butyl ketone with *n*-butylmagnesium bromide gives di-*t*-butylcarbinol. Frequently the desired alcohol can be synthesized if an alkyllithium (p. 891) is used in place of a Grignard reagent.

The mechanism of the addition of the Grignard reagents to carbonyl groups is discussed on page 123.

3. **Hydrogen Cyanide.** Anhydrous hydrogen cyanide adds to aldehydes and ketones to give α-hydroxy cyanides known as **cyanohydrins.**

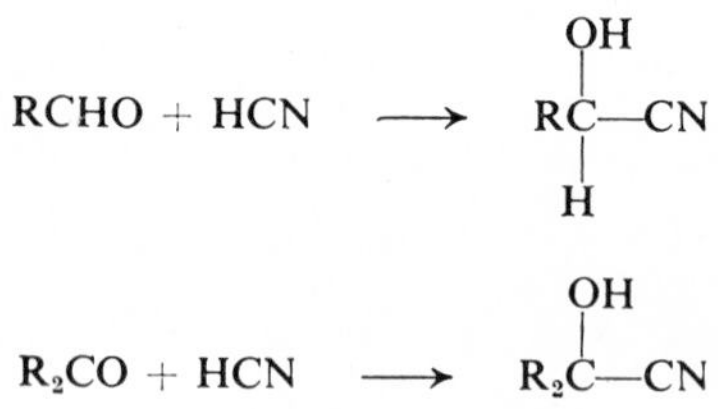

$$RCHO + HCN \longrightarrow R\overset{\overset{\textstyle OH}{|}}{\underset{\underset{\textstyle H}{|}}{C}}{-}CN$$

$$R_2CO + HCN \longrightarrow R_2\overset{\overset{\textstyle OH}{|}}{C}{-}CN$$

These compounds are named as addition products. For example that derived from acetaldehyde is known as *acetaldehyde cyanohydrin* and that from acetone as *acetone cyanohydrin.* As with any other nitrile, the cyanide group can be hydrolyzed to a carboxyl group (p. 144). Hence the cyanohydrins are intermediates for the synthesis of α-hydroxy acids (p. 781).

The reactivity of the carbonyl group depends on the ability of an electron-seeking reagent to attack the oxygen atom or of an electron-donating reagent to attack the carbon atom. Thus it was shown as early as 1903 by Lapworth[2] that the addition of hydrogen cyanide to aldehydes and ketones is accelerated by the addition of bases but retarded by the addition of acids. Therefore the active reagent is cyanide ion and not hydrogen cyanide.

$$R_2\overset{\delta_+}{C}=\overset{\delta_-}{O}: \quad \underset{\longleftarrow}{\overset{[:CN^-]}{\longrightarrow}} \quad \left[R_2\overset{|}{\underset{CN}{C}}-\overset{..}{\underset{..}{O}}: \right]^- \quad \underset{\longleftarrow}{\overset{HCN}{\longrightarrow}} \quad R_2\overset{|}{\underset{CN}{C}}-OH + [:CN^-]$$

4. Sodium Bisulfite. When shaken with a saturated aqueous sodium bisulfite solution, most aldehydes and methyl ketones will react to form a slightly soluble bisulfite addition compound in which hydrogen has added to oxygen and the sodium sulfonate group to carbon.

$$RCHO + NaHSO_3 \quad \rightleftharpoons \quad \left[R-\overset{OH}{\underset{H}{\overset{|}{\underset{|}{C}}}}-SO_3^- \right] Na^+$$

$$RCOCH_3 + NaHSO_3 \quad \rightleftharpoons \quad \left[\underset{HO}{\overset{R-C-CH_3}{\diagdown}} \underset{SO_3^-}{\diagup} \right] Na^+$$

If both groups attached to the carbonyl group are larger than methyl, the addition compound does not form unless the groups are held out of the way of the carbonyl group, as for example when they are part of a ring as in cyclohexanone (p. 793). Even if one of the groups is methyl, the reaction may be very slow if the other group is branched, e.g., a *t*-butyl group. As to nomenclature, the product from acetaldehyde is known as *acetaldehyde sodium bisulfite* or as the *bisulfite addition compound of acetaldehyde*, that from acetone is *acetone sodium bisulfite* or the *bisulfite addition compound of acetone*.

Since these compounds are salts, they are not soluble in organic solvents and may be freed from other organic compounds such as hydrocarbons or alcohols by filtering and washing with ether. The reactions are reversible, and hence the carbonyl compound is regenerated by any reagent that reacts irreversibly with bisulfite. Either alkali or acid can be used.

$$RCHOHSO_3Na + HCl \quad \longrightarrow \quad RCHO + NaCl + SO_2 + H_2O$$

$$R_2COHSO_3Na + Na_2CO_3 \quad \longrightarrow \quad R_2CO + Na_2SO_3 + NaHCO_3$$

Acids have the disadvantage that sulfur dioxide must be removed from the product. Alkalies have the disadvantage that they cause condensation reactions with aldehydes (p. 205). As a result alkalies usually are used to liberate ketones,

---

[2] Arthur Lapworth (1872–1941), professor at the University of Manchester who held in succession chairs in organic chemistry and in physical chemistry. He was a pioneer investigator of the mechanisms of organic reactions. His ideas were so advanced that his early work received little attention for many years. His investigations of the addition of hydrogen cyanide to carbonyl compounds, of the bromination of ketones, and of acid and basic catalysis now are considered classical.

Why will formaldehyde displaced higher aldehydes is it less hindered than other [?]

202 *Chemistry of Organic Compounds* Ch. 11

and acids to liberate aldehydes. An alternate procedure consists of heating the bisulfite addition compound with a slight excess of an aqueous solution of formaldehyde.

$$RCH\overset{OH}{\underset{SO_3Na}{\diagup\diagdown}} + HCHO \longrightarrow RCHO + H_2C\overset{OH}{\underset{SO_3Na}{\diagup\diagdown}}$$

$$R_2C\overset{OH}{\underset{SO_3Na}{\diagup\diagdown}} + HCHO \longrightarrow R_2CO + H_2C\overset{OH}{\underset{SO_3Na}{\diagup\diagdown}}$$

These exchange reactions take place because the position of equilibrium for the reaction of formaldehyde with bisulfite is farther to the right than it is with the other aldehydes and ketones. The chief importance of the bisulfite addition compounds is their use in separating carbonyl compounds from mixtures with other organic compounds.

5. **Water.** Although compounds having two hydroxyl groups on the same carbon atom rarely can be isolated in the pure state, it appears that they may exist in water solution. The familiar example is carbonic acid, $O{=}C(OH)_2$, which behaves like a dibasic acid in aqueous solution but can be isolated only in the form of its salts or esters or of its anhydride, carbon dioxide. Similarly when aldehydes are dissolved in water, they may exist to a considerable extent in the hydrated form. This condition is true particularly for formaldehyde whose aqueous solutions appear to contain almost exclusively dihydroxymethane.

$$HCHO + HOH \rightleftarrows H{-}\overset{\displaystyle H}{\underset{\displaystyle OH}{C}}{-}OH$$

Acetone on the other hand does not add water at a measurable rate in the absence of acids or hydroxyl ion.

Evidence for the almost complete reaction of formaldehyde with water is the absence of a characteristic carbonyl absorption band (p. 665) in the ultraviolet for aqueous solutions. Evidence for the nonreaction of acetone is the lack of exchange of the oxygen atoms of acetone and water when acetone is dissolved in water containing an increased concentration of the heavy oxygen isotope, O^{18}. Exchange takes place at a measurable rate only in the presence of acids or hydroxide ion. The mechanisms for the catalyzed reactions are expressed by the following equilibria. (For conventions, see p. 138).

$$\underset{CH_3}{\overset{CH_3}{\diagdown}}C{=}O \underset{[B^-]}{\overset{HB}{\rightleftarrows}} \left[\underset{CH_3}{\overset{CH_3}{\diagdown}}C{=}\overset{+}{O}H\right] \overset{HOH}{\rightleftarrows} \left[\underset{CH_3}{\overset{CH_3}{\diagdown}}\underset{\overset{+}{O}H}{\underset{H}{\diagup}}\overset{OH}{\underset{}{C}}\right] \underset{HB}{\overset{[B^-]}{\rightleftarrows}} \underset{CH_3}{\overset{CH_3}{\diagdown}}\underset{OH}{\overset{OH}{C}}$$

$$\underset{CH_3}{\overset{CH_3}{\diagdown}}C{=}O \overset{[OH^-]}{\rightleftarrows} \left[\underset{CH_3}{\overset{CH_3}{\diagdown}}\underset{OH}{\overset{O^-}{C}}\right] \underset{[OH^-]}{\overset{HOH}{\rightleftarrows}} \underset{CH_3}{\overset{CH_3}{\diagdown}}\underset{OH}{\overset{OH}{C}}$$

In the presence of H_2O^{18}, the reverse processes lead to the enrichment of the acetone in the O^{18} isotope.

6. **Alcohols.** In the presence of either acidic or basic catalysts, aldehydes add one mole of alcohol to form *hemiacetals*.

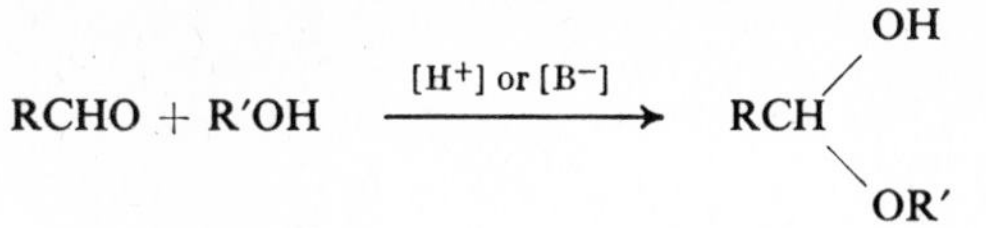

$$RCHO + R'OH \xrightarrow{[H^+] \text{ or } [B^-]} RCH \overset{OH}{\underset{OR'}{<}}$$

A hemiacetal

With an excess of alcohol and an acidic catalyst, water is eliminated and an *acetal* is formed.

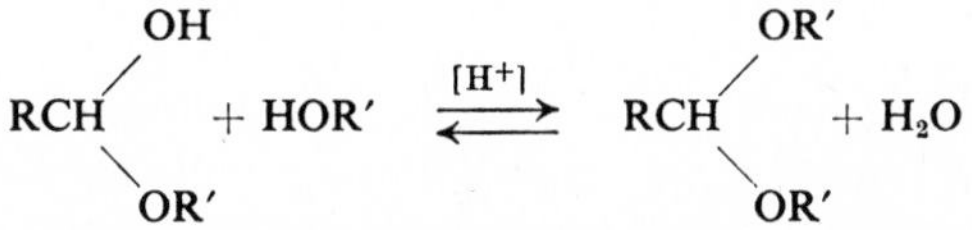

$$RCH \overset{OH}{\underset{OR'}{<}} + HOR' \underset{}{\overset{[H^+]}{\rightleftarrows}} RCH \overset{OR'}{\underset{OR'}{<}} + H_2O$$

An acetal

Bases do not catalyze the formation or hydrolysis of acetals.

Acetal also is the specific name for the product from acetaldehyde and ethyl alcohol. The product from formaldehyde and methyl alcohol has the common name **methylal.**

If an excess of hydrogen chloride or hydrogen bromide is present, α-*halogen ethers* are formed instead of acetals.

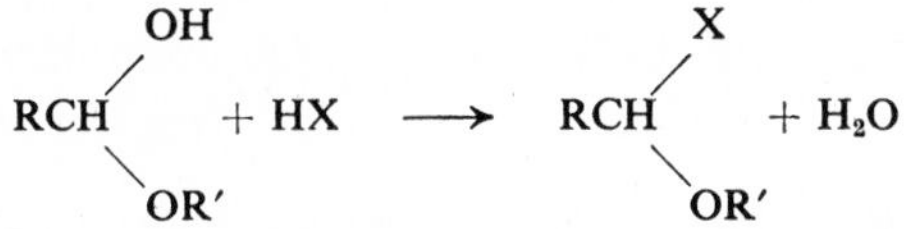

$$RCH \overset{OH}{\underset{OR'}{<}} + HX \longrightarrow RCH \overset{X}{\underset{OR'}{<}} + H_2O$$

The halogen in these compounds is very reactive and can be replaced by an alkyl group by means of Grignard reagents to give mixed ethers.

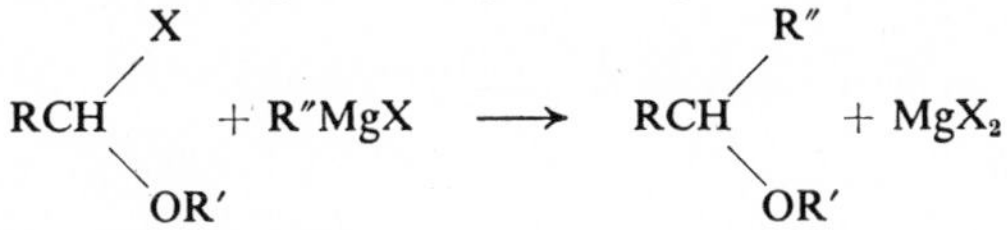

$$RCH \overset{X}{\underset{OR'}{<}} + R''MgX \longrightarrow RCH \overset{R''}{\underset{OR'}{<}} + MgX_2$$

An explanation of the fact that hemiacetal formation is catalyzed by both acids and bases, whereas acetal formation is catalyzed only by acids, is of interest. In the basic catalysis of hemiacetal formation, the alcohol must be the effective point of attack by the catalyst.

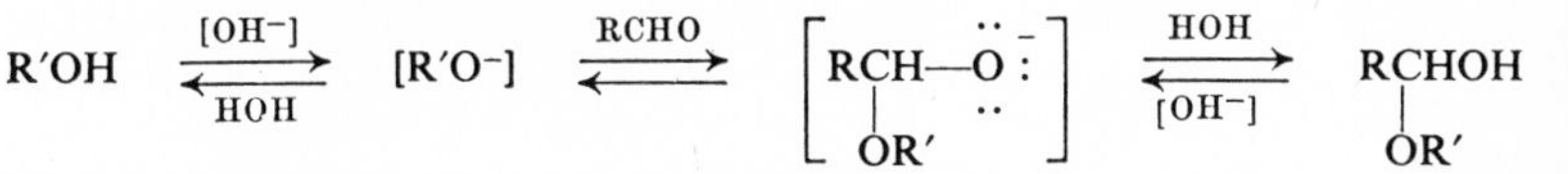

$$R'OH \underset{HOH}{\overset{[OH^-]}{\rightleftarrows}} [R'O^-] \overset{RCHO}{\rightleftarrows} \left[\underset{OR'}{\overset{..}{\underset{|}{RCH-O:}}} \right]^- \underset{[OH^-]}{\overset{HOH}{\rightleftarrows}} \underset{OR'}{\overset{|}{RCHOH}} \quad (a)$$

Although the carbon atom of the carbonyl group of the aldehyde may be attacked by a base, this does not lead to the formation of a hemiacetal, but merely to the hydrated aldehyde.

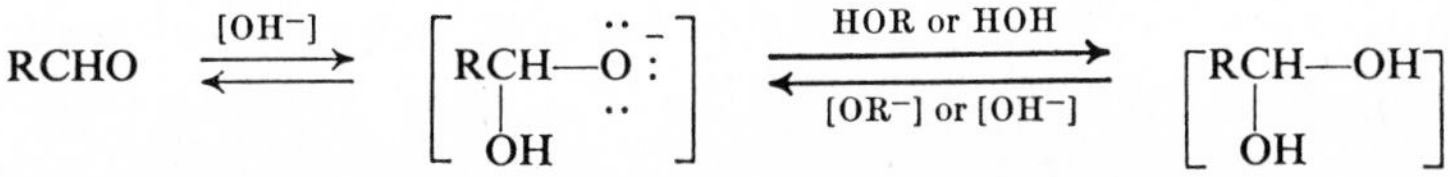

$$RCHO \overset{[OH^-]}{\rightleftarrows} \left[\underset{OH}{\overset{..}{\underset{|}{RCH-O:}}} \right]^- \underset{[OR^-] \text{ or } [OH^-]}{\overset{HOR \text{ or } HOH}{\rightleftarrows}} \left[\underset{OH}{\overset{|}{RCH-OH}} \right] \quad (b)$$

In acid catalysis, however, the effective point of attack is the carbonyl group.

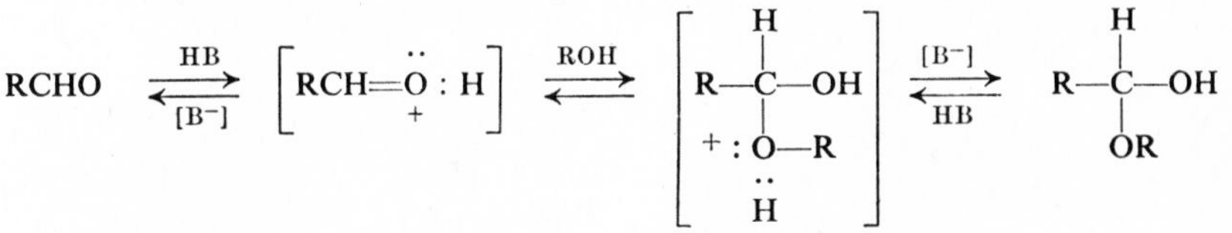

$$RCHO \underset{[B^-]}{\overset{HB}{\rightleftarrows}} \left[\underset{+}{\overset{..}{RCH=O:H}} \right] \overset{ROH}{\rightleftarrows} \left[\underset{+:\underset{H}{\overset{..}{O}}-R}{\overset{H}{\underset{|}{\underset{|}{R-C-OH}}}} \right] \underset{HB}{\overset{[B^-]}{\rightleftarrows}} \underset{OR}{\overset{H}{\underset{|}{\underset{|}{R-C-OH}}}} \quad (c)$$

The attack by the acid on the alcohol gives $[ROH_2^+]$ which can do nothing but transfer protons to the carbonyl group.

In the conversion of the hemiacetal to the acetal, bases are not effective catalysts, because they can do nothing except attack the hydroxyl of the hemiacetal, which is the reverse of hemiacetal formation (equation *a*). Acid catalysts, however, can initiate continuation of the reaction to the acetal stage. If the acid attacks the alkoxyl group, it merely is catalyzing the reverse of hemiacetal formation (equation *c*). When, however, it attacks the hydroxyl group, acetal formation can result.

$$\text{R}-\underset{\text{OR}}{\overset{\text{H}}{\text{C}}}-\text{OH} \underset{[\text{B}^-]}{\overset{\text{HB}}{\rightleftharpoons}} \left[\text{R}-\underset{\text{OR}}{\overset{\text{H}\ \ \text{H}}{\overset{+}{\text{C}}}-\overset{..}{\text{OH}}\right] \underset{\text{HOH}}{\overset{\text{HOR}}{\rightleftharpoons}} \left[\text{R}-\underset{\text{OR}}{\overset{\text{H}\ \ \text{H}}{\overset{+}{\text{C}}}-\overset{..}{\text{OR}}\right] \underset{\text{HB}}{\overset{[\text{B}^-]}{\rightleftharpoons}} \text{R}-\underset{\text{OR}}{\overset{\text{H}}{\text{C}}}-\text{OR}$$

In the reaction of ketones with alcohols, the equilibrium is so far to the left that ketals are not formed in any appreciable amount. They are made indirectly by an exchange reaction with either alkyl orthoformates (p. 175) or alkyl sulfites (p. 108).

$$\text{R}_2\text{C}{=}\text{O} + (\text{R}'\text{O})_3\text{CH} \xrightarrow{[\text{H}^+]} \text{R}_2\text{C}\underset{\text{OR}'}{\overset{\text{OR}'}{\diagup}} + \text{O}{=}\underset{\text{OR}'}{\overset{}{\text{CH}}}$$

$$\text{R}_2\text{C}{=}\text{O} + (\text{R}'\text{O})_2\text{SO} \xrightarrow{[\text{H}^+]} \text{R}_2\text{C}\underset{\text{OR}'}{\overset{\text{OR}'}{\diagup}} + \text{SO}_2$$

7. Acid Anhydrides. Aldehydes add acid anhydrides to give the ester of the hydrated aldehyde. These compounds have been classified as **acylals.**

$$\text{R}\overset{\text{H}}{\underset{}{\text{C}}}{=}\text{O} + (\text{R}'\text{CO})_2\text{O} \xrightarrow{\text{BF}_3} \text{RCH}\underset{\text{OCOR}'}{\overset{\text{OCOR}'}{\diagdown}}$$

$$\text{CH}_3\text{CHO} + (\text{CH}_3\text{CO})_2\text{O} \xrightarrow{\text{BF}_3} \text{CH}_3\text{CH}\underset{\text{OCOCH}_3}{\overset{\text{OCOCH}_3}{\diagdown}}$$

Ethylidene acetate

This reaction and the conversion to acetals may be used to "protect" an aldehyde group while carrying out a reaction, such as oxidation or reduction, on another part of the molecule. After the reaction has been completed, the alkoxyl or acyl groups are removed by hydrolysis.

$$\text{RCH}\underset{\text{OR}'}{\overset{\text{OR}'}{\diagup}} + 2\,\text{H}_2\text{O} \xrightarrow{[\text{H}^+]} [\text{RCH(OH)}_2] + 2\,\text{HOR}'$$

$$\text{RCH}\underset{\text{OCOCH}_3}{\overset{\text{OCOCH}_3}{\diagup}} + 2\,\text{NaOH} \longrightarrow [\text{RCH(OH)}_2] + 2\,\text{NaOCOCH}_3$$

$$[\text{RCH(OH)}_2] \longrightarrow \text{RCHO} + \text{H}_2\text{O}$$

Although only acids catalyze the hydrolysis of acetals, the acylals are esters of carboxylic acids and hydrolysis is catalyzed by either acid or base.

8. **Acetylenes.** Acetylenes add to aldehydes and ketones in the presence of catalysts to give *alkynols*.

$$\begin{matrix} R \\ \diagdown \\ \quad C{=}O + R''C{\equiv}CH \\ \diagup \\ R' \end{matrix} \longrightarrow \begin{matrix} R' \\ | \\ R{-}CHC{\equiv}CR'' \\ | \\ OH \end{matrix}$$

Aqueous formaldehyde and acetylene at 100° and 6 atmospheres in the presence of cuprous carbide (copper acetylide) gives **1,4-dihydroxy-2-butyne** (*butynediol*).

$$2\ HCHO + HC{\equiv}CH \xrightarrow{\ CuC_2\ } HOCH_2C{\equiv}CCH_2OH$$

Potassium hydroxide dissolved in ethers of ethylene glycol (p. 742) can be used as a catalyst for those carbonyl compounds not affected by alkali. Thus methyl ethyl ketone and acetylene give **3-hydroxy-3-methyl-1-pentyne** (*methylpentynol*) which is a useful soporific.

$$\begin{matrix} C_2H_5C{=}O + HC{\equiv}CH \\ | \\ CH_3 \end{matrix} \xrightarrow{\ KOH\ } \begin{matrix} CH_3 \\ | \\ C_2H_5{-}C{-}C{\equiv}CH \\ | \\ OH \end{matrix}$$

The HC≡C group is the *ethynyl* group and its introduction by means of acetylene is called *ethynylation*.

9. **Aldol Addition.**[3] In the presence of dilute aqueous alkalies or acids, aldehydes and ketones having at least one α hydrogen undergo self-addition reactions. These reactions may be repeated, and under certain conditions complex compounds are formed. In the presence of very dilute alkalies or acids, the product of reaction of two moles of aldehyde or ketone can be isolated. The reaction may be written as the addition of an α hydrogen to a carbonyl group, and carbon to carbon.

$$\begin{matrix} RCH{=}O + R'{-}CHCHO \\ | \\ H \end{matrix} \underset{\xleftarrow{\hspace{2cm}}}{\overset{[OH^-]\ or\ [H^+]}{\xrightarrow{\hspace{2cm}}}} \begin{matrix} R' \\ | \\ RCHOHCHCHO \end{matrix}$$

Since the product has both an alcohol and an aldehyde function, it is known as an *aldol*. **Acetaldol** was synthesized by Wurtz in 1872 (p. 126).

$$CH_3CHO + CH_3CHO \underset{\xleftarrow{\hspace{1.5cm}}}{\overset{[OH^-]\ or\ [H^+]}{\xrightarrow{\hspace{1.5cm}}}} CH_3CHOHCH_2CHO$$
$$\text{Acetaldol or aldol}$$

Since an excess of aldehyde always is present during an aldol addition, the question arises as to why the aldol first formed does not continue to react with aldehyde molecules and give polymeric products.

$$CH_3CHOHCH_2CHO + CH_3CHO \longrightarrow CH_3CHOHCH_2CHOHCH_2CHO\ \text{etc.}$$

---

[3] This reaction usually is called an aldol condensation. The term *condensation*, however, has been used very loosely by organic chemists. In this text it will be used only to mean the formation of a carbon-carbon bond with the elimination of some small molecule such as water, alcohol, or a metallic halide.

It appears that condensation between more than two molecules is prevented by the formation of a sesquiacetal between a molecule of aldol and one of acetaldehyde.

$$
\begin{array}{ccc}
\text{CH}_3\text{CHCH}_2\text{CHO} & \left[\text{CH}_3\text{CHCH}_2\text{CHO}\right] & \text{CH}_3\text{CHCH}_2\text{CHOH} \\
\underset{\text{OH}}{|} \quad + \quad \rightleftharpoons & \underset{\text{O} \quad \text{OH}}{\underset{|}{\text{CH}}} & \underset{\text{O} \quad \text{O}}{\text{CH}} \\
\text{OCHCH}_3 & \overset{|}{\underset{\text{CH}_3}{\text{CH}}} & \overset{|}{\underset{\text{CH}_3}{\text{CH}}}
\end{array}
$$

Although the equilibrium is sufficiently mobile that acetaldehyde can be removed readily by distillation, the position of equilibrium lies sufficiently far to the right to prevent further aldol condensation. On long standing two molecules of aldol react to give **paraldol**, an analogous product.

$$
\begin{array}{cc}
\text{CH}_3\text{CHCH}_2\text{CHO} & \text{CH}_2\!\!-\!\!\text{CHOH} \\
\underset{\text{OH}}{|} \quad + \quad \rightleftharpoons \quad \text{CH}_3\!\!-\!\!\text{CH} \qquad \text{O} \\
\text{OCHCH}_2\text{CHOHCH}_3 & \text{O} \!\!-\!\!\text{CHCH}_2\text{CHOHCH}_3 \\
 & \text{Paraldol}
\end{array}
$$

With ketones the equilibrium is so far to the left that special means of shifting it to the right must be employed to obtain practical amounts of product.

$$
\text{CH}_3\text{COCH}_3 + \text{CH}_3\text{COCH}_3 \xrightleftharpoons{[\text{OH}^-] \text{ or } [\text{H}^+]} \underset{\text{Diacetone alcohol}}{(\text{CH}_3)_2\text{COHCH}_2\text{COCH}_3}
$$

For the production of diacetone alcohol, the acetone is passed over an insoluble catalyst such as calcium hydroxide or barium hydroxide and the unchanged acetone separated by distillation and recycled.

The alkaline catalysis of aldol addition introduces a new point of attack for the catalyst in carbonyl compounds, namely the hydrogen atoms on a carbon atom α to a carbonyl group. The carbon atom of the carbonyl group is deficient in electrons because of the electron-attracting effect of the doubly-bound oxygen atom. The resulting positive charge in turn withdraws electrons from the α carbon atom and permits the removal of a proton by a base. The anion thus formed attacks the carbonyl carbon atom of a second molecule, and the product is stabilized by acquiring a proton from a water molecule.

$$
\begin{array}{ccccc}
\text{R} & & \text{R} & & \text{R} \\
| & [\text{OH}^-] & | & \text{R'CHO} & | \\
\text{CH}_2\text{CHO} & \underset{\text{HOH}}{\overset{}{\rightleftharpoons}} & \left[:\text{CHCHO}\right]^- & \rightleftharpoons & \text{R'CH}\!\!-\!\!\text{CHCHO} \\
 & & & & \underset{:\text{O}:}{|}
\end{array}
\xrightleftharpoons[{[\text{OH}^-]}]{\text{HOH}}
\begin{array}{c}
\text{R} \\
| \\
\text{R'CH}\!\!-\!\!\text{CHCHO} \\
| \\
\text{OH}
\end{array}
$$

Although the electrostatic effect of the oxygen atom should make the hydrogen attached directly to the carbonyl group more acidic than that on the α carbon atom, the ion $\left[\text{R}\!-\!\text{CH}_2\!-\!\bar{\text{C}}\!\!=\!\!\text{O}\right]$ is not as stable as the ion $\left[\text{R}\!-\!\bar{\text{C}}\text{H}\!-\!\text{CH}\!\!=\!\!\text{O}\right]$, because only the latter is stabilized by resonance (p. 154).

$$
\left\{\text{R}\!-\!\bar{\text{C}}\text{H}\!-\!\text{CH}\!\!=\!\!\text{O} \quad \longleftrightarrow \quad \text{R}\!-\!\text{CH}\!\!=\!\!\text{CH}\!-\!\ddot{\text{O}}\!:^- \right\}
$$

In the acid-catalyzed reaction the carbonyl group is the first point of attack, and removal of a proton from the α carbon atom follows.

$$RCH_2\overset{H}{\underset{|}{C}}{=}O \underset{[B^-]}{\overset{HB}{\rightleftharpoons}} \left[RCH_2\overset{H}{\underset{|}{\underset{H}{C}}}\overset{+}{-}C{=}\overset{+}{OH}\right] \underset{HB}{\overset{[B^-]}{\rightleftharpoons}} \left[RCH{=}\overset{H}{\underset{|}{C}}OH\right]$$

The product is known as the *enol form* of the carbonyl compound, and the process is called *enolization*. In this process the equilibrium for simple aldehydes and ketones in the fluid state[4] lies far to the left.[4] In the next stage of the reaction, the π electrons of the enol form attack the electron-deficient carbon atom of a second molecule of the conjugate acid (p. 235) of the carbonyl compound.

$$\left[RCH{=}\overset{H}{\underset{|}{C}}{-}\ddot{O}H\right] \begin{pmatrix} + \\ \end{pmatrix} \left[RCH_2\overset{+}{\underset{\underset{H}{|}}{C}}{=}\overset{+}{OH}\right] \rightleftharpoons \left[RCH{-}\overset{H}{\underset{|}{C}}{=}\overset{+}{OH} \\ RCH_2\overset{}{\underset{\underset{H}{|}}{C}}{-}OH\right] \underset{HB}{\overset{[B^-]}{\rightleftharpoons}} \begin{matrix} RCHCHO \\ | \\ RCH_2CHOH \end{matrix}$$

The aldols are characterized by the ease with which they lose water. Heating with traces of acid or iodine gives the α,β-unsaturated aldehyde or ketone.

$$CH_3CHOHCH_2CHO \underset{heat}{\overset{[H^+]}{\longrightarrow}} \underset{\text{Crotonic aldehyde}}{CH_3CH{=}CHCHO + H_2O}$$

$$(CH_3)_2COHCH_2COCH_3 \underset{heat}{\overset{I_2}{\longrightarrow}} \underset{\text{Mesityl oxide}}{(CH_3)_2C{=}CHCOCH_3 + H_2O}$$

Iodine catalyzes the above dehydrations, because it is an electron-seeking reagent. Familiar evidence for this statement is the greater solubility of iodine in potassium iodide solution than in

water because of the formation of triiodide ions by the reaction $I_2 + \left[: \ddot{I} :\right]^- \longrightarrow [I_3^-]$.

A related phenomenon is the brown color of solutions of iodine in alcohol in contrast to the violet color of solutions in hexane (cf. p. 449).

Concentrated sodium hydroxide solutions convert aldehydes having at least two α hydrogen atoms to high molecular weight complex products known as **aldehyde resins.** Aldol addition, dehydration, and polymerization types of reaction probably play a part in their formation. The product from acetaldehyde is a sticky viscous orange-colored oil with a characteristic odor.

Ketones are not affected appreciably by concentrated sodium hydroxide solutions. The amide ion, however, is a stronger base than hydroxide ion, and

---

[4] Spontaneously interconvertible isomers are called *tautomers,* and the phenomenon is known as *tautomerism* (p. 822). Tautomerism is not to be confused with resonance. Tautomers have different structures, whereas resonance does not involve a change in the positions of the atoms in the molecule.

under anhydrous conditions sodium amide converts acetone into a cyclic compound known as **isophorone,** which again is the result of a combination of aldol addition and dehydration.

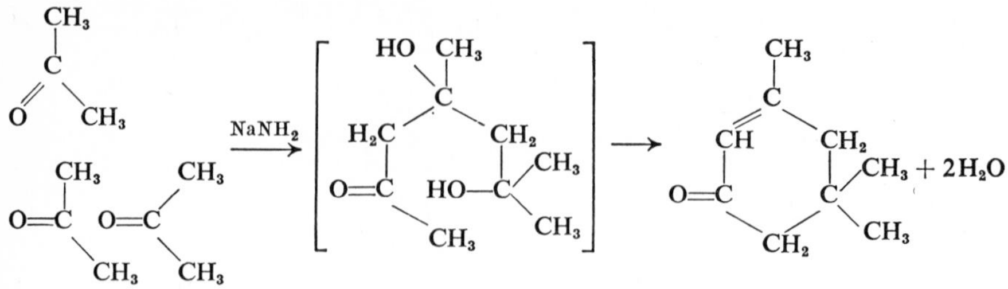

Strong acids favor the trimerization of aldehydes (see 10) but lead to addition and dehydration of ketones. For example, acetone yields mesityl oxide directly in the acid-catalyzed reaction.

$$\underset{CH_3}{\overset{CH_3}{\diagdown}}C{=}O + CH_3COCH_3 \underset{}{\overset{[H^+]}{\rightleftarrows}} (CH_3)_2COHCH_2COCH_3 \underset{H_2O}{\overset{[H^+]}{\rightleftarrows}} (CH_3)_2C{=}CHCOCH_3$$

Diacetone alcohol   Mesityl oxide

Under more vigorous conditions of catalysis and dehydration, higher condensation products are formed.

$$(CH_3)_2C{=}O + CH_3COCH_3 + O{=}C(CH_3)_2 \xrightarrow[\text{or AlCl}_3]{\text{Dry HCl, ZnCl}_2,}$$

$$(CH_3)_2C{=}CH{-}CO{-}CH{=}C(CH_3)_2 + 2\ H_2O$$
Phorone

$+ 3\ H_2O$

Mesitylene

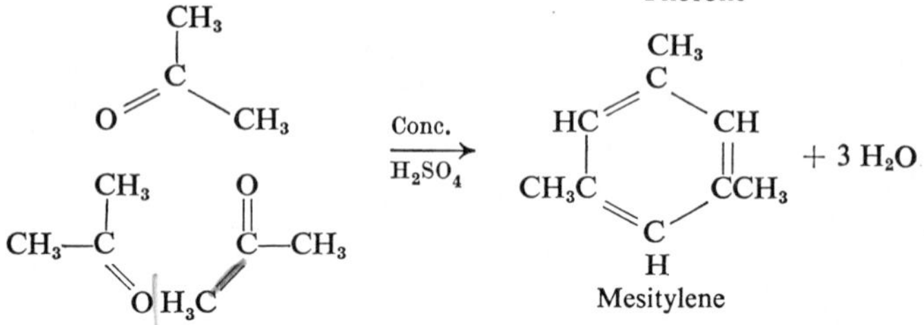

The formation of mesitylene from acetone is an example of the synthesis of an aromatic type compound (p. 416) from a member of the aliphatic series.

10. **Cyclic Trimerization.** Aliphatic aldehydes, but not ketones, undergo acid-catalyzed addition to give cyclic trimers. The reaction also takes place slowly in the absence of added catalyst.

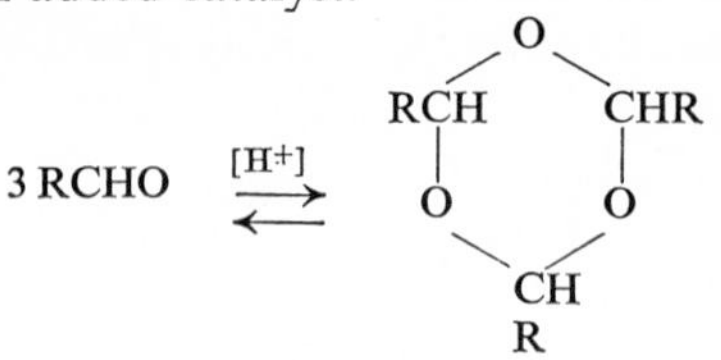

The trimer can be reconverted to the monomer by heating with or without a catalyst and removing the lower-boiling aldehyde by distillation. Other types of polymerization are discussed under the individual aldehydes.

The mechanism of the acid-catalyzed trimerization and detrimerization probably is as follows:

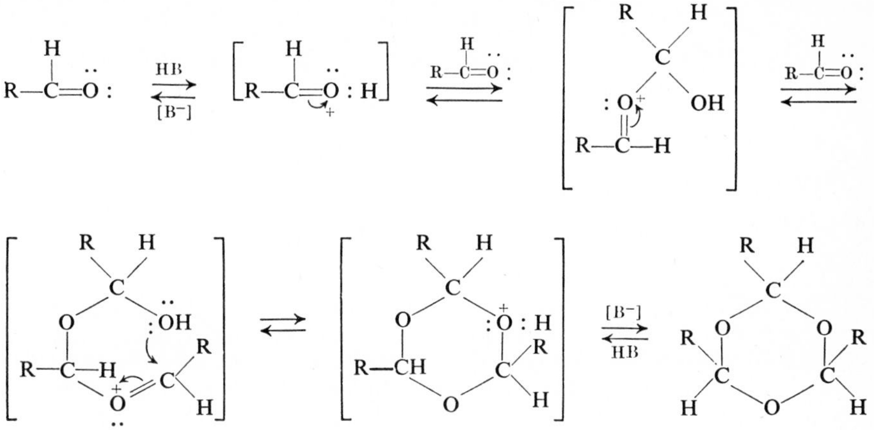

These trimers resemble the acetals in that there is no effective point of attack for basic catalysts. Hence they are stable in neutral and alkaline solutions.

11. **Addition of Aldehydes to Olefins.** Aldehydes add to the carbon-carbon double bond in the presence of acyl peroxides to give ketones. The carbonyl carbon attaches itself to the olefin carbon atom having the most hydrogen.

$$RCHO + CH_2{=}CHR \xrightarrow{(CH_3CO)_2O_2} RCOCH_2CH_2R$$

The reaction takes place by a chain mechanism catalyzed by free radicals. Initiation of the reaction is due to methyl radicals produced by the decomposition of acetyl peroxide.

$$(CH_3CO)_2O_2 \longrightarrow 2\,CH_3COO\cdot \longrightarrow 2\,CH_3\cdot + 2\,CO_2$$

$$RCHO + CH_3\cdot \longrightarrow R\overset{\cdot}{C}O + CH_4$$

$$R\overset{\cdot}{C}O + CH_2{=}CHR \longrightarrow RCOCH_2\overset{\cdot}{C}HR$$

$$RCOCH_2\overset{\cdot}{C}HR + RCHO \longrightarrow RCOCH_2CH_2R + R\overset{\cdot}{C}O$$

Light also decomposes aldehydes into free acyl radicals which can initiate the addition.

$$RCHO \xrightarrow{h\nu} R\overset{\cdot}{C}O + H\cdot$$

ADDITION AND LOSS OF WATER

1. **Ammonia.** Reaction products of aldehydes with ammonia have been isolated which appear to result from the addition of ammonia to the carbonyl

group. The initial product, however, is unstable and loses water to give an **aldimine,** RCH=NH, which polymerizes to a cyclic trimer.

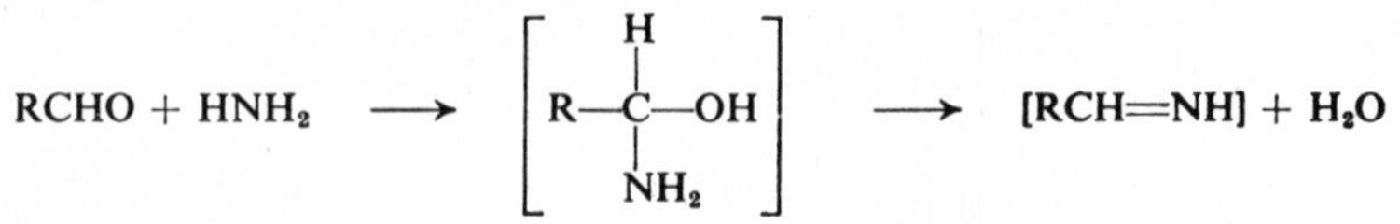

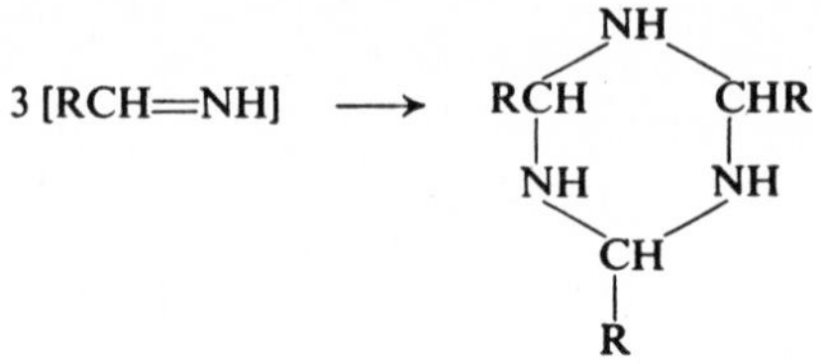

$$RCHO + HNH_2 \longrightarrow \left[\begin{array}{c} H \\ | \\ R-C-OH \\ | \\ NH_2 \end{array} \right] \longrightarrow [RCH=NH] + H_2O$$

$$3\,[RCH=NH] \longrightarrow \begin{array}{c} NH \\ R\overset{}{C}H \qquad \overset{}{C}HR \\ NH \qquad NH \\ CH \\ | \\ R \end{array}$$

The product from acetaldehyde and ammonia, known as **aldehyde-ammonia,** is a crystalline trihydrate of the cyclic compound. Ketones do not yield analogous products, but the initial addition of ammonia to the carbonyl group undoubtedly takes place in reactions such as the Strecker synthesis of α-amino acids (p. 303). Ketones may react with ammonia to give aldol-type condensation products (p. 764).

2. **Hydroxylamine.** Aldehydes and ketones add hydroxylamine, the hydroxy derivative of ammonia, to give an unstable initial product analogous to that formed by addition of ammonia to the carbonyl group, but the subsequent loss of water gives a stable monomolecular product known as an **oxime.**

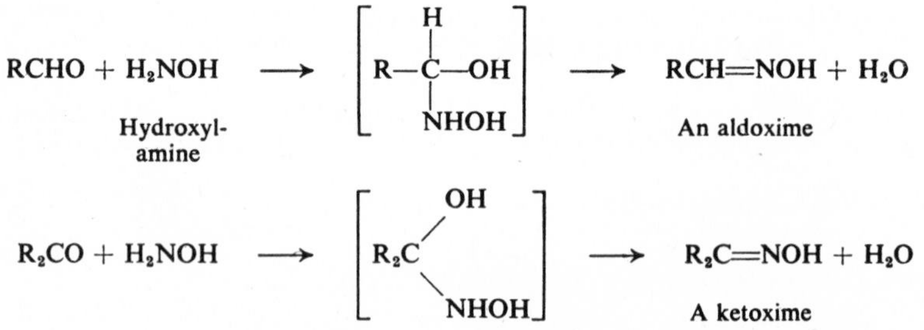

$$RCHO + H_2NOH \longrightarrow \left[\begin{array}{c} H \\ | \\ R-C-OH \\ | \\ NHOH \end{array} \right] \longrightarrow RCH=NOH + H_2O$$

$$\begin{array}{cc} \text{Hydroxyl-} & \text{An aldoxime} \\ \text{amine} & \end{array}$$

$$R_2CO + H_2NOH \longrightarrow \left[\begin{array}{c} OH \\ \diagup \\ R_2C \\ \diagdown \\ NHOH \end{array} \right] \longrightarrow R_2C=NOH + H_2O$$

$$\text{A ketoxime}$$

The product from acetaldehyde, $CH_3CH=NOH$, is called **acetaldoxime,** that from acetone is **acetoxime,** and that from methyl ethyl ketone, $CH_3(C_2H_5)C=NOH$, is **methyl ethyl ketoxime.** Homologous compounds are named in the same way.

When oximes are heated with an excess of aqueous hydrochloric acid, they are hydrolyzed with the regeneration of the aldehyde or ketone and hydroxylamine hydrochloride.

$$RCH=NOH + HCl + H_2O \longrightarrow RCHO + [HO\overset{+}{N}H_3]\,Cl^-$$

The oximes are both weak bases and weak acids. They are more soluble in cold dilute acids or cold dilute alkali than they are in water.

$$RCH=NOH + HCl \longrightarrow [RCH=\overset{+}{N}HOH]\,Cl^-$$
$$RCH=NOH + NaOH \longrightarrow [RCH=NO^-]\,Na^+ + H_2O$$

However, the oximes are much weaker bases ($K_b = 6 \times 10^{-13}$ for acetoxime) than hydroxylamine ($K_b = 1 \times 10^{-8}$). Use is made of this fact in a procedure for the estimation of aldehydes and ketones. After reaction of the carbonyl compound with hydroxylamine hydrochloride, the hydrogen chloride liberated is titrated with standard alkali using a suitable indicator (Bromophenol Blue).

$$RCHO + [H_3\overset{+}{N}OH]Cl^- \longrightarrow RCH{=}NOH + HCl + H_2O$$

Oximes frequently are crystalline solids and thus are useful derivatives for the identification of aldehydes and ketones. They are useful also for the synthesis of primary amines (p. 232) and alkyl cyanides (p. 250), and as intermediates in opening the rings of cyclic ketones (p. 841).

3. **Substituted Hydrazines.** Hydrazine has the formula H_2NNH_2, and although it reacts with aldehydes and ketones, the final product may not be typical. The substituted hydrazines having one free amino group (NH_2 group) behave in a regular fashion analogous to hydroxylamine.

$$RCHO + H_2N{-}NHR' \longrightarrow \left[\begin{matrix} RCHNH{-}NHR' \\ | \\ OH \end{matrix}\right] \longrightarrow RCH{=}N{-}NHR' + H_2O$$
An aldehyde hydrazone

$$R_2CO + H_2N{-}NHR' \longrightarrow \left[\begin{matrix} R_2C{-}NH{-}NHR' \\ | \\ OH \end{matrix}\right] \longrightarrow R_2C{=}N{-}NHR' + H_2O$$
A ketone hydrazone

The hydrazines most commonly used are (*1*) phenylhydrazine, $C_6H_5NHNH_2$, and substituted phenylhydrazines, the products being known as **phenylhydrazones,** and (*2*) semicarbazide (sometimes called semicarbazine) $H_2NNHCONH_2$, the products being known as **semicarbazones.**

$$(CH_3)_2CO + H_2NNHC_6H_5 \longrightarrow (CH_3)_2C{=}NNHC_6H_5 + H_2O$$
Acetone phenylhydrazone

$$CH_3CH{=}O + H_2NNHCONH_2 \longrightarrow CH_3CH{=}NNHCONH_2 + H_2O$$
Acetaldehyde semicarbazone

Whereas the simpler aldehydes and ketones usually are liquids, many of the phenylhydrazones and semicarbazones are crystalline solids which can be purified readily and have definite melting points. Like the oximes they are useful derivatives for the identification of aldehydes and ketones.

The reactions of aldehydes and ketones with hydroxylamine and semicarbazine take place most readily at a hydrogen ion concentration such that the reagent is half converted into its salt. A satisfactory mechanism is one in which the reaction is catalyzed by acids, but the reagent reacts by way of its free amino groups.

$$R_2C{=}O \underset{[B^-]}{\overset{HB}{\rightleftharpoons}} [R_2C{=}\overset{+}{O}H] \overset{H_2NR}{\rightleftharpoons} \left[\begin{matrix} R_2C{-}OH \\ \cdot\cdot \\ H_2N{-}R \\ + \end{matrix}\right] \underset{HB}{\overset{[B^-]}{\rightleftharpoons}}$$

$$\begin{matrix} R_2C{-}OH \\ | \\ NHR \end{matrix} \underset{[B^-]}{\overset{HB}{\rightleftharpoons}} \left[\begin{matrix} H \\ \cdot\cdot + \\ R_2C{-}\overset{\frown}{O}H \\ \overset{\frown}{} \\ :NHR \end{matrix}\right] \underset{H_2O}{\rightleftharpoons} \left[\begin{matrix} R_2C \\ || \\ +NHR \end{matrix}\right] \underset{HB}{\overset{[B^-]}{\rightleftharpoons}} \begin{matrix} R_2C \\ || \\ NR \end{matrix}$$

OXIDATION

Aldehydes are oxidized easily to acids even by mild oxidizing agents. However, in the absence of other easily oxidized groups, the common oxidizing agents such as nitric acid, chromic acid or potassium permanganate are used.

$$3\,RCHO + Na_2Cr_2O_7 + 4\,H_2SO_4 \longrightarrow 3\,RCOOH + Na_2SO_4 + Cr_2(SO_4)_3 + 4\,H_2O$$

Ketones on the other hand are fairly stable to oxidation. When oxidation is forced by using strong oxidizing agents under vigorous conditions, the carbon chain is broken and a mixture of acids having fewer carbon atoms is produced.

$$RCH_2COCH_2R' \xrightarrow[\text{oxidation}]{\text{Vigorous}} \begin{array}{c} RCOOH + HOOCCH_2R' \\ \text{and} \\ RCH_2COOH + HOOCR' \end{array}$$

Little is known about the mechanism of oxidation of aldehydes and ketones to acids. It might be expected to take place through the hydrate by a mechanism analogous to that for the oxidation of primary and secondary alcohols to aldehydes and ketones (p. 106). However, a study of the oxidation of the aromatic aldehyde, benzaldehyde, indicates that in acid solution, permanganate ion attacks the carbonyl carbon atom, whereas a free-radical mechanism operates in alkaline solution (p. 533).

Because of the difference between the ease of oxidation of aldehydes and ketones, it is possible to choose oxidizing agents which will attack aldehydes and not ketones, and to use the reaction as a distinguishing test. Some mild oxidizing agents used for this purpose are: Fehling solution, an alkaline solution of a cupric complex with sodium tartrate (p. 809); Benedict solution, a cupric complex with sodium citrate (p. 810); and Tollens reagent, an ammoniacal solution of silver hydroxide. All behave like solutions of the metallic hydroxides. With Fehling and Benedict solutions, the copper is reduced to the cuprous state, which does not form a stable complex with tartrate or citrate ion and precipitates as cuprous oxide.

$$RCHO + 2\,Cu(OH)_2 + NaOH \longrightarrow RCOO\overset{-}{}\overset{+}{Na} + Cu_2O\downarrow + 3\,H_2O$$

If the precipitation of cuprous oxide takes place in the presence of protective colloids, it is finely divided and yellow, but if formed in the absence of protective colloids, it has a larger particle size and is red. With Tollens reagent, metallic silver is the reduction product.

$$RCHO + 2\,Ag(NH_3)_2OH \longrightarrow RCOO\overset{-}{}\overset{+}{N}H_4 + 2\,Ag\downarrow + H_2O + 3\,NH_3$$

If the vessel in which the latter reaction takes place is clean and the rate of deposition slow enough, the silver deposits as a coherent silver mirror; otherwise it is a gray to black finely-divided precipitate.[5]

Neither cupric nor silver salts will oxidize aldehydes rapidly in neutral or acid solution, and alkali precipitates the very insoluble hydroxides. In order to keep the hydroxides in solution, use is made of complex ion formation. For silver hydroxide, the complex used is $Ag(NH_3)_2OH$. Fehling solution is prepared from copper sulfate, sodium hydroxide, and sodium potassium

---

[5] Tollens reagent should be freshly prepared and discarded immediately after use. On standing, silver imide, Ag_2NH, is formed along with some silver amide, $AgNH_2$ and silver azide, Ag_3N, all of which are violently explosive.

tartrate (Rochelle salts, p. 809). The reagent is not very stable, however, and the solution of copper sulfate is not mixed with the alkaline tartrate solution until just before use. Benedict solution is prepared from copper sulfate, sodium citrate (p. 810), and a milder base, sodium carbonate, and is indefinitely stable. The nature of the cupric ion complexes is discussed on page 316.

MISCELLANEOUS TESTS AND REACTIONS

1. **Schiff Fuchsin Aldehyde Reagent.** Fuchsin is a magenta dye (p. 681) which can be decolorized in aqueous solution by sulfur dioxide. In the presence of aldehydes, but not ketones, a magenta color reappears. The reaction is not specific for aldehydes, since anything which removes sulfur dioxide, for example mild alkalies, amines, or even heating or exposure to air, will regenerate the color, but in the absence of such interferences it serves to distinguish aldehydes from ketones.

The reaction with aldehydes is not merely a combination with sulfur dioxide and regeneration of the original fuchsin. The color is due to a reaction product of the aldehyde and the dye (p. 681). Thus the hue of the color produced differs with different aldehydes; for example, the color produced by formaldehyde is bluer than that produced by acetaldehyde. Moreover strong mineral acids destroy the color produced by acetaldehyde but not that produced by formaldehyde.

2. **Replacement of Oxygen by Halogen.** When aldehydes or ketones react with phosphorus pentachloride or phosphorus pentabromide, the oxygen of the carbonyl group is replaced by two halogen atoms.

$$RCHO + PX_5 \longrightarrow RCHX_2 + POX_3$$

$$R_2CO + PX_5 \longrightarrow R_2CX_2 + POX_3$$

The fact that both halogens in the product are combined with the same carbon atom is further confirmation that the oxygen atom in aldehydes and ketones is attached by a double bond to a single carbon atom. The reaction is of little importance otherwise.

3. **Salt Formation.** The hydrogen atoms on a carbon atom α to a carbonyl group are sufficiently acidic (p. 100) to react with alkali metals and form salts. Thus acetone reacts readily with metallic sodium and hydrogen is evolved.

$$CH_3COCH_3 + Na \longrightarrow [CH_3COCH_2^-]Na^+ + \tfrac{1}{2} H_2$$

Because the product can act as a basic catalyst, it is accompanied by the alkali-catalyzed condensation products of acetone (p. 208). Acetone is so weak an acid that its salts are completely hydrolyzed by water.

The ion $[RCOCH_2^-]$ is a resonance hybrid (Fig. 45; cf. p. 154). As such it is identical with

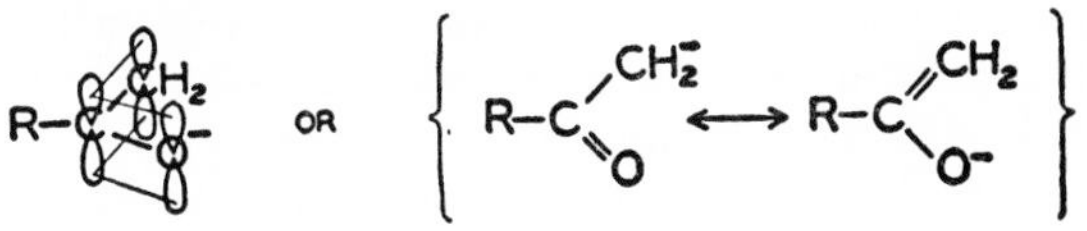

Fig. 45. Resonance in the enolate ion.

the enolate ion, $\left[\begin{array}{c} RC=CH_2 \\ | \\ O- \end{array}\right]$, by which name it usually is known. At one time it was believed that the ketone was isomerized to the enol form (p. 207) before reaction with the metal.

$$RCCH_3 \underset{}{\overset{}{\rightleftarrows}} \underset{\underset{OH}{|}}{RC=CH_2} \overset{Na}{\longrightarrow} \underset{\underset{ONa}{|}}{RC=CH_2} + \tfrac{1}{2}H_2$$
$$\underset{O}{\overset{\|}{}}$$

In acid-catalyzed reactions, for example the acid-catalyzed aldol condensation (p. 207) or the acid-catalyzed exchange of hydrogen for deuterium, the enol form undoubtedly is an intermediate.

$$\underset{\underset{O}{\|}}{RCCH_2R} \underset{[B^-]}{\overset{HB}{\rightleftarrows}} \left[\underset{_+OH}{\overset{|}{RCCH_2R}}\right] \underset{HB}{\overset{[B^-]}{\rightleftarrows}} \left[\underset{\underset{OH}{|}}{RC=CHR}\right] \underset{[B^-]}{\overset{DB}{\rightleftarrows}} \left[\underset{_+OH}{\overset{\|}{RCCHDR}}\right] \underset{HB}{\overset{[B^-]}{\rightleftarrows}} \underset{\underset{O}{\|}}{RCCHDR}$$

In base-catalyzed reactions, however, such as the base-catalyzed aldol addition (p. 206) or the base-catalyzed deuterium exchange, the enol is not a necessary intermediate.

$$RCOCH_2R \underset{HB}{\overset{[B^-]}{\rightleftarrows}} \left[\underset{\underset{O}{\|}}{RCCHR}\right] \underset{[B^-]}{\overset{DB}{\rightleftarrows}} \underset{\underset{O}{\|}}{RCCHDR}$$

4. Enol Acetate Formation. Aldehydes and ketones react with acetic anhydride in the presence of potassium acetate or with acetyl chloride to give esters of the enol form.

$$RCH_2CHO + (CH_3CO)_2O \overset{CH_3COOK}{\longrightarrow} RCH=CHOCOCH_3 + CH_3COOH$$

$$\underset{\underset{O}{\|}}{RCCH_2R} + ClCOCH_3 \longrightarrow \underset{\underset{OCOCH_3}{|}}{RC=CHR} + HCl$$

Hydrolysis of the ester regenerates the carbonyl compound, since the enol form is not stable.

$$\underset{\underset{OCOCH_3}{|}}{RC=CHR} + NaOH \longrightarrow CH_3COONa + \left[\underset{\underset{OH}{|}}{RC=CHR}\right] \longrightarrow \underset{\underset{O}{\|}}{RCCH_2R}$$

5. Halogenation and the Haloform Reaction. The α hydrogen atoms of aldehydes and ketones, like those of acyl halides (p. 162), readily undergo substitution by halogen.

$$RCH_2CHO \overset{X_2}{\longrightarrow} HX + RCHXCHO \overset{X_2}{\longrightarrow} HX + RCX_2CHO$$

$$RCOCH_3 \overset{X_2}{\longrightarrow} HX + RCOCH_2X \overset{X_2}{\longrightarrow} HX + RCOCHX_2 \overset{X_2}{\longrightarrow} HX + RCOCX_3$$

In alkaline solution hypohalite ion also acts as a halogenating agent. After one hydrogen is substituted, a second and third on the same carbon atom are substituted with increasing ease. Hence substitution once started continues on the same carbon atom until all of the hydrogen is replaced by halogen. The trisubstitution product is not stable in alkaline solution, and a secondary reaction follows in which the alkali decomposes the trisubstituted molecule to give a trihalogenated methane and the sodium salt of a carboxylic acid.

$$RCOCX_3 + HONa \longrightarrow RCOONa + HCX_3$$

Trihalogenated methanes yield formic acid on hydrolysis, which led Dumas to give them the general name *haloforms* (chloroform, bromoform, and iodoform). To obtain a haloform from a carbonyl compound, at least one group united to the carbonyl group must be methyl. The other group may be hydrogen or any group linked through carbon, provided that any hydrogen atoms remaining on this carbon atom are not substituted more readily than those of the methyl group, and provided that other substituents in the group do not reduce the reactivity of the methyl group by steric hindrance. Acetic acid does not give a haloform because the acetyl group is united to oxygen, which reduces the effect of the carbonyl group on the α hydrogen atoms by resonance (p. 154). Acetoacetic acid, CH_3COCH_2COOH, substitutes on the methylene rather than the methyl group to give CH_3COCX_2COOH, which reacts with alkali to give the sodium salts of acetic acid and a dihaloacetic acid (cf. p. 821).

$$CH_3COCX_2COOH + 2\,NaOH \longrightarrow CH_3COONa + HCX_2COONa + H_2O$$

Pinacolone (p. 217) gives bromoform but does not give iodoform because the highly branched *t*-butyl group prevents the reaction from proceeding beyond the diiodinated stage.

$$(CH_3)_3CCOCH_3 + 2\,NaOI \longrightarrow (CH_3)_3CCOCHI_2 + 2\,NaOH$$

Occasionally compounds not expected to react give iodoform. The reaction of acetoxime may be explained by the fact that it is a nitrogen analog of a ketone or that hydrolysis to acetone precedes formation of the haloform. The reaction of pulegone (p. 854) can be explained by its decomposition by alkali to give acetone. 2-Methyl-2-butene probably is converted first to methyl isopropyl ketone during the reaction (p. 742).

Not only do carbonyl compounds meeting the stated conditions undergo the haloform reaction, but all substances which oxidize to such compounds under the conditions of the reaction, for example properly constituted alcohols, also yield haloform.

$$RCHOHCH_3 + NaOX \longrightarrow RCOCH_3 + NaX + H_2O$$

$$RCOCH_3 + 3\,NaOX \longrightarrow HCX_3 + RCOONa + 2\,NaOH$$

The practical importance of the haloform reaction is its use to distinguish between different possible structures. For example acetaldehyde is the only aldehyde, and ethyl alcohol is the only primary alcohol which gives a haloform. The two largest groups of compounds responding to the reaction are the methyl ketones and alkylmethylcarbinols. For conducting such a test, the reaction with alkali and iodine is used since iodoform is a yellow crystalline solid which is identified readily by its melting point.

The halogenation of aldehydes and ketones is catalyzed by acids and by bases, and it has been shown that it is the enol form or the enolate ion that reacts with the halogenating agent (cf. p. 214). The rate of reaction is dependent on the concentration of the ketone and on the concentration of the acid or base, but is independent of the concentration or the kind of halogen. In the acid-catalyzed reaction the carbonyl group is the initial point of attack and the essential steps may be represented by the following equilibria.

The effect of adding the proton to the carbonyl group is to increase its attraction for electrons and hence make it easier for the α hydrogen to leave as a proton. Since halogen also is electron-attracting, a second hydrogen atom is replaced still more readily than the first hydrogen atom, thus accounting for the unsymmetrical substitution. In basic catalysis the initial step is removal of a proton from an α carbon atom, and the chief halogenating agent is the hypohalite ion.

$$
\underset{O}{\underset{\|}{RCCH_2R}} \underset{HB}{\overset{[B^-]}{\rightleftharpoons}} \left[\underset{O}{\underset{\|}{R\overset{..}{C}CHR}} \ \bar{} \ \right] \underset{[X^-]\,or\,[OH^-]}{\overset{X_2\,or\,HOX}{\longleftrightarrow}} \underset{O}{\overset{X}{\underset{\|}{RCCHR}}}
$$

Here again after the first hydrogen atom is substituted by halogen, the electron-attracting effect of the halogen makes the second hydrogen atom more readily removed than the first, and unsymmetrical substitution results.

The substitution of the α hydrogen of acyl halides by halogen (p. 162) undoubtedly follows the same course as the acid-catalyzed haloform reaction. Monocarboxylic acids do not halogenate readily because the electron-attracting effect of the carbonyl group is reduced by resonance (p. 154). If, however, two carboxyl groups are present on the same carbon atom, substitution proceeds rapidly (p. 303).

6. **Reduction of the Carbonyl Group to a Methyl or Methylene Group.** A carbonyl group may be converted to a methyl or methylene group by reducing first to the alcohol and then converting the alcohol to the halide and reducing the halide to the hydrocarbon (p. 126); or the alcohol may be converted to the olefin and the double bond reduced catalytically (p. 127). However more direct methods are possible. In the *Wolff-Kishner reduction* the aldehyde or ketone is heated with hydrazine in the presence of sodium ethoxide at 200°. The reduction presumably takes place by formation of the hydrazone, which decomposes under the influence of the sodium ethoxide.

$$
RCHO + H_2NNH_2 \longrightarrow H_2O + RCH{=}NNH_2 \xrightarrow[200°]{NaOC_2H_5} RCH_3 + N_2
$$

$$
R_2CO + H_2NNH_2 \longrightarrow H_2O + R_2C{=}NNH_2 \xrightarrow[200°]{NaOC_2H_5} R_2CH_2 + N_2
$$

The *Clemmensen reduction* consists of refluxing the compound with concentrated hydrochloric acid in the presence of amalgamated zinc.[6]

$$
R_2CO + 2\,Zn(Hg) + 4\,HCl \longrightarrow R_2CH_2 + 2\,ZnCl_2 + H_2O
$$

---

[6] A pair of metals in contact, one of which is above hydrogen in the electromotive series and the other one below hydrogen in the series, is known as a couple. Common examples are amalgamated aluminum, amalgamated zinc, aluminum-copper couple, and zinc-copper couple. Usually the couples are more reactive as reducing agents than are the pure metals. The reducing action of metals depends on the tendency of the metal atoms to form positive ions, leaving electrons available at the metal surface to be supplied to other ions or molecules and bring about their reduction. The positive ions formed from the pure metals tend to be held by the negative charge remaining, and the molecules or ions being reduced are prevented from reaching the electrons left on the surface of the metal. If metals like aluminum and zinc are involved and the reaction is with water, the insoluble hydroxides produced form an adherent coating on the surface of the metal, which stops the reaction. With the couples the electrons freed by solution of the active metal are transferred to the less active metal, and reduction takes place at the surface of the inactive metal, which is distant from the site of solution of the active metal.

Since sodium is one of the most active metals and sodium hydroxide is very soluble in water, reaction of sodium with water is violent. Here amalgamation decreases the reactivity by forming the much less reactive compound Na_4Hg. As a result, reductions with sodium amalgam may be carried out in aqueous and even slightly acidic solutions.

It is easier to carry out than the Wolff-Kishner reduction but is not so satisfactory for the reduction of aldehydes, because they undergo condensation and polymerization reactions too readily in the presence of strong acids.

7. **Reduction to Glycols and Pinacols.** When sodium reacts with an aldehyde in water-saturated ether, or with amalgamated magnesium, two moles couple with the formation of a 1,2-dihydroxy compound known as a **glycol**.

$$2\,RCHO + 2\,Na + H_2O(\text{in ether}) \longrightarrow RCHOHCHOHR + 2\,NaOH$$

The reduction with magnesium ordinarily is carried out under anhydrous conditions, the salt of the glycol being obtained. The glycol is liberated by a weak acid. Ketones behave similarly, and the ditertiary glycols produced are called **pinacols**.

$$2\,R_2CO + Mg(Hg) \longrightarrow \begin{bmatrix} R_2C-O^- \\ R_2C-O^- \end{bmatrix} Mg^{++} \xrightarrow{2\,CH_3COOH} R_2COHCOHR_2 + Mg(OCOCH_3)_2$$

The name *pinacol* is derived from the Greek word *pinax* meaning *plate* and refers to the crystalline structure of pinacol itself, $(CH_3)_2COHCOH(CH_3)_2$, the reduction product of acetone.

Strong acids cause dehydration and molecular rearrangement of pinacols to ketones.

$$R_2COHCOHR_2 \xrightarrow{[H^+]} R_3CCOR + H_2O$$

Pinacol rearranges to the compound $(CH_3)_3CCOCH_3$ known as **pinacolone**, and the general reaction is called a **pinacol-pinacolone rearrangement.**

The mechanism of the rearrangement may be expressed by the following series of reactions.

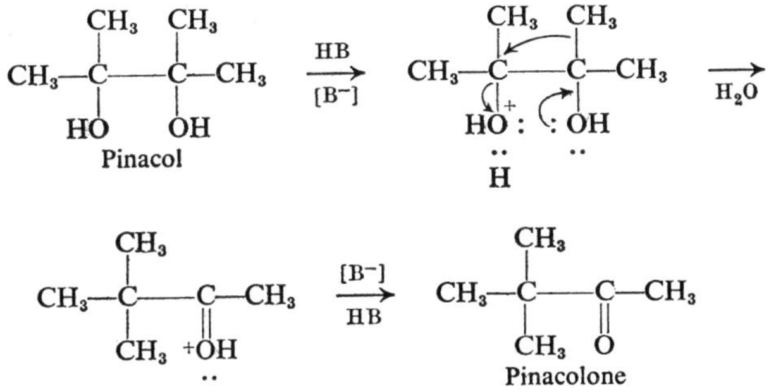

Mechanism of the Reduction of Organic Compounds by Active Metals

　　Three types of reduction of carbonyl compounds by active metals have been noted, namely reduction to alcohols, reduction to pinacols, and Clemmensen reduction to the hydrocarbon. An attempt to explain the formation of these different products is of interest.

　　Before considering the reduction of organic compounds, it may be well to discuss the reaction of active metals with proton-donating liquids to form molecular hydrogen. The electromotive series indicates the tendency of elements to lose electrons and form positive ions in solution. Hydrogen united to an electron-attracting element such as oxygen can accept an electron from any element above hydrogen in the electromotive series, the hydrogen atom leaving its electron with the electron-attracting element; that is, it leaves the compound as a proton and becomes a hydrogen atom. The hydrogen atom is adsorbed on the surface of the metal by pairing its electron with one from a metal atom. Simultaneously a metal cation goes into solution.

$$
\begin{array}{ccc}
\text{Na} \mid \cdot & & \text{Na} \mid \cdot \\
\text{Na} \mid \cdot & \text{H} : \overset{\cdot\cdot}{\text{O}} : \text{H} & \text{Na} \mid \cdot \\
\text{Na} \mid \cdot & \longrightarrow & \text{Na} \mid \cdot \\
\text{Na} \mid \cdot & & \text{Na} \mid : \text{H} \\
\text{Na} \mid \cdot & & \\
& & \text{Na}^+ : \text{OH}
\end{array}
$$

Metal Surface

It is not certain how molecular hydrogen is formed. In one likely mechanism it is assumed that numerous hydrogen atoms may be adsorbed on the metal surface and that, because of the mobility of electrons in a metal, the hydrogen atoms may migrate over the surface of the metal. When two hydrogen atoms collide, a covalent bond may be formed between them and the molecule desorbed as gaseous hydrogen.

$$
\begin{array}{ccccc}
\text{Na} \mid \cdot & & \text{Na}^+ : \overset{\cdot\cdot}{\text{O}} : \text{H} & & \\
\text{Na} \mid \cdot & \text{H} : \overset{\cdot\cdot}{\text{O}} : \text{H} & \text{Na} \mid : \text{H} & \text{Na} \mid \cdot & \text{Na} \mid \cdot \\
\text{Na} \mid \cdot & \longrightarrow & \text{Na} \mid \cdot & \text{Na} \mid : \text{H} & \text{Na} \mid \cdot \; + \\
\text{Na} \mid : \text{H} & & \text{Na} \mid : \text{H} & \text{Na} \mid : \text{H} & \text{Na} \mid \cdot
\end{array}
$$

An analogous mechanism can be used to explain the various types of reduction of carbonyl compounds. The doubly-bound oxygen atom in a carbonyl group makes the carbon atom deficient in electrons, much as the hydrogen atom of a water molecule or alcohol molecule is deficient in electrons. Accordingly this carbon atom is adsorbed at the surface of the metal just as a proton would be. In the absence of a proton-donating molecule, two such adsorbed molecules on collision could couple, giving rise to the salt of a pinacol.

$$
\begin{array}{ccccc}
\text{Na} \mid \cdot & & \text{Na}^+ \quad : \overset{-\;\cdot\cdot}{\text{O}} : & \text{Na}^+ & \text{O}^- \\
\text{Na} \mid \cdot & \overset{\text{O}}{\underset{\|}{\;}} & \text{Na} \mid : \text{C(CH}_3)_2 & \text{Na} \mid \cdot & \text{C(CH}_3)_2 \\
\text{Na} \mid \cdot + 2\,\text{C(CH}_3)_2 \longrightarrow & \text{Na} \mid \cdot & \longrightarrow & \text{Na} \mid \cdot + \text{C(CH}_3)_2 \\
\text{Na} \mid \cdot & & \text{Na} \mid : \text{C(CH}_3)_2 & \text{Na} \mid \cdot & \text{O}^- \\
\text{Na} \mid \cdot & & \text{Na}^+ : \overset{-\cdot\cdot}{\text{O}} : & \text{Na}^+
\end{array}
$$

In the presence of a proton-donating solvent, the adsorbed molecule of the carbonyl compound may react with an adsorbed hydrogen atom to give the alkoxide ion of the simple alcohol.

$$
\begin{array}{ccccc}
& \text{Na} \mid \cdot + \text{HOR} & \text{Na}^+ \,{}^-\text{OR} & & \\
\text{Na} \mid \cdot & & \text{Na} \mid : \text{H} & \text{Na} \mid \cdot & \text{H} \\
\text{Na} \mid \cdot & \longrightarrow & \text{Na} \mid \cdot & \longrightarrow & \text{Na} \mid \cdot + \text{CR}_2 \\
\text{Na} \mid \cdot & & \text{Na} \mid : \text{CR}_2 & \text{Na} \mid \cdot & \text{O}- \\
\text{Na} \mid \cdot + \text{CR}_2 & & \text{O}- & \text{Na}^+ \\
\underset{\text{O}}{\overset{\|}{\;}} & & \text{Na}^+ &
\end{array}
$$

In certain special cases the course of the reaction is different in slightly acid solution than in neutral solution. Here it may be assumed that the protonated rather than the free carbonyl compound is adsorbed, which could give rise to a differently oriented absorption complex.

$$
\begin{array}{lll}
\text{Na} \mid \cdot + \text{HOR} & \text{Na}^+ \ {}^-\text{OR} & \\[4pt]
\text{Na} \mid \cdot & \text{Na} \mid : \text{H} & \text{Na} \mid \cdot \quad \underset{|}{\text{H}} \\[4pt]
\text{Na} \mid \cdot \quad \longrightarrow & \text{Na} \mid \cdot & \text{Na} \mid \cdot \quad \underset{|}{\text{CR}_2} \\[4pt]
\text{Na} \mid \cdot & \text{Na} \mid : \underset{|}{\text{CR}_2} & \text{Na} \mid \cdot + \text{OH} \\[4pt]
\text{Na} \mid \cdot + \ \underset{||}{\text{CR}_2} & \text{Na}^+ \ \text{OH} & \\[4pt]
\quad + \ \underset{}{\text{O—H}} & &
\end{array}
$$

The Clemmensen reduction takes place in the presence of concentrated aqueous hydrochloric acid, and the best yield is obtained if the concentration of the ketone is kept low by dissolving it in a water-immiscible solvent. It would appear that the high acid concentration leads to adsorption of the oxonium salt on the metal surface. Satisfaction of the electron deficiency on the carbon atom by adsorption permits the oxygen atom to react with another proton, which permits elimination of the oxygen as a water molecule, solution of a zinc ion, and formation of an adsorbed methylene radical.

$$
\begin{array}{lllll}
& \overset{+}{:}\text{O}:\text{H} & :\text{O}:\text{H} & \overset{\overset{H}{|}}{\overset{+}{:}\text{O—H}} & \text{Zn}^{++} \quad + \text{H}_2\text{O} \\
\text{Zn} \mid : + \ \underset{||}{\text{CR}_2} & \text{Zn} \mid \overset{+}{:} \text{CR}_2 & \text{Zn} \mid \overset{+}{:} \text{CR}_2 & \text{Zn} \mid : \underset{:}{\text{CR}_2} \\
\text{Zn} \mid : & \text{Zn} \mid : & \text{Zn} \mid : & \text{Zn} \mid : \\
\text{Zn} \mid : \ \longrightarrow & \text{Zn} \mid : \ \xrightarrow{[H^+]} & \text{Zn} \mid : \ \longrightarrow & \text{Zn} \mid : \\
\text{Zn} \mid : & \text{Zn} \mid : & \text{Zn} \mid : & \text{Zn} \mid : \\
\text{Zn} \mid : & \text{Zn} \mid : & \text{Zn} \mid : &
\end{array}
$$

The adsorbed methylene radical may react successively with two adsorbed hydrogen atoms, with the formation of the hydrocarbon and positive metallic ion. By keeping the concentration of the adsorbed ketone low, the formation of bimolecular reduction products is decreased.

$$
\begin{array}{llll}
& \text{Zn}^{++} & & \\
\text{Zn} \mid : & & \text{Zn} \mid : \text{H} & \text{Zn} \mid : \quad \text{H} \\
\text{Zn} \mid : & \xrightarrow{2[H^+]} & \text{Zn} \mid : \quad \longrightarrow & \text{Zn} \mid : \ \quad \cdot\cdot \\
\text{Zn} \mid : \text{CR}_2 & & \text{Zn} \mid : \text{CR}_2 & \text{Zn} \mid : + \text{CR}_2 \\
\text{Zn} \mid : & & \text{Zn} \mid : \text{H} & \text{Zn} \mid : \quad \text{H}
\end{array}
$$

8. **Cannizzaro Reaction.** Those aldehydes that lack an α hydrogen atom cannot undergo aldol addition. When they are heated with strong alkali, however, an intermolecular oxidation and reduction takes place in which one molecule acts as a reducing agent and is oxidized to the acid, and the other acts as an oxidizing agent and is reduced to the alcohol. In the presence of the alkali, the acid appears as the salt.

$$2\ \text{HCHO} + \text{NaOH} \longrightarrow \text{HCOO}^-{}^+\text{Na} + \text{CH}_3\text{OH}$$

$$2\ \text{R}_3\text{CCHO} + \text{NaOH} \longrightarrow \text{R}_3\text{CCOO}^-{}^+\text{Na} + \text{R}_3\text{CCH}_2\text{OH}$$

The mechanism of this reaction is discussed on page 535. Under certain conditions even aldehydes having α hydrogen undergo a Cannizzaro reaction. For example, if *i*-butyraldehyde is heated with aqueous barium hydroxide in a sealed tube at 150°, a quantitative yield of *i*-butyl alcohol and barium *i*-butyrate is produced. Similarly *i*-valeraldehyde and *n*-heptaldehyde, when heated for a few hours with calcium oxide at 100°, give the corresponding alcohols and calcium salts as the chief products. With *i*-butyraldehyde an initial rapid reversible aldol addition takes place, which is followed by the slower irreversible Cannizzaro reaction.

9. Tishchenko Reaction. When aldehydes are heated with an aluminum alkoxide, usually aluminum ethoxide or isopropoxide activated by a small amount of anhydrous aluminum chloride or zinc chloride, an intermolecular oxidation and reduction similar to the Cannizzaro reaction takes place. However, instead of the alcohol and acid appearing as such, the product is the ester.

$$2\ RCHO \xrightarrow{\ Al(OR)_3\ } RCOOR$$

Thus acetaldehyde gives ethyl acetate, and *n*-butyraldehyde gives butyl butyrate.

Industrially Important Aldehydes and Ketones

Formaldehyde was prepared first by Butlerov[7] in 1859, more than fourteen years after the isolation of acetaldehyde by Liebig. In 1868 Hofmann (p. 229) obtained formaldehyde by oxidizing methanol with air in the presence of a platinum catalyst. Two methods of air oxidation are used commercially. In the older procedure a rich mixture of methanol and air (1 v. : 1 v.) is passed over a silver catalyst at 635°. Practically all of the oxygen is used, and the off-gases contain 18 to 20 per cent of hydrogen, indicating that the process is a combined dehydrogenation and oxidation. The formaldehyde and excess methanol are absorbed in water and the solution concentrated by distillation to 37 per cent formaldehyde. The formaldehyde is present in solution as methylene glycol, $CH_2(OH)_2$, and its polymers, $HO(CH_2O)_xH$, where x has an average value of 3. This solution is called **formalin.** Ordinary formalin contains 7 to 10 per cent methanol in summer and 10 to 15 per cent in winter to prevent separation of polymer. Formalin free of methanol also is transported for industrial use but must be kept warm (*ca.* 30°) to prevent precipitation of polymer. In the more recent process a lean mixture of air and 5 to 10 per cent methanol by volume is passed over an iron oxide-molybdenum oxide catalyst. Formaldehyde almost free of methanol is obtained and the off-gases contain oxygen and no hydrogen. Formaldehyde also is formed during the controlled air-oxidation of natural gas or propane-butane mixtures in the vapor phase at 350° to 450°. Methane yields chiefly methyl alcohol and formaldehyde. Propane-butane mixtures give chiefly formaldehyde, acetaldehyde, and methyl alcohol, together with acetone, propyl and butyl alcohols, and organic acids.

Although formaldehyde can be liquefied readily (b.p. −21°), it cannot be handled safely in this form because it polymerizes easily even at temperatures just above its freezing point (−118°), and no effective stabilizers are known. Besides the aqueous solution, formalin, formaldehyde is transported and stored as the polymer known as **paraformaldehyde,** which is prepared by concentrating

---

[7] Alexander Mikhailovich Butlerov (1828–1886), eminent Russian chemist and professor at the Universities of Kazan and St. Petersburg. He was the first to prepare aqueous formaldehyde, paraformaldehyde, hexamethylenetetramine, and the carbohydrate mixture formed by the action of dilute calcium hydroxide on formaldehyde. He was a strong advocate of the structural concept of organic chemistry and was the first to use the expression "the chemical structure of organic compounds." Butlerov prepared the first tertiary alcohol by the action of methylzinc on acetyl chloride. His studies of the reactions of *t*-butyl alcohol led him to the preparation of the isomeric butanes and butenes and to the discovery of the polymerization of isobutylene and the acid-catalyzed equilibrium between the two diisobutylenes (p. 62).

formalin at reduced pressure. It is a linear polymer of the formula $HO(CH_2O)_xH$, where x has an average value of around 30. When x is less than 12, the product is soluble in water, acetone, or ether, but the higher polymers are insoluble. Slow solution of the higher polymers in water is accompanied by hydrolysis to fragments of lower molecular weight.

Polymers having average molecular weights exceeding 150,000 have been obtained from pure liquid formaldehyde at low temperature. Formaldehyde also gives solid polymers when the gas comes in contact with solid surfaces at temperatures below 137°. Gaseous formaldehyde is prepared most conveniently by heating any of the solid polymers above this temperature.

When a 60–65 per cent aqueous solution of formaldehyde is distilled with 2 per cent sulfuric acid, the cyclic *trimer* (p. 208), **1,3,5-trioxane,** may be extracted from the distillate. It is a colorless highly refractive crystalline compound melting at 62° and boiling without decomposition or depolymerization at 115°. It has a pleasant odor resembling that of chloroform, in contrast to the sharp odor of formaldehyde, and is soluble in water and organic solvents. Strong acids initiate depolymerization, as with all compounds of this type, and it promises to be useful as a source of formaldehyde in reactions carried out in nonaqueous solutions.

Formaldehyde undergoes a number of reactions which most other aldehydes do not, because (*1*) it has only hydrogen atoms attached to the carbonyl group and is more reactive than other aldehydes, just as the aldehydes are more reactive than ketones, and (*2*) having only one carbon atom it does not have α hydrogen atoms and cannot undergo aldol-type additions with itself. For example, reaction with ammonia does not lead to an aldehyde-ammonia. Instead the initial addition product reacts further and a compound is obtained which has the formula $(CH_2)_6N_4$ and is called **hexamethylenetetramine.**

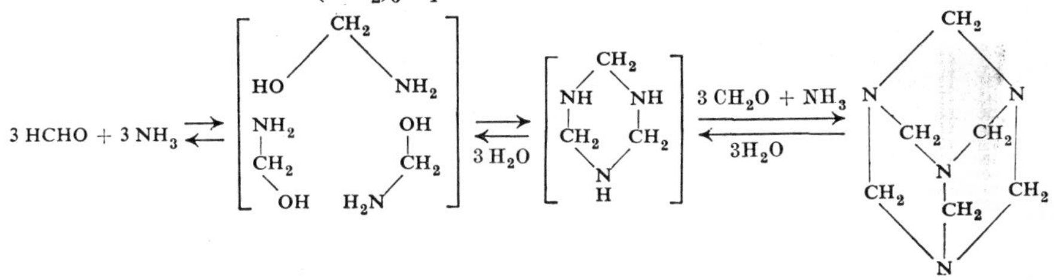

This organic compound was the first whose structure, based on valence theory and chemical reactions, was confirmed by X-ray diffraction.

Hexamethylenetetramine assumed importance during World War II as an intermediate for the manufacture of the high explosive trimethylenetrinitramine (cyclonite, hexogen, RDX). Nitration was carried out in the presence of ammonium nitrate or ammonium sulfate, which permitted utilization of 80–90 per cent of the methylene groups.

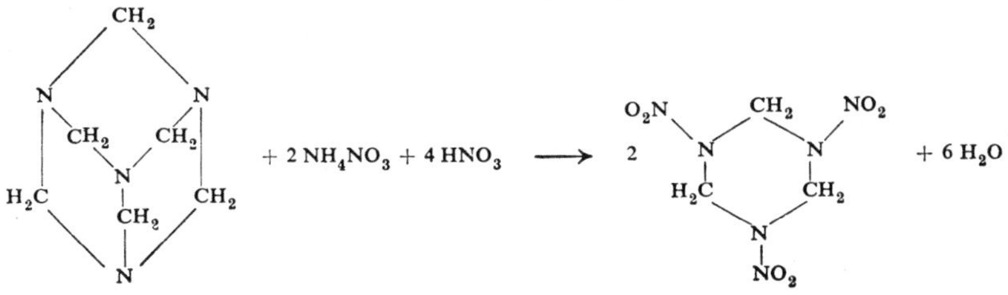

Trimethylenetrinitramine is one of the most powerful organic explosives and has a greater brisance than TNT (p. 464). Up to 30 per cent was mixed with TNT to insure complete detonation of large bombs and to increase the force of the explosion.

Lacking α hydrogen atoms, formaldehyde does not give aldehyde resins with concentrated alkali, but undergoes the *Cannizzaro reaction* (p. 219). With dilute alkali a complex series of self-additions (p. 386) produces a mixture of sugars known as *formose*.

$$6\ HCHO \xrightarrow{\text{Dil. Ca(OH}_2)} C_6H_{12}O_6$$

A *specific test for formaldehyde* is the production of a violet color with casein of milk in the presence of ferric chloride and concentrated sulfuric acid. The test is sensitive to one part of formaldehyde in 200,000 parts of milk. This test was important in the enforcement of the law against the addition of formaldehyde as a preservative. It can be used as a general test for formaldehyde simply by adding to milk the material to be tested and then applying the test. Formaldehyde can be estimated quantitatively by measuring the amount of hydrogen evolved on reaction with alkaline hydrogen peroxide solution (p. 879).

$$2\ CH_2O + H_2O_2 + 2\ NaOH \longrightarrow 2\ HCO\overset{-}{O}\overset{+}{N}a + 2\ H_2O + H_2$$

Formaldehyde has some use as a disinfectant and for the preservation of biological specimens, but its chief use is for the manufacture of synthetic resins by condensation with urea (p. 314), melamine (p. 321), or phenol (p. 511). Frequently paraformaldehyde or hexamethylenetetramine may replace formalin for this purpose. Formaldehyde is used also to make *pentaerythritol* which is important for the manufacture of drying oils (p. 187) and the high explosive *pentaerythritol nitrate* (PETN) (p. 752). Another high explosive, *trimethylene trinitramine* (cyclonite, RDX, hexogen), is derived from hexamethylene-tetramine (p. 221). Hexamethylenetetramine when taken internally is excreted in the urine and hydrolyzed to formaldehyde when the urine is acid. At one time it was used medicinally as a urinary antiseptic under the name *methenamine* or *urotropin*, but has been replaced largely by the sulfa drugs (p. 488) and mandelic acid (p. 562). In the United States the production of formalin (37 per cent) in 1940 was 181 million pounds and it increased to over 1.2 billion pounds in 1955. The unit value is around 3 cents per pound.

Acetaldehyde is made commercially by the hydration of acetylene and by the air oxidation of ethyl alcohol over a silver catalyst. Since 1945 large amounts have been produced by the controlled air-oxidation of the propane-butane mixture from natural gas (p. 220). Some acetaldehyde is obtained as a by-product of the fermentation industries (p. 91). It boils at 20°, is miscible with water and organic solvents, and behaves typically in all of its reactions. The chief importance of acetaldehyde is its use as an intermediate for the synthesis of other organic compounds, especially acetic acid (p. 159) and acetic anhydride (p. 164) by air oxidation, *n*-butyl alcohol by condensation to crotonic aldehyde followed by catalytic reduction.

$$2\ CH_3CHO \xrightarrow[\text{NaOH}]{\text{Dil.}} CH_3CHOHCH_2CHO \xrightarrow{\text{[H+]}}$$

$$CH_3CH{=}CHCHO \xrightarrow[\substack{\text{Cu} \\ \text{on pumice} \\ \text{at 200°}}]{\text{H}_2} CH_3CH_2CH_2CH_2OH$$

and ethyl acetate made by the Tishchenko reaction (p. 220). Acetaldehyde also is used in the manufacture of rubber accelerators (p. 712), of the trimer, paraldehyde, and of the tetramer, metaldehyde. **Paraldehyde** is a stable liquid, b.p. 125°, which is depolymerized readily by heating with acids, and hence is a convenient source of acetaldehyde. Paraldehyde first was used medicinally as a sleep-producer (hypnotic or soporific) in 1882. It still is considered to be very efficient and one of the least toxic hypnotics. The chief objections to its use are that it is a liquid with a burning disagreeable taste, and that, because it is eliminated largely through the lungs, a patient's breath may smell of paraldehyde for as long as twenty-four hours after administration. **Metaldehyde** is formed when acetaldehyde is treated with traces of acids or sulfur dioxide below 0°. One of the catalysts used commercially is a mixture of calcium nitrate and hydrogen bromide at −20°. The product is a solid tetramer which, like paraldehyde, has a cyclic structure.

$$4 \text{ CH}_3\text{CHO} \xrightarrow[\text{at } -20°]{\text{Ca(NO}_3)_2,\text{ HBr}}$$

$$
\begin{array}{c}
\text{CH}_3 \\
| \\
\text{CH}-\text{O} \\
\diagup \qquad \diagdown \\
\text{O} \qquad\qquad \text{CHCH}_3 \\
| \qquad\qquad\qquad | \\
\text{CH}_3\text{CH} \qquad\qquad \text{O} \\
\diagdown \qquad\qquad \diagup \\
\text{O}-\text{CH} \\
| \\
\text{CH}_3
\end{array}
$$

Like paraldehyde it is depolymerized to acetaldehyde by heat. Since it is a solid and has a fairly high vapor pressure in spite of its high melting point (m.p. 246°, sublimes below 150°), it is used as a convenient solid fuel for heating liquids or foods under unusual conditions when other fuels are not available or not satisfactory. Large quantities are used also in garden baits, the vapors being attractive and yet highly toxic to slugs and snails.

n-**Butyraldehyde** and *i*-**butyraldehyde** can be made by the dehydrogenation of the alcohols. A more important method, however, is the **oxo process** based on an American observation in 1929 and developed in Germany during World War II. It consists of bringing a slurry of cobalt salt and olefin, or a solution of preformed dicobalt octacarbonyl, $\text{Co}_2(\text{CO})_8$, and cobalt tetracarbonyl hydride, HCo(CO)_4 (p. 904), in contact with carbon monoxide and hydrogen at 150° and 200 atmospheres. Propylene gives *n*-butyraldehyde and *i*-butyraldehyde in the ratio of 3 : 2.

$$\text{CH}_3\text{CH}=\text{CH}_2 + \text{CO} + \text{H}_2 \longrightarrow \text{CH}_3\text{CH}_2\text{CH}_2\text{CHO and } \underset{\underset{\text{CHO}}{|}}{\text{CH}_3\text{CHCH}_3}$$

In the commercial operation of this reaction, a mixture of octyl alcohols containing chiefly **2-ethylhexanol** also is produced. This alcohol probably arises by aldol addition of two moles of *n*-butyraldehyde, dehydration, and hydrogenation.

$$2 \text{ CH}_3\text{CH}_2\text{CH}_2\text{CHO} \longrightarrow \underset{\underset{\text{C}_2\text{H}_5}{|}}{\text{CH}_3\text{CH}_2\text{CH}_2\text{CHOHCHCHO}} \longrightarrow$$

$$\underset{\underset{\text{C}_2\text{H}_5}{|}}{\text{CH}_3\text{CH}_2\text{CH}_2\text{CH}=\text{C}-\text{CHO}} \longrightarrow \underset{\underset{\text{C}_2\text{H}_5}{|}}{\text{CH}_3\text{CH}_2\text{CH}_2\text{CH}_2\text{CHCH}_2\text{OH}}$$

If one of the carbon atoms of the double bond is doubly substituted, only one product is formed. For example, isobutylene gives only isovaleraldehyde.

$$(CH_3)_2C = CH_2 + CO + H_2 \longrightarrow (CH_3)_2CHCH_2CHO$$

Moreover if the double bond is not terminal, isomerization to the terminal position takes place before reaction. Thus the mixture of diisobutylenes (p. 62) gives only **3,5,5-trimethylhexanal** (so-called "nonyl aldehyde").

$$\begin{array}{c} (CH_3)_3CCH_2C(CH_3) = CH_2 \\ \text{and} \\ (CH_3)_3CCH = C(CH_3)_2 \end{array} + CO + H_2 \longrightarrow (CH_3)_3CCH_2CH(CH_3)CH_2CHO$$

The aldehydes produced by the oxo synthesis usually are reduced to alcohols (p. 198) or oxidized to acids (p. 212). Thus a mixture of primary octyl alcohols is produced from the catalytic reduction of the aldehydes made from mixed heptenes. *n*-Butyraldehyde is used to manufacture rubber accelerators (p. 712) and polyvinyl butyral (p. 737). Aldehydes having seven to sixteen carbon atoms are used in perfumery. *n*-**Heptaldehyde** is one of the products of the destructive distillation of castor oil (p. 789).

Acetone is by far the most important ketone. It formerly was obtained by the destructive distillation of calcium acetate prepared from pyroligneous liquor (p. 158) but now is produced chiefly by the dehydrogenation of *i*-propyl alcohol. More recently a process has been reported in which the uncatalyzed oxidation of isopropyl alcohol with air yields acetone and hydrogen peroxide as the major products.

$$(CH_3)_2CHOH + O_2 \xrightarrow[30 \text{ sec.}]{460°} (CH_3)_2CO + H_2O_2$$

It also is one of the products of the butyl alcohol fermentation of carbohydrates (p. 96). The last process, in fact, was developed for the production of acetone during World War I because other sources were inadequate to supply the needs of the British for the manufacture of cordite, their standard smokeless powder (p. 401).[8] Since 1954 acetone has been obtained as a co-product of the synthesis of phenol (p. 511) and *p*-cresol (p. 515).

The chief use of acetone is as a solvent for cellulose acetate (p. 403), for cellulose nitrate (p. 401), and for acetylene (p. 134). In recent years large quantities have been pyrolyzed to ketene, an intermediate in the manufacture of acetic anhydride (p. 164).

$$CH_3COCH_3 \xrightarrow{700°} CH_2 = C = O + CH_4$$
$$\text{Ketene}$$

$$CH_2 = C = O + HOCOCH_3 \longrightarrow CH_3CO - O - COCH_3$$

Other uses of acetone are in the manufacture of other chemicals such as diacetone alcohol, mesityl oxide, and phorone (p. 208). Production in 1955 amounted to over 539 million pounds of which 5 per cent was obtained by fermentation, 81 per cent from *i*-propyl alcohol, and 14 per cent from other sources. The unit value was 6 cents per pound.

---

[8] Scientists rarely have influenced directly the decisions of politicians and statesmen, but it has been stated that the Balfour Declaration establishing Palestine as a national home for the Hebrews was the result of Lloyd George's gratitude to Chaim Weizmann (1874–1952) for developing this process for the production of acetone. Weizmann later became the first president of the new state of Israel.

Methyl ethyl ketone is made by the dehydrogenation of *s*-butyl alcohol and by the oxidation of butane (p. 159). It is known technically by the initials MEK and is used chiefly as a solvent for dewaxing lubricating oils. **Methyl *i*-butyl ketone** is made by the controlled catalytic reduction of mesityl oxide (p. 208).

REVIEW QUESTIONS

1. What chemical evidence can be given for the presence of a carbonyl group in aldehydes and ketones?
2. Compare the boiling points and solubilities of aldehydes and ketones with those of other types of compounds discussed so far.
3. How does the Meerwein-Ponndorf reduction differ from the Oppenauer oxidation?
4. Compare the similarities and differences in the reactions of acetals and ethers.
5. Discuss the applications and limitations of the Cannizzaro reaction.
6. Compare the reactions of formaldehyde and acetaldehyde with ammonia and with sodium hydroxide solution.
7. Discuss the polymerization of formaldehyde and acetaldehyde and compare their behavior with that of ketones.
8. Discuss the behavior of aldehydes and ketones to saturated sodium bisulfite solution. Of what value is the reaction?
9. Describe three simple tests that may be used to distinguish between aldehydes and ketones.

PROBLEMS

10. Write condensed structural formulas and give two names for each of the compounds belonging to the following groups: (*a*) aldehydes having five carbon atoms or less; (*b*) ketones having three, four, five, and six carbon atoms; (*c*) dialkyl derivatives of acetaldehyde having seven carbon atoms or less; (*d*) dialkyl ketones having nine carbon atoms.
11. Give balanced equations for the following oxidations:
    A. (*a*) Ethyl alcohol to acetaldehyde with dichromate and sulfuric acid; (*b*) *n*-butyraldehyde to *n*-butyric acid with alkaline permanganate; (*c*) lauryl alcohol to dodecanal with *t*-butyl chromate; (*d*) 2-octanol to 2-octanone with chromium trioxide in acetic acid.
    B. (*a*) *i*-Propyl alcohol to acetone with dichromate and sulfuric acid; (*b*) *n*-heptaldehyde to *n*-heptoic acid with nitric acid; (*c*) 3-pentanol to diethyl ketone with chromium trioxide in acetic acid; (*d*) hexadecanol to hexadecanal with *t*-butyl chromate.
    C. (*a*) Pelargonic aldehyde to pelargonic acid with alkaline permanganate; (*b*) *n*-propyl alcohol to propionaldehyde with acid dichromate; (*c*) di-*n*-propylcarbinol to butyrone with chromium trioxide in acetic acid; (*d*) ethyl ether to acetic acid with acid permanganate.
12. Starting with the proper aldehyde, give a reaction for the synthesis of the following compounds:
    A. (*a*) Diethylcarbinol; (*b*) 2,5-dihydroxy-3-hexyne; (*c*) propionaldoxime; (*d*) 3-hydroxybutanal; (*e*) 1-heptanol.
    B. (*a*) 3-Hydroxy-1-butyne; (*b*) *i*-butyl alcohol; (*c*) heptanaldoxime; (*d*) 2-pentanol; (*e*) 2-methyl-3-hydroxypentanal.
    C. (*a*) 3-Hydroxy-2-ethylhexanal; (*b*) *i*-butyraldoxime; (*c*) 3,6-dihydroxy-4-octyne; (*d*) 3,5,5-trimethylhexanol; (*e*) 2-methyl-3-hexanol.
13. Starting with the proper ketone, give reactions for the synthesis of the following compounds:
    A. (*a*) 2-Methyl-2-butanol; (*b*) diethylketoxime; (*c*) 3-hydroxy-3-methyl-1-pentyne; (*d*) 3,4-dimethyl-3,4-dihydroxyhexane; (*e*) methyl-*i*-propylcarbinol.
    B. (*a*) 3-Pentanol; (*b*) 2,5-dimethyl-2,5-dihydroxy-3-hexyne; (*c*) 2,3-dimethyl-2-butanol; (*d*) methyl-*i*-butyl ketoxime; (*e*) 4,5-dimethyl-4,5-dihydroxyoctane.
    C. (*a*) 4,4-Dimethyl-2-pentanone oxime; (*b*) 3,4-diethyl-3,4-dihydroxyhexane; (*c*) 2,4-dimethyl-3-hexanol; (*d*) 3-hydroxy-3-methyl-1-butyne; (*e*) methyldiethylcarbinol.
14. Give equations for the following reactions and name the organic product:
    A. (*a*) Methyl ethyl ketone and sodium hypoiodite; (*b*) acetone and semicarbazide; (*c*) propionaldehyde and acetic anhydride; (*d*) Clemmensen reduction of 5-nonanone; (*e*) 2-octanone and hydrogen cyanide; (*f*) acetaldehyde and *t*-butylmagnesium chloride.

B. (a) i-Butyraldehyde and hydrogen cyanide; (b) 2-pentanone and i-propylmagnesium bromide; (c) 2-octanol and sodium hypochlorite; (d) n-butyraldehyde and acetic anhydride; (e) diethyl ketone and hydroxylamine; (f) Meerwein-Ponndorf reduction of valerone.

C. (a) 3-Hexanone and phenylhydrazine; (b) diethylacetaldehyde and hydrogen cyanide; (c) 3-hexanone and s-butylmagnesium iodide; (d) Wolff-Kishner reduction of butyrone; (e) methyl isobutyl ketone and sodium hypobromite; (f) i-butyraldehyde and acetic anhydride.

15. Of the following groups of compounds, name the members that give a positive iodoform test: (a) aldehydes and ketones having four carbon atoms or less; (b) five-carbon ketones; (c) alcohols having four carbon atoms or less.

16. Describe a series of chemical tests that could be used to distinguish between the members of the following groups of compounds: (a) methyl-n-propylcarbinol, 3-pentanol, n-amyl alcohol, and dimethylethylcarbinol; (b) ethyl-i-propylcarbinol, dimethyl-n-propylcarbinol, methyl-i-butylcarbinol, and i-hexyl alcohol; (c) methyl alcohol, ethyl alcohol, 2-propanol and t-butyl alcohol; (d) formaldehyde, acetaldehyde, acetone, and diethyl ketone.

17. Devise procedures for obtaining the components of the following mixtures in a reasonably pure state: (a) nonyl alcohol, pelargonic aldehyde, and nonane; (b) 2-octanone, 2-octanol, and capric acid; (c) 1-nonanol, 5-nonanone, and 1-nonyne; (d) lauryl alcohol, dodecanal, and hexyl ether.

18. Give reactions indicating how the following groups of compounds could be prepared from the indicated compounds as the starting point: (a) n-butyl alcohol, n-hexyl alcohol, n-butyraldehyde, n-hexaldehyde, and 1,3-hexanediol from acetaldehyde; (b) 2-ethylhexanol, 2-ethyl-1,3-hexanediol, 2-ethylbutanol, and 2-ethyl-1,3-butanediol from n-butyraldehyde or n-butyraldehyde and acetaldehyde; (c) 5-ethyl-2-nonanol, 5,11-diethyl-8-pentadecanol, and 2-methyl-7-ethyl-4-undecanol from 2-ethylhexanal and acetone; (d) mesityl oxide, methyl i-butyl ketone, di-i-butylcarbinol, and 2-methyl-2,4-pentanediol from acetone.

19. Give a series of reactions for the following conversions: (a) n-butyraldehyde to n-hexane; (b) i-butyl bromide to i-valeraldehyde; (c) heptanoic acid to 3-nonanol; (d) i-propyl ether to i-butyl alcohol; (e) i-butyraldehyde to i-butyl iodide; (f) ethyl palmitate to hexadecanal; (g) propionic acid to methyldiethylcarbinol; (h) 1-pentene to 2-methyl-1-pentanol; (i) diethyl ketone to 2-methyl-3-ethyl-2-pentene; (j) n-butyl alcohol to 2-ethyl-3-hydroxyhexanal; (k) propionaldehyde to n-propyl ether; (l) 3-pentanol to triethylcarbinol; (m) ethyl alcohol to acetal; (n) ethyl butyrate to butyrone; (o) methyl ethyl ketone to 2-butene; (p) methylacetylene to i-propyl alcohol; (q) heptaldehyde to i-propyl n-hexyl ketone; (r) s-butyl alcohol to 3,4-dimethyl-3,4-hexanediol; (s) acetic acid to pinacol; (t) 3-hexene to 3-hexanone; (u) acetylene to ethyl alcohol; (v) oleic acid to nonyl alcohol; (w) n-amyl bromide to n-hexyl bromide.

20. A hydrocarbon having a molecular weight of 95 ± 5 decolorized aqueous permanganate with the formation of a brown precipitate. After allowing the compound to react with an excess of permanganate, two products were isolated, an acid having a neutralization equivalent of 74 and a neutral compound that formed an oxime and gave a positive iodoform test. Give a structure for the hydrocarbon and balanced equations for the reactions involved.

21. An unknown compound formed a monoxime, reduced Fehling solution, gave iodoform on treatment with hypoiodite solution, and evolved methane on treatment with methylmagnesium iodide. Oxidation gave an acid which on purification and titration was found to have an equivalent weight of 116. The acid still formed an oxime and gave a positive iodoform test but no longer reduced Fehling solution. Write a possible structural formula for the compound and show the reactions it undergoes.

22. Compound A evolved hydrogen when warmed with metallic sodium. When 0.2 g. was treated with methylmagnesium iodide in a Zerevitinov apparatus, 34.5 cc. (S.T.P.) of methane was evolved. When compound A was heated with sulfuric acid, it gave chiefly a single lower-boiling compound, B, which decolorized bromine in carbon tetrachloride. Ozonolysis of B gave two products, C and D, neither of which produced a color with Schiff reagent and both of which gave iodoform when treated with sodium hypoiodite. Reduction of D, the higher boiling of the two compounds, with hydrogen and platinum gave an alcohol which was dehydrated to an olefin E. Ozonolysis of E gave two products, one of which produced a color with Schiff reagent and the other did not. Give a structural formula for A, and the reactions that are described.

23. An unknown compound *A* reacted with hot hydrogen bromide to form two different halogen compounds *B* and *C*, which were separated by fractional distillation. Compound *B* on treatment with moist silver oxide gave a compound *D* which did not react at once with a cold mixture of concentrated hydrochloric acid and zinc chloride, but on standing gave an insoluble liquid. Compound *C* likewise gave a new substance *E* on treatment with moist silver oxide, but *E* did not react at all with cold hydrochloric acid-zinc chloride mixture. Both *D* and *E* gave iodoform on treatment with iodine in alkaline solution. When *E* was oxidized under the proper conditions, an aldehyde *F* was obtained, which on treatment with methylmagnesium iodide solution and decomposition with water gave a compound identical with *D*. Write the structural formula for *A*, and illustrate by equations all of the reactions involved.

24. A compound having the molecular formula $C_6H_{12}O$ reacted with hydroxylamine but did not reduce Tollens reagent. Reduction with hydrogen and platinum gave an alcohol which was dehydrated to give chiefly a single olefin. Ozonation and decomposition of the ozonide gave two liquid products, one of which reduced Tollens reagent but did not give a positive iodoform test whereas the other did not reduce Tollens reagent but did give a positive iodoform test. Give the structure of the original compound and show the reactions it undergoes.

25. An alkyl halide *A* was converted into the corresponding Grignard reagent which was allowed to react with *i*-butyraldehyde. After decomposition with water a compound *B* was obtained which reacted readily with hydrogen bromide to give another alkyl halide *C*. Compound *C* likewise was converted into the Grignard reagent and decomposed with water to give a fourth compound *D*. When the original compound *A* was heated with metallic sodium, a compound identical with *D* was obtained. Write a structural formula for *A* and give all of the reactions involved.

26. A compound having the molecular formula $C_7H_{16}O$ did not react with sodium or phosphorus trichloride. After warming with concentrated sulfuric acid, diluting and distilling, a mixture was obtained which could not be separated satisfactorily by fractional distillation. After the mixture was oxidized by means of dichromic acid, an acidic product was isolated having a neutralization equivalent of 74, and a neutral product which reacted with semicarbazine, but did not reduce Tollens reagent. Give the structure of the original compound and show the reactions that took place.

27. A water-insoluble compound dissolved when boiled with aqueous sodium hydroxide. A distillate from the alkaline solution gave a positive iodoform reaction. When the distillate was heated with sodium dichromate and sulfuric acid and distilled again, the distillate gave a positive Schiff reaction. When the alkaline solution was acidified, a water-insoluble compound was formed which, when passed over thoria at 400°, gave a product that no longer was soluble in aqueous alkali but formed a semicarbazone. When this product was refluxed with amalgamated zinc and hydrochloric acid, a product was formed identical with that obtained by heating undecanal with hydrazine and sodium ethoxide. Give a formula for the original compound and equations for the reactions involved.

Chapter 12

ALIPHATIC NITROGEN COMPOUNDS

Structurally the organic oxygen compounds have been considered as derivatives of the water molecule. Similarly many of the organic nitrogen compounds may be considered as ammonia molecules in which the hydrogen atoms have been replaced by other groups. Since nitrogen has three replaceable hydrogen atoms instead of two as in water, the number of possible combinations is increased.

H_2O	water	NH_3	ammonia
ROH	alcohols	RNH_2	primary amines
		R_2NH	secondary amines
ROR	ethers	R_3N	tertiary amines
RCOOH	acids	$RCONH_2$	amides.
		$RC(NH)NH_2$	amidines
RCOOR	esters	RCONHR	N-alkyl amides
		$RCONR_2$	N, N-dialkyl amides
		RC(NH)OR	imido esters
RCOOCOR	anhydrides	RCONHCOR	imides
$RCH{=}O$	aldehydes	$RCH{=}NH$	aldimines
$R_2C{=}O$	ketones	$R_2C{=}NH$	ketimines

This list is not complete, but contains the types of compounds most frequently encountered. Substituents on nitrogen other than hydrogen, alkyl, and acyl also may be present as for example in the cyanides (p. 249), the isocyanides (p. 256), the oximes (p. 210), the hydrazones (p. 211), and the nitro compounds (p. 258).

AMINES

Nomenclature

Aliphatic amines are alkyl substitution products of ammonia and are named as such, *ammonia* being contracted to *amine*. Thus CH_3NH_2 is methylamine, $(CH_3)_2NH$ is dimethylamine, and $(CH_3)_3N$ is trimethylamine. With mixed amines the alkyl groups frequently are named in the order of increasing complexity, for example $CH_3(C_2H_5)NCH(CH_3)_2$ is methylethyl-*i*-propylamine. Compounds in which the nitrogen atom is united to one carbon atom, RNH_2, are called *primary amines*; to two carbon atoms, R_2NH, *secondary amines*; and to three carbon atoms, R_3N, *tertiary amines. The terms primary, secondary, and tertiary refer here to the condition of the nitrogen atom*, whereas when used with alcohols they referred to the carbon atom to which the hydroxyl group was attached. Thus although tertiary butyl alcohol, $(CH_3)_3COH$, is a tertiary alcohol, because the carbon atom is united to three other carbon atoms, tertiary butylamine, $(CH_3)_3CNH_2$, is a primary amine, because the nitrogen atom is directly united to only one carbon atom. The NH_2 group is called the *amino group*, and primary amines having other functional groups conveniently may be named as amino substitution products; for example, $CH_3CHNH_2CH_2CH_2OH$ could be called 3-amino-1-butanol.

228

Preparation

MIXED PRIMARY, SECONDARY, AND TERTIARY AMINES

1. **From Alkyl Halides and Ammonia.** Wurtz prepared the first amines from alkyl isocyanates (p. 317) in 1849, but the most direct method for the preparation of amines is by the reaction of ammonia with an alkyl halide, reported by Hofmann[1] in 1850. In this reaction the more basic ammonia molecule displaces chlorine as a chloride ion, the alkyl group attaching itself to the unshared pair of electrons of the ammonia molecule.

$$\begin{matrix} \text{H} \\ \cdot\cdot \\ \text{H}:\text{N}: \\ \cdot\cdot \\ \text{H} \end{matrix} + \text{R}:\overset{\cdot\cdot}{\underset{\cdot\cdot}{\text{X}}}: \longrightarrow \left[\begin{matrix} \text{H} \\ \cdot\cdot \\ \text{H}:\overset{+}{\underset{\cdot\cdot}{\text{N}}}:\text{R} \\ \text{H} \end{matrix} \right] :\overset{\cdot\cdot}{\underset{\cdot\cdot}{\text{X}}}:^{-}$$

This initial reaction, however, is followed by a series of secondary reactions. Just as ammonia may be liberated from an ammonium salt by reaction with a stronger base,

$$\text{NH}_4\text{Cl} + \text{NaOH} \longrightarrow \text{NH}_3 + \text{H}_2\text{O} + \text{NaCl}$$

the free primary amine can be liberated from the alkylammonium salt.

$$\text{RNH}_3\text{X} + \text{NaOH} \longrightarrow \text{RNH}_2 + \text{H}_2\text{O} + \text{NaX}$$

Similarly the excess of ammonia present when the alkyl halide is reacting with ammonia will compete with the primary amine for the hydrogen halide. Since ammonia and the amine have about the same basicity, the reaction does not go to completion, but an equilibrium is established.

$$\text{RNH}_3\text{X} + \text{NH}_3 \rightleftarrows \text{RNH}_2 + \text{NH}_4\text{X}$$

Because of its unshared pair of electrons, the primary amine thus formed also can react with a molecule of alkyl halide and give rise to a second pair of reactions to form a secondary amine.

$$\text{RNH}_2 + \text{RX} \longrightarrow \text{R}_2\text{NH}_2\text{X}$$

$$\text{R}_2\text{NH}_2\text{X} + \text{NH}_3 \rightleftarrows \text{R}_2\text{NH} + \text{NH}_4\text{X}$$

Immediately a third pair of reactions is possible giving a tertiary amine.

$$\text{RX} + \text{R}_2\text{NH} \longrightarrow \text{R}_3\text{NHX}$$

$$\text{R}_3\text{NHX} + \text{NH}_3 \rightleftarrows \text{R}_3\text{N} + \text{NH}_4\text{X}$$

Finally a single further reaction can take place giving a quaternary ammonium salt.

$$\text{RX} + \text{R}_3\text{N} \longrightarrow \text{R}_4\text{NX}$$

The reaction stops at this point, because there is no hydrogen attached to nitrogen in the quaternary ammonium salt (nitrogen united to four carbon atoms), and hence no proton can be transferred to another base.

---

[1] August Wilhelm Hofmann (1818–1895), German chemist who received his training under Liebig, and who was professor at the Royal College of Chemistry in London from 1845 to 1864, and at the University of Berlin from 1864 until his death. He is noted particulary for his work on amines and for his investigations of aromatic compounds. The latter work laid the basis for the coal tar chemical industry.

Accordingly the reaction of alkyl halides with ammonia, known as the *Hofmann method for preparing amines*, gives rise to a mixture of primary, secondary, and tertiary amines, their salts, and the quaternary ammonium salt. Addition of strong alkali at the end of the reaction liberates a mixture of the free amines from their salts, but the quaternary salt is not affected. It is possible to control the reaction to a certain extent. If a very large excess of ammonia is used, the chance that the alkyl halide will react with ammonia molecules is greater than that it will react with amine molecules, and chiefly primary amine is produced. If increasing amounts of alkyl halide are used, more of the other products are formed.

The order of reactivity of the alkyl halides with ammonia and amines is iodides > bromides > chlorides, and methyl > primary > secondary > tertiary. Alkyl sulfates may replace alkyl halides (cf. p. 137). Because of the ease with which tertiary alkyl halides lose halogen acid, reaction with ammonia yields only olefin and ammonium halide.

$$(CH_3)_3CCl + NH_3 \longrightarrow CH_2{=}C(CH_3)_2 + NH_4Cl$$

Compounds containing an amino group attached to a tertiary carbon atom may be prepared by the Hofmann degradation of the proper amide (p. 231), which in turn is prepared readily by the hydrolysis of the nitrile (p. 254). They may be prepared also by the reaction of chloroamine with a tertiary alkyl Grignard reagent (p. 233) or by the hydrolysis of the corresponding formyl derivative (p. 255).

2. **Catalytic Reduction of Alkyl Cyanides.** Addition of four atoms of hydrogen to the carbon-nitrogen triple bond gives a primary amine.

$$RC{\equiv}N + 2\,H_2 \xrightarrow{\text{Pt or Ni}} RCH_2NH_2$$

Secondary and tertiary amines are formed at the same time by the addition of amine to the intermediate imine, followed by loss of ammonia and further reduction, or by reductive removal of the amino group.

$$RCH{=}NH + H_2NR \longrightarrow R{-}CH{-}NHR$$

$$\begin{array}{c} NH_2 \\ \end{array} \qquad H_2(\text{Pt or Ni})$$

$$NH_3 + RCH{=}NR \xrightarrow{\text{H}_2(\text{Pt or Ni})} RCH_2NHR$$

The secondary amine by a similar series of reactions gives rise to the tertiary amine. The formation of secondary and tertiary amines can be suppressed considerably by carrying out the reduction in the presence of a large excess of ammonia.

3. **Reductive Alkylation of Ammonia.** Catalytic reduction of aldehydes or ketones in the presence of ammonia gives a mixture of amines.

$$RCHO + NH_3 \longrightarrow H_2O + RCH{=}NH \xrightarrow{\text{H}_2(\text{Pt or Ni})} RCH_2NH_2$$

The secondary and tertiary amines are formed in the same way as in the catalytic reduction of alkyl cyanides. Because of side reactions, the procedure is not satisfactory when aldehydes having less than five carbon atoms are used.

Reductive alkylation of ammonia can be brought about also by heating carbonyl compounds with ammonium formate (*Leuckart reaction*). Here the reducing agent is formic acid.

$$R_2CO + HCOONH_4 \longrightarrow R_2CHNH_2 + CO_2 + H_2O$$

The primary amine may alkylate further to a secondary or tertiary amine. The primary and secondary amines are partially converted to the formamides, from which the amine is obtained by hydrolysis. The best yields of primary amines (25 to 75 per cent) are obtained from ketones boiling above 100°. The Leuckart reaction is particularly useful if other functional groups are present that would be affected by the sodium-alcohol reduction of an oxime (p. 528).

Formaldehyde and ammonium formate give trimethylamine (*Eschweiler-Clarke reaction*), and formaldehyde can be used to methylate primary or secondary amines in the presence of formic acid.

$$HCHO + HCOONH_3R \longrightarrow CH_3NHR + CO_2 + H_2O$$

PURE PRIMARY AMINES

When only one type of amine is desired, reactions that do not give mixtures are of value. In the following reactions only the primary amine is formed.

1. **From Amides (Hofmann Rearrangement).** When an amide is treated with an alkaline solution of sodium hypochlorite or sodium hypobromite, a primary amine is formed which has one less carbon atom than the amide.

$$RCONH_2 + NaOX + 2 NaOH \longrightarrow RNH_2 + Na_2CO_3 + NaX + H_2O$$

Several steps are involved which are discussed under the reactions of amides (p. 247).

When the Hofmann rearrangement is carried out in the presence of sodium hypohalite and sodium hydroxide, a side reaction takes place with the higher primary amines, for example with pentadecylamine from palmitamide, in which the amine is oxidized to a cyanide.

$$RCH_2NH_2 + 2 NaOCl \longrightarrow RCN + 2 NaCl + 2 H_2O$$

This reaction can be circumvented by using bromine and sodium methoxide as the reagents in methyl alcohol solution, when the methyl ester of a substituted carbamic acid (p. 315) is produced.

$$RCONH_2 + Br_2 + 2 NaOCH_3 \longrightarrow RNHCOOCH_3 + 2 NaBr + CH_3OH$$

Hydrolysis of the methyl ester with aqueous hydrochloric acid yields the carbamic acid, which spontaneously loses carbon dioxide. In the presence of hydrochloric acid the amine hydrochloride (p. 234) is produced.

$$RNHCOOCH_3 + H_2O \underset{}{\overset{[H^+]}{\rightleftarrows}} [RNHCOOH] + CH_3OH$$

$$[RNHCOOH] + HCl \longrightarrow RNH_3Cl + CO_2$$

Addition of a strong base liberates the free amine.

$$RNH_3Cl + NaOH \longrightarrow RNH_2 + NaCl + H_2O$$

2. **From Carboxylic Acids (Schmidt Reaction).** Carboxylic acids that are stable to concentrated sulfuric acid can be converted to primary amines having one less carbon atom by means of hydrazoic acid (p. 267).

$$RCOOH + HN_3 \xrightarrow{H_2SO_4} RNH_2 + CO_2 + N_2$$

Since hydrazoic acid is volatile and very poisonous, it is more convenient to add sodium azide to a mixture of sulfuric acid and a solution of the compound in an inert solvent such as chloroform. The Schmidt reaction yields the same product as the Hofmann or the Curtius (p. 268) rearrangements but is preferred for small scale preparations because it is more direct and the yields usually are better.

3. **Chemical Reduction of Alkyl Cyanides.** This reaction resembles the reduction of esters to alcohols (p. 172). The usual reagent is sodium and absolute alcohol.

$$RC \equiv N + 4 Na + 4 C_2H_5OH \longrightarrow RCH_2NH_2 + 4 C_2H_5ONa$$

4. **Reduction of Oximes.** Oximes of aldehydes or ketones also may be reduced by sodium and alcohol to give good yields of primary amines.

$$RCH{=}NOH + 4 Na + 3 C_2H_5OH \longrightarrow RCH_2NH_2 + NaOH + 3 C_2H_5ONa$$

This reaction provides a method for converting aldehydes and ketones to primary amines. Lithium aluminum hydride may be used as a reducing agent instead of sodium and alcohol.

5. **From Hexamethylenetetramine (Delepine Reaction).** Reaction of hexamethylenetetramine (p. 221) with primary alkyl halides yields the quaternary salt which can be hydrolyzed by aqueous acid to the primary amine.

$$(CH_2)_6N_4 + RX \longrightarrow [(CH_2)_6N_4R]^+X^-$$

$$[(CH_2)_6N_4R]^+X^- + 6 H_2O + 3 HX \longrightarrow RNH_3X + 6 CH_2O + 3 NH_4X$$

The amine is liberated from its salt by the addition of sodium hydroxide.

6. **Other Methods.** Pure primary amines can be prepared also by the reduction of nitro compounds (p. 262) and by the hydrolysis of *p*-nitroalkylacetanilides (p. 481).

PURE SECONDARY AMINES

1. **From Sodium Cyanamide and Alkyl Halides or Sulfates.** Sodium cyanamide (p. 320) reacts with alkyl halides or sulfates like many other salts, the metallic ion being replaced by covalently bound alkyl groups.

$$2 RX + Na^+_2[{=}N{-}C{\equiv}N] \longrightarrow R_2N{-}C{\equiv}N + 2 NaX$$

The dialkylcyanamide hydrolyzes readily with aqueous acids or bases giving the N,N-dialkylcarbamic acid, which loses carbon dioxide (p. 315).

$$R_2N{-}C{\equiv}N + 2 HOH \xrightarrow{[H^+] \text{ or } [OH^-]} [R_2NCOOH] + NH_3$$
$$\downarrow$$
$$R_2NH + CO_2$$

In acid solution carbon dioxide is evolved and a mixture of the amine and ammonium salts is obtained, whereas in alkaline solution the free amine, ammonia, and alkali carbonate are formed.

2. **From Chloroamines and Grignard Reagents.** Chloroamines are produced readily from amines by the action of sodium hypochlorite.

$$RNH_2 + NaOCl \longrightarrow RNHCl + NaOH$$

Grignard reagents replace the chlorine by an alkyl group.

$$RNHCl + R'MgCl \longrightarrow RNHR' + MgCl_2$$

The reaction is particularly useful for preparing amines containing tertiary alkyl groups, for example di-*t*-butylamine, which cannot be prepared by the reaction of tertiary halides with ammonia because of olefin formation. The dialkylmagnesium (p. 892) may give better yields than the alkylmagnesium chloride. The reaction also can be used to prepare primary amines from chloroamine, $ClNH_2$, and tertiary amines from dialkylchloroamines, $ClNR_2$.

3. **Other Methods.** Secondary amines can be obtained also by the dealkylation of tertiary amines (p. 239) and by the hydrolysis of *p*-nitrosodialkylanilines (p. 481).

PURE TERTIARY AMINES

Pure tertiary amines can be prepared from dialkylchloroamines and Grignard reagents.

$$R_2NCl + R'MgCl \longrightarrow R_2NR' + MgCl_2$$

More frequently a secondary amine is allowed to react with an excess of alkyl halide, and the tertiary amine is separated from the accompanying quaternary salt.

Physical Properties

Water, ammonia, and methane have very nearly the same molecular weights, but their boiling points are 100°, −33°, and −161°, respectively. The abnormally high boiling point of water is explained by proton bonding between hydrogen united to oxygen, and the unshared pair of electrons on the oxygen atom (p. 86). The boiling point of ammonia indicates that it is not so strongly associated as water. The nitrogen atom is nearer the center of the periodic table than oxygen and hence has less attraction for electrons (p. 235). Therefore the hydrogen atoms attached to nitrogen have less tendency to leave nitrogen as protons or to be shared with other atoms than do those joined to oxygen. On the other hand the unshared pair of electrons on nitrogen is shared more readily with other atoms than those on oxygen. The decrease in tendency to lose a proton accounts for the smaller degree of association.

Primary and secondary amines also are associated. Methylamine (mol. wt. 31) boils at −7° and dimethylamine (mol. wt. 45) boils at +7°, but trimethylamine (mol. wt. 59) boils at +4°. Thus even though its molecular weight is greater than that of dimethylamine, trimethylamine has the lower boiling point. The explanation is that trimethylamine no longer has a hydrogen atom capable of proton bond formation, and hence it is not associated.

There is nothing to prevent the unshared pair of electrons of tertiary amines from forming proton bonds with water molecules, and all types of amines of low molecular weight are soluble in water. Since amines have a greater tendency to share their unshared pair of electrons than do alcohols, they form stronger proton bonds with water and are somewhat more soluble. For example, *n*-butyl alcohol dissolves in water to the extent of about 8 per cent at room temperature, but *n*-butylamine is miscible with water; and although less than 1 per cent of *n*-amyl alcohol dissolves in water, this degree of insolubility is not reached in the amines until *n*-hexylamine. Like the alcohols and ethers, simple amines are soluble in most organic solvents.

The lower amines have an odor resembling that of ammonia; the odor of trimethylamine is described as "fishy." As the molecular weight increases, the odors become decidedly obnoxious, but they decrease again with increasing molecular weight and decreasing vapor pressure.

Reactions

1. **Basic Properties.** For many purposes it is sufficient to define an acid as a substance which yields hydrogen ions when dissolved in water, and a base as a substance which yields hydroxide ions when dissolved in water. A more general concept is useful in organic chemistry, because acid-base reactions are carried out in many solvents other than water. Usually an acid is considered to be any substance which can lose a proton, and a base is any substance having an unshared pair of electrons which can combine with a proton. Reaction of an acid with a base consists of the transfer of a proton from one base to another. For example when hydrogen chloride dissolves in water, the proton is transferred from the very weak base, chloride ion, to the stronger base, the water molecule.

$$H : \overset{..}{\underset{H}{O}} : \; + \; H : \overset{..}{\underset{..}{Cl}} : \quad \longrightarrow \quad \left[H : \overset{..}{\underset{H}{O}} \overset{+}{:} H \right] : \overset{..}{\underset{..}{Cl}} : \overline{}$$

Hydronium chloride

If ammonia is added to the water solution of hydrogen chloride, the proton is transferred from the water molecule to the stronger base, the ammonia molecule.

$$[H_3O^+] + : NH_3 \quad \longrightarrow \quad [NH_4^+] + H_2O$$

Similarly the hydroxide ion displaces the weaker base, ammonia, from the ammonium ion.

$$[NH_4^+] + \left[: \overset{..}{\underset{..}{O}}H \right]^- \quad \longrightarrow \quad NH_3 + H_2O$$

In general the aliphatic amines are slightly stronger bases than ammonia and form salts with acids in aqueous solution. They are liberated from their salts by stronger bases such as aqueous solutions of sodium hydroxide.

The amine salts are named either as substituted ammonium salts or as acid addition products; for example CH_3NH_3Cl may be called methylammonium chloride or trimethylamine hydrochloride. In the older literature the amine salts frequently are represented by formulas such as $CH_3NH_2 \cdot HCl$, which is equivalent to writing ammonium chloride as $NH_3 \cdot HCl$.

In the same manner as ammonia forms an insoluble salt with chloroplatinic acid, $(NH_4)_2PtCl_6$, so the amine salts, for example $(RNH_3)_2PtCl_6$, are insoluble and are used for analytical purposes. To determine the equivalent weight of an amine, it is necessary only to ignite a weighed sample of its chloroplatinate and weigh the residue of platinum.

Calcium chloride may not be used for removing water from amines, because it is solvated by them just as it is by water and ammonia. Amines usually are dried with potassium carbonate, potassium hydroxide, or barium oxide.

General Concepts of Acids and Bases

If a base is defined as a substance having an unshared pair of electrons which can combine with a proton, then differences in basicity are due to the relative availability of the unshared pair of electrons for filling the orbital of a proton. The more strongly the pair is held by the base, the weaker the basic properties of the substance; the more loosely the pair is held, the stronger the basic properties of the substance. Conversely if the pair of electrons is shared with a proton, the more strongly the pair is held by the base, the easier it is to lose a proton and the stronger the acidic properties of the substance; the more weakly the electrons are held by the base, the more difficult it is to lose a proton and the weaker the acidic properties of the substance. For example the acidity of the hydrides of carbon, nitrogen, oxygen, and fluorine increases from left to right across the periodic table. For those hydrides having an unshared pair of electrons, the basicity decreases from ammonia to water to hydrogen fluoride. Of the ions CH_3^-, NH_2^-, OH^-, and F^-, methide ion is the strongest base and fluoride ion the weakest. The order of basicity or acidity within a given series is due to the increasing charge on the nucleus of the central atom, which exerts an increasingly stronger pull on the electrons and holds them more strongly. Similarly the ions are more basic than the respective neutral molecules, because the negative charge on the ions makes the electrons less strongly held than in the case of the neutral molecules. In a series H_2O, RCH_2OH, R_2CHOH, R_3COH; or RCH_2O^-, R_2CHO^-, R_3CO^-; or NH_3, RNH_2, R_2NH, R_3N; or NH_2^-, RNH^-, R_2N^-, if R is an alkyl group, which has an electron-donating effect (p. 60), it would be expected, in the absence of steric effects (p. 117) or solvation, that in each series the basicity would increase and the acidity decrease. That other factors do play a part is shown, for example, by the order of basicity of ammonia and the methylamines in aqueous solutions which is $NH_3 < (CH_3)_3N < < CH_3NH_2 < (CH_3)_2NH$ (cf. p. 896). Substituents in the R group affect the acidity depending on whether the substituents are electron-attracting or electron-repelling. A few common types of molecules and ions are listed in the order of increasing acidity and in the order of decreasing basicity.

	INCREASING STRENGTH AS ACIDS		DECREASING STRENGTH AS BASES
Weakest	CH_4	Strongest	CH_3^-
	R_2NH, RNH_2		R_2N^-, RNH^-
	NH_3		NH_2^-
	R_3COH, R_2CHOH, RCH_2OH		R_3CO^-, R_2CHO^-, RCH_2O^-
	HOH		OH^-
	HCN		CN^-
	R_3NH^+, $R_2NH_2^+$, RNH_3^+		R_3N, R_2NH, RNH_2
	NH_4^+		NH_3
	H_2CO_3		HCO_3^-
	$RCOOH$		$RCOO^-$
	R_2OH^+, ROH_2^+		R_2O, ROH
	H_3O^+		H_2O
	$RCONH_3^+$		$RCONH_2$
	$RCOOH_2^+$		$RCOOH$
Strongest	HX	Weakest	X^-

Acids and bases related to each other, such as ammonia and ammonium ion, or hydroxide ion and water, are said to be *conjugate* to each other. Thus ammonia is the *conjugate base* of ammonium ion, and ammonium ion is the *conjugate acid* of ammonia; hydroxide ion is the conjugate base of water, and water is the conjugate acid of hydroxide ion.

This concept usually is called the Brønsted [2] theory of acids and bases although Lowry [3] had published a paper expressing similar views several months before Brønsted. It is of interest that Lewis [4] in his book on the theory of valence, which was copyrighted in 1923, the same year that the papers of Lowry and Brønsted were published, states that "the definition of an acid or a base as a substance which gives up or takes up hydrogen ion would be more general than the one used before, although it will not be universal." Thus Lewis considered the concept at least as early as Lowry and Brønsted, but discarded it in favor of a more general one.

The fundamental process being considered is the union of a proton lacking a pair of electrons with an ion or molecule that has an unshared pair of electrons.

$$H : \overset{\cdot\cdot}{\underset{H}{O}} : \ + [H^+] \ \longrightarrow \ \left[H : \overset{\cdot\cdot}{\underset{H}{O}} : H \right]^+$$

$$H : \overset{H}{\underset{H}{\overset{\cdot\cdot}{N}}} : \ + [H^+] \ \longrightarrow \ \left[H : \overset{H}{\underset{H}{\overset{\cdot\cdot}{N}}} : H \right]^+$$

$$\left[H : \overset{\cdot\cdot}{\underset{\cdot\cdot}{O}} : \right]^- + [H^+] \ \longrightarrow \ H : \overset{\cdot\cdot}{\underset{H}{O}} :$$

Entirely analogous processes, however, can take place between any ion or molecule lacking a pair of electrons in its valence shell and any ion or molecule having an unshared pair of electrons. Ammonia, for example, forms a stable complex with boron chloride.

$$H : \overset{H}{\underset{H}{\overset{\cdot\cdot}{N}}} : \ + \ \overset{Cl}{\underset{Cl}{\overset{\cdot\cdot}{B}}} : Cl \ \longrightarrow \ H : \overset{H}{\underset{H}{\overset{\cdot\cdot}{N}}} : \overset{Cl}{\underset{Cl}{\overset{\cdot\cdot}{B}}} : Cl$$

Accordingly Lewis classed boron chloride as an acid and defined an acid as a substance which can fill the valence shell of one of its atoms with an unshared pair of electrons from another molecule. In favor of this concept is the fact that substances such as boron fluoride, aluminum chloride, zinc chloride, or stannic chloride can catalyze the same types of reaction, for example polymerization of olefins (p. 63) or the formation of ethers (p. 138), as can a proton.

Lewis revived his ideas in a paper in 1938, and such compounds often are called Lewis acids. When this definition of an acid is used, it should be remembered that hydrogen chloride, sulfuric acid, acetic acid, and in fact any of the countless number of substances that from the beginning of chemistry have been called acids, are not acids under the Lewis definition. The acid as defined by Lewis is the bare unsolvated proton, which is practically incapable of existence. Moreover substances such as cupric ion, which seldom are considered as acids, are acids in the Lewis sense, because they can fill their valence shell with unshared pairs from other molecules, as when cupric ion reacts with ammonia molecules to give the cupric-ammonia complex ion.

$$Cu^{++} + 4\,NH_3 \ \longrightarrow \ \left[\begin{matrix} NH_3 \\ \cdot\cdot \\ H_3N : Cu : NH_3 \\ \cdot\cdot \\ NH_3 \end{matrix} \right]^{++}$$

[2] J. N. Brønsted (1879–1947), director of the Fysisk-Kemiske Institute of Copenhagen. His chief contributions were in the fields of electrolytes and reaction kinetics.

[3] Thomas Martin Lowry (1878–1936), professor of physical chemistry at Cambridge University. He is noted for his investigations in the fields of optical rotatory power and of proton transfer reactions.

[4] Gilbert Newton Lewis (1875–1946), professor of physical chemistry at the University of California. He is noted for his development of the electronic theory of valency, for his work in chemical thermodynamics, and for his investigations of deuterium and the absorption spectra of organic compounds.

Instead of calling all types of compounds capable of accepting a pair of electrons acids, Sidgwick[5] in his book on valency published in 1927 called them electron-acceptors, thus leaving the term acid for those compounds capable of transferring a proton to a base. Perhaps a better term than electron-acceptor for reagents, such as boron trifluoride, aluminum chloride, stannic chloride, or zinc chloride, that behave like a proton, would be **protonoid or protonoid reagent.** This term would imply properties similar to those of a proton but would not group these compounds with the substances commonly called acids.

2. **Alkylation.** Since ammonia reacts with alkyl halides to give a mixture of primary, secondary, and tertiary amines, and quaternary ammonium salt (p. 229), amines also can react with alkyl halides to give secondary or tertiary amines, or quaternary salts.

3. **Acylation.** Acyl halides, acid anhydrides, and esters react with primary and secondary amines, just as they do with ammonia, to give amides. Tertiary amines do not give amides, because they do not contain a replaceable hydrogen atom.

$$2\ RNH_2 + R'COX \longrightarrow RNHCOR' + RNH_3X$$

$$RNH_2 + (R'CO)_2O \longrightarrow RNHCOR' + R'COOH$$

$$RNH_2 + R'COOR'' \longrightarrow RNHCOR' + R''OH$$

The reaction with acyl halides requires two moles of amine, only one of which can be acylated because the second mole combines with the hydrogen halide. Although an acid is formed in the second reaction, it is a weak acid, and the salt of a weak base and a weak acid dissociates sufficiently to produce the acylated amine when heated with an excess of anhydride. Hence all of the amine can be converted into amide by this procedure.

The products formed are known as *N-substituted amides*, the *N* referring to the nitrogen atom of the amide. Thus the reaction product of methylamine with acetic anhydride, $CH_3CONHCH_3$, is called *N*-methylacetamide. Secondary amines in the above reactions yield *N,N*-disubstituted amides. *i*-Butyryl chloride and diethylamine give *N,N*-diethyl-*i*-butyramide, $(CH_3)_2CHCON(C_2H_5)_2$.

An important application of the acylation reaction is the separation of tertiary amines from a mixture with primary and secondary amines. After acetylation with acetic anhydride, the unchanged tertiary amine may be separated from the higher boiling amides by distillation, or by extraction with dilute acid. The tertiary amine is basic and forms water-soluble salts whereas the amides are neutral. Similarly acylation can be used to distinguish tertiary amines from primary or secondary amines.

4. **Isocyanide (Carbylamine) Test for Primary Amines.** When a primary amine is heated with chloroform and a few drops of an alcoholic solution of sodium hydroxide, an *isocyanide* (*isonitrile* or *carbylamine*) is formed.

$$RNH_2 + CHCl_3 + 3\ NaOH \longrightarrow RNC + 3\ NaCl + 3\ H_2O$$

Reactions involving chloroform and strong alkali appear to take place by way of the highly reactive dichloromethylene radical (p. 175).

$$CHCl_3 + KOH \longrightarrow [:CCl_2] + KCl + H_2O$$

[5] Nevil Vincent Sidgwick (1873–1952), professor of chemistry at Oxford University. His writings did much to disseminate ideas arising from the application of physical methods to organic chemical problems.

In the presence of a primary amine an inner salt is formed which resembles an ylide (p. 243).

$$R\overset{\circ\circ}{N}H_2 + [:CCl_2] \longrightarrow \left[R\overset{..}{N}H_2 \underset{-}{\overset{+}{\circ}} \overset{..}{C}Cl_2 \right]$$

Loss of two moles of hydrogen chloride gives the isocyanide.

$$\left[R\overset{..}{N}H_2 \underset{-}{\overset{+}{\circ}} \overset{..}{C}Cl_2 \right] + 2\,KOH \longrightarrow R\overset{\circ}{\underset{x}{x}}N\overset{\circ}{\underset{\circ}{\circ}}C: + 2\,KCl + 2\,H_2O$$

In the electronic structure of the isocyanide, the nitrogen atom shares with the carbon atom one pair of electrons that in the amine were owned exclusively by nitrogen. Hence nitrogen acquires a unit positive charge and the carbon atom a unit negative charge, and the formula may be written $R—N^+\!\!\equiv^-\!C$. Sometimes it is written $R—N\rightleftharpoons C$ to indicate that one pair of electrons came from the nitrogen atom. *A covalent bond in which one atom has supplied both electrons thus giving rise to a difference in charge of one electron between two atoms in the same molecule* is known as a **semipolar bond, dative bond,** or **coordinate covalence.** The ammonia-boron chloride complex (p. 236) also contains a semipolar bond.

$$\begin{array}{ccc} & H & Cl \\ & {}^{x\cdot} & {}^{\circ\cdot} \\ H & \overset{x}{\underset{\cdot x}{N}} \overset{x}{\underset{\cdot\circ}{B}} & \overset{\circ}{\underset{\cdot\circ}{Cl}}, \quad H_3\overset{+}{N}\overset{-}{—}BCl_3, \text{ or } H_3N \rightarrow BCl_3 \\ & H & Cl \end{array}$$

However, the bond formed when an ammonia or amine molecule combines with a proton is not a semipolar bond, because the proton carries with it a positive charge which neutralizes the negative charge it otherwise would have acquired by sharing half of the pair of electrons belonging to the nitrogen atom.

$$\begin{array}{c} H \\ {}^{..} \\ H:\overset{..}{N}: \\ {}^{..} \\ H \end{array} + [H^+] \longrightarrow \left[\begin{array}{c} H \\ {}^{..}\,{}^+ \\ H:\overset{..}{N}:H \\ {}^{..} \\ H \end{array} \right]$$

Thus only the nitrogen atom carries a positive charge and the four N—H bonds are all equivalent covalent bonds.

The isocyanides are characterized by a very disagreeable odor which can be detected in minute amounts and which makes the reaction suitable to distinguish primary amines from secondary and tertiary amines. When combined with the acylation reaction, which differentiates primary and secondary amines from tertiary amines, a procedure is available for distinguishing between the three types. Because of the sensitivity of the isocyanide test, secondary amines may contain enough primary amine to give a positive test. If the test is made on a sufficiently small amount of amine (less than 1 mg.), a primary amine will give a positive test, but a secondary amine containing 2 per cent primary amine as impurity will not. The sensitivity of the test naturally depends on the volatility of the isocyanide produced. A more satisfactory method for distinguishing the three types of amines is discussed on page 471.

5. **Reactions with Nitrous Acid.** The behavior of amines toward nitrous acid depends on the conditions of the reaction and on the type of amine. In the absence of a strong acid, all types of amines yield amine nitrites.

$$RNH_2 + HONO \longrightarrow RNH_3^{+-}NO_2$$

The reaction may be carried out by passing carbon dioxide into a suspension of finely divided sodium nitrite in a solution of the amine in methyl alcohol.

Di-*i*-propylammonium nitrite and dicyclohexylammonium nitrite (p. 843) are used as rust inhibitors. They volatilize slowly by dissociation into the free amine and are used in the packaging of machinery and parts.

In the presence of a strong acid, primary amines react with nitrous acid with the evolution of nitrogen. The other products of the reaction depend on the structure of the alkyl group. Usually a mixture of substances is obtained which may contain the expected alcohol or rearranged products, an olefin, an alcohol derivative such as an ether or, if the reaction is carried out in the presence of halogen acid, an alkyl halide.

$$RNH_2 + HONO \xrightarrow{\text{(HX)}} \begin{array}{l}\text{Alcohol, ether,} \\ \text{alkyl halide,} \\ \text{or olefin mixture}\end{array} + N_2 + H_2O$$

Ethylamine, for example, gives 60 per cent ethyl alcohol and traces of ethers; *n*-propylamine gives 7 per cent *n*-propyl alcohol, 32 per cent *i*-propyl alcohol, and 28 per cent propylene; *n*-butylamine gives 25 per cent *n*-butyl alcohol, 13 per cent *s*-butyl alcohol, 8 per cent *n*- and *s*-butyl chlorides, and 36 per cent 1- and 2-butenes. Although the complexity of the reaction makes it of little value for preparative purposes, the evolution of nitrogen can be made quantitative, and the reaction is used to estimate primary amino groups.

In strongly acid solutions, the nitrosating agent probably is chiefly the nitrosonium ion formed from the nitrous acid.

$$HONO + 2\,HX \longrightarrow [H_3O^+] + 2\,[X^-] + [^+NO]$$

Addition of the nitrosonium ion to the unshared pair of electrons of the amino group and loss of a proton yields the nitroso derivative which rearranges to the unstable diazohydroxide.

$$RNH_2 + [^+NO] \longrightarrow [H^+] + [RNHNO] \rightleftharpoons [RN\!\!=\!\!NOH]$$

Loss of nitrogen gives the alkyl carbonium ion.

$$[RN\!\!=\!\!NOH] + HX \longrightarrow [R^+] + N_2 + H_2O + [X^-]$$

The carbonium ion can be stabilized by loss of a proton and give the olefin, or it can, before or after rearrangement, combine with [X⁻] or abstract [OH⁻] from a water molecule or [⁻OR] from an alcohol molecule to give alkyl halides, alcohols, and ethers.

Secondary amines yield nitrosoamines, which are yellowish in color. Since they are amides of nitrous acid, they are nonbasic and insoluble in dilute acids (p. 246).

$$R_2NH + HONO \xrightarrow{[H^+]} R_2NNO + H_2O$$

Tertiary amines remain in solution as their salts, from which they can be recovered by the addition of alkali. If the reaction of tertiary amines with nitrous acid goes beyond salt formation, it is complex, the chief products being aldehydes and the nitroso derivatives of secondary amines.

6. **Conversion of Tertiary Amines to Secondary Amines** (*von Braun Reaction*[6]). Tertiary amines react with cyanogen bromide (p. 319) to give quaternary salts which decompose spontaneously into dialkylcyanamides.

$$R_3N : + Br : CN \longrightarrow [R_3\overset{+}{N}\!\!-\!\!CN]Br^- \longrightarrow R_2N\!\!-\!\!CN + RBr$$

---

[6] Julius von Braun (1875–1939), professor at Frankfurt University. His work dealt chiefly with organic nitrogen compounds. Several methods of opening nitrogen heterocycles bear his name, and he was the first to synthesize a ten-membered ring and a ring bridging the *meta* positions of a benzene ring (p. 848).

If the alkyl groups are not alike, the smallest group is eliminated preferentially as alkyl halide. Hydrolysis of the cyanamide gives the carbamic acid, which loses carbon dioxide spontaneously, forming the secondary amine (p. 232).

7. Oxidation of Tertiary Amines. When tertiary amines react with aqueous hydrogen peroxide, amine oxides are formed.

$$R_3N + H_2O_2 \longrightarrow R_3NO + H_2O$$

The mechanism of this reaction appears to be the simple displacement of hydroxide ion from a molecule of hydrogen peroxide followed by removal of a proton from the hydroxyammonium ion (p. 279).

$$R_3N: \underset{[OH^-]}{\overset{HO-OH}{\rightleftarrows}} [R_3\overset{+}{N}:OH] \underset{H_2O}{\overset{[OH^-]}{\rightleftarrows}} R_3\overset{+}{N}:\overset{-}{O}$$

Like the isocyanides (p. 238), the amine oxides contain a semipolar bond or coordinate covalency. Here it is between nitrogen and oxygen, and the formula may be written R_3N^+—^-O or $R_3N \rightarrow O$. The presence of the semipolar bond gives rise to a high dipole moment ($\mu = 4.87$ D) which in turn causes the boiling point to be abnormally high. Trimethylamine oxide of molecular weight 75 does not distill at temperatures up to 180°, where it decomposes, whereas dimethylethylamine of molecular weight 73 boils at 38°.

The amine oxides are less basic than amines but form salts with strong acids.

$$R_3N:\overset{..}{\underset{..}{O}}: + HX \longrightarrow \left[R_3\overset{+}{N}:\overset{..}{\underset{..}{O}}:H \right] X^-$$

Trimethylamine oxide has been isolated from the muscles of several varieties of marine animals such as the octopus and the spiny dogfish.

Individual Amines

Methylamine, dimethylamine, and **trimethylamine** occur in herring brine and are distributed widely in other natural products, probably as the result of the decomposition or metabolism of nitrogenous compounds. They are manufactured commercially by passing a mixture of methyl alcohol and ammonia over heated alumina.

$$CH_3OH + NH_3 \xrightarrow[400°]{Al_2O_3} \begin{array}{c} CH_3NH_2 \\ + \\ H_2O \end{array} \xrightarrow{CH_3OH} \begin{array}{c} (CH_3)_2NH \\ + \\ H_2O \end{array} \xrightarrow{CH_3OH} \begin{array}{c} (CH_3)_3N \\ + \\ H_2O \end{array}$$

This procedure has not been practical for alcohols that can be dehydrated because they yield chiefly olefins. Methylamine hydrochloride is formed along with some di- and trimethylamine hydrochlorides when a solution of ammonium chloride in formalin is evaporated to dryness.

$$NH_4Cl + 2\,HCHO \longrightarrow CH_3NH_3{}^+Cl^- + HCOOH$$

If solid ammonium chloride and paraformaldehyde are mixed and heated, trimethylamine hydrochloride is formed.

$$2\,NH_4Cl + 9\,HCHO \longrightarrow 2\,(CH_3)_3NHCl + 3\,CO_2 + 3\,H_2O$$

These reactions probably are reductive alkylations (p. 230). Trimethylamine also can be prepared by the dry distillation of beet sugar residues which contain betaine (p. 785).

$$2 \, (CH_3)_3N^+CH_2COO^- \longrightarrow 2 \, (CH_3)_3N + CH_2{=}CH_2 + 2 \, CO_2$$

Although all three amines are obtained in the commercial synthesis, dimethylamine is the most important. U.S. consumption in 1954 was over 14 million pounds. The three chief uses were for the preparation of dimethylamine salts of 2,4-D and 2,4,5-T used as herbicides (p. 514), of ultra accelerators for rubber vulcanization (p. 324), and of dimethylformamide (p. 247) used as a solvent in the spinning of acrylic fibers (p. 788). Originally dimethylamine was used chiefly as a dehairing agent for kid hides. The total quantity used for this purpose has remained about constant, but it now accounts for only about 2 per cent of production. There are numerous minor uses for methylamine but most of it is recycled. The chief use for trimethylamine is for the manufacture of choline chloride (p. 243) used in animal feeds. Excess trimethylamine may be utilized by conversion into dimethylamine and methyl chloride, or into ammonium chloride and methyl chloride.

$$(CH_3)_3NHCl + HCl \xrightarrow{\text{Heat}} (CH_3)_2NH_2Cl + CH_3Cl$$

$$(CH_3)_3NHCl + 3 \, HCl \xrightarrow{\text{Heat}} NH_4Cl + 3 \, CH_3Cl$$

n-**Butylamines** are prepared commercially from butyl chloride and ammonia, and the **amyl amines** from amyl chlorides and ammonia. All have a wide variety of uses, for example as antioxidants and corrosion inhibitors, absorbents for acid gases, and in the manufacture of oil-soluble soaps. **Higher normal amines** are made by the reduction of nitriles obtained from fat acids through the amides (p. 254).

QUATERNARY AMMONIUM SALTS

The end-product of the reaction of ammonia or of an amine with an alkyl halide is a quaternary ammonium salt (p. 229). The properties of these salts are quite unlike those of the amine salts, since the nitrogen no longer carries a hydrogen atom. They do not dissociate into amine and acid on heating, and strong alkalies have no effect on them. When a solution of a quaternary ammonium halide is shaken with silver hydroxide, or when a quaternary ammonium acid sulfate solution reacts with barium hydroxide, the insoluble silver halide or barium sulfate precipitates leaving the quaternary ammonium hydroxide in solution.

$$[R_4N^+]X^- + AgOH \longrightarrow [R_4N^+]OH^- + AgX$$

$$[R_4N^+]SO_4H^- + Ba(OH)_2 \longrightarrow [R_4N^+]OH^- + BaSO_4 + H_2O$$

The quaternary ammonium hydroxide dissociates completely into its ions in aqueous solution, and hence it has the same basic strength in water as sodium or potassium hydroxide. For example glass is etched by solutions of quaternary ammonium hydroxides just as it is by solutions of sodium hydroxide. When a quaternary ammonium salt is decomposed by heat, it dissociates into tertiary amine and alkyl halide. In other words the reaction for the formation of quaternary salts can be reversed at high temperatures.

$$[R_4N^+]X^- \xrightarrow{\text{Heat}} R_3N + RX$$

An analogous reaction can be used for the esterification of sterically hindered acids. The acid is converted to the quaternary ammonium salt which is decomposed by heat.

$$[(CH_3)_4N^+][\overline{O}OCCR_3] \longrightarrow (CH_3)_3N + CH_3OCOCR_3$$

When tetramethylammonium hydroxide is heated, the products are trimethylamine and methyl alcohol.

$$[(CH_3)_4N^+]OH^- \longrightarrow (CH_3)_3N + CH_3OH$$

If an alkyl group capable of forming an olefin is present, a tertiary amine, olefin, and water are formed.

$$[(CH_3)_3\overset{+}{N}C_2H_5]OH^- \longrightarrow (CH_3)_3N + C_2H_4 + H_2O$$

This reaction is useful for introducing the double bond into complex compounds and for opening the rings of nitrogen heterocycles (p. 621).

In the dissociation reactions of the quaternary compounds the negative ion merely displaces the amine from the ammonium ion.

$$: \overset{..}{\underset{..}{X}} \overset{-}{:} + \begin{bmatrix} R \\ R : \overset{..}{\underset{..}{N}} \overset{+}{:} R \\ R \end{bmatrix} \longrightarrow \overset{.}{.} \overset{..}{\underset{..}{X}} : R + \begin{matrix} R \\ : \overset{..}{\underset{..}{N}} : R \\ R \end{matrix}$$

$$H : \overset{..}{\underset{..}{O}} \overset{-}{:} + \begin{bmatrix} CH_3 \\ CH_3 . \overset{..}{\underset{..}{N}} \overset{+}{:} CH_3 \\ CH_3 \end{bmatrix} \longrightarrow H : O : CH_3 + \begin{matrix} CH_3 \\ \overset{..}{\underset{..}{N}} : CH_3 \\ CH_3 \end{matrix}$$

However, when a group is present which is capable of forming an olefin, a reaction analogous to the formation of an olefin from an alkyl halide takes place (p. 118). The hydroxide ion removes a proton from the β carbon with simultaneous elimination of the tertiary amine.

$$[CH_3CH_2\overset{+}{N}(CH_3)_3] \underset{H_2O}{\overset{[OH^-]}{\rightleftharpoons}} [\overline{C}H_2CH_2 : \overset{+}{N}(CH_3)_3] \longrightarrow CH_2{=}CH_2 + : N(CH_3)_3$$

The positive charge on the nitrogen atom facilitates the removal of a proton just as the electron-attraction of a halogen atom does in an alkyl halide.

A characteristic feature of the decomposition of quaternary ammonium hydroxides is that if there is more than one β carbon atom and more than one type of β hydrogen is available, the order of ease of elimination is primary > secondary > tertiary (*Hofmann rule*). For example, the decomposition of s-butyltrimethylammonium hydroxide yields 1-butene rather than 2-butene.

$$\begin{bmatrix} CH_3 \\ | \\ CH_3CH_2\overset{+}{C}H\overset{+}{N}(CH_3)_3 \end{bmatrix}[OH^-] \overset{Heat}{\longrightarrow} CH_3CH_2CH{=}CH_2 + N(CH_3)_3 + H_2O$$

This course is the opposite of that which takes place in the dehydration of alcohols or in the removal of halogen acid from alkyl halides, where the order for removal of hydrogen is tertiary > secondary > primary (*Saytzev rule*), although a similar type of mechanism is proposed in all three cases.

Choline chloride is trimethyl-(2-hydroxyethyl)-ammonium chloride, $[(CH_3)_3\overset{+}{N}CH_2CH_2OH]$ Cl$^-$. Its quaternary ammonium ion, commonly called **choline**, is an extremely important factor in biological processes and must be supplied by the diet of the animal organism. It has been shown to be a factor which (*1*) is necessary for growth, (*2*) affects fat transport and carbohydrate metabolism, (*3*) is involved in protein metabolism, (*4*) prevents hemorrhagic kidney disintegration, and (*5*) prevents the development of fatty livers in depancreatinized dogs. It also is the precursor in the animal organism of acetylcholine ion, $[(CH_3)_3\overset{+}{N}CH_2CH_2OCOCH_3]$, commonly called **acetylcholine**, which is extremely important in controlling the functions of the body.

Nerve impulses arriving at the end of a motor nerve liberate a chemical which transmits the impulse to another nerve or muscle fiber by acting on the dendrons of a postganglionic fiber at a ganglion cell or on the end-plate region at the synapse with a muscle cell. One of these chemical transmitters is acetylcholine and the other, called *sympathin*, is a mixture of epinephrine and norepinephrine (p. 529) in varying amounts. Sympathin stimulates muscular activity whereas acetylcholine causes relaxation. The action of acetylcholine is confined to the site where it is liberated, because the blood contains an esterase (an enzyme that catalyzes the hydrolysis of esters) which almost immediately converts acetylcholine into the practically inactive choline. The most toxic substances known (p. 520) are those which deactivate acetylcholine esterase and hence permit the distribution of acetylcholine throughout the organism, thus leading to total muscular relaxation and paralysis.

Excessive activity of the sympathetic nervous system can lead to high blood pressure and nervous irritability. It can be relieved by blocking the function of the nerve ganglia by the administration of quaternary ammonium salts. **Tetraethylammonium bromide** was used first for this purpose but has been replaced by **hexamethonium** (*hexamethylene-bis-triethylammonium bromide*), $\left[(C_2H_5)_3\overset{+}{N}(CH_2)_6\overset{+}{N}(C_2H_5)_3\right]Br_2{}^-$. **Succinylcholine**, $\left[(CH_3)_3\overset{+}{N}CH_2CH_2OCOCH_2{}^-\right]_2$- 2 I$^-$, is used instead of curare as an adjuvant in ether anesthesia (p. 652).

Quaternary ammonium salts in which one of the alkyl groups attached to nitrogen is a long chain hydrocarbon group, such as cetyltrimethylammonium chloride, $[C_{16}H_{33}\overset{+}{N}(CH_3)_3]$ Cl$^-$, have properties similar to soaps and are known as *invert soaps* or *cationic detergents*, because the detergent action resides in a positive ion rather than in a negative ion as is the case with ordinary soaps. Many of these invert soaps have high germicidal action.

Many attempts have been made to obtain pentacovalent nitrogen compounds but without success. Thus the reaction of a quaternary ammonium salt with an organolithium compound (p. 889) might be expected to replace the halogen by an organic group.

$$[(CH_3)_4N^+]Br^- + RLi \longrightarrow (CH_3)_4NR + LiBr$$

Instead a proton is removed to give an inner salt which is called an *ylide*. Thus tetramethylammonium bromide yields **trimethylammonium methylide**.

$$[(CH_3)_3\overset{+}{N}CH_3][Br^-] + RLi \longrightarrow (CH_3)_3\overset{+}{N}\overset{..}{—}\overset{-}{CH_2} + RH + LiBr$$

The structure of the ylide is indicated by its reaction with methyl iodide to give trimethylethylammonium iodide.

$$(CH_3)_3\overset{+}{N}\overset{..}{—}\overset{-}{CH_2} + CH_3I \longrightarrow [(CH_3)_3\overset{+}{N}CH_2CH_3][I^-]$$

AMIDES

The monoacyl derivatives of ammonia, primary amines and secondary amines, having the general formula $RCONH_2$, $RCONHR$, or $RCONR_2$, are known as *amides*. Diacyl derivatives of ammonia, $(RCO)_2NH$, and of primary amines, $(RCO)_2NR$, also are known and are called *imides*. Except for cyclic imides (pp. 553, 797) their preparation usually is more difficult because the first acyl group greatly reduces the basicity of the nitrogen. The preparation of triacyl-amines is still more difficult. From structural theory, isomeric forms of the amides should be possible, but such isomers are tautomeric (p. 207) and have not been isolated.

$$R-\overset{\overset{\textstyle O}{\|}}{C}-NH_2 \; \rightleftarrows \; R-\overset{\overset{\textstyle OH}{|}}{C}=NH$$

Preparation

Most of the methods for preparing amides have been discussed under the reactions of acids and acid derivatives and are merely summarized here.

1. From Acyl Halides and Ammonia or Amines (pp. 161, 237).

$$RCOCl + 2\,NH_3 \longrightarrow RCONH_2 + NH_4Cl$$

$$+ 2\,H_2NR \longrightarrow RCONHR + RNH_3Cl$$

$$+ 2\,HNR_2 \longrightarrow RCONR_2 + R_2NH_2Cl$$

These reactions go to completion at room temperature. Two moles of ammonia or amine are required per mole of acyl halide because of the inappreciable dissociation of the amine halide at the temperature of reaction.

2. From Acid Anhydrides and Ammonia or Amines (pp. 163, 237).

$$(RCO)_2O + 2\,NH_3 \longrightarrow RCONH_2 + RCOONH_4$$

$$+ 2\,H_2NR \longrightarrow RCONHR + RCOONH_3R$$

$$+ 2\,HNR_2 \longrightarrow RCONR_2 + RCOONH_2R_2$$

Although these reactions take place as indicated in the presence of an excess of ammonia or amine, it is possible to convert all of an amine into amide in the presence of an excess of anhydride because of the ease of dissociation of the ammonium carboxylates.

$$RCOONH_3R' \; \rightleftarrows \; RCOOH + H_2NR'$$

$$(RCO)_2O + H_2NR' \longrightarrow RCONHR' + RCOOH$$

Because of their greater basicity, amines react with acetic anhydride much more rapidly than does water. Hence amines can be acetylated in aqueous solution.

3. From Esters and Ammonia or Amines (pp. 171, 237).

$$RCOOR' + NH_3 \longrightarrow RCONH_2 + HOR'$$

$$+ H_2NR \longrightarrow RCONHR + HOR'$$

$$+ HNR_2 \longrightarrow RCONR_2 + HOR'$$

The rate of ammonolysis of an ester, like the rate of hydrolysis (p. 170), depends on the amount of branching in the alkyl groups of the ester. It also varies with the structure of the amine. The reaction of esters with amines is catalyzed by ammonium chloride.

4. **From Ammonium Salts by Thermal Decomposition** (p. 156).

$$RCOONH_4 \xrightarrow{\text{Heat}} RCONH_2 + H_2O$$

$$RCOONH_3R \xrightarrow{\text{Heat}} RCONHR + H_2O$$

$$RCOONH_2R_2 \xrightarrow{\text{Heat}} RCONR_2 + H_2O$$

Water is removed at the temperature of decomposition, forcing the reaction to completion. The reaction usually is carried out in the presence of an excess of the carboxylic acid to minimize the dissociation of the salt.

$$RCOONH_4 \rightleftharpoons RCOOH + NH_3$$

5. **From Other Amides by Acid Exchange.** When amides are heated with carboxylic acids, an exchange reaction takes place leading to an equilibrium mixture of two amides and two acids.

$$RCONH_2 + R'COOH \rightleftharpoons RCOOH + R'CONH_2$$

If urea, the amide of carbonic acid (p. 310), is heated with a carboxylic acid the unstable carbamic acid that is formed decomposes, and the reaction goes to completion.

$$CO(NH_2)_2 + RCOOH \rightleftharpoons RCONH_2 + [H_2NCOOH] \longrightarrow NH_3 + CO_2$$

6. **Other Methods.** Amides can be prepared also by the partial hydrolysis of nitriles (p. 253) and by the addition of olefins to nitriles (p. 254).

Nomenclature

The simple amides are named by replacing *ic acid* or *oic acid* in the name of the acid by *amide*. Thus $HCONH_2$ is formamide or methanamide, and $(CH_3)_2CHCONH_2$ is *i*-butyramide or methylpropanamide. Amides derived from amines are named as nitrogen substitution products; for example $CH_3CONHCH_3$ is *N*-methylacetamide, or *N*-methylethanamide.

Physical Properties

Most amides containing the $CONH_2$ group are solids. Formamide melts at 2°. The *N*-alkyl substituted amides of the aliphatic acids usually are liquids. Amides are associated by proton bonding and have high boiling points. Since they also form proton bonds with hydroxylic solvents and other oxygenated molecules, amides of monocarboxylic acids containing five carbon atoms or less are soluble in water. The liquid amides are excellent solvents for other organic compounds.

Reactions

1. **Basic and Acidic Properties.** In contrast to ammonia and the amines, the amides do not form salts that are stable in aqueous solution; that is, the replacement of a hydrogen atom of the ammonia molecule by an acyl group gives a compound that is a weaker base than water. This effect is in harmony with the effect of replacement of a hydrogen atom of a water molecule by an acyl group. The carbonyl group exerts an electron-attracting effect which increases the ease of ionization of the remaining proton of carboxylic acids and decreases the ability of the nitrogen atom of amides to share its unshared pair. If two hydrogen atoms of ammonia are replaced by acyl groups, the attraction for electrons is sufficient to permit the remaining hydrogen to be removed as a proton by strong bases in aqueous solution. In other words the imides are weak acids.

$$(RCO)_2NH + NaOH \longrightarrow (RCO)_2N^{-+}Na + H_2O$$

2. **Hydrolysis.** The hydrolysis of amides produces the acid and the amine. Like the hydrolysis of esters, the reaction is catalyzed by both acids and bases. However, with esters only the basic catalyst reacts with one of the products, whereas in the hydrolysis of the amides both the acid and basic catalyst react with one of the products, thus causing both reactions to go to completion.

$$RCONH_2 + NaOH \longrightarrow RCOONa + NH_3$$

$$RCONH_2 + HCl + H_2O \longrightarrow RCOOH + NH_4Cl$$

The mechanism of the acid-catalyzed hydrolysis of amides appears to differ from that of esters (p. 168) in that no oxygen exchange with water takes place during the hydrolysis. It is postulated that ammonia is displaced directly from the protonated amide.

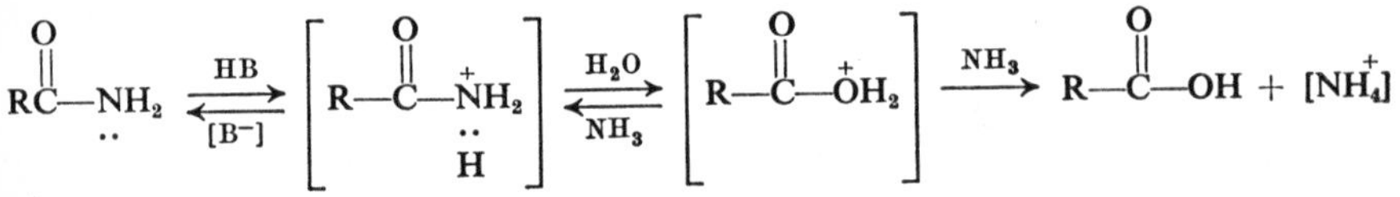

An objection to this postulate is that the proton would be expected to add to the oxygen atom of the amide rather than the nitrogen (p. 312).

Oxygen exchange during basic hydrolysis indicates that the mechanism is analogous to the basic hydrolysis of esters.

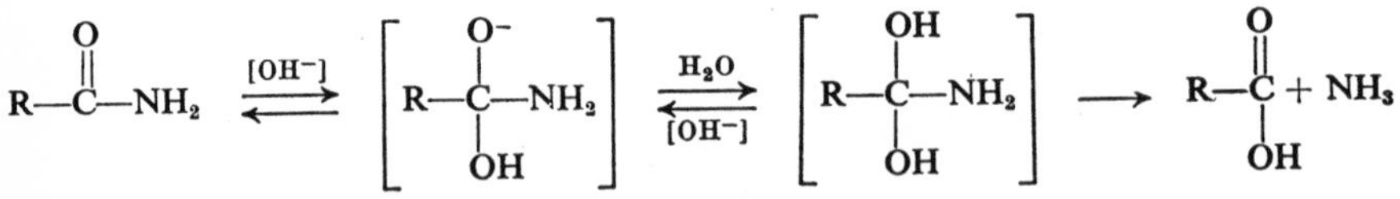

The acid reacts irreversibly with hydroxide ion to give the salt.

$$RCOOH + [OH^-] \longrightarrow [RCOO^-] + H_2O$$

3. **Dehydration.** Distillation of a mixture of an unsubstituted amide with a strong dehydrating agent yields an alkyl cyanide (p. 250).

$$RCONH_2 + P_2O_5 \longrightarrow RC{\equiv}N + 2 HPO_3$$

$$RCONH_2 + SOCl_2 \longrightarrow RC{\equiv}N + SO_2 + 2 HCl$$

4. Reaction with Nitrous Acid or Dinitrogen Tetroxide. Like primary amines, unsubstituted amides react with aqueous nitrous acid with evolution of nitrogen.

$$RCONH_2 + HONO \longrightarrow RCOOH + N_2$$

Mono-*N*-substituted amides yield nitroso derivatives.

$$RCONHR + HONO \longrightarrow RCONR + H_2O$$
$$| $$
$$NO$$

This reaction is slow and takes place only if the *N*-alkyl group is primary. Dinitrogen tetroxide, N_2O_4, reacts rapidly even at $0°$, and the *N*-alkyl group may be secondary as well as primary. Sodium acetate is added to prevent reversal by the nitric acid.

$$RCONHR + N_2O_4 \rightleftharpoons RCONR + HNO_3$$
$$|$$
$$NO$$

$$HNO_3 + NaOCOCH_3 \longrightarrow NaNO_3 + CH_3COOH$$

When *N*-alkyl-*N*-nitroso amides are heated they decompose to give chiefly the ester and nitrogen.

$$RCONR' \xrightarrow{\text{Heat}} RCOOR' + N_2$$
$$|$$
$$NO$$

Since the ester can be hydrolyzed to the alcohol, a convenient path is provided for converting a primary amine, $R'NH_2$, into the corresponding alcohol, $R'OH$.

5. Hofmann Rearrangement. One of the methods for the preparation of pure primary amines is the reaction of amides with alkaline solutions of sodium hypochlorite or hypobromite (p. 231).

$$RCONH_2 + NaOX + 2\,NaOH \longrightarrow RNH_2 + Na_2CO_3 + NaX + H_2O$$

Actually several steps are involved, namely halogenation of the amide, removal of halogen acid and rearrangement to the isocyanate (p. 317), and hydrolysis of the isocyanate to the amine and carbonic acid.

$$RCONH_2 + NaOX \longrightarrow RCONHX + NaOH$$

$$RCONHX + NaOH \longrightarrow R-N{=}C{=}O + NaX + H_2O$$
An isocyanate

$$R-N{=}C{=}O + 2\,NaOH \longrightarrow RNH_2 + Na_2CO_3$$

Although the series of reactions taking place is rather complex, it can be carried out in a single operation by adding halogen to a mixture of amide and alkali. The reaction is of some importance not only because it can be used to prepare primary amines but because it provides a method for removing one carbon atom from a carbon chain. A limitation of the reaction as a preparative method for primary amines is discussed on p. 231.

6. Reaction with Grignard Reagents. Amides having hydrogen on nitrogen react with Grignard reagents to give the hydrocarbon, but the *N,N*-dialkyl amides add the reagent to the carbonyl group. Hydrolysis of the addition product yields an aldehyde-ammonia, which loses dialkylamine to give an aldehyde or ketone.

$$RMgX + HCN(CH_3)_2 \longrightarrow RCHN(CH_3)_2 \xrightarrow{2HX} RCHO + (CH_3)_2NH_2Cl + MgX_2$$
$$\begin{array}{cc} \| & | \\ O & OMgX \end{array}$$

$$RMgX + R'CN(CH_3)_2 \longrightarrow R\!-\!CN(CH_3)_2 \xrightarrow{2HX} RCOR' + (CH_3)_2NH_2Cl + MgX_2$$
$$\begin{array}{cc} \| & / \backslash \\ O & R' \quad OMgX \end{array}$$

Most of the simple aliphatic amides are of little commercial importance. **N, N-Dimethylformamide and N, N-dimethylacetamide** are used as solvents for spinning acrylic fibers (p. 788). Since many amides are solids that can be crystallized readily and have characteristic melting points, they are used as derivatives for the identification of carboxylic acids, esters, acid halides, and nitriles. Of the more complex amides, urea and its derivatives (p. 310) are the most important.

IMIDO ESTERS AND AMIDINES

Although the difference in basicity between oxygen and nitrogen prevents the existence of an appreciable amount of the tautomeric form of the amides, $RC\!-\!OH$, the corresponding *O*-alkyl derivatives, $RC\!-\!OR$, are known and are
$$\begin{array}{cc} \| & \| \\ NH & NH \end{array}$$
called **imido esters** (less correctly *imino esters* or *imido ethers*). They are prepared most readily by passing dry hydrogen chloride into a mixture of an alkyl cyanide and an alcohol in ether solution, when the imido ester hydrochloride precipitates.

$$RC\!\equiv\!N + HOR' + HCl \longrightarrow \left[\begin{array}{c} {}^{+}NH_2 \\ \| \\ RC\!-\!OR' \end{array} \right] Cl^-$$

If the hydrochloride is neutralized with sodium carbonate in the presence of ether, the free imido ester is formed and goes into solution in the ether.

$$\left[\begin{array}{c} {}^{+}NH_2 \\ \| \\ RC\!-\!OR' \end{array} \right] Cl^- + Na_2CO_3 \longrightarrow \begin{array}{c} NH \\ \| \\ RC\!-\!OR' \end{array} + NaCl + NaHCO_3$$

Addition of water hydrolyzes the imido ester hydrochloride to an ester.

$$\left[\begin{array}{c} {}^{+}NH_2 \\ \| \\ RC\!-\!OR' \end{array} \right] [Cl^-] + H_2O \longrightarrow \begin{array}{c} O \\ \| \\ RC\!-\!OR' \end{array} + NH_4Cl$$

When the hydrochloride is warmed with an excess of alcohol, an orthoester (p. 175) is formed.

$$\left[\begin{array}{c} {}^{+}NH_2 \\ \| \\ RC\!-\!OR' \end{array} \right] [Cl^-] + 2\,HOR' \longrightarrow \begin{array}{c} OR' \\ | \\ RC\!-\!OR' \\ | \\ OR' \end{array} + NH_4Cl$$

Reaction of an imido ester with ammonia yields an **amidine.**

$$\begin{array}{c} NH \\ \| \\ RC\!-\!OR' \end{array} + NH_3 \longrightarrow \begin{array}{c} NH \\ \| \\ RC\!-\!NH_2 \end{array} + HOR'$$

The amidine hydrochlorides can be obtained by heating alkyl cyanides with ammonium chloride.

$$RC\equiv N + NH_4Cl \longrightarrow \begin{bmatrix} \overset{+}{N}H_2 \\ \parallel \\ RC-NH_2 \end{bmatrix} [Cl^-]$$

In contrast to the amides, which are very weak bases having a basic dissociation constant of about 10^{-15} (p. 246), the amidines are strong bases with a basic dissociation constant of about 10^{-2}. The high stability of the salt has been explained as the result of its high resonance energy, the contributing resonance structures being identical.

$$\left\{ \begin{array}{cc} \overset{+}{N}H_2 & NH_2 \\ \parallel & | \\ RC-NH_2 & RC=\overset{+}{N}H_2 \end{array} \right\}$$

In the amides resonance contributes very little to the stability of the cation, because the possible structures are not identical.

$$\left\{ \begin{array}{cc} \overset{+}{O}H & OH \\ \parallel & | \\ RC-NH_2 & RC=\overset{+}{N}H_2 \end{array} \right\}$$

Any resonance effect is greatly outweighed by the inductive effect of the oxygen atom (p. 153). In neither the amides nor the amidines is there any tendency for a proton to combine with an NH_2 group, since the resonance of the amide or amidine group would be destroyed without producing a more highly stabilized ion (p. 312).

ALKYL CYANIDES (NITRILES)

Nomenclature

The alkyl cyanides, $RC\equiv N$, are alkyl derivatives of hydrogen cyanide and generally are named as if they were salts; for example CH_3CN is called methyl cyanide. Organic cyanides also are called *nitriles*. The common names are derived from the common names of the corresponding carboxylic acids. They are formed by dropping *ic acid* and adding *nitrile* with a connective *o*; for example methyl cyanide, which yields acetic acid on hydrolysis, is called acetonitrile. In the Geneva system the longest chain having the nitrile group as a terminal group determines the parent name. Thus $CH_3(CH_2)_{11}CN$ is tridecanenitrile. When it is necessary to express the $C\equiv N$ group as a substituent, it is called *cyano*; for example, $N\equiv CCH_2COOH$ is cyanoacetic acid.

Preparation

The common methods of preparation already have been mentioned in connection with the reactions of alkyl halides, amides, and aldoximes.

√ 1. **From Alkyl Halides (or Sulfates) and Sodium Cyanide.**

$$RX + NaCN \longrightarrow RCN + NaX \quad \checkmark$$
$$R_2SO_4 + NaCN \longrightarrow RCN + ROSO_3Na$$
$$ROSO_3Na + NaCN \longrightarrow RCN + Na_2SO_4$$

The reactions are carried out in alcoholic or aqueous alcoholic solution. Tertiary alkyl cyanides cannot be prepared by this reaction because tertiary halides lose hydrogen halide to give olefin, sodium halide, and hydrogen cyanide. They may be prepared by the reaction of the halide with mercuric cyanide, by the alkylation of primary or secondary alkyl cyanides (p. 254), or by the addition of hydrogen cyanide to olefins (p. 255).

In the reaction of alkyl halides with sodium cyanide, a small amount of isocyanide, $R\overset{+}{N}\!\!\equiv\!\!\overset{-}{C}$ (p. 256), also is formed. The reactive agent is cyanide ion, (: C≡N :)⁻, which has unshared electrons on both carbon and nitrogen. Hence when it displaces the halide ion from the alkyl halide, either the carbon atom or the nitrogen atom may form a bond with the alkyl group. The latter process leads to the formation of isocyanide (cf. p. 259).

$$(: C\!\!\equiv\!\!N :)^- + R : \overset{..}{\underset{..}{X}} : \longrightarrow : C\!\!\equiv\!\!N : R + : \overset{..}{\underset{..}{X}} :^-$$

The isocyanide may be removed from the mixture by making use of the fact that it is more readily hydrolyzed than the cyanide.

2. **Dehydration of Amides.** Amides may be converted to nitriles by heating with dehydrating agents. Either phosphorus pentoxide or thionyl chloride is the usual reagent.

$$RCONH_2 + P_2O_5 \xrightarrow{\text{Heat}} RCN + 2\,HPO_3$$

$$RCONH_2 + SOCl_2 \xrightarrow{\text{Heat}} RCN + SO_2 + 2\,HCl$$

When phosphorus pentoxide is used, the nitrile is distilled from the reaction mixture. If thionyl chloride is used, the mixture is heated under a reflux condenser, and sulfur dioxide and hydrogen chloride are evolved. Amides may be dehydrated also by passing the vapor over a catalyst such as boron phosphate at 350° (p. 799) or alumina at 425°. The higher carboxylic acids or their amides can be converted quantitatively into nitriles by heating at 300° in a stream of ammonia with continuous removal of the water that is formed.

3. **Dehydration of Aldoximes.** The usual reagent for removing the elements of water from an aldoxime is acetic anhydride.

$$RCH\!\!=\!\!NOH + (CH_3CO)_2O \xrightarrow{\text{Heat}} RC\!\!\equiv\!\!N + 2\,CH_3COOH$$

Other dehydrating agents such as phosphorus pentoxide, phosphorus pentachloride, and phosphorus oxychloride may be used.

4. **Addition of Hydrogen Cyanide to Olefins.** Hydrogen cyanide adds to olefins in the gas phase at 350° in the presence of activated alumina, or homogeneously at 130° in the presence of dicobalt octacarbonyl (p. 904). Thus isobutylene gives *t*-butyl cyanide (*pivalonitrile*).

$$RCH\!\!=\!\!CH_2 + HCN \longrightarrow \underset{\underset{CH_3}{|}}{RCHCN}$$

The yields are best from olefins having a terminal double bond.

Physical Properties

Nitriles have abnormally high boiling points. Thus ethyl cyanide of molecular weight 55 boils at 97°, whereas trimethylamine of molecular weight 59 boils at +4°.

The abnormally high boiling points of nitriles in the absence of the possibility of proton bonding may be ascribed to the large dipole moment of the molecule. Table 15 lists a group of compounds of approximately the same molecular

TABLE 15

BOILING POINTS AND DIPOLE MOMENTS

SUBSTANCE	FORMULA	MOL. WT.	B.P.	μ	μ^2
n-Butane	$CH_3(CH_2)_2CH_3$	58	0.6	0	0
Trimethylamine	$(CH_3)_3N$	59	3.8	0.6	0.4
Methyl ethyl ether	$CH_3OC_2H_5$	60	6.4	1.2	1.4
Acetone	CH_3COCH_3	58	56.5	2.8	7.8
Ethyl isocyanide	$C_2H_5N{\equiv}C$	55	78.0	2.9	8.4
Ethyl cyanide	$C_2H_5C{\equiv}N$	55	97.0	3.3	10.9

weight which cannot form proton bonds. The differences in their boiling points therefore should be caused chiefly by differences in dipole association. The boiling points do rise with increasing dipole moment. An even more striking correlation appears on plotting the data. Figure 46 shows that the rise in

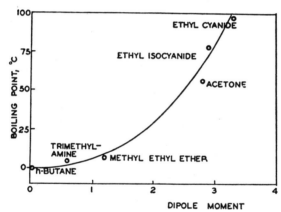

Fig. 46. Dependence of the boiling point on the dipole moment of the molecule in the absence of proton bonding.

boiling point is not directly proportional to the increase in dipole moment, but rises much more rapidly. Since the attraction is between two molecules, it would not be expected to be proportional to the dipole moment of a single molecule, but to the product of the dipole moments of two molecules. In Fig. 47, where the square of the dipole moment is plotted against the boiling point, a fairly satisfactory straight line is obtained, in spite of the numerous minor factors that have some effect.

Cyanides are less soluble in water than amines having the same number of carbon atoms. Hydrogen cyanide and acetonitrile are miscible with water, and propionitrile is fairly soluble, but the higher nitriles are only slightly soluble. The decreased tendency to form proton bonds with water can be ascribed to the reduced basicity of the nitrogen atom (reduced tendency to share the unshared pair of electrons). The cyanides do not dissolve in aqueous acids because they are too weakly basic to form salts.

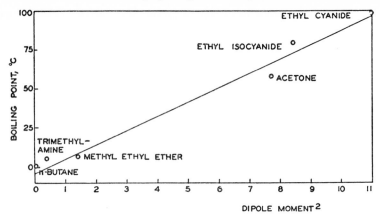

Fig. 47. Dependence of the boiling point on the square of the dipole moment.

The statement that alkyl cyanides are weaker bases than amines can be expressed in another way, namely that the conjugate acid of the nitrile, $RC\overset{+}{\equiv}N : H$, is a stronger acid than the conjugate acid of the amine, $R_3\overset{+}{N} : H$. This behavior undoubtedly is related to the increased acidity of acetylene compared with that of ethane (p. 132). Considering only inductive effects, the accumulation of electrons between two atoms should make electrons more readily available on the atoms and hence reduce the tendency to lose a proton and increase the tendency to share an unshared pair. However, in the cyanides, as in acetylene, the increased acidity coincides with a change in bond type from sp^3—s to sp—s (p. 129); that is, in the amine salt the nitrogen-hydrogen bond is formed by the overlapping of an sp^3 orbital of nitrogen with an s orbital of hydrogen, whereas in the nitrile salt the overlap is between an sp orbital and an s orbital. Moreover just as ethylene is more acidic than ethane, so the imino compounds, RCH=NR, are less basic than the corresponding secondary amines, RCH_2NHR, and the oximes, RCH=NOH, are less basic than the hydroxylamines, RCH_2NHOH. The increase in acidity or decrease in basicity here coincides with a change in bond type from sp^2—s to sp—s. That the effect is not merely coincident with the presence of a double or triple bond is indicated by the fact that the basicity of ketones, $R_2C=O$, is not greatly different from that of secondary alcohols, R_2CHOH. In both $R_2C=O : H$ and $R_2CH\overset{+}{O} : H$ the oxygen-hydrogen bonds are of

the p—s type. Quantum mechanical calculations indicate that for triply bound atoms, a fourth pair of electrons is localized about the atom and hence not readily available for covalent bond formation (p. 132).

Physiological Action

Pure alkyl cyanides have a pleasant odor and are only slightly toxic. Usually, however, they are contaminated with the disagreeably odorous and highly toxic isocyanides. α-Hydroxy and α-amino nitriles are toxic, probably because of easy loss of hydrogen cyanide.

Reactions

The more important reactions of alkyl cyanides already have been used to prepare other compounds.

1. **Hydrolysis to Acids.**

$$RCN + 2\,H_2O + HCl \longrightarrow RCOOH + NH_4Cl$$
$$RCN + H_2O + NaOH \longrightarrow RCOONa + NH_3$$

The mechanisms of acid- and base-catalyzed hydrolyses of nitriles undoubtedly are very similar to the acid- and base-catalyzed hydrolyses of esters (p. 171).

Acid-catalyzed hydrolysis:

$$
RC{\equiv}N \underset{[:B^-]}{\overset{HB}{\rightleftarrows}} [RC{\equiv}\overset{+}{N}H] \overset{HOH}{\rightleftarrows} \left[\begin{array}{c} R-C{=}NH \\ \overset{+}{:}O:H \\ H \end{array}\right] \underset{HB}{\overset{[:B^-]}{\rightleftarrows}} \left[\begin{array}{c} R-C{=}NH \\ :OH \end{array}\right] \underset{[:B^-]}{\overset{HB}{\rightleftarrows}}
$$

$$
\left\{\begin{array}{ccc} H & & H \\ R-C{=}\overset{+}{N}:H & \longleftrightarrow & R-C-\overset{..}{N}:H \\ :OH & & {}^+OH \end{array}\right\} \underset{HB}{\overset{[:B^-]}{\rightleftarrows}} \begin{array}{c} R-C-NH_2 \\ \| \\ O \end{array}
$$

Base-catalyzed hydrolysis:

$$
RC{\equiv}N \overset{[:OH^-]}{\rightleftarrows} \left[\begin{array}{c} R-C{=}N: \\ :OH \end{array}\right]^- \underset{[OH^-]}{\overset{HOH}{\rightleftarrows}} \left[\begin{array}{c} R-C{=}NH \\ :OH \end{array}\right] \underset{HOH}{\overset{[OH^-]}{\rightleftarrows}}
$$

$$
\left\{\begin{array}{ccc} RC{=}NH & \longleftrightarrow & R-C-NH^- \\ :O:{}^- & & :O: \end{array}\right\} \underset{[OH^-]}{\overset{HOH}{\rightleftarrows}} \begin{array}{c} R-C-NH_2 \\ \| \\ O \end{array}
$$

The mechanism of the hydrolysis of the intermediate amides is discussed on page 246. The rate of hydrolysis of the amides usually is so much faster than the rate of formation from the nitrile that the amides cannot be isolated as intermediates under the usual conditions of hydrolysis. For example, the rate of hydrolysis of formamide is 14,000 times faster than the rate of formation from hydrogen cyanide. Exceptions are the *t*-alkyl cyanides, hydrolysis of which stops at.the amide stage. Amides can be isolated from other alkyl cyanides by heating them with one mole of water at 200° in the absence of added catalysts, or by hydrolysis with alkaline hydrogen peroxide.

A peculiarity of the acid-catalyzed hydrolysis is of interest. At low concentrations all strong acids are equally effective as catalysts, the rate being governed by the hydronium ion concentration. At high concentrations, however, hydrogen bromide is only one tenth as effective as hydrogen chloride, and sulfuric acid is a very poor catalyst. Therefore the anion of the acid must play a part as well as the proton, and the proposed mechanism probably is valid only at low acid concentrations.

2. **Hydrolysis to Amides.** Alkaline hydrogen peroxide converts nitriles into amides in excellent yields.

$$
RCN + H_2O_2 \xrightarrow{\text{NaOH}} RCONH_2 + \tfrac{1}{2}O_2
$$

Hydroperoxide ion is the effective reagent in this reaction. The proposed steps are

$$
H_2O_2 \underset{H_2O}{\overset{[OH^-]}{\rightleftarrows}} [HO_2^-] \xrightarrow{RC{\equiv}N} \begin{array}{c} RC{=}N^- \\ | \\ O-OH \end{array} \underset{[OH^-]}{\overset{H_2O}{\rightleftarrows}} \begin{array}{c} RC{=}NH \\ | \\ O-OH \end{array}
$$

$$
\begin{array}{c} RC{=}NH \\ | \\ O-OH \end{array} + H-O-O-H \longrightarrow \begin{array}{c} R-C-NH_2 \\ \| \\ O \end{array} + O_2 + [H^+] + [OH^-]
$$

Tertiary alkyl cyanides can be hydrolyzed readily to the amide by boiling with 80 per cent sulfuric acid, since the second stage of hydrolysis to the acid is sterically hindered.

$$R_3CCN + H_2O \xrightarrow[\text{heat}]{\text{80 per cent } H_2SO_4,} R_3CCONH_2$$

3. **Alcoholysis to Esters.** To convert nitriles into esters, it is not necessary first to prepare the acid. If the nitrile is refluxed with absolute alcohol and anhydrous acid, the imido ester salt is formed (p. 248). Addition of water gives the ester.

$$RC{\equiv}N + CH_3OH + HCl \longrightarrow \left[\begin{matrix} ^+NH_2 \\ \| \\ RC{-}OCH_3 \end{matrix}\right][Cl^-] \xrightarrow{H_2O} \begin{matrix} O \\ \| \\ RC{-}OCH_3 \end{matrix} + NH_4Cl$$

Imido ester
hydrochloride

If some water is present in the alcohol or acid, the ester is obtained directly.

4. **Reduction to Primary Amines.** Nitriles may be reduced to primary amines in the same way that esters are reduced to alcohols, that is, by adding metallic sodium to a refluxing solution of the nitrile in absolute ethyl alcohol.

$$RC{\equiv}N + 4 Na + 4 C_2H_5OH \longrightarrow RCH_2NH_2 + 4 NaOC_2H_5$$

Catalytic reduction leads to a mixture of primary, secondary, and tertiary amines, but if the reaction is carried out in the presence of an excess of ammonia, good yields of primary amines are obtained (p. 230).

$$RC{\equiv}N + 2 H_2 \xrightarrow[\text{(+ NH}_3\text{)}]{\text{Raney Ni}} RCH_2NH_2$$

5. **Alkylation.** Primary and secondary nitriles are alkylated readily by heating with an alkyl halide in the presence of finely divided sodium amide.

$$RCH_2CN + R'X + NaNH_2 \longrightarrow \begin{matrix} RCHCN \\ | \\ R' \end{matrix} + NaX + NH_3$$

$$R_2CHCN + R'X + NaNH_2 \longrightarrow \begin{matrix} R_2CCN \\ | \\ R' \end{matrix} + NaX + NH_3$$

This reaction provides the most satisfactory general method for preparing tertiary alkyl cyanides.

6. **Addition of Olefins.** Dialkylethylenes add to nitriles in the presence of sulfuric acid in glacial acetic acid solution. Addition of water gives the *N-t*-alkyl amide.

$$R_2C{=}CH_2 + R'C{\equiv}N + H_2SO_4 \longrightarrow \begin{matrix} R_2C{-}N{=}CR' \\ | \qquad | \\ CH_3 \quad OSO_3H \end{matrix} \xrightarrow[H_2SO_4]{H_2O}$$

$$\left[\begin{matrix} R_2C{-}N{=}CR' \\ | \qquad | \\ CH_3 \quad OH \end{matrix}\right] \longrightarrow \begin{matrix} R_2CNHC{-}R' \\ | \qquad \| \\ CH_3 \; O \end{matrix}$$

Secondary or tertiary alcohols may be used instead of olefins in the reaction.

The products derived from alkyl cyanides are difficult to hydrolyze in basic solution and acid hydrolysis regenerates the olefin.

$$R_2CNHC—R' + HCl \longrightarrow R_2C{=}CH_2 + NH_4Cl + HOOCR'$$
$$\underset{CH_3\ O}{\overset{}{}}$$

The formamides derived from hydrogen cyanide, however, can be hydrolyzed by bases and provide a convenient synthesis for *t*-alkyl amines. Isobutylene, for example, gives *N-t*-butylformamide which can be hydrolyzed to *t*-butylamine.

Uses

Nitriles are good solvents but with the exception of hydrogen cyanide and acrylonitrile (p. 787) have not yet found large-scale commercial use. They are important intermediates, however, in the laboratory synthesis of acids, esters, amides, and amines.

The most important member of the series from a commercial viewpoint is **hydrogen cyanide (hydrocyanic acid, prussic acid).** It has been isolated from natural sources although it does not occur free in plants. It is formed by the hydrolysis of *cyanogenetic glycosides* which are widely distributed. The best known of these is **amygdalin** which is the bitter constituent of the kernels of the fruit pits of the prune family and is present in high concentration in the bitter almond. On hydrolysis amygdalin yields hydrogen cyanide, glucose and benzaldehyde (p. 537). The cyanogenetic glycosides are toxic and must be removed before the plant can be used as food. For example, the glycoside in cassava (*Manihot*, manioc) must be removed in the preparation of tapioca. Stock may be poisoned by grazing on plants containing cyanogenetic glycosides.

One common source of hydrogen cyanide is **sodium cyanide,** which is made by passing anhydrous ammonia into a mixture of sodium and charcoal in iron pots at 800°. The ammonia reacts with the sodium to give sodium amide, which at 800° reacts with carbon to give sodium cyanide. The product is withdrawn as a liquid and cast into egg-shaped lumps or cooled in thin layers on a revolving drum, scraped off, and broken into flakes.

$$Na + NH_3 \longrightarrow NaNH_2 + \tfrac{1}{2} H_2$$
$$NaNH_2 + C \xrightarrow{800°} NaCN + H_2$$

The hydrogen may be recovered and used for the resynthesis of ammonia. Hydrogen cyanide is a weak acid and is liberated from its salts by the addition of a mineral acid.

Sodium cyanide may be made also by fusing calcium cyanamide (made from calcium carbide, p. 320) with sodium chloride and carbon.

$$CaNCN + C + 2\,NaCl \longrightarrow CaCl_2 + 2\,NaCN$$

A process for the synthesis of hydrogen cyanide from ammonia and carbon monoxide which avoids the use of the electrical energy necessary to produce metallic sodium was developed in Germany during World War II. Reaction of carbon monoxide with anhydrous methyl alcohol at high pressure in the presence of sodium methoxide gave methyl formate.

$$CH_3OH + CO \xrightarrow{NaOCH_3} HCOOCH_3$$

Reaction with ammonia gave formamide, the methyl alcohol being recovered.

$$HCOOCH_3 + NH_3 \longrightarrow HCONH_2 + CH_3OH$$

The amide was dehydrated by passing the vapors over alumina at 300°.

$$HCONH_2 \xrightarrow[300°]{Al_2O_3} HCN + H_2O$$

At the end of the war, production was at the rate of 460 tons per month by this process.

Since 1948 hydrogen cyanide has been produced in the United States by catalytic synthesis from ammonia and high-purity methane. The reaction between ammonia and methane to give hydrogen cyanide and hydrogen is endothermic and heat is supplied by mixing the gases with air which burns the hydrogen and a portion of the methane.

$$2\,CH_4 + 2\,NH_3 + \underset{(air)}{3\,O_2} \xrightarrow[1000°]{Pt} 2\,HCN + 6\,H_2O \text{ (with } H_2 \text{ and CO)}$$

Conversion of ammonia to hydrogen cyanide is 67 per cent per pass and the over-all yield is 74 per cent. The hydrogen cyanide and unreacted ammonia are absorbed in an aqueous solution of pentaerythritol and boric acid. This solution is sufficiently acidic (p. 742) to hold the ammonia while the hydrogen cyanide is being stripped from it by heating to 90° under reduced pressure, but releases the ammonia when heated to 130°.

Hydrogen cyanide is a liquid which boils at 25° and freezes at −12°. It is miscible with water to give a weakly acidic solution. The acidity is less than that of carbonic acid, the acid dissociation constants being 7.2×10^{-10} and 4.3×10^{-7} respectively. Hydrogen cyanide is a useful reagent in organic chemistry. Although highly toxic, it is no more so than hydrogen sulfide and with due care can be handled with safety. It has a characteristic sweet odor, which is more like a sweet taste noticeable at the back of the throat, that gives ample warning before dangerous concentrations are reached. Since it is stated that some persons cannot detect this odor, it is advisable to determine individual sensitivity by smelling solid sodium cyanide, which liberates a small amount of hydrogen cyanide by hydrolysis.

Pure anhydrous hydrogen cyanide is stable, but in the presence of water and other impurities, particularly alkaline substances, it undergoes complex condensation and polymerization reactions to give dark colored products. These reactions may take place with explosive violence. It should be stored only in the anhydrous form. Metallic copper and cobalt oxalate appear to be the best stabilizers.

The chief commercial use for hydrogen cyanide in the United States is as an intermediate for the synthesis of other organic compounds, especially acrylonitrile (p. 787) and acetone cyanohydrin (p. 200) which are intermediates in the manufacture of certain types of synthetic rubbers (p. 718) and plastics (pp. 726, 788). The many uses for its salts are discussed in texts on inorganic chemistry.

ALKYL ISOCYANIDES (ISONITRILES)

As the name implies, the isocyanides or isonitriles are isomeric with the cyanides or nitriles. The structure of the isocyanides and the commonest method of preparation from primary amines are discussed on page 238.

$$RNH_2 + CHCl_3 + 3\,NaOH \longrightarrow R{-}\overset{+}{N}{\equiv}\overset{-}{C}: + 3\,NaCl + 3\,H_2O$$

When an alkyl halide reacts with silver cyanide instead of sodium cyanide, the isocyanide, rather than the cyanide, is the main product.

$$RX + AgCN \longrightarrow RNC + AgX$$

The difference in behavior of sodium and silver cyanides appears to be due to the ability of the silver ion to coordinate with the halogen of the alkyl halide to produce a carbonium ion which bonds with the nitrogen atom rather than with the carbon atom because of the higher electron density on nitrogen. In the absence of silver ion the reaction takes place by an S_N2 mechanism (p. 116) and the more stable carbon-carbon bond is formed (cf. p. 259).

Physical Properties

The isocyanides boil about 20° lower than the cyanides. Methyl cyanide boils at 81° and methyl isocyanide at 60°. The corresponding ethyl derivatives boil at 97° and 78°. The isonitriles have an obnoxious odor which can be detected in minute amounts, and are highly toxic.

The lower boiling points of the isocyanides presumably are due to their lower dipole moments (Table 15, p. 251). Because the isocyanide has a semipolar bond (p. 238), its dipole moment might be expected to be higher than that of the cyanide. However, since the moment due to the semipolar bond is in the opposite direction to that due to the difference in electron-attraction of carbon and nitrogen, the resulting moment is smaller for isocyanides than for nitriles.

Reactions

The isocyanides are much more reactive than the nitriles because one of the carbon atoms has an unshared pair of electrons. The initial reaction always involves this unshared pair.

1. **Rearrangement to Nitriles.** Isocyanides are less stable than nitriles and on heating rearrange to nitriles.

$$R-\overset{+}{N}\equiv\overset{-}{C} \longrightarrow RC\equiv N$$

2. **Reduction.** Isocyanides may be reduced catalytically to alkylmethylamines.

$$R\overset{+}{N}\equiv\overset{-}{C}: \xrightarrow[\text{Pt or Ni}]{H_2} [RN=CH_2] \xrightarrow[\text{Pt or Ni}]{H_2} RNHCH_3$$

Thus the reduction of isocyanides leads to secondary amines, whereas nitriles give primary amines (p. 232). The fact that a secondary amine is obtained is proof that the nitrogen must be between a single carbon atom and the alkyl group.

3. **Oxidation.** Mild oxidizing agents such as heavy metal oxides convert isocyanides into isocyanates.

$$R\overset{+}{N}\equiv\overset{-}{C}: + HgO \longrightarrow \underset{\text{Alkyl isocyanate}}{RN=C=O} + Hg$$

Sulfur similarly produces an isothiocyanate.

$$R\overset{+}{N}\equiv\overset{-}{C}: + S \longrightarrow \underset{\substack{\text{Alkyl} \\ \text{isothiocyanate}}}{R-N=C=S}$$

Bromine adds to give a dibromide.

$$R\overset{+}{N}\equiv\overset{-}{C}: + Br_2 \longrightarrow RN=CBr_2$$

4. **Hydrolysis.** Acid or alkaline hydrolysis leads to the usual scission of the multiple bond to give a primary amine and formic acid. The initial product is the formamide.

$$R—\overset{+}{N}{\equiv}\bar{C}: + H_2O \longrightarrow [RN{=}CHOH] \longrightarrow RNH—CHO$$
$$RNHCHO + H_2O + HCl \longrightarrow RNH_3Cl + HCOOH$$
$$RNHCHO + NaOH \longrightarrow RNH_2 + HCOONa$$

The isocyanides have been very important in the development of theories concerning the structure of organic molecules, but as yet have no commercial use.

NITROALKANES

Nitro compounds have the general formula RNO_2 in which the nitro (NO_2) group is linked through nitrogen to carbon. In order to maintain an octet of electrons about the nitrogen atom, one of the oxygen atoms is linked by a double bond and the other by a semipolar bond (p. 238).

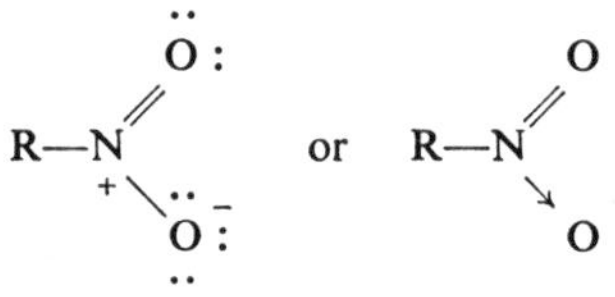

The nitro group resembles the carboxylate ion (p. 154) in that the *p* orbitals of the two oxygen atoms can overlap that of the nitrogen atom equally well and give rise to two molecular π orbitals encompassing all three nuclei as indicated by Fig. 48*a*. The nitro group also may be indicated as a resonance hybrid of two excited structures (Fig. 48*b*).

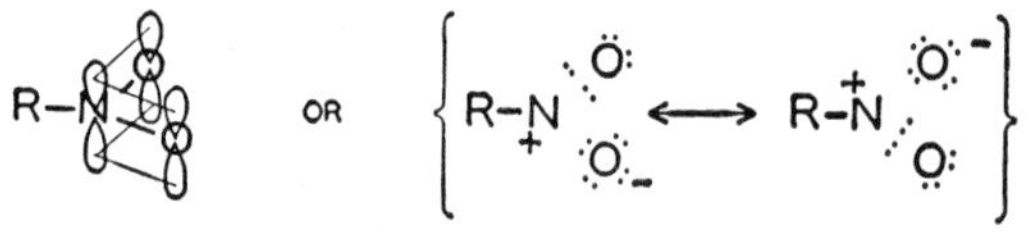

(a)　　　　　　　　　　　　(b)

Fig. 48. Resonance in the nitro group.

The barrier to free rotation about the carbon-carbon bond in ethane is about 3000 cal. per mole because the hydrogen atoms prefer to occupy staggered positions rather than opposed positions (p. 31). In contrast the barrier to free rotation about the carbon-nitrogen bond in nitromethane is only about 6 cal. per mole as determined by microwave spectroscopy (p. 657). This result confirms the view that trigonal hybridization leads to a planar distribution of the nitrogen bonds in nitro compounds, since there is no favored position for the oxygen atoms in nitromethane. When one oxygen atom is between two hydrogen atoms, the other is opposed to the third hydrogen atom.

Prior to 1940 the nitroalkanes were largely of theoretical interest. With the advent of the commercial development of vapor phase nitration of propane, however, the lower nitroalkanes were made available and their numerous reactions became of considerable importance.

Preparation

1. **From Alkyl Halides and Nitrites.** Primary and secondary alkyl bromides and iodides react with sodium nitrite in dimethylformamide containing urea (p. 310) to give 50 to 60 per cent yields of nitro compounds.

$$RX + Na^+{}^-NO_2 \longrightarrow RNO_2 + NaX$$

From 25 to 35 per cent alkyl nitrite, RONO (p. 103), also is formed. If silver nitrite in ether is used, the yields from primary alkyl bromides and iodides are 70 to 80 per cent of nitro compound, together with 10 to 15 per cent of alkyl nitrite. Tertiary halides give only olefin with sodium nitrite and chiefly alkyl nitrite with silver nitrite.

The reaction of alkyl halides with inorganic nitrites has been the subject of an extensive investigation and the results throw considerable light on the reactions of negative ions, such as the cyanide ion and nitrite ion, that have more than one point at which bond formation can take place during a displacement reaction (p. 116). The nitrite ion has unshared pairs of electrons on both oxygen and nitrogen that can be used for bond formation. If the unshared pair on nitrogen is used, a nitro compound is formed, whereas reaction of an unshared pair on oxygen leads to an alkyl nitrite. Because oxygen has a greater electron-attracting power than nitrogen, the electron density on oxygen is higher and oxygen should bond more readily than nitrogen at a point of low electron density. On the other hand nitrogen would form a more nearly covalent and hence more stable bond with carbon than would oxygen. Thus if conditions are such that carbonium ion formation is favored (p. 117), nitrites result from an S_N1 mechanism, but in the absence of such conditions the more stable nitro compounds predominate (S_N2 mechanism). This interpretation is in agreement with the fact that the relative rate of reaction of alkyl halides to give nitro compounds is primary > secondary > tertiary, whereas the relative rate to give nitrites is tertiary > secondary > primary (p. 117).

Nitromethane is prepared readily in fair yield by the reaction of an aqueous solution of sodium chloroacetate with sodium nitrite and distillation of the mixture. The intermediate sodium nitroacetate decomposes to nitromethane and sodium carbonate.

$$ClCH_2COONa + NaNO_2 \longrightarrow NO_2CH_2COONa + NaCl$$

$$2\ NO_2CH_2COONa + H_2O \longrightarrow 2\ CH_3NO_2 + CO_2 + Na_2CO_3$$

2. Vapor Phase Nitration of Hydrocarbons.

$$RH + HONO_2 \xrightarrow{420°} RNO_2 + H_2O$$

In the nitration of propane not only 1- and 2-nitropropane are obtained, but nitroethane and nitromethane also are formed by the scission of carbon-carbon bonds. These products are separated by distillation and are available commercially. The nitro compounds always are named as substitution products.

3. Oxidation of Oximes.

Primary and secondary nitro compounds can be prepared by the oxidation of oximes with peroxytrifluoroacetic acid (p. 876).

$$RCH{=}NOH + CF_3\overset{\overset{\displaystyle O}{\|}}{C}{-}O{-}OH \longrightarrow CF_3COOH + RCH{=}\overset{\overset{\displaystyle O_-}{|}\ ^+}{N}{-}OH \rightleftarrows RCH_2NO_2$$

$$R_2C{=}NOH + CF_3\overset{\overset{\displaystyle O}{\|}}{C}{-}O{-}OH \longrightarrow CF_3COOH + R_2C{=}\overset{\overset{\displaystyle O_+}{|}\ _-}{N}{-}OH \rightleftarrows R_2CHNO_2$$

The reaction is carried out best in solution in acetonitrile and in the presence of sodium bicarbonate or disodium acid phosphate to neutralize the strong trifluoroacetic acid.

4. Oxidation of *t*-Alkyl Amines.

Tertiary nitro compounds are prepared best by the oxidation of *t*-alkyl amines by aqueous potassium permanganate or alkaline hydrogen peroxide.

$$R_3CNH_2 + 3\ [O](KMnO_4\ or\ H_2O_2) \longrightarrow R_3CNO_2 + H_2O$$

5. **Addition of Nitrogen Dioxide to Olefins.** Monomeric nitrogen dioxide has an unpaired electron and adds readily to the double bond of olefins to give 1,2-dinitroalkanes and nitroalkyl nitrites in about equal amounts.

$$RCH{=}CHR + 2\,NO_2 \longrightarrow \underset{\overset{|}{NO_2}\;\overset{|}{NO_2}}{RCH{-}CHR} \text{ and } \underset{\overset{|}{NO_2}\;\overset{|}{ONO}}{RCH{-}CHR}$$

The reaction is carried out best by adding the olefin to a concentrated solution of pure nitrogen dioxide in ether between $-10°$ and room temperature.[7] Since the nitroalkyl nitrites may decompose violently, they are hydrolyzed to the nitro alcohols by the addition of water before attempting to isolate the dinitroalkanes.

Physical Properties

Because of the presence of the semipolar bond in the nitro group, the nitro-alkanes have a high dipole moment, which leads to abnormally high boiling points. Moreover the acidity of the α hydrogen probably leads to proton bonding between molecules. Thus nitromethane of molecular weight 61 boils at $101.5°$. Nitromethane dissolves in water to about the same extent as *n*-butyl alcohol, but the higher nitroalkanes are practically insoluble. They usually are good solvents for other organic compounds.

Reactions

1. **Salt Formation.** The nitro group has a strong attraction for electrons and decreases the electron-density about an atom to which it is attached. Hence hydrogen is removed more readily from a carbon atom attached to a nitro group than from an ordinary alkyl group. In fact the aliphatic nitro compounds that have an α hydrogen atom are stronger acids than water and form water-soluble salts with strong bases in aqueous solution.

$$RCH_2NO_2 + NaOH \longrightarrow [R\bar{C}HNO_2]\,Na^+ + H_2O$$

2-Nitropropane, although practically insoluble in water, will maintain the acidity of water at pH 4.3. Tertiary nitro compounds, R_3CNO_2, in which no hydrogen is united to the carbon atom bearing the nitro group, do not form salts.

This behavior of primary and secondary nitro compounds is analogous to the formation of salts from ketones (p. 213). However, when the sodium salt of a ketone reacts with water, the ketone is regenerated at once, but when the sodium salts of certain nitro compounds are acidified, an isomer of the original compound is liberated which is a fairly strong acid. The weakly acidic isomer is believed to have the nitro structure and is called the *nitro* form, whereas the

---

[7] Dinitrogen tetroxide, N_2O_4, is the colorless dimer of nitrogen dioxide and melts at $-12°$. Above its melting point of $-12°$ it dissociates into the brown monomer.

strongly ácidic isomer is believed to have an enol structure and is called the *aci* form. The *aci* form rearranges slowly to the *nitro* form.

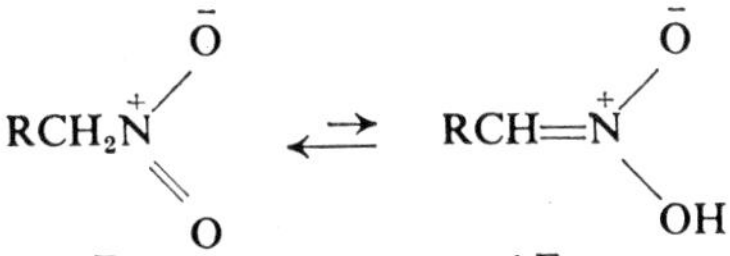

$$RCH_2N \underset{\displaystyle O}{\overset{\displaystyle \bar{O}}{\big\langle}} \quad \rightleftarrows \quad RCH{=}N \underset{\displaystyle OH}{\overset{\displaystyle \bar{O}}{\big\langle}}$$

nitro Form   *aci* Form

The *nitro* form and *aci* form are tautomeric (p. 207), but the anion of the sodium salt of a nitro compound is a resonance hybrid in which the polycentric molecular orbitals encompass not only the nitrogen and oxygen atoms but also the adjacent carbon atom.

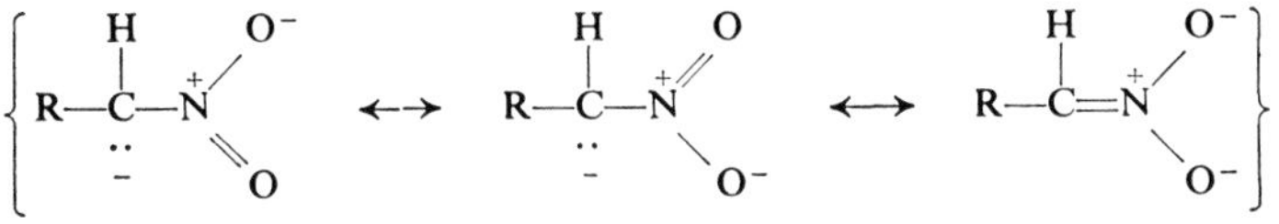

$$\left\{ \underset{\bar{}}{\overset{H}{R{-}C{-}N}}\overset{O^-}{\underset{O}{\big\langle}} \quad \leftrightarrow \quad \underset{\bar{}}{\overset{H}{R{-}C{-}N}}\overset{O}{\underset{O^-}{\big\langle}} \quad \leftrightarrow \quad \overset{H}{R{-}C{=}N}\overset{O^-}{\underset{O^-}{\big\langle}} \right\}$$

When the sodium salt is acidified, the proton combines more rapidly with an oxygen atom of the resonance hybrid anion than with the α carbon atom to give the *aci* form. However the *nitro* form is more stable thermodynamically, and the proton is transferred slowly from oxygen to nitrogen.

2. **Bromination.** Primary and secondary nitro compounds, like aldehydes and ketones (p. 214), brominate easily in alkaline solution.

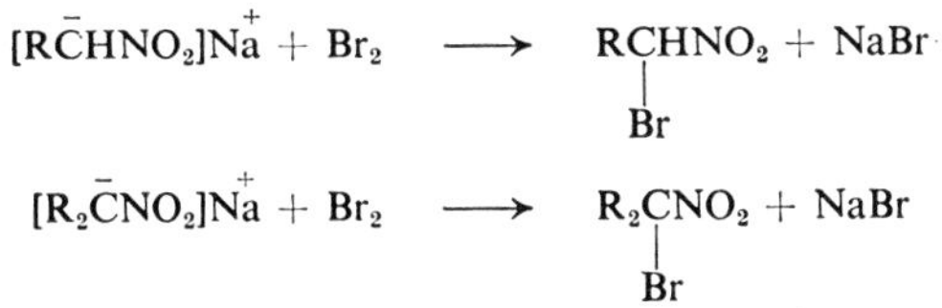

$$[R\bar{C}HNO_2]\overset{+}{Na} + Br_2 \longrightarrow \underset{Br}{RCHNO_2} + NaBr$$

$$[R_2\bar{C}NO_2]\overset{+}{Na} + Br_2 \longrightarrow \underset{Br}{R_2CNO_2} + NaBr$$

Only hydrogen on the carbon atom adjacent to the nitro group reacts. Hence tertiary nitro compounds are not brominated.

3. **Reaction with Nitrous Acid.** Primary nitro compounds react with nitrous acid to give nitroso derivatives, known as *nitrolic acids*, which dissolve in alkali to form red salts.

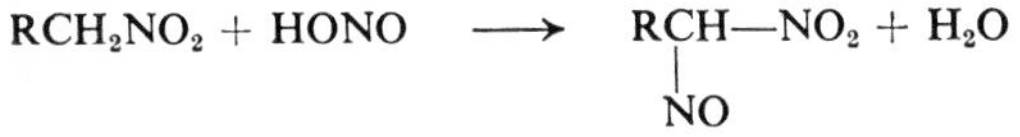

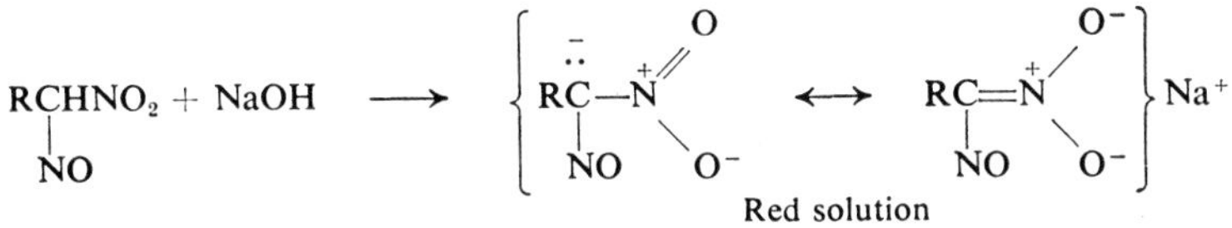

$$RCH_2NO_2 + HONO \longrightarrow \underset{NO}{RCH{-}NO_2} + H_2O$$

$$\underset{NO}{RCHNO_2} + NaOH \longrightarrow \left\{ \underset{NO}{\overset{\displaystyle \cdot\cdot}{RC{-}N}}\overset{O}{\underset{O^-}{\big\langle}} \quad \leftrightarrow \quad \underset{NO}{RC{=}N}\overset{O^-}{\underset{O^-}{\big\langle}} \right\} Na^+$$

Red solution

Secondary nitro compounds give blue nitroso derivatives which are insoluble in alkali.

$$R_2CHNO_2 + HONO \longrightarrow \underset{NO}{R_2C{-}NO_2} + H_2O$$

Blue, insoluble in
water and dilute alkali

These nitroso derivatives are blue only in the liquid monomolecular state. They solidify to white crystalline dimers which probably have the structure

$$R_2C(NO_2)-\overset{+}{N}=\overset{+}{N}-C(NO_2)R_2$$

with O^- groups on each nitrogen.

Tertiary nitro compounds do not react with nitrous acid. The difference in behavior of primary, secondary, and tertiary nitro compounds to nitrous acid and alkali may be used to distinguish between the three types and sometimes is referred to as the "red, white, and blue reaction."

4. Reduction to Primary Amines.

$$RNO_2 + 6\,[H] \longrightarrow RNH_2 + 2\,H_2O$$

The reduction may be brought about by hydrogen and a platinum or nickel catalyst, or by an active metal, for example iron, zinc, or tin, and hydrochloric acid.

5. Acid Hydrolysis. (a) HYDROLYSIS OF THE NITRO FORM OF A PRIMARY NITRO COMPOUND. When a primary nitro compound is boiled with concentrated aqueous hydrochloric acid or 85 per cent sulfuric acid, a carboxylic acid and a salt of hydroxylamine are formed. The reaction involves an oxidation of the methylene group and a reduction of the nitro group to give a hydroxamic acid. Hydrolysis of the hydroxamic acid gives the final products.

$$RCH_2NO_2 \longrightarrow \underset{\substack{| \\ OH \\ \text{A hydroxamic acid}}}{RC}=NOH \xrightarrow{HCl,\ H_2O} RCOOH + HONH_3Cl$$

The price of hydroxylamine, which formerly was produced by the reduction of nitrous acid and isolated by way of acetoxime (p. 210), has been reduced greatly because of the above process.

(b) HYDROLYSIS OF THE ACI FORM OF A PRIMARY OR SECONDARY NITRO COMPOUND. If a primary or secondary nitro compound first is converted to the salt of the aci form by alkali and then hydrolyzed by 25 per cent sulfuric acid, aldehydes and ketones are produced with the evolution of nitrous oxide (*Nef* [8] *reaction*).

$$2\,RCH{=}NOONa + 2\,H_2SO_4 \longrightarrow 2\,RCHO + N_2O + 2\,NaHSO_4 + H_2O$$

$$2\,R_2C{=}NOONa + 2\,H_2SO_4 \longrightarrow 2\,R_2CO + N_2O + 2\,NaHSO_4 + H_2O$$

6. Addition to Aldehydes or Ketones. Primary and secondary nitro compounds undergo an aldol-like addition to aldehydes or ketones in the presence of dilute

---

[8] John Ulric Nef (1862–1915), American chemist, professor at the University of Chicago. He is noted not only for his studies of the products formed by the action of alkali on carbohydrates, but also for his ideas concerning the nature of compounds containing so-called *divalent carbon*, such as the isocyanides and the fulminates.

alkali. Formaldehyde usually reacts with all α hydrogen atoms, whereas other aldehydes and ketones usually react with one.

$$RCH_2NO_2 + 2\ HCHO \xrightarrow{[OH^-]} \begin{array}{c} R \\ | \\ HOCH_2-C-CH_2OH \\ | \\ NO_2 \end{array}$$

$$R_2CHNO_2 + HCHO \xrightarrow{[OH^-]} \begin{array}{c} R \\ | \\ R-C-CH_2OH \\ | \\ NO_2 \end{array}$$

$$RCH_2NO_2 + R'CHO \xrightarrow{[OH^-]} \begin{array}{c} RCH-CHR' \\ | \quad\ | \\ NO_2\ \ OH \end{array}$$

These nitro alcohols may be reduced readily to amino alcohols (p. 754).

In the presence of formaldehyde and a secondary amine, a dialkylamino-methyl derivative is obtained (*Mannich reaction*, p. 509).

$$RCH_2NO_2 + HCHO + HNR'_2 \longrightarrow \begin{array}{c} RCHCH_2NR'_2 + H_2O \\ | \\ NO_2 \end{array}$$

7. Alkylation. When salts of nitro compounds react with alkyl halides, *O*-alkylation usually takes place.

$$[R\overset{-}{C}HNO_2]\overset{+}{Na} + R'X \longrightarrow RCH{=}\overset{+}{N}\!\!\begin{array}{c} {}^{-}O \\ \diagup \\ \diagdown \\ OR' \end{array} + NaX$$

Diazomethane (p. 266) reacts with nitro compounds to give the *O*-methyl derivative.

$$RCH{=}\overset{+}{N}\!\!\begin{array}{c} {}^{-}O \\ \diagup \\ \diagdown \\ OH \end{array} + CH_2N_2 \longrightarrow RCH{=}\overset{+}{N}\!\!\begin{array}{c} {}^{-}O \\ \diagup \\ \diagdown \\ OCH_3 \end{array} + N_2$$

The *O*-alkyl derivatives, known as *nitronic esters*, frequently decompose spontaneously into the oxime and an aldehyde or ketone.

$$RCH{=}\overset{+}{N}\!\!\begin{array}{c} {}^{-}O \\ \diagup \\ \diagdown \\ OCH_2R' \end{array} \longrightarrow RCH{=}NOH + R'CHO$$

The aliphatic nitro compounds are excellent solvents, but their chief use has been as intermediates for the synthesis of other organic compounds, especially the amino alcohols (p. 754). **Tetranitromethane** is a valuable reagent for the detection of carbon-carbon unsaturation. When a dilute solution in chloroform is added to a solution of an unsaturated compound, a yellow to red color is produced. The simpler olefins and acetylenes give a yellow color, the tetraalkyl substituted ethylenes and simple conjugated dienes (p. 707) give orange to light red colors, and the alkyl substituted dienes give a deep red color. An advantage of the test is that even unreactive double bonds that do not react with bromine or undergo catalytic reduction give a color with tetranitromethane. α,β-Unsaturated carbonyl compounds (p. 762) do not respond to the test.

Tetranitromethane is prepared by the action of nitric acid on acetic anhydride or ketene.

$$(CH_3CO)_2O + 4 HONO_2 \longrightarrow C(NO_2)_4 + CO_2 + CH_3COOH + 3 H_2O$$

$$CH_2=C=O + 4 HONO_2 \longrightarrow C(NO_2)_4 + CO_2 + 3 H_2O$$

Mixtures of tetranitromethane with organic compounds are violent explosives, and fatal accidents have occurred during its use. Only very dilute solutions should be used, and the solutions should not be heated.

Chloropicrin, Cl_3CNO_2, is made by the chlorination of nitromethane in the presence of calcium carbonate, or by the reaction of picric acid with sodium hypochlorite (p. 515). It is a powerful lachrymator and is used as a tear gas for dispelling mobs and as a warning agent for toxic gases.

Until 1949, no natural product had been known to contain a nitro group. In that year, however, **β-nitropropionic** acid, $O_2NCH_2CH_2COOH$, was shown to be a hydrolytic product of the glycoside (p. 372) **hiptagin** present in the bark of *Hiptage mandoblata* and in the kernels of *Corynocarpus laevigata*. Since then it has been isolated from cultures of the mold *Aspergillus flavus*. The antibiotic Chloromycetin (p. 530) contains an aromatic nitro group.

HYDRAZINES

The monoalkylhydrazines can be prepared by alkylation of an excess of hydrazine with alkyl sulfates in the presence of sodium hydroxide.

$$H_2NNH_2 + (RO)_2SO_2 + NaOH \longrightarrow RNHNH_2 + ROSO_3Na + H_2O$$

Because the presence of an alkyl group increases the basicity of the nitrogen to which it is attached, further alkylation gives the unsymmetrical dialkylhydrazine.

$$RNHNH_2 + (RO)_2SO_2 + NaOH \longrightarrow R_2N-NH_2 + ROSO_3Na + H_2O$$

Unsymmetrical dialkylhydrazines can be prepared also by the reduction of *N*-nitrosodialkylamines, or by the reaction of secondary amines with chloroamine.

$$R_2NNO + 4 [H](Na + C_2H_5OH, \text{ or } LiAlH_4) \longrightarrow R_2NNH_2$$

$$R_2NH + ClNH_2 \longrightarrow [R_2\overset{+}{N}HNH_2]Cl^- \overset{NaOH}{\longrightarrow} R_2NNH_2$$

Symmetrical dialkylhydrazines can be prepared only by "protecting" one hydrogen on each nitrogen atom by first replacing them with groups that can later be removed easily. In the diacylation of hydrazine, a symmetrical product is formed because the replacement of one hydrogen by an acyl group decreases the basicity of that nitrogen atom. Subsequent dialkylation followed by hydrolysis gives the symmetrical dialkylhydrazine.

$$H_2NNH_2 \xrightarrow{HCOOH} HCONHNHCHO \xrightarrow{(RO)_2SO_2 + NaOH}$$

$$\underset{\overset{|}{R}\ \overset{|}{R}}{HCON-NCHO} \xrightarrow{H_2O + HCl} RNHNHR + 2 HCOOH$$

The hydrazines can be reduced to two moles of amine, or oxidized to azo compounds.

ALIPHATIC AZO AND DIAZO COMPOUNDS

When a symmetrically disubstituted hydrazine is oxidized with sodium dichromate and sulfuric acid, an azo compound (Fr. *azote* nitrogen) is formed in which the two nitrogen atoms are joined by a double bond.

$$RNHNHR \xrightarrow{Na_2Cr_2O_7,\ H_2SO_4} RN{=}NR + H_2O$$

Azomethane, $CH_3N{=}NCH_3$, prepared from *sym*-dimethylhydrazine, is a yellow gas (p. 665). Although the nitrogen atoms each contain an unshared pair of electrons, they are not basic in aqueous solution. As with the oximes and to a greater extent the nitriles and the acetylide ion, the presence of a multiple bond reduces the availability of unshared pairs of electrons (p. 252). The azo compounds are reduced readily to the hydrazines and further to the primary amines. Azomethane is hydrolyzed on boiling with aqueous hydrochloric acid to methylhydrazine and formaldehyde, presumably because it can rearrange to the tautomeric hydrazone of formaldehyde.

$$CH_3N{=}NCH_3 \rightleftharpoons \underset{\substack{\text{Formaldehyde}\\\text{methylhydrazone}}}{CH_3NHN{=}CH_2} \xrightarrow{H_2O,\ HCl} \underset{\substack{\text{Methylhydrazine}\\\text{hydrochloride}}}{CH_3NHNH_3Cl + HCHO}$$

Frequently the azo compound cannot be isolated, because it isomerizes completely to the hydrazone.

Azomethane is unstable above 200° and yields free methyl radicals (p. 568) and nitrogen.

$$CH_3N{=}NCH_3 \longrightarrow 2\ CH_3\cdot + N_2$$

The methyl radicals may combine to give ethane, but in the presence of other molecules, they may abstract hydrogen or initiate reactions catalyzed by free radicals (p. 569).

α,α′-Azobisisobutyronitrile was prepared first by Thiele in 1896. In the reaction of acetone with potassium cyanide and hydrazine hydrochloride, free hydrazine and hydrogen cyanide first are formed. The hydrazine reacts with the acetone to give an aldehyde-ammonia, which then reacts with the hydrogen cyanide. The substituted hydrazine obtained can be oxidized to the azo compound with sodium hypochlorite.

$$2\ (CH_3)_2C{=}O + H_2NNH_2 \longrightarrow \underset{\substack{\ \ \ \ \ \ \ |\qquad\qquad|\\\ \ \ \ \ \ OH\qquad\ \ OH}}{(CH_3)_2C{-}NHNH{-}C(CH_3)_2} \xrightarrow{2\ HCN}$$

$$\underset{\substack{\ \ \ \ \ \ |\qquad\qquad\ |\\\ \ \ \ \ CN\qquad\ \ \ CN}}{(CH_3)_2C{-}NHNH{-}C(CH_3)_2} \xrightarrow{NaOCl} \underset{\substack{\ \ \ \ \ \ |\qquad\qquad\ |\\\ \ \ \ \ CN\qquad\ \ \ CN}}{(CH_3)_2C{-}N{=}N{-}C(CH_3)_2}$$

This compound decomposes on heating at 100° into nitrogen and free radicals which can act as catalysts or combine to form tetramethylsuccinonitrile (p. 792).

$$\underset{\substack{\ \ \ \ |\qquad\qquad\ |\\\ \ \ CN\qquad\ \ \ CN}}{(CH_3)_2C{-}N{=}N{-}C(CH_3)_2} \xrightarrow{100°} N_2 + 2\left[\underset{\substack{\ \ \ \ \ |\\\ \ \ \ CN}}{(CH_3)_2C\cdot}\right] \longrightarrow \underset{\substack{\ \ \ \ \ \ |\ \ \ \ |\\\ \ \ \ \ CN\ CN}}{(CH_3)_2C{-}C(CH_3)_2}$$

Since 1948 it has been widely used to catalyze free-radical polymerizations and as a foaming agent in the production of foam rubber and expanded plastics.

Compounds containing the characteristic group $>CN_2$ are known as **aliphatic diazo compounds.** They are prepared by the action of alkali on certain types of nitrosoamines. Thus the β-amino ketones prepared by the addition of primary amines to mesityl oxide (p. 207) react with nitrous acid to give the nitroso derivative. Sodium alkoxides regenerate the mesityl oxide with the formation of the diazo hydrocarbon and alcohol.

$$(CH_3)_2C{=}CHCOCH_3 + H_2NCH_2R \longrightarrow$$
Mesityl oxide

$$\underset{\underset{\text{A }\beta\text{-amino ketone}}{\overset{|}{NHCH_2R}}}{(CH_3)_2CCH_2COCH_3} \xrightarrow{HNO_2} \underset{\underset{CH_2R}{\overset{|}{N-NO}}}{(CH_3)_2CCH_2COCH_3} \xrightarrow{NaOCH(CH_3)_2}$$

$$(CH_3)_2C{=}CHCOCH_3 + RCHN_2 + HOCH(CH_3)_2 + NaOH$$
A diazo-
alkane

Nitrosoalkylureas (p. 318), *nitrosoalkylurethanes* (p. 319), and *nitrososulfonamides* (p. 473) also are used to prepare diazo hydrocarbons.

Diazomethane, CH_2N_2, the most commonly used aliphatic diazo compound, may be prepared by any of the general methods. It is a yellow, highly toxic gas that sometimes explodes even in the gaseous state at low temperatures. It usually is handled in ether solution.

From dipole moment and electron diffraction measurements, it has been concluded that diazomethane has a linear structure and is a resonance hybrid. Thus the two extreme electronic structures possible for a linear molecule coalesce because of the overlapping of p atomic orbitals of all three atoms, giving rise to π-type molecular orbitals as indicated in Fig. 49. Resonance hybrids for which all of the important contributing structures have a separation of charge have been called *mesoionic compounds.*

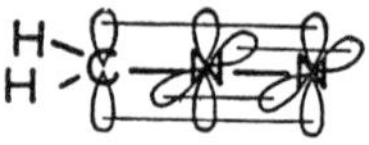

$$\text{or} \quad \left\{ \underset{+ \quad -}{CH_2{=}N{=}\overset{..}{N}:} \longleftrightarrow \underset{- \quad +}{CH_2{-}N{\equiv}\overset{..}{N}:} \right\}$$

Fig. 49. Resonance in diazomethane.

Diazomethane is a valuable reagent for preparative purposes. It reacts readily with acids to give methyl esters.

$$RCOOH + CH_2N_2 \longrightarrow RCOOCH_3 + N_2$$

Usually an ether solution of diazomethane is added to an ether solution of the acid until nitrogen evolution stops and the yellow color persists. Because the reaction takes place at room temperature to give excellent yields and negligible amounts of by-products, it is favored by research workers for preparing methyl esters from small amounts of acids.

Diazomethane converts aldehydes into methyl ketones, and ketones into the next higher homologs.

$$RCHO + CH_2N_2 \longrightarrow RCOCH_3 + N_2$$

$$RCOR + CH_2N_2 \longrightarrow RCOCH_2R + N_2$$

The mechanism of this reaction may be represented as an attack on carbon by the methylene group followed by an alkide ion shift and loss of nitrogen.

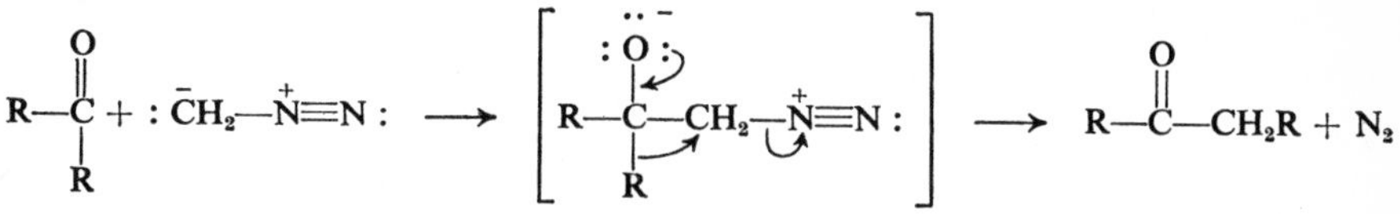

$$R-\overset{\overset{O}{\|}}{\underset{R}{C}} + :\overset{-}{C}H_2-\overset{+}{N}\equiv N: \longrightarrow \left[R-\overset{\overset{:O:^-}{\|}}{\underset{R}{C}}-CH_2-\overset{+}{N}\equiv N: \right] \longrightarrow R-\overset{\overset{O}{\|}}{C}-CH_2R + N_2$$

A very important reaction from the synthetic standpoint is known as the *Arndt-Eistert reaction*. When acyl chlorides are added to an excess of a solution of diazomethane, **diazomethyl ketones** are formed.

$$RCOCl + CH_2N_2 \longrightarrow RCOCHN_2 + HCl$$

$$CH_2N_2 + HCl \longrightarrow CH_3Cl + N_2$$

The diazomethyl ketones react with water, alcohols, or ammonia in the presence of finely divided metals such as silver, platinum, or copper to give carboxylic acids, esters, or amides having one more methylene group than the acid from which the acyl chloride was prepared. The reaction can be carried out homogeneously in triethylamine, using silver benzoate as a catalyst.

$$RCOCHN_2 \begin{cases} + HOH \\ + HOR' \\ + HNH_2 \end{cases} \xrightarrow[\text{or Cu}]{\text{Ag, Pt,}} \begin{cases} RCH_2COOH \\ RCH_2COOR' \\ RCH_2CONH_2 \end{cases} + N_2$$

Hence this method is convenient for converting an acid into its higher homologs one carbon atom at a time.

If the diazomethane is added to an excess of acyl chloride, the **chloromethyl ketone** is formed, because the hydrogen chloride reacts with the diazomethyl ketone instead of with excess diazomethane.

$$RCOCHN_2 + HCl \longrightarrow RCOCH_2Cl + N_2$$

Acetic acid reacts with diazoketones to give ketol acetates.

$$RCOCHN_2 + HOOCCH_3 \longrightarrow RCOCH_2OCOCH_3 + N_2$$

Ethyl diazoacetate (*diazoacetic ester*), a yellow oil, can be made by the direct action of nitrous acid on ethyl aminoacetate.

$$C_2H_5O\overset{\overset{O}{\|}}{C}CH_2NH_2 + HONO \longrightarrow C_2H_5O\overset{\overset{O}{\|}}{C}CHN_2 + 2 H_2O$$

The rate of decomposition of diazoacetic ester by aqueous acids is directly proportional to the hydrogen ion concentration.

AZIDES

The azides are derivatives of hydrazoic acid, HN_3. Sodium azide is prepared by passing nitrous oxide into molten sodium amide.

$$N_2O + 2 NaNH_2 \longrightarrow \underset{\substack{\text{Sodium} \\ \text{azide}}}{NaN_3} + NH_3 + NaOH$$

When an aqueous solution of sodium azide is treated with methyl sulfate, **methyl azide** is evolved and can be condensed to a liquid boiling at 20°.

$$(CH_3)_2SO_4 + NaN_3 \longrightarrow CH_3N_3 + NaCH_3SO_4$$

Methyl
azide

Ethyl azide can be prepared by a similar process.

The azide group has a linear hybrid structure analogous to that of the diazo group (p. 266). The azides may be represented by the resonance hybrid

$$\left\{ RN\overset{+}{=}\overset{-}{N}=\overset{..}{N}: \quad \longleftrightarrow \quad RN\overset{..}{-}\overset{+}{N}\equiv N: \right\}$$

The alkyl azides detonate when heated rapidly, but the decomposition in the gas phase can be controlled. Both methyl and ethyl azide give ethylene and hydrazoic acid.

$$2\,CH_3N_3 \longrightarrow CH_2{=}CH_2 + 2\,HN_3$$

$$CH_3CH_2N_3 \longrightarrow CH_2{=}CH_2 + HN_3$$

The most important azides are the acyl derivatives. They were prepared first by Curtius [9] by the action of nitrous acid on acid hydrazides.

$$RCONHNH_2 + HONO \longrightarrow RCON_3 + 2\,H_2O$$

Usually acyl azides are prepared by the reaction of an acyl chloride with sodium azide.

$$RCOCl + NaN_3 \longrightarrow RCON_3 + NaCl$$

When heated, the acid azides undergo the *Curtius rearrangement* with the formation of the isocyanate (p. 317). The reaction is analogous to the Hofmann rearrangement of amides (p. 247) except that the rearrangement of the azides can be brought about in anhydrous media, and the isocyanate can be isolated without difficulty.

$$RCON_3 \xrightarrow{\text{Heat}} RN{=}C{=}O + N_2$$

In the presence of water the Curtius rearrangement gives the same product as the Hofmann rearrangement, namely the amine with one less carbon atom.

$$RN{=}C{=}O + H_2O \longrightarrow RNH_2 + CO_2$$

Under certain conditions the acid azides act as acylating agents (p. 305).

REVIEW QUESTIONS

Amines

1. What are amines? How are they named?
2. How does the use of the terms primary, secondary, and tertiary as applied to amines differ from their use as applied to alcohols?
3. Discuss the solubility and boiling point of amines.
4. What is the most characteristic chemical property of amines? Discuss the physical properties of the product of this reaction.

---

[9] Theodor Curtius (1857–1928), professor at the University of Heidelberg. He is noted for his discovery of the aliphatic diazo compounds in 1883 and of the rearrangement of acid azides, for his work on hydrazines and heterocyclic compounds, and for his syntheses of amino acids and polypeptides.

5. Define the terms acid and base. Arrange the following types of compounds in the order of increasing acidity: water, hydronium ion, ammonia, ammonium ion, carbonic acid, mineral acids, alkanes, alcohols, carboxylic acids. Give the conjugate base of each of these types and list in the order of decreasing basicity.
6. Illustrate by reactions two methods for distinguishing between primary, secondary, and tertiary amines.
7. Outline two methods that might be satisfactory for the estimation of primary amines in the presence of other non-basic nitrogenous compounds.
8. Discuss the preparation and the physical and chemical properties of quaternary ammonium salts and hydroxides. What is choline chloride and what is its importance? What are amine oxides and how are they prepared?

Amides

9. Give equations for the general methods of preparation of amides.
10. Why is an excess of acetic acid used in the laboratory preparation of acetamide from ammonium acetate?
11. How are amides named? How is substitution on the nitrogen atom indicated?
12. Discuss the physical properties of amides. Compare the boiling points of acetic acid, acetamide, *N*-methylacetamide, and *N,N*-dimethylacetamide and explain.
13. Compare the effect of acyl groups on the basicity of water and of ammonia.
14. Compare the acid- and base-catalyzed hydrolyses of amides to the acid- and base-catalyzed hydrolyses of esters.
15. Give the steps for the Hofmann method of converting an amide to a primary amine.
16. Of what use are amides?

Alkyl Cyanides and Alkyl Isocyanides

17. Summarize the general methods for the preparation of alkyl cyanides.
18. Compare the nomenclature of cyanides with that of nitriles.
19. Compare the basicity of nitriles with that of tertiary amines. Does this difference have any bearing on the solubility of nitriles in water?
20. Give equations for the more important reactions of alkyl cyanides.
21. How are isocyanides prepared?
22. Compare the electronic structure of isocyanides with that for cyanides. Compare their boiling points and explain.
23. Compare the reduction and hydrolysis of isocyanides with the reduction and hydrolysis of cyanides.

Nitroalkanes

24. Discuss the industrial preparation of nitroalkanes.
25. Discuss the solubility of nitroalkanes in water, dilute acid, and dilute alkali, and give an explanation of the facts.
26. What is the "red, white, and blue reaction"?
27. How may primary nitro compounds be converted into amines; into carboxylic acids; into aldehydes?
28. Discuss the condensation of nitro compounds with aldehydes.
29. Give two simple procedures for distinguishing between a nitroalkane and an alkyl nitrite.

PROBLEMS

Amines

30. (*a*) Compare the number of possible alcohols having the molecular formula $C_4H_{10}O$ with the number of possible amines having the formula $C_4H_{11}N$. (*b*) Compare the number of secondary alcohols having the molecular formula $C_5H_{12}O$ with the number of secondary amines having the formula $C_5H_{13}N$. (*c*) Compare the number of primary alcohols having the molecular formula $C_5H_{12}O$ with the number of primary amines having the formula $C_5H_{13}N$.
31. Give balanced equations for the following preparations:
    A. (*a*) Ethylamine from an amide; (*b*) *n*-butylamine from an oxime; (*c*) *i*-propyl-di-*n*-butyl-amine from a chloroamine; (*d*) *n*-hexadecylamine from an acid; (*e*) *i*-butylamine from a cyanide; (*f*) diethylamine from sodium cyanamide; (*g*) *n*-octylamine from hexamethylenetetramine.

B. (a) *i*-Amylamine from hexamethylenetetramine; (b) dimethylethylamine from dimethyl-chloroamine; (c) *n*-heptylamine from an oxime; (d) *n*-dodecylamine from an acid; (e) di-*n*-amylamine from sodium cyanamide; (f) *i*-propylamine from an amide; (g) (2,2-dimethylpropyl)amine from a cyanide.

C. (a) *n*-Tetradecylamine from an acid; (b) *n*-butylamine from a nitrile; (c) *s*-butylamine from an oxime; (d) di-*n*-propylamine from sodium cyanamide; (e) methyl-di-*n*-propyl-amine from a chloroamine; (f) *i*-butylamine from an amide; (g) *n*-hexylamine from hexamethylenetetramine.

32. Write electronic formulas for each of the following compounds indicating from which atom the electrons were derived: (a) ethylamine; (b) tetramethylammonium iodide; (c) *t*-butyl-amine hydrochloride; (d) trimethylamine oxide; (e) triethylamine-boron fluoride complex; (f) nitrosodimethylamine; (g) triethylammonium nitrite; (h) methylamine sulfate; (i) diethylamine phosphate.

33. Give a series of reactions for the following conversions: (a) methyl iodide to trimethylamine oxide; (b) ethyl palmitate to *n*-pentadecylamine; (c) ethyl cyanide to *N*-acetyl-*n*-propyl-amine; (d) 2-octanone to 2-aminooctane; (e) *i*-propyl ether to *i*-propylamine; (f) 1-butene to *s*-butyl isocyanide; (g) ethyl laurate to *n*-dodecylamine; (h) capric acid to di-*n*-nonylamine; (i) *i*-amyl bromide to *i*-hexylamine; (j) triethylamine to nitrosodiethyl-amine.

34. How can one distinguish readily between the members of each of the following groups of compounds: (a) *n*-butyl alcohol, *n*-butylamine, and diethylamine; (b) propionic acid, *i*-butylamine, and ethyl ether; (c) *n*-octane, hexylamine, and triethylamine; (d) tetraethyl-ammonium bromide, ammonium bromide, and sodium bromide; (e) *n*-hexyl bromide, *n*-hexylammonium bromide, and ammonium bromide; (f) propionamide, ammonium pro-pionate, and trimethylammonium propionate; (g) *n*-butyl nitrite, di-*i*-propylammonium nitrite, and trimethylammonium nitrite; (h) diethyl ketoxime, *i*-octylamine, and caproamide; (i) *i*-butylamine, *i*-butyramide, and ethyl *i*-butyrate; (j) trimethylammonium nitrite, nitroso-dimethylamine, and ammonium nitrite.

35. Devise a procedure for obtaining in a relatively pure state each component of the following mixtures: (a) 2-octanol, *n*-octane, tri-*n*-butylamine, and methyl *i*-butyl ketone; (b) methyl-amine, acetic acid, methanol, and *n*-hexane; (c) acetone, ethyl alcohol, trimethylamine, and acetamide; (d) ethyl butyrate, *n*-butyraldehyde, tributylamine, and propionic acid; (e) ethyl alcohol, dimethylamine, trimethylamine, and tetramethylammonium bromide.

Amides

36. Give equations for the following syntheses:

A. (a) *N*-ethylpropionamide from an acyl chloride; (b) valeramide from an ester; (c) *N*,*N*-dimethyl-*n*-butyramide from an anhydride; (d) lauramide from an acid.

B. (a) Palmitamide from an acid; (b) *N*,*N*-dimethylformamide from an ester; (c) *N*-*n*-butylacetamide from an anhydride; (d) *i*-butyramide from an acyl chloride.

C. (a) Caprylamide from an acid; (b) *N*-butylcaproamide from an anhydride; (c) *N*,*N*-dimethylvaleramide from an acyl chloride; (d) *N*-ethylpropionamide from an ester.

37. Give a series of reactions for carrying out the following conversions: (a) *n*-butyramide to *N*-*n*-propylacetamide; (b) *N*-methylcaproamide to ethyl caproate; (c) *N*-*n*-butylacetamide to *n*-butyl acetate; (d) propionamide to *N*,*N*-dimethylpropionamide; (e) *N*,*N*-dimethyl-formamide to nitrosodimethylamine; (f) *N*-nitroso-*N*-tridecylacetamide to tridecyl alcohol; (g) caprylamide to *n*-octylamine; (h) *N*,*N*-di-*i*-propylacetamide to *N*,*N*-di-*i*-propyl-*n*-valer-amide; (i) *i*-amyl alcohol to *N*-*s*-butyl-*i*-valeramide; (j) methyl nonanoate to *N*-nitroso-*N*-ethylnonanoamide.

38. What can be said about the structures of the members of the following pairs of compounds: (a) Two compounds have the molecular formula C_3H_7NO. One reduces Tollens reagent but evolves no nitrogen when treated with nitrous acid, whereas the other evolves nitrogen but does not reduce Tollens reagent. On boiling with aqueous sodium hydroxide each evolves a product that turns red litmus blue. (b) Two compounds have the molecular formula $C_6H_{13}NO$. After each compound is boiled for several hours with hydrochloric acid, the nonaqueous layer from one compound gives the iodoform reaction and that from the other dissolves in dilute aqueous alkali. (c) Two compounds have the molecular formula C_3H_9NO. One evolves methane when treated with methylmagnesium iodide whereas the other does not.

Alkyl Cyanides and Alkyl Isocyanides

39. Give equations for the following preparations:

    A. (*a*) Propionitrile from an alkyl iodide; (*b*) 2-methylbutanoic acid from an alkyl cyanide; (*c*) *i*-propyl isocyanide from an amine; (*d*) (4-methylpentyl)amine from an alkyl cyanide; (*e*) 2-cyano-3-methylbutane from an olefin; (*f*) acetamide from an alkyl cyanide; (*g*) *i*-butyl cyanide from an amide; (*h*) methyl trimethylacetate from an alkyl cyanide; (*i*) *n*-hexyl cyanide from an aldoxime; (*j*) methyl-*n*-butylamine from an alkyl isocyanide.

    B. (*a*) (2-Methylbutyl)amine from an alkyl cyanide; (*b*) *t*-butyl cyanide from an olefin; (*c*) ethyl cyanide from an amide; (*d*) *n*-valeramide from a nitrile; (*e*) ethyl pentadecanoate from myristyl cyanide; (*f*) *n*-octyl cyanide from an aldoxime; (*g*) methyl-*i*-propylamine from an alkyl isocyanide; (*h*) hexanoic acid from an alkyl cyanide; (*i*) *i*-butyronitrile from an alkyl bromide; (*j*) *i*-amyl isocyanide from an amine.

    C. (*a*) Methyl undecanoate from an alkyl cyanide; (*b*) *i*-propyl cyanide from an aldoxime; (*c*) dimethylamine from an isocyanide; (*d*) valeronitrile from an alkyl halide; (*e*) propionic acid from an alkyl cyanide; (*f*) ethyl isocyanide from an amine; (*g*) α-methylheptonitrile from an olefin; (*h*) *t*-butylamine from a nitrile; (*i*) 2-methyloctanoamide from an alkyl cyanide; (*j*) *s*-butyl cyanide from an amide.

40. Give a series of reactions for the following conversions: (*a*) *n*-amyl bromide to *n*-hexylamine; (*b*) ethyl cyanide to *n*-propyl isocyanide; (*c*) *i*-amyl alcohol to 1,2-dimethylpropyl cyanide; (*d*) *n*-butyric acid to *n*-butyronitrile; (*e*) *i*-butyraldehyde to *i*-propyl cyanide; (*f*) caprylamide to *n*-heptyl isocyanide; (*g*) methyl palmitate to hexadecyl cyanide; (*h*) methyl ethyl ketone to *s*-butyl isocyanide; (*i*) *n*-butyl ether to *n*-amylamine; (*j*) propionic acid to *s*-butyl cyanide.

41. How could one distinguish readily between the members of the following groups of compounds: (*a*) *n*-butyl ether, *n*-butyl cyanide, and *n*-butylamine; (*b*) *i*-octyl cyanide, *i*-octyl isocyanide, and *i*-capramide; (*c*) butyronitrile, butyric acid, and butyrone; (*d*) acetaldoxime, acetamide, and stearonitrile; (*e*) acetonitrile, *N*,*N*-dimethylformamide, and *N*,*N*-dimethylacetamide?

Nitroalkanes

42. Give equations for the following preparations:

    A. (*a*) 2-Nitro-2-methylpropane from an amine; (*b*) *i*-propylamine from a nitro compound; (*c*) propionaldehyde from a nitro compound; (*d*) 1-nitroheptane from an oxime; (*e*) acetic acid from a nitro compound; (*f*) 1,3-dihydroxy-2-nitro-2-ethylpropane from a nitro compound.

    B. (*a*) Methyl ethyl ketone from a nitro compound; (*b*) 2-nitrobutane from an oxime; (*c*) ethylamine from a nitro compound; (*d*) 2-nitro-2-methylbutane from an amine; (*e*) 2-nitro-2-methyl-1-propanol from a nitro compound; (*f*) *i*-butyric acid from a nitro compound.

    C. (*a*) 1,3-Dihydroxy-2-nitro-2-methylpropane from a nitro compound; (*b*) 2-nitrooctane from an oxime; (*c*) valeraldehyde from a nitro compound; (*d*) *s*-butylamine from a nitro compound; (*e*) propionic acid from a nitro compound; (*f*) 3-nitro-3-methylpentane from an amine.

43. Give series of reactions that will lead to the following conversions: (*a*) *s*-butyl alcohol to 2,3-dinitrobutane; (*b*) *i*-amyl ether to 1-nitro-3-methylbutane; (*c*) 2-octanone to 2-nitrooctane; (*d*) 1-nitrobutane to *n*-propylamine; (*e*) trimethylacetamide to 2-nitro-2-methylpropane.

44. What tests may be used to distinguish between the members of the following groups of compounds: (*a*) 1-nitropropane, butyronitrile, and *n*-hexylamine; (*b*) nitromethane, 2-nitropropane, and heptanoic acid; (*c*) 2-nitro-2-methylpropane, *n*-propyl ether, and *n*-octane; (*d*) 1-nonene, 1-nitropropane, and 1-nonanol; (*e*) *s*-butyl nitrite, 2-nitrobutane, and butyronitrile.

45. Write electronic formulas for methyl nitrite, nitromethane, the aci form of nitromethane, methyl nitrate, and nitrosonitromethane.

46. Analysis indicated that two compounds had the molecular formula $C_5H_{11}NO_2$. One was fairly soluble in water and the other was insoluble but dissolved in dilute alkali. The water-soluble compound evolved ammonia on boiling with alkali, and vigorous oxidation of the hydrolysis product gave an acid having a neutralization equivalent of 66. When the alkaline solution of the water-insoluble compound was poured into hot 25 per cent sulfuric acid, a product was obtained that gave an iodoform test. What can be said about the structures of the two compounds? Give equations for the reactions involved.

Chapter 13

ALIPHATIC SULFUR COMPOUNDS

Since sulfur is the element below oxygen in the periodic table, a series of organic compounds analogous to the oxygen compounds is known.

R—S—H   Thio alcohols (thiols, mercaptans)

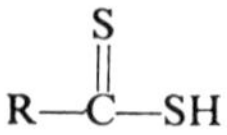

R—S—R   Sulfides (thio ethers)

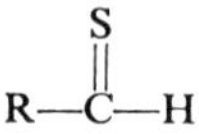

R—S—S—R   Disulfides

$$R-\overset{\overset{O}{\|}}{C}-SH \quad \text{Thio acids}$$

$$R-\overset{\overset{S}{\|}}{C}-SH \quad \text{Dithio acids}$$

$$R-\overset{\overset{S}{\|}}{C}-H \quad \text{Thio aldehydes (thials)}$$

$$R-\overset{\overset{S}{\|}}{C}-R \quad \text{Thio ketones (thiones)}$$

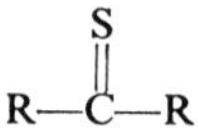

In addition to the oxygen analogs, however, several types of compounds are known in which sulfur is linked to three or four atoms or groups. In these compounds use is made of the unshared pairs of electrons on sulfur for bonding purposes. Where the third and fourth atoms are oxygen, the nature of the bond has not been established with certainty. For most purposes it is satisfactory to extend the simple octet rule to the second period and assume that the bonds to oxygen are semipolar (p. 238), both electrons being supplied by the sulfur atom.

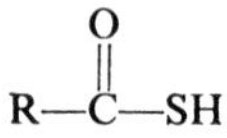

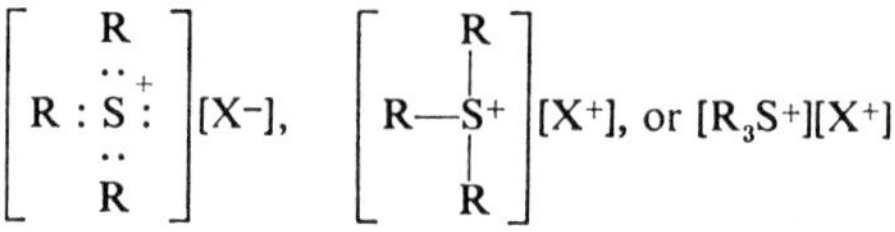

$$\begin{bmatrix} R \\ R : \overset{..}{\underset{..}{S}} : ^+ \\ R \end{bmatrix} [X^-], \quad \begin{bmatrix} R \\ R-\underset{R}{\overset{|}{S^+}} \end{bmatrix} [X^+], \text{ or } [R_3S^+][X^+] \qquad \text{Sulfonium salts}$$

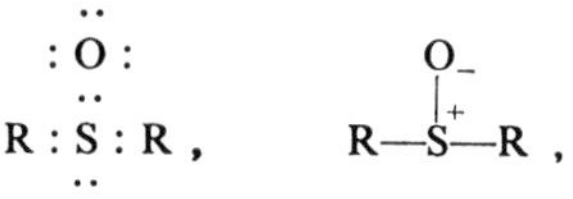

$$: \overset{..}{\underset{..}{O}} : \\ R : \overset{..}{\underset{..}{S}} : R \ , \quad R-\underset{}{\overset{\overset{O_-}{|}}{S^+}}-R \ , \quad RS(O)R, \text{ or } RSOR \qquad \text{Sulfoxides}$$

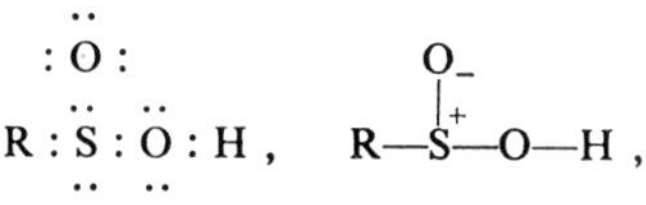

$$: \overset{..}{\underset{..}{O}} : \\ R : \overset{..}{\underset{..}{S}} : \overset{..}{\underset{..}{O}} : H \ , \quad R-\underset{}{\overset{\overset{O_-}{|}}{S^+}}-O-H \ , \quad RS(O)OH, \text{ or } RSO_2H \qquad \text{Sulfinic acids}$$

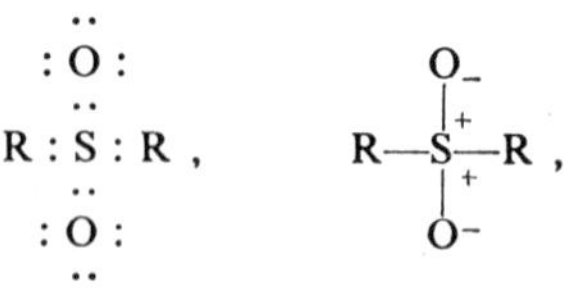

$$: \overset{..}{\underset{..}{O}} : \\ R : \overset{..}{\underset{..}{S}} : R \ , \quad R-\underset{\underset{O^-}{|}}{\overset{\overset{O_-}{|}}{S}}{}^+-R \ , \quad RS(O)_2R, \text{ or } RSO_2R \qquad \text{Sulfones} \\ : \overset{..}{\underset{..}{O}} :$$

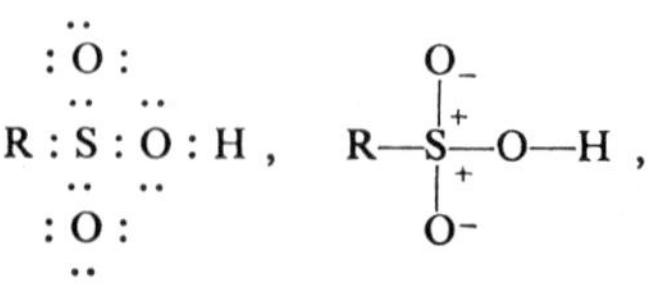

$$: \overset{..}{\underset{..}{O}} : \\ R : \overset{..}{\underset{..}{S}} : \overset{..}{\underset{..}{O}} : H \ , \quad R-\underset{\underset{O^-}{|}}{\overset{\overset{O_-}{|}}{S}}{}^+-O-H \ , \quad RS(O)_2OH, \text{ or } RSO_3H \qquad \text{Sulfonic acids} \\ : \overset{..}{\underset{..}{O}} :$$

272

Previous to the publication in 1916 of the Lewis theory of electronic structure, compounds such as the sulfoxides and sulfinic acids were considered to contain tetracovalent sulfur, one oxygen being bound to sulfur by a double bond. Similarly sulfones and sulfonic acids were considered to contain hexacovalent sulfur and two doubly-bound oxygen atoms.

$$
\begin{array}{cccc}
\underset{\text{Sulfoxides}}{R-\overset{\displaystyle O}{\overset{\|}{S}}-R} &
\underset{\substack{\text{Sulfinic}\\\text{acids}}}{R-\overset{\displaystyle O}{\overset{\|}{S}}-OH} &
\underset{\text{Sulfones}}{R-\overset{\displaystyle O}{\underset{\underset{\displaystyle O}{\|}}{\overset{\|}{S}}}-R} &
\underset{\substack{\text{Sulfonic}\\\text{acids}}}{R-\overset{\displaystyle O}{\underset{\underset{\displaystyle O}{\|}}{\overset{\|}{S}}}-OH}
\end{array}
$$

The nitrogen atom in nitric acid, nitro compounds, and amine oxides was thought to be pentacovalent.

$$
\underset{}{HO-\overset{\displaystyle O}{\overset{\|}{N}}=O} \qquad
\underset{}{R-\overset{\displaystyle O}{\overset{\|}{N}}=O} \qquad
R_3N=O
$$

Postulation by Lewis and by Langmuir of the octet rule required the nitrogen atom in the nitro group and in amine oxides to be tetracovalent, just as it is in the ammonium ion, which in turn required that the bond to one of the oxygen atoms be semipolar (p. 238). This postulation was applied also to the oxygenated compounds of sulfur and phosphorus, and compounds such as sulfur hexafluoride and phosphorus pentachloride were considered to be anomalous exceptions to the general rule.

During the next twenty years, several lines of investigation seemed to confirm the newer concept (p. 352), but in 1937 experimental results on bond distances indicated that these sulfur-oxygen bonds were shorter, and hence stronger, than would be expected for a semipolar bond. Yet it was not until 1944 that the semipolar viewpoint was questioned seriously. Since then, considerable evidence has been produced which indicates that some double bonding results from the interaction of an unshared pair of electrons on oxygen with the sulfur atom.

This interaction can be interpreted in terms of molecular orbital theory. The sulfide molecule, R_2SO, is known to be pyramidal and not planar. Hence only a p orbital or sp^3 hybrid orbital is involved in the formation of the σ bond to oxygen. The double-bonding effect arises from the overlapping of a $3d$ orbital of sulfur with a $2p$ orbital of oxygen as indicated in Figure 50.

Fig. 50. Bond formation resulting from overlapping of a $3d$ orbital with a $2p$ orbital.

Calculations show that the overlap is sufficient to form a fairly strong π bond. The double bonding accounts for the increased bond strength, decreased interatomic distance, and lower bond moment than would be expected for a single coordinate covalence. This type of interaction is not possible between oxygen and nitrogen because of the absence of $2d$ orbitals. Sulfones, R_2SO_2, and sulfonic acids, RSO_2OH, differ from the sulfoxides and sulfinic acids only in that the sulfur orbitals used for σ bond formation must be sp^3 hybrids. Similar considerations apply also to phosphorus and in modified form to silicon.

In current literature the tendency has been to revert to the old symbolism, $>S=O$ and $>S{\big\langle}{\overset{\displaystyle O}{\underset{\displaystyle O}{}}}$, to indicate the double-bond character of the sulfur-oxygen linkages. No distinction is made between a carbon-oxygen double bond and a sulfur-oxygen double bond. Yet the differences are far greater than the resemblances. In a carbon-oxygen double bond, such as that in a ketone, $R_2C=O$, the σ bond is the result of the overlapping of an sp^2 hybrid orbital and a p orbital, and the carbon valences are planar. The π bond results from the overlapping of two p orbitals (p. 50). Reagents, such as hydrogen, can add to the double bond with the formation of new strong single σ bonds. Addition of reagents to the sulfur-oxygen type of double bond does not take place because the four-lobed character of the d orbitals in general does not permit sufficient overlap of pure d orbitals or s—p—d hybrid orbitals with s, p, or s—p hybrid orbitals to permit the formation of strong σ bonds. Conceivably a new symbol for the sulfur-oxygen double bond would be useful. One way of envisioning the bond is to consider the σ p—p or sp^3—p bond as a dative bond with the sulfur atom supplying both electrons, and the π d—p bond as a dative bond with the oxygen atom supplying both electrons. This view might be symbolized as S $\rightleftarrows$ O. But if an attempt were made to use a different symbol for every type of bond, an undesirable multiplicity would result. Since in its chemical behavior the sulfur-oxygen double bond resembles the nitrogen-oxygen semipolar bond more closely than the carbon-oxygen double bond, it seems preferable to retain the semipolar symbolism with the understanding that the difference in charge and the bond distance is less than in the nitrogen-oxygen semipolar bond. When a formula is printed in a linear style, the oxygen involved may be placed in parentheses, for example, RS(O)R, to avoid confusion with the hypothetical compound R—S—O—R.

THIO ALCOHOLS (THIOLS, MERCAPTANS)

Preparation

1. **From Alkyl Halides or Sulfates, and Sodium Hydrosulfide.** Thio alcohols (mercaptans) are formed when an alkyl halide is refluxed with an alcoholic solution of sodium hydrosulfide.

$$RX + NaSH \longrightarrow RSH + NaX$$

A more convenient procedure consists of dissolving the alcohol in sulfuric acid, neutralizing with sodium carbonate, and mixing with sodium hydrosulfide solution prepared by saturating sodium hydroxide solution with hydrogen sulfide.

$$ROH + H_2SO_4 \longrightarrow ROSO_3H + H_2O$$

$$2\,ROSO_3H + Na_2CO_3 \longrightarrow 2\,ROSO_3Na + CO_2 + H_2O$$

$$ROSO_3Na + NaSH \longrightarrow RSH + Na_2SO_4$$

Whether alkyl halides or alkyl sulfates are used, some alkyl sulfide always is formed because of the equilibrium

$$RSH + NaSH \rightleftharpoons RSNa + H_2S$$

The sodium thioalkoxide (sodium mercaptide) can react with a second mole of alkyl halide or sulfate.

$$RSNa + RX \longrightarrow RSR + NaX$$

The sodium hydrosulfide ordinarily is used in large excess. Because of the alkalinity of sodium hydrosulfide solution, another competing reaction is present, namely loss of mineral acid to give olefins. Hence yields of mercaptans or sulfides are best if the alkyl group is primary, whereas only olefin is formed if it is tertiary.

2. **From Olefins and Hydrogen Sulfide.** Hydrogen sulfide adds smoothly to olefins in the liquid phase under the influence of light of short wavelength (ca. 2800 Å). Addition does not follow the Markovnikov rule, the products from 1-alkenes being primary alkyl hydrogen sulfides.

$$RCH{=}CH_2 + H_2S \xrightarrow{h\nu} RCH_2CH_2SH$$

The reaction takes place by a free-radical mechanism.

Initiation $\qquad$ $H_2S \xrightarrow{h\nu} H\cdot + \cdot SH$

Propagation $\qquad$ $RCH{=}CH_2 + \cdot SH \longrightarrow RCHCH_2SH$

$RCHCH_2SH + H_2S \longrightarrow RCH_2CH_2SH + \cdot SH$

Termination $\qquad$ $RCHCH_2SH + \cdot SH \longrightarrow RCHCH_2SH$
$$\overset{|}{S}H$$

$RCHCH_2SH + H\cdot \longrightarrow RCH_2CH_2SH$

$H\cdot + \cdot SH \longrightarrow H_2S$

Addition contrary to the Markovnikov rule is characteristic of free-radical mechanisms (p. 61).

Unsymmetrically substituted olefins add hydrogen sulfide in the liquid phase at high temperature and pressure in the presence of a silica-alumina catalyst to give tertiary alkyl hydrogen sulfides.

$$R_2CH{=}CH_2 + H_2S \xrightarrow[200°,\ 1000\ \text{p.s.i.}]{SiO_2-Al_2O_3} R_2CHSH$$
$$\overset{|}{C}H_3$$

This reaction follows the Markovnikov rule. It undoubtedly takes place by an ionic mechanism, the alumina acting as an acid catalyst.

3. **From Alkyl Dithiocarbamates.** When ammonia reacts with carbon disulfide, the ammonium salt of dithiocarbamic acid (p. 325) is formed, which can react with alkyl halides to give alkyl dithiocarbamates. The latter compounds are esters and can be saponified to the thio alcohol.

$$CS_2 + 2\ NH_3 \longrightarrow \left[H_2N{-}\overset{\overset{S}{\|}}{C}{-}S^- \right][NH_4^+]$$

$[H_2NCSS^-]NH_4^+ + RX \longrightarrow H_2NCSSR + NH_4X$

$H_2NCSSR + 2\ NaOH \longrightarrow RSNa + NaSCN + 2\ H_2O$

$RSNa + HCl \longrightarrow RSH + NaCl$

The method has been recommended for halides that lose halogen acid readily, and for making thioglycols.

4. **By Reduction of Disulfides.** The reduction may be carried out by adding zinc dust to a boiling mixture of disulfide (p. 280) and 50 per cent aqueous sulfuric acid.

$$RSSR + 2[H]\ (Zn + H_2SO_4) \longrightarrow 2\ RSH$$

5. **From S-alkylthioureas.** Alkyl halides react with thiourea (p. 326) to give S-alkylthioureas, which on heating yield mercaptans and dicyandiamide (p. 320).

$$RX + S=C\underset{NH_2}{\overset{NH_2}{\diagup}} \longrightarrow RSC\underset{NH_2}{\overset{\overset{+}{NH_2}X^-}{\diagup}} \overset{NaOH}{\longrightarrow} RSC\underset{NH_2}{\overset{NH}{\diagup}} + NaX + H_2O$$

An S-alkyl-thiourea

$$RSC\underset{NH_2}{\overset{NH}{\diagup}} \overset{Heat}{\longrightarrow} RSH + H_2NC\equiv N \overset{2\ Moles}{\longrightarrow} H_2N-\underset{\underset{NH}{\|}}{C}-NHCN$$

Cyanamide

Dicyandiamide

Nomenclature

The following examples indicate the usual methods of nomenclature: CH_3SH, methyl mercaptan or methanethiol; $CH_3CH_2CHSHCH_3$, s-butyl mercaptan or 1-methyl-1-propanethiol. The —SH group is known as the *sulfhydryl* group, or more commonly as the *mercapto* group. The last term may be used as a prefix for polyfunctional compounds, for example $HSCH_2COOH$, mercaptoacetic acid.

Physical Properties

If the boiling points of dicovalent sulfur compounds are compared with those of analogous oxygen, nitrogen, and carbon compounds of approximately the same molecular weight (Table 16) it is evident that the boiling points of mercaptans are much more nearly normal than those of alcohols or of primary or secondary amines. Although the mercaptans boil somewhat higher than

TABLE 16

BOILING POINTS OF WATER, AMMONIA, HYDROGEN SULFIDE, AND METHANE, AND OF THEIR ALKYL DERIVATIVES

OXYGEN COMPOUNDS			NITROGEN COMPOUNDS			SULFUR COMPOUNDS			CARBON COMPOUNDS		
Compd.	Mol. wt.	B.p.	Compd.	Mol. wt.	B.p.	Compd.	Mol. wt.	B.p.	Compd.	Mol. wt.	B.p.
H_2O	18	+100	NH_3	17	−33				CH_4	16	−161
CH_3OH	32	+65	CH_3NH_2	31	−7	H_2S	34	−61	C_2H_6	30	−89
C_2H_5OH	46	+78	$C_2H_5NH_2$	45	+17	CH_3SH	48	+6	C_3H_8	44	−42
$(CH_3)_2O$	46	−24	$(CH_3)_2NH$	45	+7						
n-C_3H_7OH	60	+98	n-$C_3H_7NH_2$	59	+49	C_2H_5SH	62	+37	n-C_4H_{10}	58	−1
i-C_3H_7OH	60	+82	$CH_3NHC_2H_5$	59	+32				i-C_4H_{10}	58	−10
$CH_3OC_2H_5$	60	+11	$(CH_3)_3N$	59	+4	$(CH_3)_2S$	62	+38			

hydrocarbons of the same molecular weight, the higher boiling point cannot be ascribed to proton bonding, because ethyl mercaptan and methyl sulfide boil at almost the same temperature. This behavior is in marked contrast to that of the propyl alcohols and methyl ethyl ether, or of methylethylamine and trimethylamine. The rise in boiling points of the series n-butane, trimethylamine, methyl ethyl ether, and methyl sulfide can be ascribed to the rise in dipole moment, the measured or estimated values of μ being respectively 0, 0.6, 1.2, and 1.6.

Mercaptans are much less soluble in water than the corresponding alcohols, only 1.5 g. of ethyl mercaptan being soluble in 100 cc. of water at room temperature. This low water solubility can be ascribed to the inability of sulfur to form proton bonds with hydrogen attached to oxygen, as well as with hydrogen attached to sulfur.

Physiological Properties

The volatile mercaptans have an extremely disagreeable odor. E. Fischer found that the nose can detect one volume of ethyl mercaptan in 50 billion volumes of air. This concentration expressed in terms of weight per cubic centimeter of air is 1/250 of the concentration of sodium which Kirchhoff and Bunsen were able to detect by means of the spectroscope. The obnoxious odor of mercaptans decreases with increasing molecular weight, and the odor becomes pleasant above nine carbon atoms. Like hydrogen sulfide, the lower mercaptans are toxic.

Reactions

1. **Salt Formation.** Just as hydrogen sulfide is more acidic than water, the mercaptans are more acidic than alcohols and react with aqueous solutions of strong bases to form salts. Like sodium sulfide these salts are hydrolyzed markedly in aqueous solution.

$$RSH + NaOH \rightleftharpoons RSNa + H_2O$$

The heavy metal salts, such as those of lead, mercury, copper, cadmium, and silver, are insoluble in water. The ease of formation of insoluble mercury salts gave rise to the name mercaptan (L. *mercurium captans*, seizing mercury). Standardized aqueous silver nitrate can be used for the estimation of mercaptans.

2. **Oxidation to Disulfides.** Sodium hypohalite solutions oxidize mercaptans to disulfides at room temperature.

$$2\,RSH + I_2 + 2\,NaOH \longrightarrow RSSR + 2\,NaI + 2\,H_2O$$

If a standard iodine solution is used, this reaction is suitable for the quantitative estimation of mercaptans. They are oxidized readily also by air, especially in the presence of ammonia. The *doctor process* for sweetening gasoline depends on the oxidation of mercaptans to less odorous disulfides by means of sodium plumbite solutions and a small amount of free sulfur.

$$2\,RSH + Na_2PbO_2 \longrightarrow Pb(SR)_2 + 2\,NaOH$$

$$Pb(SR)_2 + S \longrightarrow PbS + (RS)_2$$

The doctor solution is regenerated by passing air through the hot solution.

$$PbS + 4\,NaOH + 2\,O_2 \longrightarrow Na_2PbO_2 + Na_2SO_4 + 2\,H_2O$$

Doctor solution can be used also to test for the presence of the sulfhydryl group. The formation of black lead sulfide indicates a positive reaction. The oxidation of sulfhydryl groups from the cysteine portion of protein molecules (pp. 298, 303) to disulfide groups and reduction of disulfide to sulfhydryl plays an important part in biological processes.

3. Oxidation to Sulfonic Acids. This reaction usually is brought about by heating the mercaptan or a salt such as the lead mercaptide with concentrated nitric acid (p. 286).

$$RSH + 3 [O] (HNO_3) \longrightarrow RSO_3H$$

$$(RS)_2Pb + 6 [O] (HNO_3) \longrightarrow (RSO_3)_2Pb$$

4. Ester Formation. When primary thiols react with carboxylic acids, thioesters and water are formed rather than esters and hydrogen sulfide.

$$RCOOH + HSR \rightleftharpoons RCOSR + H_2O$$

This reaction was the original basis for the assumption that in the esterification of primary alcohols with acids the hydroxyl group is removed from the acid rather than from the alcohol, an assumption which has been proved by the use of the O^{18} isotope (p. 169).

Mercaptans react also with acyl halides to give thioesters.

$$RSH + ClCOR \longrightarrow RSCOR + HCl$$

In contrast to the hydroxyl group, the mercapto group is not replaced readily. For example, phosphorus trichloride reacts to give a thioester.

$$RSH + PCl_3 \longrightarrow RSPCl_2 + HCl$$

5. Thioacetal Formation. Thiols react readily with both aldehydes and ketones in the presence of hydrogen chloride or zinc chloride to give thioacetals.

$$RCHO + 2 R'SH \longrightarrow RCH(SR')_2 + H_2O$$

$$R_2CO + 2 R'SH \longrightarrow R_2C(SR')_2 + H_2O$$

These compounds are much more stable to acid hydrolysis than acetals, but the aldehyde or ketone can be regenerated by hydrolyzing in the presence of mercuric oxide.

SULFIDES

Preparation

Sulfides ordinarily are prepared by the reaction of alkyl halides or sulfates with sodium sulfide or sodium mercaptides in alcoholic solution.

$$2 RX + Na_2S \longrightarrow R_2S + 2 NaX$$

$$RX + NaSR' \longrightarrow RSR' + NaX$$

The first reaction gives simple sulfides, and the second may be used to prepare mixed sulfides.

Nomenclature

The nomenclature of sulfides is evident from the following examples: $C_2H_5SC_2H_5$, ethyl sulfide or ethylthioethane; $CH_3SCH_2CH(CH_3)_2$, methyl *i*-butyl sulfide or 1-methylthio-2-methylpropane. The Geneva names rarely are used except for polyfunctional compounds. Although names such as diethyl sulfide instead of ethyl sulfide are used, the prefix *di* is unnecessary.

Reactions

1. **Oxidation to Sulfoxides.** At room temperature sulfides react with nitric acid, chromium trioxide, or hydrogen peroxide to give sulfoxides.

$$R—S—R + [O] \, (HNO_3, \, CrO_3, \, or \, H_2O_2) \longrightarrow R—\overset{O^-}{\underset{}{\overset{|}{S^+}}}—R \quad (RSOR)$$

Sulfides can be determined quantitatively by oxidation with aqueous bromine and titration of the hydrogen bromide produced.

$$R_2S + Br_2 + H_2O \longrightarrow R_2SO + 2\,HBr$$

2. **Oxidation to Sulfones.** Hydrogen peroxide in glacial acetic acid, fuming nitric acid, or potassium permanganate at elevated temperatures oxidizes sulfides to sulfones, which are very resistant to further oxidation.

$$R—S—R + 2[O] \, (H_2O_2, \, HNO_3, \, or \, KMnO_4) \longrightarrow R—\overset{O^-}{\underset{O^-}{\overset{|+}{\underset{|+}{S}}}}—R \quad (RSO_2R)$$

Oxidation by hydrogen peroxide is catalyzed by strong acids. The mechanism of catalysis appears to be the formation of the conjugate acid of hydrogen peroxide, which, because of the positive charge on one oxygen atom, can transfer $\left[\overset{..}{\underset{..}{O}}H^+ \right]$ to the unshared pair of electrons of the sulfur atom more readily than can hydrogen peroxide.

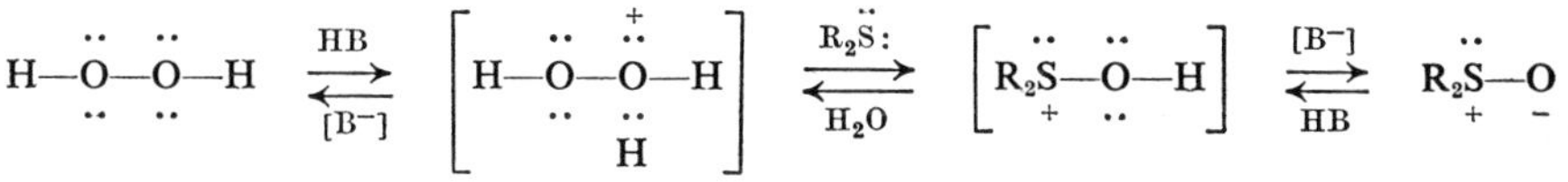

$$H—\overset{..}{\underset{..}{O}}—\overset{..}{\underset{..}{O}}—H \underset{[B^-]}{\overset{HB}{\rightleftarrows}} \left[H—\overset{..}{\underset{..}{O}}—\overset{..}{\overset{+}{O}}—H \atop H \right] \underset{H_2O}{\overset{R_2\overset{..}{S}:}{\rightleftarrows}} \left[R_2\overset{..}{\underset{+}{S}}—\overset{..}{\underset{..}{O}}—H \right] \underset{HB}{\overset{[B^-]}{\rightleftarrows}} R_2\overset{..}{S}—O \atop + \quad -$$

The oxidation of tertiary amines by hydrogen peroxide (p. 240) appears to take place by a similar mechanism.

3. **Formation of Sulfonium Salts.** Sulfides react with alkyl halides to give sulfonium salts analogous to the reaction of tertiary amines to give quaternary ammonium salts.

$$R:\overset{..}{\underset{..}{S}}: + R:X \longrightarrow \left[R—\overset{..}{\overset{+}{S}}—R \atop R \right][X^-]$$

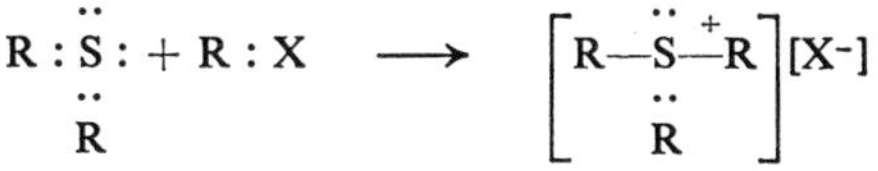

If the R groups are not all alike, this reaction is complicated by the fact that the sulfonium salts dissociate more readily than quaternary ammonium salts. For example, the following reactions may occur leading to a mixture of all the possible sulfonium salts.

$$R_2S + R'X \longrightarrow [R_2R'S^+][X^-]$$
$$[R_2R'S^+][X^-] \rightleftarrows RSR' + RX$$
$$RSR' + R'X \longrightarrow [RR'_2S^+][X^-]$$
$$R_2S + RX \longrightarrow [R_3S^+][X^-]$$
$$[RR'_2S^+][X^-] \rightleftarrows R'_2S + RX$$
$$R'_2S + R'X \longrightarrow [R'_3S^+][X^-]$$

Reaction of sulfides with halogen gives dihalides, which probably have structures analogous to those of the sulfonium salts.

$$R : \overset{..}{\underset{R}{S}} : + : \overset{..}{\underset{..}{Cl}} : \overset{..}{\underset{..}{Cl}} : \quad \longrightarrow \quad \left[R : \overset{..}{\underset{R}{S}} \overset{+}{\underset{..}{:}} \overset{..}{\underset{..}{Cl}} : \right] \left[: \overset{..}{\underset{..}{Cl}} \overset{-}{:} \right]$$

4. Scission of C—S Bond. The sulfides are even more stable to scission reactions than ethers. In this respect they resemble the amines. The C—S bond can be split by means of bromocyanogen by a reaction analogous to that used to remove an alkyl group from a tertiary amine (p. 239).

$$R_2S + BrCN \quad \longrightarrow \quad [R_2\overset{..}{S}\overset{+}{:} CN][Br^-] \quad \overset{Heat}{\longrightarrow} \quad RBr + RSCN$$

Similarly when chlorine is passed into a solution of a sulfide in acetic acid containing some water, the sulfide is cleaved with the formation of a sulfenyl chloride and alkyl chloride. The sulfenyl chloride then is oxidized to the sulfonyl chloride.

$$R_2S + Cl_2 \quad \longrightarrow \quad [R_2\overset{..}{S}\overset{+}{:} Cl][Cl^-] \quad \rightleftarrows \quad RSCl + RCl$$

$$RSCl + 2\,Cl_2 + 2\,H_2O \quad \longrightarrow \quad RSO_2Cl + 4\,HCl$$

DISULFIDES

Preparation

1. **By Oxidation of Mercaptans** (p. 277).
2. **From Alkyl Halides or Sulfates, and Sodium Disulfide.**

$$2\,RX + Na_2S_2 \quad \longrightarrow \quad RSSR + 2\,NaX$$

Sodium disulfide is prepared by dissolving an equivalent amount of sulfur in a concentrated aqueous solution of sodium sulfide. The aqueous solution is diluted with alcohol, heated to boiling, and the alkyl halide added.

Nomenclature

Disulfides are named as such; for example, $(CH_3)_2S_2$ is methyl disulfide, and $CH_3SSC_2H_5$ is methyl ethyl disulfide.

Reactions

1. **Reduction to Mercaptans.** The reduction by means of zinc dust and acid has been discussed (p. 275). A second interesting method consists of the scission with metallic sodium.

$$RSSR + 2\,Na \quad \longrightarrow \quad 2\,RSNa$$

The rate of this reaction increases rapidly with increasing molecular weight of the alkyl group. Methyl and ethyl disulfides are very unreactive, whereas the reaction of *n*-butyl disulfide must be controlled by cooling.

The reduction to mercaptans is used for the estimation of disulfides. The mercaptan formed is determined by means of standard silver nitrate solution (p. 277). The chemical reactions involved in the permanent waving of hair consist of the reduction of disulfide linkages followed by regeneration of disulfide bonds by oxidation (p. 299).

2. **Oxidation to Sulfonic Acids.** Like the mercaptans, disulfides may be oxidized to sulfonic acids by heating with strong oxidizing agents such as 50 per cent nitric acid.

$$RSSR + 5 [O] (HNO_3) + H_2O \longrightarrow 2 RSO_2OH$$

3. **Oxidation to Thiosulfonates.**

$$RS-SR + 2 H_2O_2 \longrightarrow R-\overset{\overset{O_-}{\underset{\underset{O^-}{|_+}}{|_+}}}{S}-SR + 2 H_2O$$

The product formed by this reaction is identical with that from the reaction of a sulfonyl chloride with a mercaptan.

$$RSO_2Cl + HSR \longrightarrow R-\overset{\overset{O_-}{\underset{\underset{O^-}{|_+}}{|_+}}}{S}-SR + HCl$$

4. **Addition to Olefins.** In the presence of acid catalysts, disulfides add to olefins to give thio diethers.

$$R_2S_2 + R'CH=CHR' \xrightarrow{\text{HF or BF}_3} RSCHR'CHR'SR$$

5. **Reaction with Alkyl Iodides to Give Sulfonium Salts.** This reaction takes place in the presence of mercuric iodide or ferric chloride as a catalyst.

$$RSSR + 4 RI \xrightarrow[\substack{or \\ FeCl_3}]{HgI_2} 2 [R_3S^+]I^- + I_2$$

POLYSULFIDES

The ability of sulfur atoms to bond with each other and form long chains and large rings is reflected in the existence of organic polysulfides. Thus the reaction of alkyl halides with sodium polysulfides leads to the formation of mixtures of alkyl polysulfides.

$$2 RX + Na_2S_x \longrightarrow R-S_x-R + 2 NaX$$

Physical evidence indicates that the sulfur atoms in these compounds are linked linearly even though some of the sulfur can be removed by boiling with aqueous sodium hydroxide.

THIO ALDEHYDES (THIALS) AND THIO KETONES (THIONES)

The thio aldehydes and thio ketones can be prepared from aldehydes or ketones and hydrogen sulfide in the presence of aqueous or alcoholic hydrogen chloride.

$$RCHO + H_2S \xrightarrow{HCl} R\overset{\overset{S}{||}}{C}H + H_2O$$

$$R_2CO + H_2S \xrightarrow{HCl} R_2C{=}S + H_2O$$

The aliphatic compounds polymerize to trimers, $(RCHS)_3$ and $(R_2CS)_3$, which are cyclic trisulfides and can be oxidized to trisulfones. It is said that the odor of thioacetone is so obnoxious that Baumann and Fromm had to abandon their work with the compound because of the protests of the city of Freiburg (Germany).

THIO CARBOXYLIC ACIDS AND DITHIO CARBOXYLIC ACIDS

Thio carboxylic acids may be prepared by the action of phosphorus penta-sulfide on a carboxylic acid.

$$RCOOH + P_2S_5 \longrightarrow RCOSH + P_2OS_4$$

Structural theory calls for the existence of a second isomer, RCSOH. Only one substance has been isolated, however, because the two forms readily inter-convert; that is, they are tautomeric (pp. 207, 822).

$$\underset{\text{O}}{R\overset{\text{O}}{\overset{\|}{C}}-SH} \rightleftarrows R-\overset{\text{OH}}{\underset{}{\overset{|}{C}}}=S$$

The **esters** of the two structures are stable isomers. One isomer may be made from an acid chloride and a mercaptan and the other from an imido ester hydrochloride and hydrogen sulfide.

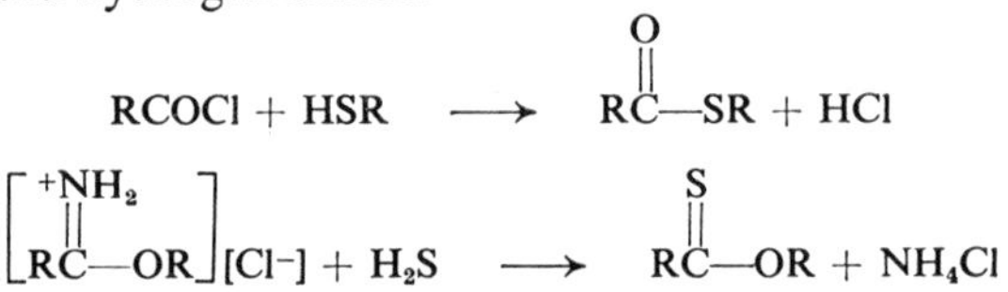

$$RCOCl + HSR \longrightarrow R\overset{\text{O}}{\overset{\|}{C}}-SR + HCl$$

$$\left[R\overset{+NH_2}{\overset{\|}{C}}-OR \right][Cl^-] + H_2S \longrightarrow R\overset{S}{\overset{\|}{C}}-OR + NH_4Cl$$

Thioamides on the other hand are again tautomeric.

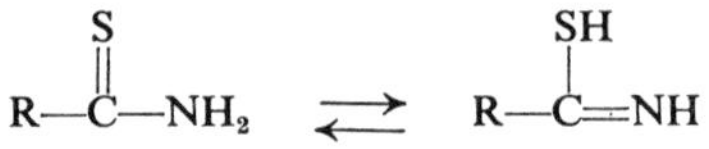

$$R\overset{S}{\overset{\|}{C}}-NH_2 \rightleftarrows R-\overset{SH}{\underset{}{\overset{|}{C}}}=NH$$

They are prepared by the reaction of an amide with phosphorus pentasulfide.

$$RCONH_2 + P_2S_5 \longrightarrow RCSNH_2 + P_2OS_4$$

The **dithio acids** are made by the reaction of carbon disulfide with Grignard reagents.

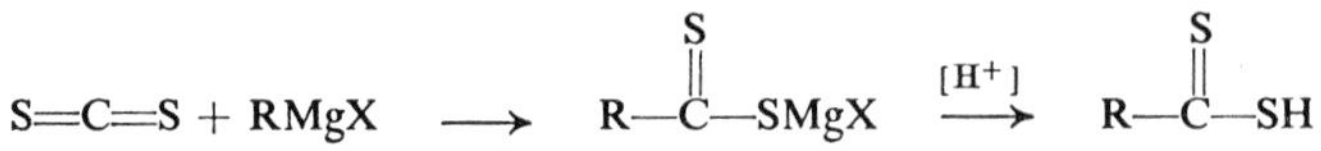

$$S=C=S + RMgX \longrightarrow R\overset{S}{\overset{\|}{C}}-SMgX \overset{[H^+]}{\longrightarrow} R\overset{S}{\overset{\|}{C}}-SH$$

They are colored oils having an unbearable odor and are oxidized by air.

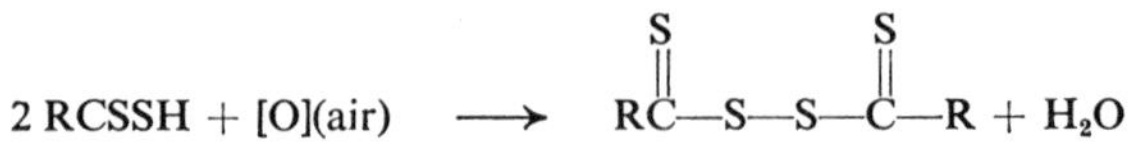

$$2\,RCSSH + [O](air) \longrightarrow R\overset{S}{\overset{\|}{C}}-S-S-\overset{S}{\overset{\|}{C}}-R + H_2O$$

Dithio esters can be made by the addition of a mercaptan to a nitrile, followed by reaction with hydrogen sulfide.

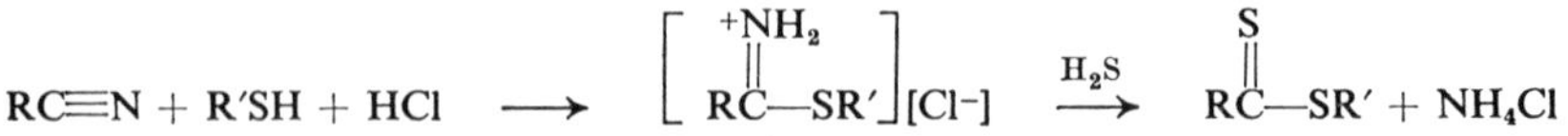

$$RC{\equiv}N + R'SH + HCl \longrightarrow \left[R\overset{+NH_2}{\overset{\|}{C}}-SR' \right][Cl^-] \overset{H_2S}{\longrightarrow} R\overset{S}{\overset{\|}{C}}-SR' + NH_4Cl$$

These reactions are analogous to those for the formation of imido ester hydro-chlorides and their hydrolysis to esters (p. 248).

SULFONIUM SALTS

Sulfonium salts, $[R_3S^+]X^-$, ordinarily formed by the reaction of sulfides or disulfides with alkyl iodides (pp. 279, 281), are strongly ionized in aqueous solution. They react with silver hydroxide to give sulfonium hydroxides.

$$[R_3S^+]X^- + AgOH \longrightarrow [R_3S^+]OH^- + AgX$$

Sulfonium hydroxides are strong bases analogous to the quaternary ammonium hydroxides (p. 241). Likewise they decompose in a similar way to give sulfides and olefins.

$$[(C_2H_5)_3S^+]OH^- \xrightarrow{\text{Heat}} (C_2H_5)_2S + C_2H_4 + H_2O$$

Sulfonium salts dissociate more easily than quaternary ammonium salts (cf. p. 279).

$$[R_3S^+]X^- \rightleftarrows R_2S + RX$$

Although the sulfur atom in the sulfonium ion still has an unshared pair of electrons, the positive charge holds the pair too strongly to permit reaction with a second molecule of alkyl halide to give a tetraalkylsulfonium ion with two positive charges of the type $[R_4S^{++}]2\ X^-$. Sulfonium salts react with halogen and with some metallic salts to give stable complexes, which probably have this type of structure.

$$[R_3S^+]X^- + X_2 \longrightarrow [R_3SX^{++}]\ 2\ X^-$$

Selenium, in which the valence electrons are farther from the nucleus, is able to form tetraalkylselenonium dihalides of the type $[R_4Se^{++}]2\ X^-$.

SULFOXIDES

Sulfoxides ordinarily are prepared by the reaction of sulfides with the theoretical amount of 30 per cent hydrogen peroxide in acetone or acetic acid solution at room temperature.

$$R_2S + H_2O_2 \longrightarrow R_2\overset{+}{S}{-}\overset{-}{O} + H_2O$$

They may be prepared also by the hydrolysis of dihalides (p. 280),

$$[R_2\overset{+}{S}Cl][Cl^-] + H_2O \rightleftarrows R_2SO + 2\ HCl$$

and by the reaction of Grignard reagents with thionyl chloride or with alkyl sulfites.

$$2\ RMgX + SOCl_2 \longrightarrow R_2SO + 2\ MgX_2$$
$$2\ RMgX + SO(OR)_2 \longrightarrow R_2SO + Mg(OR)_2 + MgX_2$$

Sulfoxides may be reduced to sulfides with zinc and acetic acid, or oxidized to sulfones with excess hydrogen peroxide in glacial acetic acid at 100° or with alkaline permanganate or hot fuming nitric acid.

If one of the alkyl groups of a sulfoxide contains hydrogen on the carbon atom α to the sulfoxide group, heating with hydrochloric acid causes a scission of the sulfoxide with the formation of an aldehyde or ketone and a mercaptan.

$$RCH_2SOR + HCl \longrightarrow \left[\overset{OH}{\underset{+}{RCH_2SR}}\right][Cl^-] \longrightarrow H_2O + [RCH{=}\overset{+}{S}R][Cl^-]$$

$$[RCH{=}\overset{+}{S}R]Cl^- + H_2O \longrightarrow RCHO + HSR + HCl$$

Ordinarily sulfoxides are named as such. In the Geneva system the *SO group* is called a *sulfinyl group*. Thus $C_4H_9SOC_4H_9$ is *n*-butyl sulfoxide or 1-butyl-sulfinylbutane, and $CH_3SOCH(CH_3)_2$ is methyl *i*-propyl sulfoxide or 2-methyl-sulfinylpropane.

The sulfoxides are solids or thick viscous oils that supercool and crystallize with difficulty. They are soluble in organic solvents, and the lower members are very soluble in water because of proton bonding of water molecules to the oxygen atom. Like amine oxides, they have a high dipole moment and a high boiling point. Methyl sulfoxide boils at 189° with some decomposition. It dissolves a wide variety of organic compounds and potentially is a valuable high-boiling solvent. It decomposes violently in the presence of organic or inorganic acid halides.

SULFINIC ACIDS

Sulfinic acids may be obtained by passing sulfur dioxide into a solution of Grignard reagent and liberating the free acid from the halomagnesium salt by adding mineral acid,

$$RMgX + SO_2 \longrightarrow R\overset{O_-}{\underset{+}{S}}-OMgX \xrightarrow{HX} R\overset{O_-}{\underset{+}{S}}-OH + MgX_2$$

or by cleavage of a sulfone or a disulfone with sodium or alkali (pp. 285, 286).

The aliphatic sulfinic acids usually are unstable and are isolated as their salts. The free acids slowly undergo oxidation and reduction (disproportionation), which is followed by esterification to give the sulfonic acid and the sulfonic thio ester as the final products.

$$2\ RSO_2H \longrightarrow [RSOH] + RSO_3H$$

$$[RSOH] + RSO_2H \longrightarrow RSO_2SR + H_2O$$

Their salts can be obtained also by reducing sulfonyl chlorides (p. 287) with zinc dust or with sodium sulfite.

$$2\ RSO_2Cl + 2\ Zn \longrightarrow (RSO_2)_2Zn + ZnCl_2$$

$$RSO_2Cl + Na_2SO_3 + 2\ NaOH \longrightarrow RSO_2Na + Na_2SO_4 + NaCl + H_2O$$

The sulfinic acids can be oxidized to sulfonic acids

$$RSOOH + [O]\ (air) \longrightarrow RSO_2OH$$

and reduced to mercaptans.

$$RSO_2H + 4\ [H]\ (Zn + H_2SO_4) \longrightarrow RSH + 2\ H_2O$$

The last reaction affords proof that the sulfur atom in sulfinic and sulfonic acids is united directly to carbon.

The **alkanesulfinyl chlorides,** RSOCl, are obtained readily by the partial hydrolysis of alkyldichlorosulfonium chlorides. The latter are prepared by the reaction of mercaptans or disulfides with chlorine.

$$RSH + 2\ Cl_2 \longrightarrow RSCl_3 + HCl$$

$$RSSR + 3\ Cl_2 \longrightarrow 2\ RSCl_3$$

$$RSCl_3 + H_2O \longrightarrow RSOCl + 2\ HCl$$

SULFONES

Sulfones usually are prepared by oxidizing sulfides or sulfoxides at elevated temperature with an excess of hydrogen peroxide in glacial acetic acid or with fuming nitric acid or potassium permanganate (p. 279). They are formed also by the reaction of alkali sulfinates with primary alkyl halides.

$$RSO_2Na + RBr \longrightarrow R_2SO_2 + NaBr$$

Alkyl sulfinates might be expected from this reaction, but the alkyl group combines with the unshared pair of electrons on the sulfur atom of the sulfinate ion, $[R—\overset{..}{\underset{..}{S}}O_2]$, rather than with an unshared pair on an oxygen atom (cf. p. 259).

Reaction of sulfinates with acyl halides yields α-oxo sulfones, and with sulfonyl halides, disulfones.

$$RSO_2Na + ClCOR \longrightarrow RSO_2COR + NaCl$$

$$RSO_2Na + ClSO_2R \longrightarrow RSO_2SO_2R + NaCl$$

Olefins react with sulfur dioxide in the presence of peroxides to give linear polymeric sulfones.

$$n\,R_2C{=}CR_2 + n\,SO_2 \longrightarrow \left[\begin{array}{c} R\;\;R \\ | \;\;\; | \\ -C-C-SO_2- \\ | \;\;\; | \\ R\;\;R \end{array} \right]_n$$

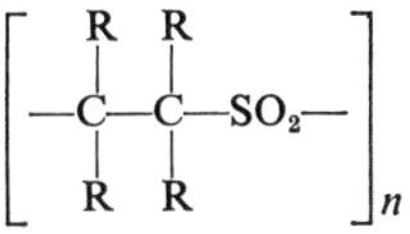

Conjugated dienes (p. 707) add sulfur dioxide in the 1,4 positions to give monomeric cyclic sulfones, which decompose to the original reactants when heated.

$$CH_2{=}CH{-}CH{=}CH_2 + SO_2 \rightleftarrows \begin{array}{c} CH{=}CH \\ | \qquad | \\ CH_2 \quad CH_2 \\ \diagdown \;\; \diagup \\ SO_2 \end{array}$$

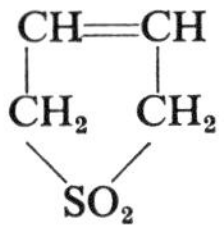

Sulfones are colorless stable solids. The lower members are soluble in water, and although high-boiling, are distillable without decomposition. In contrast to the sulfoxides, sulfones are not readily reduced to sulfides. Some can be reduced to sulfides by heating with sulfur near the boiling point. If heated with Raney nickel containing adsorbed hydrogen, the sulfur is removed completely, yielding saturated hydrocarbons.

$$R_2SO_2 + 3\,H_2 + Ni \longrightarrow 2\,RH + 2\,H_2O + NiS$$

The same type of reaction takes place with sulfoxides, sulfides, and mercaptans.

When sulfones are heated with selenium, alkyl selenides and sulfur dioxide are formed.

$$R_2SO_2 + Se \longrightarrow R_2Se + SO_2$$

When sulfones are heated with metallic sodium, the sodium sulfinate is formed. The alkyl groups that remain combine to give a saturated hydrocarbon, and also undergo disproportionation to alkene and alkane.

$$2\,C_2H_5SO_2C_2H_5 + 2\,Na \longrightarrow 2\,C_2H_5SO_2Na + C_4H_{10}\ (with\ C_2H_4 + C_2H_6)$$

The sulfone group, like the carbonyl group, has an activating effect on hydrogen or on a double bond attached to an α carbon atom (Claisen, Michael, and Knoevenagel reactions, and carbon alkylation, pp. 768, 803, 773, 820).

Disulfones of the type RSO_2SO_2R are cleaved by alkali to give sulfinate and sulfonate.

$$RSO_2SO_2R + 2\,NaOH \longrightarrow RSO_2Na + RSO_3Na + H_2O$$

Sulfones usually are named as such. In the Geneva system the SO_2 *group* is called *sulfonyl*, and sulfones are named as sulfonyl derivatives of saturated hydrocarbons. Thus $CH_3SO_2CH_3$ is methyl sulfone or methylsulfonylmethane, and $CH_3CH_2CH_2CH_2SO_2CH(CH_3)_2$ is *i*-propyl *n*-butyl sulfone or 1-(methylethylsulfonyl)butane.

SULFONIC ACIDS AND DERIVATIVES

Preparation of Sulfonic Acids

1. By the Oxidation of Mercaptans.

$$RSH + 3\,[O]\,(HNO_3) \longrightarrow RSO_2OH$$

Frequently mercaptans are purified as the lead mercaptides, and the latter are oxidized directly to lead salts of sulfonic acids (p. 278). The free acid may be obtained by passing hydrogen chloride into an alcoholic suspension of the lead sulfonate.

2. From Alkyl Halides and Alkali Sulfite.
Primary alkyl halides react with aqueous solutions of sodium or ammonium bisulfite at elevated temperatures to give alkanesulfonates.

$$RX + Na_2SO_3 \xrightarrow{200°} [RSO_3{}^-]Na^+ + NaX$$

As in the reaction of primary alkyl halides with sodium sulfinates (p. 285), the alkyl group combines with sulfur rather than oxygen to give a sulfonate rather than an alkyl sulfite (cf. p. 259).

The free sulfonic acids can be obtained by passing dry hydrogen chloride into an alcoholic solution of the sodium salt, the sulfonic acid being soluble and the sodium chloride insoluble in alcohol.

3. Sulfonyl Chlorides.
Sulfonyl chlorides are purified readily by distillation and may be hydrolyzed to the sulfonic acid by boiling with water.

$$RSO_2Cl + H_2O \longrightarrow RSO_3H + HCl$$

Since the sulfonic acids are nonvolatile, the hydrochloric acid and water may be removed by vacuum distillation leaving the pure acid as a residue.

4. Addition of Bisulfite to Double Bonds.
Sodium bisulfite adds to simple olefins only in the presence of oxygen or oxides of nitrogen. The addition takes place by a free-radical mechanism and does not follow the Markovnikov rule.

$$RCH{=}CH_2 + NaHSO_3 \xrightarrow{O_2\ or\ NO_2} RCH_2CH_2SO_3Na$$

Aldehydes and methyl ketones usually add bisulfite to give bisulfite addition compounds, which are the sodium salts of hydroxy sulfonic acids (p. 201).

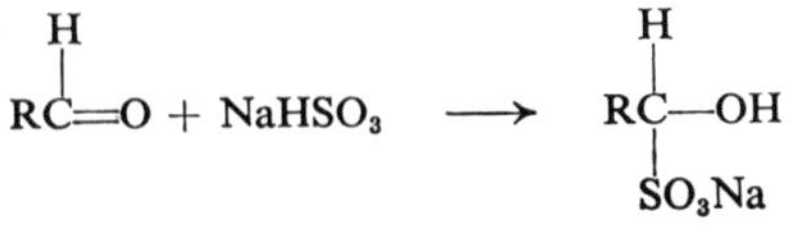

$$\overset{H}{\underset{}{R\overset{|}{C}{=}O}} + NaHSO_3 \longrightarrow \overset{H}{\underset{\underset{SO_3Na}{|}}{R\overset{|}{C}{-}OH}}$$

If a carbon-carbon double bond is conjugated with the carbonyl group, that is, if it is in the α,β position to the carbonyl group (p. 762), it also adds bisulfite.

$$
\underset{\text{Mesityl oxide}}{
\begin{array}{c}
\text{CH}_3 \\
\vert \\
\text{CH}_3\text{C}\!\!=\!\!\text{CH}\!-\!\underset{\underset{\text{O}}{\|}}{\text{C}}\text{CH}_3 + 2\,\text{NaHSO}_3
\end{array}}
\longrightarrow
\begin{array}{c}
\text{CH}_3 \qquad\quad \text{OH} \\
\vert \qquad\qquad\ \vert \\
\text{CH}_3\text{C}\!-\!\text{CH}_2\!-\!\text{C}\!-\!\text{CH}_3 \\
\vert \qquad\qquad\ \vert \\
\text{SO}_3\text{Na} \qquad \text{SO}_3\text{Na}
\end{array}
$$

Although both the double bond and the carbonyl group react, only the sulfonic acid group formed by addition to the carbonyl group is removed readily.

$$
\begin{array}{c}
\text{CH}_3 \qquad\quad \text{OH} \\
\vert \qquad\qquad\ \vert \\
\text{CH}_3\!-\!\text{C}\!-\!\text{CH}_2\!-\!\text{C}\!-\!\text{CH}_3 + \text{HCl} \\
\vert \qquad\qquad\ \vert \\
\text{SO}_3\text{Na} \qquad \text{SO}_3\text{Na}
\end{array}
\longrightarrow
\begin{array}{c}
\text{CH}_3 \\
\vert \\
\text{CH}_3\!-\!\text{C}\!-\!\text{CH}_2\!-\!\underset{\underset{\text{O}}{\|}}{\text{C}}\!-\!\text{CH}_3 + \text{SO}_2 + \text{NaCl} + \text{H}_2\text{O} \\
\vert \\
\text{SO}_3\text{Na}
\end{array}
$$

5. **Sulfonation of Paraffin Hydrocarbons.** Paraffin hydrocarbons do not react appreciably with concentrated sulfuric acid. Fuming sulfuric acid reacts with the higher hydrocarbons, and chlorosulfonic acid, ClSO_3H, reacts readily enough with the branched chain hydrocarbons to be used to remove them from normal hydrocarbons. Although sulfonic acids have been reported as products of these reactions, they have not been isolated in a pure state in good yield and the identification is uncertain. It is possible that oxidation has introduced double bonds into the molecule which subsequently react with sulfuric acid or chlorosulfonic acid.

Nomenclature

The Geneva system commonly is used in which the suffix *sulfonic acid* is added to the name of the hydrocarbon; for example $\text{CH}_3\text{SO}_3\text{H}$ is methanesulfonic acid. For higher molecular weight compounds the alkyl group frequently is named, for example, $\text{C}_{12}\text{H}_{25}\text{SO}_3\text{H}$, laurylsulfonic acid, and $\text{C}_{16}\text{H}_{33}\text{SO}_3\text{H}$, cetylsulfonic acid, but this practice should be discontinued. Unobjectionable names are dodecanesulfonic acid and hexadecanesulfonic acid.

Reactions of Sulfonic Acids and Their Derivatives

In contrast to carboxylic acids, the sulfonic acids are strong acids. Because of almost complete ionization, they are very soluble in water, insoluble in saturated hydrocarbons, and relatively nonvolatile.

Usually the **sulfonyl halides** have been prepared by the action of phosphorus pentachloride on the sodium salt.

$$\text{RSO}_2\text{ONa} + \text{PCl}_5 \longrightarrow \text{RSO}_2\text{Cl} + \text{POCl}_3 + \text{NaCl}$$

If a high temperature is used, the sulfonyl chloride group is replaced by halogen.

$$\text{RSO}_2\text{Cl} + \text{PCl}_5 \longrightarrow \text{RCl} + \text{SOCl}_2 + \text{POCl}_3$$

Phosphorus trihalides reduce the sulfonyl halide to a disulfide.

$$2\,\text{RSO}_2\text{X} + 5\,\text{PX}_3 \longrightarrow \text{RSSR} + 4\,\text{POX}_3 + \text{PX}_5$$

Sulfonyl chlorides may be prepared also by the action of chlorine and water on a variety of sulfur compounds. One of the best methods starts with disulfides.

$$RSSR + 5\,Cl_2 + 4\,H_2O \longrightarrow 2\,RSO_2Cl + 8\,HCl$$

Another good method uses alkyl thiocyanates (p. 325). Care must be exercised in carrying out this reaction because of the toxicity of the cyanogen chloride produced.

$$RSCN + 3\,Cl_2 + 2\,H_2O \longrightarrow RSO_2Cl + ClCN + 4\,HCl$$

A third procedure starting with alkyl isothioureas no longer is recommended because violent explosions have been reported.

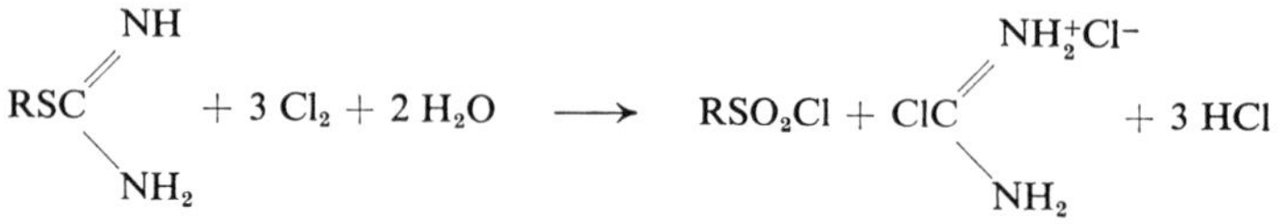

$$RSC\!\!\begin{array}{c}NH \\ \\ NH_2\end{array} + 3\,Cl_2 + 2\,H_2O \longrightarrow RSO_2Cl + ClC\!\!\begin{array}{c}NH_2^+Cl^- \\ \\ NH_2\end{array} + 3\,HCl$$

All of these oxidations are carried out in the presence of water despite the fact that an acid chloride is produced. The sulfonyl chlorides are very insoluble in water, and their rate of reaction with water is so slow that they may be removed before any appreciable hydrolysis has taken place.

Methanesulfonic acid reacts with thionyl chloride or phosphorus trichloride to give good yields of methanesulfonyl chloride, and the reactions should be general.

$$CH_3SO_2OH + SOCl_2 \longrightarrow CH_3SO_2Cl + HCl + SO_2$$

$$3\,CH_3SO_2OH + PCl_3 \longrightarrow 3\,CH_3SO_2Cl + P(OH)_3$$

Sulfonic acids do not give satisfactory yields of esters by direct esterification, or of amides by heating ammonium salts. Hence these derivatives always are made from the sulfonyl chlorides. Because of the slow rate of hydrolysis, the reactions may be carried out in the presence of water, usually with the addition of sodium hydroxide (cf. Schotten-Baumann reaction, p. 549).

$$RSO_2Cl + HOR' + NaOH \longrightarrow RSO_2OR' + NaCl + H_2O$$

$$RSO_2Cl + NH_3 + NaOH \longrightarrow RSO_2NH_2 + NaCl + H_2O$$

Sulfonamides are characterized by the relatively high acidity of the hydrogen atoms attached to nitrogen. They are sufficiently acidic to form stable salts with strong alkalies in aqueous solutions.

$$RSO_2NH_2 + NaOH \longrightarrow [RSO_2\bar{N}H][Na^+] + H_2O$$

Therefore sulfonamides derived from ammonia or primary amines are soluble in dilute sodium hydroxide solutions.

Sulfonic esters behave more like sulfuric esters than like carboxylic esters. They are hydrolyzed more readily than carboxylic esters by water and like sulfuric esters have an alkylating action. Thus ammonia yields amine salts rather than sulfonamides.

$$RSO_2OR' + NH_3 \longrightarrow [RSO_2O^-][^+NH_3R']$$

When heated with alcohols, ethers are formed.

$$RSO_2OR' + HOR'' \longrightarrow RSO_2OH + R'OR''$$

Reaction with Grignard reagents gives hydrocarbons.

$$RSO_2OR' + R''MgX \longrightarrow R'R'' + [RSO_2O-]^+MgX$$

When sulfonic acids are heated with phosphorus pentoxide, the **anhydrides** are formed.

$$RSO_2OH + P_2O_5 \longrightarrow (RSO_2)_2O + 2\ HPO_3$$

They may be prepared also from the acid and aryl carbodiimides (p. 322). The reactions of the sulfonic anhydrides are analogous to those of the sulfonyl halides but are more rapid.

When sodium alkanesulfonates are fused with sodium hydroxide, the products are olefin, water, and sodium sulfite.

$$C_2H_5SO_3Na + NaOH \longrightarrow C_2H_4 + Na_2SO_3 + H_2O$$

INDIVIDUAL SULFUR COMPOUNDS

Methyl mercaptan is made commercially by passing a mixture of methyl alcohol and hydrogen sulfide over alumina at about 400°.

$$CH_3OH + H_2S \longrightarrow CH_3SH + H_2O$$

Production capacity of one plant in the United States in 1954 was 5 million pounds per year. It is used chiefly for the synthesis of methionine (p. 765). *n*-**Propyl mercaptan** has been identified in the volatile products of freshly crushed onion. **Trichloromethanesulfenyl chloride** (*perchloromethyl mercaptan*), made by the reaction of chlorine with carbon disulfide, is the only important derivative of the unknown aliphatic sulfenic acids, R—S—OH.

$$2\ CS_2 + 5\ Cl_2 \longrightarrow 2\ Cl_3CSCl + S_2Cl_2$$

It is used in the synthesis of the powerful fungicide, Captan (p. 843). *n*-**Butyl mercaptan** has been isolated as a constituent of the malodorous secretion of skunks. *n*-**Dodecyl mercaptan** is used to regulate the chain length in the manufacture of GRS synthetic rubber (p. 717).

Methyl sulfide is made commercially by heating the spent liquor from the manufacture of kraft pulp (p. 400) with sodium sulfide. It is used as an odorant for natural gas and to make methyl sulfoxide. **Mustard gas** (*β-chloroethyl sulfide*) is one of the more powerful vesicants used in chemical warfare. It is not a gas but a heavy oily liquid boiling at 217°. It is made by reaction of ethylene and sulfur monochloride.

$$2\ CH_2{=}CH_2 + S_2Cl_2 \longrightarrow ClCH_2CH_2SCH_2CH_2Cl + S$$

It may be made also by a process which avoids the presence of sulfur in the final product.

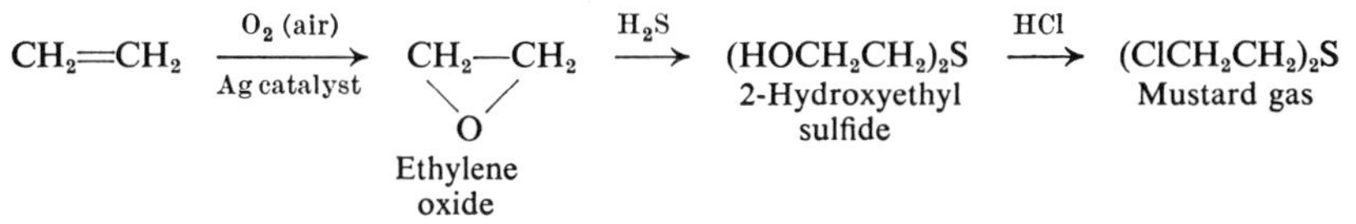

$$CH_2{=}CH_2 \xrightarrow[\text{Ag catalyst}]{O_2\ (air)} \underset{\substack{O \\ \text{Ethylene} \\ \text{oxide}}}{CH_2{-}CH_2} \xrightarrow{H_2S} \underset{\substack{\text{2-Hydroxyethyl} \\ \text{sulfide}}}{(HOCH_2CH_2)_2S} \xrightarrow{HCl} \underset{\substack{\text{Mustard gas}}}{(ClCH_2CH_2)_2S}$$

Although not used during World War II, enormous quantities of mustard gas were manufactured by both sides, which possibly acted as a deterrent to its use.

A large amount of work has been done in attempts to correlate vesicant action with structure. It has been found that the halogen must be on a carbon atom β to the sulfur atom. For example, $ClCH_2CH_2SCH_3$ has properties similar to mustard gas but $ClCH_2CH_2CH_2SCH_3$ and $ClCH_2SCH_3$ do not. These observations have led to the view that the vesicant action is related to the ability to form a sulfonium chloride having a three-membered ring.

$$\left[R-\overset{+}{S} \underset{CH_2}{\overset{CH_2}{\diagup\diagdown}} \right] [Cl^-]$$

Oil of garlic is a complex mixture of which the chief constituent appears to be allyl disulfide, $(CH_2{=}CHCH_2)_2S_2$. **Allicin,** the monosulfoxide, appears to be the immediate precursor. **Thiokols** are high molecular weight linear polymeric disulfides and polysulfides having rubber-like properties (p. 719). **Thioacetamide** is being used instead of gaseous hydrogen sulfide in qualitative and quantitative inorganic analysis. It is reasonably stable in neutral aqueous solution, but in the presence of acids or bases, especially on warming, it hydrolyzes to give hydrogen sulfide or sulfide ion.

$$CH_3CSNH_2 + H_2O + HCl \longrightarrow H_2S + CH_3COOH + NH_4Cl$$

$$CH_3CSNH_2 + 3 NaOH \longrightarrow Na_2S + CH_3COONa + NH_3 + H_2O$$

Sulfonal is a soporific which at one time had considerable use, although now it has been replaced almost completely by the barbiturates (p. 640). It is a disulfone made by oxidation of the thioacetal from acetone and ethyl mercaptan (p. 278).

$$\underset{CH_3}{\overset{CH_3}{\diagdown\diagup}}C{=}O + 2 HSC_2H_5 \longrightarrow \underset{CH_3}{\overset{CH_3}{\diagdown\diagup}}C\underset{SC_2H_5}{\overset{SC_2H_5}{\diagup\diagdown}} \xrightarrow{KMnO_4} \underset{CH_3}{\overset{CH_3}{\diagdown\diagup}}C\underset{SO_2C_2H_5}{\overset{SO_2C_2H_5}{\diagup\diagdown}}$$

Acetone ethyl thioacetal   Sulfonal

Trional, $\underset{C_2H_3}{\overset{CH_3}{\diagdown\diagup}}C\underset{SO_2C_2H_5}{\overset{SO_2C_2H_5}{\diagup\diagdown}}$, and **tetronal,** $\underset{C_2H_5}{\overset{C_2H_5}{\diagdown\diagup}}C\underset{SO_2C_2H_5}{\overset{SO_2C_2H_5}{\diagup\diagdown}}$, are increasingly

effective, and smaller amounts may be used to produce a given effect. At the time that this type of soporific was used, however, trional and tetronal could not compete with sulfonal because the starting points for their synthesis, methyl ethyl ketone and ethyl ketone, were not easily available.

The salts of many sulfonic acids having large hydrocarbon radicals are used as wetting agents and detergents (p. 187). The Aerosols (not to be confused with aerosols), for example, are manufactured by the addition of sodium bisulfite to long-chain alkyl esters of maleic acid (p. 805).

$$\underset{CH-COOR}{\overset{CH-COOR}{\parallel}} + NaHSO_3 \longrightarrow \underset{SO_3Na}{\overset{CH_2COOR}{\underset{|}{\overset{|}{CHCOOR}}}}$$

The Igepons, $RCONCH_2CH_2SO_3Na$, are fat acid amides of N-substituted
$\quad\quad\quad\quad\quad\quad\;\;|$
$\quad\quad\quad\quad\quad\quad\;\;R'$
taurines (p. 754).

Methanesulfonyl chloride (*mesyl chloride*) is used in research work for the preparation of methanesulfonates, particularly in the field of carbohydrates (p. 378).

REVIEW QUESTIONS

1. List the types of sulfur compounds that have oxygen analogs. What types have no common oxygen analogs?
2. (*a*) Compare the boiling points of water, ammonia, and hydrogen sulfide, and their alkyl derivatives and give an explanation of the facts.
   (*b*) Compare the solubilities of these compounds in water, and explain.
3. Compare the chemical properties of ethyl ether and ethyl sulfide.
4. Discuss the reaction of acetic acid with ethyl mercaptan and its bearing on the mechanism of esterification. What more direct proof has been given that this view is correct?
5. Compare the chemical properties of thioaldehydes and thioketones with those of aldehydes and ketones.
6. Give a chemical proof that in sulfonic acids, the sulfur is united directly to carbon.

PROBLEMS

7. Give balanced equations for the following oxidations using an excess of oxidizing agent:
   A. (*a*) *n*-Butyl mercaptan with dichromate and sulfuric acid; (*b*) *i*-propyl disulfide with alkaline permanganate; (*c*) ethyl sulfide with nitric acid.
   B. (*a*) Ethyl mercaptan with alkaline permanganate; (*b*) *n*-propyl sulfide with dichromate and sulfuric acid; (*c*) *n*-butyl disulfide with nitric acid.
   C. (*a*) *i*-Amyl sulfide with acid permanganate; (*b*) 1-pentanethiol with nitric acid; (*c*) *i*-butyl disulfide with dichromate and sulfuric acid.
8. Give equations for the synthesis of the following compounds: (*a*) *i*-propyl sulfide: (*b*) ethyl *n*-butyl sulfide; (*c*) methyl sulfone; (*d*) dithioacetal; (*e*) ethyl mercaptan from ethyl disulfide; (*f*) *n*-amyl disulfide from *n*-amyl chloride; (*g*) *i*-amyl mercaptan from *i*-amyl hydrogen sulfate; (*h*) *n*-butyl disulfide from *n*-butyl mercaptan; (*i*) *n*-decyl mercaptan from *n*-decyl bromide; (*j*) *n*-hexane from *n*-hexyl sulfone.
9. Give equations for the preparation of the following compounds: (*a*) thiopropionic acid; (*b*) thio-*n*-butyramide; (*c*) *S*-methyl thioacetate; (*d*) ethyl methanesulfonate; (*e*) tri-*n*-propylsulfonium iodide; (*f*) propanesulfonamide; (*g*) *i*-butanesulfonic acid from 2-methyl-1-propanethiol; (*h*) *n*-butanesulfinic acid from *n*-butyl bromide; (*i*) ethanesulfonyl chloride from ethyl disulfide; (*j*) dithioacetic acid from methyl iodide; (*k*) *n*-dodecanesulfonic acid from lauryl disulfide; (*l*) 1-pentanethiol from pentanesulfonic acid; (*m*) hexadecanesulfonic acid from cetyl iodide; (*n*) methanesulfonyl chloride from methanesulfonic acid; (*o*) neohexane from ethyl methanesulfonate; (*p*) ethanesulfinic acid from ethanesulfonyl chloride.
10. Write electronic formulas for each of the following compounds: (*a*) ethyl sulfoxide; (*b*) triethylsulfonium iodide; (*c*) potassium methyl sulfate; (*d*) ethyl *i*-propyl sulfone; (*e*) *n*-butyl sulfite; (*f*) ethyl butanesulfonate; (*g*) dithioacetic acid; (*h*) sodium ethanesulfinate; (*i*) thioacetamide.
11. Give equations for the following reactions: (*a*) thermal decomposition of dimethyl-*n*-butyl sulfonium hydroxide; (*b*) *i*-propyl sulfide with bromocyanogen; (*c*) disproportionation of ethanesulfinic acid; (*d*) heating ethyl sulfone with selenium; (*e*) air oxidation of dithiopropionic acid; (*f*) reaction of *i*-butyl sulfoxide with hydrochloric acid; (*g*) ethyl disulfide and 2-butene in the presence of boron fluoride; (*h*) *n*-propyl mercaptan with sodium plumbite in the presence of sulfur; (*i*) the action of chlorine on *n*-butyl sulfide in aqueous acetic acid; (*i*) the action of phosphorus trichloride on 2-methyl-1-propanethiol.

12. What chemical reactions may be used to distinguish between the members of each of the following groups: (*a*) methyl sulfite, methyl sulfate, and methyl methanesulfonate; (*b*) ethyl mercaptan, ethyl sulfide, and ethyl disulfide; (*c*) *n*-propyl sulfoxide, *n*-propyl sulfide, and *n*-propyl sulfone; (*d*) *i*-butyryl chloride, methanesulfonyl chloride, and trimethyl-sulfonium chloride; (*e*) ethyl hydrogen sulfate, ethanesulfonic acid, and propionic acid; (*f*) ammonium hexanesulfonate, hexanesulfonamide, and ethyl hexanesulfonate?

13. How can the following mixtures be separated into their components: (*a*) ethyl alcohol, acetic acid, and methanesulfonic acid; (*b*) decanesulfonamide, decanoamide, and ammonium decanoate; (*c*) *n*-amyl alcohol, *n*-amyl sulfide, and *n*-amyl mercaptan; (*d*) *n*-butyl ether, *n*-butyl bromide, and *n*-butyl mercaptan; (*e*) *n*-propyl sulfide, 1-pentanesulfonic acid, and 1-pentanesulfonamide?

14. Give a series of reactions for the following conversions: (*a*) ethyl mercaptan to ethane-sulfonic anhydride; (*b*) *n*-butyl bromide to *n*-butyl sulfoxide; (*c*) *i*-propyl alcohol to thio-acetone; (*d*) *n*-propyl cyanide to methyl dithiobutanoate; (*e*) *i*-propyl disulfide to methyl *i*-propyl sulfide, (*f*) methyl laurate to dodecyl mercaptan; (*g*) ethyl cyanide to thiopro-pionamide; (*h*), 1-pentanesulfonic acid to *n*-amyl mercaptan; (*i*) methyl ethyl ketone to *s*-butyl disulfide; (*j*) 1-butene to *S*-*s*-butyl thioacetate.

15. (*a*) Write structural formulas for all of the possible isomers having the molecular formula $C_3H_6O_2S$. (*b*) Give reactions that may be used to distinguish each of the above compounds from the others.

Chapter 14

PROTEINS, AMINO ACIDS, AND PEPTIDES

Proteins (Gr. *proteios*, of first importance) are complex compounds of high molecular weight that yield **α-amino acids,** RCH(NH$_2$)COOH, on hydrolysis. Proteins are present in all living tissue, but certain tissues, such as seeds and flesh, contain larger amounts than others, such as fatty and structural tissues. Plants and bacteria are the ultimate source of all proteins, because the animal organism is unable to synthesize certain essential amino acids (p. 302) from inorganic nitrogen compounds.

In the synthesis of amino acids, plants are aided by soil microorganisms. The nitrite bacteria change ammonia to nitrites, and nitrate bacteria change nitrites to nitrates. The nitrates and ammonia are converted by the plant first into α-amino acids and then into proteins. Other soil bacteria are able to change organic nitrogen into ammonia, thus completing the cycle. In addition certain soil bacteria in conjunction with the plants on whose roots they grow, namely the legumes, are capable of converting atmospheric nitrogen into amino acids. Some soil organisms can convert nitrogen into ammonium ion nonsymbiotically, and still others are able to carry out the reverse processes of reduction of nitrate and nitrite to nitrogen and ammonia. These various processes, known as the **nitrogen cycle,** are illustrated diagrammatically in Fig. 51.

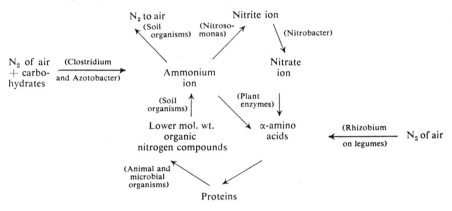

Fig. 51. The nitrogen cycle.

Because of the high molecular weight of the proteins and their similarity in being composed of amino acids, it is not possible to determine the empirical formulas of proteins from the elementary analysis. The elementary composition of all proteins is approximately 50 per cent carbon, 7 per cent hydrogen, 16 per cent nitrogen, 25 per cent oxygen, and 0–2 per cent sulfur. Phosphorus, iron, copper, and other elements also may be present. Proteins, when mixed with non-nitrogenous substances as in foodstuffs, usually are estimated by determining the total per cent nitrogen by the Kjeldahl method (p. 19) and dividing by 0.16.

The proteins are classified into **simple proteins,** yielding only α-amino acids on hydrolysis, and **conjugated proteins,** which yield α-amino acids and one or more groups of a nonprotein nature. The latter are known as **prosthetic groups** (Gr. *prosthesis,* an addition). Since the exact structures of individual proteins are unknown, the further classification of proteins is arbitrary and is based largely on their solubility characteristics. This classification was devised when there was little knowledge of the structure of proteins and is useful only as a means of dividing proteins into smaller groups. As knowledge of a pure protein increases, it frequently is found to have properties characteristic of more than one group.

Simple Proteins

Albumins are soluble in water, coagulated by heat and precipitated from solution on saturation with ammonium sulfate. Examples are *serum albumin* from blood serum, *ovalbumin* from egg white, and *lactalbumin* from milk.

Globulins are insoluble in water but soluble in dilute salt solutions, for example 5 per cent sodium chloride solution, and are precipitated by half-saturation with ammonium sulfate. They are soluble also in dilute solutions of strong acids and alkalies. They occur in serum and tissue and make up largely the proteins of seeds and nuts. Antibodies that prevent several diseases have been found in the γ-globulin fraction of human serum.

Prolamines are insoluble in water and absolute alcohol but soluble in 70–80 per cent ethyl alcohol. They are obtained principally from cereal seeds. Zein from corn is prepared industrially.

Glutelins are insoluble in water and dilute salt solutions but are soluble in dilute solutions of strong acids and alkalies. They occur in cereal seeds and are the proteins that remain after the removal of albumins, globulins, and prolamines.

Scleroproteins (albuminoids) are soluble only in concentrated solutions of strong acids and alkalies. They are the fibrous proteins having a supporting or protective function in the animal organism. Submembers are the *collagen* of the skin, tendons, and bones, the *elastins* of elastic tissues such as tendons and arteries, and the *keratins* from hair, nail, and horn.

Histones are soluble in water but are precipitated by dilute ammonia solution. They are basic compounds and occur combined as salts with acidic substances such as nucleic acids (p. 644) or heme (p. 614) in animal tissues.

Protamines are soluble in water, not coagulated by heat, and precipitated from aqueous solutions by the addition of alcohol. They are more basic than histones and simpler in structure, and are combined as salts with nucleic acids in ripe fish sperm.

Conjugated Proteins

Nucleoproteins are proteins combined with nucleic acids (p. 644), either as salts or by covalent bonds. They occur in the nucleus of every cell and sometimes in the cytoplasm as well.

Glycoproteins are proteins combined with a carbohydrate but do not contain phosphoric acid, purines, or pyrimidines. They are the *mucins* and *mucoids* (mucus-like substances) of bone, tendons, fish eggs, snails, and other tissue and glandular secretions.

Phosphoproteins have only phosphoric acid as a prosthetic group. Examples are the *casein* of milk and *vitellin* of egg yolk.

Chromoproteins are colored proteins. They contain a metallic element in the molecule, for example iron, magnesium, copper, manganese, vanadium, or cobalt, and may contain a prosthetic group, especially a metalloporphyrin (p. 614). *Hemoglobins* from red blood cells and *hemocyanins* from the blood of mollusks and arthropods are examples.

Structure of Proteins

Because of the complexity of the proteins, their high molecular weights, the large number, the complex mixtures that occur naturally, and the similarity in their chemical and physical properties, it is difficult to be certain that a protein is pure, that is, a single molecular species. Several proteins have been obtained in a crystalline state but even crystallinity does not guarantee that a protein is homomolecular. Proteins which once were thought to be pure have been separated into a number of fractions by taking advantage of the different rates of migration under an applied electromotive force (*electrophoresis*). Criteria of purity which must be applied, in addition to chemical analysis and crystalline homogeneity, are constancy of solubility at a given temperature regardless of the amount of excess protein present, constancy of diffusion rate, of rate of transfer under an electrical potential (electrophoretic mobility), of rate of sedimentation in the ultracentrifuge, and of dielectric constant.

The molecular weights of proteins are so high that methods such as those dependent on the lowering of the freezing point or elevation of the boiling point cannot be used. If the protein contains a characteristic group or atom, the equivalent weight can be found by determining the weight of the group or atom in a given weight of protein and calculating the weight of protein associated with one gram molecular weight of the group, or one atomic weight of the atom. For example, an equivalent weight can be calculated for hemoglobin from the amount of iron present. Molecular weights have been determined by the measurement of osmotic pressure, rates of diffusion, sedimentation in the ultracentrifuge, and the scattering of light. These values are particle sizes and do not preclude the possibility of subdivision into smaller units without breaking covalent bonds. For example, a particle size as high as 48,000 has been reported for the insulin molecule as determined by sedimentation, but osmotic pressure measurements indicate a value of 12,000 under conditions of maximum dissociation. Still other work supports a minimum molecular weight of about 6,000. Table 17 gives the molecular weights for a number of proteins as determined by several methods. There is fair agreement among the values obtained by the different procedures. The fact that the molecular weights are not integral multiples of the equivalent weights must be ascribed to inexact methods of analysis.

Some proteins have been shown by sedimentation in the ultracentrifuge to be definitely polymolecular; that is, they are composed of mixtures of molecules having different molecular weights. For example, the molecular weights of the molecules of lactalbumin vary from 12,000 to 25,000, of gelatin from 10,000 to 100,000, and of casein from 75,000 to 375,000.

The amino acids derived from proteins are given in Table 18. The mono-amide of aspartic acid (asparagine, $H_2NCOCH_2CH(NH_2)COOH$) and of

TABLE 17

PARTICLE SIZES OR MOLECULAR WEIGHTS OF PURIFIED PROTEINS

PROCEDURE PROTEIN	OSMOTIC PRESSURE	SEDIMENTATION- DIFFUSION	LIGHT SCATTERING	EQUIV. WT. BY CHEM. ANAL.
Insulin	12,000	6, 12, 24, 36, and 48 thousand		5734 (complete amino acid analysis)
Lysozyme	17,500	14,000–17,000	15,000	
Pepsin	36,000	35,000		
β-Lactoglobulin	35,000	41,000	36,000	
Ovalbumin	45,000	44,000	46,000	35,000 (tryptophan)
Hemoglobin	67,000	63,000		16,700 (iron)
Serum albumin (horse)	73,000	70,000	76,000	8,000 (cystine)
Hemocyanin (lobster)		760,000	625,000	
Hemocyanin (snail)		8,900,000	6,300,000	25,500 (copper)
Tobacco mosaic virus		59,000,000	40,000,000	
Influenza virus			322,000,000	

TABLE 18

AMINO ACIDS ACCEPTED AS BEING DIRECT PRODUCTS OF HYDROLYSIS OF PROTEINS

Neutral Amino Acids (equal number of amino and carboxyl groups)

1. Glycine or aminoacetic acid, $CH_2(NH_2)COOH$
2. Alanine or α-aminopropionic acid, $CH_3CH(NH_2)COOH$
3. Valine or α-aminoisovaleric acid, $(CH_3)_2CHCH(NH_2)COOH$
4. Leucine or α-aminoisocaproic acid, $(CH_3)_2CHCH_2CH(NH_2)COOH$
5. Isoleucine or α-amino-β-methylvaleric acid, $CH_3CH_2CH(CH_3)CH(NH_2)COOH$
6. Serine or α-amino-β-hydroxypropionic acid, $HOCH_2CH(NH_2)COOH$
7. Threonine or α-amino-β-hydroxybutyric acid, $CH_3CH(OH)CH(NH_2)COOH$

8. Cysteine or α-amino-β-mercaptopropionic acid, $HSCH_2CH(NH_2)COOH$
9. Cystine or bis-(2-amino-2-carboxyethyl)disulfide,

$$HOOCCH(NH_2)CH_2SSCH_2CH(NH_2)COOH$$

10. Methionine or α-amino-γ-(methylthio)butyric acid, $CH_3SCH_2CH_2CH(NH_2)COOH$
11. Phenylalanine or α-amino-β-phenylpropionic acid,*

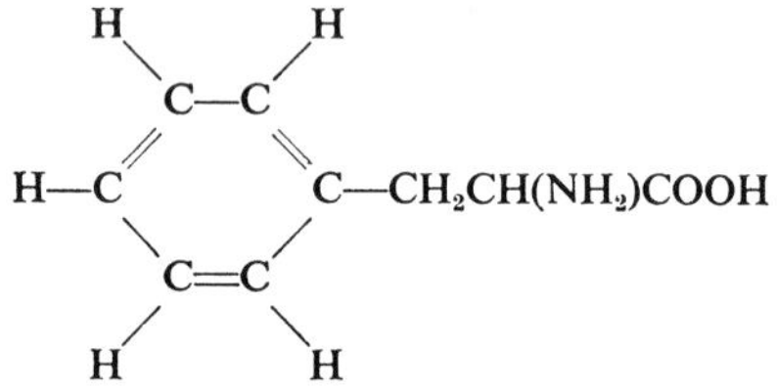

12. Tyrosine or α-amino-β-(4-hydroxyphenyl)propionic acid,*

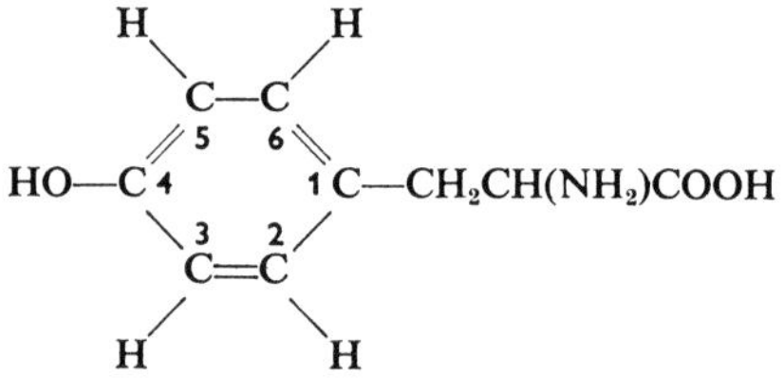

---

* Compounds containing cyclic structures are discussed in Chapters 18 to 29.

TABLE 18 (Continued)

13. Halogenated tyrosines
    (*a*) 3-Bromotyrosine
    (*b*) 3-Iodotyrosine
    (*c*) 3,5-Dibromotyrosine
    (*d*) 3,5-Diiodotyrosine (*iodogorgoric acid*)
14. Halogenated thyronines

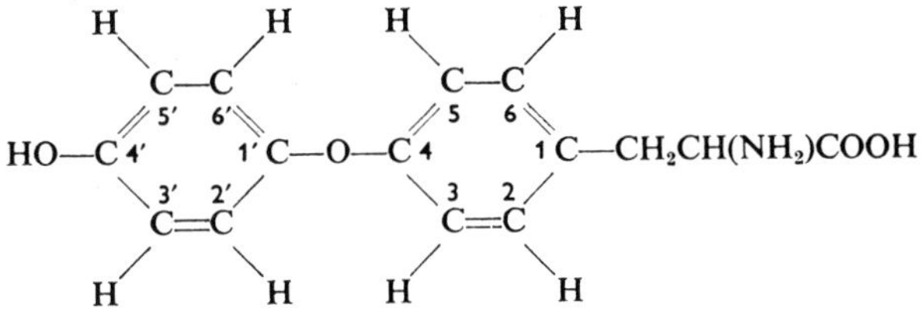

Thyronine

    (*a*) 3,5,3′-Triiodothyronine
    (*b*) 3,5,3′,5′-Tetraiodothyronine (*thyroxine*)

15. Proline or 2-pyrrolidinecarboxylic acid,*

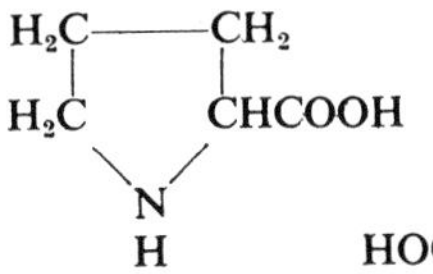

16. Hydroxyproline or 4-hydroxy-2-pyrrolidinecarboxylic acid,*

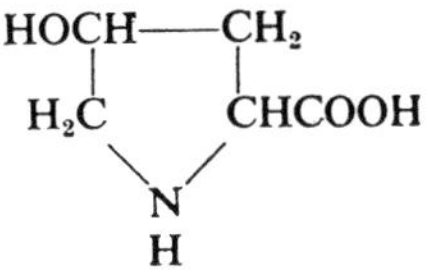

17. Tryptophan or α-amino-β-(3-indolyl)propionic acid,*

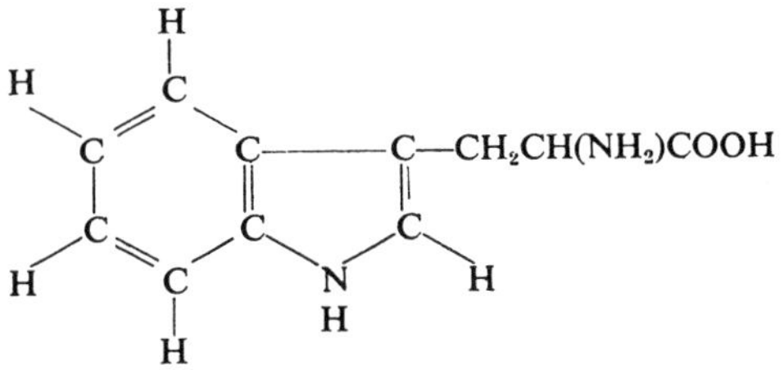

Basic Amino Acids (more basic groups than carboxyl groups)
18. Lysine or α,ε-diaminocaproic acid, $H_2NCH_2CH_2CH_2CH_2CH(NH_2)COOH$
19. Hydroxylysine or α,ε-diamino-δ-hydroxycaproic acid,
                                $H_2NCH_2CH(OH)CH_2CH_2CH(NH_2)COOH$
20. Arginine or α-amino-δ-guanidinovaleric acid,

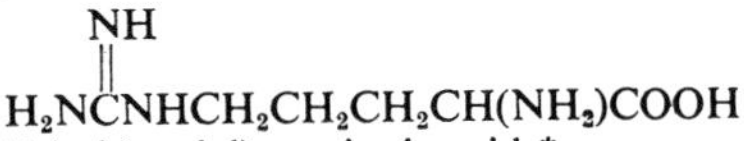

21. Histidine or α-amino-β-(5-imidazolyl)propionic acid,*

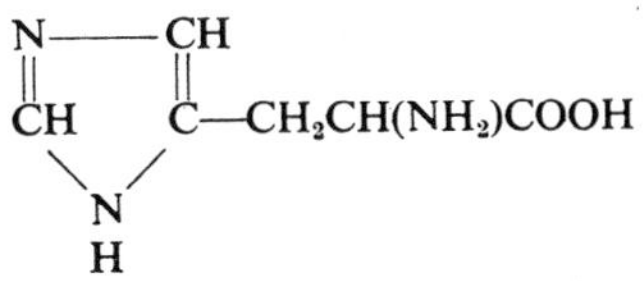

Acidic Amino Acids (more carboxyl groups than amino groups)
22. Aspartic acid or aminosuccinic acid, $HOOCCH_2CH(NH_2)COOH$
23. Glutamic acid or α-aminoglutaric acid, $HOOCCH_2CH_2CH(NH_2)COOH$

---

  * Compounds containing cyclic structures are discussed in Chapters 18 to 29.

glutamic acid (glutamine, $H_2NCOCH_2CH_2CH(NH_2)COOH$) also take part in protein structure. Numerous other α-amino acids such as citrulline, $H_2NCONH(CH_2)_3CH(NH_2)COOH$, and ornithine, $H_2N(CH_2)_3CH(NH_2)COOH$, have been isolated from natural sources but have not been established as building units of proteins.

Since often the only functional groups present are the amino group and the carboxyl group, an amide linkage is the only logical mode of joining the amino acids. If the α-amino acids are represented by the structure, $RCH(NH_2)COOH$, the protein may be represented by the partial structure I.

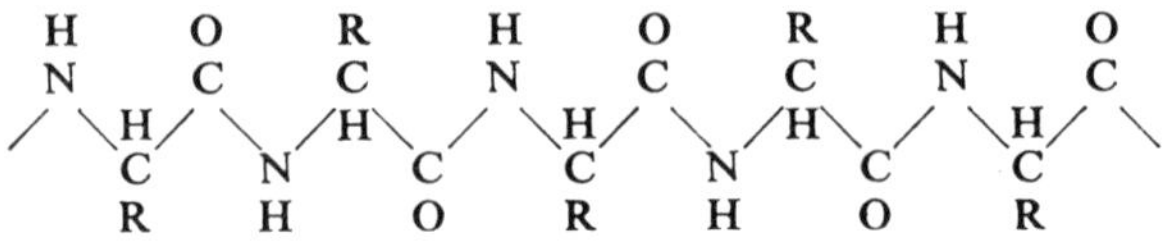

```
H    O    R    H    O    R    H    O
N    C    C    N    C    C    N    C
 / \H/ \  /H\ / \H/ \  /H\ / \H/ \
  C   N   C   C   N   C   C
  R   H   O   R   H   O   R
                 I
```

However a few of the amino acids have more than one carboxyl group and a few have more than one amino group. Therefore in a molecule such as I some free amino groups and some free carboxyl groups may be expected to be present. Since ammonia also is a product of protein hydrolysis, some of the carboxyl groups must be combined with ammonia as simple amide groups, $CONH_2$. Hence a section of a protein molecule containing lysine, aspartic acid, and glutamic acid conceivably could have the structure II.

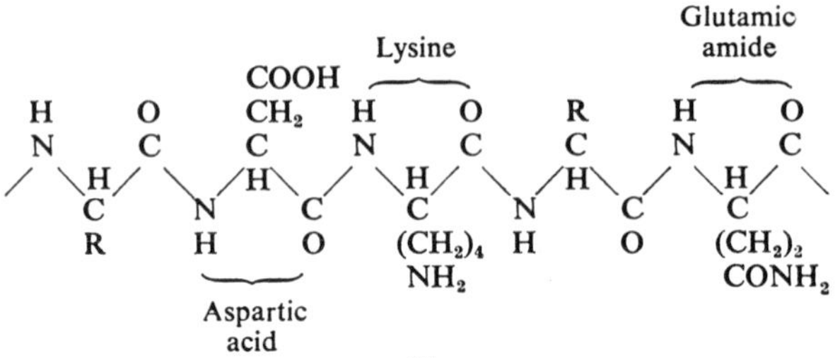

```
                                          Glutamic
                            Lysine         amide
                    COOH   ⌒⌒⌒
       H    O    CH₂   H    O    R    H    O
       N    C    C    N    C    C    N    C
        / \H/ \  /H\ / \H/ \  /H\ / \H/ \
         C   N   C   C   N   C   C
         R   H   O  (CH₂)₄ H   O  (CH₂)₂
                ⌣⌣⌣  NH₂          CONH₂
               Aspartic
                 acid
                          II
```

Moreover there is some evidence that chains of amino acids may be crosslinked by means of the disulfide linkage in the cystine portions of the molecule as represented in structure III.

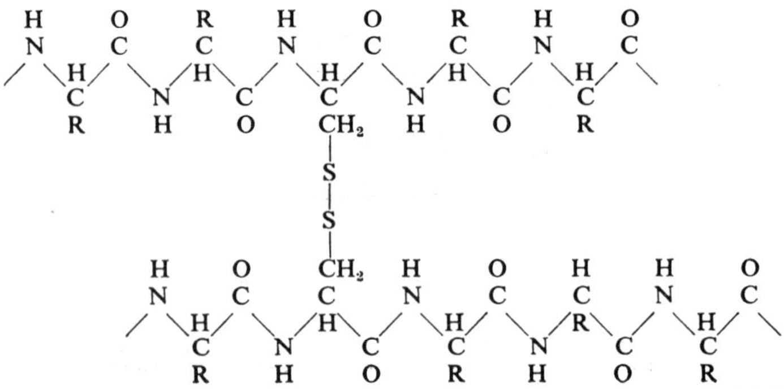

```
       H    O    R    H    O    R    H    O
       N    C    C    N    C    C    N    C
        / \H/ \  /H\ / \H/ \  /H\ / \H/ \
         C   N   C   C   N   C   C
         R   H   O   CH₂   H   O   R
                     |
                     S
                     |
                     S
                     |
       H    O   CH₂   H    O    H    H    O
       N    C    C    N    C    C    N    C
        / \H/ \  /H\ / \H/ \  /R\ / \H/ \
         C   N   C   C   N   C   C
         R   H   O   R   H   O   R
                         III
```

Other types of cross linkages, such as the amide or imide linkage, are conceivable, but there is no evidence as yet for their existence. Chains of amino acid residues linked through the carboxyl and amino groups by amide linkages frequently are called **peptides,** and this particular type of amide linkage is called a **peptide linkage.**

The fibrous proteins, such as silk, wool, hair, and connective tissues, are notably lacking in the dibasic amino acids, aspartic and glutamic, and probably are best represented by structure I. In fibroin of silk, the molecules are stretched out, but keratin of hair has a folded structure which can be stretched to a linear molecule. Globular proteins also may have their chains folded in an unknown fashion. The forces keeping the molecules in a folded structure probably are proton bonds between NH groups and C=O groups. It is possible to convert nonfibrous proteins such as zein, casein, albumin, or soybean protein into a fibrous form by dissolving in aqueous sodium hydroxide, forcing the solution through fine holes, and coagulating the filament by passing it into an acid formaldehyde bath. The molecules become uncoiled on solution, and are stretched out and oriented parallel to each other during the spinning process. The product is known as *synthetic wool.* In another process the disulfide bonds in the keratin of chicken feathers are reduced to sulfhydryl groups. The keratin then dissolves in aqueous urea and can be extruded into fibers to give artificial bristles. The permanent waving of hair is based on the reduction of the disulfide linkages with ammonium thioglycolate (p. 783) to permit shaping of the hair.

$$\text{RSSR} + 2 \text{ HSCH}_2\text{COONH}_4 \longrightarrow 2 \text{ RSH} + (\text{NH}_4\text{OOCCH}_2\text{S})_2$$

Subsequent reformation of the disulfide linkage by oxidation with potassium bromate sets the wave.

$$6 \text{ RSH} + \text{KBrO}_3 \longrightarrow 3 \text{ RSSR} + \text{KBr} + 3 \text{ H}_2\text{O}$$

The postulated structural formulas explain one other important physical property of the proteins. The proteins contain potentially free amino groups and carboxyl groups, that is, amino groups and carboxyl groups which are not joined to other carboxyl or amino groups by amide linkages. Many of these groups undoubtedly are present in salt form, the protons of the carboxyl groups having been transferred to the basic amino groups. In the presence of strong acids, however, undissociated carboxyl groups exist, and in the presence of strong bases the amino groups are free. Hence the proteins are amphoteric electrolytes. A simple amino acid molecule also contains a free amino group and a free carboxyl group, and can be used to illustrate the equilibria involved.

$$\left[\begin{array}{c} \text{R} \\ | \\ \text{H}_2\text{N}-\text{CH}-\text{COO}^- \end{array}\right] \underset{\text{H}_2\text{O}}{\overset{[\text{OH}^-]}{\rightleftarrows}} \left[\begin{array}{c} \text{R} \\ | \\ \overset{+}{\text{H}_3\text{N}}-\text{CH}-\text{COO}^- \end{array}\right] \overset{[\text{H}^+]}{\rightleftarrows} \left[\begin{array}{c} \text{R} \\ | \\ \overset{+}{\text{H}_3\text{N}}-\text{CH}-\text{COOH} \end{array}\right]$$

Basic salt form, as in the sodium salt of the amino acid	Normal salt form, as in the free amino acid	Acidic salt form, as in the amino acid hydrochloride

When the amino acid is in its normal salt form, it is a **dipolar ion (zwitter ion)** in which the negative charge on the carboxyl group balances the positive charge on the amino group. If an aqueous solution of the amino acid in this condition is subjected to a potential difference, no migration of the ion takes place. If the solution is made more strongly acid, some of the acidic salt is formed and the amino acid will be positively charged and migrate to the negative electrode. If the solution is made more strongly basic, some of the basic salt is produced and the amino acid will be negatively charged and migrate to the positive electrode. The acid concentration expressed as pH (log $1/[H^+]$) at which no migration takes place is known as the **isoelectric point.** This point is not necessarily the neutral point (pH 7), because the basicity of the amino group and the acidity of the carboxyl group vary with the structure of the amino acid and need not be the same. Since proteins also contain free amino groups and free carboxyl groups, the same considerations apply to them as apply to the amino acids. Differences in isoelectric point are important particularly in the isolation and purification of amino acids and proteins, because minimum solubility occurs at the isoelectric point, and because direction and rate of migration in an electric field can be controlled by regulating the pH of the solution.

Marked progress has been made since about 1937 in the development of methods for the separation and estimation of amino acids, and the relative amounts of the different amino acids is known for several proteins. Less is known about the order of arrangement of the amino acids in the protein molecules. That the molecules of amino acids are not randomly distributed, in which case the differences in proteins might be ascribed to differences in the number and kind of amino acids present, is known from the remarkable specificity of proteins. Thus proteins are not only specific for different tissues but also for different species of animals and even for individual members within a species. For example, whole blood of humans must be typed before blood transfusions may be made because not all of the blood proteins of two individuals are necessarily identical, and foreign proteins in the blood stream are toxic to the animal organism.

The number of possible structures for proteins is staggering. Tryptophan has the highest molecular weight (204) of the common amino acids. Therefore a protein such as ovalbumin, with a molecular weight of 45,000, must contain a minimum of 200 molecules of amino acids. It has been calculated that if only fifty molecules of nineteen different kinds, apportioned ten of one kind, four of four kinds, two of ten kinds, and one of four kinds, were present in a protein molecule, the number of possible arrangements is 10^{48}. As a comparison the diameter of the Milky Way (300,000 light years) expressed in Ångstrom units (10,000,000 per millimeter) is only 10^{32}. Nevertheless, remarkable progress is being made in determining the exact structure of proteins, and in 1954 the complete elucidation of the structure of the subunit of the **insulin** molecule of molecular weight ca. 6000 was reported.

The principle of the method for determining the constitution of a linear protein molecule is relatively simple. First it is necessary to know the amino acid composition of the protein. At one end of the chain an amino acid must have a free amino group (terminal amino group), and at the other end an amino acid must have a free carboxyl group. Moreover, regardless of the number of amide bonds broken by hydrolysis, each fragment will have the same two features. It has been found possible to "tag" the terminal amino groups by reaction with dinitrophenyl-fluoride, DNP-F, (2,4-dinitrofluorobenzene, p. 462) which reacts with the terminal amino group as would an alkyl halide.

$$HO(\!-\!\underset{\underset{O}{\|}}{C}\!-\!\underset{\underset{R}{|}}{C}HNH)_x\!-\!\underset{\underset{O}{\|}}{C}\!-\!\underset{\underset{R}{|}}{C}HNH_2 + F\!-\!DNP + NaHCO_3 \longrightarrow$$

$$HO(\!-\!\underset{\underset{O}{\|}}{C}\!-\!\underset{\underset{R}{|}}{C}HNH)_x\!-\!\underset{\underset{O}{\|}}{C}\!-\!\underset{\underset{R}{|}}{C}HNHDNP + NaF + CO_2 + H_2O$$

Hydrolysis of the product and separation and identification of the DNP derivative identifies the terminal amino acid. Next the protein is hydrolyzed partially under a variety of conditions to obtain as many different fragments as possible having two or more amino acid residues in the molecule. All of these fragments are converted into their DNP derivatives, the derivatives are separated, and the amino acid associated with DNP is determined.

Knowing the amino acid at the amino end of each fragment, it is possible to fit the amino acids together in the proper sequence. A chain of four amino acids, a, b, c, and d, may be used as a simple example. If it gives DNP-b(a,c,d) and after hydrolysis gives DNP-a(c,d), DNP-b(a,d), DNP-b-a and DNP-d-c, then the structure of DNP-(a,b,c,d) is DNP-b-a-d-c.

The insulin subunit, believed to have a molecular weight of about 6000, gives on hydrolysis 48 molecules of amino acids of sixteen different kinds. All of the sulfur in the protein is accounted for by three cystine molecules. Oxidation of the protein molecule with peroxyformic acid (p. 153) converts the disulfide linkages of the cystine units into sulfonic acid groups (p. 278) and splits the molecule into two chains. One chain, on hydrolysis, yields twenty-one molecules of amino acids, including four molecules of cysteic acid, HO_3S—$CH_2CH(NH_2)COOH$, and the other yields thirty molecules of amino acids, including two molecules of cysteic acid. The structure of each chain has been established, chiefly by the DNP procedure. Finally the mode of union of the two chains by means of disulfide linkages has been determined by isolating fragments containing the disulfide linkages and determining their constitution. The complete structure of the protein molecule is indicated schematically in the following formula.

$$H_2NCO \quad \overline{\quad\quad S—S\quad\quad}$$

H_2N–Gly–Ileu–Val–Glu–Glu–Cy–Cy–Ala–Ser–Val–Cy–Ser–Leu–Tyr–Glu–Leu–Glu–Asp–Tyr–Cy–Asp–COOH

(with CONH₂ CONH₂ CONH₂ groups and S linkages as shown)

H_2NCO $CONH_2$ S

H_2N–Phe–Val–Asp–Glu–His–Leu–Cy–Gly–Ser–His–Leu–Val–Glu–Ala–Leu–Tyr–Leu–Val–Cy–Gly–Glu–Arg–
Gly–Phe–Phe–Tyr–Thr–Pro–Lys–Ala–COOH

INSULIN

A total of twelve carboxyl groups, three from aspartic acid, seven from glutamic and two from the ends of the chains, are not used in peptide linkages. Since six molecules of ammonia are formed on hydrolysis, six of these carboxyl groups occur as simple amide groups. Hence the exact molecular weight of the insulin subunit is 5734. It is of interest that insulins from different species are not identical. The above formula is for insulin from beef pancreas. Other insulins that have been investigated differ in structure only in the portion of the molecule enclosed in the dotted rectangle. In sheep insulin this portion is alanine-glycine-valine, in horse insulin it is threonine-glycine-isoleucine, and in hog or whale insulin it is threonine-serine-isoleucine.

β-ACTH (adrenocorticotropic hormone), one of the hormones of the anterior pituitary gland, is a linear peptide made up of 39 molecules of amino acids, and **glucagon**, another pancreatic hormone, is a linear peptide of 29 amino acid molecules. The orders of linkage in both of these polypeptides have been determined also.

Metabolism of Proteins

The animal organism normally obtains its supply of nitrogen predominantly by ingesting proteins from plants and other animals. These proteins are hydrolyzed progressively to peptides (p. 302) and amino acids. The hydrolyses are catalyzed by the enzyme *pepsin* under acid conditions (pH 1–2) in the stomach and by *trypsin, chymotrypsins*, and *peptidases* under slightly acid to slightly alkaline conditions (pH 6–8) in the intestines. The amino acids pass through the walls of the intestine into the portal blood stream, which carries them to the liver and other tissues of the body. Under the influence of specific cellular enzymes, the amino acids are reconverted into proteins characteristic of the particular tissue. The liver converts the amino acids also into plasma proteins which are carried to peripheral tissues where they can be used as a source of amino acids for the synthesis of tissue proteins. That an organism can synthesize a specific protein for each particular purpose by picking out the desired amino acids from the blood stream and putting them together in the proper order is a striking example of the exactness with which life processes are regulated.

The organism also is able to convert some amino acids into others and to synthesize them from ammonium salts and α-keto acids derived from carbohydrates. Amino acids that can be so formed need not be ingested. On the other hand it is known that the rat cannot produce valine, leucine, isoleucine, phenylalanine, threonine, tryptophan, methionine, lysine, arginine,[1] or histidine, and hence they have been termed *indispensable* or *essential amino acids*. The term "indispensable" should not be taken to mean that these amino acids are more important than the "dispensable" amino acids, since all natural amino acids undoubtedly are necessary for the development and maintenance of the organism. Indispensable merely means that these amino acids must be supplied in the proteins of the diet, and cannot be synthesized from other amino acids or from ammonia nitrogen. Approximately 6 per cent of the protein intake must consist of these amino acids. Studies made so far indicate that the requirements of other species appear to be similar to those of the rat. Arginine, however, is dispensable in dogs and histidine is dispensable in man. For growing chicks glycine is an indispensable amino acid, although it is dispensable in rats. One of the more interesting facts discovered in recent years through the aid of isotopes is that the proteins in the body are being actively built up and torn down continuously, and that there is a fairly rapid turnover of amino acids. It has been calculated that the average "half-life" of proteins, that is, the time required for half of the original amino acids in the body protein to be replaced by other amino acids, is about 17 days for the rat and 80 days for the adult human.

Naturally Occurring Peptides

The term peptide usually refers to compounds having molecular weights less than 10,000, although there is no sharp distinction between the peptides of higher molecular weight and the proteins of lower molecular weight. Peptides frequently contain structures or yield hydrolytic products not characteristic of proteins.

Many naturally occurring peptides have been isolated from animals, plants, fungi, and bacteria. The structures of some have been determined. **Glutathione,** which is a widely distributed component of tissues, is the tripeptide glutamylcysteinylglycine, $HOOCCH(NH_2)CH_2CH_2CONHCH(CH_2SH)CONHCH_2COOH$. The glutamyl linkage differs from that in proteins in that it is by way of the γ carboxyl. The structure has been confirmed by synthesis. **Gramicidin-S,** one of a group of antibiotics isolated from the soil organism *Bacillus brevis*, is a cyclodecapeptide of the structure (valyl-ornithyl-leucyl-phenylalanyl-prolyl)$_2$ in which the proline carboxyls are joined to the valine amino groups by peptide linkages to form a ring. Besides lacking end groups, it contains ornithine, which does not occur in proteins, and the D form of phenylalanine instead of the

---

[1] Arginine can be produced but not at a rate sufficient for normal growth.

usual L form (p. 349). **Oxytocin** is a hormone, isolated from extracts of the posterior lobe of the pituitary, that regulates uterine contraction and lactation. It is a cyclic compound also, but the ring includes a disulfide linkage that can be opened or closed readily by reduction and oxidation. It was the first polypeptide hormone to be synthesized (p. 306).

$$\text{CONH}_2 \quad \text{CONH}_2$$
$$\text{H}_2\text{N—Cy—Tyr—Ileu—Glu——Asp—Cy—Pro—Leu—Gly—CONH}_2$$
$$\text{\textemdash S—S\textemdash}$$

Oxytocin

In Vitro Synthesis of α-Amino Acids

One of the most general methods for the synthesis of α-amino acids in the laboratory is the reaction of α-halogen acids with ammonia.

$$\underset{X}{\text{RCHCOOH}} + 2\,\text{NH}_3 \longrightarrow \text{RCH(NH}_2)\text{COOH} + \text{NH}_4\text{X}$$

A large excess of ammonia is used to decrease the amount of by-product formed by the reaction of two moles of halogen acid with one mole of ammonia. Bromo acids most commonly are used, since they are prepared readily by the Hell-Volhard-Zelinsky reaction (p. 162). When the nature of the R group does not permit the use of the Hell-Volhard-Zelinsky reaction, a substituted malonic acid (p. 800) may be brominated, since malonic acids brominate much more easily than monocarboxylic acids and lose carbon dioxide on heating (p. 795) to give the bromo acid.

$$\underset{\text{COOH}}{\overset{\text{COOH}}{\text{R—CH}}} \overset{\text{Br}_2}{\longrightarrow} \underset{\text{COOH}}{\overset{\text{COOH}}{\text{R—C—Br}}} \longrightarrow \underset{\text{COOH}}{\overset{\text{H}}{\text{R—C—Br}}} + \text{CO}_2$$

A second method is known as the *Strecker synthesis*, which consists of the reaction of an aldehyde or ketone with a mixture of ammonium chloride and sodium cyanide, followed by acid hydrolysis of the amino nitrile. The first stage of the reaction involves the formation of ammonium cyanide which dissociates into ammonia and hydrogen cyanide. Reaction of ammonia with the aldehyde or ketone gives the ammonia addition product, which reacts with hydrogen cyanide to give the amino nitrile.

$$\text{NH}_4\text{Cl} + \text{NaCN} \longrightarrow \text{NH}_4\text{CN} + \text{NaCl}$$

$$\text{NH}_4\text{CN} \rightleftarrows \text{NH}_3 + \text{HCN}$$

$$\text{RCHO} \underset{}{\overset{\text{NH}_3}{\rightleftarrows}} \underset{\text{NH}_2}{\text{RCHOH}} \underset{\text{H}_2\text{O}}{\overset{\text{HCN}}{\rightleftarrows}} \underset{\text{NH}_2}{\text{RCHCN}} \overset{\text{H}_2\text{O,[H}^+]}{\longrightarrow} \underset{\text{NH}_2}{\text{RCHCOOH}}$$

Because synthetic amino acids are important to the biochemist and physician, numerous other ingenious syntheses have been devised (pp. 635, 803). With the exception of glycine, naturally-occurring amino acids are optically active, consisting of a single form of the compound (cf. Chapter 16), whereas the synthetic amino acids are optically inactive, being composed of equal amounts of the naturally occurring L form and of a second D form that cannot be utilized by the animal organism. Of the essential amino acids, the animal organism can convert the D form of tryptophan, phenylalanine, methionine, and histidine to the L form. Hence the DL mixture is as useful as the pure L form. For the other essential amino acids only half of the synthetic mixture can be utilized, and twice the amount must be fed for a given effect. Methods are available for separating the synthetic compounds into their active components, but it usually is a difficult process.

Monosodium glutamate is used widely as a condiment and for bringing out the flavor of foods. It is prepared commercially by the hydrolysis of wheat gluten or sugar beet residues. Sixteen million pounds valued at 23 million dollars was produced in the United States in 1955. **DL-Tryptophan** is synthesized commercially (p. 803), because most of that occurring in proteins is destroyed during acid hydrolysis and, as an indispensable amino acid, it must be added to the protein hydrolysates used to treat cases of serious malnutrition. **DL-Methionine** is synthesized (p. 765) for the fortification of protein hydrolysates and for enriching foodstuffs. Small amounts fed to animals greatly increase their rate of growth. It appears also to have high therapeutic value in the treatment of metabolic deficiencies.

The marked effect of structure on biological activity is illustrated by the story of "Agenized" flour. For some years flour had been treated with small amounts of nitrogen trichloride (*Agene*) to improve its baking qualities. Then it was found that animals fed such flour developed hysteria and convulsions. The toxic agent was isolated after a long series of operations and

identified as methionine sulfoximine, $CH_3\overset{\underset{\displaystyle +}{\overset{\displaystyle NH}{|}}}{\underset{\underset{\displaystyle O}{\overset{\displaystyle +}{|}}}{S}}CH_2CH_2CH(NH_2)COOH$, formed by the action

of the nitrogen trichloride on the methionine component of the flour protein, gluten.

L-Lysine is synthesized commercially for use as a food supplement (p.760).

Synthesis of Peptides

Peptides are polyamides of low molecular weight which yield two or more moles of amino acids on hydrolysis. The terms *di-*, *tri-*, *tetra-*, and *pentapeptides* are in use, and products containing many amino acids are known as **polypeptides.** The proteins themselves may be classed as polypeptides. Since the postulation by Hofmeister[2] that proteins consist of α-amino acids joined by amide linkages, there has been continued interest in the synthesis of peptides, not only to confirm the theory but also to prepare simple compounds of known constitution for the investigation of the relation between constitution and enzyme activity.

Several obvious procedures are available for preparing high-molecular weight polypeptides having one kind of amino acid or a random distribution of a mixture of amino acids. It is more important, however, to be able to condense the amino acids stepwise to give a product of known constitution. The first

---

[2] Franz Hofmeister (1850–1922), professor of biochemistry and experimental pharmacology at the University of Prague, and later at the University of Strassburg.

general method was devised by Fischer[3] who allowed α-halogenated acid halides to react with amino acids or peptides, and subsequently replaced the α halogen by an amino group.

$$\underset{\substack{|\\X}}{\overset{\substack{R\\|}}{C}}HCOX + H_2NCHCOOH \longrightarrow XCHCONHCHCOOH \overset{NH_3}{\longrightarrow} H_2NCHCONHCHCOOH$$

The dipeptide thus formed can react with another molecule of α halogenated acid halide, and the product can react with ammonia to give a tripeptide. Making use of these reactions and others which he had devised, Fischer was able to synthesize a peptide of known constitution containing eighteen molecules of amino acids.

Since Fischer's synthesis is useful only when applied to the simpler amino acids, other methods have been devised. Attempts to protect amino groups by acylation have not been successful, because the amide linkage so formed is no more easily hydrolyzed than that linking the amino acids together, and removal of the acyl group by hydrolysis results in hydrolysis of the peptide linkage as well. This problem was solved by Bergmann[4] by the reaction of the free amino group with benzyl chloroformate (so-called carbobenzoxy chloride). The benzyloxycarbonyl group can be removed by catalytic reduction (p. 526).

$$\underset{\substack{|\\NH_2}}{RCHCOOCH_3} + C_6H_5CH_2OCOCl \longrightarrow$$

$$\underset{\substack{|\\NHCOOCH_2C_6H_5}}{RCHCOOCH_3} \overset{H_2,Pd}{\longrightarrow} \underset{\substack{|\\NH_2}}{RCHCOOCH_3} + CO_2 + C_6H_5CH_3$$

The synthesis of lysylglutamic acid is an example of the use of this reaction. In these reactions the acid with protected amino groups is converted to the azide (p. 268), rather than the acid chloride, for condensation with the glutamic acid (B = benzyl, $C_6H_5CH_2-$).

$$\underset{\substack{|\qquad\quad|\\CH_2(CH_2)_3CHCON_3}}{\overset{NHCOOB\ NHCOOB}{}} + \underset{\substack{|\\H_2NCHCOOCH_3}}{\overset{(CH_2)_2COOCH_3}{}} \longrightarrow$$

Methyl glutamate

$$\underset{\substack{|\qquad\quad|\qquad\qquad|\\CH_2(CH_2)_3CHCO-NHCHCOOCH_3}}{\overset{NHCOOB\ NHCOOB\ (CH_2)_2COOCH_3}{}} \overset{NaOH}{\longrightarrow} \underset{\substack{|\qquad\quad|\qquad\quad|\\CH_2(CH_2)_3CHCO-NHCHCOOH}}{\overset{NHCOOB\ NHCOOB\ (CH_2)_2COOH}{}} \overset{H_2,Pd}{\longrightarrow}$$

$$\underset{\substack{|\qquad\quad|\qquad\quad|\\CH_2(CH_2)_3CHCONHCHCOOH}}{\overset{NH_2\qquad\ NH_2\qquad(CH_2)_2COOH}{}}$$

Lysylglutamic acid

---

[3] Emil Fischer (1852–1919), professor of organic chemistry at the University of Berlin, and the outstanding director of organic chemical research. He and his co-workers did monumental work in the fields of amino acids and proteins, carbohydrates, and purines, and made important contributions in numerous other fields such as enzymes, stereochemistry, triphenylmethane dyes, hydrazines, and indoles. He was the second recipient of the Nobel Prize in Chemistry in 1902, the first being van't Hoff in 1901.

[4] Max Bergmann (1886–1944), German-born chemist who had been an assistant to Emil Fischer and later was the director of the Kaiser Wilhelm Institut fuer Lederforschung in Dresden. He came to the United States in 1933 and joined the staff of the Rockefeller Institute. He is noted for his work on the analysis of proteins, on the synthesis of peptides, and on the enzymatic synthesis of proteins.

A still more convenient method for producing the amide bond is by treatment of a solution of the carboxylic component and the amino component with dicyclohexylcarbodiimide (cf. p. 323).

$$RCHCOOH + H_2NCHCOOCH_3 + C_6H_{11}N=C=NC_6H_{11} \longrightarrow$$
$$\underset{NHCOOB}{|} \qquad \underset{R'}{|}$$

$$RCHCO—NHCHCOOCH_3 + C_6H_{11}NHCONHC_6H_{11}$$
$$\underset{NHCOOB}{|} \qquad \underset{R'}{|}$$

Numerous peptides of low molecular weight have been synthesized to determine what types of peptide linkages are attacked by various proteolytic enzymes. Bergmann's procedure and others developed more recently were used in 1953 to accomplish the first synthesis of a polypeptide hormone, oxytocin (p. 303).

Special Reactions of α-Amino Acids and Polypeptides

In the **ninhydrin reaction**, α-amino acids, and proteins or their degradation products that contain a free carboxyl group having an α amino group, give a blue color when treated in dilute solution with *triketohydrindene hydrate* (*ninhydrin*). One mole of carbon dioxide is evolved for each mole of α-amino acid that reacts (p. 840). Ammonium salts, dilute ammonia solutions, and certain amines also give the blue color under some conditions.

When a dilute solution of copper sulfate is added to an alkaline solution of a peptide or polypeptide, a pink to violet color is produced. This behavior is known as the **biuret reaction** because it is shown also by biuret (p. 316). The structure of the product of reaction with a section of a polypeptide chain may be represented by the formula

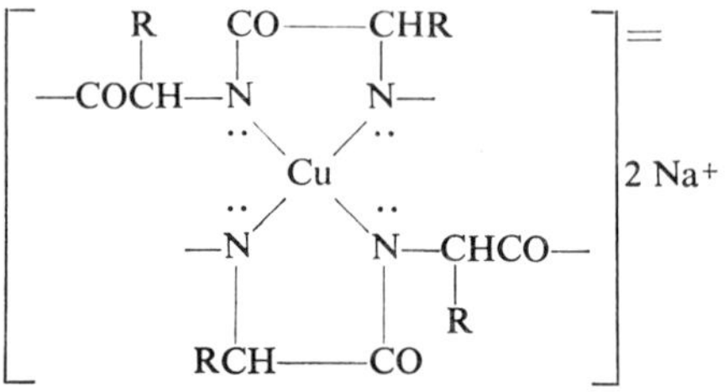

$$\left[\begin{array}{c} R \quad CO——CHR \\ | \quad | \qquad | \\ —COCH—N \qquad N— \\ \diagdown \quad \diagup \\ Cu \\ \diagup \quad \diagdown \\ —N \qquad N—CHCO— \\ | \qquad | \\ \qquad RCH——CO \end{array}\right]^{=} \quad 2\,Na^+$$

The yellow color produced when concentrated nitric acid comes in contact with skin or other proteins (**xanthoproteic reaction**) presumably is caused by the nitration of aromatic nuclei to give yellow nitro compounds (Chapter 20).

Free amino groups in either amino acids or proteins may be estimated quantitatively by measuring the volume of nitrogen liberated on reaction with nitrous acid (*Van Slyke method*).

$$RCH_2CHNH_2COOH + HONO \longrightarrow RCH=CHCOOH + N_2 + 2\,H_2O$$

Although the reaction as usually written indicates the replacement of the amino group by a hydroxyl group, unsaturated and rearranged compounds also may be formed (p. 239). The important fact is that one mole of nitrogen is eliminated for each free amino group in the molecule.

REVIEW QUESTIONS

1. Define the term *protein*. What are the sources of proteins? What is the difference between a simple protein and a conjugated protein? What is a prosthetic group?
2. Discuss the elementary composition of proteins and their molecular weights. What methods have been used to determine the molecular weights?
3. What is the generally accepted type of structure for proteins? Why do proteins give the biuret reaction? What is a peptide?
4. Approximately how many naturally occurring amino acids have been isolated? How are they usually classified?
5. Discuss the term *isoelectric point* as applied to amino acids and proteins. Why is it an important property?
6. Discuss the metabolism of proteins in the animal organism. What is meant by the term *essential* or *indispensable* amino acid?

PROBLEMS

7. Give equations for the following syntheses: (*a*) leucine from *i*-caproic acid; (*b*) valine from *i*-butyraldehyde; (*c*) alanine from propionaldehyde; (*d*) isoleucine from 2-methyl-1-butanol; (*e*) valine from *i*-butyl bromide.
8. Give a series of reactions for the synthesis of the following tripeptides: (*a*) alanylglycyl; leucine; (*b*) valylleucylalanine; (*c*) glycylalanylvaline; (*d*) isoleucylvalylglycine; (*e*) lysylalanylaspartic acid.
9. The following pentapeptides were converted to their DNP derivatives, hydrolyzed, and the products determined qualitatively and quantitatively. The peptides then were partially hydrolyzed, the products were isolated as pure DNP derivatives, and these derivatives were hydrolyzed and the products determined qualitatively and quantitatively. From the data given derive the structural formula of the peptide.

Hydrolysis Products of DNP-Pentapeptide	*Hydrolysis Products of DNP Derivatives of the Hydrolysis Products of Peptide*
A. DNP-glycine and two moles each of glycine and serine	DNP-serine, one mole of serine, and two moles of glycine
	DNP-glycine and one mole each of serine and glycine
	DNP-serine and one mole each of serine and glycine
B. DNP-cysteine and two moles each of cysteine and leucine	DNP-leucine, one mole of leucine, and two moles of cysteine
	DNP-cysteine and one mole each of cysteine and leucine
	DNP-cysteine and one mole of cysteine
C. DNP-isoleucine and two moles each of isoleucine and aspartic acid	DNP-isoleucine and one mole each of isoleucine and aspartic acid
	DNP-aspartic acid and one mole of aspartic acid
	DNP-aspartic acid and one mole of isoleucine
D. DNP-methionine, two moles of methionine, and one mole each of serine and glycine	DNP-methionine and one mole each of methionine and glycine
	DNP-methionine and one mole of methionine
	DNP-serine and one mole of methionine
	DNP-methionine and one mole each of methionine and serine

Chapter 15

DERIVATIVES OF CARBONIC ACID
AND THIOCARBONIC ACID

DERIVATIVES OF CARBONIC ACID

From the theory of structure the compound $C(OH)_4$ should exist, but the presence of more than one hydroxyl group on the same carbon atom usually results in an unstable molecule that loses water (p. 174). It is not surprising therefore that the hypothetical orthocarbonic acid has not been isolated as a stable compound. Loss of one molecule of water should give ordinary carbonic acid $O=C(OH)_2$. Although it is believed that this compound exists in aqueous solutions of carbon dioxide, all attempts to isolate it result in its decomposition to carbon dioxide and water.

$$[C(OH)_4] \underset{H_2O}{\rightleftarrows} [O=C(OH)_2] \underset{H_2O}{\rightleftarrows} O=C=O$$

Orthocarbonic acid (hypothetical)   Carbonic acid (hypothetical)   Carbon dioxide

In spite of the instability of orthocarbonic acid and carbonic acid, numerous derivatives of these compounds are known, some of which are of considerable importance. Table 19 gives the formulas and names of some of these compounds and of their sulfur analogs. Those compounds with formulas in brackets have not been isolated as pure compounds.

TABLE 19

DERIVATIVES OF CARBONIC AND THIOCARBONIC ACIDS

$O=C=O$	Carbonic anhydride, carbon dioxide
$[C(OH)_4]$	Orthocarbonic acid
CCl_4	Carbon tetrachloride
$C(OR)_4$	Alkyl orthocarbonates
$[O=C(OH)_2]$	Carbonic acid
$[HO{-}\overset{\overset{O}{\|}}{C}{-}Cl]$	Chloroformic acid (chlorocarbonic acid)
$O=CCl_2$	Carbonyl chloride, phosgene
$RO{-}\overset{\overset{O}{\|}}{C}{-}Cl$	Alkyl chloroformate (alkyl chlorocarbonate)
$O=C(OR)_2$	Alkyl carbonate
$[H_2N{-}\overset{\overset{O}{\|}}{C}{-}OH]$	Carbamic acid
$H_2N{-}\overset{\overset{O}{\|}}{C}{-}OR$	Alkyl carbamates, urethans

TABLE 19 (*continued*)

$O{=}C(NH_2)_2$	Carbamide, urea
$RNH{-}\overset{\overset{O}{\|}}{C}{-}NH_2$	*N*-Alkylureas
$RO{-}\overset{\overset{NH}{\|}}{C}{-}NH_2$	*O*-Alkylureas
$HN{=}C(NH_2)_2$	Carbamidine, guanidine
$O{=}C{=}NH \rightleftarrows HOC{\equiv}N$	Isocyanic acid $\rightleftarrows$ cyanic acid
$[ROC{\equiv}N]$	Alkyl cyanates
$O{=}C{=}NR$	Alkyl isocyanates
$RN{=}C{=}NR$	Carbodiimides
$H_2NC{\equiv}N$	Cyanamide
$ClC{\equiv}N$	Cyanogen chloride
$S{=}C{=}O$	Monothiocarbonic anhydride, carbon oxysulfide
$S{=}C{=}S$	Thiocarbonic anhydride, carbon disulfide
$[C(SH)_4]$	Orthothiocarbonic acid
$[S{=}C(OH)_2]$	Monothiocarbonic acid
$[HO{-}\overset{\overset{S}{\|}}{C}{-}SH]$	Dithiocarbonic acid
$S{=}C(SH)_2$	Thiocarbonic acid
$S{=}CCl_2$	Thiocarbonyl chloride, thiophosgene
$RO{-}\overset{\overset{S}{\|}}{C}{-}S^-{}^+Na$	Sodium alkyl dithiocarbonates, sodium alkyl xanthates
$[H_2N{-}\overset{\overset{S}{\|}}{C}{-}OH]$	Thiocarbamic acid
$H_2N{-}\overset{\overset{S}{\|}}{C}{-}OR$	Alkyl thiocarbamates, thiourethans
$H_2N{-}\overset{\overset{S}{\|}}{C}{-}SH$	Dithiocarbamic acid
$S{=}C(NH_2)_2$	Thiocarbamide, thiourea
$HSC{\equiv}N$	Thiocyanic acid
$RSC{\equiv}N$	Alkyl thiocyanates
$S{=}C{=}NR$	Alkyl isothiocyanates
$N{\equiv}CSSC{\equiv}N$	Thiocyanogen

The **derivatives of orthocarbonic acid** resemble the derivatives of orthocarboxylic acids (p. 175) in that, lacking a carbonyl group, they do not possess the properties of carboxylic acid derivatives. Carbon tetrachloride, for example, does not react like an acyl halide. It does not undergo hydrolysis, alcoholysis, or ammonolysis readily. Similarly ethyl orthocarbonate resembles the acetals rather than esters in that it is stable to alkali but hydrolyzes easily with aqueous acids. The **orthocarbonates** are prepared by the reaction of chloropicrin (trichloronitromethane, p. 264) with sodium alkoxides.

$$Cl_3CNO_2 + 4\ RONa \longrightarrow C(OR)_4 + 3\ NaCl + NaNO_2$$

Derivatives of carbonic acid, on the other hand, retain a carbonyl group or its equivalent. Their reactions therefore are those of typical carboxylic acid derivatives. Since carbonic acid contains two hydroxyl groups united to a carbonyl group, each hydroxyl group can behave like the hydroxyl of a carboxylic acid.

Phosgene, $COCl_2$, the acid chloride of carbonic acid, first was made by the action of light on a mixture of carbon monoxide and chlorine (Gr. *phos*, light; *genes*, born). In the technical process activated carbon is used as a catalyst.

$$CO + Cl_2 \xrightarrow[\text{carbon}]{\text{Activated}} COCl_2$$
$$\qquad\qquad\qquad\qquad \text{Phosgene}$$

Phosgene is a sweet-smelling gas (b.p. 8°) that is ten times as toxic as chlorine and was the principal offensive battle gas of World War I. The toxic action apparently is due to its ready hydrolysis in the lungs with the liberation of hydrogen chloride.

When phosgene reacts with alcohols, the **alkyl chloroformate** is formed first, and further reaction gives the **alkyl carbonate.**

$$\underset{\text{Phosgene}}{COCl_2 + C_2H_5OH} \longrightarrow \underset{\text{Ethyl chloroformate}}{ClCOOC_2H_5 + HCl}$$

$$ClCOOC_2H_5 + C_2H_5OH \longrightarrow \underset{\text{Ethyl carbonate}}{OC(OC_2H_5)_2 + HCl}$$

The chloroformates sometimes are called less correctly *chlorocarbonates*. Phosgene is used for the manufacture of certain ketones that are dye intermediates (p. 541) and for the preparation of **ethyl carbonate,** a useful solvent.

Urea, $CO(NH_2)_2$, is the most important derivative of carbonic acid. It may be considered as the diamide of carbonic acid, the monoamide being the unstable carbamic acid, H_2NCOOH. It is because of its relation to carbamic acid, however, that urea frequently is called *carbamide*.

Prior to the development in recent times of technical methods of synthesis and uses, urea was of interest primarily because it is the chief final product of nitrogen metabolism in mammals, being eliminated in the urine. Adult man excretes about 30 g. of urea in 24 hours. It is produced in the liver from ammonia and carbon dioxide by the ornithine cycle. Urea was isolated from urine in 1773, although it was not characterized fully and named urea until 1799. It probably was synthesized first by John Davy, a brother of Sir Humphrey Davy, who in 1811 prepared phosgene by the action of sunlight on a mixture of chlorine and carbon monoxide and in 1812 reported that the product reacted with dry ammonia to give a solid which did not evolve carbon dioxide on treatment with acetic acid and hence was not ammonium carbonate. He did not identify his product with urea, however, and credit for the synthesis of urea has been given to Woehler, who in 1828 recognized that the product obtained by boiling a solution of ammonium cyanate with water is identical with urea isolated from urine (p. 3).

$$NH_4OCN \rightleftharpoons CO(NH_2)_2$$

The mechanism of this synthesis is discussed with the chemistry of isocyanic acid (p. 315).

Since its discovery, urea has been isolated as a product of over fifty reactions, two of which have been utilized for its synthesis on a large scale. About the time of World War I, it was prepared by the hydrolysis of calcium cyanamide (p. 320), and sold for 60 cents per pound in 1920. The present commercial synthesis is from dry carbon dioxide and ammonia. Ammonia adds to one of the double bonds of carbon dioxide to yield carbamic acid, which reacts with a second molecule of ammonia to form the ammonium salt. The general method of preparing an amide by heating an ammonium salt converts the ammonium carbamate into urea. Since water is one of the products of the reaction, and since ammonium carbamate can be hydrolyzed to ammonium carbonate, which dissociates into ammonia and carbon dioxide, exact control of conditions is necessary to obtain the optimum yield of urea. The decomposition of the ammonium carbamate is carried out at 150° and 35 atmospheres pressure in the presence of a threefold excess of ammonia.

$$CO_2 + NH_3 \rightleftharpoons \left[\begin{matrix} OH \\ | \\ O\!\!=\!\!C\!\!-\!\!NH_2 \end{matrix}\right] \overset{NH_3}{\rightleftharpoons} \left[\begin{matrix} O^- \\ | \\ O\!\!=\!\!C\!\!-\!\!NH_2 \end{matrix}\right]NH_4^+ \overset{150°}{\rightleftharpoons} \begin{matrix} NH_2 \\ | \\ O\!\!=\!\!C\!\!-\!\!NH_2 \end{matrix} + H_2O$$

Carbamic acid   Ammonium carbamate   Urea

The high concentration of ammonia suppresses the following side reaction.

$$\left[\begin{matrix} O^- \\ | \\ O\!\!=\!\!C\!\!-\!\!NH_2 \end{matrix}\right]NH_4^+ + H_2O \rightleftharpoons (NH_4)_2CO_3 \rightleftharpoons 2\,NH_3 + CO_2$$

Since the development of this process the price of urea has dropped remarkably and production has greatly increased. Estimated production in the United States in 1954 was over 300 million pounds, and the price was about five cents per pound. It is used as a fertilizer and for the manufacture of urea-formaldehyde plastics (p. 314). A part of the nitrogen required by ruminants for the synthesis of proteins can be supplied by urea, and it is being added to commercial cattle feeds. A small amount is used in the manufacture of pharmaceuticals (p. 639).

Urea has the useful property of forming crystalline **inclusion compounds** (p. 97) with many straight-chain organic compounds having more than four carbon atoms, for example hydrocarbons, alcohols, mercaptans, alkyl halides, ketones, acids, and esters, but not with most branched-chain or cyclic compounds. The procedure for preparing these inclusion compounds merely involves mixing saturated methanol solutions of urea and of the compound. A crystalline precipitate forms from which the components can be separated either by extracting the urea with water or the organic compound with ether. The process can be used to improve the octane number of gasoline, to lower the freezing point of fuel for jet planes and to lower the pour point of lubricating oil by removing the normal hydrocarbons. In the laboratory it has been used to isolate and purify compounds and to resolve alkyl halides into optically active components (p. 344). Thiourea (p. 326) forms inclusion compounds with many branched and cyclic compounds.

There is no evidence that the straight-chain compounds are bound to the urea molecules by other than adsorption forces at the solid surface. The chains merely occupy channels in the urea crystal lattice. The melting point of each compound is that of urea, and the heat of formation is even less than the usual heats of adsorption on solid surfaces. Although each compound has a definite composition, the ratio of urea molecules to straight-chain molecules is not stoichiometrical but is proportional to the number of carbon atoms in the chain. Approximately two-thirds mole of urea is combined for each Ångstrom of chain length. It is of interest that unsaturated compounds included in urea crystals are not subject to autoxidation.

The reactions of urea are those of an amide. It is a very weak base, $K_b = 1.5 \times 10^{-14}$ at 25°, although it appears to be somewhat stronger than acetamide, $K_b = 3.1 \times 10^{-15}$. In spite of this low basicity, the addition of concentrated nitric acid to a concentrated aqueous solution of urea gives a precipitate of **urea nitrate** because of the insolubility of the latter in concentrated nitric acid solution.

Although the nitrogen atom of an amino group ordinarily is more basic than the oxygen atom of a carbonyl group, salt formation of an amide group undoubtedly results from addition of a proton to the oxygen rather than to the nitrogen. If the proton added to nitrogen, the resonance energy of the ion would be very low, whereas if it adds to oxygen, considerable stabilization by resonance results. Hence the cation of urea nitrate is best represented as a resonance hybrid (p. 154).

$$\left\{ \begin{array}{ccc} \overset{+}{O}H \\ \| \\ H_2N-C-NH_2 \end{array} \longleftrightarrow \begin{array}{c} OH \\ | \\ H_2\overset{+}{N}=C-NH_2 \end{array} \longleftrightarrow \begin{array}{c} OH \\ | \\ H_2N-C=\overset{+}{N}H_2 \end{array} \right\}$$

Hydrolysis of urea yields ammonium carbonate.

$$CO(NH_2)_2 + 2\,H_2O \longrightarrow [CO(OH)_2] + 2\,NH_3 \longrightarrow (NH_4)_2CO_3$$

If the reaction is catalyzed by alkali, the products are the alkali carbonate and ammonia, whereas acid catalysis yields carbon dioxide and the ammonium salt. The hydrolysis also is catalyzed rapidly at room temperature by the enzyme *urease*, which is present in soybean and jack bean, and is elaborated by certain bacteria. The hydrolysis of urea in the soil liberates the nitrogen as ammonia as part of the nitrogen cycle (Fig. 51, p. 293). Use is made of the urease catalysis for the estimation of urea in biological fluids. After hydrolysis in a suitably buffered solution, the ammonia is liberated and estimated colorimetrically or by titration with standard acid.

Since urea contains NH_2 groups, nitrogen is evolved on reaction with nitrous acid (p. 239).

$$CO(NH_2)_2 + 2\,HONO \longrightarrow CO_2 + 2\,N_2 + 3\,H_2O$$

This reaction is useful as a means of destroying nitrous acid and oxides of nitrogen.

As an amide, urea undergoes the Hofmann rearrangement (p. 247), but the product, hydrazine, is oxidized by hypobromite to nitrogen and water.

$$H_2NCONH_2 + NaOBr + 2\,NaOH \longrightarrow \underset{\text{Hydrazine}}{H_2NNH_2} + Na_2CO_3 + NaBr + H_2O$$

$$\downarrow \text{2NaOBr}$$

$$N_2 + 2\,H_2O + 2\,NaBr$$

Amides can be acylated to diacyl derivatives of ammonia, which are known as *imides*. The imides are more acidic than the amides and react with strong bases in aqueous solution to form salts (p. 246). Urea can undergo diacylation, the products being known as **ureids**.

$$CO(NH_2)_2 + 2 (CH_3CO)_2O \longrightarrow CO(NHCOCH_3)_2 + 2 CH_3COOH$$

Diacetylurea

Many of the cyclic ureids such as the barbituric acids (p. 639) and alloxan (p. 640) have important physiological properties.

When acetamide is heated with paraformaldehyde, *N*-(hydroxymethyl)-acetamide (methylolacetamide) is formed.

$$CH_3CONH_2 + HCHO \longrightarrow CH_3CONHCH_2OH$$

N-(Hydroxymethyl)-
acetamide
(methylolacetamide)

Similarly urea reacts with formaldehyde to give *N*-(hydroxymethyl)urea, commonly known as **methylolurea**.

$$H_2NCONH_2 + HCHO \longrightarrow H_2NCONHCH_2OH$$

N-(Hydroxymethyl)-
urea
(methylolurea)

When a hydroxymethyl group is united to a nitrogen atom, it readily undergoes further reaction with amino groups with elimination of water (compare the formation of hexamethylenetetramine from formaldehyde and ammonia, p. 221). Hence methylolurea can condense with a second molecule of urea.

$$H_2NCONHCH_2OH + H_2NCONH_2 \longrightarrow H_2NCONHCH_2NHCONH_2$$

Since the amide groups can condense with more formaldehyde, the reaction is capable of yielding high molecular weight chains having the general formula $(-NHCONHCH_2-)_x$. Such a long-chain polymer would be expected to be a thick viscous liquid or a thermoplastic solid. It still contains NH groups, however, which can react with formaldehyde to give *N*-hydroxymethyl groups which in turn can react with other NH groups with loss of water. If the second NH group is in a different chain, the chains would be joined together by CH_2 groups and a three-dimensional macromolecule would be formed, resulting in an insoluble nonfusible resin.

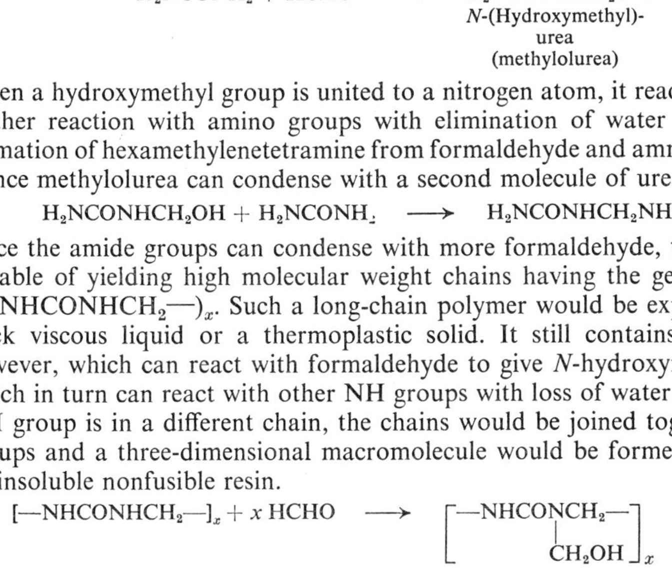

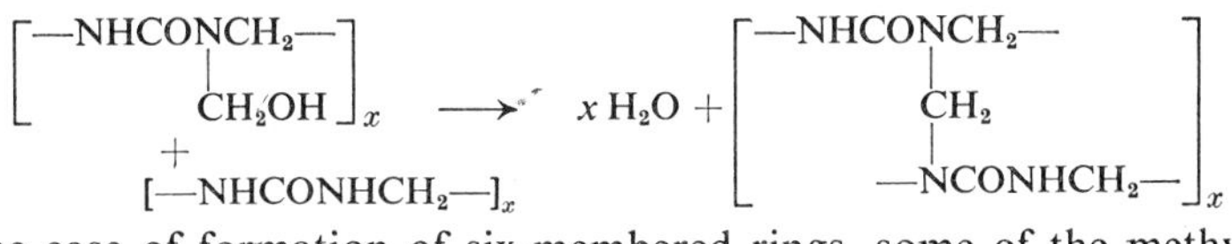

$$[-NHCONHCH_2-]_x + x\ HCHO \longrightarrow \begin{bmatrix} -NHCONCH_2- \\ \quad\quad | \\ \quad\quad CH_2OH \end{bmatrix}_x$$

$$\begin{bmatrix} -NHCONCH_2- \\ \quad\quad | \\ \quad\quad CH_2OH \end{bmatrix}_x \longrightarrow x\ H_2O + \begin{bmatrix} -NHCONCH_2- \\ \quad\quad | \\ \quad\quad CH_2 \\ -NCONHCH_2- \end{bmatrix}_x$$

$$+$$
$$[-NHCONHCH_2-]_x$$

Because of the ease of formation of six-membered rings, some of the methylolurea molecules undoubtedly produce cyclic polymers.

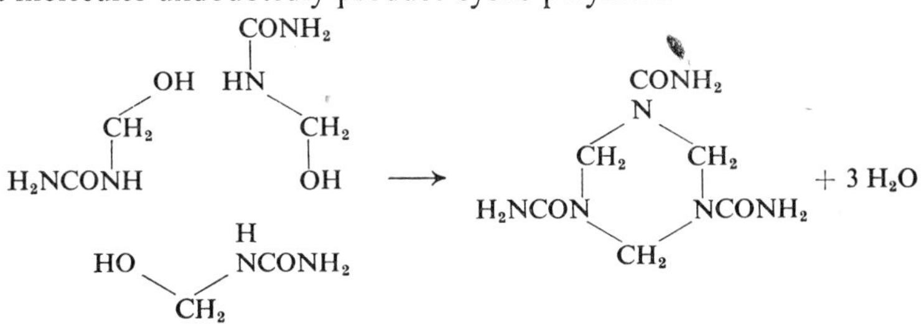

These structures still are polyamides and are capable of undergoing further reaction and entering into the structure of the macromolecule, thus increasing its complexity.

These polycondensation products constitute the commercially important group of plastics known as the **urea-formaldehyde resins.** Three moles of formaldehyde and one of urea are condensed in aqueous solution in the presence of ammonia as an alkaline catalyst. The reaction is stopped at the syrupy linear stage and mixed with a filler, usually high-grade wood pulp. The mixture is dried and ground and constitutes the thermosetting molding powder. To form an object, the powder is subjected to heat and pressure in a mold. It first flows to fill the mold and then sets to an infusible solid because of completion of the reaction in which cross-linking of the chains takes place. The urea-formaldehyde plastics are colorless, and hence color can be added to produce any desired shade. The intermediate condensation products are used widely also as water-proof adhesives in the manufacture of plywood. Some of the lower molecular weight products are used as fertilizer when a slow release of ammonia is desired. Production of urea-formaldehyde resins in the United States amounted to 220 million pounds in 1955.

When dimethylolurea is heated with 1-butanol, a butylated polymer is formed.

$$x \text{ HNCONHCH}_2\text{OH} + x \text{ C}_4\text{H}_9\text{OH} \longrightarrow \text{H}\left[-\text{N}-\text{CO}-\text{NHCH}_2-\right]_x\text{OH} + (2x-1)\text{ H}_2\text{O}$$

When added to alkyd resins used as protective coatings (p. 553) it improves the hardness and adhesion of the film. U.S. production amounted to 18 million pounds in 1955.

When urea is heated above its melting point it decomposes into ammonia and isocyanic acid. The isocyanic acid polymerizes at once to a mixture of about 70 per cent of the trimer **cyanuric acid,** and 30 per cent of the linear polymer **cyamelide.**

$$\text{H}_2\text{NCONH}_2 \longrightarrow \text{NH}_3 + \text{HN}=\text{C}=\text{O}$$

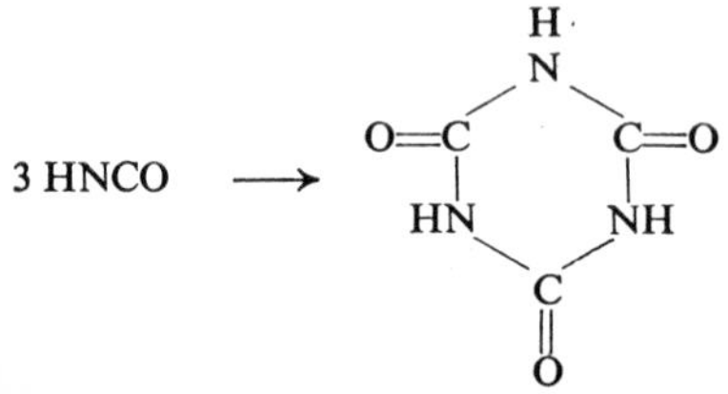

Isocyanic acid

3 HNCO $\longrightarrow$ Cyanuric acid

x HNCO $\longrightarrow$ Cyamelide

If cyanuric acid is heated to a high temperature, it depolymerizes to monomeric **isocyanic acid,** which can be condensed below 0° to a colorless liquid. When the liquid is allowed to warm to room temperature it polymerizes spontaneously and explosively to cyanuric acid and cyamelide.

Isocyanic acid is tautomeric with **cyanic acid.**

$$\text{HN}=\text{C}=\text{O} \rightleftharpoons \text{N}\equiv\text{COH}$$

Although the monomeric liquid usually is called cyanic acid, it undergoes addition reactions characteristic of compounds containing a *cumulative* or *twin double bond* (cf. ketene, p. 761). The Raman spectrum also indicates that the *iso* structure prevails. Isocyanic acid is hydrolyzed rapidly to carbon dioxide and ammonia, the intermediate carbamic acid being unstable.

$$HN{=}C{=}O + H_2O \longrightarrow [H_2NCOOH] \longrightarrow CO_2 + NH_3$$

Ammonia and amines add to isocyanic acid to give urea and *N-alkylureas*. Hence in the hydrolysis some urea is formed.

$$HN{=}C{=}O + NH_3 \longrightarrow H_2NCONH_2$$
$$+ H_2NR \longrightarrow H_2NCONHR$$
$$+ HNR_2 \longrightarrow H_2NCONR_2$$

Woehler's synthesis of urea probably is the result of the dissociation of ammonium cyanate into ammonia and cyanic acid, followed by addition.

$$NH_4NCO \rightleftarrows NH_3 + HN{=}C{=}O \longrightarrow H_2NCONH_2$$

Alcohols and isocyanic acid give the **alkyl carbamates** (*urethans*).

$$HN{=}C{=}O + HOR \longrightarrow H_2NCOOR$$

Urethans are obtained readily also by heating urea with alcohols, it being unnecessary to isolate the isocyanic acid. The alkyl carbamates also react with excess cyanic acid to give esters of allophanic acid or **allophanates.** The The allophanates frequently are valuable derivatives for hydroxy compounds.

$$HN{=}C{=}O + H_2NCOOR \longrightarrow H_2NCONHCOOR$$
An alkyl
allophanate

The mechanism of these reactions undoubtedly is the attack of the electron-deficient carbon of the isocyanic acid by the unshared pair of electrons on oxygen or nitrogen, followed by transfer of a proton.

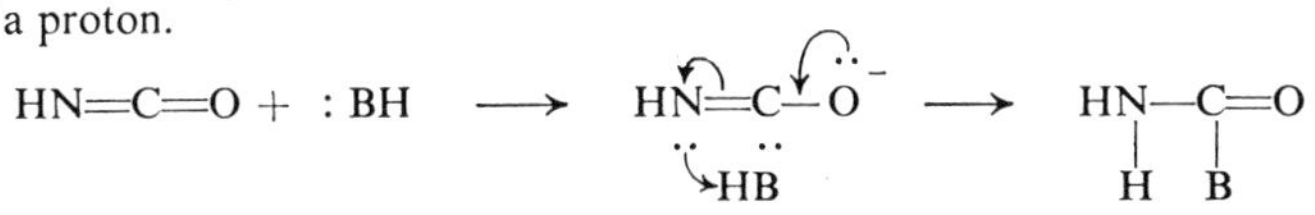

$$HN{=}C{=}O + :BH \longrightarrow HN{=}C{-}O^- \longrightarrow HN{-}C{=}O$$
$$HB \qquad\qquad H\ \ B$$

Urethans can be prepared also by the reaction of alkyl chloroformates with ammonia.

$$2\,NH_3 + ClCOOR \longrightarrow H_2NCOOR + NH_4Cl$$

Amines give *N*-substituted urethans.

$$2\,R'NH_2 + ClCOOR \longrightarrow R'NHCOOR + R'NH_3Cl$$
$$2\,R'_2NH + ClCOOR \longrightarrow R'_2NCOOR + R'_2NH_2Cl$$

The simple urethans, such as ethyl carbamate, have mild hypnotic properties. The dicarbamate derived from 2-methyl-2-*n*-propyl-1,3-propanediol is known as **meprobamate** (Equanil or Miltown) and is one of the more widely used tranquilizing (ataraxic) drugs. Production in the United States at the end of 1956 was at the rate of 50 tons per month and prescription sales at the rate of $32,000,000 per year. Sales for all tranquilizing drugs (cf. p. 643, 654) were estimated to be $150,000,000.

If urea is heated gently, the isocyanic acid first produced adds a molecule of urea to form **biuret**.

$$HN{=}C{=}O + H_2NCONH_2 \longrightarrow H_2NCONHCONH_2$$
Biuret

An alkaline solution of biuret gives a violet-pink color when copper sulfate solution is added. The color is due to the presence of a coordination complex with cupric ion in which the four water molecules normally coordinated with the cupric ion are displaced by the amino groups. The alkali removes two protons from the coordinated amino groups to give the neutral insoluble complex, and then two more protons to give the water-soluble salt.

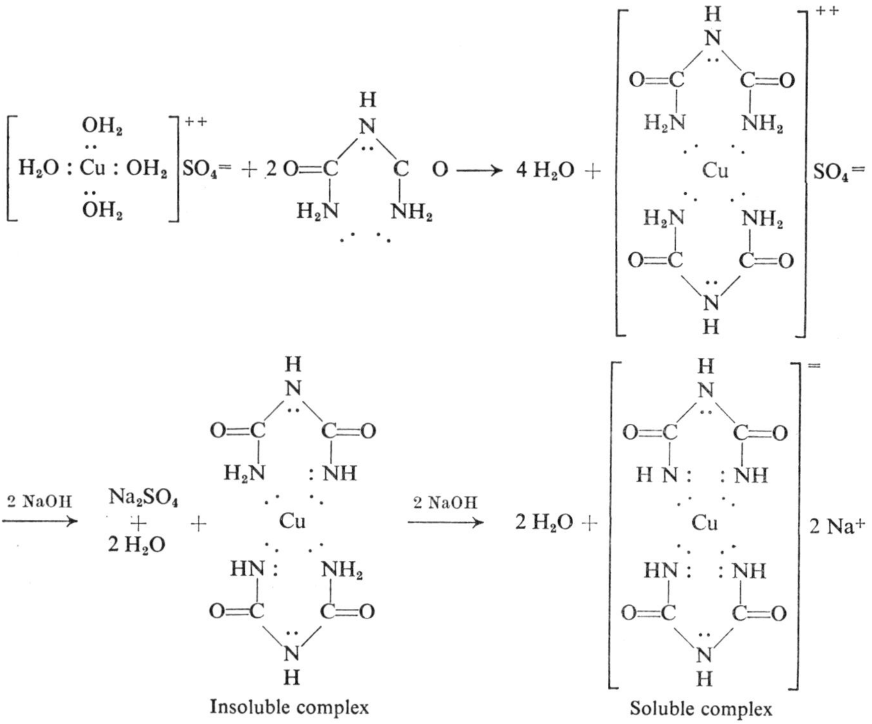

Insoluble complex   Soluble complex

The reaction takes place because of the increased stability that arises when rings are formed. Since only five- and six-membered rings can be formed readily because of the limitations imposed by bond angles, complexes of this sort are formed only when the electron-donating groups, such as the amino groups, are spaced properly in the molecule. The peptide linkage in proteins can lead to a stable complex with copper in which two five-membered rings are formed, and proteins and peptides give the biuret test (p. 306). Analogous complexes are formed with 1,2- and 1,3-dihydroxy compounds in which the hydroxyl groups are electron-donors. Examples are Fehling and Benedict solutions (p. 809).

If isocyanic acid is tautomeric, two series of alkyl derivatives (or esters) should be possible, the *alkyl cyanates*, $ROC{\equiv}N$, and the *alkyl isocyanates* ,

O=C=NR. The former are unknown in the monomeric state. When cyanogen chloride reacts with sodium alkoxide, the *alkyl cyanurate* is formed. If the alkyl cyanate is an intermediate, it polymerizes as fast as it is formed.

$$RONa + ClCN \longrightarrow [ROCN] + NaCl$$

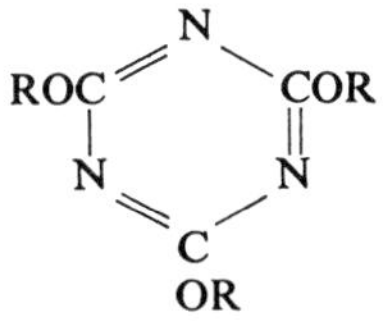

Alkyl cyanurate

The **alkyl isocyanates** on the other hand are stable compounds. They are formed when potassium cyanate is heated with an alkyl sulfate in the presence of dry sodium carbonate.

$$R_2SO_4 + KOCN \xrightarrow{Na_2CO_3} RN=C=O + RSO_4K$$

Phosgene reacts with primary amines to give alkylcarbamyl chlorides which on heating decompose to alkyl isocyanates.

$$2\,RNH_2 + COCl_2 \longrightarrow RNH_3Cl + RNHCOCl \xrightarrow{Heat} RN=C=O + HCl$$

The alkyl isocyanates are intermediates in the Hofmann conversion of amides to amines (p. 247) and in the Curtius reaction (p. 268).

Like isocyanic acid, the isocyanates readily hydrolyze with water. The final products are the primary amine and carbon dioxide.

$$RN=C=O + H_2O \longrightarrow [RNHCOOH] \longrightarrow RNH_2 + CO_2$$

It is of interest that this reaction led to the discovery of amines by Wurtz (p. 126), who first prepared methylamine and ethylamine in 1849 by the hydrolysis of methyl and ethyl isocyanates obtained from potassium cyanate and the alkyl iodides.

Alcoholysis and ammonolysis of isocyanates yield urethans and substituted ureas.

$$RN=C=O + HOR' \longrightarrow RNHCOOR'$$

$$+ HNH_2 \longrightarrow RNHCONH_2$$

$$+ HNHR' \longrightarrow RNHCONHR'$$

$$+ HNR'_2 \longrightarrow RNHCONR'_2$$

Because of the ease of reaction and the formation of solid products, the isocyanates, especially phenyl isocyanate, $C_6H_5N=C=O$ (p. 479), frequently are used to prepare derivatives of alcohols and amines for identification purposes.

Fulminic acid is isomeric with the cyanic acids. Its reactions indicate that it is a derivative of carbon monoxide rather than of carbon dioxide or carbonic acid. For example, it gives with hydrogen chloride an addition product which on hydrolysis yields formic acid and hydroxylamine hydrochloride. These reactions are explained best by considering fulminic acid to be the oxime of carbon monoxide; that is, it contains the $-\overset{+}{N}\equiv\overset{-}{C}:$ grouping present in the isocyanides.

$$HO\overset{+}{N}\equiv\overset{-}{C}: + HCl \longrightarrow HON\overset{\displaystyle H}{=}\overset{|}{C}-Cl$$
Fulminic acid

$$HON=\overset{\displaystyle H}{\underset{|}{C}}-Cl + 2\,H_2O \longrightarrow [HON\overset{+}{H_3}]\,\overset{-}{Cl} + O=\overset{\displaystyle H}{\underset{|}{C}}-OH$$

Attempts to isolate fulminic acid result in complex polymerization products, but its salts are well known. **Mercury fulminate** is prepared by the action of nitric acid on mercury and ethyl alcohol. It is highly explosive and can be detonated by heat or shock. It is used commercially in the manufacture of detonators for explosives. Liebig in 1823 showed that silver fulminate had the same composition as silver cyanate, previously analyzed by Woehler. This instance was the first recognition of the phenomenon which later became known as isomerism.

Reaction of urea with fuming sulfuric acid gives **sulfamic acid.**

$$H_2NCONH_2 + SO_3 + H_2SO_4 \longrightarrow 2\,H_2NSO_3H + CO_2$$

Ammonium sulfamate has important uses as a flame-proofing agent and as a herbicide.

When urea nitrate is dissolved in concentrated sulfuric acid, **nitrourea** is formed.

$$[H_2NC(OH)NH_2]^+\,\overset{-}{NO_3} \xrightarrow[\text{H}_2\text{SO}_4]{\text{Conc.}} \underset{\text{Nitrourea}}{H_2NCONHNO_2} + H_2O$$

Electrolytic reduction of nitrourea yields **semicarbazide** (*semicarbazine*), a valuable reagent for aldehydes and ketones (p. 211).

$$H_2NCONHNO_2 + 6\,[H](\text{electrolytic}) \longrightarrow \underset{\text{Semicarbazide}}{H_2NCONHNH_2} + 2\,H_2O$$

Semicarbazide solutions decompose slowly to form hydrazinedicarbonamide.

$$H_2NCONHNH_2 + H_2NNHCONH_2 \longrightarrow H_2NCONHNHCONH_2 + H_2NNH_2$$

This sparingly soluble compound, which melts at 245°, precipitates when solutions have been boiled for several hours and may be mistaken for a semicarbazone.

A convenient method for the preparation of **diazomethane** (p. 266) starts with urea, which when heated in aqueous solution with methylamine hydrochloride exchanges an amino group for a methylamino group to give *N*-methylurea Nitrosation gives **nitrosomethylurea**, which reacts with alkali to give diazomethane.

$$H_2NCONH_2 + CH_3NH_3Cl \longrightarrow \underset{\text{N-Methylurea}}{H_2NCONHCH_3} + NH_4Cl$$

$$H_2NCONHCH_3 + HONO \longrightarrow \underset{\substack{\displaystyle | \\ NO \\ \text{Nitroso-} \\ \text{methylurea}}}{H_2NCONCH_3} + H_2O$$

$$\underset{\substack{| \\ NO}}{H_2NCONCH_3} + KOH \longrightarrow \underset{\substack{\text{Diazo-} \\ \text{methane}}}{CH_2N_2} + KCNO + 2\,H_2O$$

When used for ring enlargement of ketones (p. 831), diazomethane is prepared best *in situ* from **nitrosomethylurethan,** which is synthesized from ethyl chloroformate.

$$CH_3NH_2 + ClCOOC_2H_5 + NaOH \longrightarrow CH_3NHCOOC_2H_5 + NaCl + H_2O$$

Ethyl
chloro-
formate

Ethyl *N*-methyl-
carbamate
(*N*-methylurethan)

$$CH_3NHCOOC_2H_5 + HONO \longrightarrow CH_3NCOOC_2H_5 + H_2O$$

|
NO
Nitroso-
methylurethan

$$CH_3NCOOC_2H_5 + 2\ KOH \longrightarrow CH_2N_2 + C_2H_5OH + K_2CO_3 + H_2O$$

| Diazo-
NO   methane

If either nitrosomethylurea or nitrosomethylurethan comes in contact with the skin, severe dermatitis may result. Diazomethane is a highly toxic gas.

Various methods are available for the preparation of *N*-**alkylureas** (pp. 315, 317). Direct alkylation of urea, however, gives *O*-**alkylureas.**

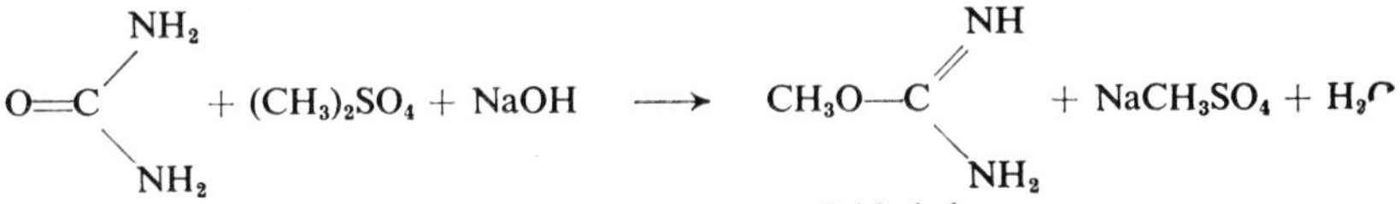

$$O=C\begin{smallmatrix}NH_2\\\\NH_2\end{smallmatrix} + (CH_3)_2SO_4 + NaOH \longrightarrow CH_3O-C\begin{smallmatrix}NH\\\\NH_2\end{smallmatrix} + NaCH_3SO_4 + H_2O$$

O-Methylurea

An explanation of *O*-alkylation of urea is one analogous to that for the formation of salts of urea in which a proton is added to the oxygen atom rather than to a nitrogen atom (p. 312). The initial product $[R\overset{+}{O}=C(NH_2)_2]$ is stabilized by resonance whereas the ion $[H_2N\overset{+}{C}ONH_2R]$ is not.

It is of interest that whereas urea and its *N*-alkyl derivatives are very weak bases, $K_B = ca.\ 10^{-14}$, the *O*-alkylureas are about as strong as the aliphatic amines, $K_B = ca.\ 10^{-4}$. The increase in basic strength is due to the stabilization of the ion by resonance. The resonance energy for the ion of the *O*-alkylureas is high, because the contributing structures are identical.

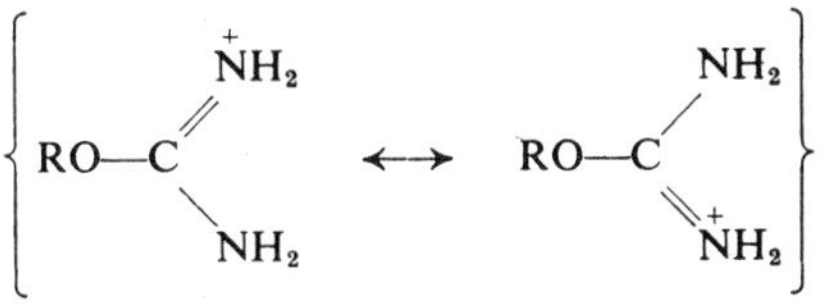

$$\left\{ RO-C\begin{smallmatrix}\overset{+}{N}H_2\\\\NH_2\end{smallmatrix} \longleftrightarrow RO-C\begin{smallmatrix}NH_2\\\\\overset{+}{N}H_2\end{smallmatrix} \right\}$$

When urea forms a salt, the proton must be located on the carbonyl oxygen (p. 312), which is much less basic than the imino nitrogen of the *O*-alkylureas. The *O*-alkylureas are less basic than the amidines (p. 249), probably because of the electron-attracting effect of the oxygen atom.

The **cyanogen halides** may be regarded as the acid halides of cyanic acid. They are prepared by the reaction of halogens on metallic cyanides.

$$MCN + X_2 \longrightarrow XCN + MX$$

They are highly toxic lachrymators. **Cyanogen chloride** melts at $-6°$ and boils at $15.5°$. **Cyanogen bromide** melts at $52°$ and boils at $61°$. **Cyanogen iodide** sublimes at atmospheric pressure. The cyanogen halides are stable when pure but polymerize readily in the presence of free halogen to give the cyanuric halides.

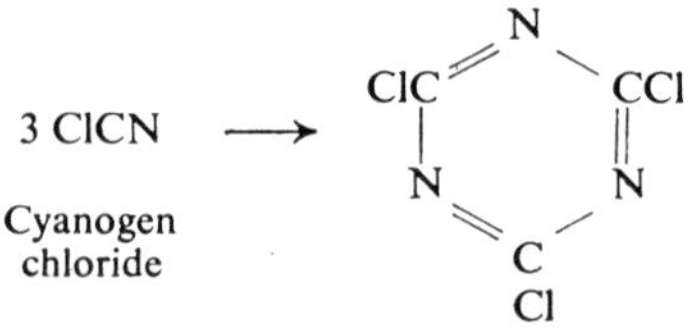

$$3\ ClCN \longrightarrow$$

Cyanogen
chloride

Cyanuric
chloride

Cyanuric chloride is prepared best by the reaction of chlorine with hydrogen cyanide, using chloroform containing 1 per cent of ethanol as a solvent. Cyanogen halides react like alkyl halides with tertiary amines to form quaternary salts (p. 239).

Cyanamide, $H_2NC \equiv N$, may be considered as the amide of hydrocyanic acid and can be prepared by the reaction of cyanogen chloride or bromide with ammonia.

$$2\ NH_3 + ClCN \longrightarrow H_2NCN + NH_4Cl$$

It can be prepared also by passing carbon dioxide into a suspension of commercial calcium cyanamide in aqueous methanol, but is obtained most readily in the laboratory by the reaction of thiourea (p. 326) with freshly precipitated mercuric oxide.

$$H_2NCNH_2 + HgO \longrightarrow H_2NC \equiv N + HgS + H_2O$$
$$\overset{\|}{S}$$

It also may be regarded as the nitrile of carbamic acid, since it yields carbamide (urea) on hydrolysis with alkali.

$$H_2NC \equiv N + H_2O \xrightarrow{[OH^-]} H_2NCONH_2$$

Its most important derivative is the calcium salt, **calcium cyanamide,** which is made by passing nitrogen through calcium carbide at about 1100°. Pure calcium carbide does not absorb nitrogen at 1200°, but in the presence of 10 per cent calcium oxide, nitrogen is absorbed readily at 1050°

$$CaC_2 + N_2 \xrightarrow{CaO} CaNCN + C$$

The mixture is brought to reaction temperature by an electrically heated carbon rod, but after the exothermic reaction has been started, the carbon rod may be removed. The cyanamide process was the first important method for the fixation of atmospheric nitrogen, and calcium cyanamide has continued to be an important nitrogen fertilizer. It is used also as a soil fumigant and as a defoliant.

Cyanamide is stable in aqueous solutions of pH < 5 but dimerizes readily to **dicyandiamide** at pH 7–12. Hence dicyandiamide is the product formed when calcium cyanamide is heated with water.

$$CaNCN + 2\ H_2O \longrightarrow Ca(OH)_2 + H_2NCN$$
$$H_2NC \equiv N + H_2NC \equiv N \longrightarrow H_2NCNHC \equiv N$$
$$\overset{\|}{NH}$$

Dicyandiamide

When dicyandiamide is heated in the presence of anhydrous ammonia and methyl alcohol, **melamine,** the cyclic trimer of cyanamide, is formed.

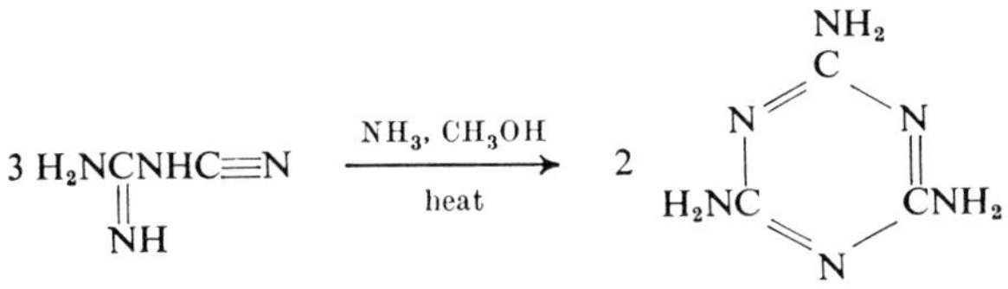

$$3 \text{ H}_2\text{NCNHC}\!\!\equiv\!\!\text{N} \xrightarrow[\text{heat}]{\text{NH}_3,\ \text{CH}_3\text{OH}} 2$$

(structure of Melamine with NH_2, ring of N and C, H_2NC, CNH_2, N)

Melamine

The amidine amino groups of melamine, like the amide amino groups of urea, condense with formaldehyde to give high molecular weight products known as **melamine resins.** They are superior to the urea formaldehyde resins in resistance to heat and water.

Guanidine, $HN\!\!=\!\!C(NH_2)_2$, the amidine (p. 248) of carbamic acid, is formed when dicyandiamide is heated with an excess of ammonia. If dicyandiamide is heated with ammonium chloride, guanidine hydrochloride is formed.

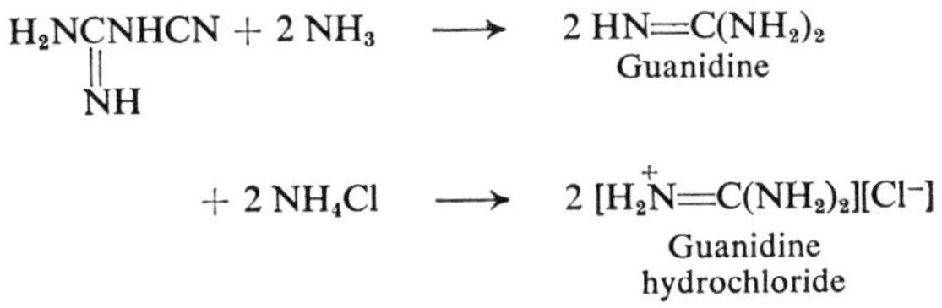

$$\text{H}_2\text{NCNHCN} + 2\text{ NH}_3 \longrightarrow 2 \text{ HN}\!\!=\!\!\text{C(NH}_2)_2$$

Guanidine

$$+ 2\text{ NH}_4\text{Cl} \longrightarrow 2 \text{ [H}_2\overset{+}{\text{N}}\!\!=\!\!\text{C(NH}_2)_2\text{][Cl}^-\text{]}$$

Guanidine
hydrochloride

Biguanide, the guanidine analog of biuret (p. 316), is an intermediate product of the reaction.

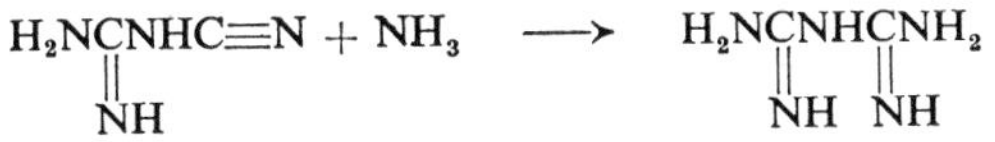

$$\text{H}_2\text{NCNHC}\!\!\equiv\!\!\text{N} + \text{NH}_3 \longrightarrow \text{H}_2\text{NCNHCNH}_2$$

Biguanide

If calcium cyanamide is heated with dilute sulfuric acid, the dicyandiamide first formed is hydrolyzed to **guanylurea** (*dicyandiamidine*), the biuret analog in which only half of the molecule contains a guanidine residue.

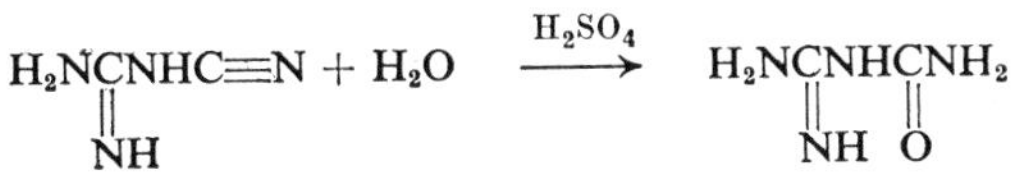

$$\text{H}_2\text{NCNHC}\!\!\equiv\!\!\text{N} + \text{H}_2\text{O} \xrightarrow{\text{H}_2\text{SO}_4} \text{H}_2\text{NCNHCNH}_2$$

Guanylurea
(dicyandiamidine)

Guanylurea phosphate is an effective rust inhibitor for iron and steel. When guanylurea is boiled with water in the presence of carbon dioxide, **guanidine carbonate** is formed in excellent yield.

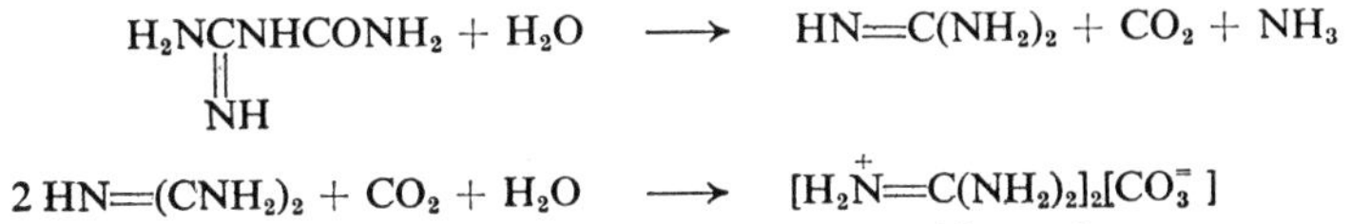

$$\text{H}_2\text{NCNHCONH}_2 + \text{H}_2\text{O} \longrightarrow \text{HN}\!\!=\!\!\text{C(NH}_2)_2 + \text{CO}_2 + \text{NH}_3$$

$$2 \text{ HN}\!\!=\!\!(\text{CNH}_2)_2 + \text{CO}_2 + \text{H}_2\text{O} \longrightarrow \text{[H}_2\overset{+}{\text{N}}\!\!=\!\!\text{C(NH}_2)_2]_2\text{[CO}_3^-\text{]}$$

Guanidine carbonate

Guanidine is the strongest organic base known, having a basic strength ($K_B=4.5\times10^{-1}$) comparable to that of hydroxide ion. The high basicity is believed to result from the large amount of resonance energy liberated when a proton adds to guanidine. The high resonance energy is to be expected since the contributing structures are identical (cf. urea, p. 312).

$$
\left\{
\begin{array}{ccccc}
\overset{+}{N}H_2 & & NH_2 & & NH_2 \\
\| & & | & & | \\
C & \longleftrightarrow & C & \longleftrightarrow & C \\
\diagup \ \diagdown & & \diagup\!\!\diagup \ \diagdown & & \diagup \ \diagdown\!\!\diagdown \\
H_2N \quad NH_2 & & H_2\overset{+}{N} \quad NH_2 & & H_2N \quad \overset{+}{N}H_2
\end{array}
\right\}
$$

Although the salts of guanidine are prepared readily, it is difficult to obtain the free base. If alcoholic solutions of the perchlorate and potassium hydroxide are mixed, potassium perchlorate precipitates. The alcoholic filtrate may be evaporated to give the free base.

When guanidine nitrate is mixed with concentrated sulfuric acid, **nitroguanidine** is formed.

$$[H_2\overset{+}{N}\!\!=\!\!C(NH_2)_2]NO_3^- \xrightarrow{\ H_2SO_4\ } \underset{\underset{NH_2}{|}}{H_2NC\!\!=\!\!NNO_2} + H_2O$$

Nitroguanidine

It is used as a component of some explosives. It is about as powerful as TNT and explodes without producing a flash. When mixed with colloided cellulose nitrate (p. 401), it gives a flashless propellant powder.

Two derivatives of guanidine are of great importance in biological processes. **Creatine** is methylguanidinoacetic acid. Its phosphoric acid derivative is **phosphagen,** which plays an important part in the muscular activity of vertebrates. Creatine is dehydrated readily to **creatinine,** which is excreted in the urine.

$$
\underset{\underset{CH_3}{|}}{H_2N^+\!\!=\!\!C\!-\!\!N\!-\!\!CH_2COO^-} \text{(or } \underset{\underset{CH_3}{|}}{HN\!\!=\!\!C\!-\!\!N\!-\!\!CH_2COOH)} \ \rightleftarrows \ HN\!\!=\!\!C\!\!\begin{array}{c}\diagup NH\!-\!\!CO \\ \diagdown \underset{\underset{CH_3}{|}}{N\!-\!\!CH_2}\end{array} + H_2O
$$

Creatine   Creatinine

The amino acid **arginine** is α-amino-δ-guanidino-*n*-valeric acid and is involved in nitrogen metabolism in mammals. It takes part also in the muscular processes of invertebrates.

The alkyl isocyanates, $O\!\!=\!\!C\!\!=\!\!NR$, are mononitrogen analogs of carbonic acid. The dinitrogen analogs, $RN\!\!=\!\!C\!\!=\!\!NR$, are known as **carbodiimides.** They are prepared from the symmetrical dialkylthioureas (p. 326) by removal of hydrogen sulfide either by means of freshly precipitated mercuric oxide or sodium hypochlorite.

$$\underset{\underset{S}{\|}}{RNHCNHR} + HgO \longrightarrow RN\!\!=\!\!C\!\!=\!\!NR + HgS + H_2O$$

$$\underset{\underset{S}{\|}}{RNHCNHR} + NaOCl \longrightarrow RN\!\!=\!\!C\!\!=\!\!NR + H_2O + S + NaCl$$

Like isocyanic acid and the alkyl isocyanates, the carbodiimides contain a twin double bond and readily undergo addition of compounds containing reactive hydrogen. Water yields the disubstituted ureas.

$$RN{=}C{=}NR + H_2O \longrightarrow \left[\begin{array}{c} RNHC{=}NR \\ | \\ OH \end{array} \right] \longrightarrow RNHCONHR$$

Alcohols give *O*-alkylureas, mercaptans give *S*-alkylthioureas (p. 327), and amines give substituted guanidines.

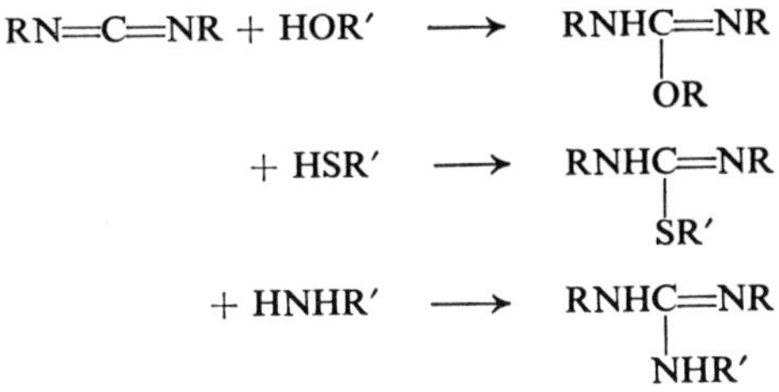

$$RN{=}C{=}NR + HOR' \longrightarrow \begin{array}{c} RNHC{=}NR \\ | \\ OR \end{array}$$

$$+ HSR' \longrightarrow \begin{array}{c} RNHC{=}NR \\ | \\ SR' \end{array}$$

$$+ HNHR' \longrightarrow \begin{array}{c} RNHC{=}NR \\ | \\ NHR' \end{array}$$

Carboxylic acids give either *N*-acyl ureas or the urea and the carboxylic anhydride.

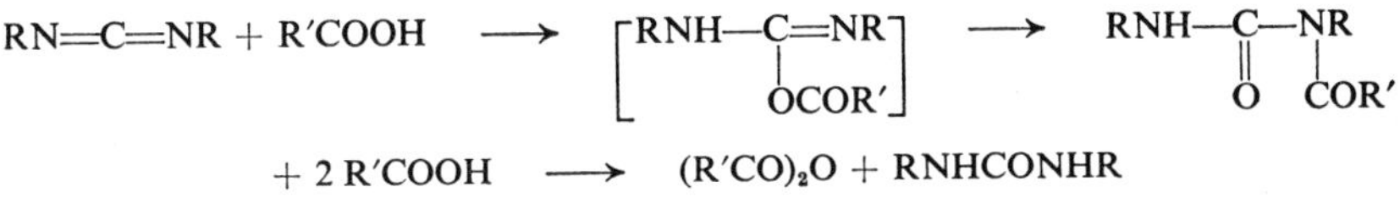

$$RN{=}C{=}NR + R'COOH \longrightarrow \left[\begin{array}{c} RNH{-}C{=}NR \\ | \\ OCOR' \end{array} \right] \longrightarrow \begin{array}{c} RNH{-}C{-}NR \\ \| \quad | \\ O \quad COR' \end{array}$$

$$+ 2 R'COOH \longrightarrow (R'CO)_2O + RNHCONHR$$

If R is an aromatic group, the acyl urea is the chief product, whereas if R is an aliphatic group the urea and the anhydride are formed. Anhydrides are produced not only from carboxylic acids but also from sulfonic acids and dialkyl esters of phosphoric acid.

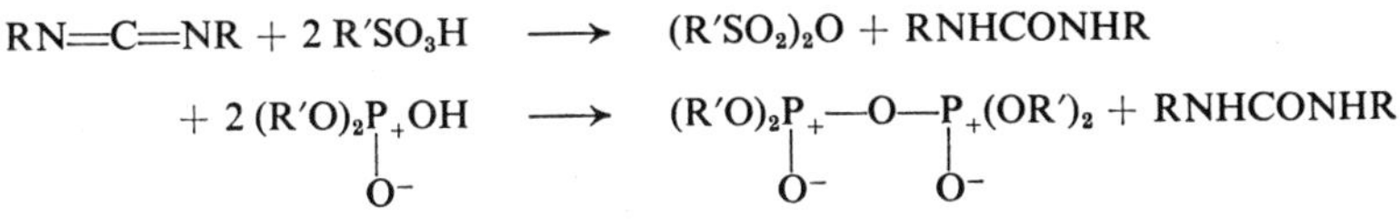

$$RN{=}C{=}NR + 2 R'SO_3H \longrightarrow (R'SO_2)_2O + RNHCONHR$$

$$+ 2 (R'O)_2P_+OH \longrightarrow (R'O)_2P_+{-}O{-}P_+(OR')_2 + RNHCONHR$$
$$\quad\quad\quad | \qquad\qquad\qquad | \quad\quad | $$
$$\quad\quad\quad O^- \qquad\qquad\qquad O^- \quad\quad O^-$$

The last reaction is useful for the synthesis of derivatives of polyphosphoric esters of biological importance (p. 645).

When an aliphatic carbodiimide reacts with a mixture of an amino compound and a carboxylic acid, an amide is formed.

$$RN{=}C{=}NR + R'COOH + R''NH_2 \longrightarrow R'CONHR'' + RNHCONHR$$

This reaction takes place even in the presence of water and other hydroxylic compounds. Its most important use is for the synthesis of peptides (p. 306).

In the formation of anhydrides, the carbodiimide cannot be functioning merely as a dehydrating agent. Undoubtedly the acid adds much more rapidly to the carbodiimide than does water. In the formation of amides the initial product, the *O*-acylurea, can act as an acylating agent for the amine.

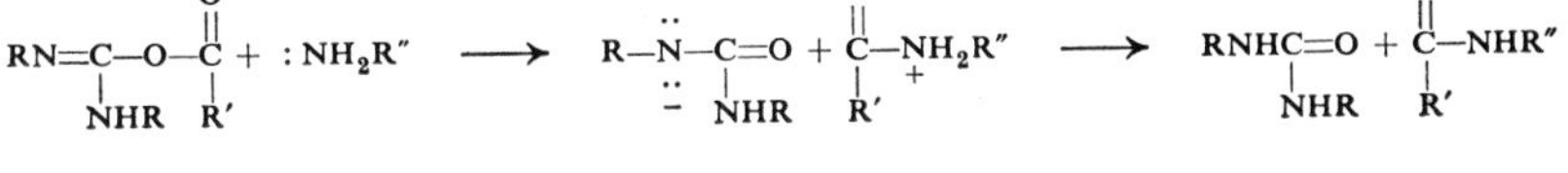

$$\begin{array}{c} O \\ \| \\ RN{=}C{-}O{-}C \\ | \qquad | \\ NHR \quad R' \end{array} + :NH_2R'' \longrightarrow \begin{array}{c} \quad O \\ \quad \| \\ R{-}N{-}C{=}O + C{-}NH_2R'' \\ | \qquad | \quad + \\ NHR \quad R' \end{array} \longrightarrow \begin{array}{c} \quad O \\ \quad \| \\ RNHC{=}O + C{-}NHR'' \\ | \qquad | \\ NHR \quad R' \end{array}$$

In the absence of amine the *O*-acylurea could rearrange to the *N*-acylurea by an analogous mechanism. Alternatively the *O*-acylurea could be attacked by another molecule of acid to give the anhydride.

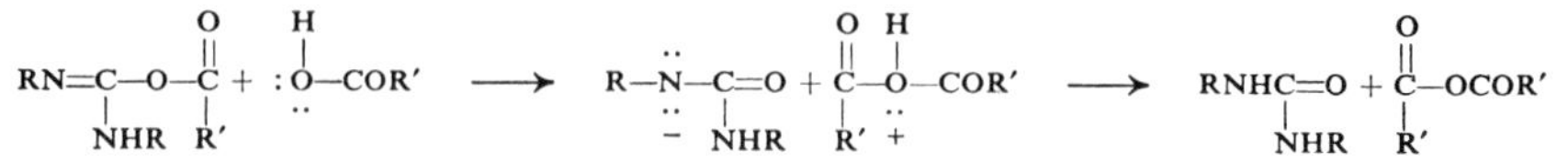

$$RN{=}C{-}O{-}\underset{\underset{R'}{|}}{\overset{\overset{O}{\parallel}}{C}} + :\overset{..}{\underset{..}{O}}{-}COR' \longrightarrow R{-}\underset{\underset{NHR}{|}}{\overset{\overset{H}{|}}{N}}{-}C{=}O + \underset{\underset{R'}{|}}{\overset{\overset{O}{\parallel}}{C}}{-}\overset{..}{\underset{..}{O}}{-}COR' \longrightarrow RNHC{=}O + \underset{\underset{R'}{|}}{\overset{\overset{O}{\parallel}}{C}}{-}OCOR'$$

DERIVATIVES OF THIOCARBONIC ACID

Many of the derivatives of carbonic acid have sulfur analogs, some of which are of general interest. Carbon oxysulfide and carbon disulfide are analogs of carbon dioxide. **Carbon oxysulfide** may be prepared by passing a mixture of carbon monoxide and sulfur vapor through a hot iron tube at 500°.

$$CO + S \xrightarrow{500°} COS$$

It is an odorless, toxic gas, boiling at $-47.5°$. **Carbon disulfide** is manufactured on a large scale by reaction of sulfur with charcoal at a high temperature, either in direct-fired retorts or in a continuous type furnace in which the charcoal is heated by the resistance it offers to the electric current.

$$C + 2S \longrightarrow CS_2$$

It can be prepared also by the reaction of methane and sulfur at 700° over an alumina catalyst.

$$CH_4 + 4S \xrightarrow[Al_2O_3]{700°} CS_2 + 2H_2S$$

Carbon disulfide is a toxic low-boiling highly flammable liquid (p. 44) that is used to some extent as a solvent, as a toxic agent for rodents, and as an intermediate for the manufacture of carbon tetrachloride (p. 722). The principal uses are in the manufacture of viscose rayon, rubber accelerators, and fungicides.

When solutions of alkali hydroxide or alkoxides in alcohols are mixed with carbon disulfide, the *alkali alkyl dithiocarbonates* are formed. These ester salts commonly are known as **xanthates.**[1]

$$C_2H_5OH + CS_2 + NaOH \longrightarrow C_2H_5O\overset{\overset{S}{\parallel}}{C}S^{-+}Na$$
Sodium ethyl
xanthate

The alkyl hydrogen dithiocarbonates decompose at room temperature into carbon disulfide and alcohol. Hence the above reaction is reversed by the addition of acid.

$$C_2H_5O\overset{\overset{S}{\parallel}}{C}S^-Na^+ + HCl \longrightarrow NaCl + \left[C_2H_5O\overset{\overset{S}{\parallel}}{C}SH \right] \longrightarrow C_2H_5OH + CS_2$$

---

[1] Originally, the reaction product of carbon disulfide, ethyl alcohol, and potassium hydroxide was known as potassium xanthate because it gave a yellow precipitate with copper sulfate (Gr. *xanthos*, yellow). Accordingly xanthic acid should be C_2H_5OCSSH. Since the chief variation in the xanthates is in the nature of the alkyl group, it is preferable to give the common name xanthic acid to the hypothetical dithiocarbonic acid, $HOCSSH$.

The **sodium alkyl xanthates** are used as collecting agents in the flotation process for the concentration of ores. The most important use of the reaction of carbon disulfide with hydroxyl groups is for the production of viscose solutions from cellulose (p. 405).

Analogous to the reaction of alcohols with carbon disulfide is the reaction of ammonia and of primary and secondary amines to give the amine salts of **dithiocarbamic acids.**

$$S=C=S + 2\,HNH_2 \longrightarrow H_2N\overset{\overset{\displaystyle S}{\|}}{C}S^{-+}NH_4$$

$$+ 2\,HNHR \longrightarrow RNH\overset{\overset{\displaystyle S}{\|}}{C}S^{-+}NH_3R$$

$$+ 2\,HNR_2 \longrightarrow R_2N\overset{\overset{\displaystyle S}{\|}}{C}S^{-+}NH_2R_2$$

In the presence of zinc oxide, the product from dimethylamine and carbon disulfide, $(CH_3)_2NCSS^{-+}NH_2(CH_3)_2$, and the zinc salt, $[(CH_3)_2NCSS^-]_2Zn^{++}$, are powerful rubber accelerators. The zinc salt and iron salts are valuable fungicides and are sold for this purpose under the trade names *Zerlate* and *Fermate*. Sodium diethyldithiocarbamate, $(C_2H_5)_2NCSS^{-+}Na$, is the preferred reagent for determining small amounts of copper.

Like all sulfhydryl compounds, the dithiocarbamates are oxidized readily to disulfides. The products are known as *thiuram disulfides*. Tetramethylthiuram disulfide, $(CH_3)_2NCSS—SCSN(CH_3)_2$, is a valuable rubber accelerator known as *Tuads* (p. 711). It is used also in fungicidal preparations for disinfecting seeds and turf. Although used as a rubber accelerator since 1918, the fungicidal properties were not recognized until 1931. Tetraethylthiuram disulfide (*Antabuse*) has been used for the treatment of chronic alcoholism. A patient who has been given the compound orally becomes violently ill on drinking alcoholic beverages because of the increase in the concentration of acetaldehyde in the blood.

The reaction of alkali thiocyanates with alkyl halides or sulfates gives **alkyl thiocyanates** in contrast to the behavior of alkali cyanates which yield alkyl isocyanates (p. 317).

$$RX + NaSCN \longrightarrow RSCN + NaX$$

Some of the alkyl thiocyanates are useful insecticides (Lethanes). Partial hydrolysis or alcoholysis in the presence of concentrated sulfuric acid yields *S*-alkyl thiocarbamates or *S*-alkyl *N*-alkylthiocarbamates.

$$RSCN + H_2O \xrightarrow{H_2SO_4} RSCONH_2$$

$$RSCN + R'OH \xrightarrow{H_2SO_4} RSCONHR'$$

In the reaction of both the cyanate and the thiocyanate ion, the product is that in which the more covalent bond has been formed, this being the usual course of reaction of a primary alkyl halide (cf. p. 259).

The **isothiocyanates,** or **mustard oils,** are obtained by the removal of hydrogen sulfide from *N*-alkyldithiocarbamates by means of a reagent such as lead nitrate that can give an insoluble sulfide.

$$RNHCSS^{-+}NH_3R + Pb(NO_3)_2 \longrightarrow RN=C=S + PbS + RNH_3NO_3 + HNO_3$$

The isothiocyanates are called mustard oils because **allyl isothiocyanate,** CH_2=$CHCH_2NCS$, is one of the hydrolytic products of a glycoside occurring in black mustard. All of the volatile mustard oils have sharp characteristic odors.

Like the alkyl isocyanates, the alkyl isothiocyanates readily add alcohols and amines, the products being **alkyl thiocarbamates** (*thiourethans*) and **thioureas.**

$$RNCS + HOR' \longrightarrow RNHCSOR'$$

$$+ HNHR' \longrightarrow RNHCSNHR'$$

$$+ HNR'_2 \longrightarrow RNHCSNR'_2$$

Solid substituted ureas formed from **phenyl isothiocyanate,** C_6H_5N=C=S (p. 482), are useful derivatives for amines. The rate of reaction with amines is so much faster than with water that the reaction can be carried out on aqueous solutions of amines.

Thiocyanogen, N≡CS—SC≡N, is prepared by the action of bromine in ether solution on lead thiocyanate. It is an unstable liquid at room temperature and usually is used in solution. It behaves like the halogens, being intermediate in reactivity between bromine and iodine. It liberates iodine from potassium iodide and adds to the olefinic double bond.

$$RCH\!=\!CHR + (SCN)_2 \longrightarrow \begin{array}{c} RCH\!-\!CHR \\ | \quad\ | \\ SCN \ SCN \end{array}$$

It is used in the estimation of unsaturation in oils (*thiocyanogen value,* p. 184).

Thiourea can be produced from ammonium thiocyanate, a product of the coal gas industry, by a reaction analogous to Woehler's synthesis of urea.

$$NH_4SCN \rightleftharpoons S\!=\!C(NH_2)_2$$

In contrast to the production of ammonium cyanate, however, the rate of the reaction is very slow at 100°, and the molten salt must be heated to about 175° for rapid reaction. At this temperature the equilibrium is not very favorable, only one fifth being converted to thiourea. After the melt has cooled the unchanged thiocyanate is dissolved in water, and the insoluble thiourea is removed. The filtrate may be concentrated and the cycle repeated until the conversion is practically complete. Thiourea can be made also by the action of hydrogen sulfide on calcium cyanamide.

$$CaNCN + 2\,H_2S \xrightarrow{\quad 150°-180° \quad} CaS + H_2NCSNH_2$$

Thiourea, like urea, forms inclusion compounds with other organic compounds (p. 311). Unlike urea it forms addition compounds with branched-chain aliphatic and with cyclic compounds, and with only those straight-chain compounds having more than fourteen carbon atoms.

N-Substituted thioureas are obtained by the reaction of amines with alkyl isothiocyanates (p. 325). Symmetrically substituted dialkylthioureas are obtained best by the thermal decomposition of the amine salts of alkyldithiocarbamic acids (p. 325).

$$RNHCSS^-{}^+NH_3R \longrightarrow RNHCSNHR + H_2S$$

The direct alkylation of thiourea gives the salt of the *S*-alkyl derivative from which the **S-alkylthiourea** (frequently called alkylisothiourea or pseudothiourea) is obtained by adding alkali.

$$(H_2N)_2C\!\!=\!\!S + RX \longrightarrow \left[\begin{array}{c} H_2N-\underset{\underset{+NH_2}{\|}}{C}-SR \end{array}\right] X^- \xrightarrow{\ \text{NaOH}\ } RSC\!\!\begin{array}{c}\nearrow NH \\ \searrow NH_2 \end{array} + NaX + H_2O$$

S-Alkylthiourea
(alkylisothiourea)

S-Substituted thioureas such as *S*-benzylthiourea, $C_6H_5CH_2SC(\!\!=\!\!NH)NH_2$, form salts with carboxylic and sulfonic acids, known as **thiuronium salts,** that crystallize readily and may be used as derivatives for the identification of the acids.

REVIEW QUESTIONS

1. Write structural formulas for orthocarbonic acid, carbonic acid, and carbon dioxide, indicating by brackets the compounds which cannot be isolated. Write structural formulas for those acid chlorides, esters, and amides, formally derivable from the above three compounds, which are known to exist as individual compounds. Give the common names for each type of derivative.
2. Which processes for the synthesis of urea have been operated commercially, and which is the present commercial process? What are the commercial uses of urea?
3. Discuss the mechanism of the conversion of ammonium cyanate into urea.
4. Discuss and give equations for the behavior of urea at elevated temperatures.
5. What is the biuret test? Write the electron formula for the product.
6. Give equations for the reaction of urea with aqueous alkali, nitrous acid, and sodium hypobromite. What is the usual procedure for the quantitative estimation of urea?
7. Discuss the basicity of urea. Why does it form a stable salt with nitric acid?
8. What are ureids? Give an example.
9. What is methylolurea and how is it prepared? Discuss its relation to the urea-formaldehyde resins and indicate the mechanism of thermosetting for this type of resin.
10. What are allophanates, how are they prepared, and of what use are they?
11. How are alkyl isocyanates prepared? Give equations for their characteristic reactions.
12. How are the *N*-alkyl derivatives of urea prepared? The *O*-alkyl derivatives?
13. Give equations for the synthesis of diazomethane starting with (*a*) urea, (*b*) ethyl chloroformate.
14. How is calcium cyanamide made? What are its uses?
15. Compare the steps in the polymerization of cyanamide to dicyandiamide to melamine, with the polymerization of cyanic acid.
16. How is guanidine made? Why is it a much stronger base than urea?
17. Give the formulas for the more common stable sulfur analogs of the derivatives of carbon dioxide.
18. How is carbon disulfide made and what are its more important uses?
19. Discuss the preparation and reactions of alkyl thiocyanates and of alkyl isothiocyanates.
20. What are xanthates, how are they prepared, and what are their uses?
21. How are thiourea and the alkyl substituted thioureas made?
22. Discuss the preparation and importance of the derivatives of dithiocarbamic acid.

PROBLEMS

23. Give equations for all the reactions that should be suitable for the preparation of urea from different types of compounds.
24. Give equations for the preparation of the following compounds: (*a*) methyl chloroformate: (*b*) *n*-butyl carbonate; (*c*) *O*-ethylurea; (*d*) *S*-*i*-butylthiourea; (*e*) *i*-propyl thiocyanate; (*f*) *S*,*N*,*N*'-triethylthiourea; (*g*) potassium *i*-amyl xanthate; (*h*) sodium *N*-methyldithiocarbamate; (*i*) di-*n*-propylcarbodiimide; (*j*) tetra-*N*-methylurea.

25. Tell how one could distinguish between the members of the following pairs of compounds, and give the reactions involved: (*a*) urea and acetamide; (*b*) ethyl isocyanate and ethyl isocyanide; (*c*) N,N'-dimethylthiourea and N,S-dimethylthiourea; (*d*) ethyl chloroformate and acetyl chloride; (*e*) urea and N,N'-dimethylurea; (*f*) ethyl carbonate and ethyl ortho-carbonate; (*g*) *i*-propyl thiocyanate and *i*-propyl isothiocyanate; (*h*) diethylcarbodiimide and N,N'-dimethylurea; (*i*) phosgene and ethyl chloride.

26. Give a series of reactions for the following syntheses: (*a*) N-methyl-N'-ethylurea from potassium cyanate; (*b*) *n*-propyl isothiocyanate from carbon disulfide; (*c*) tetraethylthiuram disulfide from diethylamine; (*d*) methyl allophanate from urea; (*e*) N,N'-methyl-thiourea from methylamine; (*f*) N,N',N''-trimethylguanidine from N,N'-dimethylthiourea; (*g*) N-ethyl-N'-*n*-butylthiourea from ethylammonium N-ethyldithiocarbamate; (*h*) ethyl N-*s*-butylcarbamate from *s*-butylamine.

27. (*a*) Predict the number of moles of ammonia that should be evolved when arginine is boiled with an aqueous solution of sodium hydroxide. Give equations illustrating the stepwise course of the reaction.
(*b*) Predict the number of moles of nitrogen that should be evolved when arginine is treated with aqueous nitrous acid. Give a series of equations illustrating the stepwise course of the reaction.

28. Compounds *A* and *B* have the same molecular formula, $C_3H_8N_2S$. Compound *A* turns black when treated with freshly precipitated mercuric oxide but *B* does not. When either *A* or *B* is boiled with aqueous sodium hydroxide and distilled into water, the distillate turns red litmus blue. The distillate from *A* when warmed with chloroform and potassium hydroxide gives a disagreeable odor but that from *B* does not. Compound *B* when treated with nitrous acid evolves nitrogen, *A* does not. Give the structural formulas for *A* and *B* and equations for the reactions that take place.

29. Compound *A* has the molecular formula $C_4H_7ClO_2$. It reacts with ammonia to give compound *B* having the molecular formula $C_4H_9NO_2$. When *B* is heated with dilute sulfuric acid, a gas is evolved that gives a precipitate when passed into a solution of barium hydroxide. When the acid solution is distilled and the distillate saturated with sodium hydroxide, an oily liquid separates. This liquid when shaken with an aqueous solution of sodium hypoiodite gives a yellow precipitate. When the acid solution is made alkaline with sodium hydroxide, a gas is evolved that turns red litmus blue. Write a structural formula for *A*, and give equations for the reactions that it undergoes.

Chapter 16

STEREOISOMERISM

The existence of two or more compounds having the same number and kinds of atoms and the same molecular weight has been called *isomerism*. Isomers have the same *composition* and are represented by the same molecular formulas. Two main types of isomerism exist. The most common type is known as **structural isomerism,** because it is assumed that the differences between the isomers result from the different order in which the atoms are attached to each other. For example, butane and isobutane differ in that butane has the carbon atoms linked in a chain, and isobutane has a branched carbon skeleton. Such structural isomers may be called *skeletal isomers*. Structural isomers may arise also from the possibility of more than one position for some other element or group as with 1-chloropropane and 2-chloropropane. These isomers are called *position isomers*. In more complex compounds, greater differences in structure may exist, giving rise to different functional groups in the molecule as with methyl ether and ethyl alcohol. Structural isomers of this type may be called *functional isomers*. The order in which atoms are joined together is spoken of as the *constitution* of the compound and is represented by a structural formula.

In the second main type of isomerism, however, the isomers have the same structural formulas. To explain this type of isomerism it is necessary to postulate a different distribution of the atoms in space, and the phenomenon is known as **stereoisomerism** (Gr. *stereos*, solid). The subject of stereoisomerism may be divided into two parts, *optical isomerism* and *geometrical isomerism*. The space arrangement of the atoms is referred to as the *configuration* of the molecule, and three-dimensional models, or perspective drawings, or projections of the space models must be used to illustrate the difference between stereoisomers.

Because of essentially free rotation about single bonds and a certain flexibility of bond angles, the same kinds of molecules, that is; molecules having the same structure and configuration, may assume different shapes in space. The particular shape that a molecule assumes is referred to as its *conformation* (p. 31). The four terms *composition, constitution, configuration,* and *conformation* have definite and distinct meanings. They should not be used interchangeably.

OPTICAL ISOMERISM
Polarized Light

Wave motion may be caused by longitudinal vibrations or transverse vibrations. In a longitudinal vibration, such as a sound wave, the vibrations are parallel to the direction of propagation and symmetrical about the line of propagation. In a transverse vibration, such as an ocean wave, the vibrations are perpendicular to the direction of propagation and there is a lack of symmetry about the line of propagation. The propagation of such a wave may be represented by Fig. 52, which shows the instantaneous magnitude of the vibrations over a given distance. The behavior of the vibrators during propagation of the wave may be visualized by moving the boundary of the wave along the direction of propagation. Each vector maintains a fixed position and direction but varies continuously in magnitude from zero to $+1$ to zero to -1 to zero.

Ordinary light does not show a lack of symmetry, but in 1669 Erasmus Bartholinus[1] discovered that a properly oriented crystal of iceland spar (calcite,

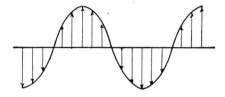

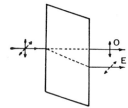

Fig. 52. Propagation of a wave by transverse vibrations.

Fig. 53. Double refraction by a calcite crystal.

a crystalline calcium carbonate) divides a single ray of ordinary light into two rays. Thus a single line viewed through the crystal appears as two lines. This phenomenon is known as *double refraction*. Eight years later Huygens[2] found that each of the rays formed by double refraction is vibrating in a single plane and that the plane of vibration of one ray is perpendicular to the plane of vibration of the other ray (Fig. 53).

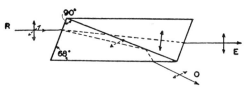

Fig. 54

Fig. 55

Fig. 54. Vibrating vectors along direction of propagation of light ray. Dotted lines indicate how each vector may be considered to be the resultant of two components vibrating at right angles to each other.

Fig. 55. Production of plane-polarized light by a Nicol prism.

Thus the symmetry of a ray of ordinary light about the direction of propagation is caused by transverse vibrations in all directions perpendicular to the direction of propagation. If two mutually perpendicular planes are passed through the ray, each vector will have a component in each plane as indicated in Fig. 54. The action of the calcite crystal is to separate the vectors into their components. The emergent rays, each of which is vibrating in a single plane, are said to be *plane-polarized*.

The Nicol prism,[3] invented in 1828, is a device for separating one plane-polarized ray from the other. The calcite crystal is a rectangular rhombohedron,

[1] Erasmus Bartholinus (1625–1698), Danish professor of mathematics and medicine at the University of Copenhagen.

[2] Christiaan Huygens (1629–1695), Dutch mathematician, astronomer, and physicist. He is known best for his contributions to physical optics.

[3] William Nicol (1768–1851), Scottish physicist who pursued his investigations privately. He devoted himself chiefly to the examination of fluid-filled cavities in crystals, to the manufacture of microscope lenses, and to the microscopic examination of fossil wood.

the acute angles measuring 71 degrees. In the Nicol prism the two end faces are cut away until these angles are reduced to 68 degrees, and the crystal is divided in a plane perpendicular to the two ends and diagonally through the corners of the obtuse angles. The surfaces are polished and the two halves cemented together with Canada balsam, which has an index of refraction less than that of calcite for one of the polarized rays and greater than that of calcite for the other. The action of the Nicol prism is illustrated in Fig. 55. A light ray, R, entering the prism parallel to the long axis is doubly refracted. The ordinary ray, O, is totally reflected from the surface of the Canada balsam. The extraordinary ray, E, is transmitted through the crystal. The reduction in the acute angles of the original calcite crystal from 71 degrees to 68 degrees is for the purpose of securing the proper angle of incidence on the balsam to produce this effect.

If a similarly oriented second Nicol prism is placed in the line of the emergent plane-polarized ray, the ray will pass through the second prism without being affected. If, however, the second prism is rotated about its long axis through 90 degrees, the effect would be the same as if the ray were vibrating at right angles to its original direction, and it would be totally reflected from the Canada balsam layer of the second prism. Two prisms so placed that the plane-polarized ray transmitted by one is not transmitted by the other are spoken of as *crossed Nicols*.

Light may be polarized by processes other than double refraction. In 1808 Malus[4] discovered that light reflected from a glass surface at a particular angle is plane-polarized. When ordinary light passes through a crystal of the mineral tourmaline, the component vibrating in one plane is absorbed much more strongly than that vibrating perpendicular to this plane. This phenomenon is known as *dichroism*. If a dichroic crystal is of the proper thickness, the more strongly absorbed component will be practically extinguished, whereas the other is transmitted in appreciable amount as plane-polarized light. The modern Polaroid operates on the same principle, the absorbing medium being a film containing properly oriented microscopic crystals of a dichroic substance such as the periodide sulfate of quinine. The transmitted light is slightly colored and not completely polarized, but it is possible by this method to make polarizing plates of large area at reasonable cost.

Optical Activity

In 1811 Arago,[5] a pupil of Malus, found that a quartz plate obtained by cutting a quartz crystal perpendicular to the crystal axis will cause the rotation of the plane of polarization of plane-polarized light. This phenomenon can be observed best by placing a plate of quartz between crossed Nicols, the face of one of the Nicol prisms being illuminated from a light source. Before the quartz plate is placed between the two Nicol prisms, no light passes through the second prism. With the quartz plate between them some light passes through the second prism,

---

[4] Etienne Louis Malus (1775–1812), French military engineer. He left the army in 1801 and died of tuberculosis in Paris at the age of 37.

[5] Dominique François Jean Arago (1786–1853), French physicist who, after successfully completing a geodetic survey through Spain, was appointed an astronomer of the French Royal Observatory, a post that he held until his death. He was active in French politics and did much to enhance the prestige of French science.

which now must be rotated through a definite angle to become dark again. *The ability to rotate the plane of polarization of plane-polarized light* is called **optical activity,** and substances possessing this ability are said to be *optically active.* The number of degrees of arc through which the second crystal must be rotated to restore the original condition is called the *optical rotation* of the optically active substance and is given the symbol α.

Häuy[6] had discovered two kinds of quartz, the crystals differing only in the location of two facets which caused the crystals to be nonidentical mirror images. Because of the mirror image relationships they were called *enantiomorphs* (Gr. *enantios,* opposite; *morph,* form). In 1815 Biot,[7] another pupil of Malus, found that plates of the same thickness from the two kinds of quartz rotate plane-polarized light the same amount but in opposite directions. The form which rotates the plane of polarization to the right when facing the light source is called *dextrorotatory* and that which rotates the plane of polarization to the left is called *levorotatory.* Biot found also that other substances such as sugar solutions and turpentine are optically active, the latter even in the vapor phase.

Measurement of Optical Rotation

The instrument used to measure the extent of rotation of plane-polarized light is called a *polarimeter* or *polariscope* (Fig. 56). It consists of a fixed Nicol prism,

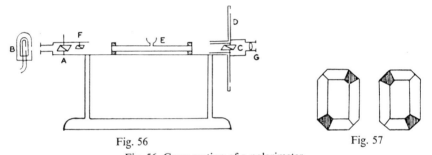

Fig. 56   Fig. 57

Fig. 56. Cross section of a polarimeter.
Fig. 57. Enantiomorphic crystals of the active forms of ammonium acid malate.

A, known as the *polarizer,* for polarizing the monochromatic light from the light source, *B.* A second Nicol prism, *C,* known as the *analyzer,* is attached to a disk, *D,* graduated in degrees and fractions of a degree, that can be rotated. The container for the sample is a tube, *E,* with clear glass ends, known as a *polarimeter tube.* The polarizer and analyzer are mounted on a suitable stand with a trough between them to hold the polarimeter tube in the path of the polarized light. Since it is easier for the eye to match two adjacent areas to the same degree of brightness than to determine a point of maximum darkness or brightness, a third smaller Nicol prism, *F,* is placed behind the polarizer and rotated through a small angle. In this way the field is divided into two halves of unequal brightness. An eyepiece, *G,* focuses on this field. By rotating the analyzer the fields may be

---

[6] Rene Just Häuy (1743–1822), French mineralogist who is regarded as one of the founders of the science of crystallography.

[7] Jean Baptiste Biot (1774–1862), French physicist who was associated with Arago in various geodetic surveys. His most important work dealt with optics, especially the polarization of light.

brought to equal brightness which provides a zero point. When an optically active substance is placed in the path of the light, the fields become unequally bright. Rotation of the analyzer returns the two fields to equal intensity. The number of degrees through which the analyzer is rotated measures the activity of the sample.

The amount of rotation depends on the number of molecules through which the light passes. Hence it is directly proportional to the length of the path through the active material, and this distance must be accurately known. For solutions the extent of rotation depends on the concentration or weight per unit volume of the substance in the solution. These statements are summarized in the equation

$$\alpha = \frac{[\alpha]gl}{v} \quad \text{or} \quad [\alpha] = \frac{\alpha v}{gl}$$

where $\quad \alpha =$ the observed rotation
$\quad g =$ grams of dissolved substance
$\quad v =$ volume of the solution in cubic centimeters
$\quad l =$ length of tube in decimeters
$\quad [\alpha] =$ a constant which is characteristic of the compound and is called the *specific rotation*.

The *molecular rotation*, $[M]$, is the specific rotation multiplied by the molecular weight, and divided by 100 to reduce the size of the figure.

$$[M] = \frac{M[\alpha]}{100}$$

The extent of rotation varies inversely with the square of the wavelength of the light. This phenomenon is known as *rotatory dispersion*. If white light were used as a source of light, each wavelength would be rotated a different amount while passing through the solution. Accordingly it is necessary to use monochromatic light when measuring optical activity. Usually the D line of sodium is used, although frequently it is preferable to use the green line of the mercury arc or the red line of the cadmium arc. The rotation varies somewhat also with the temperature. For accurate work the polarimeter tube is maintained at some fixed temperature, usually 25°. The wavelength used and the temperature of the solution are designated by subscript and superscript. For example, $[\alpha]_D^{25}$ indicates that the rotation was determined at 25° using the D line of sodium. Usually there is more or less electrical effect between solute molecules and between solvent and solute molecules, which causes the specific rotation to vary somewhat with different concentrations and with different solvents. Hence it is necessary to indicate both the concentration and the solvent used. Thus a proper description of a specific rotation would be

$$[\alpha]_D^{25} = 95.01° \text{ in methyl alcohol } (c = 0.105 \text{ g./cc.})$$

Optical Isomerism

Optical isomers may be defined as the members of a set of stereoisomers, at least two of which are optically active. By 1848 two isomeric acids were known which had been isolated from the tartar of grapes. The common acid called tartaric acid was discovered by Scheele in 1769 and found by Biot to be dextro-rotatory. Its isomer, which was isolated by Kestner [8] some time previous to 1819 and named racemic acid (L. *racemes,* a bunch of berries or grapes) by Gay-Lussac, was optically inactive. In the spring of 1848, Pasteur (p. 91) was studying the crystal structure of sodium ammonium tartrate. He noticed that the crystals were characterized by facets which eliminated certain elements of symmetry from the crystal (cf. p. 336). Such facets are known as *hemihedral facets,* since they occur in only half the number required for complete symmetry. As a result of the occurrence of the hemihedral facets, the crystals were not identical with their mirror images; that is, the mirror image could not be superposed on the crystal with coincidence at all points. Figure 57, page 332, shows enantiomorphic crystals of the active forms of ammonium acid malate (p. 808). These crystals have fewer faces than those of the sodium ammonium tartrates, and the hemi-hedral facets can be seen readily. If the hemihedral facets were lacking or if the crystals were holohedral, that is, if the facets appeared on all corners, the mirror images would be identical.

Recalling that the active quartz crystals had hemihedral facets and that Herschel [9] in 1820 had suggested that there may be a connection between the hemihedralism of quartz and its optical activity, Pasteur proceeded to examine crystals of the inactive sodium ammonium racemate, expecting to find them holohedral. He found instead that all of the crystals obtained had hemihedral facets, but that two kinds of crystals were present. One kind was identical with the crystals of sodium ammonium tartrate, and the other kind consisted of mirror images of the tartrate crystals. Pasteur separated the two types of crystals under the microscope and found that the type that looked like sodium ammonium tartrate was indeed dextrorotatory and identical with it, but that the mirror image crystals, when dissolved in water, rotated plane-polarized light exactly the same amount in the opposite direction. When equal weights of the two crystals were mixed, the solution was optically inactive. In other words, the reason that racemic acid is inactive is because it is composed of equal quantities of two different kinds of molecules, one dextrorotatory and the other levorotatory.

Quartz and other active crystals such as sodium chlorate and magnesium sulfate lose their optical activity on solution. Similarly amorphous silica is optically inactive. Hence the cause of the activity in the crystal lies in the arrangement of the atoms in the crystal. Tartaric acid, on the other hand, is active in solution. Moreover pinene from oil of turpentine is active in both the liquid and gaseous states. In these compounds the activity must be due to the arrangement of the atoms in the individual molecules. Pasteur himself came to this conclusion, but since the theories of structural organic chemistry were not

---

[8] Kestner, the owner of a chemical plant, had obtained as a by-product of tartaric acid manufacture an acid which he thought to be oxalic acid and which he sold as such. It was pointed out in a handbook in 1819 that this compound was neither oxalic nor tartaric acid. Gay-Lussac obtained a sample from Kestner and found that the analytical values were the same as those for tartaric acid, and he called the new compound racemic acid. It was not until 1830 that Berzelius convinced himself that both compounds had the same composition, and coined the term *isomerism* for the phenomenon.

[9] John Frederick William Herschel (1792–1871), noted English astronomer who by inclination was more interested in chemistry and the properties of light and made many valuable contributions in these fields.

developed until around 1860 (p. 4), he did not recognize the principle necessary to relate optical activity to molecular structure.

By 1874 the constitutions of several active compounds were known. In September and November of that year two papers appeared, one by van't Hoff [10] and the other by Le Bel,[11] in which each pointed out that in every case in which optical activity existed, at least one carbon atom was present that was combined with four different groups. The following examples may be cited, the carbon atoms under discussion being marked by an asterisk.

$$CH_3CH_2\overset{*}{C}HCH_2OH$$
$$\overset{|}{C}H_3$$

Active amyl alcohol

$$CH_3\overset{*}{C}HCOOH$$
$$\overset{|}{O}H$$

Lactic acid

$$HOOCCH_2\overset{*}{C}HCOOH$$
$$\overset{|}{O}H$$

Malic acid

$$HOOCCH_2\overset{*}{C}HCOOH$$
$$\overset{|}{N}H_2$$

Aspartic acid

Wherever a pair of isomers differing in sign of rotation was known, the members of the pair had identical chemical and physical properties with the exception of their action on plane-polarized light, and even here they differed only in the sign of rotation and not in the magnitude of rotation. Accordingly the space relationship between atoms of one isomer must be the same as that between the atoms of the other isomer. van't Hoff and Le Bel pointed out that if the four different groups about the carbon atom are placed at the four corners of a tetrahedron, two arrangements are possible. Two molecules result which are mirror images of each other, but which are not superposable and hence not identical (Fig. 58). The asymmetry of such arrangements is of the same type as the asymmetry of the quartz crystals or of the sodium ammonium tartrate crystals; that is, *the condition necessary for the existence of optical activity is that the arrangement of the atoms be such that a crystal or molecule and its mirror image are not superposable.* Objects which are not superposable on their mirror images are said to be *dissymmetric.* It should be noted that they need not be lacking in all elements of symmetry and that although all asymmetric objects are also dissymmetric, dissymmetric objects are not necessarily asymmetric. A carbon atom joined to four different atoms or groups of atoms lacks symmetry and is known as an *asymmetric carbon atom.* Two isomers that rotate plane-polarized light in equal amounts in opposite directions are known as *active components, optical antipodes, enantiomorphs,* or *enantiomers.* The term *mirror image* also frequently is used, *nonsuperposable* being implied.

Actually the presence of an asymmetric carbon atom is not necessary for optical activity. Its presence is merely the most frequently encountered condition that removes the elements of symmetry that make mirror images identical.

[10] Jacobus Hendricus van't Hoff (1852–1911), Dutch physical chemist, professor at Amsterdam University and after 1896 at the Prussian Academy of Sciences and the University of Berlin. He is noted not only for his theoretical contributions to stereoisomerism, but also for his contributions to the theories of solutions and of chemical equilibria. He was the first recipient of the Nobel Prize in Chemistry in 1901.

[11] Jules Achille Le Bel (1847–1930), French chemist who was financially independent and conducted his investigations privately. His experimental work dealt largely with the verification of predictions based on his stereochemical theories.

These elements of symmetry are (*1*) a plane of symmetry, (*2*) a center of symmetry, and (*3*) a fourfold alternating (or mirror) axis of symmetry. A *plane of symmetry* is a plane that divides an object into two halves which are mirror

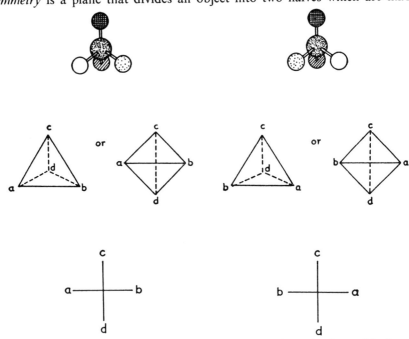

Fig. 58. Representation of nonidentical mirror images by molecular models, by tetrahedra, and by projection formulas.

images of each other. The compound *Caabd* (Fig. 59*a*), for example, has a plane of symmetry, namely that which divides the carbon atom and the groups *b* and *d* into like halves, whereas the compound *Cabde* (Fig. 59*b*) does not have a plane of symmetry.

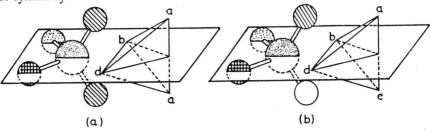

(a)　　　　　　　　　(b)

Fig. 59. (*a*) Plane of symmetry in compound *Caabd*; (*b*) lack of a plane of symmetry in compound *Cabde*.

If an object possesses a plane of symmetry, the object and its mirror image are identical. The same statement holds for the other two elements of symmetry, but since they need to be considered only infrequently, discussion of them is omitted. One example of a compound having a center of symmetry is mentioned on page 836. Examples of molecular asymmetry in the absence of an asymmetric atom are discussed on pages 580 and 605.

Expected Number of Optical Isomers

Molecules containing a single asymmetric carbon atom exist in only two forms. The asymmetric atoms may be designated as $A+$ and $A-$ for the dextrorotatory and levorotatory forms respectively. If a second asymmetric carbon atom is present, the configuration of this atom may be designated as $B+$ or $B-$. Therefore a total of four isomers is possible, namely those in which the four configurations are $A+B+$, $A+B-$, $A-B+$, and $A-B-$. Since $A+$ is the mirror image of $A-$, and $B+$ is the mirror image of $B-$, $A+B+$ is the mirror image of $A-B-$, and the two constitute an enantiomorphic pair and have identical properties except for the sign of rotation. Similarly $A+B-$ and $A-B+$ are enantiomorphic. $A+B+$, however, is not a mirror image of either $A+B-$ or $A-B+$ and has different chemical and physical properties. Similarly any active compound has only one mirror image and all others of its optical isomers differ from it in chemical and physical properties. Optical isomers which are not mirror images are called *diastereoisomers*.

If a third asymmetric atom is present, it also may exist in two forms, $C+$ and $C-$, and similarly for a fourth atom, $D+$ and $D-$. Hence two active forms exist if a single asymmetric carbon atom is present, and the number of active forms is doubled each time a new asymmetric atom is added. The total number of active forms, therefore, is 2^n, where n is the number of asymmetric carbon atoms.

To represent space models on plane paper, perspective drawings of tetrahedra may be used. It is more convenient, however, to use projection formulas. The convention has been adopted that the two groups at the top and bottom of the projection formulas always are directly over each other and behind the plane of the paper in the corresponding perspective formulas. In any comparison of projection formulas with each other, neither the formula as a whole, nor any portion of the formula may be rotated out of the plane of the paper. Otherwise the top and bottom groups would not bear the same relation to the other formulas as was assumed when the formulas were projected. Any rotation within the plane of the paper must be through 180°. If a projection formula has been rotated through 90°, it must be rotated clockwise or counterclockwise through 90° before an interpretation of the configuration can be made. General examples of several methods for representing active forms are shown in Fig. 60 and Fig. 61.

In the formulation of the 2^n rule the assumption was made that all of the asymmetric carbon atoms were different, that is, that no two of them were attached to the same four kinds of groups. If any of the asymmetric carbon atoms are alike, the number of possible isomers is decreased. Thus if a compound contains two like asymmetric carbon atoms, the possible configurations are $A+A+$, $A+A-$, $A-A+$, and $A-A-$. However since $A+A-$ is identical with $A-A+$, only three optical isomers exist. The tartaric acids investigated by Pasteur may be used for illustration. They have the constitution HOOCCHOHCHOHCOOH. Each of the two asymmetric carbon atoms bears the groups H, OH, COOH, and CHOHCOOH, and hence they are alike. The four possible combinations of active groups are shown by both perspective and projection formulas in Fig. 62.

The first two forms are nonsuperposable. The second two arrangements, however, have a plane of symmetry. These structures are not superposable in the positions shown, but if one or the other is inverted, they become superposable. Similarly in the projection formulas the dotted line indicates a plane of symmetry,

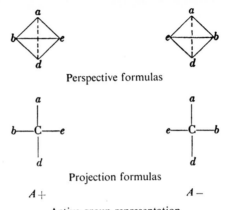

Perspective formulas

Projection formulas

A+   *A−*

Active group representation

Fig. 60. Methods of representing active forms having a single asymmetric carbon atom.

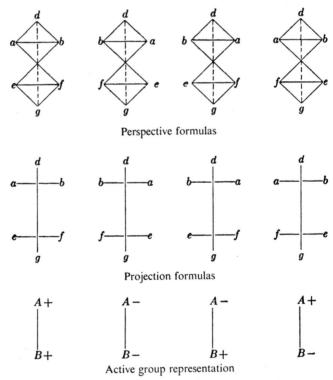

Perspective formulas

Projection formulas

Active group representation

Fig. 61. Methods of representing active forms having two different asymmetric carbon atoms.

and rotation of one or the other formula in the plane of the paper through 180° causes the two to coincide. Although it may appear that rotation of a projection formula about a vertical axis also makes it coincide with the other formula, such is not the case since the carboxyl groups are not in the plane of the paper.

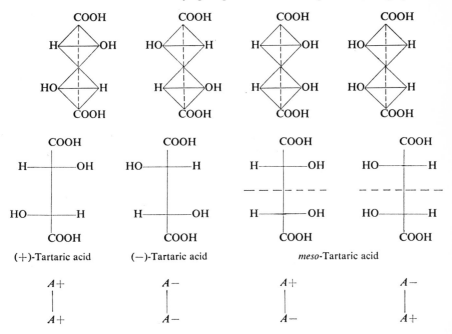

Fig. 62. Methods of representing the optical isomers of a compound having two like asymmetric carbon atoms.

    Not only is the number of optical isomers reduced from four to three when two like asymmetric carbon atoms are present, but the third form, having a plane of symmetry, is optically inactive. It is known as a *meso form* (Gr. *mesos*, middle). Therefore a compound having two like asymmetric carbon atoms has three optical isomers. Two are active enantiomorphs with identical chemical and physical properties except for their opposite effect on plane-polarized light. The third is an inactive *meso* form which is a diastereoisomer of the other two and hence differs from them in chemical and physical properties. In addition a fourth form, known as the *racemic* form (after racemic acid), consists of a mixture of equal amounts of the two active forms and hence is optically inactive. It differs from the *meso* form, however, in that it can be separated into active forms whereas the *meso* form cannot. The solid racemic form usually differs in physical properties from the other forms, but in solution it dissociates into the two active forms, and its properties in solution are identical with the properties of the active forms.

    If asymmetric carbon atoms are separated by carbon atoms attached to two like groups, the number of optical isomers remains the same. For example, *Cabd Caa Cabe* would have four active forms and *Cabd Caa Cabd* would have two active and one *meso* form. However, if two like asymmetric carbon atoms are joined to a carbon atom attached to two different nonasymmetric groups, for example *Cabd Cab Cabd*, two active forms and two *meso* forms are possible, each of the latter having a plane of symmetry. This situation is illustrated in Fig. 63.

The central carbon atom in such compounds was called a *pseudoasymmetric carbon atom* by Werner,[12] because it has four different groups attached to it when

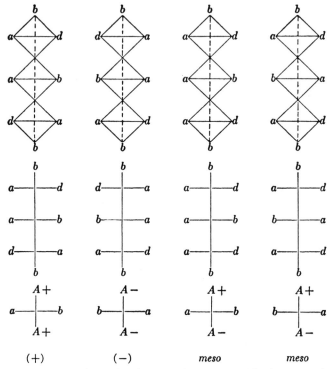

Fig. 63. Representations of the optical isomers of a compound having a pseudoasymmetric carbon atom.

two of the groups are $A+$ and $A-$, but the molecule is optically inactive because of the plane of symmetry.

The number of active and *meso* forms can be calculated from the following formulas provided all of the asymmetric carbon atoms can be considered as occurring in a chain of atoms, and none of them in a branch of the chain. In the formulas given below, $n =$ the total number of asymmetric carbon atoms including the pseudoasymmetric carbon atom if present, $a =$ the number of active forms, and $m =$ the number of *meso* forms.

1. If all of the asymmetric carbon atoms are different, $a = 2^n$, $m = 0$.

2. If the molecule contains like asymmetric carbon atoms and n is even,

$$a = 2^{(n-1)}, m = 2^{\left(\frac{n-2}{2}\right)}.$$

---

[12] Alfred Werner (1866–1919), Swiss chemist, professor at the University of Zurich. He was noted for his studies of coordination compounds and for his contributions to stereochemistry. He was awarded the Nobel Prize in Chemistry in 1913.

3. If the molecule contains like asymmetric carbon atoms and n is odd,

$$a = 2^{(n-1)} - 2^{\left(\frac{n-1}{2}\right)},\ m = 2^{\left(\frac{n-1}{2}\right)}.$$

Separation of Racemic Forms into Active Components (Resolution)

Many naturally occurring organic compounds that contain an asymmetric carbon atom are optically active. For example lactic acid, $CH_3CHOHCOOH$, isolated from muscle is the $(+)$ isomer. Lactic acid produced by fermentation may be $(+)$, or $(-)$, or racemic depending on the fermenting organism. On the other hand, lactic acid produced by synthesis always is racemic. The reason is that when the asymmetric carbon atom is formed by synthesis, there always is an equal chance of producing the $(+)$ or the $(-)$ form, and since the number of molecules involved is very large, equal quantities of both forms are produced. Suppose, for example, that lactic acid is being synthesized by brominating propionic acid to α-bromopropionic acid and hydrolyzing to the hydroxy acid. In the bromination step either of the two α hydrogen atoms may be replaced. Replacement of one gives rise to the $(+)$ form and of the other to the $(-)$ form.

Or if acetaldehyde is converted to the cyanohydrin, a racemic mixture is formed because the double bond of the carbonyl group may be attacked from either side with equal ease during the addition of hydrogen cyanide. Accordingly the separation of racemic mixtures into their active components is of considerable importance. This process is known as *resolution*, and the racemate is said to be *resolved* into its active components.

Pasteur's original separation of sodium ammonium racemate into the $(+)$-tartrate and the $(-)$-tartrate is largely of historical interest only, since not all racemates separate into enantiomorphic crystals. Even sodium ammonium tartrate does so only below $27.7°$. Furthermore the mechanical separation is tedious.

Although it has been indicated that enantiomorphs have identical chemical properties, this statement holds only if the reagent itself is not optically active; that is, if the reagent is dissymmetric, the rates at which two like bonds are broken are no longer equal. Pasteur found, for example, that many organisms destroy one form of a pair of enantiomorphs and not the other. Thus the enzymes of the mold *Penicillium glaucum*, when allowed to act on ammonium racemate, destroy ammonium $(+)$-tartrate and leave the $(-)$ form unchanged. The general procedure used is to make a solution of the racemate, add nutrient salts, and inoculate with the desired organism. This method has the serious disadvantage that one form is lost and the other form usually is obtained in poor yield. Moreover it is necessary to work with dilute solutions. The method can be applied, however, to a fairly large variety of compounds and frequently provides a simple method for determining whether a compound is capable of resolution.

Enzymic decomposition or synthesis is a complicated process, but the principles underlying the production of active compounds by means of enzymes apply also to simpler reactions. For example, if racemic lactic acid is partially esterified with an active alcohol such as (+)-amyl alcohol, the (+) and (−) forms of the lactic acid react at different rates, and the unreacted portion contains an excess of one of the forms and has some optical activity.

A closely related process is known as *asymmetric synthesis*. Catalytic reduction of pyruvic acid yields racemic lactic acid.

$$CH_3COCOOH + H_2 \xrightarrow{Pt} CH_3CHOHCOOH$$

Pyruvic acid   Racemic lactic acid

If reduction is brought about by reductase of yeast, (−)-lactic acid is produced.

$$CH_3COCOOH \xrightarrow{Reductase} CH_3CHOHCOOH$$

Pyruvic acid   (−)-Lactic acid

Moreover if (+)-amyl pyruvate is reduced catalytically and the (+)-amyl lactates hydrolyzed, the lactic acid obtained is optically active to a small extent because of an excess of one of the active forms.

$$CH_3COCOOC_5H_{11}(+) \xrightarrow{H_2, Pt} CH_3CHOHCOOC_5H_{11}(+)$$

$$\downarrow H_2O$$

$$CH_3CHOHCOOH + C_5H_{11}OH(+)$$

Active

Similarly every chemical process involving dissymmetric agents can lead to the production of active compounds. Even selective adsorption on optically active adsorbents, and asymmetric decomposition over quartz, have been used to produce active compounds from racemic mixtures.

The differences in behavior of enantiomorphs in living matter are explainable by the fact that reactions in living matter are catalyzed largely by optically active enzymes. A few examples may be given: only one form of an amino acid commonly is present in proteins and is utilizable by the organism in the synthesis of proteins; (+)-glucose is the form synthesized by plants and the only form fermentable by yeast or utilizable by living matter; (+)-leucine is sweet whereas (−)-leucine is faintly bitter; (−)-tartaric acid is more toxic than (+)-tartaric acid; (−)-epinephrine has twenty times the activity of (+)-epinephrine in raising blood pressure. These differences merely emphasize the fact that enantiomorphs have identical properties only if they are reacting with nonactive reagents.

By far the most generally practical procedure for the separation of racemic mixtures, also developed by Pasteur, involves the conversion of the enantiomorphs into compounds that are diastereoisomers. Since diastereoisomers are not mirror images, they do not have the same physical properties and may be separated by ordinary physical methods such as fractional crystallization. After the separation of the diastereoisomers, they are converted into the original reactants. If (A+) and (A−) represent the two active forms present in the racemic mixture and (B+) represents a single active form of another compound which will combine with the racemic mixture, the process of separation may be illustrated schematically as follows:

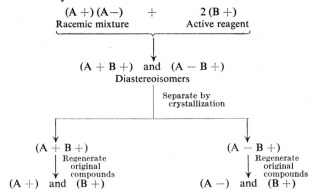

In practice the type of compound formation which takes place most readily and from which the original reactants can be regenerated most easily is salt formation. Thus a racemic acid can be resolved by an active base, or a racemic base by an active acid.

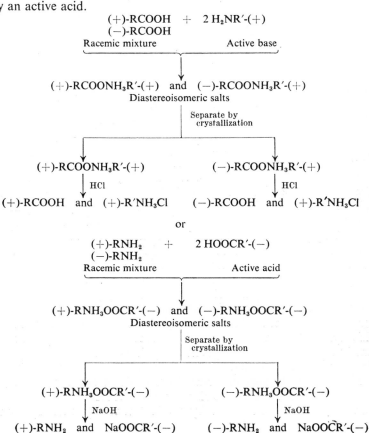

The naturally occurring alkaloids (p. 648) are active bases that give readily crystallizable salts. Those most commonly used for effecting resolution of racemic acids are (—)-brucine, (—)-strychnine, (—)-quinine, (+)-cinchonine, (+)-quinidine, and (—)-morphine. The easily available naturally occurring acids suitable for the resolution of racemic bases are (+)-tartaric acid and (—)-malic acid. Once a synthetic racemic mixture has been resolved, the active components can be used to resolve other racemic mixtures. Indirect methods and reactions other than salt formation have been used for the resolution of compounds that do not contain acidic or basic groups.

In 1952 it was found that certain compounds, for example trithymotide (p. 560) and urea, crystallize spontaneously into dissymmetric forms which are capable of occluding other compounds (p. 311). If crystallization takes place in the presence of a racemic mixture, one form can be preferentially occluded and a resolution effected. This procedure is particularly promising for resolving racemic hydrocarbons and alkyl halides which, because of the absence of reactive groups, are difficult to resolve by the usual methods.

The question arises as to how different groups must be to permit the detection of optical activity. It has been demonstrated in a number of compounds that even the difference between the isotopes hydrogen and deuterium is sufficient to give rise to observable activity. The enantiomorphs of 1-deuterobutyl acetate $CH_3CH_2CH_2CHD(OCOCH_3)$, for example, have been prepared with specific rotations of $[\alpha]_D^{25} + 0.094 \pm 0.001°$ and $[\alpha]_D^{25} - 0.090 \pm 0.007°$.

Origin of Optically Active Compounds

In all of the processes discussed so far, the production of an active compound depends on the presence of another dissymmetric compound. The question naturally arises, "How was the first compound formed?" Pasteur believed that active forms could be obtained only by the intervention of life processes. Le Bel pointed out that the formation of an asymmetric carbon atom by a reaction catalyzed by circularly-polarized light need not result in the production of equal amounts of the two isomers. It was not until 1896, however, that it was shown experimentally that *d* or *l* circularly-polarized light is absorbed to a different extent by enantiomorphs (*circular dichroism* or *Cotton effect*). Finally in 1930 an optically active substance was produced by partial photochemical decomposition using circularly-polarized light. Since light reflected from the ocean's surface is circularly polarized by the earth's magnetic field, one reasonable explanation is at hand for the origin of optically active compounds.

Another possibility is that the first organic compounds were resolved as the result of occlusion in dissymmetric crystals of nondissymmetric molecules. It is known, for example, that numerous compounds that are inactive in solution, such as quartz, sodium chlorate, benzil (p. 541), or urea, crystallize to form enantiomorphic crystals. Frequently one form is produced predominantly or exclusively. The particular form produced is governed by chance, but once the crystal starts growing in a particular configuration, all of the compound crystallizes in this form. Such a crystal could preferentially occlude or adsorb one form of an organic racemic mixture and give rise to an optical resolution. Experimentally 2-chlorooctane has been resolved by allowing it to crystallize spontaneously with urea.

Racemization

Two methods for producing racemic mixtures have been discussed, one by mixing equal amounts of the (+) and (−) forms (p. 334) and the other by producing an asymmetric carbon atom by a synthesis in which none of the reagents is optically active (p. 341). A third method consists in converting either a (+) or (−) form into a mixture of the (+) and (−). This process is known as *racemization.*

Since conversion of a (+) form to a (−) form or of a (−) form to a (+) form involves the change in position of at least two groups on the asymmetric atom, bonds must be broken during the racemization, and the molecule must pass through a nondissymmetric intermediate. In the subsequent reformation of the compound equal amounts of the two forms are produced. The most easily racemized compounds and those for which the racemization is most readily explainable are those in which a carbonyl group is α to an asymmetric atom which carries a hydrogen atom. The racemization undoubtedly involves enolization (p. 207). The enol form does not contain an asymmetric atom, and when ketonization takes place, the double bond may be attacked from either side with equal ease, and equal quantities of both (+) and (−) forms are produced. Eventually racemization becomes complete. Thus the racemization of active lactic acid may be represented by the following equilibria.

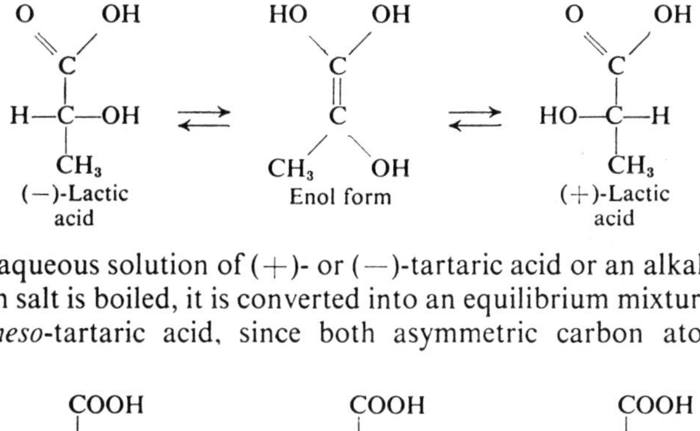

(−)-Lactic acid   Enol form   (+)-Lactic acid

When an aqueous solution of (+)- or (−)-tartaric acid or an alkaline solution of its sodium salt is boiled, it is converted into an equilibrium mixture of racemic acid and *meso*-tartaric acid, since both asymmetric carbon atoms become racemized.

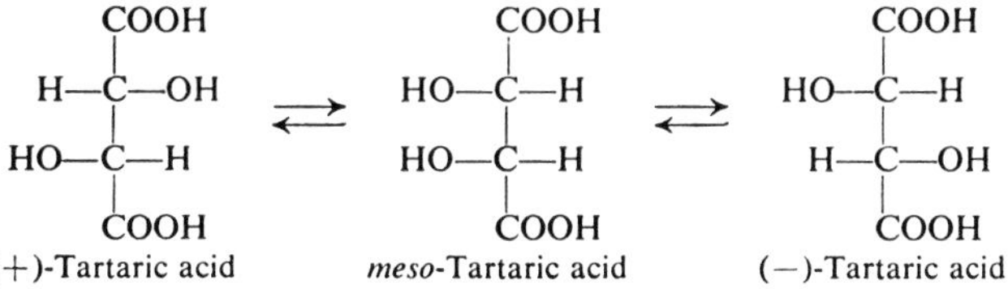

(+)-Tartaric acid   *meso*-Tartaric acid   (−)-Tartaric acid

If more than one asymmetric carbon atom is present, only those having enolizable hydrogen are isomerized. For example, an active form of 1,2-dichloropropionic acid isomerizes only to its diastereoisomer and not to the mixture of racemates

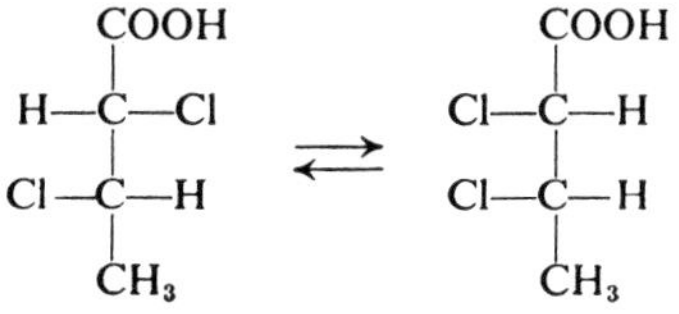

Optical isomers which differ only in the configuration of one carbon atom are called *epimers* (Gr. *epi*, beside or over), and the conversion of an active compound into its epimer is known as *epimerization*.

Racemization may take place even though enolization is not possible if the active compound is heated to a temperature sufficiently high to cause dissociation of one of the groups attached to the asymmetric atom. The resulting fragment with only three groups attached to the asymmetric atom then may assume a planar configuration. Recombination with the dissociated group can take place from either side and produces equal amounts of both forms (Fig. 64).

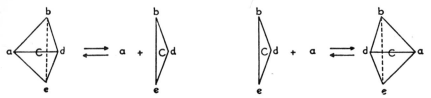

Fig. 64. Racemization by dissociation.

Active compounds whose dissymmetry results from steric effects may racemize merely by deformation of the molecule without breaking any bonds (pp. 580, 560).

Walden Inversion

When active compounds undergo reactions involving the asymmetric atom, the products may be inactive, because racemization can take place when bonds involving the asymmetric atom are broken. Frequently, however, full activity is retained. Retention of activity can be explained only by assuming that the molecule retains its asymmetry during the reaction, which could happen if the entering group merely knocked the group being eliminated out of its position and took its place. However, if the same compound is prepared in more than one way, the sign of rotation of the active form produced often varies with the number of steps involved in the reaction. For example, aspartic acid can be converted into chlorosuccinic acid either directly or by way of bromosuccinic acid. If the entering groups merely are taking the place of the groups being eliminated, the product should be the same in both cases. Actually one product is levorotatory, and the other is dextrorotatory.

$$
\begin{array}{ccc}
\text{HOOCCHNH}_2 & \xrightarrow[+\ 2\ \text{HCl}]{\text{NaNO}_2} & \text{HOOCCHCl} \\
| & & | \quad + \text{NaCl} + \text{N}_2 + 2\,\text{H}_2\text{O} \\
\text{HOOCCH}_2 & & \text{HOOCCH}_2 \\
\text{(\textminus)-Aspartic acid} & & \text{(\textminus)-Chlorosuccinic acid}
\end{array}
$$

$$
\downarrow \begin{array}{l} \text{NaNO}_2 \\ + 2\ \text{HBr} \end{array}
$$

$$
\begin{array}{ccc}
\text{HOOCCHBr} & \xrightarrow{\text{NaCl}} & \text{HOOCCHCl} \\
| & & | \\
\text{HOOCCH}_2 & & \text{HOOCCH}_2 + \text{NaBr} \\
\text{(\textminus)-Bromosuccinic} & & \text{(+)-Chlorosuccinic} \\
\text{acid} & & \text{acid}
\end{array}
$$

Therefore a change in configuration must have taken place at one or more steps of the reactions.

It seems reasonable that whatever the mechanism of the replacement of the amino group by halogen, it would be the same whether sodium nitrite and hydrogen chloride, or sodium nitrite and hydrogen bromide, are the reagents. Therefore the chloro- and bromosuccinic acids formed by this reaction would be expected to have the same configuration, and a change in configuration must take place in the conversion of bromosuccinic acid to chlorosuccinic acid. Since the reaction of the amino group with nitrous acid and hydrochloric acid is complex, only the conversion of the bromosuccinic acid to chlorosuccinic acid is considered. This step undoubtedly involves a displacement of bromide ion by chloride ion. As the chloride ion approaches the face of the molecule opposite the bromine atom, the bromide ion leaves, and an inversion of configuration takes place with the formation of a single active form (Fig. 65).

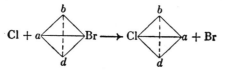

Fig. 65. Walden inversion.

The phenomenon of optical inversion was discovered by Walden[13] in 1893 and is known as the *Walden inversion*. The current interpretation of the mechanism of inversion was suggested by Werner (p. 340) as early as 1911 and again by Lewis (p. 236) in his book on valence in 1923, and by Lowry (p. 236) in 1924. If the mechanism is correct, displacement of a group on the asymmetric atom by a like group would produce the enantiomorph. Hence complete racemization eventually should result (Fig. 66).

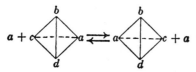

Fig. 66. Racemization by displacement.

It was shown in 1913 that the rate of racemization of active bromosuccinic acid is proportional to the bromide ion concentration, but it was not until 1935 that evidence was presented that this mechanism may be the only one involved in the racemization. It was found by the use of radioactive iodide ions that the rate of introduction of radioactive iodine into 2-iodooctane is the same as the rate of racemization of active 2-iodooctane by the iodide ions. It now is believed that most displacement reactions take place by this mechanism (p. 116), an inversion of structure taking place at each step of a reaction although the inversion is detectable only with active compounds.

Absolute and Relative Configuration

Absolute configuration is the actual configuration of the molecule in space, that is, it is the answer to the question, "Which of two enantiomorphic models represents the dextrorotatory form of a compound and which the levorotatory

---

[13] Paul Walden (1863–1957), German physical chemist, whose principal work has been in the field of electrolytes. He was awarded life pensions by each of three governments but at the end of World War II, at the age of 82, found it necessary to support himself

form?" Prior to 1951, no procedure was known by which this question could be answered. If, however, the configuration of some reference compound is assumed, it is possible to relate the configuration of other active compounds to this substance and to each other. *The configuration of a compound with reference to the arbitrarily assigned configuration of the reference substance is known as its* **relative configuration.**

The substance used for reference is glyceraldehyde, the (+) form of which is assigned the configuration represented by the perspective formula I. In this formula the asymmetric carbon atom is in the plane of the paper, the aldehyde and the hydroxymethyl groups behind the plane of the paper, and the hydrogen atom and the hydroxyl group in front of the plane of the paper. Formula II is a projection of this space formula in the plane of the paper.

CHO
H◁┼▷OH
CH₂OH

I

(+)-Glyceraldehyde

CHO
H—C—OH
CH₂OH

II

Although this configuration originally was assigned to (+)-glyceraldehyde arbitrarily, it was shown in 1951 to be the actual or *absolute* configuration. A special type of X-ray analysis of the sodium rubidium salt of (+)-tartaric acid demonstrated the absolute configuration of (+)-tartaric acid. The configuration of (+)-glyceraldehyde relative to (−)-tartaric acid already had been established by chemical methods (p. 349).

The classical chemical methods for the assignment of relative configuration depend on the assumption that no Walden inversion occurs so long as bonds or the asymmetric atom are not involved. The series of reactions shown on page 349 illustrates how the configurations of a group of compounds have been interrelated. The carbon atom corresponding to that in the reference substance is in bold-face type.

There is no apparent relationship between the configuration and the sign of rotation. Since it is the configuration and not the sign of rotation that is important, active compounds have been divided into two families. Those that are related to (+)-glyceraldehyde are said to belong to the D family, and those that are related to (−)-glyceraldehyde are said to belong to the L family. The small capital D and capital L are pronounced *dee* and *ell* respectively and not dextro and levo. They refer to configuration and not to optical rotation. The name D(+)-glyceraldehyde reveals both the configuration and the rotation.

A point that frequently is misunderstood is that it is not sufficient to say that a compound is related to (+)-glyceraldehyde configurationally without specifying the correspondence of its functional groups to those of (+)-glyceraldehyde. Thus the configuration of (+)-isoserine is the same as that of (+)-glyceraldehyde if the carboxyl group and aminomethyl group of isoserine correspond respectively to the aldehyde and hydroxymethyl groups of glyceraldehyde. If the carboxyl and aminomethyl groups of isoserine correspond to the hydroxymethyl and aldehyde groups of glyceraldehyde, then the configuration of (−)-isoserine corresponds to that of (+)-glyceraldehyde. For isoserine it is understood that the carboxyl group corresponds to the aldehyde group and the enantiomorphs are called D(+)-isoserine and L(−)-isoserine.

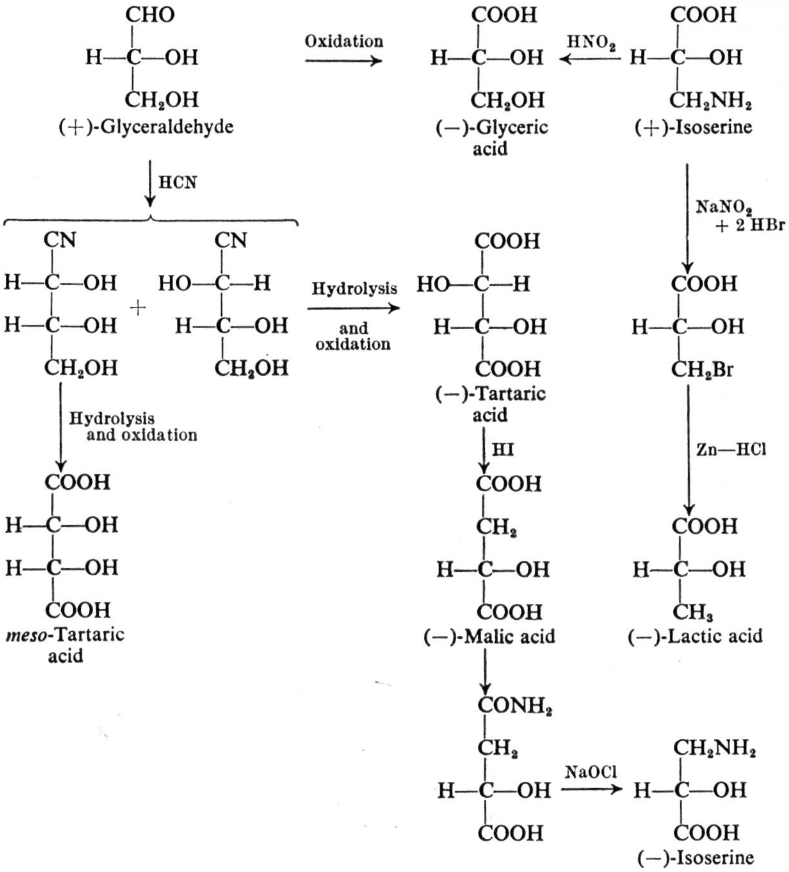

$$
\begin{array}{ccc}
\text{CHO} & \text{COOH} & \text{COOH} \\
\mid & \mid & \mid \\
\text{H—C—OH} & \text{H—C—OH} & \text{H—C—OH} \\
\mid & \mid & \mid \\
\text{CH}_2\text{OH} & \text{CH}_2\text{OH} & \text{CH}_2\text{NH}_2
\end{array}
$$

(+)-Glyceraldehyde   (−)-Glyceric acid   (+)-Isoserine

Oxidation ⟶   ⟵ HNO₂

$$
\begin{array}{ccc}
\text{CN} & \text{CN} \\
\mid & \mid \\
\text{H—C—OH} & \text{HO—C—H} \\
\mid & \mid \\
\text{H—C—OH} & + & \text{H—C—OH} \\
\mid & \mid \\
\text{CH}_2\text{OH} & \text{CH}_2\text{OH}
\end{array}
$$

HCN ↓

Hydrolysis and oxidation ⟶

$$
\begin{array}{c}
\text{COOH} \\
\mid \\
\text{HO—C—H} \\
\mid \\
\text{H—C—OH} \\
\mid \\
\text{COOH}
\end{array}
$$

(−)-Tartaric acid

$$
\begin{array}{c}
\text{COOH} \\
\mid \\
\text{H—C—OH} \\
\mid \\
\text{CH}_2\text{Br}
\end{array}
$$

NaNO₂ + 2 HBr ↓

Zn—HCl ↓

$$
\begin{array}{c}
\text{COOH} \\
\mid \\
\text{H—C—OH} \\
\mid \\
\text{CH}_3
\end{array}
$$

(−)-Lactic acid

Hydrolysis and oxidation ↓

$$
\begin{array}{c}
\text{COOH} \\
\mid \\
\text{H—C—OH} \\
\mid \\
\text{H—C—OH} \\
\mid \\
\text{COOH}
\end{array}
$$

meso-Tartaric acid

HI ↓

$$
\begin{array}{c}
\text{COOH} \\
\mid \\
\text{CH}_2 \\
\mid \\
\text{H—C—OH} \\
\mid \\
\text{COOH}
\end{array}
$$

(−)-Malic acid

$$
\begin{array}{c}
\text{CONH}_2 \\
\mid \\
\text{CH}_2 \\
\mid \\
\text{H—C—OH} \\
\mid \\
\text{COOH}
\end{array}
$$

NaOCl ⟶

$$
\begin{array}{c}
\text{CH}_2\text{NH}_2 \\
\mid \\
\text{H—C—OH} \\
\mid \\
\text{COOH}
\end{array}
$$

(−)-Isoserine

It is an interesting fact that all of the common naturally occurring amino acids have the same relative configuration. It frequently is stated that they all belong to the L family. By this it is inferred that they are configurationally related to (−)-glyceraldehyde rather than to (+)-glyceraldehyde. Again this classification is arbitrary, since it merely means that if the carboxyl, amino, hydrogen, and the residual portion R of the amino acids correspond respectively to the aldehyde, hydroxyl, hydrogen, and hydroxymethyl groups of glyceraldehyde, the common natural amino acids have the configuration

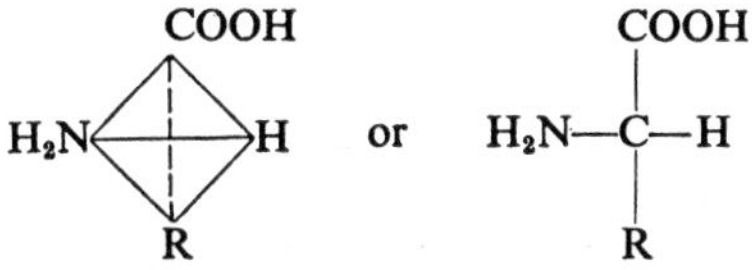

$$
\begin{array}{ccc}
\text{COOH} & & \text{COOH} \\
\mid & & \mid \\
\text{H}_2\text{N}\diamond\text{H} & \text{or} & \text{H}_2\text{N—C—H} \\
\mid & & \mid \\
\text{R} & & \text{R}
\end{array}
$$

This conclusion was based originally on analogies in physical properties. It is difficult to relate the configurations of amino acids to (+)-glyceraldehyde by chemical methods, since any interconversion involves bonds attached to the asymmetric carbon atom, and it is necessary to know whether or not Walden inversion has taken place at this step. In 1947 (+)-alanine (R = CH₃) was shown to have the L configuration by deriving it from 2-glucosamine (p. 409). The relative configuration of this compound had been determined in 1939 by a series of reactions the configurational course of which was known. This result was confirmed in 1954 when the absolute configuration of L-isoleucine hydrobromide was established by means of X-ray diffraction.

Molecular Dissymmetry Caused by Asymmetric Atoms Other Than Carbon

Silicon, germanium, tin, and lead are in the same group of the periodic table as carbon, and all may be tetracovalent with bonds distributed tetrahedrally. If these atoms are joined to four different groups, the racemic forms of the compounds are resolvable into the active forms.

The bond angles of tricovalent nitrogen compounds are predicted to be 90 degrees from theoretical considerations, but the measured angle in the ammonia molecule is about 107 degrees or nearly the tetrahedral angle. In either case compounds containing three different groups attached to nitrogen should exist in two enantiomorphic configurations.

It appears, however, that the absence of a fourth group permits the trivalent nitrogen atom to undergo Walden inversion with extreme ease.

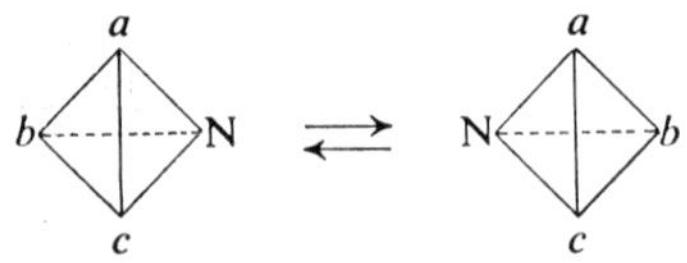

The only compound possessing molecular dissymmetry because of tricovalent nitrogen which has been resolved into active forms is a complicated molecule known as Troeger's base (p. 482). The nitrogen valences form part of a cage structure that prevents Walden inversion (Fig. 67).

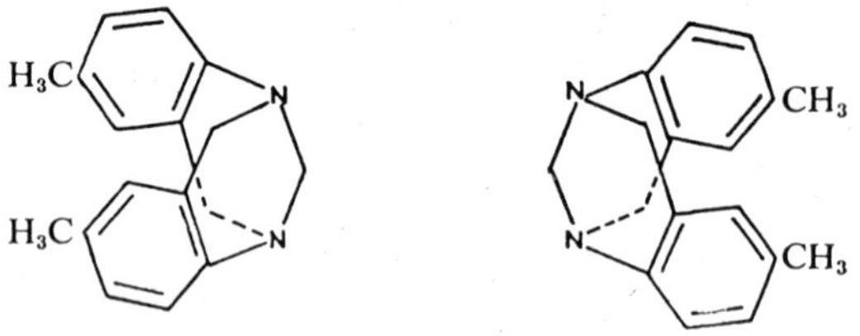

Fig. 67. Active enantiomorphs of Troeger's base.

If the nitrogen atom is tetracovalent, resolution can be brought about without difficulty. Thus in 1899 inactive methylallylphenylbenzylammonium iodide was resolved by Pope[14] into its two active forms through the (+)-camphorsulfonates (p. 856).

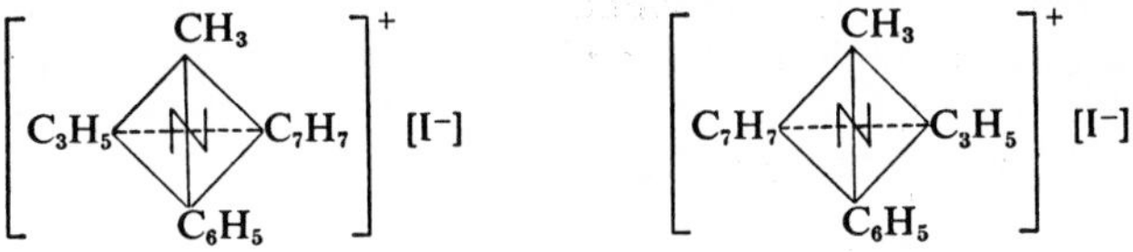

Since then all of the predictions based on a tetrahedral distribution of the valences in the ammonium ion have been realized experimentally. The amine oxides, R_3N^+——^-O (p. 240), also resemble the ammonium ion in structure, and methylethylpropylamine oxide has been resolved into active forms.

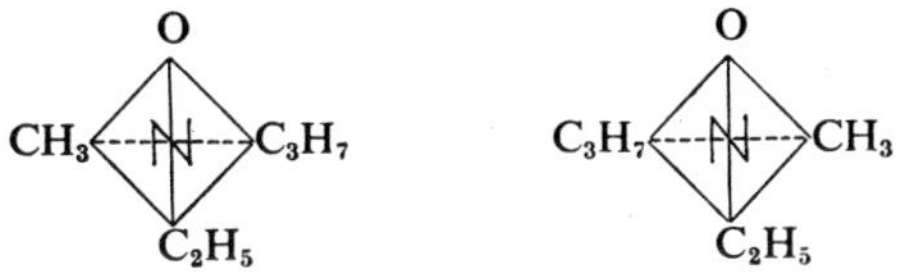

Phosphorus and arsenic compounds for the most part resemble the nitrogen compounds.

Dicovalent compounds of elements of the sixth group of the periodic table cannot exist in active forms, because the molecules contain a plane of symmetry. On the other hand the space arrangement of the covalently bound groups in the sulfonium and selenonium salts (p. 283) is analogous to that in tricovalent nitrogen compounds. Whereas the latter are configurationally unstable, the former were resolved at an early date. Thus the reaction product of methyl ethyl sulfide with chloroacetic acid was obtained in two forms in 1900.

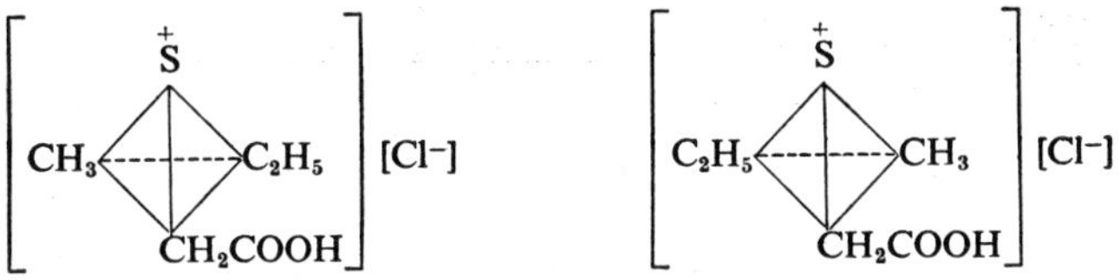

The compound $\left[\begin{array}{c} C_2H_5SCH_2CH_2SC_2H_5 \\ | \qquad\quad | \\ CH_3 \qquad CH_3 \end{array}\right]^{++}$ 2 [I$^-$] with two like asymmetric sulfur atoms exists in a *meso* form and a resolvable racemic form. The active forms of these compounds are very stable. When racemization takes place, it is not caused by inversion but by dissociation into the sulfide and alkyl halide.

$$[R_3S^+]X^- \quad \rightleftarrows \quad R_2S + RX$$

[14] William Jackson Pope (1870–1939), professor at Cambridge University and one of the founders of the International Union of Chemistry. His early work on camphorsulfonic acid (p. 651) led him to use it for the resolution of dihydropapaverine and later for the resolution of the optically active nitrogen, sulfur, and selenium compounds. He prepared the first optically active compound that did not contain an asymmetric atom and the first active compound that contained only a single carbon atom. During World War I he developed the process for making mustard gas from ethylene and sulfur monochloride (p. 289).

One of the arguments for the semipolar bond in oxygenated sulfur compounds (p. 273) has been that if the classical formula with oxygen doubly bound to sulfur were correct for sulfoxides, compounds of the type a—SO—b would not be resolvable because the molecule has a plane of symmetry. If the oxygen atom is linked by a semipolar bond, the structure resembles that of a sulfonium ion, and two active forms would be possible.

Sulfoxides with two different groups were resolved in 1926. When two such asymmetric centers are present, two active forms and one *meso* form have been obtained. The optical activity of sulforaphene, $CH_3SOCH=CHCH_2CH_2N=C=S$, isolated in 1948 from radishes, can be due only to the dissymmetry of the RSOR' grouping. Sulfinic esters, RSOOR, also have been resolved, whereas if one oxygen atom were doubly bound, resolution would not be expected.

The resolution of sulfoxides and sulfinic esters proves that the distribution of the groups must be pyramidal and cannot be planar as in the ketones. Hence any double bond character of the S—O linkage must be different from that in the carbonyl group (p. 273).

Space Arrangements Other Than Tetrahedral

The hybridization of higher orbitals may lead to the formation of strong bonds which are not directed to the corners of a tetrahedron. For example, in the cobaltic ion, two $3d$ orbitals can hybridize with the $4s$ and $4p$ orbitals to give six d^2sp^3 hybrid orbitals that are directed to the corners of an octahedron. Long before a theoretical explanation was devised, Werner showed that for several elements the number of forms predicted on the basis of an octahedral distribution of the valences could be realized experimentally. Thus the doubly-positive cation of the cobalt complex $[Co \cdot 2 NH_2CH_2CH_2NH_2 \cdot NH_3 \cdot Cl]^{++}2 [Cl^-]$ exists in two active forms and a *meso* form (Fig. 68). The bonds to cobalt are analogous to those bonding water molecules or ammonia molecules to the cupric ion.

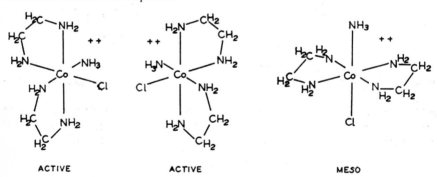

| ACTIVE | ACTIVE | MESO |

Fig. 68. Stereoisomeric forms of a cobalt complex ion.

The Cause of Optical Activity

Several theories have been proposed concerning the cause of the rotation of the plane of polarization of plane-polarized light by optically active compounds. A few of the concepts involved are discussed here. Ordinary light can be separated into two components vibrating in two mutually perpendicular planes (p. 330). Plane-polarized light also is divisible into two components of *d* and *l* circularly-polarized light. The vectors shown in Fig. 52, p. 330, are the electric vectors of the light ray. The magnetic vector of Maxwell's electromagnetic theory of light is so small for diamagnetic substances that it may be neglected. Each electric vector maintains a fixed position and direction but varies in magnitude from zero to $+1$ to zero to -1. This same behavior results from two vectors of constant magnitude rotating at constant speed in opposite directions about a point and in a plane perpendicular to the direction of propagation. In Fig. 69a the two rotating vectors neutralize each other, and the vector of the plane-polarized

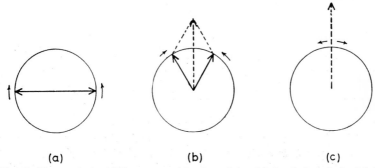

(a)   (b)   (c)

Fig. 69. Plane-polarized light as a combination of *d* and *l* circularly-polarized light.

wave is zero. In (*b*) the horizontal components of the rotating vectors still neutralize each other, but the vertical components reinforce each other, and the vector of the plane-polarized wave is increasing. In (*c*) it has reached its maximum value. As rotation of the rotating vectors continues, the vertical vector decreases to zero again and then increases to a maximum in the opposite direction. It then decreases again until the rotating vectors have returned to their original position.

Double refraction results from the retardation of the component of light vibrating in one plane over that vibrating in a perpendicular plane (p. 330). Fresnel [15] in 1825 first postulated that rotation of the plane of polarization of plane-polarized light is caused by the retardation of one circularly-polarized component with respect to the other. If after traversing the active substance the vector rotating in a clockwise direction has reached a vertical position but the other vector has been retarded more and has not reached the vertical position as in Fig. 70a,

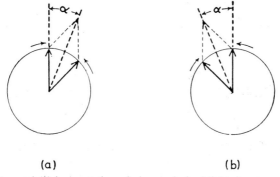

(a)   (b)

Fig. 70. (*a*) Dextro and (*b*) levo rotation of plane-polarized light due to retardation of the *l* and *d* circularly-polarized component respectively.

then the resultant plane-polarized ray that emerges will be vibrating in a plane that makes an angle α with the plane of vibration of the incident ray; in other words the plane of vibration has been rotated to the right. If on the other hand the relative positions of the two vectors are as in Fig. 70b, the plane of vibration has been rotated to the left.

---

[15] Augustin Jean Fresnel (1788–1827), French physicist who was employed as a government engineer. He began his researches in optics about 1814 and was a contemporary of Arago, Biot, La Place, and Young.

The question as to why a body whose mirror image is nonsuperposable selectively retards one of the circularly-polarized components has been more difficult to answer. Although several models have been proposed to explain selective retardation, no agreement has been reached as to which is most satisfactory. It is desirable to point out, however, that crystals containing a plane of symmetry are optically inactive only when the ray passes through the crystal or molecule perpendicular to the plane of symmetry. In all other directions the crystal is optically active. Presumably the same is true for individual molecules of optically inactive compounds in a liquid or solution. Here, however, the many molecules are randomly oriented, and for each molecule in the path of the light, there is another molecule whose orientation is such that it is a mirror image. Hence the possible rotation of the one is destroyed by the other. With optically active substances it is not possible to orient two like molecules in such a way that they are mirror images, which is another way of saying that the molecule and its mirror image are not superposable. Thus the rotation caused by one molecule is not cancelled by another. This discussion does not apply to crystals or molecules having a center of symmetry. Here the rotation is zero regardless of the direction in which the light passes through the crystal or molecule.

GEOMETRICAL ISOMERISM

Geometrical isomers may be defined most conveniently as *a set of stereoisomers, no member of which is optically active.* Geometrical isomerism frequently is associated with unsaturation. For example, oxides of nitrogen convert oleic acid, m.p. 16°, into elaidic acid, m.p. 44°, an isomer having the same constitution (p. 186). Although only one 1-butene is known, there are two 2-butenes, one

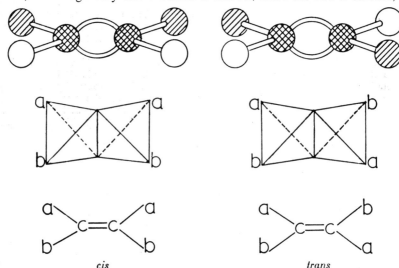

Fig. 71. Representation of *cis* and *trans* forms of geometrical isomers by molecular models, by tetrahedra, and by projection formulas.

boiling at 0.96° and the other at 3.73°. Similarly 1,1-dichloroethylene exists in only a single form, but two forms of 1,2-dichloroethylene are known, one boiling at 48.3° and the other at 60.5°. The explanation of the increased number of isomers in certain unsaturated compounds is that the two doubly-bound carbon atoms and the four atoms or groups joined to them lie in a plane and that free rotation about the double bond is not possible. Hence if the two groups on each carbon atom are different, two isomers can result (Fig. 71). If the two members of either pair of groups are alike, only one compound is possible. Accordingly in one of the 2-butenes the two methyl groups are on the same side of the molecule, and in the other they are on opposite sides. The isomer with like groups on the same side is known as the *cis* form whereas that in which like groups are on opposite sides is known as the *trans* form (L. *cis*, on this side; *trans*, across). A similar explanation accounts for the two 1,2-dichloroethylenes.

$$H \quad\quad H$$
$$\diagdown \quad \diagup$$
$$C\!\!=\!\!C$$
$$\diagup \quad \diagdown$$
$$CH_3 \quad\quad CH_3$$
cis-2-Butene

$$CH_3 \quad\quad H$$
$$\diagdown \quad \diagup$$
$$C\!\!=\!\!C$$
$$\diagup \quad \diagdown$$
$$H \quad\quad CH_3$$
trans-2-Butene

$$H \quad\quad H$$
$$\diagdown \quad \diagup$$
$$C\!\!=\!\!C$$
$$\diagup \quad \diagdown$$
$$Cl \quad\quad Cl$$
cis-1,2-Dichloroethylene

$$Cl \quad\quad H$$
$$\diagdown \quad \diagup$$
$$C\!\!=\!\!C$$
$$\diagup \quad \diagdown$$
$$H \quad\quad Cl$$
trans-1,2-Dichloroethylene

Originally it was postulated that the valences of the doubly-bound carbon atoms remained tetrahedrally distributed, and the double bond was represented as the union of two sides of the two tetrahedra (Fig. 71). Currently the double bond is represented as consisting of one σ bond and one π bond. Since the π bond results from the overlapping of two p_z atomic orbitals which are parallel to each other, rotation about the σ-type bond is prevented (p. 50). The chief practical difference between the two views is that the first assumes that the angle *aCb* is approximately 109.5 degrees, whereas the second assumes that it is more nearly 120 degrees. The infrared absorption spectra of ethylene and deuteroethylene indicate 119°55′ for the HCH angle in ethylene.

By a rather complicated procedure it has been proved that *cis*-2-butene is the isomer boiling at 3.73° and *trans*-2-butene is that boiling at 0.96°. The determination of the configuration of the two 1,2-dichloroethylenes was easier because the dipole moment of the carbon-halogen bond is much larger than that of the carbon-hydrogen bond. An examination of the proposed structures of the two isomers indicates that the *trans* isomer should have zero dipole moment, because the individual bond moments cancel each other. The *cis* compound on the other hand should have a resultant moment for the molecule as a whole. The arrow represents the direction and magnitude of the moment, the + on the tail

cis   *trans*

indicating the positive end of the moment. The melting points and moments of the 1,2-dihaloethylenes are given in Table 20, page 356. The *trans* isomer usually has the higher melting point.

The configuration of some geometrical isomers can be determined from differences in their chemical reactions. Thus of the maleic and fumaric acids, maleic acid is assigned the *cis* configuration because of the greater ease with which it forms an anhydride (p. 805).

The isomerization of the unsaturated fat acids now is understandable. The naturally occurring compounds exist as one form, which in the presence of the free-radical type catalyst is converted to its geometrical isomer. Thus the liquid

TABLE 20

DIPOLE MOMENTS OF 1,2-DIHALOETHYLENES

		M.p.	μ
1,2-Dichloroethylene	(*trans*)	-50	0
	(*cis*)	-80	1.85
1,2-Dibromoethylene	(*trans*)	-6	0
	(*cis*)	-53	1.35
1,2-Diiodoethylene	(*trans*)	$+72$	0
	(*cis*)	-14	0.75

cis oleic acid is transformed into an equilibrium mixture with its solid *trans* isomer, elaidic acid.

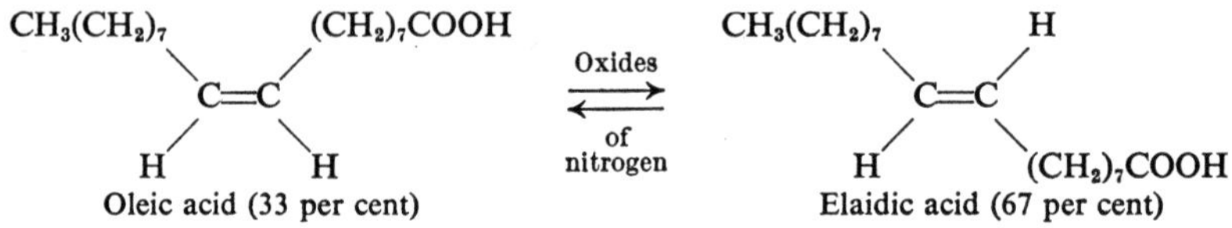

CH$_3$(CH$_2$)$_7$ ... (CH$_2$)$_7$COOH   CH$_3$(CH$_2$)$_7$ ... H
  C=C   Oxides ⇌ of nitrogen   C=C
H ... H   H ... (CH$_2$)$_7$COOH
Oleic acid (33 per cent)   Elaidic acid (67 per cent)

The stability of geometrical isomers varies with their constitution. Some isomers interconvert on standing or heating, but usually light (p. 663), or a free-radical catalyst such as oxides of nitrogen or metallic sodium, or an ionic catalyst such as halogen or hydrogen halide is required. In general at equilibrium under ordinary conditions the *trans* form is present in the greater amount.

If two double bonds are present in an unsymmetrical molecule, as in the linoleic acids, four isomeric forms should exist.

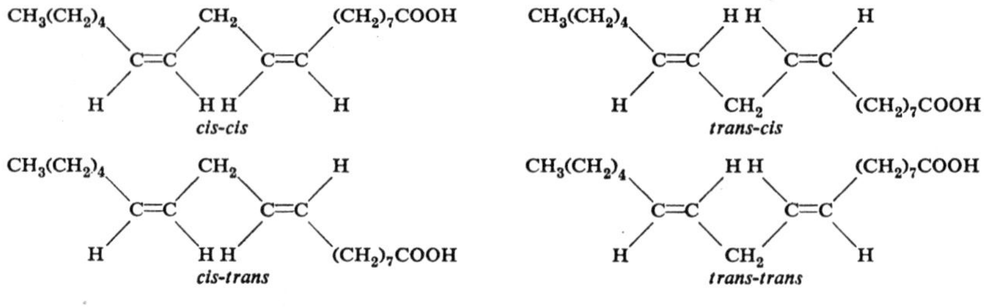

CH$_3$(CH$_2$)$_4$ ... CH$_2$ ... (CH$_2$)$_7$COOH   CH$_3$(CH$_2$)$_4$ ... H H ... H
  C=C ... C=C   C=C ... C=C
H ... H H ... H   H ... CH$_2$ ... (CH$_2$)$_7$COOH
cis-cis   *trans-cis*

CH$_3$(CH$_2$)$_4$ ... CH$_2$ ... H   CH$_3$(CH$_2$)$_4$ ... H H ... (CH$_2$)$_7$COOH
  C=C ... C=C   C=C ... C=C
H ... H H ... (CH$_2$)$_7$COOH   H ... CH$_2$ ... H
cis-trans   *trans-trans*

If the molecule is symmetrical, a smaller number of isomers is predicted. For example only three geometrical isomers are possible for 2,4-hexadiene, the *trans-cis* and *cis-trans* forms being identical.

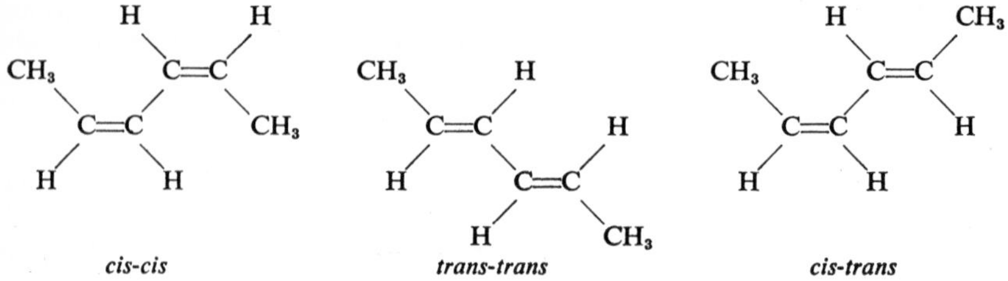

H ... H   CH$_3$ ... H   H ... CH$_3$
CH$_3$ ... C=C   C=C ... H   CH$_3$ ... C=C
  C=C ... CH$_3$ H ... C=C   C=C ... H
H ... H   H ... CH$_3$ H ... H
cis-cis   *trans-trans*   *cis-trans*

If N is the number of stereoisomers possible and n is the number of double bonds, $N = 2^n$ for unsymmetrically constituted compounds. For symmetrical compounds, $N = 2^{n-1} + 2^{\frac{n-2}{2}}$ when n is even, and $N = 2^{n-1} + 2^{\frac{n-1}{2}}$ when n is odd.

If a double bond capable of *cis-trans* isomerism is present in the molecule along with an asymmetric carbon atom, all four isomers will be optically active and give rise to two racemic mixtures. For this reason it is simpler to consider the relationship between the isomers to be that of enantiomorphs and diastereoisomers rather than that of enantiomorphs and geometrical isomers.

Examples of geometrical isomerism dependent on carbon-nitrogen and nitrogen-nitrogen double bonds and on the distribution of groups in cyclic compounds also are known (pp. 542, 500, 836, 843).

Hybridization of higher orbitals leads to planar molecules which also can exhibit geometrical isomerism. For example, in the platinous ion, a $5d$ orbital can hybridize with the $6s$ orbital and two $6p$ orbitals to give four dsp^2 hybrid orbitals directed to the corners of a square. Werner prepared amine complexes of platinous chloride having two different pairs of like groups and found that they exist in two geometrically isomeric forms.

$$\begin{bmatrix} H_3N & NH_2C_6H_5 \\ & Pt & \\ H_3N & NH_2C_6H_5 \end{bmatrix}^{++} \quad 2\,[Cl^-] \qquad \begin{bmatrix} C_6H_5NH_2 & NH_3 \\ & Pt & \\ H_3N & NH_2C_6H_5 \end{bmatrix}^{++} \quad 2\,[Cl^-]$$

REVIEW QUESTIONS

1. Define the term stereoisomerism. What are the two broad classes of stereoisomers?
2. What is meant by the term plane-polarized light? Describe two practical methods for producing it and tell how each accomplishes the polarization.
3. What is meant by the term optical activity? How is the extent of optical activity measured? On what factors does the degree of rotation depend? Tell what is meant by the term specific rotation and give a formula for calculating the specific rotation from the observed rotation and other data. What is rotatory dispersion?
4. What are the necessary and sufficient conditions for the existence of optical activity? Why does it necessarily lead to isomerism in organic molecules? What is the commonest cause of optical isomerism? What other terms are used to indicate that two different compounds are mirror images?
5. How does the optical activity of quartz differ from that of organic compounds?
6. Compare the physical and chemical properties of enantiomorphs. How do these properties compare with those of geometrical isomers? Explain the difference.
7. What is a racemic mixture? Why is it not possible to separate a racemic mixture into its components directly by ordinary methods such as fractional distillation or crystallization?
8. When an asymmetric carbon atom is introduced into a molecule by synthesis, and none of the reagents is optically active, a racemic mixture is always formed rather than an active product. Explain.
9. What are diastereoisomers? Compare their physical and chemical properties. How may a mixture of diastereoisomers be separated?
10. Give the chemical method for the resolution of a racemic mixture into its active components, and explain the principle on which the separation is based. What other procedures have been used to resolve racemic mixtures?
11. If all of the asymmetric carbon atoms in a molecule are different and form part of a chain with none of the asymmetric carbon atoms in side chains, the number of active forms possible is 2^n where n is the number of asymmetric carbon atoms. Explain.
12. What complications arise if a molecule has two like asymmetric carbon atoms? Explain. How can the *meso* forms be separated from each other and from racemic forms?
13. What is Walden inversion and how is it explained? Does it apply only to optically active compounds?

14. What conventions must be kept in mind when using plane projection formulas to represent stereoisomers?
15. What is meant by the terms absolute configuration and relative configuration?
16. How does configuration differ from conformation?
17. Define geometrical isomers. What is a frequent cause of geometrical isomerism?
18. Compare the physical and chemical properties of geometrical isomers. How does this comparison differ from that of the physical and chemical properties of enantiomorphs?
19. Compare the methods available for the separation of geometrical isomers with those for the separation of enantiomorphs.

PROBLEMS

20. Predict the number and kind of stereoisomers (active, *meso*, or geometrical) theoretically possible for each of the following compounds: (*a*) $(CH_3)_2CHCH(NH_2)COOH$; (*b*) $C_2H_5CH(CH_3)CH_2OH$; (*c*) $CH_3CHBrCH_2CHBrCH_3$; (*d*) $CH_2OH(CHOH)_4CHO$; (*e*) $CH_2(NH_2)CH_2COOH$; (*f*) $CH_2ClCHClCH_2COOH$; (*g*) $CH_3CH_2CHBrCHBrCH_3$; (*h*) $CH_3(CHOH)_2CH_3$; (*i*) serine; (*j*) threonine; (*k*) methionine; (*l*) lysine; (*m*) cystine; (*n*) arginine; (*o*) hydroxyproline; (*p*) isoleucine; (*q*) $CH_3(CH=CH)_4CH_3$; (*r*) $CH_2=CHCH_2COOH$; (*s*) $CH_3(CH=CCH_3)_2(CH=CH)_2CH_3$; (*t*) $CH_3(CH=CH)_7CH_3$; (*u*) linolenic acid; (*v*) ricinoleic acid; (*w*) farnesol; (*x*) lycopene; (*y*) bixin; (*z*) crocetin. (See index to locate formulas of unfamiliar compounds.)
21. For each compound in the following series of reactions, predict the number and kind of stereoisomers possible and give projection formulas for each. Indicate the possibility of racemic compound formation by grouping enantiomorphs together.
    (*a*) $HOOCCH(CH_3)CHOHCH(CH_3)COOH \rightarrow CH_3OOCCH(CH_3)CHOHCH(CH_3)COOH \rightarrow$
    $CH_3OOCCH(CH_3)CH=C(CH_3)COOH \rightarrow CH_3OOCCH(CH_3)CH_2CH(CH_3)COOH \rightarrow$
    $CH_3OOCCH(CH_3)CH_2CH(CH_3)COOCH_3$.
    (*b*) $C_2H_5CH(CH_3)CH_2SCH_2CH_2COOH \rightarrow C_2H_5CH(CH_3)CH_2-SO-CH_2CH_2COOH \rightarrow$
    $C_2H_5CH(CH_3)CH_2-SO-CH_2CHBrCOOH \rightarrow C_2H_5CH(CH_3)CH_2-SO-CH=CHCOOH$.
    (*c*) $CH_3CHOHCHCHO \rightarrow CH_3CHOHCH-CHOH \rightarrow CH_3CHOHCH(CH_3)CHCN \rightarrow$

            | | | |
         CH_3 CH_3 CN $C_3H_7NC_2H_5$

    $CH_3CH=C(CH_3)CHCOOH \rightarrow CH_3CH=C(CH_3)CH-N^+(CH_3)C_2H_5$

            | | |
       $C_3H_7NC_2H_5$ COO^- C_3H_7
22. (*a*) A sample of pure active amyl alcohol having a density of 0.8 g. per cc. at 20° in a 20-cm. tube gave a rotation of 9.44 degrees. Calculate the specific rotation of the alcohol.
    (*b*) A fraction of fusel oil boiling between 125° and 135° and having a density of 0.8 g. per cc. at 20° gave a rotation of 3.56 degrees in a 4-dcm. tube. What per cent of active amyl alcohol was present?
23. (*a*) When 5.678 g. of cane sugar was dissolved in water and brought to a total volume of 20 cc. at 20°, the rotation of the solution in a 10-cm. tube was 18.88 degrees. What is the specific rotation of cane sugar?
    (*b*) The observed rotation of an aqueous solution of cane sugar in a 2-dcm. tube was 10.75 degrees. What was the concentration of the sugar solution?

Chapter 17

CARBOHYDRATES

Carbohydrates are polyhydroxy aldehydes or polyhydroxy ketones or substances which yield such compounds on hydrolysis. They are distributed universally in plants and animals, and are the third important class of animal foods. The combustion of carbohydrates to carbon dioxide and water yields about 4 kcal. of energy per gram. The term *carbohydrate* came into use for these compounds because ordinarily the ratio of hydrogen to oxygen is 2 to 1, for example $C_6H_{10}O_5$, $C_6H_{12}O_6$, $C_{12}H_{22}O_{11}$. For some carbohydrates, however, this ratio does not hold; for example, rhamnose has the molecular formula $C_6H_{12}O_5$.

Nomenclature and Classification of Carbohydrates

The simpler carbohydrates commonly are called *sugars* or *saccharides* (L. *saccharon*, sugar). The ending for sugars is *ose*, for example arabinose, glucose, maltose. Frequently the generic term *glycose* is used from which is derived the prefix *glyco*. The generic terms are used when it is not desired to designate a particular sugar or derivative. The number of carbon atoms may be indicated by a prefix; for example, a sugar having five carbon atoms is called a *pentose* and one with six carbon atoms is called a *hexose*. Similarly the prefix may indicate whether the sugar contains an aldehyde group or a ketone group, giving rise to the terms *aldose* and *ketose*. Both the number of carbon atoms and the type of carbonyl group may be indicated by terms such as *aldopentose* and *ketohexose*.

Carbohydrates may be subdivided according to the following classification.

A. Monosaccharides. Carbohydrates that do not hydrolyze.

B. Oligosaccharides. Carbohydrates that yield a few molecules of monosaccharide on hydrolysis.

    1. Disaccharides. One molecule yields two molecules of monosaccharide on hydrolysis.

        (*a*) Reducing disaccharides. Disaccharides that reduce Fehling solution.

        (*b*) Nonreducing disaccharides. Disaccharides that do not reduce Fehling solution

    2. Trisaccharides. One molecule yields three molecules of monosaccharides on hydrolysis.

    3. Tetra-, penta-, and hexasaccharides.

C. Polysaccharides. Carbohydrates that yield a large number of molecules of monosaccharides on hydrolysis.

    1. Homopolysaccharides. Polysaccharides that yield only one kind of sugar on hydrolysis.

2. Heteropolysaccharides. Polysaccharides that yield more than one kind of sugar on hydrolysis.

MONOSACCHARIDES

Aldoses

The most important carbohydrate is **(+)-glucose** or **dextrose.** Since the naturally occurring isomer always is dextrorotatory, the word *glucose* without indication of sign of rotation always means (+)-glucose. Because glucose is typical of the aldoses, it is discussed in considerable detail. Only the characteristic differences of other aldoses are presented.

Glucose is obtained most readily by the hydrolysis of starch or cellulose. It also may be isolated as one of the hydrolytic products of most oligosaccharides and of many other plant products known as glucosides. It occurs free, along with fructose and sucrose, in the juices of fruits and in honey, and to the extent of about 0.1 per cent in the blood of normal mammals. Glucose in free or combined form probably is the most abundant organic compound.

Constitution. Glucose has the molecular formula $C_6H_{12}O_6$. Its constitution may be arrived at from the following chemical behavior.

(*a*) Reduction with hydrogen iodide and phosphorus yields *n*-hexane. Therefore all of the carbon atoms must be linked consecutively without branching.

(*b*) Glucose reacts with hydroxylamine to form a monoxime, or adds one mole of hydrogen cyanide to form a cyanohydrin, indicating the presence of one carbonyl group.

(*c*) On mild oxidation, for example with sodium hypobromite, glucose yields the monobasic gluconic acid, $C_5H_{11}O_5COOH$.[1] Since no carbon atoms are lost, the carbonyl group must be present as an aldehyde group, which can occupy only an end position of the chain.

(*d*) On reduction with sodium amalgam, two hydrogen atoms are added to give $C_6H_{14}O_6$, a compound known as *sorbitol* (p. 412). Sorbitol reacts with acetic anhydride to give a hexa-acetate. Accordingly the six oxygen atoms of sorbitol must be present as six hydroxyl groups. Compounds containing two hydroxyl groups on the same carbon atom are rare, and those that are known readily lose water. However sorbitol does not dehydrate easily. Hence one hydroxyl group must be located on each of the six carbon atoms. Since one hydroxyl group was formed by reduction of the aldehyde group of glucose, the constitution of glucose can be represented by $HOCH_2(CHOH)_4CHO$. Most of the isomeric aldohexoses undergo the same reactions, indicating the same constitution. Therefore they are stereoisomers of glucose.

It has been shown by similar methods that the aldopentoses, $C_5H_{10}O_5$, have the structure $HOCH_2(CHOH)_3CHO$. Similarly the aldotetroses have the structure $HOCH_2(CHOH)_2CHO$, and the simplest compound grouped with the aldoses is the triose named glycerose or glyceraldehyde, $HOCH_2CHOHCHO$.

Configuration. The structural formula for glucose has four different asymmetric carbon atoms, and hence 16 optical isomers are possible, all of which are known. Of these 16 isomers, only two besides (+)-glucose are common, namely

---

[1] This reaction is general for aldoses, the products being known as *glyconic acids* (or by the less desirable term, *aldonic acids*).

(+)-mannose and (+)-galactose. **(+)-Mannose** is one of the products of hydrolysis of a number of polysaccharides. It is obtained most readily by the hydrolysis of the vegetable ivory nut, which is the hard endosperm of the seed of the Tagua palm, *Phyletephas macrocarpa*. Vegetable ivory is used for the manufacture of buttons. **(+)-Galactose** is formed along with (+)-glucose by the hydrolysis of the disaccharide lactose or milk sugar, and is one of the products of hydrolysis of several polysaccharides. The following configurations are assigned to these three sugars.

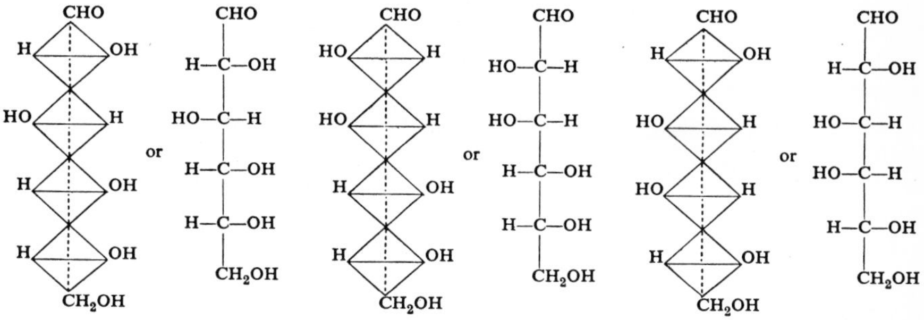

(+)-Glucose   (+)-Mannose   (+)-Galactose

(—)-Galactose has been isolated from the hydrolytic products of flaxseed mucilage.

Eight aldopentoses are possible and all are known. **(+)-Arabinose** and **(+)-xylose** may be obtained by the hydrolysis of a wide variety of plant polysaccharides. Thus corn cobs, straw, oat hulls, and cottonseed hulls yield 8 to 12 per cent of (+)-xylose. (+)-Arabinose is obtained by the hydrolysis of many plant gums. **(—)-Arabinose** has been isolated from only two sources, the glycoside *barbaloin* present in aloes, and the polysaccharide of tubercle bacilli, but it can be prepared fairly readily by the degradation of (+)-glucose (p. 381). **(—)-Ribose** is important because it is one of the products of hydrolysis of the nucleic acids (p. 644). **(+)-Apiose** (L. *apium*, parsley), a branched-chain sugar, is one of the hydrolytic products of *apiin*, a glycoside that occurs in parsley.

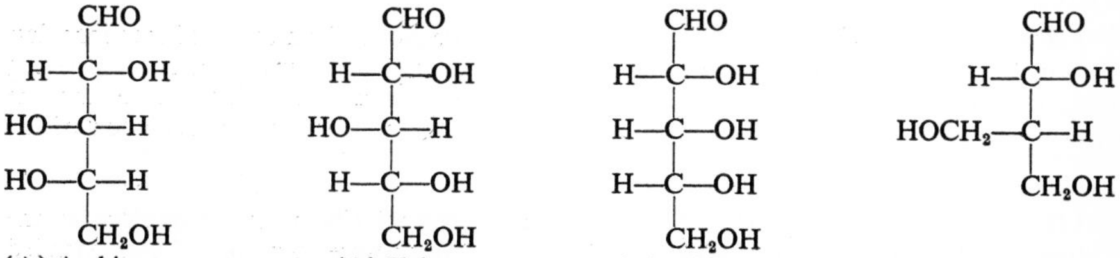

(+)-Arabinose   (+)-Xylose   (—)-Ribose   (+)-Apiose

Assignment of Configuration

The determination of the relative configuration of the sugars was a difficult task but was accomplished largely by one man, Emil Fischer (p. 305), with the assistance of the many students who worked under his direction. Any attempt to outline the actual procedures by which the relative configuration of the sixteen isomeric aldohexoses was determined would be

ne-consuming. It is relatively simple, however, to present essentially Fischer's
~~~e configuration of glucose and incidentally of mannose, gulose, and arabinose.
~~rous reactions used to determine the relative configuration of the sugars, three
~~cial importance.

. **Oxidation to Glycaric Acids.** When aldoses are oxidized by strong nitric acid, both the
aldehyde group and the primary alcohol group are converted to carboxyl groups. The dicarboxylic acids are known as **glycaric acids** (older name *saccharic acids*). By thus making both
ends of the sugar molecule alike, it is possible to determine in which aldoses the configurations
of the top and bottom pair of asymmetric atoms are enantiomorphic, since the glycaric acids
from such molecules have a plane of symmetry, and are *meso* forms and inactive. Thus (+)-
or (−)-galactose gives the inactive galactaric acid (mucic acid), whereas (+)- and (−)-mannose
give active mannaric acids (*manno-saccharic acids*).

$$
\begin{array}{ccccc}
\text{CHO} & & \text{COOH} & & \text{CHO} \\
\text{H—C—OH} & & \text{H—C—OH} & & \text{HO—C—H} \\
\text{HO—C—H} & \xrightarrow{\text{HNO}_3} & \text{HO—C—H} & \xleftarrow{\text{HNO}_3} & \text{H—C—OH} \\
\text{HO—C—H} & & \text{HO—C—H} & & \text{H—C—OH} \\
\text{H—C—OH} & & \text{H—C—OH} & & \text{HO—C—H} \\
\text{CH}_2\text{OH} & & \text{COOH} & & \text{CH}_2\text{OH}
\end{array}
$$

(+)-Galactose   Galactaric acid   (−)-Galactose
(mucic acid)
Inactive

$$
\begin{array}{ccccc}
\text{CHO} & & \text{COOH} & \text{COOH} & & \text{CHO} \\
\text{HO—C—H} & & \text{HO—C—H} & \text{H—C—OH} & & \text{H—C—OH} \\
\text{HO—C—H} & \xrightarrow{\text{HNO}_3} & \text{HO—C—H} & \text{H—C—OH} & \xleftarrow{\text{HNO}_3} & \text{H—C—OH} \\
\text{H—C—OH} & & \text{H—C—OH} & \text{HO—C—H} & & \text{HO—C—H} \\
\text{H—C—OH} & & \text{H—C—OH} & \text{HO—C—H} & & \text{HO—C—H} \\
\text{CH}_2\text{OH} & & \text{COOH} & \text{COOH} & & \text{CH}_2\text{OH}
\end{array}
$$

(+)-Mannose   Mannaric acids (*manno-saccharic*   (−)-Mannose
acids) Active

2. Conversion to the Next Higher Glyconic and Glycaric Acids. By a series of reactions first
used by Kiliani,[2] it is possible to convert an aldose into two glyconic and glycaric acids having
one more carbon atom. As a general example the conversion of an aldopentose into the
related six-carbon glyconic acids and glycaric acids is given. Since in the formation of the

[2] Heinrich Kiliani (1855–1945), director of the Medicinal Chemistry Laboratory at the
University of Freiburg. He first used several reactions which were then applied and extended
by his contemporary, Emil Fischer. Kiliani showed that most sugars were polyhydroxy aldehydes, that fructose was a ketose, and that arabinose was an aldopentose. He first used
hypobromite to oxidize aldoses to glyconic acids, which he made also by the cyanohydrin
synthesis. He converted the glyconic acids to lactones and missed the conversion of a lactone
to an aldehyde, which a few years later was accomplished by Emil Fischer, because the reduction went too far and the sugar alcohol was obtained instead. He later worked on the digitalis
glycosides (p. 869). It was under Kiliani that Windaus first began work on digitonin which led
him into a life-long investigation of the constitution of cholesterol (p. 868).

cyanohydrin a new asymmetric carbon atom is formed, a single aldopentose gives rise to two cyanohydrins, two glyconic acids, and two glycaric acids.

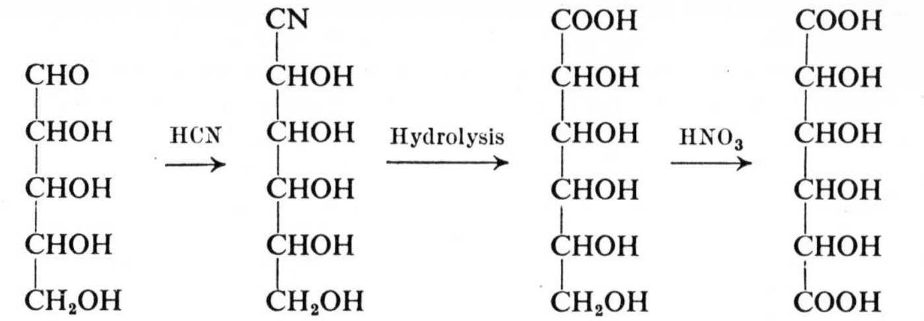

CHO
CHOH
CHOH
CHOH
CH₂OH
HCN
CN
CHOH
CHOH
CHOH
CHOH
CH₂OH
Hydrolysis
COOH
CHOH
CHOH
CHOH
CHOH
CH₂OH
HNO₃
COOH
CHOH
CHOH
CHOH
CHOH
COOH

Aldopentose Cyanohydrin Glyconic acid Glycaric acid

3. **Osazone Formation.** This reaction is discussed in more detail on page 370. It is sufficient here to note that it leads to the destruction of the asymmetry of the number 2 carbon atom.

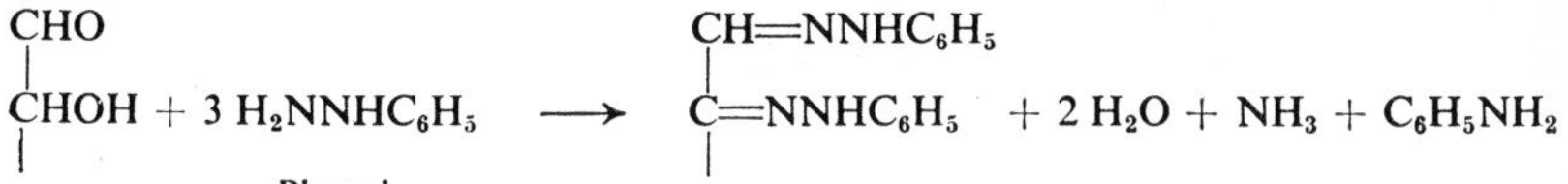

CHO
CHOH + 3 H₂NNHC₆H₅
CH=NNHC₆H₅
C=NNHC₆H₅ + 2 H₂O + NH₃ + C₆H₅NH₂

Phenyl-hydrazine A phenylosazone

Use of these reactions makes it possible to arrive at the configuration of glucose. Four sugars were available to Fischer, (−)-arabinose, (+)-glucose, (+)-mannose, and (+)-gulose. (+)-Glucose and (+)-mannose on oxidation give two different optically active glycaric acids, called saccharic and mannaric acids respectively. (−)-Arabinose when converted to the glycaric acids having six carbon atoms gives the same two dibasic acids. Accordingly the following relationship holds in which I is glucose or mannose, and II is mannose or glucose.

1
2
3
4
5
6
CHO
CH₂OH
I
HNO₃
COOH
COOH
CHO
CH₂OH
II
HNO₃
COOH
COOH
HCN, hydrolysis and oxidation
2
3
4
5
6
CHO
CH₂OH

(−)-Arabinose

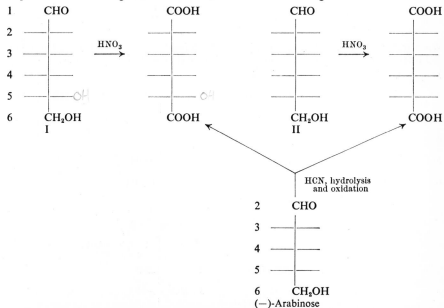

Fischer realized that it was not possible at the time to assign an absolute configuration to an active molecule, but that it was necessary to have a reference substance for determining relative configurations. Accordingly in 1891 he adopted a convention which placed the C-5 hydroxyl group on the right in the projection formula for saccharic acid. He stated then that the assignment was arbitrary and that the absolute configuration of this carbon atom remained undecided.

If the hydroxyl group at C-5 is placed on the right for saccharic acid, then the same hydroxyl must be placed on the right also for glucose and arabinose, and if on the right for arabinose, it must be on the right also for mannaric acid and mannose. (+)-Glucose and (+)-mannose give the same osazone. Therefore these sugars differ only in the configuration of C-2, and in their projection formulas the hydroxyl group at C-2 is on the right in one isomer and on the left in the other. These considerations give rise to the following partially assigned configurations.

```
1    CHO              COOH              CHO               COOH
2  H——OH           H——OH          HO——H            HO——H
3   ——     HNO3     ——             ——      HNO3     ——
4   ——      →       ——             ——       →       ——
5  H——OH           H——OH          H——OH            H——OH
6   CH₂OH           COOH            CH₂OH            COOH
      I                               II
```

Arrows converge from II and the COOH structure to:

```
                  HCN, hydrolysis,
                  and oxidation
2        CHO
3        ——
4        ——
5     H——OH
6        CH₂OH
      (−)-Arabinose
```

When arabinose is oxidized, an *active* dibasic acid is formed. Therefore the hydroxyl group on C-3 must be on the left, which also locates this hydroxyl in the other compounds.

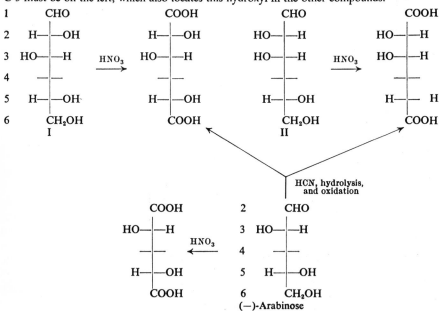

```
1     CHO              COOH              CHO               COOH
2  H——OH            H——OH          HO——H            HO——H
3  HO——H    HNO3   HO——H          HO——H    HNO3    HO——H
4   ——      →       ——             ——       →       ——
5  H——OH·           H——OH          H——OH            H——  H
6   CH₂OH            COOH            CH₂OH            COOH
      I                               II
```

```
                  HCN, hydrolysis,
                  and oxidation
        COOH              2        CHO
     HO——H                3     HO——H
      ——      HNO3        4        ——
      ——       ←          5     H——OH
     H——OH                6        CH₂OH
        COOH                   (−)-Arabinose
```

Since both glucose and mannose give *active* glycaric acids on oxidation, the hydroxyl group on C-4 must be placed on the right. Otherwise the hexose represented by structure I would give an *inactive* dibasic acid. Thus the configuration of (−)-arabinose is established.

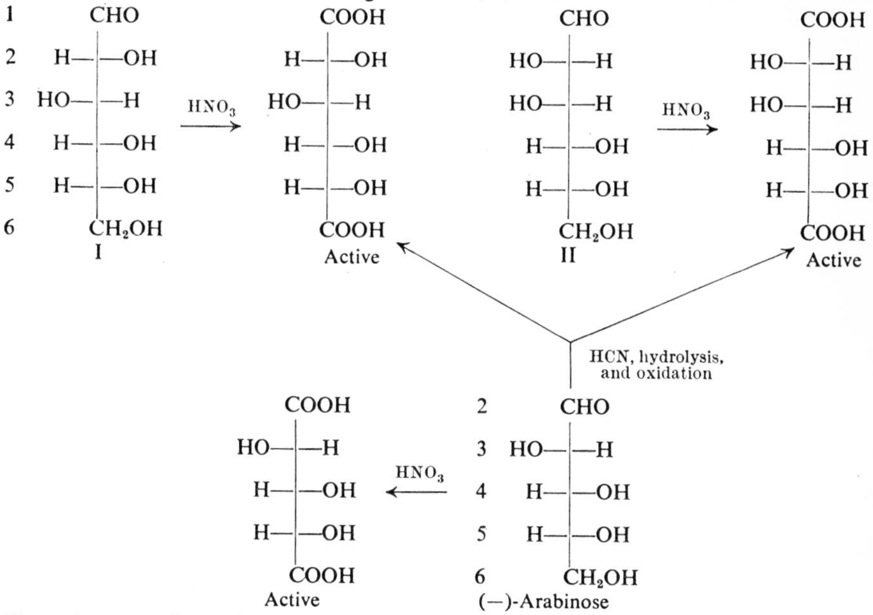

The assignment of (+)-glucose and (+)-mannose to the two structures represented by I and II rests on the fact that another sugar, (+)-gulose, on oxidation gives a dibasic acid identical with that derived from (+)-glucose. Hence these two sugars differ only in that they have their aldehyde and hydroxymethyl groups interchanged. Of the two formulas I and II, only I is in agreement with this behavior, since the structure obtained by interchanging the end groups of II does not represent a different sugar. Hence (+)-glucose is represented by formula I, and (+)-mannose by formula II. The configuration of (+)-gulose also is established.

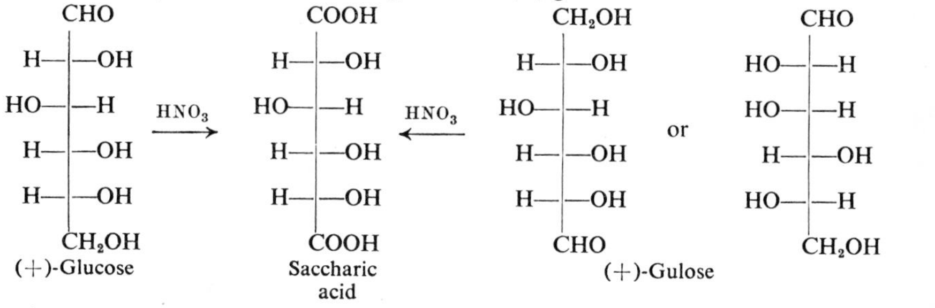

Using other reactions but essentially similar reasoning, the configurations of many sugars and related compounds have been established.

Family. Figure 72 indicates that half of the sugars may be considered as having D(+)-glyceraldehyde (p. 348) as a parent compound. Similarly their enantiomorphs may be considered as having L(−)-glyceraldehyde as a parent compound. Sugars for which the highest-numbered asymmetric carbon atom has the same configuration as D(+)-glyceraldehyde (hydroxyl group on the right in the Fischer projection formula) are said to belong to the D (*dee*) family; those having the enantiomorphic configuration belong to the L (*ell*) family (cf. p. 348).

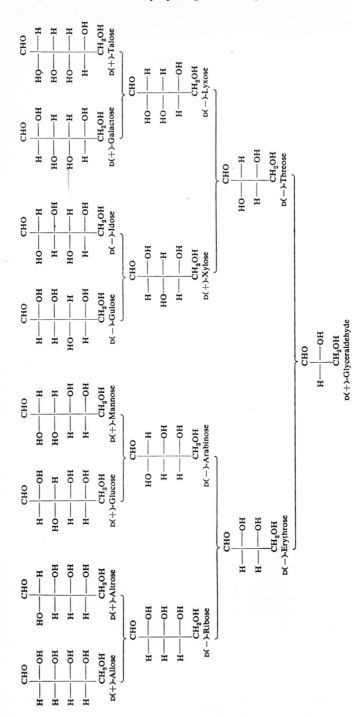

Fig. 72. Configurations of the D family of aldoses.

Although Fischer saw that the determination of relative configurations permitted the assignment of active compounds to two families (p. 348), he used (+)-glucose as a reference compound and did not recognize clearly the advantages of basing relative configurations on a compound having a single asymmetric carbon atom. These advantages first were discussed in 1906 by Rosanoff, who suggested that one of the two structures representing the active forms of glyceraldehyde, CHOCHOHCH$_2$OH, be used for reference. In order to make this reference structure correspond with Fischer's assignment of configuration, Rosanoff proposed that the structure corresponding in configuration to that of C-5 in (+)-glucose be called D-glyceraldehyde and that all compounds related to D-glyceraldehyde be placed in the D family. By 1914 Wohl and co-workers had succeeded in resolving glyceraldehyde and showing that (+)-glyceraldehyde has the D configuration by relating it to (−)-tartaric acid (p. 349). The configuration of (−)-tartaric acid had been related to (+)-glucose by M. Bergmann by the following series of reactions. Since Wohl's work the use of D-glyceraldehyde as the reference substance has been adopted generally.

$$
\begin{array}{ccccc}
\text{CHO} & & \text{COOH} & & \text{CO} \\
\text{H—C—OH} & & \text{H—C—OH} & & \text{H—C—OH} \\
\text{HO—C—H} & \xrightarrow{\text{HNO}_3} & \text{HO—C—H} & \xrightarrow{\text{Heat}} & \text{H—C} \quad\;\;\, \text{O} \\
\text{H—C—OH} & & \text{H—C—OH} & & \text{O—C—H} \\
\text{H—C—OH} & & \text{H—C—OH} & & \text{H—C—OH} \\
\text{CH}_2\text{OH} & & \text{COOH} & & \text{CO} \\
\text{(+)-Glucose} & & & &
\end{array}
$$

$$
\xrightarrow{\text{NH}_3}
$$

$$
\begin{array}{ccccc}
\text{CONH}_2 & & \left[\;\text{NH}_2\;\right] & & \\
\text{H—C—OH} & & \text{H—C—OH} & & \text{CHO} \\
\text{HO—C—H} & \xrightarrow{\text{NaOBr}} & \text{HO—C—H} & \rightarrow & \text{HO—C—H} \\
\text{H—C—OH} & & \text{H—C—OH} & & \text{H—C—OH} \\
\text{H—C—OH} & & \text{H—C—OH} & & \text{CHO} \\
\text{CONH}_2 & & \left[\;\text{NH}_2\;\right] & &
\end{array}
$$

$$
\xrightarrow[\text{H}_2\text{O}]{\text{Br}_2,}
\begin{array}{c}
\text{COOH} \\
\text{HO—C—H} \\
\text{H—C—OH} \\
\text{COOH} \\
\text{(−)-Tartaric acid}
\end{array}
$$

Deoxyaldoses

Some naturally occurring sugars have a hydrogen atom in place of one or more of the hydroxyl groups. In naming these compounds the prefix *deoxy* is used with the name of the oxygen analog to indicate the lack of oxygen, and the class as a whole is known as the **deoxy sugars**. **L(+)-rhamnose** (6-deoxy-L-mannose) is a hydrolytic product of many glycosides and the most common naturally occurring deoxy sugar. **L(−)-fucose** (6-deoxy-L-galactose) is one of the products of the hydrolysis of the cell walls of marine algae.

$$
\begin{array}{cc}
\text{CHO} & \text{CHO} \\
\text{H—C—OH} & \text{HO—C—H} \\
\text{H—C—OH} & \text{H—C—OH} \\
\text{HO—C—H} & \text{H—C—OH} \\
\text{HO—C—H} & \text{HO—C—H} \\
\text{CH}_3 & \text{CH}_3 \\
\text{L(+)-Rhamnose} & \text{L(−)-Fucose}
\end{array}
$$

Rhamnose and fucose sometimes are called *methylpentoses*, but this term may cause ambiguity when dealing with the methylated sugars (p. 373).

2-Deoxy-D-ribose is a hydrolytic product of thymus nucleosides (p. 644), and **digitoxose** (2,6-dideoxy-D-allose) is a hydrolytic product of digitoxin and other cardiac glycosides (p. 870).

```
        CHO                          CHO
         |                            |
        CH₂                          CH₂
         |                            |
   H—C—OH                      H—C—OH
         |                            |
   H—C—OH                      H—C—OH
         |                            |
        CH₂OH                   H—C—OH
                                      |
                                     CH₃
  2-Deoxy-D-ribose            2,6-Dideoxy-D-allose
                                  (digitoxose)
```

Special Reactions of the Aldoses

The Action of Alkalies. Aqueous alkali can produce two types of reactions, isomerization and degradation. *Isomerization* can be brought about by very dilute alkali at room temperature. Thus if glucose is allowed to stand for several days with dilute calcium hydroxide, a mixture is formed containing 63.5 per cent glucose, 2.5 per cent mannose, and 31 per cent of the 2-ketohexose, fructose (p. 384), along with 3 per cent of other substances. Other aldoses behave similarly. The reaction has been called the *Lobry de Bruyn* and *Alberda van Ekenstein transformation* after its discoverers, and has been used for the preparation of ketoses. The reaction is reversible, but true equilibrium is not reached. The composition of the reaction product depends on the initial sugar and on the concentration and nature of the basic catalyst.

The mechanism of the Lobry de Bruyn and Alberda van Ekenstein transformation is not known. Usually an enediol form, postulated by Nef (p. 262), is considered to be an intermediate.

```
                        CHO
                         |
                   H—C—OH
                         |
                   HO—C—H
                         |
                   H—C—OH
                         |
                   H—C—OH
                         |
                        CH₂OH
                      D-Glucose
                         ⇅
                     H      OH
                      \    /
                        C
         CHO                          CH₂OH
          |              C—OH          |
    HO—C—H               |            C=O
          |         HO—C—H             |
    HO—C—H  ⇌              ⇌   HO—C—H
          |         H—C—OH            |
    H—C—OH               |        H—C—OH
          |         H—C—OH             |
    H—C—OH               |        H—C—OH
          |             CH₂OH           |
        CH₂OH        Enediol form      CH₂OH
     D-Mannose                       D-Fructose
```

It has been shown, however, that when the transformation is carried out at 25° in 99.6 per cent deuterium oxide, no deuterium exchanges with any hydrogen atoms united to carbon. Hence the transfer of hydrogen from C-2 to C-1 cannot involve enolization but must be a direct transfer. A likely mechanism would be one related to that for the benzilic acid rearrangement (p. 542) in which the hydrogen migrates with its pair of electrons.

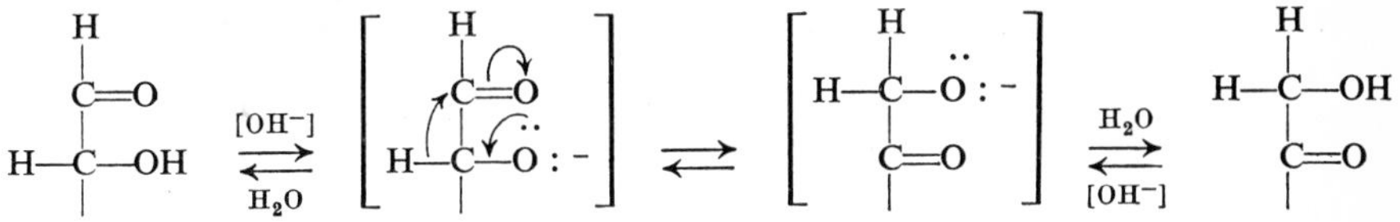

At temperatures above 40° and with stronger alkali, deuterium exchange does take place both at C-1 and C-2. Hence under these conditions a mechanism involving enolization is possible. Moreover if the hydroxyl group on C-2 is methylated as in 2,3,4,6-tetra-*O*-methylglucose (p. 390), only 2,3,4,6-tetra-*O*-methylmannose is formed, and if the isomerization is carried out in heavy water, one carbon-bound hydrogen atom is replaced by deuterium. This evidence supports the enolization hypothesis in these instances.

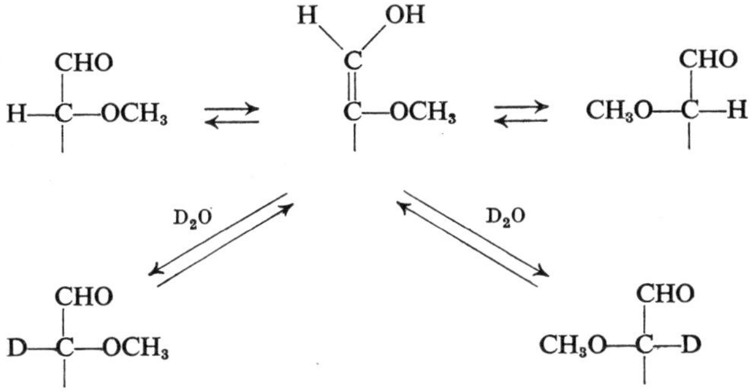

The second important type of action of alkali on monosaccharides is cleavage into smaller molecules, or *degradation*. Since aldol addition is reversible, the natural ketoses and those formed by isomerization of aldoses give rise in the presence of alkali to formaldehyde and lower-molecular weight hydroxyaldehydes and polyhydroxy ketones.

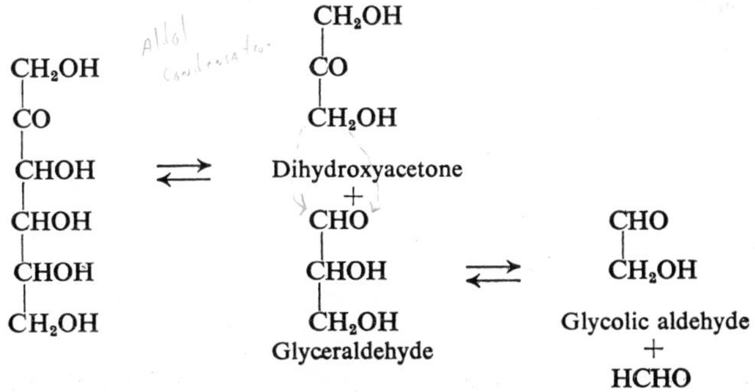

Reductone, $HOCH_2COCHO$ (p. 771), a strong reducing agent, and branched chain acidic substances known as *saccharinic acids* also have been isolated.

Oxidation by Cupric Ion in Alkaline Solution. Although the salts of many heavy metals such as copper, silver, mercury, and bismuth are reduced by alkaline sugar solutions, reagents containing copper usually are used for analytical purposes. Cupric hydroxide oxidizes carbohydrates, but its slight solubility in dilute alkali permits only a slow reaction. The rate of oxidation is increased greatly if the copper is kept in solution by the formation of a complex salt with tartrate ion (Fehling solution) or citrate ion (Benedict solution) (p. 810). The former uses sodium hydroxide for alkaline reaction, whereas the latter uses sodium carbonate. Benedict solution is the more stable and is not affected by substances such as creatine (p. 322) and uric acid (p. 645). Hence it is preferred for detecting and estimating glucose in urine.

Evidence for reduction is the formation of red cuprous oxide which precipitates because the cuprous ion does not form complexes with tartrates or citrates. If protective colloids are present, as in urine samples, the color of the precipitate may vary from yellow to red depending on the state of subdivision of the particles. In the presence of an excess of carbohydrate, some of the cuprous oxide may be reduced to metallic copper.

The equation for the oxidation of an aldehyde group to a carboxyl group requires a ratio of two moles of cupric salt per mole of aldehyde.

$$RCHO + 2\,Cu(OH)_2 \longrightarrow RCOOH + Cu_2O + 2\,H_2O$$

Actually one mole of glucose reduces between five and six moles of cupric salt depending on the conditions of the reaction. Moreover ketoses reduce just as well as aldoses, although simple ketones do not reduce Fehling solution. The explanation lies in the reaction of the sugars with alkali, which not only interconverts aldoses and ketoses but gives degradation products that have reducing properties (p. 369). Furthermore, some of the excess reduction may be caused by the CHOH groups adjacent to the carbonyl group, since even simple compounds containing this grouping are oxidized by alkaline cupric solutions to give dicarbonyl compounds.

$$\underset{\underset{\displaystyle O \quad OH}{|\quad\;|}}{R-C-CH-R} + 2\,Cu(OH)_2 \longrightarrow \underset{\underset{\displaystyle O \quad O}{|\quad\;|}}{R-C-C-R} + Cu_2O + 3\,H_2O$$

In spite of the complexity of the reaction, oxidation can be used successfully for the quantitative estimation of sugars by standardizing conditions rigidly and by using empirically determined tables relating the amount of sugar to the amount of cupric ion reduced.

Formation of Osazones. Fischer in his study of the reaction of phenylhydrazine with aldehydes and ketones found that reaction with reducing sugars introduces two phenylhydrazine residues instead of one. A yellow crystalline product known as a **phenylosazone** separates from the hot aqueous solution. The other products of the reaction are aniline (phenylamine) and ammonia. This reaction is characteristic of the grouping RCOCHOHR.

$$
\begin{array}{l}
CHO \\
| \\
CHOH \\
| \\
(CHOH)_3 \\
| \\
CH_2OH
\end{array}
\;+\; 3\,C_6H_5NHNH_2 \;\longrightarrow\;
\begin{array}{l}
CH{=}N{-}NHC_6H_5 \\
| \\
C{=}N{-}NHC_6H_5 \\
| \\
(CHOH)_3 \\
| \\
CH_2OH
\end{array}
\;+\; C_6H_5NH_2 + NH_3 + 2\,H_2O
$$

A phenylosazone   Aniline

Substituted hydrazines of the general formulas $RNHNH_2$ and R_2NNH_2 may be used to form osazones. Since the osazones from different hydrazines and different sugars differ in melting point, crystal form, and rate of formation, osazone formation is a valuable reaction for the identification of sugars. Hydrolysis of osazones yields the α dicarbonyl compounds, which are known as **osones.**

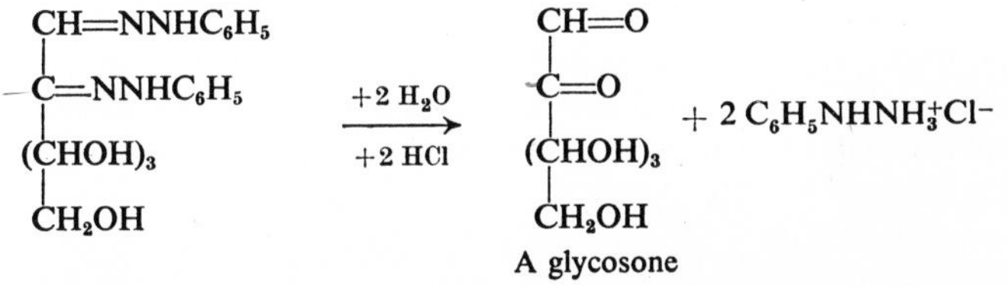

$$
\begin{array}{c}
CH\!=\!NNHC_6H_5 \\
C\!=\!NNHC_6H_5 \\
(CHOH)_3 \\
CH_2OH
\end{array}
\quad
\xrightarrow[+2\ HCl]{+2\ H_2O}
\quad
\begin{array}{c}
CH\!=\!O \\
C\!=\!O \\
(CHOH)_3 \\
CH_2OH
\end{array}
\quad +\ 2\ C_6H_5NHNH_3^+Cl^-
$$

A glycosone

When osazones are formed, the asymmetry of the α carbon atom is destroyed. Therefore sugars which differ only in the configuration of the α carbon atom, such as glucose and mannose, yield the same osazone.

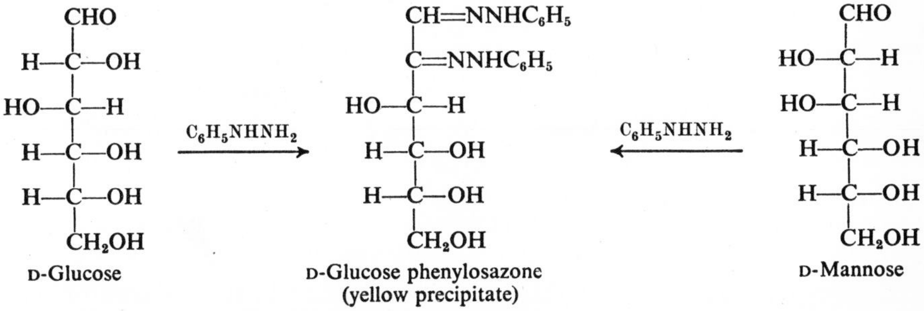

$$
\begin{array}{ccc}
CHO & CH\!=\!NNHC_6H_5 & CHO \\
H\!-\!C\!-\!OH & C\!=\!NNHC_6H_5 & HO\!-\!C\!-\!H \\
HO\!-\!C\!-\!H & HO\!-\!C\!-\!H & HO\!-\!C\!-\!H \\
H\!-\!C\!-\!OH & H\!-\!C\!-\!OH & H\!-\!C\!-\!OH \\
H\!-\!C\!-\!OH & H\!-\!C\!-\!OH & H\!-\!C\!-\!OH \\
CH_2OH & CH_2OH & CH_2OH
\end{array}
$$

D-Glucose $\xrightarrow{C_6H_5NHNH_2}$ D-Glucose phenylosazone (yellow precipitate) $\xleftarrow{C_6H_5NHNH_2}$ D-Mannose

An intermediate in this reaction is the hydrazone in which only the carbonyl group has reacted. Although glucose phenylhydrazone is soluble in water, mannose phenylhydrazone is insoluble in water and precipitates as a white solid from aqueous solution even at room temperature. This difference in behavior is used to distinguish between glucose and mannose.

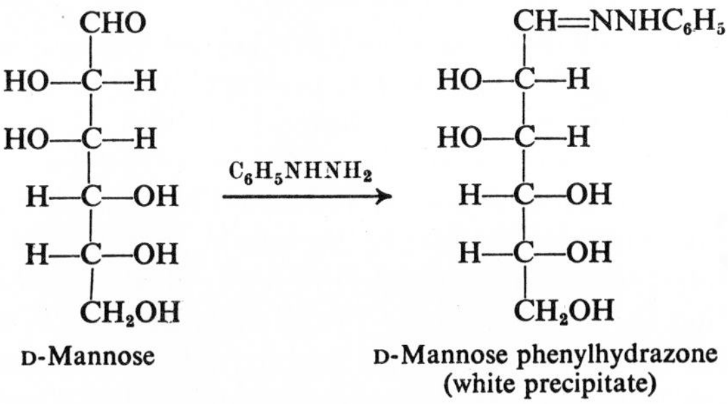

$$
\begin{array}{cc}
CHO & CH\!=\!NNHC_6H_5 \\
HO\!-\!C\!-\!H & HO\!-\!C\!-\!H \\
HO\!-\!C\!-\!H & HO\!-\!C\!-\!H \\
H\!-\!C\!-\!OH & H\!-\!C\!-\!OH \\
H\!-\!C\!-\!OH & H\!-\!C\!-\!OH \\
CH_2OH & CH_2OH
\end{array}
$$

      D-Mannose $\xrightarrow{C_6H_5NHNH_2}$ D-Mannose phenylhydrazone (white precipitate)

The course of osazone formation is not known with certainty. Fischer postulated that the phenylhydrazine oxidized the alcohol group and was reduced to aniline and ammonia.

$$
\begin{array}{c}
CH\!=\!NNHC_6H_5 \\
CHOH \\
\end{array}
\ +\ C_6H_5NHNH_2
\quad\longrightarrow\quad
\begin{array}{c}
CH\!=\!NNHC_6H_5 \\
C\!=\!O \\
\end{array}
\ +\ C_6H_5NH_2 +\ NH_3
$$

The new carbonyl group now may react with the third molecule of phenylhydrazine. An argument in favor of this behavior is that a CHOH group adjacent to a carbonyl group is easily oxidized, for example by alkaline copper solutions. More recently it has been proposed that the aniline results from the decomposition of an isomeric form of the hydrazone that arises as a result of a combination of enaminization (analogous to enolization) and ketonization.

$$
\begin{array}{c}
\text{CH=NNHC}_6\text{H}_5 \\
| \\
\text{CHOH} \\
|
\end{array}
\xrightarrow[\text{ization}]{\text{Enamin-}}
\begin{array}{c}
\text{CHNHNHC}_6\text{H}_5 \\
\| \\
\text{COH} \\
|
\end{array}
\longrightarrow
\begin{array}{c}
\text{CH}_2\text{NHNHC}_6\text{H}_5 \\
| \\
\text{C=O} \\
|
\end{array}
\xrightarrow{[\text{H}^+]}
\begin{array}{c}
\text{CH=NH} \\
| \\
\text{C=O} \\
|
\end{array}
+ [\text{C}_6\text{H}_5\text{NH}_3{}^+]
$$

Analogous types of acid-catalyzed reactions are known in other series of compounds, and optimum yields of osazones are obtained in slightly acid solutions. The osazone results from replacement of the doubly bound oxygen and imino group by the hydrazine residues.

$$
\begin{array}{c}
\text{CH=NH} \\
| \\
\text{C=O} \\
|
\end{array}
+ 2\ \text{C}_6\text{H}_5\text{NHNH}_2
\longrightarrow
\begin{array}{c}
\text{CH=NNHC}_6\text{H}_5 \\
| \\
\text{C=NNHC}_6\text{H}_5 \\
|
\end{array}
+ \text{NH}_3 + \text{H}_2\text{O}
$$

The chief argument in favor of this course for the reaction is that whereas aldoses give osazones in yields of only 40–60 per cent, compounds of the type $\text{HOCH}_2(\text{CHOH})_3\text{COCH}_2\text{NHR}$ give nearly quantitative yields of osazones. This reaction is postulated as

$$
\begin{array}{c}
\text{CH}_2\text{NHR} \\
| \\
\text{C=O} \\
|
\end{array}
\xrightarrow{\text{C}_6\text{H}_5\text{NHNH}_2}
\begin{array}{c}
\text{CH}_2\text{NHR} \\
| \\
\text{C=NNHC}_6\text{H}_5 \\
|
\end{array}
\longrightarrow
\begin{array}{c}
\text{CHNHR} \\
\| \\
\text{C}{-}\text{NHNHC}_6\text{H}_5 \\
|
\end{array}
\longrightarrow
$$

$$
\begin{array}{c}
\text{CH=NR} \\
| \\
\text{CHNHNHC}_6\text{H}_5 \\
|
\end{array}
\xrightarrow{[\text{H}^+]}
\begin{array}{c}
\text{CH=NR} \\
| \\
\text{C=NH} \\
|
\end{array}
\atop + [\text{C}_6\text{H}_5\text{NH}_3{}^+]
\xrightarrow{2\ \text{C}_6\text{H}_5\text{NHNH}_2}
\begin{array}{c}
\text{CH=NNHC}_6\text{H}_5 \\
| \\
\text{C=NNHC}_6\text{H}_5 \\
|
\end{array}
\atop + \text{RNH}_2 + \text{NH}_3
$$

In either mechanism, the driving force of the reaction would be the formation of the conjugated system. Similarly the stability of the conjugated system undoubtedly accounts for the fact that the reaction does not continue to proceed down the chain of the sugar molecule.

Glycoside Formation. Aldehydes react with alcohols in the presence of acid catalysts to form acetals. Hemiacetals are intermediates in the reaction (p. 203).

$$
\text{RCHO} + \text{HOR}' \underset{[\text{H}^+]}{\rightleftarrows} \underset{\substack{\diagup \\ \text{RCH} \\ \diagdown \\ \text{OR}' \\ \text{Hemiacetal}}}{\overset{\text{OH}}{}} \underset{\substack{\diagup \\ \text{RCH} \\ \diagdown \\ \text{OR}' \\ \text{Acetal}}}{\overset{\text{OR}'}{\underset{\text{R}'\text{OH},[\text{H}^+]}{\rightleftarrows}}} + \text{H}_2\text{O}
$$

When Fischer attempted to prepare an acetal from glucose, methyl alcohol, and hydrogen chloride, definite crystalline products were obtained, but analysis showed that although a molecule of water had been eliminated, only one methyl group had been introduced. Furthermore two isomeric products were obtained. These compounds no longer reduced Fehling solution, nor formed osazones. Moreover they behaved like acetals in that they were hydrolyzed readily in acid solutions but were stable to alkali. This behavior is explainable if it is assumed that the aldehyde group of the sugar first reacts with the alcohol group on the fifth carbon atom to form an internal cyclic hemiacetal having a six-membered ring. The hemiacetal then reacts with methyl alcohol to form the acetal. Since a new asymmetric carbon atom is produced in this process, two diastereoisomers are formed.

These acetals are called *glycosides*, and the two forms are designated α and β. Isomers of this type are known as *anomers* and the carbon atom responsible for the existence of anomers is known as the *anomeric* (Gr. *ano*, above) carbon atom. Hereafter the anomeric carbon atom is indicated by bold-faced type. It can be distinguished readily from the other carbon atoms by the fact that it is united to two oxygen atoms. For glycosides the anomeric carbon atom also is known as the *glycosidic* carbon atom. The designation α is given to the form in which the hydroxyl or substituted hydroxyl group is on the right in the projection formulas for members of the D family and on the left for members of the L family. Hence when indicating the configuration of the anomeric carbon atom, it is necessary to indicate the family of the sugar as well.

$$
\begin{array}{ccccc}
\text{H—C—OCH}_3 & \text{H—C—OH} & \text{CHO} & \text{HO—C—H} & \text{CH}_3\text{O—C—H} \\
\text{CHOH} & \text{CHOH} & \text{CHOH} & \text{CHOH} & \text{CHOH} \\
\text{CHOH} & \text{CHOH} & \text{CHOH} & \text{CHOH} & \text{CHOH} \\
\text{CHOH} & \text{CHOH} & \text{CHOH} & \text{CHOH} & \text{CHOH} \\
\text{H—C} & \text{H—C} & \text{H—C—OH} & \text{H—C} & \text{H—C} \\
\text{CH}_2\text{OH} & \text{CH}_2\text{OH} & \text{CH}_2\text{OH} & \text{CH}_2\text{OH} & \text{CH}_2\text{OH}
\end{array}
$$

Methyl α-D-glycoside   Methyl β-D-glycoside

The determination of the ring structure of the methyl glycosides originally was a difficult task. It now is done more easily by means of periodic acid oxidation, which cleaves 1,2-dihydroxy compounds, α-hydroxy aldehydes, and α-hydroxyketones between the two oxygenated carbon atoms (p. 742). The dihydroxy compounds give two moles of aldehyde, whereas α-hydroxy aldehydes and α-hydroxyketones give one mole of aldehyde and one mole of acid.

$$\text{RCHOHCH}_2\text{OH} + \text{HIO}_4 \longrightarrow \text{RCHO} + \text{HCHO} + \text{HIO}_3 + \text{H}_2\text{O}$$

$$\text{RCHOHCHOHR}' + \text{HIO}_4 \longrightarrow \text{RCHO} + \text{OCHR}' + \text{HIO}_3 + \text{H}_2\text{O}$$

$$\text{RCHOHCHO} + \text{HIO}_4 \longrightarrow \text{RCHO} + \text{HCOOH} + \text{HIO}_3$$

$$\text{RCHOHCOR}' + \text{HIO}_4 \longrightarrow \text{RCHO} + \text{R}'\text{COOH} + \text{HIO}_3$$

Five possible ring structures for the methyl glycosides of an aldohexose exist. The number of moles of periodic acid used, and of formic acid and formaldehyde produced are indicated below for each structure. The arrows indicate the points where oxidative fission takes place.

$$
\begin{array}{ccccc}
\text{CHOCH}_3 & \text{CHOCH}_3 & \text{CHOCH}_3 & \text{CHOCH}_3 & \text{CHOCH}_3 \\
\text{CH} & \text{CHOH} & \text{CHOH} & \text{CHOH} & \text{CHOH} \\
\text{CHOH} & \text{CH} & \text{CHOH} & \text{CHOH} & \text{CHOH} \\
\text{CHOH} & \text{CHOH} & \text{CH} & \text{CHOH} & \text{CHOH} \\
\text{CHOH} & \text{CHOH} & \text{CHOH} & \text{CH} & \text{CHOH} \\
\text{CH}_2\text{OH} & \text{CH}_2\text{OH} & \text{CH}_2\text{OH} & \text{CH}_2\text{OH} & \text{CH}_2
\end{array}
$$

Moles					
HIO₄	3	2	2	2	3
HCOOH	2	1	0	1	2
HCHO	1	1	1	0	0

The reactions are practically quantitative. Hence from the number of moles of periodic acid used and the moles of formic acid and formaldehyde produced, it is possible to determine the ring structure. The ordinary methyl glucosides and most methyl glycosides consume two moles of periodic acid and no formaldehyde is produced, indicating that they have a six-membered ring.

Methylation. Once the sugar is converted into a methyl glycoside, it is stable to alkali, and the remaining hydroxyl groups can be converted to methyl ethers by a modified Williamson synthesis. The original procedure, discovered by

Purdie[3] and widely used by Purdie and Irvine,[4] treated the hydroxy compound with methyl iodide in the presence of silver oxide.

$$2\ ROH + 2\ CH_3I + Ag_2O \longrightarrow 2\ ROCH_3 + 2\ AgI + H_2O$$

Later Haworth[5] developed the use of methyl sulfate in the presence of sodium hydroxide. Frequently the latter reagent brings about only partial methylation, and is completed by the Purdie procedure.

$$\begin{array}{l} CHOCH_3 \\ CHOH \\ CHOH \\ CHOH \\ CH{-\!-\!-} \\ CH_2OH \end{array}\Bigg]O + 4\ (CH_3)_2SO_4 + 4\ NaOH \longrightarrow \begin{array}{l} CHOCH_3 \\ CHOCH_3 \\ CHOCH_3 \\ CHOCH_3 \\ CH{-\!-\!-} \\ CH_2OCH_3 \end{array}\Bigg]O + 4\ NaCH_3SO_4 + 4\ H_2O$$

Methyl
glycoside

Methyl
tetra-*O*-methyl
glycoside

The methoxyl on C-1 differs markedly from the other four in that it is an acetal methoxyl whereas the others are ether methoxyls. The acetal methoxyl can be removed readily by acid hydrolysis to give the 2,3,4,6-tetra-*O*-methylglycose which, because the ring can open easily, again reduces Fehling solution.

$$\begin{array}{l} CHOCH_3 \\ CHOCH_3 \\ CHOCH_3 \\ CHOCH_3 \\ CH{-\!-\!-} \\ CH_2OCH_3 \end{array}\Bigg]O + H_2O \xrightarrow{[H^+]} CH_3OH + \begin{array}{l} CHOH \\ CHOCH_3 \\ CHOCH_3 \\ CHOCH_3 \\ CH{-\!-\!-} \\ CH_2OCH_3 \end{array}\Bigg]O \rightleftharpoons \begin{array}{l} CHO \\ CHOCH_3 \\ CHOCH_3 \\ CHOCH_3 \\ CHOH \\ CH_2OCH_3 \end{array}$$

---

[3] Thomas Purdie (1843–1916), professor of chemistry at the University of St. Andrews, Scotland. He was interested primarily in the relation of optical rotation to structure. During this work it was observed that ethyl lactate, $CH_3CHOHCOOC_2H_5$, made from the silver salt and ethyl iodide always had a higher rotation than that made by direct esterification. It was found that the former was contaminated with the ethyl ether which led to the discovery of alkylation by an alkyl iodide and silver oxide. According to Irvine, Purdie was quick to realize the application of the reaction to a study of the structure of sugars and soon found that α- and β-glucosides gave the same tetramethylglucose and hence had the same ring structure.

[4] James Colquhoun Irvine (1877–1952), student of Purdie and his successor as professor of chemistry at St. Andrews. Later he became Principal and Vice-Chancellor of St. Andrews. He made a systematic study of the methylation of sugars and laid the groundwork for the determination of the structure of di- and polysaccharides.

[5] Walter Norman Haworth (1883–1950), professor of chemistry at the University of Birmingham. He began the study of chemistry under W. H. Perkin, Jr. (p. 828) and later worked in Wallach's laboratory at Goettingen. A lectureship at St. Andrews brought him into contact with the work of Purdie and Irvine, which changed his interest from the field of terpenes to that of carbohydrates. He developed the methylation procedure using methyl sulfate and sodium hydroxide, and largely as the result of his work, the ring structures and constitutions of most of the mono- and disaccharides became established, as well as the basic structure of many polysaccharides. He was awarded the Nobel Prize in Chemistry in 1937.

However the 2,3,4,6-tetra-*O*-methylglycose can form only a hydrazone and not an osazone, because the hydroxyl group on C-2 is methylated. The methylated sugars played an important part in the determination of ring structures and of the constitution of oligo- and polysaccharides (p. 390).

Mutarotation. Many optically active compounds give solutions, the rotation of which changes with time. This phenomenon, which is called *mutarotation* (L. *mutare*, to change), must result from some chemical change in the molecule. The mutarotation of glucose solutions was reported first in 1846. By 1895 readily interconvertible isomeric modifications of lactose and glucose had been isolated. Three such forms are obtainable from glucose. The form designated α crystallizes as the hydrate from 70 per cent alcohol below 30°. Its freshly prepared aqueous solutions have a specific rotation of +112°. The β form crystallizes from aqueous solutions evaporated at temperatures above 98°. It has a specific rotation of +18.7°. The third form is obtained by adding alcohol to a concentrated aqueous solution and has a rotation of +52.7°. However only α- and β-glucose mutarotate, and each finally attains the value +52.7°. The third form therefore is nothing more than the equilibrium mixture of the α and β forms.

The existence of the two forms of glucose and their mutarotation is explainable if it is assumed that they have cyclic hemiacetal structures analogous to the acetal structures postulated for the methyl α- and β-glycosides. It usually is assumed that their interconversion takes place by way of the open chain form.

α-D-Glycose   β-D-Glycose

That the equilibrium rotation of glucose is not the average of the rotations of α- and β-glucose is not surprising, since they are not enantiomorphs and the equilibrium composition need not be a 50–50 mixture. The anomeric carbon atom of the hemiacetal structure frequently is called the *reducing* carbon atom, since it is involved in the reduction of Fehling solution. The anomeric hydroxyl group frequently is called the hemiacetal hydroxyl group.

All evidence indicates that the amount of free aldehyde form of the sugar in solution, if present at all, is very small. Thus no ultraviolet absorption band for a carbonyl group (p. 665) can be detected in aqueous glucose solutions. Moreover the aldoses do not give a color with ordinary Schiff reagent. On the other hand, if a specially prepared Schiff reagent is used, the aldoses give colors ranging from faint for glucose to intense for arabinose. Reduction at the dropping mercury electrode (*polarographic analysis*) indicates that the amount of reducible material present in dilute solutions varies from 0.02 per cent for glucose to 8.5 per cent for ribose. Solutions of glucose in strong sulfuric acid do have an absorption band in the ultraviolet corresponding to the presence of a carbonyl group.

Since the mutarotation of sugars is caused merely by an aldehyde-hemiacetal equilibrium, it is catalyzed by both acids and bases. The detailed mechanism of this type of reaction has been discussed (p. 203).

The **assignment of ring structures** to the free sugars is considerably less certain than the assignment to the glycosides, because of the ease with which the ring opens and closes. Any proof must assume that no change in ring structure takes place during the reactions used. One strong argument that glucose contains the six-membered ring is that careful enzyme hydrolysis of methyl α-glucoside yields α-glucose, and hydrolysis of methyl β-glucoside yields β-glucose. If ring changes had taken place, the equilibrium mixture of α- and β-glucose would have been expected.

In the formulas given for both the sugars and the methyl glycosides, the α isomer has been assigned the configuration with the hydroxyl group on the right and the β isomer that with the hydroxyl group on the left. This assignment was made for glucose on the basis of the conductivity of boric acid solutions in the presence of the sugars. It is known that if two hydroxyl groups on adjacent carbon atoms in a ring compound have the *cis* configuration (on the same side of the ring) boric acid forms a complex which is a stronger acid than boric acid itself. Hence the conductivity of the boric acid solution is increased.

The reaction involves the formation of the boric acid ester from three hydroxyl groups and coordination of a fourth hydroxyl group with the boron to complete the latter's electron shell (p. 741). The proton then ionizes readily from this oxygen atom to give a conducting solution. If the hydroxyl groups are on opposite sides of the ring, the bicyclic boron complex could not form without bending the bonds and changing the normal valence angles.

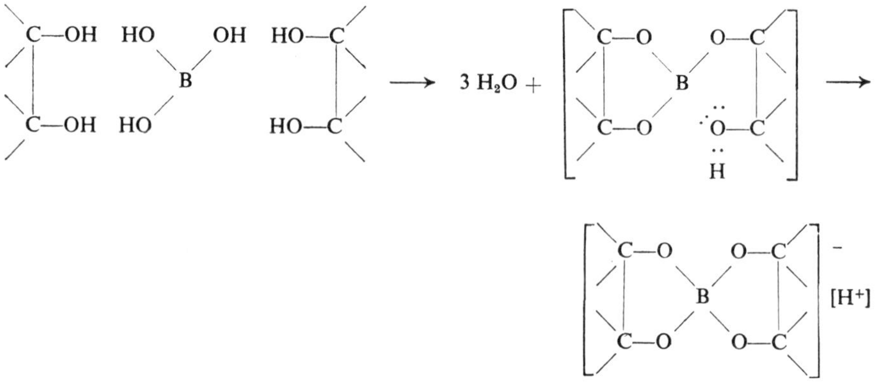

Of the two possible structures for α- and β-D-glucose, one has the hydroxyl groups on C-1 and C-2 on the same side of the ring and the other on opposite sides. Experimentally α-D-glucose gives a higher conductivity in boric acid solution than β-D-glucose and is assigned the *cis* configuration.

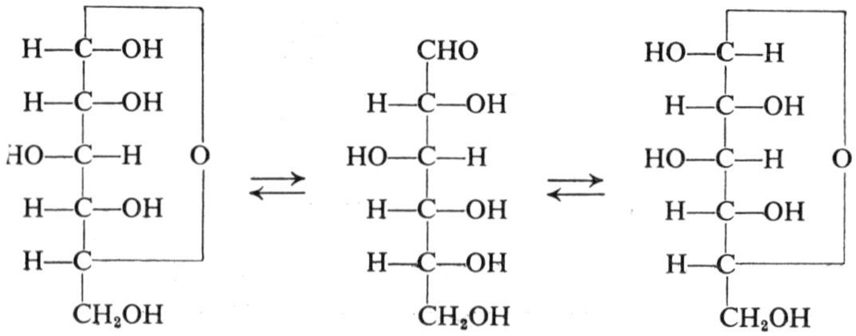

α-D-Glucose   β-D-Glucose

The conversion of methyl α-glucoside to α-glucose and of methyl β-glucoside to β-glucose establishes the configuration of these glycosides. It now is known that for sugars of the

D series the more dextrorotatory (or less levorotatory) of each α,β pair is the α isomer, and for the L series the α isomer is the more levorotatory. Actually the use of α and β by Hudson [6] to designate an anomeric pair was based originally on their optical rotations.

Ester Formation. The hydroxyl groups of sugars can be converted readily to ester groups. The aldoses acetylate with acetic anhydride in the presence of acidic or basic catalysts. The hexoses yield pentaacetates and the pentoses tetraacetates, thus indicating the presence of five and four hydroxyl groups. The acetates, however, do not reduce Fehling solution and therefore do not contain a free aldehyde group. Moreover two isomeric α and β forms of each acetate are obtained. Hence it is the cyclic form of the sugar which is acetylated. The acid catalysts commonly used are sulfuric acid or zinc chloride, and the basic catalysts are pyridine (p. 620) or sodium acetate (acetate ion).[7]

It is possible by choosing the proper catalyst and conditions to obtain chiefly α- or β-glucose pentaacetates as desired. Acids catalyze the interconversion of α and β forms of the acetates, and the equilibrium mixture of 90 per cent α and 10 per cent β is obtained. Bases catalyze the equilibrium between the free sugars (hemiacetals) but not that between the acetylated products (acetals). Since the β form of the sugar reacts faster than the α form, the base-catalyzed acetylation yields chiefly the β acetate.

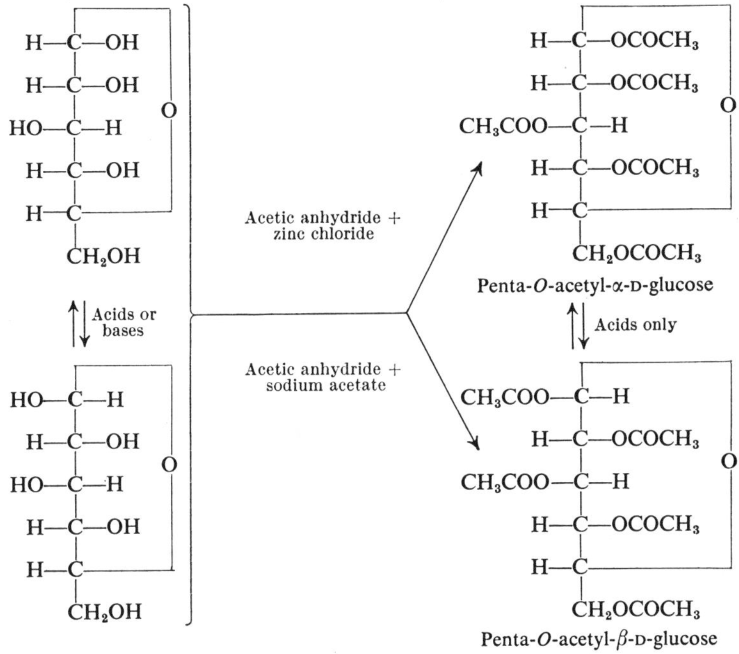

Penta-*O*-acetyl-α-D-glucose

Penta-*O*-acetyl-β-D-glucose

---

[6] Claude Silbert Hudson (1881–1952), chemist for the United States Bureau of Chemistry, the National Bureau of Standards, and the Public Health Service. When he first entered Princeton University as a graduate student, he became interested in mutarotation while determining the activity of a sample of lactose which he had been asked to purify for a professor of physics. Besides his contributions to the correlation of structure with optical activity, he first used the periodate method (p. 373) for establishing the ring structure of sugars.

[7] Zinc chloride is an acid catalyst because the zinc atom lacks electrons in its valence shell and like the proton can combine with an unshared pair of electrons. Acetate ion in acetic acid solution is a base analogous to the hydroxide ion in water solution (p. 235).

The sugar acetates are saponified readily by alkali. For preparative purposes, however, it is better to remove acetyl groups by alcoholysis catalyzed by alkoxide ion (p. 170).

$$
\begin{array}{c}
\text{CHOCOCH}_3 \\
\text{CHOCOCH}_3 \\
\text{CHOCOCH}_3 \\
\text{CHOCOCH}_3 \\
\text{CH}\!\!-\!\! \\
\text{CH}_2\text{OCOCH}_3
\end{array}\text{O} + 5\,\text{C}_2\text{H}_5\text{OH} \underset{}{\overset{\text{NaOC}_2\text{H}_5}{\rightleftarrows}}
\begin{array}{c}
\text{CHOH} \\
\text{CHOH} \\
\text{CHOH} \\
\text{CHOH} \\
\text{CH}\!\!-\!\! \\
\text{CH}_2\text{OH}
\end{array}\text{O} + 5\,\text{CH}_3\text{COOC}_2\text{H}_5
$$

Dry hydrogen bromide in glacial acetic acid replaces the glycosidic acetate group (that on the anomeric carbon atom) by bromine. The corresponding chlorine and fluorine compounds can be made by similar procedures. The products are known as *acetylglycosyl halides* or as *acetohaloglycoses* and are useful for the synthesis of glycosides and oligosaccharides.

$$
\begin{array}{c}
\text{CH}_3\text{COO}\!-\!\text{C}\!-\!\text{H} \\
\text{H}\!-\!\text{C}\!-\!\text{OCOCH}_3 \\
\text{CH}_3\text{COO}\!-\!\text{C}\!-\!\text{H} \\
\text{H}\!-\!\text{C}\!-\!\text{OCOCH}_3 \\
\text{H}\!-\!\text{C}\!\!-\!\! \\
\text{CH}_2\text{OCOCH}_3
\end{array}\text{O} \xrightarrow{\text{HBr}}
\begin{array}{c}
\text{H}\!-\!\text{C}\!-\!\text{Br} \\
\text{H}\!-\!\text{C}\!-\!\text{OCOCH}_3 \\
\text{CH}_3\text{COO}\!-\!\text{C}\!-\!\text{H} \\
\text{H}\!-\!\text{C}\!-\!\text{OCOCH}_3 \\
\text{H}\!-\!\text{C}\!\!-\!\! \\
\text{CH}_2\text{OCOCH}_3
\end{array}\text{O} + \text{CH}_3\text{COOH}
$$

Penta-*O*-acetyl-β-D-glucose   Tetra-*O*-acetyl-α-D-glucosyl bromide
(acetobromo-α-D-glucose)

Penta-*O*-acetyl-β-D-glucose yields tetra-*O*-acetyl-α-D-glucosyl bromide. The β isomers of the glucosyl halides are very unstable and rapidly isomerize to the α form. Reaction of the tetra-*O*-acetyl-α-D-glucosyl bromide with alcohols or sugars, however, yields the β-glucosides.

Many other esters of the sugars have been prepared. Among those of importance are the *benzoates* (p. 549) and the *sulfonates* (tosyl and mesyl derivatives, pp. 471, 291). Esters of some inorganic acids such as the *nitrates, carbonates,* and *phosphates* also are important. **Glucose 1-(dihydrogen phosphate)** (Cori ester) and **glucose 6-(dihydrogen phosphate)** (Robison ester) are important intermediates in the alcoholic fermentation of sugars.

Action of Strong Acids. Although dilute acids at room temperature have little effect on aldoses other than catalyzing α,β interconversion, hot strong acids produce complex changes which involve dehydration. Thus all pentoses when distilled with 12 per cent hydrochloric acid give approximately theoretical yields of furfural (p. 617). The reaction is used both as a qualitative test for pentoses or substances yielding pentoses on hydrolysis and for their quantitative estimation, by detecting or estimating the furfural that distills (p. 617). The 6-deoxyaldo-hexoses are converted into 5-methylfurfural.

$$
\begin{array}{c}
\text{CHO} \\
| \\
\text{CHOH} \\
| \\
\text{CHOH} \\
| \\
\text{CHOH} \\
| \\
\text{CH}_2\text{OH}
\end{array}
\quad
\xrightarrow[\text{acid}]{\text{Hot}}
\quad
\begin{array}{c}
\text{CHO} \\
| \\
\text{C} \\
| \quad \text{O} \\
\text{CH} \\
| \\
\text{CH} \\
\end{array}
\quad \text{or} \quad
\text{HC}\!-\!\!\!-\text{CH} \quad\quad + 3\ \text{H}_2\text{O}
$$

Furfural

Hexoses yield 5-(hydroxymethyl)furfural, but this compound is more soluble in water than furfural and is not volatile with steam. Hence it is acted upon further by the hot acid giving levulinic acid and considerable amounts of dark insoluble condensation products known as humins.

$$
\begin{array}{c}
\text{CHO} \\
| \\
\text{CHOH} \\
| \\
\text{CHOH} \\
| \\
\text{CHOH} \\
| \\
\text{CHOH} \\
| \\
\text{CH}_2\text{OH}
\end{array}
\xrightarrow[\text{acid}]{\text{Hot}}
\begin{array}{c}
\text{CHO} \\
| \\
\text{C} \\
| \quad \text{O} \\
\text{CH} \\
| \\
\text{C} \\
| \\
\text{CH}_2\text{OH}
\end{array}
\text{or}
\quad
\text{H}\!-\!\text{C}\!-\!\!\!-\text{CH} \quad \xrightarrow{2\ \text{H}_2\text{O}} \quad
\begin{array}{c}
\text{COOH} \\
| \\
\text{CH}_2 \\
| \\
\text{CH}_2 \\
| \\
\text{C}\!=\!\text{O} \\
| \\
\text{CH}_3
\end{array}
\quad + \text{HCOOH}
$$

5-(Hydroxymethyl)furfural   Levulinic acid

The different furfurals give characteristic color reactions with polyhydric phenols such as resorcinol (p. 517), orcinol (p. 517), and phloroglucinol (p. 518), which may be used to distinguish between pentoses, 6-deoxyhexoses, and hexoses.

Reactions with Aldehydes and Ketones. Compounds containing two hydroxyl groups properly spaced to give a five- or six-membered ring react readily with aldehydes or ketones to give cyclic acetals.

$$
\begin{array}{c}
\diagdown\text{C}\!-\!\text{OH} \\
| \\
\diagup\text{C}\!-\!\text{OH}
\end{array}
+ \text{OCHR} \xrightarrow[\ \ ]{[\text{H}^+]}
\begin{array}{c}
\diagdown\text{C}\!-\!\text{O} \\
| \qquad\qquad \diagdown\text{CHR} + \text{H}_2\text{O} \\
\diagup\text{C}\!-\!\text{O} \diagup
\end{array}
$$

The sugars contain the necessary grouping for this reaction, and many such derivatives have been prepared. The reaction products with acetone are of most importance and are known as **isopropylidene derivatives** or **sugar acetones.** α-D-Galactose, for example, gives a diisopropylidene derivative which is non-reducing.

$$
\begin{array}{c}
\text{H}\!-\!\text{C}\!-\!\text{OH} \\
| \\
\text{H}\!-\!\text{C}\!-\!\text{OH} \\
| \qquad\quad \text{O} \\
\text{HO}\!-\!\text{C}\!-\!\text{H} \\
| \\
\text{HO}\!-\!\text{C}\!-\!\text{H} \\
| \\
\text{H}\!-\!\text{C} \\
| \\
\text{CH}_2\text{OH}
\end{array}
+ 2\ \text{CH}_3\text{COCH}_3 \xrightarrow[\ \ ]{[\text{H}^+]} (\text{CH}_3)_2\text{C}
\begin{array}{c}
\text{H}\!-\!\text{C}\!-\!\text{O} \\
\qquad\qquad\diagdown\text{C}(\text{CH}_3)_2 \ \text{O} \\
\text{H}\!-\!\text{C}\!-\!\text{O} \\
| \\
\text{O}\!-\!\text{C}\!-\!\text{H} \\
| \\
\text{O}\!-\!\text{C}\!-\!\text{H} \\
| \\
\text{H}\!-\!\text{C} \\
| \\
\text{CH}_2\text{OH}
\end{array}
+ 2\ \text{H}_2\text{O}
$$

α-D-Galactose   1,2:3,4-Di-*O*-isopropylidene-D-galactose α-D-Glucose has only two adjacent *cis* hydroxyl groups and would be expected to form only a monoisopropylidene derivative. Instead it also reacts with two moles of acetone. To accomplish this the ring structure present in the free glucose shifts from a six-membered ring to a five-membered ring. Hence the ring structure of isopropylidene derivatives is not indicative of the original ring structure of the free sugars.

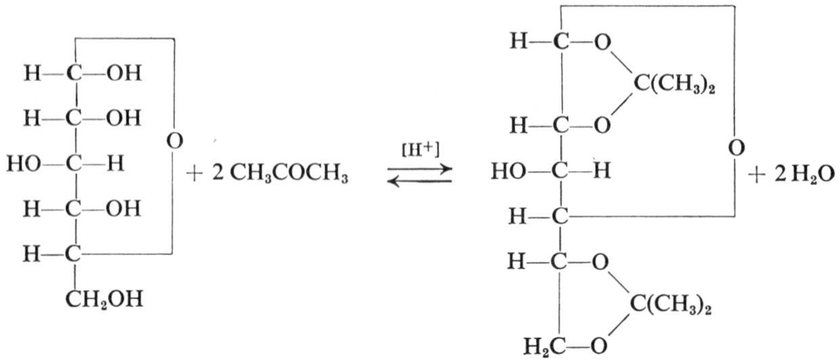

α-D-Glucose   1,2:5,6-Di-*O*-isopropylidene-D-glucose

The isopropylidene derivatives are useful for the preparation of partially substituted sugars, since they are acetals and stable to alkali, but the isopropylidene groups can be removed readily by hydrolysis with dilute acids. Thus the above diisopropylideneglucose has a free hydroxyl on C-3 which can be acetylated or methylated. Subsequent hydrolysis of the isopropylidene groups with dilute acid gives 3-*O*-acetyl- or 3-*O*-methyl-D-glucose.

Conversion to the Next Higher Sugar. Emil Fischer succeeded in converting glyconolactones into sugars, thus extending Kiliani's hydrogen cyanide synthesis of glyconic acids (p. 362) to the conversion of a sugar into the two sugars having one more carbon atom. The conversion of an aldopentose to the aldohexoses involves the following transformations.

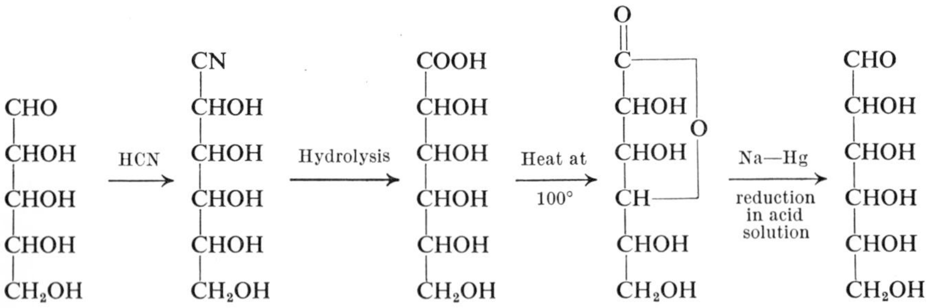

Aldopentose   Cyanohydrin   Glyconic acid   Glyconolactone   Aldohexose

The lactones in the above reactions merely are cyclic esters formed by the reaction of the carboxyl group with the hydroxyl group on the γ carbon atom (p. 783). The reaction takes place readily because a stable five-membered ring can be formed. The reduction of the lactone to the sugar under mild conditions is analogous to the reduction of a simple ester, except that the reduction of the carboxyl group is stopped at the aldehyde stage instead of continuing to a primary alcohol. Since a new asymmetric carbon atom is produced in the formation of the cyanohydrin, a single aldopentose gives rise to two aldohexoses.

This procedure is time-consuming, and the yield of the desired sugar is poor. The following simple procedure based on the Nef reaction of aliphatic nitro compounds (p. 262) can be carried out more readily and sometimes gives better yields.

$$
\begin{array}{c}
\text{CHO} \\
| \\
\text{(CHOH)}_n + \text{CH}_3\text{NO}_2 \\
| \\
\text{CH}_2\text{OH}
\end{array}
\xrightarrow{\text{NaOCH}_3}
\begin{array}{c}
\text{CH}_2\text{NO}_2 \\
| \\
\text{CHOH} \\
| \\
\text{(CHOH)}_n \\
| \\
\text{CH}_2\text{OH}
\end{array}
\xrightarrow{\text{NaOH, H}_2\text{SO}_4}
\begin{array}{c}
\text{CHO} \\
| \\
\text{CHOH} \\
| \\
\text{(CHOH)}_n \\
| \\
\text{CH}_2\text{OH}
\end{array}
$$

2-Deoxyaldoses can be synthesized by a modification of this procedure. The nitro alcohol is acetylated and one mole of acetic acid removed with sodium bicarbonate to give the unsaturated compound. Catalytic reduction of the double bond, followed by the Nef reaction and deacetylation, gives the deoxyaldose.

$$
\begin{array}{c}
\text{CH}_2\text{NO}_2 \\
| \\
\text{CHOH} \\
| \\
\text{(CHOH)}_n \\
| \\
\text{CH}_2\text{OH}
\end{array}
\xrightarrow{\text{Ac}_2\text{O}}
\begin{array}{c}
\text{CH}_2\text{NO}_2 \\
| \\
\text{CHOAc} \\
| \\
\text{(CHOAc)}_n \\
| \\
\text{CH}_2\text{OAc}
\end{array}
\xrightarrow[\text{Neutral.}]{\text{NaHCO}_3}
\begin{array}{c}
\text{CHNO}_2 \\
\| \\
\text{CH} \\
| \\
\text{(CHOAc)}_n \\
| \\
\text{CH}_2\text{OAc}
\end{array}
\xrightarrow{\text{H}_2\text{—Pd}}
$$

$$
\begin{array}{c}
\text{CH}_2\text{NO}_2 \\
| \\
\text{CH}_2 \\
| \\
\text{(CHOAc)}_n \\
| \\
\text{CH}_2\text{OAc}
\end{array}
\xrightarrow{\text{NaOH, H}_2\text{SO}_4}
\begin{array}{c}
\text{CHO} \\
| \\
\text{CH}_2 \\
| \\
\text{(CHOH)}_n \\
| \\
\text{CH}_2\text{OH}
\end{array}
$$

2-Ketoses (p. 384) can be synthesized from aldoses if 2-nitroethanol is used instead of nitromethane.

$$
\begin{array}{c}
\text{CHO} \\
| \\
\text{(CHOH)}_n + \\
| \\
\text{CH}_2\text{OH}
\end{array}
\begin{array}{c}
\text{CH}_2\text{OH} \\
| \\
\text{CH}_2\text{NO}_2
\end{array}
\longrightarrow
\begin{array}{c}
\text{CH}_2\text{OH} \\
| \\
\text{CHNO}_2 \\
| \\
\text{(CHOH)}_{n+1} \\
| \\
\text{CH}_2\text{OH}
\end{array}
\longrightarrow
\begin{array}{c}
\text{CH}_2\text{OH} \\
| \\
\text{C=O} \\
| \\
\text{(CHOH)}_{n+1} \\
| \\
\text{CH}_2\text{OH}
\end{array}
$$

Degradation to the Next Lower Sugar. Of the various degradative methods available, the best for preparative purposes involves oxidation to the glyconic acid followed by oxidation with Fenton reagent (hydrogen peroxide and ferrous sulfate, p. 886).

$$
\begin{array}{c}
\text{CHO} \\
| \\
\text{CHOH} \\
|
\end{array}
\xrightarrow{\text{NaOBr}}
\begin{array}{c}
\text{COOH} \\
| \\
\text{CHOH} \\
|
\end{array}
\xrightarrow[\text{FeSO}_4]{\text{H}_2\text{O}_2 +}
\begin{array}{c}
\text{CHO} + \text{CO}_2 + \text{H}_2\text{O} \\
|
\end{array}
$$

Epimerization. Since asymmetric atoms having a hydrogen atom α to a carbonyl group are racemized readily in the presence of alkaline catalysts (p. 345), sugars readily undergo epimerization. The action of alkalies on the free sugars, however, brings about more complex reactions (p. 368). Hence the sugar first is converted to the glyconic acid, which is epimerized by heating with the tertiary amine, pyridine (p. 620), and then reconverted to the sugar by reduction of the lactone (p. 380).

$$
\begin{array}{c}
\text{CHO} \\
| \\
\text{H—C—OH} \\
|
\end{array}
\xrightarrow{\text{NaOBr}}
\begin{array}{c}
\text{COOH} \\
| \\
\text{H—C—OH} \\
|
\end{array}
\underset{\text{Pyridine}}{\overset{}{\rightleftarrows}}
$$

$$
\begin{array}{c}
\text{COOH} \\
| \\
\text{HO—C—H} \\
|
\end{array}
\xrightarrow[100°]{\text{Heat}}
\text{Lactone}
\xrightarrow[\text{reduction}]{\text{Na—Hg}}
\begin{array}{c}
\text{CHO} \\
| \\
\text{HO—C—H} \\
|
\end{array}
$$

Aldehydo Derivatives

The sugars and their derivatives are for the most part cyclic compounds, but it is possible to prepare derivatives containing the open chain structure having a free aldehyde group. Thus when a sugar, ethyl mercaptan, and concentrated hydrochloric acid are shaken together, the diethyl mercaptal crystallizes from the mixture. The mercaptals may be methylated or acetylated. Removal of the mercaptal groups from the acetate by hydrolysis in dilute acetone solution in the presence of mercuric chloride and cadmium carbonate gives the aldehydo acetate.

$$
\begin{array}{cccc}
\begin{array}{l}\text{CHOH} \\ \text{CHOH} \\ \text{CHOH} \\ \text{CHOH} \\ \text{CH} \\ \text{CH}_2\text{OH}\end{array}\Big]\text{O}
& \xrightarrow[\text{HCl}]{\text{C}_2\text{H}_5\text{SH}}
& \begin{array}{c}\text{C}_2\text{H}_5\text{S}\diagdown\diagup\text{SC}_2\text{H}_5 \\ \text{C—H} \\ \text{CHOH} \\ \text{CHOH} \\ \text{CHOH} \\ \text{CHOH} \\ \text{CH}_2\text{OH}\end{array}
& \xrightarrow[\text{NaOAc}]{\text{Ac}_2\text{O}}
\end{array}
$$

$$
\begin{array}{cc}
\begin{array}{c}\text{C}_2\text{H}_5\text{S}\diagdown\diagup\text{SC}_2\text{H}_5 \\ \text{C—H} \\ \text{CHOAc} \\ \text{CHOAc} \\ \text{CHOAc} \\ \text{CHOAc} \\ \text{CH}_2\text{OAc}\end{array}
& \xrightarrow[\text{CdCO}_3]{\text{H}_2\text{O}+\text{HgCl}_2}
& \begin{array}{l}\text{CHO} \\ \text{CHOAc} \\ \text{CHOAc} \\ \text{CHOAc} \\ \text{CHOAc} \\ \text{CH}_2\text{OAc}\end{array}
\end{array}
$$

These aldehydo acetates give a color with Schiff reagent, form semicarbazones without loss of an acetyl group, and can be converted to dimethyl acetals. In water or alcohol they show mutarotation and give crystalline hydrates and alcoholates. This behavior probably is due to the addition of water or alcohol to the carbonyl group.

$$
\begin{array}{l}\text{CHO} \\ (\text{CHOAc})_4 \\ \text{CH}_2\text{OAc}\end{array}
\underset{}{\overset{\text{H}_2\text{O}}{\rightleftarrows}}
\begin{array}{l}\quad\ \ \text{H} \\ \text{HO—C—OH} \\ (\text{CHOAc})_4 \\ \text{CH}_2\text{OAc}\end{array}
$$

In an aqueous solution of a free sugar such as glucose, the portion present as the aldehyde form undoubtedly is hydrated. Alcohol can give rise to an equilibrium mixture of hemiacetals.

$$
\begin{array}{l}\quad\ \ \text{H} \\ \text{HO—C—OR} \\ (\text{CHOAc})_4 \\ \text{CH}_2\text{OAc}\end{array}
\rightleftarrows
\begin{array}{l}\text{CHO} \\ (\text{CHOAc})_4 \\ \text{CH}_2\text{OAc}\end{array}
\overset{\text{ROH}}{\rightleftarrows}
\begin{array}{l}\quad\ \ \text{H} \\ \text{RO—C—OH} \\ (\text{CHOAc})_4 \\ \text{CH}_2\text{OAc}\end{array}
$$

Although the structures for the oximes, hydrazones, and osazones of the sugars usually are written as open chain formulas, there is evidence that these derivatives also may exist as ring structures. Thus glucose phenylhydrazone yields a penta-acetate (*a*) from which acetylphenylhydrazine can be obtained on hydrolysis.

---

* The abbreviation *Ac* commonly is used to designate the acetyl group, CH_3CO. Thus HOAc is acetic acid, Ac_2O is acetic anhydride, and ROAc is an acetate.

The open chain structure would be expected to yield either a hexaacetate (*b*) or or a pentaacetate (*c*) which would yield phenylhydrazine on hydrolysis.

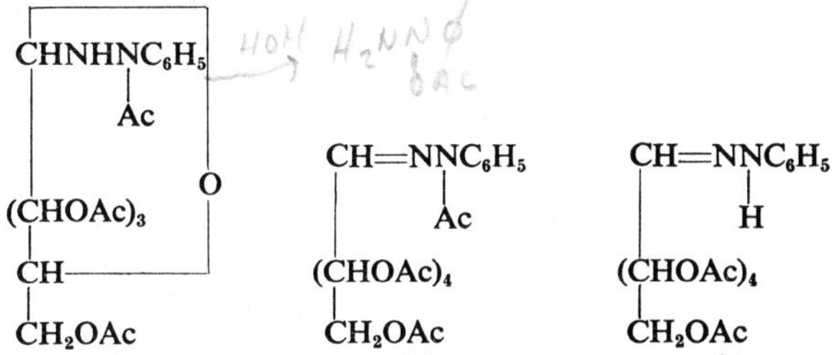

(a)   (b)   (c)

Galactose phenylhydrazone, however, appears to have the open chain structure, since acetylation yields the same product that is obtained by treating aldehydo-galactose pentaacetate with phenylhydrazine.

Representation of Ring Structures

The formulas used thus far to represent the structure of the sugars do not indicate adequately the space relationships within the molecules, particularly those of the groups on the last two carbon atoms. With a molecular model the open chain formula for glucose (I) can be represented in a coiled manner (II) to portray better the 109.5 degree angle between carbon atoms.

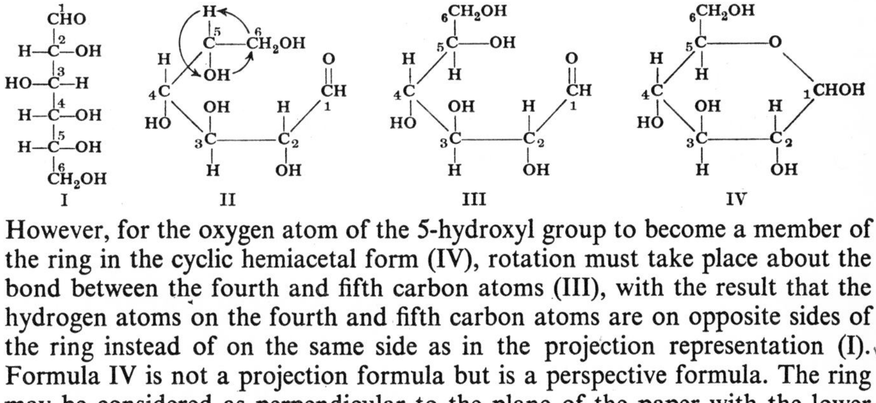

I   II   III   IV

However, for the oxygen atom of the 5-hydroxyl group to become a member of the ring in the cyclic hemiacetal form (IV), rotation must take place about the bond between the fourth and fifth carbon atoms (III), with the result that the hydrogen atoms on the fourth and fifth carbon atoms are on opposite sides of the ring instead of on the same side as in the projection representation (I). Formula IV is not a projection formula but is a perspective formula. The ring may be considered as perpendicular to the plane of the paper with the lower portion in front and the groups extending above and below the plane of the ring.

Formula IV does not indicate the configuration of the reducing carbon atom. In the following two formulas for α- and β-glucose these configurations are given. Except for the anomeric carbon atoms the ring carbon atoms are omitted.

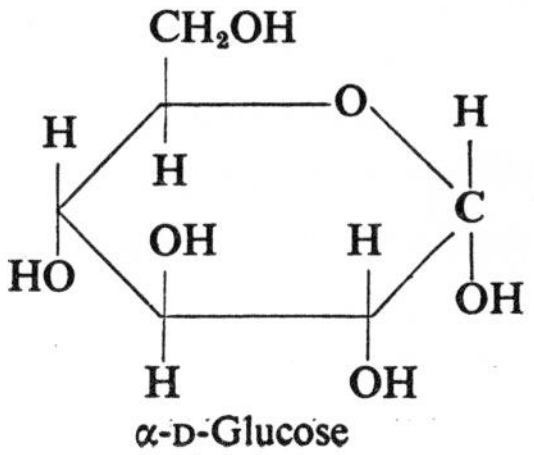

α-D-Glucose 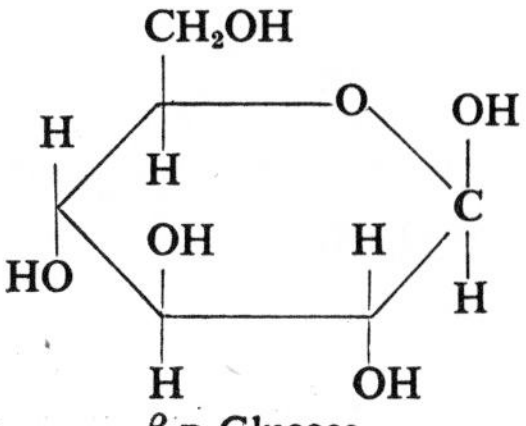   β-D-Glucose

The perspective formulas, frequently called Haworth formulas, are useful also in representing the structures of oligo- and polysaccharides (pp. 389, 399). In recent years certain properties of the sugars have been explained in terms of the conformation of the pyranose ring (p. 843).

Ketoses

The ketoses are isomeric with the aldoses having the same number of carbon atoms and differ in structure only in that the carbonyl group contains a non-terminal carbon atom. The common ketoses all have the carbonyl oxygen on the second carbon atom and may be represented by the general formula, $HOCH_2(CHOH)_nCOCH_2OH$.

Just as glyceraldehyde may be considered as the first member of the aldoses (Fig. 72, p. 366), dihydroxyacetone may be considered as the first member of the ketoses, although D-glycerotetrulose is the first member of the D family of ketoses (Fig. 73). In systematic nomenclature, the ending for ketoses is *ulose*. A prefix is used to indicate the number of carbon atoms and another, in italics, to indicate the relation of the configuration of the ketose to that of the aldose having one less carbon atom. More frequently common names for the known ketoses have been used.

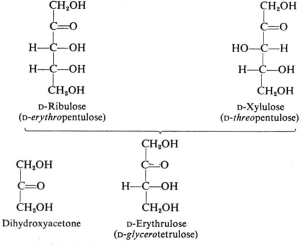

Fig. 73. Configurations of the D family of ketoses.

D(−)-**Fructose** is the most abundant ketose. It occurs free, along with glucose and sucrose, in fruit juices and honey, and combined with other sugars in oligosaccharides. It is the chief product of the hydrolysis of the polysaccharide inulin (p. 410). Naturally occurring fructose has a high negative rotation which gave rise to the common name *levulose*. It is the sweetest of the sugars.

Since individuals vary greatly in their sensory perceptions, it is possible to state only average opinions regarding taste. The results of early workers based on threshold methods, that is, the highest dilution that can be tasted, are valueless. When comparing concentrations of equal sweetness, the relative sweetness varies with the concentration. Moreover since α-glucose is sweeter than β-glucose, solutions that have reached equilibrium must be used. When compared with a 10 per cent glucose solution, the relative sweetness of some of the common sugars is lactose 0.55, galactose 0.95, glucose 1.00, sucrose 1.45, and fructose 1.65. Many synthetic compounds are known whose sweetness is from several hundred to several thousand times greater than that of the sugars (pp. 482, 556).

Fructose gives the usual addition reactions of carbonyl compounds, but it is not oxidized by hypobromite solutions to give a monocarboxylic acid. Hence it is a ketose and not an aldose. It is oxidized by Fehling solution and has a reducing power comparable to that of glucose. As a ketone it would not be expected to reduce Fehling solution. However in the presence of alkali it is in equilibrium with glucose and mannose (p. 368), which are oxidized readily. Moreover CHOH groups adjacent to a carbonyl group also are oxidized by Fehling solution (p. 541).

When fructose reacts with phenylhydrazine, a phenylosazone is formed which is identical with that obtained from (+)glucose. Hence the carbonyl group must contain C-2, the configuration of the rest of the molecule must be identical with that of (+)glucose, and (−)fructose must belong to the D family.

It was the discovery that glucose, mannose (p. 371), and fructose give the same osazone, and the realization of its significance, that led Fischer to undertake the unraveling of the configuration of the sugars. α-Methylphenylhydrazine, $C_6H_5N(CH_3)NH_2$, can be used to distinguish fructose from glucose or mannose, since conditions can be chosen such that fructose gives an osazone, whereas glucose and mannose do not.

The behavior of fructose in aqueous solution is more complex than that of glucose. Only one crystalline form of fructose is known, which is believed to be the β isomer having a six-membered ring. When it is dissolved in water, the rate of mutarotation does not follow a first order reaction law. It is believed that not only does conversion to the α form take place, but the α and β forms of structures having a five-membered ring are produced also. The latter types of sugars originally were termed "gamma" sugars.

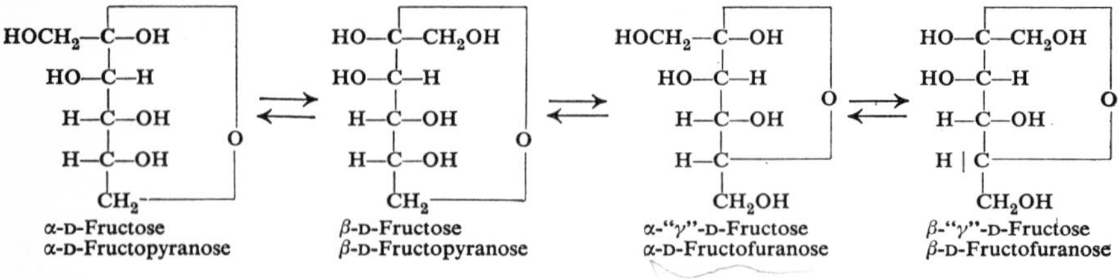

HOCH₂—C—OH	HO—C—CH₂OH	HOCH₂—C—OH	HO—C—CH₂OH
HO—C—H	HO—C—H	HO—C—H	HO—C—H
H—C—OH	H—C—OH	H—C—OH	H—C—OH
H—C—OH	H—C—OH	H—C—	H | C—
CH₂—	CH₂—	CH₂OH	CH₂OH
α-D-Fructose	β-D-Fructose	α-"γ"-D-Fructose	β-"γ"-D-Fructose
α-D-Fructopyranose	β-D-Fructopyranose	α-D-Fructofuranose	β-D-Fructofuranose

A ring containing five carbon atoms and one oxygen atom is known as a pyran ring (p. 631), and a ring containing four carbon atoms and an oxygen atom is known as a furan ring (p. 619). It now is customary to differentiate the corresponding ring structures of the sugars by the terms *pyranose* and *furanose*. Methyl glycosides of both fructopyranose and fructofuranose are known, the latter being the more rapidly hydrolyzed.

A total synthesis of D-fructose, along with D-glucose and D-mannose, has been effected. The work of Emil Fischer and others has shown that formose, the mixture of sugar-like products obtained by the action of dilute alkali on formaldehyde (p. 222), contains DL-fructose (α-*acrose*) and DL-sorbose (β-*acrose*). By a series of transformations and resolutions, Fischer was able to prepare both L-fructose and naturally occurring D-fructose from α-acrose. Later it was found that D-glyceraldehyde undergoes aldol addition with dihydroxyacetone to give D-fructose and D-sorbose. Each is obtained in 45 per cent yield. No D-psicose or D-tagatose (p. 384) was detected.

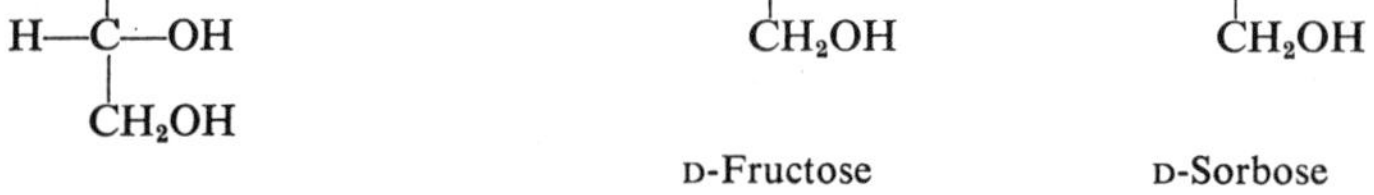

D-Fructose   D-Sorbose

The ketoses in formose probably result from the initial production of a formyl anion which attacks the carbon atom of a second molecule of formaldehyde to give hydroxyacetaldehyde (glycolic aldehyde, p. 783).

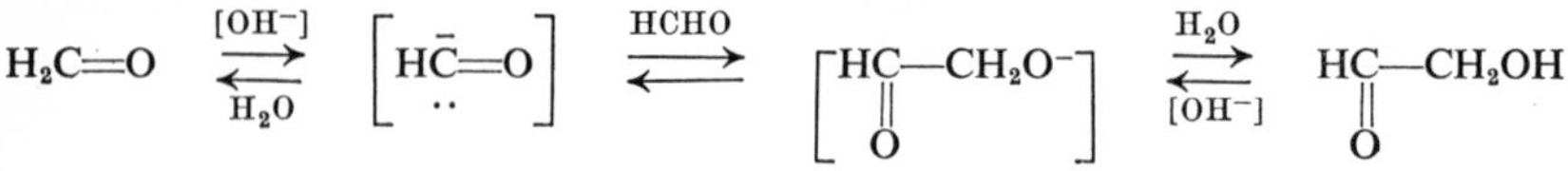

Attack of glycolic aldehyde by a formyl anion can give rise to glyceraldehyde.

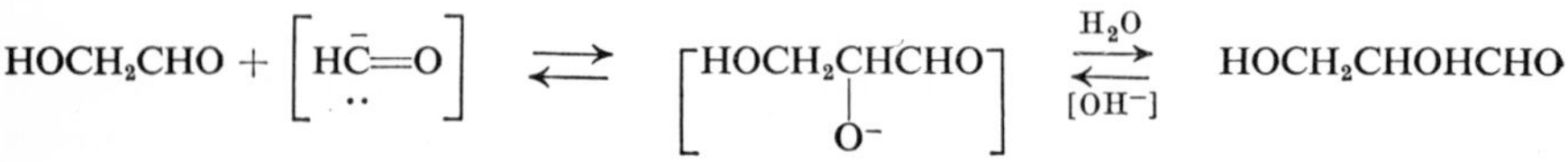

Alternatively the glyceraldehyde may arise by the aldol addition of glycolic aldehyde to formaldehyde.

$$H_2C=O + HOCH_2CHO \rightleftharpoons HOCH_2CHOHCHO$$

The glyceraldehyde, in the presence of alkali, is in equilibrium with dihydroxyacetone (p. 369) because each gives rise to the same enediol form (p. 368).

$$HOCH_2CHOHCHO \rightleftharpoons HOCH_2C(OH)=CHOH \rightleftharpoons HOCH_2COCH_2OH$$

Aldol addition of dihydroxyacetone to glyceraldehyde gives the polyhydroxy ketone.

$$HOCH_2CHOHCHO + HOCH_2COCH_2OH \longrightarrow HOCH_2(CHOH)_3COCH_2OH$$

L(—)-Sorbose is the only other ketohexose of importance. It does not occur naturally but is produced by the action of sorbose bacteria (*Acetobacter xylinum* or better *Acetobacter suboxydans*) on sorbitol (p. 412).

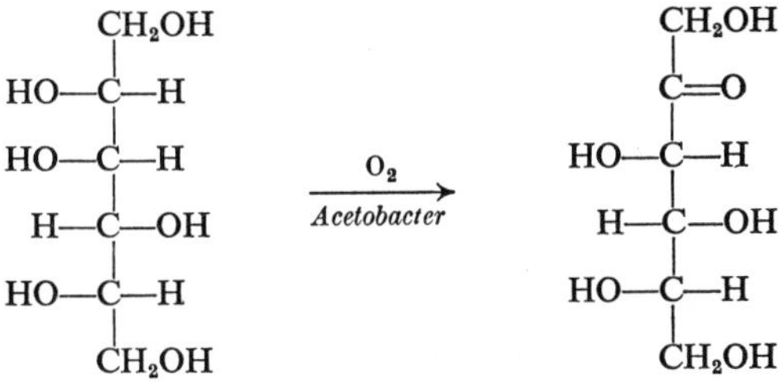

Sorbitol   L(—)-Sorbose

L-Sorbose is important as an intermediate for the commercial synthesis of **vitamin C**, otherwise known as *ascorbic acid*, which is a necessary dietary factor for the prevention of scurvy. Sorbose can be oxidized with nitric acid to 2-deoxy-2-oxo-L-gulonic acid, which on heating in water dehydrates to the 1,4-lactone. Because of the acidic properties of ascorbic acid and its ready oxidation, it is believed to exist in the enediol form.

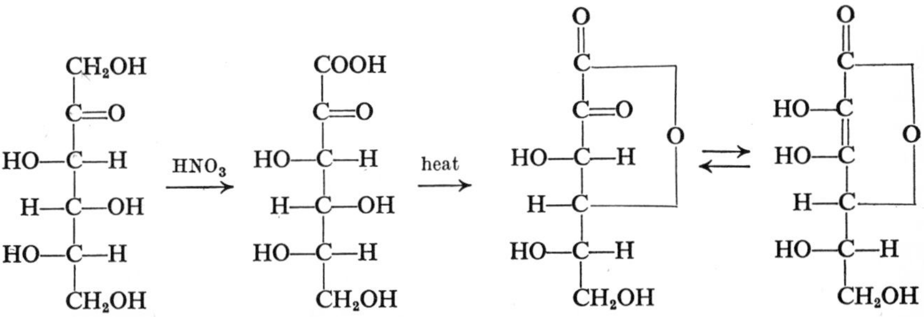

L-Sorbose   2-Deoxy-2-oxo-L-gulonic   Vitamin C
                 acid   (ascorbic acid)

Better yields are obtained in the oxidation step if the sorbose is converted first to the diisopropylidene derivative (p. 379).

D-Ribulose (D-*erythro*pentulose) and **D-sedoheptulose** (D-*altro*heptulose) play a part in the cycle whereby plants convert carbon dioxide and water to carbohydrates (photosynthetic cycle). D-Sedoheptulose was isolated originally from

Sedum spectabile, a common herbaceous garden plant. D-*Manno*heptulose is present in the fruit of the avocado tree (*Persea gratissima*). It is not metabolized but is secreted in the urine and may give rise to a positive test for glycosuria, although no glucose is present.

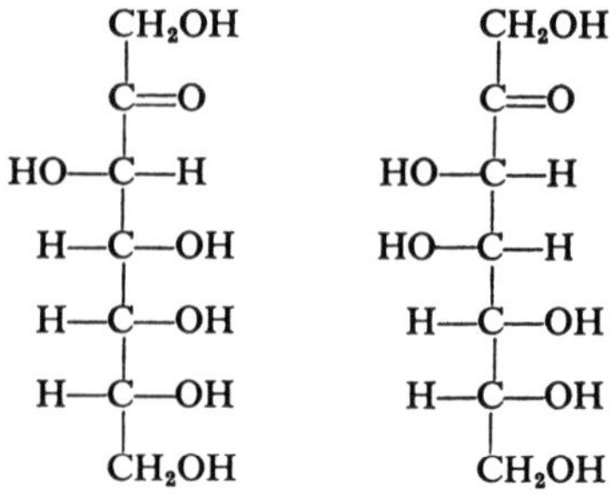

D-Sedoheptulose
(D-*altro*heptulose)

D-*Manno*heptulose

Anhydro Sugars

When aldoses or polysaccharides are heated under reduced pressure, intramolecular dehydration products are obtained. Formerly these compounds were called *sugar anhydrides* or *glycosans*, but now are known as *anhydro sugars*. Starch (p. 396) for example yields **1,6-anhydro-β-D-glucopyranose** (*levoglucosan*, *β-glucosan*). It has been obtained also by the reaction of barium hydroxide with tetra-*O*-acetyl-D-glucosyltrimethylammonium bromide which was prepared by the reaction of acetobromo-α-D-glucose with trimethylamine.

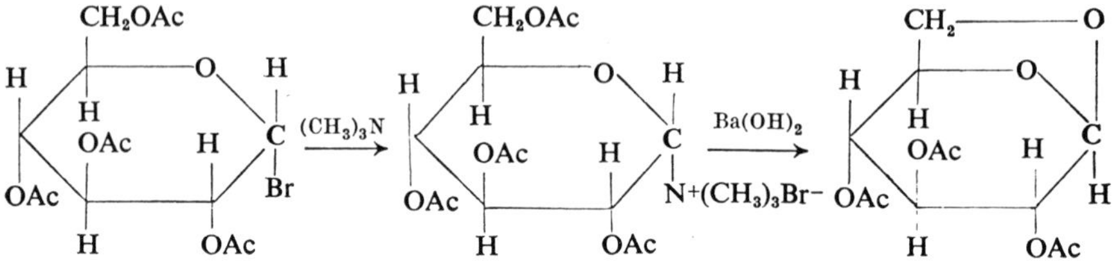

In the 1,6-anhydro sugars both of the rings are glycosidic.

When the 6-tosyl (p. 471) derivatives of methyl glycosides react with alkali, the **methyl 3,6-anhydroglycosides** are formed.

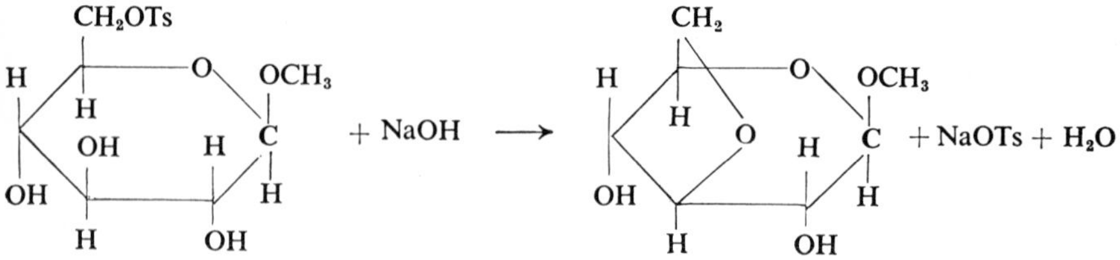

1,2-Anhydro sugars having a three-membered ethylene oxide ring, $=C\overset{\displaystyle O}{\frown}C=$, also are known (p. 395).

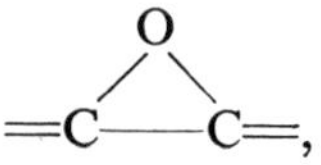

OLIGOSACCHARIDES

Disaccharides

Reducing Disaccharides. Maltose, $C_{12}H_{22}O_{11}$, is formed by the enzyme-catalyzed hydrolysis of starch.

$$(C_6H_{10}O_5)_x + \frac{x}{2}\,H_2O \xrightarrow{\text{Diastase}} \frac{x}{2}\,C_{12}H_{22}O_{11}$$

     Starch   Maltose

Acid- or enzyme-catalyzed hydrolysis of maltose yields two molecules of glucose.

$$C_{12}H_{22}O_{11} + H_2O \xrightarrow[\text{Maltase}]{\text{[H}^+\text{] or}} 2\,C_6H_{12}O_6$$

   Maltose   (α-glucosidase)   Glucose

Maltose reduces Fehling solution, forms an osazone and undergoes mutarotation. Hence it contains a potential aldehyde group and a hemiacetal ring structure. The formation of an octaacetate and octamethyl derivative indicates the presence of eight hydroxyl groups.

Hydrolysis to two molecules of glucose points to a linkage through oxygen rather than directly between two carbon atoms, and the ease of hydrolysis by enzymes and acids indicates an acetal linkage rather than an ether linkage. Degradation of methylated derivatives has shown that the two glucose units are linked through the 1 position of the nonreducing half of the molecule and the 4 position of the reducing half. Maltose is hydrolyzed by *maltase*, the α-glucosidase which hydrolyzes methyl α-glucoside, and not by *emulsin*, the β-glucosidase that hydrolyzes methyl β-glucoside. Hence the configuration of C-1 of the nonreducing portion is believed to be α. These conclusions are embodied in the following perspective formulas.

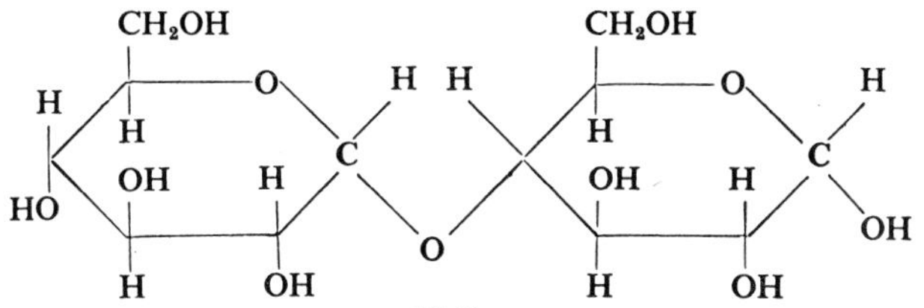

α-Maltose
4-*O*-(α-D-Glucopyranosyl)-α-D-glucopyranose

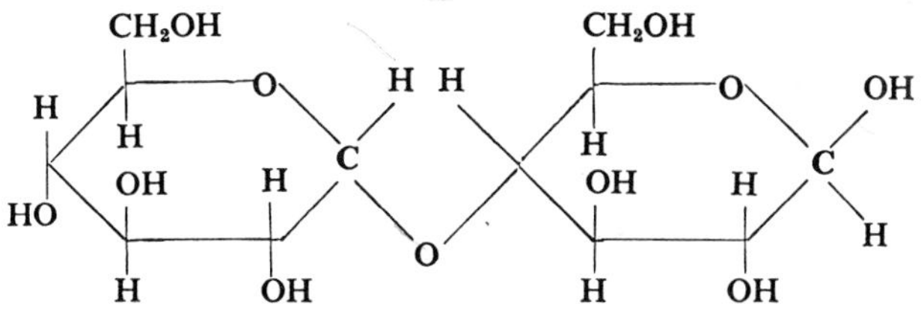

β-Maltose
4-*O*-(α-D-Glucopyranosyl)-β-D-glucopyranose

α- and β-Maltose differ only in the configuration of the anomeric carbon atom of the reducing half of the molecule. The second name given under the formulas is more descriptive in that it indicates the point at which the non-reducing half of the molecule is attached to the reducing half, and the structure and configuration of both halves. **Isomaltose,** obtained by the partial hydrolysis of dextran (p. 407), is 6-O-(α-D-glucopyranosyl)-D-glucopyranose.

A proof of the structure of maltose can be outlined briefly. If maltose is oxidized, the reducing carbon atom is converted to a carboxyl group giving maltonic acid. Methylation with methyl sulfate and sodium hydroxide converts the carboxyl group to a methyl ester, thus preventing this half of the molecule from having a ring structure. The hydroxyl groups are converted to methyl ethers. Hydrolysis of the resulting product gives 2,3,4,6-tetra-O-methylglucose, and 2,3,5,6-tetra-O-methylgluconic acid. Therefore the nonreducing half of the molecule must have had a six-membered ring which was joined to the reducing half at the 4 position.

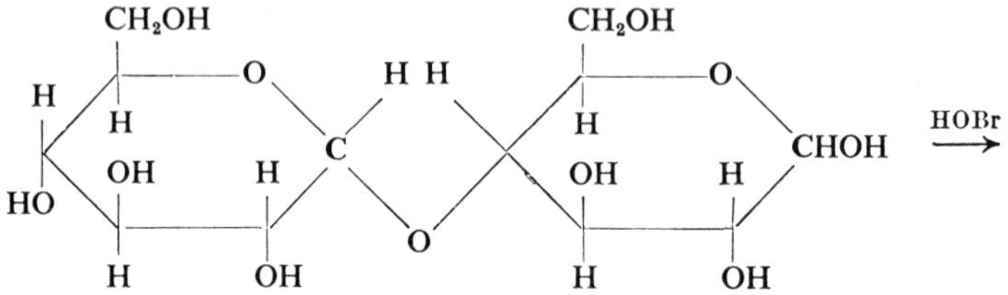

α- or β-Maltose

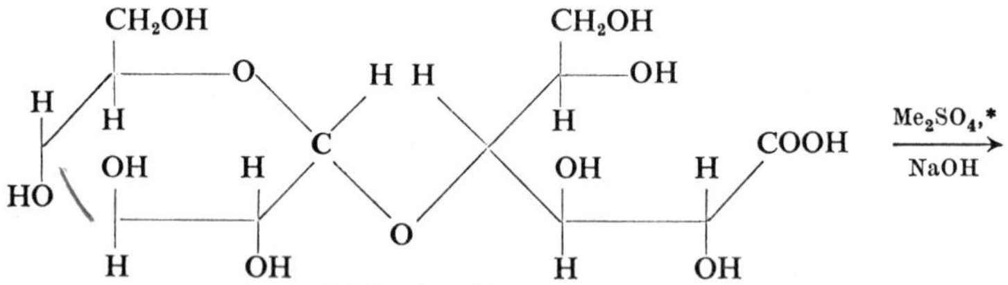

Maltonic acid

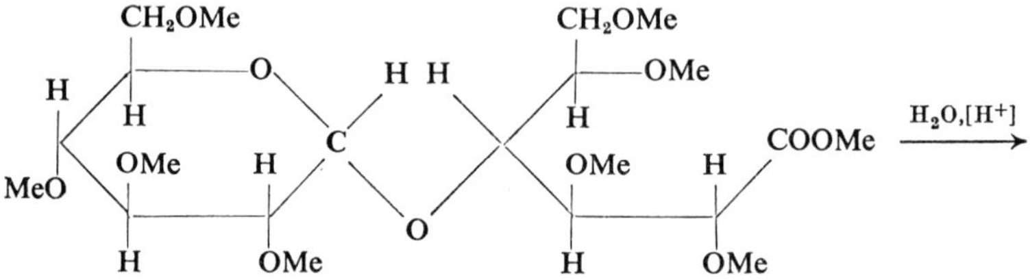

Methyl octa-O-methylmaltonate

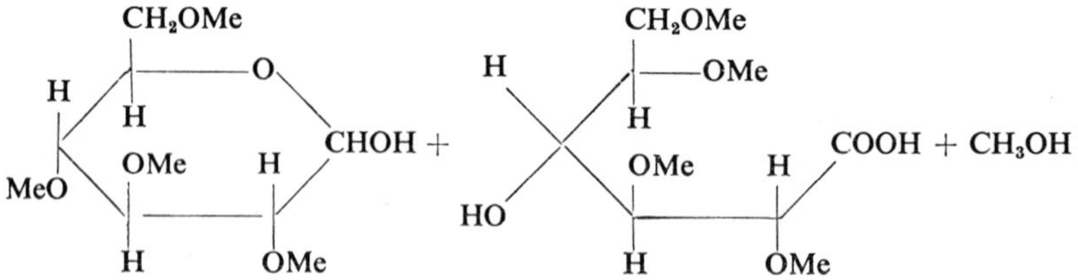

2,3,4,6-Tetra-O-methylglucose   2,3,5,6-Tetra-O-methylgluconic acid

---

* The abbreviation *Me* commonly is used to designate a methyl group, CH_3. Thus Me_2SO_4 is methyl sulfate, MeOH is methyl alcohol, and MeOR is a methyl ether.

It is assumed that the reducing half of free maltose likewise contains a six-membered ring, since methylation of maltose gives a methyl heptamethyl-*O*-maltoside which yields on hydrolysis 2,3,4,6-tetra-*O*-methylglucose and 2,3,6-tri-*O*-methylglucose.

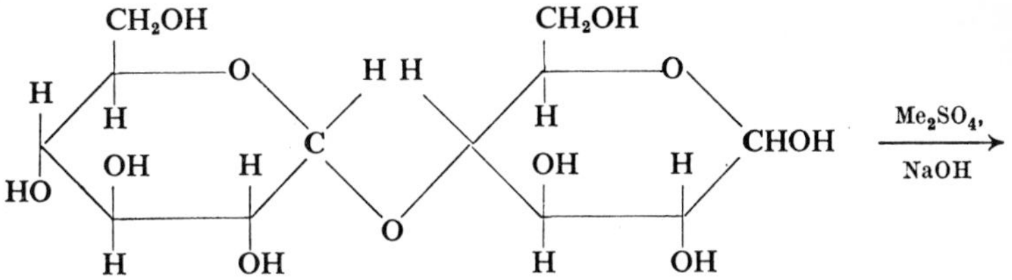

Maltose

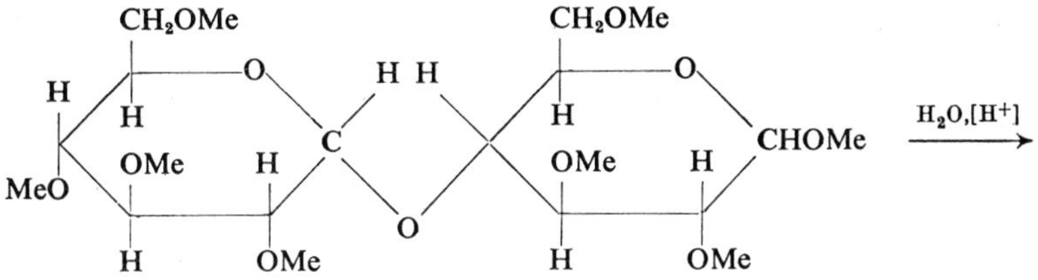

Methyl hepta-*O*-methylmaltoside

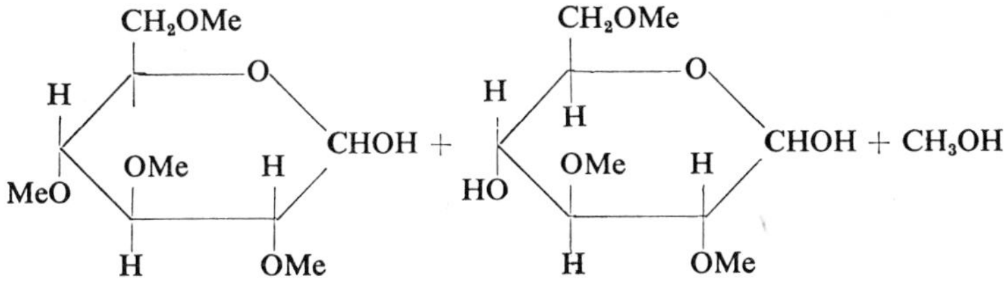

2,3,4,6-Tetra-*O*-methylglucose   2,3,6-Tri-*O*-methylglucose

Cellobiose is a disaccharide formed by the hydrolysis of its octaacetate. The latter compound is obtained in 40 per cent yield when cellulose (cotton or paper) is dissolved in a mixture of acetic anhydride and sulfuric acid, and allowed to stand for one week at 35°. Cellobiose like maltose yields two molecules of glucose on hydrolysis and undergoes all of the reactions of maltose. The results of methylation and degradation experiments indicate that it has the same structure as maltose. The only difference in behavior of the two sugars is that cellobiose is hydrolyzed in the presence of emulsin (β-glucosidase) and not in the presence of maltase (α-glucosidase). Hence cellobiose differs from maltose only in that the linkage between the two glucose units has the β-configuration instead of the α-configuration.

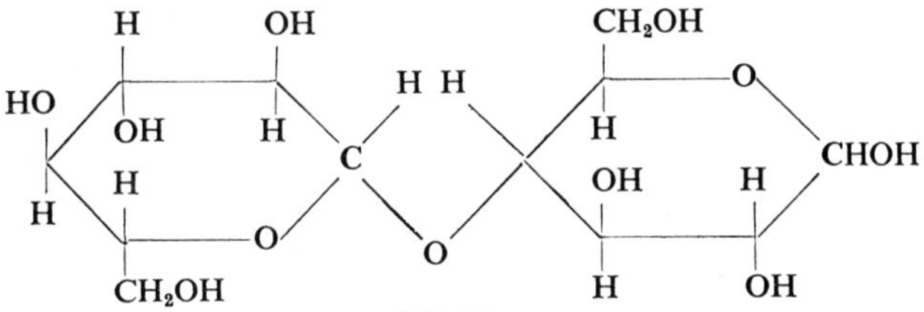

Cellobiose
4-*O*-(β-D-Glucopyranosyl)-D-glucopyranose

Lactose (*milk sugar*) is present in about 5 per cent concentration in the milk of all mammals. It is manufactured commercially from whey, the aqueous solution left after the coagulation of the proteins of milk in the manufacture of cheese. Lactose is a reducing disaccharide, and on acid or enzyme hydrolysis it yields one molecule of galactose and one molecule of glucose. If it first is oxidized to lactonic acid and then hydrolyzed, the products are galactose and gluconic acid. Hence the glucose unit contains the reducing portion of the molecule. Since lactose is hydrolyzed by β-galactosidase, the linkage between the galactose and glucose molecule is believed to be β. Methylation and degradation experiments have established its structure as 4-*O*-(β-D-galactopyranosyl)-D-glucopyranose.

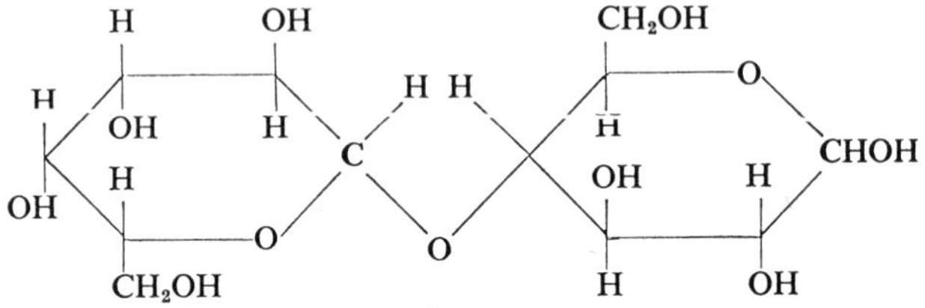

Lactose
4-*O*-(β-D-Galactopyranosyl)-D-glucopyranose

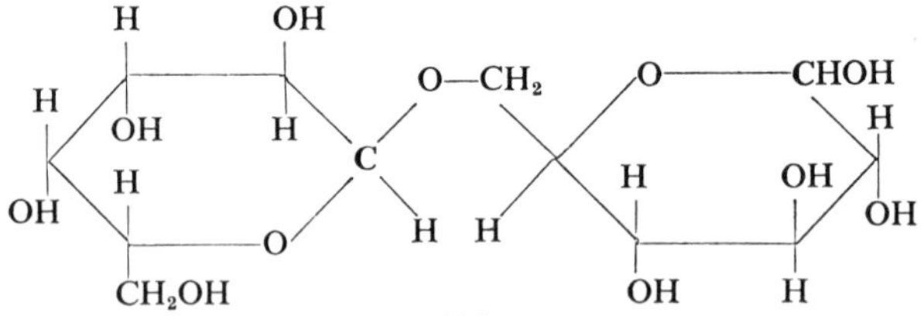

Melibiose
6-*O*-(α-D-Galactopyranosyl)-D-glucopyranose

Melibiose is a reducing disaccharide which can be obtained by the partial hydrolysis of the trisaccharide, *raffinose* (p. 395). It has been found free in plant exudations and has been shown to be 6-*O*-(α-D-galactopyranosyl)-D-glucopyranose. **Gentiobiose,** obtained by partial hydrolysis of the trisaccharide *gentianose* (p. 396) or the glycoside *amygdalin* (p. 537), is 6-*O*-(β-D-glucopyranosyl)-D-glucopyranose.

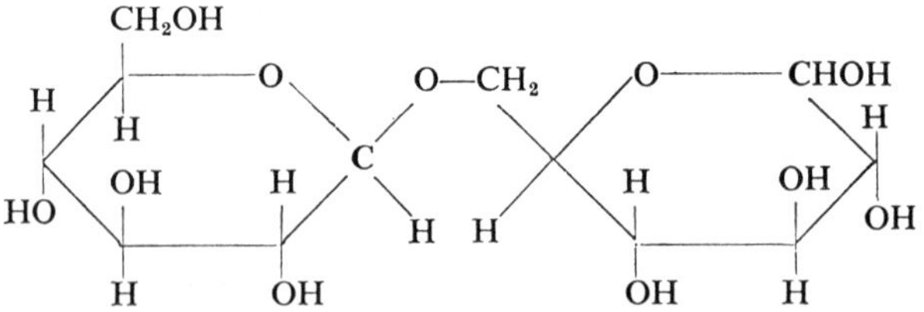

Gentiobiose
6-*O*-(β-D-Glucopyranosyl)-D-glucopyranose

Rutinose, a hydrolytic product of rutin (p. 698), is 6-*O*-(β-L-rhamnopyranosyl)-D-glucopyranose.

Although both monosaccharides and reducing disaccharides produce osazones, the reaction can be used to distinguish between them because the osazones of monosaccharides (I) are less soluble than those of disaccharides (II) and crystallize from the hot solution, whereas the osazones of disaccharides crystallize only on cooling. The difference in solubility is not surprising since the ratio of carbon atoms to oxygen and nitrogen atoms is 18:8 or 2.25:1 for one, and 24:13 or 1.85:1 for the other.

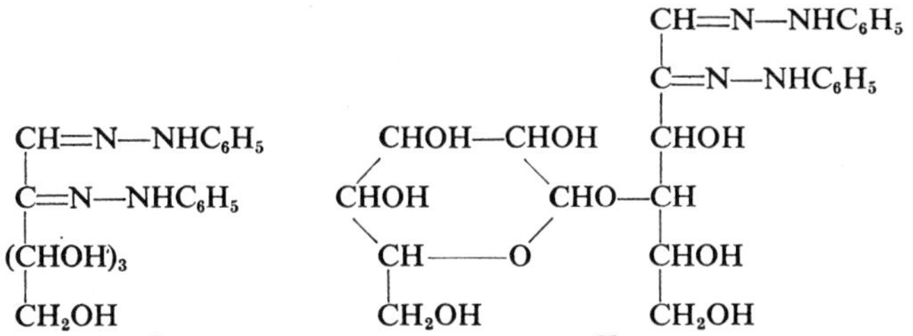

$$
\begin{array}{ccc}
 & & CH{=}N{-}NHC_6H_5 \\
 & & | \\
 & & C{=}N{-}NHC_6H_5 \\
CH{=}N{-}NHC_6H_5 & CHOH{-}CHOH & CHOH \\
| & / \qquad \backslash & | \\
C{=}N{-}NHC_6H_5 & CHOH \qquad CHO{-}CH \\
| & \backslash \qquad / & | \\
(CHOH)_3 & CH{-}{-}{-}O & CHOH \\
| & | & | \\
CH_2OH & CH_2OH & CH_2OH \\
I & II &
\end{array}
$$

Nonreducing Disaccharides. Trehalose is a disaccharide present in young mushrooms and other fungi and in the resurrection plant (*Selaginella lepidophylla*), a plant common in southwestern United States. Like maltose and cellobiose, it yields two moles of glucose on hydrolysis. Trehalose, however, does not reduce Fehling solution, does not form an osazone, and does not mutarotate or form α and β acetates or methyl glycosides. Hence the glycosidic linkage must be between the two anomeric carbon atoms. Since methylation followed by hydrolysis yields two molecules of 2,3,4,6-tetramethylglucose, both rings are six-membered. The high positive rotation, $[\alpha]_D^{20} = +178.3$, indicates that both anomeric carbon atoms have the α configuration.

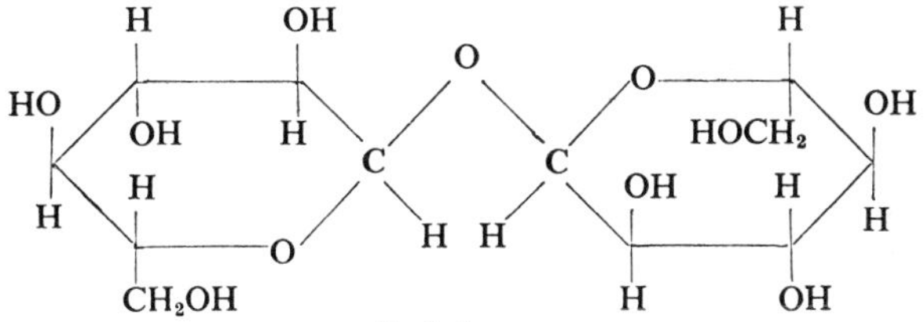

Trehalose
α-D-Glucopyranosyl-α-D-glucopyranoside

Sucrose (*cane sugar, beet sugar*) is the most important disaccharide. It occurs universally in plants and in all portions of the plant. It also is present in honey along with glucose and fructose. The principal sources are sugar cane, sugar beets, and the sugar maple tree. The great ease with which sucrose crystallizes probably accounts for its isolation in a pure state as early as 300 A.D. (p. 2). Sugar cane (*Saccharum officinarum*) belongs to the grass family and probably originated in northeastern India (Skr. *sakara*, gravel or sugar). From there it was introduced into China about 400 A.D. and into Egypt by the Arabians in 640 A.D. It is believed that it was introduced into Santo Domingo by Columbus on his second voyage to America in 1494. Although sucrose was discovered in beet juice in 1747, it was not manufactured from this source until the Napoleonic Wars (1796–1814) made the price of cane sugar prohibitive in Europe.

Sucrose is obtained from cane by grinding the stalk and expressing the juice with rollers. The juice, which contains about 15 per cent sucrose, is made slightly alkaline with lime to prevent hydrolysis. On heating, most of the impurities separate as a heavy scum and a precipitate, which are removed. This process is known as *defecation*. The clear juice is concentrated under reduced pressure and allowed to crystallize. The raw sugar is removed by centrifuging, and the filtrate is reconcentrated and crops of crystals removed until no more can be obtained economically. The final mother liquor is a dark viscous liquid that contains about 50 per cent fermentable sugars and is known as *blackstrap*. It is used for preparing cattle feeds and for the production of alcohol (p. 92).

The raw sugar is shipped to refineries where the brown color is removed by washing and by dissolving in water and passing the solution through decolorizing carbon. Concentration and crystallization yield the pure sugar of commerce. The darker colored crops from the refining operation are sold as *brown sugar*. If the white crystalline sugar is ground with 3 per cent of starch to prevent caking, the product is known as *powdered sugar*.

The white sugar beet, a cultivated variety of *Beta maritima*, has been bred to contain up to 18 per cent sucrose. The beet root, free of leaves, is washed and sliced into V-shaped pieces about 1 cm. thick. These pieces are extracted countercurrently by hot water to yield a dark solution containing about 12 per cent sucrose. By diffusing the sugar from the plant cells the amount of protein and high molecular weight impurities extracted is much less than if the beet were crushed and pressed. The warm extract is agitated with 2 to 3 per cent of lime and the mixture then saturated with carbon dioxide. The precipitate carries down most of the impurities and the yellow filtrate is decolorized with sulfur dioxide. After concentrating, crystallizing, and washing, the product is ready for market.

Production of sucrose from the sugar maple (*Acer saccharinum*) is relatively unimportant. Small amounts are prepared also from other sources such as sorghum and palm sap, but sucrose from these sources does not enter the world market.

Sucrose is manufactured in larger amount than any other pure organic chemical. World production in 1954 (excluding U.S.S.R.) was 40 million tons of which about one third was from beets and two thirds from cane. Production in the United States (mainland) was 2.6 million tons of which only one fourth was from cane. Consumption was 8 million tons or 100 pounds per capita.

Hydrolysis of sucrose in the presence of acids or of the enzyme *sucrase* (*invertase*) yields one molecule of fructose and one molecule of glucose. Sucrose has a positive rotation, $[\alpha]_D^{20} = +66.53$, but during hydrolysis the sign of rotation changes because the high negative rotation of fructose, $[\alpha]_D^{20} = -92.4$ for the equilibrium mixture, more than balances the positive rotation of glucose, $[\alpha]_D^{20} = +52.7$ for the equilibrium mixture. Because of the change in sign of rotation during hydrolysis the process is known as *inversion*, and the mixture of fructose and glucose is known as *invert sugar*. It has about the same sweetening power as sucrose (p. 385) but has much less tendency to crystallize and hence is used in the manufacture of candies and syrups. It is of interest that sucrose octaacetate is extremely bitter.

Sucrose does not reduce Fehling solution, form an osazone, undergo mutarotation or form methyl glycosides. Accordingly the fructose and glucose portions are linked through the two anomeric carbon atoms. Methylation gives octamethylsucrose, which can be hydrolyzed to 2,3,4,6-tetra-*O*-methylglucose and 1,3,4,6-tetra-*O*-methylfructose. The first product proves the presence of a six-membered ring in the glucose portion of the molecule, and the second product proves that a five-membered ring is present in the fructose portion of the molecule. Sucrose is hydrolyzed by yeast α-glucosidase and not by the β-glucosidase of emulsin. It is hydrolyzed also by sucrase, an enzyme that hydrolyzes β- but not α-fructofuranosides. Accordingly the anomeric carbon of the glucose portion is assigned the α configuration, and that of the fructose portion the β configuration.

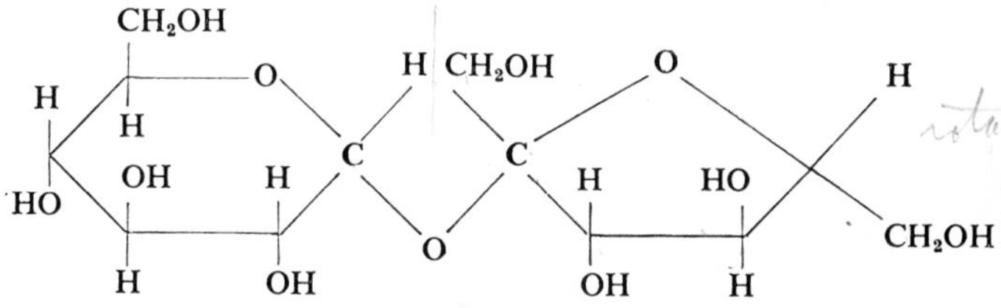

Sucrose
α-D-Glucopyranosyl-β-D-fructofuranoside

The enzymatic synthesis of sucrose from D-glucopyranose-1-phosphate and fructose was accomplished in 1943 using an enzyme from the microorganism *Pseudomonas saccharophila.* Many early attempts to synthesize sucrose by chemical methods failed because of the difficulty of obtaining the correct configuration of the glycosidic linkage. In 1953 sucrose octaacetate was obtained in 5.5 per cent yield by heating 1,2-anhydro-3,4,6-tri-*O*-acetyl-α-D-glucopyranose (cf. p. 388) with 1,3,4,6-tetra-*O*-acetyl-D-fructofuranose. Purification and deacetylation gave sucrose identical with the natural product.

Trisaccharides

Raffinose is present in small amount in many plants. It accumulates in the mother liquor during the preparation of beet sugar and can be prepared from beet sugar molasses. It may be obtained also by extracting defatted ground cottonseed with water. Complete hydrolysis of raffinose yields one mole each of glucose, fructose, and galactose. Since raffinose is nonreducing, all of the anomeric carbon atoms must be involved in glycosidic links. When raffinose is hydrolyzed in the presence of the α-galactosidase of emulsin, the products are galactose and sucrose, whereas if it is hydrolyzed by sucrase (β-fructosidase) the products are fructose and melibiose. Since the structures of sucrose and melibiose are known, the structure of raffinose is established.

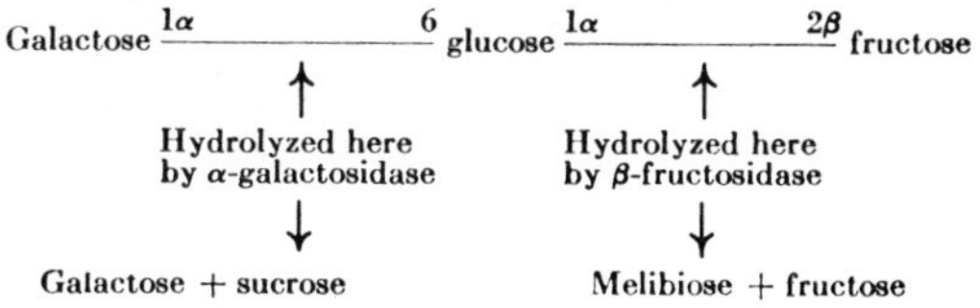

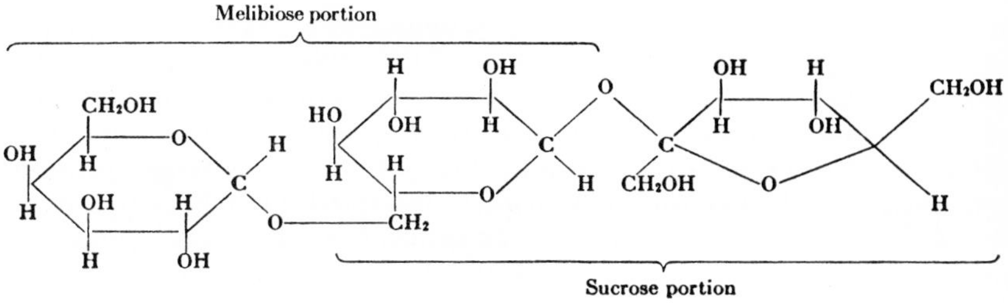

Raffinose

Gentianose is present in the rhizomes of many species of gentian. It is hydrolyzed in the presence of sucrase to fructose and gentiobiose and by the β-glucosidase of emulsin to glucose and sucrose.

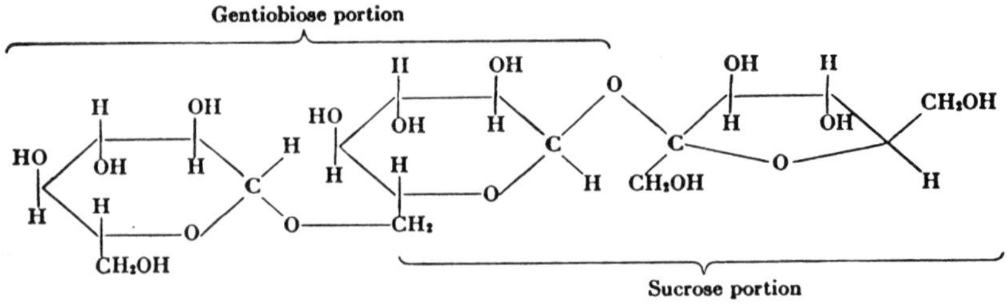

Gentianose

POLYSACCHARIDES

As the name implies, polysaccharides are high molecular weight substances (molecular weights 30,000 to 14,000,000). They are insoluble in liquids and are altered readily by the acids and alkalies required to catalyze their conversion into soluble derivatives. Hence their purification is extremely difficult. Moreover even the purified products are not molecularly homogeneous since the same substance may consist of polymers of varying molecular weight. Nevertheless the polysaccharides are considerably simpler than proteins because frequently only a single type of building unit, for example glucose, is present. Compounds containing a single type of building unit are known as *homopolysaccharides*. Some polysaccharides are derived from several different types of building units and are known as *heteropolysaccharides*. Polysaccharides such as starch, glycogen, or inulin are reserve foodstuffs for the plant or animal; others, as cellulose of plants and chitin of crustacea, have a structural function; for others, such as gums and mucilages, the function is unknown.

Homopolysaccharides

Starch. During the growth of a plant, carbohydrate is stored in various parts, such as the roots, seeds, and fruits, in the form of microscopic granules of starch. Seed may contain up to 70 per cent starch, and roots and tubers up to 30 per cent. Corn, potatoes, wheat, rice, tapioca, sago, and sweet potatoes constitute the chief commercial sources. Starch granules from different sources vary in shape, size, and general appearance.

In the United States most starch is derived from corn (maize). The corn grains are soaked until soft in warm water containing sulfur dioxide and then are shredded to free the germ. When the ground mass is mixed with water, the germ floats because of the high oil content and is collected, dried, and pressed to produce corn oil (p. 182). The remainder of the grain sinks and is ground as finely as possible without rupturing the starch granules, and the mixture is washed through screens to remove most of the hull. The starch suspension is passed through long shallow troughs where the starch granules settle, or it is removed by centrifuges. The protein constituents of the grain (gluten) are recovered from the steep water and from the water that leaves the settling tables. Corn steep water now finds an important outlet as a nutrient for the mold used in the manufacture of penicillin (p. 637). The separation of starch from potatoes is somewhat simpler in that only the grinding and settling processes are required. Annual production of cornstarch in the United States is about 4 billion pounds, and of potato starch about 100 million pounds.

When starch is heated with water, the granules swell greatly and a colloidal suspension is produced. This dispersion has been separated into two components. When it is saturated with a slightly soluble alcohol such as butanol or the commercial mixture of amyl alcohols known as Pentasol (p. 119), or with thymol (p. 515), a microcrystalline precipitate forms which is known as *A-fraction* or **amylose.** Addition to the mother liquors of a water-miscible alcohol such as methanol, or coprecipitation with aluminum hydroxide, gives an amorphous material known as *B-fraction* or **amylopectin.** Most starches contain amylose and amylopectin in the ratio of from 1 : 4 to 1 : 5. However, some genetically pure mutant varieties of grains, known as waxy corn, sorghum, millet, rice, and barley, contain only amylopectin, whereas another recessive mutant strain of wrinkled pea has been reported to contain from 70 to 98 per cent of amylose.

The two fractions differ markedly in their physical and chemical properties. Purified amylose is only sparingly soluble in hot water and the amylose reprecipitates when the solutions are allowed to stand (*retrogradation*). It disperses readily in dilute sodium hydroxide but is degraded by the alkali. Amylopectin dissolves readily in water and the solution does not gel or precipitate on standing. Solutions of native starches gel rapidly and precipitate slowly. Apparently the amylopectin acts as a protective colloid for the amylose.

The typical blue color reaction of starch with iodine is due to the amylose fraction which absorbs 18 to 20 per cent of its weight of iodine as determined by potentiometric titration. The blue product appears to be an inclusion compound (p. 311) in which iodine molecules fit into the central open spaces of a helix of C_6 units that constitute the amylose molecule. Amylopectin gives a red to purple color and absorbs only 0.5 to 0.8 per cent of iodine. Iodine titration of whole starch may be used to determine the relative amounts of the two components.

Both fractions give only glucose on complete hydrolysis by acids. More information can be obtained by partial hydrolysis by means of enzymes. Two groups of starch-splitting enzymes, the α- and β-*amylases*, have been recognized for some time. Here the α and β merely differentiate the two groups and do not refer to the configuration of the glycosidic linkage which they attack, since both are 1,4-α-glucosidases. They differ in that α-amylase hydrolyzes the linkages randomly, whereas β-amylase attacks only the second link from the nonreducing end of a chain and liberates maltose. Amylose is hydrolyzed to maltose to the extent of only about 70 per cent by pure β-maltase. In 1952 it was found that if another enzyme called *Z-enzyme* is present, hydrolysis to maltose proceeds almost to completion. Z-enzyme is a β-glucosidase. Hence it is believed that amylose consists of glucose units joined mainly by α-glycosidic links through the 1,4 positions to give an essentially linear polymer coiled into a spiral, but that there are a few single β-glucosyl units as branches. These branches prevent the β-amylase from converting the amylose completely to maltose unless the branches first are removed by the Z-enzyme. When amylose is completely methylated and then hydrolyzed, the chief product is 2,3,6-tri-*O*-methylglucose, but about 0.3 per cent of 2,3,4,6-tetra-*O*-methylglucose is obtained which results from the terminal nonreducing glucose units. Ultracentrifuge studies indicate that amylose is heterogeneous, the molecules having molecular weights between 17,000 and 225,000.

Amylopectin is hydrolyzed to the extent of only about 50 per cent by β-amylase, with or without the presence of Z-enzyme, the remainder being a high-molecular weight product known as *limit dextrin*. However, β-amylase in conjunction with another enzyme known as *R-enzyme*, a 1,6-α-glucosidase, brings about complete hydrolysis. Methylation of amylopectin, followed by hydrolysis, gives as much as 4 per cent of 2,3,4,6-tetra-*O*-methylglucose and an equal amount of 2,3-di-*O*-methylglucose. The tetra-*O*-methylglucose corresponds to about one nonreducing end for each 25 glucose units. Molecular weight determinations indicate an average value of from one to six million (6000–37000 C_6 units) from osmotic pressure measurements and 400 million (2.5×10^6 C_6 units) from light scattering. Hence amylopectin is a highly branched molecule. The branches consist of 20 to 25 glucose units joined by 1,4-α-linkages and are in turn joined to other branches by 1,6-α-linkages. Branching is believed to be random rather than to follow any regular pattern.

The chief use of starch is as food. It is hydrolyzed stepwise by the *salivary amylases*, the final product being maltose if the reaction goes to completion. Since these enzymes are destroyed by strong acid, starch digestion stops as soon as the food is completely mixed with hydrochloric acid of the stomach. Digestion continues, however, in the intestine, where the hydrochloric acid is neutralized and *pancreatic amylase* completes the hydrolysis to maltose. Before passage through the mucous membrane of the intestine, disaccharides such as maltose, sucrose, and lactose are hydrolyzed by specific intestinal enzymes to the monosaccharides. There is some evidence that glucose, fructose, and galactose may undergo phosphorylation and dephosphorylation during the process of passing through the walls of the intestine into the blood stream. These sugars are removed rapidly from the blood by the liver and muscle tissue and converted into glycogen.

Industrially starch is converted by acid hydrolysis into **corn syrup** or **crystalline glucose,** both of which are used as food. Large quantities of starch are used as stiffening agents and adhesives, often after modification to dextrins. Starch can be converted to esters and ethers, but so far these functional derivatives have not found large-scale uses. **Starch nitrates** containing 11 to 13 per cent nitrogen (so-called *nitrostarch*) have been used as a demolition explosive to replace TNT.

Glycogen. This reserve carbohydrate of animals does not occur as granules but is distributed throughout the protoplasm. Some of it is water-soluble, but the remainder is bound to protein. The best source is mussels. Glycogen is isolated by hydrolyzing the tissue with hot aqueous alkali, neutralizing, and precipitating with alcohol. Glycogen gives a violet to brown color with iodine. Acid hydrolysis yields only glucose, but diastase gives up to 30 per cent maltose. Methylation and hydrolysis indicates one end group for each 12 C_6 units. Glycogen preparations are very heterogeneous and molecular weights vary from 3 to 15 million (osmotic pressure). The shorter chain length and higher molecular weight indicate that glycogen is even more highly branched than amylopectin, but that otherwise it has a similar structure.

Cellulose. This polysaccharide constitutes the cell membranes of the higher plants. It makes up about 10 per cent of the dry weight of leaves, about 50 per cent of the woody structures of plants, and 98 per cent of cotton fiber. Pure cellulose is obtained best from cotton by dewaxing with an organic solvent, and removing pectic substances (p. 407) by extracting with hot 1 per cent sodium hydroxide solution.

Like starch, cellulose yields only glucose on hydrolysis, and 90–95 per cent yields of 2,3,6-tri-*O*-methylglucose have been obtained from methylated cellulose. Unlike starch, no tetra-*O*-methylglucose is obtained provided the methylation has been carried out in the absence of air. Hence either the molecule is so large that the amount of tetra-*O*-methylglucose produced cannot be detected, or the molecule has a cyclic structure. By the ultracentrifugal method molecular weights of one to two million (6000 to 12,000 C_6 units) are indicated.

Since acetolysis yields 40–50 per cent of cellobiose octaacetate which has a β glycosidic linkage (p. 391), it is assumed that the glucose units are linked entirely by a β linkage through the 1,4 positions.

Cellulose

In spite of the fact that cellulose contains five oxygen atoms for each six carbon atoms, it is insoluble in water and alcohols. Evidently because of the high molecular weight and the linear nature of the molecule, strong van der Waals forces prevent dispersion in solvents. Cellulose is soluble in sulfuric acid and concentrated solutions of zinc chloride, but since a scission of glycosidic links takes place in the presence of acids, the product regenerated by pouring the solution into water has a much lower molecular weight than the original cellulose. Such products are said to be *degraded*. Degradation also takes place on exposure to air in the presence of alkali.

The best solvent for cellulose is an aqueous solution of cupric ammonium hydroxide, $Cu(NH_3)_4(OH)_2$, which is known as *cuprammonium solution* or *Schweitzer reagent*. A more convenient reagent currently used is *cupriethylene-diamine*, $Cu(H_2NCH_2CH_2NH_2)_2(OH)_2$, made by dissolving cupric hydroxide in ethylenediamine (p. 754) and diluting with water to the desired concentration. Since the viscosity of solutions decreases with decreasing chain length of a molecule, the extent of degradation of cellulose can be estimated by determining the viscosity of solutions in these reagents. Cellulose regenerated by acidifying cuprammine solutions gives a solution having a lower viscosity than the original cellulose. Hence even these reagents bring about some degradation. The degradation is greater if the solutions are exposed to air.

Although considerable study of these solutions has been made, little is known about the constitution of the solute. In concentrated copper solutions, one atom of copper combines with each C_6 unit. It seems likely that complexes are formed analogous to those existing in Fehling solution (p. 809). The large size of the copper atom increases the distance between the chains and renders inoperative the van der Waals forces between the chains, thus permitting hydration and solution (cf. p. 404).

Commercial Sources of Cellulose. The technical uses of cellulose are dependent chiefly on its fibrous form and on the strength and flexibility of products prepared from it. Cotton fibers have an average tensile strength of 80,000 p.s.i. compared with 65,000 p.s.i. for medium steel. Fiber length varies with the source. The bast fibers, such as flax, jute, and hemp, vary from 20 to 350 cm. in length. Cotton, which is a seed hair, has fibers 1.5 to 5.5 cm. long. Wood fibers vary from 0.2 to 5 mm. in length. The long fibers are used chiefly for making textiles, and cotton is by far the most important for this purpose.

After removal of moisture, wood consists of 40 to 50 per cent cellulose, 15 to 25 per cent other polysaccharides known as *hemicelluloses*, 30 per cent lignin (p. 527), which acts as a matrix for the cellulose fibers, and 5 per cent of other substances such as mineral salts, sugars, fat, resin, and protein. Wood pulp is manufactured by dissolving the lignin with hot solutions of (*1*) sodium hydroxide, (*2*) calcium, magnesium, or ammonium bisulfite, or (*3*) a mixture of sodium hydroxide and sodium sulfide (made from lime and reduced sodium sulfate). The products, known as soda pulp, sulfite pulp, or sulfate (kraft) pulp, respectively, consist of impure cellulose that has been more or less degraded. Most wood pulp is used in the manufacture of paper where the length of the fibers and the strength are most important. Fermentable sugars can be recovered from sulfite liquors and used as a source of alcohol. The sulfate process yields for each ton of paper about 50 pounds of **tall oil** (Sw. *tallolja*, pine oil), which consists of about 50 per cent unsaturated fatty acids, chiefly oleic and linoleic acids, and 50 per cent resin acids. It is used in the manufacture of soap (p. 188) and synthetic protective coatings (p. 553).

Mercerized Cotton. John Mercer, an English chemist and calico printer, attempted in 1814 to filter a concentrated solution of sodium hydroxide through cotton cloth and found that the fibers swelled and stopped the filtration. After the cloth was washed free of sodium hydroxide and dried, it dyed more readily than the original cloth. He patented his process in 1850. This treatment, however, shrinks the cloth considerably. Around 1889 Horace Lowe, another English technical chemist, attempted to prevent this shrinkage mechanically by carrying out the whole process with the cloth or yarn under tension. Not only was shrinkage prevented, but the surface irregularities of the fiber were removed giving it a high luster like silk. Moreover the strength of the fiber increased about 20 per cent. This process now is known as *mercerization* and the product is called *mercerized cotton*. It is by far the most widely used chemical finish for cotton in which the fiber is modified. About 45 million pounds of yarn and 800 million yards of cloth are mercerized each year in the United States.

Parchment Paper. When paper is treated for a few seconds with about 80 per cent sulfuric acid, an alteration of the surface of the fiber takes place, and after washing and drying, the paper is stiffer and tougher and does not disintegrate in water. Because of its resemblance to parchment, it is called *parchment paper*.

Glucose. Cellulose can be hydrolyzed to glucose and in this way becomes usable for food or for the production of alcohol or yeast by fermentation. In the technical processes the wood chips are extracted with 40 per cent hydrochloric acid at 20° (Bergius process) or 0.5 per cent sulfuric acid at 130° (Scholler process). The cellulose dissolves leaving the lignin as a solid. Concentration of the extract yields the sugars. Acetic acid also may be recovered from the extracts. The residual lignin can be briquetted and distilled to give charcoal and methyl alcohol. Wood saccharification has been operated in countries with a controlled economy, particularly in Germany before World War II, although even there the operation was not so extensive as generally is believed. Attempts have been made periodically since 1900 to operate plants in the United States, but they have never been feasible economically.

Cellulose Esters. Many important products are derived from cellulose by esterifying the hydroxyl groups. These derivatives are soluble in organic solvents and thus permit the formation of films or fibers. Formerly the cellulose used for this purpose was chiefly purified cotton linters, the short cotton fibers cut from the cotton seed after the removal of the long fibers by the cotton gin. More recently wood pulp having a high α-*cellulose* content has become the dominant raw material. α-Cellulose is a technical term for the portion of wood pulp that is insoluble in alkali of mercerizing strength (17.5 per cent). The soluble portion consists of the so-called *hemicelluloses*, which are chiefly pentosans and mannans (p. 407), and of sugars and lower molecular weight substances.

The **cellulose nitrates** were the first esters to be of technical importance. Dry purified cotton linters are soaked in a mixture of nitric and sulfuric acid. It is desirable to carry out the reaction for as short a time (15–30 minutes), and at as low a temperature (30°–40°) as possible and to keep the water concentration low to reduce degradation. After centrifuging and washing, the nitrated cotton is boiled with water to hydrolyze sulfates and to produce good stability. It is stored wet and dehydrated before use by washing with ethanol or butanol. Three chief types of cellulose nitrate are produced: (*1*) *celluloid pyroxylin* containing 10.5–11 per cent nitrogen, soluble in ethanol-ether mixture and in absolute ethanol; (*2*) *soluble pyroxylin* (*collodion cotton,* or *dynamite cotton*) containing 11.5–12.3 per cent nitrogen and soluble in absolute ethanol; and (*3*) *guncotton,* containing 12.5–13.5 per cent nitrogen. Guncotton containing over 13 per cent nitrogen is insoluble in ethanol-ether and in absolute ethanol. All of the commercial nitrates dissolve in acetone and in the lower molecular weight esters. The dinitrates of cellulose should contain 11.11 per cent nitrogen and the trinitrate 14.15 per cent nitrogen. Hence the commercial products are mixtures rather than pure compounds.

Guncotton is the least degraded, having a chain length of about 3000 C_6 units. It gives solutions of extremely high viscosity. It is used for making smokeless powder, the chief propellant explosive. The guncotton is *gelatinized* or *colloided* to a dough by mixing with a solvent, and expressed and cut into cylindrical perforated pellets called *grains.* The perforations permit a progressive increase in burning area and hence an increasing rate of combustion as the projectile moves through the barrel of the gun. The United States military forces use a propellant made from guncotton having 12.5 per cent nitrogen and gelatinized with ethanol-ether mixture. The British military forces use a propellant made from guncotton having over 13 per cent nitrogen and gelatinized with acetone. Powders having a higher nitrogen content give a somewhat longer range but are more corrosive on the bore of the gun. **Cordite** and **ballistite** consist of guncotton plasticized with nitroglycerin (p. 749). The equation for the decomposition of cellulose trinitrate may be written as

$$2 \begin{bmatrix} -CH(CHONO_2)_2-CH-O- \\ CH\underline{\hspace{3cm}}O \\ CH_2ONO_2 \end{bmatrix}_x \longrightarrow 9x\,CO + 3x\,CO_2 + 7x\,H_2O + 3x\,N_2$$

Sufficient oxygen is present to convert the compound completely to gaseous products, and the large amount of energy liberated in transferring oxygen from nitrogen to hydrogen and carbon raises the gases to a high temperature and produces the pressure necessary to expel the projectile at high velocity.

In 1865 Alexander Parkes, an Englishman, obtained a horn-like mass by mixing cellulose nitrate, alcohol, and camphor. In 1869 the American inventor John Wesley Hyatt obtained a patent for a similar product, which he had developed as a substitute for ivory for billiard balls, and for which he coined the name **celluloid.** It is made by mixing two parts of celluloid pyroxylin with one part of powdered camphor (p. 856) and kneading in a mixer with enough alcohol to form a dough. The soft mass is pressed into various forms or rolled into sheets. In the curing the alcohol evaporates and the articles solidify. Celluloid has many disadvantages, such as undesirable odor and taste, non-resistance to acid and alkali, discoloration in light, and high flammability. Yet for about fifty years it was the only important plastic.

Thin cellulose nitrate sheet, formerly used chiefly as a base for motion picture film, is made by dissolving soluble pyroxylin in a mixture of methanol and acetone together with camphor as a plasticizer, and coating on the highly polished surface of a wheel 20 to 30 feet in diameter. As the wheel rotates slowly, the solvent evaporates sufficiently to permit the film to be stripped continuously from the opposite side and passed through drying rooms where the rest of the solvent is removed.

Prior to the development of the vinyl plastics (p. 736), large quantities of pyroxylin were used for the manufacture of **artificial leather.** Viscous solutions containing treated castor oil (p. 182) as plasticizer, together with pigment, were coated in several layers on cotton fabric and embossed to resemble leather.

Celluloid pyroxylin and soluble pyroxylin are more degraded than guncotton, having chain lengths of only 500 to 600 C_6 units. It is this smaller molecular size that permits them to give free-flowing solutions at fairly high concentration. Solutions of sufficient concentration to leave a film thick enough to act as a binding agent for pigments and to serve as a protective coating are, however, too viscous to be applied with a brush or spray gun. Further degradation can be brought about by heating the pyroxylin with water in pressure digestors. Pyroxylin giving solutions of almost any desired viscosity thus can be obtained, but the lower the viscosity the shorter the chain length, and hence the lower the film strength and the greater the brittleness of the film. The material commonly used in lacquers is known as **half-second cotton,** the viscosity being measured by the time required for a ball of specified size and material to drop through a solution of specified composition under standard conditions. It has a chain length of 150 to 200 C_6 units.

Nitrocellulose lacquers consist of pigment, half-second cotton, and a mixture of solvents. The solvents are grouped as *low boilers, medium boilers,* and *high* *boilers.* The low boilers evaporate rapidly leaving a thick film that still can flow enough to remove brush or spray marks. Evaporation of the medium boilers leaves a dry film. The high boilers remain in the film to plasticize it, that is, to keep it flexible. Lacquers were introduced as finishes for automobiles in 1924, to replace varnish, and the ease of application, rapid drying, and durability revolutionized the industry. It is said that the development of chromium plating received its chief impetus because the new body finishes outlasted the nickel plated trim. Nitrocellulose lacquers have been supplanted largely by synthetic alkyd baking enamels (p. 553) for automobile finishes but still are used extensively for refinishing automobiles and for household decoration.

The **cellulose acetates** are the most important esters. The maximum amount of acetyl that can be introduced by direct esterification corresponds to the acetylation of one of the three hydroxyl groups, and the product is not soluble in organic solvents and has no commercial use. When cellulose is pretreated by soaking under carefully controlled conditions in a dilute solution of sulfuric acid in glacial acetic acid and then is added to a mixture of acetic anhydride and acetic acid, it dissolves to give a viscous solution. Dilution with water precipitates an almost completely acetylated cellulose known as the **triacetate.** In the past the triacetate was little used, because it was soluble only in the expensive and highly toxic tetrachloroethane (p. 723), or in chloroform containing a small amount of alcohol. Moreover the product was not thermoplastic and films and threads made from it were brittle. Recently, however, a type of triacetate has been developed which is soluble in methylene chloride and which gives flexible films. In 1949 the largest manufacturer of photographic film in the United States started producing all of its safety film base from this triacetate and has since discontinued the use of nitrate film base entirely. Textile fibers based on the triacetate (p. 406) first were introduced in 1955.

The older commercial material is the so-called **cellulose diacetate.** After acetylation to the triacetate stage, some water is added to the acetylation mixture, and hydrolysis is permitted to take place until approximately the diacetate is formed. The product is precipitated with water, washed, and dried. It is soluble in acetone and gives flexible films and fibers. This material is not molecularly homogeneous but is a mixture having approximately the composition of the diacetate.

Usable diacetates cannot be prepared by stopping the acetylation at the diacetate stage. Those hydroxyl groups that are most readily esterified give the acetate groups that are most readily hydrolyzed. Hence a diacetate formed by the esterification of two of the three hydroxyl groups is a different product from one formed by hydrolyzing one of the three acetate groups.

Cellulose acetate is more expensive than the nitrate. In the first place cellulose nitrate is not soluble in the nitrating mixture, and most of the excess reagents can be recovered without dilution, whereas the acetate must be precipitated by water and large volumes of dilute acetic acid must be concentrated. Secondly the reagents for the preparation of the nitrate are cheaper than those for the acetate. Another disadvantage of the acetate is that it is more highly degraded than pyroxylin, having an average chain length of 175 to 300 units. Hence fibers and films made from it are weaker and more brittle. Nevertheless because of its lower flammability, its freedom from spontaneous decomposition, and its greater stability to discoloration, it has largely displaced cellulose nitrate in technical applications. Thus U.S. production of cellulose nitrate plastics in 1955 amounted to only 5 million pounds compared to 134 million pounds for acetate plastics.

More recently **acetatepropionates** and **acetatebutyrates** have been prepared by using propionic or butyric acid along with acetic anhydride during the acetylation. These products are thermoplastic without being partially hydrolyzed, and since they contain fewer free hydroxyl groups, they are less permeable to water, weather better, and are more compatible with gums and plasticizers.

Cellulose Ethers. A number of cellulose ethers are of technical importance. **Ethylcellulose** is prepared by soaking high α-cellulose wood pulp or cotton linters with 17 to 18 per cent sodium hydroxide solution and removing the excess solution in a hydraulic press. The product is known as *alkali cellulose* and has the approximate composition $(C_6H_{10}O_5 \cdot 2 \text{ NaOH})_x$, although it does not seem to be a definite compound. The alkali cellulose is shredded to crumbs and treated in an autoclave with ethyl chloride at 120° to 130° for 8 to 12 hours. The ethoxyl content obtained depends on the concentration of the alkali and on the time and number of treatments. Like the acetates, the ethylcelluloses differ in solubility characteristics depending on the extent of reaction. Products containing 0.8 to 1.4 ethoxyl groups per C_6 unit are soluble in water, whereas those containing more than 1.5 ethoxyl groups are soluble in most organic solvents. The most widely used commercial product contains 2.2 to 2.6 ethoxyl groups. It is highly compatible with resins and plasticizers and is soluble in mixtures of alcohol and hydrocarbons. Its use is increasing rapidly in the manufacture of coatings, films, and plastics. Unlike the esters, it is very resistant to the action of alkalies.

The **methylcelluloses** of low methoxyl content are soluble in cold water and precipitate on heating. They are used chiefly as thickeners for textile printing, for pastes, cosmetics, sizing, and finish for textile fibers.

The water solubility of the lower acetates and ethers seems anomalous, since acylation or etherification of a hydroxyl group ordinarily decreases the solubility in water. The insolubility of cellulose in water, however, may be explained by strong van der Waals forces between chains (pp. 39, 86). Since the replacement of a few hydrogen atoms by hydrocarbon or acyl groups separates the chains and renders these forces inoperative, hydration of the hydroxyl groups becomes more important. In accord with this view, the solubility in water decreases at higher temperatures, because the hydrates become less stable.

Carboxymethylcellulose (CMC) is prepared by the reaction of alkali cellulose with sodium chloroacetate.

$$\text{ROH} + \text{ClCH}_2\text{COONa} + \text{NaOH} \longrightarrow \text{R—O—CH}_2\text{COONa} + \text{NaCl} + \text{H}_2\text{O}$$

The commercial product contains about 0.5 carboxymethyl groups per C_6 unit, and the sodium salt is soluble in both cold and hot water. Metallic salts other than those of the alkali metals are insoluble in water. The *sodium salt* is used on a large scale as a thickening agent and protective colloid, as an additive for synthetic detergents, and as a size for textiles. It was used widely in Germany during World War II to extend detergents and as a replacement for starch. Significant commercial production began in the United States in 1946 and reached 27 million pounds in 1955. A purified product called *cellulose gum* is used as a thickening agent in foods, especially ice cream. **Hydroxyethylcellulose** also is manufactured commercially and used as a water-soluble thickening agent.

Oxidized cellulose is not an ether but has properties similar to carboxy-methylcellulose because carboxyl groups are present. Nitrogen dioxide, in the presence of sufficient water to form nitric acid, oxidizes the primary hydroxyl group to carboxyl without affecting the rest of the molecule appreciably except for considerable reduction in chain length.

$$3 NO_2 + H_2O \longrightarrow 2 HNO_3 + NO$$

$$3 \begin{bmatrix} -CH-(CHOH)_2CH-O- \\ | \\ CH-\!-\!-O- \\ | \\ CH_2OH \end{bmatrix}_x + 4x\,HNO_3 \longrightarrow 3 \begin{bmatrix} -CH(CHOH)_2CH-O- \\ | \\ CH-\!-\!-O- \\ | \\ COOH \end{bmatrix}_x \begin{array}{l} + 5x\,H_2O \\[1em] + 4x\,NO \end{array}$$

Cellulose	Oxidized cellulose

Rayon. Synthetic fibers are textile fibers produced from a homogeneous solution or melt, whether the raw material is a synthetic or a natural product. Thus the raw material for some synthetic fibers is coke, but that for others is essentially unmodified cellulose or protein. Synthetic fibers derived from cellulose are known as **rayon.**

In all of the processes the same operations are involved, namely solution of the cellulose or a derivative, forcing the solution through the fine holes of a die called a *spinneret*, and precipitation of the cellulose or evaporation of the solvent to give a thread. The threads have smooth cylindrical surfaces which reflect light and give them a high luster. The strength of the threads can be increased greatly by stretching them, which brings about a linear orientation of the molecules and hence an increase in the attractive forces between the molecules.

Viscose rayon manufacture is based on the reaction of the hydroxyl groups of cellulose with carbon disulfide in the presence of sodium hydroxide to give *xanthates* (p. 324) which are soluble in water. The reaction can be reversed by acidification.

$$ROH + CS_2 + NaOH \longrightarrow \begin{bmatrix} & S \\ & \| \\ RO\!C & -S^- \end{bmatrix} Na^+ + H_2O$$

$$\begin{bmatrix} & S \\ & \| \\ RO\!C & -S^- \end{bmatrix}{}^+Na + NaHSO_4 \longrightarrow ROH + CS_2 + Na_2SO_4$$

Alkali cellulose (p. 404) from high α-cellulose sulfite pulp or from cotton linters is treated in rotating drums with an amount of carbon disulfide equal to 30 to 40 per cent of the weight of dry cellulose (calculated amount for 1 mole of carbon disulfide per C_6 unit is 47 per cent). An orange-colored crumbly product is formed, which is dissolved in 3 per cent sodium hydroxide solution to give the viscous solution known as *viscose*, in which the cellulose molecule has been degraded to an average chain length of 400 to 500 C_6 units. The solution initially is unstable and the viscosity drops rapidly during the first day of standing. A slow hydrolysis of xanthate radicals then takes place with a gradual rise in viscosity for about eight days when it rapidly sets to a gel. Spinning of the solution is carried out after the solution has ripened four to five days when the viscosity is not changing rapidly and after considerable hydrolysis has taken place. The filaments from the spinneret are passed through a bath of sodium bisulfate and additives, where the hydrolysis is completed to give a regenerated cellulose fiber. After coagulation and twisting of the filaments into a thread, the product is thoroughly washed and sometimes bleached. The number of holes in the spinneret depends on the number of filaments desired in the thread and may vary from 15 to 500. The size of the filaments or thread is measured in *denier*, which is the weight in grams of 9000 meters of thread. The common size of the filaments is 2 to 3 denier and of the thread 150 denier, but rayon thread is made as fine as 50 and as coarse as 1000 denier. Ordinary viscose rayon has 50 to 80 per cent of the strength of silk and loses 50 to 60 per cent of its strength when wet. If the spinning is carried out under tension while the filaments still are plastic, orientation of the molecules takes place and the product has a strength equal to that of silk, wet or dry. Since around 1930, filaments of 1 to 20 denier have been cut to lengths of 1 to 6 inches to give **staple fiber.** Here the number of filaments from a single spinneret may be as high as 10,000. Staple fiber is combined with wool, cotton, or linen fibers in spun yarn, or is converted to **spun rayon** by the usual spinning process for cotton or wool.

Viscose solution is converted into **cellophane** by extruding through a slot into the coagulating bath. The addition of glycerol improves the flexibility, and a coating of wax and nitrocellulose lacquer makes it impervious to water vapor. Modification of the extruding die gives sausage casings, artificial straw, or filaments containing bubbles. Sealing caps of cellophane are kept moist and pliable in dilute glycerol. When placed over a bottle top, they dry and shrink to a tight fit. Synthetic sponges are made by incorporating crystals of Glauber's salt ($Na_2SO_4 \cdot 10\ H_2O$) of all sizes in the viscose solution and coagulating in blocks. Leaching with warm water dissolves the crystals and leaves the sponge-like mass.

Acetate rayon is made by dissolving cellulose diacetate in acetone or triacetate in methylene chloride and forcing the solution through spinnerets into warm air, where the solvent evaporates. The thread does not require a finishing treatment, and since two thirds or more of the hydroxyl groups are esterified, it has a higher wet strength than ordinary viscose rayon. The smaller number of hydroxyl groups, however, makes direct dyeing more difficult and special dyes are required (p. 675). Alternatively the dye may be incorporated in the spinning solution to give a colored thread. Acetate rayon can be distinguished easily from the other rayons by the fact that it still is soluble in acetone or methylene chloride. Viscose, cuprammonium, and nitrate rayons are regenerated cellulose and hence insoluble in organic solvents.

The **cuprammonium process** is essentially the same as the viscose process except that the purified cellulose is dissolved directly in Schweitzer reagent. The cellulose is precipitated by passing the filament into a sodium bisulfate bath which neutralizes the ammonia and forms copper sulfate.

The **Chardonnet nitrate process** was the first commercially successful process, but by the time it became established it was superseded by the viscose process. Filaments of pyroxylin are spun from a solvent as for acetate rayon. Because of the high flammability, however, the nitrate groups must be removed. Alkaline or acid hydrolysis is not possible because of the side reactions that take place. Cleavage by reduction with ammonium sulfide gives a satisfactory product, but it cannot compete economically with viscose or acetate rayon.

World production of rayon was 2.2 million tons in 1954, of which about half was filament yarn and half staple fiber. Of this amount over .80 per cent was made by the viscose process, 15 per cent by the acetate process, 4 per cent by the cuprammonium process, and a fraction of 1 per cent by the nitrate process. In the United States viscose rayon accounts for 60 per cent and acetate rayon for 40 per cent of production.

Pentosans and Hexosans. In the early literature the ending *an* was given to polysaccharides, other than starch and cellulose, having an indefinite composition or unknown structure. The **pentosans** give chiefly pentoses on hydrolysis, and the **hexosans** yield chiefly hexoses. The ending *an* has been used also in naming intramolecular anhydrides of monosaccharides, but such compounds now are called anhydro sugars (p. 388).

An **araban** has been isolated from *peanut hulls* which yields only arabinose on hydrolysis. Hydrolysis of methylated araban yields equimolar amounts of 3-methylarabinose, 2,3-dimethylarabinose, and 2,3,5-trimethylarabinose. These products indicate a highly branched structure in which there is one terminal group, one group linked to two other groups, and one group linked to three other groups for each three arabinose units. **Xylans** are present in all land plants and are most abundant in corncobs, straw, and grain hulls, which serve as the raw material for the commercial production of furfural (p. 617). Some xylans give only xylose on hydrolysis, and it is believed that they are made up of β-D-xylopyranose units linked through the 1,4 positions. This structure is like that of cellulose with hydrogen replacing the hydroxymethyl group. Native xylan may contain a small number of L-arabinose and D-glucuronic acid residues.

Dextrans are highly branched glucosans produced by the fermentation of sucrose solutions by certain bacteria (*Leuconostoc mesenteroides, Betacoccus arabinosaceus*). Dextrans having 90 per cent of the molecules in the molecular weight range of 50,000 to 100,000, obtained by partial hydrolysis of native dextran, are used as blood plasma extenders in the treatment of shock caused by loss of body fluids. Industrial uses for nonclinical dextrans also are being developed. A **mannan** has been isolated from *yeast* which, after methylation and hydrolysis, gives 3,4-dimethylmannose, 2,4,6-trimethylmannose, 3,4,6-trimethylmannose, and 2,3,4,6-tetramethylmannose in the molecular ratio of 2 : 1 : 1 : 2, together with small amounts of 2,3,4-trimethylmannose. Hence three types of linkages, 1,2-, 1,3-, and 1,6-, are present in the ratio of 3 : 1 : 2.

Pectins and Pectic Acids. Fruits and berries contain water-insoluble complex carbohydrates known as *protopectins*, which on partial hydrolysis yield **pectins** or **pectinic acids.** Pectins have the property of forming gels with sugar and acid under proper conditions and are the agents necessary for the production of jellies from fruit juices. The pectins or pectinic acids contain both carboxyl groups and carbomethoxy groups. Removal of the remainder of the methoxy groups by hydrolysis yields the **pectic acids.** Enzyme hydrolysis of purified pectic acids gives up to 85 per cent of D-galacturonic acid and no other carbohydrates have been identified. The pectic acids contain one free carboxyl group per C_6 unit. These and other experimental data have led to the view that the pectic acids essentially are linear polygalacturonides with α linkages. In the pectins the carboxyl groups are esterified partially with methyl groups.

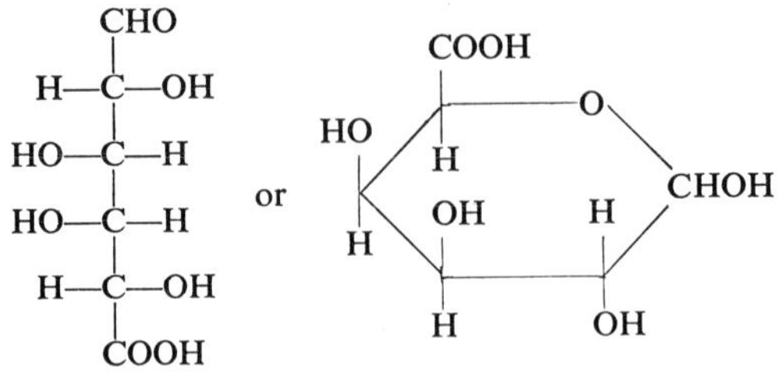

D-Galacturonic acid

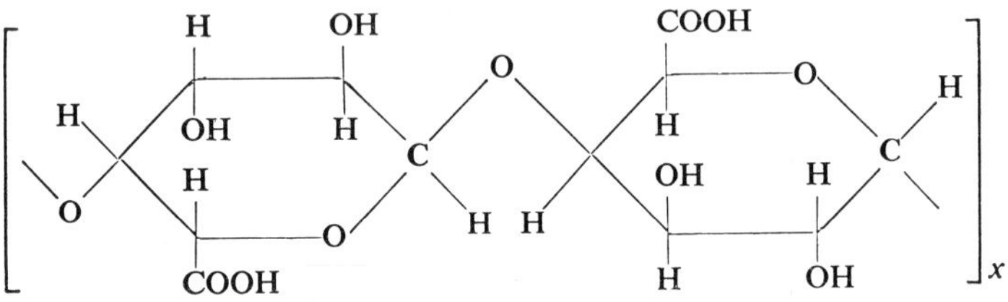

Pectic acid

Galacturonic acid belongs to the group of substances known as **uronic** or **glycuronic acids** in which the end carbon atom of the aldose is present in a carboxyl group, the aldehyde group being unchanged. In the *glyconic acids* (p. 360) the aldehyde group is replaced by the carboxyl group, and in the *glycaric acids* (p. 362) both terminal carbon atoms are in carboxyl groups. The uronic acids and their polymers, when heated with 12 per cent hydrochloric acid, lose one mole of carbon dioxide for each carboxyl group. The other

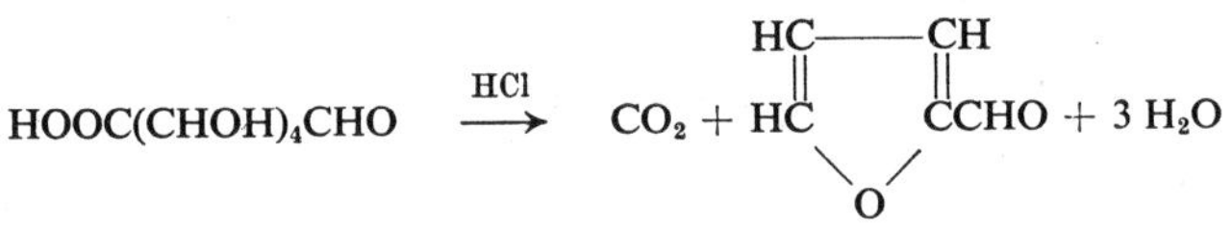

$$HOOC(CHOH)_4CHO \xrightarrow{HCl} CO_2 + HC \underset{O}{\overset{HC---CH}{\underset{\diagdown\diagup}{||\quad\quad||}}} CCHO + 3\,H_2O$$

products are furfural and water. The reaction is used for the quantitative estimation of uronic acid and polyuronides by absorbing the carbon dioxide in barium hydroxide solution and weighing the amount of barium carbonate that precipitates.

The polyuronides are difficult to hydrolyze and difficult to methylate. When methylation with methyl sulfate and sodium hydroxide has failed, recourse has been had to the formation of salts with thallium hydroxide, or with sodium in liquid ammonia, followed by reaction with methyl iodide. Frequently methylation is carried out partially with methyl sulfate and sodium hydroxide until the product becomes soluble in organic solvents, and then is completed with methyl iodide in the presence of silver oxide.

Alginic Acid. Extraction of the brown seaweed (*Laminaria digitata*) yields a substance known as **alginic acid,** which finds its chief use as a thickening agent for foods, especially ice cream. It yields only D-*mannuronic acid* on hydrolysis and is believed to be a linear polymannuronide with β linkages between the 1,4 positions.

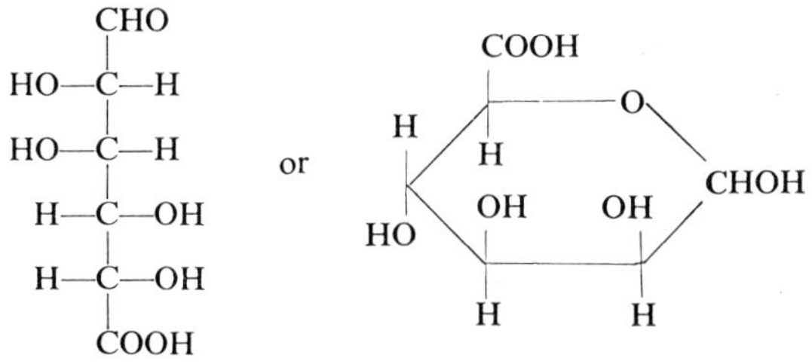

D-Mannuronic acid

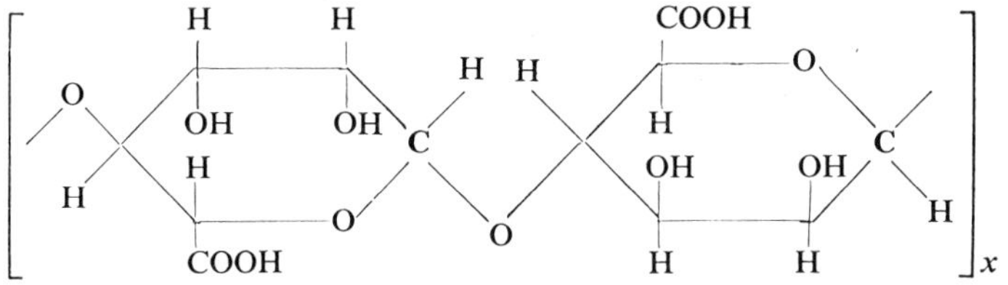

Alginic acid

It is of interest that both pectic acid and alginic acid have the geometrical pattern of cellulose, even though pectic acid has the α linkage like starch.

Chitin. The shells of crustacea and the structural substance of insects and fungi consist of the polysaccharide **chitin,** which contains nitrogen. Enzyme hydrolysis yields N-acetyl-2-amino-2-deoxyglucose (N-acetyl-2-glucosamine). The structure of chitin appears to be identical with that of cellulose except that the acetylamino group replaces the hydroxyl at C-2.

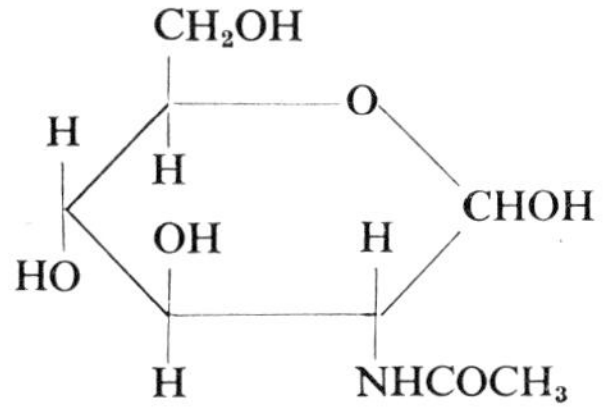

N-Acetyl-2-amino-2-deoxyglucose
(N-acetyl-2-glucosamine)

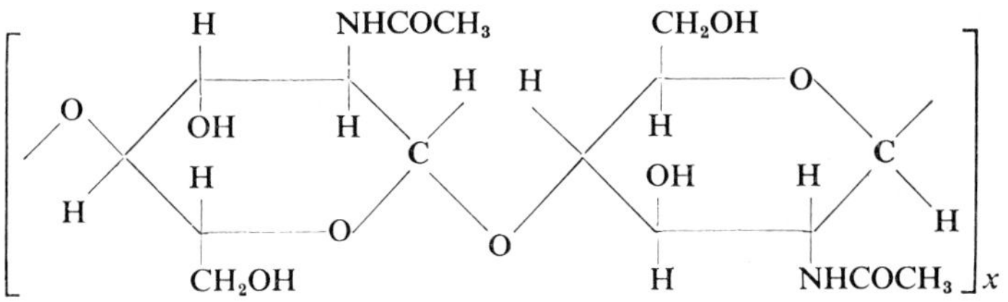

Chitin

Heteropolysaccharides

Inulin. This starchlike substance occurs in many plants, particularly members of the *Compositae*, for example inula, Jerusalem artichoke, goldenrod, dandelion, dahlia, and chicory. It is obtained readily from dahlia tubers or chicory roots. Hydrolysis yields fructose and a small amount of glucose. Methylation followed by hydrolysis yields 91 per cent 3,4,6-tri-*O*-methylfructose, 3 per cent of a tetra-*O*-methylfructose, 2 per cent of a tetra-*O*-methylglucose and smaller amounts of a mixture of tri-*O*-methylglucoses. The amount of tetra-*O*-methyl-fructose indicates a chain length of about 33 C$_6$ units. Osmotic pressure measurements on the acetate and methyl ether indicate a molecular weight corresponding to about 30 C$_6$ units. Hydrolysis by sucrase and the levo rotation of solutions point to a β linkage. From these data it may be concluded that the structure is a chain of β-fructofuranose units joined at the 1 and 2 positions and terminated with a sucrose-type linkage to glucose. Possibly a second glucose unit also forms a part of the molecule.

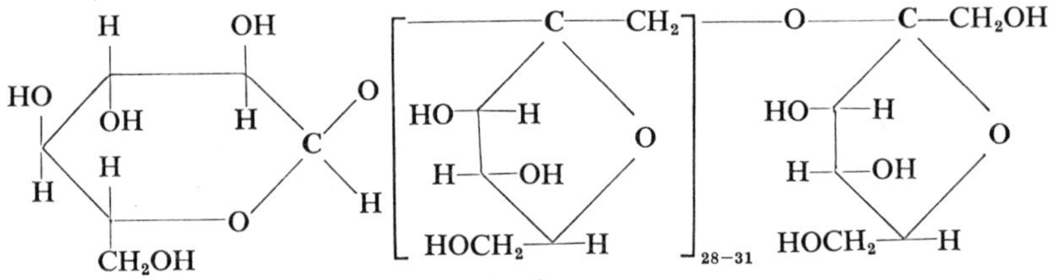

Inulin

Agar. Hot water extracts of certain East Indian seaweeds (various species of *Gelidium*) set to a gel on cooling. Freezing of the gel and subsequent thawing precipitates a material that can be removed by filtration. Drying of the precipitate to about 35 per cent moisture content gives translucent flakes known as **agar.** Solutions of agar in hot water again set to a gel on cooling. Its chief use is to prepare a support for nutrient media in the growing of microorganisms. The dry product swells in warm water without dissolving and is indigestible, making it useful as a bulk cathartic.

Hydrolysis of agar yields chiefly D-galactose, together with some 3,6-anhydro-L-galactose and sulfuric acid. Methylation and hydrolysis indicates a chain of D-galactose units joined by a β linkage through the 1,3 positions which in turn is linked to the 4 position of the 6-acid sulfate of L-galactose. The 3,6-anhydro-L-galactose is thought to arise from the loss of sulfuric acid during hydrolysis. Failure to detect tetra-*O*-methylgalactose indicates a high molecular weight.

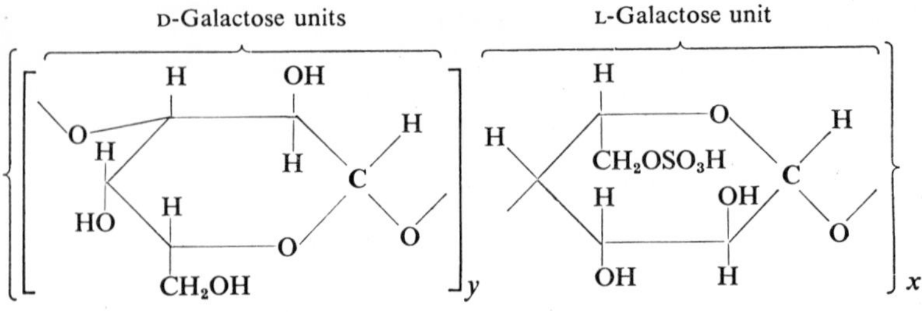

Agar

Hyaluronic Acid. This polysaccharide was isolated first from the vitreous humor of the eyes of cattle (Gr. *hyalos*, glass). It is distributed widely in animals and is largely responsible for the viscosity of body jellies and lubricating fluids. Hydrolysis gives equimolar amounts of D-glucuronic acid and N-acetyl-D-glucosamine. It is not certain whether the molecule is linear or branched. Molecular weights up to 400,000 are indicated by viscosity measurements.

Plant Gums and Mucilages. Many plants yield water-soluble exudations or extractives that give viscous mucilaginous solutions which are used widely as adhesives and thickening agents. Heteropolysaccharides are the predominant constituents. **Gum arabic** is the most important polysaccharide gum of commerce, the annual production being around 50 million pounds. It is obtained from the bark of various species of *Acacia*, particularly *Acacia verek*, and is chiefly the calcium salt of **arabic acid.** The latter on hydrolysis yields L-arabinose, L-rhamnose, D-galactose, and D-glucuronic acid. **Mesquite gum,** an exudation of the stems and branches of the desert shrub *Prosopsis juliflora* of Mexico and southwestern United States, is a salt resembling gum arabic. Hydrolysis yields L-arabinose, D-galactose, and methylglucuronic acid. It is the best source of L-arabinose, since the latter can be removed by mild hydrolysis leaving a residue, resistant to hydrolysis, which contains the galactose and uronic acid. **Damson gum** is the exudation of the injured bark of a species of plum tree and yields on hydrolysis L-arabinose, D-xylose, D-galactose, D-mannose, and D-glucuronic acid. **Gum tragacanth,** an exudation of shrubs of the genus *Astragalus*, contains an acidic and a neutral polysaccharide. The acidic portion on hydrolysis yields fucose, xylose, galactose, and galacturonic acid, and the neutral portion yields L-arabinose and D-galactose. **Slippery elm mucilage** is a polysaccharide of L-rhamnose, D-galactose, 3-methyl-D-galactose, and D-galacturonic acid, and **flaxseed mucilage** is a polysaccharide of L-arabinose, D-xylose, L-rhamnose, L-galactose and D-galacturonic acid. The seeds of many legumes contain **galactomannans. Locust bean** or **carob bean flour** from the endosperm of the seed of the Mediterranean locust tree (*Ceratonia siliqua*) is a commercial product. Hydrolysis yields mannose and galactose in the ratio of about 5 : 1. **Guar flour** is a similar product from the endosperm of the guar bean (*Cyamopsis proraloides* or *C. tetragona*), a native of India which now is grown commercially in southern United States.

Immunopolysaccharides. Pneumococci and many other bacteria produce polysaccharides which are responsible for the immunological specificity of the organisms. The polysaccharide of pneumococcus type III has been investigated extensively. It appears to be a linear molecule in which glucose units linked through the 1,4 positions alternate with glucuronic acid units linked through the 1,3 positions. The molecular weight appears to be of the order of 10^5–10^6.

Polysaccharides Associated with Proteins. Polysaccharides are associated with proteins and must play an important part in biological processes, but little is known about their structure. The glycoprotein **ovomucoid** from egg albumin yields after enzymic digestion a carbohydrate made up of N-acetyl-2-D-glucosamine, D-mannose, and D-galactose.

Chondroitin sulfuric acid is present to the extent of 20 to 40 per cent in cartilage where it is bound as a salt to the protein *collagen* and from which it can be extracted by alkali. It is present also in skin and connective tissues. Hydrolysis gives equimolar amounts of 2-amino-2-deoxy-D-galactose, D-glucuronic acid, sulfuric acid, and acetic acid. Molecular weights from 10,000 to 260,000 have been proposed. The molecule is believed to be linear with alternating glucuronic acid and galactosamine units having pyranose structures. They are joined by β linkages through the 1,3 positions. The amino group of the galactosamine units are acetylated and the C-6 hydroxyl groups are esterified with sulfuric acid.

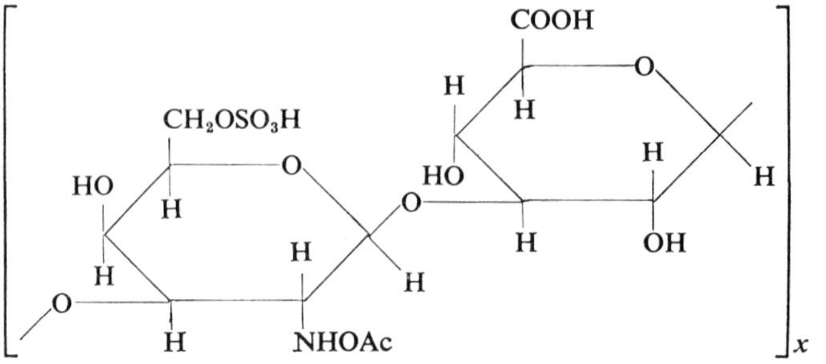

Chondroitin sulfuric acid

SUGAR ALCOHOLS

Although sugar alcohols are not carbohydrates in the strict sense, the naturally occurring sugar alcohols are so closely related to the carbohydrates that they are discussed here rather than with other polyhydric alcohols (p. 739). The sugar alcohols most widely distributed in nature are sorbitol (identical with D-glucitol), D-mannitol, and galactitol (dulcitol). They correspond to the reduction products of glucose, mannose, and galactose.

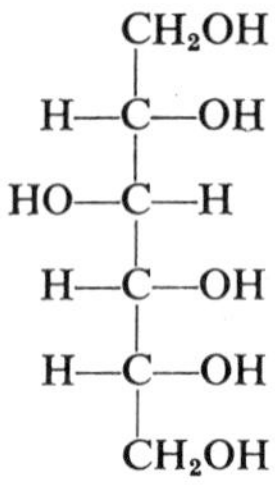

Sorbitol (D-glucitol)	D-Mannitol	Galactitol (dulcitol)
CH_2OH	CH_2OH	CH_2OH
H—C—OH	HO—C—H	H—C—OH
HO—C—H	HO—C—H	HO—C—H
H—C—OH	H—C—OH	HO—C—H
H—C—OH	H—C—OH	H—C—OH
CH_2OH	CH_2OH	CH_2OH

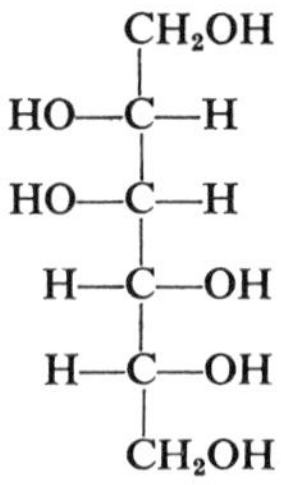

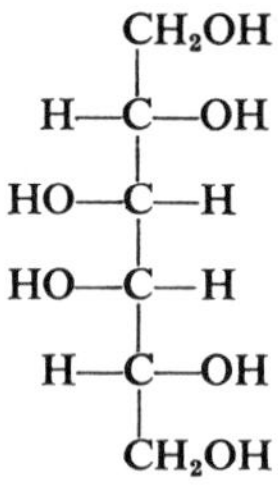

Since the reduction of the sugars gives compounds in which the end groups are identical, the reduction products of two different sugars frequently are identical. Thus L-arabitol is identical with L-lyxitol. Similarly D-glucose on reduction gives a sugar alcohol identical with sorbitol, one of the two reduction products of L-sorbose. Sorbitol was the name first assigned to the naturally occurring compound and commonly is used rather than D-glucitol. The designation of family for *meso* forms such as erythritol and galactitol is meaningless.

Sorbitol first was isolated from the berries of the mountain ash (*Sorbus aucuparia*) in 1872. The red seaweed, *Bostrychia scorpoides*, contains almost 14 per cent sorbitol. It has been isolated in appreciable quantities from many other plants ranging from the algae to the higher orders. Sorbitol is the most important of the sugar alcohols and is manufactured by the catalytic hydrogenation of glucose. Electrolytic reduction of glucose at pH 10–13 produces a mixture of mannitol and sorbitol because of the epimerizing effect of the alkali on the glucose. Sorbitol is very soluble in water giving thick viscous solutions that can replace glycerol for many purposes. It dehydrates readily to derivatives of tetrahydropyran and tetrahydrofuran.

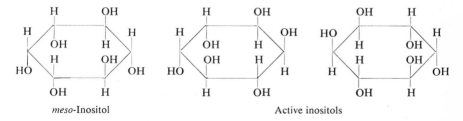

The monoesters of the cyclic dehydration products with long chain fat acids (*Spans*) or of their reaction products with ethylene oxide (*Tweens*) are used as nonionic emulsifying and wetting agents. Sorbitol also is an intermediate for the synthesis of vitamin C (p. 387).

D-**Mannitol** occurs in many land and marine plants and, in contrast to sorbitol, is present frequently in the plant exudates known as *mannas*, for example in the exudates of the manna ash (*Fraxinus ornus*), of the olive, and of the plane trees. The amount of mannitol in the seaweed *Laminaria digitata*, from which alginic acid is obtained (p. 408), varies from as low as 3 per cent (dry weight) in the winter months to as high as 37 per cent in the summer. **Galactitol** (dulcitol) also is present in many plants and plant exudates and can be made by the catalytic hydrogenation of galactose.

Related to the sugar alcohols are the polyhydroxycyclohexanes, of which the hexahydroxy derivatives, known as the **inositols,** are of most interest. Nine stereoisomeric forms are possible, two of which are optically active and seven of which are *meso* forms. One of the *meso* forms is distributed widely in nature, and it is this form which is meant by the designation **inositol** or *meso*-**inositol.**

It is found in microorganisms, plants, and animals. It occurs both free and combined in many organs of the animal body and in the body fluids. The hexaphosphoric acid ester is called **phytic acid,** and its calcium magnesium salt, known as **phytin**, is present in plants. The best source of phytin is corn steep liquor (p. 396), from which inositol is prepared commercially. *meso*-Inositol is a component (**bios I**) of the vitamin B complex and is a dietary requirement for both lower and higher forms of animal life. Hence it is one of the vitamins.

Pinitol is a monomethyl ether of (+)-inositol, which occurs in various conifers, especially the California sugar pine (*Pinus lambertiana*). **Quebrachitol** is a monomethyl ether of (—)-inositol that is present in quebracho bark and in the latex of the rubber tree (*Hevea braziliensis*). **Scyllitol**, the fourth inositol known to occur in nature, has been found in small amount in elasmobranch fish and in several plants. It is the completely *trans* form. (**+**)-**Quercitol** is a deoxyinositol found in acorns and oak bark.

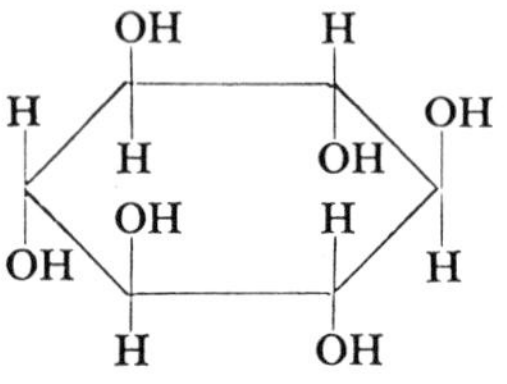

| Scyllitol | (+)-Quercitol | Streptamine |

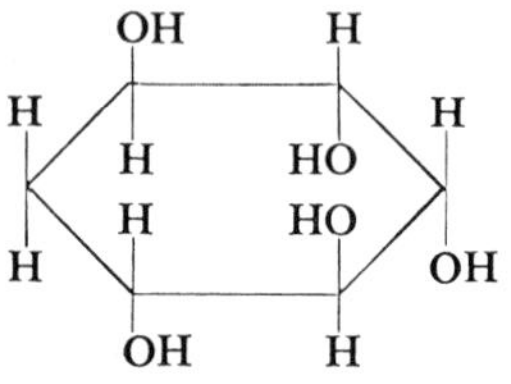

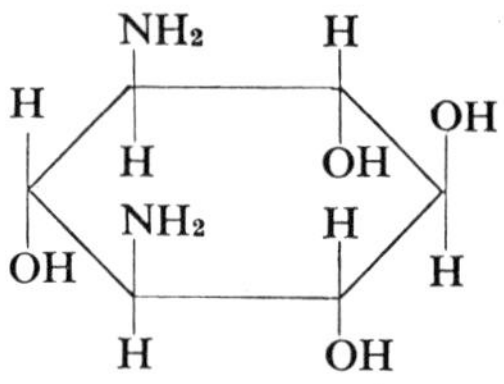

Streptomycin, an antibiotic from *Streptomyces griseus* that is more active against gram-negative organisms than penicillin (p. 637), yields **streptamine** as one of the products of hydrolysis. Streptamine has two amino groups instead of two of the hydroxyl groups of scyllitol. The amino groups are derived from guanidyl groups in the streptomycin molecule. The other constituents appear to be a dialdehydodeoxy sugar named **streptone**, and *N*-methyl-L-glucosamine.

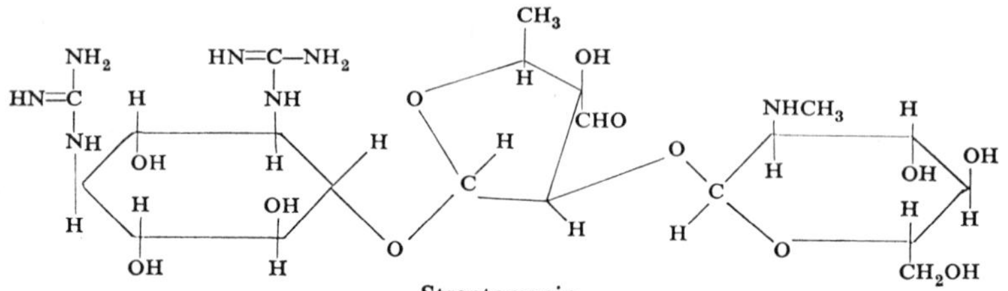

Streptomycin

REVIEW QUESTIONS

1. Define the term carbohydrate.
2. Give in outline form a classification of the carbohydrates.
3. Give a group of reactions which establish the accepted open chain structure of glucose. Explain the part of each reaction in the proof of structure.
4. Why is the open chain formula for glucose not an entirely satisfactory representation? How are these phenomena explained?
5. Why can one hydroxyl group of reducing sugars be methylated with methyl alcohol and hydrogen chloride, whereas the other four cannot? Why is one methyl group of methyl-α-2,3,4,6-tetra-*O*-methylglucoside removed more readily by hydrolysis than the other four?
6. What are the configurations of glucose, mannose, and galactose?
7. How many straight-chain aldoheptoses are possible excluding α and β forms?
8. What is meant by the term *relative configuration*; D-family of sugars?
9. Why do glucose, mannose, and fructose give the same osazone?

10. Why does fructose reduce Fehling solution? Why must empirical tables be used when estimating sugars by oxidation methods? What is the difference in composition between Fehling solution and Benedict solution, and what advantage has one over the other?
11. How can aldohexoses be distinguished from aldopentoses?
12. What is the meaning of *pyranose* and *furanose*?
13. Explain the difference in structure of maltose, cellobiose, lactose, and sucrose.
14. Compare the reactions of reducing and nonreducing disaccharides.
15. What are the more important differences in the chemical constititution of starch, glycogen, inulin, and cellulose?
16. How is cellulose nitrate made? What is the difference between guncotton, soluble pyroxylin or collodion cotton, and half second cotton? For what are they used?
17. Discuss the preparation and properties of cellulose triacetate, cellulose diacetate, and cellulose acetate-butyrate.
18. How does viscose rayon differ from acetate rayon? How are they made? What is cellophane?
19. What are methylcellulose, ethylcellulose, carboxymethylcellulose, and oxidized cellulose, and for what are they used?

PROBLEMS

20. Give reactions for the preparation of the following compounds: (*a*) L-arabinaric acid; (*b*) D-galactonic acid; (*c*) L-rhamnonolactone; (*d*) methyl β-D-mannoside; (*e*) D-glucosone; (*f*) isopropylidene methyl β-D-arabinoside; (*g*) D-xylose phenylosazone; (*h*) methyl β-D-mannose tetraacetate.
21. How may the members of the following pairs of compounds be distinguished easily from each other: (*a*) arabinose and glucose; (*b*) ribose and arabinose; (*c*) glucose and mannose; (*d*) rhamnose and arabinose; (*e*) xylose and galactose; (*f*) glucose and maltose; (*g*) sucrose and trehalose; (*h*) maltose and lactose; (*i*) lactose and trehalose; (*j*) cellobiose and sucrose; (*k*) inulin and starch; (*l*) pectic acid and alginic acid; (*m*) cellulose acetate and cellulose nitrate; (*n*) viscose rayon and acetate rayon; (*o*) ethylcellulose and cellulose acetate?
22. Give reactions for carrying out the following conversions: (*a*) D-xylose to D-gulonic acid; (*b*) D-galactose to D-talose; (*c*) D-arabinose to D-altrose; (*d*) D-ribose to 2-deoxy-D-allose; (*e*) D-xylose to D-sorbose; (*f*) D-galactose to D-lyxose.
23. Write perspective formulas for the following disaccharides: (*a*) 4-(α-L-arabinopyranosyl)-β-D-galactopyranose; (*b*) 6-(β-D-ribofuranosyl)-α-D-glucopyranose; (*c*) β-D-mannopyranosyl-α-L-rhamnopyranoside; (*d*) 4-(α-D-mannofuranosyl)-α-D-xylopyranose; (*e*) β-L-fucopyranosyl-β-D-glucofuranoside.
24. Give a series of reactions for preparing the following compounds starting with the proper sugar: (*a*) 2,3,4,6-tetra-*O*-methyl-D-mannose; (*b*) 2,3,6-tri-*O*-methyl-D-glucose; (*c*) 2,3,4-tri-*O*-methyl-L-arabinose; (*d*) 6-*O*-methyl-D-galactose; (*e*) 3-*O*-methyl-D-glucose; (*f*) 2,3,4,5,6-penta-*O*-methyl-D-mannose; (*g*) 2,3,4,6-D-galactose tetraacetate.
25. A pentose of the D-family gave an optically active glycaric acid on oxidation. When it was degraded to the tetrose and the tetrose was oxidized, *meso*-tartaric acid was formed. What is the configuration and name of the pentose?
26. A pentose of the D-family gave an optically active dibasic acid on oxidation. It was converted to a pair of diastereoisomeric hexoses, one of which gave an optically active glycaric acid when oxidized and the other an optically inactive glycaric acid. What are the configurations and names of the hexoses and the pentose?
27. A pentose gave an optically inactive glycaric acid on oxidation. It was converted to a pair of diastereoisomeric hexoses, one of which was oxidized to a glycaric acid identical with that derived from D-glucose. What are the configurations and names of the hexoses and the pentose?
28. An aldoheptose belonging to the D-family was oxidized with nitric acid and gave a *meso* pentahydroxy dibasic acid. When the heptose was degraded to the hexose and oxidized to the dibasic acid, an active form was obtained. If the hexose first was made to undergo epimeric change and then oxidized, the dibasic acid was inactive. What is the configuration of the heptose?

Chapter 18

BENZENE AND ITS HOMOLOGS.
SOURCES OF AROMATIC COMPOUNDS

Most of the compounds considered thus far are classed as aliphatic, because their composition is related to that of the fats insofar as the hydrocarbon portion of the molecule is concerned (Gr. *aliphatos*, fat). It was recognized at an early date that many other compounds had a hydrocarbon portion with a higher ratio of carbon to hydrogen and with distinctly different chemical properties. These substances frequently were pleasantly odorous or derivable from aromatic substances. For example, the essential components of the volatile oils of cloves, cinnamon, sassafras, anise, bitter almonds, wintergreen, and vanilla exhibited these properties. The hydrocarbon *benzene* received its name because it was obtained by the decarboxylation of benzoic acid isolated from the aromatic substance *gum benzoin*, and the name *toluene* was assigned to another hydrocarbon because it had been obtained by heating the fragrant *tolu balsam*. Loschmidt[1] in 1861 was the first to state that most of the aromatic compounds could be considered as derivatives of benzene, C_6H_6, just as the aliphatic compounds were considered as derivatives of methane, CH_4. Since then the term *aromatic compounds* has been applied to those compounds having the characteristic chemical properties of benzene.

BENZENE AND ITS HOMOLOGS

Isolation and Structure of Benzene

During the latter part of the eighteenth century an illuminating gas was manufactured in England by the thermal decomposition of whale oil and other fat oils. When this gas was compressed for distribution in tanks, a light mobile liquid separated. This liquid was brought to the attention of Michael Faraday (p. 92) in 1820, and in 1825 he reported the isolation, by distillation and crystallization, of a compound which he called *bicarburet of hydrogen*. In 1833 Mitscherlich[2] reported the isolation of the same hydrocarbon by distilling benzoic acid with lime. He named his product *benzin*, but Liebig, as editor of the Annalen der Chemie, added a note to Mitscherlich's paper stating that a more suitable name would be *benzol*, the ending *ol* indicating that it was a liquid (L. *oleum*, oil) obtained from the solid benzoic acid. Benzol still is the

---

[1] Joseph Loschmidt (1821–1895), Austrian physicist and professor at the University of Vienna. He originally was a chemist and published privately in 1861 his views on the use of graphic constitutional formulas in organic chemistry. In this work he proposed formulas for 368 compounds of which 121 belonged to the aromatic series.

[2] Eilhard Mitscherlich (1794–1855), professor of chemistry at the University of Berlin. He first specialized in Oriental languages, particularly Persian, and began the study of medicine because as a physician he would have more freedom than other Europeans to travel in Persia. He soon became so interested in chemical subjects that he gave up his aspirations in the other fields. He is noted chiefly for his work on isomorphism.

common term in the German chemical literature and is used in all countries by technicians in the coal tar industry. It has been replaced in the English and French literature by the term *benzene*, the ending *ol* being reserved for alcohols. Although the separation of benzene from the products of the destructive distillation of coal (p. 426) usually is credited to Leigh (1842) and Hoffmann (1845), Liebig's note to Mitscherlich's work indicates that Faraday's compound was recognized then as one of the products of the distillation of coal.

The data of both Faraday and Mitscherlich indicated that benzene has the molecular formula C_6H_6. Since the corresponding alkane has the molecular formula C_6H_{14}, benzene would be expected to be highly unsaturated. On the contrary, it is almost as stable to oxidation and to the usual addition reactions as the saturated hydrocarbons. Hydrogen adds catalytically (p. 830) and chlorine or bromine adds in the presence of sunlight (p. 432), but only six atoms add and not eight. Moreover the number of isomers formed on replacing hydrogen atoms by other elements or groups does not correspond to that expected for the aliphatic hydrocarbons. Thus only one monosubstitution product, for example, one chlorobenzene, one hydroxybenzene, or one amino-benzene, is known. Hence each hydrogen atom bears the same relationship to the molecule as a whole as every other hydrogen atom; that is, the molecule is symmetrically constituted.

Kekulé, who originated or consolidated most of the views concerning the structure of organic compounds (p. 4), assigned the first definite structural formula to benzene in 1865. He proposed that the six carbon atoms were at the corners of a regular hexagon and that one hydrogen atom was joined to each.

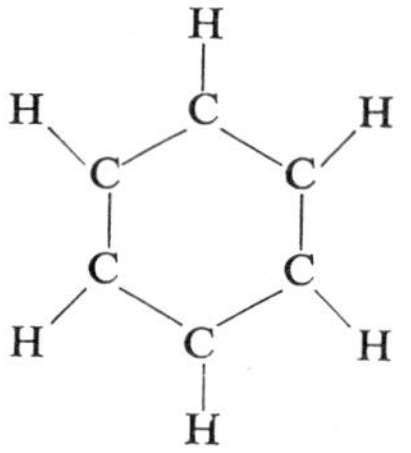

Four years earlier Loschmidt (p. 416) had represented the benzene nucleus by a circle but had made no attempt to indicate the arrangement of the carbon atoms in the nucleus. Kekulé's formula accounts also for the fact that if two hydrogen atoms are replaced by other groups, *Y*, three and only three isomers are known. If two adjacent hydrogen atoms are replaced, the resulting compound is known as the *ortho* isomer; if two alternate hydrogen atoms are replaced, the compound is known as the *meta* isomer; and if two opposite hydrogen atoms are replaced, it is known as the *para* isomer.

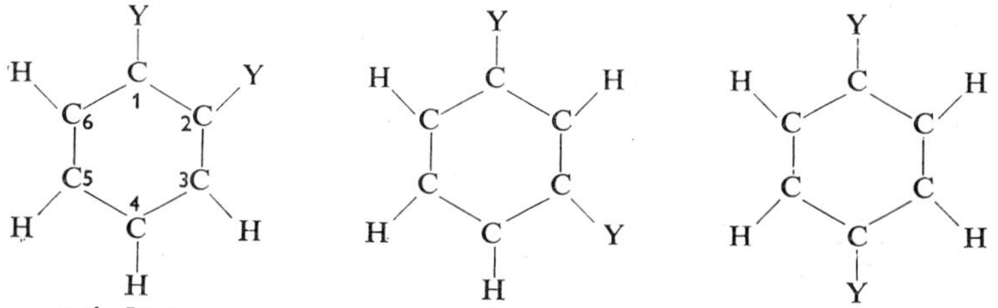

ortho Isomer   *meta* Isomer   *para* Isomer

Regardless of which two adjacent hydrogen atoms are replaced the same compound results. For example, if hydrogen atoms at positions 3 and 4 are replaced instead of those at 1 and 2, rotation through 120 degrees in the plane of the paper brings the two molecules into coincidence. Similar considerations hold for the *meta* and *para* isomer. Moreover the two groups, Y, may be alike or different without changing the number of isomers.

Objections to the simple hexagon formula for benzene are that it violates Kekulé's own advocacy of the tetravalence of carbon, and that it does not explain the addition of six atoms of halogen or six atoms of hydrogen. Both objections are overcome by the introduction of three double bonds in continuous conjugation. Now, however, the objection arises that two *ortho* substitution products would be expected, one in which the two carbon atoms carrying the Y groups are linked by a double bond (*a*), and another in which they are linked by a single bond (*b*). To overcome this difficulty, Kekulé proposed in 1872

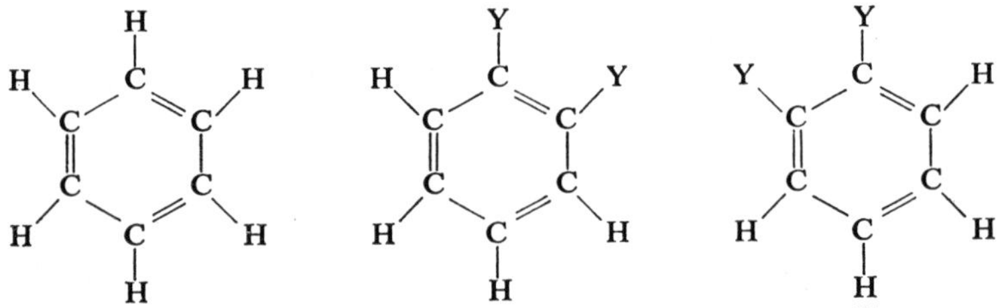

that the positions of the double bonds are not fixed, but that an equilibrium exists between two structures which is so mobile that individual isomers such as (*a*) and (*b*) cannot be isolated.

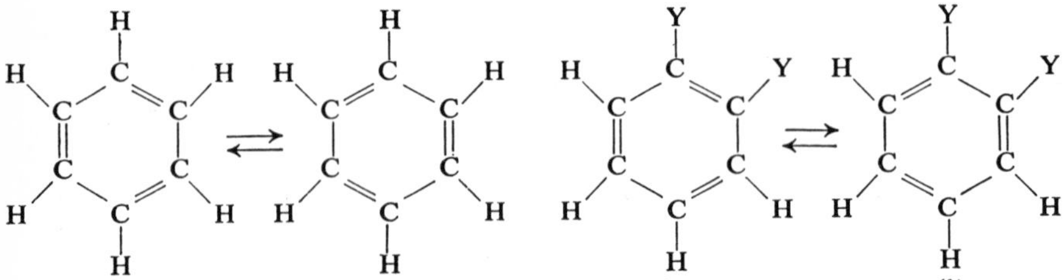

The current view is that in neither benzene nor its derivatives do molecules of two structures exist in mobile equilibrium with each other, but that only one kind of molecule is present which is a hybrid of the two structures. The most direct evidence for this view comes from the measurement of the distances between carbon atoms by means of electron diffraction. In ethane and other saturated compounds the distance between adjacent carbon atoms is 1.55 Å, in ethylene the carbon-carbon distance is 1.34 Å, and in acetylene it is 1.20 Å. In other words the distance is shorter for a double bond than for a single bond and shorter for a triple bond than for a double bond (p. 51). This result is to be expected, because the attraction between atoms increases with the formation of each bond. In compounds containing both single bonds and double bonds, both distances are observed, but for benzene only a single carbon-carbon distance can be detected, namely 1.39 Å, which lies between the single bond and double bond distances. Therefore all of the carbon-carbon bonds in benzene are alike and have properties intermediate between those of a single bond and of a double bond.

The problem of benzene structure is the same as that for the carboxylate ion (p. 153) and the nitro group (p. 258). The two classical Kekulé structures correspond to two equivalent electronic structures. The so-called *resonance hybrid* of the two electronic structures is more stable than either single structure by the resonance energy, which for benzene is about 36 kcal. per mole. The nature of the resonance hybrid probably can be made clear most readily by the use of molecular orbitals. Each carbon atom is bonded to three other atoms. Hence sp^2 hybridization of the atomic orbitals of the carbon atoms takes place on bonding, and three σ-type molecular orbitals are formed making angles of 120 degrees to each other and causing the four atoms to lie in a plane (p. 12). Therefore all of the atoms of benzene lie in a plane and all bond angles are 120 degrees. These σ-type bonds are indicated by the usual dash. One p orbital containing an unpaired electron remains at each carbon atom as illustrated in Fig. 74a. If the p orbitals overlapped as three pairs as indicated in Fig. 74b, one of the Kekulé structures with

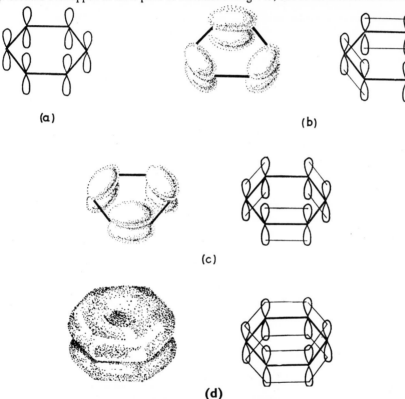

(a)

(b)

(c)

(d)

Fig. 74. Resonance in benzene.

three double bonds would be obtained, whereas if they overlapped as in Fig. 74c, the other Kekulé structure would be obtained. However since any p orbital overlaps both p orbitals on either side of it equally well, all six orbitals overlap each other giving a hexagonal π orbital above and below the plane of the carbon atoms (Fig. 74d). These structures are shown schematically by drawing light lines connecting p orbitals to indicate overlapping. The heavier lines indicate the σ-type bonds between the atoms (p. 10). The movement of the π electrons about six positive nuclei instead of only two accounts for the greater stability of this system and the large resonance energy of the aromatic ring. Because of the Pauli exclusion principle (p. 5), the molecular π orbital indicated can accommodate only two electrons. Hence two additional π orbitals must be available to accommodate the remaining four electrons. These two π orbitals also encompass all six nuclei, but each has a nodal plane perpendicular to the plane of the ring in addition to that coinciding with the plane of the ring.

Nomenclature

Aromatic compounds may be named as derivatives of benzene or of some other aromatic compound. Thus the compound in which a chlorine atom has replaced a hydrogen atom in benzene is known as chlorobenzene. When more than one substituent is present the positions occupied are indicated by numbers. The six carbon atoms of benzene are numbered from 1 to 6, the starting point being that which gives the substituents the smaller numbers. Usually a formula is written with one group at the top carbon atom of the hexagon, which then becomes the number 1 carbon atom. It is preferable to name the substituent groups in alphabetical order. When only two substituents are present, the designations *ortho, meta,* or *para* may be used. Sometimes these terms are combined with numerals, but this practice should be discontinued because it frequently leads to ambiguity.

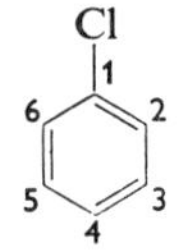

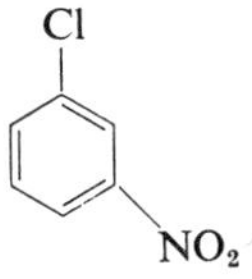

1-Chloro-3-nitrobenzene
3-Chloronitrobenzene
m-Chloronitrobenzene

Chlorobenzene

In these and subsequent formulas the carbon and hydrogen atoms of the benzene ring are represented by the simple hexagon and only those groups replacing hydrogen are given. The double bonds are included to indicate that the ring is aromatic and not alicyclic (p. 64), but it is understood that they are not the same as fixed aliphatic double bonds (p. 418).

Common names are used even more extensively for aromatic compounds than for aliphatic compounds. Thus many of the hydrocarbons have common names. Methylbenzene is called *toluene,* and 1,2-, 1,3-, and 1,4-dimethylbenzene are known as *ortho-, meta-,* and *para-xylene.*

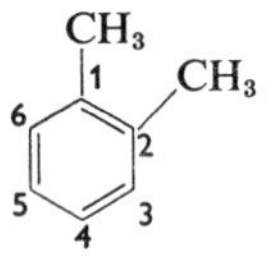

o-Xylene 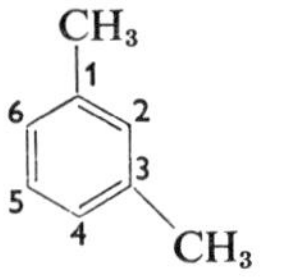   *m*-Xylene 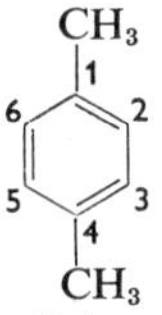   *p*-Xylene

1,3,5-Trimethylbenzene is called *mesitylene,* isopropylbenzene is *cumene,* 1,2,4,5-tetramethylbenzene is *durene,* and 4-isopropyltoluene is *p-cymene.*

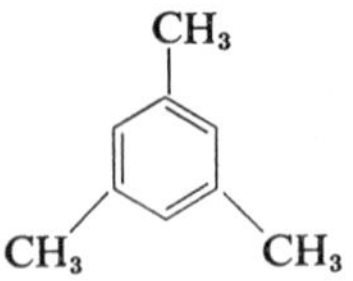

Mesitylene 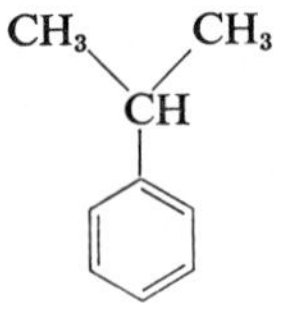   Cumene 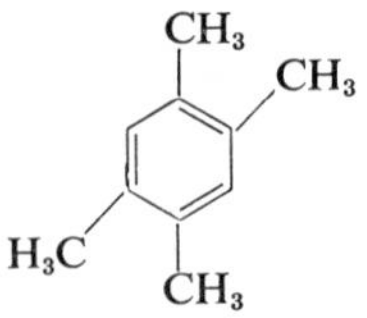   Durene 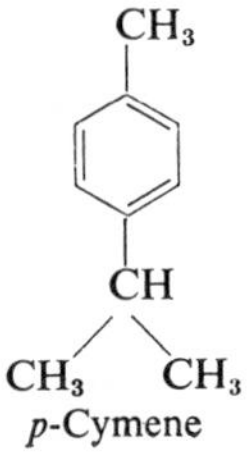   *p*-Cymene

Kekulé introduced the terms *ring* and *nucleus* to designate the characteristic portion of aromatic compounds. The aliphatic portions he called *side chains*. Groups obtained by dropping a hydrogen atom from the nucleus are called *aryl* groups. Frequently they are indicated by the symbol Ar, just as R is used to designate an alkyl group. The group C_6H_5 derived from benzene is known as *phenyl*. This name is derived from *phene*, a name that was proposed by Laurent (p. 535) for benzene, because it is present in illuminating gas (Gr. *phainein*, to bring to light). If two hydrogen atoms are dropped, the residue, C_6H_4, is known as a *phenylene* group. Since the two hydrogen atoms may be removed in three ways, there are *o-*, *m-*, and *p-*phenylene groups. If a hydrogen atom is dropped from the methyl group of toluene, the residue is known as a *benzyl* group, but if from the nucleus, three *tolyl* groups, *ortho*, *meta*, and *para*, result. The term *xylyl* appears in the literature, but it should be dropped, because it has been used to mean $(CH_3)_2C_6H_3{}^-$ as well as $CH_3C_6H_4CH_2{}^-$.

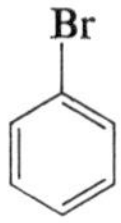

Br

Bromobenzene
(phenyl bromide)

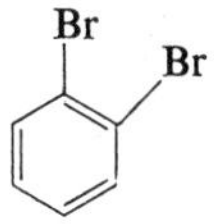

Br
Br

o-Dibromobenzene or
1,2-dibromobenzene
(*o*-phenylene bromide)

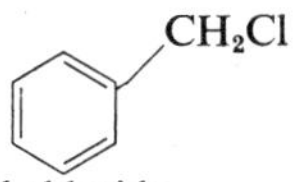

CH₂Cl

Benzyl chloride
(phenylmethyl chloride)

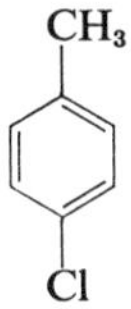

CH_3

Cl

p-Chlorotoluene
(*p*-tolyl chloride)

Physical Properties of Benzene

Hexane, C_6H_{14}, boils at 68.8°, and since benzene has a lower molecular weight, its boiling point might be expected to be lower. Actually benzene boils at 80.1°. The higher boiling point can be ascribed to the fact that the benzene molecules have a rigid flat structure, whereas the hexane chains can undergo considerable twisting and bending on thermal agitation. Hence the van der Waals forces can operate more effectively between the benzene molecules. The more symmetrical structure for benzene accounts also for its relatively high melting point of +5.5° compared with −95° for hexane or for toluene.

Being a hydrocarbon, benzene is practically insoluble in water, but the solubility at 15° of 0.18 g. per 100 g. of water is over ten times that of the 0.014 g. per 100 g. of water for *n*-hexane. The greater attraction of benzene for water molecules would be expected because of the greater polarizability of the unsaturation electrons. The solubility of water in benzene is 0.06 g. per 100 g. of benzene. In general the solubility of highly associated liquids and solids in aromatic hydrocarbons and of aromatic hydrocarbons in associated liquids is greater than the corresponding solubilities of the saturated hydrocarbons. It is for this reason that aromatic hydrocarbons are more useful as solvents and diluents for paints, lacquers, and synthetic enamels than are petroleum fractions.

They can be used only with proper precautions, however, because of their high toxicity. They cause the destruction of red blood corpuscles, and even very low concentrations are dangerous on prolonged exposure. All workers using materials containing volatile aromatic hydrocarbons should be subjected to frequent blood counts to detect signs of poisoning.

Reactions of the Benzene Nucleus

The usual reagents for double bonds do not add readily to the benzene nucleus. As a measure of the relative reactivity of benzene and olefins to addition, the heat liberated on catalytic hydrogenation may be cited. A doubly substituted olefin such as *cis*-butene liberates 28.6 kcal. per mole on catalytic hydrogenation. If three ordinary double bonds were present in benzene, the heat liberated should be $3 \times 28.6 = 85.8$ kcal. The actual amount of heat liberated is 49.8 kcal. The difference of 36 kcal. is the resonance energy of benzene; that is, of the 85.8 kcal. that is liberated on the catalytic hydrogenation of three double bonds, 36 kcal. is used up overcoming the resonance energy of the benzene molecule. Since the heat liberated on hydrogenating 1,3-cyclohexadiene, the cyclic compound with two conjugated double bonds, is 57.2 kcal., the hydrogenation of benzene to cyclohexadiene actually is endothermic by 7.4 kcal. Similarly in other addition reactions, energy must be supplied to get the first mole of reagent to react. In general the reactivity of the unsaturation electrons of benzene is so low that the double bonds usually can be disregarded. Frequently they are not even indicated in the formula for benzene.

In contrast to the nonreactivity of the double bonds, the hydrogen atoms of the aromatic nucleus are substituted more readily than those of the alkanes. The following characteristic reactions of aromatic compounds are the most important ones.

1. **Controllable Halogenation.** Paraffin hydrocarbons react with chlorine or bromine at high temperatures or in the presence of light of short wave length, but the reaction is violent, the position of substitution is random, and considerable quantities of polysubstitution products are formed (p. 119). At ordinary temperatures and in the absence of light, reaction is very slow. Benzene reacts with chlorine or bromine in the presence of light, but addition takes place rather than substitution. On the other hand benzene reacts rapidly with chlorine or bromine in the presence of a catalyst such as ferric chloride or bromide at moderately elevated temperatures to give halogen substitution products.

Chlorobenzene

Since a second halogen substitutes with more difficulty, the reaction can be controlled to give chiefly the monosubstitution product.

2. **Controllable Nitration.** Propane or *n*-butane reacts with oxides of nitrogen at high temperatures. However, not only are all the isomeric monosubstitution

products obtained, but also all of the possible nitro compounds resulting from breaking of the carbon-carbon bonds (p. 259). In contrast, benzene reacts with fuming nitric acid at moderate temperature, or better with concentrated nitric acid in the presence of concentrated sulfuric acid, to give good yields of the mononitro substitution products.

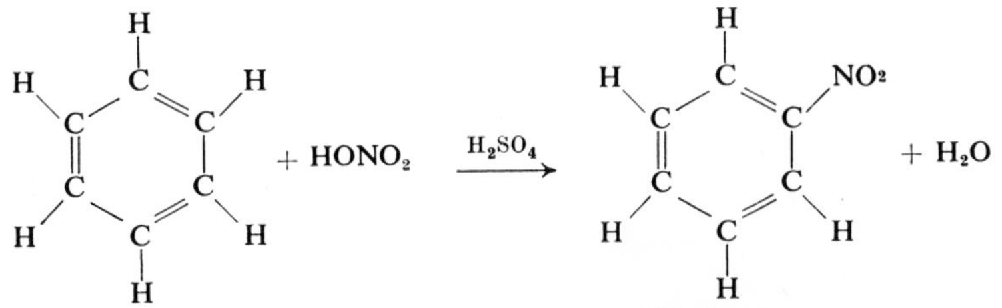

$$+ \text{HONO}_2 \xrightarrow{\text{H}_2\text{SO}_4} \quad + \text{H}_2\text{O}$$

Nitrobenzene

3. **Direct Sulfonation.** Straight chain alkanes do not react with concentrated sulfuric acid, and although branched-chain alkanes react, there is some indication that oxidation to olefins is the first step (p. 287). Sulfonation of benzene takes place readily to give the monosulfonic acid in good yield.

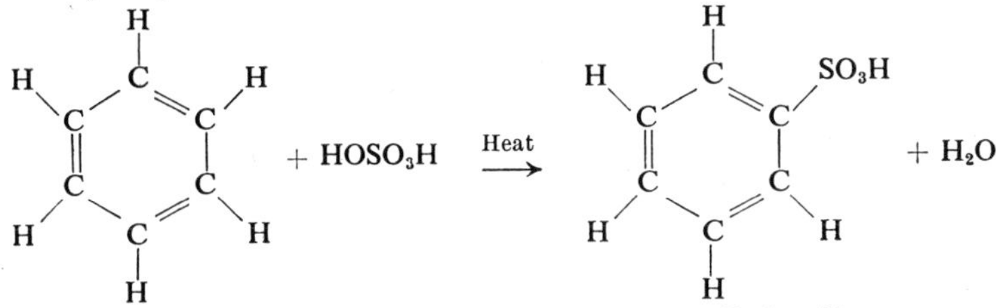

$$+ \text{HOSO}_3\text{H} \xrightarrow{\text{Heat}} \quad + \text{H}_2\text{O}$$

Benzenesulfonic acid

4. **Friedel-Crafts Reaction.** Aromatic hydrocarbons react with acyl halides in the presence of anhydrous aluminum chloride to give good yields of ketones. The reaction is known as the Friedel-Crafts reaction.[3,4]

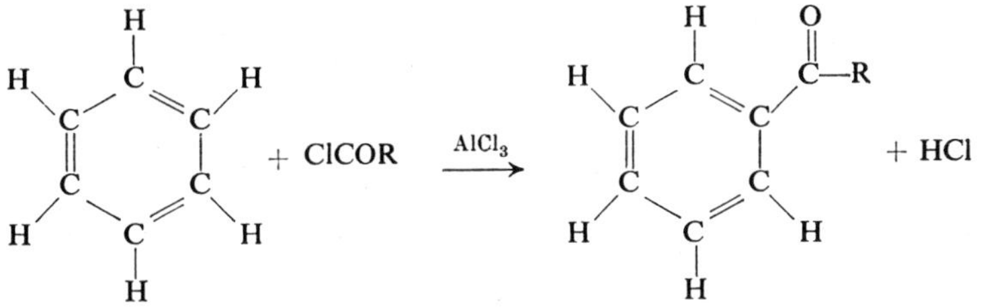

$$+ \text{ClCOR} \xrightarrow{\text{AlCl}_3} \quad + \text{HCl}$$

[3] Charles Friedel (1832–1899), successor to Wurtz at the Sorbonne. He was the first to produce isopropyl alcohol by the reduction of acetone, and to report, with Crafts, transesterification. He investigated the preparation of organosilicon compounds, and in his later years devoted himself to the chemical aspects of mineralogy.

[4] James Mason Crafts (1839–1917), graduate of Harvard University and student of Bunsen and Wurtz. He became professor of chemistry first at Cornell and then at Massachusetts Institute of Technology, but resigned his post in 1874 because of poor health. He revisited the laboratory of Wurtz, planning to stay about a year, and remained there for seventeen years. Much of this time he worked in collaboration with Friedel. He returned to the United States in 1891 and resumed teaching at the Institute. He became head of the chemistry department in 1895 and was president of the Institute from 1897 until he resigned in 1900 to continue his scientific investigations.

It is the ability to undergo these substitution reactions that is characteristic of benzene and its derivatives. Compounds exhibiting these properties constitute the *aromatic compounds*.

5. **Oxidation of Side Chains.** Although this reaction does not involve the aromatic nucleus, it usually is considered as one of the typical reactions of aromatic compounds. When the alkylbenzenes are subjected to vigorous oxidation with dichromic acid (sodium dichromate and sulfuric acid) or potassium permanganate, or to catalytic air oxidation, the alkyl group is converted to a carboxyl group.

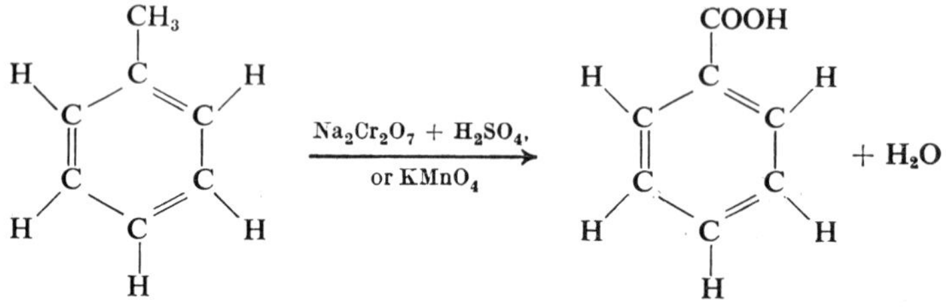

Toluene

Benzoic acid

Since the point of attack is the carbon atom attached to the benzene nucleus, a carboxyl group results regardless of the size of the alkyl group or the type of substituent present in the alkyl group.

Orientation of Substituents in the Benzene Nucleus

Whenever more than one substituent is present in a benzene nucleus, several structural isomers may exist, and it is desirable to know which structure to assign to a particular isomer. For example, three xylenes are known (p. 420). One boils at 138.4° and melts at +13.4°, another boils at 139.3° and melts at −47.4°, and the third boils at 144.1° and melts at −25°. The question is, "Which isomer has the methyl groups in the *ortho* position, which in the *meta* position, and which in the *para* position?" The procedure for assigning structures to isomeric benzene derivatives is known as *orientation.* Two methods have found general use. One is known as the Koerner absolute method, and the other may be called the interconversion method.

Koerner [5] Absolute Method. If a third group is introduced into each member of any set of three isomeric disubstituted benzenes in which the two original substituents are alike, the *ortho* isomer should yield two trisubstitution products, the *meta* three trisubstitution products, and the *para* only one trisubstitution

[5] Wilhelm Koerner (1839–1925), assistant to Kekulé and Cannizzaro and later professor of chemistry and director of the School of Technology and Agriculture in Milan. He devised one of the chemical proofs of the equivalence of the six hydrogen atoms of benzene, and first proposed the accepted structural formula for pyridine (p. 621).

product. For example, o-xylene on mono-nitration should yield two nitro-o-xylenes, m-xylene should yield three nitro-m-xylenes, and p-xylene should yield one nitro-p-xylene.

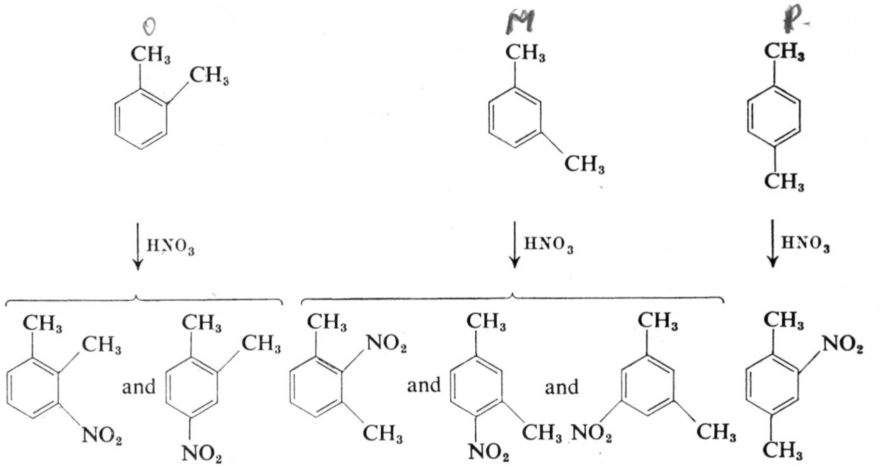

The nitro group has, of course, a larger total number of positions to enter, but more than one position may yield the same compound. For example, in p-xylene four hydrogen atoms may be replaced by a nitro group but replacement of any one of them yields the same product.

When the three known xylenes are subjected to monosubstitution, that boiling at 138.4° yields only one compound and hence is the *para* isomer; that boiling at 139.3° yields three compounds and hence is the *meta* isomer; that boiling at 144.1° yields only two compounds and hence is the *ortho* isomer. The constitution of a number of disubstituted benzenes has been determined by this procedure, and the principle can be extended to other types of substitution products.

The orientation of substituents in several polysubstituted benzenes had been determined previously by less general procedures. For example, in 1874, the year prior to the publication of Koerner's work, Griess (p. 492) had determined the structure of the three diaminobenzenes by a procedure which was the reverse of Koerner's method. Six different diaminobenzene carboxylic acids were known which could be decarboxylated to the diamines.

$$C_6H_3(NH_2)_2COOH \longrightarrow C_6H_4(NH_2)_2 + CO_2$$

Three of the acids gave the same diamine, which therefore was *meta*diaminobenzene. Two of the acids gave a second diamine which must be the *ortho* compound. The remaining acid gave a third diamine which was the *para* diamine.

Interconversion Method. Once the orientation of the groups in a substituted benzene has been determined, the orientation is known for all compounds that can be derived from it by converting one or more substituents into other groups. For example, three benzenedicarboxylic acids are known. One called *phthalic acid* melts with decomposition at about 200°, another, *isophthalic acid*, melts at 348°, and a third, *terephthalic acid*, sublimes without melting at 300°. These acids can be formed respectively by the vigorous oxidation of *o-*, *m-*, and *p*-xylene and hence are the *o-*, *m-*, and *p*-dicarboxylic acids.

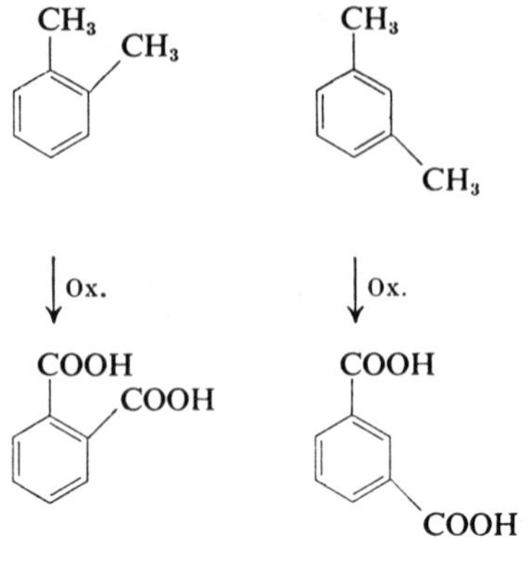

Phthalic acid   Isophthalic acid   Terephthalic acid

Since the three methylbenzenecarboxylic acids (toluic acids) also yield the three phthalic acids on oxidation, their constitution likewise is established.

SOURCES OF AROMATIC COMPOUNDS

Carbonization of Coal

Coal is a compact stratified mass derived from plants which have suffered partial decay and have been subjected to various degrees of heat and pressure. Most normal banded coals are believed to have originated in peat swamps. The substances peat, lignite, soft or bituminous coal, and anthracite or hard coal are progressive stages of metamorphosis in which the ratio of the amount of carbon to the amount of other elements increases. When bituminous coal is heated to a sufficiently high temperature (350°–1000°) in the absence of air, volatile products are formed, and a residue of impure carbon remains which is called *coke*. The process is known as the *destructive distillation* or *carbonization* of coal. When the volatile products cool to ordinary temperature, a portion condenses to a black viscous liquid known as *coal tar*. The noncondensable gases are known as *coal gas*. One ton of coal yields about 1500 pounds of coke, 8 gallons of tar, and 10,000 cubic feet of coal gas. About 20 pounds of ammonium sulfate is obtained by removing ammonia from the gas by washing with sulfuric acid. Production of coal tar in the United States in 1955 was over 900 million gallons.

The principal reason for the commercial carbonization of coal is the production of **coke,** which is used for the reduction of ores in blast furnaces. Coke is used also as a smokeless industrial and household fuel.

Coal gas varies in composition during the course of the distillation but consists chiefly of hydrogen and methane in about equal volumes, along with some carbon monoxide, ethane, ethylene, benzene, carbon dioxide, oxygen, and nitrogen, and smaller amounts of cyclopentadiene (p. 837), toluene, naphthalene (p. 582), water vapor, ammonia, hydrogen sulfide, hydrogen cyanide, cyanogen, and nitric oxide. After removal of the noxious components the gas is run into mains for use as illuminating gas and as a domestic fuel. When economically desirable, the benzene, toluene, and other less volatile hydrocarbons also are removed by washing (*scrubbing*) with a high-boiling petroleum fraction (b.p. 285°–350°) known as *straw oil.* The hydrocarbons are recovered by heating (*stripping*) the oil and condensing the vapors. The liquid obtained contains chiefly benzene and toluene and is known as *light oil* because of its low specific gravity. Although the benzene and toluene are liquids at room temperature, the coal gas is saturated with them, and a larger amount can be obtained by washing the coal gas than can be obtained by distilling the coal tar. About three gallons of light oil can be recovered per ton of coal carbonized.

The composition of **coal tar** varies with the process used for carbonization. Tar obtained from high temperature distillation is the most useful for chemical purposes. The first step in the separation of the black foul-smelling liquid into its components is distillation. The fractions obtained in a typical procedure are (*1*) *light oil* (so-called because it floats on water) distilling up to 200°, 5 per cent; (*2*) *middle oil* (carbolic oil), 200°–250°, 17 per cent; (*3*) *heavy oil* (dead oil, creosote oil), 250°–300°, 7 per cent; (*4*) *anthracene oil* (green oil), 300°–350°, 9 per cent; and (*5*) *pitch*, the residue, 62 per cent.

The further separation of the fractions depends on a combination of chemical and physical methods. Three main groups of substances are present: (*1*) *neutral compounds*, chiefly hydrocarbons; (*2*) *tar acids*, very weakly acidic substances soluble in sodium hydroxide solution; (*3*) *tar bases*, weakly basic substances soluble in dilute sulfuric acid.

The **light oil** fraction from coal tar is rather small, but about eight times as much can be recovered by scrubbing coal gas. It usually is separated directly into its components by fractional distillation. The so-called *crude 90 per cent benzol* is a fraction, 90 per cent of which distills between 80° and 100°; *crude 90 per cent toluol, solvent naphtha,* and *heavy naphtha* are the fractions, 90 per cent of which distill between the ranges 100° to 120°, 130° to 160°, and 160° to 210° respectively. They consist chiefly of aromatic hydrocarbons and olefins. Most of the tar bases remain behind with the tar acids. The fractions are treated with concentrated sulfuric acid to polymerize the olefins and then are washed with 10 per cent aqueous sodium hydroxide and distilled to give benzene, toluene, and xylenes.

The **middle** or **carbolic oil** is combined with the high-boiling fraction from the light oil and cooled in large shallow pans. The solid hydrocarbon *naphthalene* (p. 582) crystallizes and is removed by centrifuging. The crude naphthalene is distilled, washed while molten with sulfuric acid, water, and aqueous alkali, and distilled again to give refined naphthalene. The oil that is separated from the crude naphthalene is washed with aqueous sodium hydroxide to remove the tar acids. Steam is passed into the aqueous extract to remove volatile materials, and then the solution is cooled and saturated with carbon dioxide, which precipitates the weakly acidic tar acids from their salts. The tar acid layer is separated and fractionally distilled to give phenol (p. 509), which is purified further by crystallization. The aqueous sodium carbonate layer is reconverted to sodium hydroxide solution (causticized) by the addition of lime, and the precipitate of calcium carbonate is reconverted to lime and carbon dioxide by heating in lime kilns. The oil remaining after the extraction of acidic substances with alkali is washed with aqueous sulfuric acid, which forms salts with the tar bases and takes them into solution. The tar bases are liberated by the addition of sodium hydroxide and distilled to give chiefly *pyridine* (p. 620). The oil remaining from the acid treatment is distilled to give solvent naphtha and a solid residue of polymerized olefins known as *cumar resin*.

The **heavy oil** may be treated in much the same way to yield naphthalene, the higher tar acids (cresols, p. 502), and the higher tar bases (quinolines, p. 628). The **anthracene oil** is run into tanks and allowed to crystallize over a period of one to two weeks. After filtration the nearly dry cakes are subjected to about 60,000 pounds pressure in a warm hydraulic press to remove more liquid impurities and then ground and washed with solvent naphtha to remove most of the hydrocarbon *phenanthrene* (p. 602), and with pyridine to remove most of a nitrogen-containing compound, *carbazole* (p. 616). The residue is sublimed to give the hydrocarbon *anthracene* (p. 596) of 85 to 90 per cent purity. With the development of commercial methods of synthesis for pyridine, pyridine derivatives, anthracene derivatives, and carbazole, the tendency has been not to separate the higher fractions into their components but to use them as wood preservatives under the name *creosote oil*.

Over 215 individual compounds have been isolated from coal tar, the first being naphthalene, described in 1820. Anthracene was isolated in 1832, phenol, aniline (p. 475), quinoline, and pyrrole (p. 610) in 1834, and chrysene (p. 603) in 1837. Forty-six components were isolated during the thirty year period 1861–1890 and over 100 during the 15-year period 1931–1946. The remainder are scattered over the intervening years. The period 1861–1890 was that of the most intensive development of the chemistry of coal tar. The large number of compounds isolated during the period 1931–1946 reflected new techniques for separation and an exhaustive effort to identify all of the components of coal tar. The more important components are listed in Table 21. The amounts of

TABLE 21

CHIEF COMPONENTS OF COAL TAR

COMPOUND	PER CENT	COMPOUND	PER CENT
Benzene	0.1	Phenanthrene	4.0
Toluene	0.2	Anthracene	1.1
Xylenes	1.0	Carbazole	1.1
Naphthalene	10.9	Crude tar bases	2.0
α- and β-Methylnaphthalenes	2.5	(Pyridine 0.1)	
Dimethylnaphthalenes	3.4	Crude tar acids	2.5
Acenaphthene	1.4	(Phenol, 0.7, cresols, 1.1,	
Fluorene	1.6	xylenols, 0.2)	

benzene and toluene given are those present in coal tar and do not include the light oil fraction extracted from coal gas by scrubbing (p. 427).

In 1952 an experimental plant which has the primary object of producing aromatic chemicals rather than coke, from coal, was placed in operation in the United States. A mixture of powdered coal and heavy oil from the product stream is partially hydrogenated at 5000 p.s.i. and 500° in the presence of an iron catalyst, whereby 90 per cent of the coal is converted to a liquid crude oil. Distillation of the oil yields about 10 per cent aliphatic compounds, 50 per cent aromatic compounds, and 40 per cent coke. In this process the yield of naphthalene is increased 5 to 8 times, of phenol 60 to 80 times, of cresols 100 to 200 times, and of tar bases 300 to 500 times over that obtained by conventional coking processes.

Aromatic Hydrocarbons from Petroleum

With increased demand for aromatic compounds and the development of newer processes, the production of aromatic compounds from petroleum by isomerization and dehydrogenation (pp. 64, 66, 76) has become economically feasible. In 1955 the total U.S. production of benzene was 410 million gallons of which one fourth came from petroleum. Of the 334 million gallons of toluene produced, 45 per cent came from petroleum, as did 50 per cent of the 208 million gallons of xylenes.

Before 1950 benzene had been produced commercially only from coal gas and coal tar (p. 427). As late as 1940, the amount available from this source was more than adequate, since less than a third of the potential United States supply of 125 million gallons per year was refined to pure benzene for solvent and chemical use. The balance was blended with gasoline for use as motor fuel. During World War II more aniline, phenol, and styrene were required, all of which are made from benzene. This demand continued to rise after the war with the result that insufficient benzene was available as a by-product of coke manufacture, since production of coke is limited by the production of steel. The price rose from 15 cents per gallon in 1946 to 30 cents in 1950, when it became profitable to produce benzene from petroleum. In 1955 the price was 40 cents per gallon. About 35 per cent was used for the manufacture of styrene, 20 per cent for phenol, 10 per cent for synthetic detergents, 5 per cent for aniline, and 30 per cent for other chemical intermediates and as solvent.

The economic picture of toluene is exactly the opposite. Prior to World War II, most of the United States production of 30 million gallons per year from coke manufacture was refined, although it was used chiefly as a solvent rather than for chemical purposes. During the war the demand for toluene for the manufacture of TNT required its production from petroleum. Annual capacity from petroleum reached 175 million gallons, giving a total capacity of over 200 million gallons. After the war, production dropped to 80 million gallons but slowly rose again to 208 million gallons in 1955. The price during this time remained almost constant at about 25 cents per gallon.

Other Sources of Benzene Homologs

Alkyl halides, as well as acyl halides, can be used in the Friedel-Crafts reaction (p. 423) to give alkyl instead of acyl derivatives.

$$\text{benzene} + RCl \xrightarrow{\text{AlCl}_3} \text{C}_6\text{H}_5\text{R} + HCl$$

Since an alkylbenzene substitutes even more readily than benzene (p. 449), these reactions lead to mixtures with higher alkylated compounds rather than to a single product. Thus in the reaction of benzene with methyl chloride in the presence of anhydrous aluminum chloride, not only toluene but also the xylenes and higher-alkylated benzenes are produced. By using a large excess of benzene, it is possible to obtain chiefly the monoalkylated benzene.

Higher primary alkyl halides give rearranged products in the Friedel-Crafts reaction. For example *n*-propyl halides give chiefly *i*-propylbenzene, *n*-butyl halides give *s*-butylbenzene, and *i*-butyl halides give *t*-butylbenzene.

The alkylbenzenes undergo intra- and intermolecular exchange of alkyl groups in the presence of Friedel-Crafts catalysts such as aluminum chloride-hydrogen chloride and boron fluoride-hydrogen fluoride. For example, any of the xylenes in the presence of small amounts of boron fluoride-hydrogen fluoride at 100° gives a mixture of toluene, xylenes, and trimethyl-benzenes. The xylenes are present in the equilibrium concentration required by their relative thermodynamic stability ($o:m:p = 16:60:24$). If, however, a high concentration of catalyst is present (1 mole per mole of hydrocarbon), the xylene present is entirely *m*-xylene. Similarly the trimethylbenzenes under these conditions isomerize completely to 1,3,5-trimethylbenzene (mesitylene). This behavior is due to the fact that *m*-xylene and 1,3,5-trimethylbenzene are the strongest bases of the various isomers, and form the most stable complex salts (cf. p. 449).

Alcohols or olefins also may be used to alkylate aromatic compounds. Concentrated sulfuric acid, phosphoric acid, or anhydrous hydrogen fluoride may be used as catalysts as well as the aluminum chloride-hydrogen chloride complexes. For commercial production the olefins are particularly useful, and several important hydrocarbons are synthesized by this process. Thus although the mixed xylene fraction derived from petroleum contains about 20 per cent of ethylbenzene, the boiling points of *m*-xylene, 139°, *p*-xylene, 138°, and ethylbenzene, 136°, are so close that it is easier to synthesize **ethylbenzene** than to separate it in the required purity from this mixture.

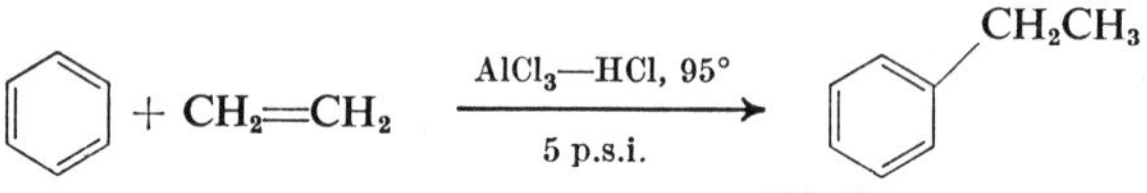

Ethylbenzene

The catalyst is a liquid aluminum chloride-hydrogen chloride-hydrocarbon complex through which the mixture of ethylene and an excess of benzene vapor is passed. The aromatic hydrocarbons are insoluble in the complex and are separated readily and the ethylbenzene is purified by distillation. Unreacted benzene and the higher-alkylated benzenes are recycled to give over-all yields of better than 95 per cent based on either the ethylene or benzene. The sole use for pure ethylbenzene is as an intermediate for the production of styrene (p. 574), which requires over a third of the total production of benzene. The production of over one billion pounds in 1955 was greater than that of any other synthetic aromatic compound and was exceeded only by that of methanol among the synthetic aliphatic compounds.

Cumene (*isopropylbenzene*) similarly is synthesized from benzene and propylene. Here the preferred catalyst is a supported phosphoric acid similar to that used for the polymerization of olefins (p. 62). The reaction is carried out at higher temperatures and pressures.

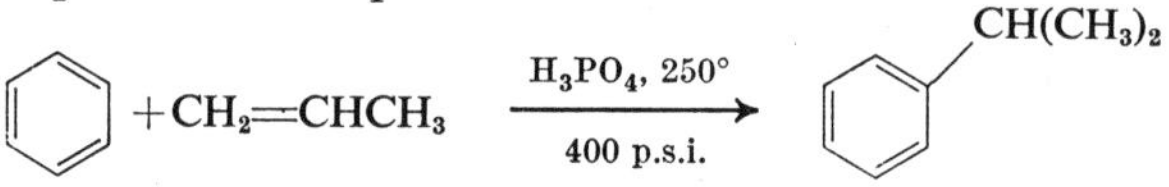

Cumene is used as a high-octane component of aviation fuel, and as an intermediate for the synthesis of phenol (p. 511).

Mesitylene is made by the condensation of three moles of acetone in the presence of concentrated sulfuric acid.

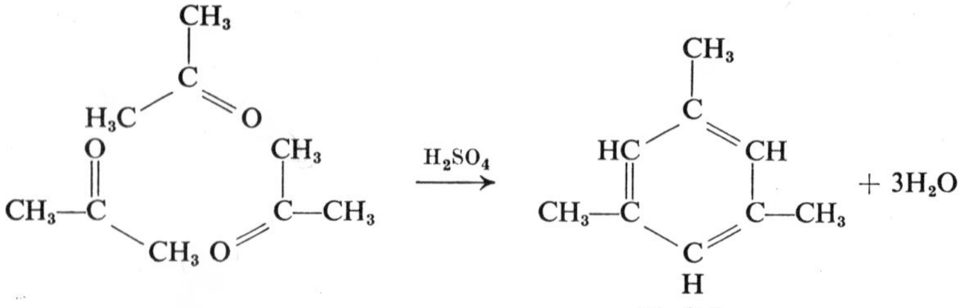

Mesitylene

The reaction illustrates one of a number of syntheses in which aromatic compounds are derived from aliphatic compounds. *p*-**Cymene** is one of the minor products of the sulfite process for making wood pulp (p. 400). The crude material is called *spruce turpentine*.

REVIEW QUESTIONS

1. What is the chief source of aromatic compounds? How are the various components separated?
2. Give the experimental facts on which the accepted structural formula of benzene is based.
3. Discuss and illustrate by equations the more important differences in the chemical behavior of aliphatic and aromatic hydrocarbons.
4. Discuss the Koerner absolute method for distinguishing between *ortho-*, *meta-*, and *para-* disubstituted benzenes when both groups are identical. What other procedure may be used?
5. Write structural formulas for toluene, the xylenes, mesitylene, *p*-cymene, cumene. What methods of preparation or sources of these compounds are available other than direct isolation from coal tar?
6. What are the formulas for the phenyl, phenylene, benzyl, and tolyl groups?
7. Compare the economic importance of benzene with that of toluene.

PROBLEMS

8. Give structural formulas and name all of the possible compounds in each of the following groups: (*a*) the tri- and tetramethylbenzenes; (*b*) the monochloromononitrotoluenes; (*c*) the monochlorodinitrobenzenes; (*d*) the monobromotrimethylbenzenes.
9. Show why it is not possible to use the simple Koerner method to distinguish between *ortho*, *meta*, and *para* disubstituted benzenes when the two groups are different.
10. What are the possible structural formulas of an aromatic hydrocarbon, $C_{10}H_{14}$, that meets the following specifications: (*a*) oxidation gives a monocarboxylic acid; (*b*) nitration can give three mononitro derivatives and oxidation a dicarboxylic acid; (*c*) nitration can give two mononitro derivatives and oxidation a dicarboxylic acid; (*d*) nitration can give two mononitro derivatives and oxidation a tricarboxylic acid?
11. Three tribromobenzenes are known, which melt at 44°, 87.4°, and 119°. When each is nitrated, they give respectively three, two, and one mononitrotribromobenzenes. Give the structures of the tribromobenzenes and of their nitration products.
12. Six dibromonitrobenzenes melt respectively at 57.8°, 61.8°, 82.6°, 83.6°, 85.2°, and 104.5°. When the nitro group is replaced by hydrogen by a series of reactions, the compound melting at 83.6° gives a dibromobenzene melting at 87°. The two dibromonitrobenzenes melting at 57.8° and 85.2° give a dibromobenzene boiling at 225°. The remaining three dibromonitrobenzenes give a dibromobenzene boiling at 219°. Assign structures to the three dibromobenzenes.
13. Three chloronitrobenzenes, *A*, *B*, and *C*, when nitrated further give two, four, and four dinitro derivatives respectively. When *o*-dinitrobenzene is monochlorinated, one of the products is identical with one of the four products obtained from *B* and with one of the four products obtained from *C*. The other isomer also is obtained from *C* but not from *B*. Assign structures to the three chloronitrobenzenes.

Chapter 19

HALOGEN DERIVATIVES OF AROMATIC HYDROCARBONS

In a strict sense aromatic halides are halogen compounds in which the halogen is attached directly to an aromatic nucleus. It is convenient, however, to consider also those halogen compounds formed by addition of halogen to the double bonds of the nucleus, and those in which the halogen is present in a side chain.

Reactions of Aromatic Hydrocarbons with Halogen

Halogen may react with aromatic hydrocarbons in three ways: (*1*) it may add to the double bonds of the nucleus giving a product which no longer has aromatic properties; (*2*) it may replace a hydrogen atom of the benzene nucleus to give an aryl halide; (*3*) if an alkyl side chain is present, it may replace a hydrogen atom of the side chain to give an aralkyl halide.

Addition of Halogen. Exposure of a mixture of benzene and chlorine or bromine to light of short wavelength causes the addition of six atoms of halogen to give a mixture of stereoisomeric benzene hexachlorides or hexabromides.

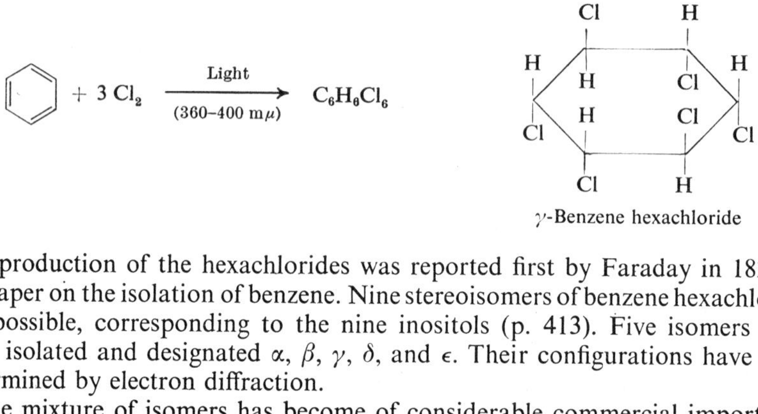

$$\bigcirc + 3\,Cl_2 \xrightarrow[\text{(360–400 m}\mu)]{\text{Light}} C_6H_6Cl_6$$

γ-Benzene hexachloride

The production of the hexachlorides was reported first by Faraday in 1825 in his paper on the isolation of benzene. Nine stereoisomers of benzene hexachloride are possible, corresponding to the nine inositols (p. 413). Five isomers have been isolated and designated α, β, γ, δ, and ε. Their configurations have been determined by electron diffraction.

The mixture of isomers has become of considerable commercial importance because of the discovery of its insecticidal properties in 1943. Production in the United States in 1955 was over 49 million pounds. It is called **BHC** or **666,** abbreviations of its name or of the formula $C_6H_6Cl_6$. It must be used at the proper dilution because of its persistent musty odor at higher concentrations. The insecticidal property is due solely to the γ form, which makes up only 18 per cent of the mixed halides. The insecticidal products are sold on the basis of the content of the γ isomer, which has been given the names *gammexane* and *lindane* (after van der Linden, who established the existence of the first four isomers in 1912). Pure γ-isomer is reported to be free of the musty odor.

When the hexachlorides or hexabromides are heated with alcoholic potassium hydroxide, three moles of halogen acid are removed to give 1,2,4-trihalobenzene.[1]

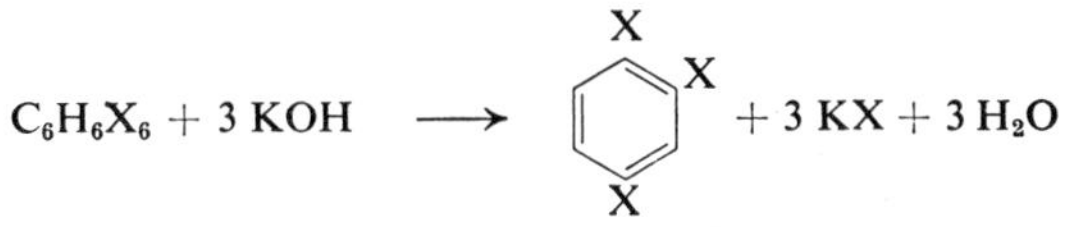

$$C_6H_6X_6 + 3\ KOH \longrightarrow \underset{X}{\overset{X}{\bigcirc}}^{X} + 3\ KX + 3\ H_2O$$

Nuclear Substitution. When aromatic hydrocarbons are warmed with chlorine or bromine in the presence of iron, substitution of nuclear hydrogen takes place with the evolution of halogen acid. The actual catalyst is ferric chloride or ferric bromide formed by the action of halogen on the iron. Anhydrous aluminum chloride and bromide also are effective catalysts.

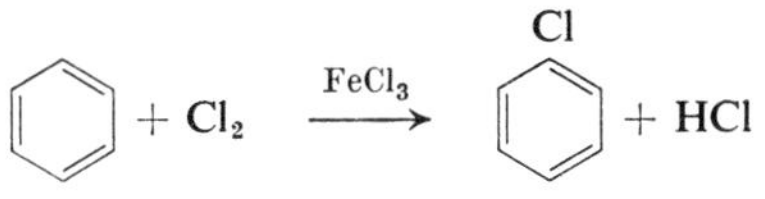

$$\bigcirc + Cl_2 \xrightarrow{FeCl_3} \overset{Cl}{\bigcirc} + HCl$$

Chlorobenzene

During these reactions some disubstitution takes place, the product being a mixture of the *ortho* and *para* isomers with very little *meta*.

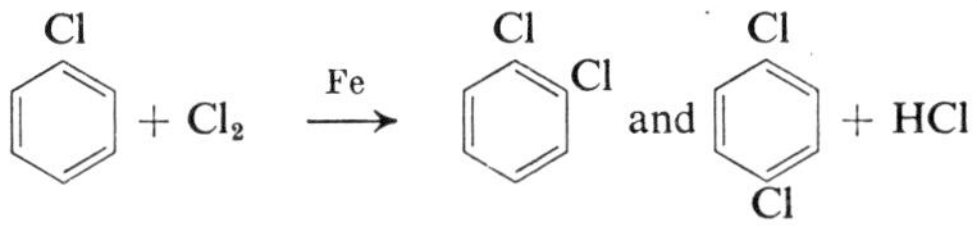

$$\overset{Cl}{\bigcirc} + Cl_2 \xrightarrow{Fe} \overset{Cl}{\bigcirc}^{Cl} \text{ and } \underset{Cl}{\overset{Cl}{\bigcirc}} + HCl$$

o-Dichloro-   p-Dichloro-
benzene   benzene

The introduction of one halogen atom into the benzene ring makes it more difficult to replace a second hydrogen atom, the relative rates of substitution of benzene and chlorobenzene being about 8.5 : 1. Hence by regulating the amount of halogen and the time and temperature of the reaction, it is possible to produce predominantly mono- or polysubstitution products as desired. Usually in commercial operations, chlorination is carried out until practically all of the benzene has reacted. The composition of the resulting mixture is about 80 per cent chlorobenzene, 17 per cent *p*-dichlorobenzene, 2 per cent *o*-dichlorobenzene, and 1 per cent higher substitution products.

Chlorobenzene is an intermediate in the manufacture of phenol, aniline, DDT, and dyes. *p*-Dichlorobenzene is used as a larvicide against the clothes moth and the peach-tree borer. *o*-Dichlorobenzene containing 4 per cent of the *para* isomer is used as a heat transfer medium in the 150°–250° range. The relative technical importance of chlorobenzene, *p*-dichlorobenzene, and *o*-dichlorobenzene is indicated by the production in the United States in 1955 of 436, 57, and 26 million pounds respectively.

---

[1] In the formula for this compound and subsequently, bonds usually are not indicated between the substituent and the aromatic ring.

Other aromatic compounds halogenate in a similar manner. For example, toluene on chlorination or bromination in the presence of iron yields a mixture of *o*- and *p*-chloro- or bromotoluenes.

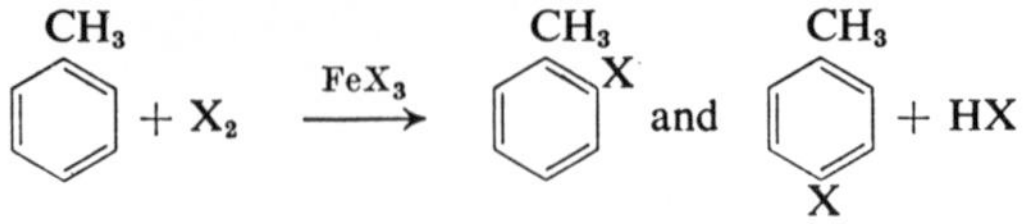

$$\text{(Ph)CH}_3 + X_2 \xrightarrow{\text{FeX}_3} \text{(Ph)CH}_3\text{-X} \quad \text{and} \quad \text{(Ph)CH}_3 + HX$$

As with aliphatic hydrocarbons, iodination does not occur because the position of equilibrium is unfavorable. Iodination of aromatic hydrocarbons can be brought about in the presence of nitric acid or mercuric oxide, presumably because the equilibrium is shifted by the oxidation of hydrogen iodide.

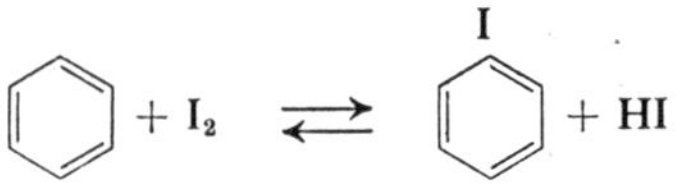

$$\text{(Ph)} + I_2 \rightleftharpoons \text{(Ph)I} + HI$$

$$4\,HI + 2\,HNO_3 \longrightarrow 2\,I_2 + N_2O_3 + 3\,H_2O$$

$$2\,HI + HgO \longrightarrow HgI_2 + H_2O$$

Direct halogenation is the usual method for the preparation of aryl halides. The replacement of a hydroxyl group by halogen, which is of primary importance in the preparation of alkyl halides, seldom is used, because it is difficult to replace a hydroxyl group attached to a benzene ring (p. 504). Methods for the replacement of the amino group by halogen are discussed on page 494.

Side-chain Substitution. The chemical properties of side chains are for the most part those of aliphatic compounds. Hence if a mixture of toluene vapor and halogen is exposed to light of short wavelength, halogenation takes place in the side chain more rapidly than substitution in the nucleus or than addition to the double bonds. Since for aliphatic hydrocarbons the rates of replacement of a second and third hydrogen atom by halogen differ little from the rate of replacement of the first hydrogen atom, mono-, di-, and trisubstitution products are formed.

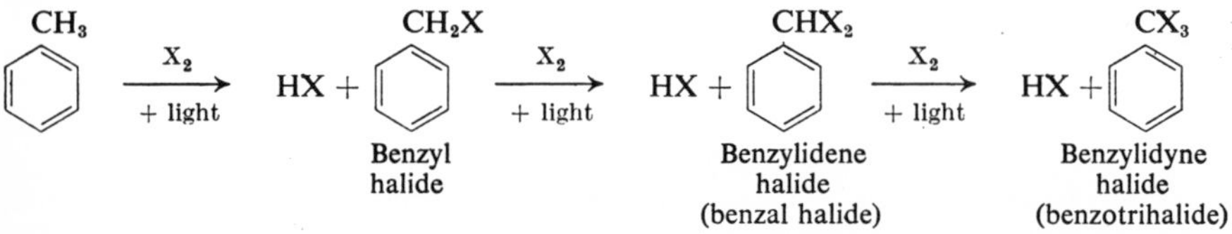

$$\text{(Ph)CH}_3 \xrightarrow[+\text{ light}]{X_2} HX + \text{(Ph)CH}_2X \xrightarrow[+\text{ light}]{X_2} HX + \text{(Ph)CHX}_2 \xrightarrow[+\text{ light}]{X_2} HX + \text{(Ph)CX}_3$$

| | Benzyl halide | Benzylidene halide (benzal halide) | Benzylidyne halide (benzotrihalide) |

A certain amount of regulation of the ratio of mono- to di- to trisubstitution can be obtained by varying the hydrocarbon-halogen ratio. In the technical preparation of benzyl chloride, reaction takes place at 130°–140°. This temperature is above the boiling point of toluene (111°) but below the boiling point of benzyl chloride (179°). Hence the benzyl chloride condenses as it is formed and further chlorination is prevented. The reaction is carried out in a lead-lined vessel illuminated internally with quartz mercury vapor lamps. At higher temperatures the reaction takes place in the absence of light.

Benzyl chloride can be prepared also by the reaction of benzene with formaldehyde and hydrogen chloride in the presence of zinc chloride or phosphoric acid.

$$\text{C}_6\text{H}_6 + \text{HCHO} + \text{HCl} \xrightarrow[\text{or H}_3\text{PO}_4]{\text{ZnCl}_2} \text{C}_6\text{H}_5\text{CH}_2\text{Cl} + \text{H}_2\text{O}$$

The process is known as **chloromethylation** and is another substitution reaction that is applicable to aromatic compounds in general. Either the formaldehyde condenses with the aromatic compound to give a benzyl alcohol which then reacts with hydrogen chloride, or the hydrogen chloride adds to the formaldehyde to give chloromethyl alcohol, which reacts with the aromatic compound to give the benzyl chloride.

Reactions of Aryl and Aralkyl Halides

Aryl Halides. Unlike the alkyl halides the simple aryl halides are very unreactive. No observable reaction takes place with sodium hydroxide, silver salts, sodium alkoxide, sodium cyanide, sodium sulfide, or ammonia under the conditions that bring about displacement reactions with the alkyl halides (p. 114). The reactivity may, however, be increased greatly by the presence of other substituents in the benzene ring (p. 461). Aryl bromides and iodides react readily with magnesium in ether solution to give Grignard reagents which undergo all of the usual reactions (pp. 121, 173, 175, 196, 199, 203, 248).

$$\text{C}_6\text{H}_5\text{Br} \xrightarrow[\text{ether}]{\text{Mg in}} \text{C}_6\text{H}_5\text{MgBr}$$

Phenylmagnesium
bromide

When the iodides are heated with activated copper powder, coupling of two aromatic nuclei takes place (*Ullmann reaction*).

$$\text{C}_6\text{H}_5\text{I} + 2 \text{ Cu} + \text{IC}_6\text{H}_5 \longrightarrow \text{C}_6\text{H}_5-\text{C}_6\text{H}_5 + 2 \text{ CuI}$$

Biphenyl

When a mixture of aryl halide and alkyl halide is allowed to stand for a long time in the presence of metallic sodium, a mixed coupling takes place (*Wurtz-Fittig*[2] *reaction*).

$$\text{C}_6\text{H}_5\text{Br} + 2 \text{ Na} + \text{BrR} \longrightarrow \text{C}_6\text{H}_5\text{R} + 2 \text{ NaBr}$$

This reaction has been used for the synthesis of benzene homologs. It was particularly valuable as a means of interconverting compounds during the early work on orientation (p. 425).

At temperatures between 200° and 300°, particularly in the presence of copper salts, aryl halides react with aqueous solutions of sodium hydroxide,

---

[2] Rudolph Fittig (1835–1910), professor at the University of Strassburg. He discovered the pinacol reaction in 1858, and applied the Wurtz reaction to mixed alkyl and aryl halides in 1863. He is known also for his synthesis of β-naphthol from benzaldehyde (1883) and his discovery of the interconversion of α,β- and β,γ-unsaturated acids by alkali (1894).

sodium cyanide, or ammonia to give the corresponding hydroxy, cyano, or amino compounds (pp. 486, 510). The removal of halogen acid with the formation of a triple bond does not take place even in strongly alkaline solutions because the bonds —C≡C— are linear (p. 129) and cannot be combined with 120 degree bond angles in a six-membered ring to give a stable product. Current theory concerning the nonreactivity of unsubstituted aryl halides is discussed on page 462.

Polyvalent Iodine Compounds. The iodine atom in aryl iodides can exist in higher states of oxidation. Thus iodobenzene in chloroform adds one mole of chlorine to give **iodobenzene dichloride,** a yellow solid. Heating the dichloride to 120° gives *p*-chloroiodobenzene. Aqueous sodium hydroxide hydrolyzes the dichloride to **iodosobenzene.**

$$C_6H_5I + Cl_2 \longrightarrow C_6H_5ICl_2 \begin{cases} \xrightarrow{120°} p\text{-}ClC_6H_4I + HCl \\ \xrightarrow[\text{(aq.)}]{2\,NaOH} C_6H_5IO + 2\,NaCl + H_2O \\ \qquad\qquad \text{Iodoso-} \\ \qquad\qquad \text{benzene} \end{cases}$$

Iodosobenzene results also from the action of ozone on iodobenzene. Iodosobenzene is unstable and slowly disproportionates (intermolecular oxidation and reduction) to iodobenzene and **iodoxybenzene.** This reaction takes place rapidly on boiling with water, which removes the iodobenzene by steam distillation.

$$2\,C_6H_5IO \longrightarrow C_6H_5I + C_6H_5IO_2$$
$$\text{Iodoxy-}$$
$$\text{benzene}$$

Iodoxybenzene can be prepared directly by the oxidation of iodobenzene with potassium persulfate and sulfuric acid (*Caro reagent*) or by the oxidation of iodosobenzene with hypochlorite.

Iodoso compounds react with acetic acid to give the **iodoso acetates.**

$$ArIO + 2\,CH_3COOH \longrightarrow ArI(OCOCH_3)_2 + H_2O$$

Iodosobenzene acetate is prepared best by the reaction of iodobenzene with peroxyacetic acid in the presence of acetic anhydride.

$$C_6H_5I + CH_3CO_3H + (CH_3CO)_2O \longrightarrow C_6H_5I(OCOCH_3)_2 + CH_3COOH$$

The iodoso acetates have properties analogous to those of lead tetraacetate (p. 742).

Condensation of iodoso compounds with aromatic hydrocarbons in the presence of concentrated sulfuric acid yields **diaryliodonium salts.** The acid sulfates are soluble in water, but the water-insoluble halides precipitate on adding aqueous solutions of the sodium halides.

$$ArIO + Ar'H + H_2SO_4 \longrightarrow H_2O + [Ar\overset{+}{-}I-Ar][^-SO_4H] \xrightarrow{NaX}$$

$$[Ar-\overset{+}{I}-Ar'][X^-] + NaHSO_4$$

The iodonium salts undergo displacement reactions with a wide variety of bases, including the amines and most negative ions.

$$[Ar\overset{+}{-}I\!-\!Ar]\,[X^-] + [\,:\,B^-] \longrightarrow Ar:B + ArI + [X^-]$$

There is little direct evidence concerning the structure of the polyvalent iodine compounds. The dicovalent iodonium salts probably are analogous to the other "onium" compounds and make use of $5p$ orbitals or hybrids of the $5s$ and $5p$ orbitals. The tricovalent iodobenzene dichloride and iodosobenzene acetate, however, must make use of one $5d$ orbital either for bonding purposes or to accept an unshared pair of electrons. X-ray diffraction of iodobenzene dichloride indicates that the Cl—I—Cl bonds are linear and perpendicular to the plane of the benzene ring. The structures of the iodoso and iodoxy compounds may be analogous to those of the sulfoxides and sulfones (p. 273).

Aralkyl Halides. In general, halogen in the side chain undergoes the same reactions as that in simple alkyl halides (p. 114). Even the rates of reaction are about the same if the halogen is located beyond the carbon atom attached directly to the ring. If the halogen is located on the carbon atom attached to the ring, the reactivity is greatly increased. For example, although benzyl chloride is a primary halide, it is hydrolyzed readily by aqueous solutions of sodium carbonate, and benzyl bromide reacts with tertiary amines to form quaternary salts about 300 times faster than *n*-propyl bromide. The high reactivity of benzyl halides is explainable by current theory (p. 463).

Grignard reagents prepared from benzyl halides frequently react abnormally in that the product is an *ortho* methyl derivative instead of a benzyl derivative. Thus benzylmagnesium chloride and formaldehyde give *o*-methylbenzyl alcohol instead of 2-phenylethyl alcohol (p. 527).

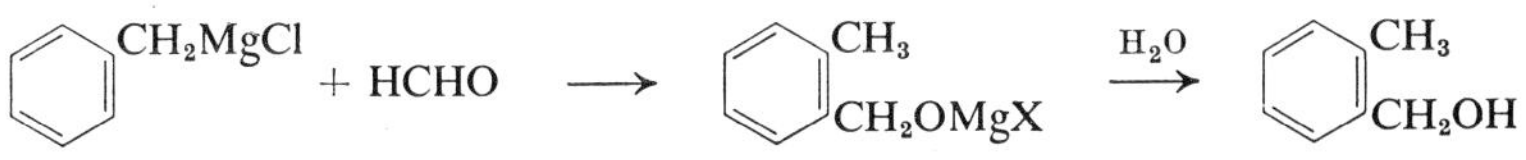

Similarly acetyl chloride gives *o*-tolyl methyl ketone.

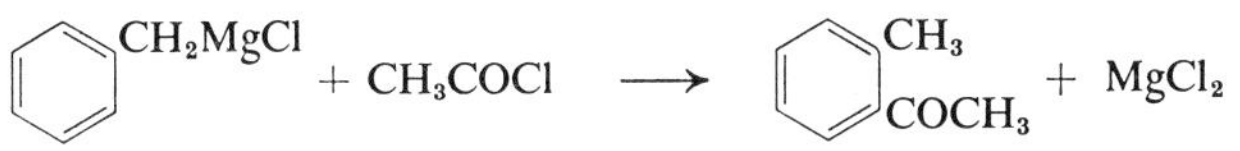

Methyl sulfate and chloroamine on the other hand give the normal reaction products.

$$2\,C_6H_5CH_2MgCl + 2\,(CH_3O)_2SO_2 \longrightarrow 2\,C_6H_5CH_2CH_3 + MgCl_2 + Mg(CH_3OSO_2O)_2$$

$$C_6H_5CH_2MgCl + ClNH_2 \longrightarrow C_6H_5CH_2NH_2 + MgCl_2$$

The initial step in the addition of a Grignard reagent to a carbonyl group involves the formation of a complex in which an unshared pair of electrons from the carbonyl group occupies an empty orbital of the magnesium atom. By a rearrangement of bonds, the carbon atom attached to magnesium becomes bonded to the carbon atom of the carbonyl group.

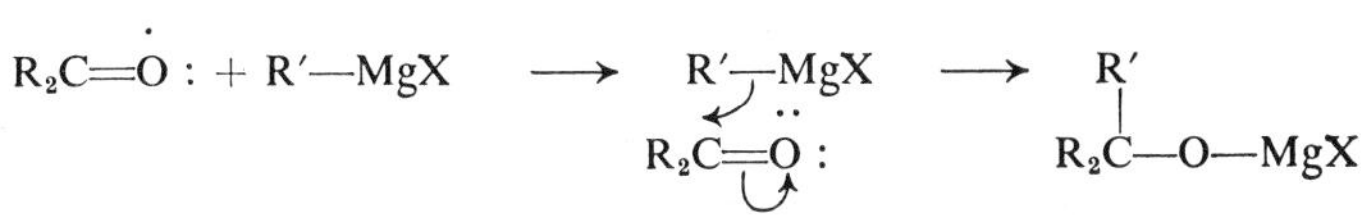

In the complex with benzylmagnesium halide, the carbon atom of the carbonyl group can approach within bonding distance of the *ortho* position, and a transfer of electrons can take place with the result that the *ortho* carbon atom may bond rather than the carbon atom attached to magnesium.

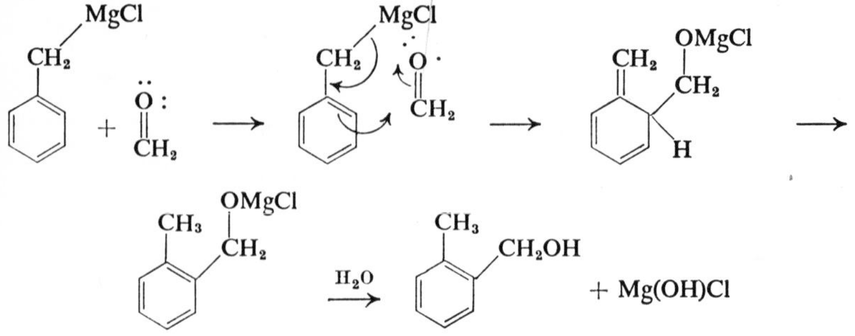

REVIEW QUESTIONS

1. How does the usual method for the preparation of aryl halides differ from that for alkyl halides and why?
2. What are the usual conditions for causing addition of halogen to the benzene nucleus, and what conditions are used to cause substitution by halogen?
3. Compare the conditions for substitution of aromatic hydrogen by iodine with those for substitution by chlorine or bromine.
4. Discuss in detail the several aspects of the halogenation of toluene.
5. How do aryl iodides differ from aryl chlorides and bromides in their chemical behavior?
6. Compare the reactivities of chlorobenzene, benzyl chloride, 2-phenylethyl chloride and *n*-butyl chloride.
7. What is meant by the term "abnormal Grignard reaction" as applied to benzylmagnesium halides?

PROBLEMS

8. Write perspective formulas (cf. p. 383) for the nine stereoisomers of benzene hexachloride. Indicate which forms would be optically active.
9. Give reactions for the preparation of the following compounds: (*a*) benzene hexabromide; (*b*) *o*- and *p*-chlorocumene; (*c*) *o*-methylbenzyl bromide; (*d*) *o*- and *p*-bromochlorobenzene; (*e*) *p*-iodosotoluene; (*f*) *o*-iodoxyethylbenzene; (*g*) 1,3-dimethyl-4-iodobenzene dichloride; (*h*) 4-methylbiphenyl; (*i*) di-*o*-tolyliodonium acid sulfate; (*j*) *p*-di(chloromethyl)benzene.
10. Give a series of reactions for the following conversions: (*a*) toluene to phenylacetic acid; (*b*) *m*-xylene to *m*-methylethylbenzene; (*c*) benzene to *p*-*i*-propylbenzyl chloride; (*d*) mesitylene to bromobenzene-2,4,6-tricarboxylic acid; (*e*) *p*-xylene to 1,4-dimethyl-3-*n*-propylbenzene; (*f*) durene to iodosodurene acetate; (*g*) acetone to iodomesitylene.
11. Give reactions that may be used to distinguish between the members of each of the following pairs of compounds: (*a*) benzene and *n*-hexane; (*b*) bromobenzene and benzyl bromide; (*c*) chlorobenzene and *m*-xylene; (*d*) benzyl chloride and benzylidene chloride; (*e*) benzyl chloride and *t*-amyl chloride; (*f*) iodobenzene and bromobenzene; (*g*) *o*-, *m*-, and *p*-dichlorobenzenes; (*h*) iodosobenzene and iodoxybenzene; (*i*) *p*-dichlorobenzene and *p*-dibromobenzene.

Chapter 20

AROMATIC NITRO COMPOUNDS. MECHANISM OF AROMATIC SUBSTITUTION

Although aliphatic nitro compounds have been manufactured commercially only since 1940 (p. 259), aromatic nitro compounds long have been technically important. They have been used as intermediates for the manufacture of dyes since the discovery of mauve by Perkin in 1856. Other technical developments have led to their use as explosives and as intermediates for the manufacture of pharmaceuticals and many other aromatic compounds of commercial importance.

Preparation of Nitro Compounds

The factor contributing most to the widespread use of aromatic nitro compounds is the ease of preparation by direct nitration of aromatic compounds. When benzene is warmed with fuming nitric acid or with a mixture of concentrated nitric acid and sulfuric acid, the chief product is nitrobenzene.

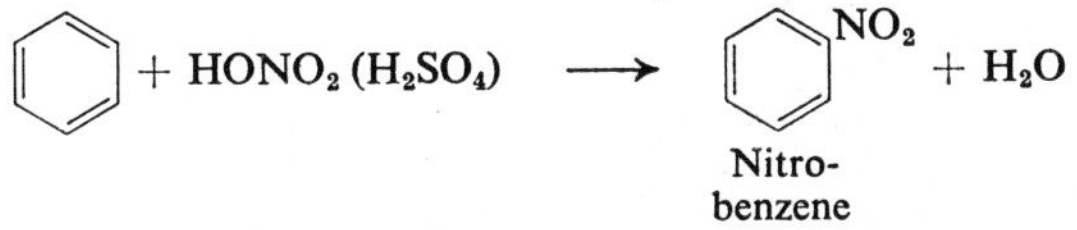

$$\bigcirc + HONO_2\ (H_2SO_4) \longrightarrow \bigcirc^{NO_2} + H_2O$$

Nitro-
benzene

The presence of a nitro group in a benzene ring decreases the rate of substitution of a second hydrogen atom even more so than does a halogen atom; consequently more concentrated acids and higher temperatures are needed to obtain appreciable quantities of the dinitrated product. When substitution of a second hydrogen takes place, the nitro group enters chiefly at the *meta* position.

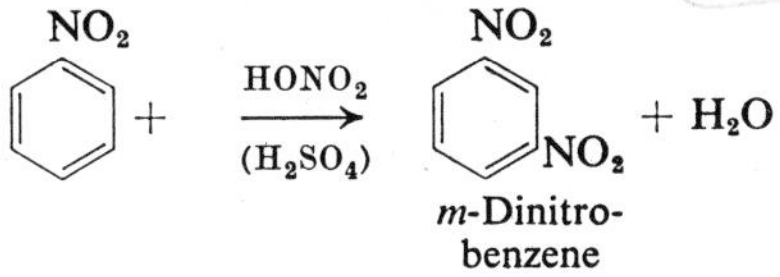

$$\bigcirc^{NO_2} + \xrightarrow[\text{(H}_2\text{SO}_4)]{\text{HONO}_2} \bigcirc^{NO_2}_{NO_2} + H_2O$$

m-Dinitro-
benzene

It is very difficult to introduce a third nitro group into benzene by direct nitration.

Toluene nitrates more readily than benzene. The principal products are first a mixture of o- and p-nitrotoluene, then 2,4-dinitrotoluene, and finally 2,4,6-trinitrotoluene (TNT).

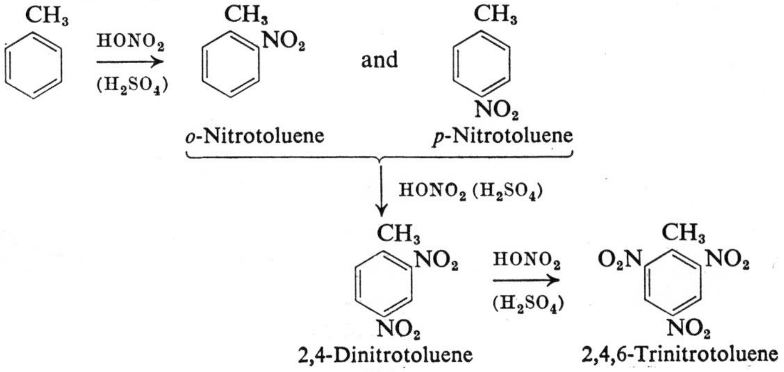

$$\bigcirc^{CH_3} \xrightarrow[\text{(H}_2\text{SO}_4)]{\text{HONO}_2} \bigcirc^{CH_3}_{NO_2} \quad \text{and} \quad \bigcirc^{CH_3}_{NO_2}$$

o-Nitrotoluene   p-Nitrotoluene

$$\downarrow \text{HONO}_2\ (\text{H}_2\text{SO}_4)$$

$$\bigcirc^{CH_3}_{NO_2}{}^{NO_2} \xrightarrow[\text{(H}_2\text{SO}_4)]{\text{HONO}_2} \bigcirc^{CH_3}_{NO_2}{}^{NO_2}_{O_2N}$$

2,4-Dinitrotoluene   2,4,6-Trinitrotoluene

439

Chloro- and bromobenzene nitrate somewhat less readily than benzene and give chiefly a mixture of the *ortho* and *para* isomers.

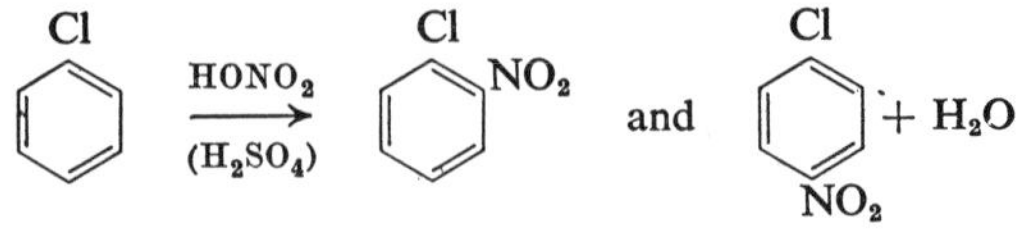

o-Nitrochloro-
benzene
  p-Nitrochloro-
benzene

On the other hand, chlorination or bromination of nitrobenzene gives chiefly the *meta* isomer,

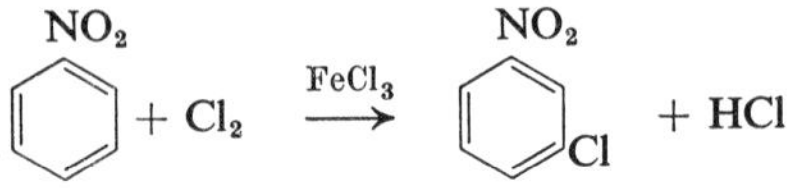

m-Nitrochloro-
benzene

Since iron reduces nitro groups (p. 457), anhydrous ferric chloride is the preferred catalyst for the halogenation of nitro compounds.

Occasionally during the nitration of an aromatic compound groups other than hydrogen are replaced by a nitro group. For example, the nitration of phenol-2,4-disulfonic acid leads to 2,4-dinitrophenol, nitration of 2,4-dihydroxybenzoic acid gives chiefly 2,4,6-trinitroresorcinol, and nitration of *p*-cymene can give 2,4-dinitrotoluene.

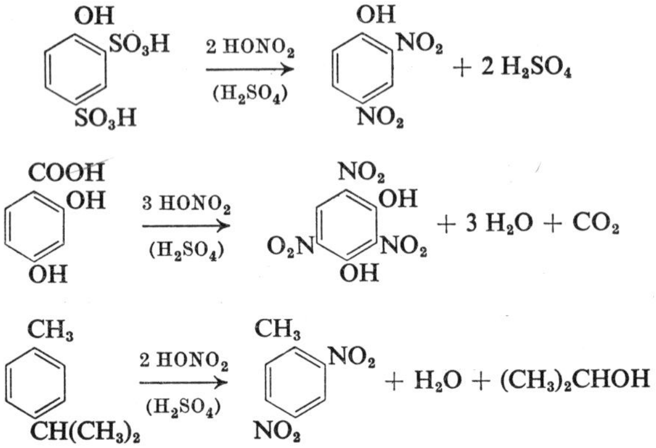

Rules for Substitution in the Benzene Nucleus

Two striking facts are evident from the substitution reactions discussed so far: (*1*) in some reactions a substituting group enters chiefly the positions that are *ortho* and *para* to the group already present in the ring as in the halogenation or nitration of toluene and chlorobenzene, and in other reactions it enters chiefly the *meta* position as in the halogenation or nitration of nitrobenzene; (*2*) the substituent already present, for example a methyl group, may make a second hydrogen more readily substituted than a hydrogen atom of benzene, or a substituent such as a halogen atom or a nitro group may make it more difficult to replace a hydrogen atom.

Many investigations of the products formed in substitution reactions between a variety of reagents and a large number of aromatic compounds have led to the following generalizations:

(*1*) A number of groups, such as halogen (X), nitro (NO_2), sulfonic acid (SO_3H), alkyl (R), and acyl (RCO or ArCO), may be introduced directly into the benzene nucleus, hydrogen being displaced.

(*2*) When a second substituent is introduced into a benzene nucleus, the relative amounts of the *ortho*, *meta*, and *para* isomers should be 40, 40, and 20 per cent respectively on a statistical basis. Usually this ratio is not obtained. The relative amounts of the isomers depends primarily on the nature of the group already present in the ring, although the nature of the entering group and the conditions of the reaction, such as temperature and concentrations, have some influence.

(*3*) Groups vary greatly in their directing power, from the $[\overset{+}{N}R_3]$ group, which causes substitution almost exclusively in the *meta* position, to the $[O^-]$ group, which causes substitution almost exclusively in the *ortho* and *para* positions. Other groups fall between these extremes in directing power (Table 22). Groups causing the production of more than 60 per cent of the *ortho* and *para* isomers combined are called *ortho,para-directing groups*, and those causing the

TABLE 22

RELATIVE AMOUNTS OF *meta*, *ortho*, AND *para* ISOMERS FORMED IN THE NITRATION OF MONOSUBSTITUTED BENZENES

GROUP PRESENT IN RING	ISOMERS FORMED ON NITRATION (PER CENT)			
	meta	*ortho*	*para*	*o* + *p*
OH*	0	73	27	100
I	trace	34	66	100
Br	trace	42	58	100
Cl	trace	30	70	100
F	trace	12	88	100
$NHCOCH_3$	2	19	79	98
CH_3	4	59	37	96
$CH_2COOC_2H_5$	11	42	47	89
$CH_2CH_2NO_2$	13	35	52	87
CH_2Cl	16	32	52	84
$CHCl_2$	34	23	43	66
$[\overset{+}{N}H_3]$	47	1	52	53
CH_2NO_2	48			52
$COCH_3$	55	45	0	45
CCl_3	64	7	29	36
$CONH_2$	70	27	3	30
$COOC_2H_5$	72	24	4	28
SO_3H	72	21	7	28
CHO	72	19	9	28
COOH	80	19	1	20
CN	81	17	2	19
NO_2	93	7	trace	7
SO_2CH_3	99	trace	trace	1
$[\overset{+}{N}(CH_3)_3]$	100	0	0	0

* In the absence of nitrous acid.

production of more than 40 per cent of the *meta* isomer are called *meta-directing groups*.

(4) *ortho,para*-Directing groups, *with the exception of halogen*, increase the ease with which a second hydrogen can be displaced. Such groups are said to *activate* the ring. *meta*-Directing groups *and halogen* decrease the ease with which a second hydrogen can be displaced; that is, they are *deactivating* groups. Activation and deactivation are reflections of the rates of substitution compared with benzene. The effect of a group on the relative amounts of the three isomers formed reflects the relative rates of substitution at the unsubstituted positions. When the group already present is activating and *ortho,para*-directing, it increases the rate of substitution over that of benzene, and at the *ortho* and *para* positions more than at the *meta* positions. When a group is deactivating and *meta*-directing, it decreases the rate of substitution compared with that for benzene, but decreases the rate less at the *meta* positions than at the *ortho* and *para* positions. Halogen, which is deactivating and *ortho,para*-directing, decreases the rate of substitution over that for benzene, but decreases the rate less at the *ortho* and *para* positions than at the *meta* positions.

Table 23 gives the relative rates of mononitration in the *ortho*, *meta*, and *para* positions for those compounds for which quantitative data are available. The relative total rates were obtained by allowing two compounds, for example benzene and toluene, to compete for a limited amount of nitric acid and determining the relative amounts of the nitro compounds produced. For comparison the rate of replacement of a hydrogen atom in benzene is taken as unity. Since it has six equivalent hydrogen atoms the total rate would be six. The relative rates for the *ortho*,

TABLE 23

RELATIVE RATES OF MONONITRATION

GROUP PRESENT IN RING	TOTAL RATE	RATE AT EACH POSITION		
		ortho	*meta*	*para*
CH_3	147.0	43	3	55
$CH_2COOC_2H_5$	22.0	4.6	1.2	10.4
H (benzene)	6.0	1	1	1
CH_2Cl	1.8	0.3	0.15	0.9
Cl	0.20	0.03	0	0.14
Br	0.18	0.04	0	0.10
$COOC_2H_5$	0.022	0.0025	0.008	0.001

meta, and *para* positions for a particular substituted benzene were arrived at from the relative total rates and the relative amounts of the isomers produced on nitrating a single compound. To take a specific example, the nitration of toluene gives 59 per cent *ortho*nitrotoluene, 4 per cent *meta*, and 37 per cent *para*. Since there are two *ortho* and two *meta* positions, 29.5 per cent of the total relative rate of 147 or 43 is accounted for by each *ortho* position, 2 per cent or 3 by each *meta* position, and 37 per cent or 55 by the *para* position. The figures in Table 23 show that the methyl and ethoxycarbonylmethyl groups activate all positions but activate more strongly in the *ortho* and *para* positions. The chloromethyl and halogen groups are deactivating but deactivate the *ortho* and *para* positions less strongly than the *meta* position and hence still are *ortho,para*-directing. The ethoxycarbonyl group, however, deactivates the *ortho* and *para*-positions more than the *meta* position and hence is *meta*-directing.

From Table 22 an approximate order of directive influence of different groups can be obtained. *These results hold only for nitration and for the particular conditions of the experiment.* For example, nitration of chlorobenzene yields 30 per cent *o*-, 70 per cent *p*-, and no *m*-nitrochlorobenzene, but chlorination of chlorobenzene yields 39 per cent *o*-, 55 per cent *p*-, and 6 per cent *m*-dichlorobenzene. Bromination of bromobenzene in the presence of aluminum chloride yields 8 per cent *o*-, 30 per cent *m*-, and 62 per cent *p*-dibromobenzene, whereas bromination in the presence of ferric chloride yields 13 per cent *o*-, 2 per cent *m*-, and 85 per cent *p*-dibromobenzene. Nitration of benzenesulfonic acid at 20°–30° yields 21 per cent *o*-, 72 per cent *m*-, and 7 per cent *p*-nitrobenzenesulfonic acid, but nitration at 90°–100° yields 29 per cent *o*-, 58 per cent *m*-, and 13 per cent *p*-nitrobenzenesulfonic acid. Thus although the group present in the ring is the dominant factor in determining the position taken by the entering group, the nature of the reagent and the conditions under which the reactions take place also influence the relative amounts of the isomers formed.

Moreover the ratio of *ortho* to *para* is rarely the 2 : 1 expected statistically. Usually the amount of *para* actually exceeds the amount of *ortho*, because the *ortho* positions are sterically hindered. The exceptions usually are those compounds having a strongly deactivating group in which the atom joined to the ring is united to another atom by a double bond. A steric effect is observable also as regards the entering group. Thus the ratio of *ortho* to *para* substitution decreases in the order chlorination, nitration, bromination, sulfonation. This order is the same as that of the relative size of the entering group.

Table 22 does not list the free NH_2, NHR, or NR_2 groups nor the $[O^-]$ group, because they cannot exist as such in acid solution. These groups are known to direct strongly to the *ortho* and *para* positions from other reactions such as halogenation.

If several groups are all strongly *ortho,para*-directing, it is difficult to determine their relative directing power, because so little of the *meta* isomer is formed. An answer has been obtained by determining which isomer is produced in larger amount when a third group enters a *para*-disubstituted compound. For example, chlorination of *p*-hydroxytoluene gives chiefly 3-chloro-4-hydroxytoluene, indicating that the hydroxyl group is more strongly *ortho,para*-directing than the methyl group.

CH₃   ⬡ + Cl₂ ⟶ ⬡Cl + HCl   OH

By such methods the relative order of directive influence has been shown to be $[O^-] > NH_2 > OH > I > Br > Cl > F > CH_3$.

When two substituents are present in the benzene ring, the position taken by the entering group is influenced by both groups already present. If these groups direct to the same position, a third group enters almost exclusively at this position. For example, further nitration of either 2-nitrotoluene or 4-nitrotoluene leads to 2,4-dinitrotoluene (p. 439). In the first compound the 4 position is *para* to the methyl group and *meta* to the nitro group, and in the second compound the 2 position is *ortho* to the methyl group and *meta* to the nitro group. Similarly two *ortho,para*-directing groups or two *meta*-directing groups in the *meta* position to each other direct to a single position.

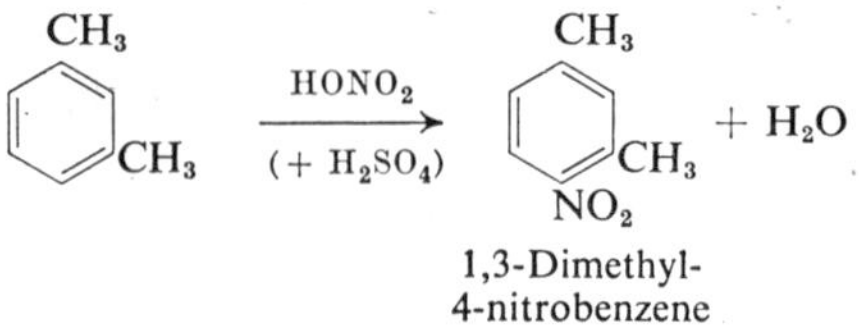

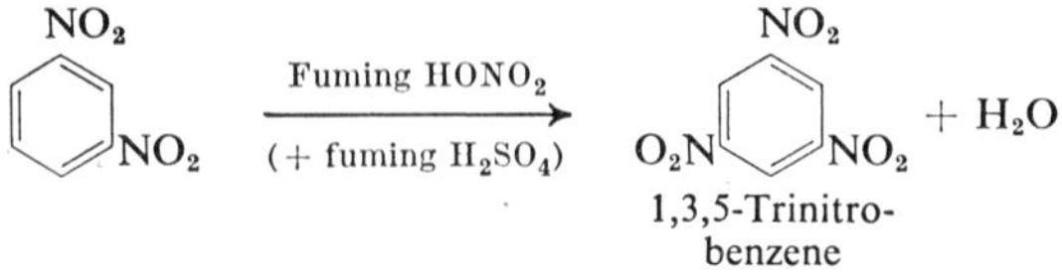

$$CH_3 \quad \xrightarrow[\text{(+ H}_2\text{SO}_4)]{\text{HONO}_2} \quad CH_3 \ / \ NO_2 \quad + H_2O$$

1,3-Dimethyl-
4-nitrobenzene

$$NO_2 \quad \xrightarrow[\text{(+ fuming H}_2\text{SO}_4)]{\text{Fuming HONO}_2} \quad O_2N \quad NO_2 \quad + H_2O$$

1,3,5-Trinitro-
benzene

When two *ortho,para*-directing groups or two *meta*-directing groups are *ortho* or *para* to each other, that with the stronger directive power determines the predominant isomer. Thus in the chlorination of *p*-hydroxytoluene, the product is 3-chloro-4-hydroxytoluene.

If an *ortho,para*-directing group is *meta* to a *meta*-directing group, the influence of the *ortho,para*-directing group usually predominates over that of the *meta*-directing group. For example, in the nitration of *m*-nitrotoluene, a third nitro group enters the 2, 4, and 6 positions but not the 5 position.

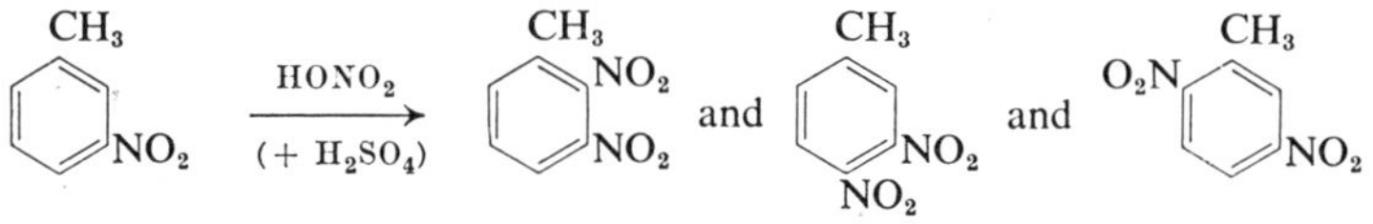

$$CH_3 \ NO_2 \quad \xrightarrow[\text{(+ H}_2\text{SO}_4)]{\text{HONO}_2} \quad CH_3 \ NO_2 \ NO_2 \quad \text{and} \quad CH_3 \ NO_2 \ NO_2 \quad \text{and} \quad O_2N \ CH_3 \ NO_2$$

Many rules have been formulated for remembering whether a group is predominantly *ortho,para*-directing or predominantly *meta*-directing. Some are purely empirical and others have some theoretical basis, but none is quantitative. Probably the simplest empirical rule is that halogen and groups in which the atom joined to the ring is united to other elements by single homopolar bonds or carries a negative charge are chiefly *ortho,para*-directing, whereas groups in which the atom joined to the ring is united to other elements by multiple bonds or semipolar bonds or carries a positive charge are chiefly *meta*-directing. The principal exceptions to this rule are the trichloromethyl group (CCl_3), which directs chiefly to the *meta* position, and the vinyl group ($CH{=}CH_2$), which directs chiefly to the *ortho* and *para* positions.

Mechanism of Substitution in the Benzene Nucleus by Electron-seeking (Electrophilic) Reagents and the Theory of Directive Influence

Mechanism of Substitution in the Benzene Nucleus. Much of the current theory of the mechanism of organic reactions had its beginnings in attempts to explain aromatic substitution, particularly the directive influence of groups. Although unsaturation electrons usually are omitted in writing the reactions of aromatic compounds, they undoubtedly are responsible for the characteristic substitution reactions.

In the mechanism proposed for the addition of halogen acids to olefins (p. 60), it is postulated that as the molecule H : X approaches the olefin molecule, the hydrogen atom exerts an attraction for the unsaturation electrons, and forms a π complex. The resulting deficiency in electrons attracts the halogen atom of another hydrogen halide molecule, which bonds with it to give the addition product and a proton.

$$RCH\text{---}CHR + H : X : \longrightarrow [RCH\text{---}CHR] + \left[: X : ^- \right]$$

$$[RCH\text{---}CH R] + : X : H \longrightarrow RCHX\text{---}CH_2R + [H^+]$$

Combination of $[H^+]$ and $\left[: X : ^- \right]$ gives $H : X :$, or alternatively $\left[: X : ^- \right]$ may add to $\left[RCH\text{---}CHR \right]$.

Undoubtedly benzene starts to react with proton donors in the same way, the hydrogen being attracted to the π electrons to give a π complex. Toluene for example forms a 1 : 1 complex with hydrogen chloride at $-78°$. No reaction takes place, however, because the energy necessary to overcome the resonance energy of benzene and the energy necessary to separate a proton from the halide ion is too great. If a compound such as anhydrous aluminum chloride, having an electron-deficient orbital, also is present, the liberation of a proton from the halogen is facilitated and reaction with the electrons takes place to give what is called a σ complex. Here the hydrogen is covalently bonded in a positive ion which still is stabilized considerably by resonance.

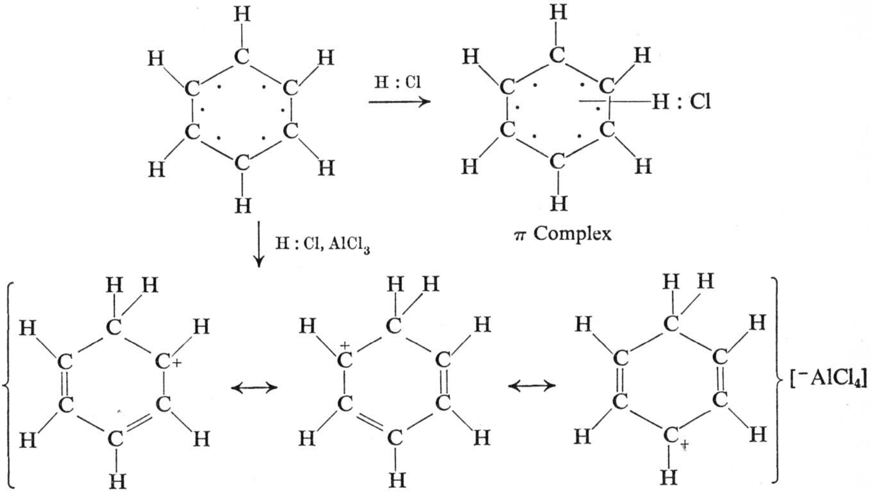

π Complex

σ Complex

In the simplified symbolism used in this reaction the six dots in the first formula represent the six electrons in the molecular π orbitals of benzene, the double bonds indicate conjugated or ethylenic π orbitals, and the $+$ indicates the presence of an empty p orbital. Figure 75a attempts to picture the nature of this intermediate positive ion in which the entering proton has formed a σ bond and the positive charge is distributed over five of the carbon atoms of the ring. Figure 75b is a simpler symbolism for indicating that the transition state is a resonance hybrid.

If the subsequent steps of the reaction followed the course of the olefins, the intermediate ion of the above reaction would combine with halide ions at the *ortho* and *para* positions to give addition products. Such a course, however, would involve destruction of the resonance of the ion as well as of the benzene nucleus. Moreover, because of the considerable resonance energy, the intermediate positive ion is less reactive than the corresponding alkyl carbonium

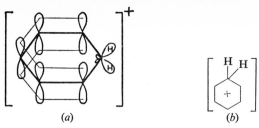

(a)   (b)

Fig. 75. Representation of intermediate ion or transition state after proton transfer to benzene.

ion from an olefin. Hence the carbon atom to which the proton becomes attached loses a proton, and the benzene resonance is retained. Thus only an exchange of hydrogen atoms can result.

$$\left[\begin{array}{c} \text{H H} \\ + \end{array}\right]\text{[-AlCl}_4\text{]} \longrightarrow \begin{array}{c}\text{H}\\ \end{array} + \text{HCl} + \text{AlCl}_3$$

There are several facts pointing to the marked difference in properties of the π complex and the σ complex and to the existence of the latter. The solution of hydrogen chloride in toluene is colorless and its absorption spectrum does not differ greatly from that of toluene, indicating that there is little disturbance of the electronic structure of toluene. The solution does not conduct the electric current and hence the complex is not appreciably ionized. If deuterium chloride is used in place of hydrogen chloride there is no exchange of deuterium with the hydrogen of the toluene. Thus there is no bonding of the deuterium with the carbon atoms of toluene in the π complex. On the other hand, although aluminum chloride is not appreciably soluble in toluene at $-78°$, it dissolves readily in the presence of hydrogen chloride to give a green solution. This solution has high electrical conductivity, and if deuterium chloride is present, there is a rapid exchange of deuterium for hydrogen in the toluene, the deuterium entering chiefly the *ortho* and *para* positions.

$$\begin{array}{c}\text{CH}_3\\ \end{array} + \text{DCl} \xrightarrow{\text{AlCl}_3} \begin{array}{c}\text{CH}_3\\ \text{D}\\ \end{array} \text{ and } \begin{array}{c}\text{CH}_3\\ \\ \text{D}\end{array} + \text{HCl}$$

Since there is no evidence for the formation of complexes of the type $[\text{H}^+][^-\text{AlCl}_4]$, it is unlikely that the formation of the σ complex is preceded by a reaction between the aluminum chloride and the hydrogen chloride.[1]

---

[1] Aluminum chloride and aluminum bromide are double molecules having the molecular formula Al_2X_6 in which two halogen atoms form bridges between the two aluminum atoms by supplying electron pairs to the unfilled orbitals (a). Solid complexes of toluene with hydrogen

$$\begin{array}{ccc}\text{X} & \text{X} & \text{X}\\ \text{Al} & & \text{Al}\\ \text{X} & \text{X} & \text{X}\end{array}$$
(a)

$$[\text{ArH}_2]^+ \left[\begin{array}{c}\text{Br}\\ \text{Br : Al : Br}\\ \text{Br}\end{array}\right]^-$$
(b)

$$[\text{ArH}_2]^+ \left[\begin{array}{c}\text{Br} \quad\quad \text{Br}\\ \text{Br : Al : Br : Al : Br}\\ \text{Br} \quad\quad \text{Br}\end{array}\right]^-$$
(c)

bromide and aluminum bromide have been isolated, having the compositions $\text{C}_6\text{H}_5\text{CH}_3 \cdot \text{HBr} \cdot \text{AlBr}_3$ and $\text{C}_6\text{H}_5\text{CH}_3 \cdot \text{HBr} \cdot \text{Al}_2\text{Br}_6$, which may be considered to have structures as in (b) and (c). Because of the high solubility of aluminum halides in the liquid complexes, it is probable that even more than two moles may be associated with each mole of hydrocarbon and hydrogen halide. However, since the catalytic activity of aluminum halides resides in the monomeric form, it is unnecessary to use polymeric formulas.

+ heavy hydrogen (see Forsham text).

Here then is another type of substitution reaction. The attack is not from the back side with Walden inversion, as was postulated in the simple displacement reaction (p. 116), because the reagent cannot approach from the inside of the ring, and the ring structure could not be maintained if Walden inversion took place. Instead the reagent attacks from one side of the ring, and the displaced group leaves from the other side.

Most other substitution reactions are believed to follow a similar course. Halogenation and alkylation by primary halides probably form σ complexes without prior ionization of the reagent.

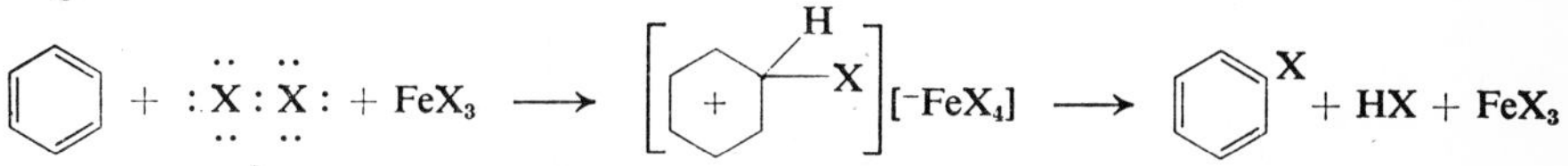

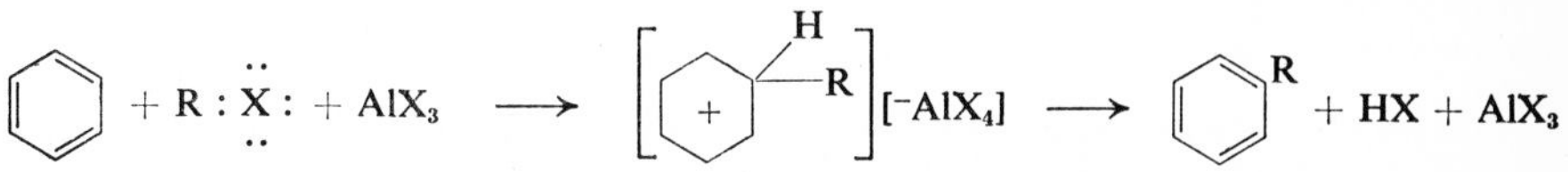

The more basic reagents would be expected to form initial complexes with the strongly acidic catalysts.

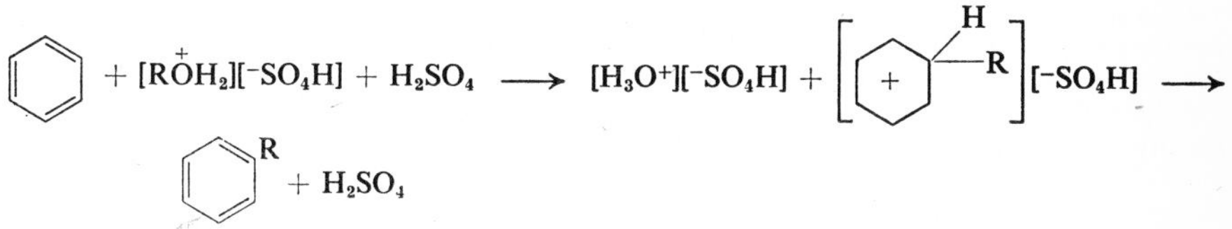

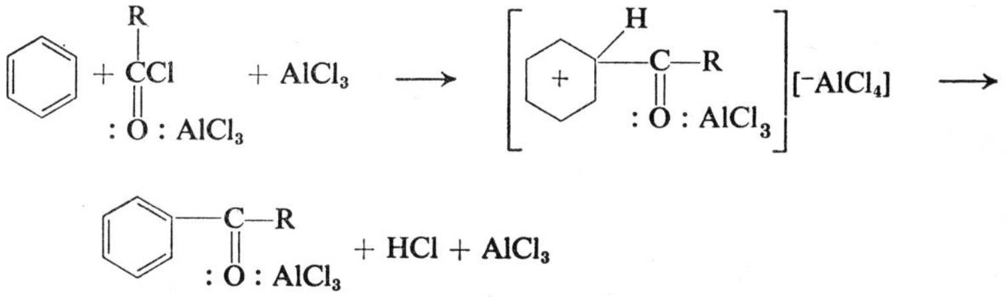

Aluminum chloride catalyzes the reaction of olefins with aromatic compounds only in the presence of hydrogen chloride, although the more reactive olefins react in the presence of hydrogen fluoride or of concentrated sulfuric or phosphoric acid.

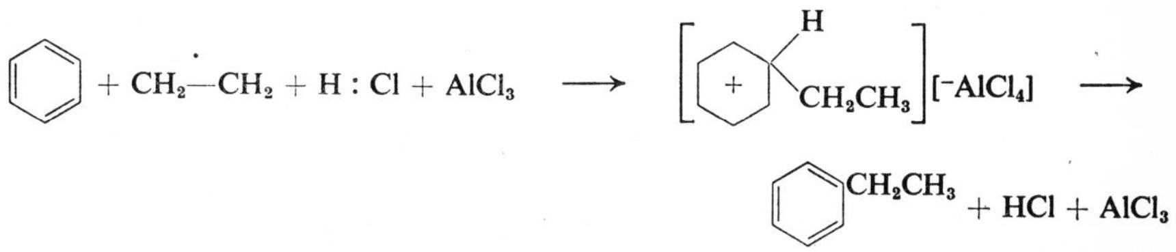

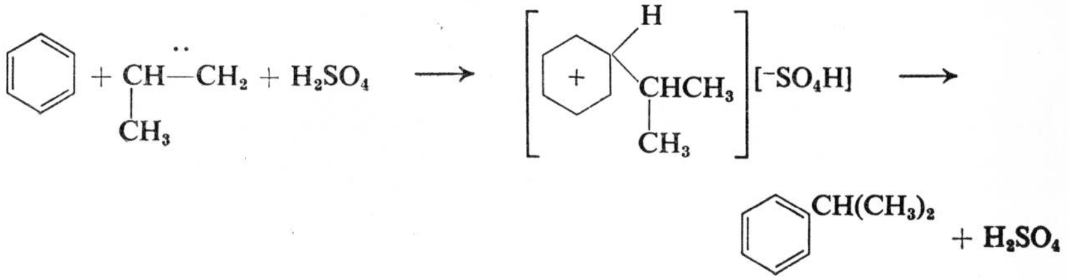

Concerning the nitration of aromatic compounds, there is considerable evidence that the active agent in a mixture of nitric acid and concentrated sulfuric acid is the nitronium ion, $[NO_2^+]$, which arises from the reaction

$$HONO_2 + 2 H_2SO_4 \longrightarrow [NO_2^+] + [H_3O^+] + 2[HSO_4^-]$$

Evidence for the above ionization is as follows: (*1*) the partial pressure of nitric acid is at a maximum in sulfuric acid monohydrate and zero in 100 per cent sulfuric acid; (*2*) adding nitric acid to sulfuric acid monohydrate has little effect on the conductivity but addition to 100 per cent sulfuric acid greatly increases the conductivity; (*3*) on electrolysis of a solution of nitric acid in sulfuric acid, nitric acid migrates to the cathode; (*4*) the molal lowering of the freezing point of 100 per cent sulfuric acid by nitric acid is 3.8 times the value expected for nitric acid, indicating the formation of four entities from each molecule of nitric acid; (*5*) the characteristic ultraviolet absorption spectra of the $[NO_3^-]$ ion and of free HNO_3 are absent in solutions of nitric acid in 100 per cent sulfuric acid, and the Raman spectrum indicates the presence of $[NO_2^+]$.

That $[NO_2^+]$ is the active nitrating agent is indicated (*a*) by the fact that although the free nitric acid concentration is at a maximum in sulfuric acid monohydrate, the nitrating action of the solution is weak, whereas in 90 per cent sulfuric acid in which the ultraviolet absorption spectrum indicates the absence of free HNO_3 or $[NO_3^-]$ the nitrating action is at a maximum; and (*b*) by the observed rates of nitrations which can be accounted for by the estimated concentrations of $[NO_2^+]$. Therefore along with the attack of the benzene nucleus by protons, which merely results in hydrogen exchange, attack by $[NO_2^+]$ ions takes place. Again because of the large amount of energy involved in destroying the benzene resonance, and because of the considerable resonance stabilization of the intermediate ion, a negative ion does not add to the positive ion intermediate, but instead a proton is lost to give the substitution product.

Simultaneously nitro compounds can be formed from the more reactive aromatic compounds by nitrosation with nitrous acid followed by oxidation by nitric acid.

$$ArH + HONO \longrightarrow ArNO + H_2O$$

$$ArNO + HNO_3 \longrightarrow ArNO_2 + HNO_2$$

The nitrous acid need not be present initially in the nitric acid because phenols and amines are oxidized readily by nitric acid with the production of nitrous acid. The nitrosating agent is the nitrosonium ion $[^+NO]$ formed by the reaction of nitrous acid with nitric acid.

$$HONO + 2 HNO_3 \longrightarrow [H_3O^+] + [^+NO] + 2[NO_3^-]$$

Nitrous acid in the presence of nitric acid exists chiefly in the form of dinitrogen tetroxide which may be considered as the reaction product of nitrosonium ion and nitrate ion. Dinitrogen tetroxide also is an effective nitrosating agent, acting as a carrier of the nitrosonium ion.

$$[ON^+] + [NO_3^-] \rightleftarrows ON-O-NO_2$$

Sulfonation follows a different course from nitration in that the active agent is sulfur trioxide rather than the bisulfonium ion, $[^+SO_3H]$. Sulfur trioxide is one of the components of sulfuric acid because of the reaction

$$2 H_2SO_4 \rightleftarrows SO_3 + [H_3O^+] + [HSO_4^-]$$

The three oxygen atoms in sulfur trioxide greatly decrease the electron density on sulfur, making sulfur trioxide a strongly electron-seeking reagent.

The interconversion of the xylenes and of other polyalkylated benzenes in the presence of hydrogen chloride-aluminum chloride or of hydrogen fluoride-boron fluoride (p. 429) is believed to result from the migration of an alkide ion in the σ complex.

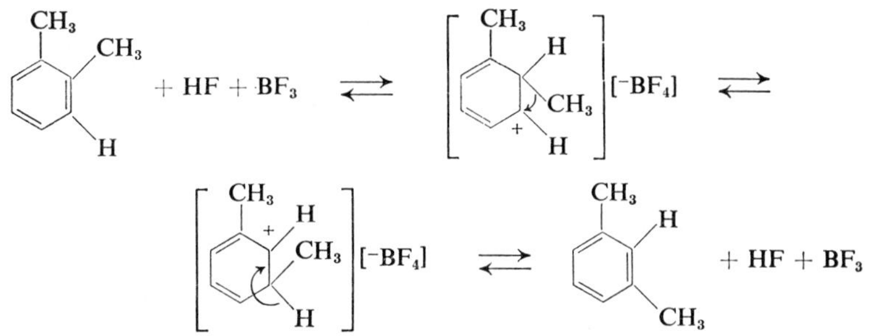

Similarly a methyl group can migrate from *m*-xylene to give *p*-xylene.

The fact that *m*-xylene is the most basic of the dimethylbenzenes and mesitylene is the most basic of the trimethylbenzenes is ascribed to the greater ability of the methyl groups to stabilize the salt when they are *meta* to each other than when they are *ortho-para* to each other. In the salt with *o*-xylene, for example, the electron-donating power of only one methyl group can aid in neutralizing the positive charge, whereas in *m*-xylene both methyl groups are effective (cf. p. 60).

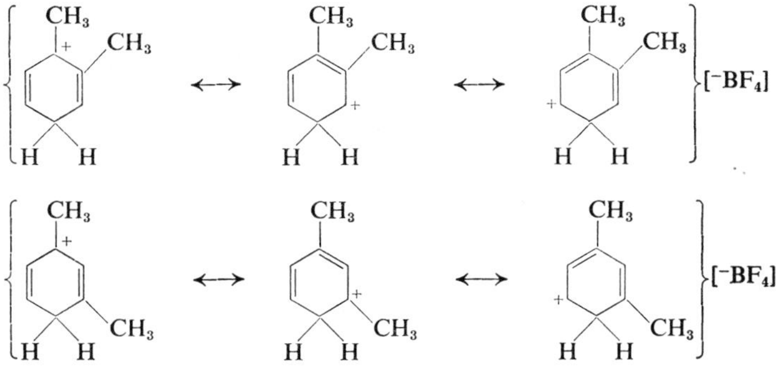

The increase in basicity, that is, in electron-donating ability, in the series hexane, benzene, toluene, *m*-xylene, mesitylene, acetic acid, ethanol can be observed visually using dilute solutions of iodine in these liquids. Solutions of iodine in hexane are violet, the absorption maximum being at 520 mμ. This absorption is that of the iodine molecule, essentially unaffected by interaction with solvent molecules. Solutions of iodine in alcohol are yellow, the absorption maximum being at 360 mμ. This absorption is that of the iodine-alcohol complex,

$$\left[\overset{+}{\underset{H}{C_2H_5O}} : \ddot{\underset{\cdot\cdot}{I}} : \right] \left[\overset{-}{:} \ddot{\underset{\cdot\cdot}{I}} : \right].$$ At equal concentrations of iodine in the above series of solvents,

the color changes progressively from violet to yellow.

Activation and Deactivation of the Benzene Nucleus. The next question concerns the effect of groups other than hydrogen on the ease of substitution. In the first place the most strongly activating group is the [O⁻] group which carries a full negative charge of one electron, whereas the most strongly deactivating group is the [NR₃⁺] group which carries a full positive charge equivalent to one electron. This behavior is consistent with the views expressed so far, since a negatively charged group should hold electrons less strongly than a hydrogen atom and increase the availability of the nuclear electrons for the electron-seeking reagent, whereas a positively charged group should hold electrons more strongly than hydrogen and decrease the availability of the nuclear electrons. For groups that do not carry a full negative or positive charge, the relative effectiveness in increasing or decreasing the rate of substitution should depend on the size and direction of the electrical dipole of the monosubstituted benzene.

Electrical Dipole Moments and Their Direction. The methyl group is believed to increase the electron density at an unsaturated carbon atom (p. 60). If a change in electron distribution takes place when one group replaces another, it should lead to a change in the electrical dipole moment (p. 197) unless the two groups being joined have the same attraction for electrons.

The dipole moment of benzene is zero, as is that of methane, p-xylene, and all other symmetrically constituted compounds (p. 197). If there were no difference between the phenyl group and the methyl group in their ability to attract or repel electrons, the moment of toluene would be zero, as is true for ethane or biphenyl. Toluene, however, has a moment of 0.3 D. Hence there is a shift of the electron density either towards the phenyl group or towards the methyl group.

The direction of the polarization has been determined by comparing the moment of nitrobenzene with that of p-nitrotoluene. For nitrobenzene the moment is 4.0 D. The high dipole moment of nitro compounds is explained by assuming the presence of a semipolar bond in which the nitrogen is positive with respect to the oxygen atoms. Hence the effect of the group must be to decrease the electron density of the ring, which agrees with its deactivating property. Since p-dinitrobenzene has zero moment, the moment caused by the nitro groups must be opposed to each other and lie on a line passing through the *para* positions.[2] If now any other group is *para* to the nitro group and the vector representing the electric moment that it induces lies on the line passing through the *para* positions, the moment of the disubstituted benzene will be greater or less than that of nitrobenzene depending on whether the moment is in the same direction as that caused by the nitro group or is opposed to it. Thus if the methyl group has a greater attraction for electrons than a hydrogen atom, the moment of p-nitrotoluene should be less than that of nitrobenzene and should approximate $4.0 - 0.3 = 3.7$ D, but if the methyl group has less attraction for electrons than hydrogen (electron-repelling or electron-donating),

---

[2] Here is direct evidence that the structure of the nitro group is that of a resonance hybrid of

the structures $-\overset{+}{N}\diagdown\diagup^{O^-}_{O}$ and $-N\diagup^{O}_{\overset{+}{O^-}}$. If it were unsymmetrically constituted as represented

by one of these structures, p-dinitrobenzene could have zero moment only when the $N \longleftrightarrow O$ vectors are opposed to each other. In all other positions the molecule would have a resultant moment. Since isomeric forms cannot be isolated, free rotation about the nitrogen carbon bond

$\mu = 0$ $\mu = $ maximum

must be assumed. Therefore the moments of unsymmetrical nitro groups would not always be opposed, and the molecule would have a resultant electric moment. Hence the zero moment must be ascribed to a symmetrical structure for the nitro group.

$\mu = 0$

Groups known to have unsymmetrical structures, such as the hydroxyl group and the amino group, give rise to electrical moments in the *para* disubstituted compounds.

$\mu = 2.5$ D $\qquad\qquad\qquad \mu = 1.5$ D

the moment of *p*-nitrotoluene should be larger than that of nitrobenzene and should approximate $4.0 + 0.3 = 4.3$ D. The observed moment for *p*-nitrotoluene is 4.5 D, and hence the methyl group increases the electron density of the benzene nucleus, which agrees with its activating effect. It is convenient to indicate the direction of the induced moments by the sign $+\!\!\rightarrow$. The arrow symbolizes the direction in which electron density is increased, the tail being the positive end of the dipole.

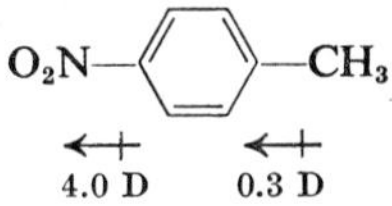

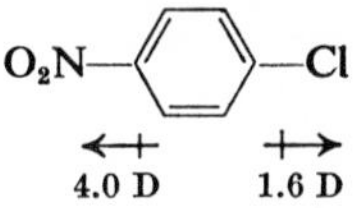

$$O_2N\!-\!\!\bigcirc\!\!-\!CH_3 \qquad\qquad O_2N\!-\!\!\bigcirc\!\!-\!Cl$$

$\leftarrow\!\!+$	$\leftarrow\!\!+$	$\leftarrow\!\!+$	$+\!\!\rightarrow$
4.0 D	0.3 D	4.0 D	1.6 D

Difference = 3.7 D	Difference = 2.4 D
Sum = 4.3 D	Sum = 5.6 D
Experimental = 4.5 D	Experimental = 3.1 D

Chlorobenzene has a moment of 1.6 and *p*-chloronitrobenzene 2.6. Hence the chlorine atom has a greater attraction for electrons than hydrogen, in agreement with its deactivating effect. The directions of the moments for other groups have been determined by similar methods and are listed in Table 24.

TABLE 24

MAGNITUDE AND DIRECTION OF ELECTRIC MOMENTS OF BENZENE DERIVATIVES

GROUP A IN C_6H_5-A	ELECTRIC MOMENT OF C_6H_5-A	DIRECTION OF MOMENT C_6H_5-A $\leftarrow\!\!+$　or　C_6H_5-A $+\!\!\rightarrow$
$N(CH_3)_2$	1.6	
OH	1.6	
NH_2	1.5	
SH	1.3	$\leftarrow\!\!+$
OCH_3	1.2	
CH_3	0.3	
H	0.0	
I	1.4	
Br	1.5	
Cl	1.6	
COOH	1.6	
CH_2Cl	1.8	
$COOC_2H_5$	1.9	
$CHCl_2$	2.0	
CCl_3	2.1	
CHO	2.8	$+\!\!\rightarrow$
$COCH_3$	2.8	
NO	3.1	
SO_3H	3.8	
CN	4.0	
NO_2	4.0	

The moments of the amino and substituted amino groups and of all the oxygen-containing groups except the nitro group, the phenoxide ion, and the carboxylate ion, are not collinear with the axis of the benzene ring but make an angle with it (see footnote 2, p. 450). Hence for these groups the component affecting the bond to the ring may be considerably different from the observed moment for the molecule.

Directive Influence of Substituents. The general increase or decrease in the availability of the unsaturation electrons of the nucleus does not account for the greater reactivity of one position over another. When an *ortho,para*-directing group is present, the σ complex or transition state in which the electron-seeeking reagent has bonded to a carbon atom in the *ortho* or *para* position must be formed more readily, that is, the activation energy necessary for its formation must be less, than if it had bonded to a *meta* position. The reverse must be true for *meta*-directing groups.

If A is the directing group and Z the entering group, the more stable resonance forms will be those in which the positive charge is located at the positions *ortho* and *para* to Z. Resonance forms in which the positive charge is located *meta* to Z are not important because they would require the unpairing of electrons and a separation of charge in the molecule. When Z is *ortho* or *para* to A, a positive charge is located at the ring carbon atom to which A is attached in (a) and (d) of transition states I and II, whereas if Z is *meta* to A as in transition state III, this carbon does not bear a positive charge in any of the resonance forms.

If A is an electron-donating group, it will stabilize a positive charge adjacent to it, and hence favor the formation of the transition states I and II in which Z is the in *ortho* and *para* positions, over III in which Z is in the *meta* position. On the other hand, if A is electron-attracting, it is more difficult to withdraw electrons from the carbon atom to which A is attached, and transition states I and II can be formed less readily than transition state III. Thus electron-donating groups favor *ortho,para*-substitution, whereas electron-attracting groups favor *meta* substitution.

If A is a group that is not complicated by having unshared electrons or multiple bonds on the atom joined to the ring, such as a methyl group, CH_3, or a trichloromethyl group, CCl_3, these considerations hold. Thus when a methyl group is combined with a group that can accept electrons, it can supply the electrons better than a hydrogen atom joined to the same group (Table 24). Hence the rate of substitution at the *ortho* and *para* positions is increased over that expected statistically. This type of directive influence of the group A is known as an **inductive effect**. According to Table 24 the trichloromethyl group attracts electrons more strongly than a hydrogen atom; that is, it has an inductive effect opposite to that of a methyl group, and by decreasing the electron density tends to prevent the formation of transition states I and II. Hence the rate of substitution at the *ortho* and *para* positions is decreased over that expected statistically, resulting in a higher proportion of *meta* substitution.

The series NO_2, CH_2NO_2, and $CH_2CH_2NO_2$ of Table 22, page 441, indicates that the effect of a group rapidly diminishes as saturated hydrocarbon groups are interposed between it and the ring. The series CH_3, CH_2Cl, $CHCl_2$, CCl_3 illustrates the effect of replacing a less strongly electron-attracting group by a more strongly electron-attracting group.

Halogen appears to be anomalous. Since it is more electron-attracting than hydrogen, its inductive effect deactivates the nucleus. Nevertheless it directs *ortho* and *para*. A clue to the problem is afforded by the interatomic carbon-chlorine distances and the dipole moments of *t*-butyl chloride and chlorobenzene. The respective distances are 1.76 A and 1.69 A, and the moments are 2.14 D and 1.56 D. Both the shortening of the bond and the lower moment for the aromatic compound can be explained by the interaction of an unshared pair of electrons in a *p* orbital of the chlorine atom with the unsaturation electrons of the aromatic nucleus as

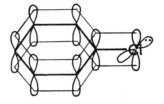

Fig. 76. Interaction of the unshared electrons of the chlorine atom in chlorobenzene with the unsaturation electrons of the benzene nucleus.

indicated in Fig. 76 or by the resonance hybrid symbolism

The effect of this electronic interaction is opposite to that of the inductive effect, but it is not sufficient to overcome the inductive effect, and the chlorine atom remains deactivating. How-ever, on the approach of an electron-seeking reagent, such as a nitronium ion, this type of electronic interaction is sufficient to render the transition states having the nitro group attached to the *ortho* or *para* position (I or II) more stable than that having the nitro group at the *meta* position (III).

Hence the rate of reaction is greater at the *ortho* and *para* positions than at the *meta* position although less than the rate of reaction of benzene. This effect has been called the **electromeric, tautomeric, mesomeric, or resonance effect.**[3]

The hydroxyl and amino groups also are electron-attracting as is indicated by the fact that hydroxylamine, $HONH_2$, $(K_B = 1.1 \times 10^{-8})$ and hydrazine, H_2NNH_2, $(K_B = 3.0 \times 10^{-6})$ are weaker bases than ammonia $(K_B = 1.8 \times 10^{-5})$. However, the resonance effect overbalances the inductive effect as is evident from the size and direction of the dipole moments of the monosubstituted benzenes (Table 24, p. 451). Hence these groups are activating as well as *ortho,para*-directing.

---

[3] A somewhat subtle distinction is made between the electromeric or tautomeric effect and the mesomeric effect. The mesomeric effect is that which is present in the nonreacting molecule and gives rise to the decreased moment of chlorobenzene as compared with *t*-butyl chloride. The electromeric or tautomeric effect is that which permits the molecule to be readily polarized and to supply a pair of electrons to the electron-seeking reagent in the transition state for the reaction. The term "resonance effect" is used for either or both effects.

The hydroxyl group is more strongly activating in alkaline solution than in neutral or acid solution, because the negative charge on the oxygen atom in the phenoxide ion reverses the inductive effect; moreover, the resonance effect is increased because no separation of charge is present in the resonance structures of the phenoxide ion.

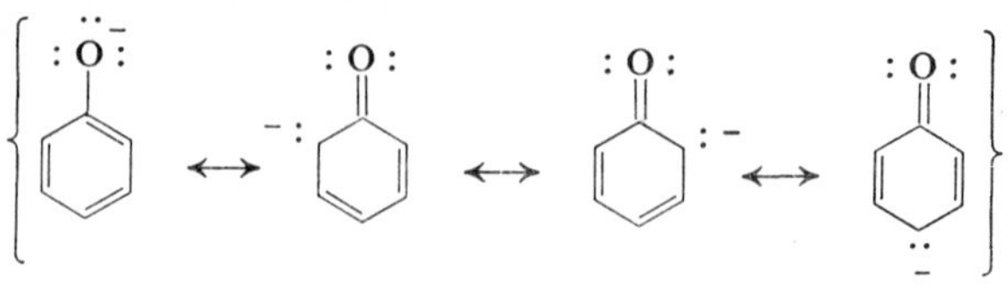

Since the inductive and resonance effects now reinforce each other, the negatively-charged oxygen atom is the strongest activating and strongest *ortho,para*-directing group.

The amino group is less strongly electron-attracting than the hydroxyl group. Hence the effect of the amino group lies between that of the undissociated hydroxyl group and the negatively-charged oxygen atom. In acid solution the unshared pair of electrons of the amino group acquires a proton and the group a positive charge, thereby removing the resonance effect and increasing the electron-attracting power of the group, with the result that it becomes deactivating and *meta*-directing. In the nitration of aniline in acid solution most of the *ortho* and *para* isomers arise from the reaction of the free amine that is in equilibrium with its salt. Thus the proportion of the *meta* isomer increases with increasing concentration of acid.

Substituted vinyl groups are *ortho,para*-directing even though they may be electron-attracting. Thus β-nitrophenylethylene (β-nitrostyrene) gives only 2 per cent of the *meta* isomer on nitration. As with the halogenobenzenes, the transition state is more stable when the substituent is attached to the *ortho* or *para* position (I or II) than when it is attached to the *meta* position (III).

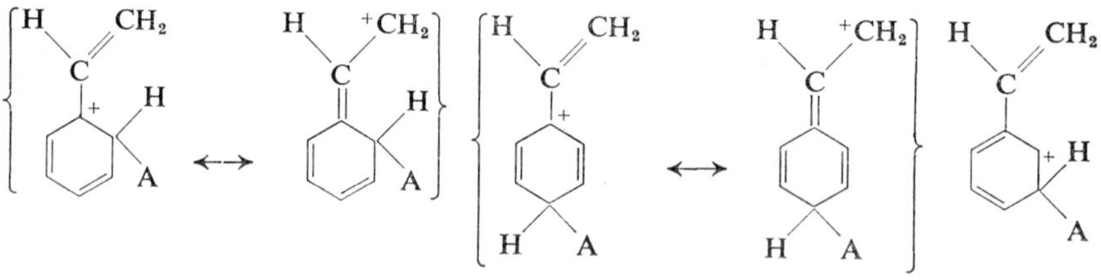

I   II   III

The discussion thus far applies to substitution by an electron-seeking reagent. Substitutions in the aromatic nucleus are known, however, in which the active agent is electron-donating. An example is the formation of *o*-nitrophenol (*o*-hydroxynitrobenzene) when nitrobenzene is heated with potassium hydroxide in the presence of air.

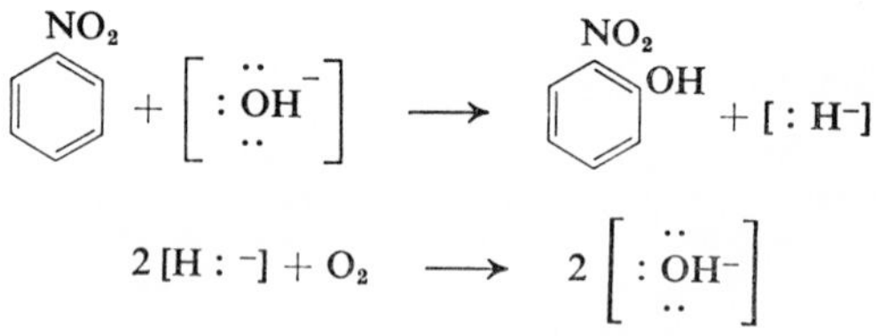

The theory can accommodate these reactions also. Groups that are activating for electron-seeking reagents are those that increase the electron density of the ring nucleus, and hence they are deactivating for electron-donating reagents. Groups that are deactivating for electron-seeking reagents withdraw electrons from the nucleus and are activating for electron-donating reagents. Concerning directive influence, the transition states for electron-donating reagents would have an unshared pair of electrons and hence a negative charge instead of a positive charge in the resonance structures of the transition states represented on page 452. Thus electron-attracting groups would lead to *ortho,para* substitution and electron-donating groups to *meta* substitution. Moreover the nitro group is particularly activating because both the inductive effect and the resonance effect stabilize the transition state when Z is at the *ortho* or *para* position.

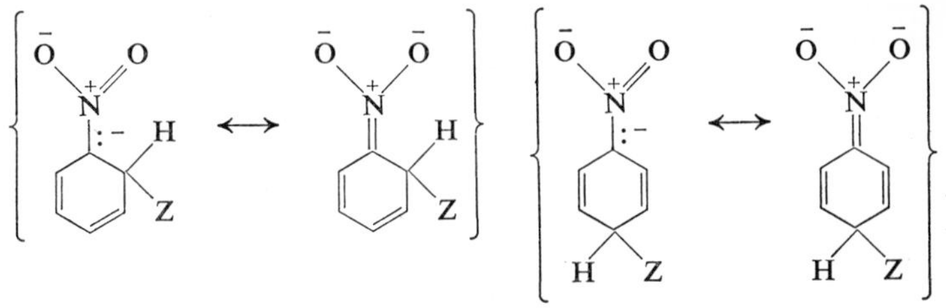

Physical Properties of Nitro Compounds

Aromatic nitro compounds usually are solids, either colorless or yellow. Only a few mononitro hydrocarbons are liquids at room temperature. Because of the presence of the semipolar bond, the nitro group has a high dipole moment, and the nitro compounds have high boiling points. The lowest boiling aromatic nitro compound, nitrobenzene, has a dipole moment of 4.0 D and boils at 209°. The ability of nitro groups to produce crystallinity and high melting point in aromatic compounds has led to the extensive use of nitro compounds, such as 2,4-dinitrophenylhydrazine (p. 462) and 3,5-dinitrobenzoyl chloride (p. 551), for the preparation of derivatives for identification purposes.

Aromatic nitro hydrocarbons are practically insoluble in water. The liquids are good solvents for most organic compounds and fair solvents for many inorganic salts, especially those such as zinc chloride or aluminum chloride that can accept an unshared pair of electrons and form a complex.

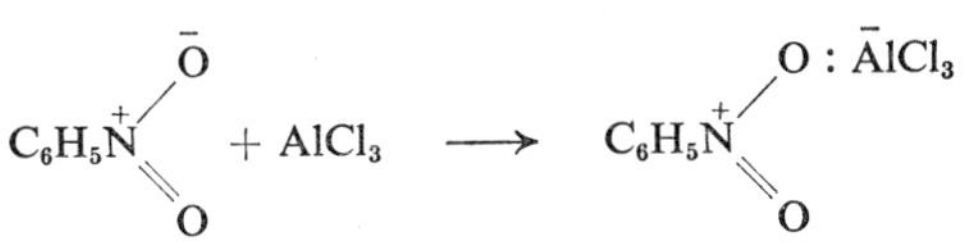

Nitrobenzene strongly absorbs ultraviolet light just beyond the visible (Fig. 96, p. 665). Electronic disturbances, produced by other groups in the molecule or by the approach of other molecules, may shift the absorption band to longer wavelengths, causing the compounds or their solutions to be yellow, orange, or red (pp. 461, 666).

Physiological Action

Nitro compounds having a sufficiently high vapor pressure have strong characteristic odors. For the most part they are highly toxic substances. Even those compounds with low vapor pressures are dangerous because they are absorbed readily through the skin, particularly from solutions. Symptoms of poisoning are dizziness, headache, irregular pulse, and cyanosis (blue lips and finger tips caused by a change in the hemoglobin of the blood). Prolonged contact or exposure leads to death.

Reactions of the Aromatic Nitro Group

Displacement Reactions. In general the nitro group does not undergo displacement reactions. In some polynitro compounds, however, one nitro group frequently undergoes a displacement reaction with basic reagents, nitrite being the other product.

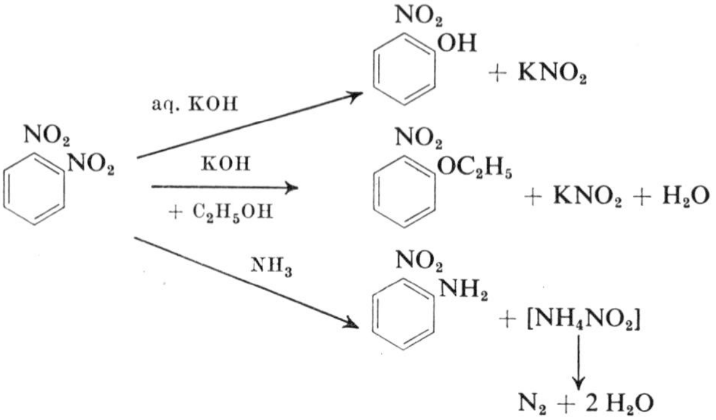

p-Dinitrobenzene behaves similarly but not *m*-dinitrobenzene. On the other hand 1,3,5-trinitrobenzene reacts with sodium methoxide in methanol solution to give 1,3-dinitro-5-methoxybenzene.

Frequently in displacement reactions the entering group does not occupy the same position as the group displaced. For example, *p*-bromonitrobenzene and potassium cyanide give some *m*-bromobenzonitrile; *o*-bromoanisole and sodium amide in liquid ammonia give *m*-aminoanisole; and *o*-, *m*-, or *p*-chlorotoluene with aqueous sodium hydroxide at 350° gives a mixture of the three hydroxytoluenes in which the *meta* isomer predominates.

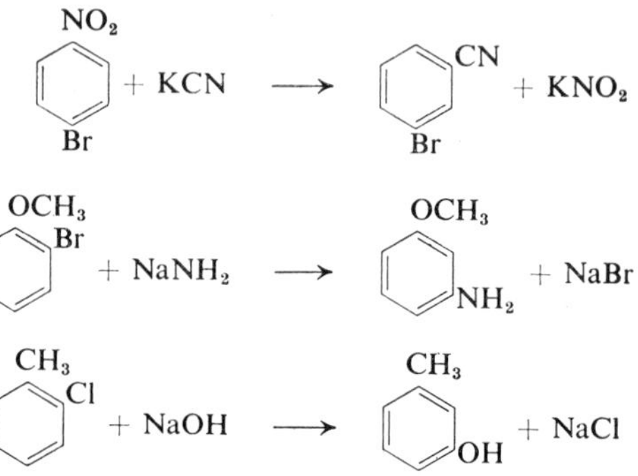

It has been shown that these products are not formed by rearrangement of the expected compounds but are formed during the displacement reaction. The term *cine substitution* (Gr. *kinein*, to move) has been applied to these reactions. They were the cause of considerable difficulty in the early attempts to establish the constitution of aromatic substitution products.

Reduction. Like the aliphatic nitro compounds, the aromatic nitro compounds are reduced readily to primary amines. The reduction may be brought about by hydrogen and a hydrogenation catalyst at room temperature and atmospheric pressure. Because of the large amount of heat evolved and the speed of the reaction, proper precautions should be taken, when hydrogenating large quantities of nitro compounds in a closed system, to keep the reaction always under control.

$$C_6H_5NO_2 + 3 H_2 \xrightarrow[\text{Raney Ni}]{\text{Pt or}} C_6H_5NH_2 + 2 H_2O$$
$$\text{Aniline}$$

Hydrazine may be used conveniently as a source of hydrogen.

$$2 C_6H_5NO_2 + 3 H_2NNH_2 \xrightarrow{\text{Raney Ni}} 2 C_6H_5NH_2 + 4 H_2O + 3 N_2$$

Ordinarily reduction to the amine is brought about by active metals in acid solution. The reagents commonly used are iron or tin in the presence of hydrochloric acid. When an excess of tin is used, the product is the arylammonium chlorostannite from which the amine is liberated by the addition of alkali.

$$2 C_6H_5NO_2 + 6 Sn + 24 HCl \longrightarrow (C_6H_5\overset{+}{N}H_3)_2\overset{=}{S}nCl_4 + 5 H_2SnCl_4 + 4 H_2O$$

Phenylammonium   Chlorostan-
chlorostannite   nous acid

$$\downarrow 6\,\text{NaOH}$$

$$2 C_6H_5NH_2 + Na_2SnO_2 + 4 NaCl + 4 H_2O$$
Aniline   Sodium
stannite

Stannous chloride in the presence of hydrochloric acid reduces nitro compounds to amines, the actual product being the chlorostannate.

$$2 C_6H_5NO_2 + 6 SnCl_2 + 24 HCl \longrightarrow (C_6H_5\overset{+}{N}H_3)_2\overset{=}{S}nCl_6 + 5 H_2SnCl_6 + 4 H_2O$$

Phenylammonium   Chlorostannic
chlorostannate   acid

If standardized solutions of stannous chloride are used, the reaction may be used for the quantitative estimation of nitro groups. Zinc and hydrochloric acid is not a satisfactory reducing agent because considerable amounts of chloroanilines are formed (see below).

Commercially nitrobenzene is reduced to aniline by scrap iron and water in the presence of about one-fortieth of the calculated amount of hydrochloric acid. Hence the reduction is brought about essentially by iron and water, the iron being converted to black oxide of iron, Fe_3O_4 (p. 486).

$$4 C_6H_5NO_2 + 9 Fe + 4 H_2O \xrightarrow{\text{(HCl)}} 4 C_6H_5NH_2 + 3 Fe_3O_4$$

If two nitro groups are present in the ring, it is possible to reduce one group without reducing the other. Ammonium or sodium sulfide is the preferred reagent.

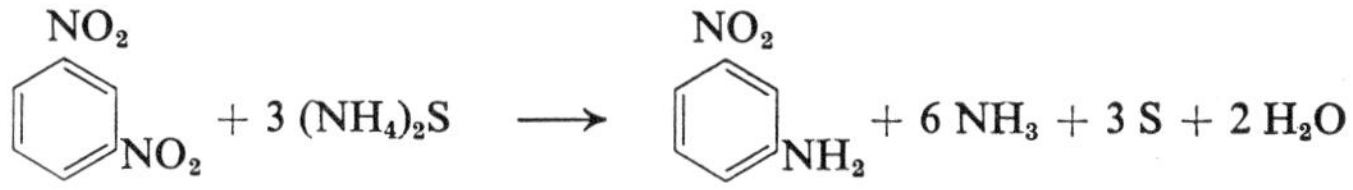

This behavior is understandable, since the electron-attracting properties of the nitro groups mutually increase their strength as oxidizing agents and enable one of them to be reduced more easily than if a single nitro group were present. After one nitro group is reduced, the smaller electron-attracting power of the amino group decreases the ease of reduction of the remaining nitro group.

Although primary amines are the final reduction products of both aliphatic and aromatic nitro compounds, it is possible with aromatic nitro compounds to isolate a number of intermediate reduction products, which may be obtained in good yield by the use of milder and controlled reducing conditions. Thus nitrobenzen. when boiled with an aqueous solution of ammonium chloride and zinc dust gives **N-phenylhydroxylamine** (also called β-phenylhydroxylamine).

$$C_6H_5NO_2 + 2\,Zn + 4\,NH_4Cl \longrightarrow C_6H_5NHOH + 2\,ZnCl_2 + H_2O + 4\,NH_3$$
N-Phenylhydroxylamine

N-Phenylhydroxylamine is a colorless solid that melts at 81°. It is not stable, however, the molecules undergoing mutual intermolecular oxidation and reduction and condensation to give a mixture of the various reduction products of nitrobenzene (p. 460). When a solution of β-phenylhydroxylamine in ether is treated with dry ammonia and an alkyl nitrite the ammonium salt of *N*-phenyl-*N*-nitrosohydroxylamine precipitates.

$$C_6H_5NHOH + NH_3 + C_4H_9ONO \longrightarrow \underset{\underset{NO}{|}}{C_6H_5NO^{-+}NH_4} + C_4H_9OH$$

It is known as **cupferron** and is used in analytical chemistry for the separation of certain metal ions, such as those of copper, iron, and titanium, that react with it to form insoluble chelate coordination compounds (p. 742).

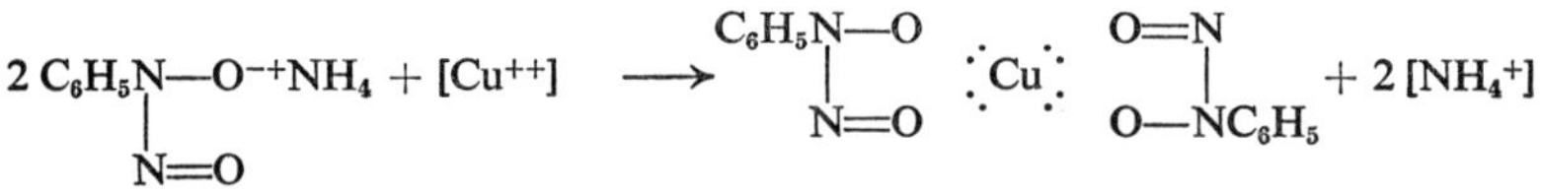

$$2\,C_6H_5\underset{\underset{N=O}{|}}{N-O^{-+}NH_4} + [Cu^{++}] \longrightarrow \underset{N=O}{\overset{C_6H_5N-O}{|}} \,\,:Cu:\,\, \underset{O-NC_6H_5}{\overset{O=N}{|}} + 2\,[NH_4^+]$$

If zinc and hydrochloric acid are used to reduce nitrobenzene, the main product is aniline, but a considerable amount of *o*- and *p*-chloroaniline is formed, presumably by rearrangement of *N*-chloroaniline produced from *N*-phenylhydroxylamine.

NHOH $\qquad$ NHCl $\qquad$ NH$_2$ $\qquad$ NH$_2$

$+\,HCl \longrightarrow H_2O + \qquad \longrightarrow \qquad$ and

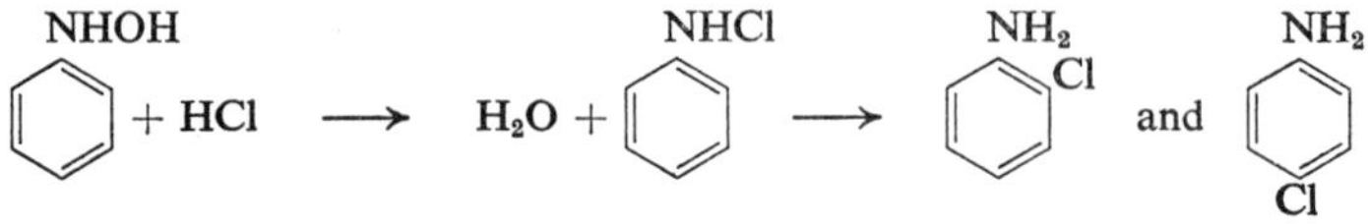

Although **nitrosobenzene** has been shown to be an intermediate reduction product of nitrobenzene, it has not been isolated, because it is reduced very rapidly to *N*-phenylhydroxylamine (p. 458). It can, however, be prepared by oxidation of the latter compound.

$$3\,C_6H_5NHOH + Na_2Cr_2O_7 + 4\,H_2SO_4 \xrightarrow{0°} 3\,C_6H_5NO + Na_2SO_4 + Cr_2(SO_4)_3 + 7\,H_2O$$
Nitrosobenzene

Sodium methoxide in alcohol, or sodium arsenite solution, gives **azoxybenzene**, in which a coupling of two molecules has taken place.

$$4\,C_6H_5NO_2 + 3\,NaOCH_3 \longrightarrow 2\,\underset{\underset{\underset{\text{Azoxybenzene}}{O^-}}{|+}}{C_6H_5N=NC_6H_5} + 3\,NaOCHO + 3\,H_2O$$
(or 6 Na$_3$AsO$_3$) $\qquad\qquad\qquad\qquad$ Sodium formate
$\qquad\qquad\qquad\qquad\qquad\qquad\qquad\qquad$ (or 6 Na$_3$AsO$_4$)

Oxidation of azobenzene with hydrogen peroxide in acetic acid also yields azoxybenzene.

$$C_6H_5N=NC_6H_5 + H_2O_2 \longrightarrow \underset{\underset{O^-}{|+}}{C_6H_5N=NC_6H_5} + H_2O$$

The oxygen atom in azoxybenzene is believed to be linked to nitrogen by a semipolar bond as in the amine oxides (p. 240). In accordance with this view oxidation of unsymmetrical azo compounds yields two structurally isomeric products.

$$C_6H_5N{=}NC_6H_4NO_2 \xrightarrow{\text{H}_2\text{O}_2} \underset{\overset{|}{\underset{O^-}{+}}}{C_6H_5N{=}NC_6H_4NO_2} \quad \text{and} \quad \underset{\overset{|}{\underset{O^-}{+}}}{C_6H_5N{=}NC_6H_4NO_2}$$

Azobenzene can be prepared by heating azoxybenzene with iron filings,

$$\underset{\overset{|}{\underset{O^-}{+}}}{3\,C_6H_5N{=}NC_6H_5} + 2\,Fe \longrightarrow 3\,C_6H_5N{=}NC_6H_5 + Fe_2O_3$$

but the usual laboratory method of preparation is by the oxidation of hydra-zobenzene with hypobromite solution.

$$\underset{\text{Hydrazobenzene}}{C_6H_5NHNHC_6H_5} + NaOBr \longrightarrow C_6H_5N{=}NC_6H_5 + NaBr + H_2O$$

The oxidation may be brought about also by passing air through an alkaline alcoholic solution of hydrazobenzene.

When nitrobenzene is heated with zinc dust and aqueous sodium hydroxide, the product is **hydrazobenzene.**

$$2\,C_6H_5NO_2 + 5\,Zn + 10\,NaOH \longrightarrow C_6H_5NHNHC_6H_5 + 5\,Na_2ZnO_2 + 4\,H_2O$$

Any of the intermediate reduction products can be reduced to aniline using a strong reducing agent. The reactions of nitrobenzene are summarized in Fig. 77.

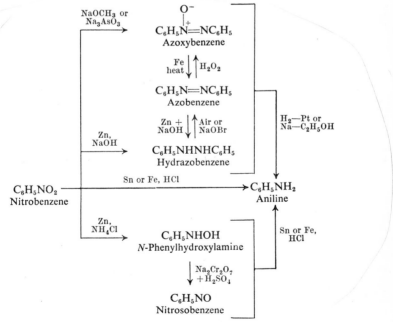

Fig. 77. Reduction products of nitrobenzene.

The bimolecular reduction products of nitrobenzene obtained in alkaline solution arise from secondary reactions of nitrosobenzene and phenylhydroxylamine. The first bimolecular product is azoxybenzene, formed by the condensation of nitrosobenzene and *N*-phenylhydroxylamine in alkaline solution.

$$C_6H_5NHOH + ONC_6H_5 \longrightarrow \underset{\underset{O^-}{|+}}{C_6H_5N}{=}NC_6H_5 + H_2O$$

Further reduction of the azoxybenzene gives hydrazobenzene but not azobenzene.

$$\underset{\underset{O^-}{|+}}{C_6H_5N}{=}NC_6H_5 + 4\ [H] \longrightarrow C_6H_5NHNHC_6H_5 + H_2O$$

The azobenzene arises from the oxidation of hydrazobenzene by nitrobenzene.

$$C_6H_5NHNHC_6H_5 + C_6H_5NO_2 \longrightarrow C_6H_5N{=}NC_6H_5 + C_6H_5NO + H_2O$$

Hence the particular reduction product formed in largest amount depends not only on the reducing power of the reagent but also on the relative rates of the reduction of nitrobenzene and of the secondary reactions.

Molecular Complex Formation. A striking property of polynitro compounds is their ability to form molecular complexes with aromatic compounds. Table 25 lists a few representative examples.

TABLE 25

Molecular Complex Compounds of Polynitro Hydrocarbons

POLYNITRO HYDROCARBON	SECOND COMPONENT	M.P. OF COMPLEX	COLOR OF COMPLEX
1,3-Dinitrobenzene	naphthalene	53	colorless
	aniline	42	red
1,3,5-Trinitrobenzene	benzene	dec.	colorless
	naphthalene	152	colorless
	phenanthrene	158	orange
	anthracene	174	scarlet
	α-naphthol	179	orange
	aniline	124	orange-red
	dimethylaniline	107	dark violet
	α-naphthoic acid	183	pale yellow
	biphenylene oxide	96	lemon yellow
2,4,6-Trinitrotoluene	naphthalene	98	colorless
	α-naphthol	110	orange
	aniline	84	red
Hexanitroethane	naphthalene	dec.	red

Over 700 complexes of polynitro compounds had been recorded in the literature by 1927 and many more have been added since. In about 85 per cent of the compounds, the molecular ratio is one mole of nitro compound to one mole of the second component. The compounds usually are decomposed easily into their components, but most are sufficiently stable to be purified by crystallization and have characteristic melting points. They are useful as derivatives, particularly for complex hydrocarbons and compounds that do not have a reactive functional group. 1,3,5-Trinitrobenzene, 2,4,6-trinitrophenol (picric acid, p. 514), 2,4,6-trinitroresorcinol (styphnic acid, p. 517), and 2,4,7-trinitrofluorenone (p. 840) are used most frequently for this purpose. The addition products usually are highly colored although the components are colorless. The formation of molecular complexes is not limited to the aromatic polynitro compounds. Hexanitroethane, for example, gives red addition products with naphthalene, aniline, and phenol.

Frequently nitro compounds give colors with other compounds even though there is no evidence for compound formation. Nitrobenzene gives lemon-yellow solutions when mixed with aliphatic amines and orange to red solutions with aromatic amines. The purplish to red colors produced when polynitro aromatic compounds are dissolved in acetone and a few drops of aqueous alkali added may be similar in nature. Tetranitromethane (p. 263) gives yellow to red colors with olefins and aromatic hydrocarbons, and brown colors with amines.

The nature of the forces holding the molecules together and the cause of the color have been the subject of considerable discussion. It is believed that in spite of the well-defined properties of the molecular complexes, no bond formation in the usual chemical sense takes place between the two components. *m*-Dinitrobenzene and 1,3,5-trinitrobenzene form a complex with each other with practically no change in color. Here the molecules must be held together by dipole association alone. On the other hand 1,3,5-trinitrobenzene dissolved in liquid ammonia conducts the electric current and the trinitrobenzene migrates to the anode, indicating a transfer of an electron from the ammonia to the trinitrobenzene to give an ionic complex. In general the stability of a complex increases with increasing electron-donating ability of one component and increasing electron-accepting ability of the second component. However, it seems likely that for most colored complexes the transfer of an electron is accompanied by the formation of an intermolecular electron-pair bond to give a complex resembling somewhat the σ complexes postulated as transition states for electrophilic substitution of aromatic compounds (p. 445).

This type of complex would be expected to have considerable stability and yet dissociate readily into the original components. The high electric moment associated with resonance among equivalent electronic structures would account for the intense color of the complexes which often approaches that of the dyes (pp. 662, 666, 667). Undoubtedly the intermolecular forces in molecular complexes which exist in solution range from pure dipole association, through π complexes (p. 445) and σ complexes, to ionic compounds with complete transfer of an electron.

Effect of the Nitro Group and of Other *meta*-Directing Groups on the Reactivity of Other Nuclear Substituents

Halogen attached to an aryl group is very unreactive in the usual displacement reactions (p. 435). If, however, a nitro group or other *meta*-directing group is in a position *ortho* or *para* to the halogen atom, the reactivity is greatly increased. The reactivity is greater yet when two nitro groups are present in the 2,4 position and reaches a maximum with three nitro groups in the 2,4,6 positions. For example although chlorobenzene reacts with concentrated alkali only at 200°–300° in the presence of copper, 2,4-dinitrochlorobenzene is hydrolyzed by boiling with an aqueous solution of sodium carbonate.

2,4-Dinitrochlorobenzene   2,4-Dinitrophenol

Similarly aqueous sodium hydrogen sulfide gives 2,4-dinitrothiophenol, sodium sulfide gives 2,4-dinitrophenyl sulfide, sodium disulfide gives 2,4-dinitrophenyl disulfide, ammonia gives 2,4-dinitroaniline, and hydrazine gives 2,4-dinitro-phenylhydrazine. The last compound is a valuable reagent for the preparation of derivatives of aldehydes and ketones. 2,4-Dinitrofluorobenzene, prepared by the reaction of 2,4-dinitrochlorobenzene with potassium fluoride in nitrobenzene at 190°, has found important use in determining the structure of polypeptides (p. 300). The high reactivity of the fluorine permits reaction with free amino groups under relatively mild conditions.

Other *meta*-directing groups such as carbonyl also have an activating effect when present in the positions *ortho* and *para* to the halogen. If the group is *meta* to the halogen atom it has less effect on reactivity. *meta*-Directing groups in the *ortho* and *para* positions and to a less extent in the *meta* position increase also the reactivity of other groups such as alkyl (p. 489). They also increase the acidity of the carboxyl and phenolic hydroxyl groups (pp. 548, 503) and decrease the basicity of amino groups (p. 478). Electron-donating groups in the *para* position have the opposite effect (pp. 468, 548).

Mechanism of Displacement of Aromatic Halogen

When a halogen atom in an alkyl halide is displaced by an electron-donating group such as a hydroxide ion or an ammonia molecule, the reaction may take place in one of two ways. In the usual bimolecular mechanism (p. 116) the reagent approaches the carbon atom on the side opposite the halogen atom, and as the new bond is formed and the halogen ion leaves, the carbon atom undergoes a Walden inversion. In other reactions, such as the hydrolysis of tertiary halides, a so-called unimolecular mechanism has been proposed in which a slow ionization of the alkyl halide takes place, followed by a rapid combination of the carbonium ion with the electron-donating reagent (p. 117).

For aromatic halides, neither of these mechanisms is possible. Because of the ring of carbon atoms, the reagent cannot approach from the back side; and if it managed to do so, Walden inversion could not take place without rupture of the ring. Moreover the halogen has less tendency to ionize than that in an alkyl halide because of the resonance with the benzene ring (Fig. 76, p. 453). Hence the only possibility appears to be a direct replacement analogous to substitution by electron-donating reagents (p. 454).

When an electron-attracting group is in the *ortho* or *para* position, it assists the formation of the transition state by relieving the increased electron density at these positions. The nitro and carboxyl groups are particularly effective, because either can provide a favorable site for the location of the negative charge.

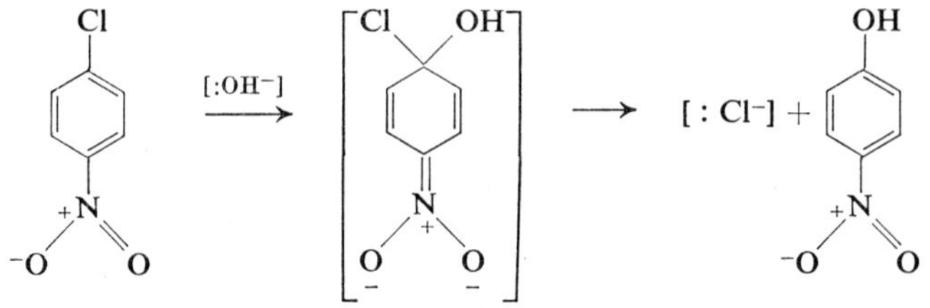

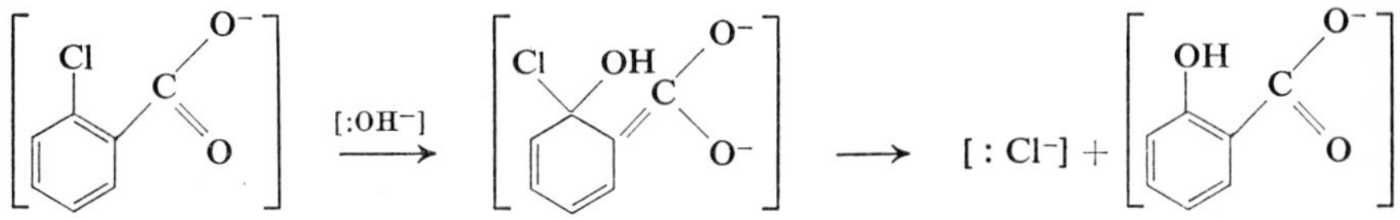

The current explanation of the high reactivity of halogen located on a carbon atom attached to the ring can be illustrated by the phenylmethyl halides (p. 437). In the displacement of halide ion by an electron-donating group the transition state must involve an increase in electron density about the carbon atom from which the halogen is being displaced. The ability of the aromatic ring to relieve this pressure of electrons permits easier formation of the transition state and increases the reactivity of benzyl halides over that of primary alkyl halides.

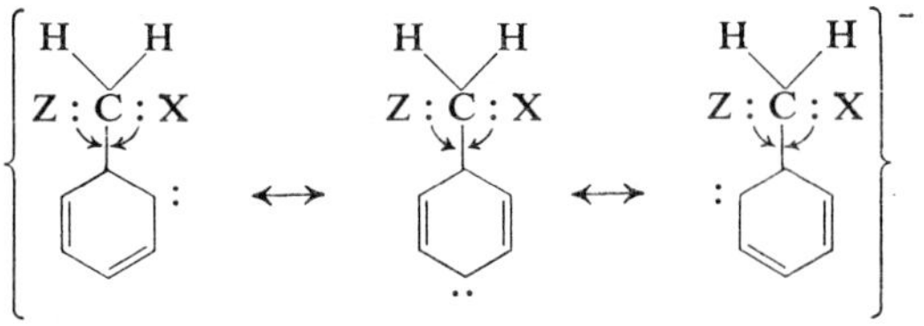

Important Nitro Hydrocarbons

Nitrobenzene was prepared first in 1834 by Mitscherlich, who called it *nitrobenzid*. It is the most important of the nitro aromatic hydrocarbons in times of peace. Production in the United States rose from 69 million pounds in 1940 to 125 million pounds in 1943 because of World War II. Production has remained at a high figure, being 176 million pounds in 1955 when the selling price was about 11 cents per pound. Very little nitrobenzene is used as such, practically all being converted to aniline. Because of its odor, nitrobenzene was called *oil of mirbane* or *artificial oil of bitter almonds*. It once was used as a flavoring principle and as a perfume for soaps, and to adulterate oil of bitter almonds. Its high toxicity soon led to a discontinuance of this practice. Because it penetrates leather, it long was used as a solvent for shoe dyes, but here again poisoning occurred by absorption of the vapors through the skin, and such formulations now are prohibited in most countries.

Some of the di- and trinitroalkylbenzenes have a musk-like odor and are used in perfumery. Methoxyl or acetyl groups also may be present. They are known as **"synthetic musks"** or **"nitro musks"** although they are not related chemically to the true musks which are cyclic ketones (p. 847).

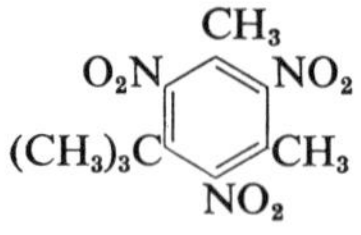

Musk xylene	Musk tibetine	Musk ambrette	Musk ketone

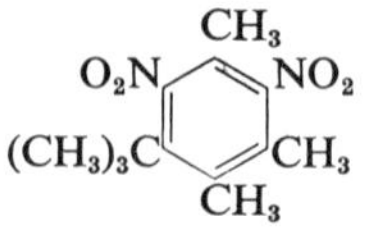

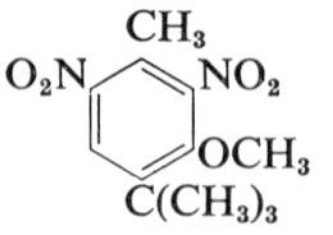

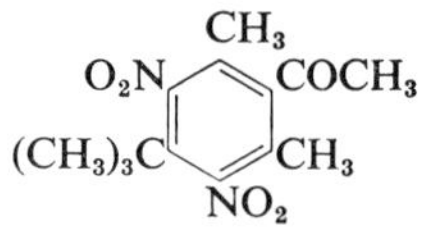

1,3,5-Trinitrobenzene is a more powerful explosive than TNT, but it cannot be made in satisfactory yields by direct nitration of benzene because of the difficulty of introducing a third nitro group unless an activating group also is present. It is prepared on a small scale for reagent purposes by decarboxylating 2,4,6-trinitrobenzoic acid, which is obtained by the oxidation of TNT.

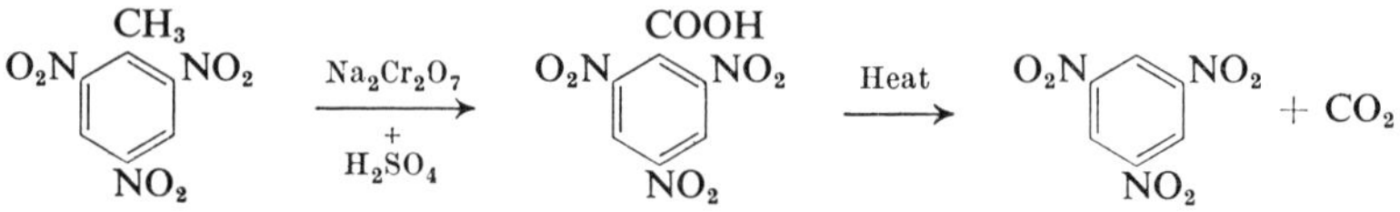

2,4,6-Trinitrobenzoic acid decarboxylates more readily than most benzoic acids. Decomposition is by way of the anion, the strong electron-attracting effect of the nitro groups facilitating the formation of the intermediate carbanion.

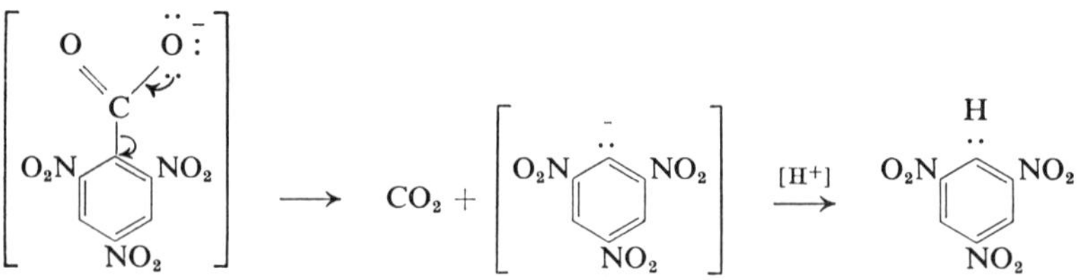

2,4,6-Trinitrotoluene, commonly known as TNT, is an important military explosive. It is used for filling bombs, shells, and hand grenades either alone or with other explosives (pp. 222, 752). Since it melts at 81° and does not explode until 280°, it can be poured into shells in a liquid state and allowed to solidify. It is relatively insensitive to shock and must be exploded by a detonator. Production in the United States during World War II probably reached a rate of one million tons per year. The first H-bomb exploded is believed to have had a force equivalent to the explosion of around 14 million tons of TNT.

REVIEW QUESTIONS

1. Compare the direct nitration of aromatic hydrocarbons with that of aliphatic hydrocarbons.
2. Compare the boiling points of aromatic hydrocarbons, halides, and nitro compounds of approximately the same molecular weight. Compare the melting points of the *ortho*, *meta*, and *para* nitro derivatives of toluene, chlorobenzene, and nitrobenzene.
3. Discuss the effect of substituents on the position taken by an entering group in substitution reactions of aromatic compounds.
4. What is meant by the terms *activation* and *deactivation* as applied to aromatic compounds?
5. What is meant by the term molecular complex compound? Give an example.

PROBLEMS

6. Give the formulas and names of the chief product or products that would be expected when one more group is introduced by the following substitution reactions:

   A. (*a*) Nitration of bromobenzene; (*b*) chlorination of nitrobenzene; (*c*) sulfonation of toluene; (*d*) bromination of benzoic acid; (*e*) nitration of benzenesulfonic acid; (*f*) chlorination of *m*-xylene in the presence of ferric chloride; (*g*) light-catalyzed bromination of *o*-xylene; (*h*) nitration of *m*-dinitrobenzene; (*i*) sulfonation of *o*-nitrocumene; (*j*) bromination of chlorobenzene.

   B. (*a*) Sulfonation of chlorobenzene; (*b*) chlorination of bromobenzene; (*c*) nitration of ethylbenzene; (*d*) bromination of nitrobenzene; (*e*) sulfonation of benzenesulfonic acid; (*f*) nitration of fluorobenzene; (*g*) bromination of *p*-nitrotoluene; (*h*) chlorination of *m*-dinitrobenzene; (*i*) light-catalyzed chlorination of *o*-xylene; (*j*) sulfonation of *m*-diethylbenzene.

   C. (*a*) Chlorination of benzenesulfonic acid; (*b*) nitration of cumene; (*c*) sulfonation of phenol; (*d*) bromination of benzenesulfonic acid; (*e*) sulfonation of nitrobenzene; (*f*) nitration of chlorobenzene; (*g*) chlorination of *m*-bromotoluene; (*h*) sulfonation of *p*-nitroethylbenzene; (*i*) light-catalyzed bromination of *p*-xylene; (*j*) chlorination of *m*-benzenedisulfonic acid.

7. Give equations for the following reactions:

   A. (*a*) *p*-Nitrotoluene with iron and hydrochloric acid; (*b*) *o*-nitrocumene with sodium methoxide; (*c*) *p,p'*-dimethylazobenzene with hydrogen peroxide; (*d*) *p*-nitroethylbenzene with zinc dust and sodium hydroxide; (*e*) *m*-chloronitrobenzene with zinc dust and ammonium chloride; (*f*) hydrazocumene with sodium hypobromite; (*g*) *N*-*o*-tolylhydroxylamine with dichromate and sulfuric acid.

   B. (*a*) *o*-Nitrochlorobenzene with hydrogen and Raney nickel; (*b*) *p,p'*-diethylazobenzene and hydrogen peroxide; (*c*) *o*-nitrocumene with zinc dust and sodium hydroxide; (*d*) *p*-nitroethylbenzene with sodium arsenite; (*e*) *N*-*p*-ethylphenylhydroxylamine with dichromate and sulfuric acid; (*f*) *p,p'*-dimethylhydrazobenzene with sodium hypobromite; (*g*) *m*-nitrotoluene with zinc dust and ammonium chloride.

   C. (*a*) *p*-Nitrocumene and sodium methoxide; (*b*) *m,m'*-diethylhydrazobenzene and sodium hypobromite; (*c*) *m*-chloronitrobenzene with iron and hydrochloric acid; (*d*) *N*-*p*-bromophenylhydroxylamine with dichromate and sulfuric acid; (*e*) *p*-nitroethylbenzene with zinc dust and ammonium chloride; (*f*) *m*-nitrotoluene with zinc dust and sodium hydroxide; (*g*) *p,p'*-di-*i*-propylazobenzene and hydrogen peroxide.

8. Give a series of reactions for the synthesis of the following compounds from an aromatic hydrocarbon:

   A. (*a*) *m*-Bromonitrobenzene; (*b*) 2,4-dimethyl-5-nitrochlorobenzene; (*c*) 2-nitro-4-bromoethylbenzene; (*d*) *p*-chlorobenzenesulfonic acid; (*e*) 4-nitro-2-chlorotoluene; (*f*) *m*-nitrobenzoic acid; (*g*) *p*-bromobenzoic acid; (*h*) 2,4-dinitrochlorobenzene.

   B. (*a*) 2-Nitro-4-chlorotoluene; (*b*) *m*-chlorobenzenesulfonic acid; (*c*) *m*-chlorobenzoic acid; (*d*) 4-nitro-2-bromocumene; (*e*) *p*-bromonitrobenzene; (*f*) 2,4-dimethyl-5-bromobenzenesulfonic acid; (*g*) *p*-nitrobenzoic acid; (*h*) 3,5-dinitrochlorobenzene.

   C. (*a*) *p*-Bromobenzenesulfonic acid; (*b*) 4-nitro-2-bromoethylbenzene; (*c*) 5-bromo-2,4-dimethylnitrobenzene; (*d*) *m*-bromobenzoic acid; (*e*) 2-nitro-4-chlorocumene; (*f*) *m*-chloronitrobenzene; (*g*) *p*-chlorobenzoic acid; (*h*) 3-nitro-4-chlorobenzenesulfonic acid.

9. How could one distinguish by a chemical reaction between the members of the following pairs of compounds: (*a*) nitrobenzene and 1-nitrohexane; (*b*) azoxybenzene and hydrazobenzene; (*c*) *m*-nitrochlorobenzene and 2,4-dinitrochlorobenzene; (*d*) nitrobenzene and *N*-phenylhydroxylamine; (*e*) *m*-chloronitrobenzene and 2-chloro-4-nitrotoluene.

10. Arrange the following compounds in the order of increasing ease with which halogen is displaced by a negative ion: bromobenzene, *o*-nitrochlorobenzene, *m*-nitrochlorobenzene, chlorobenzene, 3,5-dinitrochlorobenzene, 2,4-dinitrochlorobenzene, benzyl chloride, 2,4,6-trinitrochlorobenzene.

Chapter 21

AROMATIC SULFONIC ACIDS AND THEIR DERIVATIVES

SULFONIC ACIDS

Since aromatic sulfonic acids can be obtained by direct sulfonation, they are more readily available than aliphatic sulfonic acids. The aromatic sulfonic acids are used as intermediates for the introduction of other groups, and to confer water-solubility on aromatic compounds, particularly dyes.

Nomenclature

Sulfonic acids are named by attaching the ending *sulfonic* to the name of the compound that has been substituted and adding *acid*. The positions of the sulfonic acid groups are indicated by numbers or letters.

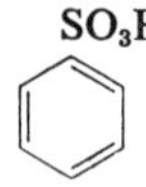

| Benzenesulfonic acid | 2-Chlorobenzenesulfonic acid or *o*-chlorobenzenesulfonic acid | Nitrobenzene-3,5-disulfonic acid |

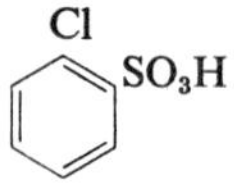

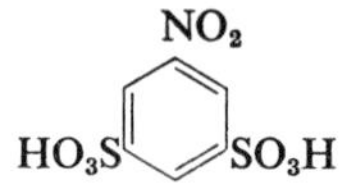

Physical Properties

Sulfonic acids are strong acids, being ionized completely in aqueous solution. They are very soluble in water but are insoluble or only slightly soluble in nonoxygenated solvents. The pure acids are hygroscopic and difficult to obtain anhydrous. They usually crystallize from aqueous solutions with water of hydration.

Sulfonic acids are relatively nonvolatile, although some can be distilled without decomposition at low pressures. Thus benzenesulfonic acid boils at 135°–137° at a pressure below 0.01 mm. of mercury. The melting points of the anhydrous sulfonic acids are lower than those of the corresponding carboxylic acids.

Preparation

Aromatic sulfonic acids generally are prepared by direct sulfonation. The ease of sulfonation depends on the substituents already present in the ring. Thus if activating groups are present, concentrated sulfuric acid at room temperature may suffice to bring about sulfonation. When deactivating groups are present the use of elevated temperatures and fuming sulfuric acid (oleum) containing varying amounts of dissolved sulfur trioxide may be necessary. Benzene can be converted to the monosulfonic acid using 10 per cent fuming sulfuric acid (100 per cent sulfuric acid containing 10 per cent sulfur trioxide)

466

at room temperature. To convert the monosulfonic acid to the *m*-disulfonic acid a temperature of 200°–245° is used, and to convert the *m*-disulfonic acid to the 1,3,5-trisulfonic acid a temperature of 280°–300° is required.

Benzenesulfonic acid — *m*-Benzenedisulfonic acid — 1,3,5-Benzenetrisulfonic acid

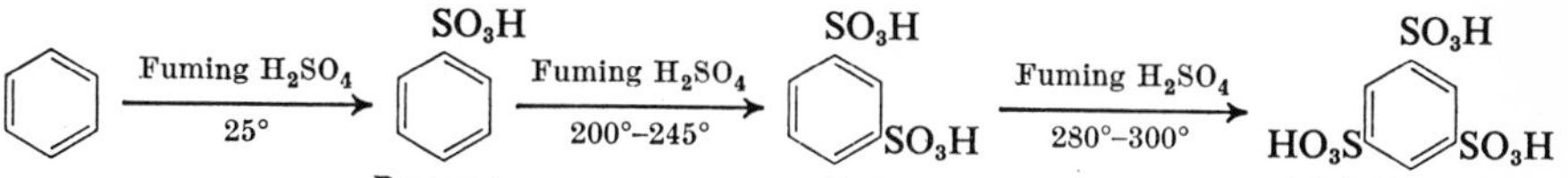

Since 1947 a stabilized form of liquid sulfur trioxide has been available commercially. Because it is much more reactive than sulfuric acid, it can be used in stoichiometric amounts, and the product is free of excess sulfuric acid. When fuming sulfuric acid or sulfur trioxide is used some *sulfone* (p. 285) may be formed as a by-product. Since the sulfone is insoluble in water, it can be removed after dilution of the sulfonation mixture.

$$C_6H_5SO_2OH + C_6H_6 + SO_3 \longrightarrow \underset{\text{Phenyl sulfone}}{C_6H_5SO_2C_6H_5} + H_2SO_4$$

In general sulfonation follows the rules for substitution outlined for nitration (p. 440). It appears, however, to be less predictable and more influenced by conditions. Phenol, for example, gives chiefly *o*-phenolsulfonic acid, whereas chlorobenzene gives chiefly *p*-chlorobenzenesulfonic acid. Temperature and catalysts such as mercuric sulfate frequently have a pronounced influence on the position taken by the sulfonic acid group. The mechanism of sulfonation is discussed on p. 448.

Most sulfonic acids are used in the form of their salts. Fortunately the salts can be isolated much more readily than the sulfonic acid. The sodium salts usually are less soluble than the sulfonic acid, particularly in a solution saturated with sodium chloride. Hence they can be isolated by *salting out.* The reaction mixture is poured into water and a brine solution is added.

$$C_6H_5SO_3H + NaCl \longrightarrow \underset{\text{Sodium benzenesulfonate}}{C_6H_5SO_3Na} + HCl$$

The *calcium*, *barium*, and *lead sulfonates* are soluble in water in contrast to the sulfates. After dilution of the sulfonation mixture with water, the hydroxide, oxide, or carbonate of calcium, barium, or lead can be added to precipitate the sulfate present and leave the sulfonate in solution. Evaporation of the filtrate gives the calcium, barium, or lead sulfonate.

Commercially the **sodium salts** are most useful and are prepared by the *liming out process.* After dilution of the sulfonation mixture, slaked lime is added, and the precipitate of calcium sulfate is removed by filtration. Addition of sodium carbonate to the filtrate precipitates calcium carbonate and leaves the sodium sulfonate in solution. Removal of the calcium carbonate and evaporation give the sodium salt.

Free sulfonic acids can be obtained by adding sufficient sulfuric acid to an aqueous solution of a calcium, barium, or lead salt to precipitate the metallic sulfate, and evaporating the filtrate. Usually it is more convenient to hydrolyze the pure sulfonyl chloride (p. 470).

Reactions of Aromatic Sulfonic Acids and Their Salts

SUBSTITUTION OF THE NUCLEUS

The aromatic ring can be halogenated or nitrated, the SO_3H group being deactivating and *meta*-directing.

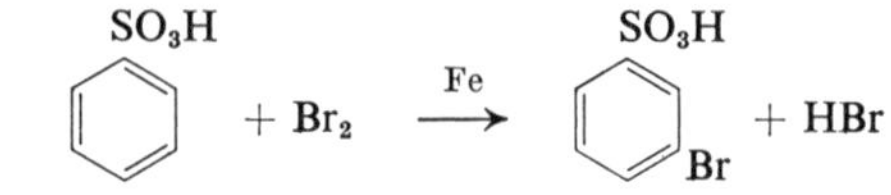

Frequently the sulfonic acid group is displaced, especially when the reaction is carried out in the presence of water.

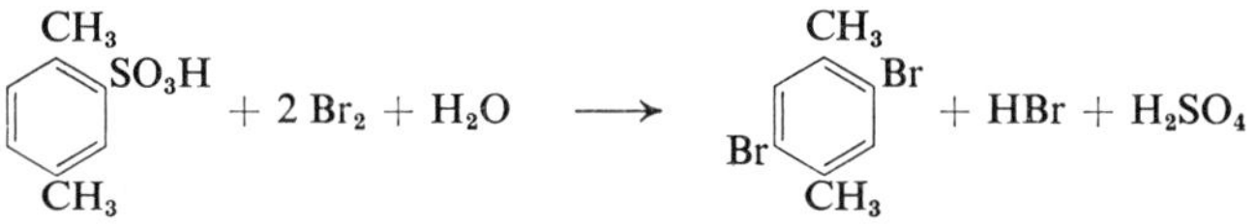

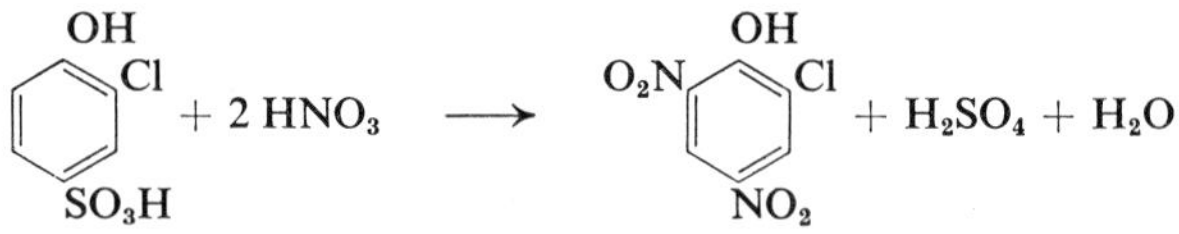

REACTIONS OF FREE SULFONIC ACIDS

1. **Salt Formation and Strength as Acids.** Sulfonic acids react with strong bases to form neutral salts. Salts from weak bases give an acid reaction when dissolved in water. Benzenesulfonic acid is about as strong as sulfuric acid. Electron-attracting groups in the *ortho* and *para* positions increase the acidity, but electron-donating groups decrease the acidity (p. 462). Thus 2,4-dinitro-benzenesulfonic acid is stronger than sulfuric acid, whereas 2,4-dimethoxy-benzenesulfonic acid is weaker than sulfuric acid, although it is stronger than nitric acid.

2. **Hydrolysis.** The sulfonation reaction is reversible. Hence if sulfonic acids are boiled with an excess of water, the sulfonic acid group slowly is removed. A high concentration of an added mineral acid greatly increases the rate of hydrolysis. The reaction is fairly rapid if carried out in a sealed tube at 150°–170°.

$$C_6H_5SO_3H + H_2O \underset{HCl}{\overset{Heat}{\rightleftarrows}} C_6H_6 + H_2SO_4$$

REACTIONS OF SODIUM SULFONATES

1. **Replacement by Hydroxyl.** When a sodium sulfonate is heated with molten sodium hydroxide, the sodium salt of a phenol and sodium sulfite are formed.

$$C_6H_5SO_3Na + 2\ NaOH \xrightarrow{Fusion} C_6H_5ONa + Na_2SO_3 + H_2O$$
$$\text{Sodium}$$
$$\text{phenoxide}$$

2. **Replacement by the Nitrile Group.** Fusion of a sodium salt with sodium cyanide yields a nitrile and sodium sulfite.

$$C_6H_5SO_3Na + NaCN \xrightarrow{\text{Fusion}} C_6H_5CN + Na_2SO_3$$

Phenyl cyanide
(benzonitrile)

Uses of Sulfonic Acids and Their Salts

The free sulfonic acids find very little use. Because they are strong acids and have a much weaker oxidizing action than sulfuric acid, they frequently are used as acid catalysts.

An important use of the sodium sulfonates is for the manufacture of phenols by fusion with sodium hydroxide (p. 509). The sodium sulfonate group usually is present in direct or substantive dyes (p. 673), its function being to confer water solubility on the dyestuff. Sodium salts of alkylated aromatic sulfonic acids are important synthetic detergents. Since their calcium, magnesium, and iron salts are soluble in water, they are as effective in hard water as in soft water (cf. p. 188). In one process of manufacture, benzene is alkylated with tetrapropylene (p. 62) and the product is sulfonated and converted to the sodium salt.

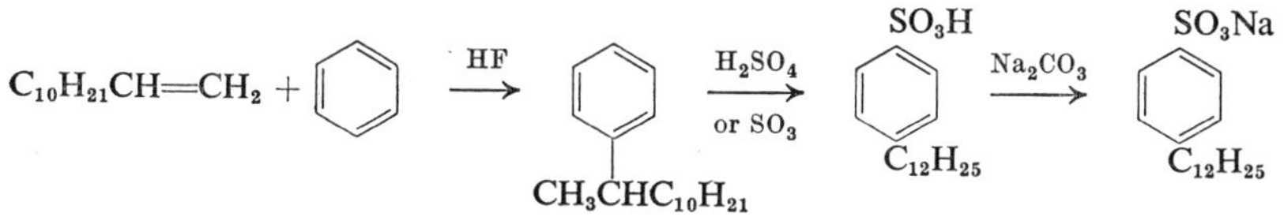

In a second process a C_{12} kerosene fraction is chlorinated, the product is condensed with benzene, and the alkylated benzene is sulfonated and converted to the sodium salt.

$$C_{12}H_{26} + Cl_2 \longrightarrow C_{12}H_{25}Cl \xrightarrow[\text{AlCl}_3]{C_6H_6} C_6H_5C_{12}H_{25} \xrightarrow[\text{or SO}_3]{H_2SO_4}$$

$$C_{12}H_{25}C_6H_4SO_3H \xrightarrow{Na_2CO_3} C_{12}H_{25}C_6H_4SO_3Na$$

In the product made by the first process the aromatic group is near the end of the chain, whereas in the second process chlorination of the aliphatic hydrocarbon takes place at random in the chains. Hence the aromatic ring is located in some molecules at the end of the chain and in others at the middle of the chain and at all intermediate points. Detergents having the water-soluble group at the end of the chain are claimed to be more efficient, and are the most widely used. Synthetic products accounted for over 60 per cent of the total production of soaps and detergents in the United States in 1954, and their preparation is now the most extensive use of the sulfonation reaction.

Alkylbenzenesulfonic acids of high molecular weight are obtained by sulfonating the aromatic components of highly-refined lubricating oils, and as by-products in the manufacture of "white oils" (p. 82). The calcium or barium salts are added to lubricating oils to keep internal combustion engines free of carbon. They are valuable particularly in compounding lubricating oils for Diesel engines.

DERIVATIVES OF SULFONIC ACIDS

Derivatives of both the aliphatic sulfonic acids (p. 286) and the aromatic sulfonic acids, such as the amides and esters, are prepared from the acid chlorides. All of the methods used for the preparation of alkanesulfonyl chlorides (p. 287) can be used for the preparation of aromatic sulfonyl chlorides. However, the latter usually are prepared by a method applicable only to aromatic compounds, namely direct chlorosulfonation by means of chlorosulfonic acid. Two moles of chlorosulfonic acid are required per mole of aromatic compound. Toluene yields a mixture of *o*- and *p*-toluenesulfonyl chlorides.

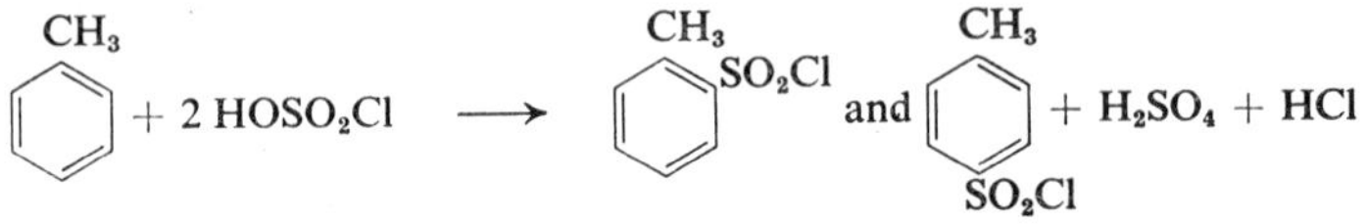

o-Toluene-sulfonyl chloride
p-Toluene-sulfonyl chloride

Undoubtedly sulfonation is brought about by sulfur trioxide formed by dissociation of the chlorosulfonic acid and is followed by conversion of the sulfonic acid to the acid chloride.

$$HOSO_2Cl \rightleftharpoons SO_3 + HCl$$

$$C_6H_6 + SO_3 \rightleftharpoons C_6H_5SO_2OH$$

$$C_6H_5SO_2OH + ClSO_3H \rightleftharpoons C_6H_5SO_2Cl + H_2SO_4$$

Benzenesulfonyl chloride

Readily available aryl disulfides, such as 2,4-dinitrophenyl disulfide (p. 462), can be converted to the sulfonyl chlorides by the action of chlorine and water (p. 288).

The sulfonyl chlorides boil much lower than the sulfonic acids. They are insoluble in water and soluble in organic liquids. Hence they can be isolated more readily than sulfonic acids and can be purified by distillation or crystallization.

Because of the insolubility of sulfonyl chlorides in water, they react only slowly with it. Boiling with water hydrolyzes the sulfonyl chloride to the sulfonic acid and hydrogen chloride, and evaporation at reduced pressure gives the free sulfonic acid.

$$p\text{-}CH_3C_6H_4SO_2Cl + H_2O \xrightarrow{\text{Heat}} p\text{-}CH_3C_6H_4SO_3H + HCl$$

Alcohols and amines react more rapidly than water. Hence the reactions may be carried out in the presence of water, usually with the addition of alkali to remove the hydrogen chloride.

$$ArSO_2Cl + HOR + NaOH \longrightarrow ArSO_2OR + NaCl + H_2O$$

In the absence of alkali, the ester acts as an alkylating agent and undergoes side reactions with the hydrogen chloride and excess alcohol.

$$ArSO_2OR + HCl \longrightarrow ArSO_3H + RCl$$

$$ArSO_2OR + HOR \xrightarrow{[H^+]} ArSO_3H + ROR$$

Pyridine, a tertiary amine (p. 620), frequently is used instead of aqueous alkali in the preparation of sulfonic acid esters. Not only does it act as a basic catalyst and combine with the hydrogen chloride formed in the reaction, but it is a solvent for the sulfonyl chlorides and the alcohol. The reaction of *p*-toluenesulfonyl chloride (*tosyl chloride*) with alcohols frequently is called *tosylation*. It finds important use in preparing the *p*-toluenesulfonyl (*tosyl*) derivatives of carbohydrates (p. 378). The esters are called *tosylates*. *p*-Bromo-benzenesulfonyl chloride is called *brosyl chloride* and its esters *brosylates*. The general behavior of sulfonic esters has been discussed (p. 288). Because of their alkylating action and ready availability, the *p*-toluenesulfonates have been used frequently for the preparation of hydrocarbons, quaternary salts, and esters of carboxylic acids.

$$p\text{-}CH_3C_6H_4SO_2OR + R'MgX \longrightarrow R\text{---}R' + p\text{-}CH_3C_6H_4SO_2OMgX$$

$$+ 2 NR_3 \longrightarrow p\text{-}CH_3C_6H_4SO_3^-{}^+NR_4$$

$$+ Na^+{}^-OCOR' \longrightarrow ROCOR' + p\text{-}CH_3C_6H_4SO_3^-{}^+Na$$

The last reaction is a simple displacement reaction. Hence if in group R the carbon atom attached to oxygen is asymmetric, its configuration is inverted (p. 347).

Ammonia and primary and secondary amines, like the alcohols, react with sulfonyl chlorides in the presence of water. Here also an equivalent quantity of a strong alkali is used but for a different reason. The hydrogen chloride produced in the reaction combines at once with unreacted amine. Since the amine salt cannot react with the sulfonyl chloride, only half of the amine can be converted to the sulfonamide.

$$ArSO_2Cl + 2 HNHR \longrightarrow ArSO_2NHR + RNH_3Cl$$

If an equivalent quantity of strong base is present, it reacts with the hydrogen chloride, and all of the amine is convertible into sulfonamide.

$$ArSO_2Cl + HNHR + NaOH \longrightarrow ArSO_2NHR + NaCl + H_2O$$

The availability of benzenesulfonyl chloride and of *p*-toluenesulfonyl chloride has made their reaction with amines important as a means of distinguishing between primary, secondary, and tertiary amines, and of separating mixtures of different types of amines. This procedure is known as the *Hinsberg reaction*. It is based on the fact that sulfonamides prepared from primary amines are sufficiently acidic to form sodium salts in aqueous solution and hence are soluble in dilute aqueous alkali (p. 288). Those from secondary amines cannot form a salt and do not dissolve in dilute alkali. Tertiary amines do not react with sulfonyl chlorides in the presence of water.

$$C_6H_5SO_2Cl + H_2NR + 2 NaOH \longrightarrow [C_6H_5SO_2\bar{N}R]Na^+ + NaCl + 2 H_2O$$
Soluble in water; reacts with dilute acid to give water-insoluble sulfonamide

$$C_6H_5SO_2Cl + HNR_2 + NaOH \longrightarrow C_6H_5SO_2NR_2 + NaCl + H_2O$$
Insoluble in dilute alkali or dilute acid

$$C_6H_5SO_2Cl + NR_3 \longrightarrow$$
No reaction; tertiary amine soluble in dilute acids

Two sources of error may be present in applying the Hinsberg reaction as a test or for separating mixtures. Some primary amines react with two moles of sulfonyl chloride to give imides which are not soluble in dilute alkali.

$$2 C_6H_5SO_2Cl + H_2NR + 2 NaOH \longrightarrow (C_6H_5SO_2)_2NR + 2 NaCl + 2 H_2O$$

Secondly amides from primary amines of high molecular weight may be insoluble in dilute alkali. These errors can be detected and obviated in the following ways: (*1*) reaction of the imide with sodium ethoxide in alcohol solution gives the sodium salt of the amide;

$$(C_6H_5SO_2)_2NR + NaOC_2H_5 \longrightarrow (C_6H_5SO_2\bar{N}R)Na^+ + C_6H_5SO_2OC_2H_5$$

(*2*) the alkali insoluble amides of primary amines dissolved in ether react with metallic sodium to give sodium salts that are insoluble in ether.

$$C_6H_5SO_2NHR + Na \longrightarrow [C_6H_5SO_2\bar{N}R]Na^+ + \tfrac{1}{2} H_2$$
Insoluble in ether

Although tertiary amines do not react with benzenesulfonyl chloride in the presence of water, they react in anhydrous solvents to give the sulfonamide of a secondary amine and the quaternary ammonium chloride of the amine.

$$C_6H_5SO_2Cl + 2 N(CH_3)_3 \text{ (in ether)} \longrightarrow C_6H_5SO_2N(CH_3)_2 + [(CH_3)_4N^+]Cl^-$$

Sulfonamides are hydrolyzed with difficulty. The best reagent is 30 per cent hydrogen bromide in acetic acid containing phenol.

$$ArSO_2NHR + 2 HBr \longrightarrow ArSO_2Br + RNH_3^{+-}Br$$

The phenol prevents side reactions by reacting with the bromine formed by the oxidizing action of the sulfonyl bromide on hydrogen bromide.

Sulfonamides having hydrogen on the nitrogen atom react with alkaline hypochlorite solutions to give *N*-halo derivatives.

$$ArSO_2NHR + NaOCl \rightleftharpoons ArSO_2\underset{\underset{Cl}{|}}{N}R + NaOH$$

p-Toluenesulfonamide gives the sodium salt, which is soluble in water. It commonly is called **Chloramine-T.**

$$p\text{-}CH_3C_6H_4SO_2NH_2 + NaOCl \rightleftharpoons [p\text{-}CH_3C_6H_4SO_2\bar{N}Cl]Na^+ + H_2O$$
Sodium salt of *N*-chloro-
p-toluenesulfonamide
(Chloramine-T)

Since the product is stable when dry and the reaction is reversible in aqueous solution, the *N*-chlorosulfonamides have the antiseptic properties of hypochlorite solutions. The analogous compound from benzenesulfonamide is known as **Chloramine-B.** If the chlorination is carried further, a dichloro derivative is formed which is soluble in oils and salves.

$$p\text{-}CH_3C_6H_4SO_2NH_2 + 2 NaOCl \longrightarrow p\text{-}CH_3C_6H_4SO_2NCl_2 + 2 NaOH$$
N,N-Dichloro-*p*-
toluenesulfonamide
(Dichloramine-T)

Since *p*-toluenesulfonyl chloride is a co-product of the manufacture of saccharin (p. 556), conversion to the amide and to Chloramine-T and Dichloramine-T is one method of utilization.

Nitrous acid reacts with *N*-methyl-*p*-toluenesulfonamide to give the *N*-nitroso derivative which may be used for the preparation of diazomethane (p. 266).

$$p\text{-CH}_3\text{C}_6\text{H}_4\text{SO}_2\text{NHCH}_3 + \text{HONO} \longrightarrow p\text{-CH}_3\text{C}_6\text{H}_4\text{SO}_2\underset{|}{\text{N}}\text{CH}_3 + \text{H}_2\text{O}$$
$$\text{NO}$$

$$p\text{-CH}_3\text{C}_6\text{H}_4\text{SO}_2\underset{|}{\text{N}}\text{CH}_3 + \text{NaOH (in alcohol)} \longrightarrow p\text{-CH}_3\text{C}_6\text{H}_4\text{SO}_2\text{O}^{-+}\text{Na} + \text{CH}_2\text{N}_2 + \text{H}_2\text{O}$$
$$\text{NO}$$

When arylsulfonhydrazides are heated, they decompose with the evolution of nitrogen and are used as foaming agents in the production of foamed rubbers and plastics. Presumably the sulfenic acid is the other product but it is unstable and gives the disulfide and the thiosulfonic ester.

$$\text{ArSO}_2\text{NHNH}_2 \longrightarrow \text{N}_2 + \text{H}_2\text{O} + [\text{ArSOH}]$$

$$4\,[\text{ArSOH}] \longrightarrow \text{ArSSAr} + \text{ArSO}_2\text{SAr} + 2\,\text{H}_2\text{O}$$

The decomposition product of sulfonhydrazidophenyl ether (Celogen), $\text{H}_2\text{NNHSO}_2\text{C}_6\text{H}_4\text{OC}_6\text{H}_4\text{SO}_2\text{NHNH}_2$, is polymeric and odorless.

Sulfonyl chlorides can be reduced to sulfinic acids and to mercaptans (p. 284). These reactions are valuable in the aromatic series as a means of obtaining **sulfinic acids** and **thiophenols**.

$$2\,\text{C}_6\text{H}_5\text{SO}_2\text{Cl} + 2\,\text{Zn (in ether)} \longrightarrow (\text{C}_6\text{H}_5\text{SO}_2)_2\text{Zn} + \text{ZnCl}_2$$
Zinc benzene-
sulfinate

$$\downarrow 2\,\text{HCl}$$

$$\text{C}_6\text{H}_5\text{SO}_2\text{H} + \text{ZnCl}_2$$
Benzenesul-
finic acid

$$2\,\text{C}_6\text{H}_5\text{SO}_2\text{Cl} + 6\,\text{Zn} + 5\,\text{H}_2\text{SO}_4 \text{ (in water)} \longrightarrow 2\,\text{C}_6\text{H}_5\text{SH} + \text{ZnCl}_2 + 5\,\text{ZnSO}_4 + 4\,\text{H}_2\text{O}$$
Thiophenol

Sulfonyl chlorides undergo the Friedel-Crafts reaction with aromatic compounds in the presence of anhydrous aluminum chloride to yield **sulfones**.

$$\text{C}_6\text{H}_5\text{SO}_2\text{Cl} + \text{C}_6\text{H}_6 \xrightarrow{\text{AlCl}_3} \text{C}_6\text{H}_5\text{SO}_2\text{C}_6\text{H}_5 + \text{HCl}$$
Phenyl sulfone

DERIVATIVES OF SULFENIC ACIDS

Although the sulfonic acids and the sulfinic acids are obtained readily, only one example of the sulfenic acids, RSOH, is known. The sulfur chlorides, RSCl, however, may be considered as the acid chlorides of the sulfenic acids. Of these, **2,4-dinitrosulfenyl chloride**, prepared by the action of chlorine on 2,4-dinitrophenyl disulfide (p. 462) is of most interest.

Its reactions in general are analogous to those of an alkyl halide, and it has been used to prepare derivatives of a wide variety of compounds.

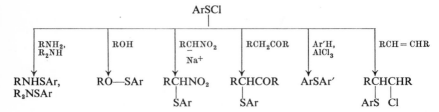

REVIEW QUESTIONS

1. How are aromatic sulfonic acids prepared? What is a common co-product?
2. What is the *liming out process?* How may sulfonic acids be obtained in a pure state?
3. Compare the properties of sulfonic acids with those of carboxylic acids.
4. What is meant by the terms tosylation and brosylation?
5. What is the Hinsberg reaction and of what value is it?
6. What types of detergents have been discussed so far?
7. Give equations for the various methods by which aromatic sulfonyl chlorides may be prepared.
8. How are amides and esters of sulfonic acids prepared? Why is sodium hydroxide used in these reactions?
9. List some commerical uses for the salts of aromatic sulfonic acids; for sulfonamides.
10. Summarize the various methods that have been discussed for the synthesis of diazomethane.
11. Compare the reactions of the esters of carboxylic acids with those of the esters of sulfonic acids.
12. What is the general formula of a sulfenic acid? What derivative of a sulfenic acid is of importance and for what purpose is it used?

PROBLEMS

13. Give equations for the preparation of the following compounds:
    A. (a) *p*-Tolyl sulfone; (b) *o*-methylthiophenol; (c) *N*-methylbenzenesulfonamide; (d) *n*-butyl *p*-toluenesulfonate; (e) *p*-bromobenzenesulfonyl chloride; (f) 2,4-dimethylbenzenesulfinic acid.
    B. (a) *N,N*-dimethyl-*p*-toluenesulfonamide; (b) *i*-amyl benzenesulfonate; (c) 2-ethylphenyl sulfone; (d) *m*-nitrobenzenesulfonyl chloride; (e) 2,4-dimethylthiophenol; (f) *o*-chlorobenzenesulfinic acid.
    C. (a) *p*-Ethylbenzenethiol; (b) *N*-ethyl-*N*-*i*-propylbenzenesulfonamide; (c) *n*-propyl *p*-bromobenzenesulfonate; (d) 2,4-dimethylphenyl sulfone; (e) *p*-toluenesulfinic acid; (f) *m*-chlorobenzenesulfonyl chloride.
14. Give equations for the following reactions: (a) ethyl *p*-toluenesulfonate and benzylmagnesium chloride; (b) *N*-chlorobenzenesulfonamide and water; (c) *N*-methyl-*N*-nitroso-*p*-toluenesulfonamide and alcoholic sodium hydroxide; (d) cumene and *p*-toluenesulfonyl chloride in the presence of aluminum chloride; (e) 2,4-dinitrobenzenesulfenyl chloride and diethylamine; (f) 3,5-dibromobenzenesulfonic acid boiled with aqueous hydrochloric acid; (g) sodium *m*-benzenesulfonate and phosphorus pentachloride; (h) 2,4-dinitropheny l disulfide, chlorine, and water; (i) fusion of sodium *p*-toluenesulfonate with sodium hydroxide; (j) *n*-propyl benzenesulfonate and ammonia.
15. Describe a test for distinguishing between the members of the following pairs of compounds: (a) methyl *p*-chlorobenzenesulfonate and benzenesulfonyl chloride; (b) sodium benzenesulfonate and sodium sulfate; (c) benzenesulfonyl chloride and *p*-chlorophenyl sulfone; (d) *N*-methylbenzenesulfonamide and *N,N*-dimethylbenzenesulfonamide; (e) *N*-chlorobenzenesulfonamide and *p*-chlorobenzenesulfonamide; (f) benzenesulfonic acid and phenyl sulfone; (g) benzyl chloride and benzenesulfonyl chloride; (h) ethyl *p*-toluenesulfonate and *N,N*-dimethyl-*p*-toluenesulfonamide; (i) ethyl *p*-nitrobenzenesulfonate and *N,N*-dimethylbenzenesulfonamide.

Chapter 22

AROMATIC AMINES

Compounds classed as aromatic amines have an amino group or an alkyl- or aryl-substituted amino group attached directly to an aromatic nucleus. Usually they are made by a different procedure from aliphatic amines and undergo additional reactions.

Nomenclature

Aromatic amines may be primary, secondary, or tertiary, and in the secondary or tertiary amines, one or two of the hydrocarbon groups may be aliphatic. Usually the primary amines are named as the amino derivatives of the aromatic hydrocarbon or as aryl derivatives of ammonia, but some are known best by common names such as aniline or toluidine.

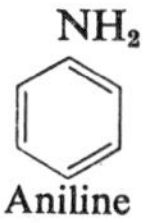

Aniline
(aminobenzene or
phenylamine)

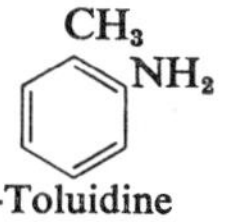

o-Toluidine
(o-aminotoluene or
o-tolylamine)

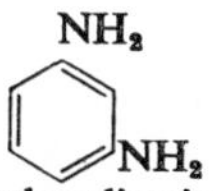

m-Phenylenediamine
(m-diaminobenzene)

Secondary and tertiary amines are named as derivatives of the primary amine, or as derivatives of ammonia.

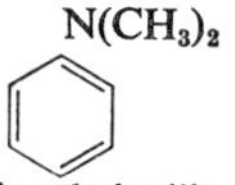

N,N-Dimethylaniline
(dimethylaniline)

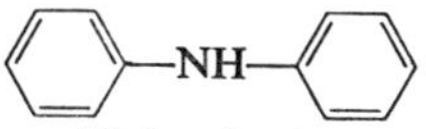

Diphenylamine

Structure

In the structure assigned to the aromatic amines, an amino group is attached to an aromatic ring. If three double bonds are placed in the aromatic nucleus, the amino group is attached to a carbon atom united to another carbon atom by a double bond. Such enamine structures are unstable in the aliphatic series and rearrange to the imine structure which usually polymerizes.

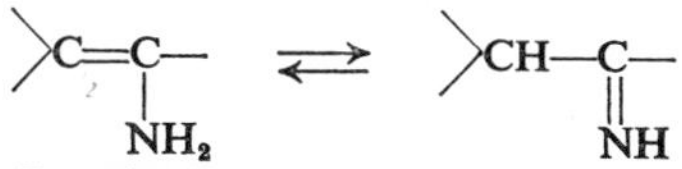

Enamine form;
stable structure in
aromatic systems

Imino form;
stable structure in
aliphatic systems

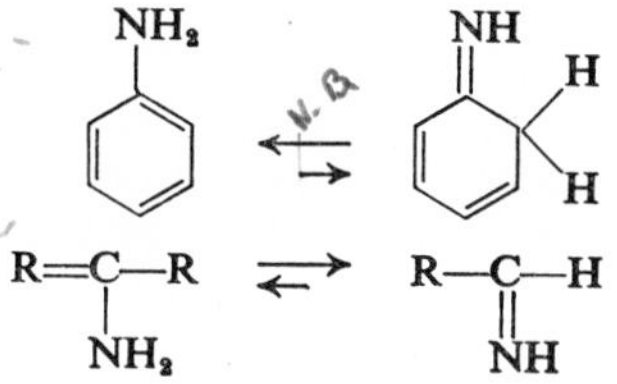

475

The stability of the amino structure in aromatic amines is due to the high resonance energy of the aromatic nucleus, which is absent in the dienimine structure.

Physical Properties

The physical properties of the aromatic amines are about what would be expected. Just as benzene (b.p. 80°) boils at a higher temperature than *n*-hexane (b.p. 69°), so aniline (b.p. 184°) has a higher boiling point than *n*-hexylamine (b.p. 130°). The greater difference in the boiling points of the second pair may be ascribed to the fact that aniline has a higher dipole moment ($\mu = 1.6$) than *n*-hexylamine ($\mu = 1.3$). Methylaniline (b.p. 195°) boils at a higher temperature than aniline, but dimethylaniline (b.p. 193°) boils at a lower temperature than methylaniline despite the increase in molecular weight, because proton bonding is not possible for dimethylaniline.

Aniline is somewhat more soluble in water (3.6 g. per 100 g. of water) than *n*-hexylamine (0.4 g. per 100 g. of water). Water dissolves in aniline to the extent of about 5 per cent. Aniline is miscible with benzene but not with *n*-hexane.

As is true for all of the disubstituted benzenes, the *para*-substituted anilines, being the most symmetrical, have the highest melting point. Thus *p*-toluidine is a solid at room temperature whereas both the *ortho* and *meta* isomers are liquids.

Physiological Properties

The aromatic amines, like the hydrocarbons and their halogen and nitro derivatives, are highly toxic. The liquids are absorbed readily through the skin, and low concentrations of the vapors produce symptoms of toxicity when inhaled for prolonged periods. Aniline vapors may produce symptoms of poisoning after several hours of exposure to concentrations as low as 7 parts per million. Aniline affects both the blood and the nervous system. Hemoglobin of the blood is converted into methemoglobin with reduction of the oxygen-carrying capacity of the blood and resultant cyanosis. A direct depressant action is exerted on heart muscle. Continued exposure leads to mental disturbances. Aromatic amines appear to be responsible also for bladder irritation and the formation of tumors in workers engaged in the manufacture of dye intermediates.

The chloro and nitro nuclear-substituted amines, the *N*-alkylated and acylated amines, and the diamines all are highly toxic. The *N*-phenylamines are considerably less toxic than the *N*-alkyl derivatives. The phenolic hydroxyl group also decreases the toxicity somewhat. Toxicity is greatly reduced by the presence of free carboxylic or sulfonic acid groups in the ring.

Preparation

1. **By Reduction of More Highly Oxidized Nitrogen Compounds.** Aromatic nitro compounds yield a series of reduction products, the final product being the primary amine (Fig. 77, p. 459). Therefore aromatic amines may be prepared from nitro compounds, or from the less highly oxidized nitroso, hydroxylamino, azoxy, azo, and hydrazo compounds, by reduction with tin or iron and hydrochloric acid, or by catalytic hydrogenation.

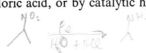

2. **By Ammonolysis of Halogen Compounds.** Halogen attached to an aromatic nucleus usually is very stable to hydrolysis or ammonolysis, and rather drastic conditions are required to bring about reaction (p. 486). If, however, electron-attracting groups are present in the *ortho* and *para* positions, the halogen is more easily displaced. Thus 2,4,6-trinitrochlorobenzene (*picryl chloride*) reacts readily with ammonia to yield 2,4,6-trinitroaniline (*picramide*).

$$\text{2,4,6-Trinitrochlorobenzene (picryl chloride)} + 2\ NH_3 \longrightarrow \text{2,4,6-Trinitroaniline (picramide)} + NH_4Cl$$

2,4,6-Trinitro-
chlorobenzene
(picryl chloride)

2,4,6-Trinitro-
aniline
(picramide)

Reactions

Reactions of the Amino Group

1. **Basicity.** An amino group attached to an aromatic nucleus is in general much less basic than one attached to an alkyl radical, although it still is considerably more basic than an amino group attached to an acyl group. Thus the basic dissociation constants of methylamine, aniline, and acetamide are 4.4×10^{-5}, 3.8×10^{-10}, and 3.1×10^{-15} respectively. The presence of electron-attracting groups in the nucleus decreases the basicity still further. For example, the basic dissociation constants for *o*-, *m*-, and *p*-nitroaniline are 1×10^{-14}, 4×10^{-12}, and 1×10^{-12} respectively. Similarly the introduction of a second aromatic nucleus on the nitrogen atom greatly decreases the basicity, the basic dissociation constant for diphenylamine being 7.6×10^{-14}. On the other hand the introduction of alkyl groups increases the basicity, the dissociation constants for *N*-methylaniline and *N*,*N*-dimethylaniline being 7.1×10^{-10} and 1.1×10^{-9} respectively.

The decreased basicity of aniline compared with aliphatic amines can be explained by the electronic interaction or resonance of the unshared pair of electrons on the nitrogen atom with the unsaturation electrons of the nucleus (Fig. 78). This interaction reduces the availability of

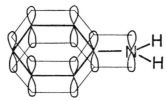

Fig. 78. Interaction of the unshared electrons of the nitrogen atom in aniline with the unsaturation electrons of benzene.

the unshared pair for bonding with a proton. As with chlorobenzene (p. 453), the molecular orbital representation may be replaced by the symbolism for a resonance hybrid.

The effects of other substituents in the aromatic nucleus depend both on their inductive and resonance effects. The inductive effects depend on the distance separating the groups concerned, and hence the order of effectiveness when in the various positions is $o > m > p$. Resonance effects, however, can be transmitted best through conjugated systems and therefore are most effective in the *ortho* and *para* positions and least in the *meta* positions.

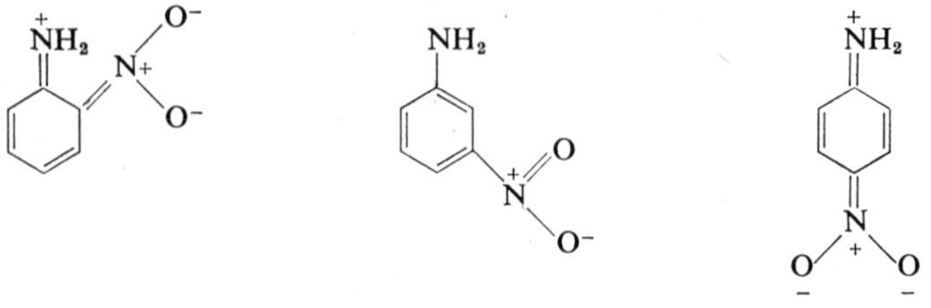

Resonance strong and induction strong   Resonance weak and induction fair   Resonance strong and induction weak

In general resonance effects are more important than inductive effects. For the nitro group the inductive and resonance effects are in the same direction. Although the inductive effect in the *para* position is less than that in the *meta* position, *p*-nitroaniline is a weaker base than *m*-nitroaniline because resonance can take place and the resonance effect is more important. *o*-Nitroaniline is the weakest base, because the resonance effect is operative and the inductive effect is at a maximum.

2. **Alkylation and Arylation.** Like the aliphatic amines, the primary aromatic amines react with alkyl halides to give secondary and tertiary amines and quaternary ammonium salts.

$$C_6H_5NH_2 + RX \longrightarrow [C_6H_5\overset{+}{N}H_2R]X^- \xrightarrow{\text{NaOH}} C_6H_5NHR + NaX + H_2O$$
N-Alkylani-
line

$$C_6H_5NHR + RX \longrightarrow [C_6H_5\overset{+}{N}HR_2]X^- \xrightarrow{\text{NaOH}} C_6H_5NR_2 + NaX + H_2O$$
N,N-Di-
alkylaniline

$$C_6H_5NR_2 + RX \longrightarrow [C_6H_5\overset{+}{N}R_3]X^-$$
Phenyltrialkyl-
ammonium halide

Simple aryl halides react with difficulty. Although diphenylamine is a minor co-product of the commercial production of aniline from chlorobenzene (p. 486), it is made best by heating aniline with aniline hydrochloride.

$$C_6H_5NH_2 + [C_6H_5\overset{+}{N}H_3]Cl^- \xrightarrow{220°} (C_6H_5)_2NH + NH_4Cl$$
Diphenyl-
amine

Triphenylamine is made by heating diphenylamine with iodobenzene, potassium carbonate, and copper bronze.

$$(C_6H_5)_2NH + IC_6H_5 \xrightarrow{K_2CO_3 (Cu)} (C_6H_5)_3N + KI + KHCO_3$$
Triphenyl-
amine

3. **Acylation.** Acid anhydrides and acyl halides convert primary and secondary amines into the amides.

$$C_6H_5NH_2 + (CH_3CO)_2O \longrightarrow C_6H_5NHCOCH_3 + CH_3COOH$$
Acetanilide

$$2\ C_6H_5NHCH_3 + CH_3COCl \longrightarrow C_6H_5N(CH_3)COCH_3 + [C_6H_5\overset{+}{N}H_2CH_3]Cl^-$$

N-Methylaniline	*N*-Methylacetanilide	*N*-Methylaniline hydrochloride (phenylmethylammonium chloride)

Acylation can be brought about also by heating the amine salts of carboxylic acids.

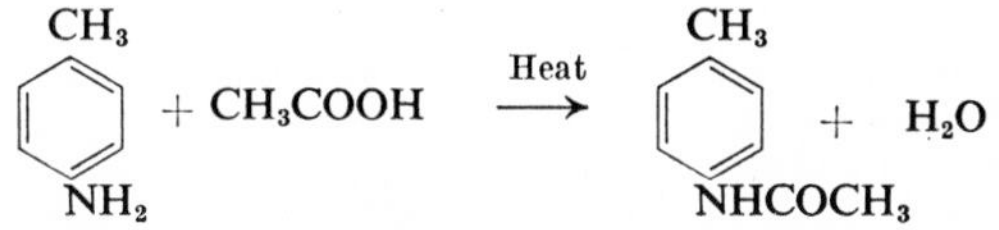

p-Toluidine	Aceto-*p*-toluidide

When aniline reacts with phosgene, phenylcarbamyl chloride is formed. On heating, hydrogen chloride is lost and **phenyl isocyanate,** a valuable reagent for alcohols and amines (p. 317), is produced.

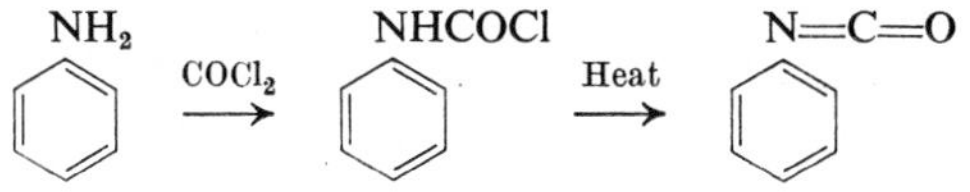

Phenyl isocyanate

Phenyl isocyanate also is useful for the identification of alkyl halides because the latter can be converted to Grignard reagents which add to phenyl isocyanate. Hydrolysis of the addition product gives a solid anilide.

$$C_6H_5N{=}C{=}O + RMgX \longrightarrow C_6H_5N{=}\overset{\overset{OMgX}{|}}{C}R \overset{H_2O}{\longrightarrow} \left[C_6H_5N{=}\overset{\overset{OH}{|}}{C}R\right] \longrightarrow C_6H_5NH\overset{\overset{O}{||}}{C}R$$

Diisocyanates such as that made from 2,4-diaminotoluene (so-called toluene diisocyanate) have become of commercial importance for the production of urethan rubbers (p. 799).

4. **Reaction with Nitrous Acid.** The behavior of aromatic amines toward nitrous acid, like that of the aliphatic amines, depends on whether the amine is primary, secondary, or tertiary. However, the reactions of primary and tertiary aromatic amines differ from those of primary and tertiary aliphatic amines (p. 238).

(*a*) PRIMARY AMINES. At temperatures below 0° in strongly acid solution, nitrous acid reacts with the primary aromatic amine salts to give water-soluble compounds known as *diazonium salts.* The properties and uses of these

$$[C_6H_5\overset{+}{N}H_3]Cl^- + HONO(NaNO_2 + HCl) \longrightarrow [C_6H_5\overset{+}{N}_2]Cl^- + 2\ H_2O$$

Aniline hydrochloride	Benzenediazonium chloride

important compounds are described in Chapter 23.

(b) SECONDARY AMINES. Secondary aromatic amines behave like secondary aliphatic amines, yielding *N*-nitroso derivatives.

$$C_6H_5NHCH_3 + HONO \longrightarrow C_6H_5NCH_3 + H_2O$$

Methyl-
aniline

(under second product:) NO
N-Nitroso-
methylaniline

(c) TERTIARY AMINES. Tertiary aromatic amines having an unsubstituted *para* position yield *p*-nitroso derivatives.

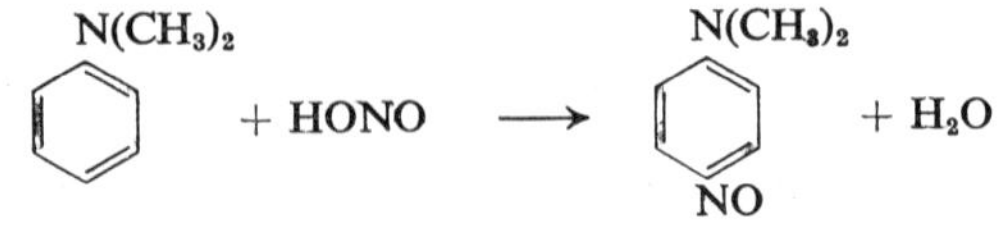

Dimethyl-
aniline

p-Nitrosodi-
methylaniline

This reaction takes place because of the strong activating effect of the dimethyl-amino group. Although most of the dimethylaniline is present as the salt in the acid solution, and the dimethylammonium group is deactivating and *meta*-directing, sufficient free dimethylaniline is in equilibrium with the salt to react with nitrous acid, and the equilibrium shifts until nitrosation is complete. Nitrous acid does not bring about the nitrosation of benzene or even of toluene or mesitylene.

Activation by the dimethylamino group depends on the resonance effect (p. 453) which requires that the dimethylamino group must be able to take up a position coplanar with the benzene ring.

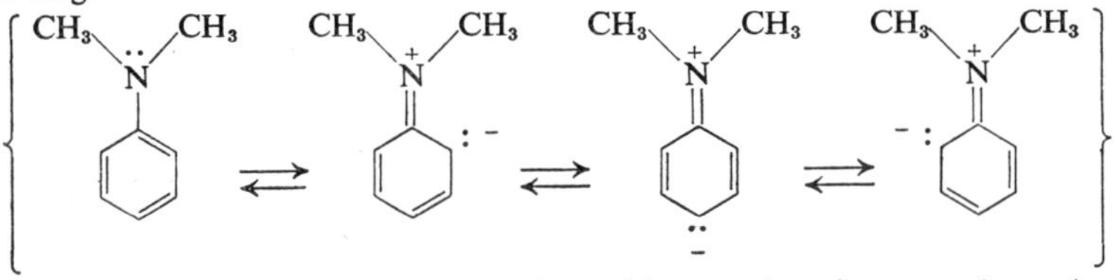

If groups larger than hydrogen occupy the *ortho* positions, coplanarity cannot be attained, and activation of the ring is not possible. Thus 2,6-dimethyl-*N*,*N*-dimethylaniline does not undergo reactions that require strong activation of the nucleus such as nitrosation and coupling with diazonium salts (p. 498).

Although both secondary and tertiary aromatic amines yield nitroso derivatives, the reaction still can be used to distinguish between them, because the *N*-nitroso derivatives are amides of nitrous acid. Hence they are not basic and do not dissolve in dilute acids. The *p*-nitroso derivatives, however, form yellow salts with mineral acids. The diazonium salts from primary amines can be detected readily by reaction with aromatic amines or phenols to give highly colored azo compounds (p. 676).

It appears that salt formation does not take place with the tertiary amino group, but with the nitroso group, stabilization being brought about by resonance with the quinonoid structure (p. 520).

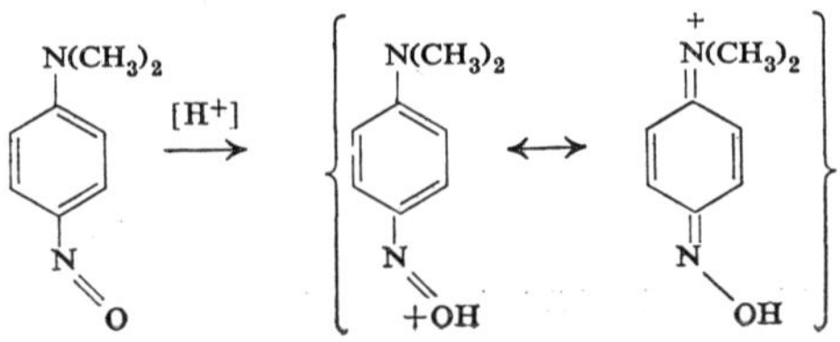

5. **Hydrolysis.** As in the aliphatic series, an aromatic amino group usually is stable to hydrolysis, although in the presence of water at high temperatures equilibrium exists between the aromatic amine and the phenol. This reaction is of little importance in the benzene series but finds commercial application in

$$C_6H_5NH_2 + H_2O \underset{\rightleftarrows}{\overset{200°}{}} C_6H_5OH + NH_3$$

the naphthalene series (pp. 588, 590).

If, however, a strongly electron-attracting group is present in the *para* position, a strong base will displace the amino group under relatively mild conditions. The reaction is useful for the preparation of pure primary and pure secondary aliphatic amines. For the primary amines the starting point is the *N*-alkylaniline which is acetylated and nitrated and then hydrolyzed with sodium hydroxide solution.

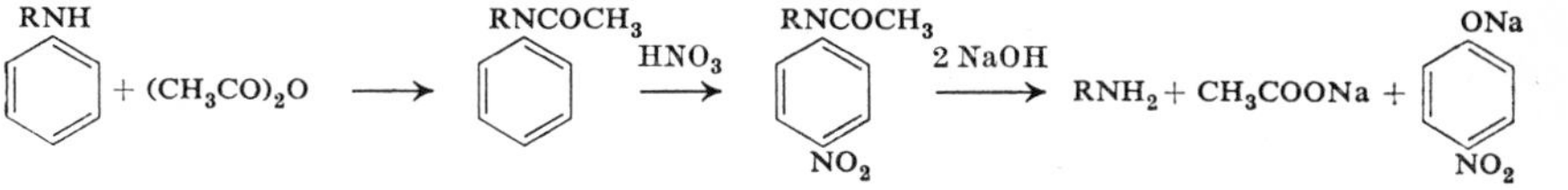

Sodium *p*-nitro-
phenoxide

Secondary amines are obtained from *p*-nitrosodialkylanilines.

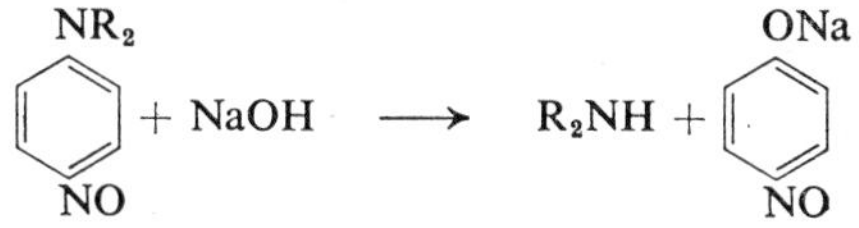

The function of the nitro or nitroso group can be explained by assuming that on the approach of a hydroxide ion in the neighborhood of the amino group, the nitro or nitroso group can take up a pair of electrons from the benzene ring and permit attachment of a pair of electrons from the hydroxide ion. Subsequent loss of the amide ion, with a reversal of the electronic shift and reaction of the amide ion with the phenol, yields the amine.

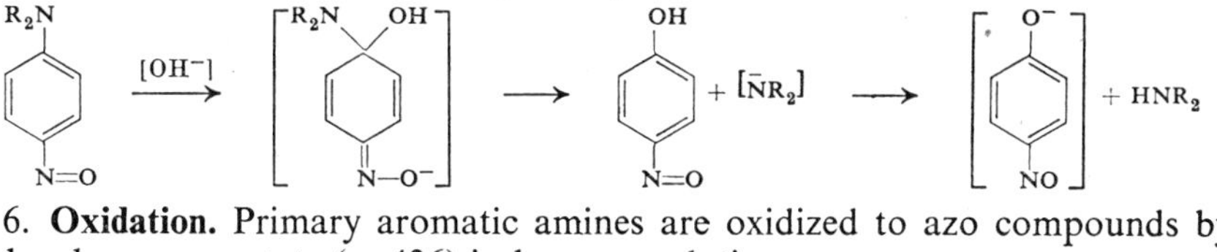

6. **Oxidation.** Primary aromatic amines are oxidized to azo compounds by iodosobenzene acetate (p. 436) in benzene solution.

$$2\,ArNH_2 + 2\,C_6H_5I(OCOCH_3)_2 \longrightarrow ArN{=}NAr + 2\,C_6H_5I + 4\,CH_3COOH$$

Peroxytrifluoroacetic acid (hydrogen peroxide and trifluoroacetic acid) oxidizes the amino group to the nitro group. The reaction is particularly useful to prepare compounds that cannot be obtained by direct substitution, such as *p*-dinitrobenzene.

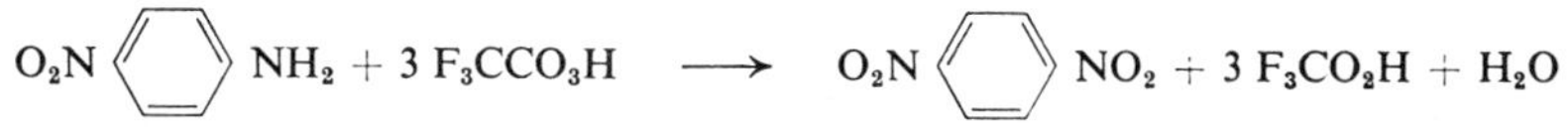

7. **Other Reactions.** Aromatic amines undergo most of the reactions described for aliphatic amines. Thus they give condensation products with aldehydes and ketones. Intermediate condensation products frequently are more stable than those of the aliphatic amines. For example, the products of reaction of an aldehyde with one or two moles of aniline can be isolated.

$$C_6H_5NH_2 + OCHR \longrightarrow C_6H_5N{=}CHR + H_2O$$
$$2\,C_6H_5NH_2 + OCHR \longrightarrow (C_6H_5NH)_2CHR + H_2O$$

The products from one mole each of amine and aldehyde are known as *Schiff bases* or *anils*. These intermediates undergo further polymerization and condensation. The condensation products have been used as rubber accelerators and antioxidants (p. 712). *p*-Toluidine reacts with formaldehyde in acid solution to give a cyclic condensation product known as *Troeger's base*, which is of stereochemical interest (p. 350).

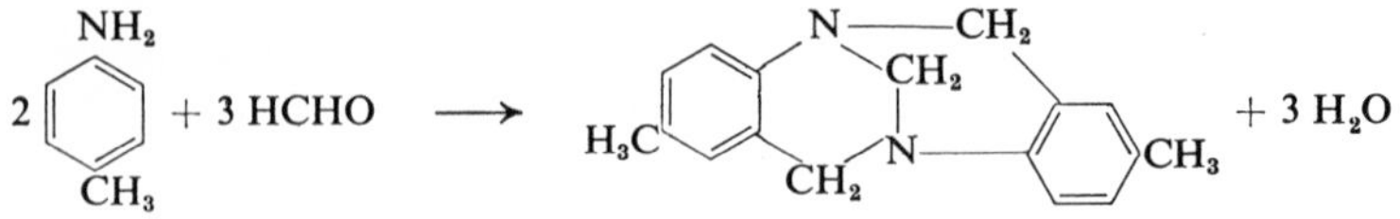

$$2 \underset{CH_3}{\underset{|}{\overset{NH_2}{\overset{|}{\bigcirc}}}} + 3 \ HCHO \longrightarrow \quad + 3 \ H_2O$$

Unlike the aliphatic amines, aniline does not react with carbon disulfide at room temperature to give the dithiocarbamate (p. 325). When a solution of aniline and carbon disulfide in alcohol is refluxed, hydrogen sulfide is evolved with the formation of **thiocarbanilide.**

$$2 \ C_6H_5NH_2 + CS_2 \longrightarrow \quad C_6H_5NHCSNHC_6H_5 + H_2S$$
Thiocarbanilide
(diphenylthiourea)

Thiocarbanilide at one time was an important rubber accelerator. It now is used chiefly for the preparation of 2-mercaptobenzothiazole which has supplanted it (p. 636).

When thiocarbanilide is boiled with strong hydrochloric acid, **phenyl isothiocyanate** (*phenyl mustard oil*), a very pungent compound, is produced.

$$C_6H_5NHCSNHC_6H_5 + HCl \longrightarrow \quad C_6H_5N{=}C{=}S + C_6H_5NH_3{}^+{}^-Cl$$

Phenyl isothiocyanate reacts readily with primary and secondary amines to give thioureas which are useful for the identification of amines.

$$C_6H_5N{=}C{=}S + H_2NR \longrightarrow \quad C_6H_5NHCSNHR$$

Reaction with ammonia gives **phenylthiourea,** $C_6H_5NHCSNH_2$, which is of interest in that it is extremely bitter to some persons and tasteless to others. The ability to taste the compound has been shown to be hereditary. ***p*-Ethoxyphenylurea** (*Dulcin*), *p*-$C_2H_5OC_6H_4NHCONH_2$, on the other hand, is about 100 times sweeter than sucrose.

In the presence of ammonia, aniline reacts with carbon disulfide to give **ammonium phenyldithiocarbamate.**

$$C_6H_5NH_2 + CS_2 + NH_3 \longrightarrow \quad C_6H_5NHCSS{}^-{}^+NH_4$$

Removal of hydrogen sulfide from the salt by reaction with lead nitrate (p. 325) gives phenyl isothiocyanate.

$$C_6H_5NHCSS{}^-{}^+NH_4 + Pb(NO_3)_2 \longrightarrow \quad C_6H_5N{=}C{=}S + PbS + NH_4NO_3 + HNO_3$$

Primary aromatic amines when heated with chloroform and alkali give the *isocyanides* or *carbylamines* (p. 237).

REACTIONS OF THE NUCLEUS

1. **Oxidation.** Aliphatic amines are fairly stable to oxidation, but aromatic amines oxidize readily. Unless carefully purified, they soon darken on standing in air. Stronger oxidizing agents produce highly colored products. Even the

simplest aromatic amine, aniline, can give rise to numerous and frequently complex oxidation products. It is not surprising that, depending on the oxidizing agent used, azobenzene, azoxybenzene, phenylhydroxylamine, nitrosobenzene, and nitrobenzene have been isolated, since aniline is a reduction product of these compounds. In addition to the amino group, however, the hydrogen atoms of the benzene ring that are *ortho* and *para* to the amino group are oxidized to hydroxyl groups. Thus when sodium hypochlorite solution is added to aniline, *p*-aminophenol is formed along with azobenzene and other products.

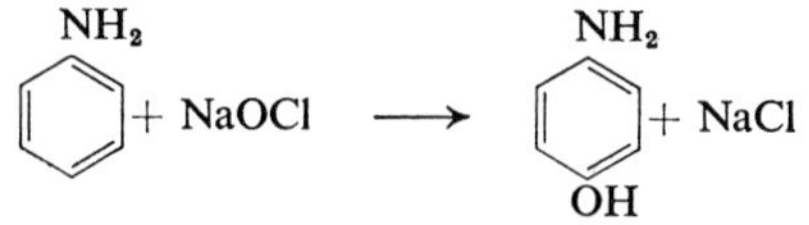

These hydroxy amines are oxidized very readily to quinones (p. 520), which undergo further oxidation and condensation reactions. For example, the violet color produced when aniline is mixed with a solution of bleaching powder is due to a series of reactions which form a blue compound known as *indoaniline*.

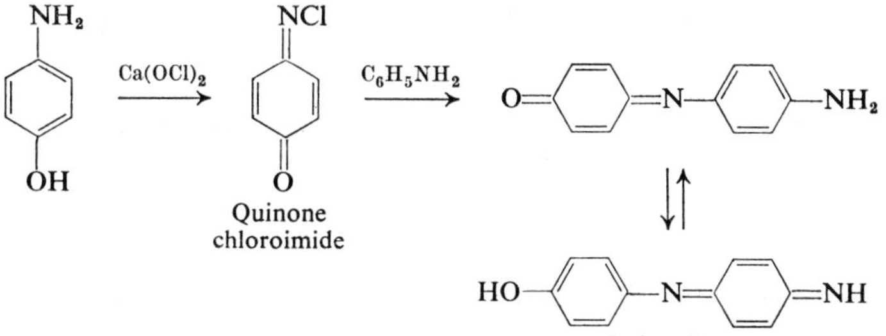

Quinone
chloroimide

Indoaniline

Some of the more complicated reactions are considered in the discussion of quinones (p. 522), and of the Aniline Blacks (p. 696).

Amine salts are much less readily oxidized than the free amines because the positive charge greatly reduces the electron-donating property of the molecule. Replacement of both hydrogen atoms of the amino group by alkyl groups also hinders some types of oxidation. Lack of hydrogen on the nitrogen atom prevents the formation of compounds such as azobenzene and phenylhydroxylamine. It also prevents oxidation of nuclear hydrogen, since this reaction appears to be dependent on the presence of small amounts of the tautomeric imino forms of the amine (p. 475).

2. **Halogenation.** Because of the strong activating effect of the amino group, no catalyst is required in the halogenation of the nucleus. Furthermore, halogenation takes place in aqueous solution and is so rapid that the only product readily isolated is 2,4,6-trichloro- or 2,4,6-tribromoaniline. The three halogen atoms in the *ortho* and *para* positions reduce the basicity of the amino group, and the salt does not form in aqueous solution.

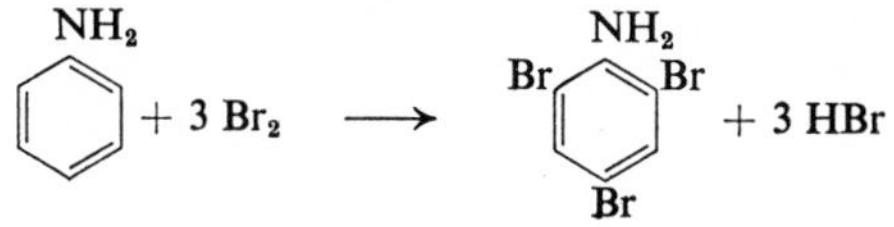

2,4,6-Tribromo-
aniline

Actually trichloroaniline or tribromoaniline is formed even when chlorine or bromine is added to an aqueous solution of an aniline salt. This behavior seems anomalous at first, since salt formation should lead to deactivation and *meta* orientation. The experimental results can be explained by the presence of free amine formed by hydrolysis of the salt in aqueous solution. This view is confirmed by the fact that aniline dissolved in concentrated sulfuric acid is not chlorinated or brominated at room temperature. At higher temperatures the *meta* substitution product is formed.

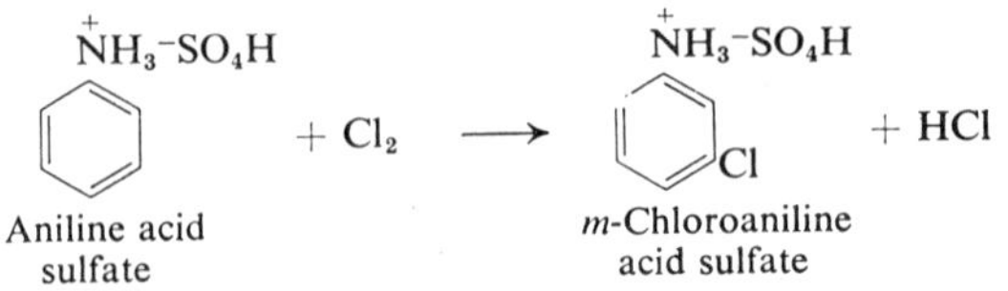

$\overset{+}{N}H_3^-SO_4H$ + Cl$_2$ ⟶ $\overset{+}{N}H_3^-SO_4H$ (Cl)   + HCl

Aniline acid sulfate   *m*-Chloroaniline acid sulfate

Even the less reactive iodine substitutes aniline directly, the hydrogen iodide combining with unreacted aniline.

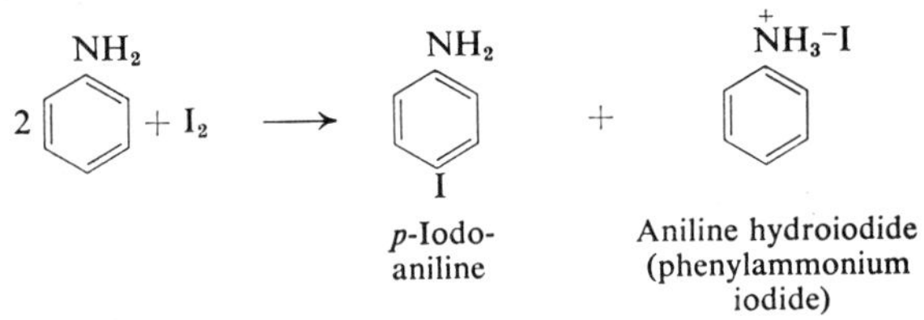

2 NH$_2$ + I$_2$ ⟶ NH$_2$(I) + $\overset{+}{N}H_3^-I$

p-Iodo-aniline   Aniline hydroiodide (phenylammonium iodide)

If the activating effect of the amino group is reduced by conversion to the acetamino group, monochloro or monobromo derivatives can be obtained.

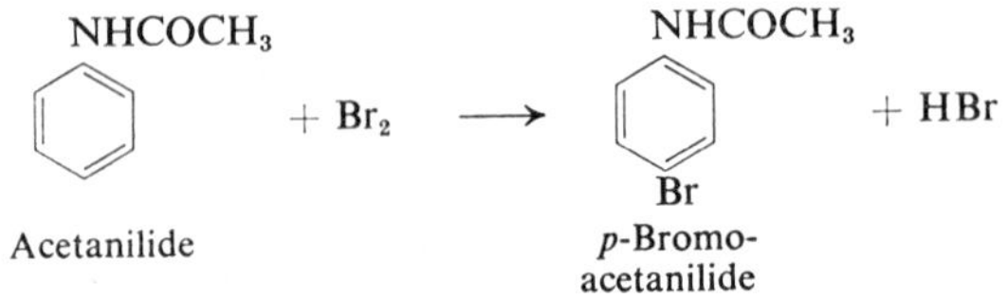

NHCOCH$_3$ + Br$_2$ ⟶ NHCOCH$_3$(Br) + HBr

Acetanilide   *p*-Bromo-acetanilide

Usually monohalogenated anilines are prepared by reduction of the halogenated nitro compounds.

3. **Nitration.** Because of the ease of oxidation of free aniline (p. 482), only the salt can be nitrated efficiently, and nitration is carried out in concentrated sulfuric acid solution. Hence the chief product is *m*-nitroaniline.

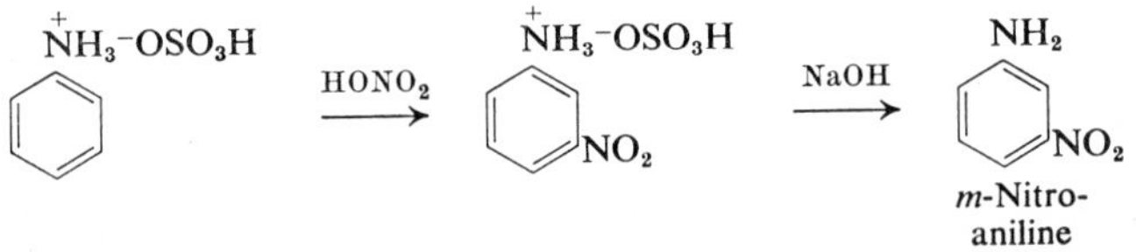

$\overset{+}{N}H_3^-OSO_3H$ $\xrightarrow{HONO_2}$ $\overset{+}{N}H_3^-OSO_3H$(NO$_2$) $\xrightarrow{NaOH}$ NH$_2$(NO$_2$)

m-Nitro-aniline

Some *o*- and *p*-nitroaniline also are formed, probably by nitration of the small amount of free amine in equilibrium with its salt, since the amount of *meta* increases with the concentration of the sulfuric acid. The three nitroanilines differ in basicity (p. 477) and can be separated by fractional precipitation from their salts with alkali. The order of precipitation is *ortho*, then *para*, then *meta*. *m*-Nitroaniline usually is made by the partial reduction of *m*-dinitrobenzene (p. 457).

If salt formation is prevented by the conversion of the basic amino group to the neutral acetamido group, nitration in acetic acid takes place almost exclusively in the *para* position. If the nitration is carried out in the presence of acetic anhydride, the *ortho* isomer is the chief product.

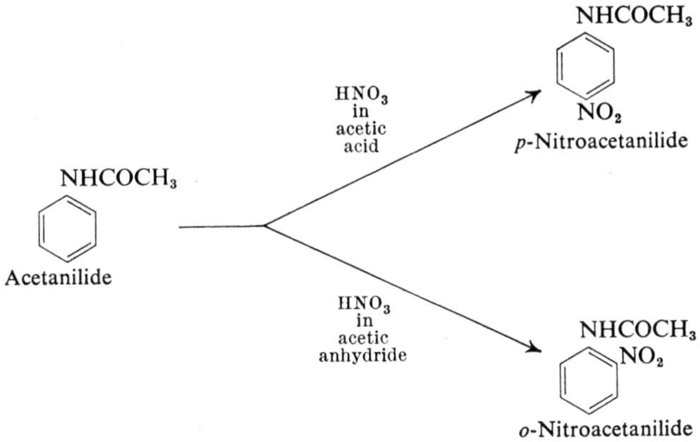

NHCOCH₃

NO₂

p-Nitroacetanilide

HNO₃
in
acetic
acid

NHCOCH₃

Acetanilide

HNO₃
in
acetic
anhydride

NHCOCH₃
NO₂

o-Nitroacetanilide

Saponification of the nitroacetanilides with sodium hydroxide solution gives the nitroanilines. *p*-Nitroaniline is an intermediate for the manufacture of Para Red (p. 677).

4. **Sulfonation.** Sulfonation of aniline at room temperature with fuming sulfuric acid gives a mixture of *o*-, *m*-, and *p*-aminobenzenesulfonic acids. Since the effect of the [⁺NH₃] group should be comparable to that of the [⁺NR₃] group, it should lead to pure *meta* substitution. Hence, as in nitration (p. 484), the *ortho* and *para* isomers must arise from the sulfonation of the small amount of free amine in equilibrium with the salt. When aniline is heated with concentrated sulfuric acid for several hours at 180° (*baking process*), the sole product is the *para* isomer, sulfanilic acid. There is some evidence that here the initial product is the sulfamic acid, which should be *ortho,para*-directing.

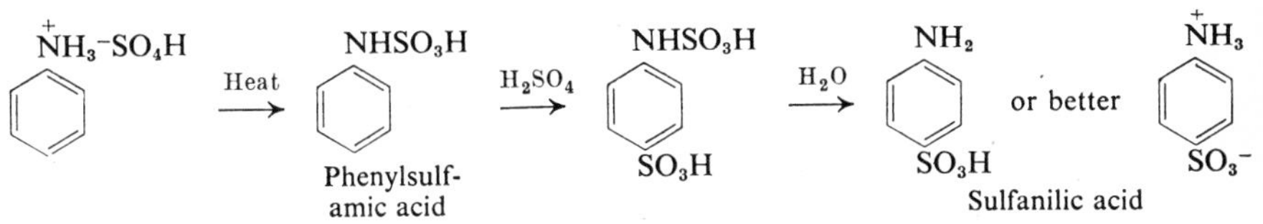

$\overset{+}{N}H_3{}^-SO_4H$

Heat

NHSO₃H

Phenylsulf-
amic acid

H₂SO₄

NHSO₃H

SO₃H

H₂O

NH₂

SO₃H

or better

$\overset{+}{N}H_3$

SO₃⁻

Sulfanilic acid

However, *N,N*-dimethylaniline behaves in the same way as aniline, and since it cannot form a sulfamic acid, *para* substitution is assumed to result from sulfonation of the free amine at both low and high temperatures.

Although the formulas for the sulfonated amines frequently are written as aminosulfonic acids, they actually are inner salts or dipolar ions (cf. p. 299). Thus sulfanilic acid decomposes at 280°–300° without melting, whereas aniline is a liquid, benzenesulfonic acid is a low melting solid, and both can be distilled. Whereas the amino carboxylic acids are more soluble in either strong base or strong acid than in water, sulfanilic acid is more soluble only in strong bases because the sulfonic acid group is as strong as any of the mineral acids in aqueous solution.

The common names for o-, m-, and p-aminobenzenesulfonic acids are *orthanilic*, *metanilic*, and *sulfanilic* acids respectively. Metanilic acid is prepared by the reduction of m-nitrobenzenesulfonic acid. Orthanilic acid is not readily available but can be obtained by removing the bromine atom in 4-bromoaniline-2-sulfonic acid by reduction, or from o-nitrophenyl disulfide (p. 462) by oxidation.

Technically Important Aromatic Amines and Their Derivatives

Aniline is by far the most important amine from the technical viewpoint. Over 131 million pounds were produced in the United States in 1955, the selling price being about 19 cents per pound. Aniline was discovered in 1826 in the products of the destructive distillation of indigo (p. 683) and given the name *krystallin*, because it readily formed crystalline salts. It was detected in coal tar in 1834 and called *kyanol*, because it gave a blue color with bleaching powder. It was rediscovered in the distillation products of indigo in 1841 and called *aniline* from *añil*, the Spanish word for indigo. In the same year it was produced by the reduction of nitrobenzene with ammonium sulfide and called *benzidam*. In 1843 Hofmann (p. 229) proved that all four substances are identical.

Both the reduction of nitrobenzene and the ammonolysis of chlorobenzene are used in the commercial production of aniline. In the reduction process scrap cast-iron turnings and water are placed in a cast-iron vessel fitted with a stirrer and a reflux condenser. A small amount of hydrochloric acid or ferric chloride is added, and the mixture is heated to remove oxides from the surface of the iron, the hydrochloric acid or ferric chloride being converted to ferrous chloride. Nitrobenzene then is added with vigorous stirring. The iron is converted to black iron oxide, Fe_3O_4, which is recovered and used as a pigment (p. 457). The aniline is distilled with steam, and the mixed vapors are condensed. The aniline layer of the distillate is separated from the water layer and purified by distillation at reduced pressure. Since aniline is soluble in water to the extent of about 3 per cent, it must be recovered from the aqueous layer of the distillate. In order to avoid extraction with a solvent and recovery of the solvent, the aniline-saturated aqueous layer is returned to the steam generator for processing a subsequent batch. In another procedure the aniline is extracted from the water with nitrobenzene, and the extract put through the reduction process. Operation of a continuous catalytic hydrogenation process began in 1956.

Since 1926 aniline has been prepared on a large scale by the reaction of chlorobenzene with ammonia. The chlorobenzene is heated in a pressure system with 28 per cent aqueous ammonia (mole ratio 1 : 6) in the presence of cuprous chloride (introduced as cuprous oxide) at 190°–210°. A pressure of around 900 p.s.i. develops. The process is continuous, the reactants entering at

$$C_6H_5Cl + 2\,NH_3 \xrightarrow[190°-210°]{CuCl} C_6H_5NH_2 + NH_4Cl$$

one end of the system and the products leaving the other end. About 5 per cent of phenol and 1 to 2 per cent of diphenylamine are formed as co-products.

$$C_6H_5Cl + H_2O + NH_3 \longrightarrow \underset{\text{Phenol}}{C_6H_5OH} + NH_4Cl$$

$$C_6H_5Cl + H_2NC_6H_5 + NH_3 \longrightarrow \underset{\text{Diphenylamine}}{C_6H_5NHC_6H_5} + NH_4Cl$$

These side reactions would take place to a greater extent were it not for the presence of the large excess of ammonia. At the end of the reaction the liquid is blown into a column. The free ammonia and aniline vaporize and are condensed. Caustic soda is added to the residue to liberate ammonia and aniline from their hydrochlorides, convert the phenol into its sodium salt, and precipitate the copper salts.

The first technical use for aniline was in 1856 for the production of mauve, the first commercial synthetic dye (p. 672). Aniline still is used almost exclusively as an intermediate in the production of other compounds. About half of the total production is used in the manufacture of rubber accelerators and anti-oxidants (p. 711), about 20 per cent for dyes and dye intermediates, and about 5 per cent for drug manufacture.

The **toluidines, xylidines, phenylenediamines,** and most other primary aromatic amines are prepared by similar procedures involving reduction of the nitro compounds. **m-Nitroaniline** is prepared commercially by the partial reduction of *m*-dinitrobenzene using sodium sulfide as the reducing agent (p. 457).

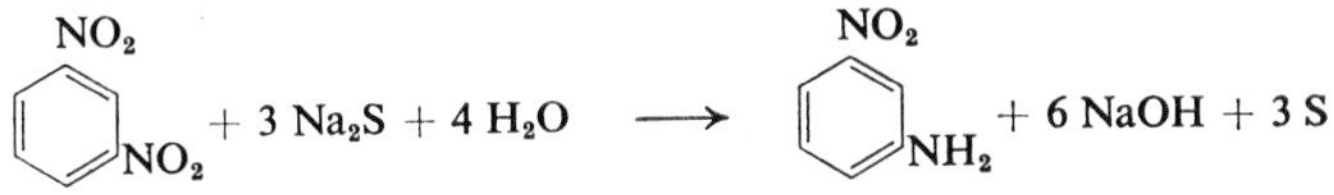

o- or *p*-**Nitroaniline** may be prepared by the ammonolysis of *o-* or *p*-nitrochloro-benzene. This reaction takes place more readily than the ammonolysis of chlorobenzene because of the activating effect of nitro groups in the *ortho* or *para* position (p. 461).

Acetanilide was produced to the extent of about 6 million pounds in 1945, but output has fallen to about half this amount since 1948 because of the decrease in the production of sulfa drugs (p. 488). A small amount is used as a dye intermediate. Acetanilide was introduced as an antipyretic in 1886 under the name *antifebrine*, and at one time it was used widely for this purpose and as an analgesic. It is highly toxic, however, being similar to aniline in its action, and it has been displaced largely by the relatively safer salicylates (p. 559), especially aspirin which was introduced in 1899. Because of its cheapness, however, acetanilide still is used in some proprietary headache and pain-killing remedies.

Xylocaine, a new type of local anesthetic (p. 141), is the hydrochloride of α-diethylamino-2,6-dimethylacetanilide and is prepared by the following series of reactions.

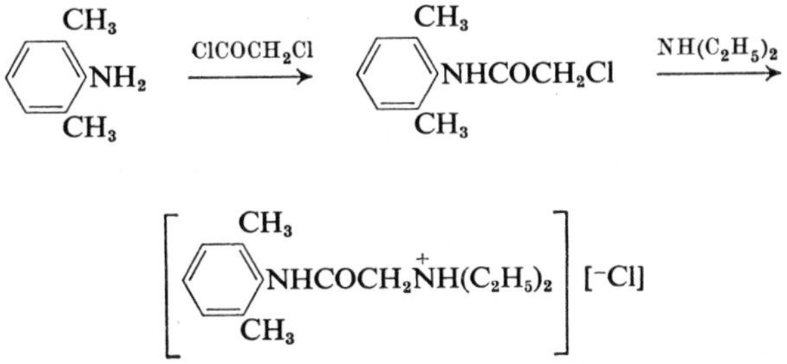

About 7 million pounds of **N,N-dimethylaniline** was produced in 1955. It is made by heating aniline and methyl alcohol in the presence of hydrochloric or sulfuric acid in a pressure reactor at 220°.

$$C_6H_5NH_2 + 2\ CH_3OH \xrightarrow[220°]{H_2SO_4} C_6H_5N(CH_3)_2 + 2\ H_2O$$

It can be made also by passing aniline and methyl ether vapors over activated alumina at 260°.

$$C_6H_5NH_2 + (CH_3)_2O \xrightarrow[260°]{Al_2O_3} C_6H_5N(CH_3)_2 + H_2O$$

Dimethylaniline is used as a dye intermediate (pp. 490, 541, 681) and in the manufacture of tetryl (p. 490). **N,N'-Di-s-butyl-p-phenylenediamine,** p-$(s$-$C_4H_9NH)_2C_6H_4$, is one of the more widely used antioxidants (p. 886) for preventing the polymerization of the unsaturated components of cracked gasoline. Long-chain alkyl derivatives, such as **N,N'-di-2-octyl-p-phenylene-diamine,** are used as antioxidants for synthetic rubber.

Diphenylamine is the principal stabilizer for smokeless powder (p. 401), being added in amounts of 1 to 8 per cent of the finished product. Its function is to combine with any oxides of nitrogen that are liberated, which otherwise would catalyze further decomposition. Large quantities of diphenylamine are used also in the manufacture of phenothiazine (p. 643), an intestinal disinfectant for animals. When a solution of diphenylamine in concentrated sulfuric acid reacts with nitrous or nitric acid or with their salts or esters, a deep blue color is formed (p. 572). The reaction can be used as a test for diphenylamine or for nitrous or nitric acid or their salts or esters.

Sulfanilic acid and **p-toluidine** are used principally as dye intermediates. The production of **sulfa drugs,** which amounted to about 6 million pounds in 1945, dropped to 2.5 million pounds in 1948 and has remained there because of the increased use of penicillin and other antibiotics. Preparation of the sulfa drugs, however, still consumes a considerable quantity of aniline. The forerunner of the sulfanilamides was *Prontosil*, an azo dye patented by I. G. Farbenindustrie in 1932 and definitely established clinically by 1935 as effective against streptococcal infections. Fourneau, a French chemist, and his co-workers showed in 1935 that prontosil is converted into sulfanilamide in the body, and in 1936 that sulfanilamide is equally effective. Sulfanilamide soon was shown to be effective against other cocci infections such as pneumonia and gonorrhea, and other bacterial infections. These results led to the synthesis and testing of hundreds of derivatives of sulfanilamide. *Sulfanilamide* is synthesized from aniline by a series of reactions.

Most of the derivatives of sulfanilamide that have proved to be superior to it differ from it in structure only in that one of the hydrogen atoms of the sulfonamide group is replaced by a more complex organic group. These derivatives are made by substituting another amine for ammonia in the step in which the amide is formed. One exception is *marfanil* in which the nuclear amino group is separated from the benzene ring by a methylene group. It is more effective than the sulfanilamides against anaerobic bacteria, such as the anthrax bacillus, and is used for dusting into open wounds.

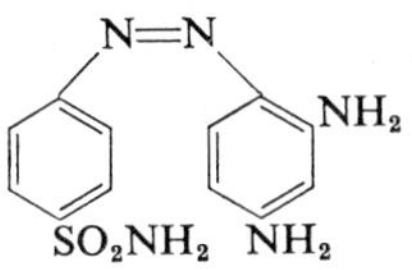

Prontosil

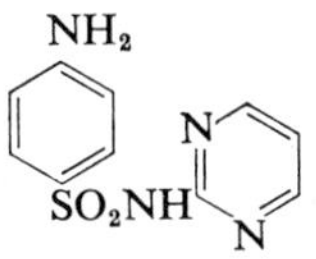

Sulfadiazine

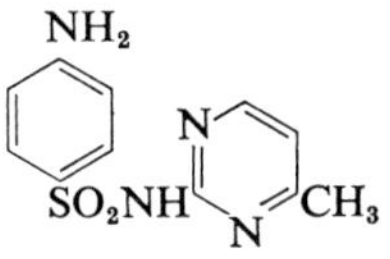

Sulfamerazine

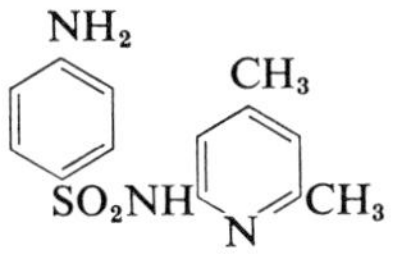

Sulfamethazine

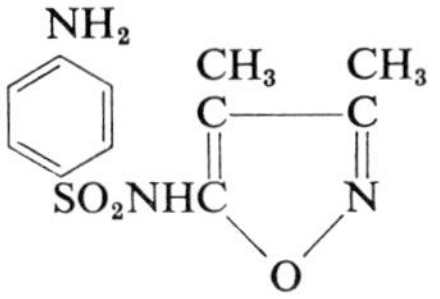

Sulfisoxazole

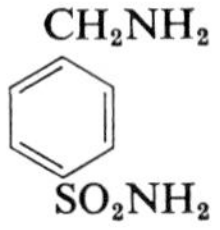

Marfanil

The disadvantage of the sulfanilamides has been their low solubility in water, which has led to deposition in the kidneys and renal damage. This difficulty has been alleviated by administering a mixture of three different compounds. The combined dose is as effective as an equal amount of any one drug, but the concentration of each is only one third. *Sulfisoxazole* has the advantage that it has a relatively high solubility in urine.

Clinical tests reported in 1955 indicated that *p*-aminobenzenesulfonyl and *p*-tolylsulfonyl derivatives of *n*-butylurea are effective orally in lowering the blood sugar in mild cases of diabetes, although some cause serious undesirable side effects. *p*-Aminophenyl sulfone (diaminodiphenyl sulfone) and its derivatives are effective in the treatment of Hansen's disease (leprosy). It is useful also as a hardening agent for epoxy resins (p. 750).

$SO_2NHCONHC_4H_9$-*n*
N-(*p*-Tolylsulfonyl)-*N'*-(*n*-butyl)urea
(Orinase)

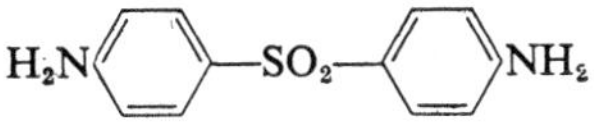

p-Aminophenyl sulfone
(diaminodiphenyl sulfone)

p-Nitrosodimethylaniline is made commercially by the nitrosation of dimethylaniline (p. 480). It condenses with activated methyl groups such as those present in α-picoline (p. 626) or 2,4-dinitrotoluene (p. 439). Hydrolysis of the condensation product gives the aldehyde.

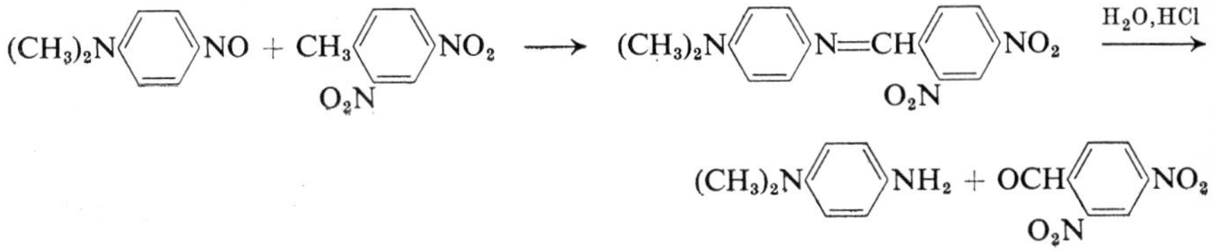

Reduction of *p*-nitrosodimethylaniline gives **p-dimethylaminoaniline,** which is used in the manufacture of Methylene Blue (p. 696). *p*-Dimethylaminoaniline is useful also for the separation of aldehydes and ketones, since only aldehydes react to give the anils (p. 481). The zinc chloride double salts of diazotized *p*-dimethylaminoaniline and of diazotized **p-diethylaminoaniline** are used in diazotype photographic processes (pp. 493, 697). *p*-Diethylaminoaniline is used also as a developer in color photography (p. 692).

Tetryl, 2,4,6-trinitrophenylmethylnitramide, is the standard booster charge for high explosive shells. The explosion of a shell is initiated by the primary explosive such as mercury fulminate (p. 318) which is sensitive to heat or shock. Detonation of the primary charge causes the explosion of the less sensitive booster charge, which in turn detonates the still less sensitive main charge such as TNT. Tetryl may be made by the reaction of dinitrochlorobenzene with methylamine, followed by further nitration.

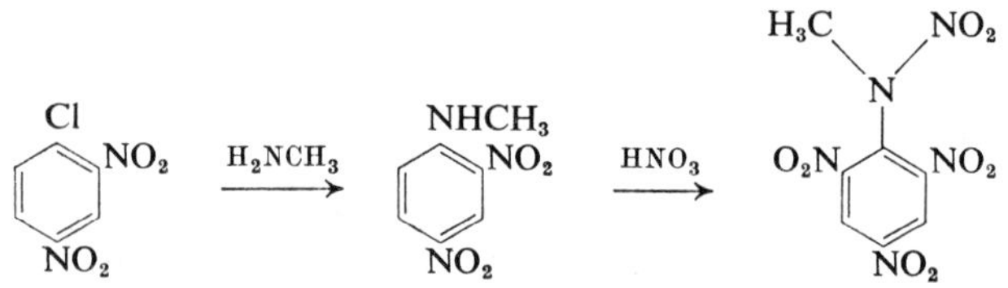

Tetryl

It usually is manufactured by the nitration of dimethylaniline in concentrated sulfuric acid. During the course of the reaction one of the methyl groups is removed by oxidation.

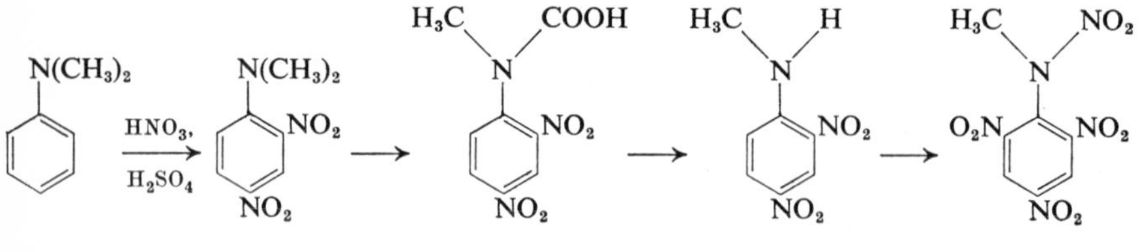

REVIEW QUESTIONS

1. Compare the boiling points of aniline, *n*-hexylamine, methylaniline, and dimethylaniline, and explain.
2. Look up the melting points of the *ortho, meta,* and *para* isomers of toluidine, nitroaniline, and chloroaniline, note any regularities, and explain.
3. Discuss the physiological action of aromatic amines.
4. Summarize the methods for preparing primary, secondary, and tertiary aromatic amines.
5. Discuss the bromination, nitration, and sulfonation of aniline.
6. Summarize the methods for the preparation of *o-, m-,* and *p*-nitroaniline.
7. Discuss the properties and structure of *p*-aminobenzenesulfonic acid.
8. Compare the basicity of aniline with that of aliphatic amines and of acid amides. Discuss the effect of substituents attached to the nitrogen atom and of substituents in the ring on the basicity of the amino group.
9. Compare the reactions of primary, secondary, and tertiary aromatic amines with those of the corresponding types of aliphatic amines.
10. Compare the ease of oxidation of aromatic amines with that of their salts.
11. What are the sulfanilamides? How is sulfanilamide synthesized, starting with benzene? Why is aniline not chlorosulfonated directly?

PROBLEMS

12. Give equations for the preparation of the following compounds:
    A. (*a*) *p*-Toluidine from toluene; (*b*) *N*-nitrosodiphenylamine from aniline; (*c*) di-*n*-butyl-amine from *N,N*-di-*n*-butylaniline; (*d*) *p*-chlorophenyl isocyanate from *p*-chloroaniline; (*e*) *N,N'*-di-*s*-butyl-*p*-phenylenediamine from *p*-nitroaniline; (*f*) *p*-nitroacetanilide from aniline.
    B. (*a*) *m*-Phenyl diisocyanate from *m*-phenylenediamine; (*b*) 2,4-dimethylaniline from *m*-xylene; (*c*) *N*-nitroso-*N*-methyl-*p*-toluidine from *p*-toluidine; (*d*) *i*-butylamine from *N*-isobutylacetanilide; (*e*) *p*-bromoacetanilide from aniline; (*f*) *p*-diethylaminoaniline from *N,N*-diethylaniline.
    C. (*a*) *N*-Nitroso-*N*-ethylaniline from aniline; (*b*) *p*-tolyl isocyanate from *p*-toluidine; (*c*) *p*-isopropylaniline from cumene; (*d*) *o*-nitroaniline from acetanilide; (*e*) *p*-dimethyl-aminoaniline from *N,N*-dimethylaniline; (*f*) diethylamine from *N,N*-diethylaniline.
13. Give equations for the following reactions and name the product formed:
    A. (*a*) Ethylmagnesium bromide with phenyl isocyanate; (*b*) nitrous acid with 2,4-dimethyl-aniline hydrochloride; (*c*) sulfanilic acid with trifluoroperoxyacetic acid; (*d*) *p*-toluidine heated with *p*-toluidine hydrochloride; (*e*) phenylisothiocyanate with dimethylamine; (*f*) 2,6-dinitrotoluene with ammonium sulfide.
    B. (*a*) *o*-Nitroaniline with trifluoroperoxyacetic acid; (*b*) benzylmagnesium chloride with *p*-tolyl isocyanate; (*c*) *o*-chloroaniline heated with *o*-chloroaniline hydrochloride; (*d*) nitrous acid with *p*-nitroaniline hydrochloride; (*e*) 1,2-dimethyl-4,5-dinitrobenzene with ammonium sulfide; (*f*) *p*-chlorophenyl isothiocyanate with *n*-butylamine.
    C. (*a*) Nitrous acid with *o*-chloroaniline hydrochloride; (*b*) 3-nitro-4-aminotoluene with trifluoroperoxyacetic acid; (*c*) 3,5-dinitrobenzenesulfonic acid with ammonium sulfide; (*d*) phenylmagnesium bromide with *p*-chlorophenyl isocyanate; (*e*) *p*-tolyl isothiocyanate with diethylamine; (*f*) *o*-toluidine heated with *o*-toluidine hydrochloride.
14. Describe a procedure for distinguishing between the following pairs of compounds: (*a*) thiocarbanilide and diphenylurea; (*b*) aniline and *n*-hexylamine; (*c*) acetanilide and acetamide; (*d*) *o*-toluidine and *o*-nitrotoluene; (*e*) phenyl isocyanate and phenyl isocyanide; (*f*) *N*-methylaniline and *N,N*-dimethylaniline; (*g*) *o*-chloroaniline and aniline hydrochloride; (*h*) diphenylamine and acetanilide; (*i*) thiocarbanilide and *p*-toluenesulfonamide; (*j*) *m*-toluidine and *N*-methylaniline.
15. Which member of the following pairs of compounds is the stronger base: (*a*) diphenylamine and *N*-methylphenylamine; (*b*) *p*-nitroaniline and 2,4-dinitroaniline; (*c*) *p*-toluidine and *N,N*-dimethylaniline; (*d*) aniline and *p*-toluidine; (*e*) aniline and *n*-amylamine; (*f*) *m*-chloroaniline and *p*-chloroaniline?
16. Five compounds, *A*, *B*, *C*, *D*, and *E*, have the molecular formula C_7H_9N. All are soluble in dilute hydrochloric acid. All react with benzenesulfonyl chloride in the presence of aqueous sodium hydroxide to give soluble products except *A*, which gives a product that is not soluble in dilute alkali. When subjected to vigorous oxidation, *B* yields an acid having a neutralization equivalent of 122, but the remainder give only products of low molecular weight. All of the compounds are liquids at room temperature except *E*, which is a solid. When *C* and *D* are oxidized first with trifluoroperoxyacetic acid and then with sodium dichromate and sulfuric acid, they yield acids having neutralization equivalents of 167. The acid from *C* melts at 140° and that from *D* at 147°. Give possible structural formulas for the five compounds and equations for the reactions that they undergo.
17. Compound *A* has the molecular formula $C_{15}H_{16}N_2S$. When boiled with hydrochloric acid, it gives an oil having a sharp odor. The acid aqueous layer, when made alkaline, gives a solid precipitate, *B*. When a mixture of the oil and the solid are warmed and then allowed to cool, a solid is obtained which, after purification, is found to be identical with the starting compound, *A*. When *A* is heated with mercuric oxide, a compound free of sulfur is obtained. This compound reacts with water to give compound *C*, which has the molecular formula $C_{15}H_{16}N_2O$. When *C* is boiled with aqueous hydrochloric acid it goes completely into solution. When the solution is made alkaline, a compound precipitates that is identical with *B*. Give a structural formula for *A*, and show by equations the reactions that take place.

Chapter 23

DIAZONIUM SALTS AND DIAZO COMPOUNDS

DIAZONIUM SALTS

Diazonium salts and Grignard reagents constitute the two most versatile types of reagents known to organic chemists. The value of Grignard reagents is limited by the fact that for the most part they can be prepared only from the halogen derivatives of aliphatic or aromatic hydrocarbons; that is, few other functional groups may be present. This type of limitation does not exist for the formation of diazonium salts. On the other hand the latter can be prepared only if an amino group is attached to an aromatic nucleus.

Diazonium salts were prepared first by Peter Griess[1] in 1858 by the action of nitrous acid on the salt of an aromatic amine.

$$ArNH_3{}^+Cl^- + HONO \longrightarrow ArN_2{}^+Cl^- + 2\,H_2O$$

The importance of these compounds soon was recognized, and within the course of the next five years, their reactions had been widely investigated and azo dyes derived from them were being manufactured commercially. Moreover the investigations concerning the structure of diazonium salts, and of diazo compounds in general, have played an important part in the development of the theoretical aspects of organic chemistry.

Physical Properties, Structure, and Nomenclature

In acid solutions the aromatic diazo compounds show all of the properties of salts. They are solids, soluble in water, and insoluble in organic solvents. Electrical conductivity measurements show that they are completely ionized in dilute solution. The only reasonable structure is that in which one of the nitrogen atoms is quaternary as in ammonium salts and in which the nitrogen atoms are joined by a triple bond.

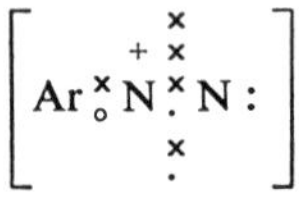

$$\left[Ar\overset{+}{\underset{\cdot}{\overset{\times\times}{\text{N}}}}\overset{\times\times}{\underset{\cdot}{\text{N}}}: \right][^-X] \quad \text{or} \quad [Ar{-}\overset{+}{N}{\equiv}N][^-X]$$

In naming these compounds the name of the hydrocarbon from which they are derived is affixed to *diazonium* and the name of the acid radical.

$$\left[\text{⟨◯⟩}\overset{+}{N}{\equiv}N \right][\bar{C}l] \qquad \left[O_2N\text{⟨◯⟩}\overset{+}{N}{\equiv}N \right][\bar{O}SO_3H]$$

Benzenediazonium
chloride

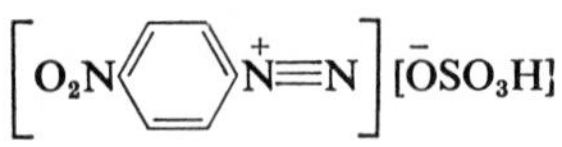

p-Nitrobenzenediazonium
acid sulfate

---

[1] Johan Peter Griess (1829–1888) discovered the diazonium salts while working on a problem suggested by Kolbe. He continued his investigations first as an assistant to Hofmann and then throughout his life in whatever time he could spare while working as a chemist for an English brewery.

The term *azo* comes from the French word *azote* meaning nitrogen. In compounds such as azobenzene, $C_6H_5N{=}NC_6H_5$, *one* nitrogen atom is present for each aromatic nucleus. In the diazo compounds, *two* nitrogen atoms are present for each aromatic nucleus.

Preparation

In general diazonium salts are not isolated as pure compounds but are prepared and used in aqueous solution. The reaction of the amine salt with nitrous acid is known as *diazotization* and must be carried out in strongly acid solution to prevent the diazonium salt from coupling with unreacted amine (p. 498). The nitrous acid usually is generated *in situ* by the addition of sodium nitrite to the suspension of amine salt in excess mineral acid. The diazonium salts generally are unstable at room temperature. Hence the reaction ordinarily is carried out at 0°, and the solution is used immediately.

Solid diazonium salts may be obtained by dissolving the amine salt in an acid solution of alcohol and adding an alkyl nitrite.

$$[Ar\overset{+}{N}H_3]Cl^- + C_2H_5ONO \longrightarrow [Ar\overset{+}{N}_2]\bar{C}l + C_2H_5OH + H_2O$$

In this procedure no inorganic salts are introduced or formed, and the diazonium salt can be precipitated by the addition of ether. The solid salts are crystalline and colorless but darken in air. They explode when heated or subjected to mechanical shock. The stability of diazonium salts varies greatly with the structure of the molecule. *p*-Nitrobenzenediazonium chloride is considerably more stable than benzenediazonium chloride. Double salts with zinc chloride and the salts of some acids such as 1,5-naphthalenedisulfonic acid (p. 587) are more stable than salts of the mineral acids. Their wet pastes may be kept for some time at room temperature without decomposition and are used in certain types of dyeing and in diazotype printing (p. 697).

The mechanism of diazotization appears to be the attack by dinitrogen trioxide, nitricidium ion or nitrosonium ion on the free amine that is present in equilibrium with its salt.

$$ArNH_2 + O{=}N{-}O{-}N{=}O \longrightarrow \left[\begin{array}{c} Ar\overset{+}{N}H_2 \\ \overset{\cdot\cdot}{N}O \end{array} \right] + [^-NO_2]$$

$$+ [ON\overset{+}{O}H_2] \longrightarrow \left[\begin{array}{c} Ar\overset{+}{N}H_2 \\ \overset{\cdot\cdot}{NO} \end{array} \right] + H_2O$$

$$+ [^+NO] \longrightarrow \left[\begin{array}{c} Ar\overset{+}{N}H_2 \\ \overset{\cdot\cdot}{N}O \end{array} \right]$$

Loss of water from the arylnitrosoammonium ion by a series of steps gives the diazonium ion.

$$\left[\begin{array}{c} Ar\overset{+}{N}H_2 \\ \overset{\cdot\cdot}{N}O \end{array} \right] \underset{[H^+]}{\rightleftarrows} [ArNHN{=}O] \rightleftarrows [ArN{=}NOH] \underset{H_2O}{\overset{[H^+]}{\rightleftarrows}} [Ar\overset{+}{N}{\equiv}N]$$

Reactions

WITH ELIMINATION OF NITROGEN

1. **Replacement by Hydrogen.** Numerous reducing agents can be used to replace the diazonium group by hydrogen. Hypophosphorous acid generally gives the best yields, although alkaline formaldehyde may be equally satisfactory.

$$[ArN_2^+]^-OSO_3H + H_3PO_2 + H_2O \longrightarrow ArH + N_2 + H_2SO_4 + H_3PO_3$$

$$[ArN_2^+]^-OSO_3H + HCHO + 3\,NaOH \longrightarrow ArH + N_2 + Na_2SO_4 + NaOCHO + 2\,H_2O$$

Reductions of this type frequently are valuable because an amino group can be used to activate the nucleus or bring about a desired orientation and then can be removed by diazotization and reduction. These principles are illustrated by the following series of reactions for the preparation of 1,3,5-tribromobenzene.

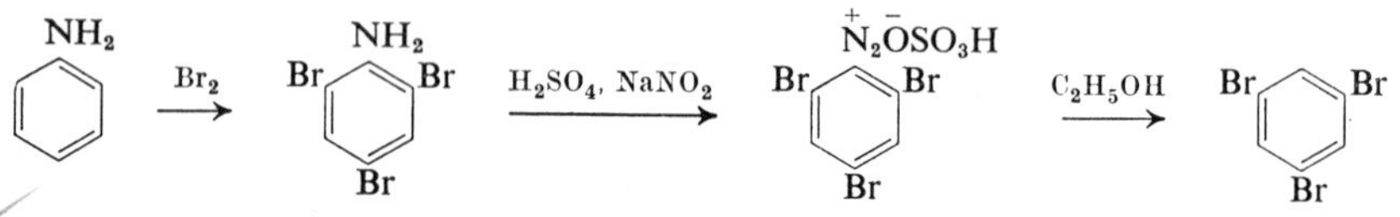

2. **Replacement by Hydroxyl.** If an aqueous solution of the diazonium sulfate is heated, nitrogen is evolved and the phenol is formed.

$$[ArN_2^+]^-OSO_3H + H_2O \xrightarrow{\text{Heat}} ArOH + N_2 + H_2SO_4$$

3. **Replacement by Alkoxyl.** Frequently when a solution of diazonium salt in an alcohol is heated, the diazonium group is replaced by alkoxyl.

$$[ArN_2^+]^-OSO_3H + CH_3OH \longrightarrow ArOCH_3 + N_2 + H_2SO_4$$

4. **Replacement by Halogen.** The diazonium group can be replaced readily by any of the halogens, although different conditions may be required. For replacement by chlorine or bromine the aqueous solution of the corresponding salt is heated either with copper bronze (*Gattermann reaction*) or with cuprous chloride or cuprous bromide (*Sandmeyer reaction*). In general the cuprous halides give better yields.

$$[ArN_2^+]Cl^- \xrightarrow[\text{heat}]{\text{Cu or CuCl}} ArCl + N_2$$

$$[ArN_2^+]Br^- \xrightarrow[\text{heat}]{\text{Cu or CuBr}} ArBr + N_2$$

To replace the diazonium group with iodine it is necessary only to add potassium iodide to the aqueous solution of the sulfate and heat.

$$[ArN_2^+]^-OSO_3H + KI \longrightarrow ArI + N_2 + KHSO_4$$

Fluorine compounds are prepared by adding a solution of the diazotized aromatic amine to a solution of fluoboric acid. The fluoborate precipitates and is washed and dried. When heated, it decomposes to yield the fluoro derivative and boron fluoride.

$$ArN_2^+Cl^- + HBF_4 \longrightarrow [ArN_2^+]^-BF_4 + HCl$$

$$\downarrow \text{Heat}$$

$$ArF + N_2 + BF_3$$

From these reactions it is evident that for replacement by groups other than halogen, it is preferable to use the diazonium sulfates rather than the diazonium halides, since the latter always yield some of the halogen substitution product. Although chlorine and bromine compounds can be prepared by direct substitution, the preparation from the diazonium salt frequently has an advantage because the halogen enters only at the position formerly occupied by the diazonium group. Hence single products are obtained and isomers can be made which may not be available by direct halogenation because of unfavorable directive influences.

5. Replacement by the Cyano (and Carboxyl) Group. If a neutral solution of a diazonium salt is added to a solution of cuprous cyanide-sodium cyanide complex, a precipitate is formed which decomposes to the nitrile when heated.

$$[ArN_2^+]^-OSO_3Na + NaCu(CN)_2 \longrightarrow ArCN + N_2 + CuCN + Na_2SO_4$$

Since the nitrile can be hydrolyzed to the acid, the reaction affords a method for replacing the diazonium group by a carboxyl group as well.

6. Replacement by the Nitro Group. If a diazonium fluoborate is heated with sodium nitrite in the presence of copper bronze, the nitro group enters to give yields of 10 to 60 per cent.

$$ArN_2BF_4 + NaNO_2 \xrightarrow{Cu} ArNO_2 + N_2 + NaBF_4$$

This type of reaction may be useful when the desired nitro compound cannot be made by direct nitration.

7. Replacement by the Mercapto Group. When a diazonium salt reacts with potassium ethyl xanthate (p. 324), an aryl ethyl dithiocarbonate is formed, which can be saponified to a thiophenol.

$$[ArN_2^+]^-OSO_3K + K^+\left[-S\overset{\overset{\displaystyle S}{\|}}{C}OC_2H_5\right] \longrightarrow N_2 + K_2SO_4 + Ar S\overset{\overset{\displaystyle S}{\|}}{C}OC_2H_5 \xrightarrow{5\ KOH}$$

$$K_2S + K_2CO_3 + C_2H_5OH + 2\,H_2O + [ArS^-]^+K \xrightarrow{HCl} ArSH + KCl$$

The reaction must be controlled carefully, because violent explosions may result if the reaction is carried out improperly.

8. Replacement by the Arsono Group. Solutions of diazonium salts react with sodium arsenite in neutral solution in the presence of copper bronze to give arsonic acids (*Bart reaction*).

$$[ArN_2^+]^-OSO_3H + Na_2HAsO_3 \xrightarrow{Cu} ArAsO_3H_2 + N_2 + Na_2SO_4$$

9. Replacement by Mercury. When mercuric chloride is added to a solution of a diazonium chloride, a complex addition product precipitates.

$$ArN_2Cl + HgCl_2 \longrightarrow ArN_2Cl \cdot HgCl_2$$

If this precipitate is suspended in acetone, copper powder added, and the mixture heated, the arylmercuric chloride is formed (*Nesmejanow reaction*).

$$ArN_2Cl \cdot HgCl_2 + 2\,Cu \xrightarrow{\text{Heat in acetone}} ArHgCl + N_2 + 2\,CuCl$$

If ammonia is present during the decomposition, a diarylmercury is produced.

$$2\,ArN_2Cl \cdot HgCl_2 + 5\,Cu \xrightarrow[\text{in acetone}]{\text{Heat with NH}_3} Ar_2Hg + HgCl + 2\,N_2 + 5\,CuCl$$

These reactions work well only if the aryl group is unsubstituted or if it contains electron-donating groups such as methyl or methoxyl. If electron-attracting groups such as nitro or carboxyl are present, it is preferable to start with the fluoborate.

$$[ArN_2{}^+]^-BF_4 + HgCl_2 + SnCl_2 \longrightarrow ArHgCl + N_2 + SnCl_3BF_4$$

Numerous other types of replacement reactions are known which yield, for example, thiocyanates, sulfides, disulfides, sulfinic acids, and stibonic acids. Since the diazonium group carries a positive charge and, like a nitro group, increases the ease of displacement of groups in the *ortho* and *para* positions (p. 461), it is not surprising that 2,4-dibromobenzenediazonium chloride can be converted in hydrochloric acid solution into the 2-bromo-4-chlorobenzene-diazonium salt.

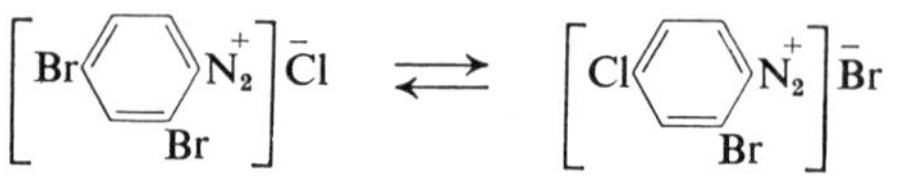

$$\left[Br\!\!\bigcirc\!\!N_2{}^+ \atop Br \right]\bar{C}l \rightleftharpoons \left[Cl\!\!\bigcirc\!\!N_2{}^+ \atop Br \right]\bar{B}r$$

10. Union of Aromatic Nuclei. When a diazonium salt is treated with copper bronze, some biaryl is formed as a co-product of the Gattermann reaction.

$$2\,ArN_2Cl + 2\,Cu \longrightarrow Ar_2 + N_2 + 2\,CuCl$$

The yield of biphenyl from benzenediazonium chloride is about 20 per cent, but the amount of coupling is greater for some diazonium salts.

If a solution of the diazonium salt is mixed with a liquid aromatic compound at 5°–10° and the mixture made alkaline with sodium hydroxide, from 10 to 45 per cent yields of product are obtained in which the two aromatic nuclei are united (*Gomberg reaction*).

$$ArN_2X + H\!\!\bigcirc\!\!R \xrightarrow{NaOH} Ar\!\!\bigcirc\!\!R + N_2 + NaX + H_2O$$

11. Arylation of Unsaturated Compounds (*Meerwein Reaction*). Diazonium halides add to a carbon-carbon double bond in the presence of cuprous salts. The reaction goes particularly well with α,β-unsaturated esters or nitriles. It usually is carried out in acetone solution in the presence of catalytic amounts of cupric chloride, but it has been shown that only the cuprous ion formed by reduction of the cupric chloride by acetone is effective.

$$2\,CuCl_2 + CH_3COCH_3 \longrightarrow 2\,CuCl + ClCH_2COCH_3 + HCl$$

$$ArN_2Cl + CH_2{=}CHCOOCH_3 \xrightarrow{CuCl} ArCH_2CHClCOOCH_3 + N_2$$

$$ArN_2Cl + CH_2{=}CHCN \xrightarrow{CuCl} ArCH_2CHClCN + N_2$$

With certain unsaturated compounds the product corresponds to the dehydro-halogenated addition product, and α,β-unsaturated acids lose carbon dioxide to give the arylated alkene.

$$ArN_2Cl + CH_2{=}CHCOOH \longrightarrow ArCH{=}CH_2 + N_2 + HCl + CO_2$$

Mechanisms of the Decomposition Reactions of Diazonium Salts

Although diazonium salts are completely ionized in strongly acid solutions, they can exist as covalent diazo compounds in weakly acid to alkaline solutions (p. 499). It appears that those reactions involving elimination of nitrogen take place by either ionic mechanisms through the diazonium salt, or free-radical chain mechanisms through the covalent diazo compound.

Replacement by Hydroxyl or Methoxyl. In strongly acid solution in water or methanol an ionic mechanism predominates.

$$[ArN_2^+][^-SO_4H] + H_2O \longrightarrow [HSO_4^-] + N_2 + [Ar\overset{+}{O}H_2] \longrightarrow ArOH + [H^+]$$

$$+ CH_3OH \longrightarrow [HSO_4^-] + N_2 + \left[Ar\overset{+}{\underset{..}{O}}CH_3 \atop H \right] \longrightarrow ArOCH_3 + [H^+]$$

Reduction by Hypophosphorous Acid. Reductions probably take place by way of free radicals.

$$[ArN_2^+][X^-] \rightleftarrows Ar{-}N{=}N{-}X \longrightarrow [Ar \cdot] + N_2 + [\cdot X]$$

$$[Ar \cdot] + HPO_2H_2 \longrightarrow ArH + [O{=}\overset{\cdot}{P}HOH]$$

$$[ArN_2^+] + [O{=}PHOH] \longrightarrow [Ar \cdot] + N_2 + [O{=}\overset{+}{P}HOH]$$

$$[O{=}\overset{+}{P}HOH] + [X^-] \longrightarrow HX + HPO_2$$

Sandmeyer Reaction. Here cuprous chloride initiates a free-radical decomposition.

$$[ArN_2^+] + \cdot Cu : Cl \longrightarrow [Ar \cdot] + N_2 + [\overset{+}{Cu} : Cl]$$

$$[Ar \cdot] + [\overset{+}{Cu} : Cl] \longrightarrow ArCl + [\cdot Cu^+]$$

$$[\cdot Cu^+] + [^- : Cl] \longrightarrow \cdot Cu : Cl$$

Cupric chloride is not a catalyst for the reaction, and the rate decreases with increasing chloride ion concentration because of the formation of the $[^=CuCl_3]$ complex ion.

Gomberg Reaction. This reaction long has been known to involve free radicals.

$$[ArN_2^+] + [^-OH] \rightleftarrows ArN{=}NOH \longrightarrow [Ar \cdot] + N_2 + [\cdot OH]$$

$$[Ar \cdot] + Ar'H \longrightarrow ArAr' + [H \cdot]$$

$$[H \cdot] + [\cdot OH] \longrightarrow H_2O$$

With aliphatic compounds the chief reaction is transfer of a hydrogen atom.

$$[Ar \cdot] + HR \longrightarrow ArH + R \cdot$$

It is for this reason that the second reactant must be an aromatic liquid, since any solvent would be attacked by the intermediate free radical. Free-radical substitution does not follow the rules for either electrophilic or nucleophilic substitution. Both electron-donating and electron-attracting groups are activating, and the average isomer distribution in the product is roughly 50 per cent *ortho* and 25 per cent each of *meta* and *para*.

WITHOUT ELIMINATION OF NITROGEN

1. **Reduction to Hydrazines.** When a diazonium salt is reduced with zinc dust and acetic acid, with sulfur dioxide, with sodium hydrosulfite, or with stannous chloride, an arylhydrazine is formed.

$$[C_6H_5\overset{+}{N}{\equiv}N]\overset{-}{Cl} + 2 H_2SO_3 + 2 H_2O \longrightarrow [C_6H_5NHNH_3^+]\overset{-}{Cl} + 2 H_2SO_4$$

Since the reaction is general, many of these valuable reagents are easily available. It was the discovery of phenylhydrazine by Emil Fischer in 1875 that led to his work on the structure of the sugars (p. 385).

2. **The Coupling Reaction.** Diazonium salts react with phenols and tertiary amines in weakly acid, neutral, or alkaline solution, causing substitution in the position *para* to the hydroxyl or amino group with the production of highly colored azo compounds (p. 676).

$$[C_6H_5\overset{+}{N}{\equiv}N]Cl^- + H\langle\;\rangle OH + NaOH \longrightarrow C_6H_5N{=}N\langle\;\rangle OH + NaCl + H_2O$$

p-Hydroxyazobenzene

$$+ H\langle\;\rangle N(CH_3)_2 + NaOH \longrightarrow C_6H_5N{=}N\langle\;\rangle N(CH_3)_2 + NaCl + H_2O$$

p-Dimethylaminoazobenzene

In the coupling reaction the diazonium salt is known as the *primary component*, and the compound with which it couples is called the *secondary component*. If the *para* position of the secondary component is occupied, coupling takes place in the *ortho* position. If the *para* position and both *ortho* positions are blocked, coupling usually does not take place, although occasionally the group in the *para* position is displaced.

Coupling is a substitution reaction analogous to nitration, sulfonation, and halogenation, the active agent being the diazonium ion, $[ArN_2{}^+]$. Like nitrous acid, however, a diazonium salt is a very weak reagent and displaces hydrogen only from aromatic nuclei that contain a strongly activating group such as an amino or hydroxyl group. Coupling does not take place in strongly acid solution, because the amino groups form salts and become deactivating, and the hydroxyl group is undissociated and not so strongly activating as the phenoxide ion (p. 454).

Coupling takes place with primary and secondary aliphatic amines to give *diazoamino compounds.*

$$[Ar\overset{+}{N}_2]\overset{-}{Cl} + 2\ HNHR \longrightarrow ArN{=}N{-}NHR + RNH_3Cl$$

Some of the primary and secondary aromatic amines also undergo this reaction. For example aniline couples with benzenediazonium chloride buffered with sodium acetate to give diazoaminobenzene.

$$C_6H_5N_2Cl + H_2NC_6H_5 + NaOCOCH_3 \longrightarrow C_6H_5N{=}N{-}NHC_6H_5 + NaCl + CH_3COOH$$
Diazoaminobenzene

It is to prevent this reaction that diazotization is carried out in strongly acid solution, since the amine salt does not couple.

If the diazoamino compound is heated in the presence of an amine salt to catalyze the reaction, rearrangement to the aminoazo compound takes place.

$$C_6H_5N{=}N{-}NHC_6H_5 \xrightarrow{\text{Heat } (+ C_6H_5NH_3Cl)} C_6H_5N{=}N\langle\;\rangle NH_2$$

p-Aminoazobenzene

From many primary aromatic amines, for example the naphthylamines (p. 588), the diazoamino compounds cannot be isolated, the nuclear-substituted azo compounds being formed directly.

Victor Meyer reported in 1875 that benzenediazonium salts couple with nitroethane in alkaline solution.

$$RCH_2NO_2 + ArN_2Cl + NaOH \longrightarrow \underset{\underset{N=NAr}{|}}{RCHNO_2} + NaCl + H_2O$$

If the aliphatic component has two active hydrogen atoms, the product is tautomeric with the hydrazone.

$$\underset{\underset{N=NAr}{|}}{RCHNO_2} \rightleftarrows \underset{\underset{NNHAr}{||}}{RCNO_2}$$

Other compounds having an active methylene group, such as malonic esters (p. 800), β-keto esters (p. 817), acetoacetanilides (p. 703), and β-diketones (p. 771), also couple with diazonium salts.

DIAZO COMPOUNDS

When sodium hydroxide is added to an aqueous solution of an ordinary quaternary ammonium salt, such as tetramethylammonium bromide, nothing happens because the quaternary ammonium hydroxide is completely ionized, and the solution contains only tetramethylammonium ions, sodium ions, bromide ions, and hydroxide ions. If silver oxide is added, silver bromide precipitates, and the solution is strongly basic and contains tetraethylammonium and hydroxide ions (p. 241). The behavior of the diazonium salts is entirely different. The addition of sodium hydroxide or silver oxide yields a sodium or silver salt of a compound having the diazo group in a negative ion instead of a positive ion. The sodium salt in aqueous solution is only weakly alkaline, indicating that it is the salt of a fairly strong acid. The composition of the salts indicates that the acid is isomeric with the diazonium hydroxide. It may be called an **aryldiazoic acid,** and the salts **diazoates.** The acids also have been called *diazohydrates* and the salts *diazotates.* The free diazoic acids have not been isolated. They have been assigned the structure $ArN=NOH$, which would be expected to have about the same acidity as nitrous acid, $O=NOH$. Accordingly the reaction of a diazonium salt with sodium hydroxide is believed to be the reaction of hydroxide ion with the diazonium ion to give the diazoic acid, which is stabilized by salt formation.

$$[Ar\overset{+}{N}\equiv N]\overset{-}{Cl} \xrightarrow{\text{NaOH}} NaCl + \underset{\substack{\text{Aryldiazoic}\\\text{acid}}}{[ArN=NOH]} \xrightarrow{\text{NaOH}} H_2O + \underset{\substack{\text{Sodium}\\\text{aryldiazoate}}}{[ArN=NO^-]\overset{+}{Na}}$$

When the diazoate solution is acidified, the reverse reaction takes place and the diazonium salt is formed.

$$[ArN=NO^-]\overset{+}{Na} \xrightarrow{\text{HCl}} NaCl + [ArN=NOH] \xrightarrow{\text{HCl}} H_2O + [Ar\overset{+}{N}\equiv N]\overset{-}{Cl}$$

Sodium cyanide behaves like sodium hydroxide, yielding a diazocyanide.

$$[ArN_2{}^+]Cl^- + NaCN \longrightarrow ArN=NCN + NaCl$$

The diazocyanides are not electrolytes and are soluble in organic solvents. Hence the nitrile group is bound covalently to nitrogen.

If the diazoates are heated with excess alkali or if the diazocyanides are allowed to stand in the solid state or in alcoholic solution, isomeric compounds sometimes can be isolated. Hantzsch[2] proposed that these isomers owe their existence to geometrical isomerism caused by the spatial distribution of the nitrogen bonds and the double bond between the two nitrogen atoms, analogous to the *cis-trans* isomers caused by carbon-carbon double bonds (p. 354). Instead of calling them *cis* and *trans*, Hantzsch used the terms *syn* and *anti*.

$$
\begin{bmatrix} \underset{\text{N}}{\overset{\text{Ar}}{\diagdown}} \\ \underset{\text{N}}{\overset{\|}{}} \\ \underset{\text{-O}}{\diagup} \end{bmatrix}
\quad
\begin{bmatrix} \underset{\text{N}}{\overset{\text{Ar}}{\diagdown}} \\ \underset{\text{N}}{\overset{\|}{}} \\ \underset{\text{O}^-}{\diagdown} \end{bmatrix}
\quad
\underset{\text{NC}}{\overset{\text{Ar}}{\diagdown}} \! \underset{}{\overset{\text{N}}{\underset{\text{N}}{\overset{\|}{}}}}
\quad
\overset{\text{Ar}}{\underset{\text{N}}{\diagdown}} \underset{\text{CN}}{\overset{\|}{\underset{\text{N}}{}}}
$$

syn-Diazoate   anti-Diazoate   syn-Diazocyanide   anti-Diazocyanide

Hantzsch's views have been contested recently but still appear to be the most satisfactory interpretation of the facts.

The ability of the nitrogen-nitrogen double bond to give rise to stereoisomers has been confirmed by the isolation of two forms of azobenzene. Irradiation of solutions of the stable *trans* form by light converts it partially into the *cis* isomer, which can be isolated by crystallization or by adsorption on alumina. Many azo dyes in solution undergo a reversible color change when exposed to light (*phototropism*), because the *cis* form has a different color than the *trans* form.

REVIEW QUESTIONS

1. Discuss the physical properties of diazonium salts and their bearing on the structure of this class of compounds.
2. Give equations and conditions for the replacement of a diazonium group by hydroxyl, hydrogen, halogen, and nitrile groups.
3. How is phenylhydrazine prepared?
4. Discuss the coupling reaction of diazonium salts. Why does coupling take place only in alkaline or weakly acid solutions? Why is it necessary that the reaction mixture contain a large excess of mineral acid during the preparation of diazonium salts?
5. Devise a colorimetric procedure for the estimation of nitrous acid. (Hint: use a diazonium salt as an intermediate.)
6. Discuss the isomerism of aromatic azo compounds.

[2] Arthur Rudolf Hantzsch (1857–1935) made his Habilitationsschrift in 1882 on the synthesis of pyridines. He succeeded Victor Meyer at the Polytechnicum in Zurich as a full professor at the age of 28, and then succeeded Emil Fischer at Wuerzburg in 1893, and Wislicenus at Leipzig in 1903. Up to 1890 his research was concerned largely with the synthesis of heterocyclic compounds. After Meyer had proven that the benzil monoximes were not structural isomers, Hantzsch and Werner put forward their stereochemical explanation. This view led to the investigation of diazo compounds. Later he investigated the tautomeric forms of aliphatic nitro compounds. Under the influence of the strong school of physical chemistry at Leipzig, he was led to the application of physical chemical methods, such as conductivity and freezing point depression, to the study of organic chemical problems. Following 1906 he concerned himself largely with the absorption spectra of organic compounds and the relation between color and chemical constitution.

PROBLEMS

7. Making use of diazonium salts, give reactions for the synthesis of the following compounds from the proper amine:

   A. (a) p-Hydroxytoluene; (b) o-chlorobromobenzene; (c) phenyl cyanide; (d) p-hydroxy-p'-nitroazobenzene; (e) m-bromophenylhydrazine; (f) 2,4-dimethylthiophenol; (g) p-nitrobenzenearsonic acid; (h) bi-o-tolyl; (i) phenylmercuric chloride; (j) o-dinitrobenzene.

   B. (a) 2,4-Dimethylcyanobenzene; (b) p-tolylhydrazine; (c) m-nitrophenol; (d) p-dimethylamino-o'-methylazobenzene; (e) o-iodotoluene; (f) p-methoxyphenylmercury; (g) 2-methylbiphenyl; (h) p-i-propylthiophenol; (i) p-nitrobenzenesulfonic acid; (j) m-toluenearsonic acid.

   C. (a) Fluorobenzene; (b) o-chloro-p'-hydroxyazobenzene; (c) m-bromocyanobenzene; (d) p-chlorophenylhydrazine; (e) 2,4-dimethylphenol; (f) m-chlorobiphenyl; (g) p-i-propylbenzenearsonic acid; (h) m-nitrotoluene; (i) o-methylphenylmercuric chloride; (j) o-ethylthiophenol.

8. Give a series of reactions for the preparation of the following compounds starting with an aromatic hydrocarbon: (a) 2-cyano-4-chlorotoluene; (b) m-dibromobenzene; (c) p-bromofluorobenzene; (d) 3,3'-dinitrobiphenyl; (e) 3-bromo-4-methylthiophenol; (f) m-iodonitrobenzene; (g) p-methylbiphenyl; (h) m-chlorophenol; (i) o-chlorothiophenol; (j) 2,5-dimethylphenylhydrazine; (k) 1,3,5-trichlorobenzene.

9. Assuming that the properties of the three phthalic acids are known, devise a procedure for determining the orientation of (a) the three nitroanilines; (b) the three nitrotoluenes.

10. Assuming that the properties of the three nitroanilines are known, and that Y and Z are two groups which can be introduced by way of the diazonium salts, list the disubstituted benzenes whose orientation readily could be determined.

Chapter 24

PHENOLS, AMINOPHENOLS, AND QUINONES

PHENOLS

The phenols are compounds having a hydroxyl group attached directly to an aromatic nucleus. In general their methods of preparation and reactions differ from those of the alcohols.

Occurrence and Nomenclature

The name *phenol* for hydroxybenzene is derived from *phene*, an old name for benzene (p. 535). The hydroxy derivatives of toluene have the common name *cresols*, and those of xylene are called *xylenols*. Phenols in general are named as derivatives of phenol.

CH₃
OH

o-Cresol
(*o*-methylphenol)

NH₂

OH
p-Aminophenol

Phenol, cresols, and xylenols occur in coal tar, wood tar, and petroleum distillates along with other phenolic compounds and are known as *tar acids*. The mixed phenols from the cresol fraction is known technically as *cresylic acid*. Derivatives of phenols frequently occur as plant products (pp. 515, 516).

Structure

Whereas the enol forms of simple aldehydes and ketones are unstable and pass almost completely into the keto forms, most phenols exist entirely in the enol form. The greater stability of the enol form for the phenols is due to its high resonance energy, compared with that of the keto form. The situation is exactly analogous to that discussed for the aromatic amines (p. 475).

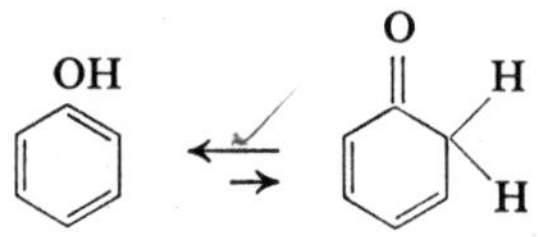

OH

O
‖ H
H

Preparation

This section summarizes the general methods discussed previously.

1. From Aromatic Sulfonic Acids (p. 468).

$$\text{ArSO}_3\text{Na} + 2\,\text{NaOH} \xrightarrow[300°]{\text{Fusion}} \text{ArONa} + \text{Na}_2\text{SO}_3 + 2\,\text{H}_2\text{O}$$

2. From Aryl Halides.

$$\text{ArCl} + 2\,\text{NaOH} \longrightarrow \text{ArONa} + \text{NaCl} + \text{H}_2\text{O}$$

This reaction goes readily only if the halogen is activated by electron-attracting groups (p. 461), but it is applied industrially to nonreactive halides by using a catalyst and a high temperature (p. 510).

3. **From Diazonium Salts** (p. 494).

$$[Ar\overset{+}{N_2}]\overset{-}{O}SO_3H + H_2O \xrightarrow{\text{Heat}} ArOH + N_2 + H_2SO_4$$

Physical Properties

The pure phenols are colorless solids or liquids, although as usually encountered they are colored red by oxidation products. Like the aromatic amines (p. 476), they boil higher than the normal aliphatic analogs of the same molecular weight. For example, phenol boils at 181° whereas 1-hexanol boils at 157°. Phenol is soluble in water to the extent of 9 g. per 100 g. of water at 25° and becomes miscible at 65°. Water is soluble in phenol to the extent of 29 g. per 100 g. Since the melting point of phenol is only 42°, a small amount of water lowers the melting point below room temperature. This liquid form containing about 5 per cent water is called **carbolic acid**. In the monosubstituted phenols, the *para* isomer has the highest melting point.

Reactions

REACTIONS INVOLVING THE HYDROXYL GROUP

1. **Acidity.** Phenols are considerably more acidic than alcohols or water, but weaker than carboxylic acids and weaker even than carbonic acid. Thus the acid dissociation constant of acetic acid is 1.8×10^{-5}; carbonic, 4.3×10^{-7}; hydrocyanic, 7.2×10^{-10}; phenol, 1.3×10^{-10}; and water, 1.8×10^{-16}. Hence phenols react with sodium hydroxide solutions to form water-soluble salts but not with aqueous sodium carbonate. Moreover water-insoluble phenols are precipitated from their salts by carbonic acid.

$$ArOH + NaOH \longrightarrow [Ar\overset{-}{O}]\overset{+}{Na} + H_2O$$

$$[Ar\overset{-}{O}]\overset{+}{Na} + CO_2 + H_2O \longrightarrow ArOH + NaHCO_3$$

These reactions are used to distinguish phenols and to separate them from alcohols or carboxylic acids.

These statements apply to phenols which do not contain strongly electron-attracting groups in the nucleus. Thus the acid dissociation constants of some of the nitrophenols are: *o*-nitrophenol, 6.8×10^{-8}; *m*-nitrophenol, 5.3×10^{-9}; *p*-nitrophenol, 6.5×10^{-8}; 2,4-dinitrophenol, 8.3×10^{-5}; and 2,4,6-trinitrophenol (picric acid), 4.2×10^{-1}. In the mononitrophenols, the effect of the nitro group is greater in the *ortho* or *para* position than in the *meta* position. Two nitro groups in the *ortho* and *para* positions give an acid approximately as strong as a carboxylic acid. The strength of picric acid with three nitro groups in the *ortho* and *para* positions approaches that of the mineral acids.

The greater acidity of phenols compared with alcohols can be explained by the overlapping of a *p* orbital of the oxygen atom with a *p* orbital of the adjacent carbon atom, leading to interaction of the unshared pair of electrons of the oxygen atom with the unsaturation electrons of the nucleus as indicated for chlorobenzene (Fig. 76, p. 453) and aniline (Fig. 78, p. 477).

This resonance effect decreases the electron density on the oxygen atom and permits loss of a proton more easily from a phenol than from an alcohol. The resonance effect in phenols is not so pronounced as in the carboxylic acids (p. 153), because the extreme resonance structures of the phenoxide ion (p. 454) are not equivalent as are those of the carboxylate ion. This factor, together with the lack of the inductive effect of the second oxygen atom, accounts for the lower acidity of phenols when compared with carboxylic acids. The inductive and resonance effects of nitro groups operate to increase the acidity of phenols in the same way that they do to decrease the basicity of aromatic amines (p. 477).

2. **Colored Complexes with Ferric Chloride.** Enols in general give colored water-soluble complexes with ferric chloride. The exact nature of these colored compounds is uncertain, although it seems likely that a coordination compound is formed in which the iron is hexacovalent. The reaction with phenols probably is complicated by the formation of colored oxidation products (p. 505). Whereas with simple enols the color produced is a burgundy red, the phenols give colors that are less pure and usually purplish or greenish. This reaction is a convenient test for phenols and other enols.

3. **Ester Formation.** Phenols do not esterify directly with carboxylic acids. Esters can be prepared by reaction with anhydrides or acid chlorides.

$$\underset{\text{Phenol}}{C_6H_5OH} + (CH_3CO)_2O \xrightarrow{\text{(H}_2\text{SO}_4)} \underset{\text{Phenyl acetate}}{C_6H_5OCOCH_3} + HOCOCH_3$$

$$C_6H_5OH + CH_3COCl \longrightarrow C_6H_5OCOCH_3 + HCl$$

4. **Ether Formation.** Phenols form ethers very easily by the Williamson synthesis (p. 137). Since sodium aryl oxides are hydrolyzed only partially in aqueous solution, the reaction can be carried out in this medium.

$$ArONa + XR \longrightarrow ArOR + NaX$$

The methyl ethers are most important, because they can be prepared readily by agitating an alkaline solution of the phenol with methyl sulfate.

$$[C_6H_5\overset{-}{O}]\overset{+}{Na} + (CH_3)_2SO_4 \longrightarrow \underset{\substack{\text{Anisole} \\ \text{(methyl phenyl} \\ \text{ether)}}}{C_6H_5OCH_3} + CH_3HSO_4$$

Sodium phenoxide

Ethyl phenyl ether is known as *phenetole*. *Phenyl ether* (phenyl oxide) is a co-product of one of the commercial methods for the synthesis of phenol (p. 510).

5. **Replacement by Halogen.** The hydroxyl group of phenols, unlike that of alcohols, is difficult to replace by halogen. Halogen acids are without action, and phosphorus trihalides yield only phosphorous esters. If phosphorus pentachloride or pentabromide is used, some replacement occurs, but the reaction is not used for preparative purposes.

$$ArOH + PX_5 \longrightarrow ArX + POX_3 + HX$$

6. **Replacement by Hydrogen.** When phenols are heated with zinc dust the oxygen is removed from the molecule.

$$ArOH + Zn \xrightarrow{\text{Heat}} ArH + ZnO$$

The reaction, although of no value for synthesis, has been useful in arriving at the fundamental structure of aromatic products. The method was used first by Baeyer in his elucidation of the structure of indigo (p. 684).

7. **Replacement by the Amino Group.** Equilibrium can be established between phenol, aniline, water, and ammonia (p. 481). Ordinarily the replacement of a hydroxyl group by an amino group is brought about by heating the phenol with the complex of ammonia and zinc chloride or of ammonia and calcium chloride.

$$4\,ArOH + Zn(NH_3)_4Cl_2 \longrightarrow 4\,ArNH_2 + Zn(H_2O)_4Cl_2$$

REACTIONS INVOLVING THE NUCLEUS

1. **Oxidation.** Like the amino group in aromatic amines, the hydroxyl group can supply electrons to the nucleus and permits ready oxidation. Complex mixtures of oxidation products are formed by either air or other oxidizing agents. One of the oxidation products of phenol by air is *quinone* (p. 520), which forms a brilliant red addition product with phenol known as *phenoquinone*.

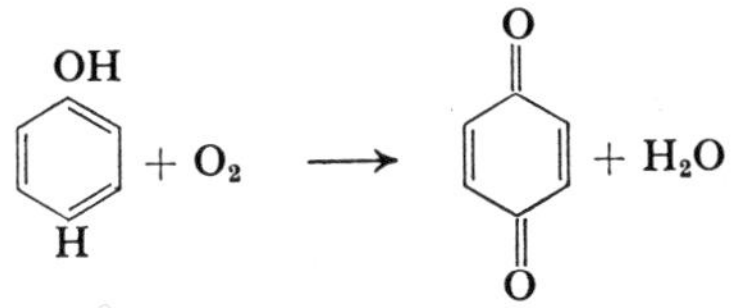

Quinone

$$C_6H_4O_2 + 2\,C_6H_5OH \longrightarrow C_6H_4O_2 \cdot 2\,C_6H_5OH$$
Phenoquinone

The X-ray diffraction pattern of crystalline phenoquinone indicates that the quinone molecule is sandwiched between the two phenol molecules with the planes of the benzene rings parallel. The bonding forces in such complexes are analogous to those in complexes formed by polynitro compounds (p. 461).

2. **Sulfonation.** Because of the strong activating effect of the hydroxyl group, sulfonation takes place very readily. At room temperature concentrated sulfuric acid yields chiefly the *ortho* isomer, whereas at 100° the *para* isomer predominates.

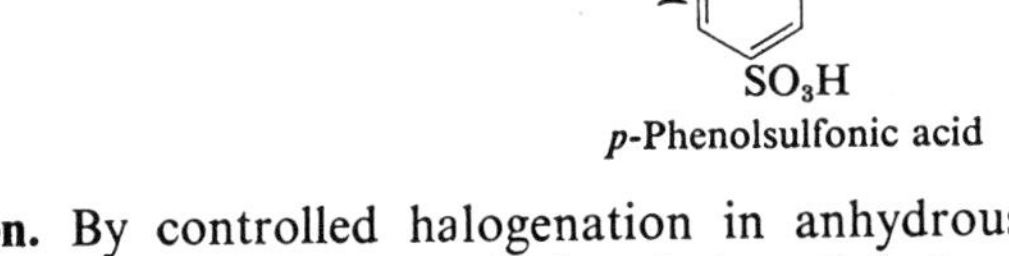

o-Phenolsulfonic acid

p-Phenolsulfonic acid

3. **Halogenation.** By controlled halogenation in anhydrous solvents, it is possible to obtain the monohalogenated phenols in satisfactory yields.

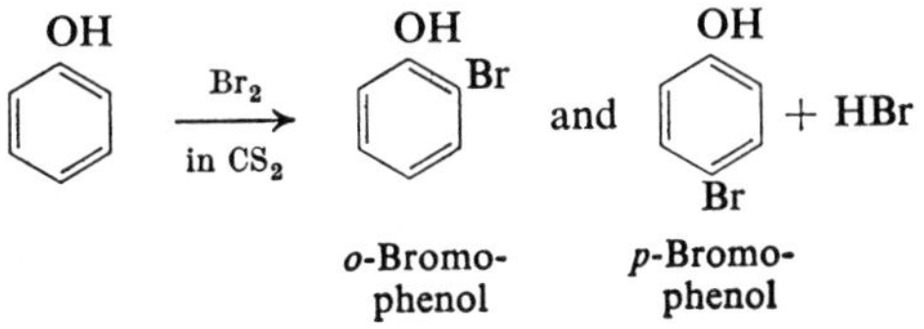

o-Bromo-
phenol

p-Bromo-
phenol

When bromine water is added to an aqueous solution of phenol, a quinonoid tetrabromo derivative precipitates. Addition of sodium bisulfite produces 2,4,6-tribromophenol.

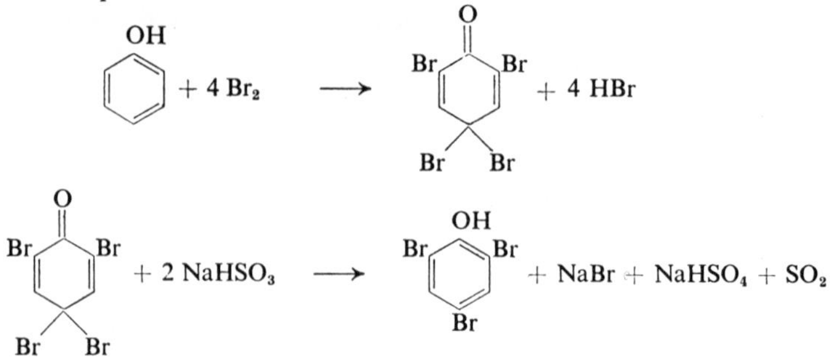

4. **Nitrosation.** The activating effect of the hydroxyl group is so great that phenol reacts with nitrous acid to give **p-nitrosophenol.** This compound is tautomeric with the monoxime of quinone (p. 520).

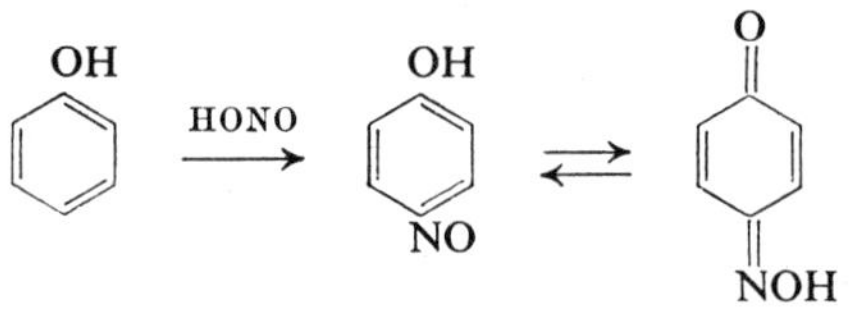

p-Nitroso-   Quinone
phenol   monoxime

If the reaction is carried out in the presence of concentrated sulfuric acid, further condensation with phenol takes place to give a dark blue solution of phenolindophenol acid sulfate. When the acid solution is diluted with water, the red **phenolindophenol** is liberated. When excess sodium hydroxide is added, the deep blue sodium salt is formed.

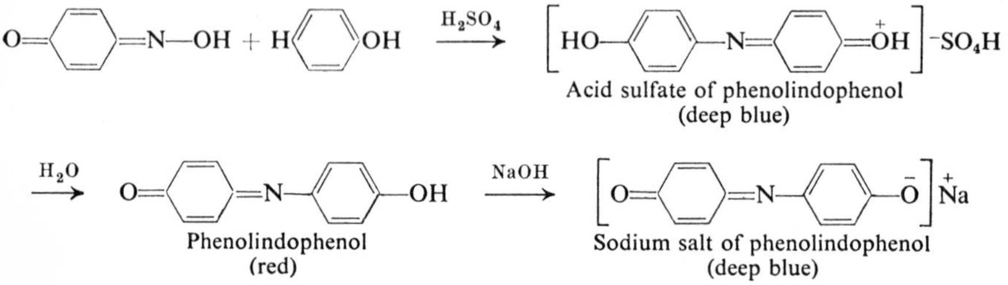

Acid sulfate of phenolindophenol
(deep blue)

Phenolindophenol   Sodium salt of phenolindophenol
(red)   (deep blue)

Compounds of this type are called phenolindophenols, because they are hydroxy analogs of indophenol which contains an amino group instead of a hydroxyl group. The reaction is used as a test for nitrites and is known as the **Liebermann nitroso reaction.**[1] Even some nitrates and aliphatic nitro compounds give the test, since reduction to nitrite takes place in the concentrated sulfuric acid solution.

---

[1] Carl Theodor Liebermann (1842–1914), professor at the Berlin Technische Hochschule. His work dealt chiefly with natural dyes and with the chemistry of anthracene (p. 596).

The deep blue color in either strongly basic or strongly acidic solutions is due to the complete resonance of the ions (p. 667).

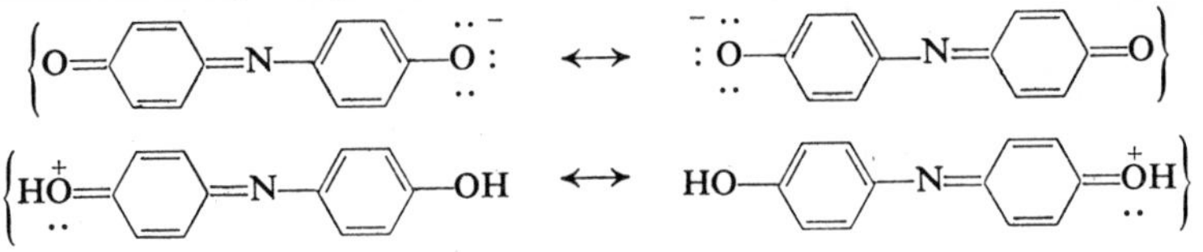

5. Nitration. Phenol nitrates so rapidly that if mononitration is desired, dilute nitric acid at room temperature is used.

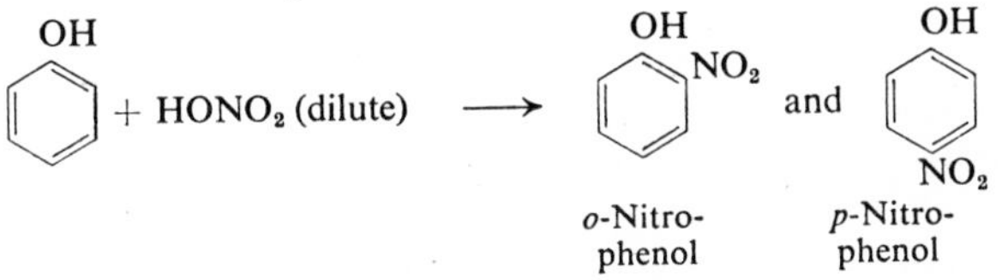

o-Nitro-
phenol

p-Nitro-
phenol

The isomers can be separated by steam distillation, since the *ortho* isomer is much more volatile.

Ortho, meta, and para isomers usually boil within 10° of each other, but *o*-nitrophenol boils at 214° and *p*-nitrophenol boils at 245°. The *ortho* isomer also is less soluble in water than the *meta* or *para* compound. Thus the *ortho* isomer has much less tendency to associate with itself or with other hydroxylic compounds. An explanation of this behavior is that the spatial arrangement of the groups permits the hydrogen atom of the hydroxyl group in the *ortho* isomer to form an internal proton bond with the nitro group in the *ortho* position but not with a nitro group in the *meta* or *para* position.

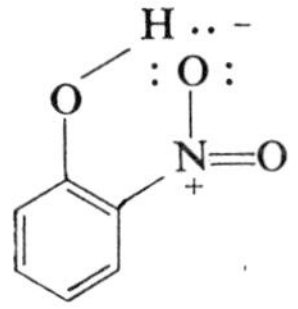

Nonassociated
o-nitrophenol

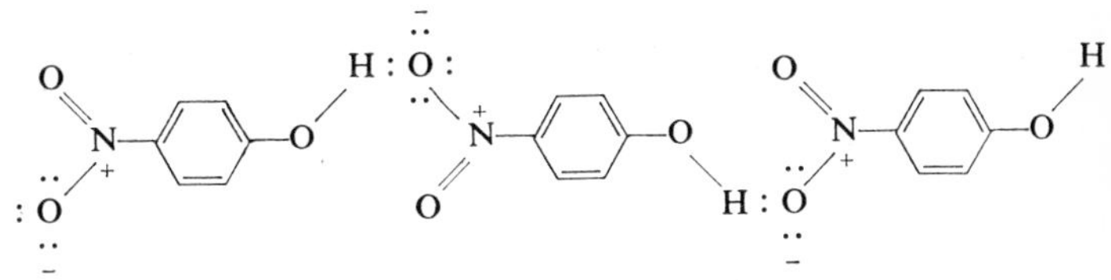

Associated *p*-nitrophenol

Nitration of phenol with concentrated nitric acid gives 2,4,6-trinitrophenol (picric acid), but the amount of oxidation is excessive, and indirect methods of preparation are used. The nitrophenols are colorless or pale yellow. Their salts are deep yellow (p. 666).

The nitration of phenols by dilute nitric acid appears to result from nitrosation followed by oxidation of the nitroso group by nitric acid (p. 448). If urea is added to destroy nitrous acid present in the nitric acid or formed by reduction of the nitric acid by the phenol, no nitration takes place.

6. Ring Alkylation. Because of the activating effect of the hydroxyl group, phenols alkylate in the aromatic ring much more readily than hydrocarbons. Usually warming the phenol with an olefin or an alcohol in the presence of sulfuric acid is sufficient for reaction.

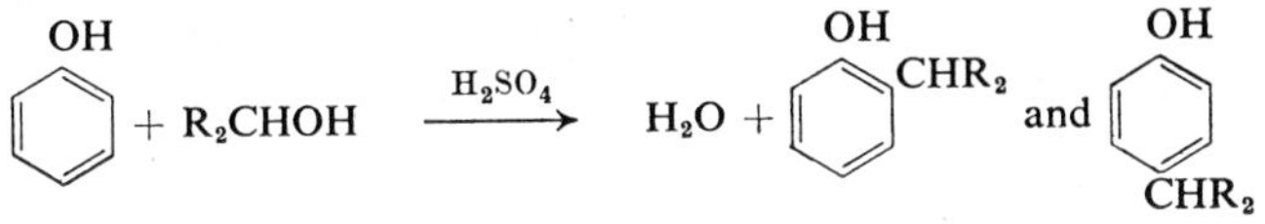

7. Condensation with Aldehydes and Ketones. The activating effect of the hydroxyl group also permits condensation with aldehydes and ketones in the *ortho* and *para* positions. Thus phenol undergoes an aldol-type condensation with formaldehyde in the presence of dilute alkali (*Lederer-Manasse reaction*).

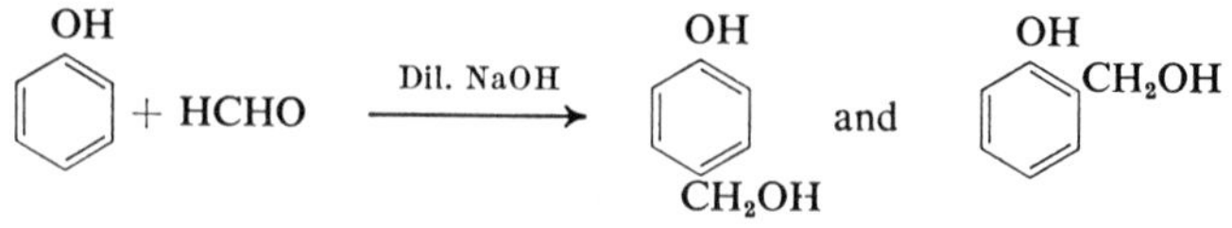

p-Hydroxy-
benzyl
alcohol

o-Hydroxybenzyl
alcohol
(saligenin)

Unless the reaction is controlled carefully, these products undergo further condensation to yield phenol-formaldehyde resins (p. 511).

Aldehydes which resinify in the presence of alkali condense with phenols under acid conditions, usually with two molecules of phenol.

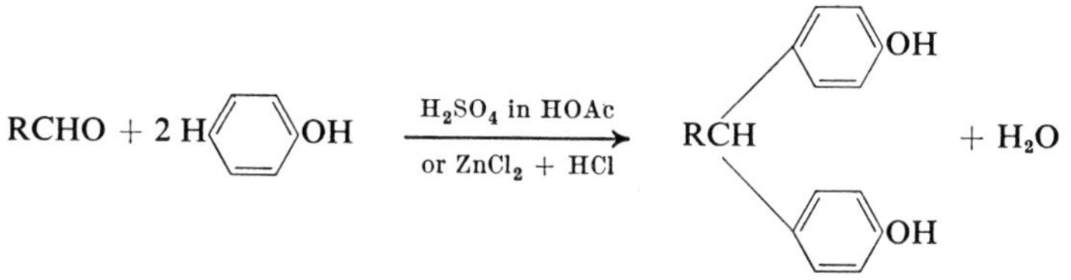

At higher temperatures ketones give the same type of reaction.

The condensation with aldehydes or ketones is a typical substitution reaction. In alkaline solution the formation of the phenoxide ion greatly increases the electron density of the aromatic ring, permitting attack by the carbonyl carbon atom at the *ortho* and *para* positions with ready formation of the transition state.

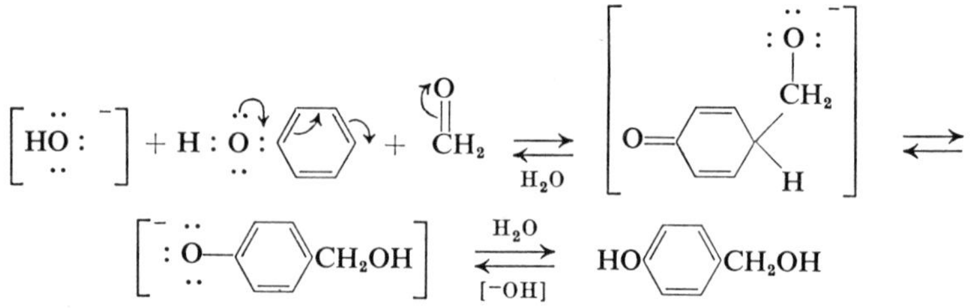

In acid solution, the formation of the oxonium salt of the aldehyde or ketone makes the carbonyl carbon atom a stronger electron-seeking reagent.

8. Mannich Reaction. The *ortho* and *para* hydrogen atoms in phenols are sufficiently reactive to undergo the *Mannich reaction* with formaldehyde and secondary amines. Phenol gives the trisubstitution product, and *p*-cresol gives a mixture of mono- and disubstitution products.

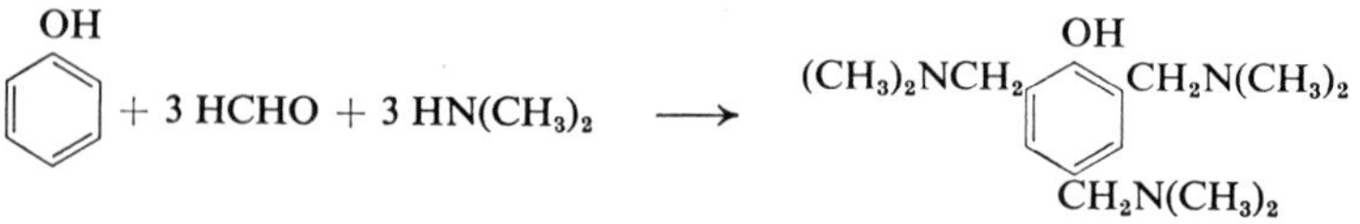

The Mannich reaction is fairly general for compounds having reactive hydrogen atoms. Thus thiophene (p. 608) and compounds having hydrogen α to a carbonyl group (p. 767) or acetylenic hydrogen also condense with formaldehyde and amines.

Physiological Action

All phenols having a sufficiently high vapor pressure have a characteristic odor. Phenol is highly toxic, killing all types of cells. It precipitates proteins, and, when applied to the skin, produces a white spot which soon turns red; later the dead skin sloughs. If allowed to remain in contact with the skin, it penetrates to the deeper tissues and severe burns result. It also is absorbed into the blood stream and acts as a systemic poison. Phenol is eliminated in the urine as sodium phenyl sulfate, $C_6H_5OSO_3Na$. Frequently other toxic aromatic compounds, for example naphthalene and bromobenzene, are detoxified in the body by oxidation to the phenol and elimination as the ester of sulfuric acid.

The phenols in general are toxic to microorganisms. Although many substances had been discovered empirically to have a preservative and healing action long before the nature of bacterial infection was known, phenol itself was the first compound to be used widely for the avowed purpose of antisepsis. It was introduced by Lister in 1867. Much more effective and less toxic compounds have been developed since then, but antiseptic activity still is reported in terms of the *phenol coefficient*, a number which compares the effectiveness of a preparation with that of a 5 per cent solution of phenol against *Staphylococcus aureus*.

Phenol and Some Important Derivatives

Phenol in 1955 held third place among the synthetic aromatic chemicals, the volume of production being exceeded only by styrene (p. 573) and ethylbenzene (p. 430). The quantity produced in the United States by synthesis was 8 million pounds in 1928, 274 million pounds in 1948, and 475 million pounds in 1955. In the same years the amount of natural phenol obtained from coal tar was 2, 23, and 38 million pounds. About 4 million pounds was obtained also from the refining of petroleum.

Production of Phenol. Numerous processes have been developed for the synthesis of phenol. At least four different processes are competitive in the United States.

1. SULFONATION AND CAUSTIC FUSION. This process is the oldest. It was discovered independently in 1867 by Kekulé, Wurtz, and Dusart. The commercial application originally involved sulfonation with fuming sulfuric acid, conversion to the sodium salt by liming out (p. 467), and fusion with sodium hydroxide. In 1918 a continuous process was developed in which a large excess of benzene runs counter-current to the sulfonating acid, which starts out at a concentration of 98 per cent and ends up as 77 per cent. The sulfonic acid remains dissolved in the benzene at a concentration of 2 per cent. It is washed out with water and neutralized with sodium sulfite recovered from the caustic fusion. The solution of sodium salt is concentrated and run into fused sodium hydroxide at 320°–350°. The melt is treated with a minimum of water to dissolve the sodium phenoxide,

leaving the sodium sulfite undissolved. The phenol is liberated or *sprung* by passing carbon dioxide into the solution. The sodium carbonate is reconverted to caustic soda by the addition of lime, and the calcium carbonate that precipitates is converted to carbon dioxide and lime in the lime kilns. Alternatively the phenol may be liberated with sulfur dioxide formed when the benzenesulfonic acid is converted to the sodium salt, or the benzenesulfonic acid itself may be used. With the exception of losses, only benzene, sodium hydroxide, and sulfuric acid are consumed in the process, the products being phenol and sodium bisulfite (or sulfur dioxide and sodium sulfite). The over-all process therefore is the oxidation of benzene by sulfuric acid. Since sulfuric acid is made by the oxidation of sulfur dioxide with air, the latter is the ultimate oxidizing agent.

2. HYDROLYSIS OF CHLOROBENZENE (DOW PROCESS). Since 1928 phenol has been manufactured in large quantities by the hydrolysis of chlorobenzene, which is emulsified with 10 per cent sodium hydroxide solution and then circulated and recirculated with turbulation in copper-lined iron tubes at 320°. The product is bled out of the system at the rate at which the original emulsion enters, making the process continuous. Almost 100 per cent reaction occurs. Besides phenol, about 20 per cent of phenyl ether and smaller amounts of o- and p-phenylphenol are formed.

$$C_6H_5Cl + 2\,NaOH \longrightarrow C_6H_5ONa + NaCl + H_2O$$

$$C_6H_5Cl + NaOC_6H_5 \longrightarrow C_6H_5OC_6H_5 + NaCl$$
Phenyl ether

$$C_6H_5Cl + C_6H_5ONa + NaOH \longrightarrow$$

The phenyl ether is extracted with chlorobenzene and the phenol is liberated with hydrochloric acid. The phenol is purified and separated from the phenyl-phenols by distillation.

Some phenyl ether is used in the perfume industry, and a large quantity is used to form with biphenyl (p. 578) a eutectic mixture, which serves as a heat transfer medium in industrial operations. This mixture of 74 parts of phenyl ether and 26 parts of biphenyl is stable up to 400° at 135 p.s.i. If the amount of phenyl ether produced during the manufacture of phenol is greater than the demand, it can be recycled, since at 320° in the presence of sodium hydroxide it is in equilibrium with sodium phenoxide.

$$C_6H_5OC_6H_5 + 2\,NaOH \rightleftharpoons 2\,C_6H_5ONa + H_2O$$

3. RASCHIG PROCESS. This process was introduced into the United States from Germany about 1940. As in the Dow process two stages are involved, the chlorination of benzene and hydrolysis. However hydrogen chloride and air replace electrolytic chlorine, water replaces caustic soda, and the process is carried out in the vapor phase. In the first stage benzene, hydrogen chloride, and air are passed over a catalyst.

$$C_6H_6 + HCl + \tfrac{1}{2} O_2 \text{ (air)} \xrightarrow[\text{Cu–Fe cat.}]{230°} C_6H_5Cl + H_2O$$

Although carried out in one step, the process undoubtedly involves the intermediate formation of chlorine by the old Deacon process from hydrogen chloride and air in the presence of cupric chloride. The conversion is about 10 per cent per pass, but the chlorobenzene is separated readily and the unchanged reagents are recycled.

In the second stage the chlorobenzene is hydrolyzed with water. Here again the conversion is about 10 per cent.

$$C_6H_5Cl + H_2O \xrightarrow{\;425° \,+\, cat.\;} C_6H_5OH + HCl$$

The recovery of hydrogen chloride for use in the first stage is about 97 per cent. About 10 per cent of co-products are formed including 6 per cent of dichlorobenzene in the first stage. This process like the first is an indirect air oxidation of benzene.

4. FROM CUMENE. Since 1954 phenol has been synthesized starting with cumene, prepared from benzene and propylene (p. 430). Oxidation by air gives cumene hydroperoxide (p. 874). Strong acids catalyze the decomposition of the hydroperoxide into phenol and acetone.

$$C_6H_5CH(CH_3)_2 + O_2 \text{ (air)} \longrightarrow \underset{\displaystyle O-OH}{C_6H_5C(CH_3)_2} \xrightarrow{\;H_2SO_4\;} C_6H_5OH + (CH_3)_2CO$$

Cumene   Cumene hydroperoxide

Small amounts of methanol, acetophenone (p. 541), and α-methylstyrene (p. 575) also are formed

The acid-catalyzed decomposition takes place by an ionic mechanism. The strong acid removes hydroxide ion from the hydroperoxide to give an intermediate ion with a positive charge on oxygen. Migration of the phenyl group and acquisition of a molecule of water gives the oxonium salt of a hemiacetal which decomposes into phenol, acetone, and a proton.

$$\underset{\displaystyle O-OH}{C_6H_5C(CH_3)_2} \underset{H_2O}{\overset{[H^+]}{\rightleftarrows}} \left[C_6H_5\overset{\displaystyle O^+}{\underset{\displaystyle}{C(CH_3)_2}} \right] \rightleftarrows \left[\underset{\displaystyle {}^+C(CH_3)_2}{OC_6H_5} \right] \overset{H_2O}{\rightleftarrows}$$

$$\underset{\displaystyle H_2\overset{+}{O}C(CH_3)_2}{OC_6H_5} \rightleftarrows \underset{\displaystyle HO\overset{}{C}(CH_3)_2}{\overset{+}{H}OC_6H_5} \longrightarrow [H^+] + HOC_6H_5 + O{=}C(CH_3)_2$$

Uses of Phenol and Its Derivatives. The chief use for phenol is for the manufacture of phenol-formaldehyde resins and plastics. Production of these *phenolics* in the United States amounted to 563 million pounds in 1955. Although the reaction of phenol and formaldehyde to give resins was reported by Baeyer in 1872, it was not until 1909 that a commercially useful product was developed by Baekeland, a Belgian-born American chemist, who was looking for a substitute for shellac. For a long time the term *Bakelite* was synonymous with phenol-formaldehyde plastics. The trade name now is owned by the Union Carbide and Carbon Corporation and is used to designate all of their plastics except the vinyl polymers (p. 736).

Two general processes of manufacture are in use. The *one-step process* produces cast phenolics, which usually are converted into useful objects by machining. Phenol and somewhat more than one molecular equivalent of aqueous formaldehyde are heated for a short time with a basic catalyst such as ammonia or sodium hydroxide. A *resole* or *A-stage resin* is formed which is fusible and soluble in organic solvents. It is a linear polymer, condensation having taken place in the *ortho* and *para* positions. This molten resin is drawn off and cast into molds which then are heated at 75°–85° until the reaction is complete. During this stage the linear polymeric chains are cross-linked by the excess formaldehyde, and the infusible, insoluble resin is formed.

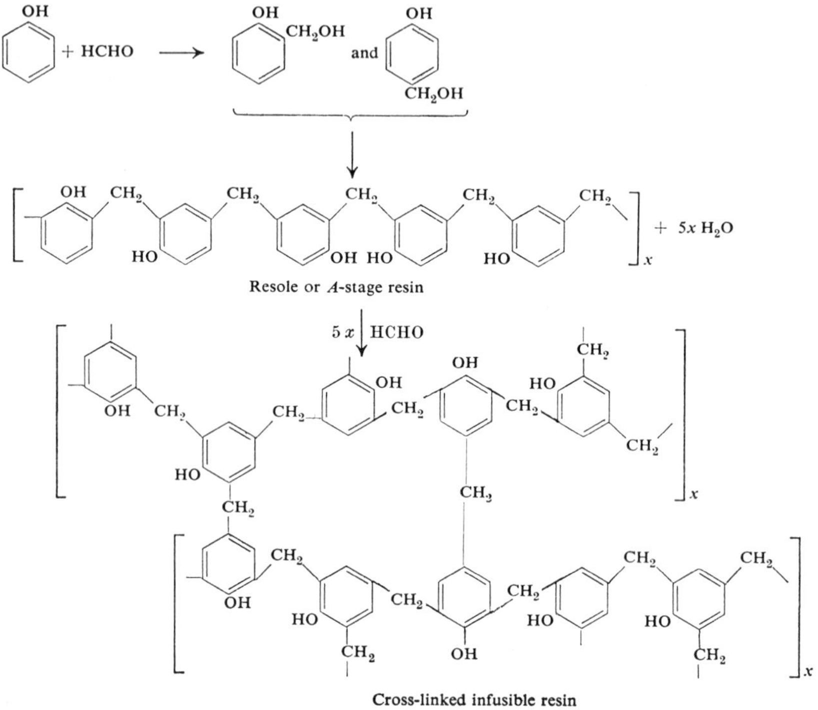

Resole or *A*-stage resin

Cross-linked infusible resin

The above formulas merely indicate possible modes of linkage. In the actual resin these various types of linkage undoubtedly are distributed randomly.

The *two-step process* is used for the compression molding of objects. Phenol and about 0.8 molecular equivalent of formaldehyde is heated with about 0.1 per cent of hydrogen chloride as an acid catalyst. After two hours the water is removed by distillation at reduced pressure, and the resole is run into pans or onto the floor, where it is cooled to a glassy solid. It is broken into pieces which are ground in ball mills with lime to neutralize the acid. It then is mixed with hexamethylenetetramine (p. 221), a mold lubricant such as zinc stearate, a filler such as sawdust, and a brown or black coloring matter. After compacting and granulating, it is known as *molding powder*. When the proper amount of the powder is placed in a mold and subjected to heat and pressure, the material flows to fill the interstices of the mold, and the hexamethylenetetramine supplies the additional formaldehyde and ammonia necessary to produce cross linking and setting of the resin.

The phenol-formaldehyde plastics usually are dark colored. They are brittle, the strength of the finished product being dependent largely on the filler. However they are cheap, have a good finish, high heat resistance and high dielectric strength. If *para*-substituted phenols are used, for example *p*-cresol or *p-t*-butylphenol, the cross-chain reaction is blocked and the product is thermoplastic. About half of the phenolic resin production is used for molding purposes. Most of the remainder is used as a bonding agent in the manufacture of plywood and other laminated materials, and as water-proof adhesives for other purposes.

If a phenolsulfonic acid is condensed with formaldehyde and phenol, the resulting resin contains sulfonic acid groups and can act as an ion-exchange material. The chief use is for softening water. Hard water contains alkaline earth and heavy metal salts which form insoluble precipitates with soaps (p. 188) and deposit insoluble salts in water heaters and boilers. When such water is passed over the sodium salt of an ion-exchange material, these undesirable ions are replaced by sodium ions, the salts of which are more soluble.

$$\left[\text{—} \bigcirc \text{SO}_3^-\text{Na}^+ \right]_x + x\,\text{M}^+\text{A}^- \rightleftharpoons \left[\text{—} \bigcirc \text{SO}_3^-\text{M}^+ \right]_x + x\,\text{Na}^+\text{A}^-$$

In the above equilibrium M^+ is any cation and A^- any anion, which need not be monovalent. When exchange has taken place to the extent that the undesirable cations no longer are removed sufficiently from solution, the ion exchanger is regenerated by allowing it to stand with a concentrated salt solution, which shifts the equilibrium to the left. Sulfonated polystyrenes (p. 575) behave in the same way.

If the ion-exchange resin is used as the free acid, it exchanges hydrogen ions for other cations and can be regenerated with concentrated hydrochloric acid.

$$\left[\text{—} \bigcirc \text{SO}_3^-\text{H}^+ \right]_x + x\,\text{M}^+\text{A}^- \rightleftharpoons \left[\text{—} \bigcirc \text{SO}_3^-\text{M}^+ \right]_x + x\,\text{H}^+\text{A}^-$$

A solution which has exchanged its metallic ions for hydrogen ions can be passed over a basic resin, such as one produced by condensing *m*-phenylenediamine (p. 475) with formaldehyde, to give substantially ion-free water.

$$\left[\bigcirc \begin{smallmatrix} \text{NH}_2 \\ \text{NH}_2 \end{smallmatrix} \right]_x + 2x\,\text{H}^+\text{A}^- \longrightarrow \left[\bigcirc \begin{smallmatrix} \text{NH}_3^+\text{A}^- \\ \text{NH}_3^+\text{A}^- \end{smallmatrix} \right]_x$$

When the basic resin is converted fully to its salt, it can be regenerated with sodium hydroxide solution.

Since the aromatic amino groups are only weakly basic (p. 477), these resins are not very efficient for removing weak acids. To provide groups that are more basic and have a high capacity, polybasic aliphatic amines such as tetraethylene-pentamine (p. 755) are condensed with the aromatic diamine and formaldehyde (Mannich reaction, p. 508), or a tertiary amine is formed which can be converted to a quaternary hydroxide.

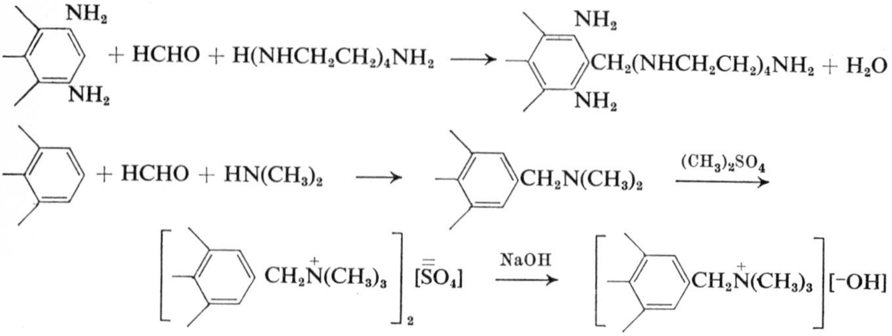

Bisphenol-A is the condensation product from acetone and two moles of phenol.

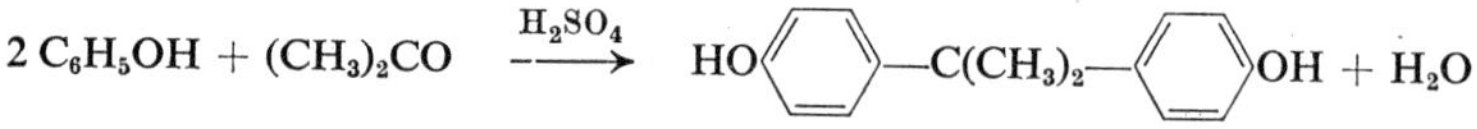

$$2\ C_6H_5OH + (CH_3)_2CO \xrightarrow{H_2SO_4} HO\!\!-\!\!\bigcirc\!\!-\!\!C(CH_3)_2\!\!-\!\!\bigcirc\!\!-\!\!OH + H_2O$$

It is an important intermediate for the production of epoxy resins (p. 750). **Pentachlorophenol** dissolved in oil is used extensively for treating wood to prevent destruction by fungi and termites. The sodium salt is used to treat industrial water to prevent the growth of slime and algae. The salts and esters of the halogenated phenoxy aliphatic acids are important selective weed killers. **2,4-Dichlorophenoxyacetic acid** (*2-4-D*) is made from sodium 2,4-dichlorophen-oxide and sodium chloroacetate.

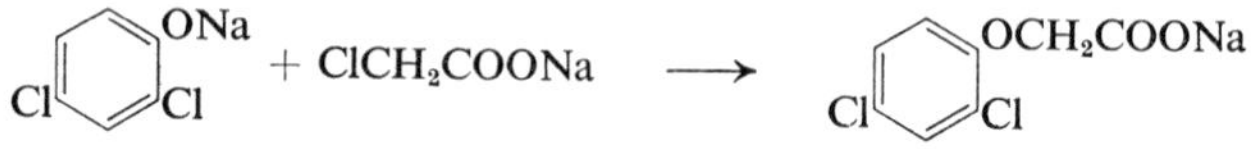

2,4,5-Trichlorophenoxyacetic acid (*2,4,5-T*) is made in the same way from 2,4,5-trichlorophenol. The latter compound results from the hydrolysis of 1,2,4,5-tetrachlorobenzene obtained by direct chlorination of benzene.

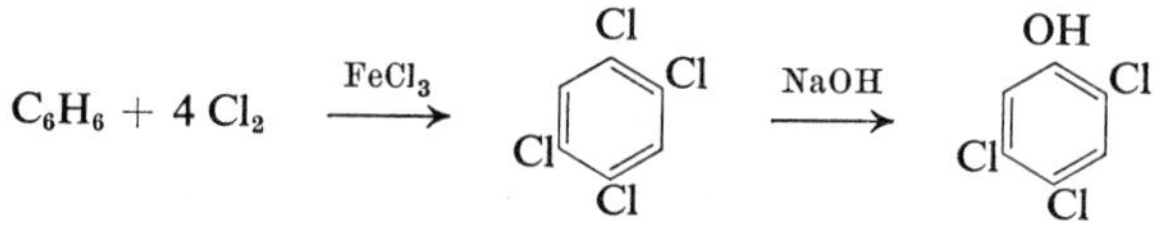

2,4,6-Trinitrophenol, because of its high acidity and its bitter taste, was given the name **picric acid** (Gr. *pikros*, bitter). At times it has been used as a yellow dye for silk and as a military explosive. In addition to procedures starting with phenol, other processes of manufacture have been developed. For example, if chlorobenzene is nitrated to 2,4-dinitrochlorobenzene, the halogen can be removed readily by hydrolysis and the nitration completed in good yield.

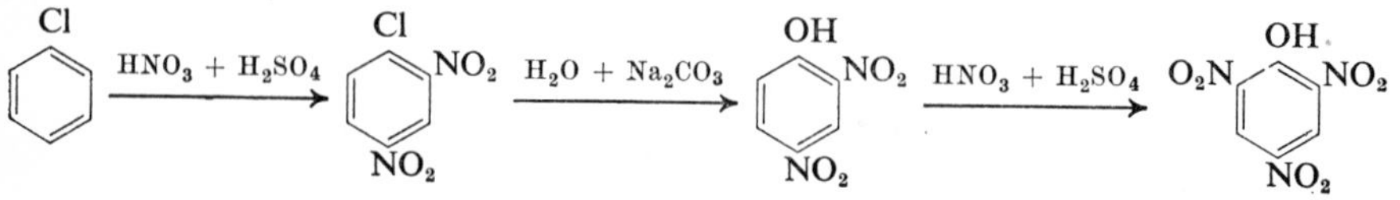

The aromatic ring of trinitrophenol is oxidized by alkaline hypochlorite to give **chloropicrin** (trichloronitromethane, p. 264).

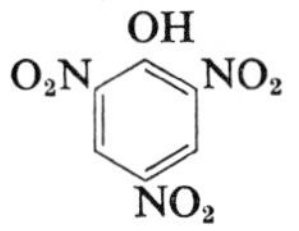

$$\text{(O}_2\text{N)(NO}_2\text{)C}_6\text{H}_2(\text{OH})(\text{NO}_2) + 11\ \text{NaOCl} \longrightarrow 3\ \text{Cl}_3\text{CNO}_2 + 3\ \text{Na}_2\text{CO}_3 + 3\ \text{NaOH} + 2\ \text{NaCl}$$

The *aryl phosphates* are made by the reaction of the phenol with phosphorus oxychloride.

$$3\ \text{ArOH} + \text{POCl}_3 \longrightarrow (\text{ArO})_3\text{PO} + 3\ \text{HCl}$$

They are used extensively as plasticizers and flame retarders. **Phenyl phosphate** (triphenyl phosphate) is used in photographic film base to increase flexibility, to produce flat sheets, and to decrease flammability. Technical **tricresyl phosphate,** prepared from the mixed cresols, is one of the most important of the plasticizers, particularly for vinyl polymers. It is used also as a nonflammable hydraulic fluid and as an additive for lubricating oils. More recently it has been added to gasoline under the trade name **TCP** to prevent preignition and the fouling of spark plugs. Production in the United States in 1955 was 34 million pounds.

Creosote oil, a coal, wood, or petroleum tar fraction boiling at $225°-270°$, contains considerable amounts of the **cresols** and is used on a large scale for wood preservation. **p-Cresol** is synthesized from the hydroperoxide formed by the air-oxidation of *p*-cymene (cf. phenol from cumene, p. 511). **Thymol,** *3-hydroxy-4-isopropyltoluene*, occurs in thyme oil. In the absence of a sufficient supply of the natural product, it is synthesized from *m*-cresol and propylene (p. 430). Alkylation of *p*-cresol with isobutylene gives **2,6-di-*t*-butyl-4-methyl-phenol,** which is used widely as an antioxidant (p. 886) for gasoline, lubricating oils, rubber and edible fats and oils. It does not dissolve in dilute aqueous alkali and does not give a color with ferric chloride. Phenols which have large groups in the *ortho* position and do not give the usual reactions of phenols have been called *cryptophenols.*

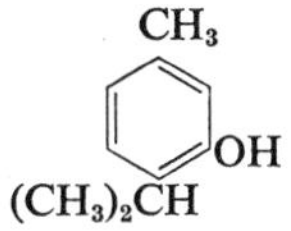

Thymol

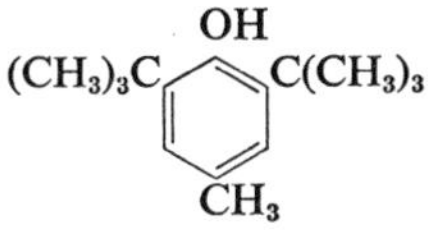

2,6-Di-*t*-butyl-
4-methylphenol

Thymol is antiseptic in high dilutions. It has a more pleasant aromatic odor than phenol or the cresols, and frequently is used in proprietary antiseptic preparations. Thymol is the starting point for the synthesis of menthol (p. 854). **Carvacrol,** *2-hydroxy-4-isopropyltoluene*, also occurs in some essential oils. Many other phenols or phenol ethers are responsible for the aromatic properties of essential oils. **Anethole,** the chief constituent of anise oil, is 4-propenylanisole.

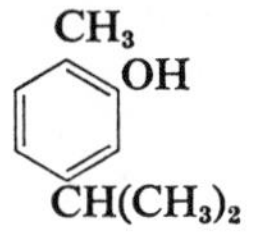

Carvacrol

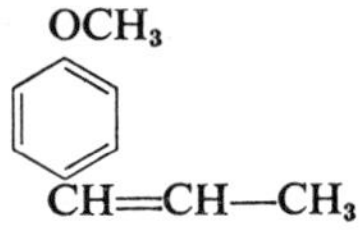

Anethole

Cardanol is a technical product obtained from the oil in cashew nut shells. It is composed principally of the monohydric phenols substituted in the 3 position with an unbranched 15-carbon side chain which may be saturated or contain one, two, or three double bonds. The double bonds are located at the 8, the 8,11, and the 8,11,14 positions. Cardanol is used in the manufacture of certain phenol-formaldehyde resins. Because of the unsaturation in the side-chain these resins have drying properties similar to those of the drying oils, but since they are not esters, they are more resistant to hydrolysis. Moreover the long chain confers a toughness to the resin and overcomes the brittleness usually associated with phenol-formaldehyde resins.

POLYHYDRIC PHENOLS AND AMINOPHENOLS

The *o*-, *m*-, and *p*-dihydroxybenzenes are known as *pyrocatechol, resorcinol,* and *hydroquinone* respectively. **Pyrocatechol** is so named because it is one of the distillation products of *gum catechu*, obtained from certain Asiatic tropical plants. It can be prepared by the general method of synthesis, namely the fusion of sodium *o*-phenolsulfonate with caustic soda, or by the acid hydrolysis of its monomethyl ether (guaiacol). **Guaiacol** occurs in the distillation products of

Guaiacol $\quad$ Pyrocatechol

guaiac, the resin from American tropical trees of the genus *Guaiacum*, but is produced commercially from wood tar. The technical product, because of its antioxidant properties, is used as an anti-skinning agent for paints. Guaiacol carbonate is used as an expectorant in cough remedies. Methylation of guaiacol with methyl sulfate and sodium hydroxide (p. 504) gives the dimethyl ether of pyrocatechol, which is known as **veratrole.** Veratrole also is formed on decarboxylation of veratric acid (p. 561). **Eugenol** from oil of cloves is 2-methoxy-4-allylphenol, and **safrole** from oil of sassafras and from camphor oil is the formaldehyde acetal of 4-allylpyrocatechol. Being an acetal, safrole is hydrolyzed easily by dilute acids.

Guaiacol carbonate $\qquad\qquad$ Eugenol $\qquad\qquad$ Safrole

The toxic irritants of poison ivy (*Rhus toxicodendron*), poison oak (*Rhus diversiloba*), and certain related plants of the *Anacardiaceae* are mixtures of pyrocatechols having unbranched 15-carbon side chains in the 3 position. As with cardanol, four compounds have been isolated from poison ivy in which the side chain is saturated or contains one, two or three double bonds in the 8, the 8,11, and the 8,11,14 positions. Three of the components of **urushiol,** the toxic principle of one of the lac trees (*Rhus vernicifiua*), are identical with three of the compounds obtained from poison ivy, but the triply unsaturated compound has two of the double bonds conjugated in the 12,14 positions.

Resorcinol is a product of the distillation of natural resins but is manufactured by the fusion of sodium *m*-benzenedisulfonate with caustic soda. It undergoes substitution reactions readily in the 4 position. The condensation products with formaldehyde are used as cold-setting adhesives. Resorcinol also is an intermediate for the preparation of azo dyes (p. 676), fluorescein (p. 683), and **n-hexylresorcinol.** The last compound is a popular antiseptic and is synthesized by Clemmensen reduction of hexanoylresorcinol (cf. pp. 216, 539).

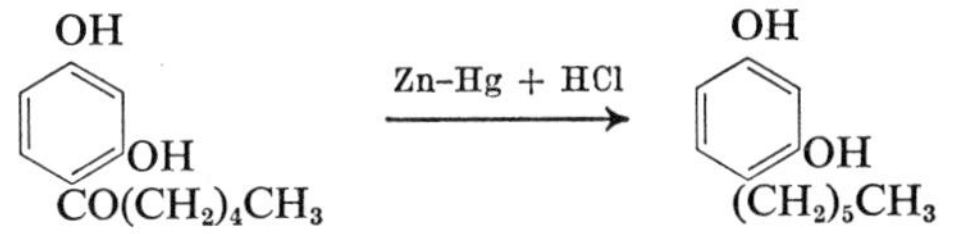

OH　　　　　　　　　　　　　　　OH

　　　　　Zn–Hg + HCl
　　OH　　　　────────→　　　　OH
CO(CH₂)₄CH₃　　　　　　　　　(CH₂)₅CH₃

The antiseptic power of phenol is increased greatly by the substitution of alkyl groups into the nucleus. Thus the cresols are nearly as toxic as phenol, but their phenol coefficients are about 3. As the length of the alkyl group is increased the effectiveness increases up to six carbon atoms, and then decreases. *n*-Hexylphenol is 500 times more effective than phenol. Evidently a hydrocarbon chain of six carbon atoms corresponds to the optimum solubility in water and in fats, both of which are present in cells. The effect of the compound in lowering the surface tension of water also is important.

2,4,6-Trinitroresorcinol is known as **styphnic acid** and like picric acid is used to prepare derivatives of organic compounds (p. 461). **Orcinol,** which can be obtained from certain lichens and aloes, is 5-methylresorcinol. It is used as a reagent to distinguish between pentoses, methylpentoses, and hexoses (p. 379).

Hydroquinone is manufactured by the reduction of quinone (p. 521) with iron and water.

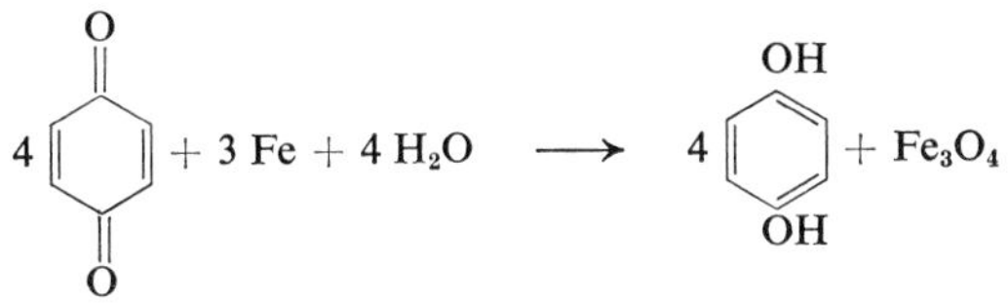

O　　　　　　　　　　　　　　　　　　OH

4 ‖ ‖ + 3 Fe + 4 H₂O ⟶ 4 ‖ ‖ + Fe₃O₄

O　　　　　　　　　　　　　　　　　　OH

Quinone　　　　　　　　　　　　Hydroquinone

Hydroquinone and some of its derivatives, for example the monobenzyl ether, have the undesirable property of causing permanent depigmentation of the skin. **Pyrogallol** (pyrogallic acid) is *1,2,3-trihydroxybenzene* and is prepared by decarboxylating gallic acid, obtained by hydrolysis of gallotannin (p. 561).

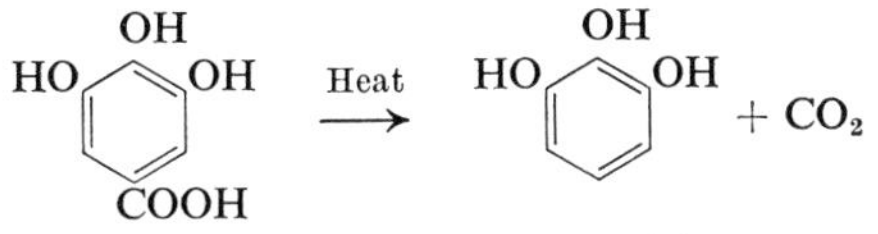

　　　OH　　　　　　　　　　OH
HO　　OH　　Heat　　HO　　OH
　　　‖ ‖　　────→　　　‖ ‖　　+ CO₂
　　COOH

Gallic acid　　　　　　　Pyrogallol

Hydroquinone and pyrogallol are important photographic developers (p. 519). Alkaline pyrogallol solutions absorb oxygen very readily and are used to remove oxygen from mixtures with other gases. Hydroquinone is used extensively to prevent unwanted autoxidation and polymerization of organic compounds (p. 886).

Benzoic acids having hydroxyl or amino groups in the *ortho* and *para* positions decarboxylate more readily than the unsubstituted acid. The resonance effect increases the electron density at the carbon atom bearing the carboxyl group and facilitates displacement of the carboxyl group by a proton.

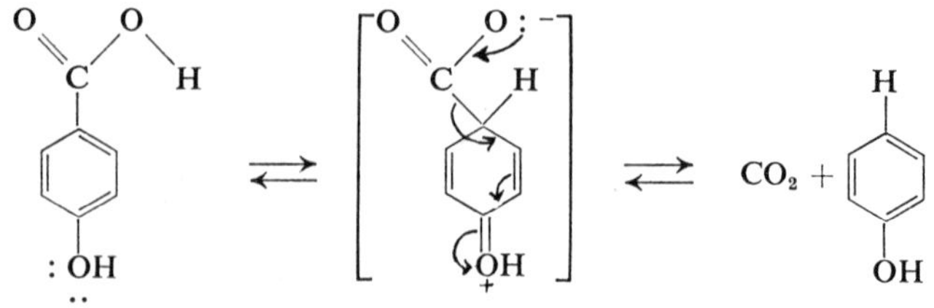

Phloroglucinol (*sym. trihydroxybenzene, 1,3,5-trihydroxybenzene*) is a useful reagent for the estimation of furfural and hence of pentoses (p. 379). It is made by a series of reactions starting with trinitrotoluene,

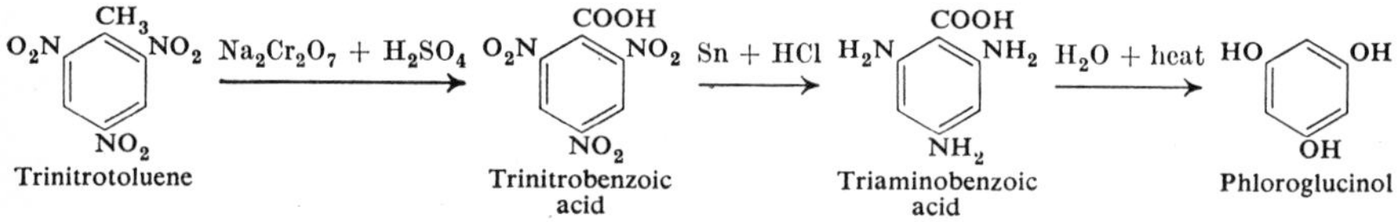

| Trinitrotoluene | Trinitrobenzoic acid | Triaminobenzoic acid | Phloroglucinol |

or by the caustic fusion of quercitin (p. 698).

Whereas simple ketones behave as if very little of the enol form is present and simple phenols behave as if very little of the keto form is present, phloroglucinol reacts as if both forms are present or are in very mobile equilibrium with each other.

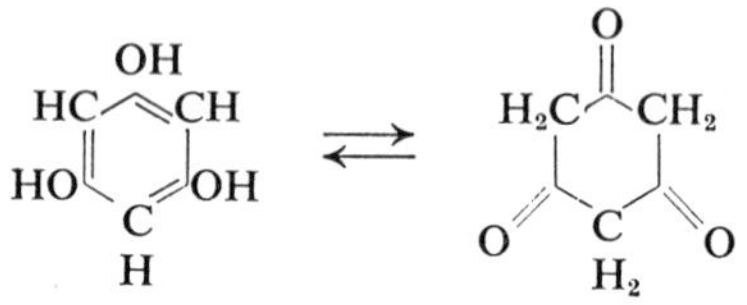

Thus it gives a blue-violet color with ferric chloride and forms a trimethyl ether with diazomethane (p. 266).

On the other hand it reacts with ammonia and with hydroxylamine, reactions characteristic of ketones. It is conceivable that the latter reactions merely indicate that the hydroxyl groups are

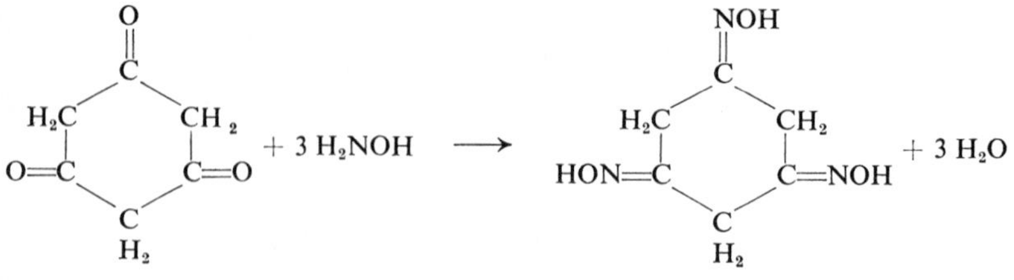

displaced readily and that the trioxime is really the trihydroxylamino derivative of benzene. However when phloroglucinol is alkylated with methyl iodide in alcoholic potassium hydroxide solution, alkylation takes place on carbon rather than on oxygen to give as a final product a hexamethyl derivative which can have only the keto structure.

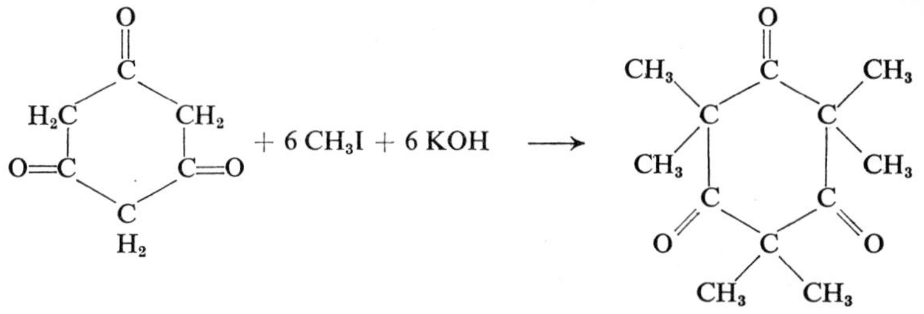

This behavior is characteristic of compounds containing a methylene group between two carbonyl groups (p. 773).

Of the aminophenols, **p-aminophenol** (P.A.P.) is the most important because of its use as a photographic developer. It is made by the nitrosation of phenol followed by reduction.

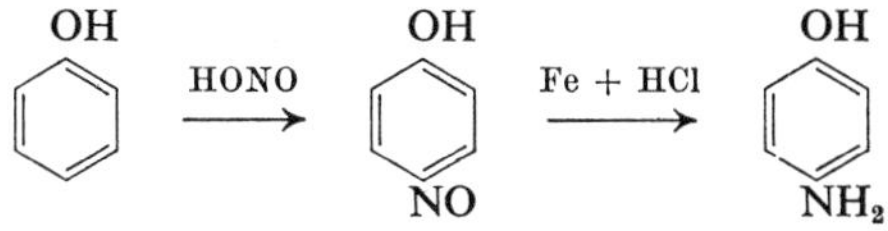

It can be made also by the electrolytic reduction of nitrobenzene in acid solution. *N*-Phenylhydroxylamine is formed which rearranges in acid solution to the salt of *p*-aminophenol.

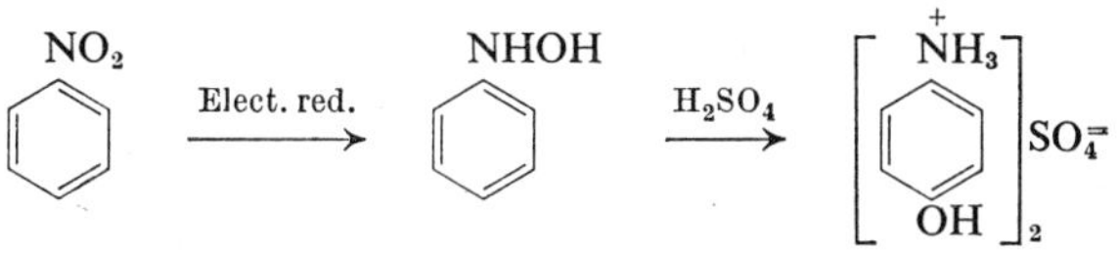

p-Hydroxyphenylglycine (photographer's *Glycine*) is made by the condensation of *p*-aminophenol with sodium chloroacetate.

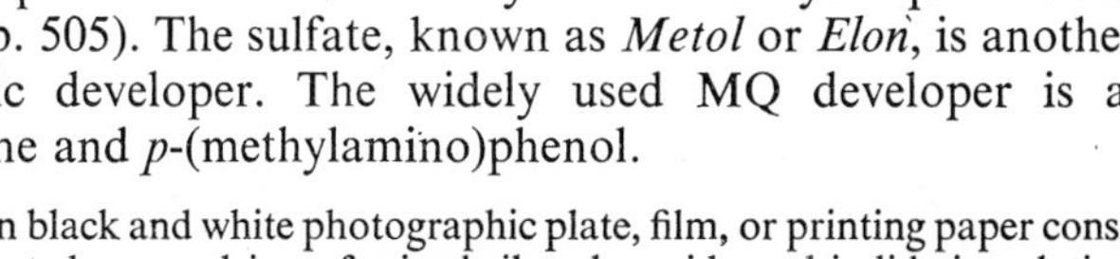

When *p*-hydroxyphenylglycine is heated in a mixture of cresols, decarboxylation takes place to give **p-(methylamino)phenol.** This compound can be made also by heating an aqueous solution of methylamine and hydroquinone in an autoclave at 100° (cf. p. 505). The sulfate, known as *Metol* or *Elon*, is another commercial photographic developer. The widely used MQ developer is a mixture of hydroquinone and *p*-(methylamino)phenol.

The common black and white photographic plate, film, or printing paper consists of a support on which is coated an emulsion of mixed silver bromide and iodide in gelatin solution. Silver halides darken on exposure to light. The light energy dissociates the silver halide into silver and halogen atoms, the number of silver atoms formed depending on the intensity of the light falling on the silver halide and the time of exposure. If a photographic plate were exposed long enough to a light image, enough silver would be formed to produce a silver image on the plate. A more satisfactory procedure is to give a short exposure and produce an invisible latent image on the plate. Each silver particle thus formed then can act as a nucleus for the deposition of more silver when the plate is subjected to mild chemical reduction. During this reduction a visible image develops because the density of the silver deposited is proportional to the number of silver nuclei which in turn is proportional to the intensity of the light which fell on the plate. After the desired amount of development, the unreduced silver halide is removed by dissolving with sodium thiosulfate solution (photographer's *hypo*) leaving the silver image on the plate, film, or print.

The most important developers are hydroquinone, pyrogallol, and *p*-aminophenol and its derivatives, because they bring about the chemical reduction of the silver halide at the desired rate. The introduction of amino and hydroxyl groups into the benzene nucleus increases the ease of oxidation by increasing the availability of the unsaturation electrons (pp. 483, 505). The ease of oxidation is increased greatly in alkaline solution and decreased in acid solution because the availability of electrons on an oxide ion or on a free amino group is much greater than that on a hydroxyl group or an ammonium ion. If two hydroxyl groups or amino groups are *ortho* or *para* to each other, the ease of oxidation is increased greatly because such compounds can be oxidized to quinones (p. 520). Different developers produce different types of deposition of silver and hence influence the characteristics of the developed image. Usually a combination of developers is used to produce the desired effect.

The methyl ethers of the aminophenols are known as *anisidines* and the ethyl ethers as *phenetidines*. **p-Phenetidine** and the acetyl derivative, known as **acetophenetidine** or **phenacetine**, have antipyretic and analgesic action. Although less toxic than acetanilide, they also reduce the oxygen-combining power of the blood.

The quaternary salts of the carbamates of *m*-aminophenol are strong inhibitors of acetylcholine esterase (p. 243) and certain derivatives are among the most toxic compounds known. **Prostigmin** is used medicinally in the treatment of *myasthenia gravis*, a spastic condition of the skeletal muscle. The methods for its synthesis are typical for this class of compounds.

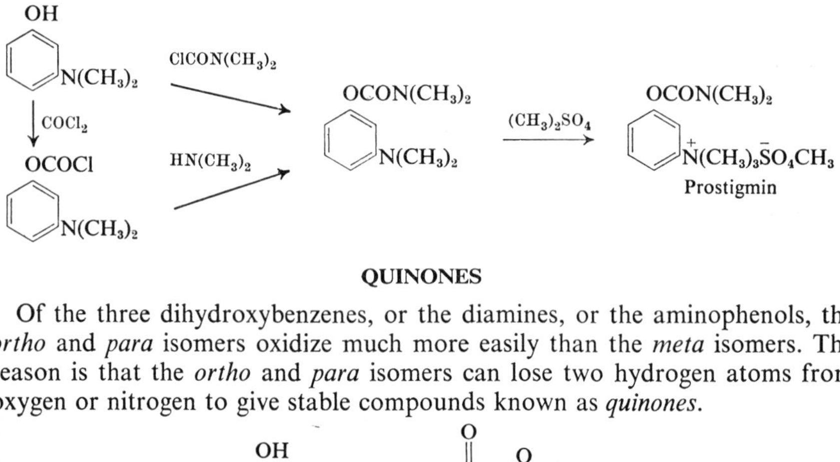

QUINONES

Of the three dihydroxybenzenes, or the diamines, or the aminophenols, the *ortho* and *para* isomers oxidize much more easily than the *meta* isomers. The reason is that the *ortho* and *para* isomers can lose two hydrogen atoms from oxygen or nitrogen to give stable compounds known as *quinones*.

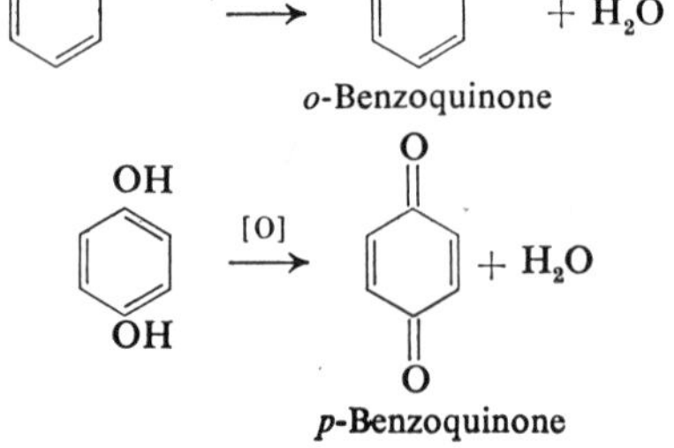

o-Benzoquinone

p-Benzoquinone

This type of oxidation is not possible for the *meta* isomers because no stable structure can be written for a *meta* quinone. Quinones are formed also by the oxidation of aminophenols and diamines, because the intermediate quinonimines and quinonediimines are hydrolyzed rapidly in aqueous solution.

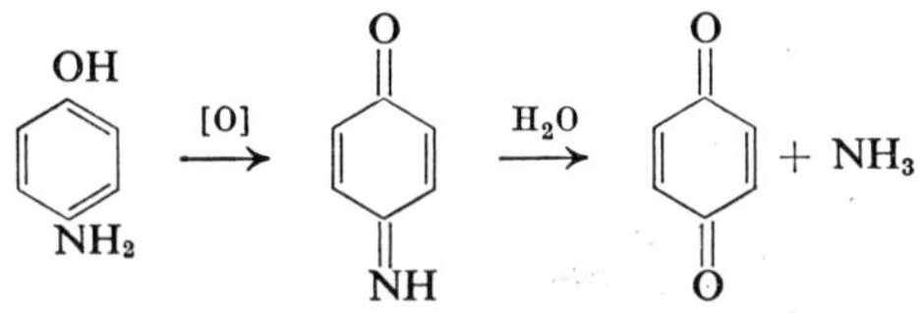

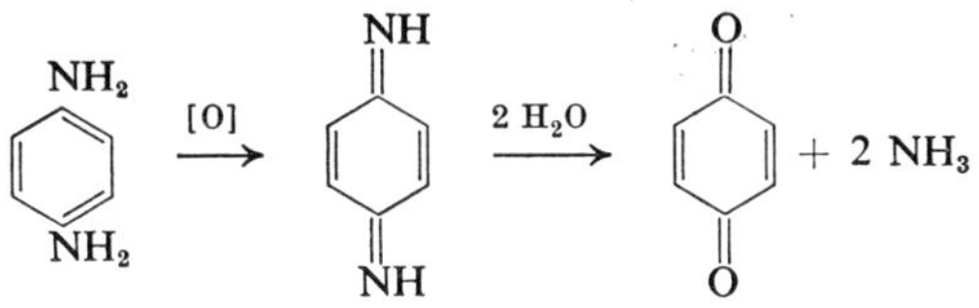

Quinone is a generic term for the above class of compounds but frequently is used as a specific name for *p*-benzoquinone. The name *quinoyl* was assigned to this compound when it first was obtained by the oxidation of quinic acid (p. 842) extracted from cinchona bark. Berzelius later changed the name to *quinone*. It is prepared commercially by the oxidation of aniline with manganese dioxide and sulfuric acid.

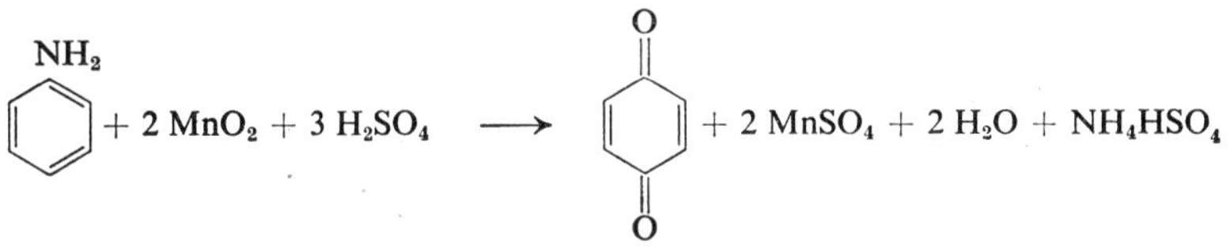

Quinone is a bright yellow solid with a sharp odor. Its reactions are those of α,β-unsaturated ketones, involving 1,4 addition (p. 763), rather than those of aromatic compounds. If the initial product can rearrange to an aromatic compound a substituted hydroquinone results.

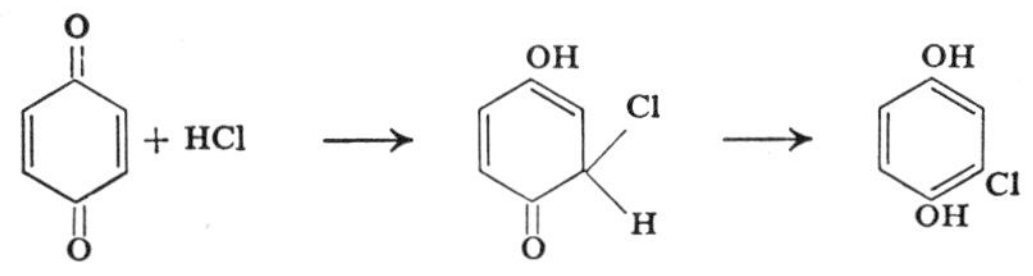

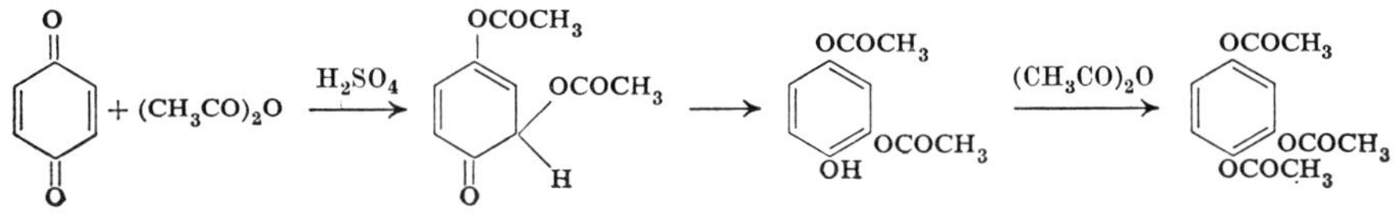

If quinone is a stronger oxidizing agent than the substituted quinone, the latter and hydroquinone are the final products. This behavior accounts for the formation of 2,5-dimethoxyquinone by the reaction of quinone with methyl alcohol.

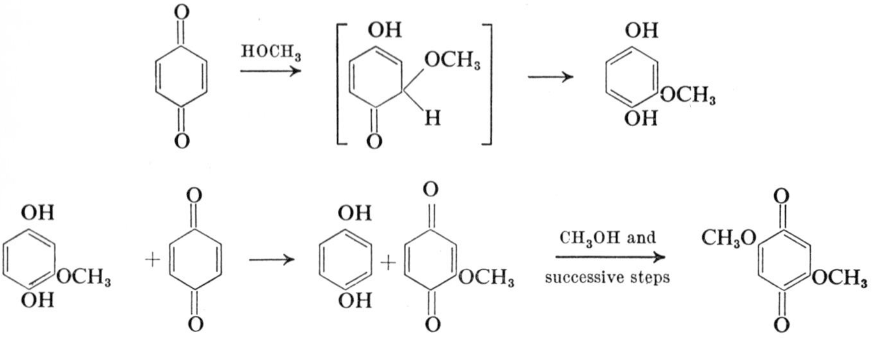

Similar addition and oxidation reactions can account for the presence of **2,5-dianilinoquinone** and its mono- and dianil (**azophenin**) among the colored oxidation products of aniline (p. 482).

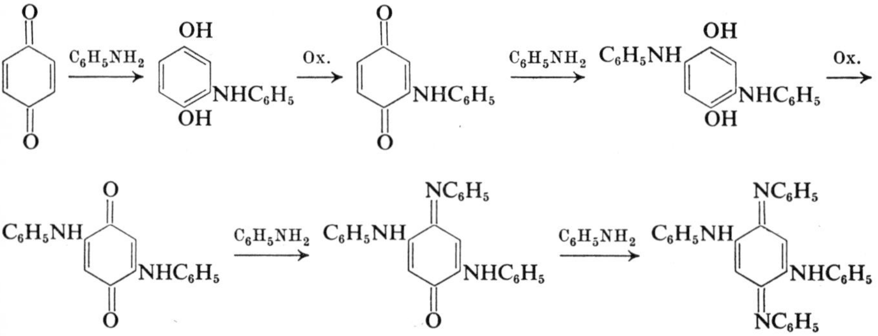

2,5-Dianilinoquinone   Azophenin

In general, groups which are electron-donating decrease the oxidizing power of the quinone and increase the reducing power of the quinol. Electron-attracting groups increase the oxidizing power of the quinone and decrease the reducing power of the quinol. The relative effect of different groups is approximately that of their effect on orientation in the aromatic nucleus. Tetrachloroquinone is known as **chloranil** and has been used as a dehydrogenating agent for organic compounds.

Quinones couple with diazonium salts in weakly acid solution with loss of nitrogen. This behavior is analogous to the Gomberg reaction (p. 496) and probably takes place by a free-radical mechanism.

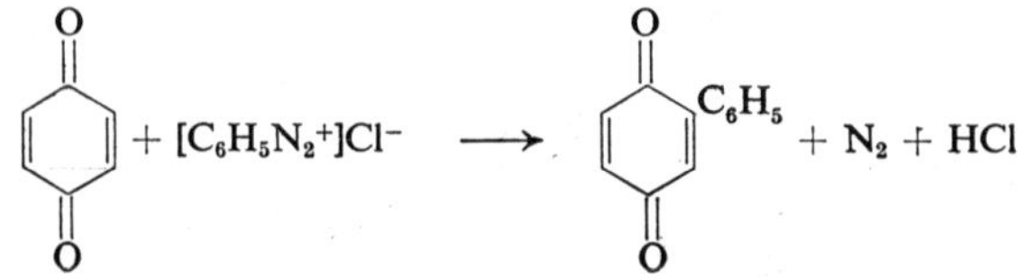

Quinone and hydroquinone combine directly in equimolecular proportions to give **quinhydrone,** which is an almost black crystalline solid and gives deeply colored solutions. The association appears to be due to proton bonding (p. 571). In aqueous solution it behaves like an equimolar mixture of quinone and hydroquinone, and since the interconversion of the two compounds is quantitative and readily reversible, a platinum electrode in a saturated solution can be used instead of a hydrogen electrode for measuring hydrogen ion concentration.

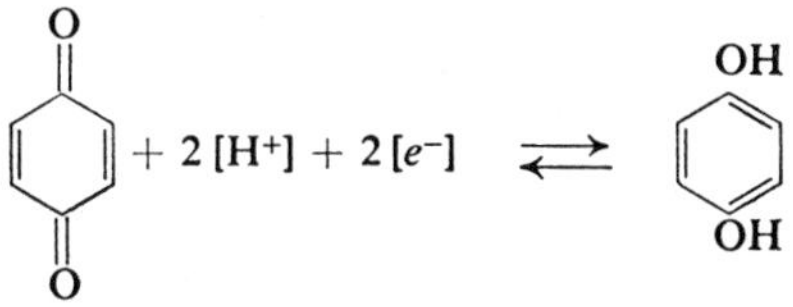

However both the hydrogen electrode and the quinohydrone electrode have been supplanted almost entirely by the glass electrode.

When a salt of 2,6-dichloro- or 2,6-dibromo-4-aminophenol reacts with hypochlorite solution, the **quinone chloroimide** is formed.

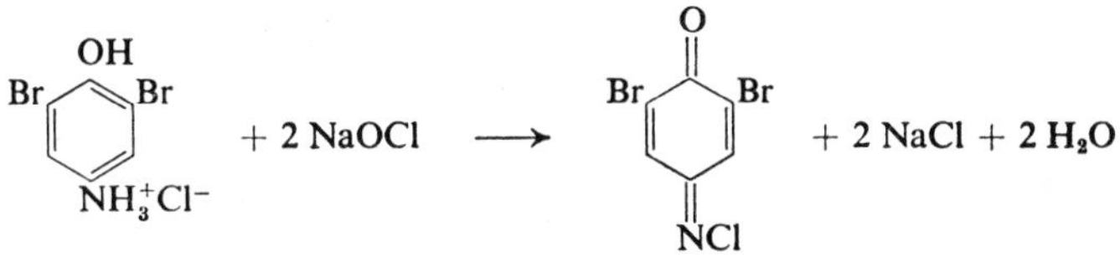

These compounds are valuable reagents for the detection of small amounts of phenol in water, since reaction in alkaline solution gives the intensely colored phenolindophenols (p. 506).

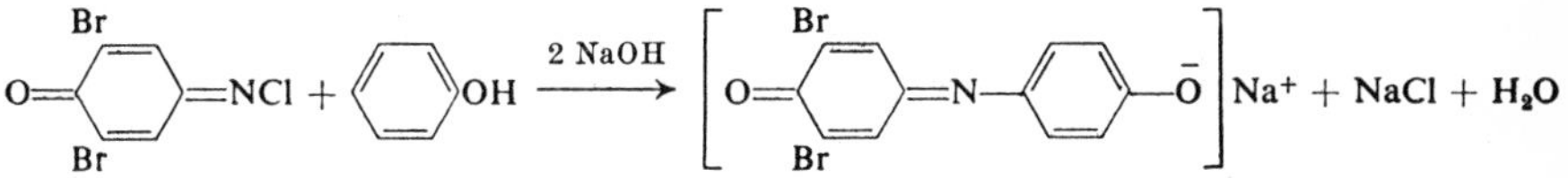

REVIEW QUESTIONS

1. Give reactions for the general methods for the synthesis of phenols.
2. Compare the reactions of the hydroxyl group in phenols with the reactions of alcoholic hydroxyl groups and explain the differences.
3. Give three reactions of phenol which illustrate the marked effect of the hydroxyl group on the ease of substitution in the benzene ring.
4. What is the Liebermann nitroso reaction? What other reaction discussed in this chapter resembles it?
5. Give two practical methods for the synthesis of picric acid. Why is direct nitration of phenol unsatisfactory?
6. Give reactions for the commercial processes for the synthesis of phenol. What are its chief uses?
7. What are the formulas and sources of the cresols; thymol; catechol; resorcinol; quinone; hydroquinone; pyrogallol; phloroglucinol?
8. Discuss the effect of substituents in the benzene ring on the acidity of phenol.
9. Give reactions suitable for the synthesis of *p-t*-butylphenol. What is meant by the term *phenol coefficient?*
10. Why are catechol, hydroquinone, and *p*-aminophenol useful as photographic developers whereas resorcinol and *m*-aminophenol are not?
11. Indicate by reactions the probable steps involved in the formation of azophenin by the oxidation of aniline.

PROBLEMS

12. Give reactions for the synthesis of the following compounds starting with an aromatic hydrocarbon: (a) p-methoxytoluene; (b) o-nitrophenyl acetate; (c) m-nitrophenol; (d) 2,4-dinitroanisole; (e) 2,4-dimethylphenyl benzyl ether; (f) m-chlorophenol; (g) m-phenolsulfonic acid; (h) 1,3-dihydroxy-4,6-dimethylbenzene; (i) p-bromophenyl carbonate; (j) p-methoxybenzenesulfonamide.

13. Give equations for the synthesis of the following compounds from readily available chemicals: (a) o-cresyl phosphate; (b) thymol; (c) p-methylaminophenol; (d) o-anisidine; (e) p-diethylaminophenyl di-n-propylcarbamate; (f) acetphenetidine; (g) styphnic acid; (h) 2-n-butyl-5-methylphenol; (i) veratrole; (j) 2,6-dichloroquinone chloroimide.

14. Making use of differences in physical and chemical properties, describe a procedure for the separation of the following mixtures, obtaining each component in a relatively pure state: (a) p-cymene, p-cresol, benzenesulfonic acid, and aniline; (b) N-methylaniline, N,N-dimethylaniline, o-chlorophenol, and benzoic acid; (c) acetanilide, n-butyric acid, phenol, and sulfanilic acid; (d) o-dichlorobenzene, benzenesulfonamide, phenol, and p-phenolsulfonic acid; (e) o-nitrophenol, p-nitrophenol, 2,4,6-trinitrophenol, aniline, and 2,4,6-trinitroaniline.

15. Write the structural formulas for the components of (a) cardanol, (b) the toxic principles of poison ivy and poison oak, and (c) urushiol.

16. Compound A has the molecular formula $C_9H_{12}O_2$. It gives a positive iodoform test and evolves two moles of methane when treated with methylmagnesium iodide. When heated with sodium bisulfate, it gives compound B, $C_9H_{10}O$, which is reduced catalytically to C, $C_9H_{12}O$. When C is distilled with zinc dust, compound D, C_9H_{12}, is obtained, which is converted by vigorous oxidation to terephthalic acid. Compound A reacts with thionyl chloride to give a product having the molecular formula $C_9H_{10}O_3S$. Give the structural formula for A and equations for the reactions that take place.

17. Compound A has the molecular formula $C_{15}H_{14}O_5$. It is insoluble in water but dissolves completely when boiled with aqueous sodium hydroxide. When the alkaline solution is distilled only water comes over. When the alkaline solution is acidified, effervescence takes place and an oil separates. The gas gives a white precipitate when passed into a solution of barium hydroxide. The oil gives a color with ferric chloride. When the oil is boiled with constant-boiling hydrobromic acid, methyl bromide is evolved. Distillation of the excess hydrogen bromide under reduced pressure leaves an oil which solidifies at room temperature. It proves to be identical with the compound obtained by fusing sodium m-benzenedisulfonate with sodium hydroxide and acidifying the melt. Give a structural formula for A and equations for the reactions that take place.

18. Compound A has the molecular formula $C_{10}H_{11}NO_3$. It is insoluble in dilute alkali or dilute acid. When boiled with dilute sulfuric acid, and distilled, the distillate is acid to litmus and gives a Duclaux value of 6.8. When a portion of the residue in the flask is made alkaline no precipitate forms. When the remainder of the acid solution is cooled to 0° and sodium nitrite is added, there is no evolution of gas, but when this solution is warmed, nitrogen is evolved. When the solution is cooled, a solid crystallizes. An aqueous solution of the solid reduces Tollens reagent and gives a transient green color with ferric chloride. As more ferric chloride is added, a yellow precipitate forms. Give the structural formula for A and equations for the reactions that take place.

Chapter 25

AROMATIC ALCOHOLS, ARALKYLAMINES, ALDEHYDES AND KETONES. STEREOCHEMISTRY OF THE OXIMES

ALCOHOLS AND ARALKYLAMINES

The methods for preparing compounds containing hydroxyl or amino groups in alkyl side chains of aromatic nuclei and the reactions of these groups are the same as the methods of preparation and reactions of aliphatic alcohols and amines. The chief difference is a considerably greater reactivity of the groups that are attached to the carbon atom adjacent to the ring.

Benzyl alcohol is made by the hydrolysis of benzyl chloride (p. 434).

$$C_6H_5CH_2Cl + H_2O + Na_2CO_3 \longrightarrow C_6H_5CH_2OH + NaHCO_3 + NaCl$$

When benzyl alcohol is mixed with sulfuric acid, a high molecular weight insoluble hydrocarbon is formed by self condensation in the *ortho* and *para* positions.

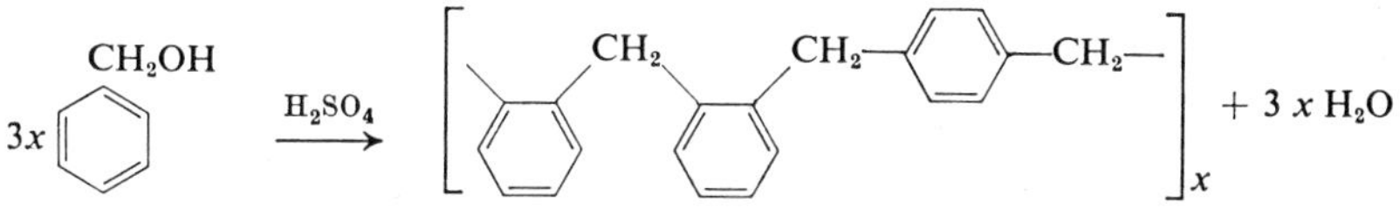

Benzyl alcohol is added to the extent of 1 to 3 per cent to solutions or suspensions intended for intramuscular or subcutaneous injections in order to minimize pain at the site of the injection. **Benzyl acetate** is used for the preparation of perfumes of the jasmine or gardenia type, and **benzyl benzoate** (p. 535) is used as a miticide. The antipyretic (fever-reducing) power of willow bark (*Salix alba*) was known to the ancients and is due to the bitter glucoside **salicin,** first isolated in 1827. Hydrolysis yields glucose and **saligenin** (*o-hydroxybenzyl alcohol*, p. 508).

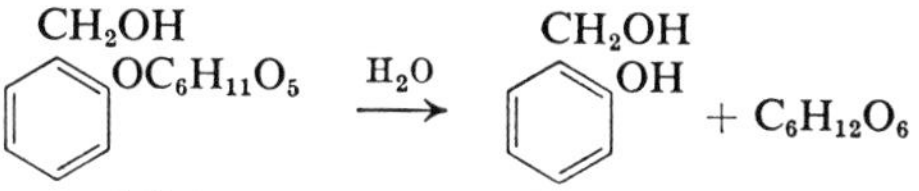

Salicin   Saligenin   Glucose

Methylphenylcarbinol is made by the catalytic reduction of methyl phenyl ketone (acetophenone, p. 541).

$$C_6H_5COCH_3 + H_2 \xrightarrow[\text{150°, 100 p.s.i.}]{\text{Cu-Cr-Fe}} C_6H_5CHOHCH_3$$

α-Methylbenzyl ether, $[C_6H_5CH(CH_3)]_2O$, made by dehydration of the carbinol, is used as a softening agent for nitrile synthetic rubbers (p. 718).

Diphenylcarbinol (*benzhydrol*) is made by the reduction of phenyl ketone (benzophenone, p. 541).

$$C_6H_5COC_6H_5 + Zn + 2\,NaOH \longrightarrow C_6H_5CHOHC_6H_5 + Na_2ZnO_2$$

It dehydrates with extreme ease to form **benzhydryl ether,** dilute acids being sufficient to cause reaction.

$$2 (C_6H_5)_2CHOH \longrightarrow (C_6H_5)_2CHOCH(C_6H_5)_2 + H_2O$$

Benadryl, $(C_6H_5)_2CHOCH_2CH_2N(CH_3)_2$, the β-dimethylaminoethyl ether of benzhydrol, was one of the first synthetic chemicals to be used widely in the treatment of histamine allergies (p. 634). It also is one of the more effective preventives and cures for seasickness. It is synthesized by a modified Williamson synthesis from diphenylmethyl bromide and β-dimethylaminoethanol.

Met. alkoxide + RX → ROR

$$(C_6H_5)_2CHBr + HOCH_2CH_2N(CH_3)_2 \xrightarrow[140°]{K_2CO_3} (C_6H_5)_2CHOCH_2CH_2N(CH_3)_2$$
$$+ KBr + KHCO_3$$

Triphenylcarbinol usually is prepared by the action of phenylmagnesium bromide on ethyl benzoate.

NB

$$C_6H_5COOC_2H_5 + 2 C_6H_5MgBr \longrightarrow (C_6H_5)_3COMgBr + MgBr(OC_2H_5)$$
$$\downarrow{H_2O}$$
$$(C_6H_5)_3COH + MgBr(OH)$$

The carbinol dissolves in concentrated sulfuric acid to give an orange-colored solution (halochromic salt, p. 573) from which the carbinol is regenerated by pouring into water. Reaction with concentrated aqueous hydrochloric acid gives **triphenylmethyl chloride** (*trityl chloride*).

$$(C_6H_5)_3COH + HCl \longrightarrow (C_6H_5)_3CCl + H_2O$$

Triphenylmethyl chloride in the presence of pyridine reacts with the primary alcohol groups of sugars to give triphenylmethyl ethers, a process frequently called *tritylation.*

$$RCH_2OH + ClC(C_6H_5)_3 + C_5H_5N \longrightarrow RCH_2OC(C_6H_5)_3 + C_5H_5NHCl$$

The remaining hydroxyl groups can be methylated or acetylated. The triphenylmethyl group then can be removed selectively, since triphenylmethyl ethers are hydrolyzed more readily in acid solution than are methyl ethers or esters.

An important characteristic of the benzyl-oxygen bond is that it is cleaved easily by hydrogenation, either catalytic or chemical.

$$ArCH_2OR \xrightarrow[\text{or Na—ROH}]{H_2\text{—Pt or Ni}} ArCH_2OH + HOR$$

Hydrogenolysis of the benzyl-sulfur or the benzyl-nitrogen bond also takes place readily. Hence a benzyl group can be used to protect a hydroxyl, mercapto, or amino group while carrying out another reaction and then can be removed by hydrogenolysis (cf. p. 305).

β-Phenylethyl alcohol (*phenethyl alcohol*) is an important component of oil of roses. The synthetic product is made either by the sodium-alcohol reduction of ethyl phenylacetate, or by a Friedel-Crafts reaction between benzene and ethylene oxide (p. 743).

$$C_6H_5CH_2COOC_2H_5 + 4\,Na + 3\,C_2H_5OH \longrightarrow C_6H_5CH_2CH_2OH + 4\,NaOC_2H_5$$

$$C_6H_6 + CH_2\!-\!CH_2 \xrightarrow{AlCl_3} C_6H_5CH_2CH_2OAlCl_2 \xrightarrow{H_2O} C_6H_5CH_2CH_2OH$$

Cinnamyl alcohol is made by the Meerwein-Ponndorf reduction of cinnamaldehyde (p. 537).

$$C_6H_5CH\!=\!CHCHO + (CH_3)_2CHOH \xrightarrow{Al(OPr\text{-}i)_3} C_6H_5CH\!=\!CHCH_2OH + (CH_3)_2CO$$

It has a hyacinth-like odor. The alcohol and its esters are used in perfumery.

Coniferin, which has been isolated from the cambial sap of conifers, is the glucoside of **coniferyl alcohol.**

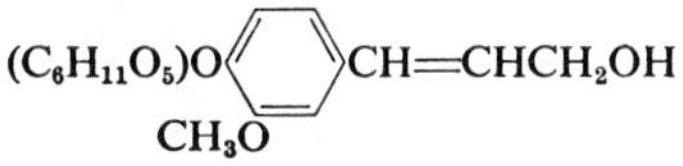

$$(C_6H_{11}O_5)O\langle\ \rangle CH\!=\!CHCH_2OH \qquad HO\langle\ \rangle CH\!=\!CHCH_2OH$$
$$CH_3O \qquad\qquad\qquad CH_3O$$

Coniferin 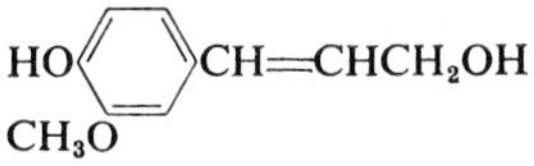   Coniferyl alcohol

The lignin of conifers (p. 400) appears to be an oxidative polymerization product of coniferyl alcohol. Alkaline oxidation of the lignin yields up to 25 per cent as vanillin (p. 538). The lignin of deciduous trees yields a mixture of vanillin and syringic aldehyde, the amount of syringic aldehyde frequently exceeding the amount of vanillin. Accordingly the lignin of deciduous trees appears to be derived not only from coniferyl alcohol but also from **syringenin,** which first was obtained from the glycoside **syringin** present in bark of the lilac, *Syringa vulgaris.*

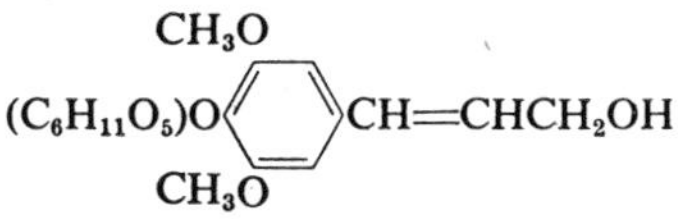

$$CH_3O \qquad\qquad\qquad CH_3O$$
$$(C_6H_{11}O_5)O\langle\ \rangle CH\!=\!CHCH_2OH \qquad HO\langle\ \rangle CH\!=\!CHCH_2OH$$
$$CH_3O \qquad\qquad\qquad CH_3O$$

Syringin 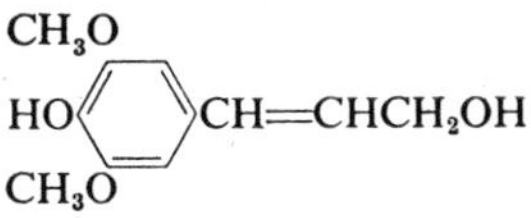   Syringenin

Benzylamine, dibenzylamine, and **tribenzylamine** are formed when ammonia reacts with benzyl chloride. They are only slightly less basic than the aliphatic amines. The benzyl-nitrogen bond is cleaved readily by catalytic hydrogenation. Hence the benzyl group can be used to protect an amino group during condensation reactions of other portions of the molecule, and then can be removed.

$$R_2NCH_2C_6H_5 + H_2 \xrightarrow{Raney\ Ni} R_2NH + CH_3C_6H_5$$

Primary and secondary aralkylamines can be made also from aromatic aldehydes or ketones by reductive alkylation of ammonia or of a primary amine (p. 230).

$$ArCHO + NH_3 + H_2 \xrightarrow{Ni} ArCH_2NH_2 + H_2O$$

$$ArCOR + H_2NR' + H_2 \xrightarrow{Ni} \underset{NHR}{ArCHR} + H_2O$$

α-Phenylethylamine (*α-methylbenzylamine*) usually is made in the laboratory from acetophenone by the Leuckart reaction (p. 231).

$$C_6H_5COCH_3 + HCOONH_4 \longrightarrow C_6H_5CH(CH_3)NH_2 + CO_2 + H_2O$$

It can be resolved readily into the two active forms, which are useful for the resolution of racemic acids. An important advantage of the Leuckart reaction over other reductive methods is that halogen and nitro groups that may be present in the aromatic nucleus are not affected.

β-Phenylethylamine (*phenethylamine*) may be regarded as the parent substance of a large group of medicinally important compounds known as *sympathomimetic amines*. The name was coined to indicate that they mimic the action of the sympathetic nervous system. For example, they dilate the pupil of the eye (*mydriatic action*), strengthen the heart beat, and increase blood pressure (*pressor activity*). It now is believed that the sympathetic system performs these functions by the elaboration of epinephrine (Adrenalin) and norepinephrine (Arterenol), which are substituted β-phenylethylamines. Formulas for only a few of these important compounds are given.

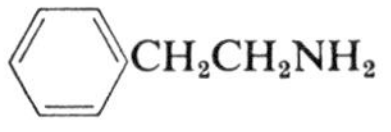

β-Phenylethylamine

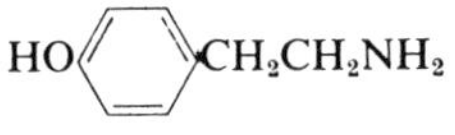

Tyramine

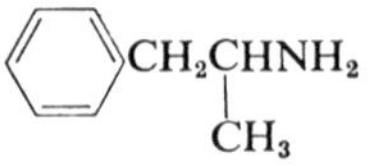

Benzedrine

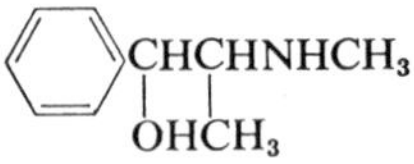

Ephedrine

Propadrine

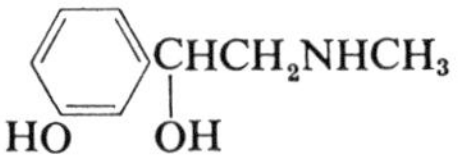

Neo-Synephrine

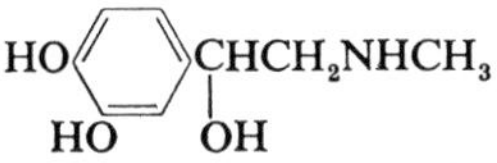

Epinephrine
(Adrenalin)

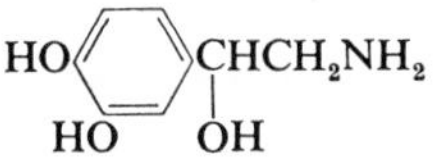

Norepinephrine
(Arterenol)

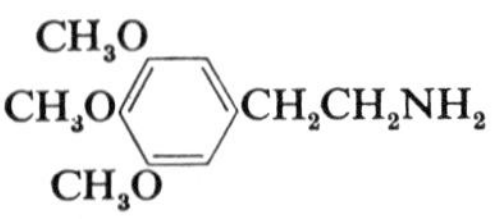

Mescaline

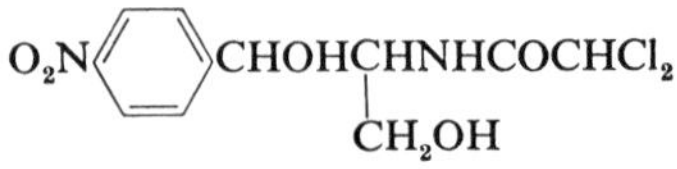

Chloromycetin

Various procedures have been used for the synthesis of β-phenylethylamines and their hydroxy derivatives. A few are indicated in the following series of reactions.

(a) $ArCH_2Cl \xrightarrow{NaCN} ArCH_2CN \xrightarrow{H_2,Ni} ArCH_2CH_2NH_2$

(b) $ArCH_2COR \xrightarrow{H_2NOH} ArCH_2\underset{\underset{NOH}{\|}}{C}R \xrightarrow{Na,C_2H_5OH} ArCH_2\underset{\underset{NH_2}{|}}{C}HR$

(c) $ArCHO \xrightarrow{RCH_2NO_2} ArCHOH\underset{\underset{R}{|}}{C}HNO_2 \xrightarrow{H_2,Pt} ArCHOH\underset{\underset{R}{|}}{C}HNH_2$

(d) $ArCOCH_2R \xrightarrow{HONO} \left[ArCO\underset{\underset{NO}{|}}{C}HR \right] \longrightarrow ArCO\underset{\underset{NOH}{\|}}{C}R \xrightarrow{Na,C_2H_5OH} ArCHOH\underset{\underset{NH_2}{|}}{C}HR$

(e) $ArCOCH_2Cl \xrightarrow{HNR_2} ArCOCH_2NR_2 \xrightarrow{Na,C_2H_5OH} ArCHOHCH_2NR_2$

Benzedrine has a powerful action on the central nervous system leading to temporary increase in alertness, lessened fatigue, and increased irritability and sleeplessness. This action is followed by fatigue and mental depression; hence considerable danger lies in promiscuous use of the drug. The dextrorotatory form is two to four times more active than racemic Benzedrine and is sold under the trade name Dexedrine. It reduces gastric contractions and is prescribed as an anorexic to prevent overeating.

The closely related compound **ephedrine** is present in the herb *Ma Huang* (*Ephedra vulgaris*) used medicinally by Chinese physicians for thousands of years. The active principle was isolated by Japanese workers in 1885, but it did not become well known in the western world until about 1925 after the investigations of Chen and Schmidt in the United States. It is administered for the treatment of bronchial asthma, and for a few years was used in nose drops for contracting the capillaries and relieving nasal congestion caused by colds. For the latter purpose it has been replaced largely by other synthetic arylethyl-amines such as **Neo-Synephrine**. **Propadrine** is used orally for this purpose. It is of interest that Propadrine differs from Benzedrine only in having an additional hydroxyl group; yet it is much less likely to cause central stimulation.

Epinephrine (*Adrenalin*) and **norepinephrine** (*Arterenol*) are the active principles produced by the adrenal medulla and by the postganglionic nerve endings (p. 243). Epinephrine was the first hormone to be isolated in crystalline form (Abel, 1897) and the first hormone to be synthesized (Stolz, 1904, and Dakin, 1905). Hormones (Gr. *hormaein*, to excite) are chemical substances produced by the cells of one part of an organism and transported by the fluids of the organism to another site where they exert their specific action. Although it was suspected for a long time that the sympathin liberated by nerve endings (p. 243) consisted of two substances, designated as *sympathin E* and *sympathin I*, it was not until after 1948 that it was proven that sympathin I is chiefly epinephrine and sympathin E almost pure norepinephrine, and that ordinary epinephrine from adrenal glands (U.S.P. epinephrine) contains from 12 to 18 per cent of norepinephrine. Epinephrine in very small amounts increases the blood pressure by increasing the force and the rate of the heart beat and by constricting the arteries. This pressor effect is diminished by a dilating action on the peripheral and capillary blood vessels. Norepinephrine has an action similar to epinephrine but lacks the last property and hence has about 1.5 times the pressor activity of epinephrine. U.S.P. epinephrine is administered with local anesthetics (p. 558) to prolong their action by constricting the blood vessels locally and preventing the anesthetic from being carried away from the site of injection. Epinephrine also is a powerful bronchodilator and is used in the treatment of bronchial asthma. It is about 100 times more effective than norepinephrine for this purpose. Both epinephrine and norepinephrine contain an asymmetric carbon atom, and the naturally occurring (−) forms are around twenty times more active than the (+) forms.

Mescaline has been isolated from mescal buttons, the tops of tubercles on the dumpling cactus (*Lophophora williamsii*). Mescal is employed by the Indians of southwestern United States and northern Mexico in religious ceremonies for the psychic effects and hallucinations that it produces. **Tyramine** is found in ergot and putrefying meat, and probably is formed by the decarboxylation of the amino acid tyrosine (Table 18, p. 296). Its pressor activity is about the same as that of β-phenylethylamine.

Chloromycetin (*chloramphenicol*), isolated from a species of *Streptomyces*, a soil organism, is the first antibiotic to be synthesized by a practical procedure. It is a relatively simple molecule and contains an aromatic nitro group and a dichloroacetyl group. Neither structural feature had been found previously in a natural product. Chloromycetin is especially effective against typhus and Rocky Mountain fever.

ALDEHYDES

Preparation

The aromatic aldehydes can be prepared by any of the general methods used to prepare aliphatic aldehydes (p. 194). Additional methods are available that are applicable only to aromatic compounds. Usually some one procedure is preferable for a particular aromatic aldehyde. The more commonly used procedures are summarized below.

1. **Oxidation of Side Chains.** (*a*) METHYL SIDE CHAINS. The presence of a phenyl group increases to some extent the ease of oxidation of an alkyl group. If the oxidation is carried out in the presence of acetic anhydride, the further oxidation of the aldehyde is prevented by the formation of the diacetate. Hydrolysis yields the aldehyde.

$$ArCH_3 + 2\ MnO_2 + 2\ H_2SO_4 \longrightarrow ArCHO + 3\ H_2O + 2\ MnSO_4$$

$$ArCHO + (CH_3CO)_2O \longrightarrow ArCH(OCOCH_3)_2$$

$$ArCH(OCOCH_3)_2 + H_2O \longrightarrow ArCHO + 2\ CH_3COOH$$

An interesting oxidation of a methyl group to an aldehyde group is the production of *p*-aminobenzaldehyde in 75 per cent yield by heating *p*-nitrotoluene with sodium polysulfide.

$$3\ CH_3\!\!\left\langle\!\!\bigcirc\!\!\right\rangle\!\!NO_2 + Na_2S_4 \longrightarrow 3\ OCH\!\!\left\langle\!\!\bigcirc\!\!\right\rangle\!\!NH_2 + Na_2S_2O_3 + 2\ S$$

(*b*) HYDROXYMETHYL SIDE CHAINS. Several oxidizing agents convert primary or secondary aromatic alcohols to aldehydes or ketones. Among these may be mentioned *t*-butyl hypochlorite (p. 109), or *N*-chlorosuccinimide (p. 797) in carbon tetrachloride solution, along with one mole of pyridine to combine with the hydrogen chloride formed.

$$ArCH_2OH + t\text{-}C_4H_9OCl + C_5H_5N \longrightarrow ArCHO + t\text{-}C_4H_9OH + C_5H_5NHCl$$

t-Butylchromate in petroleum solvent, dinitrogen tetroxide in chloroform, and nitric acid also have been used as oxidizing agents.

(*c*) UNSATURATED SIDE CHAINS. If the side chain contains a double bond adjacent to the ring, it can be oxidized to give aromatic aldehydes. The latter are less easily oxidized to acids by chemical reagents such as potassium permanganate than are aliphatic aldehydes.

$$ArCH{=}CHCH_3 \xrightarrow{\text{KMnO}_4} ArCHO + CH_3COOH$$

2. Hydrolysis of Dihalides. Usually it is preferable to oxidize a methyl group indirectly by halogenating to the dihalide (p. 434) and hydrolyzing.

$$ArCH_3 + 2 Cl_2 \longrightarrow ArCHCl_2 + 2 HCl$$

$$ArCHCl_2 \xrightarrow{\text{H}_2\text{O(Na}_2\text{CO}_3)} HCl + [ArCH(OH)Cl] \longrightarrow ArCHO + HCl$$

3. Gattermann[1] Carbon Monoxide Synthesis (Gattermann–Koch Reaction). Formyl chloride is stable only at liquid air temperature, but a mixture of carbon monoxide and hydrogen chloride in the presence of anhydrous aluminum chloride and cuprous chloride behaves like formyl chloride in its reactions with aromatic compounds (p. 423).

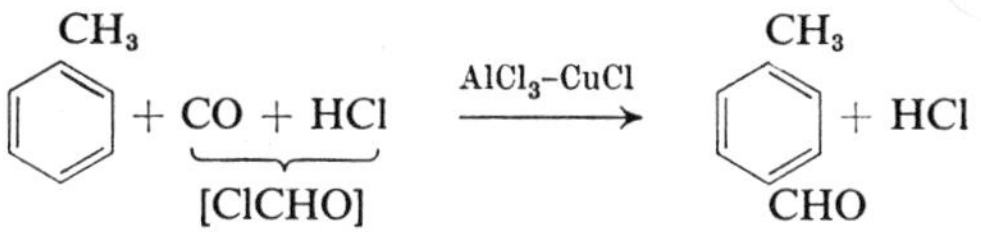

An equimolecular mixture of carbon monoxide and hydrogen chloride can be prepared conveniently by adding chlorosulfonic acid to formic acid.

$$HCOOH + ClSO_3H \longrightarrow CO + HCl + H_2SO_4$$

4. Gattermann Hydrogen Cyanide Synthesis. This procedure is used chiefly on phenols and phenol ethers which substitute with greater ease than hydrocarbons. It again is a Friedel-Crafts type of reaction (p. 423), an addition product of hydrogen chloride and hydrogen cyanide probably being the active reagent.

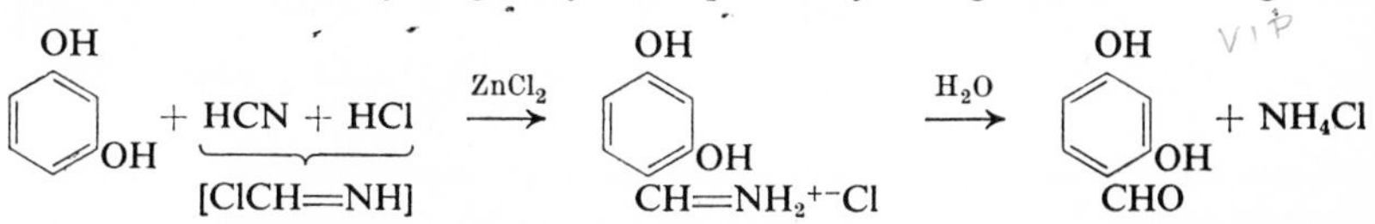

---

[1] Ludwig Gattermann (1860–1920), professor at Heidelberg. He is best known for his work with diazonium salts (p. 494), for his syntheses of aromatic aldehydes, and for his popular laboratory textbook.

Zinc chloride is a sufficiently active catalyst for resorcinol. Zinc cyanide and hydrogen chloride may be used in place of anhydrous hydrogen cyanide, or the hydrogen cyanide may be replaced by bromocyanogen. Formerly the reaction was believed to be useful only with phenols and phenol ethers, but it has been shown to give 85 to 100 per cent yields with toluene or xylene if carried out at 100°.

5. **Reimer-Tiemann Reaction.** This reaction takes place only with phenols.

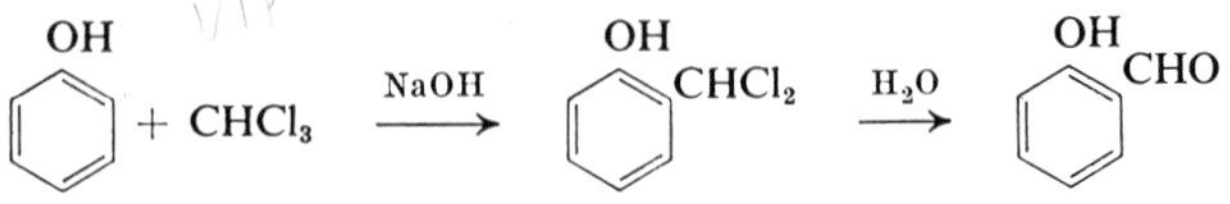

Salicylaldehyde

It involves both substitution and hydrolysis. *Ortho* substitution usually predominates unless the *ortho* positions are occupied, when *para* substitution takes place.

As with other reactions of chloroform in strongly alkaline solution (p. 175), the Reimer-Tiemann reaction appears to involve a dichloromethylene intermediate.

$$CHCl_3 + [^-OH] \longrightarrow H_2O + [^- : CCl_3] \longrightarrow [Cl^-] + [: CCl_2]$$

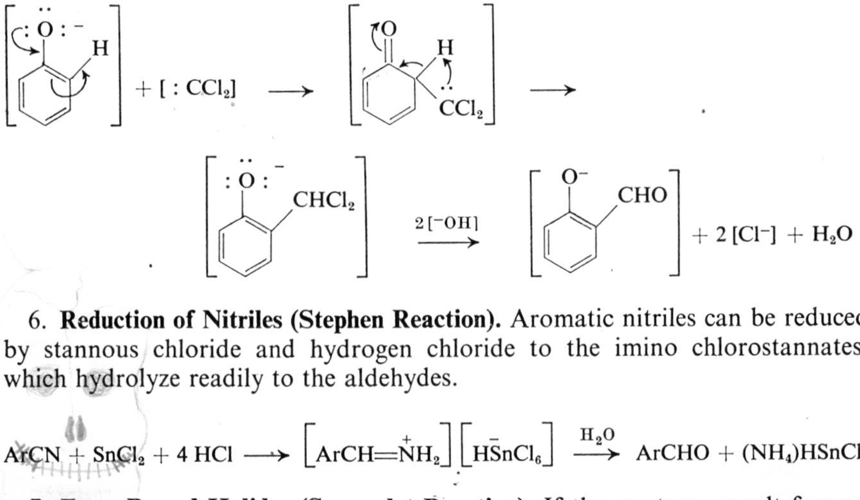

6. **Reduction of Nitriles (Stephen Reaction).** Aromatic nitriles can be reduced by stannous chloride and hydrogen chloride to the imino chlorostannates, which hydrolyze readily to the aldehydes.

$$ArCN + SnCl_2 + 4 HCl \longrightarrow \left[ArCH=\overset{+}{N}H_2 \right]\left[H\bar{S}nCl_6 \right] \xrightarrow{H_2O} ArCHO + (NH_4)HSnCl_6$$

7. **From Benzyl Halides (Sommelet Reaction).** If the quaternary salt formed by the reaction of a benzyl chloride with hexamethylenetetramine (p. 221) is boiled in aqueous alcohol, the aromatic aldehyde is obtained in good yield.

$$ArCH_2[(CH_2)_6N_4]^+Cl^- + 6 H_2O \longrightarrow ArCHO + CH_3NH_3Cl + 3 NH_3 + 5 CH_2O$$

Reaction of the ammonia and formaldehyde gives rise to a mixture of methylamines (p. 231).

The Sommelet reaction appears to proceed initially as in the Delepine reaction (p. 232) with the formation of the primary amine.

$$ArCH_2[(CH_2)_6N_4]^+Cl^- + 6 H_2O \longrightarrow ArCH_2NH_2 + 2 NH_3 + NH_4Cl + 6 CH_2O$$

Reaction of the primary amine with formaldehyde gives the imino derivative which is in tautomeric equilibrium with the benzylidene derivative of methylamine. Hydrolysis of the benzylidene derivative gives the aromatic aldehyde.

$$ArCH_2NH_2 + HCHO \longrightarrow ArCH_2N{=}CH_2 \rightleftarrows ArCH{=}NCH_3 \xrightarrow{H_2O}$$

$$\left[\begin{array}{c} ArCHNHCH_3 \\ | \\ OH \end{array} \right] \longrightarrow ArCHO + H_2NCH_3$$

8. Through Aldehyde-Ammonia Intermediates. Several other methods for preparing aldehydes involve the intermediate formation of an aldehyde-ammonia which decomposes to the aldehyde and amine. Thus an activated aromatic nucleus reacts with *N,N*-dimethylformamide or *N*-methylformanilide in the presence of phosphorus oxychloride to give the aromatic aldehyde.

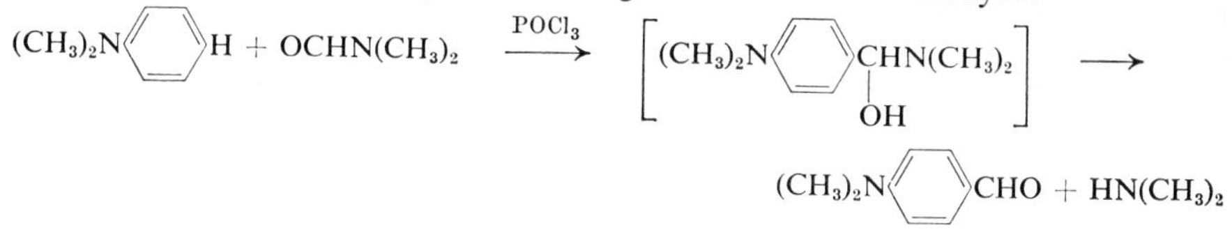

$$(CH_3)_2N\langle\bigcirc\rangle H + OCHN(CH_3)_2 \xrightarrow{POCl_3} \left[(CH_3)_2N\langle\bigcirc\rangle\underset{\underset{OH}{|}}{C}HN(CH_3)_2 \right] \longrightarrow$$

$$(CH_3)_2N\langle\bigcirc\rangle CHO + HN(CH_3)_2$$

p-Dimethylamino-
benzaldehyde

Similar intermediates can be formed by the addition of reactive organometallic compounds to *N*-methylformanilide or by reduction of the *N*-methylanilides of other carboxylic acids with lithium aluminum hydride.

$$C_6H_5N(CH_3)CHO + ArLi \longrightarrow \left[\begin{array}{c} C_6H_5N(CH_3)CHAr \\ | \\ O^{-+}Li \end{array} \right] \xrightarrow{H_2O}$$

$$C_6H_5NHCH_3 + OCHAr + LiOH$$

$$C_6H_5N(CH_3)COR + LiAlH_4 \longrightarrow \left[\begin{array}{c} C_6H_5N(CH_3)CHR \\ | \\ O^- \end{array} \right]_4 Li^+Al^{+++} \xrightarrow{H_2O}$$

$$C_6H_5NHCH_3 + OCHR + LiOH + Al(OH)_3$$

Reactions

Aromatic aldehydes undergo most of the general addition reactions of aliphatic aldehydes such as reduction and oxime formation, but they do not polymerize. They are oxidized by air to the acid, by way of the peroxide (p. 885). However they are not oxidized by solutions of oxidizing agents as readily as aliphatic aldehydes. For example, benzaldehyde does not reduce Fehling solution.

The oxidation of benzaldehyde by permanganate is subject to general acid catalysis and specific hydroxide ion catalysis. In the neutral and acid-catalyzed oxidation, attack of the protonated aldehyde by the permanganate ion gives the permanganate ester of the hydrated aldehyde, which loses a proton and MnO_3^- to give the acid.

$$ArCH{=}O \xrightarrow{[H^+]} \left[ArCH{=}\overset{+}{O}H \right] \xrightarrow{[\,:OMnO_3]} Ar\underset{\underset{O-MnO_3}{|}}{\overset{\overset{OH}{|}}{C}}{-}H \longrightarrow ArCOOH + [H^+] + [MnO_3^-]$$

The $[MnO_3^-]$ ion is rapidly converted to manganese dioxide and permanganate ion.

$$3\,[MnO_3^-] + H_2O \longrightarrow 2\,MnO_2 + [MnO_4^-] + 2\,[^-OH]$$

In accordance with this mechanism, O^{18} is introduced into the acid when $[^-MnO_4{}^{18}]$ is used as the oxidizing agent. This mechanism resembles that for the oxidation of alcohols by chromic acid (p. 106) in that an ester is an intermediate. It differs, however, in that the oxygen in the ester linkage is supplied by the permanganate, whereas in the chromic acid oxidation it is supplied by the alcohol.

Oxidation by alkaline permanganate follows a different course. Here the oxygen introduced into the product comes mainly from the solvent water molecules rather than from the permanganate. Indications are that oxidation takes place by a free-radical mechanism through hydroxyl free radicals.

$$[MnO_4{}^-] + [^- : OH] \longrightarrow [MnO_4{}^=] + [\cdot OH]$$

$$
R-\overset{\displaystyle O}{\underset{\displaystyle H}{\overset{\|}{C}}} + [\cdot OH] \longrightarrow \left[R-\overset{\displaystyle O \cdot}{\underset{\displaystyle H}{\overset{|}{\underset{|}{C}}}-OH \right]
$$

$$
\left[R-\overset{\displaystyle O \cdot}{\underset{\displaystyle H}{\overset{|}{\underset{|}{C}}}-OH \right] + [MnO_4{}^-] \longrightarrow RCOOH + [MnO_3{}^-] + [\cdot OH]
$$

Little O^{18} is introduced into the benzoic acid when $[^-MnO_4{}^{18}]$ is used because of the rapid exchange of the oxygen of hydroxyl radical with water molecules.

$$[HO \cdot] + HOH \rightleftarrows HOH + [\cdot OH]$$

Special consideration of some of the more important reactions is of value.

1. **Halogenation of the Aldehyde Group.** The hydrocarbon portion of the molecule of aliphatic aldehydes is halogenated in the position α to the carbonyl group more rapidly than is the aldehyde group itself. Since no α hydrogen is present in aromatic aldehydes and since the aromatic ring does not substitute in the absence of special catalysts, it is possible to bring about the direct substitution of the hydrogen atom of the aldehyde group by halogen, the product being an acyl halide.

$$\underset{\substack{\text{Benzalde-}\\\text{hyde}}}{C_6H_5CHO} + Cl_2 \longrightarrow \underset{\substack{\text{Benzoyl}\\\text{chloride}}}{C_6H_5COCl} + HCl$$

2. **Cannizzaro Reaction.** Like all aldehydes that do not have hydrogen on an α carbon atom, aromatic aldehydes undergo the Cannizzaro reaction (p. 219).

$$2\,C_6H_5CHO + NaOH \longrightarrow \underset{\substack{\text{Benzyl}\\\text{alcohol}}}{C_6H_5CH_2OH} + \underset{\substack{\text{Sodium}\\\text{benzoate}}}{C_6H_5COONa}$$

Because formaldehyde is oxidized more easily than the aromatic aldehydes, the latter can be converted completely to the alcohol by heating a mixture of the aromatic aldehyde with an excess of formaldehyde in the presence of concentrated aqueous sodium hydroxide (*crossed Cannizzaro reaction*).

$$C_6H_5CHO + HCHO + NaOH \longrightarrow C_6H_5CH_2OH + HCOONa$$

If a hydroxyl group is present in the *ortho* or *para* position, the Cannizzaro reaction takes place only when catalyzed by finely divided metals, especially silver.

The Cannizzaro reaction appears to take place through the intermediate formation of the ester. The initial attack is by hydroxide ion on the carbonyl carbon, which then attacks a second molecule of benzaldehyde. The transfer of hydrogen must take place intramolecularly, because no deuterium enters the methylene group of the benzyl alcohol when the reaction is carried out in the presence of heavy water. Apparently this step involves the transfer of the negative hydride ion. The final step is the rapid saponification of the ester.

$$\text{ArCHO} \underset{\longleftarrow}{\overset{[\text{OH}^-]}{\longrightarrow}} \left[\begin{array}{c} \text{H} \\ \text{Ar}-\overset{|}{\underset{|}{\text{C}}}-\text{O}^- \\ \text{OH} \end{array} \right] \underset{\longleftarrow}{\overset{\text{ArCHO}}{\longrightarrow}} \left[\begin{array}{c} \text{H} \quad \text{H} \\ \text{Ar}-\overset{|}{\text{C}}-\text{O}-\overset{|}{\text{C}}-\text{Ar} \\ \text{OH} \quad :\text{O}: \end{array} \right] \underset{[\text{OH}^-]}{\rightleftharpoons}$$

$$\overset{\overset{\displaystyle O}{\parallel}}{\text{ArCH}_2\text{OCAr}} \xrightarrow{[\text{OH}^-]} \text{ArCH}_2\text{OH} + \left[\overset{\overset{\displaystyle O}{\parallel}}{^-\text{O}-\text{CAr}} \right]$$

Benzaldehyde is converted into benzyl benzoate by the catalytic action of aluminum ethoxide (Tishchenko reaction, p. 220).

$$2\,\text{C}_6\text{H}_5\text{CHO} \xrightarrow{\text{Al(OC}_2\text{H}_5)_3} \text{C}_6\text{H}_5\text{COOCH}_2\text{C}_6\text{H}_5$$

3. **Reaction with Ammonia.** Acetaldehyde reacts with ammonia in the mole ratio 1 : 1 to give an addition product, acetaldehyde-ammonia, which dehydrates to ethylidenimine or its polymer (p. 210). With formaldehyde the mole ratio of the reactants is 6 : 4 and the dehydration is spontaneous to give hexamethylenetetramine having a cage structure (p. 221). Benzaldehyde reacts with ammonia in the mole ratio of 3 : 2 with spontaneous dehydration to give a product known as **hydrobenzamide.**

$$3\,\text{C}_6\text{H}_5\text{CHO} + 2\,\text{NH}_3 \longrightarrow \underset{\underset{\text{Hydrobenzamide}}{\overset{|}{\text{C}_6\text{H}_5}}}{\text{C}_6\text{H}_5\text{CH}{=}\text{NCHN}{=}\text{CHC}_6\text{H}_5} + 3\,\text{H}_2\text{O}$$

This name was assigned by Laurent[2] because he thought that benzaldehyde was a type of acid which differed from benzoic acid in that it did not form ammonium salts and yet formed amides. He called benzaldehyde a *hydrogen acid* and the reaction product with ammonia a *hydrogen amide* or *hydramide*. Actually the product is not an amide but is the dibenzylidene derivative of benzylidenediamine. In the reactions of all aldehydes with ammonia, the aldehyde-ammonia undoubtedly is the initial product.

4. **Condensation with Primary Amines.** Aromatic aldehydes condense with primary aliphatic or aromatic amines to give imino derivatives known as *Schiff bases*. The products from aromatic amines are known also as *anils*.

$$\text{C}_6\text{H}_5\text{CHO} + \text{H}_2\text{NCH}_3 \longrightarrow \underset{\substack{N\text{-Methylbenzyli-}\\\text{denimine}}}{\text{C}_6\text{H}_5\text{CH}{=}\text{NCH}_3} + \text{H}_2\text{O}$$

$$\text{C}_6\text{H}_5\text{CHO} + \text{H}_2\text{NC}_6\text{H}_5 \longrightarrow \underset{\text{Benzylideneaniline}}{\text{C}_6\text{H}_5\text{CH}{=}\text{NC}_6\text{H}_5} + \text{H}_2\text{O}$$

---

[2] Auguste Laurent (1807–1853) first studied mining engineering and then became an assistant to Dumas under whose direction he isolated anthracene from coal tar. He also was the first to prepare anthraquinone (1832), phthalic acid (1836), and adipic acid (1837), and did other work on naphthalene and phenol. He coined the word *phene* (p. 421) for benzene which persists in the words *phenol* and *phenyl*. Laurent was the first to draw a clear distinction between atom, equivalent, and molecule. In his later years he was warden of the Mint at Paris.

Schiff bases do not polymerize and in general are more stable than *N*-alkyl-alkylidenimines, RCH=NR, because the conjugation of the double bond with the aromatic nucleus greatly reduces its reactivity.

Schiff bases can be reduced easily by hydrogen and Raney nickel to the secondary amines. It is not necessary to isolate the Schiff bases. An alcoholic solution of aromatic aldehyde and primary amine is shaken with hydrogen in the presence of the catalyst.

5. **Aldol-Type Condensations with Aliphatic Aldehydes and Ketones.** Aromatic aldehydes condense with other aldehydes and ketones having two α hydrogen atoms. However, the intermediate aldols lose water even more readily than the aliphatic aldols (p. 207), because the double bond formed by loss of water is conjugated not only with the carbonyl group but also with the aromatic ring.

$$C_6H_5CHO + CH_3CHO \xrightarrow{\text{Dil. NaOH}} C_6H_5CH=CHCHO + H_2O$$
$$\text{Cinnamaldehyde}$$

$$C_6H_5CHO + CH_3COCH_3 \xrightarrow[\text{10 per cent}]{\text{NaOH}} C_6H_5CH=CHCCH_3 + H_2O$$
$$\overset{\|}{O}$$
$$\text{Benzylideneacetone}$$

$$C_6H_5CH=CHCCH_3 + OCHC_6H_5 \xrightarrow[\text{10 per cent}]{\text{NaOH}} C_6H_5CH=CHCCH=CHC_6H_5 + H_2O$$
$$\overset{\|}{O} \qquad\qquad\qquad\qquad\qquad \overset{\|}{O}$$
$$\text{Dibenzylideneacetone}$$

The yield of cinnamaldehyde is not so good as that of either benzylidene- or dibenzylideneacetone because of the polymerizing action of the alkali on the aliphatic aldehyde. Aldehyde condensations with ketones brought about by the use of 10 per cent sodium hydroxide are known as *Claisen reactions*. The benzylideneacetones give highly colored halochromic salts with strong acids in anhydrous media (p. 573).

6. **Perkin Synthesis.** An aldol type of addition of anhydrides to aromatic ketones was discovered by Perkin (p. 672). The basic catalyst for the reaction usually is the sodium salt of the acid corresponding to the anhydride used.

$$ArCHO + (RCH_2CO)_2O \xrightarrow[100°]{\text{NaOCOCH}_2R} \left[ArCH=\overset{\overset{\displaystyle R}{|}}{C}-\overset{\overset{\displaystyle O}{\|}}{C}-O-\overset{\overset{\displaystyle O}{\|}}{C}-CH_2R + H_2O \right]$$

$$\downarrow$$

$$ArCH=\overset{\overset{\displaystyle R}{|}}{C}COOH + RCH_2COOH$$

The final product is an α,β-unsaturated acid formed by the hydrolysis of the intermediate anhydride.

7. **Benzoin Condensation.** When benzaldehyde is shaken with an aqueous alkali cyanide solution, two molecules condense to give a keto alcohol known as **benzoin.**

$$2\,C_6H_5CHO \xrightarrow{\text{KCN}} C_6H_5CCHOHC_6H_5$$
$$\overset{\|}{O}$$
$$\text{Benzoin}$$

Formally this reaction appears to take place by the addition of the hydrogen of one aldehyde group to the carbonyl group of the other and union of the carbon atoms. That the reaction is not simply an aldol-type condensation, however, is indicated by the fact that it is not catalyzed by ordinary bases but specifically by alkali cyanides. Lapworth (p. 201) proposed that the first step is the addition of cyanide ion followed by proton transfer to give the cyanohydrin. The cyanohydrin contains a hydrogen α to a nitrile group and hence can undergo a base-catalyzed condensation with a second molecule of aldehyde. The resulting cyanohydrin of benzoin then loses hydrogen cyanide.

$$ArCHO \xrightleftharpoons{[:CN^-]} \left[\begin{array}{c} ArCHO: \\ | \\ CN \end{array} \right]^- \xrightleftharpoons[[:OH^-]]{H_2O} ArCHOH \xrightleftharpoons{[:OH^-].} \left[\begin{array}{c} \ddots \\ ArCOH \\ | \\ CN \end{array} \right] \xrightleftharpoons{ArCHO}$$

$$\left[\begin{array}{c} O: \\ \| \\ Ar-C-CHAr \\ | \quad | \\ CN \quad OH \end{array} \right] \xrightleftharpoons[[:OH^-]]{H_2O} \begin{array}{c} Ar-C-CHOHAr \\ | \quad | \\ CN \quad OH \end{array} \xrightleftharpoons{[:OH^-]} \left[\begin{array}{c} Ar-C-CHOHAr \\ | \quad | \\ CN \quad O: \end{array} \right] \xrightleftharpoons{[:CN^-]} \begin{array}{c} ArCCHOHAr \\ \| \\ O \end{array}$$

8. Pinacol Formation. When aromatic aldehydes react with metallic sodium in ether solution, pinacols are formed analogous to those obtained from aliphatic ketones (p. 217).

$$2 C_6H_5CHO + 2 Na \longrightarrow \begin{array}{c} C_6H_5CH\text{----}CHC_6H_5 \\ | \quad\quad | \\ ONa \quad ONa \end{array} \xrightarrow{H_2O} \underset{Hydrobenzoin}{C_6H_5CHOHCHOHC_6H_5} + 2 NaOH$$

Important Aromatic Aldehydes

Benzaldehyde is one of the products of hydrolysis of the cyanogenetic glycoside, *amygdalin* (Gr. *amygdalon*, almond), which is present in the seeds of members of the prune family (p. 255). It once was called *oil of bitter almonds*.

$$\underset{\underset{Amygdalin}{OC_{12}H_{21}O_{10}}}{C_6H_5CHCN} \xrightarrow{H_2O} 2 \underset{Glucose}{C_6H_{12}O_6} + \underset{\substack{Benzaldehyde \\ cyanohydrin}}{C_6H_5CHOHCN} \longrightarrow \underset{Benzaldehyde}{C_6H_5CHO} + HCN$$

Benzaldehyde played an important part in the work which laid the foundations of structural organic chemistry, because Liebig and Woehler showed that the radical benzoyl, C_6H_5CO, could be transported intact through a large number of chemical transformations. Benzaldehyde is prepared commercially by the hydrolysis of benzylidene chloride, one of the products of the side-chain chlorination of toluene (p. 434). It is used to some extent as a flavoring agent and as a perfume, but chiefly for the synthesis of other organic compounds.

Cinnamaldehyde, $C_6H_5CH{=}CHCHO$, is the chief component of cassia oil and oil of cinnamon, the volatile oils of the bark of *Cinnamonium cassia* and *Cinnamonium ceylonicum*. It is synthesized by the aldol condensation of benzaldehyde with acetaldehyde (p. 536).

Anisaldehyde is prepared by the oxidation of anethole (p. 515).

$$\underset{Anethole}{CH_3O\langle\bigcirc\rangle\text{--}CH{=}CHCH_3} + 2 KMnO_4 \longrightarrow \underset{Anisaldehyde}{CH_3O\langle\bigcirc\rangle CHO} + 2 MnO_2 + CH_3COOK + KOH$$

Anisaldehyde is used in perfumery under the name *aubepine*. It has the odor of hawthorn flowers with no resemblance to the odor of anisole, benzaldehyde, or anethole. The floral character of the odor is completely lacking in the *ortho* and *meta* isomers.

Vanillin is the principal odorous constituent of vanilla beans, the long podlike capsules of a tropical climbing orchid, *Vanilla planifolia*. It probably is the most widely used flavoring material with the exception of salt, pepper, and vinegar. Annual production of the synthetic product in the United States is over half a million pounds. Besides being used to produce a desired odor or flavor of vanilla, it has a pronounced effect in masking undesirable odors. For example, one part in 2000 will mask the undesirable odor of fresh paint. The masking and neutralizing of the odors of articles manufactured from rubber, textiles, and plastics is an important phase of the perfumer's art.

The price of vanilla beans has fluctuated greatly whereas that of synthetic vanillin has continuously decreased. Since one pound of vanillin is equivalent in flavoring power to about 100 pounds of a good grade of vanilla beans, the first synthetic vanillin placed on the market in 1875 at $80 per pound could compete with vanilla beans at $2.50 per pound. The price of synthetic vanillin was $8 per pound in 1925 when that of vanilla beans was $9 per pound, the natural product competing only by virtue of the sales appeal of the phrase "pure vanilla extract" over "imitation" or "artificial vanilla flavor." In the depression year, 1932, the price of vanilla beans dropped to $0.50 per pound. The price of synthetic vanillin has been in the neighborhood of $2 per pound since 1940.

Numerous processes have been developed for the synthesis of vanillin. For many years the cheapest synthetic method started with eugenol from natural oil of cloves. The eugenol was isomerized to isoeugenol, in which the double bond is conjugated with the benzene ring, and the side chain then was oxidized with permanganate under controlled conditions.

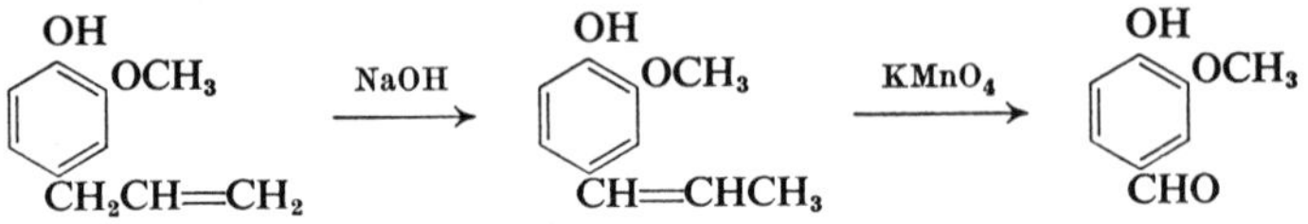

Guaiacol reacts readily with formaldehyde, and the resulting vanillyl alcohol can be oxidized to vanillin by one of several mild oxidizing agents such as *p*-nitrosodimethylaniline (p. 489).

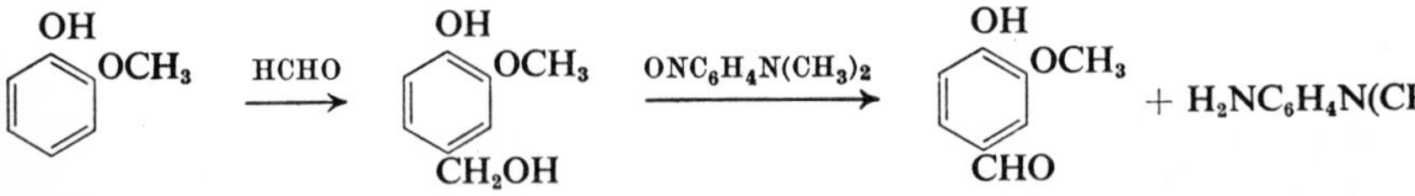

Currently vanillin is being obtained by heating the lignin sulfonates from waste sulfite liquors (pp. 400, 527) with alkali. **Ethavan** is the trade name of a synthetic product containing an ethoxy group in place of the methoxy group. It has 3.5 times the flavoring power of vanillin.

Methylation of vanillin with methyl sulfate and alkali yields **veratral** (3,4-dimethoxybenzaldehyde), a material useful in organic synthesis. **Piperonal** (*heliotropin*) is 3,4-methylenedioxybenzaldehyde and is made from safrole (p. 516) by a process analogous to the production of vanillin from eugenol.

It has a pleasant odor and is used in perfumery. It also is valuable in organic synthesis. In contrast to benzaldehyde and cinnamic aldehyde, which rapidly oxidize in air to the acids, anisaldehyde, vanillin, and piperonal are highly stable to autoxidation (p. 887).

KETONES

Ketones that do not have the carbonyl group adjacent to an aromatic ring are prepared by the general procedures described for aliphatic ketones (p. 194). Those ketones having a carbonyl group adjacent to the ring usually are prepared by the Friedel-Crafts reaction (p. 423). Either an acyl halide or an acid anhydride may be used. With acyl halides one equivalent of anhydrous aluminum chloride is required, because a stable addition product of the ketone and catalyst is formed. With acid anhydrides two moles of aluminum chloride are required, because the carboxylic acid formed also reacts with aluminum chloride.

$$ArH + ClCOR \text{ (or Ar)} + AlCl_3 \longrightarrow ArCR \text{ (or Ar)} + HCl$$
$$\underset{O : AlCl_3}{\|}$$
$$\downarrow H_2O$$
$$ArCOR \text{ (or Ar)} + H_2O : AlCl_3$$

$$ArH + (RCO)_2O + 2 AlCl_3 \longrightarrow ArCR + RCOOAlCl_2 + HCl$$
$$\underset{O : AlCl_3}{\|}$$
$$\downarrow 2 H_2O$$
$$ArCOR + RCOOH + H_2O : AlCl_3 + HOAlCl_2$$

Only one acyl group substitutes, because the carbonyl group is sufficiently deactivating to prevent a second substitution. For the same reason halogen and *meta*-directing groups prevent the Friedel-Crafts reaction from taking place. Nitrobenzene frequently is used as a solvent for these reactions. On the other hand, activating groups permit reactions of the Friedel-Crafts type to take place that do not occur with aromatic hydrocarbons. Resorcinol, for example, gives ketones by condensation with carboxylic acids in the presence of zinc chloride.

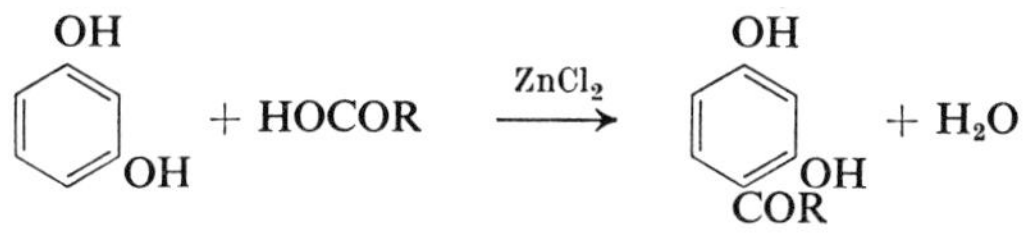

The deactivating effect of a carbonyl group involves both an inductive and a resonance effect. For the resonance effect to be operable, it must be possible for the oxygen atom of the carbonyl group to become coplanar with the benzene ring in order that the π orbital of the carbonyl group can overlap with the π orbital of the benzene ring.

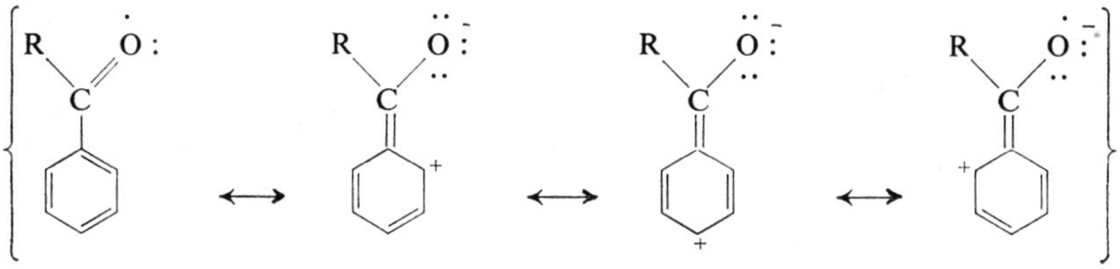

If this coplanarity is prevented by the blocking effect of groups in the *ortho* positions, the inductive effect alone is not sufficient to prevent substitution by a second acyl group. Thus although a second acetyl group cannot be introduced into 2,5-dimethylacetophenone by the Friedel-Crafts reaction, 2,6-dimethylacetophenone in which the resonance effect is blocked gives the diacetyl derivative.

Another modification of the Friedel-Crafts reaction is the *Fries reaction* in which phenolic ketones are obtained by heating phenol esters with aluminum chloride in nitrobenzene solution.

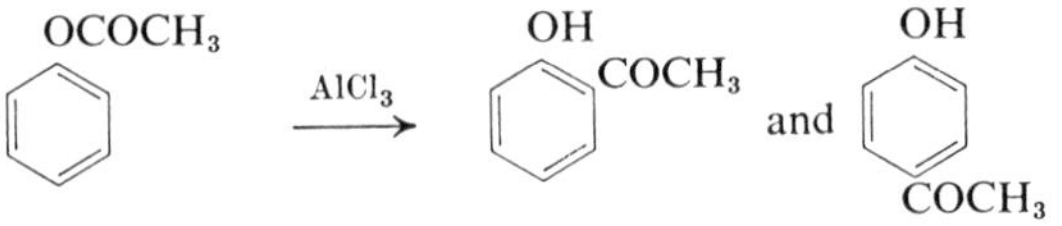

Aromatic ketones result also from the hydrolysis of the addition products of Grignard reagents with aryl cyanides.

$$ArC{\equiv}N + RMgCl \longrightarrow Ar\overset{\underset{\displaystyle R}{|}}{C}{=}NMgCl \xrightarrow{H_2O\,+\,2\,HCl} \underset{\underset{\displaystyle O}{\|}}{ArCR} + NH_4Cl + MgCl_2$$

This reaction is less useful with aliphatic nitriles containing α hydrogen, because the latter is sufficiently acidic to give the hydrocarbon.

$$RCH_2C{\equiv}N + R'MgCl \longrightarrow [RCHC{\equiv}\overset{+}{N}]MgCl + R'H$$

Aromatic ketones undergo the same general reactions as aliphatic ketones. They readily undergo bimolecular reduction to pinacols. Magnesium and magnesium iodide (so-called magnesious iodide) is the preferred reducing agent.

$$2\,(C_6H_5)_2CO + Mg \xrightarrow{MgI_2} \left[\underset{\underset{\displaystyle O^-\ \ O^-}{|\ \ \ \ |}}{(C_6H_5)_2C{-}C(C_6H_5)_2} \right] Mg^{++} \xrightarrow{2\,H_2O}$$

$$\underset{\underset{\displaystyle OH\ \ OH}{|\ \ \ \ |}}{(C_6H_5)_2C{-}C(C_6H_5)_2} + Mg(OH)_2$$

Benzpinacol

A reaction which is valuable particularly in the aromatic series is the conversion of aryl alkyl ketones to amides by the *Willgerodt reaction*.

$$ArCO(CH_2)_nCH_3 + 2\,(NH_4)_2S + S \xrightarrow{160°} Ar(CH_2)_{n+1}CONH_2 + 3\,NH_4SH$$

In the rearranged product the carbonyl group always is on the terminal carbon atom of the side chain. The principal use of the Willgerodt reaction has been for the preparation of aryl-substituted aliphatic acids. If the ketone is heated with equimolar amounts of sulfur and an anhydrous amine instead of aqueous ammonium polysulfide, the thioamide is formed, which can be hydrolyzed to the acid or reduced electrolytically to the amine.

$$ArCOCH_3 \xrightarrow{(CH_3)_2NH\,+\,S} ArCH_2CSN(CH_3)_2 \begin{array}{l} \xrightarrow{H_2O} ArCH_2COOH \\[2mm] \xrightarrow{4\,[H]} ArCH_2CH_2N(CH_3)_2 \end{array}$$

Acetophenone is methyl phenyl ketone and **benzophenone** is phenyl ketone. Both have some use in perfumery and are valuable intermediates for organic synthesis. They have been made by the Friedel-Crafts reaction from benzene and acetyl chloride or acetic anhydride, and from benzene and benzoyl chloride respectively. Acetophenone now is made commercially by the catalytic air-oxidation of ethylbenzene.

$$C_6H_5CH_2CH_3 + O_2 \xrightarrow[130°,\ 50\ \text{p.s.i.}]{Mn(OAc)_2} C_6H_5COCH_3 + H_2O$$

It is used chiefly as an intermediate for the synthesis of styrene (p. 573), but other organic compounds also are being made from it (pp. 525, 528). The Claisen reaction of benzaldehyde with acetophenone (p. 536) gives **benzylidene-acetophenone**, $C_6H_5COCH{=}CHC_6H_5$. It was given the name *chalcone* because its hydroxy derivatives have a reddish yellow color (Gr. *chalkos*, copper). **Michler ketone**, *p*-dimethylaminophenyl ketone, is made from dimethylaniline and phosgene. It is used as a dye intermediate (p. 681).

$$4\ (CH_3)_2NC_6H_5 + COCl_2 \xrightarrow{ZnCl_2} (CH_3)_2N\langle\ \rangle CO\langle\ \rangle N(CH_3)_2 + 2\ C_6H_5\overset{+}{N}H(CH_3)_2\overset{-}{Cl}$$

Michler ketone

Chlorination or bromination of acetophenone gives **ω-chloro-** or **ω-bromo-acetophenone** (*phenacyl chloride* or *phenacyl bromide*). Both are relatively harmless but potent lachrymators, and chloroacetophenone is used extensively as a tear gas for dispelling mobs. The phenacyl chlorides and bromides react with the sodium salts of carboxylic acids to give solid esters which serve as derivatives for the identification of carboxylic acids. *p*-**Nitrophenacyl bromide** is particularly useful for this purpose.

$$p\text{-}NO_2C_6H_4COCH_2Br + NaOCOR \longrightarrow p\text{-}NO_2C_6H_4COCH_2OCOR + NaBr$$

p-Nitrophenacyl ester

Benzyl alkyl ketones can be made from an aldehyde and a primary aliphatic nitro compound by way of the oxime.

$$ArCHO + RCH_2NO_2 \longrightarrow \underset{R}{ArCH{=}CNO_2} \xrightarrow{Fe,\ HCl} \left[\underset{R}{ArCH{=}CNHOH}\right] \rightleftarrows$$

$$\underset{R}{ArCH_2C{=}NOH} \xrightarrow{H_2O,\ HCl} ArCH_2COR + HONH_3Cl$$

Benzil, a 1,2-diketone, is obtained easily by the oxidation of benzoin (p. 536). Even mild oxidizing agents such as Fehling solution or copper sulfate in pyridine bring about the reaction.

$$\underset{\text{Benzoin}}{C_6H_5COCHOHC_6H_5} + 2\ CuSO_4 + 2\ C_5H_5N \longrightarrow \underset{\text{Benzil}}{C_6H_5COCOC_6H_5} + Cu_2SO_4 + (C_5H_5NH)_2SO_4$$

The cupric sulfate can be regenerated by passing air into the cuprous solution. Benzil on heating with aqueous or alcoholic alkali undergoes the **benzilic acid rearrangement** to give sodium benzilate.

$$C_6H_5COCOC_6H_5 + NaOH \longrightarrow (C_6H_5)_2COHCOONa$$

The benzilic acid rearrangement appears to proceed by a mechanism analogous to that for the Cannizzaro reaction (p. 535) in that the rearrangement involves the intramolecular shift of a group with its pair of electrons.

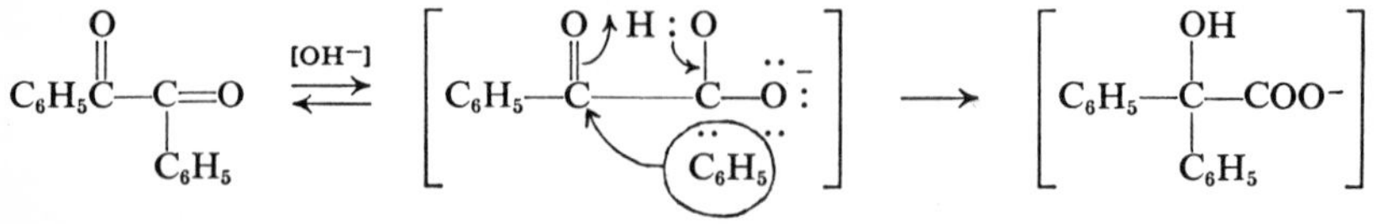

$$C_6H_5\overset{O}{\underset{C_6H_5}{\underset{|}{C}}}-C=O \underset{\longleftarrow}{\overset{[OH^-]}{\rightleftharpoons}} \left[C_6H_5-\overset{O}{\overset{||}{C}}\overset{H:O}{\underset{C_6H_5}{C}}-\overset{..}{\underset{..}{O}}: \right]^- \longrightarrow \left[C_6H_5-\overset{OH}{\underset{C_6H_5}{\underset{|}{C}}}-COO^- \right]$$

If sodium ethoxide is used instead of sodium hydroxide, the products are ethyl benzoate and benzaldehyde.

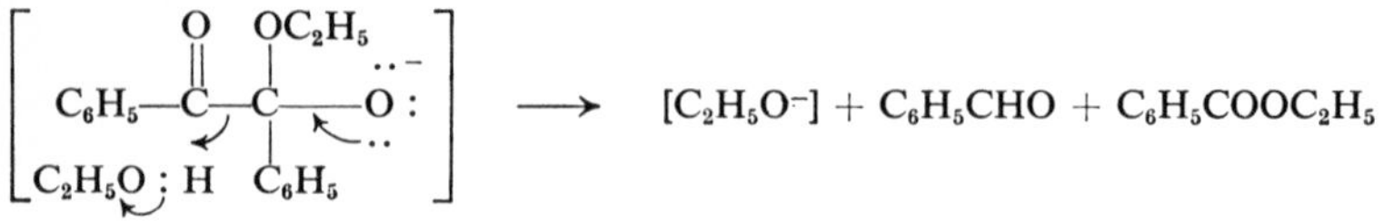

$$\left[C_6H_5-\overset{O}{\overset{||}{C}}\overset{OC_2H_5}{\underset{C_2H_5O:H}{C}}\overset{..}{\underset{C_6H_5}{O:}} \right] \longrightarrow [C_2H_5O^-] + C_6H_5CHO + C_6H_5COOC_2H_5$$

✳ STEREOCHEMISTRY OF THE OXIMES ✳

When benzaldehyde reacts with hydroxylamine, an oxime called α-benzaldoxime, melting at 34°, is formed. If this oxime is dissolved in ether and dry hydrogen chloride is added, a hydrochloride precipitates. Decomposition of the hydrochloride with sodium carbonate solution yields an oxime called β-benzaldoxime, which melts at 128°–130°. Both oximes on hydrolysis yield benzaldehyde and hydroxylamine. Benzophenone gives only a single oxime, but mixed ketones give two oximes. For example, phenyl *p*-tolyl ketone gives an α-ketoxime, m.p. 153°–154°, and a β-ketoxime, m.p. 115°–116°.

Hantzsch and Werner (pp. 500, 340) in 1890 proposed a stereochemical explanation for the isomerism. They assumed that the three nitrogen valences are nonplanar and that a carbon-nitrogen double bond can give geometrical isomers in the same way as a carbon-carbon double bond (p. 354). Hantzsch proposed the terms *syn* and *anti* for the two forms. For the aldoximes the prefixes refer to the relative positions of the hydrogen and hydroxyl group, and for the ketoximes they refer to the relative positions of the hydroxyl group and the group adjacent to the prefix.

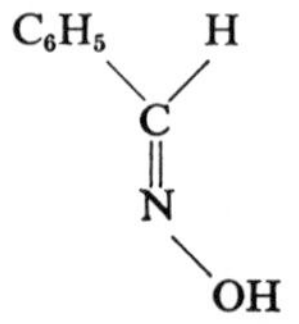

$$\begin{array}{cc} C_6H_5 & H \\ & \diagdown \diagup \\ & C \\ & || \\ & N \\ & \diagdown \\ & OH \end{array} \qquad \begin{array}{cc} C_6H_5 & H \\ & \diagdown \diagup \\ & C \\ & || \\ & N \\ & \diagup \\ HO & \end{array}$$

syn-Benzaldoxime 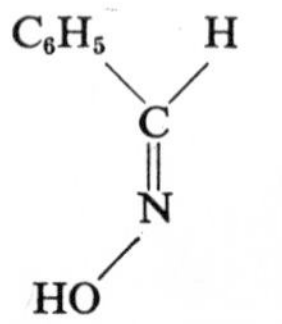 　　　　　*anti*-Benzaldoxime

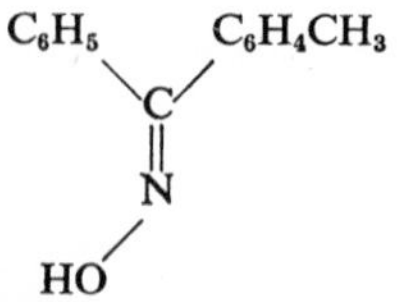

$$\begin{array}{cc} C_6H_5 & C_6H_4CH_3 \\ & \diagdown \diagup \\ & C \\ & || \\ & N \\ & \diagup \\ HO & \end{array} \qquad \begin{array}{cc} C_6H_5 & C_6H_4CH_3 \\ & \diagdown \diagup \\ & C \\ & || \\ & N \\ & \diagdown \\ & OH \end{array}$$

syn-Phenyl tolyl ketoxime 　　　*syn*-Tolyl phenyl ketoxime
or *anti*-tolyl phenyl ketoxime 　 or *anti*-phenyl tolyl ketoxime

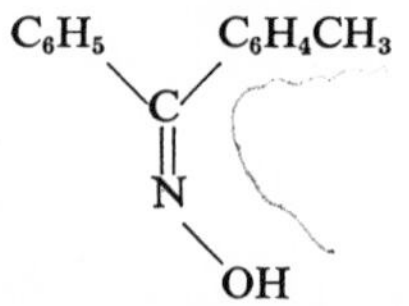

The currently accepted configurations of the isomeric forms were assigned by Meisenheimer.[3] If a reactive halogen atom is *ortho* to the aldoximino group, one form of the aldoxime undergoes ring formation easily in the presence of alkali, whereas the other form gives the same product much more slowly. It seems likely therefore that the form undergoing ready cyclization is the *anti* aldoxime, and that the *syn* aldoxime first must rearrange to the *anti* form before cyclization takes place. Furthermore the form that undergoes easy ring closure gives an acetate which reacts with alkali to form a nitrile, whereas the acetate

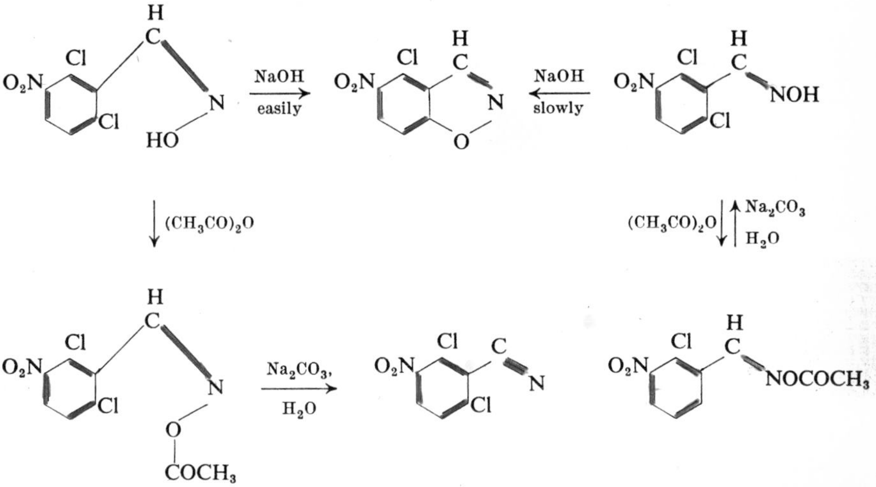

of the other form regenerates the original oxime. Thus a procedure is at hand for determining the configuration of other aldoximes that cannot undergo ring closure. For example, α-benzaldoxime gives an acetate, m.p. 14°–16°, which regenerates the oxime when warmed with sodium carbonate solution, whereas β-benzaldoxime gives an acetate, m.p. 55°–56°, which by the same treatment yields benzonitrile. Hence it seems likely that α-benzaldoxime is the *syn* form and that β-benzaldoxime is the *anti* form.

Ring closure first was used by Meisenheimer in 1921 to determine the configuration of ketoximes.

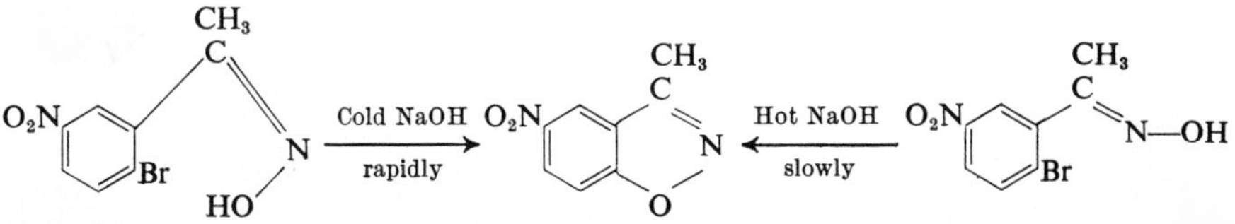

---

[3] Jacob Meisenheimer (1876–1934), student of Baeyer and successor to Wislicenus at the University of Tuebingen. He is known not only for his work on the configuration of the oximes, but also for his resolution of amine oxides and phosphine oxides, and his attempts to resolve tricovalent nitrogen compounds.

This behavior also has been correlated with a difference in chemical behavior not dependent on ring closure. When ketoximes are treated with a variety of acidic reagents such as concentrated sulfuric acid, acetyl chloride, or phosphorus pentachloride in ether solution, rearrangement to an amide takes place.

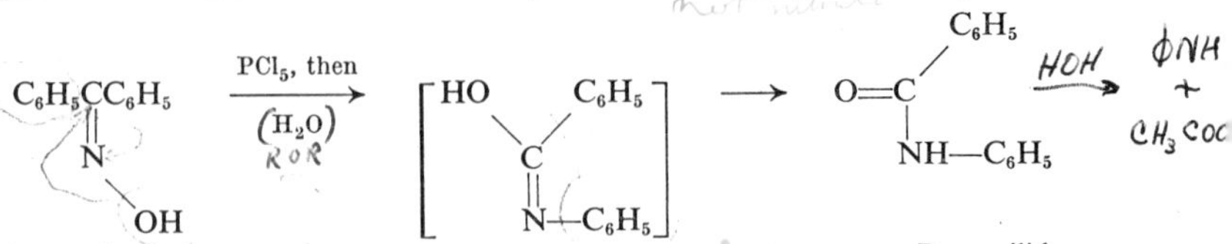

Benzophenone oxime

Benzanilide

This reaction is known as the **Beckmann [4] rearrangement**. The *syn* and *anti* ketoximes yield different products. For the bromonitroacetophenone oximes, the isomer that undergoes easy ring closure gives the *N*-methylamide of 2-bromo-5-nitrobenzoic acid, whereas the other isomer gives the 2-bromo-5-nitroanilide of acetic acid.

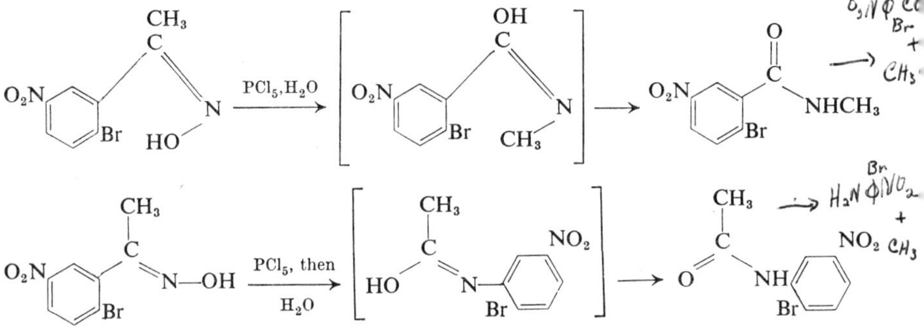

Thus the groups that exchange places in the rearrangement are those that are *anti* to each other. Hence the Beckmann rearrangement can be used to determine the configuration of ketoximes that cannot undergo ring closure. For example the α isomer of phenyl tolyl ketoxime yields an anilide which can be hydrolyzed to *p*-toluic acid and aniline, and is assigned the *anti*-phenyl tolyl ketoxime structure, whereas the β isomer yields an anilide which can be hydrolyzed to benzoic acid and toluidine, and is assigned the *syn*-phenyl tolyl ketoxime structure.

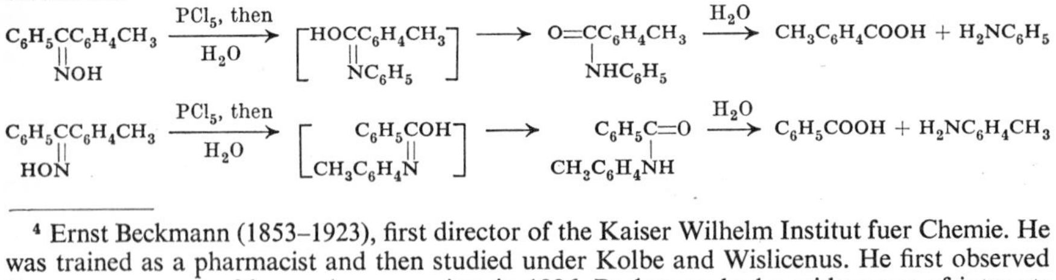

[4] Ernst Beckmann (1853–1923), first director of the Kaiser Wilhelm Institut fuer Chemie. He was trained as a pharmacist and then studied under Kolbe and Wislicenus. He first observed the rearrangement of benzophenone oxime in 1886. Beckmann had a wide range of interests and occupied chairs in organic, physical, and pharmaceutical chemistry, and in food technology and nutrition. He developed many pieces of laboratory apparatus such as the sodium press, the differential thermometer, electromagnetic stirrers, and electrical heating apparatus. Beckmann redesigned the laboratories at Leipzig, and the Kaiser Wilhelm Institut was built largely according to his plans.

These conclusions have been confirmed by other chemical reactions and particularly by the determination of the dipole moments of properly substituted aldoximes and ketoximes. Aliphatic aldehydes and ketones do not give isomeric oximes, probably because one form is much more stable than the other.

The mechanism of the Beckmann rearrangement has been of considerable interest. Energetically the reaction is favored, because an arrangement in which oxygen and nitrogen are linked to carbon is more stable than one in which two electron-attracting elements such as nitrogen and oxygen are linked to each other. The rearrangement is intramolecular, rather than intermolecular, and the migration of the *anti* R′ group with its pair of electrons takes place simultaneously with the loss of the group attached to nitrogen.

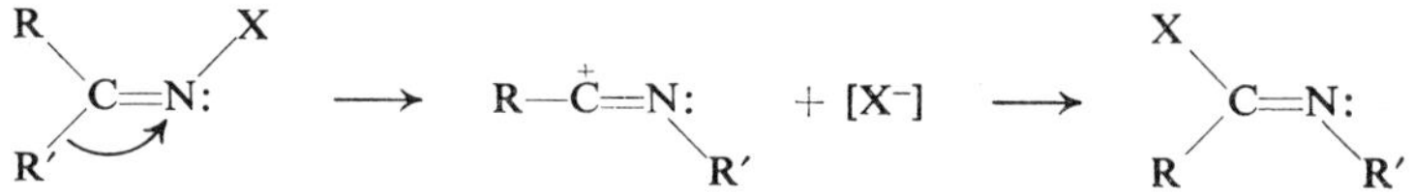

Fig. 79. Beckmann rearrangement of oximes.

The function of the catalysts is to facilitate the removal of the hydroxyl group with the pair of electrons by adding a proton, by forming an ester, or by replacing the hydroxyl group with chlorine.

When the monoximes of benzil are subjected to the conditions of the Beckmann rearrangement, cleavage of the molecule results. α-Benzil monoxime gives benzonitrile whereas β-benzil monoxime gives phenylisocyanide.

$$C_6H_5\underset{\underset{\text{HON}}{\|}}{C}COC_6H_5 \longrightarrow C_6H_5CN + C_6H_5COOH$$

α-Benzil monoxime

$$C_6H_5\underset{\underset{\text{NOH}}{\|}}{C}COC_6H_5 \longrightarrow C_6H_5NC + C_6H_5COOH$$

β-Benzil monoxime

Reactions of this type have been called *second order* Beckmann rearrangements.

REVIEW QUESTIONS

1. Compare the chemical behavior of benzyl chloride, benzylamine, and benzyl alcohol with that of chlorobenzene, aniline, and phenol.
2. What is the Gattermann carbon monoxide synthesis; the Gattermann hydrogen cyanide synthesis; the Reimer-Tiemann synthesis?
3. Give equations for the reaction of benzaldehyde with concentrated aqueous sodium hydroxide; ammonia; dilute potassium cyanide solution.
4. Discuss the mechanism of the benzoin condensation and compare with the aldol condensation.
5. Discuss the Friedel-Crafts reaction for the preparation of alkyl aryl ketones and diaryl ketones, including reagents and limitations of the reaction.
6. What is the Claisen reaction? Illustrate by reactions for the preparation of benzylidene-acetophenone, benzylideneacetone, and dibenzylideneacetone.
7. What are *anils* or *Schiff bases* and how are they prepared? What is formed on acid hydrolysis of anils; on catalytic reduction?

8. Discuss the isomerism of the aldoximes and the ketoximes. What is the Beckmann rearrangement and how may it be used to determine the configuration of ketoximes? What method is available for determining the configuration of aldoximes?

PROBLEMS

9. Give equations for the following preparations:

   A. (a) p-Chlorobenzaldehyde from toluene; (b) p-tolualdehyde from a nitrile; (c) ethylphenylcarbinol using a Grignard reagent; (d) p-methylacetophenone from an acyl halide; (e) o-methylbenzylamine from o-xylene; (f) p,p'-dimethoxybenzil from anisaldehyde; (g) o-nitrobenzaldehyde from o-nitrobenzyl chloride; (h) piperonylideneacetone from safrole; (i) 2,4-dimethylbenzaldehyde from a hydrocarbon; (j) diethylbenzylamine from benzaldehyde.

   B. (a) Anisylideneacetone from anethole; (b) benzyldimethylamine from toluene; (c) 2,2'-dimethylbenzil from o-tolualdehyde; (d) p-nitrobenzaldehyde from toluene; (e) diphenylmethylcarbinol using a Grignard reagent; (f) o-chlorobenzaldehyde from a nitrile; (g) m-tolualdehyde from m-methylbenzyl chloride; (h) p-methoxypropiophenone from an ether; (i) 3,4-dimethoxybenzylmethylamine from veratraldehyde; (j) p-tolualdehyde from a hydrocarbon.

   C. (a) p-Ethylbenzaldehyde from p-(chloromethyl)ethylbenzene; (b) cinnamylideneacetone from benzaldehyde; (c) p-i-propylbenzaldehyde from a hydrocarbon; (d) (m-methylbenzyl)phenylamine from m-xylene; (e) p-bromobenzaldehyde from a nitrile; (f) 3,3'-dichlorobenzil from m-chlorobenzaldehyde; (g) o-bromobenzaldehyde from toluene; (h) p,p'-dimethylbenzophenone from a hydrocarbon; (i) p-methoxybenzyldimethylamine from anisaldehyde; (j) benzyldiphenylcarbinol using a Grignard reagent.

10. Give equations for the conversion of benzaldehyde into the following compounds: (a) $C_6H_5CH_2OH$; (b) C_6H_5COCl; (c) C_6H_5COOH; (d) $C_6H_5CHOHCH_3$; (e) $C_6H_5CH=CHCHO$; (f) $C_6H_5CHOHCOC_6H_5$; (g) m-BrC_6H_4CHO; (h) C_6H_5CN; (i) $C_6H_5CHOHCN$; (j) $C_6H_5CH=N-NHCONH_2$; (k) $C_6H_5CH=NNHC_6H_5$; (l) $C_6H_5N=CHC_6H_5$; (m) $C_6H_5CHOHCHOHC_6H_5$; (n) $CH_3COCH=CHC_6H_5$; (o) $C_6H_5CHCl_2$; (p) $C_6H_5CH_2OCOC_6H_5$; (q) $C_6H_5CH=CHCOOH$; (r) $C_6H_5CH=CHNO_2$.

11. Give reactions for the following syntheses: (a) triphenylmethyl chloride from ethyl benzoate; (b) β-phenylethylchloride from benzyl chloride; (c) benzyl methyl ketone from nitroethane; (d) benzedrine from phenylacetic acid; (e) anisaldehyde from phenol; (f) propadrine from benzaldehyde; (g) coniferyl alcohol from vanillin; (h) tyramine from phenol; (i) veratral from eugenol; (j) hydroxydiphenylacetic acid from benzaldehyde.

12. Indicate a possible series of reactions for the synthesis of the following compounds starting only with hydrocarbons as the source of the aromatic nuclei: (a) α-methylbenzyl ether; (b) β-phenylethylamine; (c) anisaldehyde; (d) Michler ketone; (e) m-nitrobenzaldehyde; (f) ω-chloroacetophenone; (g) p-dimethylaminobenzaldehyde; (h) 2,4-dinitrobenzaldehyde; (i) p-nitrophenacyl bromide; (j) benzpinacol.

13. How could one distinguish by a chemical reaction between the members of the following pairs of compounds: (a) phenylethyl alcohol and phenetole; (b) anethole and anisaldehyde; (c) vanillin and piperonal; (d) p-tolualdehyde and anisaldehyde; (e) benzylaniline and diphenylamine; (f) acetophenone and isobutyrophenone; (g) nitrobenzene and benzaldehyde; (h) biphenyl and benzophenone; (i) benzyl phenyl ether and phenyl ether; (j) benzylamine and dibenzylamine.

14. Write the structural formulas and configurations for the oximes that give the following products when the amides formed by Beckmann rearrangement are hydrolyzed: (a) benzoic acid and p-toluidine; (b) p-bromobenzoic acid and p-aminocumene; (c) m-toluic acid and p-chloroaniline; (d) o-nitrobenzoic acid and aniline.

15. It is desired to prepare the following compounds with radioactive carbon at the starred position. Give the series of reactions by which this may be accomplished, starting with radioactive barium carbonate, $BaC*O_3$, and any other readily available materials: (a) $C_6H_5C*H_2CH_2CH_2OH$; (b) $C_6H_5C*H=CH_2$; (c) $C_6H_5COOC*H_2CH_3$; (d) $C_6H_5C*HOHCOOH$; (e) $(C_6H_5)_2C*(OH)C_2H_5$; (f) m-$C_6H_4(C*OOH)COOH$.

Chapter 26

AROMATIC CARBOXYLIC ACIDS
AND DERIVATIVES

The effect of an aromatic nucleus on the properties of a carboxyl group attached to it is less pronounced than the effect on other groups such as halogen, amino, and hydroxyl groups. Nevertheless the effect is sufficient to warrant special attention being given to some of the methods of preparation and reactions of aromatic carboxylic acids. Many of the derivatives of carboxylic acids are important compounds.

Preparation

Strictly aromatic acids, in which the carboxyl group is attached to the ring, can be prepared by the general methods available for aliphatic carboxylic acids. Some of these general methods become particularly important in the aromatic series.

1. **Carbonation of Grignard Reagents.** Arylmagnesium halides react with carbon dioxide to give salts of carboxylic acids.

$$ArMgX \xrightarrow{CO_2} ArCO_2MgX \xrightarrow{HX} ArCOOH$$

2. **Hydrolysis of Nitriles.** Aryl cyanides can be prepared by the reaction of aryl halides with sodium cyanide (p. 435), from sulfonates by cyanide fusion (p. 469), or from amines through the diazonium salts (p. 495). Acid- or base-catalyzed hydrolysis yields the acid.

$$ArCN \begin{array}{c} \xrightarrow{NaOH + H_2O} ArCOONa + NH_3 \\ \\ \xrightarrow{HCl + 2 H_2O} ArCOOH + NH_4Cl \end{array}$$

3. **Hydrolysis of the Trichloromethyl Group.** Since the trichloromethyl group frequently can be formed by direct chlorination (p. 434), hydrolysis of this group becomes an important procedure for preparing aromatic acids.

$$C_6H_5CCl_3 + 2 Na_2CO_3 \text{ (aqueous)} \longrightarrow C_6H_5COONa + 3 NaCl + 2 CO_2$$
Benzotrichloride   Sodium benzoate

4. **Oxidation of Side Chains.** Although only primary alcohols and aldehydes are oxidized to acids without loss of carbon in the aliphatic series, even a methyl group attached to an aromatic nucleus can be oxidized to a carboxyl group in good yield.

$$ArCH_3 \xrightarrow[\text{or } KMnO_4]{Na_2Cr_2O_7 + H_2SO_4,} ArCOOH + H_2O$$

547

The aryl group makes the carbon atom attached to the ring more easily oxidized than atoms further away from the ring. Once this carbon is oxidized, further oxidation takes place still more readily; hence side chains longer than methyl also give aromatic acids.

$$ArCH_2R \xrightarrow{\text{Ox.}} ArCHOHR \longrightarrow ArCOR \longrightarrow ArCOOH$$

Most side chains in which a carbon atom is attached to the nucleus are converted to a carboxyl group on strong oxidation. The reaction is useful not only for preparing aromatic acids, but also for locating the position of side chains in the aromatic nucleus, since the constitutions of the more common aromatic acids are known. The reaction is limited to compounds that do not contain hydroxyl or amino groups in the nucleus, because the latter increase the ease of oxidation of the ring.

Reactions

For the most part the reactions of aromatic acids are identical with those of aliphatic acids, the more important differences being in degree rather than in kind.

1. **Acidity.** The unsubstituted benzene ring gives rise to a slightly stronger acid than an unsubstituted alkyl group (benzoic acid, $K_a = 6.6 \times 10^{-5}$, acetic acid $K_a = 1.8 \times 10^{-5}$). The effect of substituents in the nucleus on the ionization of benzoic acid has been studied extensively. Ionization constants for a few compounds are listed in Table 26.

TABLE 26

IONIZATION CONSTANTS OF BENZOIC ACID AND DERIVATIVES

SUBSTITUENT	POSITION		
	ortho	*meta*	*para*
H	6.6×10^{-5}	6.6×10^{-5}	6.6×10^{-5}
CH_3	1.2×10^{-4}	5.3×10^{-5}	4.2×10^{-5}
OH	1.1×10^{-3}	8.3×10^{-5}	3.3×10^{-5}
OCH_3	8.0×10^{-5}	8.2×10^{-5}	3.4×10^{-5}
Br	1.4×10^{-3}	1.5×10^{-4}	1.0×10^{-4}
Cl	1.2×10^{-3}	1.5×10^{-4}	1.0×10^{-4}
NO_2	6.7×10^{-3}	3.1×10^{-4}	3.7×10^{-4}

Substituents in the *ortho* position increase the acidity regardless of the nature of the group, indicating that factors other than the inductive and resonance effects are important. Certain correlations are discernible for substituents in the *meta* and *para* positions. The electron-donating effect of a methyl group is transmitted to the carboxyl group and the increased electron density decreases the tendency to lose a proton. The hydroxyl and methoxyl groups in the *meta* position decrease the electron density through their inductive effect, which is electron-attracting, and increase the acidity. The resonance effect is in the opposite direction, and since it can operate in the *para* position, it overbalances the inductive effect and the acid is weaker. The inductive effect is stronger and the resonance effect weaker for a halogen atom than for an oxygen atom, and halogen increases the acidity when in either the *meta* or the *para* position. For the nitro group the inductive and resonance effects operate in the same direction and cause increased acidity when in either position. It is of interest that a correlation has been established between the effect of a wide variety of substituents in the *meta* and *para* positions on the rates of reaction and the position of equilibrium for a large number of reactions. If $k°$ is the rate or equilibrium constant for the unsubstituted benzene derivative and k that for the same compound with a substituent in the *meta* or *para* position, then

$$\log k - \log k° = \rho\sigma$$

where ρ is a constant that depends on the particular reaction being carried out and is independent of the substituent, and σ is a constant that depends on the nature of the substituent and is independent of the nature of the reaction (Hammett equation). Therefore if the values of ρ and σ are known, it is possible to calculate the rate or position of equilibrium for a reaction from the rate or position of equilibrium of the unsubstituted compound.

2. **Esterification.** If no substituents are present in the *ortho* positions, direct esterification of the carboxyl group proceeds as with straight chain aliphatic acids. If, however, one of the *ortho* positions is substituted, the rate of esterification is greatly decreased, and if both *ortho* positions are occupied, esterification does not take place. This behavior was noted first by Victor Meyer (p. 21) and sometimes is called the *Victor Meyer esterification law*. The esters of *ortho*-substituted benzoic acids can be prepared by the reaction of the silver salts with alkyl halides. However once they are formed, they cannot be hydrolyzed easily.

These effects are observed regardless of the nature of the substituents. Apparently a **steric effect (steric hindrance,** p. 117) is involved analogous to that noted for secondary and tertiary aliphatic carboxylic acids (p. 165). Groups larger than hydrogen so effectively occupy the space surrounding the carbon atom of the carboxyl group that there is insufficient room to form the intermediate or transition state necessary for the formation or the saponification of the ester.

3. **Acyl Halide Formation.** In general the hydroxyl group of aromatic acids is replaced with more difficulty than that of aliphatic acids, and phosphorus pentachloride is the preferred reagent instead of phosphorus trichloride.

$$ArCOOH + PCl_5 \longrightarrow ArCOCl + POCl_3 + HCl$$

Thionyl chloride also can be used. Sometimes the acid chloride can be prepared conveniently by the chlorination of the aldehyde (p. 534).

The aromatic acyl chlorides (frequently called *aroyl chlorides*) are insoluble in water and hence react with it very slowly. As a result alcohols and amines can be acylated in aqueous solution. When dilute alkali is used to combine with the hydrogen chloride formed, the reaction is called the *Schotten-Baumann reaction.*

$$ArCOCl + ROH + NaOH \longrightarrow ArCOOR + NaCl + H_2O$$

$$ArCOCl + H_2NR + NaOH \longrightarrow ArCONHR + NaCl + H_2O$$

A more recent procedure uses a tertiary amine such as pyridine (p. 620) as both solvent and base.

$$ArCOCl + HOR + C_5H_5N \longrightarrow ArCOOR + C_5H_5NHCl$$

4. **Decarboxylation.** When the salt of an aromatic carboxylic acid is fused with alkali, the carboxyl group is replaced by hydrogen. The usual reagent is *soda lime*, a mixture of sodium hydroxide and calcium hydroxide.

$$ArCOONa + NaOH \xrightarrow{\text{Heat}} ArH + Na_2CO_3$$

This reaction takes place with aliphatic carboxylic acids also, but except for sodium acetate which yields methane, the side reactions are so complex that the reaction has no practical value.

5. **Reduction of the Carboxyl Group.** Aromatic acids are reduced to benzyl alcohols in 80 to 99 per cent yields by lithium aluminum hydride (p. 172). As with aliphatic compounds, reduction of the esters or acyl halides is preferred because they are more soluble in ether, and one third less reagent is required. Reduction of aromatic esters with sodium and alcohol (p. 172) is not satisfactory for the preparation of benzyl alcohols because the ethoxycarbonyl group is reduced to a methyl group instead of a hydroxymethyl group.

$$C_6H_5COOC_2H_5 + 6\,Na + 4\,C_2H_5OH \longrightarrow C_6H_5CH_3 + 5\,C_2H_5ONa + NaOH$$

6. **Reduction of the Nucleus.** In contrast to the aromatic hydrocarbons and most of their derivatives, the nucleus of the carboxylic acids can be reduced by chemical reagents. Thus sodium benzoate in aqueous solution is reduced by sodium amalgam to sodium tetrahydrobenzoate, an increase in alkalinity being prevented by passing carbon dioxide into the solution.

$$C_6H_5COONa + 4\,Na(Hg) + 4\,H_2O \longrightarrow C_6H_9COONa + 4\,NaOH$$

Sodium and boiling amyl alcohol yield hexahydrobenzoic acid (cyclohexane carboxylic acid).

$$C_6H_5COONa + 6\,Na + 6\,C_5H_{11}OH \longrightarrow C_6H_{11}COONa + 6\,NaOC_5H_{11}$$

This behavior is analogous to that of α,β-unsaturated carbonyl compounds in general (p. 763).

Important Aromatic Acids and Derivatives

Benzoic acid was described in 1560 as a product of the distillation of Siam gum benzoin, an aromatic resin. The term *benzoin* is a corruption of the Arabic *luban jawi* which means the *frankincense of Java*. Its composition was established by Liebig and Woehler in 1832. It has been manufactured technically by the oxidation of toluene, by the hydrolysis of benzotrichloride, and by the partial decarboxylation of phthalic acid (p. 553). The benzoyl derivative of glycine, $C_6H_5CONHCH_2COOH$, occurs in the urine of horses and other herbivora and is known as **hippuric acid** (Gr. *hippos*, horse). When benzoic acid is ingested by animals, including humans, it is detoxified by combination with glycine and eliminated in the urine as hippuric acid. **Sodium benzoate** frequently is added to foods as a preservative. Since only free benzoic acid is effective in inhibiting the growth of microorganisms, the pH of the food must be less than 4.5. *o*-**Iodohippuric acid** also is excreted by the kidneys and, because iodine is opaque to X-rays, it is used for X-ray examination of the urinary tract. **3-Acetylamino-2,4,6-triiodobenzoic acid** has a much higher iodine content and is used for the same purpose.

Benzoyl chloride is made by the chlorination of benzaldehyde. It is a liquid having a characteristic odor and strong lachrymatory action, and is used as a benzoylating agent. When benzoyl chloride is shaken with sodium peroxide in water or with an alkaline solution of hydrogen peroxide, **benzoyl peroxide** is formed.

$$2\ C_6H_5COCl + Na_2O_2 \longrightarrow C_6H_5\overset{O}{\overset{\|}{C}}-O-O-\overset{O}{\overset{\|}{C}}C_6H_5 + 2\ NaCl$$

Benzoyl peroxide

Benzoyl peroxide is used as a bleaching agent for edible oils and fats and for flour and as a catalyst for polymerization reactions (pp. 574, 726). When it reacts with sodium methoxide, methyl benzoate and sodium peroxybenzoate are formed. Removal of the methyl benzoate, acidification, and extraction with chloroform gives a chloroform solution of **peroxybenzoic acid.**

$$(C_6H_5COO)_2 + NaOCH_3 \longrightarrow CH_3OOCC_6H_5 + C_6H_5\overset{O}{\overset{\|}{C}}-O-ONa \xrightarrow{HCl} C_6H_5\overset{O}{\overset{\|}{C}}-O-OH$$

Peroxybenzoic acid

Peroxybenzoic acid reacts quantitatively with nonconjugated double bonds to form the oxide, a valuable preparative procedure.

$$RCH{=}CHR + C_6H_5CO_3H \longrightarrow RCH-CHR + C_6H_5COOH$$
$$\underset{O}{\diagdown\diagup}$$

Since the peroxybenzoic acid liberates iodine from potassium iodide, the chloroform solution can be standardized and the reaction used for the *quantitative estimation of double bonds.*

3,5-Dinitrobenzoic acid is made by the nitration of benzoic acid. Reaction with phosphorus pentachloride gives **3,5-dinitrobenzoyl chloride,** a valuable reagent for the identification of alcohols. The latter react with it even in aqueous solution by the Schotten-Baumann reaction (p. 549) to give solid 3,5-dinitrobenzoates.

The methylbenzoic acids are called **toluic acids.** They are obtained by the partial oxidation of *o-*, *m-*, and *p*-xylene. **p-t-Butylbenzoic acid** is made commercially by the liquid phase air-oxidation of *t*-butyltoluene in the presence of a soluble cobalt salt as a catalyst. It can replace advantageously some of the fat acids in alkyd resins (p. 553).

The *o-*, *m-*, and *p*-benzenedicarboxylic acids are known as *phthalic, isophthalic,* and *terephthalic acids.* **Phthalic acid** on heating above 180° rapidly loses water to form the cyclic anhydride.

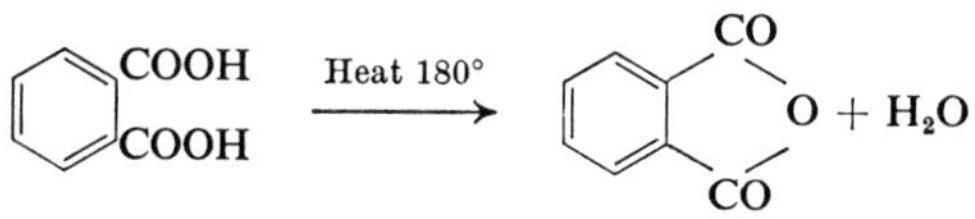

Phthalic acid   Phthalic anhydride

Hence in the usual methods for synthesizing phthalic acid, namely the high temperature oxidation of *o*-xylene or naphthalene (p. 582), it is the anhydride that is obtained.

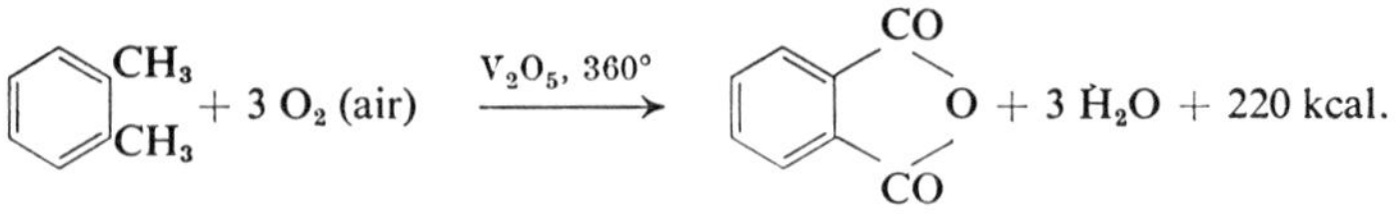

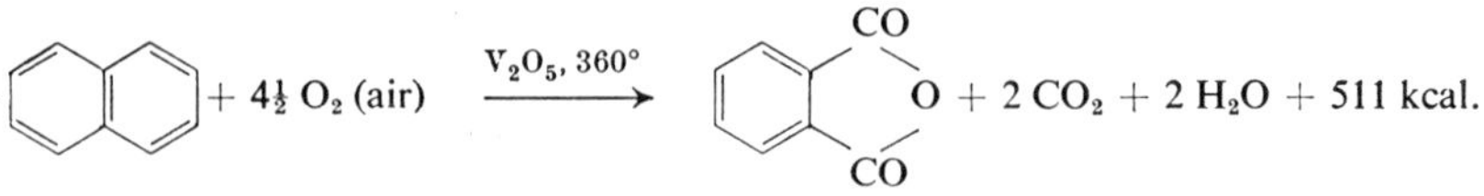

Naphthalene

Naphthalene is cheaper than *o*-xylene, but the oxidation of *o*-xylene is more readily controlled because less than half as much heat is evolved per mole of anhydride formed. Prior to the development of this process by Gibbs in 1917, sulfuric acid in the presence of mercuric sulfate had been used as the oxidizing agent (p. 685).

Over 330 million pounds of phthalic anhydride was produced in 1955 at a price of about $0.20 per pound. About half of the phthalic anhydride is used to produce the **methyl, ethyl, butyl,** and **higher alkyl esters** of phthalic acid, which are used as plasticizers of synthetic polymers, especially polyvinyl chloride. Production of the esters in millions of pounds in 1955 was as follows: methyl, 4; ethyl, 16; butyl, 24; 2-ethylhexyl, 72. **Methyl phthalate** (dimethyl phthalate, DMP) is an effective insect repellent.

Most of the remainder of the phthalic anhydride is used for the manufacture of polyester resins of which the **glyptal** (glycerol and phthalic anhydride) type is·the simplest. Since both phthalic acid and glycerol are polyfunctional, heating a mixture gives polymeric esters. If three moles of phthalic anhydride to two of glycerol are used, a fusible resin first is obtained which on further heating gives an infusible solid, insoluble in organic solvents. The cross-links occur not only between two polymeric chains as indicated, but between large numbers of chains.

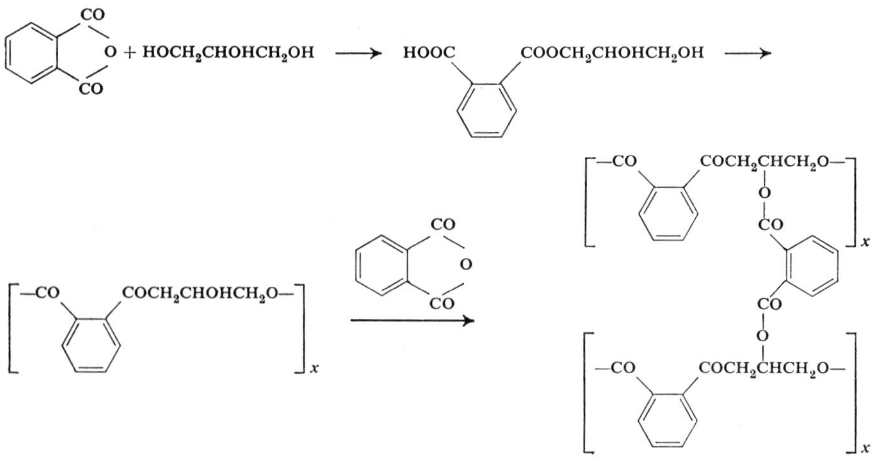

Fusible resin

Infusible resin

If one mole of phthalic anhydride, one mole of glycerol, and one mole of a monocarboxylic acid (a modifying agent) is heated, one of the hydroxyl groups is esterified with the monocarboxylic acid and cross-linking is prevented, thus forming a fusible solid, soluble in organic solvents. If unsaturated mono-carboxylic acids such as those from the drying oils are used, the resin after coating on a surface can undergo further oxidative polymerization like a drying oil to give very tough, elastic, weather-resistant films. It is these synthetic enamels that are used so extensively for the finishing of automobiles and household appliances. The glyptal resins belong to a more general class of polymeric substances derived from polyhydric alcohols and polybasic acids known as **alkyd resins.** Other types of polyester resins are used for laminating fiber glass (p. 807) and for making rubber-like products (p. 799).

A considerable quantity of phthalic anhydride is used for the manufacture of anthraquinone (p. 597) and its derivatives, which are intermediates for the synthesis of anthraquinone dyes (p. 687). Smaller amounts are used for miscellaneous purposes such as the manufacture of phthalein and xanthene dyes (p. 683), benzoic acid, and phthalimide.

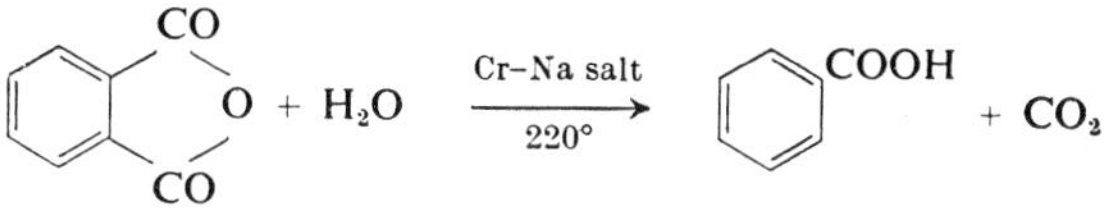

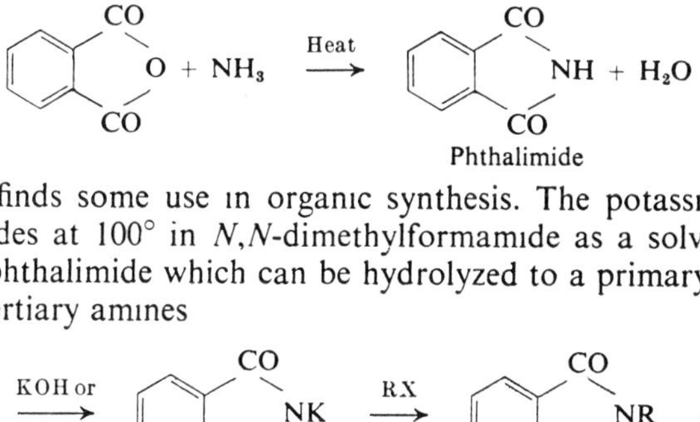

$$
\text{(phthalic anhydride)} \quad + H_2O \xrightarrow[220°]{\text{Cr–Na salt}} \text{(C}_6\text{H}_4\text{COOH)} + CO_2
$$

$$
\text{(phthalic anhydride)} \quad + NH_3 \xrightarrow{\text{Heat}} \text{(phthalimide)} + H_2O
$$

Phthalimide

Phthalimide finds some use in organic synthesis. The potassium salt reacts with alkyl halides at 100° in *N,N*-dimethylformamide as a solvent to give an *N*-substituted phthalimide which can be hydrolyzed to a primary amine free of secondary or tertiary amines

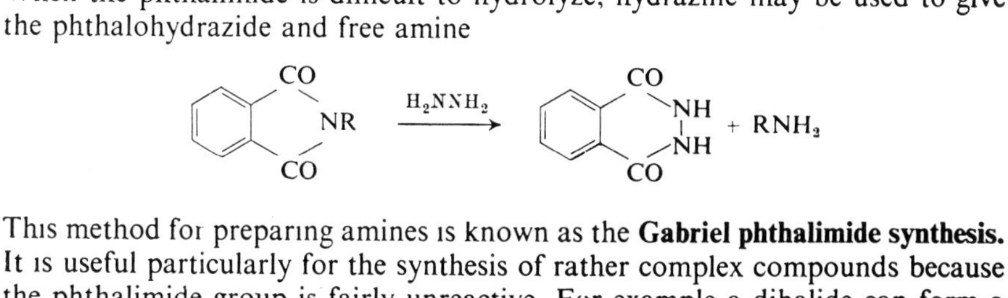

$$
\text{NH} \xrightarrow[K_2CO_3]{\text{KOH or}} \text{NK} \xrightarrow[190°]{RX} \text{NR} \xrightarrow[H_2O]{HCl} \text{(C}_6\text{H}_4(\text{COOH})_2) + RNH_3Cl
$$

When the phthalimide is difficult to hydrolyze, hydrazine may be used to give the phthalohydrazide and free amine

$$
\text{NR} \xrightarrow{H_2NNH_2} \text{(phthalohydrazide, NH–NH)} + RNH_2
$$

This method for preparing amines is known as the **Gabriel phthalimide synthesis.** It is useful particularly for the synthesis of rather complex compounds because the phthalimide group is fairly unreactive. For example a dihalide can form a monophthalimide, $C_6H_4(CO)_2N(CH_2)_xBr$, and the remaining halogen can undergo most of the reactions of an alkyl halide. Halogenated esters give phthalimide derivatives, $C_6H_4(CO)_2N(CH_2)_xCOOR$, which can be saponified, converted to the acid chloride, and used in a Friedel-Crafts reaction. Following these reactions the phthalyl group can be removed to give the free amino group.

When phthalic anhydride reacts with phosphorus pentachloride, the liquid symmetrical phthalyl chloride is obtained (m.p. 12°–16°), which can be converted to a solid unsymmetrical form (m.p. 87°–89°) by heating with anhydrous aluminum chloride.

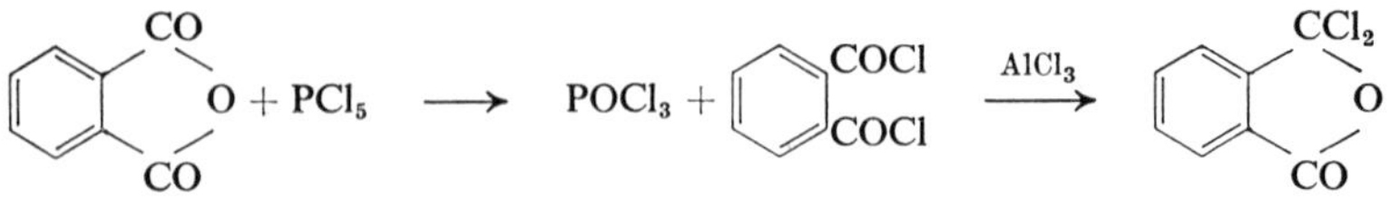

When heated above its melting point, the unsymmetrical form reverts to the symmetrical form. The ordinary liquid form reacts as if it is in equilibrium with the unsymmetrical form. Thus hydrazine gives the cyclic hydrazide, but reduction with zinc and hydrochloric acid gives phthalid, and ammonia yields *o*-cyanobenzoic acid.

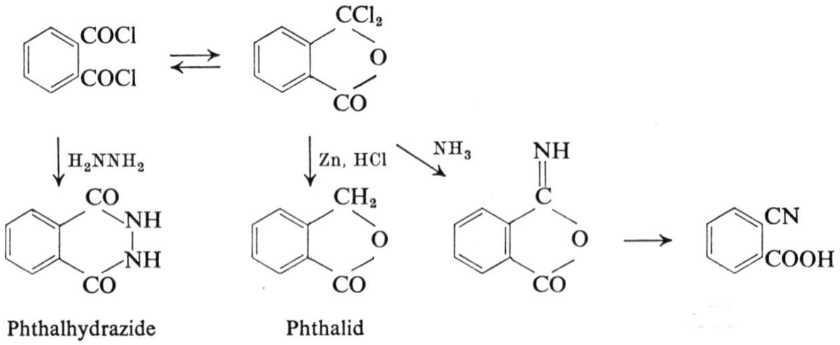

Phthalhydrazide   Phthalid

A similar tautomerism can exist in the acyl halides of those half esters of dibasic acids that can yield a cyclic intermediate. Thus 2-methoxycarbonyl-6-nitrobenzoyl chloride is in equilibrium with 2-methoxylcarbonyl-3-nitrobenzoyl chloride.

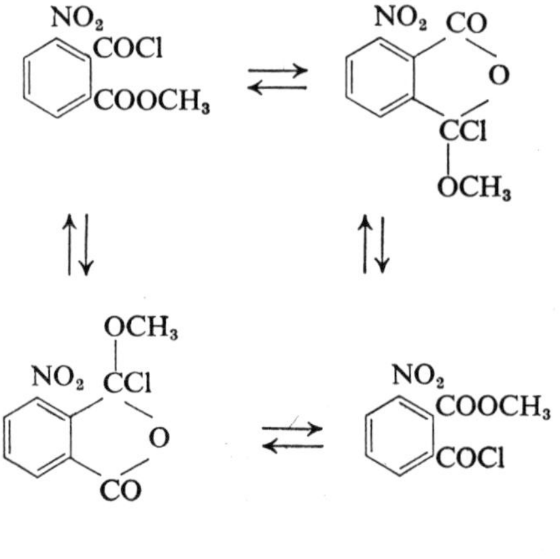

Reaction of phthalic anhydride with an alkaline solution of hydrogen peroxide followed by acidification gives the **monoperoxyphthalic acid**. It can be used for the same purposes as peroxybenzoic acid (p. 551).

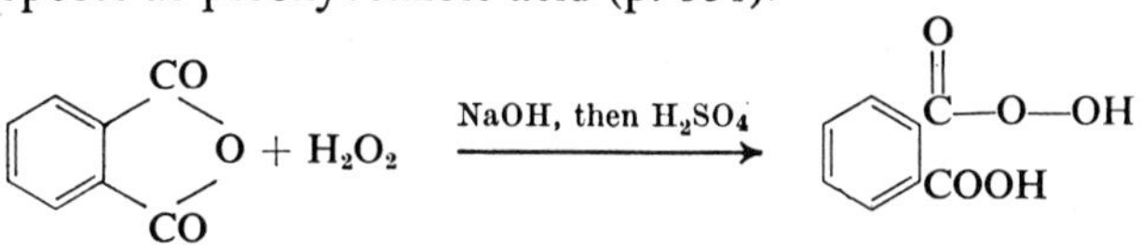

Monoperoxy-
phthalic acid

Isophthalic and **terephthalic acids** have become of technical importance only since 1950. They cannot be made by the same process used for phthalic anhydride because they cannot form volatile monomeric anhydrides. Usually the oxidation of *m*- or *p*-xylene is brought about in several steps. The xylene in the liquid phase and in the presence of a soluble cobalt or manganese salt is oxidized by air to the toluic acid. The toluic acid is converted to the methyl ester, which is oxidized to the methyl hydrogen phthalate. The latter is isolated as the dimethyl ester.

$$C_6H_4(CH_3)_2 \xrightarrow[140°]{O_2, \text{ Co or Mn salt}} C_6H_4(CH_3)COOH \xrightarrow[[H^+]]{CH_3OH}$$

m- or *p*-Xylene   *m*- or *p*-Toluic
acid

$$C_6H_4(CH_3)COOCH_3 \xrightarrow[\text{salt}]{O_2, \text{ Co or Mn}} C_6H_4(COOH)COOCH_3 \xrightarrow[[H^+]]{CH_3OH} C_6H_4(COOCH_3)_2$$

Methyl *m*- or   Methyl hydrogen iso or   Methyl iso or
p-toluate   terephthalate   terephthalate

Alternatively, the toluic acids can be further oxidized in alkaline solution. For most purposes methyl isophthalate and methyl terephthalate are preferable to the free acids, although the latter can be obtained by hydrolysis. Isophthalic acid confers desirable properties on alkyd resins and other polyesters. British investigators, extending some earlier work of Carothers (p. 719), found that fibers spun from the polymeric ester of terephthalic acid with the dihydric alcohol, ethylene glycol (p. 742), had superior properties. Textile fibers made from polyethylene terephthalate are called **Terylene** or **Dacron**. Transparent films are sold as **Mylar** and photographic film as **Cronar**. The product is made by alcoholysis of methyl terephthalate with ethylene glycol to give hydroxyethyl terephthalate. Further alcoholysis with removal of ethylene glycol by distillation gives the polymer for which *n* has a value of 80 to 130.

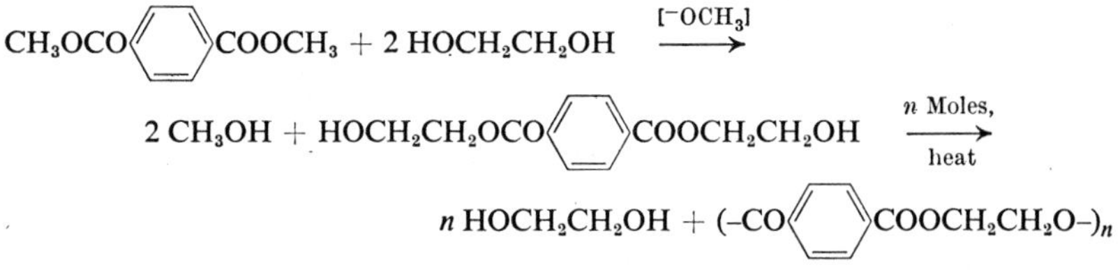

Terylene or Dacron

N,N'-Dimethyl-N,N'-dinitrosoterephthalamide (*NTA*) is used as a blowing agent for foamed rubbers and plastics. When heated, it decomposes to nitrogen and methyl terephthalate.

The benzenepolycarboxylic acids usually are made by the oxidation of the appropriate polymethylbenzenes. For example, **trimesic acid** (1,3,5-benzene-tricarboxylic acid) can be made by the oxidation of mesitylene, and **pyromellitic acid** (1,2,4,5-benzenetetracarboxylic acid) by the oxidation of 1,2,3,5-tetra-methylbenzene (durene). When heated above its melting point (270°), pyro-mellitic acid gives **pyromellitic anhydride,** which is used in the manufacture of alkyd resins.

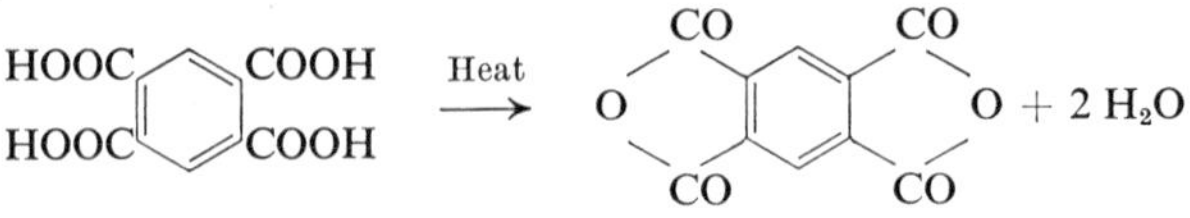

Pyromellitic acid　　　　　　　　Pyromellitic anhydride

Mellitic acid is benzenehexacarboxylic acid. It was isolated in 1799 from its aluminum salt, which occurs in lignite as the mineral *mellite* (*honeystone*), so-called because of its honey color. Mellitic acid is prepared best by the oxidation of wood charcoal with fuming nitric acid or of graphite with permanganate. This behavior agrees with the interlocking benzene ring structure for graphite.

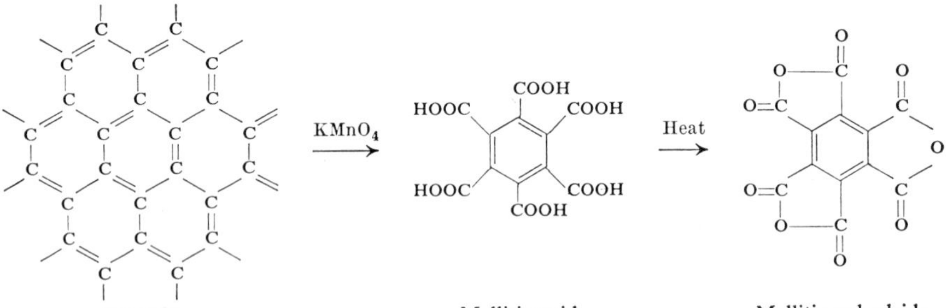

Graphite　　　　　　　　　　Mellitic acid　　　　　　　Mellitic anhydride

Mellitic anhydride, $C_{12}O_9$, is an oxide of carbon.

When phthalid is heated with potassium cyanide, the potassium salt of the nitrile of homophthalic acid is formed. Hydrolysis gives **homophthalic acid.**

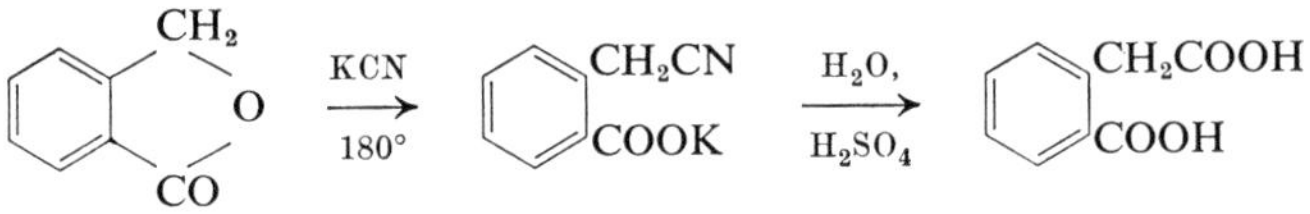

Homophthalic acid is converted to the cyclic anhydride when heated or treated with dehydrating agents.

Saccharin, discovered by Remsen,[1] is the imide of the mixed anhydride of *o*-carboxybenzenesulfonic acid. It usually is stated to have a sweetness from 550 to 750 times that of cane sugar. Relative sweetness, however, depends on the

---

[1] Ira Remsen (1846–1927), professor of chemistry at Johns Hopkins University, later president of the university. He established the first adequate graduate school in chemistry in the United States. He was an outstanding teacher, and his textbooks in both inorganic and organic chemistry were used throughout the world. He established in 1879 the American Chemical Journal, which later was combined with the Journal of the American Chemical Society. Remsen was interested in the effect of substituents on the reactivity of other groups, and it was while investigating the effect of substituents on the oxidation of side chains that he discovered saccharin.

method of determination and the individual (p. 385). For most tastes a $\frac{1}{2}$ grain (0.03 gram) tablet replaces a heaping teaspoon (10 grams) of sucrose, indicating a sweetening power about 300 times that of sucrose. Saccharin has no food value and is used only when it is desirable to reduce the consumption of sugar. Saccharin has been made from toluene by a series of reactions.

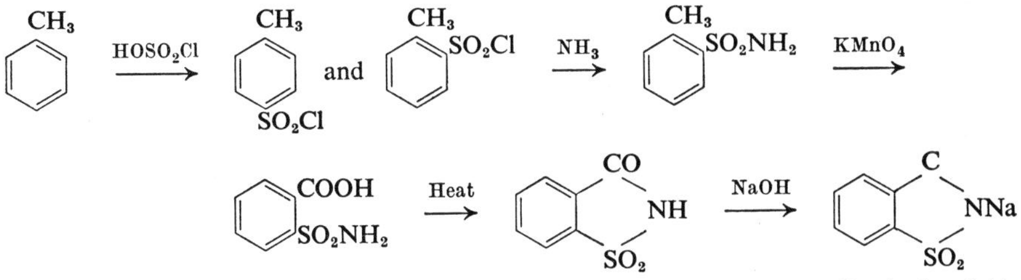

Saccharin   Saccharin soluble
                         (sodium salt)

The imide is converted to the sodium salt to increase the solubility in water.

It is reported that the slight bitter taste associated with saccharin is caused by the presence of *o*-toluamide. Moreover the disposal of the *p*-toluenesulfonyl chloride obtained as a by-product in the above process has been a problem. Both of these objections are overcome by two new processes, one starting with thianaphthene (p. 609) and the other with anthranilic acid.

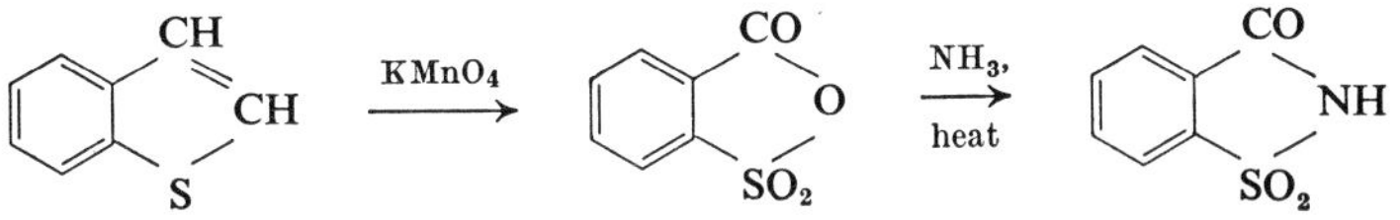

Thianaphthene

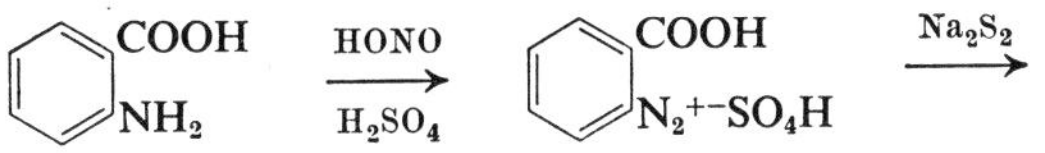

Anthranilic
acid

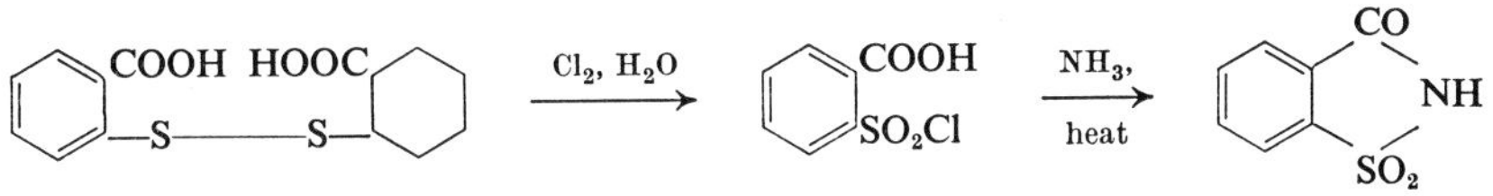

p-Toluenesulfonyl chloride, obtained as a co-product of the chlorosulfonation of toluene, can be converted to the amide and oxidized to *p*-carboxybenzenesulfonamide. Reaction with hypochlorous acid gives the dichloroamide known as **Halazone.**

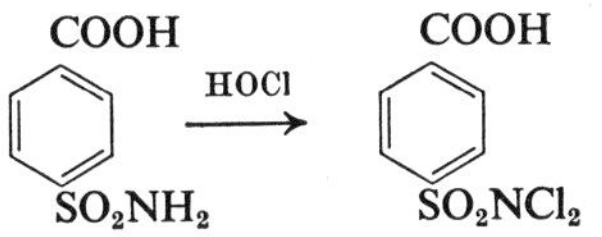

COOH   COOH

Halazone 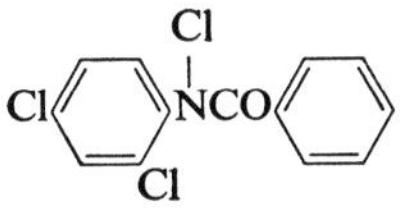   Impregnite

Tablets of Halazone and sodium carbonate, when dissolved in water, form sodium hypochlorite, which acts as a sterilizing agent. The *N*-chloro derivative of benz-2,4-dichloroanilide is called **Impregnite.** It has been used to impregnate clothing and canvas as a protection against mustard gas (p. 289), which it oxidizes to the nonvesicant sulfoxide.

Anthranilic acid, *o*-aminobenzoic acid, is made by the action of alkaline sodium hypochlorite on phthalimide. The reaction involves hydrolysis to the sodium salt of phthalamic acid and a Hofmann rearrangement (p. 231).

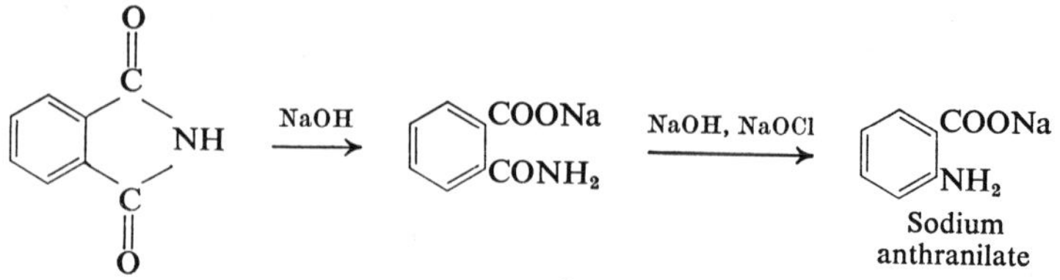

Sodium anthranilate

At one time a large quantity of anthranilic acid was used for the synthesis of indigo (p. 685). It still is used as an intermediate for the synthesis of thioindigo (p. 687) and other dyes, but production was only 404,000 pounds in 1955. **Methyl anthranilate** is present in several odorous oils and contributes to the odor and flavor of grape juice. The synthetic product is used in grape flavors.

Although **p-aminobenzoic acid** is present in the mixture of substances known as the vitamin B complex and makes up a portion of the folic acid molecule (p. 647), its necessity in the human diet has not been established. Certain bacteria, however, must be supplied with it, presumably for the synthesis of the folic acid group of vitamins, which are necessary for their growth. Apparently this need accounts for the effectiveness of the sulfa drugs in combating infections by such organisms. A sufficiently high concentration of the sulfanilamides prevents the formation of folic acid and hence inhibits the growth of the organism. Compounds that are related in structure to normal metabolic compounds but which inhibit essential metabolic processes are called *antimetabolites*. They are playing an increasingly important role in chemotherapy.

Since *m*-nitrobenzoic acid is the chief product of the nitration of benzoic acid, *p*-aminobenzoic acid is made by the oxidation of *p*-nitrotoluene followed by reduction.

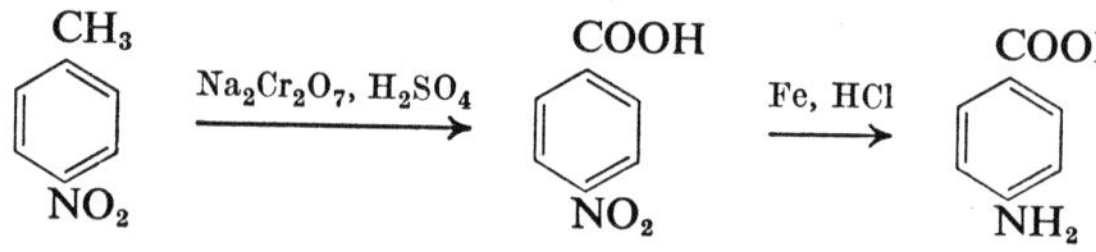

Certain *p*-aminobenzoic esters have a local anesthetic action. The ethyl ester is known as **Anesthesin** (*benzocaine*) and the butyl ester as **Butesin.** They are used for relieving the pain of burns and open wounds. The most important derivatives are the aminoalkyl *p*-aminobenzoates, which on injection at the proper site anesthetize nerve fibers or endings, or block the transmission of pain by the nerve trunks. Their development resulted from attempts to find agents less toxic than cocaine, the first local anesthetic (p. 650). **Novocain** (*procaine,* β-diethyl-aminoethyl *p*-aminobenzoate hydrochloride) was synthesized by Einhorn in 1905. It still is the most frequently used local and spinal anesthetic, although literally thousands of related compounds have been synthesized and many placed on the market. Its method of synthesis is that generally used for all of the compounds of this type.

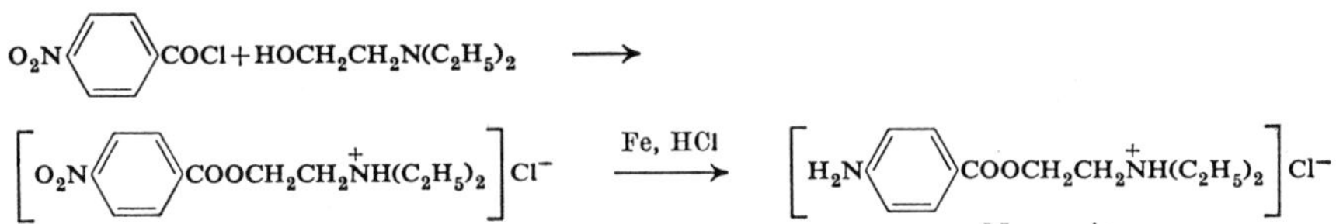

$$O_2N\langle\bigcirc\rangle COCl + HOCH_2CH_2N(C_2H_5)_2 \longrightarrow$$

$$\left[O_2N\langle\bigcirc\rangle COOCH_2CH_2\overset{+}{N}H(C_2H_5)_2\right]Cl^- \xrightarrow{\text{Fe, HCl}} \left[H_2N\langle\bigcirc\rangle COOCH_2CH_2\overset{+}{N}H(C_2H_5)_2\right]Cl^-$$

Novocain
(procaine)

Butyn is more active but also is more toxic than Novocain. **Pontocaine** (*tetracaine*) is used for surface anesthesia of the eye and for spinal anesthesia.

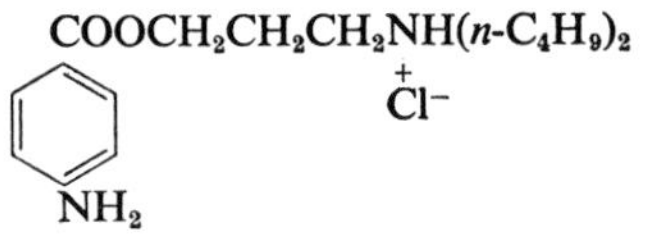

$$\text{COOCH}_2\text{CH}_2\text{CH}_2\text{NH}(n\text{-}C_4H_9)_2$$
$$\overset{+}{\text{Cl}^-}$$

$$\text{NH}_2$$

Butyn

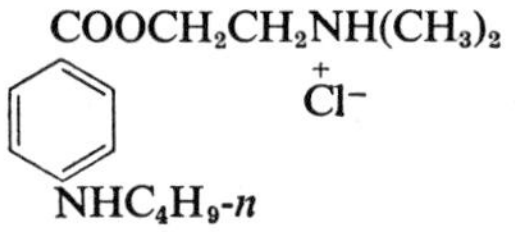

$$\text{COOCH}_2\text{CH}_2\text{NH}(CH_3)_2$$
$$\overset{+}{\text{Cl}^-}$$

$$\text{NHC}_4H_9\text{-}n$$

Pontocaine (tetracaine)

Of the hydroxy acids, the *ortho* isomer, **salicylic acid,** is by far the most important. It is prepared by the action of carbon dioxide on sodium phenoxide at 150° (*Kolbe synthesis*).

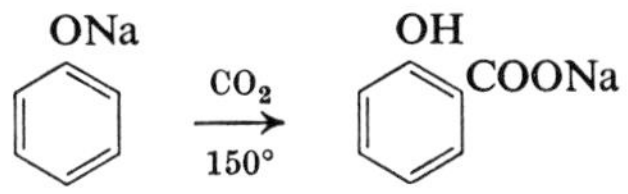

$$\text{ONa} \xrightarrow[150°]{\text{CO}_2} \text{OH, COONa}$$

Sodium salicylate

If potassium phenoxide is used instead of sodium phenoxide, the chief product is the *para* isomer. Salicylic acid was prepared first by Piria in 1838 from salicyl-aldehyde, which derived its name from the fact that it could be obtained by the oxidation of saligenin from the glucoside salicin (p. 525). Salicylic acid also was known as *spirsaeure* in the older German literature because salicylaldehyde is present in the volatile oil from the blossoms and leaves of various species of *Spiraea*.

The importance of salicylic acid and its derivatives lies in their antipyretic and analgesic action. **Sodium salicylate** was used first for this purpose in 1875. In the following year it was used for the treatment of rheumatic fever. The irritating action of sodium salicylate on the lining of the stomach led to the investigation of the action of various derivatives.

Salol (*phenyl salicylate*) was introduced in 1886. It passes unchanged through the stomach and is hydrolyzed to phenol and salicylic acid in the alkaline juices of the intestines. Since, however, the weight of phenol liberated is almost equal to that of salicylic acid, there is considerable danger of phenol poisoning. Salol now is used only as an enteric coating for medicinals that otherwise would be destroyed by the secretions of the stomach. When the pill reaches the alkaline intestines the salol is hydrolyzed and dissolved, and the medicinal is liberated. Salicylic acid now is administered almost exclusively as the acetyl derivative, which is known as **aspirin** (from the German *acetylspirsaeure*). Like salol it passes through the stomach unchanged and is hydrolyzed to salicylic acid in the intestines.

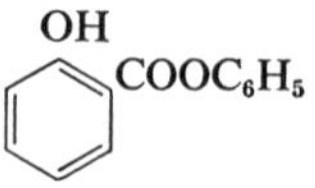

OH
⬡ COOC$_6$H$_5$

Salol

OCOCH$_3$
⬡ COOH

Aspirin

Salicylates lower body temperature rapidly and effectively in subjects having fever (antipyretic action) but have little effect if the temperature is normal. They are mild analgesics relieving certain types of pain such as headaches, neuralgia, and rheumatism. The threshold for cutaneous pain by heat is raised about 35 per cent when 2 grams of aspirin is taken orally. The extensive use of aspirin is indicated by the production in the United States in 1955 of about 15 million pounds, enough for one hundred and twenty-five 5-grain pills for every member of the entire population. Although the toxic dose is large, promiscuous use of salicylates is not without danger. Single doses of 5 to 10 grams have caused death, and 12 grams taken over a period of twenty-four hours causes symptoms of poisoning. Moreover, in some persons salicylates cause skin rashes.

The chief component of oil of wintergreen (*Gaultheria procumbens*) was identified as **methyl salicylate** in 1843. It is used to a considerable extent as a flavoring agent and in rubbing liniments. It has a mild irritating action on the skin and acts as a counterirritant for sore muscles.

When salicylic acid is heated, two, three or four molecules react to give cyclic lactones having eight, twelve, and sixteen atoms in the ring. The analog from three moles of **thymosalicylic acid** has the common name **trithymotide.**

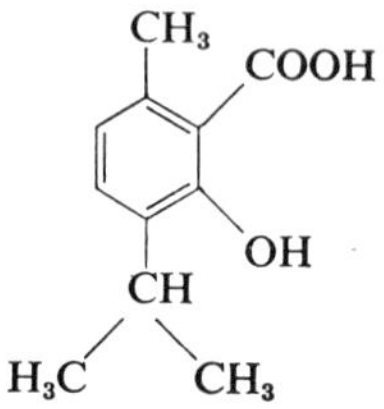

CH$_3$ COOH
⬡
CH
H$_3$C   CH$_3$
Thymosalicylic acid

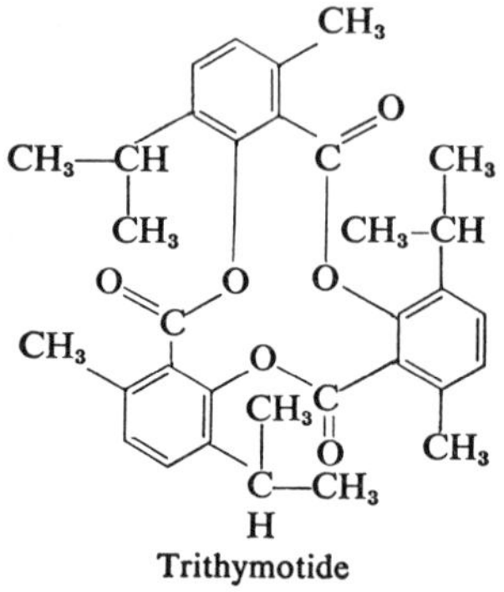

Trithymotide

Spatial interference of the isopropyl and carbonyl groups forces the rings into a screw propeller arrangement which may be right-handed or left-handed. Crystallization may give one or the other form depending on which first starts to crystallize. If the crystals are removed after partial crystallization, the remaining solution is optically active. Moreover trithymotide forms inclusion compounds with many liquids (p. 311). Since the cavity in a trithymotide crystal is dissymmetric, trithymotide can be used to resolve racemic mixtures of other dissymmetric compounds (p. 344).

2-Hydroxy-4-aminobenzoic acid, commonly called *p*-aminosalicylic acid or PAS, can be made by the Kolbe synthesis (p. 559) from *m*-aminophenol. It is being used along with streptomycin in the treatment of tuberculosis.

Vanillic acid can be obtained in good yields by fusing vanillin with sodium hydroxide below 240°, hydrogen being evolved. At higher temperatures demethylation takes place to give **protocatechuic acid.**

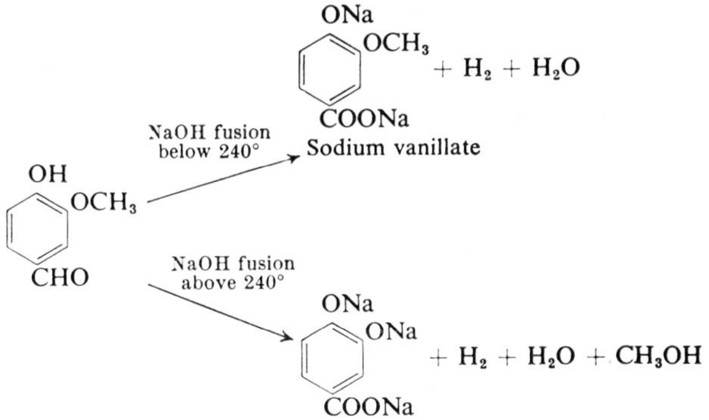

$$+ H_2 + H_2O$$

Sodium vanillate

NaOH fusion below 240°

NaOH fusion above 240°

$$+ H_2 + H_2O + CH_3OH$$

Sodium protocatechuate

Ethyl vanillate (ethyl 3-methoxy-4-hydroxybenzoate) is effective in preventing the growth of molds. It has been proposed as a food preservative and as a remedy for skin diseases caused by molds.

Veratric acid, the dimethyl ether of protocatechuic acid, was obtained first from the seeds of *Sabadilla veratrum.*

Gallic acid (3,4,5-trihydroxybenzoic acid) is found free in sumach, tea, and many other plants. It is prepared by the hydrolysis of the **tannin (tannic acid)** present in oak galls (gall nuts or nutgall), which are the excrescences on young twigs of oaks caused by parasitic insects. This particular tannin, called *gallotannin,* is a mixture of gallic acid esters of glucose. One product isolated by E. Fischer was shown to be a *pentadigalloylglucose.* The digallic acid is itself an ester, *m*-galloylgallic acid.

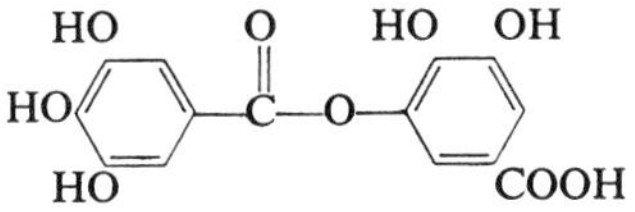

m-Galloylgallic acid

Compounds of this type are known as **depsides** (Gr. *depsein,* to tan) because many of them have tanning properties. Tannins in general are substances that have the property of rendering the gelatin of hides insoluble, thereby converting the hide to leather.

Gallic acid and tannic acid are used in the manufacture of permanent writing inks. They form colorless water-soluble ferrous salts, which on oxidation by air give black insoluble ferric salts. The latter are more permanent to light than the dye used to make the ink initially visible. Gallic acid is decarboxylated to produce pyrogallol (p. 517).

Hydrolysis of benzyl cyanide, prepared from benzyl chloride and sodium cyanide, gives **phenylacetic acid.** The α-hydrogen atoms in phenylacetic acid and its esters are more acidic than those in purely aliphatic compounds. Thus phenyl-acetic acid liberates two moles of methane from solutions of methylmagnesium bromide.

$$C_6H_5CH_2COOH + 2 CH_3MgBr \longrightarrow C_6H_5\underset{\overset{|}{\overset{+}{MgBr}}}{C}HCOO^{-+}MgBr + 2 CH_4$$

The resulting product behaves like a Grignard reagent and is known as the *Ivanov reagent*. It reacts with carbon dioxide to give the dibasic phenylmalonic acid and with aldehydes or ketones to give α-phenyl-β-hydroxy acids.

$$C_6H_5\underset{\overset{|}{\overset{+}{MgBr}}}{C}HCOO^{-+}MgBr$$

$$\xrightarrow{CO_2} C_6H_5\underset{\overset{|}{COO^{-+}MgBr}}{C}HCOO^{-+}MgBr \xrightarrow{[H^+]} C_6H_5CH(COOH)_2$$

$$\xrightarrow{RCHO} C_6H_5\underset{\overset{|}{R-CHO^{-+}MgBr}}{C}HCOO^{-+}MgBr \xrightarrow{[H^+]} C_6H_5\underset{\overset{|}{RCHOH}}{C}HCOOH$$

Mandelic acid (α-hydroxyphenylacetic acid) is prepared by the hydrolysis of benzaldehyde cyanohydrin (mandelonitrile).

$$C_6H_5CHO \xrightarrow{HCN} \underset{\text{Mandelonitrile}}{C_6H_5CHOHCN} \xrightarrow{HCl} \underset{\text{Mandelic acid}}{C_6H_5CHOHCOOH}$$

Its name arises from the fact that it first was obtained by heating an extract of bitter almonds (Ger. *mandel*, almond) with hydrochloric acid (p. 527). Mandelic acid administered orally is excreted unchanged in the urine. Since it is bacteri-cidal in acid medium, it is used in the treatment of urinary infections. It may be administered as its salt with hexamethylenetetramine (p. 221), which also is eliminated in the urine and has antiseptic properties. *p*-**Bromomandelic acid** is used to determine the ratio of hafnium to zirconium in mixtures of their salts.

Cinnamic acid is made by the Perkin synthesis (p. 526).

$$C_6H_5CHO + (CH_3CO)_2O \xrightarrow{NaOCOCH_3} [C_6H_5CH=CHCOOCOCH_3 + H_2O] \longrightarrow$$

$$\underset{\text{Cinnamic acid}}{C_6H_5CH=CHCOOH + HOOCCH_3}$$

Cinnamic acids, when heated strongly, lose carbon dioxide to give arylethylenes.

$$ArCH=CHCOOH \xrightarrow{Heat} ArCH=CH_2 + CO_2$$

When salicylaldehyde is subjected to the Perkin reaction, the resulting free acid is unstable and cyclizes spontaneously to the lactone known as **coumarin.** Coumarin is present in the tonka bean, the seed of a tropical South American

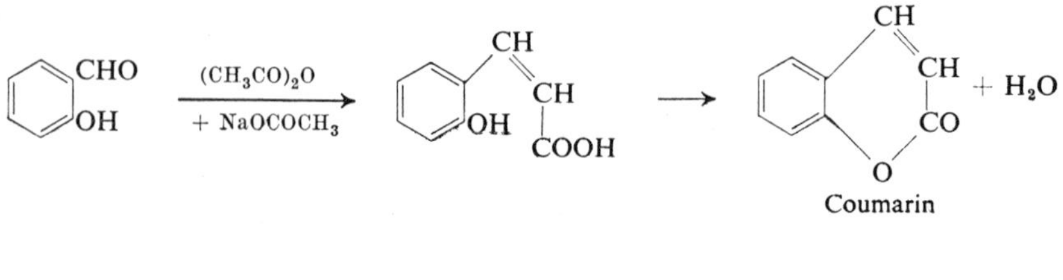

Coumarin

tree (*Dipteryx odorata*) known to the natives as *cumaru*. It has been isolated also from numerous other plants. It has the odor of newly mown hay and is used in perfumery. It was the first natural perfume to be synthesized from a coal tar chemical (p. 672). Its use as a flavoring agent has been discontinued because of its toxicity.

Dicumarol (dicoumarin) prevents the coagulation of blood and is the agent responsible for the hemorrhagic disease that results when cattle eat spoiled sweet clover. Dicumarol and certain related compounds are used medicinally to reduce the possibility of blood clot formation, for example, after surgery or in the treatment of coronary thrombosis. Another coumarin derivative, called *Warfarin*, is an effective rat poison.

Dicumarol (dicoumarin)   Warfarin

The acetylenic acid, **phenylpropiolic acid,** is made by the reaction of ethyl cinnamate dibromide with alcoholic potassium hydroxide.

$$C_6H_5CHBrCHBrCOOC_2H_5 \xrightarrow{\text{Alc. KOH}} C_6H_5C{\equiv}CCOO^{-+}K \xrightarrow{[H^+]} C_6H_5C{\equiv}CCOOH$$

Phenylpropiolic
acid

REVIEW QUESTIONS

1. Compare the reactions of aromatic carboxylic acids with those of aliphatic acids. What is the effect of *ortho* substitution on the rate of esterification of aromatic acids and on the ease of hydrolysis of esters?
2. What are the raw materials for the commercial synthesis of phthalic anhydride? What are its principal uses?
3. What is Gabriel's phthalimide method for the synthesis of primary amines?
4. How is benzoyl chloride made commercially? In what other way may it be prepared? What is the Schotten-Baumann reaction and why is it not applicable with acetyl chloride?
5. Give reactions for the preparation of benzoyl peroxide and peroxybenzoic acid. Of what use is the latter reagent and what are its limitations?
6. What is the Kolbe synthesis of salicylic acid? What is oil of wintergreen; aspirin?
7. Give equations for the synthesis of saccharin starting with toluene. What is the chief co-product of the synthesis and how is it used?

PROBLEMS

8. Give reactions for the following preparations:
    A. (*a*) *o*-Toluic acid from *o*-nitrotoluene; (*b*) benzanilide from benzotrichloride; (*c*) methyl *o*-toluate from *o*-xylene; (*d*) *m*-chlorobenzyl alcohol from *m*-chlorobenzoic acid; (*e*) benzoic acid from bromobenzene.
    B. (*a*) *p*-Methylbenzyl alcohol from *p*-toluic acid; (*b*) 2,4-dimethylbenzoic acid from 2,4-dimethylbromobenzene; (*c*) *p-i*-propylbenzoic acid from cumene; (*d*) ethyl benzoate from benzotrichloride; (*e*) 3-bromo-1,4-benzenedicarboxylic acid from *p*-xylene.
    C. (*a*) *p*-Chlorobenzamide from *p*-chlorobenzotrichloride; (*b*) 2,4-dimethylbenzoic acid from *m*-xylene; (*c*) *p*-chlorobenzoic acid from toluene; (*d*) *m*-di-(hydroxymethyl) benzene from isophthalic acid; (*e*) *p-s*-butylbenzoic acid from *p*-bromo-*s*-butylbenzene.
9. Give equations illustrating the steps necessary for the replacement of the indicated group in each of the following compounds by hydrogen: (*a*) COOH in *p*-toluic acid; (*b*) NH₂ in 3,4-dichloroaniline; (*c*) SO₃H in 3,5-dinitrobenzenesulfonic acid; (*d*) OH in 2,4,6-trimethyl-phenol; (*e*) Br in *p*-bromo-*s*-butylbenzene; (*f*) NO₂ in 2,4-dimethylnitrobenzene; (*g*) CH₃ in 2,4-dinitrotoluene; (*h*) SO₂NH₂ in sulfanilamide; (*i*) C₂H₅O in ethyl *p*-tolyl ether; (*j*) C₆H₅CH₂ in *N*-benzyl-*p*-chloroaniline; (*k*) CHO in 3,5-dinitrobenzaldehyde.

10. Give a series of reactions for preparing the following compounds starting with an aromatic hydrocarbon as the source of the aromatic nucleus: (*a*) *o*-iodohippuric acid; (*b*) peroxybenzoic acid; (*c*) 3,5-dinitrobenzoyl chloride; (*d*) methyl *m*-toluate; (*e*) aspirin; (*f*) Anesthesin; (*g*) 2-hydroxy-4-aminobenzoic acid; (*h*) phenylacetic acid; (*i*) phenyl salicylate; (*j*) *p-t*-butylbenzoic acid; (*k*) 3-acetylamino-2,4,6,triiodobenzoic acid; (*l*) Impregnite; (*m*) *m*-aminobenzoic acid.

11. Give a series of reactions for the following preparations: (*a*) methyl anthranilate from phthalic anhydride; (*b*) butyn from toluene and trimethylene chlorohydrin; (*c*) thymosalicyclic acid from *m*-cresol; (*d*) veratric acid from vanillin; (*e*) 3,4,5-trimethoxybenzaldehyde from gallic acid; (*f*) trimesic acid from acetone; (*g*) α-phenyl-β-hydroxybutyric acid from phenylacetic acid; (*h*) phenylpropiolic acid from benzaldehyde; (*i*) *i*-amylamine from phthalic anhydride; (*j*) Pontocaine from toluene and ethylene chlorohydrin.

12. For the members of each of the following groups of compounds, predict the order of increasing acid strength: (*a*) benzenesulfonic acid, hexanoamide, benzoic acid, *p*-nitrobenzoic acid, *p*-toluic acid, benzamide, phenol; (*b*) benzoic acid, 2,4,6-trinitrobenzoic acid, diphenylamine, phthalimide, trimesic acid, saccharin, 2,4,6-trichlorobenzoic acid; (*c*) phenylacetic acid, 2,4-dichlorobenzoic acid, 2,3-dimethylbenzoic acid, *p*-chlorobenzoic acid, *p*-toluamide, benzenesulfonamide, 2,4,6-trichlorobenzoic acid.

13. Give reactions for four procedures for the synthesis of *p*-toluic acid starting with toluene or *p*-xylene.

14. The following compounds all have the molecular formula C_9H_{12}. From the indicated behavior deduce the structural formula of the compound: (*a*) Nitration gives only two mononitro derivatives and oxidation gives an acid having a neutralization equivalent of 83; (*b*) nitration gives only two mononitro derivatives and oxidation gives an acid having a neutralization equivalent of 70; (*c*) nitration gives only three mononitro derivatives and oxidation gives an acid with a neutralization equivalent of 122; (*d*) nitration gives only three mononitro derivatives and oxidation gives an acid having a neutralization equivalent of 70.

15. Compound *A* has the molecular formula $C_{18}H_{18}O_3$. It is insoluble in dilute sodium hydroxide, but when boiled with the alkali it goes into solution. The saponification equivalent is 141. When the alkaline solution is distilled, only water comes over. Acidification of the alkaline solution gives a precipitate, *B*, which has a neutralization equivalent of 150. Strong oxidation of *B* gives *C*, which is an acid having a neutralization equivalent of 83. When *C* is heated above its melting point, it evolves a gas and forms a compound that dissolves only slowly in aqueous alkali. Write a structural formula for *A* and give equations for the reactions that take place.

16. Compound *A* has the molecular formula $C_{14}H_{10}N_2O_5$. It is soluble in aqueous bicarbonate and insoluble in dilute hydrochloric acid. When *A* is shaken with hydrogen in the presence of platinum catalyst, a product *B* is obtained that is soluble in either dilute acid or dilute alkali. When *B* is boiled with strong hydrochloric acid for some time and the solution is neutralized to pH 7, a single compound *C* is obtained that is soluble in both acid and alkali and has the molecular formula $C_7H_7NO_2$. Write a possible structural formula for *A* and give equations for the reactions that take place.

17. Compound *A* has the molecular formula $C_9H_{12}ClNO_2$. It is soluble in water and gives a precipitate with silver nitrate. When the aqueous solution is made alkaline, a precipitate *B* is formed which is free of halogen. When *B* is refluxed with alkali, it dissolves. When the alkaline solution is distilled, the distillate gives a positive iodoform test. When the alkaline residue is neutralized to pH 7, a precipitate *C* is formed which is soluble in either acid or alkali. When a cold acid solution of *C* is treated with sodium nitrite, no nitrogen is evolved. Addition of a cuprous cyanide–sodium cyanide solution yields a product which evolves ammonia when it is boiled with alkali. After ammonia no longer is formed, the alkaline solution is acidified. A precipitate is obtained which is identical with terephthalic acid. Write a structural formula for *A* and give equations for the reactions that take place.

Chapter 27

ARYLALKANES. FREE GROUPS. ARYLALKENES AND ARYLALKYNES. BIPHENYL AND ITS DERIVATIVES

ARYLALKANES

The simplest of the arylalkanes is **toluene** (p. 65). **Diphenylmethane** can be synthesized by the Friedel-Crafts reaction either from benzyl chloride or methylene chloride and benzene.

$$C_6H_5CH_2Cl + C_6H_6 \xrightarrow{\text{AlCl}_3} C_6H_5CH_2C_6H_5 + HCl$$

$$CH_2Cl_2 + 2\,C_6H_6 \xrightarrow{\text{AlCl}_3} \underset{\text{Diphenylmethane}}{C_6H_5CH_2C_6H_5} + 2\,HCl$$

Oxidation of diphenylmethane yields benzophenone, which is more stable to further oxidation than aliphatic ketones because further oxidation requires rupture of a benzene ring.

$$C_6H_5CH_2C_6H_5 \xrightarrow{\text{Na}_2\text{Cr}_2\text{O}_7,\ \text{H}_2\text{SO}_4} C_6H_5\overset{\text{O}}{\overset{\|}{C}}C_6H_5 + H_2O$$

Hexachlorophene (2,2′-dihydroxy-3,5,6,3′,5′,6′-hexachlorodiphenylmethane) is used as a germicide, especially in soaps.

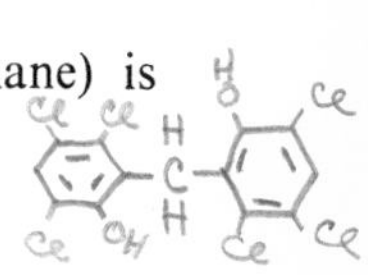

Triphenylmethane may be prepared from chloroform and benzene.

$$3\,C_6H_6 + CHCl_3 \xrightarrow{\text{AlCl}_3} (C_6H_5)_3CH + 3\,HCl$$

A better method is from benzene and carbon tetrachloride. The intermediate complex of triphenylmethyl chloride and aluminum chloride is reduced by the addition of ether.

$$CCl_4 + 3\,C_6H_6 \xrightarrow{\text{AlCl}_3} (C_6H_5)_3C^+{}^-AlCl_4 + 3\,HCl$$

$$(C_6H_5)_3C^+{}^-AlCl_4 + (C_2H_5)_2O \longrightarrow (C_6H_5)_3CH + CH_3CHO : AlCl_3 + C_2H_5Cl$$

The reducing agent undoubtedly is ethoxide ion formed by the splitting of the ether with aluminum chloride (p. 140).

The accumulation of phenyl groups in triphenylmethane increases the acidity of the CH group sufficiently to permit reaction with potassium amide in liquid ammonia to give a potassium salt; that is, triphenylmethane is a stronger acid than ammonia (cf. p. 235).

$$(C_6H_5)_3CH + KNH_2 \longrightarrow (C_6H_5)_3C\,\overset{-}{:}\overset{+}{K} + NH_3$$

The solution of the potassium salt in liquid ammonia is red. If electron-attracting groups are present, the acidity is increased. For example, tri-*p*-nitrotriphenylmethane gives a blue salt with potassium hydroxide in alcoholic solution. The reason for the acidity of triphenylmethane and for the color of solutions of its salts is discussed under free groups (p. 569).

Direct oxidation of triphenylmethane yields triphenylcarbinol. The reaction stops at this point because the tertiary alcohol cannot be oxidized further without destroying a benzene ring.

$$(C_6H_5)_3CH \xrightarrow{Na_2Cr_2O_7, \ H_2SO_4} (C_6H_5)_3COH$$

Triphenyl-
carbinol

Tetraphenylmethane is difficult to prepare because the replacement of a halogen atom by a fourth bulky group is slow. A yield of about 5 per cent is obtained by the reaction of triphenylmethyl chloride and phenylmagnesium bromide.

$$(C_6H_5)_3CCl + C_6H_5MgBr \longrightarrow (C_6H_5)_4C + MgBrCl$$

Derivatives of **1,1-diphenylethane** are important insecticides. The first to be used for this purpose was 1,1-bis(*p*-chlorophenyl)-2,2,2-trichloroethane, known as **DDT**. It is manufactured by the action of sulfuric acid on a mixture of chlorobenzene and chloral (trichloroacetaldehyde, p. 739).

$$2 \ ClC_6H_5 + OCHCCl_3 \xrightarrow{H_2SO_4} (p\text{-}ClC_6H_4)_2CHCCl_3 + H_2O$$

Chloral   DDT

Although first prepared in 1874, the insecticidal properties did not become known until 1942. During World War II it was used in delousing powders to prevent the spread of typhus, and as a mosquito larvicide to render swampy areas habitable. Since then it has been used widely as an agricultural insecticide and in household sprays. Production in the United States was over 117 million pounds in 1955. A large number of related compounds have been prepared and their properties investigated. **DDD** or **TDE** is 1,1-bis(*p*-chlorophenyl)-2,2-dichloroethane and **Methoxychlor** is 1,1-bis(*p*-methoxyphenyl)-2,2,2-trichloroethane.

Hexaphenylethane was prepared by Gomberg[1] in 1900 by the action of finely divided metals on a benzene solution of triphenylmethyl chloride.

$$2 \ (C_6H_5)_3CCl + 2 \ Ag \ (or \ Zn) \longrightarrow (C_6H_5)_3CC(C_6H_5)_3 + 2 \ AgCl \ (or \ ZnCl_2)$$

Hexaphenylethane

Hexaphenylethane is a colorless crystalline solid, but its solutions are deep yellow. The solutions rapidly absorb oxygen from the air to give triphenylmethyl peroxide.

$$(C_6H_5)_3CC(C_6H_5)_3 + O_2 \longrightarrow (C_6H_5)_3C\text{—}O\text{—}O\text{—}C(C_6H_5)_3$$

They decolorize iodine with the formation of triphenylmethyl iodide and react with alkali metals to give brick red metallic salts.

$$(C_6H_5)_3CC(C_6H_5)_3 + I_2 \longrightarrow 2 \ (C_6H_5)_3CI$$

$$+ \ 2 \ K \longrightarrow 2 \ (C_6H_5)_3CK$$

---

[1] Moses Gomberg (1866–1947), Russian-born American chemist who obtained both undergraduate and graduate training at the University of Michigan and then worked with Baeyer and Victor Meyer. After synthesizing tetraphenylmethane, he returned to Michigan and attempted to synthesize hexaphenylethane with the result that he discovered stable free radicals.

None of these reactions would be expected from the structure of the hydrocarbon. The explanation lies in the dissociation of hexaphenylethane in solution into two free **triphenylmethyl** groups, each with an unpaired electron.

$$(C_6H_5)_3C : C(C_6H_5)_3 \rightleftharpoons 2 [(C_6H_5)_3C \cdot]$$

These unpaired electrons can pair with the unpaired electrons of the oxygen molecule or with that of an iodine atom to form covalent bonds, or can accept an electron from a metallic atom to form an ionic bond.

FREE GROUPS

Free Radicals

Stable Free Radicals. With the recognition during the latter part of the eighteenth century that chemical compounds are built of component parts, designated as radicals by Lavoisier (L. *radicalis*, having roots), attempts were made to isolate these parts. Partial success seemed to reward these efforts during the first half of the nineteenth century. Thus free *ammonium* was isolated as an amalgam by Berzelius in 1808, and in 1815 Gay-Lussac prepared cyanogen gas, believing it to be the free cyanogen radical. Frankland in 1849 believed that he had isolated the ethyl radical by heating ethyl iodide with zinc. It was Cannizzaro, however, who pointed out in 1858 the necessity for making molecular weight determinations based on Avogadro's hypothesis, and it became recognized that cyanogen is $(CN)_2$ and that Frankland's ethyl was $(C_2H_5)_2$ or butane. In other words any reaction that might lead to the formation of a free radical was followed by a combination of the radicals. These results led to the view that compounds containing di- or trivalent carbon, with the exception of carbon monoxide, are incapable of existence. Although Victor Meyer showed in 1880 from vapor density measurements at high temperatures that a molecule of iodine dissociates reversibly into two free iodine atoms, the marked success attending the application of Kekulé's rules of valence to the synthesis of new organic compounds during the last half of the nineteenth century banished any thoughts that groups having abnormal valencies might be capable of independent existence. Hence Gomberg's discovery of free triphenylmethyl (p. 566) was received with great interest and considerable skepticism. Additional experimental results of Gomberg and his co-workers and of other investigators who entered the field soon confirmed the discovery.

The existence of an equilibrium between the free triphenylmethyl radical and the undissociated hexaphenylethane is observable without difficulty, since the solid ethane when first dissolved gives a colorless solution which soon turns yellow. On shaking with air the color is discharged, but in the absence of oxygen, the color returns as more of the ethane dissociates. The process can be repeated several times until all of the ethane has been converted to peroxide. Molecular weight determinations show that, as a 3 per cent solution in benzene, hexaphenylethane is dissociated to triphenylmethyl to the extent of about 2 per cent at 20° and about 9 per cent at 75°.

The most conclusive proof that free radicals containing an unpaired electron are present is from the magnetic susceptibility. Because electrons are in motion about the positive nucleus, a magnetic field induces a magnetic dipole in all matter. The induced dipole gives rise to a magnetic field which is opposed to the applied field, and hence the substance is said to be *diamagnetic* and is repelled by the applied field. If the molecules composing a substance contain an unpaired electron, a permanent magnetic dipole will be present. When near an external field, these dipoles so align themselves that their fields reinforce the applied field. Such substances are said to be *paramagnetic* [2] and are attracted by the applied field, the effect of the permanent dipole far outweighing the induced diamagnetism. Thus nitric oxide, NO, nitrogen dioxide, NO_2, and chlorine dioxide, ClO_2, which must contain an unpaired electron, are paramagnetic. Surprisingly the diatomic oxygen molecule, O_2, also is strongly paramagnetic, indicating that it is a diradical having two unpaired electrons. Solutions of hexaphenylethane are paramagnetic, and the extent of dissociation calculated from the magnetic susceptibility agrees roughly with that determined by other methods.

Another physical method for the detection of free radicals is the catalysis of the interconversion of *ortho* and *para* hydrogen, which differ in that the spins of the two hydrogen nuclei

---

[2] Paramagnetism is not to be confused with ferromagnetism which is a thousand or more times greater than any paramagnetic effect.

in *ortho* hydrogen are in the same direction, whereas those in *para* hydrogen are in opposite directions. Each is stable and thermal interconversion is slow at ordinary temperatures. If, however, a sufficiently strong magnetic field is brought close enough to a hydrogen molecule, the direction of a nuclear spin can be reversed, and the conversion of *ortho* or *para* hydrogen to the equilibrium mixture (25 per cent *para*, 75 per cent *ortho*) results. Nitric oxide, nitrogen dioxide, oxygen, and solutions of triphenylmethyl catalyze the interconversion of *ortho* and *para* hydrogen.

The recent development of apparatus for the detection of electron spin resonance absorption (p. 669) has provided a means for detecting unpaired electrons, and hence free radicals, in concentrations as low as 10^{-8} molar. These studies have confirmed the existence of free radicals and have shown the presence of free radicals not previously detected. Moreover, the distribution of the unpaired electron over the whole group in a free radical such as triphenyl-methyl has been confirmed, since the interaction of the unpaired electron with all of the hydrogen atoms, whose nuclei also have a magnetic moment (p. 668), has been observed.

Short-lived Free Radicals. The demonstration of the existence of stable free radicals lent support to the attractive hypothesis that short-lived free radicals might play a part as intermediates in organic reactions. In 1929 Paneth and his associates demonstrated the independent existence of **free methyl radicals.** When a stream of inert gas saturated with tetramethyllead vapor is passed through a silica tube heated at one spot, a lead mirror forms at this spot because of the decomposition of the tetramethyllead. If then the tube is heated some distance nearer the source of the gas stream, a new mirror is formed, and at the same time the first mirror disappears. Evidently the decomposition of tetramethyllead yields free methyl radicals which can exist for a sufficient length of time to travel the distance to the first lead mirror and convert it to volatile tetramethyllead.

$$Pb(CH_3)_4 \xrightarrow{\text{Hot}} Pb + 4[CH_3 \cdot]$$

$$Pb + 4[CH_3 \cdot] \xrightarrow{\text{Cold}} Pb(CH_3)_4$$

From the rate of streaming of the gas and the distance between the two mirrors, the average life of the methyl radical under the conditions of the experiment was calculated to be 8.4×10^{-3} second. Thus even in the gaseous state at 1 to 2 mm. pressure, the methyl radicals are rapidly destroyed by collision with gaseous particles or with the walls of the tube. Methyl radicals are formed similarly in the pyrolysis of acetone at 700°, butane at 600°, azomethane at 200° (p. 265), and in many similar thermal decompositions. Their presence can be demonstrated by removal of a lead mirror a short distance from the pyrolysis zone, and the production of tetramethyllead.

Certain types of compounds decompose even more readily than azomethane to give short-lived free radicals. Thus acetyl peroxide on heating at relatively low temperatures yields free acetate radicals which can decompose further into methyl radicals and carbon dioxide.

$$CH_3CO\text{—}O\text{—}O\text{—}COCH_3 \xrightarrow{\text{Heat}} 2[CH_3CO\text{—}O \cdot]$$

$$[CH_3CO\text{—}O \cdot] \longrightarrow [CH_3 \cdot] + CO_2$$

Benzoyl peroxide yields benzoate and phenyl radicals. Diazoacetates, diazohydroxides and diazocyanides (p. 499) also readily decompose to yield free radicals.

$$C_6H_5N\text{=}NOCOCH_3 \longrightarrow [C_6H_5 \cdot] + N_2 + [\cdot OCOCH_3]$$

When free radicals are generated in the absence of solvent, combination of the free radicals takes place. Benzoyl peroxide gives chiefly biphenyl with a little phenyl benzoate and benzene. In a solvent, however, displacement reactions with the solvent molecules are more probable than combination of two free radicals. When benzoyl peroxide is decomposed by boiling a solution in benzene, the products are carbon dioxide, biphenyl, and benzoic acid, together with phenyl benzoate, terphenyls, and quaterphenyls. The benzoic acid arises by a displacement of phenyl from benzene by benzoate radical.

$$[C_6H_5COO \cdot] + C_6H_6 \longrightarrow C_6H_5COOH + [C_6H_5 \cdot]$$

Biphenyl results from the combination of two phenyl radicals, but the terphenyls must be formed by conversion of biphenyl into a free radical which then combines with a phenyl radical.

$$2\,[C_6H_5 \cdot]\ \longrightarrow\ C_6H_5\!-\!C_6H_5$$
$$\text{Biphenyl}$$

$$C_6H_5C_6H_5 + [C_6H_5 \cdot]\ \longrightarrow\ [C_6H_5\!-\!C_6H_4 \cdot] + C_6H_6$$

$$[C_6H_5C_6H_4 \cdot] + [C_6H_5 \cdot]\ \longrightarrow\ C_6H_5C_6H_4C_6H_5$$
$$\text{Terphenyl}$$

Quaterphenyl arises from terphenyl by a similar series of displacement reactions. If the solvent is toluene, chlorobenzene, or nitrobenzene, the corresponding substituted biphenyls are produced.

Inasmuch as free radicals can by displacement reactions generate other free radicals from a solvent, chain reactions initiated by a small amount of a substance that readily yields free radicals soon become characteristic of the solvent. Hence acyl peroxides are important as catalysts for reactions taking place by a free-radical chain mechanism. For example, acetyl peroxide catalyzes the addition of carbon tetrachloride to olefins (p. 725).

$$(CH_3CO)_2O_2\ \longrightarrow\ 2\,[CH_3 \cdot] + 2\,CO_2$$
$$[CH_3 \cdot] + CCl_4\ \longrightarrow\ CH_3Cl + [\cdot\,CCl_3]$$
Chain initiating reactions

$$RCH\!=\!CH_2 + [\cdot\,CCl_3]\ \longrightarrow\ [RCH\!-\!CH_2CCl_3]$$

$$[RCH\!-\!CH_2CCl_3] + CCl_4\ \longrightarrow\ \underset{\overset{|}{Cl}}{RCH}\!-\!CH_2CCl_3 + [\cdot\,CCl_3]$$
Chain propagating reactions

Explanation of the Stability of Long-lived Free Radicals. The markedly greater stability of the triphenylmethyl free radical compared to the methyl free radical can be ascribed to the large resonance energy of the former. In the methyl free radical, three sp^2 hybrid bonds join the carbon atom to three hydrogen atoms, and an unpaired electron is in the remaining p orbital (Fig. 80*a*). There is a great tendency to pair with another electron and hence to bond

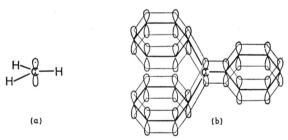

(a)   (b)

Fig. 80. Representations of the electronic structures of (*a*) the methyl free radical and (*b*) the triphenylmethyl free radical.

with another atom or group leading to tetrahedral sp^3 hybridization. In the triphenylmethyl free radical, the p orbital of the methane carbon atom can overlap the p orbitals of the unsaturated carbon atoms of the aromatic rings, permitting the unpaired electron to interact with the unsaturation electrons of the aromatic rings (Fig. 80*b*). This resonance may be indicated also by the hybrid symbolism.

Since electronic interaction takes place with all three benzene nuclei, there are ten possible positions for the unpaired electron, and a total of 44 valence bond structures can be written. If more aromatic nuclei are conjugated with the system, the possibility for resonance increases and the free radicals become still more stable. Thus replacement of the phenyl groups of hexaphenylethane successively by *p*-biphenyl groups (xenyl groups) increases the degree of dissociation. In 3 per cent solutions in benzene, triphenylmethyl exists to the extent of about 2 per cent in equilibrium with its dimer, xenyldiphenylmethyl 15 per cent, dixenylphenylmethyl 79 per cent, and trixenylmethyl 100 per cent.

Biradicals can exist if it is not possible for the unpaired electrons to form an electron-pair bond within the molecule. For example, *m,m′*-bis(diphenylmethyl)biphenyl exists as a biradical, but the *ortho* and *para* analogs have predominantly the quinonoid structure (cf. p. 669).

$(C_6H_5)_2C=\!\!\!\bigcirc\!\!\!-\!\!\!\bigcirc\!\!\!=\!C(C_6H_5)_2$

$(C_6H_5)_2C\cdot$ $\cdot C(C_6H_5)_2$

Metal Ketyls. When a solution of benzophenone in toluene is allowed to react with metallic sodium under anhydrous conditions and in the absence of air, a deep blue solution results, which reacts rapidly with air to regenerate the ketone. Water yields benzhydrol and not benzpinacol (p. 540). An excess of sodium gives a violet disodium derivative. These reactions were interpreted as indicating the formation of a compound containing trivalent carbon, a view which has been confirmed by the demonstration that the solutions are paramagnetic. These metallic derivatives of aromatic ketones are known as *metal ketyls*.

$$(C_6H_5)_2C=\!\!O + \cdot Na \longrightarrow [(C_6H_5)_2\overset{.}{C}-ONa]$$

$$2\,[(C_6H_5)_2\overset{.}{C}-ONa] + O_2 \longrightarrow 2\,(C_6H_5)_2C=\!\!O + Na_2O_2$$

$$2\,[(C_6H_5)_2\overset{.}{C}-ONa] + 2\,H_2O \longrightarrow (C_6H_5)_2CHOH + (C_6H_5)_2CO + 2\,NaOH$$

$$[(C_6H_5)_2\overset{.}{C}-ONa] + \cdot Na \longrightarrow \overset{Na}{\underset{}{(C_6H_5)_2\overset{..}{C}-ONa}}$$

Di-*t*-butyl ketone on treatment with sodium yields only the sodium derivative of the pinacol.

$$2\,(CH_3)_3CCOC(CH_3)_3 + 2\,Na \longrightarrow \overset{[(CH_3)_3C]_2\overset{.}{C}-ONa}{\underset{[(CH_3)_3C]_2C-ONa}{|}}$$

Moreover, when metal ketyls are hydrolyzed with dilute acids, a high yield of pinacol is obtained.

$$2\,[(C_6H_5)_2\overset{.}{C}-ONa] + 2\,HCl \longrightarrow 2\,[(C_6H_5)_2\overset{.}{C}-OH] + 2\,NaCl$$

$$\downarrow$$

$$(C_6H_5)_2C-OH$$
$$(C_6H_5)_2\overset{|}{C}-OH$$

The stability of the metal ketyl may be ascribed to (1) the ability of the unpaired electron to interact with the electrons of the aromatic nuclei and (2) the tendency of the negative charge on the oxygen atom to force the electron into the nuclei and decrease the probability of location on the methane carbon atom.

Stable Nitrogen and Oxygen Free Radicals. That nitrogen and oxygen exhibit anomalous valence and can exist in molecules with an unpaired electron is indicated by the paramagnetism of nitric oxide and oxygen. Their chemical reactions are in agreement with this view. Thus nitric oxide and oxygen combine readily with triphenylmethyl to give the nitroso derivative and the peroxide.

$$[(C_6H_5)_3C\cdot] + [\cdot NO] \longrightarrow (C_6H_5)_3C-NO$$

$$2\,[(C_6H_5)_3C\cdot] + [O-O] \longrightarrow (C_6H_5)_3C-O-O-C(C_6H_5)_3$$

More closely allied to triphenylmethyl is **diphenylnitrogen.** When a cold solution of diphenylamine is oxidized with permanganate, the colorless solid tetraphenylhydrazine is obtained.

$$2 (C_6H_5)_2NH \xrightarrow{\text{Ox.}} (C_6H_5)_2N\text{—}N(C_6H_5)_2$$

Tetraphenylhydrazine

Its solutions in nonionizing solvents turn green when heated (*thermochromism*), and react with nitric oxide, metallic sodium, and triphenylmethyl. This behavior undoubtedly is due to dissociation into free radicals.

$$(C_6H_5)_2N : N(C_6H_5)_2 \rightleftarrows 2 [(C_6H_5)_2N \cdot]$$

$$[(C_6H_5)_2N \cdot] + [\cdot NO] \longrightarrow (C_6H_5)_2N\text{—}NO$$

$$+ [\cdot Na] \longrightarrow [(C_6H_5)_2N \overset{..}{:}] Na^+$$

$$+ [(C_6H_5)_3C \cdot] \longrightarrow (C_6H_5)_2N\text{—}C(C_6H_5)_3$$

2,4,6-Tri-*t*-butylphenol when oxidized with lead dioxide or potassium ferricyanide in benzene gives a deep blue solution, and a dark blue crystalline solid on evaporation of the solvent. The compound is extremely sensitive to air, and its reactions and paramagnetic properties indicate that it is an oxygen free radical.

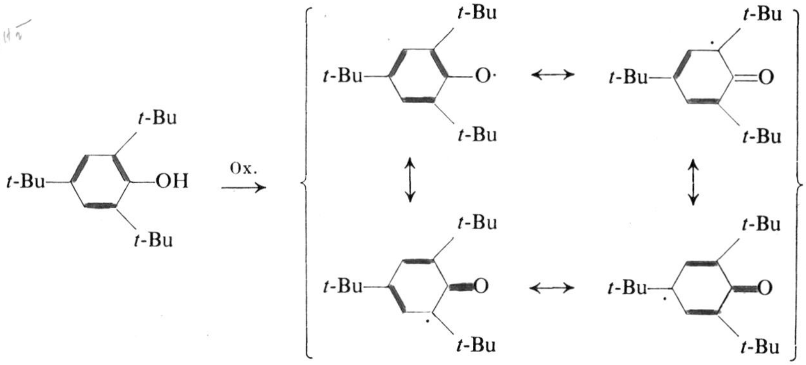

Bimolecular coupling of the free radicals undoubtedly is prevented by the bulky *t*-butyl groups in the 2,4, and 6 positions. The yellow peroxide formed by reaction with air is assigned the structure

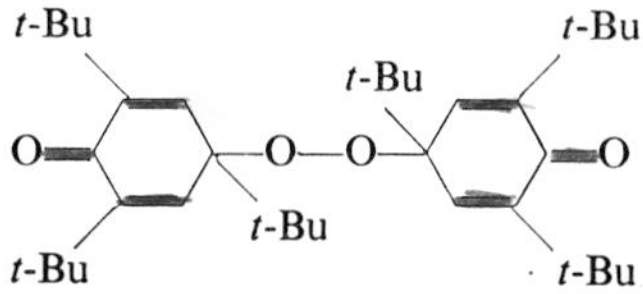

The **quinhydrones** are bimolecular addition products in which the association is due to proton bonding (p. 87). In alkaline solutions, however, these compounds are paramagnetic and have the properties of free radicals. Evidently an electron transfer takes place from the hydroquinone ion to the quinone molecule to give semiquinone ions which are stabilized by resonance.

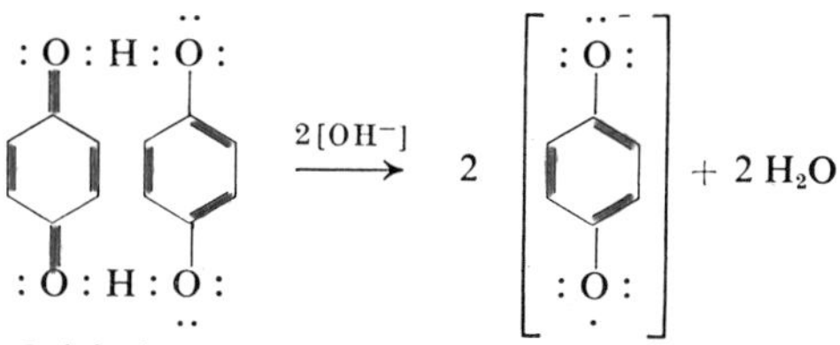

Quinhydrone   Semiquinone

When *p*-phenylenediamine and its alkyl derivatives are oxidized with bromine in acid solution, deeply colored products are formed which are known as **Wurster salts**. They are similar to the semiquinones and can be formed only when the symmetry of the molecule is sufficiently high for resonance between identical or almost identical structures.

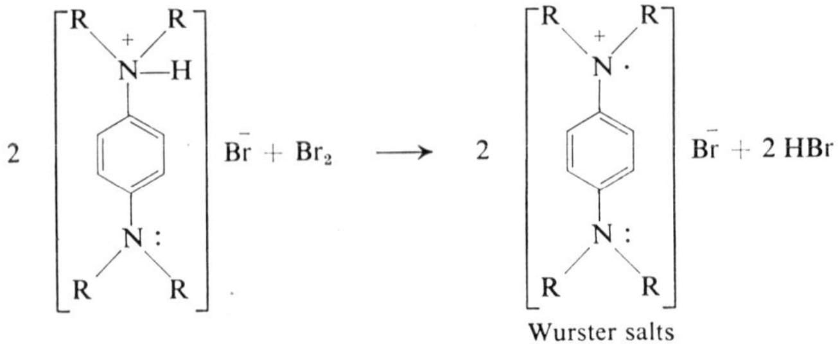

Wurster salts

The Wurster salt from *p*-phenylenediamine is stable only in the pH range of 3.5 to 6 because only the ion of the monoacid salt (II) is symmetrical and permits sufficient stabilization by resonance. The free base (I) and the ion of the diacid salt (III) are unsymmetrical.

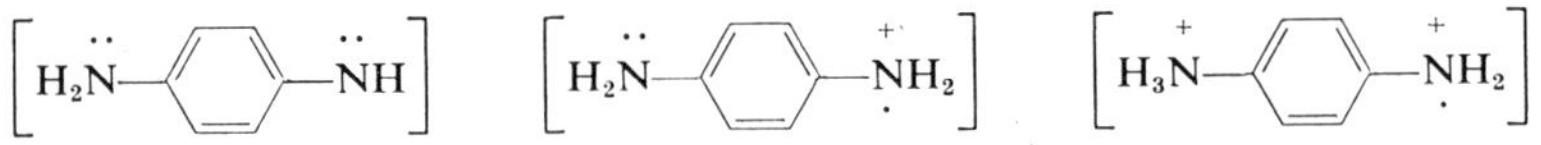

The deep blue compound formed when a solution of diphenylamine in concentrated sulfuric acid reacts with nitrites or nitrates (p. 488) probably has an analogous constitution. The initial oxidation product is tetraphenylhydrazine, which undergoes a benzidine rearrangement (p. 578) and then further oxidation.

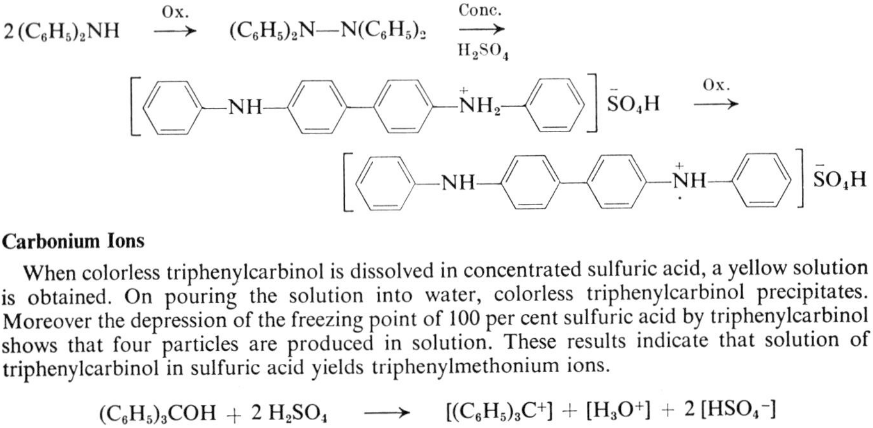

$$2\,(C_6H_5)_2NH \xrightarrow{\text{Ox.}} (C_6H_5)_2N\!-\!N(C_6H_5)_2 \xrightarrow[\text{H}_2\text{SO}_4]{\text{Conc.}}$$

Carbonium Ions

When colorless triphenylcarbinol is dissolved in concentrated sulfuric acid, a yellow solution is obtained. On pouring the solution into water, colorless triphenylcarbinol precipitates. Moreover the depression of the freezing point of 100 per cent sulfuric acid by triphenylcarbinol shows that four particles are produced in solution. These results indicate that solution of triphenylcarbinol in sulfuric acid yields triphenylmethonium ions.

$$(C_6H_5)_3COH + 2\,H_2SO_4 \longrightarrow [(C_6H_5)_3C^+] + [H_3O^+] + 2\,[HSO_4^-]$$

The triphenylmethonium ion is stabilized by resonance in the same way as the triphenylmethyl free radical (p. 569).

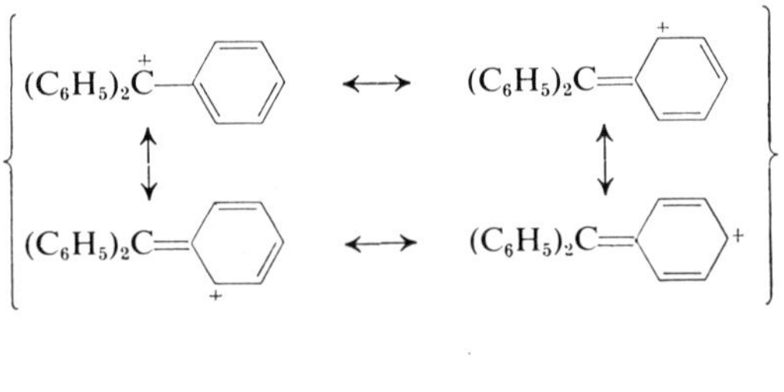

Highly colored compounds formed by the reaction of organic compounds with protonoid reagents are known as **halochromic salts.** Other examples are the deep blue solutions obtained in the Liebermann nitroso reaction (p. 506) and the red to purple solutions of dibenzylidene-acetone and its derivatives in concentrated sulfuric acid. The same color is obtained whether the reagent is sulfuric acid or solutions of anhydrous aluminum chloride, zinc chloride, or boron trifluoride. The ease with which these highly colored solutions are formed depends on the "basicity" of the organic compound, that is the availability of an unshared pair of electrons, and on the "acidity" of the protonoid reagent, that is, its attraction for a pair of electrons. Because of the indicator action of the organic compounds, their relative basicity or the relative acidity of the protonoid reagents can be easily determined. Thus it can be shown that the ability of the reagents to acquire a pair of electrons is in the order—anhydrous aluminum chloride in nitrobenzene > concentrated sulfuric acid > anhydrous zinc chloride in nitrobenzene—which order is the same as the catalytic activity of these reagents in condensation reactions.

Carbanions

The **triphenylmethide ion** can be formed by the reaction of triphenylmethyl with metallic sodium or by the reaction of potassium amide with triphenylmethane.

$$[(C_6H_5)_3C \cdot] + [\cdot Na] \longrightarrow [(C_6H_5)_3C : ^-]Na^+$$

$$(C_6H_5)_3CH + KNH_2 \longrightarrow [(C_6H_5)_3C : ^-]K^+ + NH_3$$

The solution of potassium triphenylmethyl in liquid ammonia is deep red. The stability of the triphenylmethide ion also can be accounted for by resonance, since its planar conformation permits the overlapping of the p orbital of the methane carbon atom with those of the adjacent carbon atoms of the aromatic rings and interaction of the unshared pair of electrons with the unsaturation electrons of the aromatic rings (p. 569).

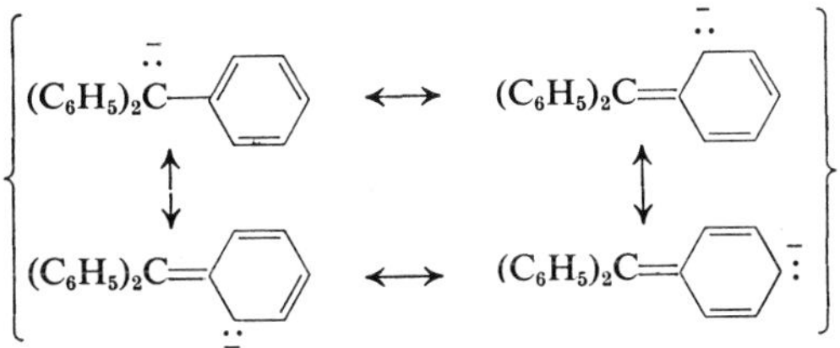

Triptycene (*9,10-o-phenylene-9,10-dihydroanthracene*), in which the methane carbon atoms are part of a cage structure and cannot assume a planar configuration (Fig. 81), does not form a potassium salt.

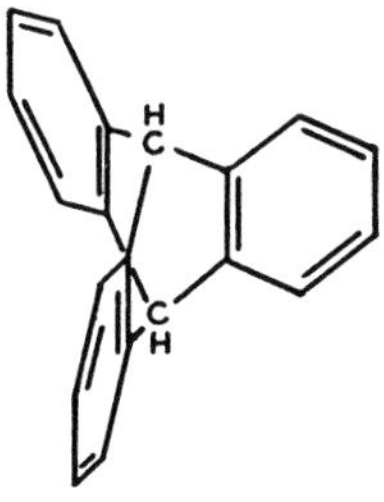

Fig. 81. Triptycene.

ARYLALKENES AND ARYLALKYNES

From a practical viewpoint the simplest of the arylalkenes, **phenylethylene,** is a very important substance. Over one billion pounds was produced in the U.S. in 1955, exceeding the production of any other synthetic aromatic chemical. The common name **styrene** arises from the fact that it was obtained first in 1831 by the distillation of *liquid storax*, a fragrant balsam from *Liquidambar* *styraciflua* and *Liquidambar orientalis*. It probably is formed from the cinnamic acid present, which decomposes on slow distillation (p. 562).

$$C_6H_5CH{=}CHCOOH \xrightarrow{\text{Heat}} \underset{\text{Styrene}}{C_6H_5CH{=}CH_2 + CO_2}$$

Styrene is present also in coal tar, which was the first commercial source. At present it is made by dehydrogenating ethylbenzene (p. 430) catalytically. The catalyst is either iron oxide or zinc oxide with small amounts of promoters such as chromic oxide. Superheated steam is used to supply the heat for the endothermic reaction and to shift the equilibrium by reducing the partial pressure of the reactants.

$$C_6H_5CH_2CH_3 \xrightarrow[650°]{Fe_2O_3 \text{ or } ZnO} C_6H_5CH{=}CH_2 + H_2$$

The conversion of ethylbenzene to styrene is about 40 per cent per pass and the over-all yield about 90 per cent. Purification of the styrene is difficult because its boiling point of 145° is close to that of ethylbenzene (136°) and because it polymerizes readily. Sulfur is used as an inhibitor and the temperature is kept below 90° by distilling at reduced pressure. In a more complex commercial process used on a smaller scale, the difficult fractionation is avoided by the series of reactions ethylbenzene → acetophenone (p. 541) → methylphenyl-carbinol (p. 525) → styrene. The dehydration step is carried out by passing the carbinol over titanium oxide at 250°. For storage and shipment an antioxidant such as *t*-butylcatechol is added and the temperature kept low by refrigeration.

The importance of styrene lies in its easy polymerization, which was observed as early as 1839. As late as 1930, however, polystyrene had little commercial use because the product was very brittle. Subsequently the brittle polymers were avoided by proper purification of the monomer to remove the small amounts of impurities which cause cross-linking. Very pure styrene polymerized at room temperature gives a fibrous tough solid having a molecular weight of about 500,000, which is a thermoplastic linear polymer, soluble in benzene. To carry out the polymerization, the antioxidant is removed by washing with alkali, and benzoyl peroxide is added as a catalyst.

$$x\,C_6H_5CH{=}CH_2 \xrightarrow{(C_6H_5CO)_2O_2} \left[\begin{array}{c}{-}CH_2CH{-}\\ \quad\quad | \\ \quad C_6H_5\end{array}\right]_x$$

If as little as 0.01 per cent of divinylbenzene, $CH_2{=}CHC_6H_4CH{=}CH_2$, is present, the product no longer is thermoplastic and only swells in benzene, because cross-linking of the linear chains has taken place.

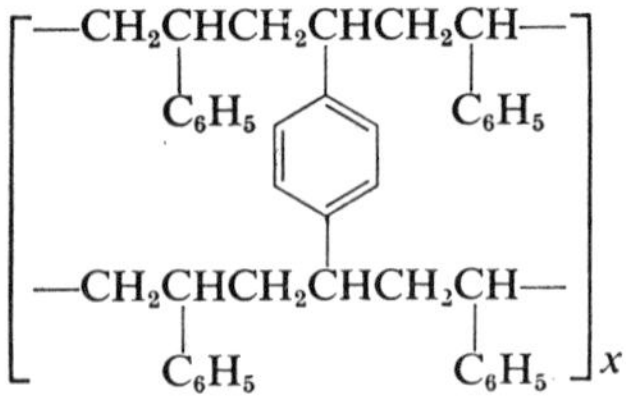

Polystyrene has high transparency and strength and, being a hydrocarbon, it is a good electrical insulator, is chemically resistant, and is light in weight.

The cross-linked copolymer of styrene and divinylbenzene is sulfonated to give cation-exchange resins. Chloromethylation (p. 435) followed by reaction with trimethylamine gives a quaternary salt. Conversion to the quaternary hydroxide gives a strongly basic anion-exchange resin (cf. p. 514). Styrene also is copolymerized with butadiene to give the most important type of synthetic rubber, Buna-S or GRS (p. 717), and with unsaturated alkyd resins to give polyester resins (p. 807). Emulsions of styrene-butadiene copolymers are used as a vehicle for aqueous latex paints. When polystyrene containing a volatile solvent is heated and subjected to reduced pressure, a rigid polystyrene foam is produced which is light in weight and has good insulating properties.

α-**Methylstyrene** (*2-phenylpropylene*) and the *m*- and *p*-**methylstyrenes** (*vinyltoluenes*) are made by the catalytic dehydrogenation of cumene (p. 430) and of the methylethylbenzenes. They can be substituted for styrene for most purposes. α-Methylstyrene has the advantage that it does not polymerize as readily as styrene, and hence there is less difficulty in shipping and storage and greater freedom in processing operations. The *m*- and *p*-methylstyrenes have the advantage that the raw material is toluene instead of benzene. Toluene is available in large amounts from reforming operations (p. 76) and can be produced more cheaply from petroleum than benzene. However, more products are produced in the ethylation of toluene than in the ethylation of benzene (p. 430), and *o*-ethyltoluene must be removed before dehydrogenation because it yields more indene than *o*-methylstyrene.

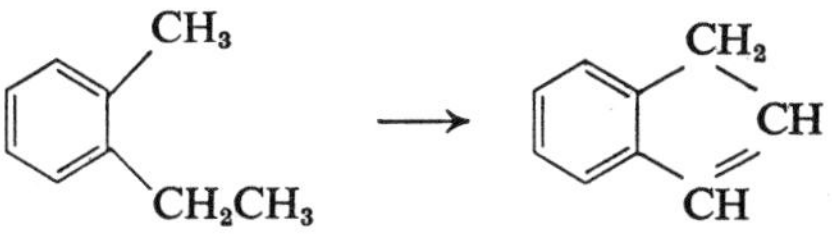

Indene

Moreover the separation of the methylstyrenes by distillation is even more difficult than the separation of styrene.

Styrene adds hypochlorous acid to give a mixture of the two chlorohydrins which are difficult to separate by distillation. Reaction of the mixture with alkali gives **styrene oxide.** It is made commercially for use in epoxy resin formulations (p. 750) and for the preparation of other compounds.

$$C_6H_5CH{=}CH_2 \xrightarrow{\text{HOCl}} \begin{array}{c} C_6H_5CHOHCH_2Cl \\ \text{and} \\ C_6H_5CHClCH_2OH \end{array} \xrightarrow{\text{NaOH}} C_6H_5CH{-}CH_2$$

Styrene oxide

Arylethylenes react with paraformaldehyde in acetic acid solution in the presence of concentrated sulfuric acid to give unsaturated alcohols, glycols or their acetates, or cyclic formals (*Prins reaction*).

$$ArCH{=}CH_2 + HCHO \xrightarrow{H_2SO_4} ArCH{=}CHCH_2OH \xrightarrow{H_2O}$$

$$ArCHCH_2CH_2OH \xrightarrow{HCHO} ArCHCH_2CH_2$$

The formal is a benzyl ether and can be reduced catalytically or with sodium and alcohol (p. 526) to give the hemiacetal of formaldehyde. Loss of formaldehyde, with its concurrent reduction to methanol, gives the 3-arylpropanol.

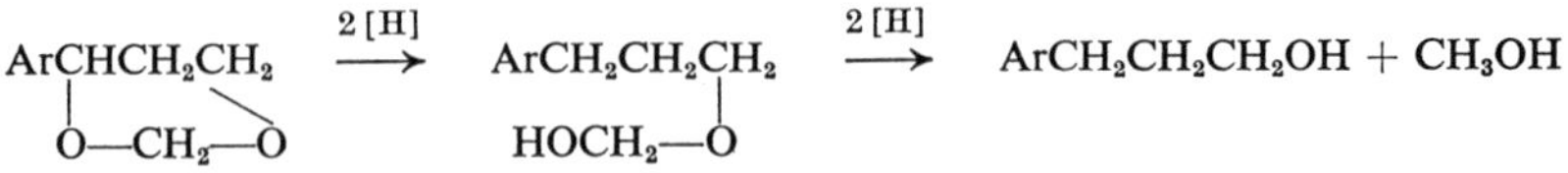

$$ArCHCH_2CH_2 \xrightarrow{2\,[H]} ArCH_2CH_2CH_2 \xrightarrow{2\,[H]} ArCH_2CH_2CH_2OH + CH_3OH$$
$$\underset{O-CH_2-O}{|} \qquad \underset{HOCH_2-O}{|}$$

Purely aliphatic olefins also undergo the Prins reaction, but in general a more complex mixture of products is formed.

ω-Bromostyrene is obtained when cinnamic acid dibromide is boiled with a solution of sodium carbonate.

$$C_6H_5CHBrCHBrCOONa \longrightarrow C_6H_5CH{=}CHBr + CO_2 + NaBr$$

When ω-bromostyrene is dropped on fused potassium hydroxide, **phenylacetylene** distills.

$$C_6H_5CH{=}CHBr + KOH \xrightarrow{200°} C_6H_5C{\equiv}CH + KBr + H_2O$$

Three diphenylethylenes are possible. **1,1-Diphenylethylene** can be made by the reaction of acetophenone and phenylmagnesium bromide. The intermediate carbinol can be dehydrated readily to the olefin.

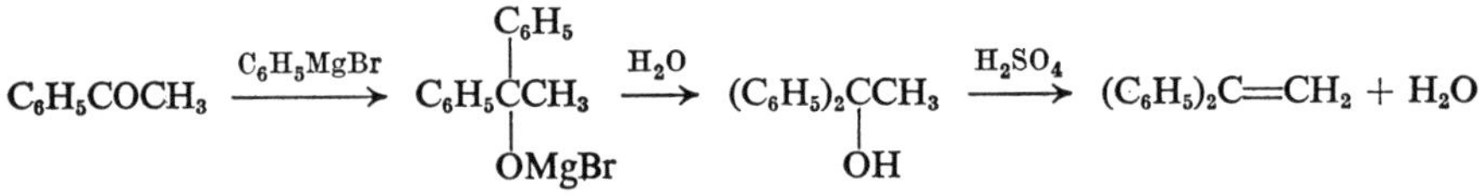

$$C_6H_5COCH_3 \xrightarrow{C_6H_5MgBr} \underset{OMgBr}{\overset{C_6H_5}{C_6H_5\overset{|}{\underset{|}{C}}CH_3}} \xrightarrow{H_2O} \underset{OH}{(C_6H_5)_2\overset{|}{\underset{|}{C}}CH_3} \xrightarrow{H_2SO_4} (C_6H_5)_2C{=}CH_2 + H_2O$$

The two *1,2-diphenylethylenes* are known as *cis* and *trans*-stilbene (p. 354). *trans*-Stilbene is the stable isomer and is obtained by the dehydration of benzylphenylcarbinol.

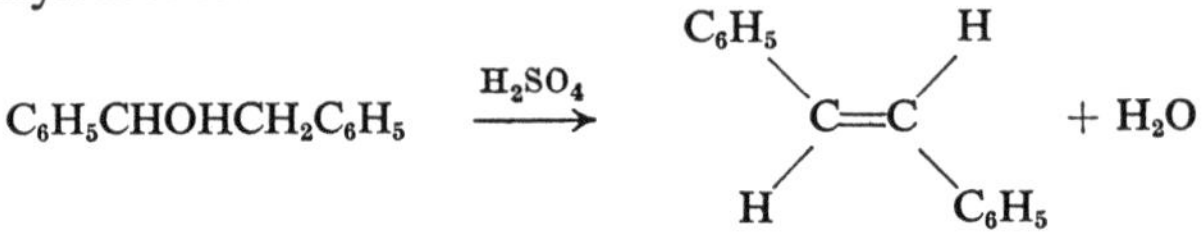

$$C_6H_5CHOHCH_2C_6H_5 \xrightarrow{H_2SO_4}$$

C=C with C_6H_5 and H on left, H and C_6H_5 on right + H_2O

trans-Stilbene

Irradiation with ultraviolet light converts it to *cis*-stilbene (p. 663).

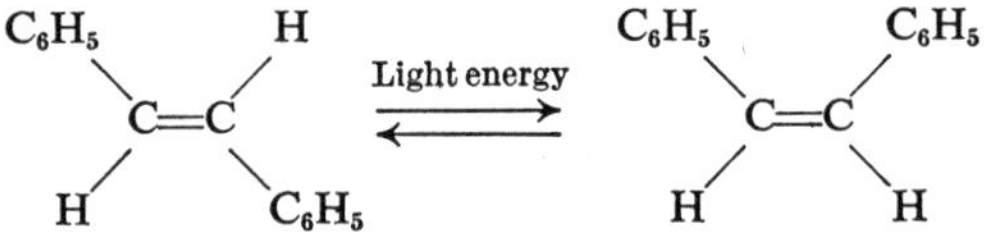

C=C with C_6H_5, H / H, C_6H_5 ⇌ (Light energy)   C=C with C_6H_5, C_6H_5 / H, H

cis-Stilbene

When stilbene dibromide is boiled with alcoholic potassium hydroxide, it is converted first into bromostilbene and then into **diphenylacetylene** (*tolan*).

$$C_6H_5CHBrCHBrC_6H_5 \xrightarrow{KOH} C_6H_5CH{=}CBrC_6H_5 \xrightarrow{KOH} C_6H_5C{\equiv}CC_6H_5$$

It can be prepared also by the oxidation of the dihydrazone of benzil.

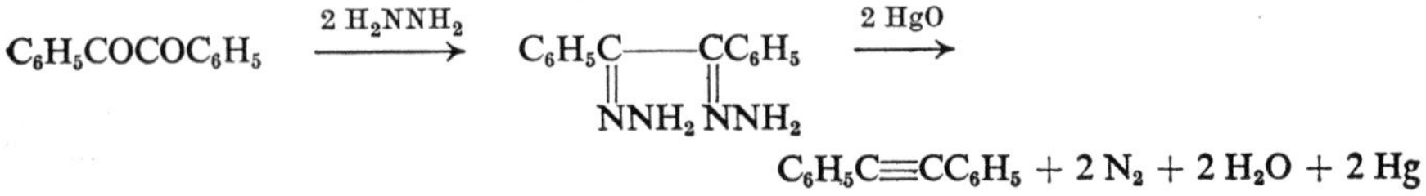

$$C_6H_5COCOC_6H_5 \xrightarrow{2\,H_2NNH_2} \underset{NNH_2\;NNH_2}{C_6H_5\overset{||}{C}{-}{-}\overset{||}{C}C_6H_5} \xrightarrow{2\,HgO}$$

$$C_6H_5C{\equiv}CC_6H_5 + 2\,N_2 + 2\,H_2O + 2\,Hg$$

Triphenylethylene may be prepared by dehydration of diphenylbenzylcarbinol or phenylbenzhydrylcarbinol. **Tetraphenylethylene** is formed when diphenyldichloromethane, prepared by the action of phosphorus pentachloride on benzophenone, is heated with zinc dust.

$$2\,(C_6H_5)_2CO \xrightarrow{2\ PCl_5} 2\,(C_6H_5)_2CCl_2 \xrightarrow{2\ Zn} (C_6H_5)_2C{=}C(C_6H_5)_2 + 2\ ZnCl_2$$

Stilbene adds bromine less readily than ethylene, triphenylethylene less readily than styrene, and tetraphenylethylene less readily than stilbene. Nevertheless styrene adds bromine more readily than ethylene, and triphenylethylene more readily than stilbene; that is, as long as the phenyl groups replace hydrogen symmetrically, they reduce the reactivity, but unsymmetrical compounds are more reactive than less highly phenylated symmetrical compounds. An explanation is that the phenyl groups permit stabilization of the intermediate ion by resonance. The greater the number of phenyl groups on the electron-deficient carbon atom, the greater the stability of the ion and the more likely it will form. Thus ion II is more stable than I, and IV than III. Although the ions II and III and the ions IV and V have about the same stability, the electrons of the π bond of the original olefin are less available in the compound having the greater number of phenyl groups.

$$\overset{+}{CH_2}CH_2Br$$

I

$$C_6H_5\overset{+}{C}HCH_2Br$$

II

$$C_6H_5\overset{+}{C}HCHBrC_6H_5$$

III

$$(C_6H_5)_2\overset{+}{C}CHBrC_6H_5$$

IV

$$(C_6H_5)_2\overset{+}{C}CBr(C_6H_5)_2$$

V

The accumulation of phenyl groups on a carbon-carbon double bond permits alkali metals to react with the π electrons because the ions formed are stabilized by resonance. With 1,1-diphenylethylene the intermediate ion-radical dimerizes to give the disodium derivative of 1,1,4,4-tetraphenylbutane.

$$2\,(C_6H_5)_2C{=}CH_2 + 2\,[Na\cdot] \longrightarrow 2\left[\underset{\overset{..}{\underset{Na^+}{}}}{(C_6H_5)_2CCH_2\cdot}\right] \longrightarrow \underset{\overset{..}{\underset{Na^+}{}}}{(C_6H_5)_2CCH_2} : \underset{\overset{..}{\underset{Na^+}{}}}{CH_2C(C_6H_5)_2}$$

With tetraphenylethylene the intermediate ion-radical is sufficiently stable to react with a second atom of the metal to give a disodium derivative.

$$(C_6H_5)_2C{=}C(C_6H_5)_2 \xrightarrow{Na\cdot} \left[\underset{\overset{..}{\underset{Na^+}{}}}{(C_6H_5)_2C{-}\overset{\cdot}{C}(C_6H_5)_2}\right] \xrightarrow{Na\cdot} \underset{\overset{..}{\underset{Na^+}{}}\ \overset{..}{\underset{Na^+}{}}}{(C_6H_5)_2C{-}\!\!-\!\!C(C_6H_5)_2}$$

These metallic derivatives are highly colored solids and react like organometallic compounds. Thus water gives the saturated hydrocarbon, and carbon dioxide gives the dicarboxylic acid.

$$(C_6H_5)_2CH{-}CH(C_6H_5)_2 + 2\ NaOH$$

$$\underset{\overset{..}{\underset{Na^+}{}}\ \overset{..}{\underset{Na^+}{}}}{(C_6H_5)_2C{-}\!\!-\!\!C(C_6H_5)_2}\ \overset{2\ H_2O}{\nearrow}\ \underset{2\ CO_2}{\searrow}$$

$$\underset{COONa\quad COONa}{(C_6H_5)_2C{-}\!\!-\!\!-\!\!-\!\!C(C_6H_5)_2}$$

BIPHENYL AND ITS DERIVATIVES

Biphenyl and its derivatives form the largest group of compounds having benzene rings directly united. **Biphenyl** is obtained when benzene is heated to a high temperature. In the laboratory preparation the vapor from refluxing benzene is allowed to come in contact with a spiral of electrically heated Nichrome wire, but in the commercial method the vapor is passed through molten lead or hot tubes.

$$2 C_6H_6 \xrightarrow{700°-800°} C_6H_5C_6H_5 + H_2$$

Since the initial stage in the formation of biphenyl undoubtedly is the decomposition of benzene into phenyl radicals and hydrogen atoms, it is not surprising that small amounts of the terphenyls, **m-** and **p-diphenylbenzene,** and the quaterphenyls, **1,3,5-triphenylbenzene** and **4,4′-bi(biphenyl),** also are produced.

Besides the use of biphenyl in the eutectic with phenyl ether as a heat transfer medium (p. 510), some of its substitution products are important. The halogenated biphenyls (Arochlors) are used as transformer oils and as nonflammable heat exchange mediums, and some of the aminobiphenyls are used as dye intermediates. Direct substitution reactions lead to *ortho* and *para* mono-substitution products, but since the groups introduced usually are deactivating, a second substitution takes place in the second ring.

The most important derivative of biphenyl, *p,p′*-diaminobiphenyl or **benzidine,** is not made from biphenyl but by the *benzidine rearrangement* of hydrazobenzene (p. 459). It is an important intermediate for the synthesis of direct dyes for cotton (p. 678).

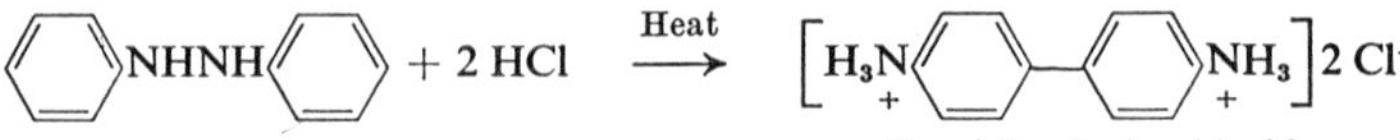

Benzidine hydrochloride

o-**Tolidine** (*p,p′-diamino-m,m′-dimethylbiphenyl*) is made similarly from *o*-hydrazotoluene, and **dianisidine** (*p,p′-diamino-m,m′-dimethoxybiphenyl*) from *o*-hydrazoanisole. If one or both *para* positions in the hydrazo compound are blocked, a diphenylamine derivative is formed rather than a biphenyl derivative.

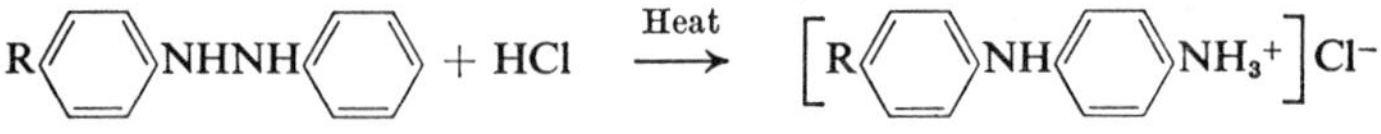

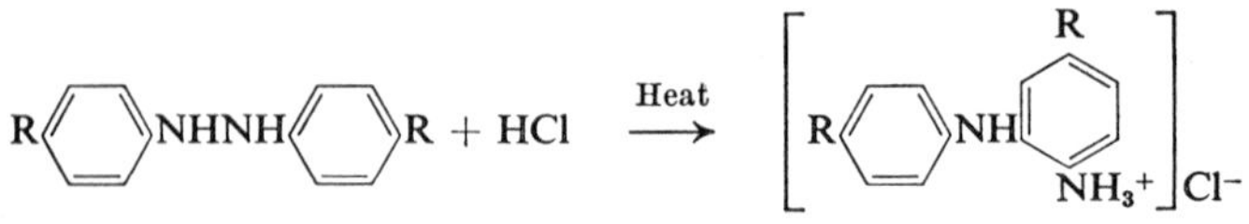

This type of reaction is called the *semidine rearrangement.*

The mechanism of the benzidine rearrangement has been the subject of many investigations. It has been difficult to explain because the rearrangement is known to be entirely intramolecular; that is, the molecule never separates into two distinct entities during the rearrangement. It has been shown that it must be the dihydrochloride of hydrazobenzene that rearranges, and it is assumed that the adjacent positive charges cause a repulsion of the nitrogen atoms and permit formation of a *para* quinonoid structure which loses two protons to give the benzidine.

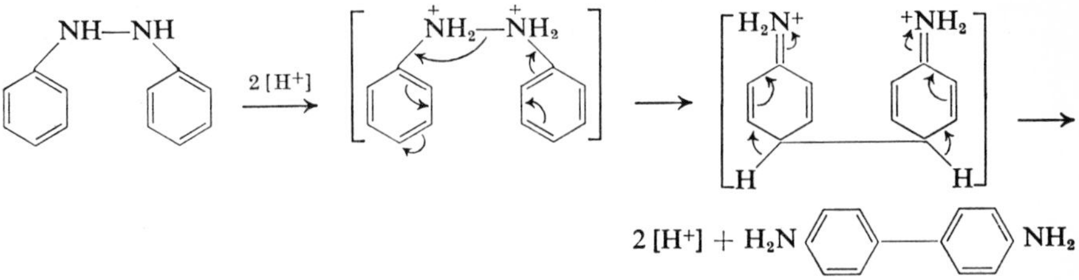

$$2\,[H^+] + H_2N\!\!-\!\!\langle\;\rangle\!\!-\!\!\langle\;\rangle\!\!-\!\!NH_2$$

Benzidine is oxidized under certain conditions to give the intensely colored **Benzidine Blue.** This reaction has been used as the basis of tests for hydrogen peroxide and peroxidases; of sensitive spot tests for readily reduced ions of metals such as cerium, manganese, cobalt, and copper; and for bromide, iodide, cyanide and thiocyanate ions. The test for copper is even more sensitive if tolidine is used instead of benzidine.

The test for hydrogen peroxide or peroxidases depends on the ability of the peroxidases to cause dissociation of hydrogen peroxide into free hydroxyl radicals which can remove a hydrogen atom from benzidine acetate to give a free-radical semiquinone ion similar to Wurster salts (p. 572).

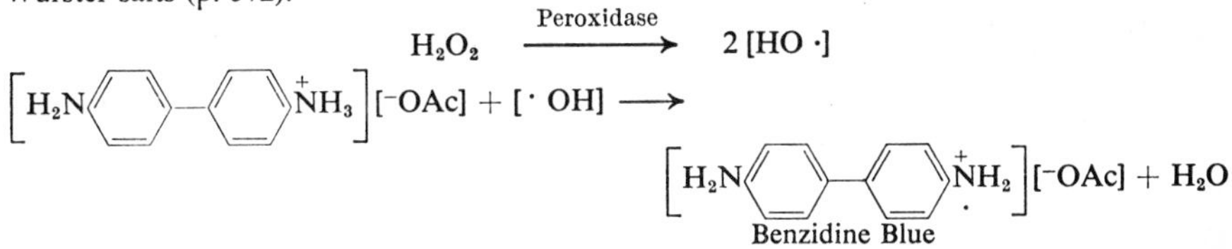

$$H_2O_2 \xrightarrow{\text{Peroxidase}} 2\,[HO\cdot]$$

The tests for the metals depend on their ability to oxidize the benzidine acetate and be reduced to a lower valence state.

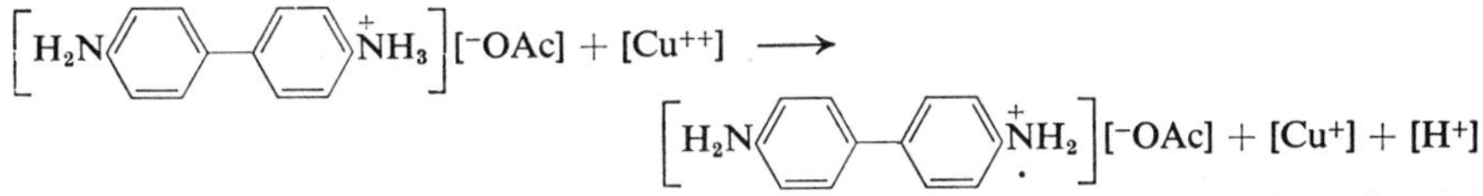

The cupric ion is not a sufficiently strong oxidizing agent to produce the blue color unless the cuprous ion formed is removed from solution. Cyanide, bromide, iodide or thiocyanate ions form sufficiently insoluble cuprous salts to permit cupric ion to give a positive test. Benzidine acetate in the presence of cyanide ion is converted to Benzidine Blue also by certain adsorbent clays, such as Bentonite, which have crystal lattice defects.

Biphenyl derivatives can be prepared by heating iodobenzenes with finely divided copper (*Ullmann reaction*). The reaction is valuable because it permits the synthesis of derivatives of known constitution and of compounds that cannot be prepared readily in other ways.

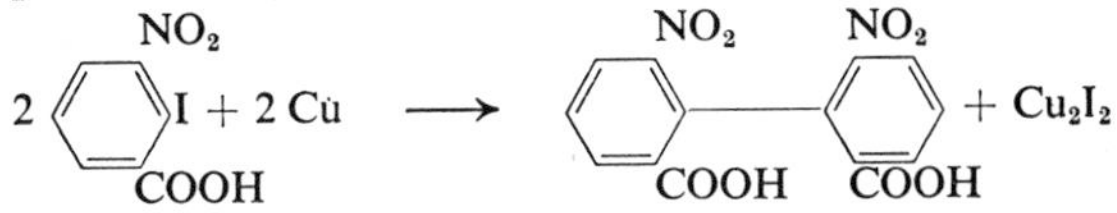

2,2'-Dinitro-6,6'-
biphenyldicarboxylic
acid

Biphenyl and its derivatives also are products of the reaction of diazonium salts with aromatic hydrocarbons in the presence of alkali (p. 496).

The derivatives of biphenyl have been of interest from the theoretical viewpoint. 2,2′-Dinitro-6,6′-biphenyldicarboxylic acid, for example, can be resolved into two optically active isomers, although it does not contain an asymmetric carbon atom. Many derivatives of biphenyl have been studied, and it has been found that only those having substituents in the *ortho* positions are capable of resolution. Moreover active forms of compounds having four *ortho* substituents are very stable to racemization, but those having three *ortho* substituents racemize more easily. The ease of racemization decreases with increasing size of the group on the ring having the single *ortho* substituent. Figure 82 shows that if two *ortho* groups have an apparent diameter greater

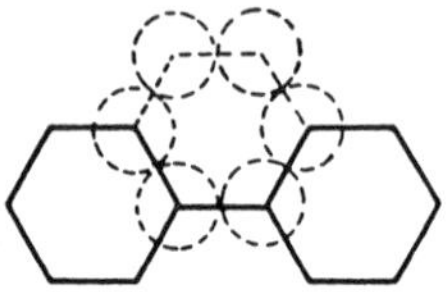

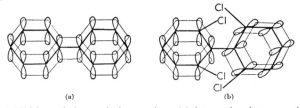

Fig. 82 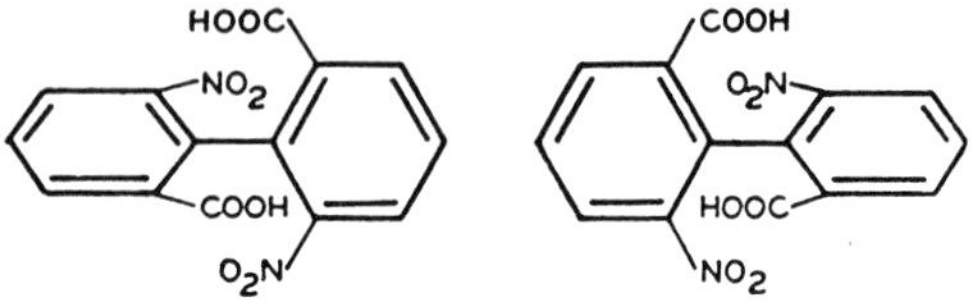   Fig. 83

Fig. 82. Shortest internuclear distance between *ortho* groups that will permit free rotation in biphenyl derivatives.

Fig. 83. Active forms of 2,2′-dinitrobiphenyl-6,6′-dicarboxylic acid.

than that of the aromatic carbon atom (1.39 Å), these groups cannot pass each other, and free rotation about the bond joining the two phenyl groups will be prevented. If the two phenyl groups are restricted to a nonplanar configuration and the resulting molecule lacks a plane, center, or alternating axis of symmetry (p. 336), then two configurations are possible which are nonsuperposable mirror images (Fig. 83). The racemization of tri-*o*-substituted biphenyls is understandable, since a small amount of bending of the bond joining the two phenyl groups might permit two *ortho* groups to pass each other without causing the third *ortho* group to interfere with the *ortho* hydrogen atom. If a group is large enough to interfere with an *ortho* hydrogen, one such group in each ring should permit resolution. 2,2′-Biphenyldisulfonic acid appears to be an example. There is indication that a single trimethylarsonium group is large enough to prevent free rotation even with bending of the bond between the phenyl groups.

Evidence differing entirely from resolvability confirms the inability of tetra-*ortho*-substituted biphenyls to assume a planar configuration. The ultraviolet absorption spectrum of biphenyl exhibits characteristic bands because of the interaction of the unsaturation electrons of one nucleus with those of the other. This interaction is possible only because the rings can become coplanar permitting the *p* orbitals of the carbon atoms joining the rings to overlap. In 2,2′,6,6′-tetrachlorobiphenyl the rings cannot become planar, and the bands characteristic of biphenyl are absent (Fig. 84).

(a)   (b)

Fig. 84. Steric inhibition of electronic interaction: (*a*) interaction between planar rings; (*b*) noninteraction between nonplanar rings.

The prevention of free rotation about single bonds and of coplanarity by the blocking effect of groups has been extensively investigated and found to exist in a wide variety of compounds other than the biphenyls. For example, compound I has been resolved and the active form is not racemized in boiling butanol. Compound II has been resolved whereas III, which has a plane of symmetry, has not.

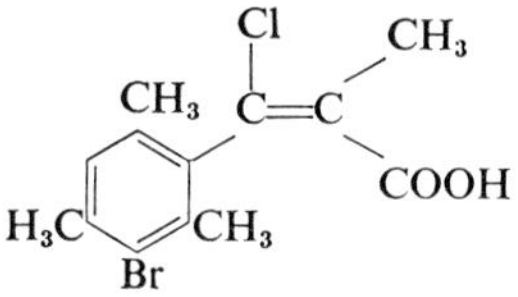

Hence the activity of II must be due to restricted rotation and not to the asymmetry of the nitrogen atom. Restricted rotation about single bonds which leads to inhibition of resonance also affects the reactivity of aromatic compounds (pp. 480, 539).

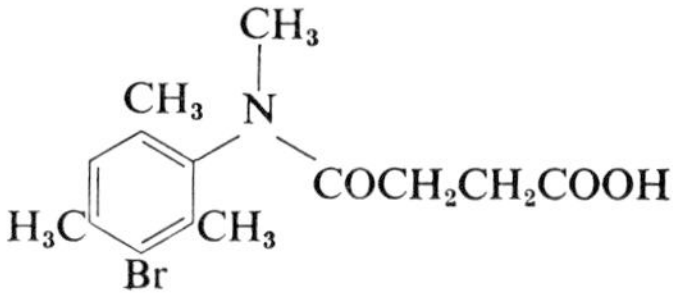

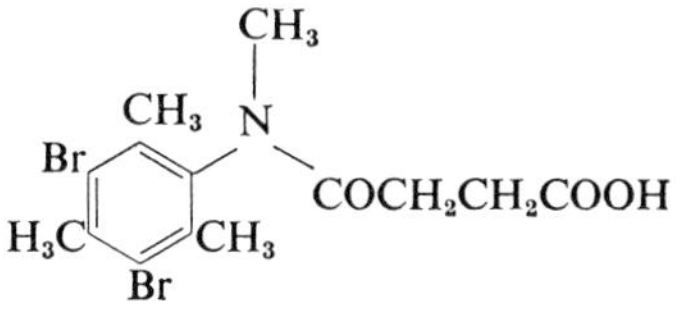

Ellagic acid, the dilactone of 4,5,6,4′,5′,6′-hexahydroxydiphenic acid, is obtained by the hydrolysis of the ellagic tannins present in many plants. These tannins are the mixed glucose esters of the hexahydroxydiphenic acid and of gallic acid (p. 561). In the tannin the hexahydroxydiphenic acid is present as the (+) active form but the free acid spontaneously lactonizes with consequent destruction of the asymmetry.

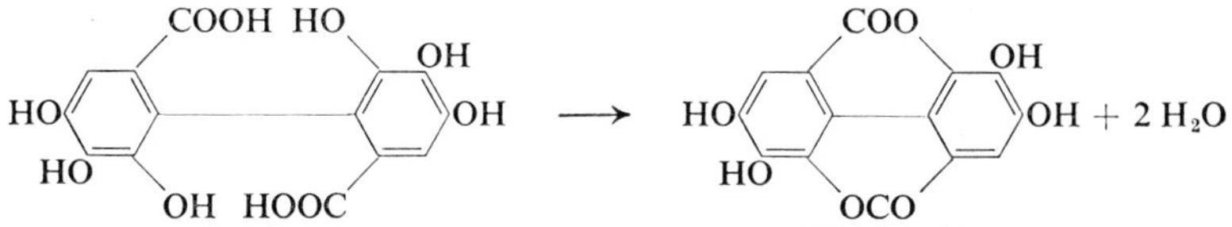

Ellagic acid

REVIEW QUESTIONS

1. How is triphenylmethylsodium prepared? What is unusual about solutions of the compound and how are the unusual properties explained?
2. Discuss the method of preparation and chemical properties of hexaphenylethane. How are these properties explained? What are the three classes of *free groups?*
3. How is styrene made and of what use is it?
4. What reaction does tetraphenylethylene undergo that is not given by tetramethylethylene?
5. What is biphenyl and how is it made? Of what use is it?
6. In the direct substitution reactions of biphenyl, what positions are taken by the entering groups and why?
7. What is the common name for *p,p′*-diaminobiphenyl, and how is it made?
8. Discuss the isomerism of tri- and tetra-*ortho*-substituted biphenyls.
9. What is Benzidine Blue? Explain the use of benzidine in a test for certain cations and anions.

PROBLEMS

10. Give a series of reactions for the following syntheses: (*a*) Methoxychlor from phenol; (*b*) ω-bromostyrene from benzaldehyde; (*c*) 3-phenyl-1-propanol from styrene; (*d*) *o*-tolidine from toluene; (*e*) 2-amino-4′,5-dimethyldiphenylamine from toluene; (*f*) styrene from benzaldehyde; (*g*) triphenylmethyl from benzene; (*h*) diphenylacetylene from benzyl alcohol; (*i*) *p,p′*-biphenyldicarboxylic acid from toluene; (*j*) *p,p′*-diiodobiphenyl from nitrobenzene.
11. How could one distinguish by chemical reactions between the members of the following pairs of compounds: (*a*) *p*-methylbiphenyl and diphenylmethane; (*b*) biphenyl and triphenylmethane; (*c*) *sym*-diphenylethylene and *p,p′*-dimethylbiphenyl; (*d*) styrene and phenylacetylene; (*e*) *sym*-diphenylethylene and *unsym*-diphenylethylene.

Chapter 28

CONDENSED NUCLEAR HYDROCARBONS
AND THEIR DERIVATIVES

Condensed nuclear compounds are compounds in which two or more carbon atoms are shared in common by two or more aromatic rings. The most common compounds of this type are naphthalene and anthracene and their derivatives. Numerous systems that are more complex are known.

NAPHTHALENE

Occurrence and Structure

Naphthalene, isolated some time before 1820, was the first pure compound to be obtained from the distillation products of coal. The reason for its early discovery is that it is a beautiful crystalline solid that sublimes readily. It was noticed first as a deposit in the condensers during the distillation of the naphtha fraction and hence was called naphthalene. Naphthalene is obtained chiefly by allowing the carbolic and creosote fractions of coal tar to crystallize (p. 427).

The empirical formula, C_5H_4, was established by Faraday in 1826 by the analysis of barium naphthalenesulfonate, but it was not until after Kekulé propounded his theory of aromatic structure that Erlenmeyer[1] proposed in 1866 a satisfactory structure for the molecular formula, $C_{10}H_8$. Erlenmeyer's formula contains two aromatic nuclei having two carbon atoms in common.

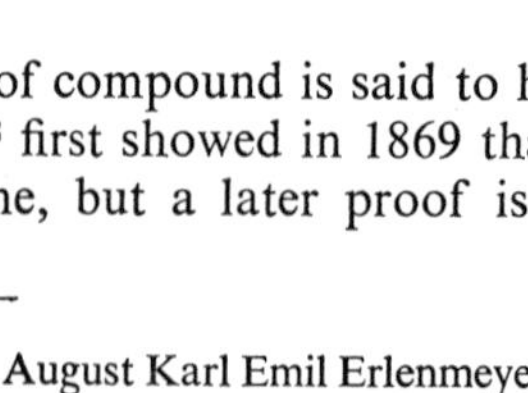

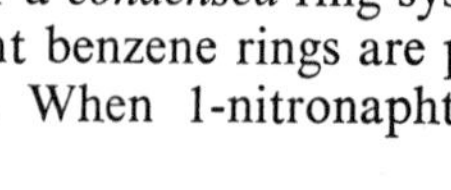

This type of compound is said to have a *fused* or a *condensed* ring system.

Graebe[2] first showed in 1869 that two different benzene rings are present in naphthalene, but a later proof is more direct. When 1-nitronaphthalene is

---

[1] Richard August Karl Emil Erlenmeyer (1825–1909), professor at the University of Munich. He is well known for the still popular conical flask which he devised.

[2] Carl Graebe (1841–1927), student of Bunsen and Baeyer and later professor at the University of Geneva. He is known chiefly for determining the structure of alizarin and synthesizing it but did important work in the fields of polynuclear compounds and dyes in general.

582

oxidized, 3-nitrophthalic acid is formed, but if the nitro group first is reduced to the amino group, the product of subsequent oxidation is phthalic acid.

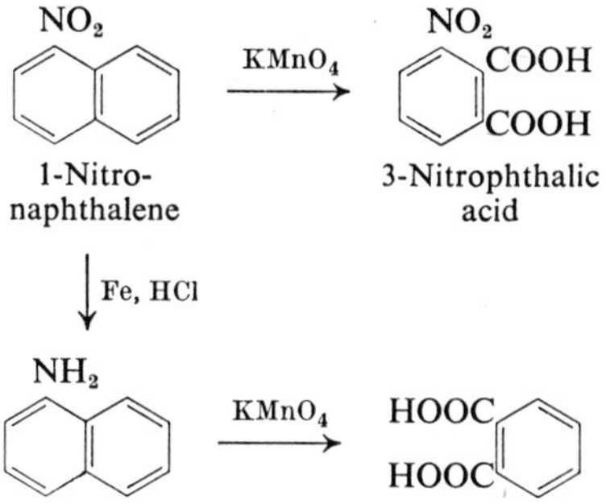

1-Nitro-
naphthalene

3-Nitrophthalic
acid

Fe, HCl

KMnO₄

The reason for the difference in behavior on oxidation is that the nitro group makes an aromatic ring harder to oxidize than an unsubstituted benzene ring, whereas the amino group increases the ease of oxidation of the ring to which it is attached (p. 482).

Several syntheses of naphthalene substantiate Erlenmeyer's formula. One of the more unequivocal syntheses is that of Fittig which involves the cyclization of β-benzylidenepropionic acid to 1-naphthol and reduction to naphthalene.

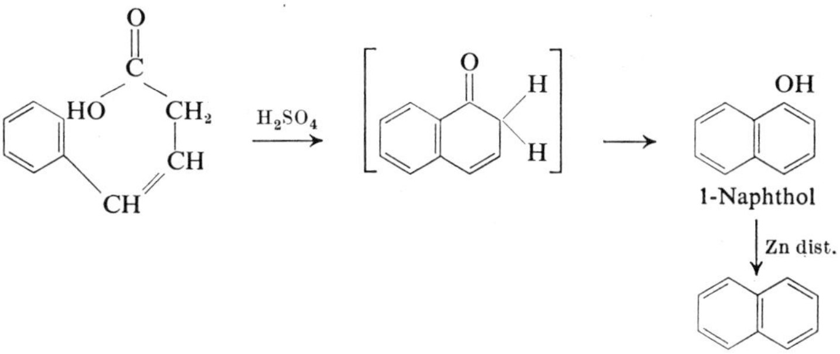

1-Naphthol

Zn dist.

The formula accounts for the existence of two monosubstitution products, frequently designated as α and β, and ten disubstitution products when both groups are alike. Up to ten hydrogen atoms can be added to naphthalene indicating five potential double bonds.

As with benzene, the unsaturation electrons are in molecular orbitals characteristic of closed conjugated systems (p. 419). Naphthalene, like benzene, usually is represented as a resonance hybrid of the conventional bond structures. The resonance energy of naphthalene is 61 kcal. per mole. Since the resonance energy of benzene is 36 kcal. per mole, the additional resonance energy contributed by the second ring is only 25 kcal. per mole. This decreased resonance energy is reflected in a greater reactivity of naphthalene compared to benzene.

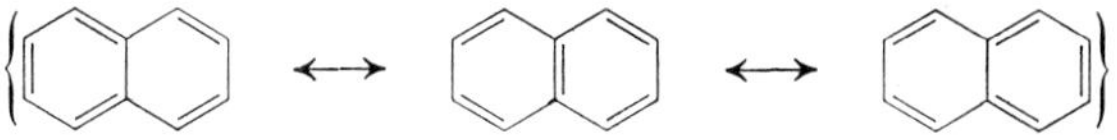

Reactions

Addition Reactions. One ring of naphthalene undergoes addition reactions more readily than benzene. Reaction with sodium and ethyl alcohol produces a

1,4-dihydro derivative. At the higher temperature of boiling *i*-amyl alcohol, the 1,2,3,4-tetrahydro derivative (tetralin) is formed.

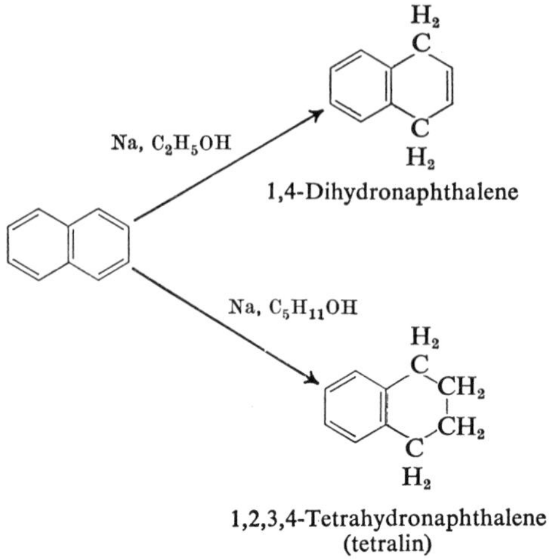

1,4-Dihydronaphthalene

1,2,3,4-Tetrahydronaphthalene (tetralin)

Catalytically the reduction may be carried to the tetrahydro or the decahydro stage.

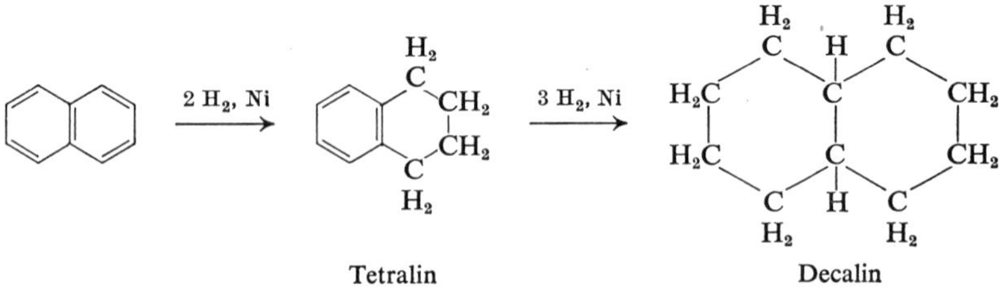

Tetralin

Decalin

Tetralin and **decalin** find some use as solvents. Decalin is of interest in that it exists in two stereoisomeric configurations, *cis*-decalin in which the methylidyne (CH) hydrogen atoms are on the same side of the ring union, and *trans*-decalin in which they are on opposite sides (p. 843).

Naphthalene adds one or two molecules of chlorine more easily than does benzene. The addition products when heated lose hydrogen chloride.

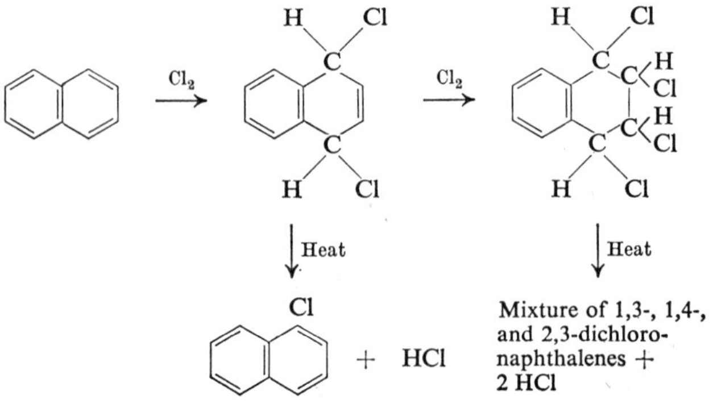

Mixture of 1,3-, 1,4-, and 2,3-dichloro-naphthalenes + 2 HCl

Because of this behavior **naphthalene tetrachloride** is used as a component of soldering pastes, the hydrogen chloride generated on heating being available for removing metallic oxide films.

Naphthalene adds the alkali metals also. In methyl ether solution, two atoms of sodium add, presumably to give the 1,2 and 1,4 addition products, since reaction with water or with carbon dioxide gives a mixture of the dihydronaphthalenes or the dicarboxylic acids.

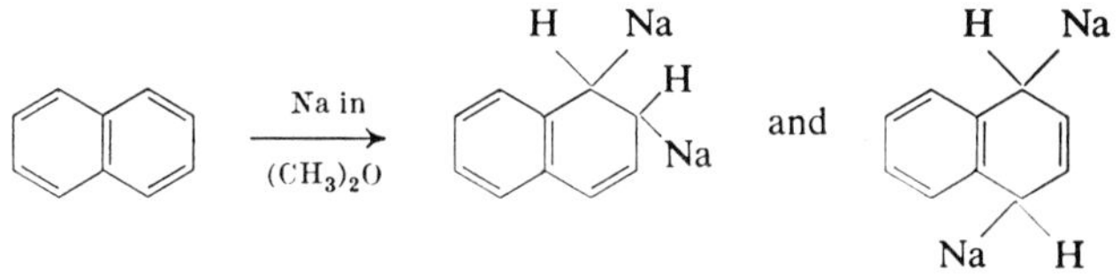

In liquid ammonia four atoms of sodium add, but three are ammonolyzed immediately. The fourth atom can be replaced by hydrogen by adding ammonium chloride.

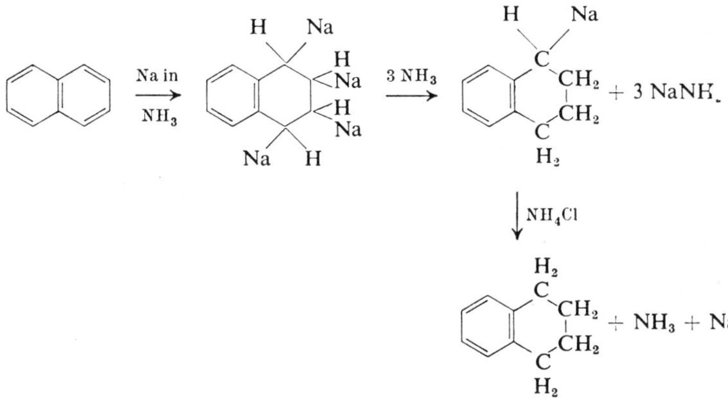

This procedure may be used for the commercial preparation of tetralin, the sodium amide being a valuable co-product.

Substitution Reactions. Naphthalene undergoes all of the substitution reactions of benzene, using the same reagents and catalysts. **Direct halogenation** in the presence of iron gives 95 per cent of α-chloronaphthalene and about 5 per cent

α-Chloronaphthalene (95 per cent) β-Chloronaphthalene (5 per cent)

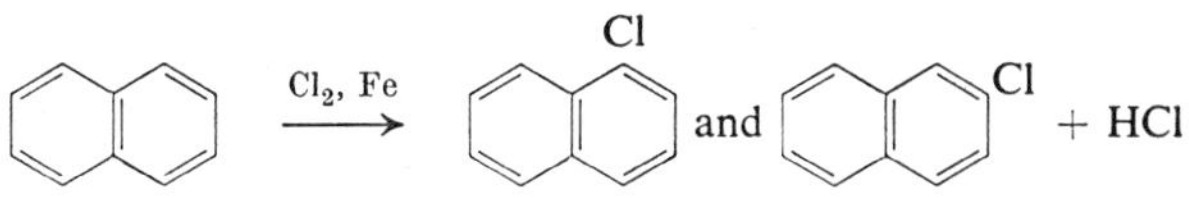

of the β isomer. Similarly nitration with a mixture of nitric and sulfuric acids yields 95 per cent of α-nitronaphthalene together with about 5 per cent of

β-nitronaphthalene. Sulfonation of naphthalene below 80° gives chiefly the α-sulfonic acid, whereas above 120° the β-sulfonic acid is the main product.

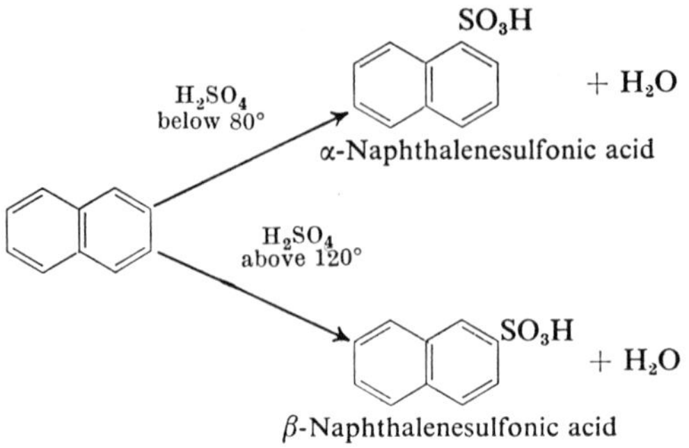

α-Naphthalenesulfonic acid

β-Naphthalenesulfonic acid

This behavior is important because it provides the principal method for introducing a functional group into the β position. Most β-substituted naphthalenes are prepared by way of the β-sulfonic acid. The reason for this behavior appears to be that the rate of sulfonation in the α position is very much faster than in the β position, but the position of equilibrium for the β-sulfonic acid is more favorable. Since the reaction is reversible, the β isomer eventually predominates. Mixtures of the α and β acids are separated by crystallization of the calcium salts, the calcium salt of the α isomer being the more soluble.

The Friedel-Crafts reaction also gives mixtures of α and β substitution products, the relative amounts of which can be controlled by varying the conditions of the reaction. Reaction with acetyl chloride in carbon disulfide gives about three-fourths α and one-fourth β substitution, whereas in nitrobenzene solution the β isomer is formed almost exclusively.

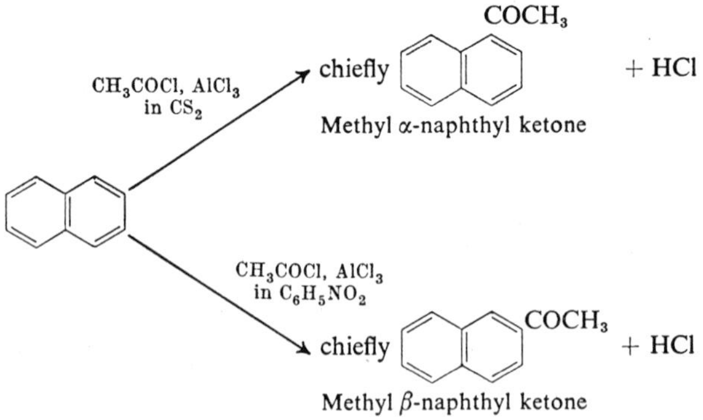

Methyl α-naphthyl ketone

Methyl β-naphthyl ketone

Disubstitution follows essentially the same rules as for benzene, although the reversibility of some reactions frequently permits rearrangement of the initial product to a more stable isomer. If the group in a monosubstituted naphthalene is deactivating, a second substituent will enter the second ring usually in one of the α' positions, except for sulfonation which can take place in a β' position.

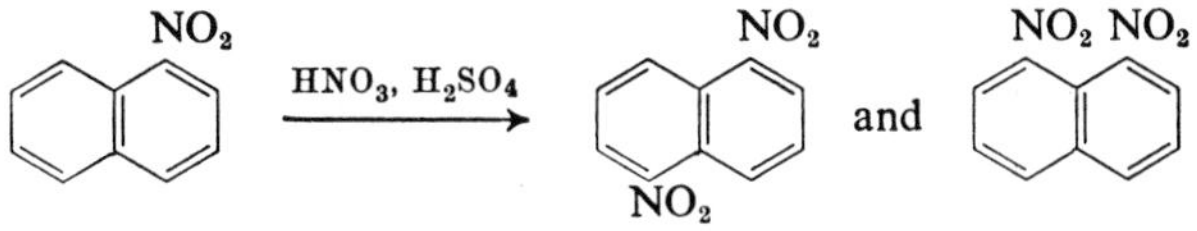

NO₂

HNO₃, H₂SO₄

NO₂

and

NO₂ NO₂

NO₂

1,5-Dinitro-naphthalene

1,8-Dinitro-naphthalene

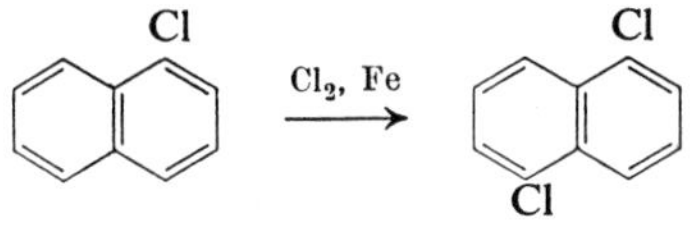

Cl

Cl₂, Fe

Cl

Cl

1,5-Dichloro-naphthalene

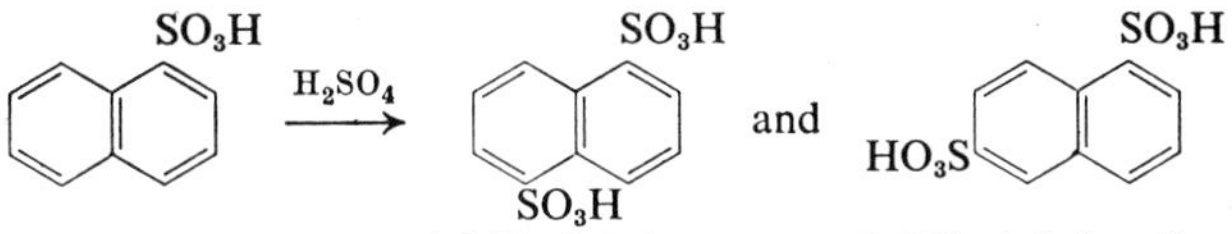

SO₃H

H₂SO₄

SO₃H

and

SO₃H

SO₃H

HO₃S

1,5-Naphthalene-disulfonic acid

1,6-Naphthalenedi-sulfonic acid

SO₃H

H₂SO₄

SO₃H

HO₃S

and

HO₃S

SO₃H

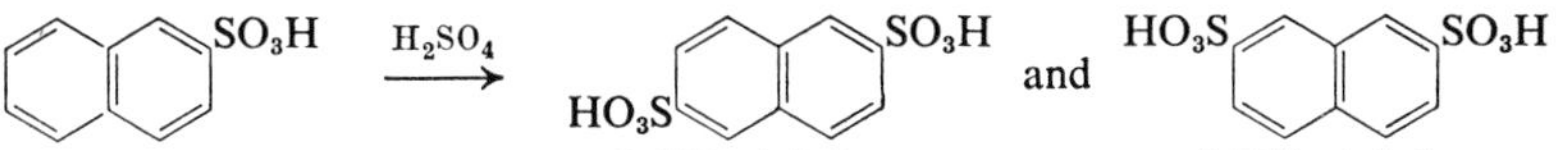

2,6-Naphthalene-disulfonic acid

2,7-Naphthalene-disulfonic acid

If the group present is activating and in the α position, a second substituent enters the 4 (*para*) position, except that in sulfonation a rearranged product may result. If an activating group is in the β position, a second substituent enters the α position. Again sulfonation may give anomalous products (p. 590).

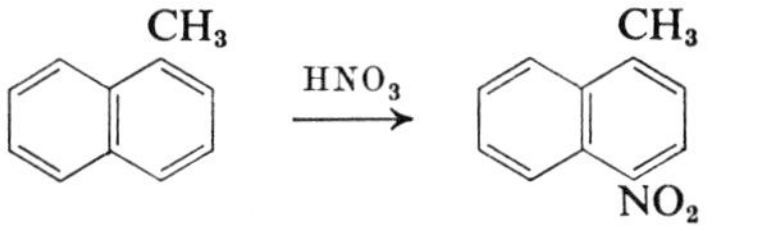

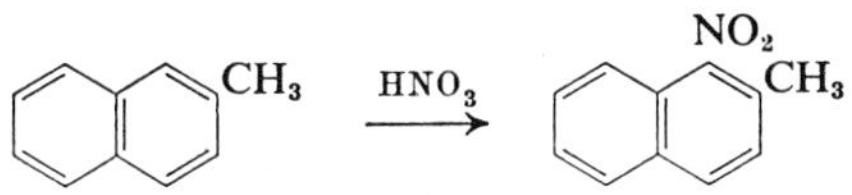

CH₃

HNO₃

CH₃

NO₂

CH₃

HNO₃

NO₂

CH₃

Preference of the 1 position over the 3 position in the second reaction can be explained by noting that two of the resonance structures in the transition state for substitution at the 1 position have a benzene nucleus, whereas in that for substitution at the 3 position only one structure has an aromatic ring.

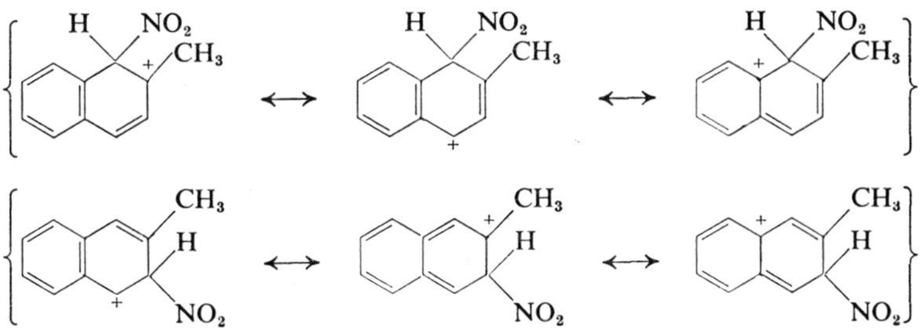

H   NO₂
CH₃

⟷

H   NO₂
CH₃

⟷

H   NO₂
CH₃

CH₃
H

⟷

CH₃
H

⟷

CH₃
H

NO₂

NO₂

NO₂

Naphthalene Derivatives

Alkyl Derivatives. α- and β-Methylnaphthalene are isolated commercially from coal tar. α-**Methylnaphthalene** has been selected as the standard fuel with zero rating in testing Diesel fuels, because of its poor burning characteristics in the Diesel engine (p. 81).

Naphthols. α- and β-Naphthol are prepared from the corresponding sodium sulfonates by fusion with sodium hydroxide. They not only are important dye intermediates themselves but are used for the synthesis of other dye intermediates. β-Naphthol is the more important, production being forty to fifty times that of the α isomer. Pure α-naphthol is made by the hydrolysis of α-naphthylamine (p. 588).

Halogenated Naphthalenes. α-Chloro- and α-bromonaphthalene are made by direct halogenation. The β isomers are only of research interest. They can be made by the action of phosphorus pentahalides on the naphthol or by the Sandmeyer reaction from diazotized β-naphthylamine.

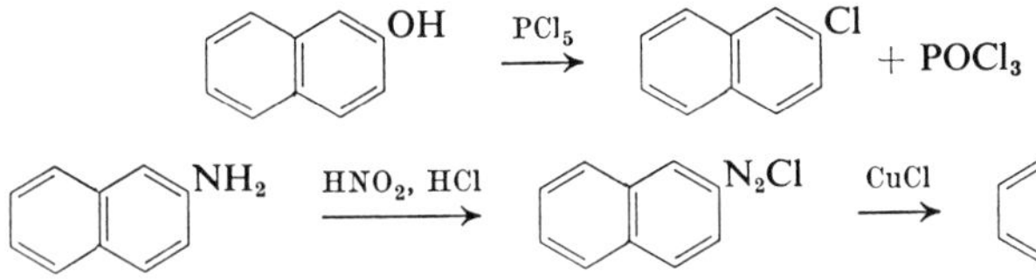

The polychloronaphthalenes made by direct chlorination are solids which find use as nonflammable impregnating agents for electrical insulating materials under the trade name *Halowax*.

Naphthylamines. α-Naphthylamine is made by the reduction of α-nitronaphthalene with iron and water (p. 457). β-Naphthylamine is made by the ammonolysis of β-naphthol. This reaction, which is slow in the benzene series (p. 505), can be brought about easily in the naphthalene series by aqueous ammonia and ammonium sulfite, and is known as the **Bucherer reaction.**

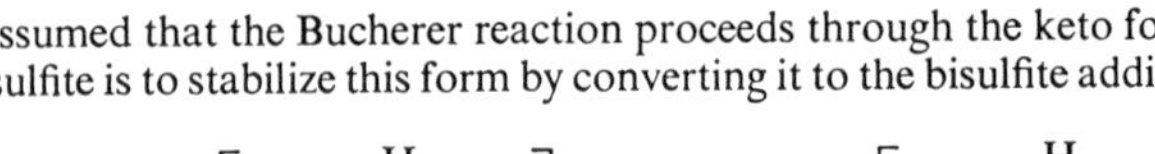

Amines other than ammonia can be used to give substituted aminonaphthalenes. The reaction is reversible and is used to prepare naphthols from naphthylamines if the naphthylamine is more readily available. For example, pure α-naphthol is obtained best from pure α-naphthylamine.

It usually is assumed that the Bucherer reaction proceeds through the keto form and that the function of the sulfite is to stabilize this form by converting it to the bisulfite addition compound.

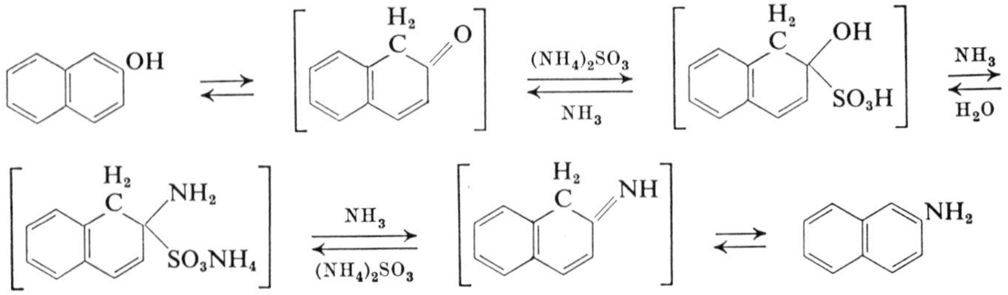

Sulfonated Naphthols and Naphthylamines. Naphthols and naphthylamines couple with diazonium salts to give azo compounds which absorb light of longer wavelength than the simpler azo compounds derived from benzene derivatives, because of increased opportunity for resonance (p. 667). In order that these colored compounds be water-soluble, however, strongly water-solubilizing groups must be present. Hence azo dyes for direct dyeing always contain sulfonic acid groups, and the sulfonated naphthols and naphthylamines are used widely as dye intermediates. Usually these intermediates have common names which were assigned by dye manufacturers because the constitution of the compound was unknown when it first came into use, or because the originator did not care to be overly helpful to his competitors.

Naphthionic acid is made from α-naphthylamine by the baking process described for the preparation of sulfanilic acid (p. 485).

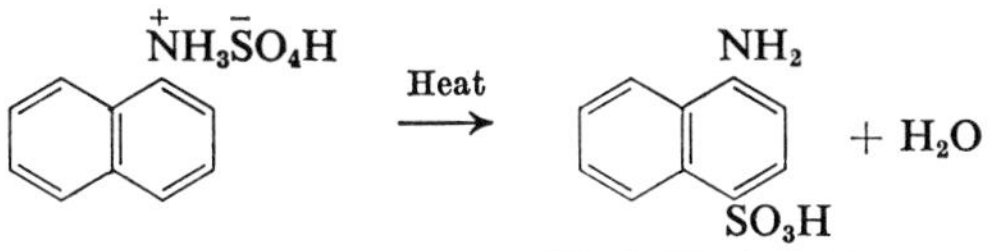

Naphthionic acid

Nitration of α-naphthalenesulfonic acid gives a mixture of 5- and 8-nitrosulfonic acids which are reduced by iron to the mixed amines. Neutralization to pH 4 precipitates the 8-amino-1-naphthalenesulfonic acid, called **Peri acid,** and further neutralization to pH 5 gives the 5-amino-1-naphthalene sulfonic acid, known as **Laurent acid.**

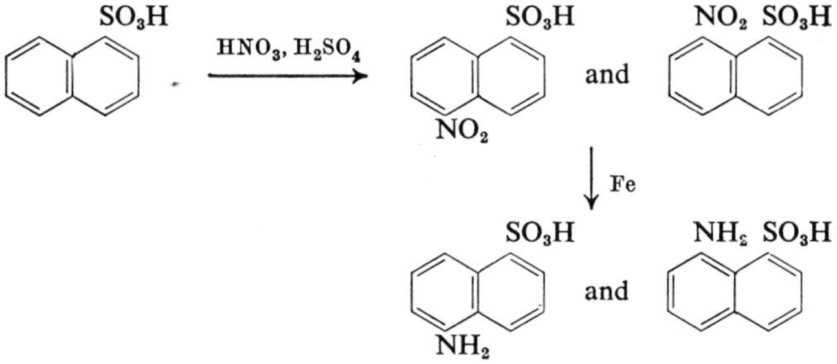

Laurent acid   Peri acid

When β-naphthalenesulfonic acid is nitrated, the nitro group again enters the 5 and 8 positions. Reduction gives rise to the corresponding aminosulfonic acids which are known as **Cleve acids.**

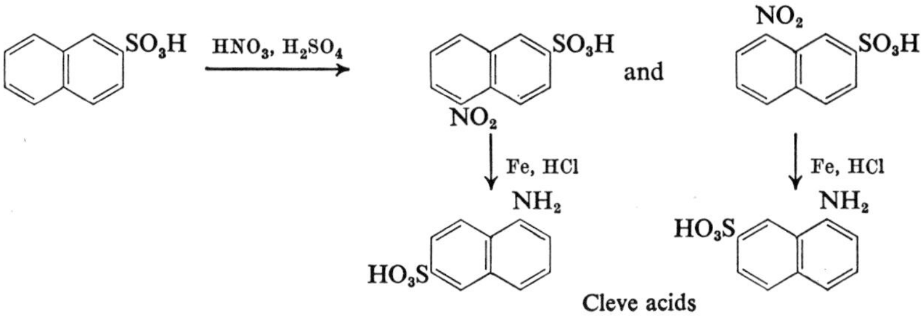

Cleve acids

Naphthionic acid is hydrolyzed to 1-naphthol-4-sulfonic acid (**Nevile-Winther acid**) by boiling with aqueous sodium bisulfite.

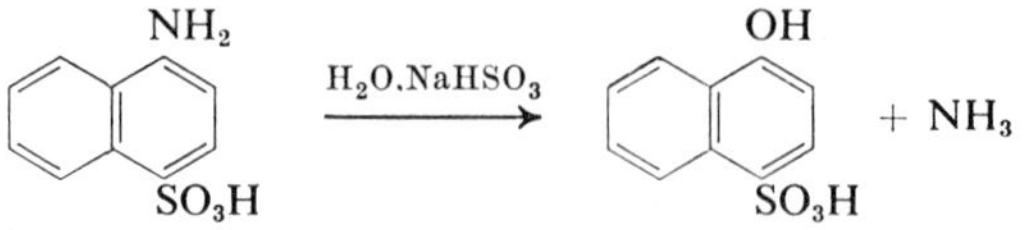

1-Naphthol-4-sulfonic acid
(Nevile-Winther acid)

This reaction was known but not openly published eight years before Bucherer discovered it in 1904, but Bucherer demonstrated the general usefulness and the reversibility of the reaction.

Sulfonation of β-naphthol at a low temperature gives the 1-sulfonic acid, which rapidly rearranges to the 8-sulfonic acid, and at higher temperatures to the 6-sulfonic acid (**Schaeffer acid**). With an excess of sulfuric acid the 3,6- and 6,8-disulfonic acids (**R-acid and G-acid**) are formed.

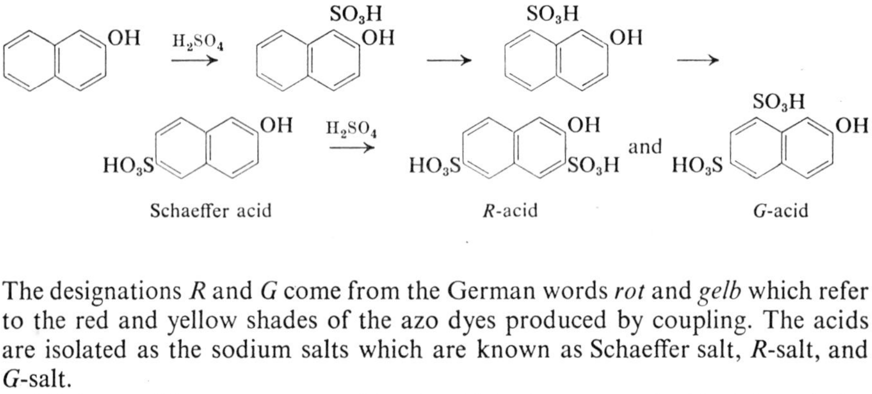

Schaeffer acid   *R*-acid   *G*-acid

The designations *R* and *G* come from the German words *rot* and *gelb* which refer to the red and yellow shades of the azo dyes produced by coupling. The acids are isolated as the sodium salts which are known as Schaeffer salt, *R*-salt, and *G*-salt.

All three acids are important but *G*-acid is the most valuable. The relative amounts of the isomers can be varied by changing the conditions of sulfonation. Thus 1 part of naphthol to 2 parts of 100 per cent sulfuric acid at 80°–110° gives 1 part of Schaeffer salt and 0.5 part of *R*-salt, whereas 1 part of naphthol to 3 parts of sulfuric acid at 30°–35° for two to three days gives 1 part of *G*-salt, and 1 part of *R*-salt.

If β-naphthol is sulfonated at a low temperature in an anhydrous solvent with one mole of chlorosulfonic acid, the 2-naphthol-1-sulfonic acid is obtained. It is converted to the technically important **Tobias acid** by the Bucherer reaction (p 588)

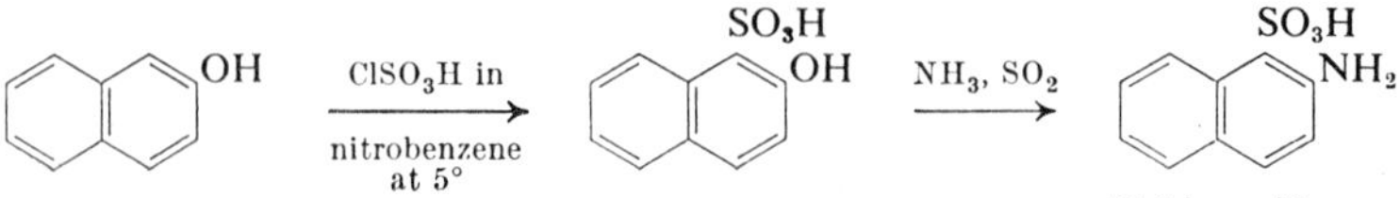

Tobias acid

Aminonaphthols. 4-Amino-1-naphthol and 1-amino-2-naphthol are prepared best by coupling α- or β-naphthol with diazotized sulfanilic acid and reducing the azo dye with sodium hydrosulfite.

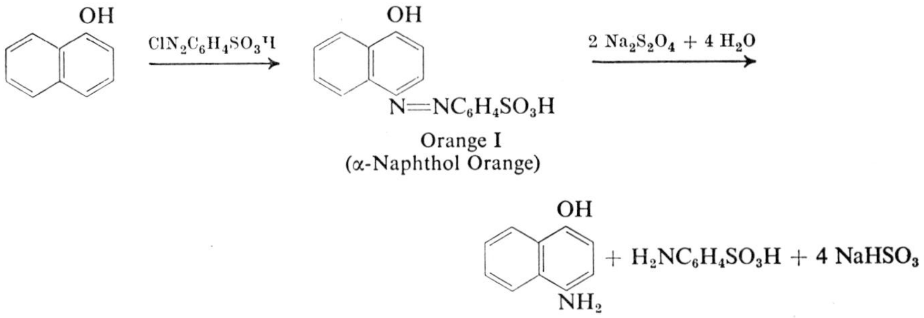

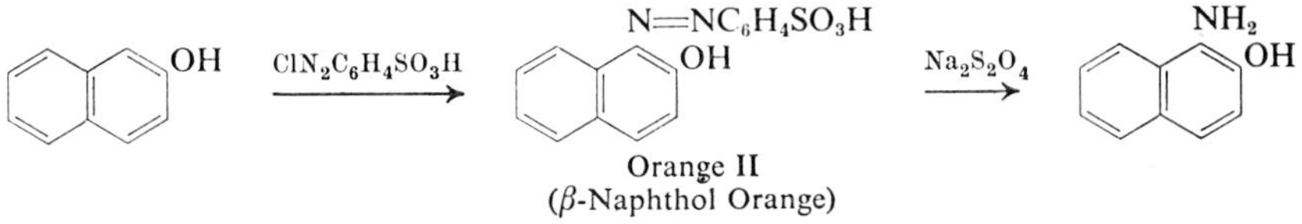

Orange I
(α-Naphthol Orange)

Orange II
(β-Naphthol Orange)

Other aminonaphthols can be made by the fusion of salts of amino sulfonic acids with sodium hydroxide, or of hydroxy sulfonic acids with sodium amide.

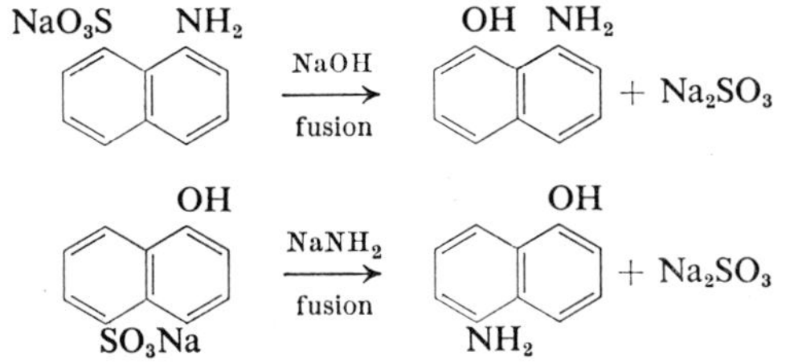

Aminonaphtholsulfonic Acids. The most important derivative of an amino-naphthol is **H-acid,** which is made by the controlled sodium hydroxide fusion of 1-naphthylamine-3,6,8-trisulfonic acid (**Koch acid**), the sulfonic acid group in the 8 position being easily replaced.

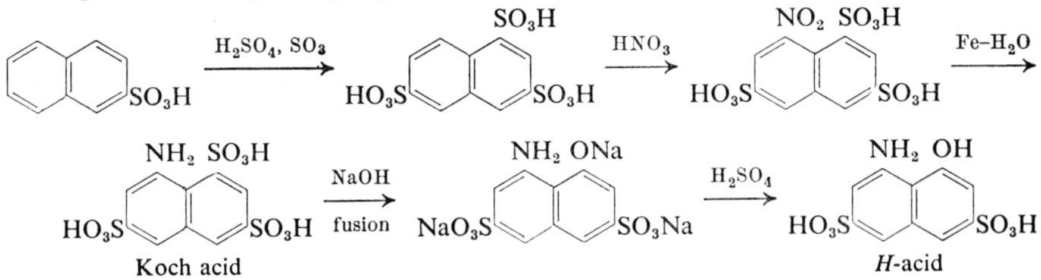

Koch acid   *H*-acid

Sulfonation of β-naphthylamine gives a mixture of 2-aminonaphthalene-6,8-disulfonic acid and 2-aminonaphthalene-1,5,7-trisulfonic acid. Controlled caustic fusion of the disulfonic acid gives **γ-acid,** 2-amino-8-hydroxynaphthalene-6-sulfonic acid. Partial hydrolysis of the trisulfonic acid gives 2-amino-5,7-naphthalenedisulfonic acid, which is converted by caustic fusion to 2-amino-5-hydroxy-7-naphthalenesulfonic acid, known as **J-acid.**

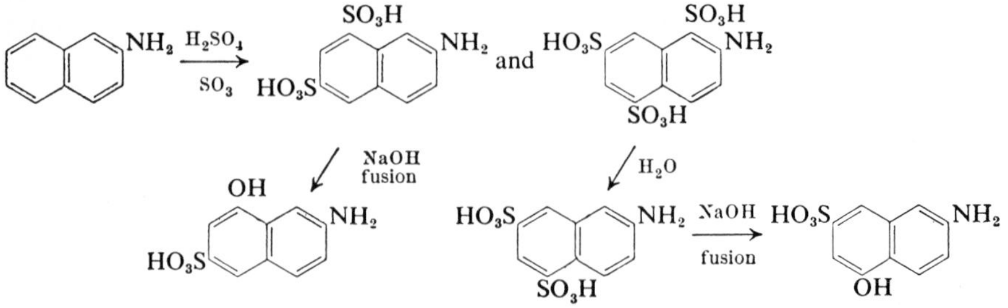

γ-acid   J-acid

The only aminonaphtholsulfonic acid whose commercial production does not involve an alkali fusion is 1-amino-2-hydroxy-4-naphthalenesulfonic acid commonly called **1,2,4-acid.** Nitrosation of β-naphthol is followed by reaction with sodium sulfite, which reduces the nitroso group and is itself oxidized to sulfuric acid, which brings about sulfonation.

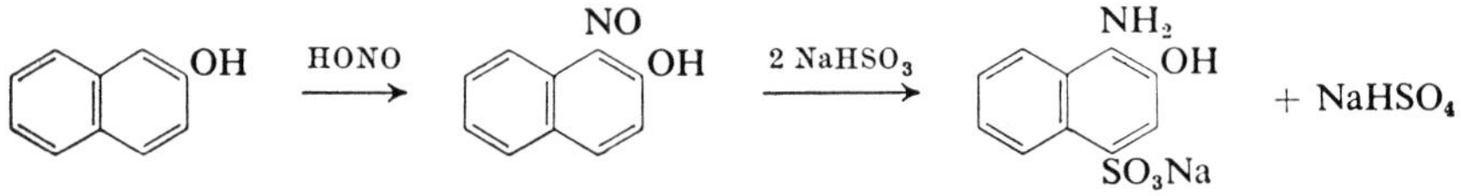

1,2,4-Acid

The relative importance of these intermediates is indicated by the U.S. production in 1955 of approximately 3 million pounds each of *H*-acid and Tobias acid, 2 million pounds of 1,2,4-acid, and 1 million pounds each of *J*-acid and γ-acid.

Naphthoquinones. Whereas the benzene ring permits the existence of only two benzoquinones, the *ortho* and *para*, the naphthalene ring system permits a third. α- and β-Naphthoquinones are prepared by the oxidation of 4-amino-1-naphthol and 2-amino-1-naphthol respectively. The latter are obtained more readily than the dihydroxy or diamino derivatives. The third naphthoquinone, called *amphi*, is obtained by the oxidation of 2,6-dihydroxynaphthalene.

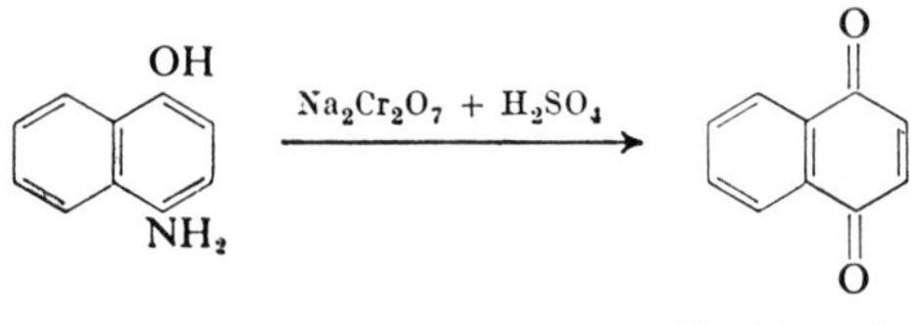

α-Naphthoquinone
(1,4-naphthoquinone)

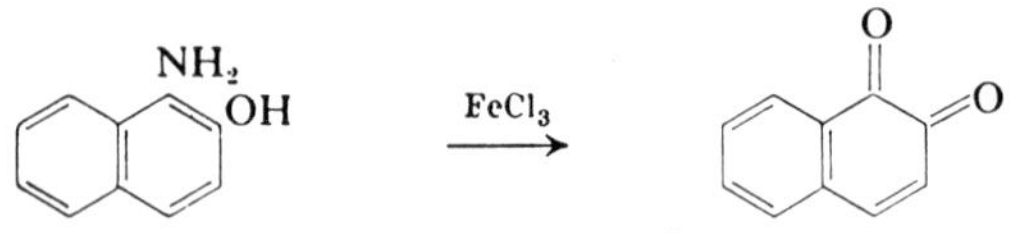

β-Naphthoquinone
(1,2-naphthoquinone)

Amphi-naphthoquinone
(2,6-naphthoquinone)

Numerous derivatives of α-naphthoquinone have been isolated from natural sources, where they early attracted attention because of their color. The fleshy hulls of walnuts (*Juglans regia*) contain 1,4,5-trihydroxynaphthalene, which on oxidation with air gives the dark colored quinhydrone from which **juglone** was isolated in 1856.

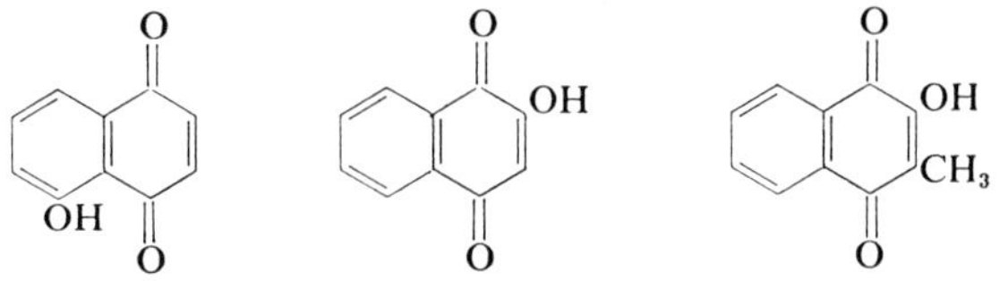

Juglone   Lawsone   Phthiocol

Lawsone is a yellow pigment isolated from Indian henna (*Lawsonia alba*). A paste of henna leaves and an extract of *Acacia catechu* was used for dyeing the hair red and gives rise to the term *henna* for this particular hue. **Phthiocol** is obtained by the saponification of the ether-soluble fraction (lipid fraction) of tubercle bacilli.

1,4-Quinones having a hydroxyl group in the 2 position are tautomeric with 4-hydroxy-1,2-quinones, although the 1,4-quinone is the more stable. On the other hand 2-hydroxy-1,4-iminoquinone exists entirely as the 1,2-quinone except in strongly alkaline solutions.

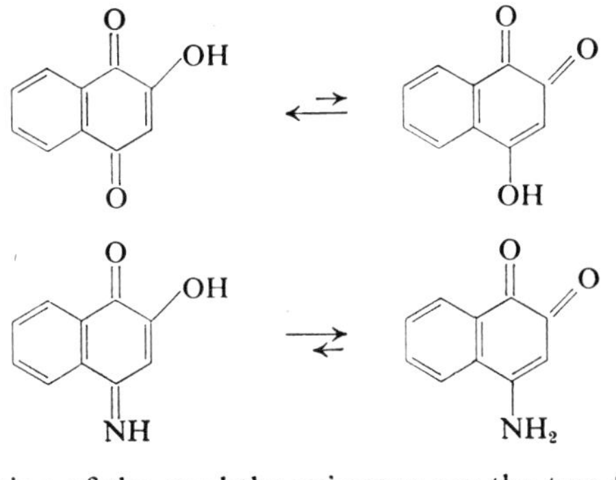

The most interesting of the naphthoquinones are the two forms of **vitamin K.** Vitamin K_1 is found in green plants such as alfalfa and K_2 in putrefied fish meal. One of the K vitamins must be supplied by the diet for the adequate clotting of blood, and so they are termed *antihemorrhagic factors*. Although modifications

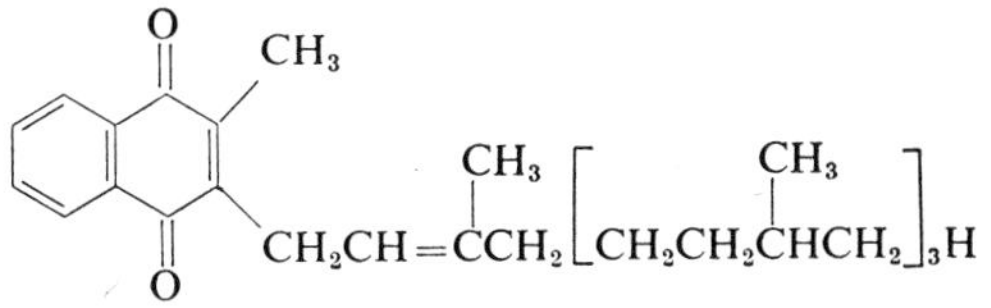

Vitamin K_1

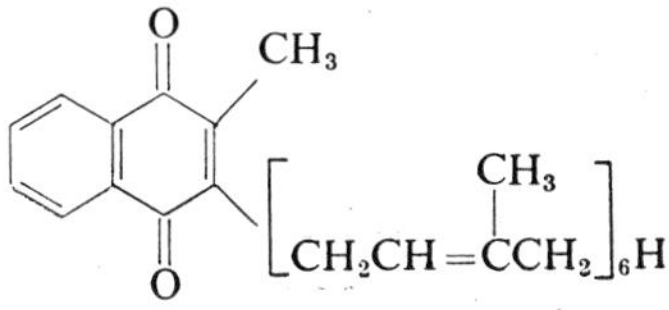

Vitamin K_2

in the structure of vitamin K_1 usually decrease its activity, it has been found that **2-methyl-1,4-naphthoquinone** is more potent on a weight basis and almost as potent on a mole basis. This compound can be synthesized readily by the direct oxidation of β-methylnaphthalene and is used therapeutically under the name *Menadione*.

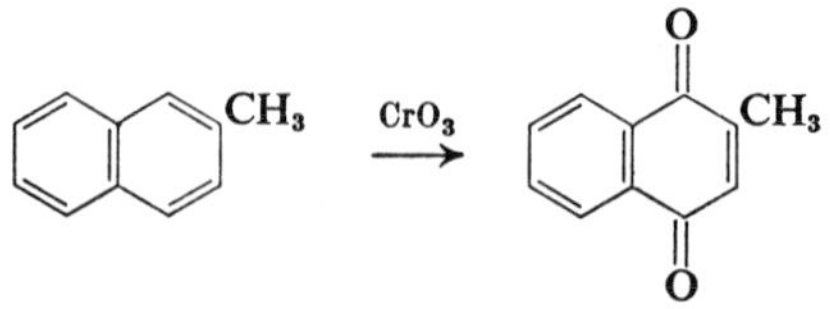

It has been suggested that the methyl quinone serves as a precursor for the biological synthesis of an active compound by the animal organism.

The synthesis of the 2,3-dimethyl-1,4-naphthoquinone is of interest because it results from direct methylation of 2-methyl-1,4-naphthoquinone with lead tetraacetate or acetyl peroxide, presumably by a free-radical mechanism.

$$Pb(OCOCH_3)_4 \longrightarrow Pb(OCOCH_3)_2 + 2\,[CH_3CO_2 \cdot\,]$$

$$2\,[CH_3 \cdot\,] + 2\,CO_2$$

$$\text{or } CH_3\overset{O}{\underset{}{C}}OO\overset{O}{\underset{}{C}}CH_3 \longrightarrow 2\,[CH_3CO \cdot\,]$$

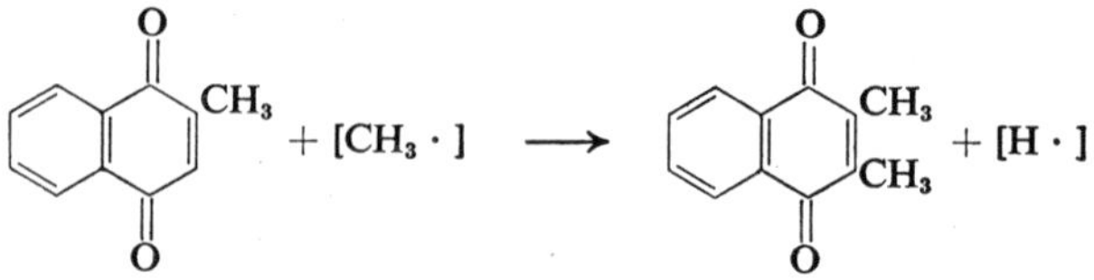

$$[H \cdot\,] + [CH_3COO \cdot\,] \longrightarrow CH_3COOH$$

Carboxylic Acids. α- or β-Naphthoic acid can be made by hydrolysis of the corresponding nitrile. The latter is prepared from the sulfonic acid by fusion with sodium cyanide, or from the amine through the diazo reaction. α-Naphthoic acid can be obtained also from α-bromonaphthalene through the Grignard reagent. The oxidation of side chains, which is an important method for benzenecarboxylic acids (p. 547), may or may not be useful for the preparation of naphthalenecarboxylic acids. Thus although β-ethylnaphthalene on oxidation yields β-naphthoic acid, β-methylnaphthalene gives 2-methyl-1,4-naphthoquinone. Oxidation of α-methylnaphthalene with chromium trioxide gives 5-methyl-1,4-naphthoquinone.

3-Hydroxy-2-naphthoic acid (β-oxynaphthoic or *BON* acid) is made on a large scale by a Kolbe synthesis from β-naphthol.

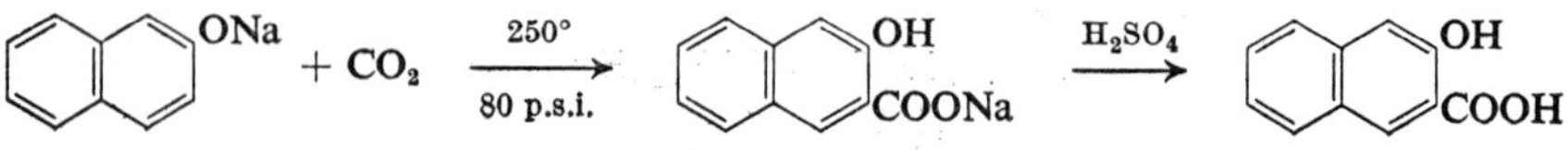

It is used to make the anilide known as **Naphtol AS,** an important intermediate for the preparation of azoic dyes (p. 677).

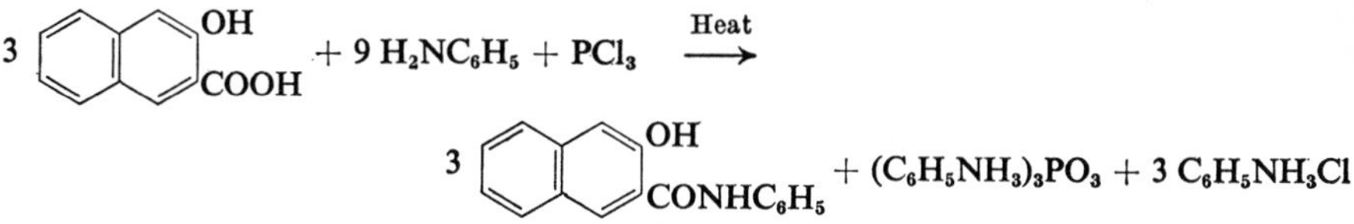

$$3 \quad \text{(naphthol-COOH)} + 9\ H_2NC_6H_5 + PCl_3 \xrightarrow{\text{Heat}}$$

$$3 \quad \text{(naphthol-CONHC}_6H_5) + (C_6H_5NH_3)_3PO_3 + 3\ C_6H_5NH_3Cl$$

Naphtol AS

Over one million pounds was produced in 1955. Other aryl amides also are used but in smaller amounts.

The most important dibasic acid is **naphthalic acid** prepared by the oxidation of acenaphthene, a component of coal tar.

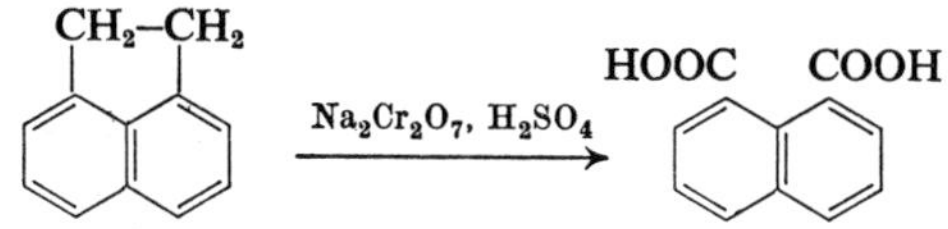

$$\text{Acenaphthene} \xrightarrow{Na_2Cr_2O_7,\ H_2SO_4} \text{Naphthalic acid (HOOC COOH)}$$

Acenaphthene   Naphthalic acid

The spatial relation of the two carboxyl groups is such that naphthalic acid closely resembles phthalic acid in its properties. On heating, it yields an anhydride which can be converted to the imide.

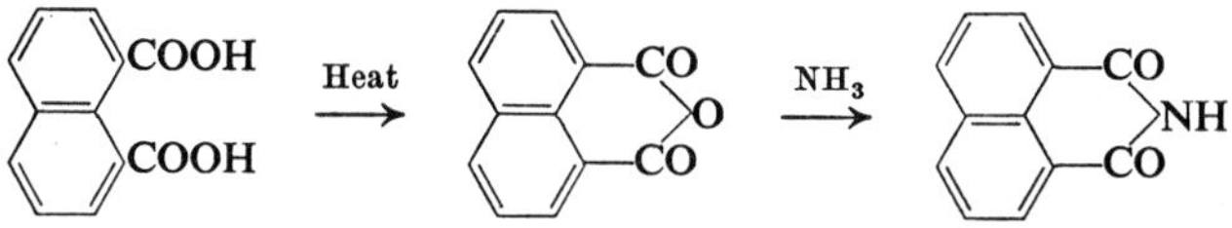

$$\text{(COOH, COOH)} \xrightarrow{\text{Heat}} \text{(CO-O-CO)} \xrightarrow{NH_3} \text{(CO-NH-CO)}$$

Naphthalic   Naphthalimide
anhydride

Certain chemicals present in plants accelerate the growth of cells and are known as **auxins.** Many synthetic compounds have similar properties and are used by nurserymen to increase the ease of rooting of cuttings and by orchardists to prevent premature bud formation and premature dropping of fruit. One of the more widely used substances for this purpose is α-**naphthylacetic acid** which can be made by the chloromethylation of naphthalene, conversion to the nitrile, and hydrolysis.

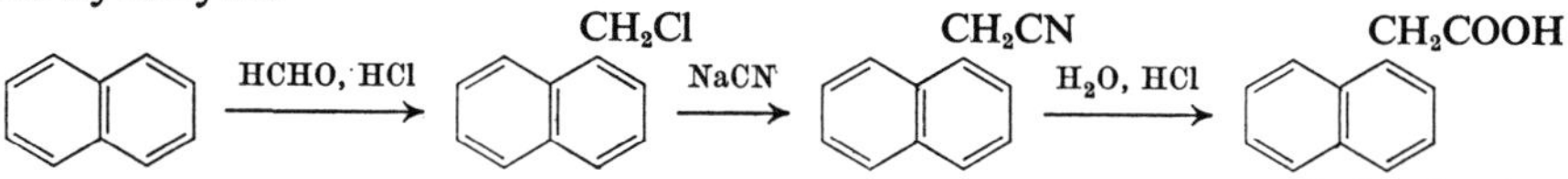

$$\text{naphthalene} \xrightarrow{HCHO,\ HCl} \text{CH}_2\text{Cl} \xrightarrow{NaCN} \text{CH}_2\text{CN} \xrightarrow{H_2O,\ HCl} \text{CH}_2\text{COOH}$$

α-Naphthylacetic
acid

α-Naphthylacetic acid is obtained more readily by a less conventional procedure, namely the reaction of naphthalene with acetic anhydride in the presence of potassium permanganate. Apparently carboxymethyl free radicals are intermediates.

$$(CH_3CO)_2O + KMnO_4 \longrightarrow 2[\cdot CH_2COOH] + KMnO_3$$

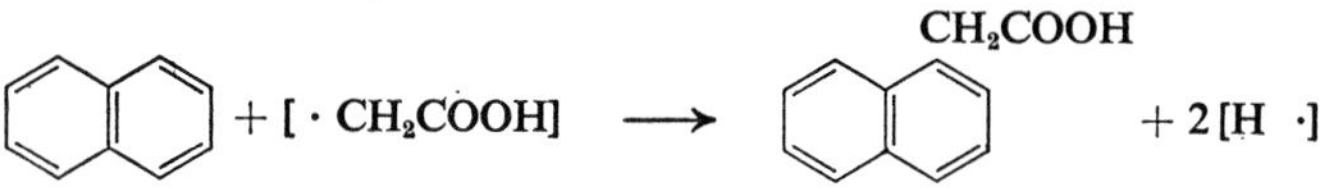

$$\text{naphthalene} + [\cdot CH_2COOH] \longrightarrow \text{CH}_2\text{COOH} + 2[H\ \cdot]$$

$$2[H\cdot] + KMnO_4 \longrightarrow H_2O + KMnO_3$$

Commercial Use of Naphthalene. Of the 477 million pounds of naphthalene produced in 1955, 70 per cent was used for the production of phthalic anhydride, 8 per cent for β-naphthol, 5 per cent each for other dye intermediates and for insecticidal use and 3 per cent each for wetting agents and for chlorinated and hydrogenated naphthalene. About 70 per cent of the naphthalene available from domestic coal tar was recovered.

ANTHRACENE AND DERIVATIVES

The coal tar fraction boiling at 300°–350° is known as **anthracene oil,** or as **green oil** because of its dark green fluorescence. It is run into tanks and allowed to crystallize over a period of one to two weeks and filtered. The nearly dry cakes are hot-pressed at 50,000 to 70,000 pounds pressure to give a mixture of anthracene, phenanthrene, and carbazole. The press cake is ground and washed with coal tar naphtha to remove most of the phenanthrene and then with pyridine to remove the carbazole. Anthracene was the second compound to be isolated from coal tar (p. 428) although less than 1 per cent is present. At first it was believed to be an isomer of naphthalene and was called paranaphthalene, but later the name was changed to anthracene (Gr. *anthrax,* coal). At one time anthracene was the sole source of the anthraquinone dyes, but intermediates for the latter now are synthesized from benzene.

Anthracene has the molecular formula $C_{14}H_{10}$. It has both unsaturated and aromatic properties. Thus it readily adds one mole of hydrogen, chlorine, or bromine, and two atoms of sodium. It also sulfonates directly and can be oxidized to anthraquinone, $C_{14}H_8O_2$. Its structure is arrived at from the rational synthesis of some of its derivatives. Thus when *o*-bromobenzyl bromide reacts with metallic sodium, a dihydroanthracene is formed, identical with that obtained by the reduction of anthracene. Mild oxidation converts it to anthracene.

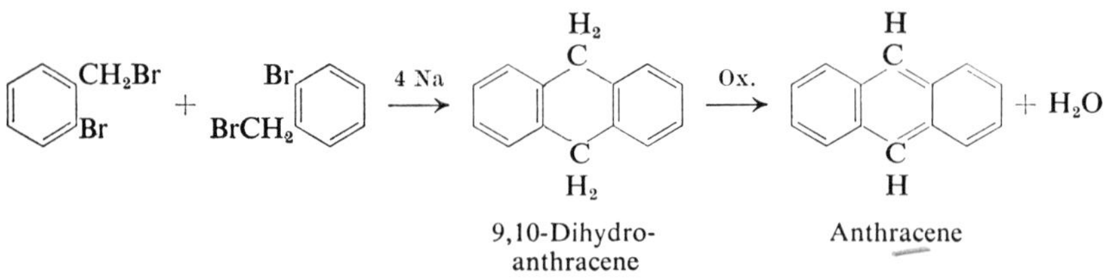

9,10-Dihydro-
anthracene   Anthracene

9,10-Anthraquinone is obtained in good yield by condensing benzene with phthalic anhydride and cyclizing with sulfuric acid.

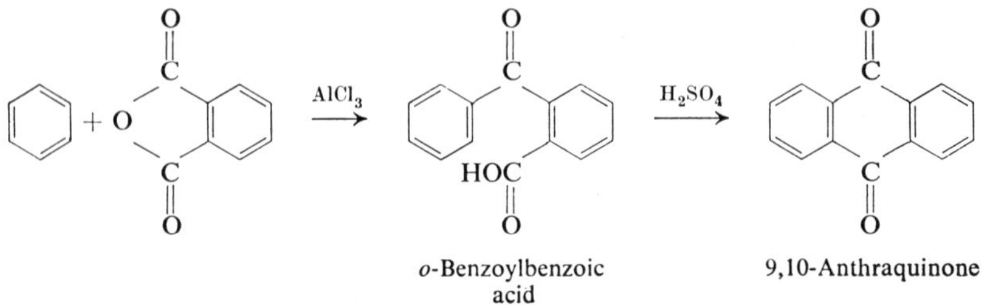

o-Benzoylbenzoic   9,10-Anthraquinone
acid

From these syntheses it is clear that anthracene contains three fused rings, and that addition and oxidation take place at the two central carbon atoms which are designated as the 9,10 positions.

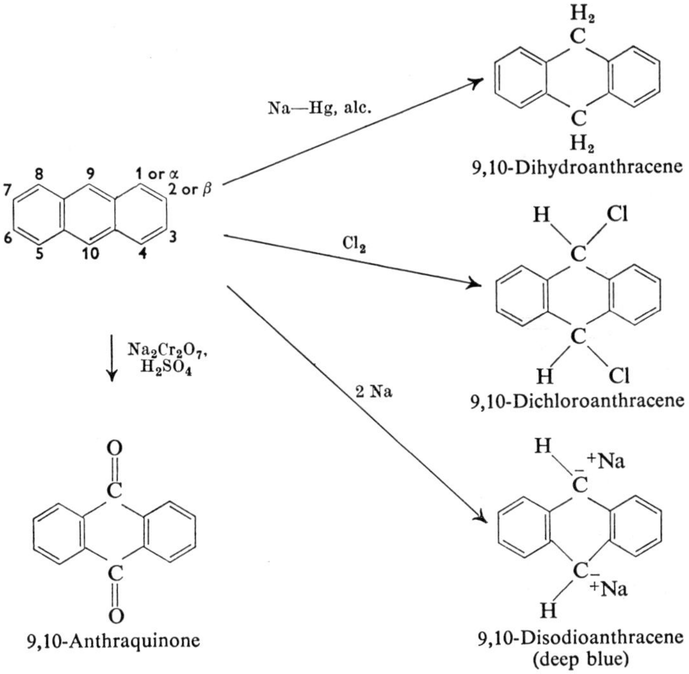

Na—Hg, alc.

9,10-Dihydroanthracene

Cl$_2$

9,10-Dichloroanthracene

2 Na

9,10-Disodioanthracene
(deep blue)

Na$_2$Cr$_2$O$_7$,
H$_2$SO$_4$

9,10-Anthraquinone

Anthracene itself has little use. When pure it is colorless and has a strong pale blue fluorescence when exposed to ultraviolet light. Ordinary anthracene has a pale yellow color and exhibits a strong greenish-yellow fluorescence.

Anthracene, like other aromatic hydrocarbons, is considered to be a resonance hybrid.

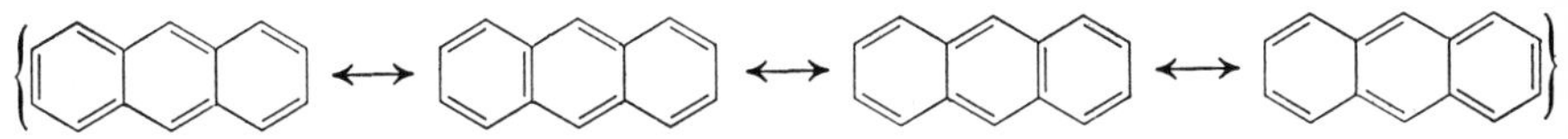

The resonance energy of anthracene is 84 kcal. per mole. Since the resonance energy of two benzene rings is 72 kcal., the resonance energy for the additional ring is only 12 kcal. which is in accordance with the high reactivity of anthracene. Reaction at the 9,10 positions leaving two benzene rings takes place more readily than at an end ring because the latter course would leave a naphthalene nucleus with resonance energy of only 61 kcal.

Of the several anthraquinones, the 9,10 isomer is the only one of importance, and usually it is designated simply as **anthraquinone.** Its derivatives are of great importance in the dye industry (p. 687). Formerly anthraquinone was made by the oxidation of anthracene, but now it is made by the cyclization of o-benzoyl-benzoic acid. Since halogen or nitro groups may be introduced into phthalic anhydride by direct substitution, and since it or its derivatives may be condensed with any aromatic derivative capable of undergoing the Friedel-Crafts reaction, the general method of synthesis can lead to a large number of derivatives of anthraquinone.

The cyclization of carboxylic acids to ketones is a general reaction. Thus γ-phenylbutyric acid cyclizes readily to α-tetralone. The reaction may be interpreted as a substitution reaction

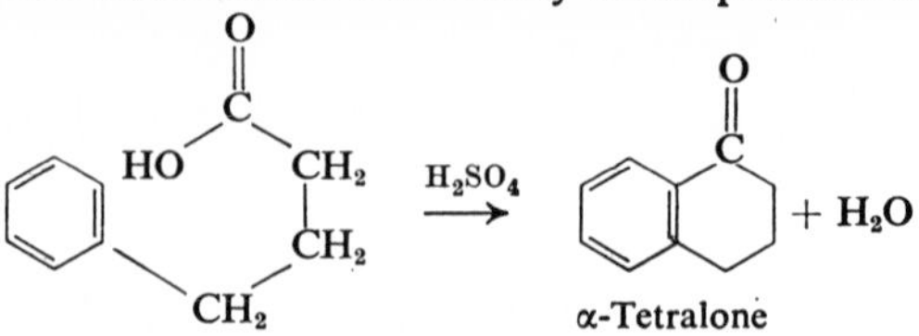

α-Tetralone

of the Friedel-Crafts type. The transfer of a proton from the sulfuric acid to the carbonyl group decreases the electron density on the carbonyl carbon atom, which then attacks the *ortho* position as does any electron-seeking reagent.

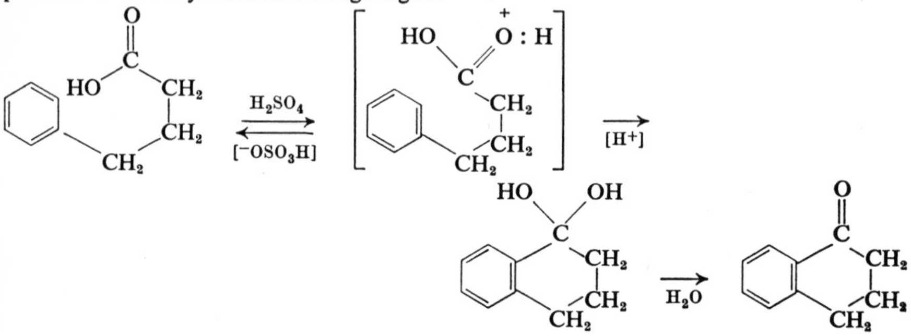

Because of the presence of the deactivating carbonyl groups, anthraquinone does not undergo substitution readily by electron-seeking reagents. Thus halogenation is difficult and Friedel-Crafts type reactions do not take place. On the other hand, the carbonyl groups increase the ease of displacement of hydrogen and other groups by electron-donating reagents.

Sulfonation catalyzed by mercuric sulfate at 120° gives chiefly **α-anthraquinonesulfonic acid,** whereas the uncatalyzed sulfonation at 140° gives chiefly **β-anthraquinonesulfonic acid.** The sodium salt of the β isomer, obtained by the liming out process (p. 467), is known as **silver salt** because of its silvery gray appearance.

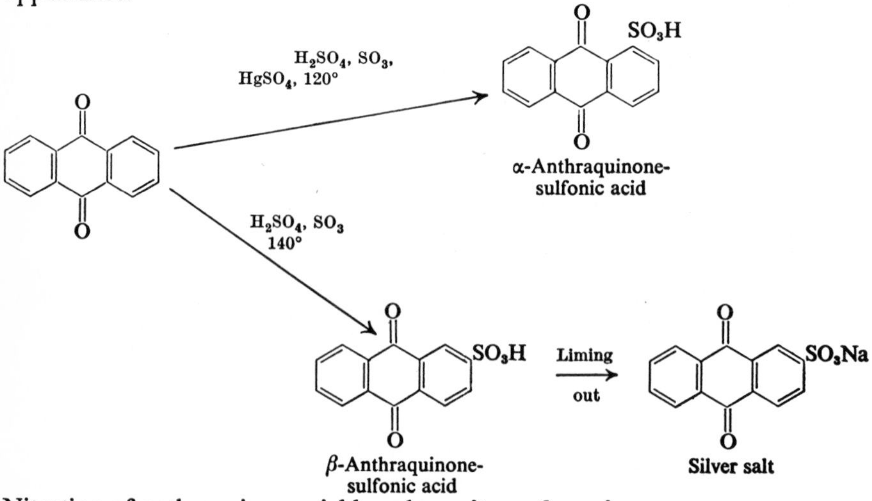

α-Anthraquinone-
sulfonic acid

β-Anthraquinone-
sulfonic acid

Silver salt

Nitration of anthraquinone yields only **α-nitroanthraquinone.**

α- or β-Anthraquinonesulfonates yield the corresponding α- or **β-hydroxy-anthraquinones** when heated with milk of lime at 180°. Under the more drastic conditions of fusion with sodium hydroxide used to make phenols, the α sulfonate breaks down to benzene derivatives. When silver salt is fused with sodium hydroxide, the α hydrogen as well as the sulfonate group is displaced by hydroxyl (cf. p. 454). To prevent the simultaneous reduction of the anthraquinone, an oxidizing agent is added.

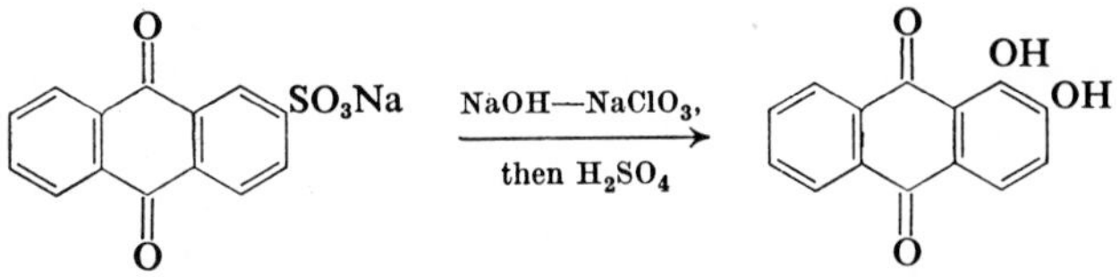

Alizarin

The product is **alizarin,** formerly an important mordant dye (p. 687).

The 1,4 isomer, **quinizarin,** is an important dye intermediate. It is made by the reaction of phthalic anhydride with *p*-chlorophenol. Condensation, cyclization, and hydrolysis take place in a single operation.

Quinizarin

About fifty anthraquinone derivatives have been identified as pigments in plants, fungi, lichens, and insects. Many are hydroxymethylanthraquinones. **Emodin** has strong cathartic properties and is an active principle of cascara, senna, aloes, and rheum (rhubarb). **Physcion** occurs widely in molds and lichens.

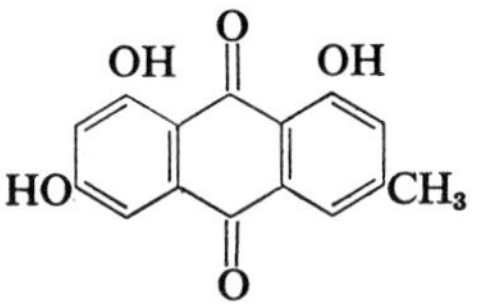

Emodin 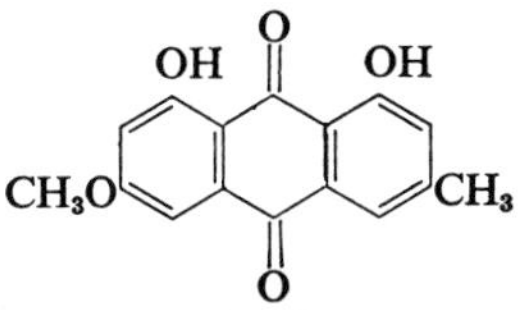   Physcion

When either α- or β-anthraquinonesulfonate is treated with chlorine (sodium chlorate and hydrogen chloride), the sulfonic acid group is displaced to give α- or **β-chloroanthraquinone.**

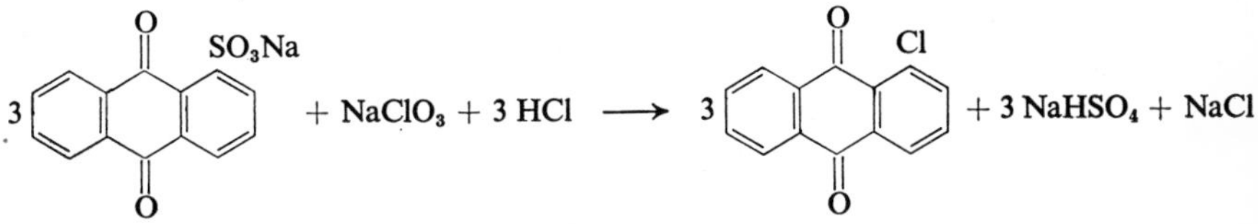

However, β-chloroanthraquinone is prepared commercially from chlorobenzene and phthalic anhydride.

α-Aminoanthraquinone can be made by reduction of α-nitroanthraquinone or by the action of ammonia on the salt of the α sulfonate in the presence of barium chloride.

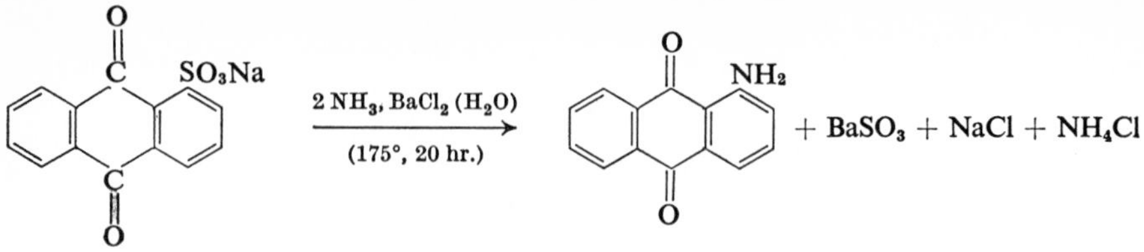

α-Aminoanthra-
quinone

β-Aminoanthraquinone is made from silver salt by a similar process using calcium chloride instead of barium chloride at 195°. A second technical process for this important dye intermediate is the ammonolysis of β-chloroanthraquinone.

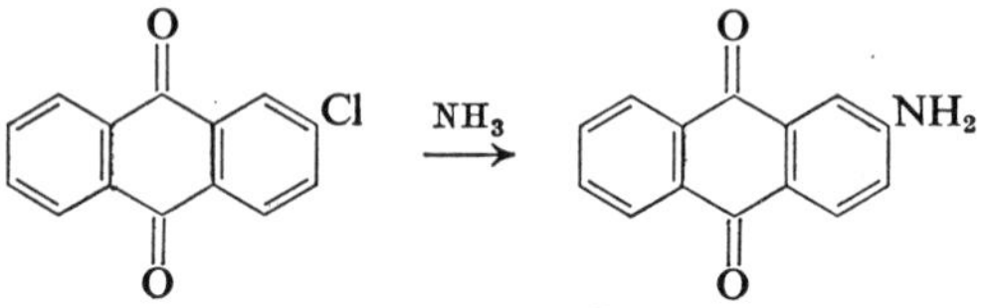

β-Aminoanthra-
quinone

The aminoanthraquinones do not couple with diazonium salts, presumably because of the deactivating effect of the carbonyl groups. The dihydro derivatives, in which the carbonyl groups are converted to hydroxyl groups, couple readily. **1,4-Diaminoanthraquinones** can be made by heating quinizarin with aqueous ammonia or with aliphatic or aromatic amines.

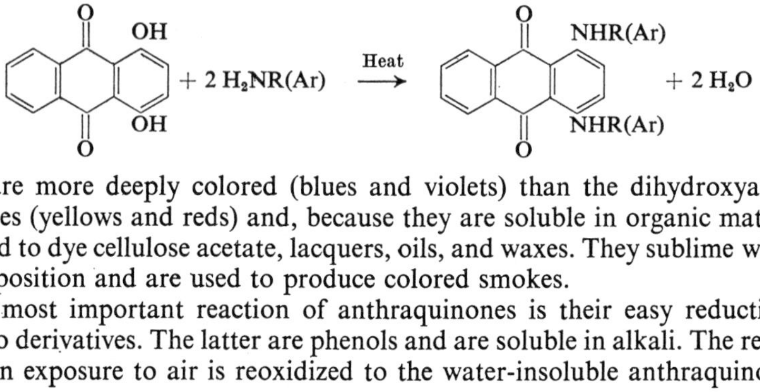

They are more deeply colored (blues and violets) than the dihydroxyanthraquinones (yellows and reds) and, because they are soluble in organic materials, are used to dye cellulose acetate, lacquers, oils, and waxes. They sublime without decomposition and are used to produce colored smokes.

The most important reaction of anthraquinones is their easy reduction to dihydro derivatives. The latter are phenols and are soluble in alkali. The reduced form on exposure to air is reoxidized to the water-insoluble anthraquinone.

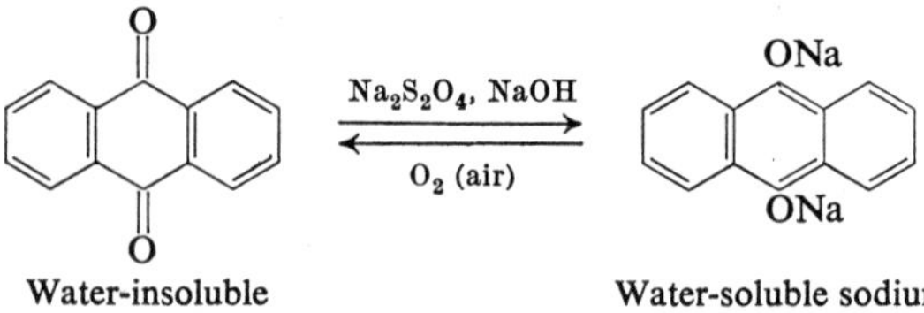

Water-insoluble
anthraquinone

Water-soluble sodium
salt of dihydroanthra-
quinone

These reactions are the basis for the application of the anthraquinone vat dyes to cotton cloth (p. 689).

Reduction of anthraquinone with tin and hydrochloric acid in glacial acetic acid gives **anthrone.**

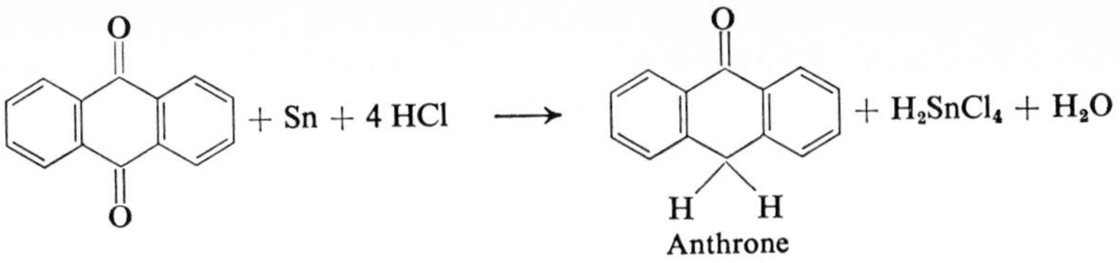

Anthrone is insoluble in water but dissolves in hot aqueous alkali to give a salt from which **anthranol**, the enol form of anthrone, can be precipitated with acid. Heating anthranol with acids regenerates anthrone.

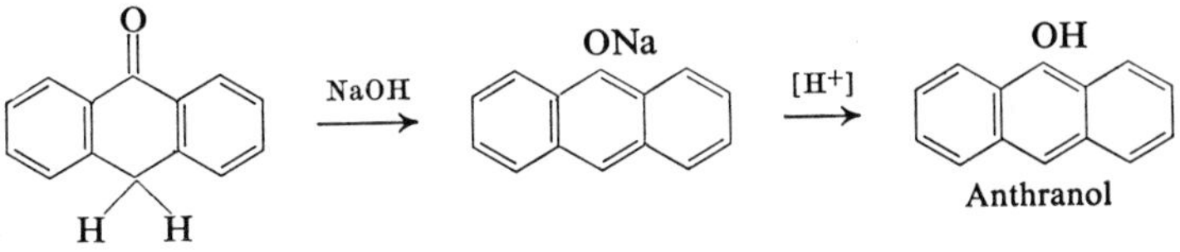

Anthrone is used for the qualitative detection and quantitative estimation of carbohydrates. All known saccharides, polysaccharides, and glycosides give a blue-green color with a solution of anthrone in sulfuric acid. Furfural is the only noncarbohydrate that has been reported to give a positive reaction in this test. Condensation of anthrone with acrolein (p. 764) and oxidation by sulfuric acid gives **benzanthrone,** an important dye intermediate.

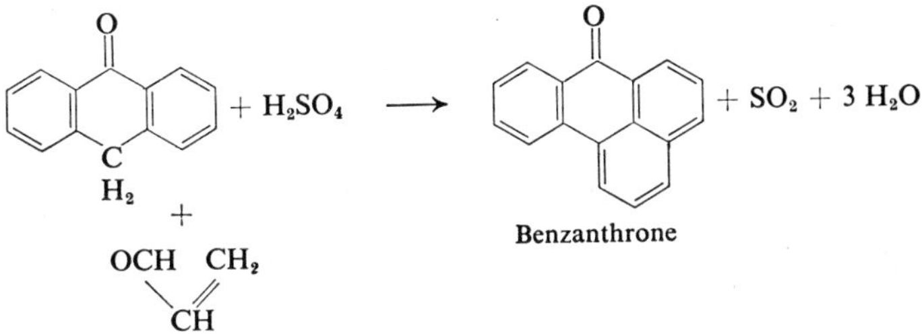

Benzanthrone can be obtained directly by heating anthraquinone with iron powder, glycerol and sulfuric acid. The iron reduces the anthraquinone, and the glycerol dehydrates to supply the acrolein (p. 764).

2-Ethylanthraquinone, made from phthalic anhydride and ethylbenzene, is of some interest because it has been used in a nonelectrolytic process for the synthesis of hydrogen peroxide.

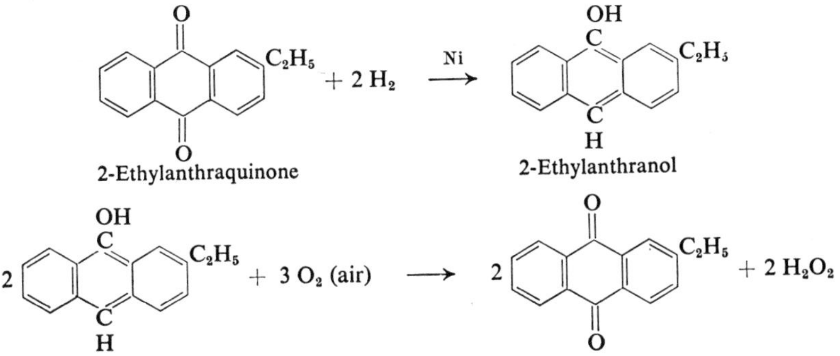

The reactions are carried out in an organic solvent, and the hydrogen peroxide is extracted with water. The disadvantage as a method for the production of 90 to 100 per cent hydrogen peroxide is that it is difficult to remove organic impurities which catalyze the explosive decomposition of peroxide solutions of high concentration.

OTHER CONDENSED RING SYSTEMS

Phenanthrene is isomeric with anthracene. Its structure can be deduced from its oxidation to 9,10-phenanthraquinone and diphenic acid (2,2'-biphenyl-dicarboxylic acid).

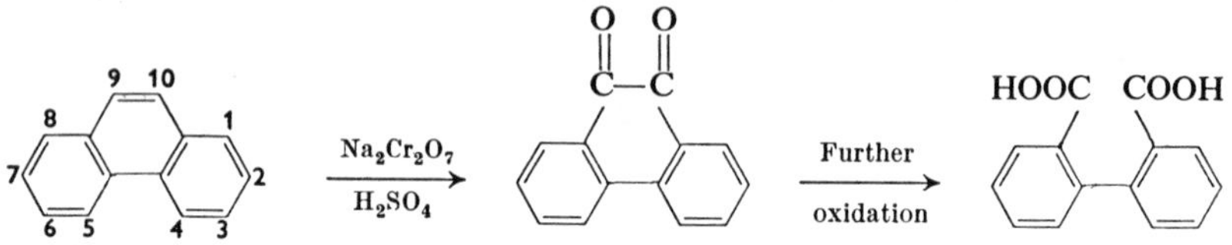

Phenanthrene

$\xrightarrow[\text{H}_2\text{SO}_4]{\text{Na}_2\text{Cr}_2\text{O}_7}$

9,10-Phenanthra-quinone

Further oxidation

Diphenic acid

Like anthracene it yields a 9,10-dibromide and a 9,10-dihydro derivative.

The resonance energy of phenanthrene is 92 kcal. per mole or 22 kcal. above that for two benzene rings. In accordance with this value, its reactivity lies between that of naphthalene and that of anthracene (pp. 583, 597).

Phenanthrene, though readily available from coal tar, is of little practical importance, chiefly because of the large number of difficultly separable isomers that are formed in substitution reactions. However, the carbon skeleton of phenanthrene is present as a nonaromatic ring system in many natural products. When these products are heated with sulfur or selenium, dehydrogenation takes place and phenanthrene derivatives are formed. Since the aromatic hydrocarbon usually can be purified easily and its constitution determined more readily than that of the original compound, these dehydrogenation products have played an important part in elucidating the constitution of complex natural products. For example, the ring system in abietic acid, the chief constituent of pine rosin (p. 861), was identified by the isolation of **retene**, 1-methyl-7-isopropylphenanthrene, from the dehydrogenation products.

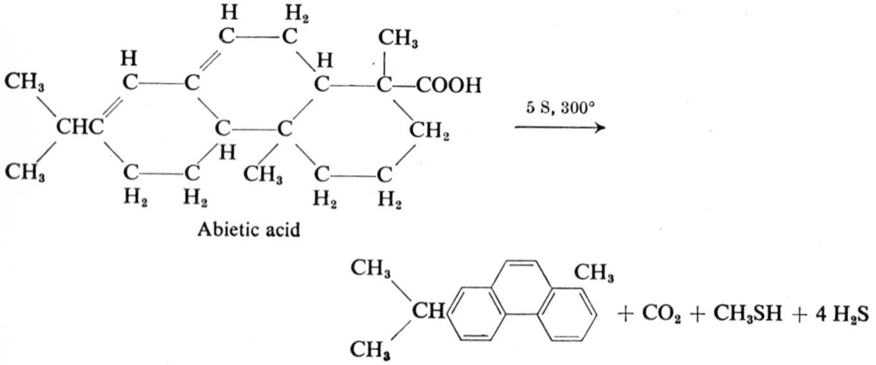

Abietic acid

$\xrightarrow{5 \text{ S, } 300°}$

Retene $+ CO_2 + CH_3SH + 4 H_2S$

Numerous syntheses of phenanthrene derivatives have been devised in order to prove the structure of the various dehydrogenation products. The following series of reactions illustrates one procedure for the synthesis of retene which also can be modified to yield other alkylated phenanthrenes.

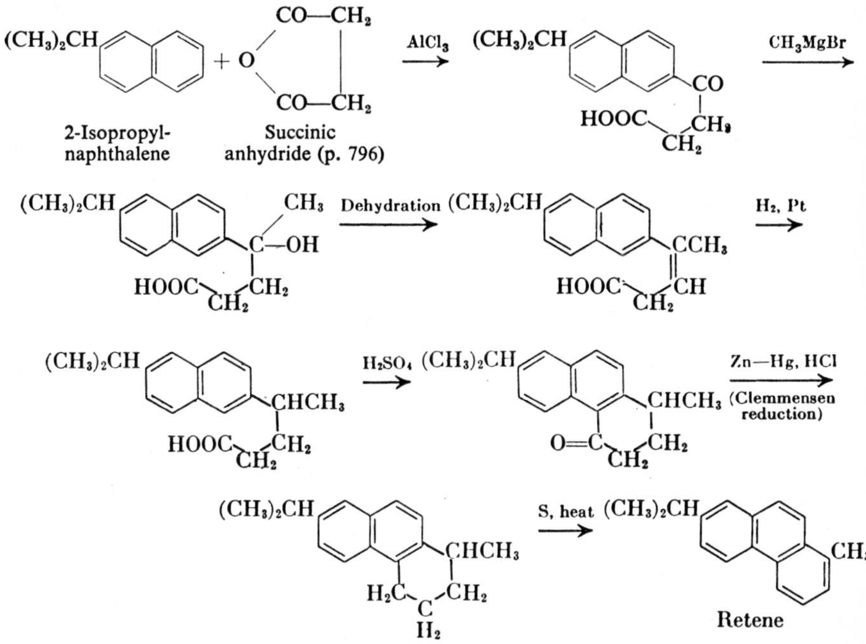

2-Isopropyl-naphthalene

Succinic anhydride (p. 796)

The following formulas illustrate the structures of other interesting aromatic hydrocarbons with condensed nuclei. The more complicated polynuclear aromatic hydrocarbons may be named as benzologs or napthologs of hydrocarbons having common names. To avoid confusion of the peripheral numbering of the compound with that of the parent compound, the sides of the latter may be lettered *a*, *b*, *c*, etc., with the 1,2 side lettered *a*.

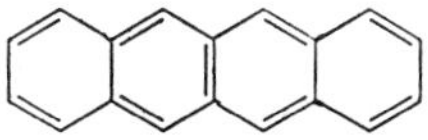

Naphthacene
(2,3-benzanthracene, benzo(*b*)anthracene)

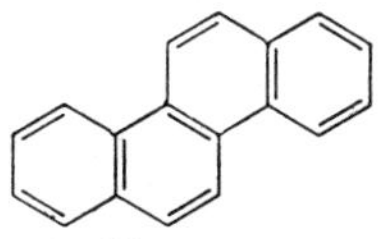

Chrysene
(1,2-benzophenanthrene, benzo(*a*)phenanthrene)

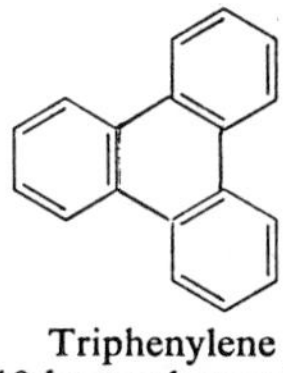

Triphenylene
(9,10-benzophenanthrene, benzo(*l*)phenanthrene)

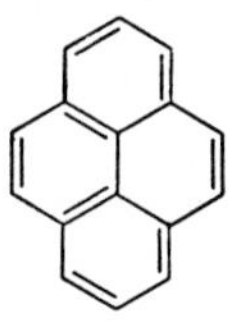

Pyrene
(benzo(*def*)-phenanthrene)

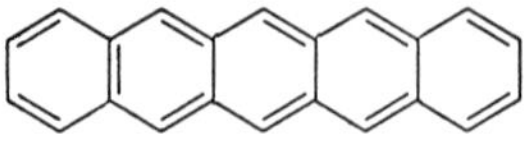

Pentacene
(benzo(*b*)naphthacene)

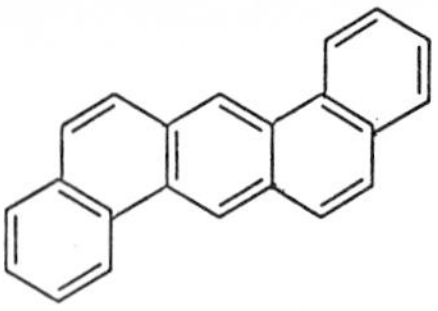

1,2 : 5,6-Dibenzanthracene
(dibenz(*ah*)anthracene)

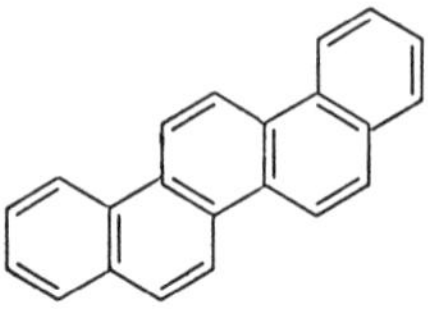

Picene
(dibenz(*ai*)phenanthrene)

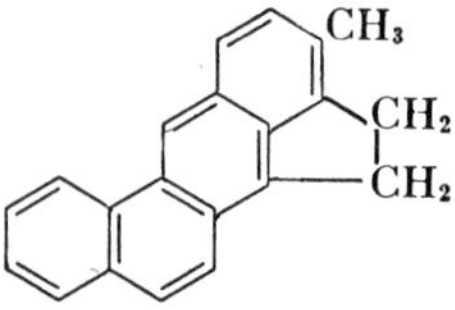

Methylcholanthrene

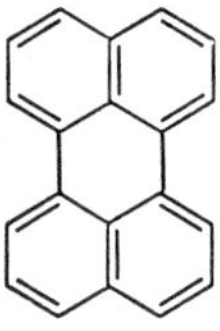

Perylene
(dibenz(*de, kl*)-
anthracene)

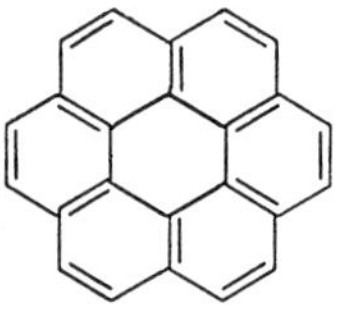

Coronene
(dibenz(*ghi, pqr*)-
perylene)

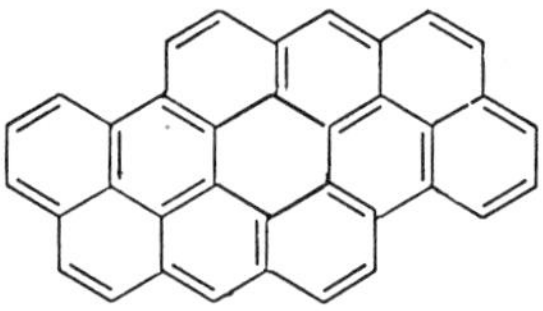

Dinaphtho(*abc, jkl*)coronene

Anthracene has an absorption band in the near ultraviolet and is colorless, but naphthacene is orange-yellow and pentacene is purple (p. 666).

Two important antibiotics are complex derivatives of a partially hydrogenated naphthacene nucleus. **Terramycin** is obtained from *Streptomyces rimosus* and **Aureomycin** from *Streptomyces aureofaciens*.

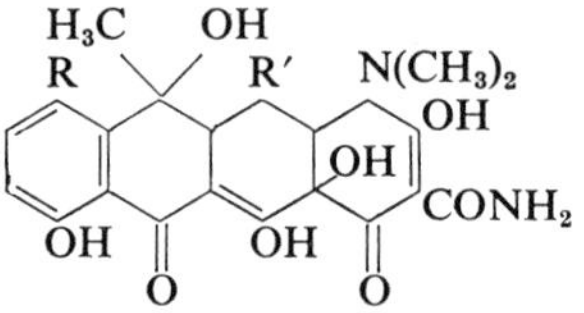

Tetracycline R = H, R′ = H

Terramycin R = H, R′ = OH

Aureomycin R = Cl, R′ = H

They are called broad-spectrum antibiotics because they are effective against a large variety of organisms. **Tetracycline,** obtained by the replacement of either a hydroxyl group or a chlorine atom by hydrogen, also is an effective antibiotic. Aureomycin is used to delay the spoilage of meats (*Acronizing process*).

1,5-Dibenzanthracene and **methylcholanthrene** are powerful carcinogenic hydrocarbons; that is, they produce skin cancers when applied over a considerable period of time. Numerous other polynuclear aromatic hydrocarbons also are carcinogenic. Derivatives of picene are obtained by dehydrogenating many natural products belonging to the triterpene group (p. 863). Dinaphthocoronene, $C_{36}H_{16}$, contains 96.4 per cent carbon and sublimes without decomposition at 500°.

In some of the polynuclear hydrocarbons, for example benzo(*c*)phenanthrene, substituents in the 1,12 positions prevent the rings from being coplanar and lead

to molecular asymmetry. Thus 1,12-dimethylbenzo(*c*)phenanthrene-5-acetic acid
has been resolved into active isomers although no asymmetric atom is present.

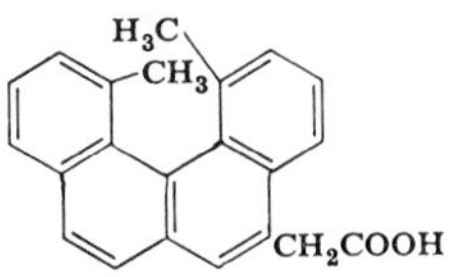

1,12-Dimethylbenzo(*c*)-
phenanthrene-5-acetic acid

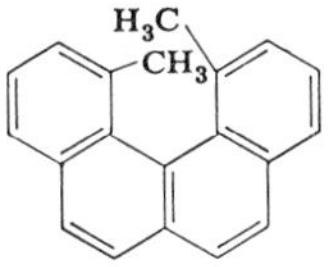

1,12-Dimethylbenzo(*c*)-
phenanthrene

As would be expected, the nonplanarity of the aromatic rings in 1,12-dimethylbenzo(*c*)-
phenanthrene increases the reactivity with methyl radicals as compared to that of other
methylbenzophenanthrenes, presumably because of a decrease in resonance energy.

REVIEW QUESTIONS

1. What is the source of naphthalene? Compare its abundance with that of other compounds
which accompany it.
2. Give a proof of the structure of naphthalene, including evidence from analysis, reactions,
synthesis, and the number of monosubstitution products.
3. What monosubstitution products are formed by the direct halogenation, nitration, and
sulfonation of naphthalene?
4. How many naphthoquinones are known and how are they prepared? What are the
vitamins K_1 and K_2?
5. Give a reaction for the conversion of acenaphthene into naphthalic acid.
6. Give equations for the reaction of anthracene with halogen; dichromic acid; metallic
sodium; sodium amalgam and alcohol.
7. What product is formed on reduction of anthraquinone; nitration; sulfonation?
8. How is β-aminoanthraquinone made; alizarin?
9. What is emodin?
10. What is the structure of phenanthrene? Give reactions for its conversion into phenanthraquinone and diphenic acid.
11. What happens when phenanthraquinone is heated with alkali? (Hint: compare the structure
of phenanthraquinone with that of benzil.)
12. What are the structural formulas for indene; fluorene; chrysene; 1,2 : 5,6-dibenzanthra-
cene; benzo(*c*)phenanthrene?

PROBLEMS

13. Give structural formulas for the theoretically possible isomers, including stereoisomers,
for each of the following groups of compounds: (*a*) dinitronaphthalenes; (*b*) trichloro-
naphthalenes; (*c*) dinaphthylethylenes; (*d*) bromo-β-nitronaphthalenes.
14. Predict the chief product or products formed when one more group is introduced by the
following reactions: (*a*) nitration of 1-bromonaphthalene; (*b*) bromination of β-naph-
thalenesulfonic acid; (*c*) nitration of β-naphthol; (*d*) chlorination of α-methylnaphthalene;
(*e*) bromination of β-chloronaphthalene; (*f*) chlorination of β-naphthylamine; (*g*) sulfonation of 8-hydroxy-1-naphthylamine.
15. Give reactions for the synthesis of the following compounds starting with naphthalene:
(*a*) α-naphthylamine; (*b*) β-naphthylamine; (*c*) α-naphthol; (*d*) β-naphthol; (*e*) α-naphthoic
acid; (*f*) β-naphthoic acid; (*g*) α-naphthaldehyde; (*h*) β-naphthaldehyde; (*i*) α-naphtho-
quinone; (*j*) β-naphthoquinone; (*k*) α-naphthylacetic acid; (*l*) β-naphthylacetic acid; (*m*)
β-isopropylnaphthalene.
16. What would be the chief product expected on oxidation of each of the following compounds:
(*a*) α-naphthoic acid; (*b*) β-naphthol; (*c*) β-chloroanthracene; (*d*) 1,4-dihydroxyanthra-
quinone; (*e*) β-naphthalenesulfonic acid; (*f*) phenanthrene; (*g*) 2,6-diaminonaphthalene?
17. Give a practical synthesis of the following compounds starting with an aromatic hydrocarbon: (*a*) 3-chlorophthalic anhydride; (*b*) 4-nitrophthalic anhydride; (*c*) β-chloroanthra-
quinone; (*d*) 1,4-dianilinoanthraquinone; (*e*) 2-methyl-1-nitroanthraquinone; (*f*) 2-methyl-
5-nitroanthraquinone.
18. Suggest the probable intermediate steps that take place in the synthesis of (*a*) alizarin from
silver salt, and (*b*) quinizarin from phthalic anhydride and *p*-chlorophenol.

Chapter 29

HETEROCYCLIC COMPOUNDS. ALKALOIDS

Compounds in which three or more atoms are joined to form a closed ring are known as cyclic compounds. If all of the ring atoms are carbon, the compound is said to be *carbocyclic*, but if different kinds of atoms constitute the ring, the compound is said to be *heterocyclic*. Theoretically any atom capable of forming at least two covalent bonds can be a member of a ring, but the heterocyclic compounds encountered most frequently contain nitrogen, oxygen, and sulfur as the hetero atoms.

RING COMPOUNDS CONTAINING ONE HETERO ATOM

Three- and Four-membered Rings

The members of this group that are of most importance are the ethylene oxides. Their methods of preparation and reactions are discussed on page 744.

Five-membered Rings

Thiophenes. In 1879 Baeyer reported that when benzene is mixed with isatin (p. 684) and concentrated sulfuric acid a blue color is produced. This behavior was called the *indophenin reaction* (p. 686) and was believed to be characteristic of benzene until Victor Meyer in 1882 attempted to demonstrate the reaction on a sample of benzene that had been prepared by the decarboxylation of benzoic acid. The lecture demonstration failed, and the resulting investigation as to the cause of the failure led to the discovery that the indophenin reaction is not characteristic of benzene, but of a sulfur compound with physical and chemical properties resembling those of benzene so closely that the few tenths of a per cent present in coal tar benzene had not been detected previously. This compound was named *thiophene*. Subsequent development of thiophene chemistry was so rapid that five years after its isolation in 1883, Meyer published a 300-page book on the subject.

Thiophene has the molecular formula C_4H_4S and forms two monosubstitution products. It has been assigned a cyclic structure with two double bonds, which is supported by the methods of synthesis. Until 1946 thiophene was synthesized by heating sodium succinate (p. 792) with phosphorus heptasulfide (sometimes called phosphorus trisulfide).

$$2 \underset{\substack{| \\ \text{ONa}}}{\overset{\substack{\text{CH}_2-\text{CH}_2 \\ |}}{\text{O}=\text{C}}} \quad \underset{\substack{| \\ \text{ONa}}}{\text{C}=\text{O}} + \text{P}_4\text{S}_7 \longrightarrow 2 \quad \underset{\substack{5 \\ \text{S} \\ 1}}{\overset{\substack{4 \quad\quad 3 \\ \text{HC}-\text{CH}}}{\underset{\text{HC}\alpha' \quad \alpha\text{CH}}{\overset{\beta' \quad \beta}{|\;\;\;\;|}}}} + 4 \text{NaPO}_2\text{S} + \text{S}$$

Sodium succinate   Thiophene[1]

---

[1] *Chemical Abstracts* and the *Ring Index* orient the formulas of heterocyclic compounds with the hetero atom at the top. By custom, however, it usually is placed at the bottom for the simpler molecules, or in whatever position it assumes if other features of the molecule have a customary orientation. As an aid to memory it seems better to follow custom even though the Ring Index system may have some points of logic in its favor.

Homologs of thiophene can be made by the reaction of 1,4-diketones (p. 775) with phosphorus pentasulfide.

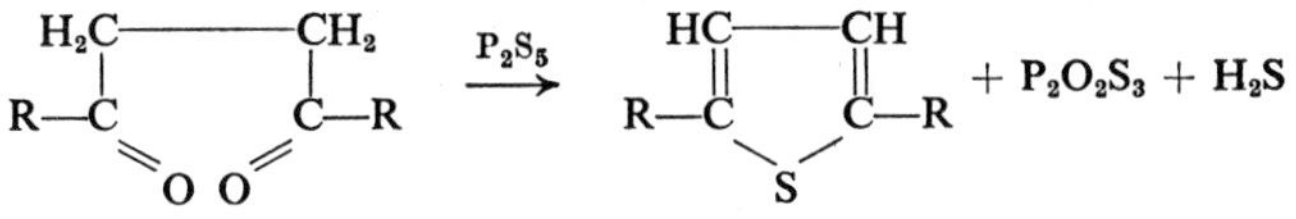

$$
\underset{\text{A 1,4-diketone}}{
\begin{array}{c}
\text{H}_2\text{C}\!-\!\!-\!\!-\!\text{CH}_2 \\
\mid \qquad\quad \mid \\
\text{R}\!-\!\text{C} \qquad \text{C}\!-\!\text{R} \\
\underset{\text{O O}}{\diagdown}
\end{array}
}
\xrightarrow{\text{P}_2\text{S}_5}
\begin{array}{c}
\text{HC}\!-\!\!-\!\!-\!\text{CH} \\
\parallel \qquad\quad \parallel \\
\text{R}\!-\!\text{C} \qquad \text{C}\!-\!\text{R} \\
\diagdown\,\text{S}\,\diagup
\end{array}
+ \text{P}_2\text{O}_2\text{S}_3 + \text{H}_2\text{S}
$$

Renewed interest in the chemistry of thiophene and its derivatives has developed with the commercial production of thiophene from butane and sulfur.

$$
\text{CH}_3\text{CH}_2\text{CH}_2\text{CH}_3 + 4\,\text{S} \xrightarrow{650°}
\begin{array}{c}
\text{HC}\!-\!\!-\!\!-\!\text{CH} \\
\parallel \qquad\quad \parallel \\
\text{HC} \qquad \text{CH} \\
\diagdown\,\text{S}\,\diagup
\end{array}
+ 3\,\text{H}_2\text{S}
$$

The butane and sulfur vapor are preheated separately to 600° and mixed in the reaction tube at 650° for a contact time of 0.07 second, after which the exit gases are cooled rapidly. The unreacted materials are recycled. A longer reaction time leads to a more complex mixture of products. It can be prepared also by the reaction of butenes with sulfur dioxide.

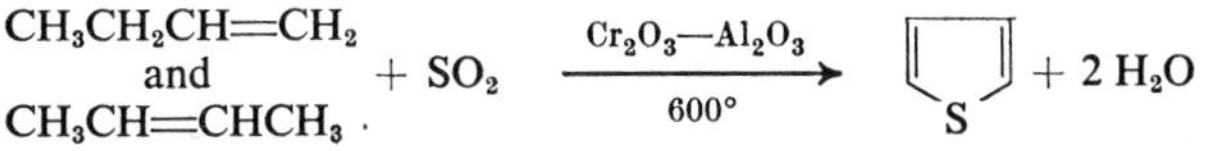

$$
\begin{array}{c}
\text{CH}_3\text{CH}_2\text{CH}\!=\!\text{CH}_2 \\
\text{and} \\
\text{CH}_3\text{CH}\!=\!\text{CHCH}_3
\end{array}
+ \text{SO}_2 \xrightarrow[600°]{\text{Cr}_2\text{O}_3\text{—Al}_2\text{O}_3}
\underset{\text{S}}{\boxed{}}
+ 2\,\text{H}_2\text{O}
$$

The only true thiophene compound known to occur in plants is **α-terthienyl** isolated from the Indian marigold (*Tagetes erecta*).

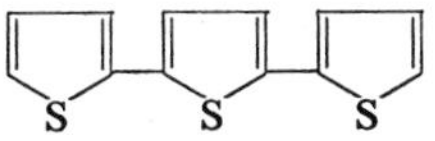

α-Terthienyl

Thiophene boils at 84°, and the boiling points of its homologs and derivatives also are close to those of the benzene analogs. The replacement of a benzene ring in physiologically active compounds by a thiophene ring has little effect on their activity. Thus the thiophene analogs of cocaine or atropine (p. 650) have similar local anesthetic or mydriatic action. 2-Thiophenecarboxylic acid when ingested is eliminated in the urine as the amide of glycine, just as benzoic acid is eliminated as hippuric acid (p. 550).

Thiophene undergoes the typical substitution reactions of aromatic compounds and is considerably more reactive than benzene. When possible, substitution usually takes place almost exclusively in the 2 or 5 position. If either a *meta*- or an *ortho,para*-directing group is present in the 2 position, a second group enters the 5 position. When substituents are in the 3 (or 4) position mixtures of isomers usually are formed.

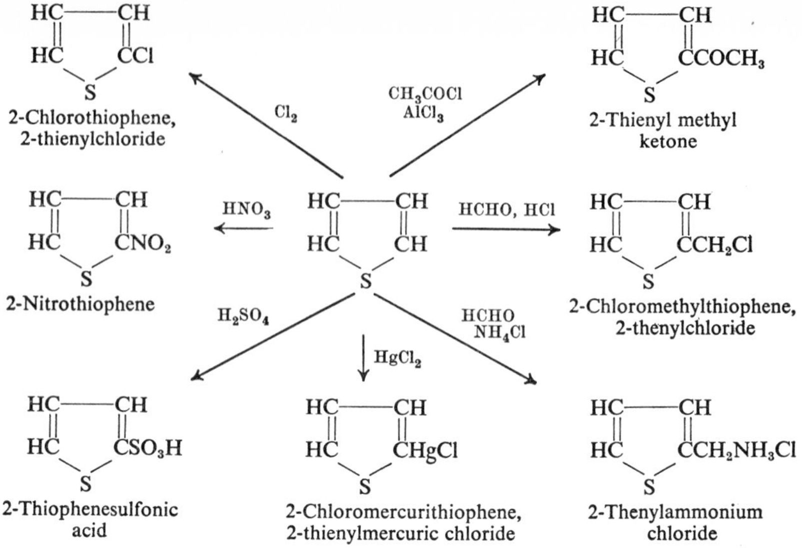

HC——CH
HC CCl
  S
2-Chlorothiophene,
2-thienylchloride

Cl_2

CH_3COCl
$AlCl_3$

HC——CH
HC CCOCH$_3$
  S
2-Thienyl methyl
ketone

HC——CH
HC CNO$_2$
  S
2-Nitrothiophene

HNO_3

HC——CH
HC CH
  S

HCHO, HCl

HC——CH
HC CCH$_2$Cl
  S
2-Chloromethylthiophene,
2-thenylchloride

H_2SO_4

HCHO
NH_4Cl

$HgCl_2$

HC——CH
HC CSO$_3$H
  S
2-Thiophenesulfonic
acid

HC——CH
HC CHgCl
  S
2-Chloromercurithiophene,
2-thienylmercuric chloride

HC——CH
HC CCH$_2$NH$_3$Cl
  S
2-Thenylammonium
chloride

An exception to exclusive 2 substitution is the alkylation with isobutylene which yields about equal amounts of the 2- and 3-*t*-butylthiophenes.

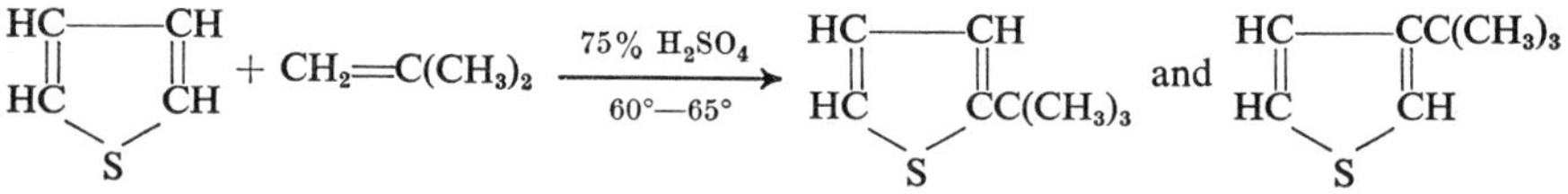

HC——CH
HC CH
  S
+ CH$_2$=C(CH$_3$)$_2$

$\xrightarrow[60°—65°]{75\% \; H_2SO_4}$

HC——CH
HC CC(CH$_3$)$_3$
  S

and

HC——CC(CH$_3$)$_3$
HC CH
  S

The greater reactivity of thiophene over benzene permits the reactions to be carried out under milder conditions that are more nearly like those used for phenols. Thus halogenation takes place without a catalyst. Unless special conditions are observed, direct nitration gives 2,5-dinitrothiophene. Concentrated sulfuric acid reacts at room temperature, preferably in an inert solvent. The Friedel-Crafts reaction is carried out in petroleum ether solution, or a milder catalyst such as stannic chloride is used rather than aluminum chloride. The greater ease of sulfonation is the basis for the removal of thiophene from benzene by shaking with concentrated sulfuric acid.

Thiophene and its homologs do not behave like sulfides. For example, oxidation does not produce the sulfoxide or the sulfone, and alkyl halides do not give sulfonium salts. The impure sulfone has been obtained indirectly by a series of reactions, but it readily undergoes intermolecular addition, followed by loss of sulfur dioxide, to give a dihydrobenzothiophene sulfone.

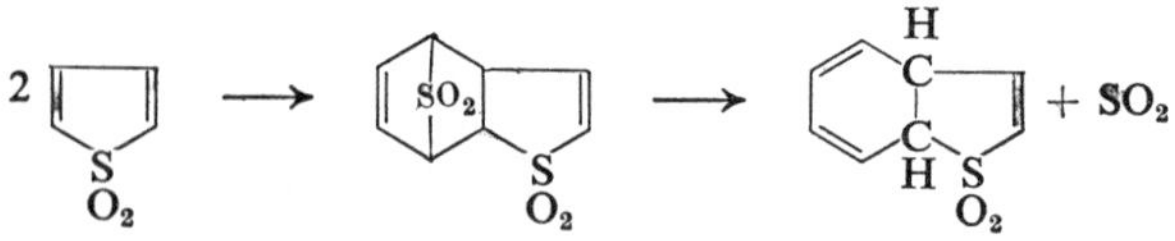

$$2 \; \underset{O_2}{\overset{}{\bigsqcup_S}} \longrightarrow SO_2 \longrightarrow + SO_2$$

Although some derivatives of thiophene behave like the corresponding benzene analogs, most of them are too reactive to give satisfactory yields of simple products. Thus the halogen derivatives form Grignard reagents, and 2-acetylthiophene can be oxidized to 2-thiophenecarboxylic acid. On the other hand reduction of 2-nitrothiophene to the amine is difficult because the ring also is reduced with the production of hydrogen sulfide. 2-Aminothiophene can be obtained as the chlorostannate by careful reduction with tin and hydrochloric acid. The free amine darkens and solidifies on exposure to oxygen. It couples with benzenediazonium chloride to give the azo derivative, but does not itself undergo a true diazotization.

The resemblance of thiophene to benzene can be ascribed to similar molecular weights, similar shapes of the molecules, and most of all to the similar electronic interactions. The *p* orbitals of the carbon atoms of the benzene ring overlap to form molecular orbitals above and below the plane of the ring (Fig. 74, p. 419); likewise a *p* orbital of the sulfur atom overlaps with the *p* orbitals of the carbon atoms to form molecular orbitals above and below the plane of the ring (Fig. 85). One molecular orbital of thiophene has a single nodal plane in the plane of the ring, and two additional nodal planes perpendicular to the plane of the ring.

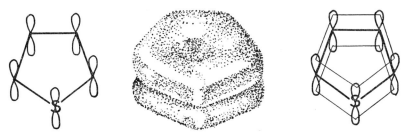

Fig. 85. Resonance in the thiophene molecule.

The increased reactivity of thiophene compared to benzene results from the higher electron-density of the thiophene ring because of the unshared electrons on sulfur. On the approach of electron-seeking reagents transition complexes can be formed more readily at the 2 position than at the 3 position because the positive charge can be more widely dispersed over the ring.

Benzothiophenes. 2-Benzothiophene is known as **thianaphthene**. It is obtained in 60 per cent yield by the catalyzed reaction of styrene with hydrogen sulfide.

Strong oxidation of thianaphthene gives benzenecarboxylicsulfonic anhydride (p. 557). **Dibenzothiophene** is formed in 65 per cent yield when biphenyl is heated with sulfur in the presence of anhydrous aluminum chloride.

Oxidation with dichromic acid gives the sulfone which can be reconverted to dibenzothiophene by heating with sulfur.

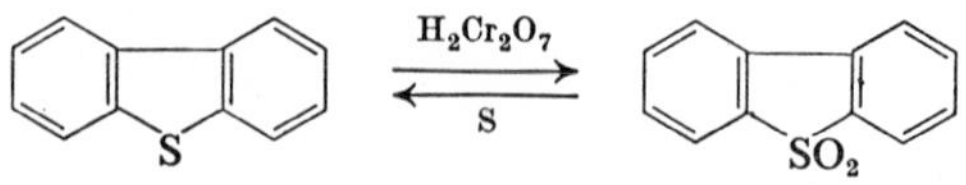

Pyrroles. Pyrrole, C_4H_5N, is the nitrogen analog of thiophene. It is present in coal tar and in the tars obtained by the distillation of waste animal matter such as bones (*bone oil* or *Dippel's oil*), horn, and scrap leather. Its presence in bone oil was detected in 1834 by the red color which is produced when its vapors come in contact with a pine splint dipped in concentrated hydrochloric acid (Gr. *pyrros*, red). It was not isolated in a pure state from these sources until 1858.

The **structure** of pyrrole is most obvious from its formation by distilling succinimide (p. 797) with zinc dust.

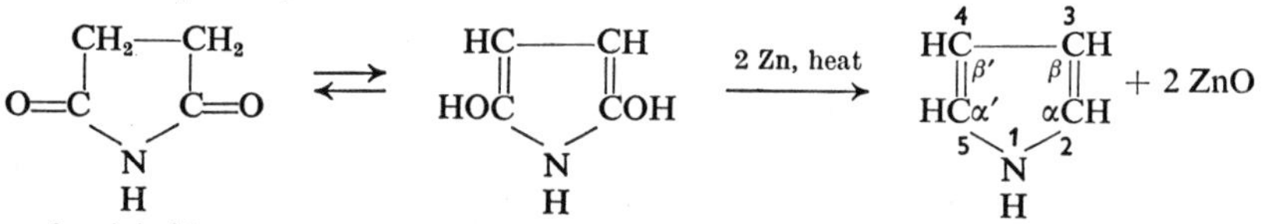

It is **prepared** best by heating ammonium salts of glycaric acids (p. 362) in a stream of ammonia. Ammonium saccharate gives the best yield, but ammonium mucate is more readily obtainable. At the high temperature used, the ammonium salt undoubtedly dissociates into the free acid, which dehydrates, decarboxylates, and reacts with ammonia.

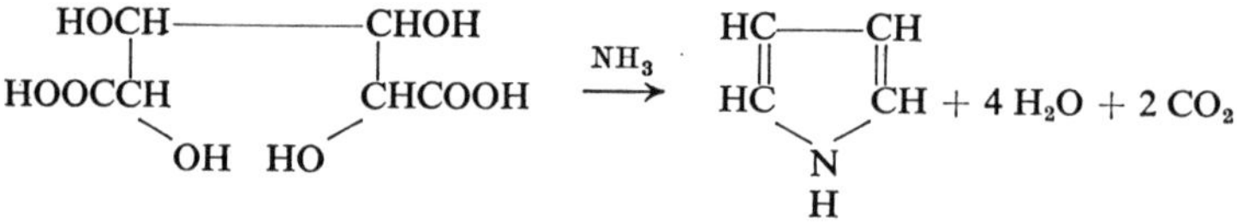

Pyrrole is produced commercially from furan and ammonia (p. 619). One of the more general methods that have been used for the synthesis of substituted pyrroles is the reaction of 1,4-diketones (p. 775) with ammonia or an ammonium salt.

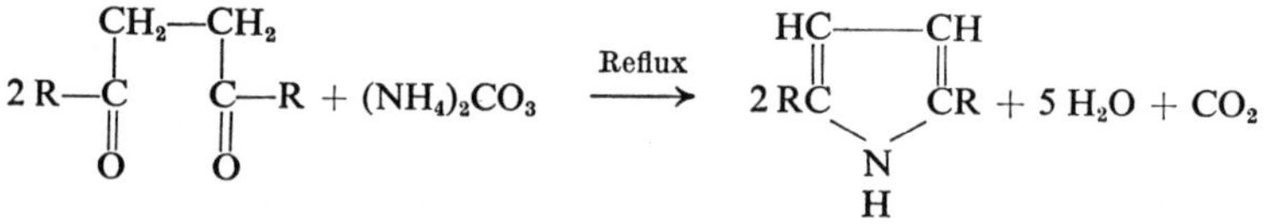

Pyrrole derivatives can be prepared also from β-keto esters (p. 819).

The **physical properties** of pyrrole are distinctly anomalous. It has the exceptionally high boiling point of 131° compared with 78° for *n*-butylamine. It is practically insoluble in water, whereas *n*-butylamine is miscible with water. The dipole moment of 1.83 D is high, but it is lower than the moment of 2.11 D for pyridine, C_5H_5N, which boils lower and is miscible with water (p. 621).

In regard to their **chemical properties,** pyrrole and its simple derivatives are characterized by their ease of oxidation by air to give dark-colored resins, and by their sensitivity to strong acids, which produce polymeric red substances.

It has been suggested that the sensitivity to acids is due to the destruction of the aromatic resonance (cf. thiophene, p. 609) by salt formation. The resulting product is a conjugated diene which polymerizes easily.

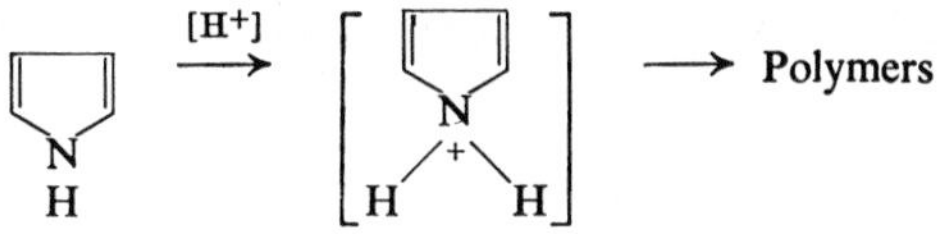

However, conjugated dienes such as 1,3-butadiene (p. 707) do not polymerize readily in the presence of acids. An alternate mechanism is one analogous to the acid-catalyzed polymerization of olefins (p. 62).

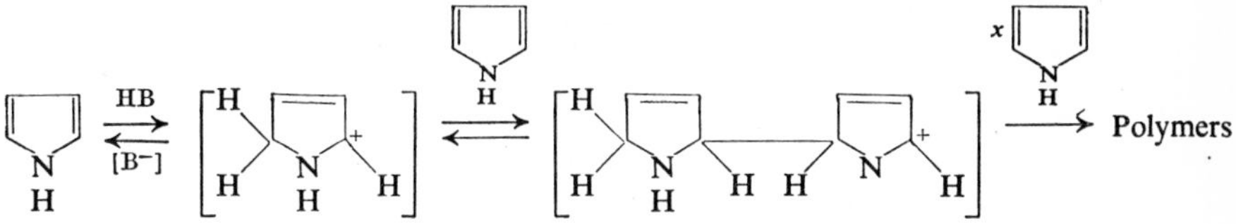

Pyrrole is both a weaker base and a stronger acid than an amine. Its basic and acidic properties are about the same as those of water. It forms a potassium salt by reaction with solid potassium hydroxide, but the reaction is reversed if an excess of water is added to the potassium salt.

$$C_4H_4NH + KOH \rightleftarrows [C_4H_4N^-]K^+ + H_2O$$

The weaker basicity and the higher acidity of pyrroles compared to secondary amines is understandable in terms of the resonance picture. Since the unshared electrons on nitrogen are interacting with the other unsaturation electrons, they are less available for bonding with a proton, and the low electron density on nitrogen permits the hydrogen to leave more readily as a proton.

Methylmagnesium bromide reacts with pyrrole to give methane and an *N*-magnesium bromide derivative. These derivatives behave as if the magnesium were combined at the 2 position, since reagents yield **2-substituted pyrroles.**

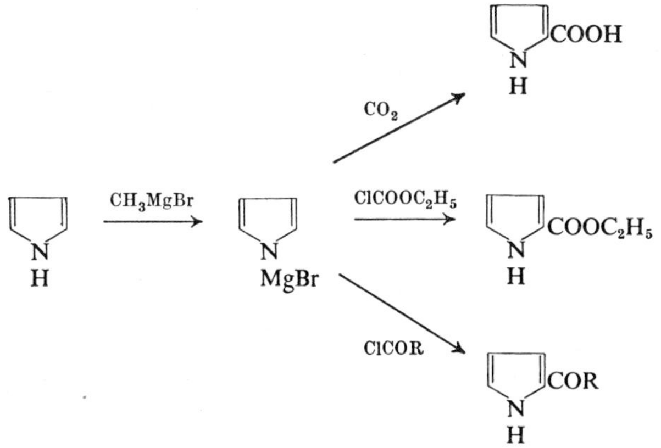

This behavior resembles that of the benzylmagnesium halides (p. 437) and can be explained by a similar mechanism.

The pyrrole nucleus undergoes many reactions characteristic of aromatic compounds. Since it is destroyed by strong acids, however, halogenation, nitration, sulfonation, and Friedel-Crafts reactions under the usual conditions are not applicable. On the other hand the NH group activates the ring even more strongly than the sulfur atom in thiophene, and many substitution reactions take place under mild conditions. Halogenation is conducted under alkaline conditions, when even iodine gives **tetraiodopyrrole.**

$$C_4H_4NH + 4 I_2 + 4 NaOH \longrightarrow C_4I_4NH + 4 NaI + 4 H_2O$$

3-Nitropyrrole results from reaction with amyl nitrate and sodium ethoxide.

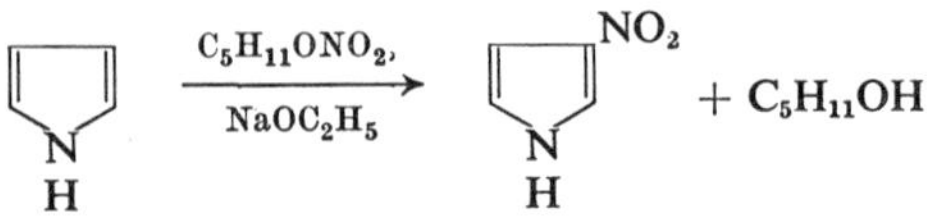

Other nuclear reactions resemble those of other highly activated nuclei such as that in phenol (pp. 508, 498).

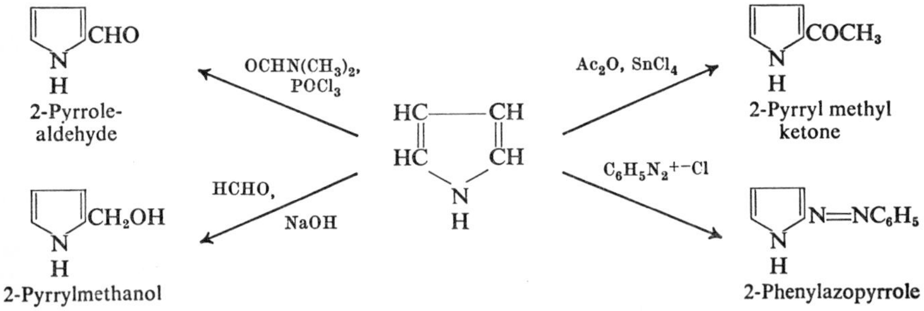

The Reimer-Tiemann reaction (p. 532) gives some **2-pyrrolealdehyde** but chiefly 3-chloropyridine by ring enlargement.

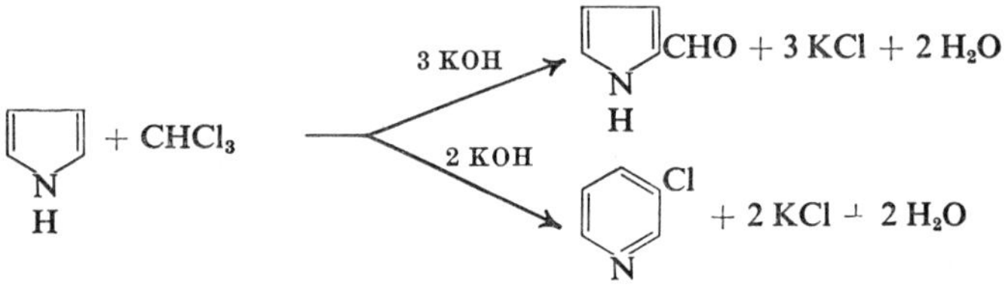

The mechanism of the formation of 2-pyrrolealdehyde is analogous to that for the formation of salicylaldehyde (p. 532).

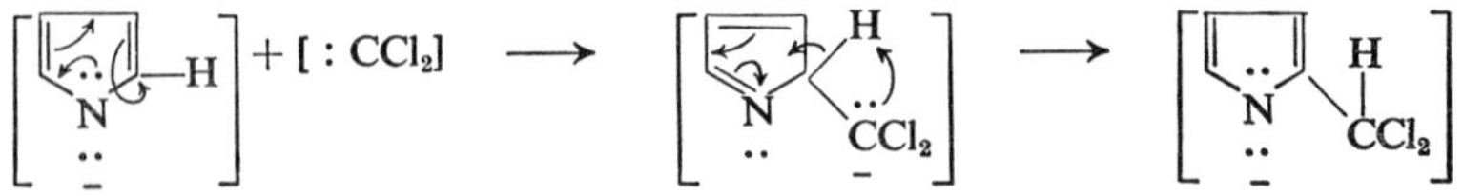

The intermediate addition product, however, can form the more stable pyridine derivative by loss of a chloride ion.

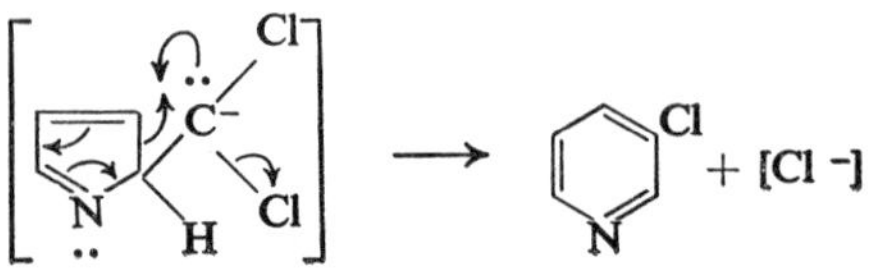

Pyrrolecarboxylic acids lose carbon dioxide on heating, a behavior characteristic of phenolcarboxylic acids (p. 518).

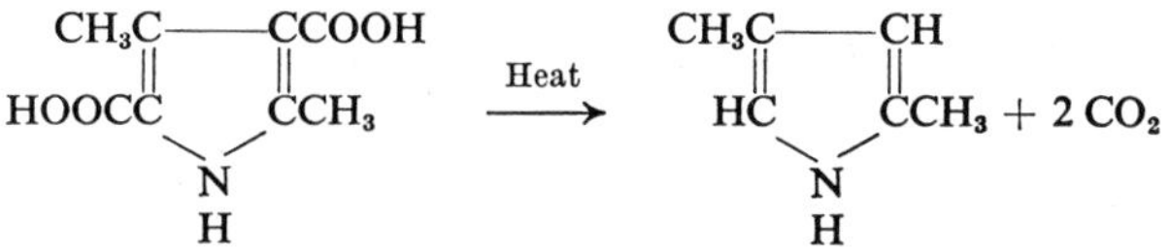

$$CH_3C\text{---}CCOOH \qquad \xrightarrow{\text{Heat}} \qquad CH_3C\text{---}CH$$
$$HOOCC \quad CCH_3 \qquad\qquad HC \quad CCH_3 + 2\,CO_2$$
$$\underset{H}{N} \qquad\qquad\qquad \underset{H}{N}$$

Reduction of pyrrole with zinc and acetic acid yields 2,5-dihydropyrrole (**pyrroline**), and catalytic reduction yields the tetrahydro derivative, **pyrrolidine.** The formation of pyrrolidine hydrochloride when 1-chloro-4-aminobutane is heated is a proof of the structure of pyrrolidine.

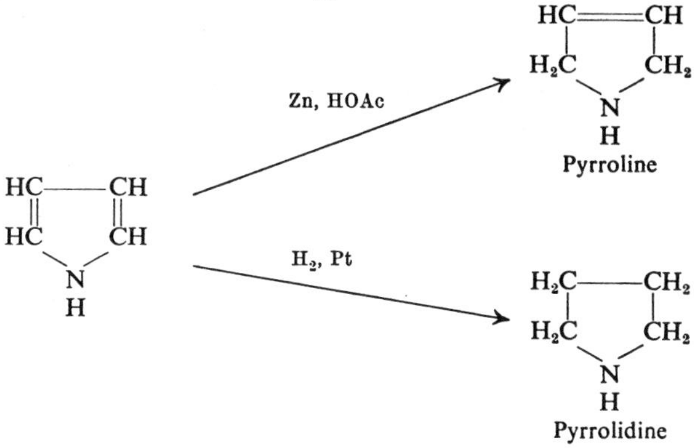

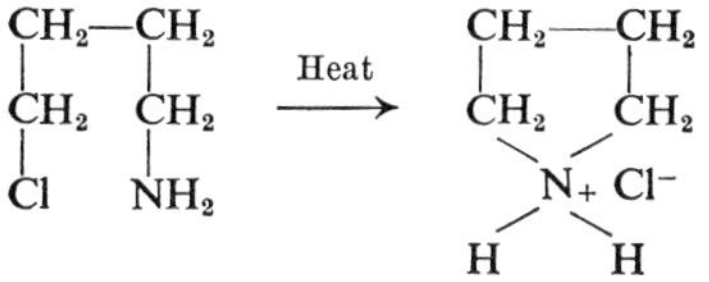

$$HC\text{====}CH$$
$$H_2C \quad CH_2$$
$$\underset{H}{N}$$
Pyrroline

$$\xrightarrow{\text{Zn, HOAc}}$$

$$HC\text{----}CH$$
$$HC \quad CH$$
$$\underset{H}{N}$$

$$\xrightarrow{H_2,\ Pt}$$

$$H_2C\text{----}CH_2$$
$$H_2C \quad CH_2$$
$$\underset{H}{N}$$
Pyrrolidine

$$CH_2\text{---}CH_2$$
$$CH_2 \quad CH_2$$
$$\underset{Cl}{|} \quad \underset{NH_2}{|}$$
$$\xrightarrow{\text{Heat}}$$
$$CH_2\text{---}CH_2$$
$$CH_2 \quad CH_2$$
$$\underset{H}{N_+}\ Cl^-$$
$$\underset{H}{}$$
Pyrrolidine
hydrochloride

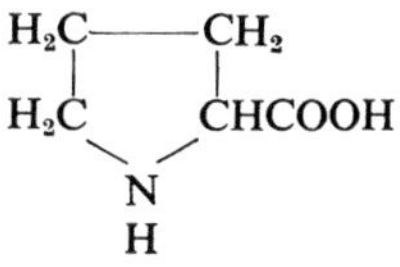

$$H_2C\text{----}CH_2$$
$$H_2C \quad CHCOOH$$
$$\underset{H}{N}$$
Proline

Pyrrolidine is a typical secondary aliphatic amine. It is miscible with water, its basic dissociation constant is 1.3×10^{-3}, and it boils at 88°. **Proline** (*2-pyrrolidinecarboxylic acid*) and **hydroxyproline** (*4-hydroxy-2-pyrrolidinecarboxylic acid*) are natural amino acids (Table 18, p. 297). The **pyrrolidones** are lactams of γ-amino acids (p. 784).

Porphin Derivatives. Alkylated pyrrole nuclei form the building units for many biologically important pigments, for example those of bile and blood, and the green coloring matter of plants. Hence pyrrole and the alkylated pyrroles are present in bone oil (p. 610), which arises from the decomposition of bone marrow, the source of the blood pigments. These pigments have a basic structure known as the **porphin nucleus** which contains a flat 16-membered ring. The **porphyrins** derived from natural pigments (Gr. *porphyra*, purple) have substituents in the eight β positions of the pyrrole nuclei. The natural pigments themselves are metal chelate complexes (p. 742) of the porphyrins. Thus reaction of **protoporphyrin** with ferric chloride in alkaline solution gives **hemin**. The synthesis of hemin has been reported, but the method of synthesis is not sufficiently rational

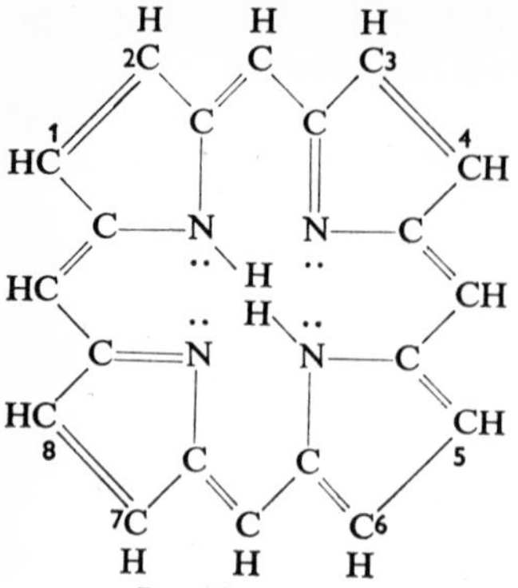

Porphin nucleus

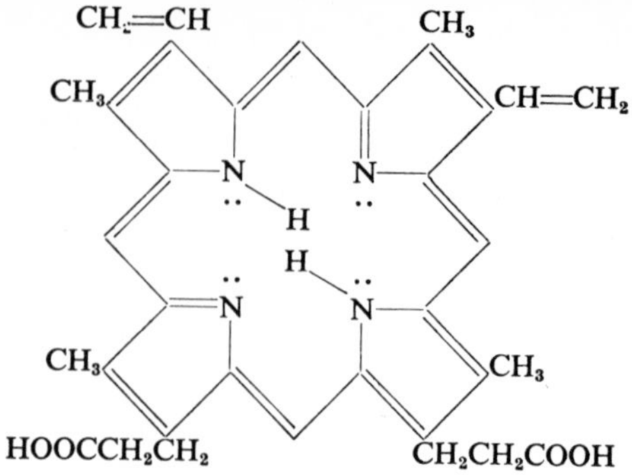

Protoporphyrin

to be an unequivocal proof of structure. The reduced compound lacking the chloride ion is the **heme** of hemoglobin (p. 295).

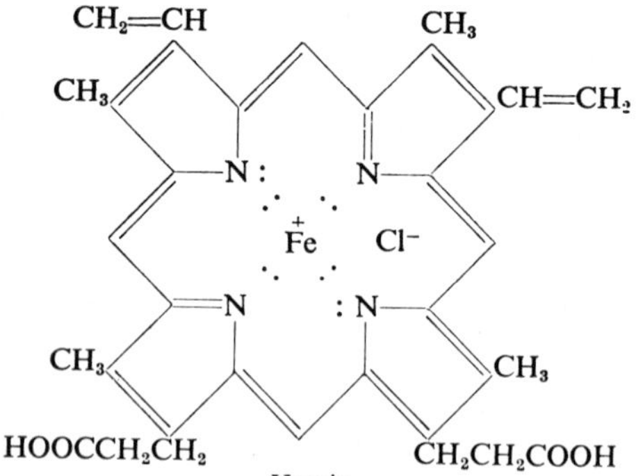

Hemin

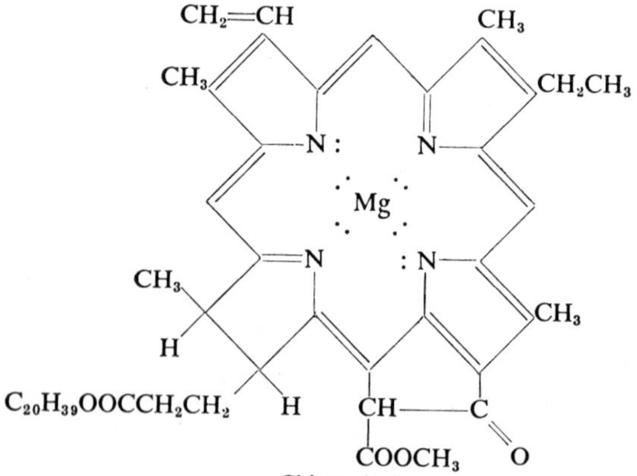

Chlorophyll *a*

The **chlorophylls** are magnesium complexes of porphyrins esterified with the long-chain alcohol phytol, $C_{20}H_{39}OH$ (p. 860). Chlorophyll *b* differs from chlorophyll *a* in that it has an aldehyde group replacing the methyl group in the 3 position. By the use of isotopically labelled molecules it has been shown that the porphyrin nucleus of both heme and chlorophyll is synthesized biologically from glycine and acetic acid and that the steps of the synthesis by the red blood cell and by the chloroplast of the plant are identical.

The **cytochromes** and **catalases** are enzymes concerned with biological oxidations and reductions. They are proteins having an iron-containing prosthetic group identical with or related to heme.

In the metabolic degradation of the porphyrins to the **bile pigments,** the porphin nucleus is opened to give a linear arrangement of the four pyrrole rings. The formula for **bilirubin** illustrates the general nature of these compounds.

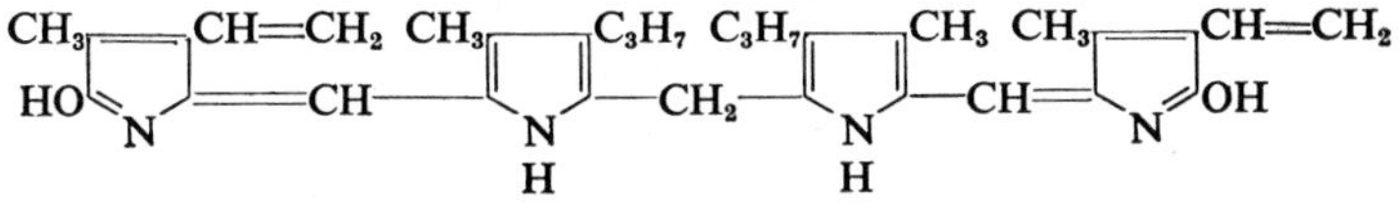

Bilirubin

Vitamin B$_{12}$, isolated from liver and effective in the treatment of pernicious anemia, is a cobalt complex containing a porphin nucleus. Its structure was elucidated completely by chemical and X-ray analysis in 1955. The molecular formula is $C_{63}H_{90}O_{14}N_{14}PCo$, and it is the most complicated nonprotein organic compound of known structure. Nickel and vanadium complexes of porphyrins occur in petroleum and lead to difficulties in the processing operations.

Benzopyrroles. 2-Benzopyrrole is known as **indole** because it was obtained first by Baeyer[2] in 1866 by distilling oxindole, a degradation product of indigo (p. 684), with zinc dust. It first was synthesized in 1869 and was not found in coal tar until 1910. Numerous syntheses of indole and its derivatives have been developed. One which clearly indicates the structure of indole is the intramolecular condensation of formo-o-toluidide (*Madelung synthesis*).

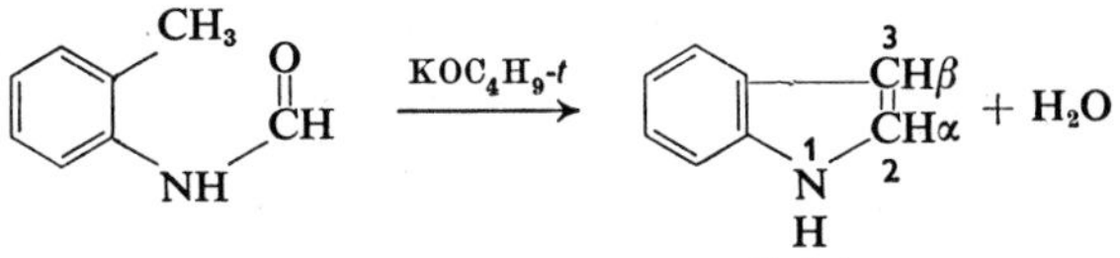

Indole

Indole and 3-methylindole (skatole) are formed during the putrefaction of proteins. They contribute to the characteristic odor of feces. In contrast, pure indole in high dilution has a flowery odor and is used in the preparation of jasmine, orange blossom, and lilac blends. In fact it is present in natural jasmine, orange blossom, and jonquil extracts. **Skatole** can be synthesized by the *Fischer indole synthesis*, which consists of heating the phenylhydrazones of aldehydes, ketones, or keto acids with zinc chloride or alcoholic sulfuric acid.

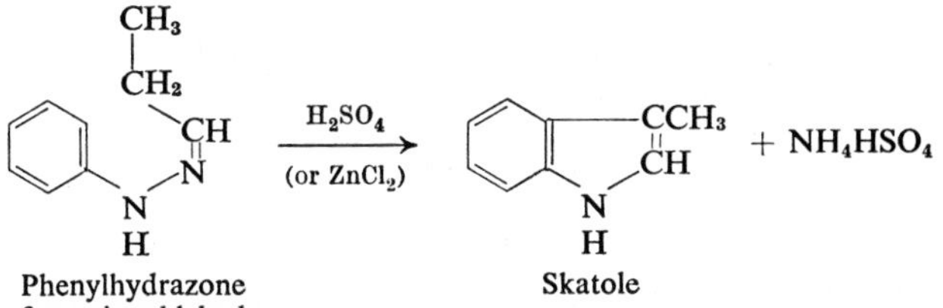

Phenylhydrazone
of propionaldehyde

Skatole

---

[2] Johann Friedrich Wilhelm Adolf von Baeyer (1835–1917), student of Bunsen and Kekulé and successor to Liebig at the University of Munich. He was awarded the Nobel Prize in Chemistry in 1905. Of the many who studied under Baeyer may be mentioned Emil and Otto Fischer, Perkin Jr., Friedlaender, Bamberger, Curtius, Rupe, and Willstaetter.

The indoles behave like pyrroles. They resinify with mineral acids, form potassium salts, and undergo substitution reactions under alkaline conditions. In contrast to pyrrole, substituents usually enter the β position.

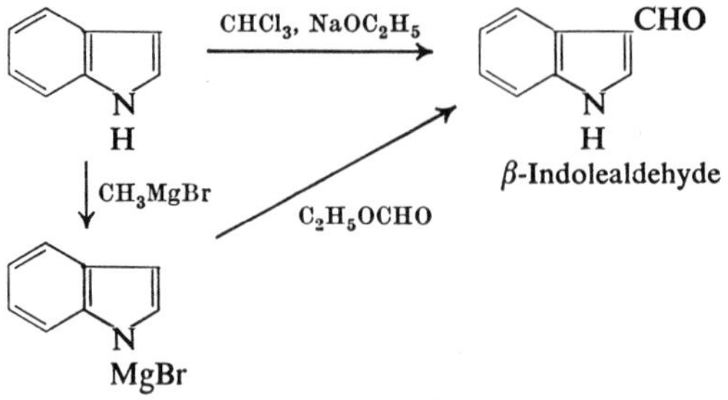

β Substitution in preference to α substitution may be explained by the fact that in the transition state for β substitution the positive charge can be stabilized by resonance without destroying the resonance of the benzene ring.

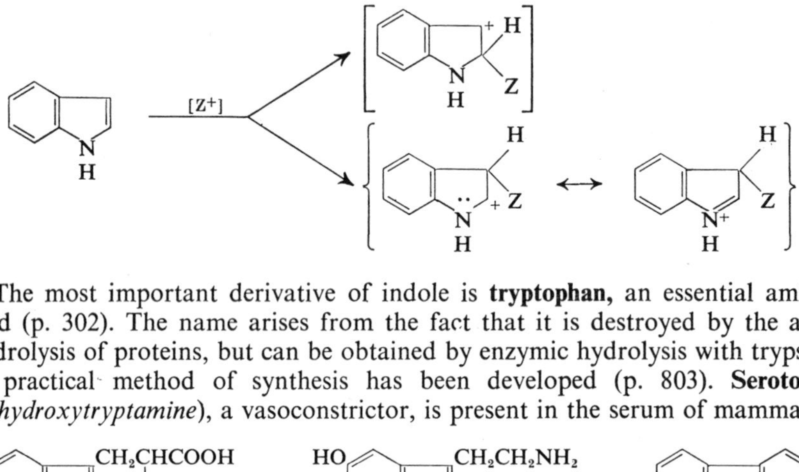

The most important derivative of indole is **tryptophan,** an essential amino acid (p. 302). The name arises from the fact that it is destroyed by the acid hydrolysis of proteins, but can be obtained by enzymic hydrolysis with trypsin. A practical method of synthesis has been developed (p. 803). **Serotonin** (*5-hydroxytryptamine*), a vasoconstrictor, is present in the serum of mammals.

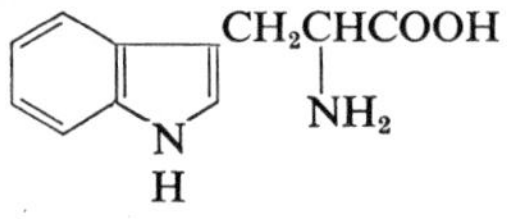

Tryptophan 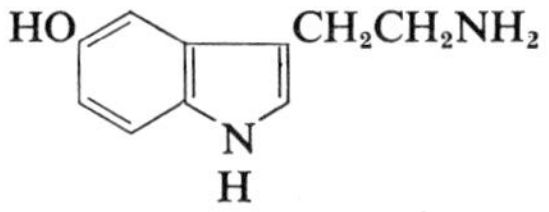   Serotonin 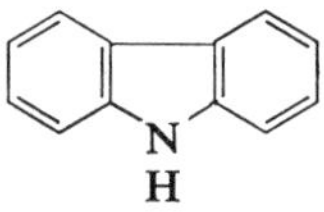   Carbazole

Carbazole, 2,4-dibenzopyrrole, is present to the extent of over 1 per cent in coal tar. It can be isolated from the anthracene fraction as the potassium salt. The demand, however, exceeded the supply from coal tar with the result that a synthetic process from *o*-aminobiphenyl was developed which made the recovery from coal tar uneconomical.

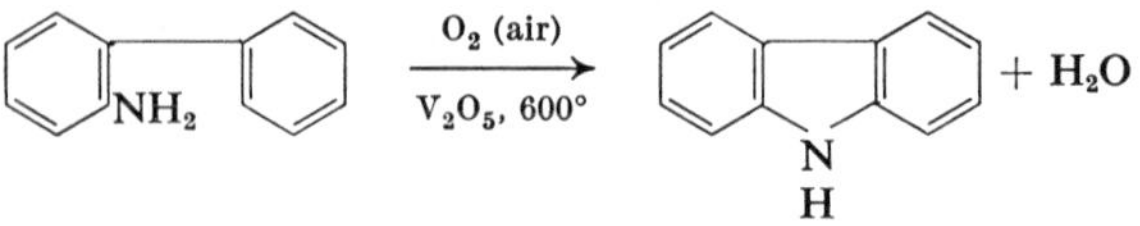

The chief use is for the preparation of blue sulfur dyes (p. 692). It is used also to make **polyvinylcarbazole,** a high-melting plastic with good dielectric properties.

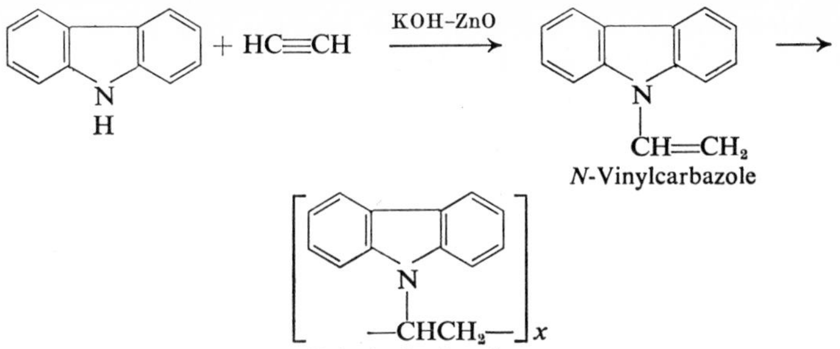

N-Vinylcarbazole

Polyvinylcarbazole

Other important derivatives of indole are discussed under indigo (p. 684).

Furans. Furan, C_4H_4O, is the oxygen analog of thiophene. The most available derivative of furan is the α aldehyde, **furfural,** from which most other furans are prepared. Furfural first was obtained in 1840 by the distillation of bran (L. *furfur*) with dilute sulfuric acid. It results from the dehydration of pentoses formed by the hydrolysis of the pentosans in the bran (p. 407).

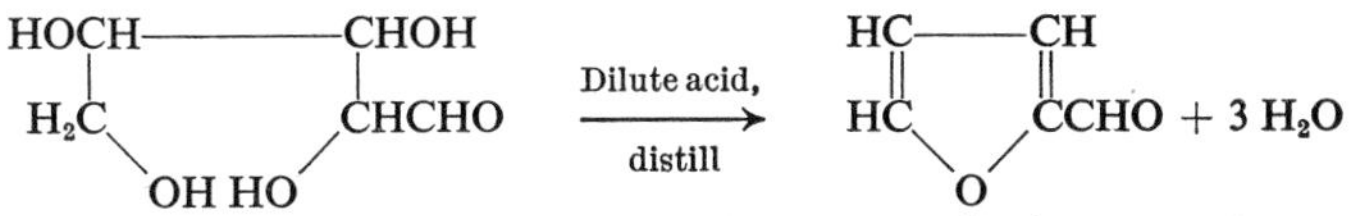

The commercial production since 1922 by the hydrolysis of oat hulls stemmed from an attempt to produce an improved cattle feed from them. The availability of cheap furfural led to several large-scale applications, and now it is made also from other agricultural wastes that contain pentosans, such as corncobs and straw. Because of increased use and technical improvements in the process, the price dropped from $1.00 per pound in 1922 to 12 cents per pound in 1955.

Furfural is a colorless liquid with a pleasant characteristic odor. It is oxidized by air, the color changing through shades of yellow and brown to almost black. The initial products after peroxide formation appear to be formic acid and β-formylacrylic acid, $OCHCH=CHCOOH$. The latter undergoes condensation reactions to give high molecular weight polymers. These changes can be prevented by storing in the absence of oxygen or by adding an antioxidant (p. 886).

Furfural can be detected by the brilliant red color that it gives with aniline in the presence of acetic acid. Apparently two moles of aniline condense with one of furfural with opening of the ring.

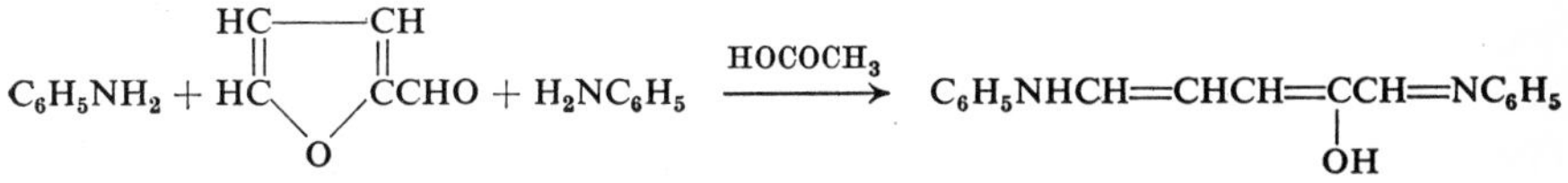

Reaction of furfural with an acid solution of phloroglucinol (p. 518) gives a dark green precipitate of unknown and probably variable composition. The weight of precipitate formed has been related empirically to the weight of furfural from which it was produced. Hence the reaction can be used for the quantitative estimation of furfural, and indirectly of pentoses and pentosans (p. 378).

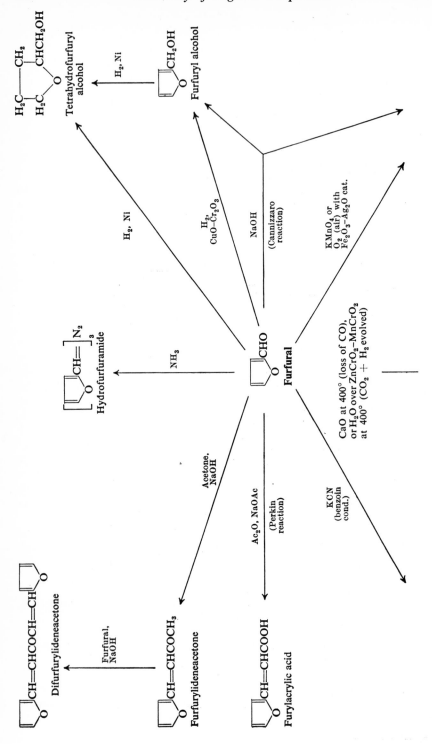

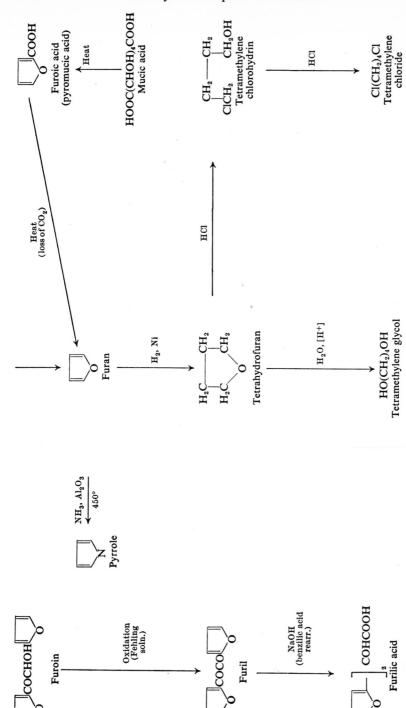

Fig. 86. Reactions of furfural and derived products.

Furfural and furans in general undergo ring scission by acids, which is followed by complex condensation reactions. Nitration of furfural in the presence of acetic anhydride gives **5-nitrofurfural diacetate.**

$$\text{[furan]}\text{CHO} + HNO_3 + 2 (CH_3CO)_2O \longrightarrow O_2N\text{[furan]}CH(OCOCH_3)_2$$
$$+ 2 CH_3COOH$$

Numerous nitrofurans have antibacterial properties. 5-Nitrofurfural semicarbazone, known as **nitrofurazone** or **Furacin,** is used for prevention and treatment of surface infections and for the control of animal diseases. In alkaline or neutral solution, furfural gives all of the reactions of benzaldehyde. The more commonly used reactions are summarized in Fig. 86, p. 618.

Furfural is used on a large scale as a solvent for refining lubricating oils (p. 81), and for removing butadiene from its mixtures with butene and butane (p. 716). With the developing shortage of benzene, a process has been developed (p. 799) to use furfural as an alternate raw material for the preparation, through tetramethylene chloride and tetramethylene cyanide, of hexamethylenediamine, $H_2N(CH_2)_6NH_2$, one of the components of nylon salt from which nylon is made (p. 798). **α-Furfuryl mercaptan,** the thiol corresponding to furfuryl alcohol, is one of the essential constituents of the aroma of roasted coffee. At high concentrations the synthetic product has an intense odor of onions, but at high dilution (1 : 10^6) it has the aroma of roasted coffee and is used in perfumes and flavoring agents. **Tetrahydrofuran** has been synthesized on an industrial scale from acetylene (p. 717), as well as from furfural (p. 619).

One general method for the synthesis of furans is the dehydration of 1,4-diketones (p. 775).

$$\begin{array}{c}\text{CH}_2\text{---}\text{CH}_2 \\ R\text{--}C \quad\quad C\text{--}R \\ \text{O} \quad \text{O}\end{array} \xrightarrow{\text{Conc. HCl}} \begin{array}{c}\text{HC}\text{---}\text{CH} \\ R\text{--}C \quad\quad C\text{--}R \\ \text{O}\end{array} + H_2O$$

The reaction can be reversed and acetonylacetone can be made best by the hydrolysis of **2,5-dimethylfuran,** a co-product in the preparation of ketene by the thermal decomposition of acetone (p. 164).

$$\begin{array}{c}\text{HC}\text{---}\text{CH} \\ CH_3C \quad\quad CCH_3 \\ \text{O}\end{array} \xrightarrow{H_2O,\ HCl} \left[\begin{array}{c}\text{HC}\text{---}\text{CH} \\ CH_3C \quad\quad CCH_3 \\ \text{OH} \quad \text{OH}\end{array}\right] \rightleftharpoons CH_3COCH_2CH_2COCH_3$$

2,5-Dimethylfuran   Acetonylacetone

Benzofuran (*coumarone*) is present in the naphtha fraction of coal tar. It is polymerized by sulfuric acid to give **coumarone resins** used chiefly in varnish making and as a bonding agent.

Six-membered Rings

Pyridines. Pyridine, C_5H_5N, was isolated first from bone oil in 1851 and then from coal tar in 1854. Until around 1950, coal tar was the sole commercial source, although less than 0.1 per cent of pyridine is present (Table 21, p. 428).

It now is synthesized from acetylene and ammonia but no details of the process are available.

Pyridine boils at 115° and is miscible with water. It also is a good solvent for most organic compounds, and dissolves many inorganic salts. Like most of the higher amines, it has a disagreeable odor.

Pyridine is a typical tertiary amine. It reacts with alkyl iodides to give quaternary ammonium salts.

$$C_5H_5N : + CH_3I \longrightarrow [C_5H_5\overset{+}{N} : CH_3]I^-$$
N-Methylpyridinium
iodide

It is considerably weaker as a base ($K_b = 2.3 \times 10^{-9}$) than aliphatic tertiary amines ($K_b = $ ca. 10^{-4}) but stronger than aniline ($K_b = 3.8 \times 10^{-10}$). Reduction with sodium and alcohol gives a hexahydro derivative known as *piperidine*. Since three monosubstitution products are known, pyridine can be represented best as an analog of benzene in which a CH group is replaced by nitrogen.

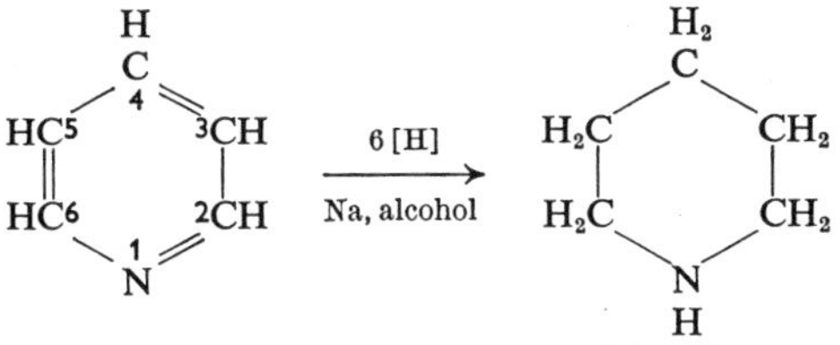

Pyridine　　Piperidine

Piperidine is a typical secondary amine having a basicity ($K_b = 1.6 \times 10^{-3}$) and other properties resembling those of secondary aliphatic amines. The assigned structure is supported by its synthesis from pentamethylenediamine hydrochloride (p. 756).

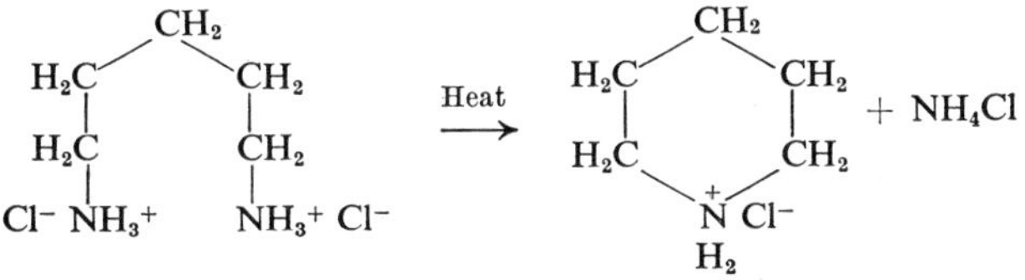

Pentamethylenediamine
hydrochloride

Piperidine
hydrochloride

Piperidine can be converted to a quaternary ammonium hydroxide which decomposes on heating with opening of the ring (p. 242).

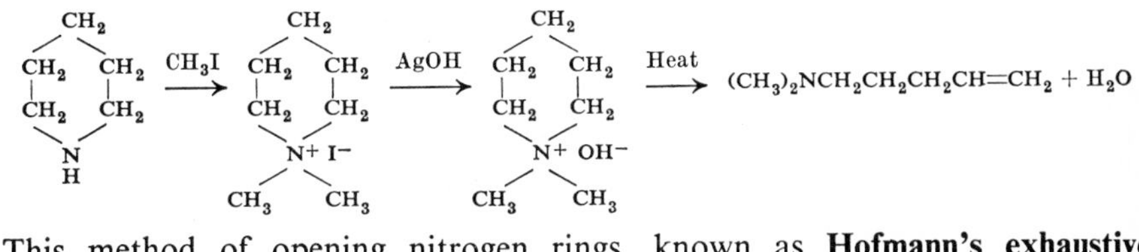

This method of opening nitrogen rings, known as **Hofmann's exhaustive methylation** procedure, has been valuable in determining the structure of alkaloids (p. 648) and other nitrogen heterocycles of unknown constitution.

Excluding its basic properties, pyridine is less reactive than any type of compound with the exception of the saturated hydrocarbons. It is not affected by boiling with alkaline permanganate, concentrated nitric acid, or dichromic acid. The action of chlorine on pyridine hydrochloride at 120° for several weeks yields a complex mixture containing di-, tetra-, and pentachloropyridines. Bromine reacts with the hydrobromide to give **3-bromo-** and **3,5-dibromopyridine.** Bromination in the vapor phase at 300° gives **3-bromopyridine,** but at 500° the product is **2-bromopyridine.** Distillation of pyridine sulfate with concentrated sulfuric acid in the presence of vanadium sulfate gives a 50 per cent yield of **3-pyridinesulfonic acid.** Pyridine is not sulfonated by sulfur trioxide but forms a stable addition complex, $C_5H_5NSO_3$, which can be used to sulfonate other compounds such as furans and pyrroles that are sensitive to strong acids.

Similarly it forms a stable solid **pyridinium bromide perbromide** $[C_5H_5N\overset{+}{B}r]\,[^-Br_3]$ that is a convenient brominating agent for other compounds. **3-Nitropyridine** is obtained in a 22 per cent yield by heating with concentrated sulfuric and fuming nitric acids at 300° in the presence of iron salts. On the other hand the amino group can be introduced directly into pyridine by heating with sodium amide (*Chichibabin* [3] *reaction*). The main product is **2-aminopyridine,** although some **4-aminopyridine** and several other products also are formed.

The inertness of pyridine to substitution reactions with acidic reagents and the comparative ease of substitution by amide ion, as well as the positions taken by the substituents, is understandable. In the first place the nitrogen atom, having a greater positive charge on the nucleus, has a greater attraction for electrons than a carbon atom and decreases the availability of the unsaturation electrons. What is more important, combination with a proton or other electron-seeking reagent gives it a positive charge which holds the electrons still more strongly. Hence the rate of substitution by electron-seeking reagents is very low (cf. p. 449). Moreover attack of the electrophilic reagent at the 2 or 4 position would require an increase in the positive charge on nitrogen in the transition state whereas attack at the 3 position does not. Hence the rate of substitution is faster at the 3 position than at the 2 or 4 position.

The effect of nitrogen in reducing the electron density of the ring makes pyridine more easily substituted than benzene by electron-donating reagents. Moreover the ability of nitrogen to accept a negative charge favors the reaction with electron-donating reagents at the 2 and 3 positions and accounts also for the greater ease of hydrolysis of 2- and 4-chloropyridine over that of 3-chloropyridine (cf. p. 462).

---

[3] Aleksei Eugenievitsch Chichibabin (1871–1945), professor of chemistry at the Imperial College of Technology of Moscow until 1929. From 1931 until his death he worked at the Collège de France in Paris. He is noted chiefly for his studies of the chemistry of pyridine compounds.

The weaker basicity of pyridine compared with aliphatic tertiary amines can be ascribed to the fact that the best orbital which the proton can use is an sp^2 hybrid; that is, its basicity, like that of the imines, lies between that of the amines and the nitriles (p. 252).

2- or 4-Hydroxypyridine can be obtained by diazotizing 2- or 4-aminopyridine, and **3-hydroxypyridine** or **3-cyanopyridine** is formed when the sodium sulfonate is fused with sodium hydroxide or sodium cyanide. The 2- and 4-hydroxypyridines are tautomeric with the keto forms.

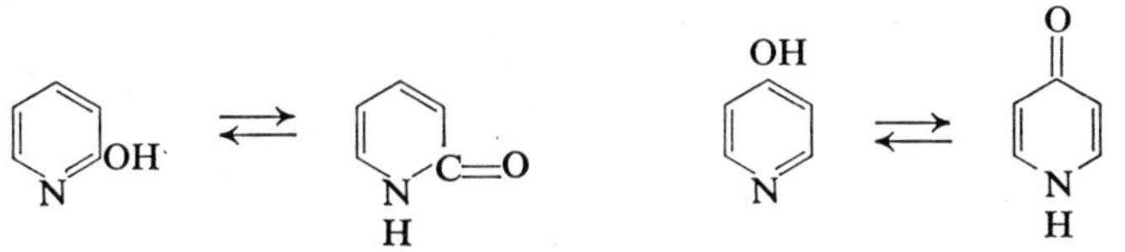

α-Pyridone   γ-Pyridone

A corresponding structure is not possible for 3-hydroxypyridine. The **N-alkyl-α-pyridones** are obtained by the oxidation of the quaternary hydroxides. The latter strong bases appear to be in equilibrium with the α-hydroxydihydropyridines, which are called *pseudo bases.*

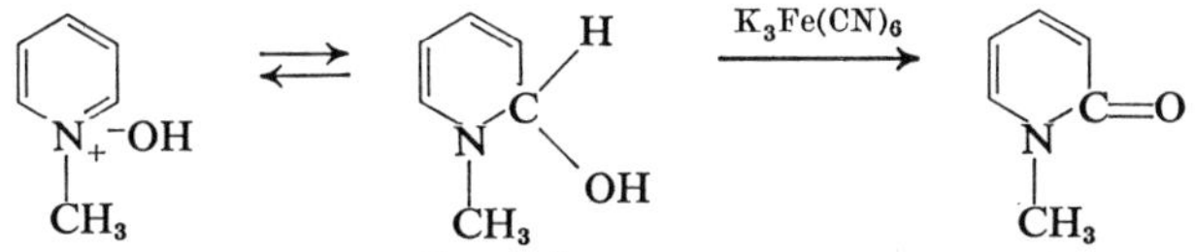

Quaternary   Pseudo base   N-Methyl-
base   pyridone

The hydroxyl groups of α- and γ-hydroxypyridine can be replaced by chlorine using phosphorus trichloride or phosphorus pentachloride. α- or γ-Halogenated pyridines hydrolyze much more easily than the β isomers.

When quaternary pyridinium iodides are heated in a sealed tube to high temperatures (ca. 300°) **alkylpyridine hydroiodides** are formed. The reaction is known as the *Ladenburg*[4] *rearrangement.*

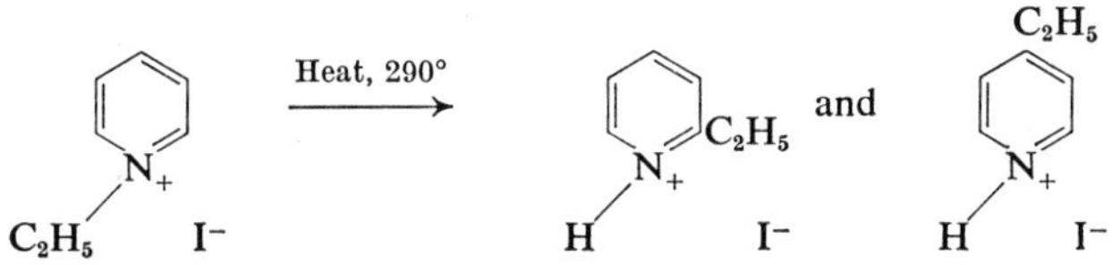

The chief commercial use for crude pyridine has been as a denaturant for ethyl alcohol. More recently it is being used as an intermediate for the manufacture of certain pharmaceuticals. **α-Aminopyridine,** for example, is used in the manufacture of sulfapyridine (p. 488). Pyridine finds important use in organic synthesis as a basic solvent whereby it not only can exert a catalytic action but also combines with acids produced in reactions. For example, acetylations and benzoylations take place smoothly in pyridine solution.

$$ROH + ClCOC_6H_5 + C_5H_5N \longrightarrow ROCOC_6H_5 + C_5H_5NHCl$$

---

[4] Albert Ladenburg (1842–1911), student of Bunsen, Friedel, and Kekulé, and later professor at the University of Breslau. He is known for his proof of the equivalence of the hydrogen atoms of benzene, for early work on organosilicon compounds (p. 911), and for his investigations of heterocyclic compounds and alkaloids.

For this purpose the pyridine must be anhydrous since water in the presence of pyridine hydrolyzes the reagent. The presence of interfering amounts of water in pyridine can be detected easily by adding pure benzoyl chloride free of benzoic acid. If water is present an immediate precipitate of the slightly soluble benzoic anhydride is formed.

$$C_6H_5COCl + H_2O + C_5H_5N \longrightarrow C_6H_5COOH + C_5H_5NHCl$$

$$C_6H_5COOH + ClCOC_6H_5 + C_5H_5N \longrightarrow (C_6H_5CO)_2O + C_5H_5NHCl$$

Pyridine reacts with peroxy acids or with 30 per cent hydrogen peroxide in acetic acid solution to give good yields of **pyridine-N-oxide.**

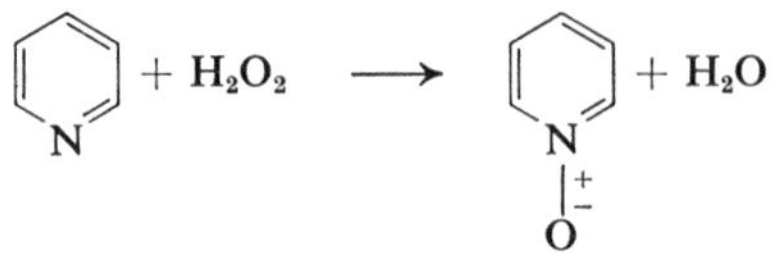

In contrast to pyridine, the *N*-oxide nitrates readily to give an 85 per cent yield of **4-nitropyridine-N-oxide.**

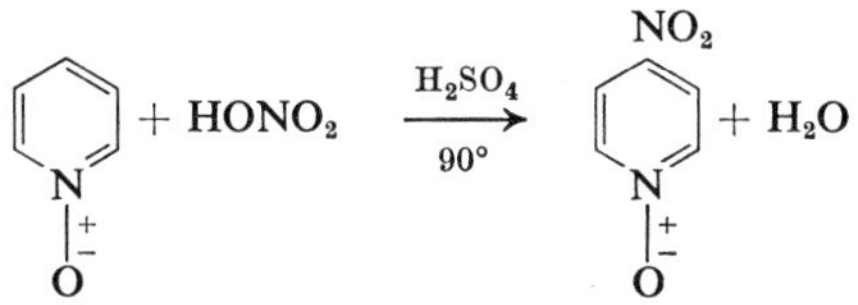

From the nitro *N*-oxide, **4-aminopyridine** can be obtained by reduction with iron and acetic acid.

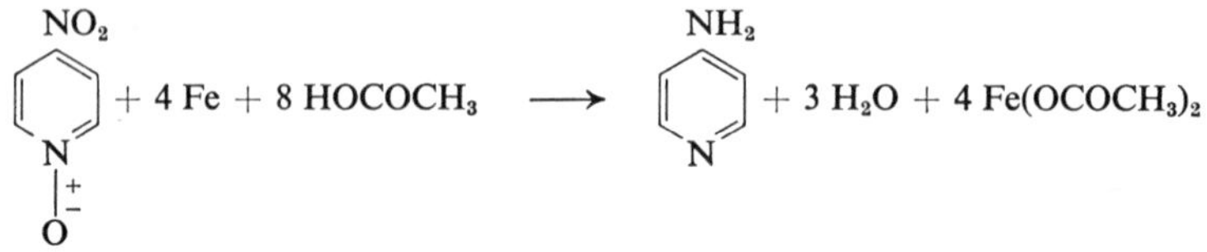

Reaction of the nitro compound with acyl chlorides or bromides gives the **4-chloro-** or **4-bromopyridine-N-oxide.** The 4-chloropyridine-*N*-oxide can be reduced to **4-chloropyridine.**

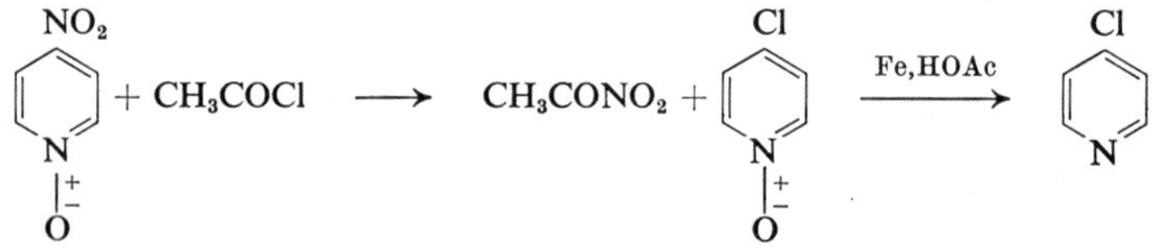

The nitro group can be displaced also by alkoxy and phenoxy groups.

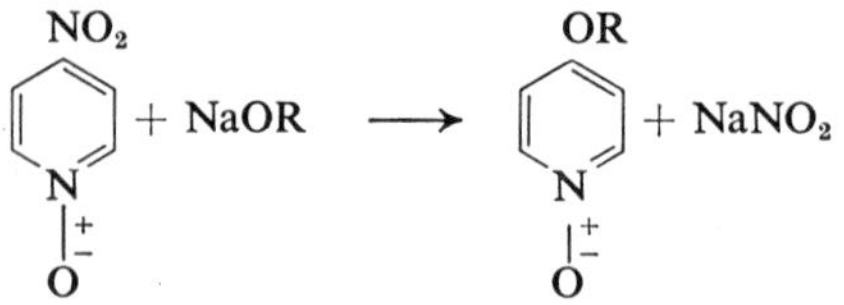

Catalytic reduction of 4-benzyloxypyridine-*N*-oxide gives **4-hydroxypyridine** (cf. p. 526).

The three methylpyridines are known as **α-, β-**, and **γ-picolines** (L. *pix, picis,* pitch). They occur in bone oil, but the commercial source is coal tar. The α isomer is present in largest amount and was isolated first in 1846. The β isomer was isolated in 1879, and the γ isomer, which is present in smallest amount, in 1887. Oxidation of the three isomers with permanganate yields the three **carboxylic acids.**

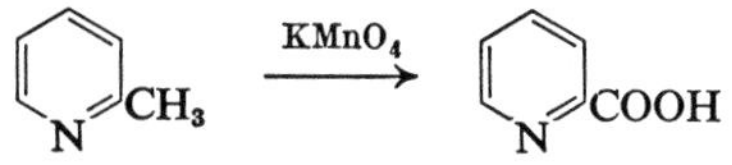

α-Picoline

$\xrightarrow{\text{KMnO}_4}$

α-Picolinic acid
(picolinic acid)

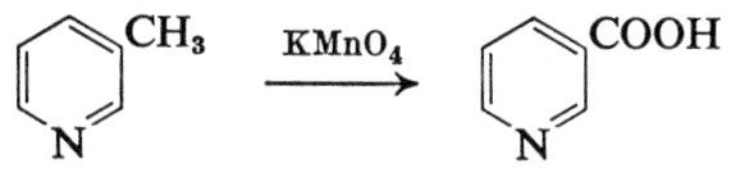

β-Picoline

$\xrightarrow{\text{KMnO}_4}$

β-Picolinic acid
(nicotinic acid)

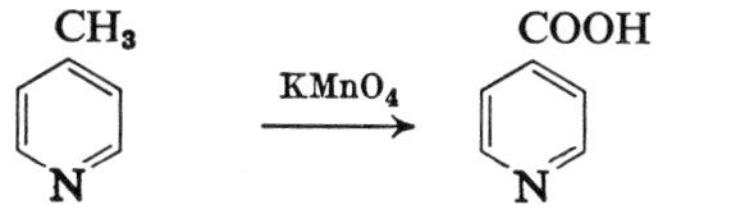

γ-Picoline

$\xrightarrow{\text{KMnO}_4}$

γ-Picolinic acid
(isonicotinic acid)

The α and γ acids when heated lose carbon dioxide with the formation of pyridine. The name **nicotinic acid** for the β isomer arises because it first was obtained in 1867 by the oxidation of nicotine. This reaction elucidated the structure of half of the nicotine molecule.

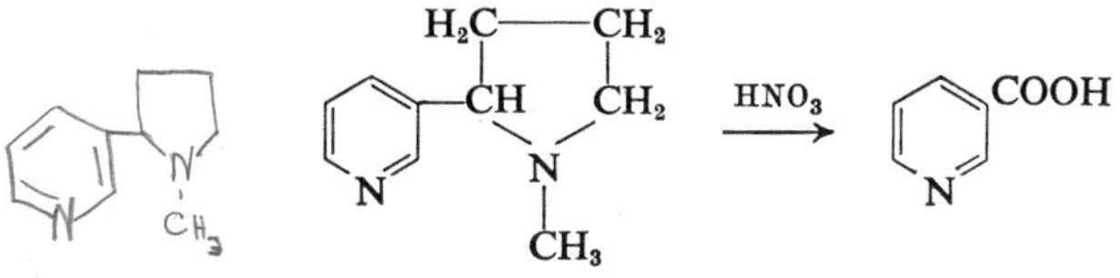

Nicotine

$\xrightarrow{\text{HNO}_3}$

It was not until 1937 that it was recognized that the absence of nicotinic acid or its amide from the diet resulted in the deficiency disease known as *pellagra* in humans and *black tongue* in dogs. Over two million pounds of the acid and amide valued at over 6 million dollars was manufactured in the United States in 1955 for use in fortified wheat flour and vitamin preparations. The names *niacin* and *niamide* have been coined for the acid and its amide because they are considered to be more acceptable to the public.

Nicotinic acid is required in the diet for the production of *coenzymes I* and *II* which act as hydrogen acceptors in the presence of dehydrogenating enzymes.

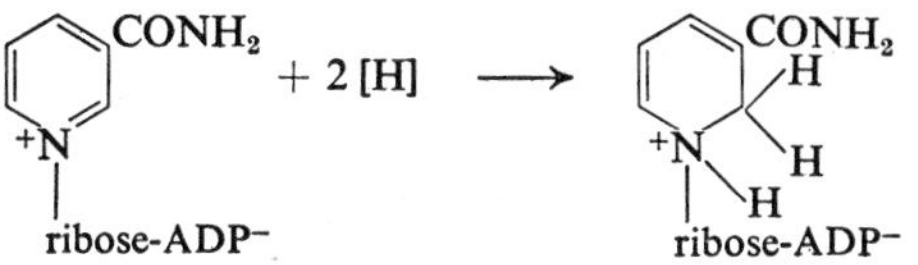

ribose-ADP⁻
Coenzyme I

$+ \, 2\,[\text{H}] \longrightarrow$

ribose-ADP⁻
Dihydrocoenzyme I

Coenzyme II contains adenosine triphosphate (ATP) instead of adenosine diphosphate (ADP) in the molecule (p. 644).

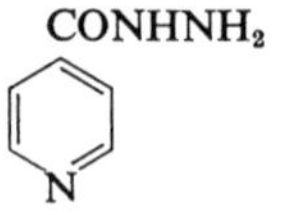

Isonicotinic acid hydrazide (*isoniazid*) is one of the more effective tuberculostatic drugs, although it allows the emergence of resistant strains of the organism. It also has been used in the treatment of leprosy.

CONHNH₂ ... CONHNH₂ ... CH=NOH

CH₃⁻SO₃C₆H₄CH₃-*p*   CH₃⁻I

Isonicotinic acid   *N*-Methyl-*p*-toluenesulfonate of   2-Pyridinealdoxime
hydrazide   nicotinic acid hydrazide   methiodide (*PAM*)

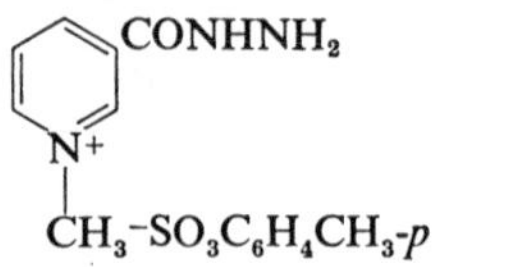

The **N-methyl-p-toluenesulfonate** of **nicotinic acid hydrazide** is a useful reagent for preparing water-soluble derivatives of aldehydes and ketones.

Air oxidation of α- or γ-picoline in the vapor phase gives **2- or 4-pyridinealdehyde**. **2-Pyridinealdoxime methiodide** appears to be an effective antidote for poisons such as the nerve gases (p. 910) that inhibit choline esterase (p. 243). **3-Pyridinealdehyde** has been obtained from 3-bromopyridine through the Grignard reagent (p. 196).

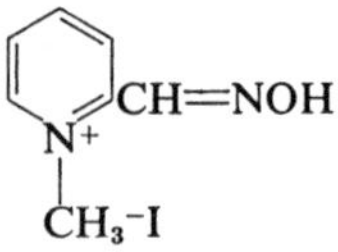

α- and γ-Picolines condense with aromatic aldehydes to give benzylidine derivatives, but β-picoline does not.

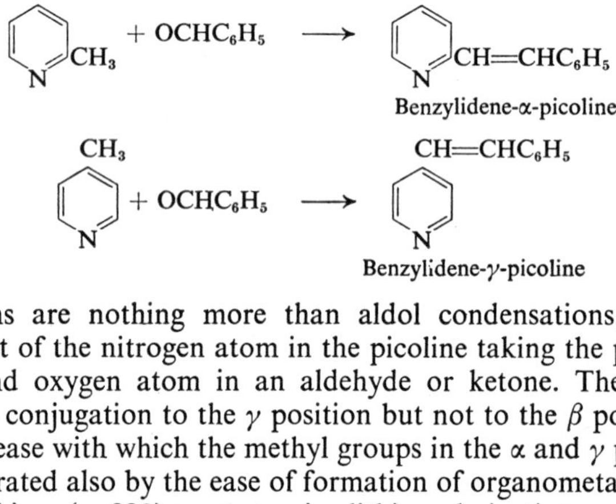

CH₃ + OCHC₆H₅ ⟶ CH=CHC₆H₅

Benzylidene-α-picoline

CH₃ + OCHC₆H₅ ⟶ CH=CHC₆H₅

Benzylidene-γ-picoline

These reactions are nothing more than aldol condensations, the electron-attracting effect of the nitrogen atom in the picoline taking the place of that of a doubly-bound oxygen atom in an aldehyde or ketone. The effect can be transmitted by conjugation to the γ position but not to the β position.

The greater ease with which the methyl groups in the α and γ positions lose a proton is illustrated also by the ease of formation of organometallic derivatives. Thus phenyllithium (p. 889) reacts to give lithium derivatives, which react with carbon dioxide to give lithium salts of the **pyridylacetic acids.**

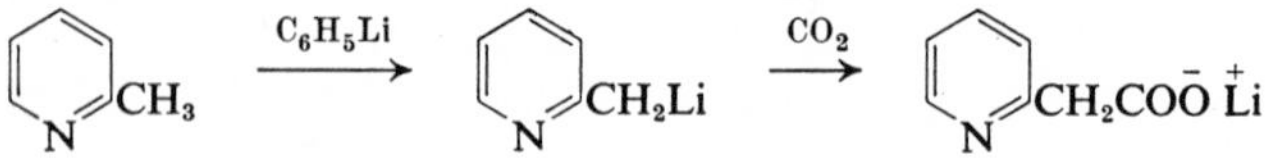

CH₃ $\xrightarrow{C_6H_5Li}$ CH₂Li $\xrightarrow{CO_2}$ CH₂COO⁻ Li⁺

Condensation of α- or γ-picoline with formaldehyde gives the **hydroxyethylpyridines** which can be dehydrated to the **vinylpyridines.**

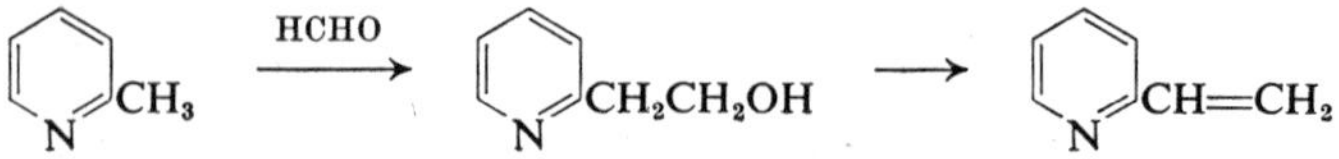

CH₃ $\xrightarrow{HCHO}$ CH₂CH₂OH ⟶ CH=CH₂

2-Vinylpyridine

2-Vinylpyridine when copolymerized with butadiene gives an elastomer that adheres to rayon and nylon cord and makes possible cord tires. When copolymerized with acrylonitrile it introduces a basic group which permits polyacrylonitrile fibers (p. 788) to be dyed more readily.

The dimethylpyridines were called **lutidines,** because they are isomeric with the toluidines. All six possible isomers are known. The trimethylpyridines are called **collidines** (Gr. *kolla*, glue) and occur with the other pyridine and pyrrole bases in coal tar and in the decomposition products of animal matter.

2-Methyl-5-ethylpyridine (*aldehyde-collidine* or *aldehydine*) can be synthesized in good yield by heating paraldehyde with ammonia at 220°. The paraldehyde depolymerizes to acetaldehyde which probably undergoes a multiple aldol addition, reaction with ammonia, dehydration and rearrangement.

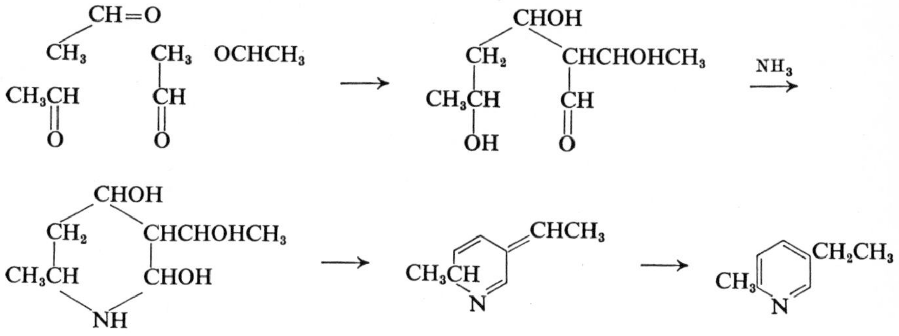

It is used to supplement the limited amount of β-picoline available from coal tar for the synthesis of nicotinic acid. Oxidation gives 2,5-pyridinedicarboxylic acid, but since carboxyl groups in the 2 and 4 positions are readily lost, the final product is nicotinic acid.

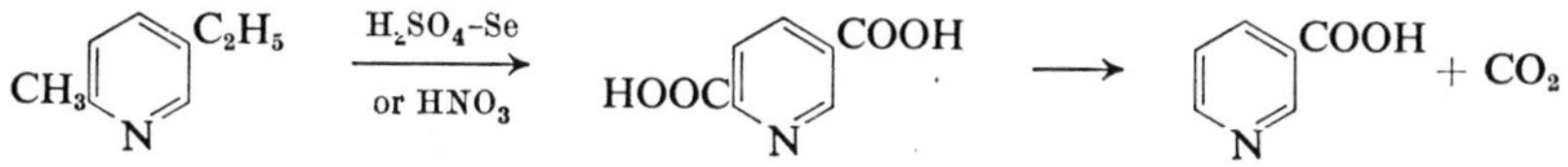

Loss of carbon dioxide from a carboxyl group in a 2 or 4 position takes place by way of the dipolar ion, the intermediate being stabilized by the ability of the nitrogen to accept a pair of electrons. This mechanism is not available to carboxyl groups in the 3 position.

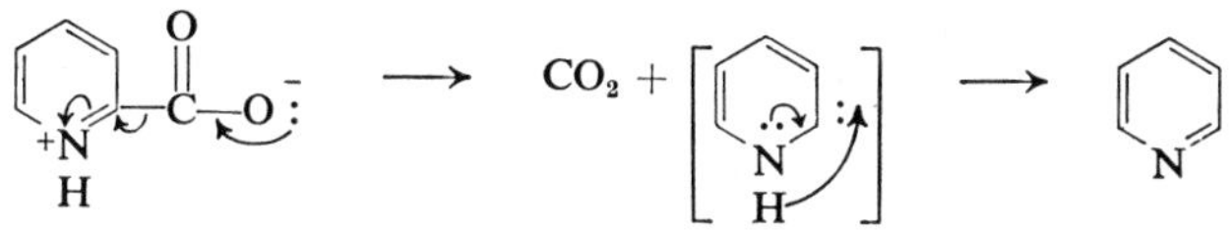

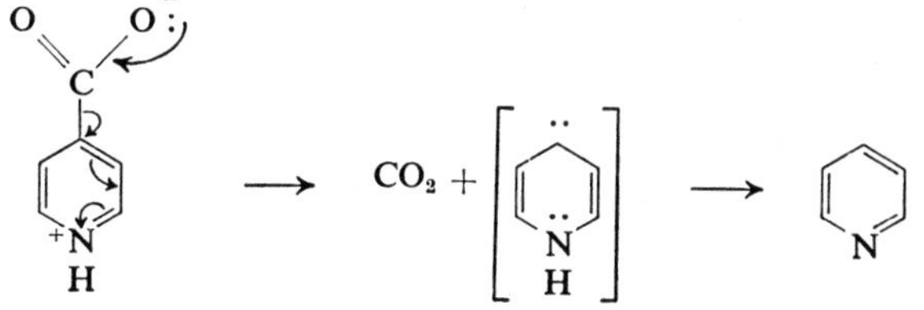

The α- and γ-pyridylacetic acids also decarboxylate readily by an analogous mechanism.

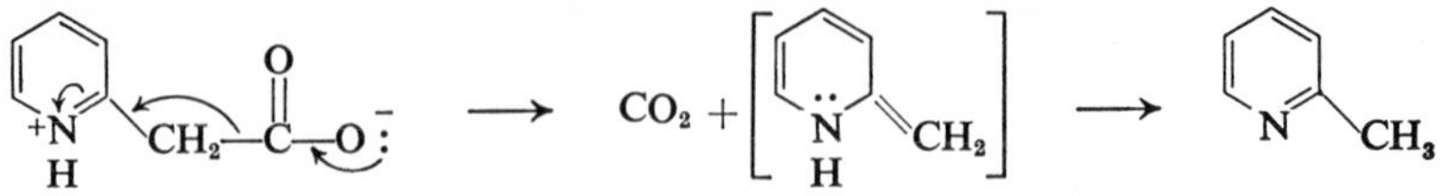

Pyridoxine (*vitamin B$_6$*), **pyridoxamine,** and **pyridoxal** function in certain enzyme systems. Although the biological activity of all three compounds is the same for higher animals, it appears that pyridoxal phosphate is the active agent. Among other functions it plays a part in enzymic transamination and decarboxylation of α-amino acids.

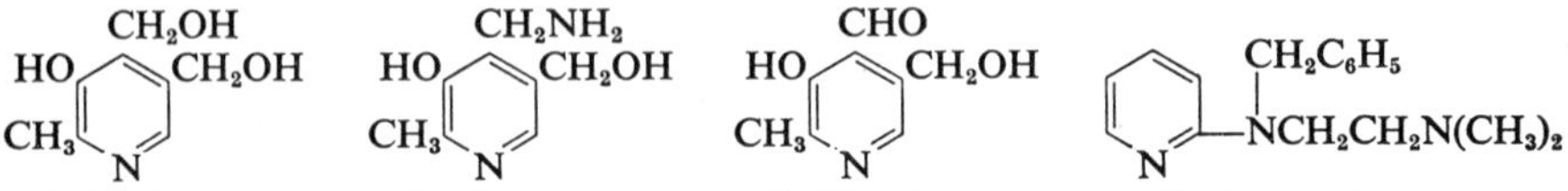

Pyridoxine
(vitamin B$_6$)   Pyridoxamine   Pyridoxal   Pyribenzamine

Pyribenzamine is one of the more widely used antihistaminics (p. 634).

Quinolines. Quinoline is 2,3-benzopyridine. It first was isolated from coal tar in 1834. It was obtained also by the distillation of quinine alkaloids with alkali in 1842. However, both products were accompanied by impurities that gave different color reactions, and they were not proven to be identical until 1882.

The structure of quinoline is indicated clearly by the *Friedlaender synthesis* from *o*-aminobenzaldehyde and acetaldehyde in the presence of dilute alkali.

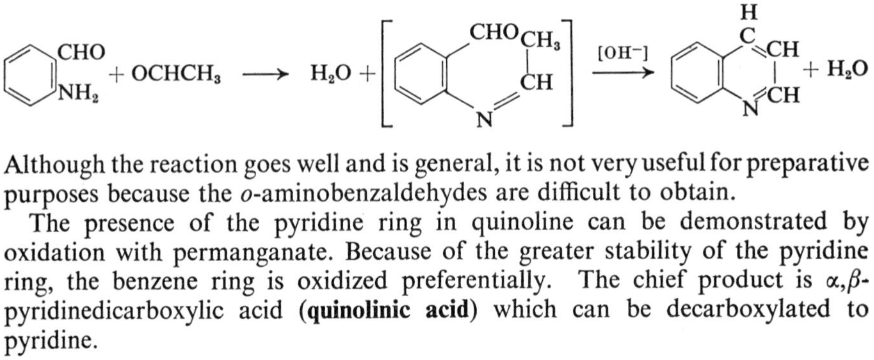

Although the reaction goes well and is general, it is not very useful for preparative purposes because the *o*-aminobenzaldehydes are difficult to obtain.

The presence of the pyridine ring in quinoline can be demonstrated by oxidation with permanganate. Because of the greater stability of the pyridine ring, the benzene ring is oxidized preferentially. The chief product is α,β-pyridinedicarboxylic acid (**quinolinic acid**) which can be decarboxylated to pyridine.

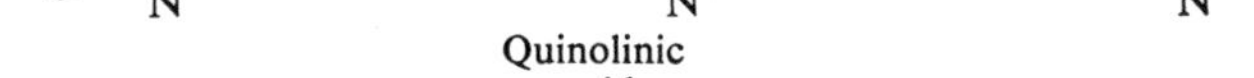

Quinolinic
acid

Pure quinoline is obtained best by the *Skraup synthesis*, which results when a mixture of glycerol and aniline is heated with concentrated sulfuric acid and a mild oxidizing agent such as arsenic acid or nitrobenzene. Ferrous sulfate and boric acid usually are added to moderate the reaction. Presumably the first stage is the dehydration of the glycerol to the unsaturated aldehyde, acrolein. Aniline then adds 1,4 to the conjugated unsaturated aldehyde. Subsequent ring closure and oxidation yields the quinoline. The method can be used also for the synthesis of quinoline derivatives.

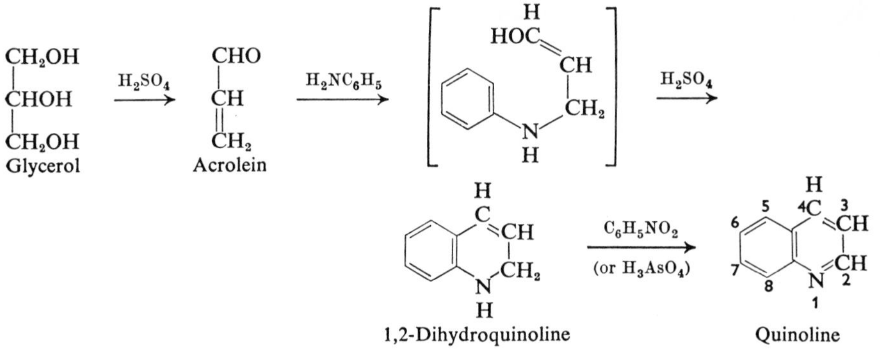

$$\begin{array}{c}CH_2OH \\ | \\ CHOH \\ | \\ CH_2OH \\ \text{Glycerol}\end{array} \xrightarrow{H_2SO_4} \begin{array}{c}CHO \\ | \\ CH \\ \| \\ CH_2 \\ \text{Acrolein}\end{array} \xrightarrow{H_2NC_6H_5} \cdots \xrightarrow{H_2SO_4}$$

1,2-Dihydroquinoline   Quinoline

2-Methylquinoline, known as **quinaldine,** occurs in coal tar. It can be synthesized by a reaction similar to that of Skraup and known as the *Doebner-Miller synthesis.* It consists of heating aniline with paraldehyde in the presence of sulfuric acid. The steps of the reaction probably are the intermediate formation of crotonic aldehyde, 1,4 addition of aniline, cyclization, and oxidation. Co-products of the reaction are ethylaniline and *n*-butylaniline, indicating that the hydrogen acceptors in the dehydrogenation of the dihydroquinaldine are the anils of acetaldehyde and crotonic aldehyde.

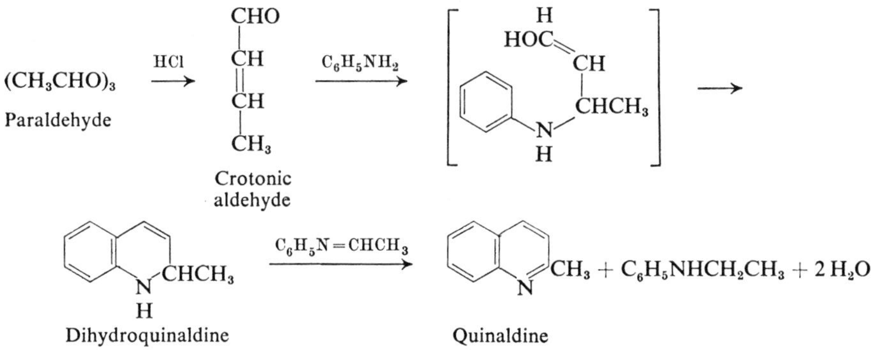

$$(CH_3CHO)_3 \xrightarrow{HCl} \begin{array}{c}CHO \\ | \\ CH \\ \| \\ CH \\ | \\ CH_3\end{array} \xrightarrow{C_6H_5NH_2} \cdots \longrightarrow$$

Paraldehyde   Crotonic aldehyde

Dihydroquinaldine $\xrightarrow{C_6H_5N=CHCH_3}$ Quinaldine $+ C_6H_5NHCH_2CH_3 + 2H_2O$

Quinolines result also from the reaction of aromatic amines with 1,3-diketones (p. 773).

4-Methylquinoline (**lepidine**) accompanies quinoline in the decomposition products of quinine alkaloids. The methyl groups of both quinaldine and lepidine are reactive, resembling those of the 2- and 4-picolines (p. 626).

Reduction of *o*-nitrocinnamic acid gives the amino acid which spontaneously cyclizes to the amide. The resulting product is α-quinolone, which is tautomeric with 2-hydroxyquinoline, known as **carbostyril.**

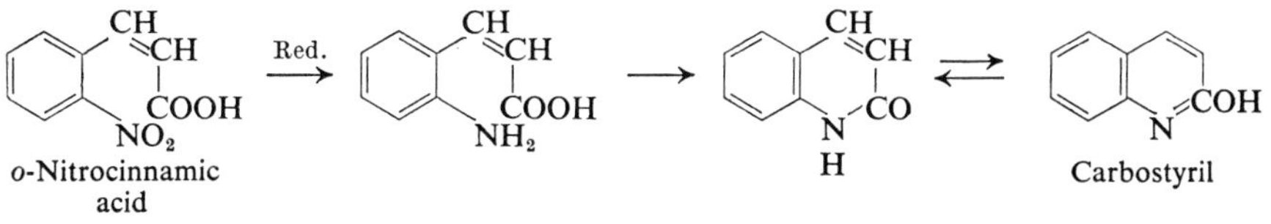

o-Nitrocinnamic acid   Carbostyril

8-Hydroxyquinoline is made from *o*-aminophenol by the Skraup reaction. The space relationship of the hydroxyl group and the unshared pair of electrons on the nitrogen atom is such that insoluble chelate (p. 742) coordination complexes are formed with metallic ions, making it a valuable reagent in analytical chemistry.

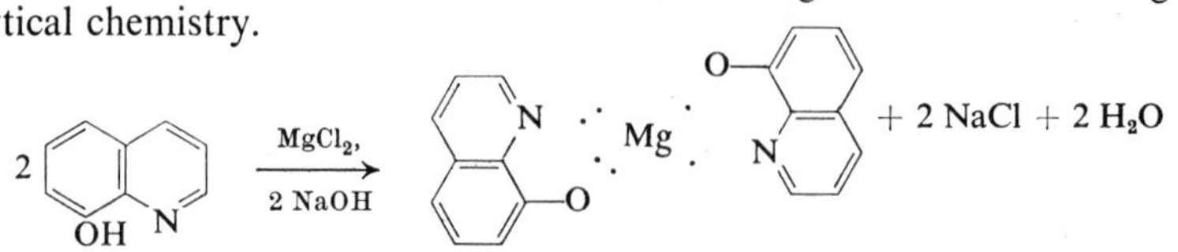

8-Hydroxy-quinoline

When quinoline reacts with benzoyl chloride in the presence of aqueous potassium cyanide, addition of benzoyl to nitrogen and cyanide to carbon takes place to give what is known as a **Reissert compound.** Acid hydrolysis gives benzaldehyde and **quinaldinic acid** (*2-quinolinecarboxylic acid*).

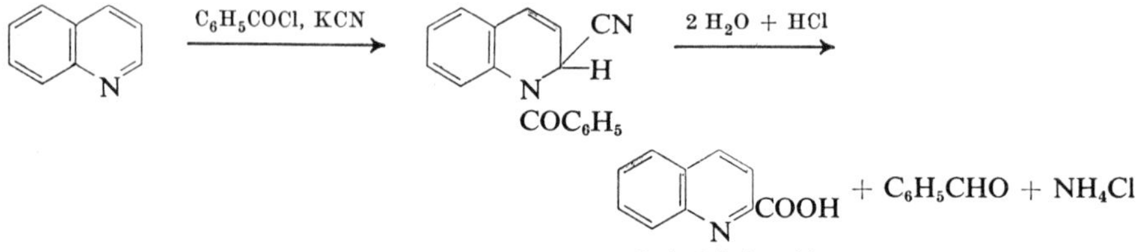

Quinaldinic acid

Cinchoninic acid (*4-quinolinecarboxylic acid*) was obtained first by the oxidation of the alkaloid cinchonine. Its derivatives may be prepared by the *Pfitzinger reaction* from isatin (p. 684) and aldehydes or ketones.

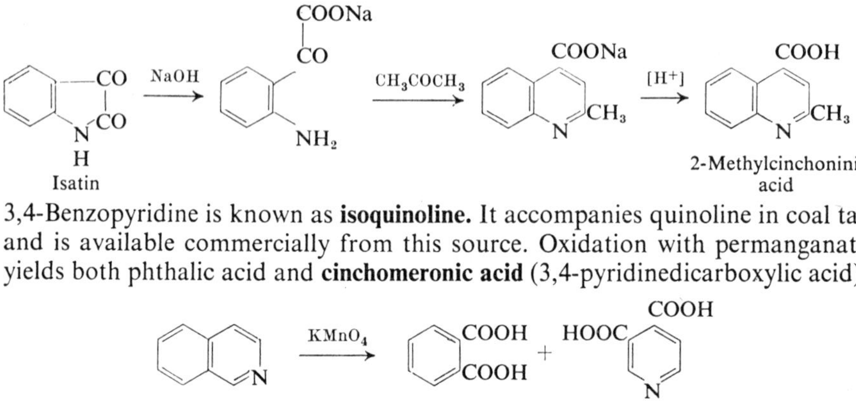

Isatin

2-Methylcinchoninic acid

3,4-Benzopyridine is known as **isoquinoline.** It accompanies quinoline in coal tar and is available commercially from this source. Oxidation with permanganate yields both phthalic acid and **cinchomeronic acid** (3,4-pyridinedicarboxylic acid).

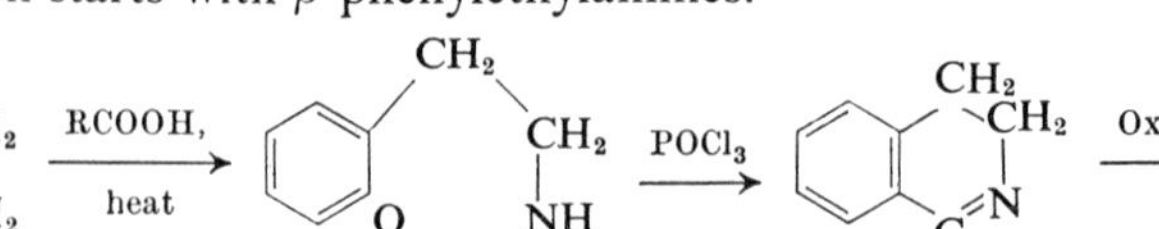

Isoquinoline

Cinchomeronic acid

The most general synthesis of isoquinolines is the *Bischler-Napieralski reaction* which starts with β-phenylethylamines.

Several natural alkaloids are benzylisoquinolines (p. 651).

Acridine is 2,3:5,6-dibenzopyridine. It received its name from its irritating

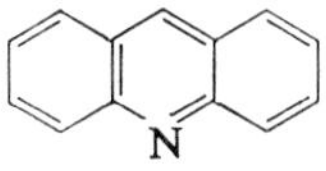

Acridine 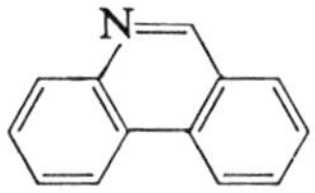   Phenanthridine

action on the skin and mucous membranes. 2,3:4,5-Dibenzopyridine is known as **phenanthridine** because of its relation to phenanthrene.

o-**Phenanthroline** contains two nitrogen atoms replacing two CH groups of the phenanthrene nucleus. The position of the nitrogen atoms is such that *o*-phenanthroline can form stable complex cations with metal ions. The *iron chelate complex* (p. 742), in which iron has a coordination number of six, is a valuable oxidation-reduction indicator, being intensely red in the reduced form and faintly blue in the oxidized form.

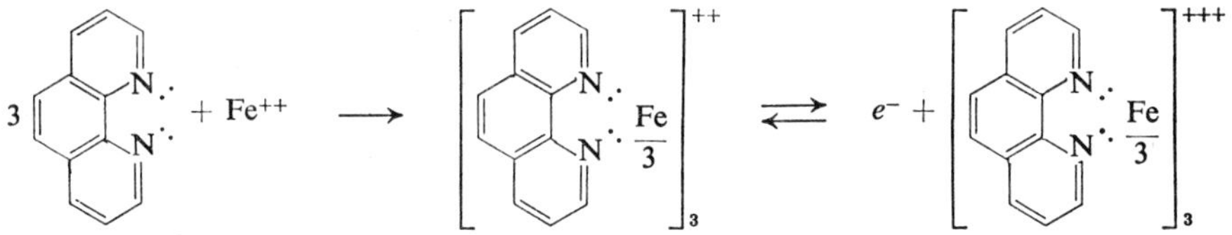

o-Phenanthroline   Intense red   Faint blue

o-Phenanthroline is used also as a nonmetallic catalyst for the polymerization of drying oils. It can be made by a Skraup synthesis from *o*-phenylenediamine.

Pyrans. The six-membered ring containing a single oxygen atom and two double bonds is known as the *pyran ring*. The oxonium salts containing an aromatic system are known as *pyrylium salts*.

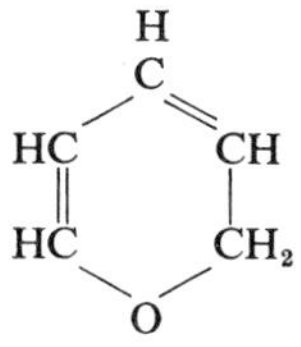

α-Pyran 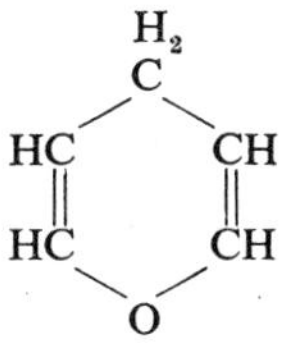   γ-Pyran 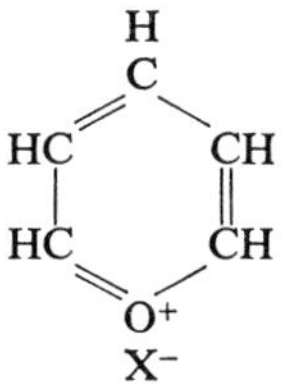   Pyrylium salt

No simple pyran or pyrylium salt is known. **Dihydropyran** is made by the catalytic dehydration with ring enlargement of tetrahydrofurfuryl alcohol. Catalytic hydrogenation of dihydropyran gives **tetrahydropyran.**

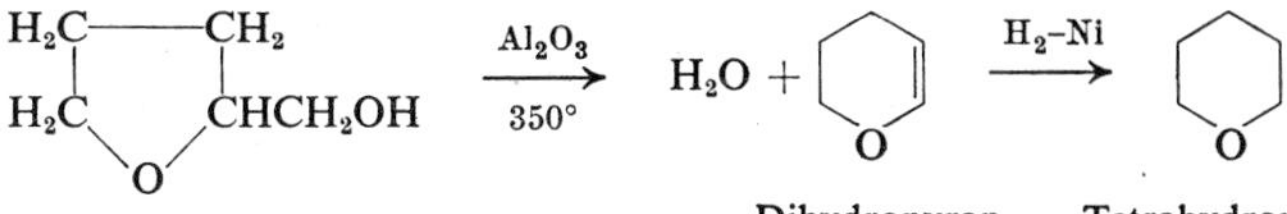

Dihydropyran   Tetrahydropyran

Hydrolysis of dihydropyran gives **δ-hydroxyvaleraldehyde.** Hydrolysis with concurrent hydrogenation yields **1,5-pentanediol.**

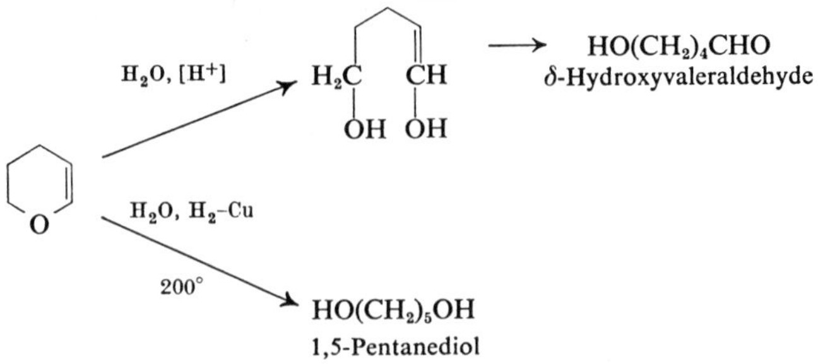

H2O, [H+]
H2C CH
OH OH
HO(CH2)4CHO
δ-Hydroxyvaleraldehyde
O
H2O, H2-Cu
200°
HO(CH2)5OH
1,5-Pentanediol

Alcohols add readily to give cyclic acetals.

O
+ HOR
[H+]
H
O
OR

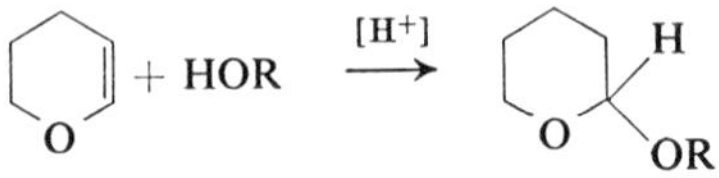

The acetals are stable to alkali, reducing, and acylating agents, and the alcohol can be regenerated by acid hydrolysis. The reaction has been used to protect hydroxyl groups while carrying out other reactions on complicated molecules.

2-Aldehydo-2,3-dihydro-γ-pyran is readily available as the dimer of acrolein (p. 764). It can be hydrogenated to **2-(hydroxymethyl)tetrahydropyran.**

CH2
CH
CH
O
+
CH2
CHCHO
CHO
O
H2-Ni
CH2OH
O

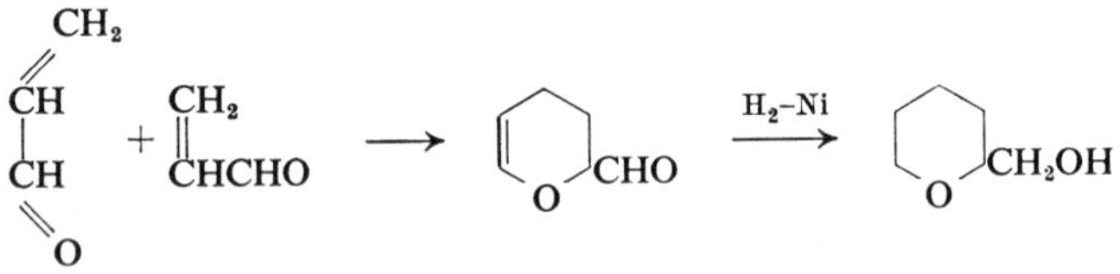

Kojic acid, formed in the fermentation of starch by *Aspergillus oryzae*, **maltol**, first isolated from larch bark, and **chelidonic acid**, from the greater celandine (*Chelidonium majus*), are γ-pyrones.

O
HO
CH2OH
O
O
OH
CH3
O
O
HOOC
COOH
O

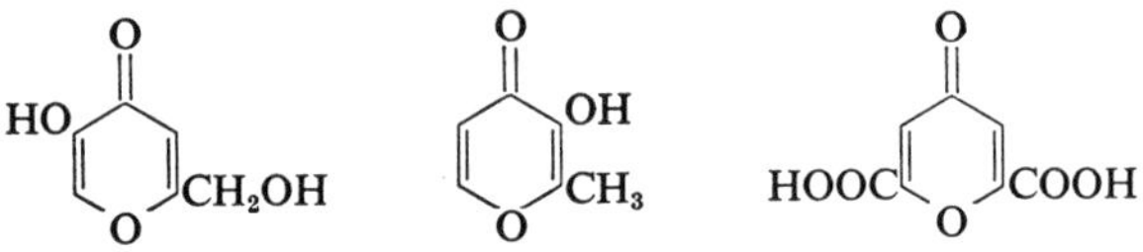

Kojic acid | Maltol | Chelidonic acid

The weakly acidic properties of kojic acid are due to the enolic hydroxyl. Maltol is a product also of the dry distillation of carbohydrates and hardwood. It has the property of enhancing nonnitrogenous flavors much as monosodium glutamate enhances nitrogenous flavors (p. 304).

Benzopyrans frequently are present in plants, and many are of considerable interest. Thus the germ oil of seeds, especially wheat germ oil, contains substances designated as *vitamin E* which are necessary for the growth and normal reproduction of the rat. At least four compounds are present that have this activity and they have been called the *tocopherols* (Gr. *tokos*, childbirth; *pherein*, to bear). The most active is **α-tocopherol,** the racemic form of which has been synthesized from trimethylhydroquinone and phytyl bromide (p. 860).

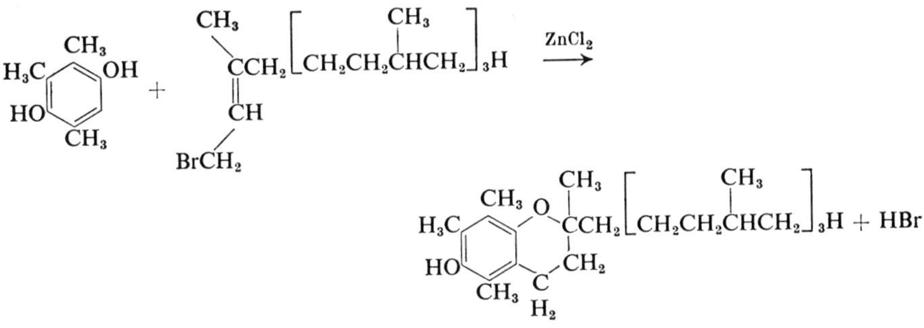

$$
\begin{array}{c}
\text{CH}_3 \\
\text{H}_3\text{C} \overset{\text{CH}_3}{\bigcirc} \text{OH} \\
\text{HO} \bigcirc \\
\text{CH}_3
\end{array}
\;+\;
\begin{array}{c}
\text{CH}_3 \\
\overset{|}{\text{CCH}_2}\left[\text{CH}_2\text{CH}_2\overset{\text{CH}_3}{\overset{|}{\text{CHCH}_2}}\right]_3\text{H} \\
\text{CH} \\
\text{BrCH}_2
\end{array}
\xrightarrow{\text{ZnCl}_2}
$$

$$
\begin{array}{c}
\text{CH}_3 \; \text{O} \\
\text{H}_3\text{C} \bigcirc \overset{\text{CH}_3}{\overset{|}{\text{CCH}_2}}\left[\text{CH}_2\text{CH}_2\overset{\text{CH}_3}{\overset{|}{\text{CHCH}_2}}\right]_3\text{H} \;+\; \text{HBr} \\
\text{HO} \bigcirc \text{CH}_2 \\
\text{CH}_3 \; \underset{\text{H}_2}{\text{C}}
\end{array}
$$

α-Tocopherol

The tocopherols are distributed widely in food, and their use as a supplement to the diet of man and animals for therapeutic purposes has been controversial. The tocopherols have a marked antioxidant action and decrease the rate at which rancidity develops in foods containing fats (p. 886).

The resin from the flowering tops of hemp (*Cannabis sativa*) has been used since antiquity for its physiological effects. The resin is known as *hashish* or *bhang* and the dried tops as *marijuana*. The active constituents are believed to be isomeric **tetrahydrocannabinols,** one of which has been synthesized.

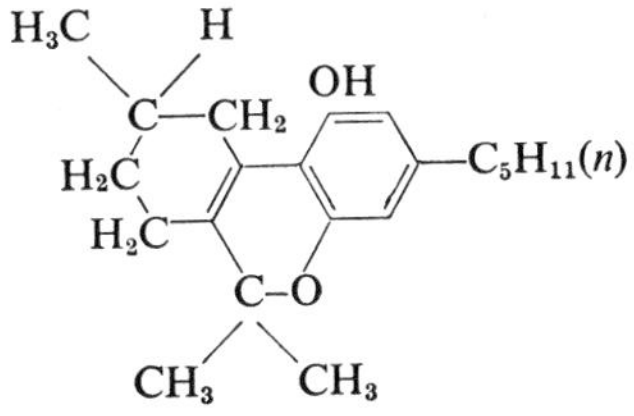

Tetrahydrocannabinol 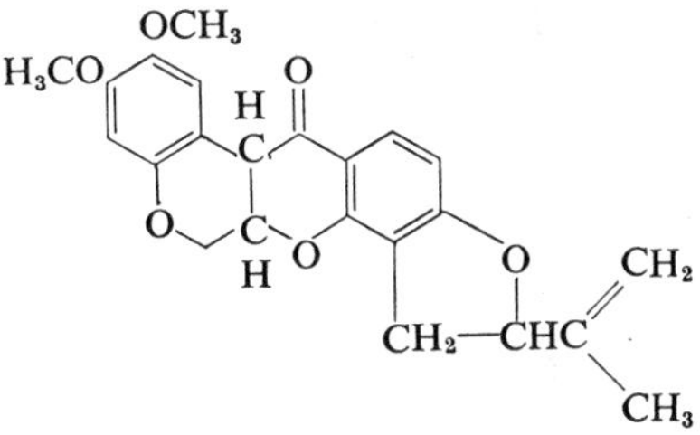   Rotenone

Rotenone contains two dihydropyran rings and a dihydrofuran ring. It is one of the active constituents of several plants that are used as insecticides. They are highly toxic to fish also but are relatively harmless to human beings. Hence they are safe to use on plants bearing food. Rotenone and related compounds have been identified in sixty-seven species of plants, but the chief commercial sources are the roots of *Derris elliptica* (tuba) cultivated in Malaya and the East Indies, and of *Lonchocarpus nicou* (timbo or cube) grown in South America. Many of the brilliant coloring matters of flowers contain a pyran ring. These **anthocyanins** are discussed in Chapter 31.

Xanthone (*dibenzo-γ-pyrone*) is made by the thermal decomposition of phenyl salicylate.

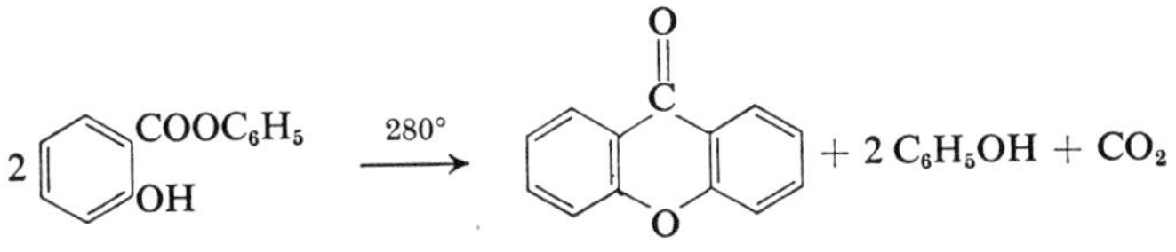

$$
2 \;\; \overset{\text{COOC}_6\text{H}_5}{\underset{\text{OH}}{\bigcirc}} \;\; \xrightarrow{280°} \;\; \text{(xanthone)} \;+\; 2\,\text{C}_6\text{H}_5\text{OH} + \text{CO}_2
$$

Xanthone

Reduction of xanthone gives **xanthydrol** which is useful for the preparation of derivatives for the identification of primary amides and for the quantitative determination of urea.

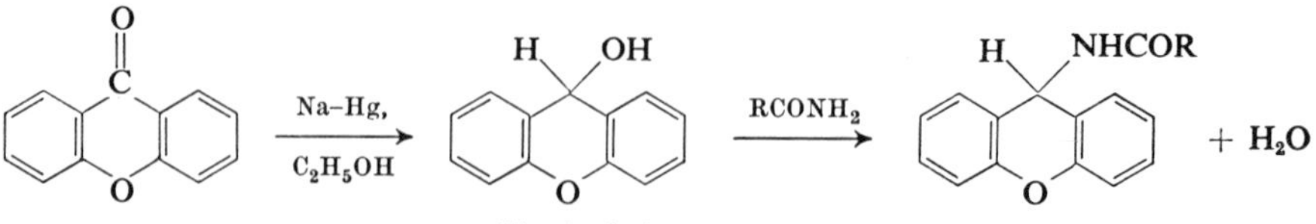

Xanthydrol

RING COMPOUNDS CONTAINING TWO OR MORE HETERO ATOMS

The number of possible compounds falling into this group is very large. Only a few of the more important ones are considered.

Five-membered Rings

Pyrazole and **imidazole** each contain two hetero nitrogen atoms. **Histidine,** which contains the imidazole ring, is an essential amino acid (p. 302).

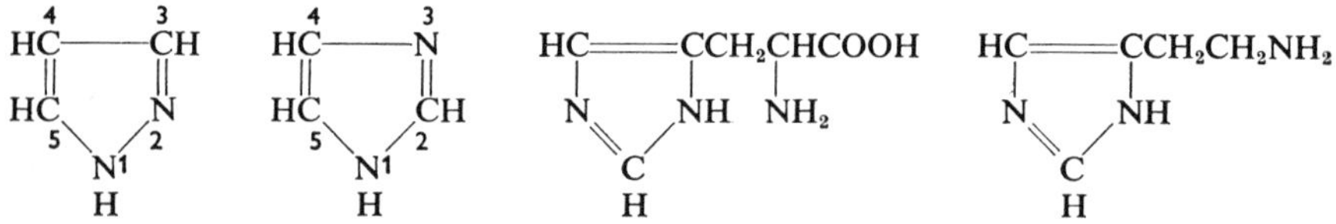

Pyrazole   Imidazole   Histidine   Histamine

Histamine probably is derived from histidine by decarboxylation and is present in all tissues of the body. It is extremely toxic when administered parenterally, that is, by means other than absorption through the intestines, and hence it must be present in the tissues in a combined form with protein. No other chemical has such a wide variety of actions. Nearly every tissue responds to it in some way. Excessive amounts of free histamine are believed to be the cause of many allergies. Since 1941 many synthetic organic compounds have been found to relieve allergic symptoms such as those caused by hay fever, poison ivy and poison oak, and the common cold. They are known as *antihistaminics* (pp. 526, 628, 641).

The *hydantoins* contain the imidazole ring system. **Hydantoin** may be prepared by the cyclization of hydantoic acid obtained by boiling glycine with urea. The name hydantoin was assigned by Baeyer because he obtained it by reduction

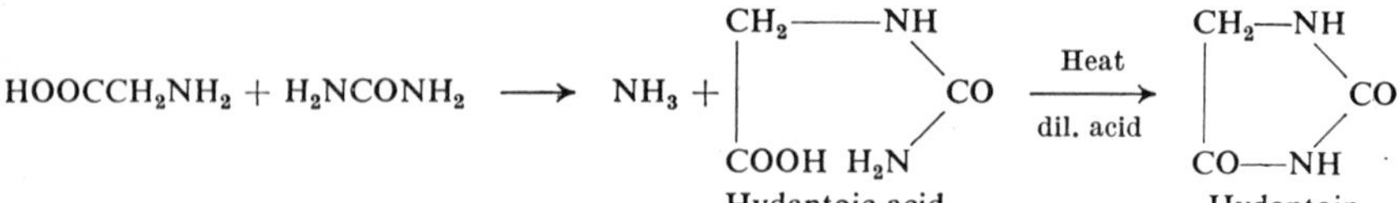

Hydantoic acid   Hydantoin

of allantoin (p. 645) with hydrogen iodide. Hydantoic acid was prepared first by the hydrolysis of hydantoin. The sodium salt of diphenylhydantoin, known as **Dilantin Sodium,** is used in the treatment of epilepsy. It has an anticonvulsant action equal to that of phenobarbital (p. 640) but is less depressant.

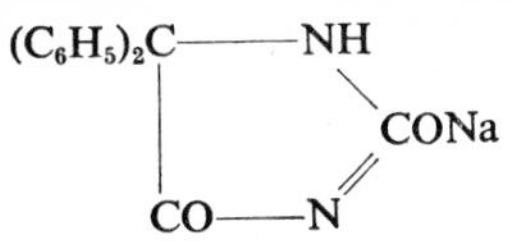

$$(C_6H_5)_2C\text{———}NH$$
$$|\qquad\qquad\diagdown CONa$$
$$CO\text{———}N\diagup$$

Dilantin Sodium

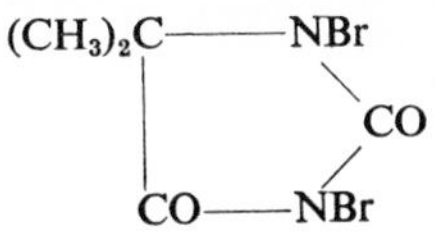

$$(CH_3)_2C\text{———}NBr$$
$$|\qquad\qquad\diagdown CO$$
$$CO\text{———}NBr$$

1,3-Dibromo-5,5-di-
methylhydantoin

$$H_2C\text{———}CH(CH_2)_4COOH$$
$$H_2C\qquad S$$
$$\diagdown S\diagup$$

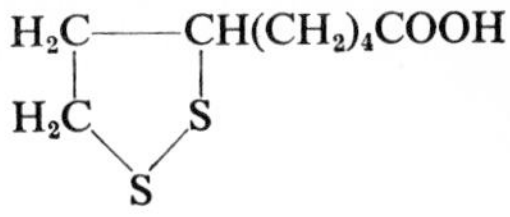

Lipoic acid

1,3-Dibromo-5,5-dimethylhydantoin is more stable than *N*-bromosuccinimide (p. 797) and can be used for the same purposes. The chlorine analog reacts with water to give hypochlorous acid and can be used as a dry stable bleaching agent in laundry preparations.

Lipoic acid contains the *1,2-dithiole* ring. It plays a part in the enzyme systems involved in photosynthesis and carbohydrate metabolism.

The five-membered ring containing one oxygen and one nitrogen atom in adjacent positions is known as the **isoxazole** ring, and that in which they occupy the alternate position is called the **oxazole** ring. The sulfur-nitrogen analogs are the **isothiazoles** and the **thiazoles.**

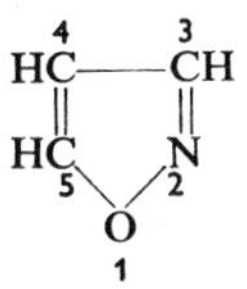

$$\underset{\underset{1}{O}}{\overset{4\qquad3}{\underset{\overset{HC\text{———}CH}{HC\diagdown\diagup N}}{}}}$$

Isoxazole

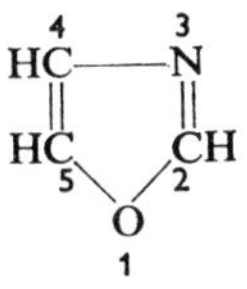

$$\overset{4\qquad3}{\underset{1}{HC\text{———}N}}$$
$$HC\qquad CH$$
$$O$$

Oxazole

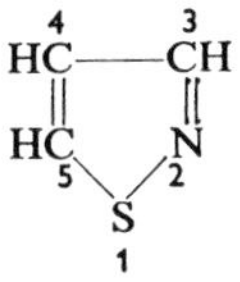

$$\overset{4\qquad3}{HC\text{———}CH}$$
$$HC\qquad N$$
$$S$$

Isothiazole

$$\overset{4\qquad3}{HC\text{———}N}$$
$$HC\qquad CH$$
$$S$$

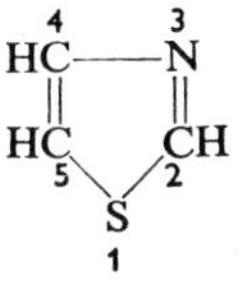

Thiazole

Azlactones contain the oxazole ring. They are formed by the cyclodehydration of acylated glycines with acetic anhydride. Condensation with an aldehyde can be brought about simultaneously to give a product that can be reduced and hydrolyzed to an α-amino acid.

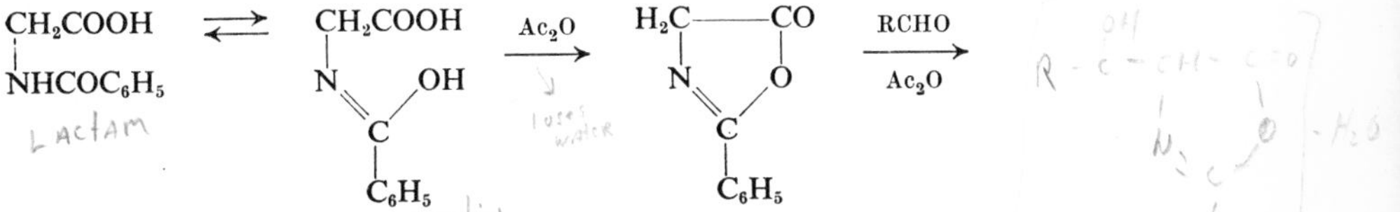

$$CH_2COOH$$
$$|$$
$$NHCOC_6H_5$$

$$\rightleftharpoons$$

$$CH_2COOH$$
$$|$$
$$N\diagdown OH$$
$$C$$
$$|$$
$$C_6H_5$$

$$\xrightarrow{Ac_2O}$$

$$H_2C\text{———}CO$$
$$N\qquad O$$
$$\diagdown\diagup$$
$$C$$
$$|$$
$$C_6H_5$$

Azlactone of
hippuric acid

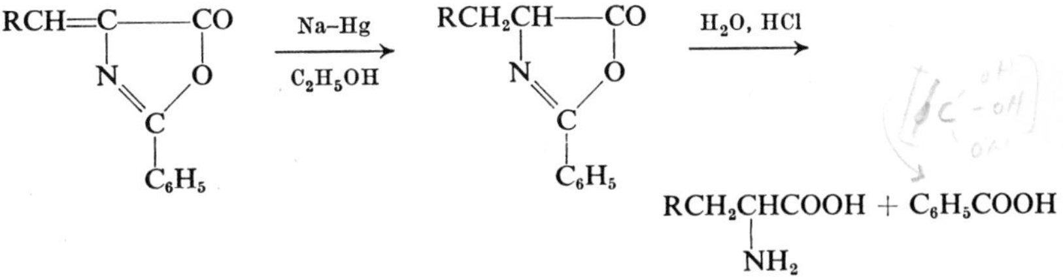

$$\xrightarrow[Ac_2O]{RCHO}$$

$$RCH{=}C\text{———}CO$$
$$N\qquad O$$
$$\diagdown\diagup$$
$$C$$
$$|$$
$$C_6H_5$$

$$\xrightarrow[C_2H_5OH]{Na\text{–}Hg}$$

$$RCH_2CH\text{———}CO$$
$$N\qquad O$$
$$\diagdown\diagup$$
$$C$$
$$|$$
$$C_6H_5$$

$$\xrightarrow{H_2O,\ HCl}$$

$$RCH_2CHCOOH + C_6H_5COOH$$
$$|$$
$$NH_2$$

Rhodanine (*2-mercapto-4-hydroxythiazole*) results from the reaction of sodium chloroacetate with ammonium dithiocarbamate. It is a useful reagent in organic synthesis, because the methylene group of the keto form condenses with

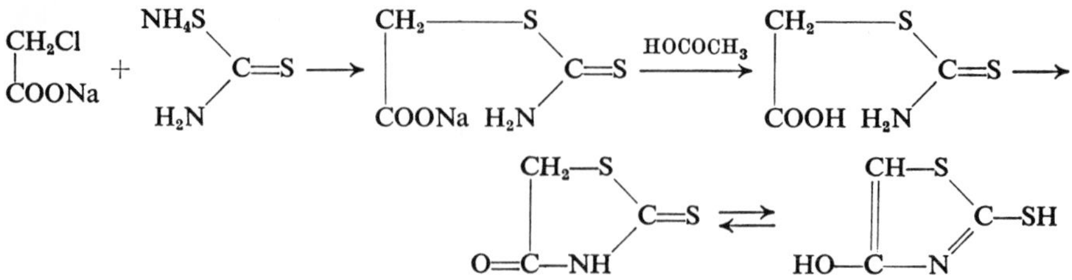

$$CH_2Cl \atop COONa + NH_4S \atop H_2N C{=}S \longrightarrow CH_2{-}S \atop COONa \; H_2N C{=}S \xrightarrow{HOCOCH_3} CH_2{-}S \atop COOH \; H_2N C{=}S \longrightarrow$$

$$CH_2{-}S \atop O{=}C{-}NH C{=}S \rightleftharpoons CH{-}S \atop HO{-}C{-}N C{-}SH$$

Rhodanine

aldehydes. The ring, being an imido thioester, can then be saponified to give thiopyruvic acids. Hydroxylamine converts the thiopyruvic acids into oximes of the pyruvic acids, which can be converted into α-amino acids, nitriles, amines, and substituted acetic acids.

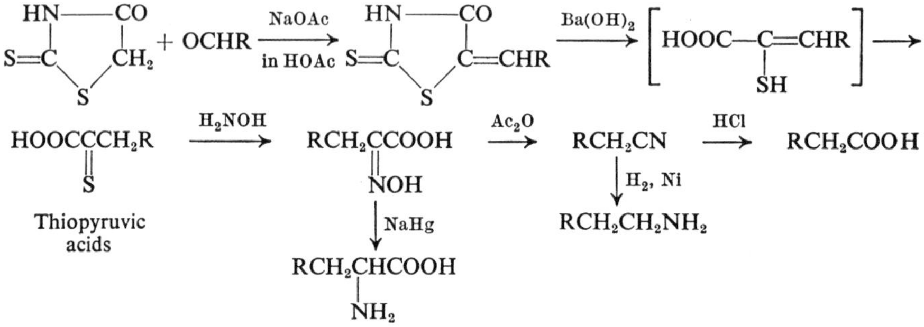

$$HN{-}CO \atop S{=}C \; CH_2 \atop S + OCHR \xrightarrow[\text{in HOAc}]{NaOAc} HN{-}CO \atop S{=}C \; C{=}CHR \atop S \xrightarrow{Ba(OH)_2} \left[HOOC{-}C{=}CHR \atop \quad\quad SH \right] \longrightarrow$$

$$HOOCCCH_2R \atop \quad S \xrightarrow{H_2NOH} RCH_2CCOOH \atop \quad NOH \xrightarrow{Ac_2O} RCH_2CN \xrightarrow{HCl} RCH_2COOH$$

Thiopyruvic
acids

$$\downarrow NaHg$$

$$RCH_2CHCOOH \atop \quad NH_2$$

$$\downarrow H_2, Ni$$

$$RCH_2CH_2NH_2$$

These reactions are valuable particularly for the synthesis of aryl substituted compounds starting with aromatic aldehydes.

2-Methylbenzothiazole results from the oxidation of thioacetanilide.

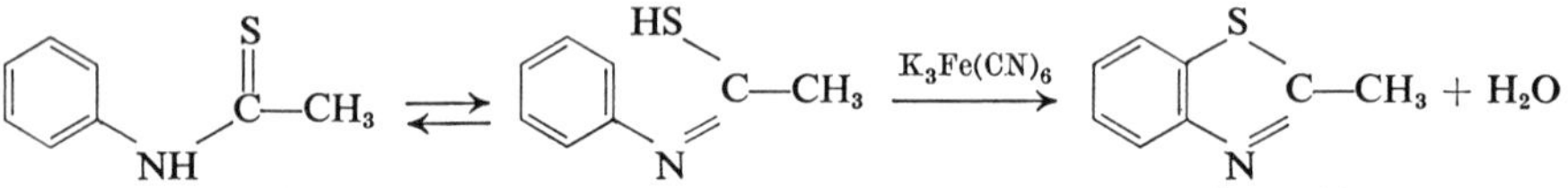

$$\underset{\text{Thioacetanilide}}{\overset{S}{\underset{NH}{\bigcirc}C{-}CH_3}} \rightleftharpoons \underset{N}{\overset{HS}{\bigcirc}C{-}CH_3} \xrightarrow{K_3Fe(CN)_6} \underset{\underset{\text{2-Methylbenzothiazole}}{N}}{\overset{S}{\bigcirc}C{-}CH_3} + H_2O$$

The methyl group, like that in α-picoline or quinaldine, is activated by the doubly-bound nitrogen atom and undergoes condensation reactions like those of a methyl ketone.

2-Mercaptobenzothiazole (*Captax*) is an important rubber accelerator. It is formed by heating thiocarbanilide (p. 482) with carbon disulfide and sulfur.

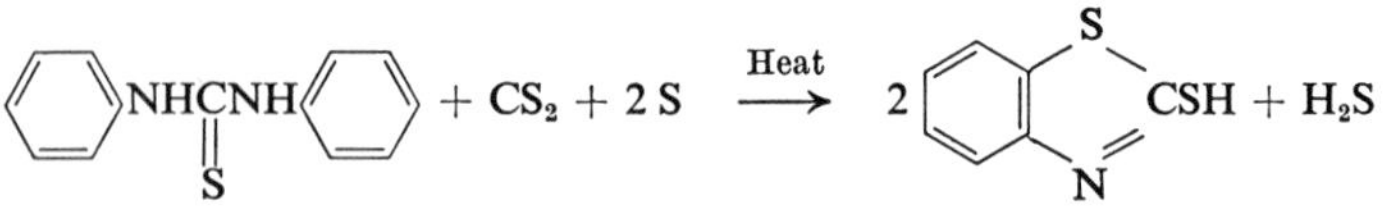

$$\underset{\text{Thiocarbanilide}}{\bigcirc NHCNH \bigcirc \atop S} + CS_2 + 2S \xrightarrow{Heat} 2 \underset{\underset{\text{2-Mercaptobenzothiazole} \atop (Captax)}{N}}{\overset{S}{\bigcirc}CSH} + H_2S$$

The natural **penicillins,** the first antibiotics to be used in medicine, contain the thiazole ring system. Around 455,000 pounds in terms of penicillin G valued at 44 million dollars was produced in the United States in 1955, chiefly from the mold *Penicillium chrysogenum*. It has been estimated that during World War II a thousand chemists in thirty-nine laboratories in Great Britain and the

United States worked on the problem of the structure and synthesis of penicillin at a cost of $20,000,000. A successful synthesis was not developed, however, until 1957.

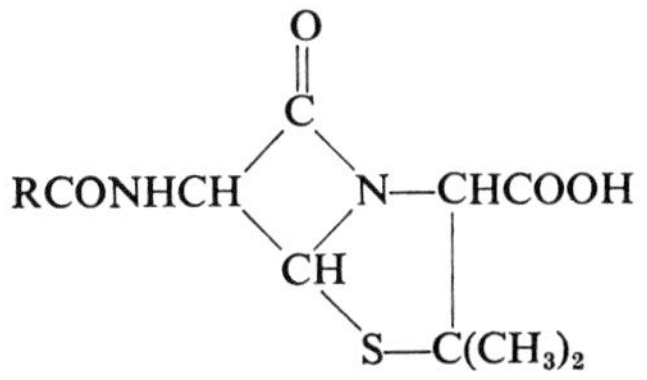

	PENICILLIN	R
	G or II	$C_6H_5CH_2-$
	X or III	p-$HOC_6H_4CH_2-$
	F or I	$CH_3CH_2CH=CHCH_2-$
	Dihydro F	$CH_3(CH_2)_4-$
	Flavicidin	$CH_3CH=CH(CH_2)_2-$
	K or IV	$CH_3(CH_2)_6-$
	V	$C_6H_5OCH_2-$

Natural Penicillins

The cyclic acetals and carbonates formed from 1,2-glycols (p. 741) contain a five-membered ring with two hetero oxygen atoms.

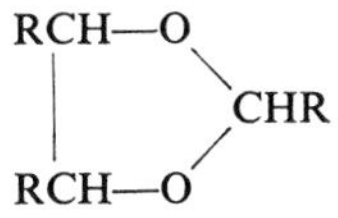

A cyclic acetal 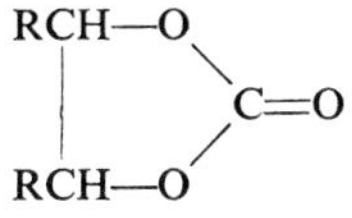   A cyclic carbonate

When *N*-nitroso-*N*-phenylglycine is heated with acetic anhydride, water is lost and a compound having a 1,2,3-oxadiazole ring structure is formed. Compounds of this type, which are called *sydnones* after the University of Sydney where they were discovered, first were formulated as having a three-membered ring fused to a four-membered ring. Dipole moment measurements indicate that they are resonance-hybrid dipolar molecules for which the term *mesoionic* has been coined (p. 266).

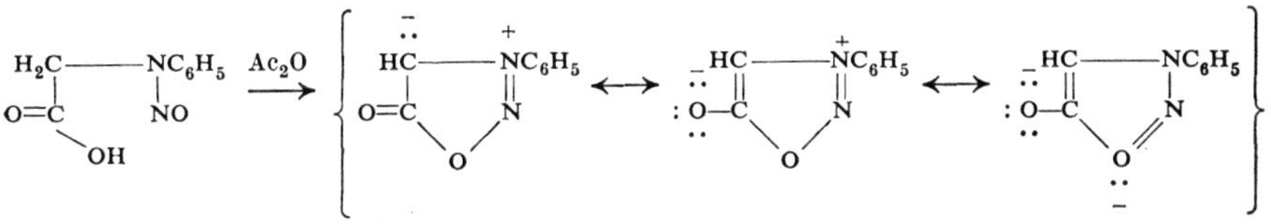

Several tetrazole derivatives are of practical importance. **Tetracene** is a primary explosive that can replace lead azide or mercury fulminate. It results from a complex series of reactions when aminoguanidinium nitrate is treated with sodium nitrite.

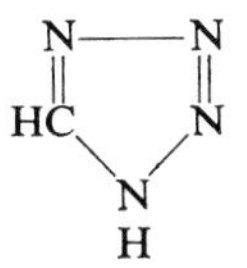

Tetrazole 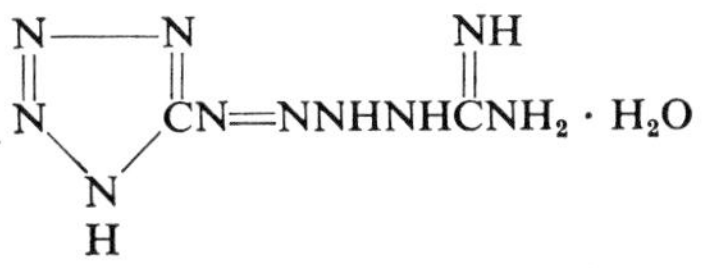   Tetracene

Arylhydrazones couple with diazonium salts to give highly colored water-insoluble *formazans*. The latter can be oxidized to colorless water-soluble **tetrazolium salts**.

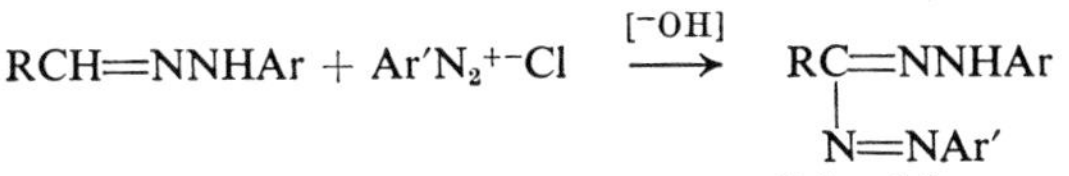

$$RCH=NNHAr + Ar'N_2{}^+Cl^- \xrightarrow{[^-OH]} \begin{array}{c} RC=NNHAr \\ | \\ N=NAr' \end{array}$$

Colored formazan

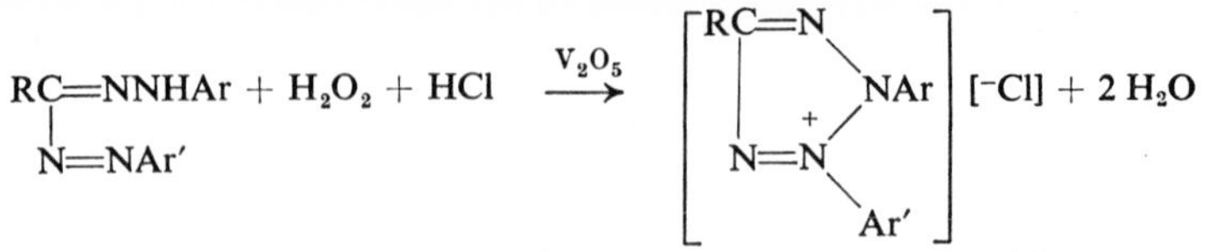

$$RC\!\!=\!\!NNHAr + H_2O_2 + HCl \xrightarrow{V_2O_5} \begin{bmatrix} RC\!\!=\!\!N \\ | \quad\quad\quad NAr \\ N\!\!=\!\!N \\ \quad\quad\quad Ar' \end{bmatrix}^{+} [^-Cl] + 2\,H_2O$$

Colorless tetrazolium chloride

The reduction of tetrazolium salts to the formazan can be brought about readily by various reagents including biological systems. When tissues are treated with a tetrazolium salt, the colored insoluble formazan is deposited at the site where reduction is taking place. **Triphenyltetrazolium chloride**, which is most used, is made from benzaldehyde phenylhydrazone and benzenediazonium chloride and gives a red formazan. The diformazan from benzaldehyde phenyl-hydrazone and diazotized *o*-dianisidine is called **Tetrazolium Blue.**

Six-membered Rings

Three six-membered ring systems containing two nitrogen atoms are known, namely the 1,2-diazines or pyridazines, the 1,3-diazines or pyrimidines, and the 1,4-diazines or pyrazines.

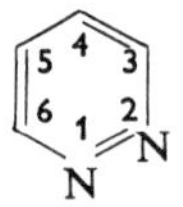

| 1,2-Diazine or pyridazine | 1,3-Diazine or pyrimidine | 1,4-Diazine or pyrazine |

Pyridazines are formed when 1,4-diketones react with hydrazine in the presence of air. The group as a whole is of little importance.

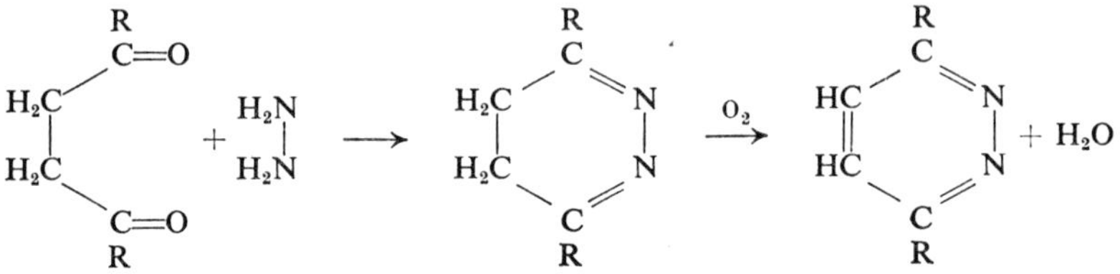

Compounds containing the **pyrimidine** ring are present in all living cells. Hydrolysis of nucleic acids obtained from nucleoproteins yields the pyrimidines **cytosine, 5-methylcytosine, uracil,** and **thymine,** along with purines, D-ribose or 2-deoxy-D-ribose, and phosphoric acid.

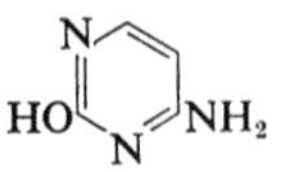

| Cytosine (2-hydroxy-4-amino-pyrimidine) | 5-Methylcytosine (2-hydroxy-4-amino-5-methylpyrimidine) | Uracil (2,4-dihydroxy-pyrimidine) | Thymine (2,4-dihydroxy-5-methylpyrimidine) |

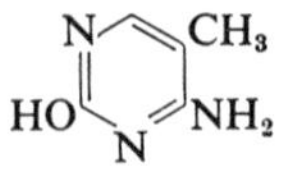

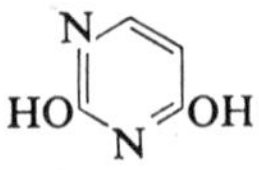

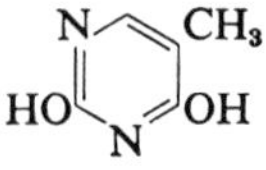

Most of the methods for the synthesis of pyrimidines consist of the reaction of a malonic ester (p. 800) or a β-keto ester (p. 817) with amidines, urea, or thiourea. For example, **barbituric acid**[5] (*2,4,6-trihydroxypyrimidine*) results from the reaction of urea with ethyl malonate (p. 792). Reaction of barbituric acid with phosphorus trichloride gives the trichloro derivative, which can be reduced to pyrimidine with zinc dust and water.

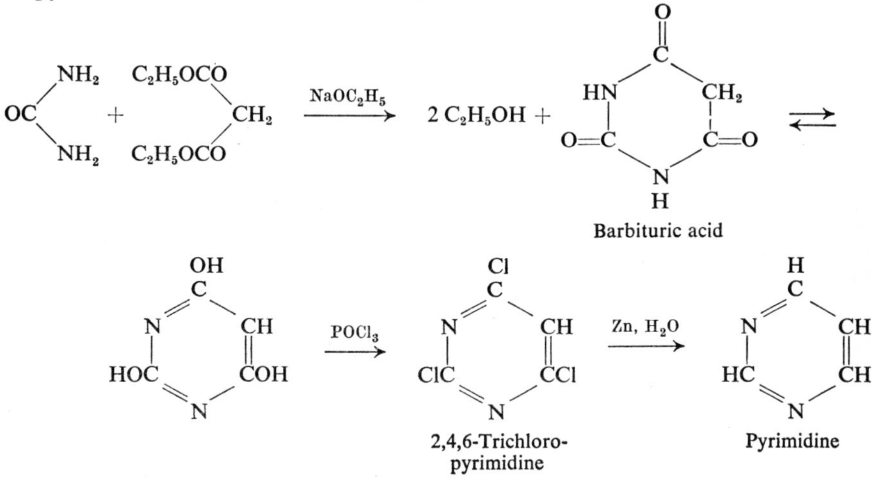

$$\begin{array}{c}\text{NH}_2 \\ \text{OC} \\ \text{NH}_2\end{array} + \begin{array}{c}\text{C}_2\text{H}_5\text{OCO} \\ \text{CH}_2 \\ \text{C}_2\text{H}_5\text{OCO}\end{array} \xrightarrow{\text{NaOC}_2\text{H}_5} 2\,\text{C}_2\text{H}_5\text{OH} + \begin{array}{c}\text{O} \\ \| \\ \text{C} \\ \text{HN} \qquad \text{CH}_2 \\ \text{O=C} \qquad \text{C=O} \\ \text{N} \\ \text{H}\end{array} \rightleftharpoons$$

Barbituric acid

OH C → POCl₃ → Cl C → Zn, H₂O → H C

2,4,6-Trichloro-pyrimidine   Pyrimidine

Condensation of ethyl formylacetate (p. 815) with guanidine yields 2-amino-4-hydroxypyrimidine which can be converted to **2-aminopyrimidine,** the intermediate for sulfadiazine (p. 489).

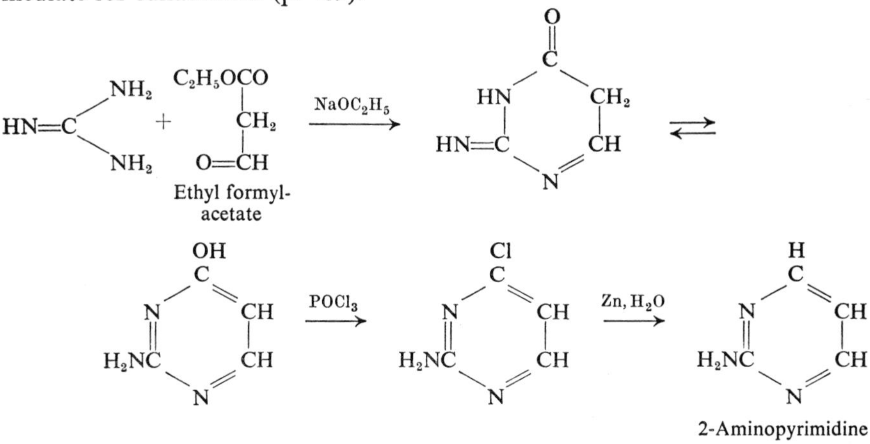

$$\text{HN}{=}\text{C}\begin{array}{c}\text{NH}_2 \\ \\ \text{NH}_2\end{array} + \begin{array}{c}\text{C}_2\text{H}_5\text{OCO} \\ \text{CH}_2 \\ \text{O=CH}\end{array} \xrightarrow{\text{NaOC}_2\text{H}_5} \begin{array}{c}\text{O} \\ \| \\ \text{C} \\ \text{HN} \qquad \text{CH}_2 \\ \text{HN=C} \qquad \text{CH} \\ \text{N}\end{array} \rightleftharpoons$$

Ethyl formyl-acetate

OH C, H₂NC → POCl₃ → Cl C, H₂NC → Zn, H₂O → H C, H₂NC

2-Aminopyrimidine

Thymine can be synthesized from ethyl 2-formylpropionate and *S*-methylthiourea.

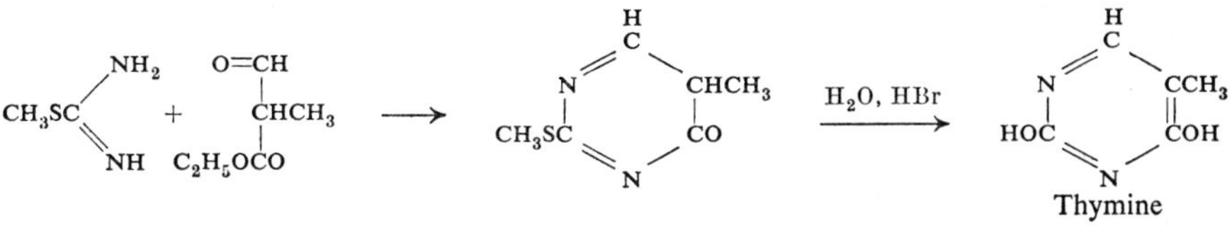

$$\text{CH}_3\text{SC}\begin{array}{c}\text{NH}_2 \\ \\ \text{NH}\end{array} + \begin{array}{c}\text{O=CH} \\ \text{CHCH}_3 \\ \text{C}_2\text{H}_5\text{OCO}\end{array} \longrightarrow \begin{array}{c}\text{H} \\ \text{C} \\ \text{N} \qquad \text{CHCH}_3 \\ \text{CH}_3\text{SC} \qquad \text{CO} \\ \text{N}\end{array} \xrightarrow{\text{H}_2\text{O, HBr}} \begin{array}{c}\text{H} \\ \text{C} \\ \text{N} \qquad \text{CCH}_3 \\ \text{HOC} \qquad \text{COH} \\ \text{N}\end{array}$$

Thymine

---

[5] Barbituric acid was prepared first from uric acid by Baeyer (p. 615), who named it after a friend, Barbara. A less intriguing story is that it was so named because it was discovered on St. Barbara's Day.

The **barbiturates** form an important group of pyrimidine derivatives. They are cyclic diimides prepared by condensing urea or thiourea with disubstituted malonic esters, and form stable sodium salts.

$$
\begin{array}{c}
R_1 \diagdown \diagup COO_2CH_5 \quad H_2N \diagdown \\
C \qquad\qquad + \qquad CO \\
R_2 \diagup \diagdown COOC_2H_5 \quad H_2N \diagup
\end{array}
\xrightarrow{\;NaOC_2H_5\;}
\begin{array}{c}
R_1 \diagdown \diagup CO{-}\overset{-}{N}\overset{+}{N}a \\
C \qquad\qquad CO \;+\; 3\,C_2H_5OH \\
R_2 \diagup \diagdown CO{-}NH
\end{array}
$$

Barbituric acid is stabilized in the enol form by resonance of the pyrimidine ring. The electron-attracting properties of the two nitrogen atoms greatly increase the acidity of the COH group between them, and barbituric acid ($K_a = 1 \times 10^{-4}$) is even stronger than acetic acid ($K_a = 1.8 \times 10^{-5}$). The two alkyl substituents in the barbiturates prevent the molecule from becoming aromatic in type, but the imino group situated between two carbonyl groups still is considerably more acidic ($K_a = ca.\ 10^{-8}$) than phenol ($K_a = 10^{-10}$). Hence these barbituric acid derivatives also form water-soluble sodium salts.

Although these compounds as a class are called **barbiturates** by the medical profession, the free compounds as well as their sodium salts are used medicinally. The ending commonly used for the free compound is *al*, and *sodium* is added as a separate word to indicate the sodium salt, for example, *barbital* and *barbital sodium*.

The barbiturates have a depressant action on the central nervous system and are valuable sedatives and soporifics. **Barbital** (R_1 and $R_2 = C_2H_5$) was synthesized first in 1882 by the reaction of ethyl iodide with the silver salt of barbituric acid. In 1903 von Mering discovered its hypnotic properties and called it *Veronal* because he considered Verona to be the most restful city in the world. Barbital is its nonproprietary name. The synthesis from ethyl diethylmalonate was developed by Emil Fischer. **Phenobarbital** ($R_1 =$ ethyl, $R_2 =$ phenyl) was introduced several years later under the trade name *Luminal*. It has a specific action in preventing epileptic seizures. **Amytal** ($R_1 =$ ethyl, $R_2 =$ isoamyl), and **pentobarbital (Nembutal)** ($R_1 =$ ethyl, $R_2 =$ 1-methylbutyl) act more quickly but have a shorter duration of action than either barbital or phenobarbital. **Seconal** ($R_1 =$ allyl, $R_2 =$ 1-methylbutyl) acts still more quickly and for a relatively short period.

Unfortunately the indiscriminate distribution and use of barbiturates and the danger of overdosage make them a hazard to a large proportion of the population. Over 430,000 pounds of phenobarbital and an equal amount of other barbiturates having a value of $2,800,000 were produced in the United States in 1955. This amount is equivalent to twelve 0.2-gram doses per capita.

Pentothal Sodium is a thiobarbiturate that is used for general anesthesia by intravenous injection. The use of barbiturates for general anesthesia requires

$$
\begin{array}{c}
C_2H_5 \diagdown \diagup CO{-}N^-Na^+ \\
C \qquad\qquad CS \\
CH_3CH_2CH_2CH \diagup \diagdown CO{-}NH \\
\;\;\;\;|\;\;\;\;\; \\
\;\;\;\;CH_3
\end{array}
\qquad\qquad
\begin{array}{c}
CO{-}NH \\
\diagup \qquad \diagdown \\
CO \qquad\quad CO \\
\diagdown \qquad \diagup \\
CO{-}NH
\end{array}
$$

Pentothal Sodium (*sodium thiopental*)   Alloxan

careful technique, since the anesthetic dose is 50 to 70 per cent of the lethal dose. However, their ease of administration and rapid action, and the rapid recovery of the patient, led to their use for major surgical operations in the front battle lines during World War II, and the experience gained has been carried over to civilian practice.

Alloxan was isolated from the oxidation products of uric acid in 1817 (p. 645). The discovery in 1943 that either oral or parenteral administration to animals brings about destruction of the islets of Langerhans in the pancreas, resulting in diabetes, brought about renewed interest in the compound.

Thiamine (*vitamin B₁, aneurin*) contains a pyrimidine nucleus joined through a methylene group to a thiazole nucleus. Its absence from the diet causes the deficiency diseases known as beriberi in man and polyneuritis in birds. The pyrophosphate is **cocarboxylase,** which is necessary for the enzymic decarboxylation of pyruvic acid (p. 812). There is evidence that the active portion of the enzyme is the lipoic acid amide of cocarboxylase (p. 635).

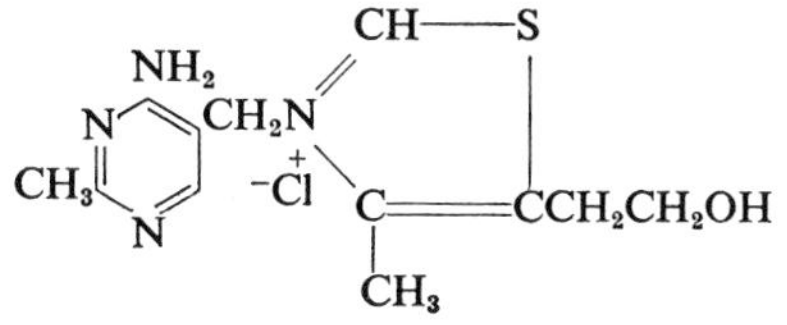

Thiamine
(vitamin B₁, aneurin)

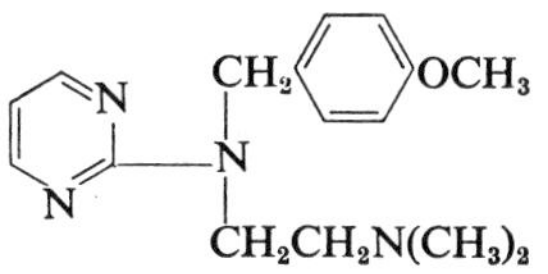

Neohetramine

Neohetramine was among the first of the antihistaminics (p. 634) that the U. S. Federal Drug Administration permitted to be sold without a physician's prescription.

Pyrazines can be synthesized by the air oxidation of the condensation products of α-amino aldehydes or α-amino ketones.

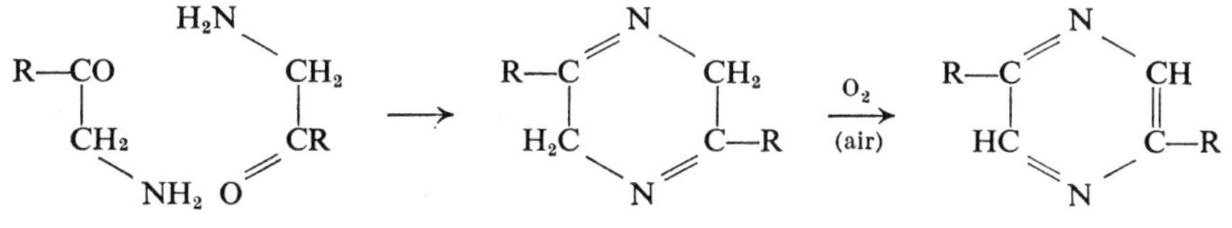

Hexahydropyrazines are called **piperazines.** Their hydrochlorides are formed on heating the hydrochlorides of 1,2-diamines.

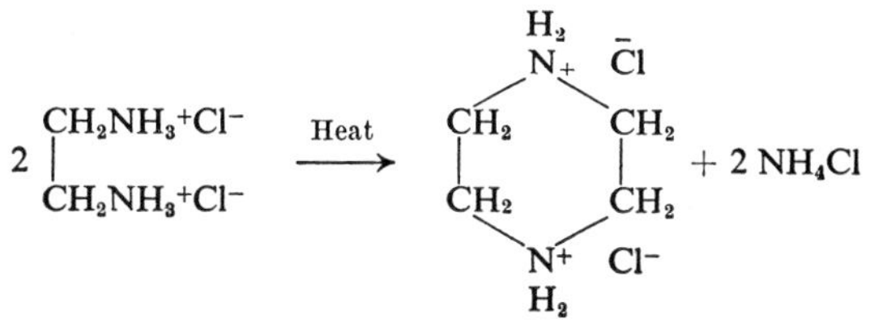

Piperazine dihydrochloride

The **2,5-diketopiperazines** are cyclic amides formed by heating α-amino acids (p. 784).

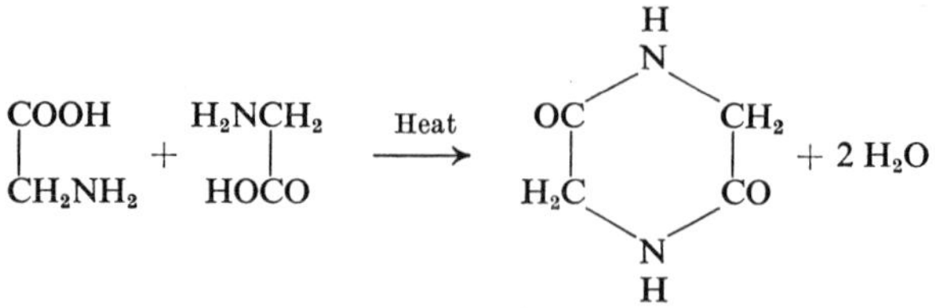

$$\underset{\text{CH}_2\text{NH}_2}{\overset{\text{COOH}}{|}} + \underset{\text{HOCO}}{\overset{\text{H}_2\text{NCH}_2}{|}} \xrightarrow{\text{Heat}} \quad + \ 2\,\text{H}_2\text{O}$$

2,5-Diketopiperazine

Benzopyrazines, which are known as **quinoxalines,** are formed by reaction of *o*-phenylenediamines with 1,2-dicarbonyl compounds. Their formation is used as a diagnostic test for the latter.

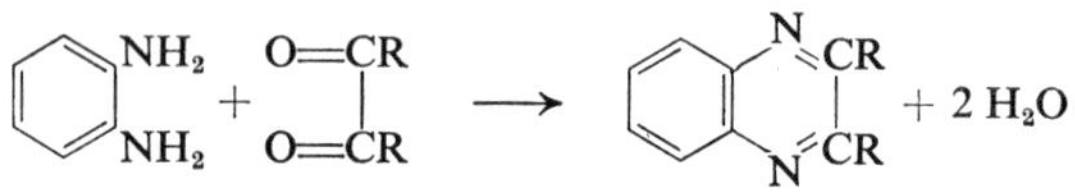

$$\underset{\text{NH}_2}{\overset{\text{NH}_2}{\bigcirc}} + \underset{\text{O}=\text{CR}}{\overset{\text{O}=\text{CR}}{|}} \longrightarrow \quad + \ 2\,\text{H}_2\text{O}$$

Oxidation of quinoxalines yields dicarboxylic acids of pyrazines, which can be decarboxylated easily.

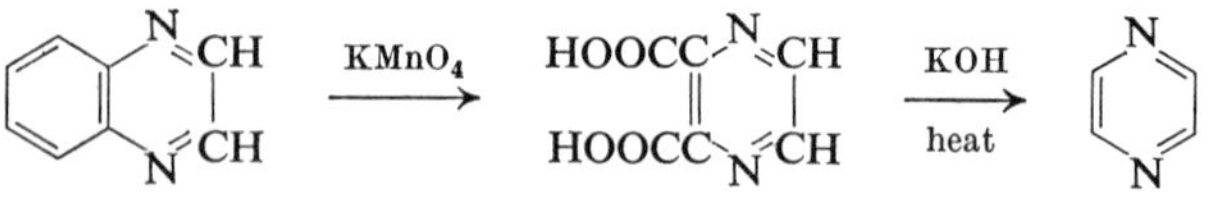

$$\text{Quinoxaline} \xrightarrow{\text{KMnO}_4} \underset{\text{HOOCC}\diagdown\text{N}\diagup\text{CH}}{\overset{\text{HOOCC}\diagup\text{N}\diagdown\text{CH}}{}} \xrightarrow[\text{heat}]{\text{KOH}} \text{Pyrazine}$$

Quinoxaline   2,3-Pyrazinedi-   Pyrazine
                     carboxylic acid

Phenazine (dibenzopyrazine) is prepared most readily by the condensation of *o*-phenylenediamine with *o*-benzoquinone.

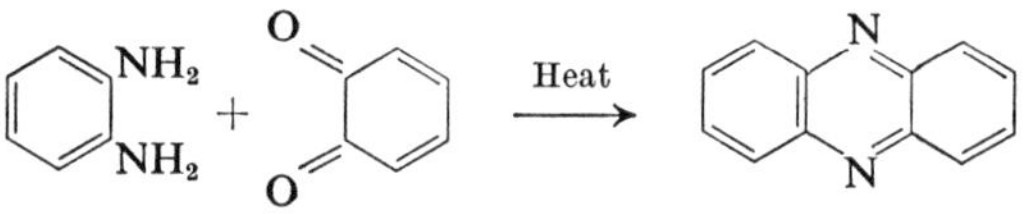

$$\underset{\text{NH}_2}{\overset{\text{NH}_2}{\bigcirc}} + \overset{\text{O}}{\underset{\text{O}}{\bigcirc}} \xrightarrow{\text{Heat}} \text{Phenazine}$$

Phenazine

The phenazine nucleus is present in several classes of dyes (pp. 689, 696).

A few six-membered heterocycles containing oxygen or sulfur are important. **1,4-Dioxane** is made by the dehydration of ethylene glycol or of diethylene glycol (p. 744), and **morpholine** by the dehydration of diethanolamine (p. 752).

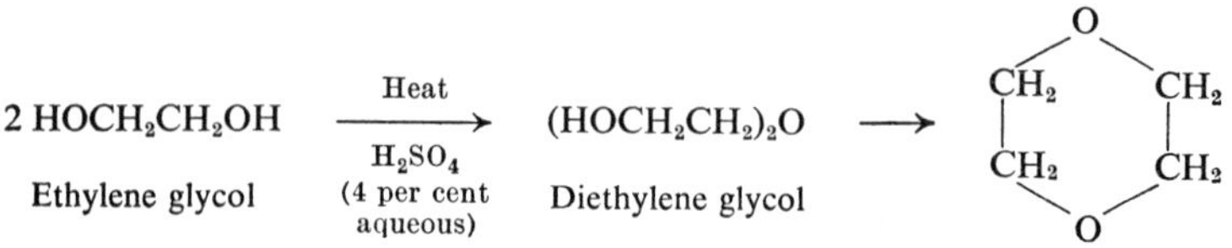

$$2\ \text{HOCH}_2\text{CH}_2\text{OH} \xrightarrow[\substack{\text{H}_2\text{SO}_4 \\ (4\ \text{per cent} \\ \text{aqueous})}]{\text{Heat}} (\text{HOCH}_2\text{CH}_2)_2\text{O} \longrightarrow$$

Ethylene glycol   Diethylene glycol   1,4-Dioxane

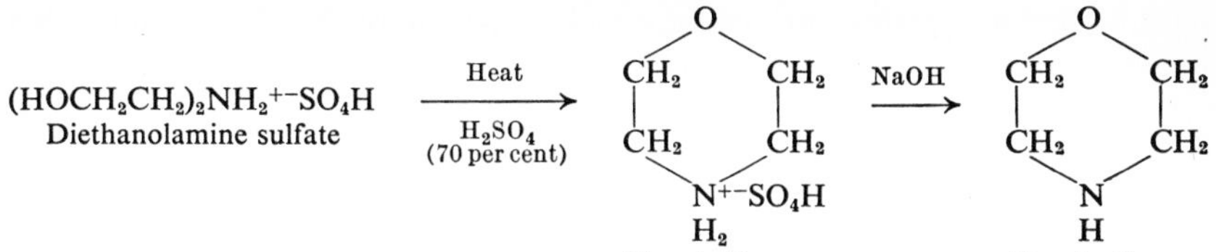

$$(HOCH_2CH_2)_2NH_2{}^{+-}SO_4H$$
Diethanolamine sulfate

$$\xrightarrow[\substack{H_2SO_4 \\ (70 \text{ per cent})}]{\text{Heat}}$$

Morpholine
sulfate

$$\xrightarrow{\text{NaOH}}$$

Morpholine

The cyclic anhydrides of hydroxy sulfonic acids and the cyclic amides of amino sulfonic acids contain sulfur and oxygen, or sulfur and nitrogen in a ring. They are known as **sultones** and **sultams.**

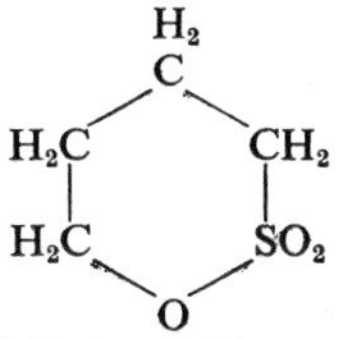

4-Hydroxy-1-butane-
sulfonic acid sultone

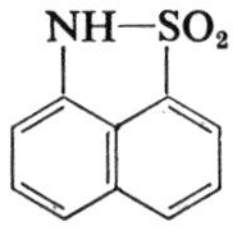

8-Amino-1-naphthalene-
sulfonic acid sultam

A few dibenzo-1,4-thiazines are important. **Phenothiazine** (sometimes called thiodiphenylamine) is prepared by heating diphenylamine with sulfur. It is used extensively as an intestinal antiseptic for cattle and poultry. **Chlorpromazine** is one of the more widely used tranquilizing psychiatric drugs.

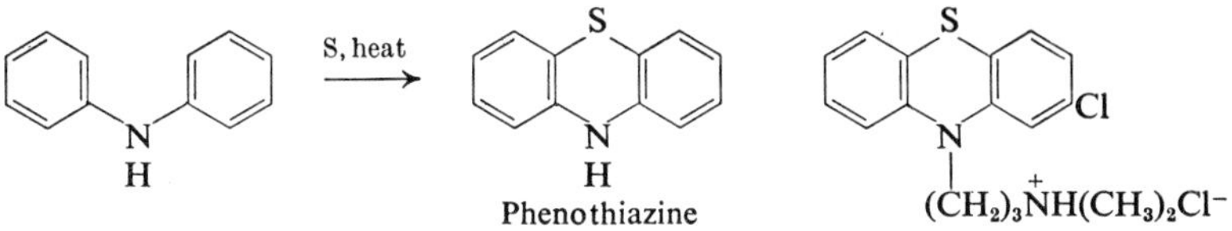

$$\xrightarrow{\text{S, heat}}$$

Phenothiazine

$$(CH_2)_3\overset{+}{N}H(CH_3)_2Cl^-$$
Chlorpromazine

COMPOUNDS WITH CONDENSED HETERO RINGS

The **purines** are the most important class of compounds containing two condensed heterocyclic rings. They contain both a pyrimidine ring and an imidazole ring.

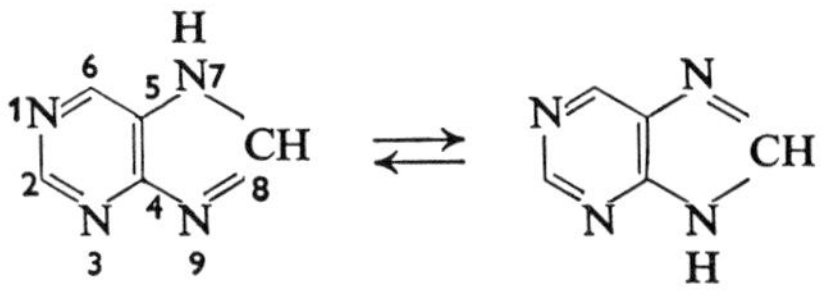

Purine

Amino and hydroxy derivatives of purine accompany pyrimidines as the hydrolysis products of nucleic acids (p. 294). **Adenine** is 6-aminopurine, **hypoxanthine** is 6-hydroxypurine, **guanine** (from guano) is 2-amino-6-hydroxy-purine, and **xanthine** is 2,6-dihydroxypurine. The chemical properties of nucleic acids in general and of ribonucleic acid in particular are illustrated diagrammatically in Fig. 87.

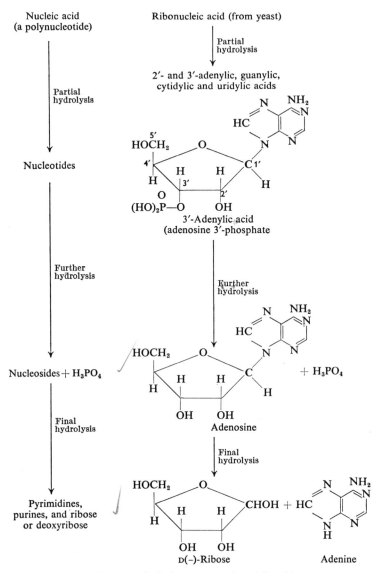

Fig. 87. Hydrolytic products of nucleic acids.

Muscle adenylic acid is adenosine 5'-monophosphate (AMP). Its reversible conversion to adenosine 5'-diphosphate (ADP) and adenosine 5'-triphosphate (ATP), in which all of the phosphoric acid units are joined to each other by phosphoric anhydride linkages, plays an important part in carbohydrate metabolism. **Coenzyme A**, which is essential for the metabolism of carbohydrates and fats and for the formation of acetylcholine, is an ester of pantetheine (p. 786) and a polyphosphorylated adenosine.

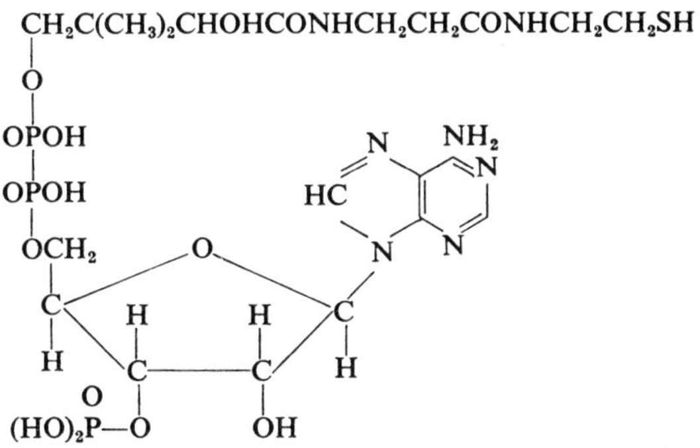

$$CH_2C(CH_3)_2CHOHCONHCH_2CH_2CONHCH_2CH_2SH$$

Coenzyme A

Uric acid is 2,6,8-trihydroxypurine. It is present in blood and urine and can cause the formation of urinary calculi, from which it first was isolated by Scheele in 1776. Crystals of the monosodium salt deposited in the joints cause the painful condition known as gout. Although uric acid is eliminated only in small amounts by mammals, it is the chief product of nitrogen metabolism by caterpillars, birds, and reptiles. Guano, which contains about 25 per cent uric acid, is one of the best sources.

The empirical formula, $C_5H_4N_4O_3$, was established by Liebig and Mitscherlich in 1834. Its constitution is indicated by the formation of alloxan and urea on oxidation with nitric acid, and of allantoin on oxidation with lead dioxide. Reduction of allantoin with hydrogen iodide gives hydantoin (p. 634). A rational synthesis by Emil Fischer from barbituric acid confirms the assigned structure.

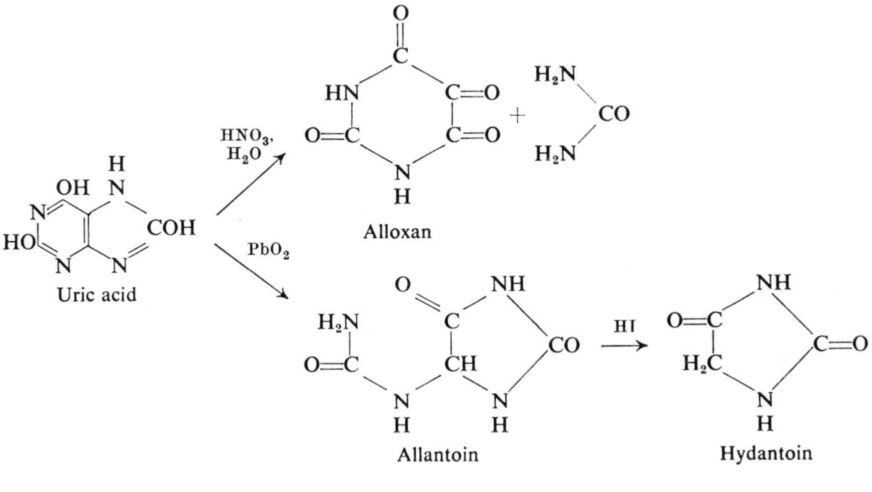

Uric acid

Alloxan

Allantoin

Hydantoin

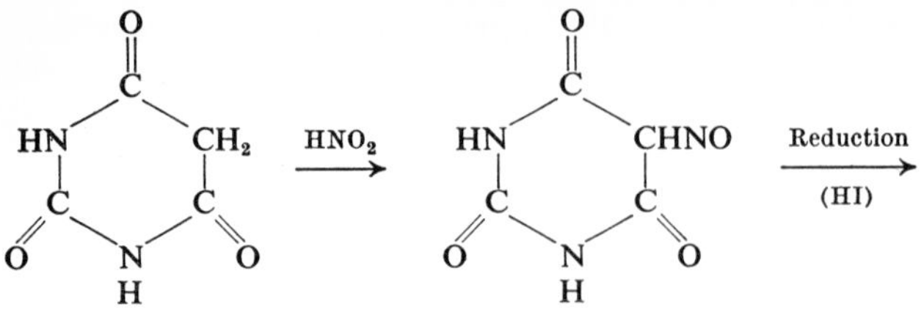

Barbituric acid → Violuric acid (HNO$_2$), Reduction (HI)

Barbituric acid

Violuric acid

Uramil (KOCN, H$_2$O, (HN=C=O)) → Pseudouric acid (HCl)

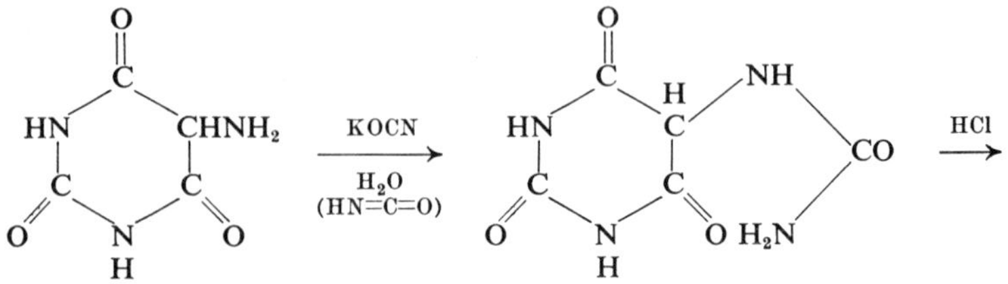

Uramil

Pseudouric acid

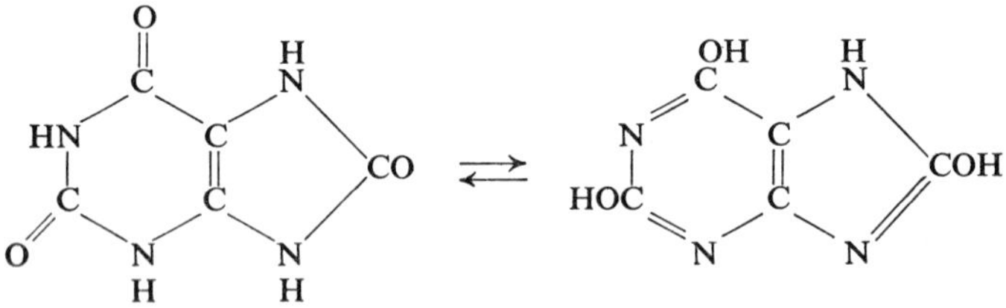

Uric acid

The compounds responsible for the stimulating action of coffee, tea, and cocoa are methyl derivatives of xanthine. **Theophylline** is present in tea (*Thea sinensis*), **theobromine** in cocoa (*Theobroma cacao*), and **caffeine** in tea, coffee (*Coffea arabica*), cola nuts (*Cola acuminata*), maté (*Ilex paraguayensis*), and many other plants. Numerous legends are told concerning the origin of the use

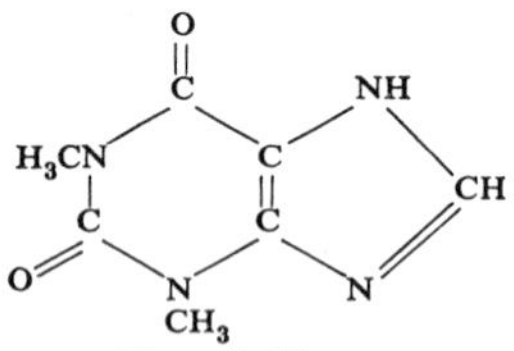

Theophylline

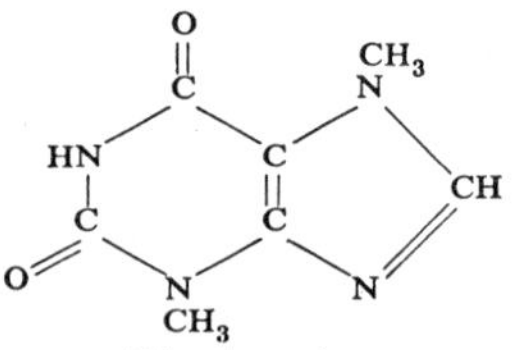

Theobromine

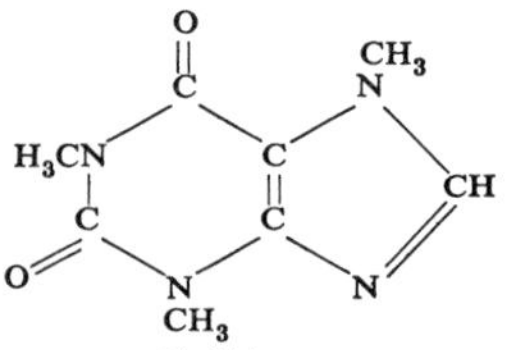

Caffeine

of coffee and tea as beverages. It is of interest that wherever plants having a high caffeine content are indigenous to an area, the natives use extracts of the plant as a beverage. All of these compounds stimulate the central nervous system, caffeine being most active and theobromine least. The effective dose of caffeine is 150 to 250 mg., corresponding to 1 to 2 cups of coffee or tea. About 80 per cent is broken down in the body to urea, and the remainder excreted unchanged or partially demethylated. The fatal dose of caffeine has been estimated as 10 grams, but no deaths from it have been reported. In recent years the use of caffeine-containing beverages has increased enormously, largely because of their stimulating effect. Production of natural and synthetic caffeine in the United States in 1955 was 1,153,000 pounds valued at over $3,600,000. This amount is equivalent to over 3.5 billion 150-mg. doses or about twenty per capita. Large amounts of theobromine are prepared from ground cocoa shells and from the press cake remaining after the manufacture of chocolate. The base is liberated with lime and extracted with solvent. About 100 pounds of theobromine is obtained from each 6500 pounds of raw material. The theobromine that is not sold as a drug is converted to caffeine by methylation. Caffeine also is synthesized starting with urea and cyanoacetic acid.

Theophylline is a stronger acid ($K_a = 1.69 \times 10^{-9}$) than phenol ($K_a = 1.3 \times 10^{-10}$) and is soluble in aqueous ammonia. The salt of 8-chlorotheophylline and Benadryl (p. 526) is called **Dramamine** and is used for the prevention of motion sickness. Its effectiveness appears to be due entirely to the Benadryl content.

Several biologically important compounds have the *pteridine nucleus* in which a pyrimidine ring is fused to a pyrazine ring. The **pterins** (Gr. *pteron*, wing) are colorless or yellow compounds found in the wings of various species of butterflies and wasps, in the skin and eyes of fish, and in the liver and urine of mammals. They are characterized by marked fluorescence in neutral solution.

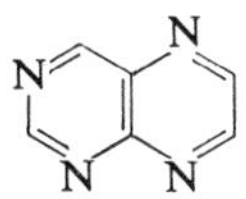

Pteridine 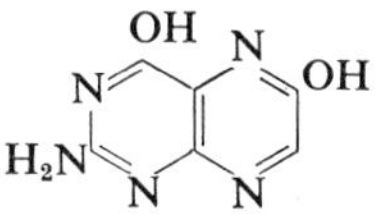   Xanthopterin 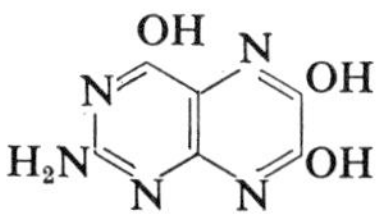   Leucopterin

The **folic acids** are necessary for the growth of certain micro-organisms. The portion remaining after removal of the glutamic acid units by hydrolysis is

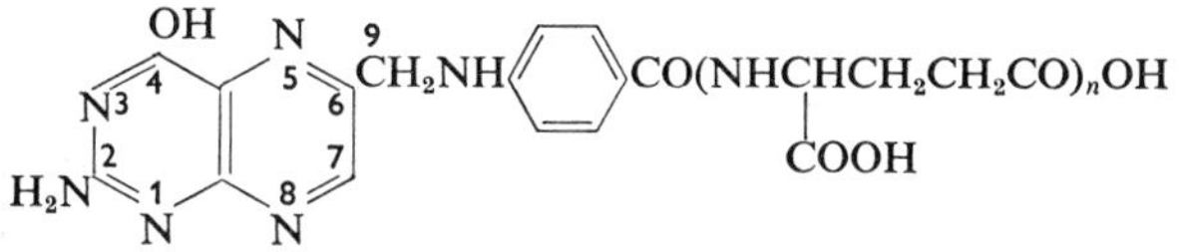

Folic acids

called **pteroic acid** and the folic acids have been termed *pteroylglutamic acids*. **Pteroylglutamic acid** ($n = 1$) is synthesized commercially for use in the treatment of various types of anemia. It appears to be a precursor of the so-called *citrovorum factor* which is a 5,6,7,8-tetrahydro *N*-formyl derivative and is required for cell division in mammals. **Aminopterin** has an amino group instead of a hydroxyl group in the 4 position. It is an antimetabolite (p. 558) that inhibits cell division and has been used in the treatment of acute leukemia.

Riboflavin is the prosthetic group of the various *yellow enzymes* or *flavoproteins*. They play a part in the metabolism of α-amino acids and in aerobic carbohydrate metabolism. Riboflavin is yellow and its solutions are highly fluorescent in ultraviolet light. The polyhydroxy side chain has the D-ribose configuration.

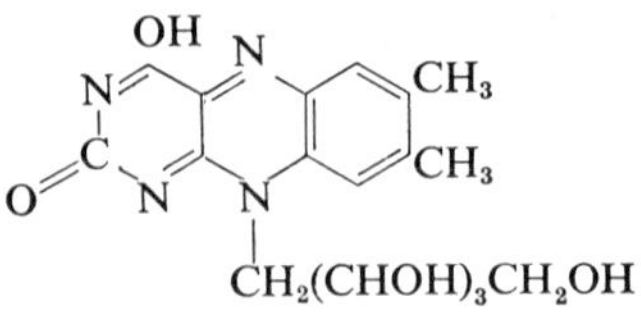

Riboflavin (vitamin B₂)

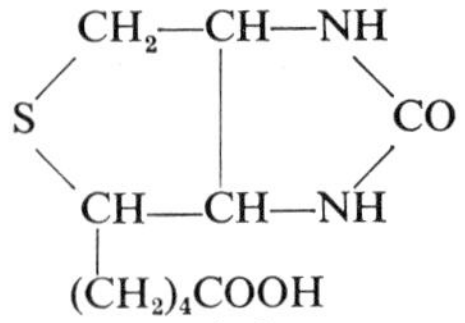

$CH_2(CHOH)_3CH_2OH$

Biotin

$(CH_2)_4COOH$

Production of riboflavin in the United States in 1955 amounted to 311,000 pounds valued at over 6 million dollars.

Biotin, another member of the vitamin B complex that may be involved in the metabolism of pyruvic acid, contains an imidazole ring fused to a thiophene ring.

"Oxa-aza" Nomenclature. The difficulty of remembering the names of heterocyclic structures has led to increasing use of the "oxa-aza" system whereby heterocycles are named from the corresponding homocyclic compound. *Oxa,* or *thia,* for example, denotes replacement of CH_2 by oxygen or sulfur, and *aza,* or *phospha,* denotes replacement of CH by nitrogen or phosphorus. Thus dioxane becomes 1,4-dioxacyclohexane, and xanthopterin becomes 2,8-dihydroxy-6-amino-1,4,5,7-tetrazanaphthalene.

ALKALOIDS

The term *alkaloid* means *like an alkali,* and alkaloids usually are defined as basic nitrogenous plant products having a marked physiological action when administered to animals. Some compounds, however, are included under the term which do not conform to this definition. For example piperine, the alkaloid of pepper, is not basic and has practically no physiological activity. On the other hand some compounds such as caffeine are so innocuous that though they definitely are alkaloids, they frequently are not considered as such. Furthermore, some compounds either are so closely related in structure to the alkaloids or have such similar physiological action that it is natural to think of them along with the alkaloids even though they do not come within the usual definition. Thus epinephrine and ephedrine are closely related but only ephedrine is a plant product; opium and hashish (marijuana) are both habit-forming drugs having similar action, yet the active principle of the latter is not basic and does not contain nitrogen (p. 633).

Coniine is present in all parts of the poison hemlock (*Conium masculatium*; Gr. *konas,* to whirl around). It is α-*n*-propylpiperidine, and the simplest of the alkaloids. It has been synthesized from α-picoline.

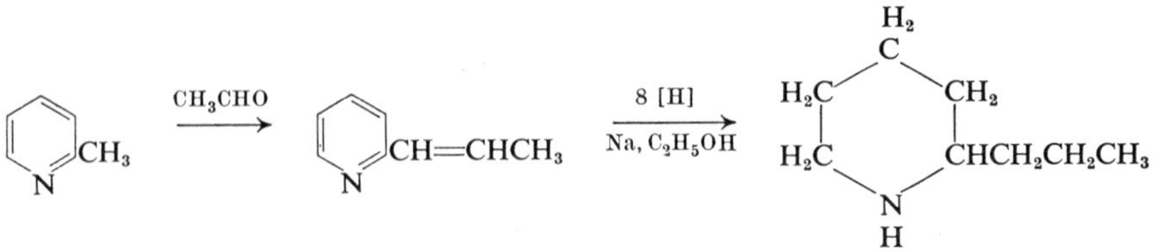

α-Picoline

Coniine

At least ten alkaloids are present in tobacco (*Nicotiana tabacum*). About three fourths of the total alkaloids is **nicotine.** An interesting synthesis starts with 3-cyanopyridine and the Grignard reagent of γ-bromopropyl ethyl ether.

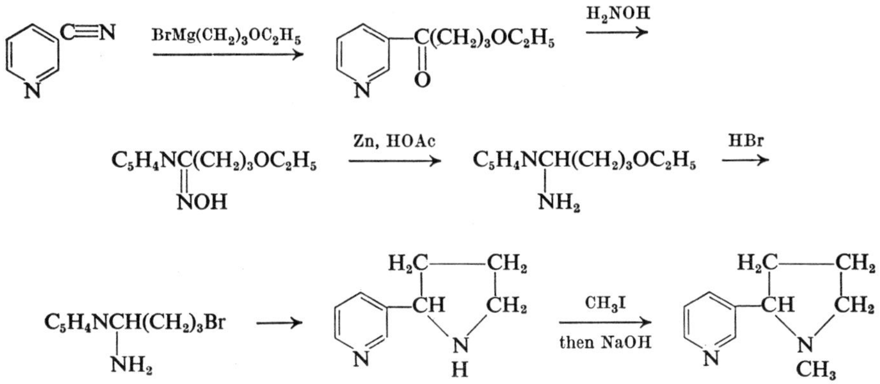

Nornicotine

Nicotine

Nicotine is highly toxic to animals, but in small amounts it causes an initial and transient stimulation followed by depression. It is used extensively as a contact insecticide.

Piperine is the alkaloid of black pepper (*Piper nigrum*). The piperine content varies from 5 to 9 per cent. Hydrolysis yields piperidine and piperic acid, indicating an amide linkage. Piperic acid, $C_{12}H_{10}O_4$, contains two double bonds, and oxidation gives piperonal.

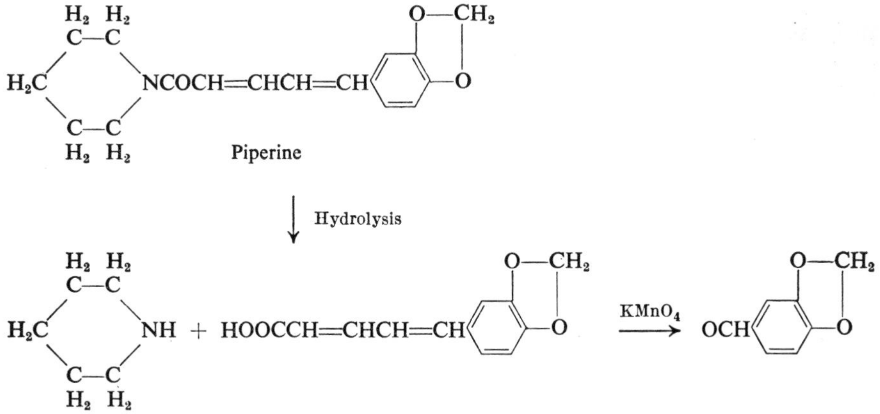

Piperine

Hydrolysis

Piperidine   Piperic acid   Piperonal

Capsaicin is the pungent principle of tabasco (*Capsicum* species), cayenne or red pepper (*Capsicum fastigatum*), and paprika (*Capsicum annuum*), the relative pungencies being proportional to the capsaicin content. Capsaicin yields on hydrolysis vanillylamine and a C_{10} unsaturated acid. The latter on hydrogenation gives isocapric acid, and on oxidation adipic acid.

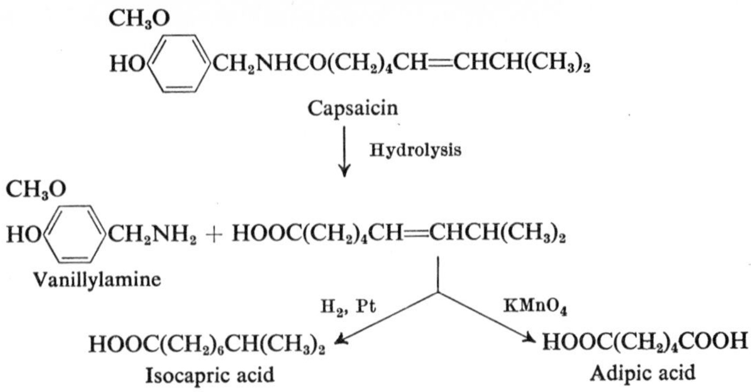

$$CH_3O$$

$$HO\langle\;\rangle CH_2NHCO(CH_2)_4CH\!=\!CHCH(CH_3)_2$$

Capsaicin

↓ Hydrolysis

$$CH_3O$$

$$HO\langle\;\rangle CH_2NH_2 + HOOC(CH_2)_4CH\!=\!CHCH(CH_3)_2$$

Vanillylamine

H_2, Pt $KMnO_4$

$$HOOC(CH_2)_6CH(CH_3)_2 \longleftarrow \qquad \longrightarrow HOOC(CH_2)_4COOH$$

Isocapric acid   Adipic acid

A number of alkaloids have a **tropane ring system,** in which two methylene groups bridge the 2,6 positions of a reduced pyridine ring. **1-Hyoscyamine** is the chief alkaloid of many plants of the family *Solanaceae,* especially henbane (*Hyoscyamus niger*), belladonna (*Atropa belladona*), and the deadly nightshade

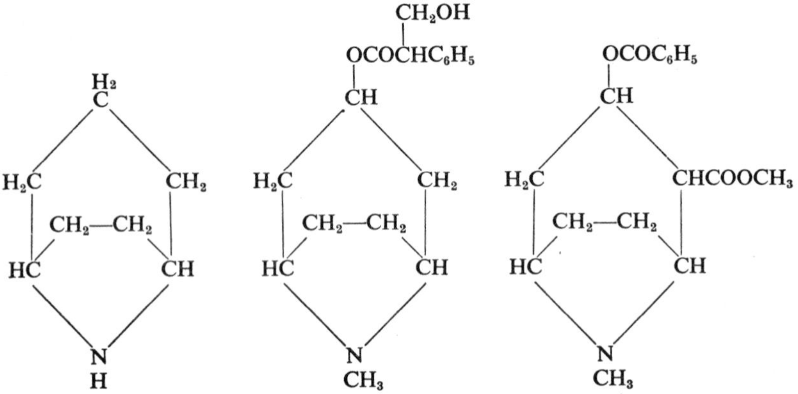

Tropane   1-Hyoscyamine and atropine   Cocaine

(*Datura stramonium*). It is racemized readily to **atropine,** which probably does not occur naturally in more than traces. **Cocaine** is the chief alkaloid in the leaves of the Peruvian bush, *Erythroxylum coca.*

All of the alkaloids of this group are characterized by their mydriatic action. Atropine causes dilation of the pupil of the eye at a dilution of 1 in 130,000 parts of water. Cocaine is noted particularly for its stimulating action on the central nervous system, permitting great physical endurance, and for its local anesthetic action. Before the dangers of addiction were understood, it was self-administered widely in Europe and was a component of many patent medicines. The development of the local anesthetics of the procaine type (p. 558) resulted from the observation that the toxic effects of cocaine are associated with the carbomethoxy group, whereas the anesthetic action is due to the portion that is the benzoic ester of an amino alcohol.

At least twenty-four different alkaloids are present in **opium** (Gr. *opion,* poppy juice), the dried latex of the species of poppy (*Papaver somniferum*) that is indigenous to Asia Minor. These alkaloids fall chiefly into two groups, the benzylisoquinoline group and the phenanthrene group. In the former are **papaverine, narcotine,** and **laudanine,** and in the latter **morphine, codeine,** and **thebaine.**

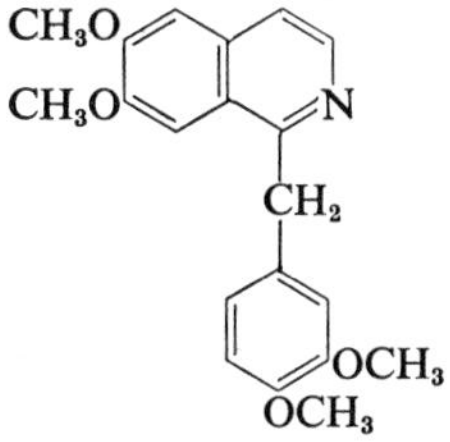

Papaverine

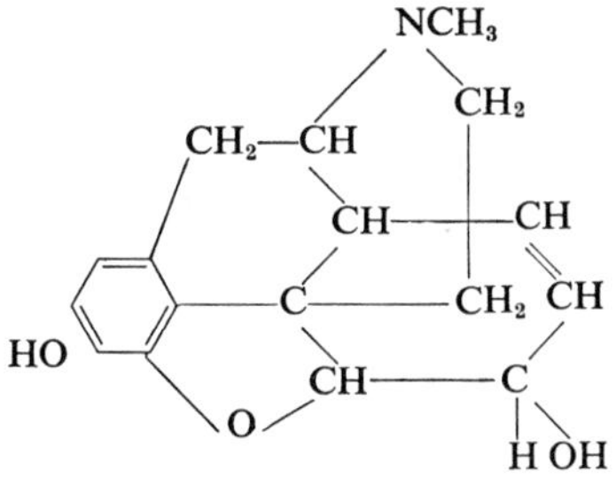

Morphine

One of the hydroxyl groups of morphine is phenolic and can be methylated readily, the resulting methyl ether being identical with natural **codeine. Thebaine** is the dimethyl derivative. Acetylation of morphine gives the diacetate, **heroine,** which does not occur in opium.

The effects of opium were known before recorded history, and it has been and remains one of the most valuable drugs at the disposal of the physician. Morphine, which constitutes about 10 per cent of opium, was isolated by Sertuerner in 1805, and the isolation of other pure components soon followed. Since then the individual alkaloids have been used medicinally. The benzyliso-quinoline alkaloids have very little action on the central nervous system but relax smooth muscle. Papaverine is the most important member of the group and is a valuable antispasmodic. Morphine exerts a simultaneous depressing and stimulating action on the central nervous system, producing drowsiness and sleep, yet causing excitation of smooth muscle with resulting nausea and vomiting. The most important use for morphine is for the relief of pain. Its synthesis was completed in 1952.

At one time it was thought that the phenanthrene portion of the molecule might be the source of the analgesic properties of morphine. Much experimental work was done preparing and testing phenanthrene derivatives, in the hope that one might be found which would have the desirable properties of morphine and yet not lead to addiction. These efforts were unsuccessful, but in 1939 it was discovered accidentally that a relatively simple synthetic compound, which has been named **pethidine** (*Demerol*), when injected into rats caused them to hold their tails in a position such as that assumed when morphine is injected. This observation led to the discovery that pethidine has a marked analgesic action although less than that of morphine. It has the advantage that it does not cause nausea.

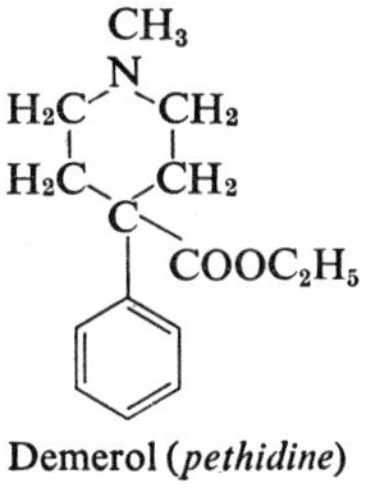

Demerol (*pethidine*)

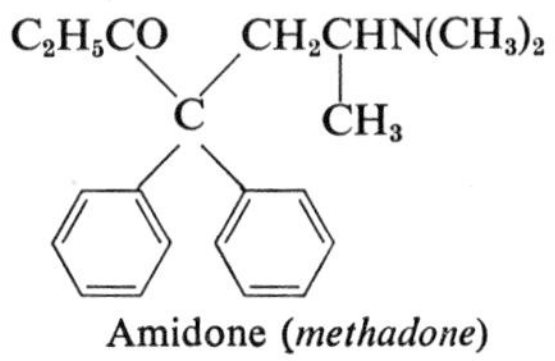

Amidone (*methadone*)

This discovery turned attention to the fact that morphine also contains a phenylpiperidine structure. Accordingly many derivatives of phenylpiperidine were synthesized and tested, and some of them were found to have marked analgesic activity. About 1941 a compound, which has been named **methadone** (*Amidone*), was found to be even more effective than morphine as an analgesic. Although certain structural features are present in methadone that may be said to be present in morphine, the relationship is rather remote. Unfortunately continued use of either pethidine or methadone also leads to addiction.

World production of morphine in 1954 was 181,000 pounds of which only 12,000 pounds was used as such. The remainder was converted into other derivatives, especially codeine. Production of codeine was 163,000 pounds, of pethidine 27,000 pounds, and of methadone 1,300 pounds.

The material known as **curare** is used as an arrow poison by the South American aborigines. It has been difficult to determine the origin of curare, but three types are recognized. They are called *tube, calabash,* and *pot curare,* according to the type of container in which they are packed. In 1935 a crystalline active alkaloid was isolated from tube curare and called **d-tubocurarine chloride.** Later the same alkaloid was isolated from a sample of curare known to have been prepared from a single plant species, *Chondodendron tomentosum.* This alkaloid is a double tetrahydroisoquinoline related to papaverine, in which both nitrogen atoms are quaternary.

d-Tubocurarine chloride

The paralytic or curariform activity is general for quaternary ammonium salts.

Curare has no effect on the central nervous system but causes complete relaxation of the muscles. Death is due to respiratory failure. *d*-Tubocurarine chloride, as well as standardized preparations of curare, is used for the treatment of spastic and other paralytic conditions. These substances also are important as adjuvants to general anesthesia. Administration of curare makes it possible to produce complete relaxation with very light anesthesia, thus avoiding the detrimental effects of deep anesthesia. It is being replaced for this purpose by the synthetic diquaternary salt, succinylcholine (p. 243).

Another important group of alkaloids is that derived from **cinchona bark.** The name commonly is thought to be derived from that of Countess Anna del Chinchon, wife of the Spanish Viceroy to Peru, who was cured of malaria by treatment with it in 1638. It has been suggested also that the name was derived from the Inca word *kinia* meaning *bark.*

The bark probably reached Europe about 1632, and its use was widespread by 1640. The genus *Cinchona* was established by Linnaeus in 1742, and the tree known as *Cinchona officinalis,* which is native to the high eastern slopes of the Andes, was described by him in 1753. The alkaloids **quinine** and **cinchonine** were not isolated until 1820 by Pelletier and Caventou. By about 1860 the near extinction of the native trees caused such a rise in price of the drug that attempts were made to cultivate cinchona elsewhere. It was grown successfully in India, Ceylon, and Java. Today more than 90 per cent of the quinine produced comes from plantations in Java. The total alkaloid content of the bark of the cultivated trees is 6 per cent, of which 70 per cent is quinine. The last phase of a total synthesis of quinine was completed successfully in 1944.

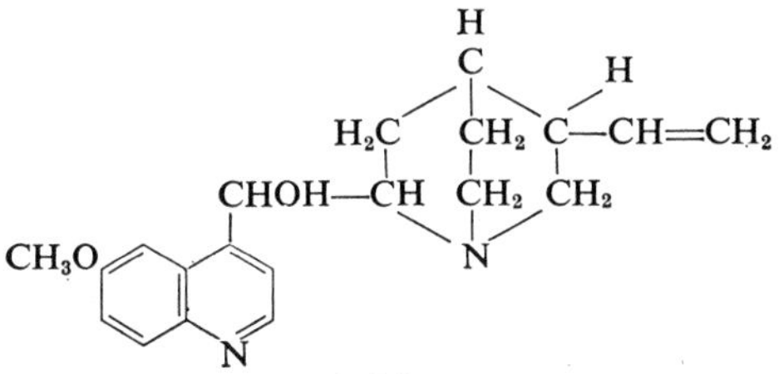

Quinine

Over twenty other alkaloids have been isolated from various species of *Cinchona* and *Cuprea*. **Epiquinine, quinidine,** and **epiquinidine** are stereoisomers of quinine. **Cinchonine, cinchonidine,** and **cinchonicine** are stereoisomeric with each other, and differ from quinine and its isomers in that they lack the methoxyl group.

The value of quinine lies in its specific action in the treatment of malaria. It is estimated that throughout the world there are several hundred million cases of malaria per year, resulting in 3 million deaths and partial or total debilitation for the remainder. Although annual production of quinine has reached 600 tons it is only a fraction of what would be needed to treat all cases even if the cost were not prohibitive for most of the victims. Starting from the observation of Ehrlich (p. 903) in 1891 that methylene blue (p. 696) has anti-malarial action, chemists at the I. G. Farbenindustrie of Germany began an extensive program of synthesis and testing which resulted in the introduction of **Plasmochin** (pamaquine) in 1926. It had the desirable property not possessed by quinine of being able to kill the sexual form of the parasite, thus preventing the spread of malaria by mosquitoes. Its toxic effects precluded its general use, however, and **Atabrine** (quinacrine) was introduced in 1930.

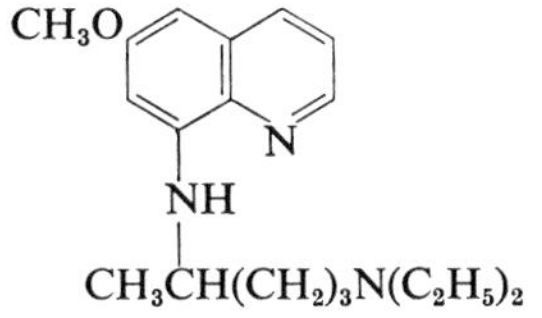

Plasmochin (pamaquine) 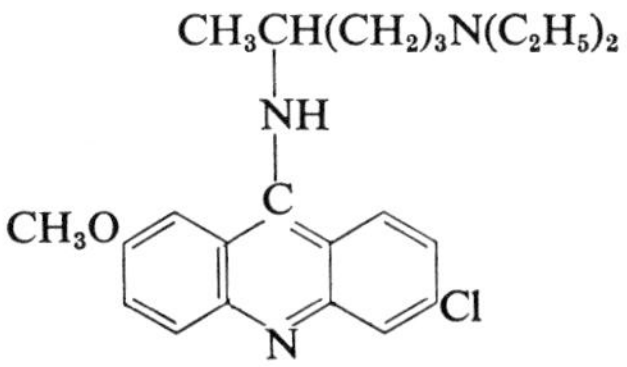   Atabrine (quinacrine)

Atabrine, like quinine, acts on the schizont stage of the parasite and reduces the formation of the gametocytes whose asexual reproduction causes the destruction of red blood corpuscles and leads to the symptomatic chills and fever. Atabrine was not used extensively, however, until World War II cut off supplies of quinine from Java. Having become familiar with Atabrine, physicians preferred it to quinine. However, its use was abandoned because it causes the skin to become yellow.

Between 1920 and 1930, during the development of Plasmochin and Atabrine, over 12,000 compounds were prepared and tested. With the advent of tropical warfare in World War II, an intensive search for better antimalarials was undertaken in the United States, Canada, and England. In this program over 14,000 compounds were screened. The formulas are given for several that have been found useful. **Chloroquine** proved to be more satisfactory than Atabrine in extensive clinical trials with human patients, but it now is being superseded by **primaquine.**

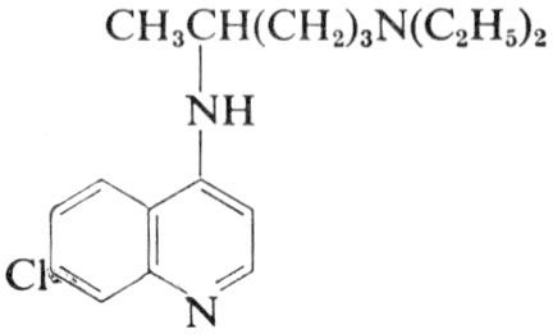

Chloroquine
(Aralen)

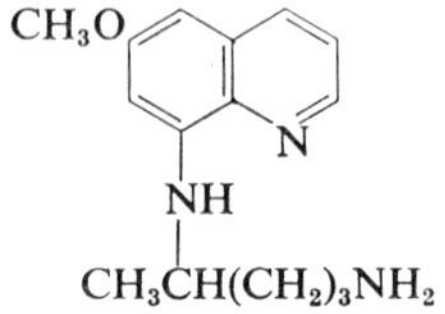

Primaquine

Daraprim and **paludrine** are of interest in that they do not contain the quinoline nucleus.

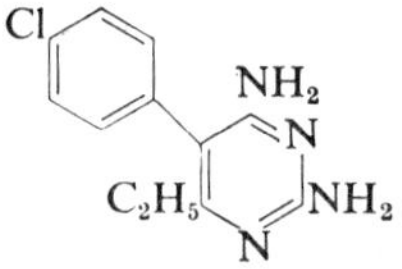

Daraprim

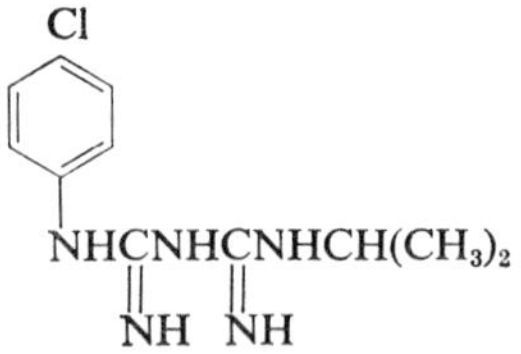

Paludrine

The **ergot alkaloids** are derived from ergot, a fungus that grows on rye and other cereals. They are responsible for a disease known as *ergotism* that was prevalent in the Middle Ages. All are amides of **lysergic acid. Ergonovine,** which is the amide of 2-amino-1-propanol, is used medicinally to induce uterine contractions at childbirth. The administration of the synthetic **diethylamide** produces a psychosis resembling schizophrenia.

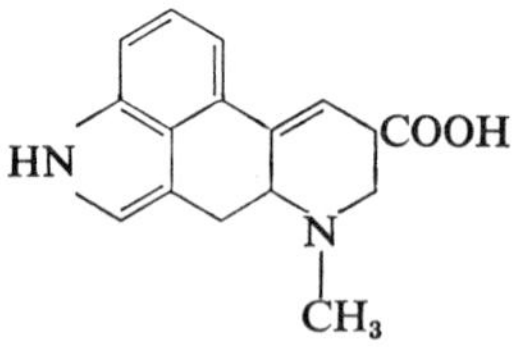

Lysergic acid

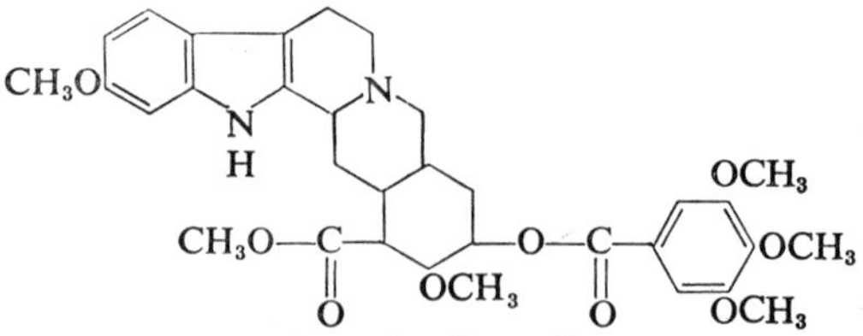

Reserpine (Serpasil)

Rauwolfia serpentina (Indian snake root) is a shrub that grows in the hot moist regions of India. Extracts of the root have been used as a remedy for fever, snake bite, and dysentery. In recent times it has been used to lower blood pressure and to treat some types of insanity. The active alkaloid was isolated in a pure state in 1952 and named **reserpine** or **Serpasil.** Since then it has been used extensively in the treatment of hypertension and as a general sedative. Violent schizophrenics are calmed without being put to sleep. Thus they become amenable to psychiatric treatment, and frequently the necessity of hospitalization is avoided. Reserpine is a striking example of the commercial aspects of a new drug. First isolated in 1952, it accounted for over a fourth of the total sales of a large pharmaceutical company in 1954. Although a complicated molecule, its structure was established by 1955 and its synthesis announced in 1956. Chlorpromazine (p. 643) and meprobamate (p. 315) are widely used synthetic tranquilizing drugs, and numerous others are rapidly being introduced.

REVIEW QUESTIONS

1. Define the term *heterocyclic compound*. What are the more common hetero atoms?
2. Compare the physical and chemical properties of thiophene and benzene? How did thiophene happen to be discovered? How is it synthesized?
3. Give a laboratory method for the preparation of pyrrole? Compare its physical properties with those of pyridine.
4. The reactions of pyrrole usually are stated to resemble those of phenol. Give specific examples to illustrate this point.
5. What is the *porphin nucleus* and why is it important?
6. Write structural formulas for proline, indole, tryptophan, and skatole, and indicate a source or method of preparation for each.
7. What compound is used as a starting point for the synthesis of furan and its more common derivatives? How is this compound prepared?
8. Give reactions for the action on furfural of aqueous permanganate; hydrogen and a platinum catalyst; strong aqueous sodium hydroxide; dilute aqueous potassium cyanide; acetone and sodium hydroxide; ammonia; acetic anhydride in the presence of sodium acetate.
9. What are the sources of pyridine? Why is it more stable to substitution reactions than benzene? What are some of its common laboratory uses?
10. Give a reaction for the conversion of pyridine into a piperidine. Give a reaction for the synthesis of piperidine that can be considered to be a proof of structure. What are the chemical properties of piperidine?
11. What are the picolines; the lutidines; the collidines?
12. What reaction do α- and γ-picoline undergo that β-picoline does not?
13. How can β-picolinic acid be made? What is another name for it and why is it important?
14. Give reactions illustrating what is believed to take place in the Skraup synthesis of quinoline; the Doebner-Miller synthesis of quinaldine.
15. What is the structural formula for isoquinoline; for phenanthridine?
16. What are the pyrimidines and purines? What is the fundamental ring structure of each?
17. What are the sources and structures of uric acid; theophylline; theobromine; caffeine?
18. Define the term *alkaloid*. What is the constitution of coniine; piperine; cocaine; morphine; quinine?

PROBLEMS

19. Tell how one may distinguish readily by chemical reactions between the members of the following pairs of compounds: (*a*) benzaldehyde and furfural; (*b*) pyridine and piperidine; (*c*) α-picoline and β-picoline; (*d*) thiophene and benzene; (*e*) furoic acid and benzoic acid; (*f*) α-picolinic acid and β-picolinic acid; (*g*) quinoline and quinaldine; (*h*) quinoline and tetralin; (*i*) phthalic acid and quinolinic acid; (*j*) phenanthridine and *o*-phenanthroline; (*k*) 6-hydroxyquinoline and 8-hydroxyquiniline; (*l*) 2-hydroxyquinoline and 3-hydroxyquinoline; (*m*) pyrrole and pyrrolidine; (*n*) coniine and nicotine; (*o*) capsaicin and piperine; (*p*) pethidine and methadone; (*q*) *o*-phenylenediamine and *m*-phenylenediamine; (*r*) benzil and dibenzoylmethane.
20. Give a series of reactions for the following preparations: (*a*) 2-thiophenecarboxylic acid from thiophene; (*b*) thienylacetic acid from thiophene; (*c*) methyl α-pyrryl ketone from pyrrole; (*d*) pyrrolidine from galactose; (*e*) pyrrolidone from tetrahydrofuran; (*f*) β-methylindole from aniline; (*g*) α-methylindole from *o*-toluidine; (*h*) 4-methoxypyridine from pyridine; (*i*) 4-bromopyridine from pyridine; (*j*) 2-hydroxypyridine from pyridine; (*k*)

1-phenyl-2-α-pyridylethane from α-picoline; (*l*) 2-ethylpyridine from α-picoline; (*m*) 3-pyridinealdehyde from pyridine.

21. Give reactions for the following syntheses: (*a*) 5-nitrofurfural semicarbazone from furfural; (*b*) proline from tetrahydrofuran; (*c*) isonicotinic acid hydrazide from γ-picoline; (*d*) 2-pyridinealdoxime methiodide from α-picoline; (*e*) Pyribenzamine from pyridine and other readily available chemicals; (*f*) 2-chloroquinoline from *o*-nitrobenzaldehyde; (*g*) papaverine from vanillin; (*h*) phenylalanine from hippuric acid; (*i*) 1,3-dichloro-5,5-dimethylhydantoin from *i*-butyric acid; (*j*) Dilantin from benzaldehyde; (*k*) leucine from rhodanine; (*l*) triphenyltetrazolium chloride from benzaldehyde and aniline; (*m*) Tetrazolium Blue from benzaldehyde and *o*-anisole; (*n*) 8-hydroxyquinoline from phenol; (*o*) 6-chloroquinoline from benzene; (*p*) *o*-phenanthroline from *o*-nitroaniline; (*q*) 6-methoxyquinaldine from anisole; (*r*) tetrahydropyran from furfural; (*s*) 2,3-diphenylquinoxaline from benzaldehyde.

22. Anthranilic acid is treated in hydrochloric acid solution at 0° with sodium nitrite, cuprous chloride is added, and the solution warmed. The resulting compound *A* is heated with a mixture of nitric and sulfuric acids to give *B*, which when heated with aniline gives *C*, $C_{13}H_{10}N_2O_4$. *C* is treated with tin and hydrochloric acid to give *D*, which, after isolation, is dissolved in hydrochloric acid and cooled. Sodium nitrite is first added and then hypophosphorous acid and the solution warmed. The product *E* has the formula $C_{13}H_{11}NO_2$. When *E* is heated with concentrated sulfuric acid, compound *F*, $C_{13}H_9NO$, is obtained which, when heated with zinc dust, yields *G*, $C_{13}H_9N$. Give the reactions involved, with structural formulas and names for the organic products.

23. Compound *A* is optically active and has the molecular formula $C_8H_{14}O_2S_2$. It dissolves readily in aqueous bicarbonate and is precipitated unchanged by acidifying the alkaline solution. Reduction with zinc and hydrochloric acid gives *B*, $C_8H_{16}O_2S_2$, which is reconverted to *A* with sodium hypoiodite solution. When *A* is heated with Raney nickel containing adsorbed hydrogen, it is converted to octanoic acid. No acetic acid is formed when *A* is heated with chromium trioxide and distilled (cf. p. 144). Give the likely structures for *A* and equations for the reactions that it undergoes.

24. Compound *A*, $C_{10}H_{13}N$, is soluble in dilute hydrochloric acid and reacts with benzenesulfonyl chloride to give a derivative insoluble in dilute aqueous sodium hydroxide. When subjected to the Hofmann exhaustive methylation and decomposition of the quaternary hydroxide, *A* is converted into compound *B*, $C_{12}H_{17}N$. *B* is soluble in dilute acid but does not react with acetyl chloride. When the exhaustive methylation and decomposition procedure is repeated on *B*, compound *C*, $C_{10}H_{10}$, is formed. *C* decolorizes bromine in carbon tetrachloride rapidly without the evolution of hydrogen bromide. Vigorous oxidation converts either *A*, *B*, or *C* into compound *D*. *D* is soluble in dilute alkali and has a neutralization equivalent of 83. When heated, *D* is converted into compound *E*, $C_8H_4O_3$. Give a structural formula for *A* and equations for the reactions involved.

25. Give equations for the following reactions with structural formulas for the organic compounds: Vanillin treated with methyl sulfate and sodium hydroxide gives compound *A*. When an alcoholic solution of *A* is shaken with hydrogen and platinum catalyst, compound *B* is formed. *B* reacts with dry hydrogen chloride to give *C*, which reacts with sodium cyanide in the presence of cuprous cyanide to give *D*. When *D* is boiled with alcohol containing sulfuric acid, *E* is obtained. When *D* is shaken with hydrogen at 250 pounds pressure in the presence of Raney nickel, compound *F* is obtained. Heating *E* and *F* together in tetralin at the boiling point gives *G*. Refluxing *G* in toluene solution with phosphorus oxychloride gives *H*. When *H* is heated with platinum black, compound *I* is obtained, which has the molecular formula $C_{20}H_{21}NO_4$.

26. Give equations for the following transformations: Vigorous sulfonation of benzene, liming out, concentration, and fusing with sodium hydroxide gives a melt from which, after acidification, compound *A*, $C_6H_6O_2$, can be isolated. When hydrogen chloride is passed into a mixture of *A* and zinc cyanide in benzene and the reaction product is decomposed with water, compound *B*, $C_7H_6O_3$, is obtained. Heating *B* with acetic anhydride and sodium acetate gives *C*, $C_{13}H_{12}O_6$. Saponification of *C* and acidification gives compound *D*, $C_9H_6O_3$.

Chapter 30 ✓

VIBRATIONAL AND ELECTRONIC ABSORPTION SPECTRA. NUCLEAR- AND ELECTRON-SPIN RESONANCE

The application of physical methods always has been important for the characterization and the determination of structure of organic compounds. The routine use of these methods by organic chemists has depended on the complexity of the apparatus, the time and patience required for the measurements, the training and knowledge required for the operation of the equipment and for the interpretation of the results, and the usefulness of the information that is obtained. Among the simplest procedures may be mentioned the determination of melting point, boiling point, refractive index, and optical rotation. The usefulness of the last procedure is being extended by making measurements with ultraviolet as well as visible light. Among the more complicated procedures should be mentioned the X-ray diffraction of crystals and the electron diffraction of gases, liquids, or solids. They yield valuable information regarding the distances and bond angles between atoms but are too complicated both as to equipment and interpretation for routine use. One exception to this statement is the comparison of the X-ray diffraction pattern of a known and unknown compound for the purpose of establishing identity or nonidentity of the samples. The determination of molecular weights by mass spectrometry, sedimentation and diffusion, or light-scattering is somewhat less complicated, but the use of these procedures is limited to compounds of very low and very high molecular weights.

It long has been recognized that valuable information concerning the structure of organic molecules can be obtained by determining the intensity of the absorption of electromagnetic radiation at different wavelengths. Three regions of the spectrum are important for this purpose. The wavelengths absorbed by a molecule in the portion of the **microwave region** from one millimeter to a few centimeters in wavelength are due to the differences in energy of the various rotational states of the molecule. They give the principal moments of inertia of the molecule from which intermolecular distances and bond angles of simple molecules may be calculated. Moreover, although the absorption spectrum in this region cannot be used to identify functional groups in a molecule, it is characteristic of the molecule as a whole and can be used to identify the molecule. Thus far, the organic chemist has made little use of microwave spectroscopy.

Far different is the situation as regards absorption in the portion of the **infrared region** from wavelength 2.5 microns (2.5 μ = 0.0025 mm.) to 15 microns (15 μ = 0.015 mm.) and in the portion of the **ultraviolet** and **visible region** from 200 millimicrons (200 mμ = 0.2 μ = 0.0002 mm.) to 800 millimicrons (800 mμ). The magnitude of the energy of radiation in the infrared is such as to cause vibrations within the molecule, whereas the higher energy of the visible and ultraviolet radiation can cause electronic transitions. Both are intimately connected with the bonding forces between atoms within the molecule and can be

TABLE 27

REGIONS OF THE ELECTROMAGNETIC SPECTRUM

REGION	WAVELENGTH*,†
Cosmic rays	0.00005 mμ
Gamma rays	0.001–0.14 mμ
X-rays	0.01–15 mμ
Far ultraviolet	15–200 mμ
Near ultraviolet	200–400 mμ
Visible	400–800 mμ
Near infrared	0.8–2.5 μ
Vibrational infrared	2.5–25 μ
Far infrared	0.025–0.5 mm.
Microwave radar	0.5–300 mm.
Short radio	0.3–30 m.
Broadcast radio	30–550 m.
Long radio	above 550 m.

* 1 Millimicron (mμ) = 0.001 micron (μ); 1 micron = 0.001 millimeter (mm.); 1 millimeter = 0.001 meter (m.).

† The dividing lines between the various regions are not sharply defined. Each portion overlaps the adjacent portions at both ends.

used in the determination of structure. Moreover, since around 1940, commercial instruments have become available which anyone can operate and which in a matter of minutes record a complete spectrum as a graph.

More recently equipment has become available for determining nuclear- and electron-spin resonance, which makes use of the **radio frequency range** of the electromagnetic spectrum for their detection. This new research tool also is rapidly coming into use for arriving at the structure of chemical compounds.

VIBRATIONAL OR INFRARED SPECTRA

The positions of atoms in molecules are equilibrium positions; that is, they are the positions at which the attraction of nuclei for electrons balances the repulsion of nuclei for nuclei and of electrons for electrons. Hence atoms can be forced closer together or pushed farther apart, and bond angles can be decreased or increased. On removal of the distorting force the atoms return to their original positions. Thus the bonds between atoms may be looked upon as springs subject to stretching, bending, and twisting vibrations. Each vibration has its natural period, which depends on the mass of the atoms and the strength of the bonds. Furthermore a difference in charge usually exists between two bonded atoms, one being slightly more negative or more positive than the other. As an electromagnetic wave passes a molecule, the wave's electric field intensifies the vibrations of the atoms, pushing them together or pulling them apart. Since this electric field is oscillating (p. 330), it will be most effective when its frequency matches the natural frequency of a particular vibration. If this vibration causes a change in the dipole moment of the molecule, some of the radiant energy is absorbed, and the intensity of the radiation at this particular wavelength is decreased on passing through the substance. Thus carbon dioxide, a linear molecule, has three nonequivalent modes of vibration: (*a*) that in which one oxygen atom moves toward the carbon atom as the other moves away; (*b*) that in which both oxygen atoms move toward the carbon atom or away from it simultaneously; and (*c*) that in which the molecule is deformed by a back and forth bending motion about the center of the molecule.

(*a*)   O⌇C⌇O   O⌇C⌇O   O⌇C⌇O   Antisymmetrical stretching

(*b*)   O⌇C⌇O   O⌇C⌇O   O⌇C⌇O   Symmetrical stretching

(*c*)   [bent structure]   O⌇C⌇O   [bent structure]   Deformation

Carbon dioxide absorbs radiation, however, at only two wavelengths, namely 4.2 μ corresponding to the antisymmetrical stretching and 15 μ corresponding to the deformation. The symmetrical stretching does not cause a change in dipole moment and does not absorb energy from the radiation.

Energy can be transferred only in packets known as *quanta*. The energy of a quantum of electromagnetic radiation, called a *photon*, is equal to the product of the Planck constant and the velocity of light, divided by the wavelength. Hence the shorter the wavelength, the greater the amount of energy in the packet; the longer the wavelength the less the energy in the packet. The wavelengths that possess just the right energy to cause molecular vibrations lie in the infrared portion of the spectrum. Although the infrared region extends from 0.8 μ to 500 μ (Table 27, p. 658), the portion from 2 μ to 15 μ, commonly called the vibrational region, is most useful to the chemist, and it is this region that is covered by commercial instruments and is usually meant when infrared spectra are discussed.

The mechanical operation of determining infrared spectra consists of placing a sample of the substance in the path of a source of infrared radiation, usually a rod of carborundum heated to 1200°, and measuring from the shortest to the longest wavelength the per cent of the original intensity of the radiation that is transmitted by the sample. The instrument records the result as a graph in which the per cent transmission usually is plotted against the wavelength in microns. In such graphs the absorption maxima or peaks appear as minima or valleys. It should be stated here that the graphical representation of absorption spectra has not been standardized. Per cent absorption or other methods of expressing absorption may be used, and wavelength frequently is replaced by *wavenumber*, which is the reciprocal of the wavelength in centimeters, or 10,000 divided by the wavelength in microns.

Figure 88 gives the spectra for several simple compounds. The assignment that has been made for some of the absorption bands is indicated. The intensity of the absorption (depth of the band) is proportional roughly to the change in the dipole moment caused by the vibration. Hence bonds that have a high bond moment, such as O—H, N—H, C—O and C—N, show intense absorption. The region of absorption for single bonds between atoms differing greatly in mass, for example O—H, N—H, or C—H, lies between 2.7 μ and 3.7 μ, that for triple bonds lies between 4.4 μ and 4.8 μ, and that for double bonds between 5.3 μ and 6.7 μ. These bands are caused by stretching vibrations. The region between 6.7 μ and 15 μ commonly is called the *profile region*. Here the various

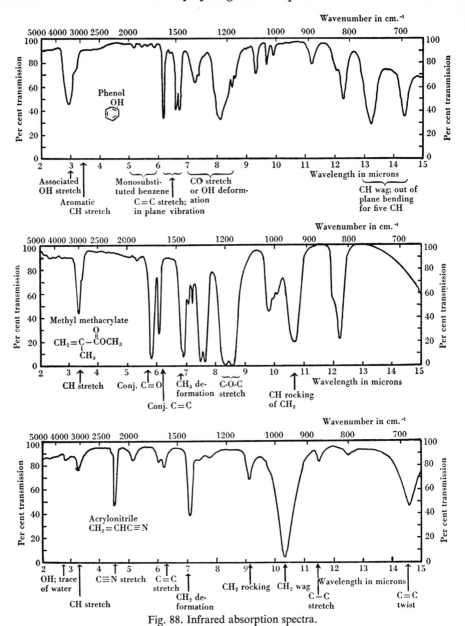

Fig. 88. Infrared absorption spectra.

absorption bands arise from the stretching, bending, and twisting vibrations of single bonds. Because of the large number of possible modes of vibration, it usually is difficult to assign the individual bands to a specific type of vibration, but the spectrum is very characteristic of the particular compound.

In addition to the bands resulting from fundamental modes of vibration, overtones may appear at wavelengths corresponding to frequencies that are an even multiple of the fundamental frequency. These bands usually are very weak, but the intensity may amount to as much as 10 per cent of that of the fundamental frequency. If the latter is a strong band, the overtone may be as strong as some of the weaker bands caused by fundamental vibrations.

Although it frequently is possible to determine from the infrared spectrum the presence of specific structural details in an unknown compound, it is not always a simple procedure and the interpretation must be confirmed by chemical evidence. Theoretically every different compound, except for enantiomorphs, has a different infrared spectrum, and comparison of spectra is one of the best methods for establishing the identity or nonidentity of a compound of unknown structure with one of known structure.

ELECTRONIC (ULTRAVIOLET AND VISIBLE) SPECTRA

The graphical representation ordinarily used for ultraviolet and visible spectra differs from that used for infrared spectra. The unit of wavelength is the millimicron (1 mμ = 0.001 μ). The absorption is expressed as the **extinction**, E, (also called *optical density*, D, or *absorbance*) which is the logarithm of the ratio of the intensity, I_0, of the incident light to the intensity, I, of the transmitted light. The intensity of ultraviolet and visible light can be measured accurately more readily than the intensity of infrared radiation, and absorption usually is expressed on a quantitative rather than on a qualitative basis. Frequently the extinction is given for a solution thickness of 1 cm. and a concentration of 1 per cent, for which the symbol is $E_{1\,cm.}^{1\%}$. If the molecular weight of the compound is known, the absorption usually is expressed as the molecular extinction coefficient, ϵ, which is defined by the equation

$$\epsilon = \log \frac{I_0}{I} \times \frac{\text{Mol. wt.}}{c\,d}$$

where c is the concentration in grams per liter, and d is the thickness in centimeters of the solution through which the light passes. The maximum value of ϵ to be expected is about 10^5. For large values the extinction usually is expressed as log E or log ϵ. Since absorption is being plotted rather than transmittance, the absorption peaks are maxima in the ultraviolet and visible curves rather than minima as in the infrared curves.

In contrast to the absorption of infrared radiation, which is caused by molecular vibrations, the absorption of ultraviolet and visible radiation results from electronic excitation. In molecules at ordinary temperatures the electrons are in orbitals having the lowest possible energy, a condition known as the *ground state*. Higher orbitals are empty, but it requires energy to cause the transfer (transition) of an electron from a lower orbital to a higher orbital, and the kinetic energy of the molecules is not sufficiently high to do this except at high temperatures. It happens, however, that electromagnetic vibrations having wavelengths between 100 mμ and 1300 mμ, that is, in the ultraviolet, visible, and near infrared, have just the right energy range to cover the energy range of the lower electronic transitions of molecules. Hence the energy of a light wave can be used to transfer an electron from its ground state to the next higher orbital, during which process light of that particular wavelength is absorbed.

When an electronic transition takes place in atoms, only a single wavelength which has just the right energy to bring about the transfer of an electron to a higher orbital is absorbed. The result is a line spectrum. For the hydrogen atom the single electron in the ground state is in the $1s$ orbital. The orbital of next higher energy is the $2s$ orbital. However in order for the light wave to be able to transfer its energy to the atom with a high degree of probability, a quantum-mechanical condition, namely the existence of a nonvanishing transition dipole, must be met by the occupied and unoccupied orbitals. The $1s \longrightarrow 2s$ transition does not satisfy this condition, but the next higher transition, $1s \longrightarrow 2p$ does. The energy associated with this change is 235 kcal. per mole and accounts for the strong line in the far ultraviolet at 120 mμ (Fig. 89).

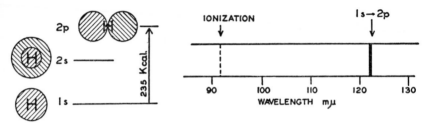

Fig. 89. First electronic transition and the resulting absorption spectrum of the hydrogen atom (after Bowen).

Molecules, however, have more than one positive nucleus, and when an electronic transition takes place, an alteration in the internuclear distance results and changes take place in the rotational and vibrational energies. Hence absorption is not confined to a single wavelength but extends over a broad spectral region and gives what is known as a *band system*. Thus in the ground state of the hydrogen molecule, two electrons are in a cylindrically symmetrical molecular orbital designated as σ_g. The next higher molecular orbital is dumb-bell-shaped with a nodal plane perpendicular to the internuclear axis and designated as σ_u. Transition of one electron from the σ_g to the σ_u orbital results from the absorption of light in the region of 110 mμ, but a number of wave-lengths are absorbed because of the accompanying rotational and vibrational changes (Fig. 90).

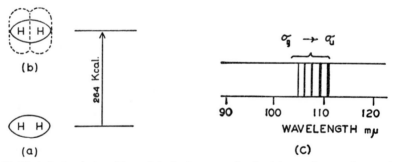

Fig. 90. First electronic transition of the hydrogen molecule: (*a*) two electrons in σ_g orbital; (*b*) one electron in σ_g and one in σ_u orbital; (*c*) absorption spectrum resulting from the transition.

The single bonds in organic molecules consist of a pair of electrons in σ-type orbitals and absorption is in the far ultraviolet as for the hydrogen molecule. It makes little difference whether hydrogen, carbon, nitrogen, or oxygen atoms are combined as long as only single bonds are involved. If a double bond is present, however, one pair of electrons is in a π orbital, designated as π_u, which has a nodal plane in the plane of the single links (p. 50 and Fig. 91a). The next higher π orbital, called π_g, has in addition a nodal plane perpendicular to the σ-type C—C linkage (Fig. 91b). The energy difference between the π_u and the π_g

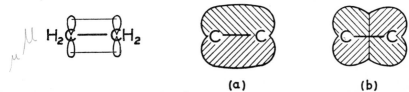

Fig. 91. π Orbitals of ethylene: (a) π_u orbital; (b) π_g orbital.

orbitals is less than that between a σ_g and a σ_u orbital; that is, the electrons are bound less strongly, and light of lower energy (longer wavelength) can bring about the transition. Thus the longest wavelength absorbed by ethane is 140 mμ, whereas ethylene absorbs at 162 mμ. In the excited state the presence of one electron in an orbital having a nodal plane perpendicular to the σ bond reduces the energy necessary to cause free rotation about the bond, which explains the effect of light on *cis-trans* isomerization (pp. 356, 500, 576).

If two isolated double bonds are present in a molecule, the absorption represents simply the sum of the separate absorptions. If, however, the double bonds are conjugated, it is possible for the wave functions of all four p orbitals to coalesce, giving rise to an entirely new set of molecular orbitals (Fig. 92). The most stable of these orbitals, π_u, results from the coalescence of all four p

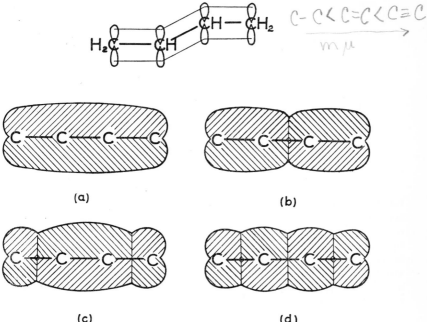

(a)   (b)

(c)   (d)

Fig. 92. π Orbitals of 1,3-butadiene, CH_2=$CHCH$=CH_2.

orbitals in such a way that the number of nodal planes is a minimum as represented by (a). Like all orbitals, the π_u orbital can contain at most two electrons in accordance with the Pauli exclusion principle. Hence the second pair is in a π_g orbital having a second nodal plane perpendicular to the first as illustrated in (b). These two orbitals together with the σ_g orbitals accommodate all of the valence electrons in the ground state. The next two higher orbitals, (c) and (d), have two and three nodal planes perpendicular to the first nodal plane. Absorption of light of the proper wavelength causes transition of an electron from either (a) or (b) to either (c) or (d), giving rise to four band systems. The transition requiring the least energy and hence the absorption of the longest wavelength is (b) $\longrightarrow$ (c). The energy difference of (b) and (c) is only 130 kcal. per mole and causes strong absorption ($\epsilon = 10^4$) at about 220 mμ. Since air does not transmit light of shorter wavelength than about 200 mμ, this band is the first that can be observed conveniently for organic molecules.

As the number of double bonds in conjugation increases, the number of π orbitals necessary to accommodate the unsaturation electrons increases. Since an electron can be transferred from any ground state orbital to that of the lowest excited state, the number of band systems equals the square of the number of double bonds in conjugation. Moreover the difference in energy between the highest occupied π orbital in the ground state and that for the first excited state decreases with each additional double bond, and the longest wavelength absorption moves toward the red (Fig. 93). By the time eight or nine double

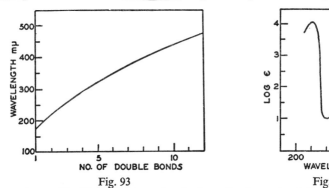

Fig. 93 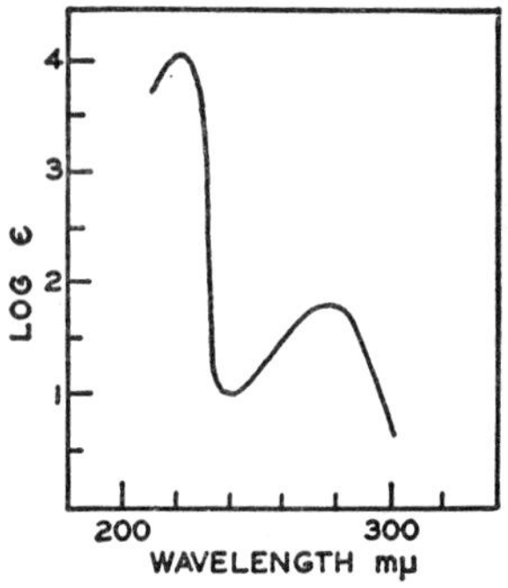   Fig. 94
Fig. 93. Longest wavelength absorption by conjugated polyenes.
Fig. 94. Absorption spectrum of mesityl oxide, $(CH_3)_2C{=}CHCOCH_3$, a conjugated unsaturated ketone.

bonds are in conjugation, absorption is taking place in the blue region of the spectrum and the compound appears yellow. As conjugation continues to increase, the absorption progresses through the visible causing color changes through orange, red, and purple. A compound is colorless again if the band moves into the infrared unless, as usually happens, a new band moves into the visible. If two or more bands are sufficiently close together, several may appear in the visible simultaneously, and the color depends on the remainder of the light that is transmitted or reflected (p. 670). The position of the absorption maximum is influenced to some extent by the replacement of hydrogen by other groups. For 1,3-dienes the band $\lambda_{max.} = 217$ mμ is shifted about 5 mμ towards the red for each hydrogen atom replaced by an alkyl group.

Carbon-oxygen and carbon-nitrogen double bonds resemble carbon-carbon double bonds in that the two pairs of electrons forming the double bond are in a σ orbital and a π orbital. Hence similar electronic transitions occur. Formaldehyde absorbs at 190 mμ, corresponding possibly to the absorption at 162 mμ by ethylene, because of the transition of an electron from the π_u orbital to the π_g orbital. Formaldehyde, however, and other aldehydes and ketones as well, absorb also at about 280 mμ ($\epsilon = 10^2$), whereas ethylene and its homologs do not. This band appears to be the result of a transition not of a π electron, but of one of the p electrons of the oxygen atom to the unoccupied π_g orbital. Similarly azomethane, $CH_3N{=}NCH_3$, gives a high intensity absorption at $\lambda_{max.} = 245$ mμ and a low intensity band at $\lambda_{max.} = 345$ mμ. The latter band is sufficiently broad to extend well into the visible, and azomethane is yellow. Neither the carboxyl group nor the nitrile group exhibits appreciable absorption in the ultraviolet.

A carbon-carbon double bond conjugated with a carbonyl group gives rise to a high intensity absorption ($\epsilon = 10^4$) at about the same place ($\lambda_{max.} = 220$ mμ) as two conjugated carbon-carbon bonds. Again the position of the maximum is shifted to the red with increasing substitution at the carbon-carbon double bond. The lower intensity absorption due to the carbonyl group remains at about 280 mμ (Fig. 94).

If two carbonyl groups are in conjugation as in diacetyl, $CH_3COCOCH_3$, two absorption bands occur, one at 280 mμ and the other in the visible extending from about 400 to 460 mμ (Fig. 95), and the compound is yellow. The short

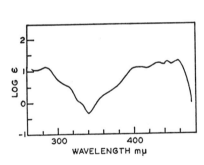

Fig. 95. Absorption spectrum of diacetyl, $CH_3COCOCH_3$, a conjugated diketone.

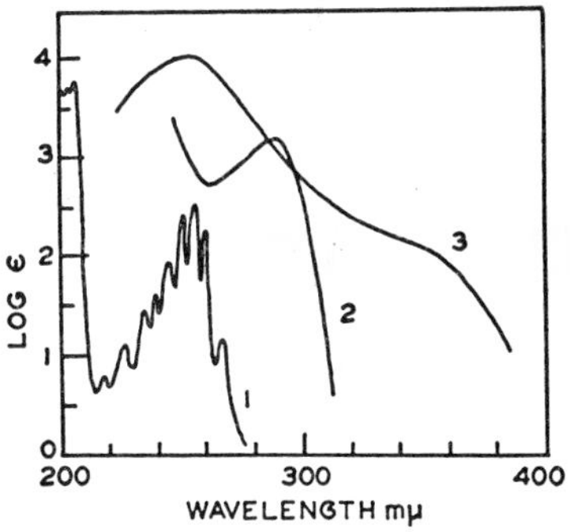

Fig. 96. Absorption spectra of (*1*) benzene, (*2*) aniline, and (*3*) nitrobenzene.

wavelength band corresponds to the 220 mμ band of conjugated dienes, but the transition causing the long wavelength absorption probably involves an electron from an oxygen p orbital rather than one from a π_u orbital. Similarly conjugation of N=N with phenyl groups in azobenzene (p. 459) shifts the long wavelength band of yellow azomethane further towards the red ($\lambda_{max.} = 448$ mμ), and the compound is orange. The short wavelength band ($\lambda_{max.} = 313$ mμ) corresponds to that for colorless *trans*-stilbene ($\lambda_{max.} = 300$ mμ).

For an electronic transition to occur with high probability, a transition dipole must exist (p. 662). This condition is related closely to the symmetry of the molecule. Benzene with three conjugated double bonds might be expected to absorb strongly in the ultraviolet. Although a band appears at about 260 mμ, it is relatively weak (Fig. 96). For a perfectly hexagonal molecule the transition corresponding to this band is not possible, since the transition dipole is zero. Hence the faint band at this position, observed even with solid benzene at liquid hydrogen temperatures, must be due to the slight distortion of some molecules by crystal forces. In liquid or dissolved benzene at ordinary temperatures, the band is of moderate strength because of the effect of atomic vibrations in the molecule. Substituted benzenes absorb more strongly because the substituents cause a further disturbance of the symmetry of the molecular π orbitals. An amino or hydroxyl group not only greatly increases the intensity of absorption but also shifts the band to longer wavelengths because of the interaction of the unshared pair of electrons with the unsaturation electrons of the ring (p. 477); that is, the π orbitals now encompass the oxygen or nitrogen atom as well as the benzene ring, and the number of π orbitals is increased from three to four. With a nitro group as a substituent, the π orbitals encompass the benzene nucleus, the nitrogen atom, and the oxygen atoms, and the number of orbitals is further increased. Hence the absorption is still more intense and is shifted further towards the visible (Fig. 96).

p-Nitrophenol has a high intensity band near the ultraviolet ($\epsilon = 10^4$) because the excited electron vibrates across a considerable distance between polar groups, which gives rise to a high transition moment. In alkaline solution the absorption band is shifted to the visible giving a yellow salt. The removal of the proton and the resulting negative charge on the oxygen atom makes it easier for the unshared electrons to interact with the nucleus and the nitro group, thus permitting longer wavelengths to bring about the transition. The intensity of the absorption remains unchanged (Fig. 97). On the other hand, when a nuclear amino group

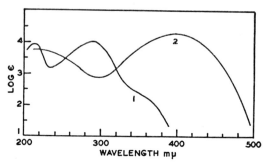

Fig. 97. Absorption spectra of *p*-nitrophenol (*1*) in hexane, and (*2*) in 0.1 *N* sodium hydroxide solution.

is converted to a salt, combination of the proton with the unshared pair of electrons prevents their interaction with those of the nucleus, and the absorption is shifted to shorter wavelengths. Thus the absorption of the anilinium ion is almost identical with that of benzene.

Increasing the number of fused nuclei in condensed aromatic ring systems leads to absorption at increasing wavelengths. Thus the long wavelength band of benzene is at 260 mμ, of naphthalene at 280 mμ, of anthracene at 375 mμ, of naphthacene at 450 mμ, and of pentacene at 575 mμ. Benzene, naphthalene, and anthracene are colorless, but naphthacene is orange and pentacene is purple. However, phenanthrene has the same number of fused rings as anthracene but absorbs at a shorter wavelength (350 mμ). Likewise coronene absorbs at a shorter wavelength (400 mμ) than naphthacene. Evidently this behavior is to be ascribed to the more completely aromatic character (higher resonance energy) of phenanthrene and coronene (p. 602), and consequently to a lower energy level for the highest filled molecular orbital.

Benzene	Naphthalene	Anthracene	Phenanthrene
$\lambda_{max.} = 260$ mμ	$\lambda_{max.} = 280$ mμ	$\lambda_{max.} = 375$ mμ	$\lambda_{max.} = 350$ mμ

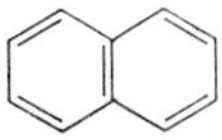

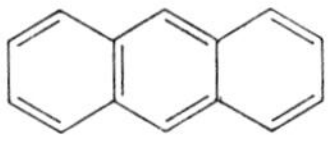

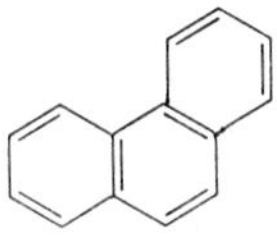

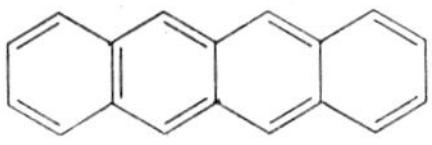

Naphthacene	Pentacene	Coronene
$\lambda_{max.} = 450$ mμ	$\lambda_{max.} = 575$ mμ	$\lambda_{max.} = 400$ mμ

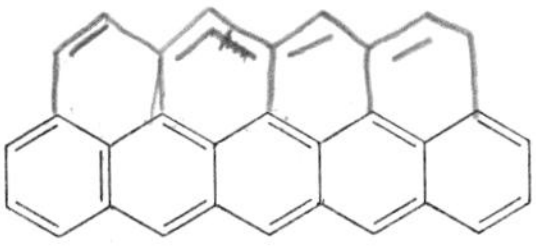

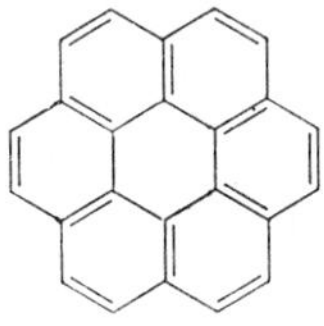

High intensity absorption in the visible is characteristic of organic dyes. They all have (*1*) a large number of conjugated double bonds, giving rise to a large number of π orbitals differing little in energy, and (*2*) two or more polar groups a considerable distance apart, which causes a large transition dipole.

Complexity of Spectra

The preceding abbreviated discussion may give the impression that it is an easy matter to identify the absorption bands of organic compounds with specific structural features of the molecule. Such is the case only for relatively simple chromophoric systems under certain conditions. Almost any external influence modifies the absorption spectrum of a molecule. Solvent molecules may produce electric and magnetic fields about the molecule which change the energy differences between the ground state and excited states, they may form solvates, or they may act as an acid or a base and alter the proportions in which a compound exists as a base and its conjugated acid. The solute itself may dissociate, polymerize, or isomerize in solution. All of these factors alter and increase the complexity of molecular spectra. Moreover many different electronic systems can give rise to absorption in the same region of the spectrum.

Fate of Absorbed Light; Fluorescence

Although the energy of absorbed electromagnetic radiation in the range 100 mμ–1300 mμ is used to bring about electronic transitions, the molecules do not remain in the excited state but revert almost instantly to the ground state. Ordinarily the mean life of an excited molecule is about 10^{-8} sec. The energy liberated usually is converted by collision or other processes into heat; that is, the material which absorbs light becomes warmer. The energy may be dissipated also by inducing photochemical reaction, which accounts for the fading of colored substances in light. Some molecules, however, are resistant to electronic deactivation by collision or by photochemical reaction, and the energy is re-emitted as light, a phenomenon known as fluorescence. Since some of the absorbed energy has been used to produce vibrational excitation which is removed readily by collision, the re-emitted light is of lower energy, that is, of longer wavelength, than the absorbed light. Thus a colorless substance like anthracene, having an absorption band in the near ultraviolet, fluoresces in the visible.

NUCLEAR- AND ELECTRON-SPIN RESONANCE

The nuclei of certain isotopes have a magnetic moment caused by the spin of the nucleus. If a substance that contains an isotope having a spin quantum number of one half, such as H^1, F^{19}, or P^{31}, is placed in a strong magnetic field, the nuclear magnetic moment lines up either parallel or antiparallel to the applied field. A difference in energy exists for these two states. If electromagnetic radiation of the right frequency in the radio range is passed into the substance, the nuclei absorb it and go from the state of lower energy to that of higher energy. The frequency at which this takes place is called the *resonance frequency*. If the extent of absorption at various frequencies is plotted against the frequency, a graph is obtained that is characteristic of the compound. This graph is called the *nuclear magnetic resonance (NMR) spectrum* or the *nuclear-spin resonance (NSR) spectrum of the compound*.

Of the abundant isotopes that have a strong nuclear magnetic moment, hydrogen is the most important to the organic chemist. Carbon, oxygen, and sulfur have zero nuclear magnetic moment and cannot be detected, and the moment of nitrogen is weak. Boron, fluorine and phosphorus have strong moments which can be observed when these elements are present in organic compounds. Most elements have at least one isotope with a reasonably strong moment, for example C^{13} and O^{17}, that can be introduced into organic compounds if necessary for special purposes. However, except for special applications, routine determination of nuclear magnetic resonance spectra (usually called NMR) is confined mostly to hydrogen. Here it is considered sufficiently important to justify the high cost ($20,000 to $40,000) for the necessary equipment. The reason is that the nuclear magnetic spectrum is characteristic of the structural environment of hydrogen, which is difficult to determine by other physical methods. The effective magnetic field at the hydrogen nucleus is not the same as the applied field because of the shielding effect of the electrons around it. Hence the amount of resonance energy that must be supplied is different for different electron densities about the nucleus. Figure 98a is a trace of the nuclear magnetic resonance signals for ethanol. Not only does the position of the maximum

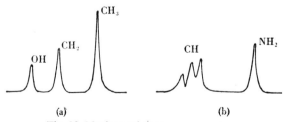

(a)   (b)

Fig. 98. Nuclear-spin resonance spectra.

indicate the kind of hydrogen present, but the areas under the peaks give the relative number of each kind of hydrogen. Because of the electron-attracting effect of the oxygen atom, the order of electron-shielding of the protons is $OH < CH_2 < CH_3$. Figure 98*b* shows the same effect of nitrogen in aniline on the protons in the amino group and in the *ortho*, *meta*, and *para* positions of the benzene ring. Here the H—C bands are to the left of the H—N bands because of the high electron density of the benzene nucleus. Higher resolution shows that the main peaks are accompanied by a fine structure which further characterizes the structural environment of the hydrogen atoms.

The spin of an unpaired electron also produces a magnetic moment and, when present in free radicals, can give rise to resonance phenomena analogous to those caused by nuclear spin. *Electron-spin resonance (ESR)* also is called *electron paramagnetic resonance (EPR)*. Electron-spin resonance is more complicated than nuclear-spin resonance. The number of absorption lines observable is equal to one plus twice the magnetic quantum number of the nucleus with which the unpaired electron is associated. Thus an unpaired electron in the neighborhood of a C^{12} nucleus, for which the nuclear spin is zero, gives a single line. For H^1, with nuclear spin 1/2, splitting of the absorption line into two components occurs, and N^{14}, with nuclear spin 1, gives three lines. Moreover if the electron interacts with several "equivalent" nuclei, the total magnetic quantum number applies. Thus if interaction is with two nitrogen nuclei, five lines $[2(1 + 1) + 1]$ are observed, if with three hydrogen nuclei, four lines $[2(1/2 + 1/2 + 1/2) + 1]$. The observation that for stable free radicals the absorption line is split into numerous components is experimental evidence for the delocation of the electron. At high resolution triphenylmethyl gives a number of groups of multiple lines, indicating that the unpaired electron is interacting with all the nuclei of the molecule (cf. p. 569). The observation of 13 lines in the ESR spectrum of tetramethylsemiquinone anion (cf. p. 571) indicates that the unpaired electron is interacting with all twelve hydrogen atoms in the methyl groups. Resonance interaction involving the electrons of carbon-hydrogen bonds in methyl groups with unsaturation electrons has been postulated on chemical grounds and is known as *hyperconjugation*.

The extremely low concentration at which unpaired electrons now can be detected has made it possible to establish the existence of free radicals which were unobservable by static susceptibility methods. For example susceptibility measurements could not detect paramagnetism in *p,p'-bis*(diphenylmethyl)-biphenyl (*Chichibabin hydrocarbon*, p. 570), but ESR absorption indicates that about 4 per cent is in the form of biradicals. Free radicals also have been detected in polymers formed by free-radical catalyzed polymerizations and in substances that have been irradiated by high-energy particles. Moreover ESR absorption has been observed in substances not previously considered to contain molecules with unpaired electrons. Thus carbonium ions (p. 572) and carbanions (p. 573) appear to contain some ions in the biradical state.

Chapter 31

COLOR. DYES AND DYEING.
ORGANIC PIGMENTS

Color always has played an important role in the life of man, even though its significance is almost wholly esthetic. Throughout man's history dyes and pigments, both natural and synthetic, have been an important article of commerce.

COLOR

Color Sensation

The human eye is sensitive only to electromagnetic vibrations having a wavelength between 400 mμ and 750 mμ. This region of the electromagnetic spectrum is known as the *visible* (cf Table 28). The mixture of all wavelengths in the visible having the relative intensities produced by a body at a white heat is known as *white light*. If the light striking the retina of the eye does not contain all of the wavelengths of the visible spectrum, or if the intensity of some of them is reduced considerably, the sensation of color results.

Light may be colored because only a limited region of the spectrum is emitted by a light source, as for example the yellow light of the sodium flame. Or light may be colored because of the separation or removal of certain wavelengths of the visible light. Because light of different wavelengths is refracted (velocity reduced) to different degrees on passing through a transparent medium, it is possible to separate the different wavelengths of white light by the use of a prism and produce a colored spectrum. Another way in which portions of the spectrum may be removed is by interference. When light is reflected from the two surfaces of a thin film, the thickness of the film may be such that a light wave reflected from the far surface travels a sufficiently longer path to be thrown out of phase with a light wave reflected from the near surface. Cancellation of this wavelength results, and if white light is being reflected, the reflected light is colored. Colored

TABLE 28

RELATION BETWEEN ABSORPTION AND VISUAL COLOR

WAVELENGTHS ABSORBED (mμ)	COLOR ABSORBED	VISUAL COLOR
400–435	violet	yellow-green
435–480	blue	yellow
480–490	green-blue	orange
490–500	blue-green	red
500–560	green	purple
560–580	yellow-green	violet
580–595	yellow	blue
595–605	orange	green-blue
605–750	red	blue-green

670

bird feathers and colors of soap bubbles are examples of this phenomenon. Finally certain wavelengths of white light may be removed by absorption, which is by far the most common cause of color. The color may be observed as the light transmitted through a solution of the substance in a transparent medium, or as the light reflected from an opaque substance.

The visual color is complementary to the color absorbed; that is, it is the color sensation produced by all of the wavelengths minus the wavelengths absorbed. Table 28 gives the observed colors when relatively narrow bands of the visible spectrum are absorbed. If the absorption bands are broader or if more than one absorption band is present, the visible color is altered.

Color and Chemical Structure

Until very recently chemists contented themselves with attempts to correlate visual color with structural features of the molecule. As early as 1868 Graebe and Liebermann discussed the importance of unsaturation in producing color, and noted that reduction of a colored compound always led to a colorless product.

In 1876 Witt pointed out that two types of groups usually are present in highly colored compounds, unsaturated groups which he called **chromophores** (Gr. *chroma*, color; *phoros*, from *pherein*, to bear) and groups that intensified the color which he called **auxochromes** (Gr. *auxein*, to increase). To the chromophores he assigned the groups NO_2, $C=O$, and $N=N$. Later $C=C$, $C=N$, $C=S$, and $N=O$ were added to the list. In 1888 Armstrong[1] added the very important chromophoric quinonoid structure, $=\langle\ \rangle=$, pointing out that the structures of most highly colored substances containing an aromatic ring could be written in such a way that they contained a quinonoid structure. The important auxochromes were the hydroxyl group, the amino group and the alkylated amino group. Witt associated the effect of the auxochromes with their salt-forming properties, since acetylation of the amino group or methylation of the hydroxyl group destroys the effect, but methylation of the amino group does not. Moreover the salts of the phenolic compounds are more strongly colored than the free phenols. Numerous other empirical observations have been made. For example, auxochromes do not affect the color when in the *meta* position to the chromophore.

At the time that Witt discussed the effect of salt-forming groups on color, he mentioned also the necessity for their presence if the colored compound was to act as a dye, that is, to have the ability to fix itself to a fiber. This dual property of auxochromes has led to some confusion, since both properties are not always exhibited simultaneously.

The inconsistencies and inadequacy of the chromophore-auxochrome theory long have been recognized, and in recent years it has been reinterpreted and extended in terms of current electronic theory as discussed under electronic spectra in Chapter 30. There it is shown that the entire conjugated system is responsible for color, and that either nitro groups or amino groups shift the absorption to longer wavelengths (p. 665). The chromophores of Witt are

---

[1] Henry Edward Armstrong (1848–1937), professor of chemistry at Central Technical College, South Kensington, England. He is remembered not only for his contributions to the theory of color and the structure of benzene, but also for his sharp criticisms of contemporary thinking in the field of chemistry.

electron-accepting groups and the auxochromes are electron-donating groups. When they are connected through a conjugated system, they extend the conjugation and increase the transition dipole moment. Hence absorption is shifted to still longer wavelengths. Acylation of the amino or the hydroxyl group merely decreases the availability of an unshared pair of electrons for interaction with the conjugated system. The nature of fixation of a dye to the fiber, and especially to mordants, also now is better understood, and the function of hydroxyl and amino groups in this respect has been separated from their effect on color.

DYES AND DYEING

Historical

Natural coloring matters have been used by man since the beginnings of civilization. The first synthetic dye was picric acid, made by Woulfe in 1771 by the action of nitric acid on natural indigo. Not until 1855 was a technical method introduced to prepare it from coal tar. The first dye prepared from coal tar was *aurin* or *rosolic acid* reported by Runge[2] in 1834. He noted that with the usual mordants it produced red colors and lakes which rivaled those produced from cochineal and madder. Since little was known about the components of coal tar at that time and Kekulé's theory of the structure of benzene was not proposed until 1865, Runge's observations were not extended.

As early as 1843, Hofmann had observed that aniline, as prepared at that time, gave red colors under certain conditions. In 1856 Perkin[3] oxidized aniline

---

[2] Friedlieb Ferdinand Runge (1794–1867), professor of chemistry at the University of Breslau and later technical director of the Chemical Products factory at Oranienburg. He was the first to isolate aniline, quinoline, pyrrole, and phenol from coal tar in 1834. He discovered Aniline Black (p. 696) and pioneered in the use of absorbent paper for spot tests.

[3] William Henry Perkin (1838–1907) entered the Royal College of Chemistry in London in 1853 to study chemistry under Hofmann. He discovered anthraquinone while trying to nitrate anthracene, but did no further work with this compound until 1869, when he devised a commercial synthesis of alizarin from it (p. 687).

In his report on the work of the Royal College of Chemistry in 1849, Hofmann had remarked that the synthesis of quinine would be very desirable. Seven years later Perkin, now 18 years old and research assistant to Hofmann, was impressed by this remark. At that time the chief lead to the structure of a compound was the difference between its molecular formula and that of a known compound. Perkin thought that quinine might result by the oxidation of allyl-toluidine.

$$2\ C_{10}H_{13}N + 3\ [O] \longrightarrow C_{20}H_{24}N_2O_2 + H_2O$$
Allyl-　　　　　　　　　　Quinine
toluidine

During the Easter vacation of 1856, he made allyltoluidine in his home laboratory and oxidized the sulfate with potassium dichromate. He obtained only a dirty reddish-brown precipitate, but this behavior interested him, and he decided to try the reaction on a simpler base. On treating aniline sulfate with dichromate, he obtained a black precipitate from which he extracted a purple compound that had the property of a dye and was fast to light. After submitting samples to dyers and receiving favorable comments, he resigned his post at the Royal College and with the aid of his father and brother began manufacture in 1857. The dye was known as *aniline purple* or *mauve*. Material dyed with it became so popular that it gave its name to the *mauve decade*. It is of interest that the total synthesis of quinine was not accomplished until 1944.

Perkin became a successful industrialist but never gave up scientific research. In 1867 he published his first paper on what now is known as the Perkin reaction (p. 536), and in 1868 announced the synthesis of coumarin (p. 562), the first natural perfume to be synthesized from a coal tar component. In 1874 at the age of 36, Perkin retired from business to devote full time to scientific research, especially to the study of the effect of the magnetic field on optical rotation.

sulfate with potassium dichromate and obtained a purple dye called *mauve* (p. 696), which became the first synthetic coal tar dye to be manufactured commercially. In 1859 a process was patented in France for the oxidation of aniline with stannic chloride to give a dye having a color resembling that of fuchsia flowers and named *fuchsin*. After Hofmann showed that fuchsin is a derivative of triphenylmethane, this class of dyes was investigated extensively and came into widespread use.

Meanwhile the azo dyes were discovered by Griess in 1862, the theory of aromatic structure became established, alizarin was synthesized by Graebe and Liebermann in 1868, and indigo was synthesized by Baeyer in 1879. Sulfur colors from coal tar derivatives were produced in 1893, anthraquinone vat dyes in 1901, acridine dyes in 1910, acetoacetarylides in 1923, and phthalocyanins in 1934.

The synthetic coal tar dye industry developed first in England under Perkin, Nicholson, and others, but gradually passed into German hands. By 1913, just before World War I, Germany produced three fourths of the world production of dyes and 90 per cent of the dyes used in England and the United States. France and Switzerland also had flourishing dye industries, but they were connected with the German cartel. Among the reasons for German predominance were (*1*) favorable American patent laws which permit a foreign country to patent processes and products without requiring manufacture in the United States, (*2*) vigorous research programs by German manufacturers with close collaboration with university laboratories, (*3*) low tariff restrictions, and (*4*) cartel control of prices with price-cutting and dumping to prevent competition. Along with control of the dye industry went control of the manufacture of synthetic medicinals and all other organic chemicals.

During World War I Germany lost control of the organic chemical market because the United States and England had to make their own dyes and pharmaceuticals, and these countries realized that the dye plants with their facilities for nitration and for the manufacture of chlorine and phosgene were potential munitions factories. The Chemical Foundation took over German patents in this country and licensed them to firms in the United States, and after the war adequate tariff laws were passed to ensure the continuance and growth of the organic chemical industry. Since then the general industrial development and aggressive research programs have permitted the organic chemical industry to flourish.

Dyeing

Not all colored substances are dyes. A true dye may be defined as a colored substance that will attach itself to a material from solution and that is fast to light and washing.

The mechanism of dyeing must differ with the nature of the material, that is, whether it is protein, cellulose, or some synthetic substance. The dyeing of wool and silk at one time was held to be chemical, the acidic or basic group in a dye combining with basic or acidic groups in the protein. It now is thought that the acidic and basic groups in the dye aid in the initial adsorption of the dye on the surface of the fiber, but that this process is followed by solution and diffusion of the dye into the fiber.

Direct or Substantive Dyes. The **direct** or **substantive dyes** are those that are applicable by immersing the fiber or cloth in a hot solution of the dye in water. Those dyes suitable for dyeing *animal fibers* are divided into **acid dyes** and **basic dyes. Acid dyes** are sodium salts of sulfonic acids and are dyed from a bath acidified with sulfuric or acetic acid. **Basic dyes** are the hydrochlorides or zinc chloride complexes of dyes having basic groups. They are dyed from a neutral bath, usually on a fiber that has been treated with tannic acid. Basic dyes frequently also contain sodium sulfonate groups to make them more soluble in water. Some basic dyes now are used for dyeing acrylic fibers (p. 680).

In cellulose there are no strongly acidic or basic groups, and the colored compounds of lower molecular weight that dye protein fibers are not fixed by cotton or viscose rayon. However, dyes that have a molecular weight sufficiently high to give colloidal solutions are adsorbed more strongly and are **direct dyes for cotton and viscose rayon.** These dyes also are called **salt colors** because adsorption on the fiber usually is assisted by the addition of a salt such as sodium sulfate.

Mordant or Adjective Dyes, and Chrome Dyes. A mordant is any substance which can be fixed to the fiber (L. *mordere*, to bite) and which later can be dyed. Thus albumin was used as a mordant for printing cotton cloth to produce calico. The protein was coagulated on the cotton fiber by heat, and then dyed with an acid dye. Tannic acid was used as a mordant for basic dyes. The terms mordant and chrome dye, however, are reserved for those dyes that can form insoluble complexes with metallic oxides. Usually the oxide first is precipitated in the fiber and then dyed. For example, cotton is soaked in a solution of aluminum acetate or formate and steamed. The aluminum salt hydrolyzes, and the volatile organic acid vaporizes. Reaction of the aluminum hydroxide with an alkaline solution of alizarin (p. 687) produces a colored, high molecular weight, insoluble chelate complex (p. 742) which is adsorbed strongly by the fiber.

Sometimes a cloth is dyed with a direct dye and then treated with a chromium salt to produce on the fiber a complex that is faster or has a more desirable shade. This process is known as *after chroming*. Dyes also can be *prechromed* and used as direct dyes, or the chroming may be done during the dyeing of the cloth, a process called *meta chroming*.

Azoic Dyes. Azoic dyes are water-insoluble azo dyes that are formed on the fiber. They usually are used on cotton. The **ice colors** are applied by impregnating the cloth with a compound capable of coupling with a diazonium salt and then immersing in an ice-cold solution of a diazotized amine. In **developed dyeing** the cloth is dyed with a direct dye containing a free amino group. The dye then is diazotized on the fiber and developed by coupling with an amine or phenol. The new dye on the fiber is faster to washing because of its higher molecular weight. It usually has a deeper color.

Sulfur Dyes. This class includes those sulfur-containing dyes that are applied to cotton from their solution in aqueous sodium sulfide. The soluble reduced form of the dye is substantive to cotton. After dyeing, the cloth is exposed to air or chemical oxidizing agents which regenerate the insoluble dye on the fibers.

Vat Dyes. Vat dyes are water-insoluble but can be rendered water-soluble by reduction in alkaline solution. Cotton adsorbs the reduced form of the dye from this solution. Reconversion of the adsorbed dye to the oxidized form is accomplished as in sulfur dyeing. The reduction formerly was carried out by fermentation in large vats and gave rise to the name *vat dye*.

Disperse Dyes. Direct dyes are not suitable for synthetic fibers such as cellulose acetate, or for the polyester (p. 555) or polyamide (p. 799) fibers, because the lack of hydroxyl or amino groups makes the fiber still less adsorbing than cellulose. Vat and azoic dyeing cannot be used because the alkaline and acid solutions bring about partial hydrolysis of the ester or amide groups and deluster and weaken the fiber. Dyeing can be brought about, however, by colloidal aqueous dispersions of azo or anthraquinone dyes that lack sulfonic acid groups and are soluble in the organic polymer. The colors must be very finely divided to increase the rate of solution in water, because the dyeing mechanism appears to involve the removal by the fiber of the small amount of dye that is dissolved in the water. Disperse dyes are not very fast to washing. A peculiar weakness is that they are subject to fading even in the dark. This fading is due to oxides of nitrogen and of sulfur in the atmosphere and is called *gas fading*.

Oil and Spirit-Soluble Dyes. Many colored compounds lacking sulfonic acid groups are soluble in organic solvents and are used to dye gasoline, plastics, fats, oils and waxes, spirit printing inks, and stains.

Whites or Blankophors. Colorless compounds that have an affinity for fibers and have a blue fluorescence when exposed to near ultraviolet light are used widely as whitening agents. They are known as *direct whites, blankophors*, or *optical bleaches*.

Of the total production in 1955, vat dyes accounted for 32 per cent; direct dyes for cotton, 20 per cent; sulfur dyes, 14 per cent; acid dyes, 9 per cent; basic dyes, 5 per cent; azoic dyes, 5 per cent; disperse dyes, 4 per cent; and mordant and chrome dyes, 3 per cent.

CHEMICAL CLASSES OF DYES

Nitro and Nitroso Compounds

Of the older nitro dyes, **Naphthol Yellow S** still is used to some extent. It is made by sulfonating naphthol and nitrating the trisulfonic acid.

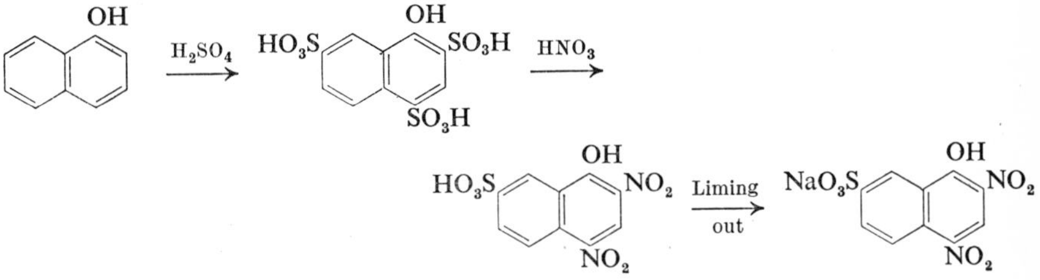

Flavianic
acid

Naphthol
Yellow S

The free acid, known as **flavianic acid,** is an important precipitant for the isolation of the amino acid arginine. The most important members of the nitro dyes today are the **nitrophenylamines** which give yellow, orange, and brown shades. They are made by the reaction of an aromatic amine with an aromatic nitro compound having reactive halogen.

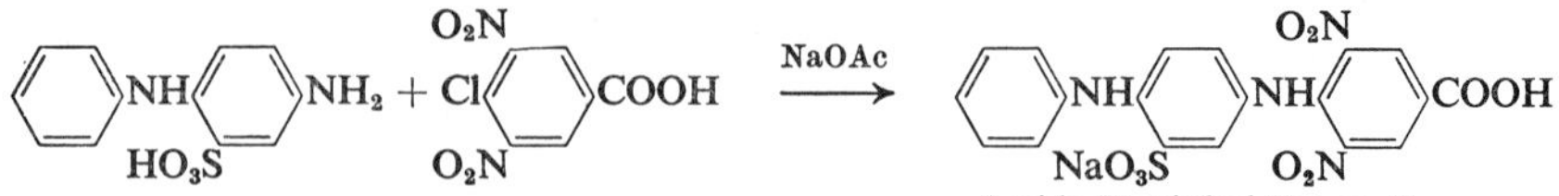

Amido Naphthol Brown G

Some of the simpler nitrophenylamines are used as disperse dyes for cellulose acetate and nylon. **Naphthol Green B,** made by the nitrosation of Schaeffer's salt (p. 590), is used with an iron mordant.

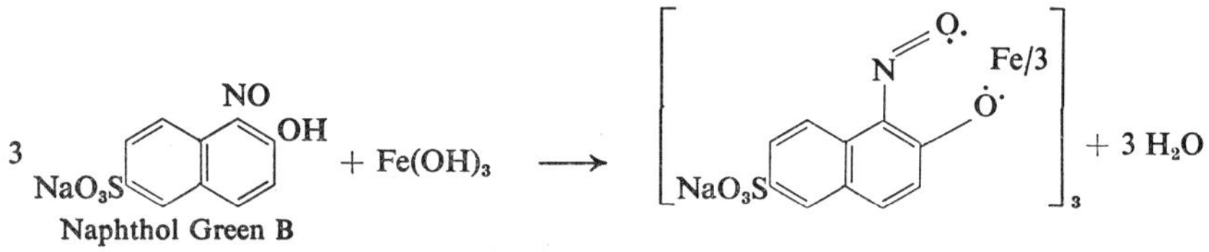

Naphthol Green B

Azo Dyes

This class constitutes the largest single group of dyes, making up over half of the total number of synthetic colors of known structure. It accounted for about 37 per cent of the total production by weight and 42 per cent by value in 1955. Over 65 million pounds were produced at an average unit price of $1.36 per pound. Most azo dyes are sulfonic acids. Those of high molecular weight containing two, three, and four azo groups (disazo, trisazo, and tetrakisazo dyes) are substantive for cotton.

Azo dyes are prepared by coupling a diazotized aromatic amine, the *primary component,* with a phenol or an aromatic amine, the *secondary component* (p. 498). In the benzene series coupling takes place *para* to the hydroxyl or amino group, or *ortho* if the *para* position is occupied. If all *ortho* and *para* positions are occupied, no coupling takes place. Occasionally a group such as the carboxyl group in the *para* position may be displaced. Phenols when coupled in strongly alkaline solution undergo some *ortho* substitution. With diamines and dihydroxy compounds only the *meta* isomers couple.

In the naphthalene series, α-naphthol and α-naphthylamine couple in the 4 position. If the 4 position is occupied or if a sulfonate group is in the 3 or 5 position, coupling takes place in the 2 position. β-Naphthol and β-naphthylamine couple only in the 1 position. If both an amino group and a hydroxyl group are present, the amino group directs in weakly acid solution, and the hydroxyl group directs in alkaline solution.

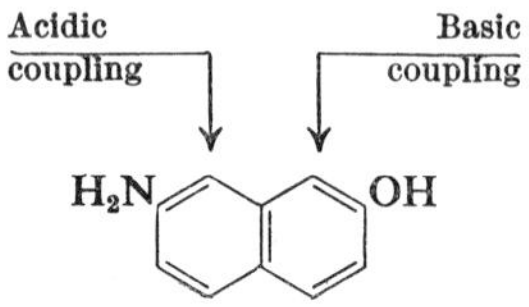

Monoazo Dyes. (*a*) BASIC. Only a few monoazo basic dyes still are in use. **Chrysoidine Y,** the first azo dye made commercially in 1875, was produced to the extent of over half a million pounds in 1955 for dyeing leather and paper.

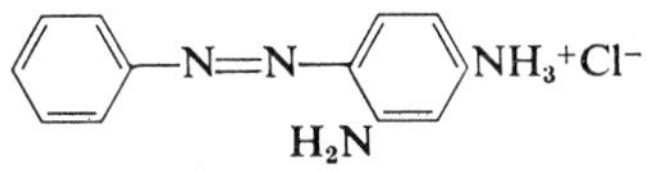

Chrysoidine Y 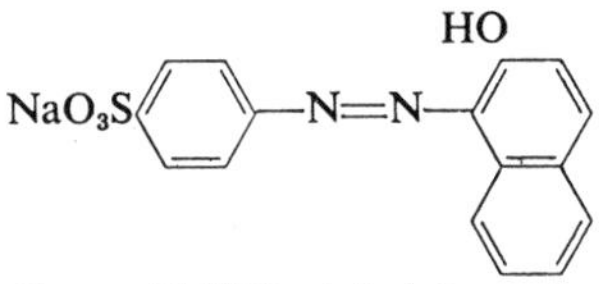   Orange II (*β*-Naphthol Orange)

(*b*) ACID. The acid monoazo dye produced in largest amount in 1955 (900,000 pounds) was **Orange II.**

(*c*) AZOIC. **Para Red** was the first ice color to be used, the cloth being impregnated first with an alkaline solution of *β*-naphthol and then dipped into an ice-cold solution of diazotized *p*-nitroaniline. Much faster colors are obtained, however, if anilides of 3-hydroxy-2-naphthoic acid (BON acid, p. 595) are used as the secondary component. These compounds are known as the **Naphtol AS** series (from the German *Anilid Saeure*). The best primary components are amines having an electron-donating group *ortho* to the amino group and an electron-attracting group *para* to the amino group. The free amines are sold as *Fast Bases* and the stabilized diazotized amines as *Fast Salts*. About 30 Naphtols and 50 bases or salts are available commercially, making 1500 combinations possible. Not all combinations are used, however, because many of the colors overlap and not all of the colors produced have the best possible properties. Azoic dyes are used not only for solid dyeing but also for print-dyeing of cloth. Most of the colors do not have specific names since they are not sold as such but in the form of their components. **Fast Scarlet R** is the color produced from Fast Scarlet R salt and Naphtol AS.

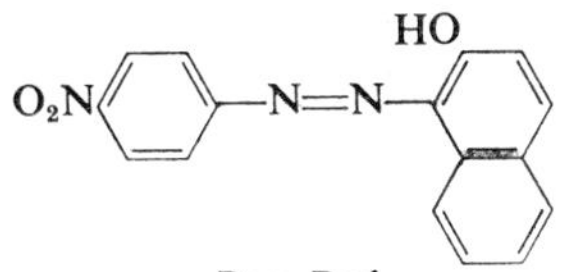

Para Red 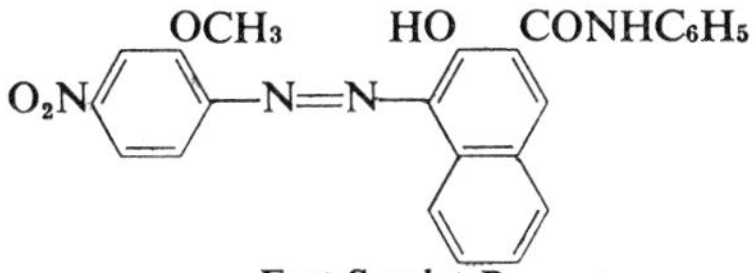   Fast Scarlet R

Since the azoic colors are insoluble in water, many are used as pigments for paints and printing inks. Total production of azoic colors and components amounted to about 9 million pounds or over 5 per cent of all dyestuffs in 1955.

(*d*) DISPERSE and OIL-SOLUBLE DYES. **Celliton Fast Yellow G** is an example of a widely-used disperse dye for cellulose acetate. **Oil Orange** (*Sudan I*) is representative of oil-soluble colors.

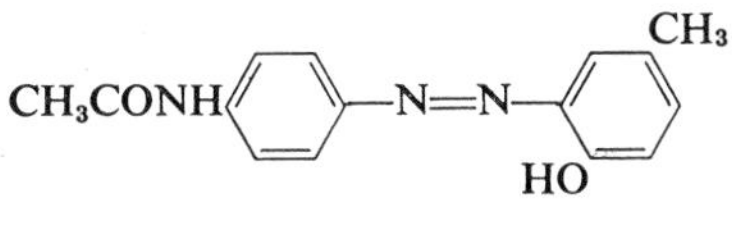

Celliton Fast Yellow G 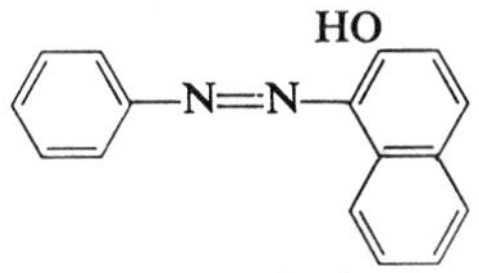   Oil Orange (Sudan I)

(*e*) MORDANT. **Chrome Blue Black R** is a widely used monoazo mordant dye (2 million pounds, 1955). The fiber may be treated with chroming solution before, after, or during the dyeing (p. 674). The chroming deepens the color and produces on the fiber a molecule of much higher molecular weight and hence of greater fastness.

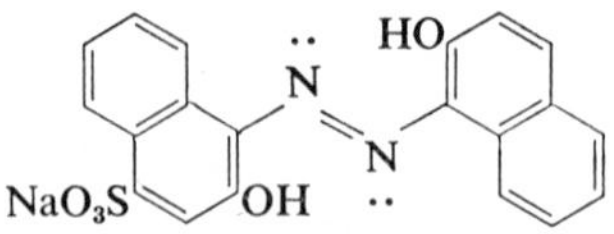

Chrome Blue Black R

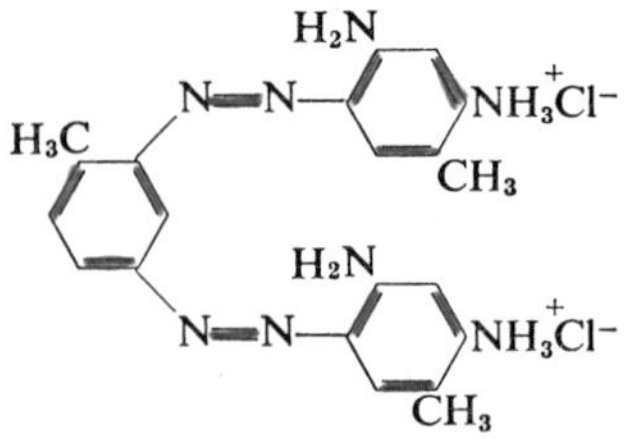

Bismarck Brown R

Disazo Dyes. (*a*) BASIC. **Bismarck Brown R** is made by the action of nitrous acid on 2,4-diaminotoluene (*m*-toluylenediamine). The original Bismarck Brown from *m*-phenylenediamine was discovered by Martius in 1863.

(*b*) ACID. The discovery that the disazo acid dyes derived from benzidine are direct dyes for cotton gave enormous impetus to the synthetic dye industry. **Congo Red,** derived from benzidine and naphthionic acid, was the first dye of this class, but it is sensitive to acids. The direct cotton dye which established the Badische Anilin und Soda Fabrik in Germany was **Benzopurpurin 4B** made from *o*-tolidine (p. 578) and naphthionic acid (p. 589).

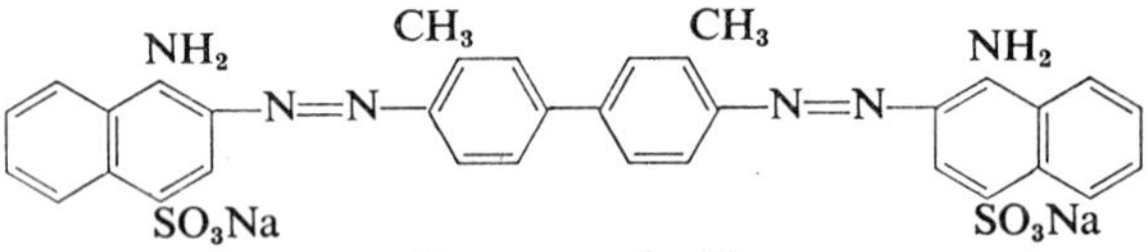

Benzopurpurin 4B

Many other important dyes are derived from benzidine. Thus **Direct Blue 2B** is made by coupling diazotized benzidine with H-acid (p. 591).

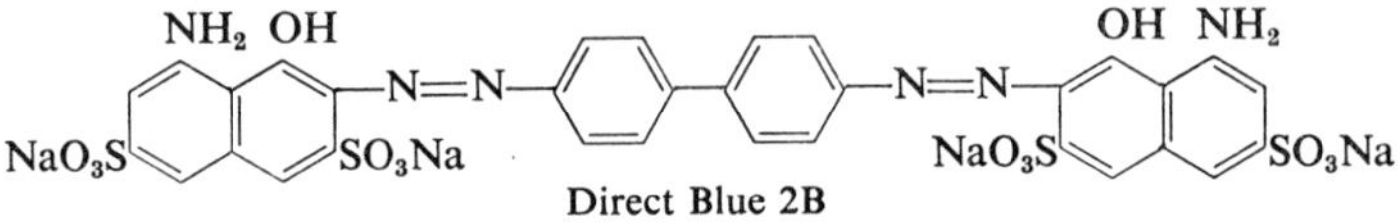

Direct Blue 2B

(*c*) DEVELOPED COLORS. **Developed Black BH** (2.7 million pounds, 1955) is made by coupling diazotized benzidine first with one mole of γ-acid (p. 592) and then with one mole of H-acid in alkaline solution.

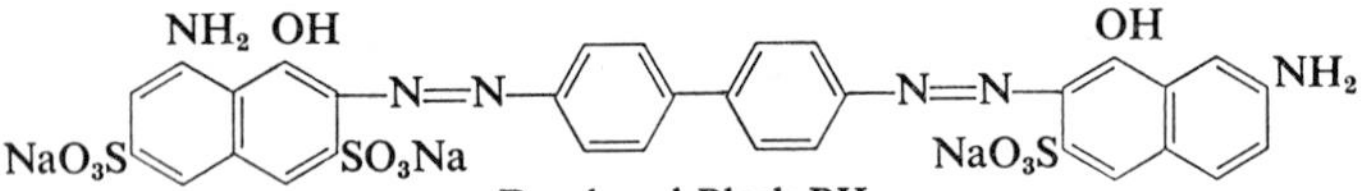

Developed Black BH

It dyes cotton a bright blue. When diazotized on the fiber and coupled with β-naphthol, it gives a navy blue; if coupled with *m*-phenylenediamine, a black color is produced.

Trisazo Dyes. The most widely used black azo dye is **Direct Black EW** (6 million pounds, 1955), discovered in the United States in 1901 by Oscar Mueller. It is made by coupling diazotized benzidine with one mole of *H*-acid in acid solution, and then coupling diazotized aniline with the H-acid portion in alkaline solution. Finally the second diazonium group of the benzidine portion is coupled with *m*-phenylenediamine.

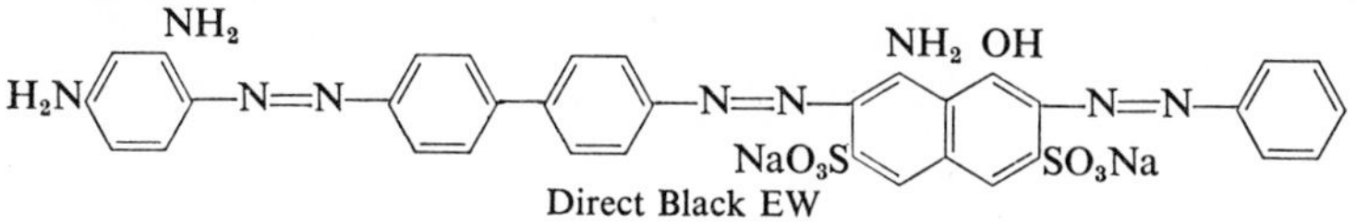

Direct Black EW

Stilbene Dyes. These yellow to orange direct dyes for cotton are azo or azoxy compounds that are not made by the usual coupling reaction but are derived from 4-nitro-2-toluenesulfonic acid (*para acid*) by boiling it with dilute aqueous sodium hydroxide and oxidizing or reducing the products. The initial product from para acid is the sodium salt of 4,4'-dinitroso-2,2'-stilbenedisulfonic acid.

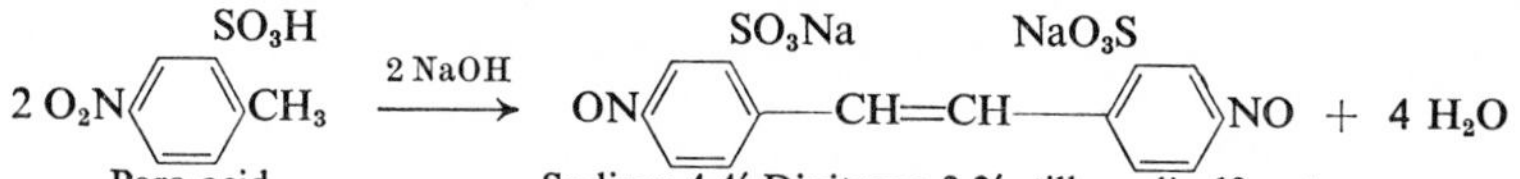

Para acid   Sodium 4,4'-Dinitroso-2,2'-stilbenedisulfonate

The constitutions of the dyes resulting by oxidation and reduction are uncertain. Stilbene dyes amounted to 7 million pounds or 4 per cent of total production in 1955.

Reduction of the dinitrosostilbenedisulfonic acid gives the diamine. Reaction of the latter with phenyl isocyanate gives **Blankophor R,** one of the first of the optical bleaches (p. 675).

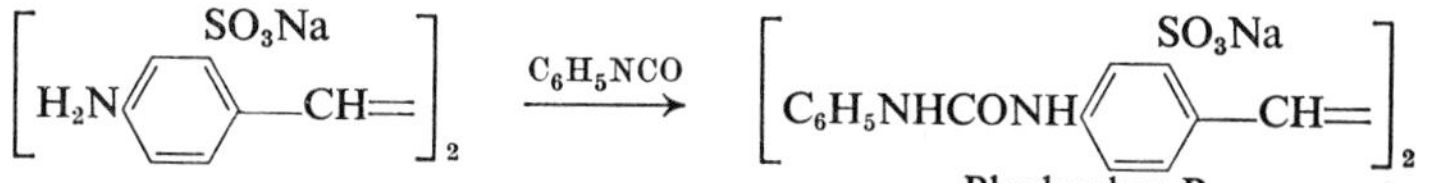

Blankophor R

Pyrazolones. Tartrazine, an important yellow acid dye for wool (0.4 million pounds, 1955), is made by coupling the pyrazolone from ethyl oxalacetate (p. 815) and *p*-hydrazinobenzenesulfonic acid with diazotized sulfanilic acid.

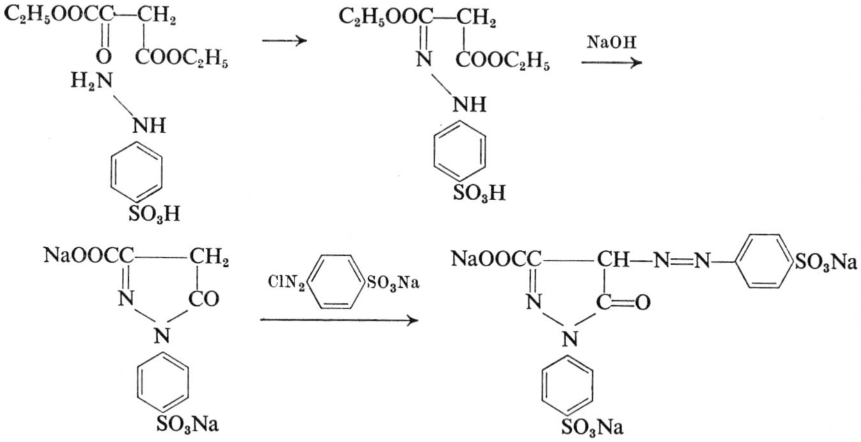

Tartrazine

Triphenylmethane Dyes

Triphenylmethane dyes are basic dyes for wool or silk, or for cotton mordanted with tannic acid. From the time of their discovery in 1859 to the development of the anthraquinone vat dyes, the triphenylmethane dyes were regarded highly because of their brilliant colors; that is, they not only absorb strongly some parts of the spectrum, but they reflect strongly other parts of the spectrum. However they are not fast to light or washing, except when applied to acrylic fibers.

Malachite Green Series. Dyes of this group are derivatives of bis(*p*-aminophenyl)phenylmethane. **Malachite Green** is made by condensing benzaldehyde with dimethylaniline to give bis(*p*-dimethylaminophenyl)phenylmethane, which is known as the *leuco base* (Gr. *leukos*, white). Oxidation converts it to the carbinol which also is colorless and is known as the *color base* or the *carbinol base*. Strong acids convert the color base into the colored dye.

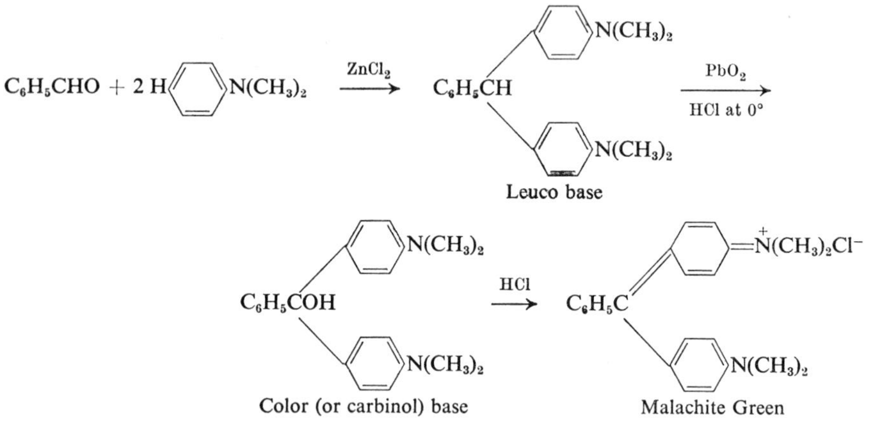

Leuco base

Color (or carbinol) base

Malachite Green

Rosaniline Series. The rosanilines are derivatives of tris(*p*-aminophenyl)-methane.

(*a*) PARAROSANILINE. **Pararosaniline,** patented by Verguin in France in 1859, was the first triphenylmethane dye. Like mauve, it was prepared by the oxidation of aniline, but with stannic chloride, nitrobenzene, or arsenic oxide, instead of dichromate. The dye was manufactured by the Society for Chemical Industry in Basle (Ciba) until the plant was forced to shut down because the aniline imported from France no longer gave satisfactory yields. Hofmann found that the formation of the dye depended on the presence of toluidine in the aniline, and the results of his investigations established the structure of rosaniline. The methyl group of the *p*-toluidine supplies the methylidyne (CH) carbon atom of the leuco base.

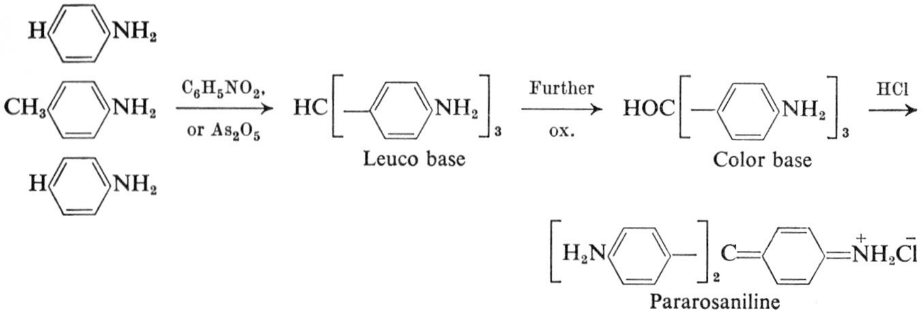

Leuco base

Color base

Pararosaniline

The commercial **fuchsins, rosanilines,** and **magentas** usually are mixtures of pararosaniline with its methyl homologs. The names *fuchsin* and *rosaniline* were given because of the fuchsia or rose colors of the dyes, but *magenta* was named in honor of the victory of Napoleon III in the battle of Magenta, Italy, in 1859.

The decolorization of fuchsin by sulfur dioxide appears to involve the formation of the leucosulfonic acid and also the addition of sulfur dioxide to two amino groups. Subsequent reaction with an aldehyde gives an addition product which loses sulfurous acid to form a new colored compound.

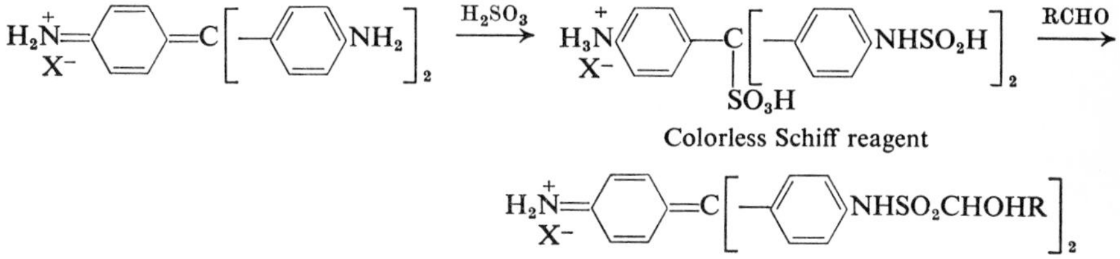

$$H_2\overset{+}{N}\!\!=\!\!\underset{X^-}{\bigcirc}\!\!=\!\!C\!\left[\bigcirc\!\!NH_2\right]_2 \xrightarrow{H_2SO_3} \underset{X^-}{H_3\overset{+}{N}}\bigcirc\!\!-\!\!\underset{\underset{SO_3H}{|}}{C}\!\left[\bigcirc\!\!NHSO_2H\right]_2 \xrightarrow{RCHO}$$

Colorless Schiff reagent

$$\underset{X^-}{H_2\overset{+}{N}}\!\!=\!\!\bigcirc\!\!=\!\!C\!\left[\bigcirc\!\!NHSO_2CHOHR\right]_2$$

Colored aldehyde addition product

(*b*) METHYL VIOLET AND CRYSTAL VIOLET. These dyes are the only members of the triphenylmethane group that are of real importance today. Production of **Methyl Violet** in the United States amounted to about 1.5 million pounds in 1955. It is the dye commonly used in purple inks, indelible pencils, and typewriter ribbons. Methyl Violet is made by oxidizing dimethylaniline with cupric chloride. It is believed that one methyl group of a molecule of dimethylaniline is oxidized to formaldehyde, which then undergoes condensation and further oxidation.

$$C_6H_5N(CH_3)_2 + [O] \xrightarrow[NaCl]{CuSO_4} C_6H_5NHCH_3 + HCHO$$

$$HCHO + C_6H_5NHCH_3 + 2\,C_6H_5N(CH_3)_2 \xrightarrow{[O]} \underset{\diagdown C_6H_4N(CH_3)_2}{\overset{\diagup C_6H_4NHCH_3}{HC\!-\!C_6H_4N(CH_3)_2}} \xrightarrow{[O]}$$

$$\underset{\diagdown C_6H_4N(CH_3)_2}{\overset{\diagup C_6H_4NHCH_3}{HOC\!-\!C_6H_4N(CH_3)_2}} \xrightarrow{HCl} \underset{\diagdown C_6H_4N(CH_3)_2}{\overset{\diagup C_6H_4NHCH_3}{C\!\!=\!\!\bigcirc\!\!=\!\!\overset{+}{N}(CH_3)_2\bar{Cl}}}$$
Methyl Violet

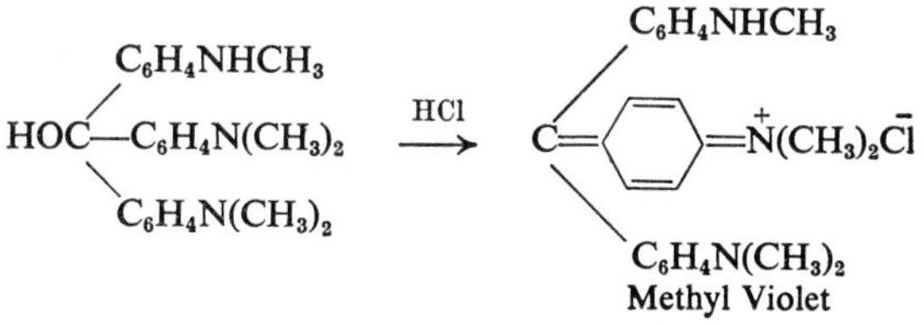

Crystal Violet is the completely methylated compound obtained by condensing Michler ketone (p. 541) with dimethylaniline.

$$[(CH_3)_2NC_6H_4]_2CO + C_6H_5N(CH_3)_2 \xrightarrow{POCl_3} HOC[C_6H_4N(CH_3)_2]_3 \xrightarrow{HCl}$$

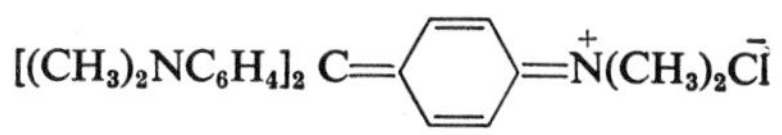

$$[(CH_3)_2NC_6H_4]_2\,C\!\!=\!\!\bigcirc\!\!=\!\!\overset{+}{N}(CH_3)_2\bar{Cl}$$
Crystal Violet

Gentian Violet, which is used as an antiseptic, is a mixture of Methyl Violet and Crystal Violet.

Aurins. Aurin or rosolic acid is of interest because it was the first dye to be synthesized from coal tar, preceding the synthesis of mauve by over twenty years. It was obtained by Runge in 1834 by boiling a solution of the mixed phenols of coal tar in calcium hydroxide for several hours. It is synthesized best by oxidizing a mixture of phenol and formaldehyde.

$$HCHO + 3\ C_6H_5OH \xrightarrow{[O]} \left[HO\!\!\bigcirc\!\!- \right]_2 C\!=\!\bigcirc\!=\!O$$

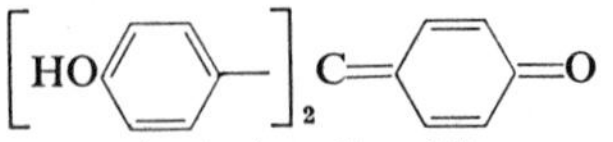

Aurin (rosolic acid)

Its only use at present is as a neutral indicator.

Phthaleins. Although not used as a dye, **phenolphthalein** is the most important member of this group of which it is typical. It is prepared by condensing phthalic anhydride and phenol in the presence of an anhydrous acid catalyst.

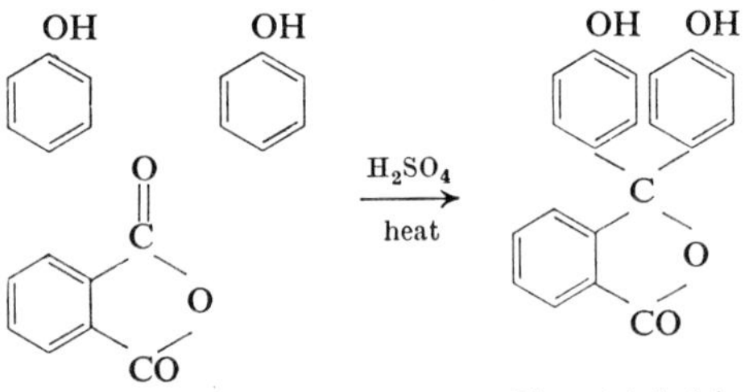

Phenolphthalein

Although used to some extent as an acid-base indicator (p. 700), the chief commercial importance of phenolphthalein is as a medicinal. It is the usual active ingredient of the candy-type laxatives. **Tetraiodophenolphthalein** is made by the direct iodination of phenolphthalein in alkaline solution. It is used in the X-ray examination of the gallbladder, because it accumulates there, and the heavy iodine atoms are opaque to X-rays.

The **sulfonphthaleins** result from the condensation of phenols with sulfobenzoic anhydride.

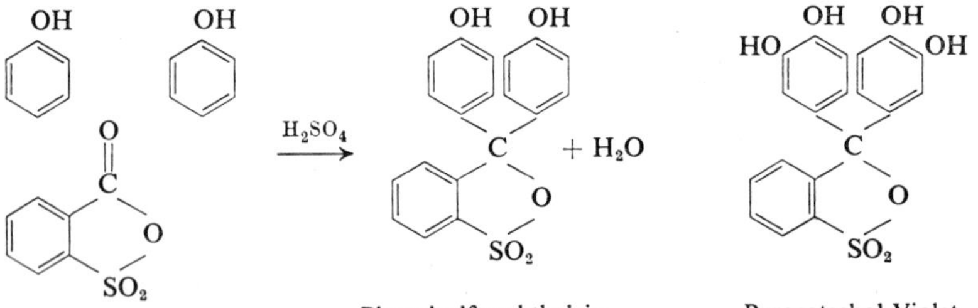

Phenolsulfonphthalein   Pyrocatechol Violet

Like phenolphthalein and its derivatives, the sulfonphthaleins are used as acid-base indicators. **Pyrocatechol Violet** is a sulfonphthalein used as an indicator in chelatometric titrations. Because of the *ortho* hydroxyl groups it forms chelate complexes with metal ions. These coordination compounds have a different color than the indicator itself. If a solution of the metal ions containing the indicator is titrated with a solution of a compound such as ethylenediaminetetraacetic acid (p. 755) that coordinates more strongly with the metal ion than does the indicator, a change in color takes place when all of the metal ion has been removed from the solution.

Xanthenes. The xanthenes are related to the phthaleins and are made in the same way. They are derived, however, from *m*-dihydroxy compounds or *m*-hydroxy amines, which permit the formation of the xanthene (1,5-dibenzopyran) ring system. A typical example is **fluorescein,** the sodium salt of which is called **Uranine.**

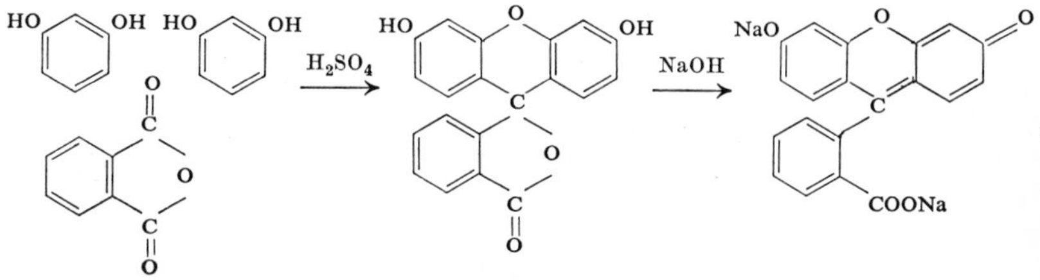

Fluorescein   Uranine

Aqueous solutions of the sodium salt of fluorescein, even at very low concentration, have an intense yellow-green fluorescence when exposed to sunlight. There is distinct visual evidence of its presence at one part in 40 million parts of water. It has been used to trace the course of underground waters and to detect the source of contamination of water supplies. Production in normal times is negligible but over a million pounds was manufactured in the United States in 1943. It was supplied in packets to airmen during World War II for use as a sea marker, and many rescued men owe their lives to this dye. Other dyes that fluoresce brilliantly also found wartime use. For example, planes were landed at night on aircraft carriers by signal men whose dyed flags and clothing were made to glow by illumination with ultraviolet light.

Tetrabromofluorescein, prepared by direct bromination, is known as **eosin,** and the sodium salt is the usual dye in red ink. **Mercurochrome,** an antiseptic dye (p. 895), is the sodium salt of hydroxymercuridibromofluorescein. **Erythrosin,** a red dye used as a food color and photographic sensitizer (p. 693), is tetraiodofluorescein.

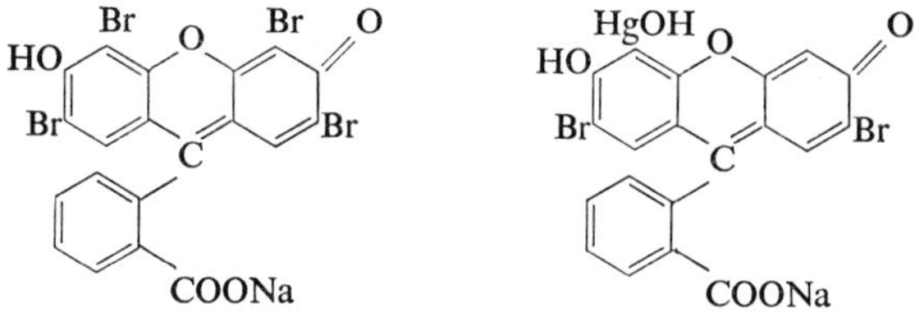

Eosin   Mercurochrome

Indigoid Dyes

Indigos. The oldest known recorded use of an organic dye is that of **indigo.** Egyptian mummy cloths estimated to be over four thousand years old were dyed with it. It is present in many plants as a glucoside, *indican,* but has been obtained in the western world from woad (*Isatis tinctoria*), and from plants of the *Indigofera* species.

The earliest source of indigo in Europe was the woad plant, which was known to the ancient Indo-Germanic tribes. It is believed that the art of cultivation and methods of application had spread to them from India. The growing of woad continued to modern times, although towards the end it was used only for the fermentative reduction of indigo (p. 686). Woad was last cultivated in France in 1887, in Germany in 1910, and in England in 1931. Indigo from the *Indigofera* species, which grow only in tropical countries, was known to the Greeks and Romans, but was not known in Europe between the fifth and twelfth centuries. After the twelfth century it became an important article of commerce. Production reached a maximum of about five million pounds in 1890, valued at about $3 per pound. In India alone, 250,000 acres were planted to indigo.

The source of natural indigo is a glucoside, *indican*, which on acid or enzymic hydrolysis yields glucose and *indoxyl*. Air oxidation of indoxyl yields the water-insoluble indigo. Indigo has the molecular formula $C_{16}H_{10}N_2O_2$. Aniline first was obtained by the destructive distillation of indigo in 1826 (p. 486). In 1841 anthranilic acid was obtained by the action of alkali on indigo. The names for both compounds were derived from the Spanish word for indigo, *añil*, which in turn was derived through the Arabic *al-nil* from the Sanskrit *nila* meaning dark blue.

In 1841 *isatin* was obtained by the oxidation of indigo. Baeyer began his investigations of indigo in 1865. He reduced isatin stepwise to dioxindole and oxindole, and synthesized the latter by the simultaneous hydrolysis and reduction of *o*-acetylaminomandelic acid with hydrogen iodide.

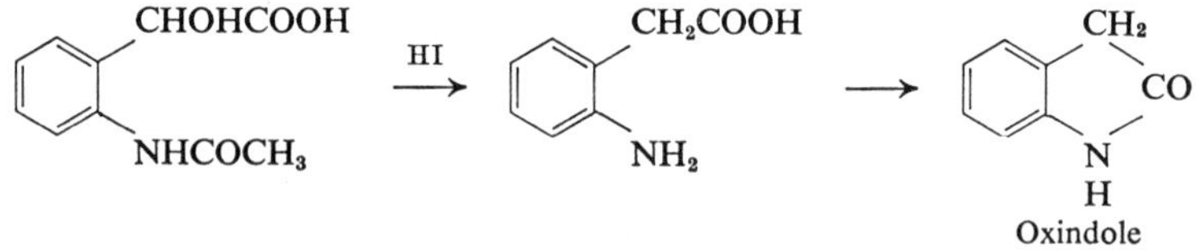

He proposed the name *indole* for the parent compound and obtained it by heating oxindole with zinc dust. This synthesis of indole was the first use of this valuable method for removing oxygen from complex organic compounds (p. 504). On the basis of these results structures were assigned which accounted for the reactions of indigo and its derivatives.

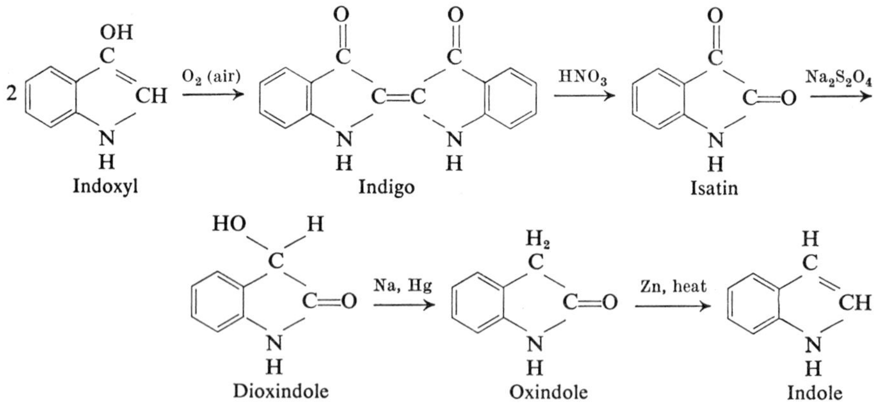

The first synthesis of indigo from a product not derived from it was reported by Baeyer in 1880. He tried to make it commercially by another process in 1882, but it was not until 1897, eighteen years after the first synthesis of indigo in the laboratory, that the Badische Anilin und Soda Fabrik placed synthetic indigo on the market at a price below that of the natural product. For the development of its process, this firm used the profits from the manufacture of synthetic alizarin (p. 688).

Two processes for the commercial synthesis of indigo have been important, the basic reactions of both having been discovered by Heumann in 1890. One involves cyclization of *N*-phenylglycine to indoxyl and the other of *N*-phenylglycine-o-carboxylic acid to indoxylic acid by fusion with sodium hydroxide. Either product on air oxidation yields indigo. The second process, which starts with naphthalene, was the one decided upon by Badische.

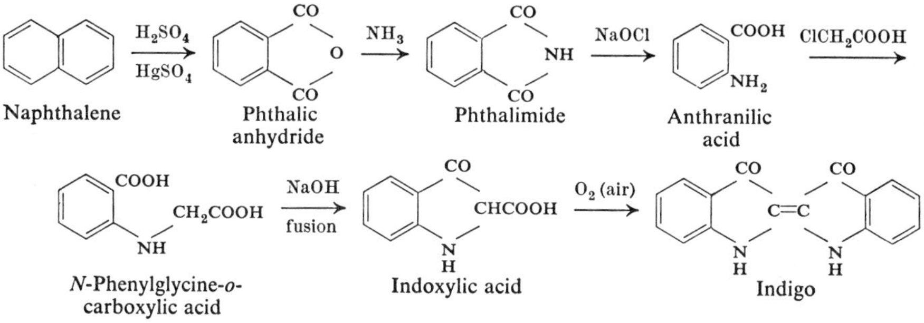

Naphthalene → Phthalic anhydride → Phthalimide → Anthranilic acid

N-Phenylglycine-o-carboxylic acid → Indoxylic acid → Indigo

It required cheap phthalic anhydride to make anthranilic acid, cheap chlorine to make chloroacetic acid and hypochlorite, and cheap caustic soda for the condensation. The first requirement was met after Sapper accidentally broke a thermometer and discovered the mercury-catalyzed oxidation of naphthalene by sulfuric acid. The need for cheap chlorine and sodium hydroxide led to the development of the electrolytic method of production.

Shortly after the Badische process went into operation, a modification of Heumann's other process, previously discarded by Badische, was developed at the Hoechst dye works. This process, which starts with aniline and chloroacetic acid, was found to be practical if sodium amide was substituted for sodium hydroxide in the cyclization step. It soon became the standard method of synthesis.

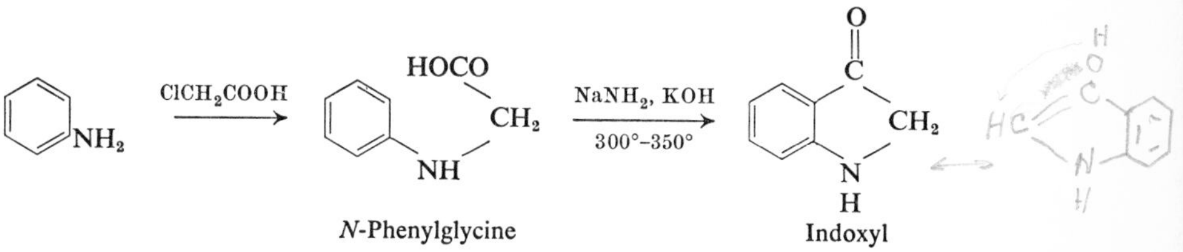

N-Phenylglycine → Indoxyl

Recent developments have been the synthesis of *N*-phenylglycine from aniline, formaldehyde, bisulfite, and sodium cyanide, or from aniline, formaldehyde, and hydrogen cyanide.

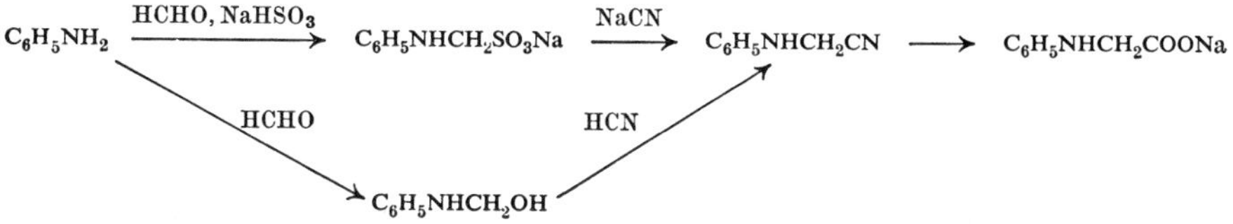

$C_6H_5NH_2 \xrightarrow{HCHO, NaHSO_3} C_6H_5NHCH_2SO_3Na \xrightarrow{NaCN} C_6H_5NHCH_2CN \longrightarrow C_6H_5NHCH_2COONa$

$C_6H_5NHCH_2OH$

Indigo is a deep blue water-insoluble substance having a bronze reflex. Its application to textiles depends on its easy reduction to a bright yellow dihydroxy compound known as *indigo white*. The latter is soluble in alkali because of the acidic nature of the hydroxyl groups. The cloth is dyed in the hot indigo white solution and then exposed to air, which rapidly oxidizes the indigo white and deposits the insoluble indigo within the fiber.

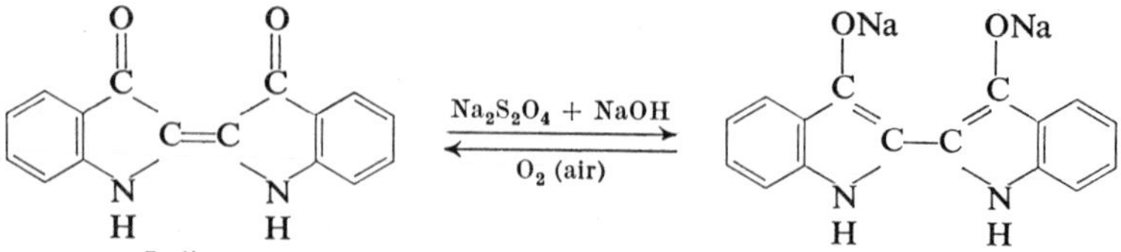

Indigo
(water-insoluble)

Indigo white
(water-soluble)

Formerly indigo was reduced by a fermentation process. The necessary bacteria to start the process were supplied by the natural fermentation of woad. Sugars, lime and indigo paste were added as needed to keep the bath at the desired strength of indigo white. Since the process was carried out in large open vats, it was called *vat dyeing*. The woad vat and other fermentation processes have been discontinued in industrialized countries, the commonly used reducing agent being alkaline sodium hydrosulfite solution. However, the term *vat dye* still is retained for dyes applied in a reduced form. They usually are supplied as aqueous pastes containing 10 to 20 per cent of the insoluble dye, in order to permit easy dispersion in water for the reduction process. Indigo is fairly fast to light and washing. Its cheapness makes it still the most widely used blue dye. Production in 1955 amounted to 2.5 million pounds on a 100 per cent basis. The selling price was $1.45 per pound.

Ordinary indigo is the *trans* form. The *cis* form was unknown until 1939. It is of interest that the indigo white is adsorbed on the fiber as the *cis* form, and the product first formed on air oxidation is *cis* indigo, which goes over to the *trans* form in the solid state on the fiber.

Tyrian Purple is another natural dye used by the ancients. It is believed to have been used in Crete as early as 1600 B.C. It was derived from several species of mollusk of the family *Murex*. The term *royal purple* and the phrase *born to the purple* testify to its limited use, 9000 mollusks being required to yield one gram of dye. Modern investigations have shown that the chief constituent of the dye is 6,6'-dibromoindigo. 5,5',7,7'-Tetrabromoindigo (**Bromindigo Blue 2BD)** sold for $5.00 per pound on a 100 per cent basis, and 85,000 pounds was made in 1955.

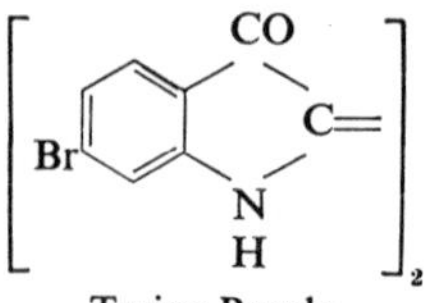

Tyrian Purple

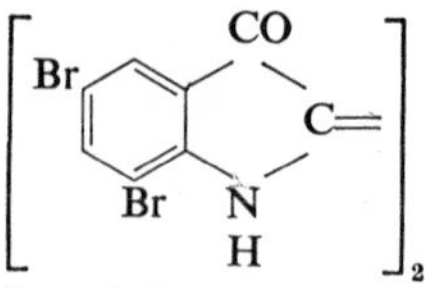

Bromindigo Blue 2BD

The blue color of the indophenin reaction (p. 606) is due to the formation of compounds related to indigo. Two products have been isolated, α- and β-indophenin.

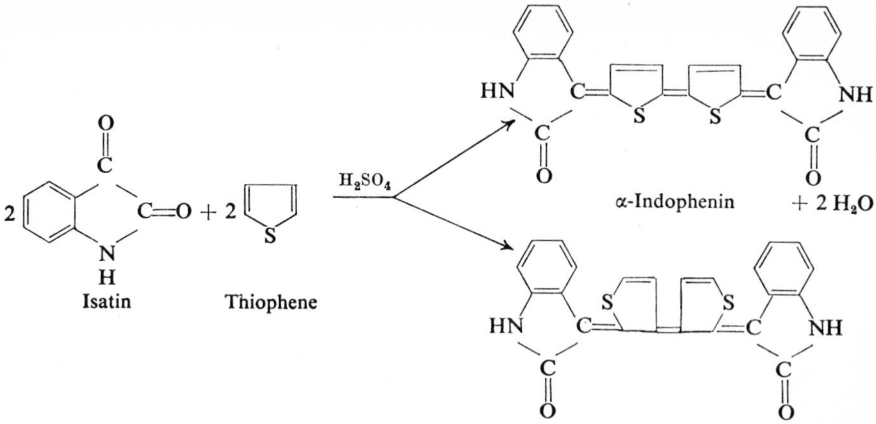

α-Indophenin + 2 H₂O

β-Indophenin

Thioindigos. In these dyes a sulfur atom replaces the NH group of the indole ring of indigo. They may be made by analogous reactions and are applied in the same way as indigo to give a variety of fast colors.

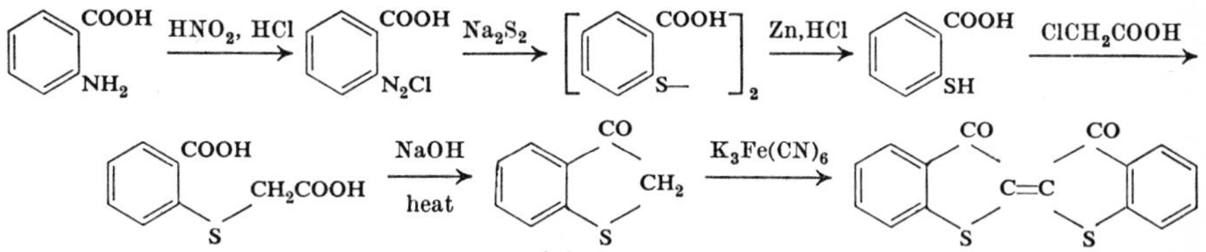

Thioindoxyl　　　　　Thioindigo (Vat Red B)

Of more importance than thioindigo are **Helindon Pink R, Vat Orange R,** and **Indanthrene Brown RRD.**

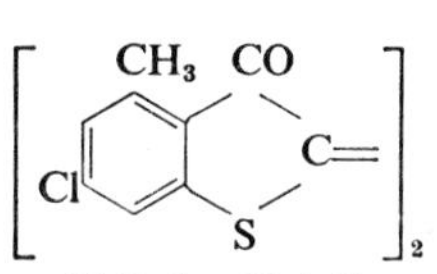

Helindon Pink R 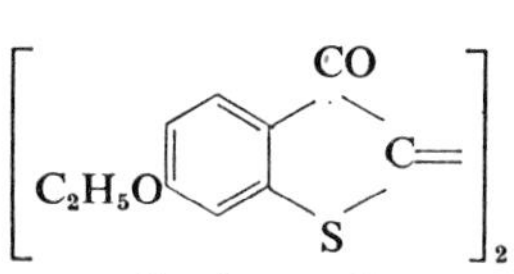　　　　　Vat Orange R 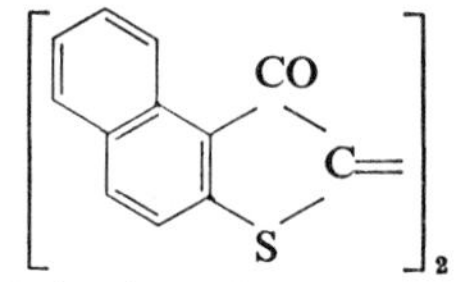　　　　　Indanthrene Brown RRD

Anthraquinone Dyes

Mordant Dyes. The best known member of this class is **alizarin,** another natural dye known to the ancient Egyptians and Persians. It occurs in the root of the madder (*Rubia tinctorum:* Fr. *garance,* Ger. *krapp,* Ar. *alizari*). Cultivation in Europe resulted in a production of 70,000 tons of madder in 1868. Although alizarin had been isolated in 1826, all early attempts to determine its structure failed, chiefly because chemists assumed that it was a naphthalene derivative. In 1868 Graebe and Liebermann applied Baeyer's newly discovered reduction method, namely distillation with zinc dust, and obtained anthracene. From the similarity in behavior of alizarin to 5,6-dihydroxynaphthoquinone (naphthazarin), they guessed that alizarin was 1,2-dihydroxyanthraquinone. In the following year they synthesized alizarin by fusing 1,2-dibromoanthraquinone with alkali. This process was not technically useful, but in the same year patents were issued in England to Caro, Graebe, and Liebermann, and almost simultaneously to Perkin, for the production of alizarin from sodium β-anthraquinonesulfonate (p. 598).

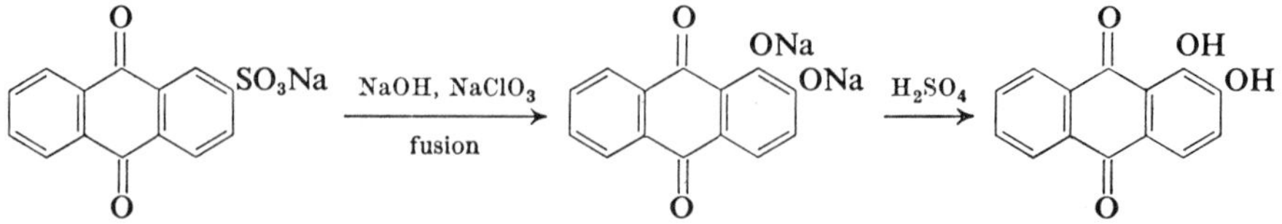

Alizarin

In contrast to the story of indigo, the process immediately was technically successful and soon drove the natural product from the market. Needless to say a considerable disturbance to the agricultural economy of Western Europe resulted. The cost of alizarin (100 per cent) dropped from $15 per pound in 1870 to $0.55 per pound in 1914.

Alizarin is *polygenetic*, yielding different colors with different mordants. Thus a magnesium mordant gives a violet color, calcium a purple-red, barium a blue, aluminum a rose-red, chromium a brown-violet, and ferrous iron a black-violet. Alizarin was used chiefly to produce the color known as *Turkey Red* on cotton mordanted with aluminum hydroxide (p. 674) in the presence of sulfated castor or olive oil. Although the dye now is obsolete, sulfated oils still are known as Turkey Red oil (p. 191).

Acid Dyes. The acid dyes derived from anthraquinone are sulfonated amino or hydroxy derivatives. **Acid Alizarin Blue B** and **Alizarin Cyanine Green** are important. They produce on wool a purity of shade equal to that of the triphenylmethane dyes and are very fast to light.

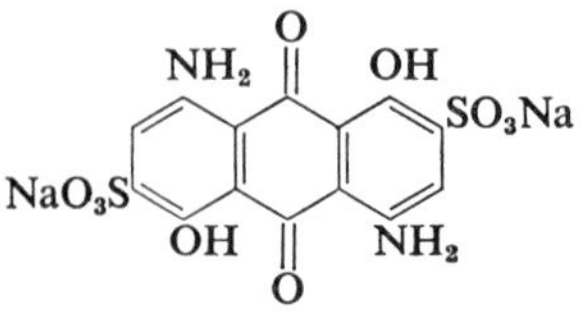

Acid Alizarin Blue B 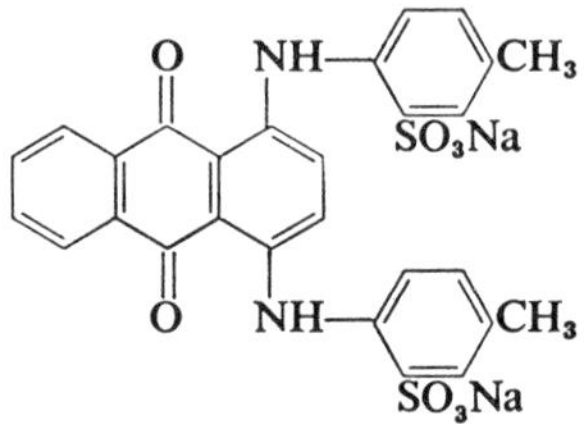   Alizarin Cyanine Green

Disperse Dyes. Dyes for cellulose acetate, nylon, and polyester fibers generally are simple aminoanthraquinones or derivatives having one or more hydrogen atoms of the amino groups replaced by other groups. **Celliton Fast Pink B** (80,000 pounds, 1955) and **Celliton Fast Blue FFR** (606,000 pounds, 1955) are examples.

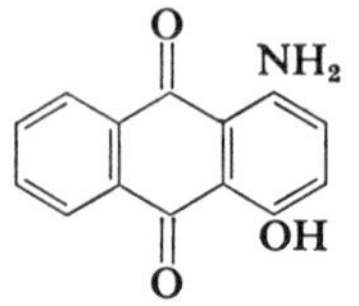

Celliton Fast Pink B 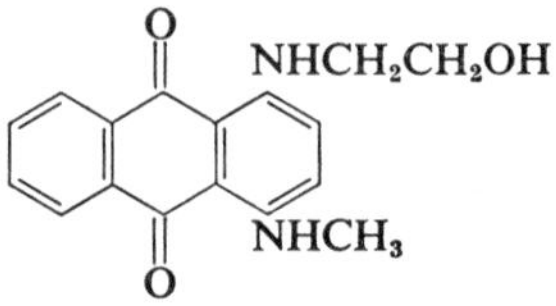   Celliton Fast Blue FFR

Vat Dyes. The anthraquinones, like indigo, give on reduction dihydro derivatives that are soluble in alkali and are oxidized back to the insoluble anthraquinone on exposure to air or by chemical oxidizing agents (p. 600). The simple quinones are not fixed to animal or vegetable fibers, but the more complex compounds are.

(*a*) ACYLAMINOANTHRAQUINONES. Although the vats of the aminoanthra- quinones have no affinity for cotton, they become substantive if an amino group in the α position is acylated with an aromatic acyl group. The resulting products are the simplest of the vat dyes. Examples are **Indanthrene Red 5GK** and **Indan- threne Brilliant Violet RK.**

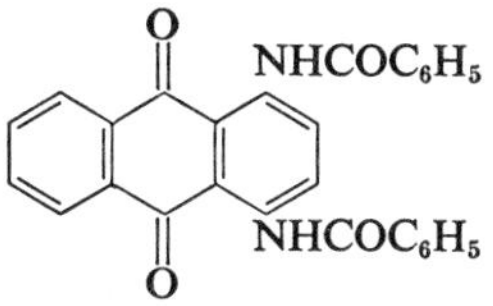

Indanthrene Red 5GK 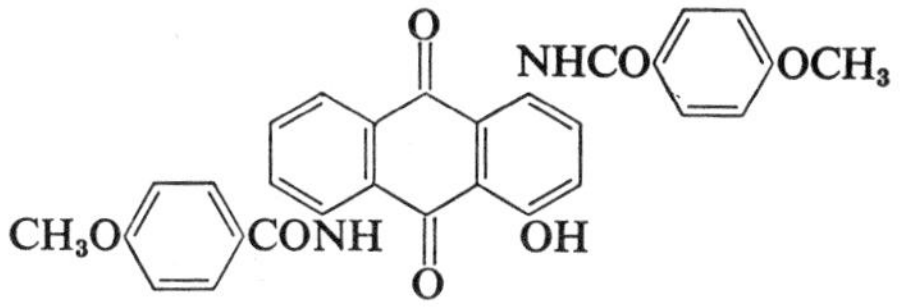   Indanthrene Brilliant Violet RK

(*b*) HYDROAZINES. This group is the oldest of the anthraquinone vat dyes. **Indanthrene Blue R,** the first anthraquinone vat dye, was discovered accidentally by Bohn in 1901. He was trying to make diphthaloylindigo by the alkaline fusion of the glycine derived from β-aminoanthraquinone. A blue vat dye was obtained which proved to be a dehydrogenation product of β-aminoanthraquinone. He found that the dye could be made by the action of alkali on β-aminoanthra- quinone in the presence of an oxidizing agent.

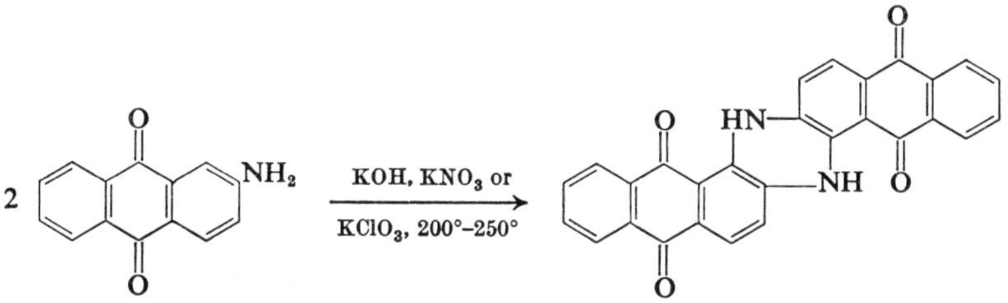

Indanthrene Blue R
(Anthraquinone Vat Blue RS)

Indanthrene Blue is one of the most stable organic compounds known. It can be heated in air at 470°, with strong hydrochloric acid at 400°, and with potassium hydroxide at 300° without decomposition. When applied to cloth, it is extremely fast to washing and light, a property shared by most anthraquinone vat colors. **Anthraquinone Vat Blue GCD,** a dichloro derivative of Indanthrene Blue, is manufactured currently on a large scale.

(*c*) CARBAZOLE DERIVATIVES. These dyes are made by condensing an amino- anthraquinone with a chloroanthraquinone and cyclizing to form a carbazole nucleus, the latter step involving an oxidation or dehydrogenation.

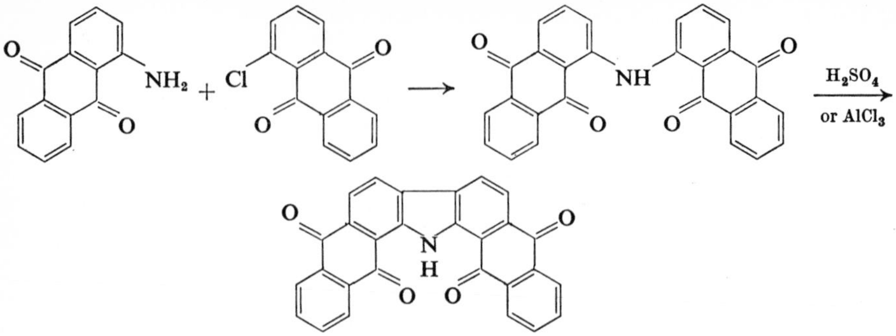

Indanthrene Yellow FFRK

Indanthrene Brown BR (1 million pounds, 1955) is made from one mole of 1,4-diaminoanthraquinone and two moles of 1-chloroanthraquinone. **Indanthrene Khaki GG** was one of the major products of the dyestuff industry during World War II. It is made from one mole of 1,4,5,8-tetrachloroanthraquinone and four moles of 1-aminoanthraquinone.

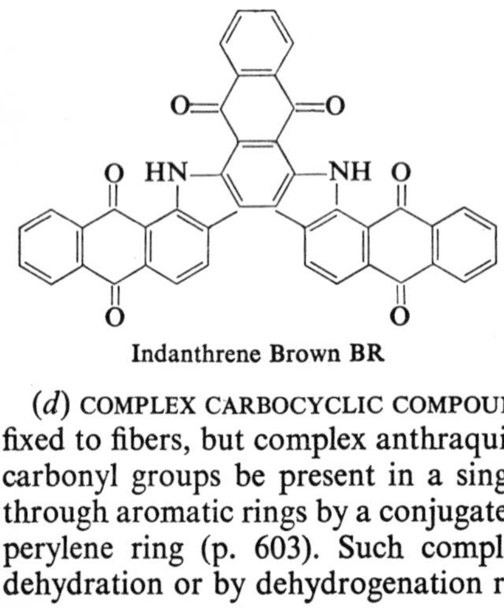

Indanthrene Brown BR

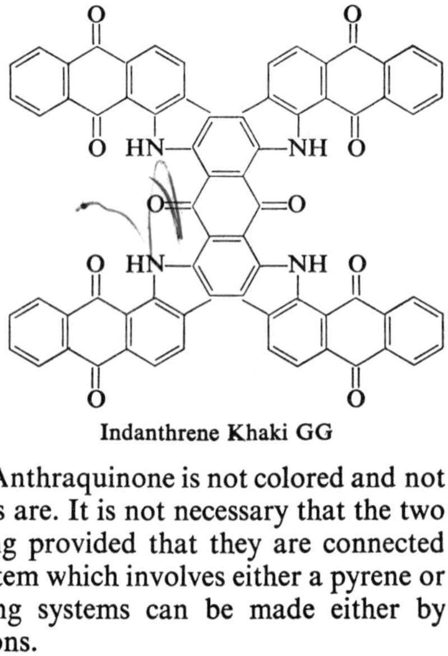

Indanthrene Khaki GG

(*d*) COMPLEX CARBOCYCLIC COMPOUNDS. Anthraquinone is not colored and not fixed to fibers, but complex anthraquinones are. It is not necessary that the two carbonyl groups be present in a single ring provided that they are connected through aromatic rings by a conjugated system which involves either a pyrene or perylene ring (p. 603). Such complex ring systems can be made either by dehydration or by dehydrogenation reactions.

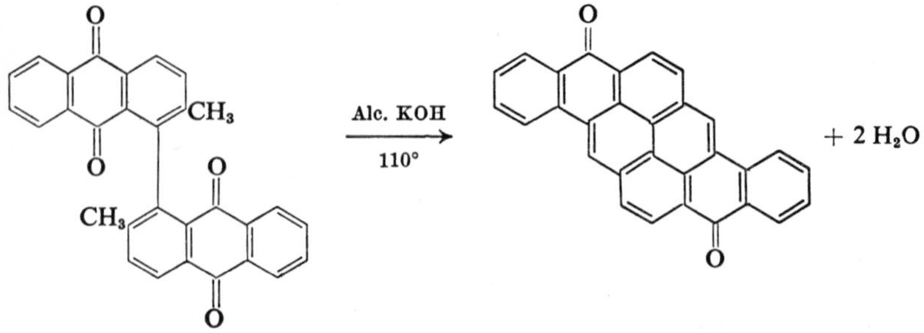

Anthraquinone Vat Golden Orange G

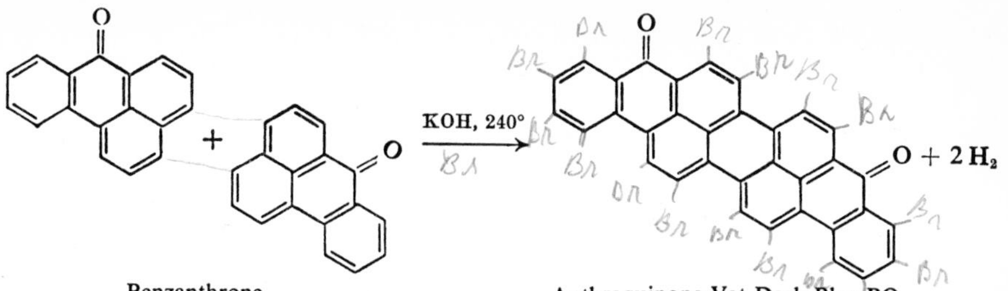

Benzanthrone   Anthraquinone Vat Dark Blue BO

Caledon Jade Green, a British discovery first produced in 1920, is considered by dye chemists to be the finest cotton dye. It is a dimethoxy derivative of Dark Blue BO.

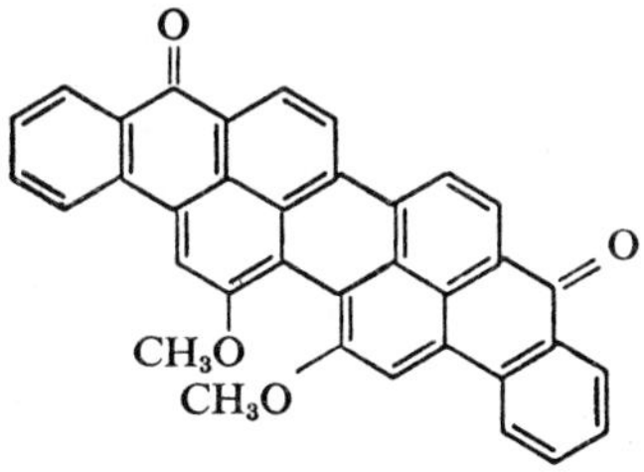

Caledon Jade green

About 380,000 pounds (100 per cent basis) valued at over $4.5 million was produced in the United States in 1955.

Anthraquinone vat dyes are applied from a hydrosulfite bath (p. 600) which must be considerably more strongly alkaline than that for dyeing indigo. Hence in the past they have been used only on cotton and viscose rayon. More recently processes have been developed for applying them to wool at a lower temperature than is used for cotton. The greater difficulty of manufacture has made the anthraquinone vats more expensive than most other dyes. Thus the average price per pound for various classes of dyes (100 per cent basis) in 1955 was sulfur, $0.26; azo, $1.36; indigoid, $1.85; anthraquinone vat, $9.70. Nevertheless, the superior fastness of anthraquinone vats to light and washing, the brilliance of their colors, and their high tinctorial power have resulted in a rapid expansion in their use in recent years. The value of their annual sales in 1955 was about $44,000,000 compared to $77,000,000 for azo dyes, $7,800,000 for indigoid dyes, and $6,600,000 for sulfur dyes.

Sulfur or Sulfide Dyes

This important class of dyes ordinarily includes those dyes made by heating organic materials with sulfur and sodium sulfide, a process known as *thionation*, and does not include other sulfur-containing dyes such as the thiazines, thio-indigos, and the thiazoles. The first sulfur dyes were yellows and browns produced by heating sawdust, bran, or manure with sulfur. In 1893 Vidal introduced the use of derivatives of benzene and naphthalene to produce black dyes, and later blues, greens, yellows, and oranges were developed. Sulfur dyes are insoluble in water but are reduced by sodium sulfide to water-soluble products that are substantive to cotton and from which the insoluble dye is regenerated by air or chemical oxidation. They are used only for cotton, since they are applied from the sodium sulfide solution, which attacks protein and ester fibers.

The exact chemical structures of the sulfur dyes is unknown, but they are complex compounds and may contain thiazole, phenothiazine, and 9,10-dithia-anthracene ring systems. Thionation also introduces mercapto or disulfide groups, which accounts for the solubilization by alkaline reduction and precipitation by oxidation.

$$DH \xrightarrow{S} DSH \xrightarrow{NaOH} DSNa \xrightarrow{O_2, H_2O} DS-SD$$

Since little is known about the constitution of the dyes and since the products of various manufacturers differ, they usually are grouped together according to color. The most important of the **blacks** is made from 2,4-dinitrophenol. At $0.20 per pound, it is the cheapest dye and the volume of production (16 million pounds, 1955) is several times that of any other single dye. **Blues** are made from indophenols (p. 692), from diphenylamine derivatives, and from carbazole and *p*-nitrosophenol. **Greens** are made by adding copper salts to melts for blue dyes. **Yellows, oranges,** and **browns** are made from compounds having reactive groups in the *meta* position such as *m*-toluylenediamine.

Quinonimines

The formation of these colored compounds of simple structure is discussed under the Liebermann nitroso reaction (p. 506) and the quinonechloroimide test for phenols (p. 523). The dye **Indophenol Blue** can be used as a vat dye, the reduced form being soluble in alkali.

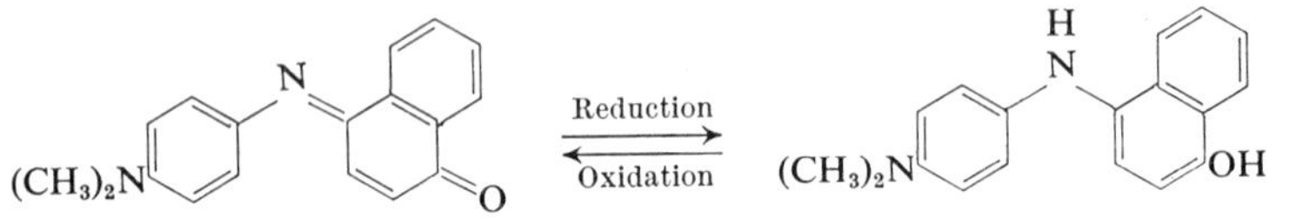

Indophenol Blue

It is almost as fast as indigo but is sensitive to acids. The chief use of the indophenols is as intermediates for blue sulfur dyes (p. 692).

The dyes formed when film for color photography is developed are quinonimines. If *p*-diethylaminoaniline is used as the developing agent, it is oxidized by the silver bromide to the quinonoid salt, which then can react with a coupler such as α-naphthol to give a blue-green indophenol. Developing is carried out in a buffered alkaline solution, which neutralizes the hydrogen bromide.

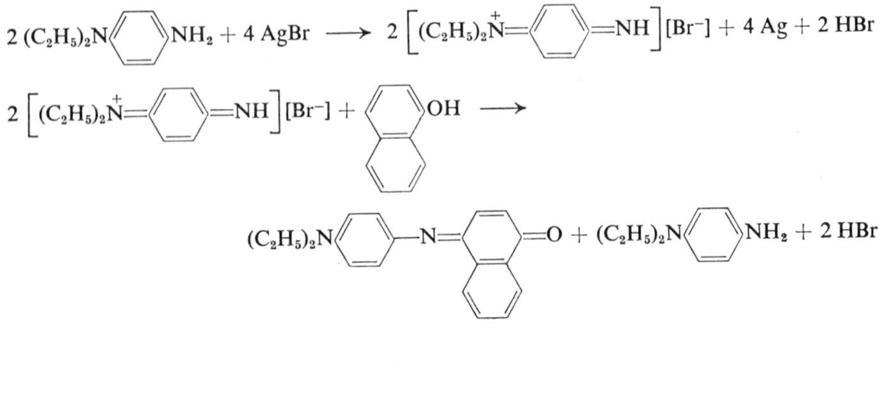

The dye is deposited at the site where the silver bromide was reduced and in an amount proportional to the amount of silver bromide reduced (p. 519). Removal of the silver leaves a dye image. By using a three-layer emulsion and three couplers that give blue-green, magenta, and yellow dyes with the same developer, together with the proper sensitizers for the silver halide and dyes to act as filters, a colored photograph results.

Methylidyne and Polymethylidyne Dyes

This class of dyes contains one or more methylidyne groups in the chromophoric system. For many years their chief use was as photographic sensitizers, but in recent years several of them have been introduced as dyes for cellulose acetate.

The development of these dyes as photographic sensitizers has made possible modern high speed and color photography. Like all photochemical reactions, the action of light on silver halide takes place only when light is absorbed. White silver chloride is sensitive only in the violet and ultraviolet regions of the spectrum. Silver bromide is yellow and is sensitive into the blue, and mixtures of silver bromide and silver iodide, which are darker colored than either halide alone, are sensitive up to 500 mμ, All longer wavelengths do not affect the emulsion. They register as black on a photographic print and hence the picture does not give the relative intensities of dark and light as registered by the eye. Moreover color photography using such an emulsion would be impossible, since red, orange, yellow, and most of the green region would not affect the photographic plate.

In 1873 Vogel discovered that the addition of small amounts of dyes made the emulsions sensitive to longer wavelengths, and it soon was found that the region in which a dye sensitizes corresponds roughly to the region in which the dye absorbs light, although the sensitivity usually extends 20 to 40 mμ further into the red. It now is known that the sensitizing action is due to a band characteristic of an adsorption complex in which several layers of dye molecules are oriented on the surface of the silver halide crystals.

Although many dyes increase sensitivity in a particular region of the spectrum, most of them have a deleterious action on the emulsion, causing fogging or desensitization at other regions of the spectrum. With the exception of erythrosin (tetraiodofluorescein), the dyes that have proved to be most useful are the **cyanine dyes** derived from quinoline derivatives. The simple **cyanines** can be prepared by the reaction of a quinaldine ethiodide with a 2-iodoquinoline ethiodide in the presence of a base.

| Quinaldine ethiodide | 2-Iodoquinoline ethiodide | 1,1′-Diethyl-2,2′-cyanine iodide |

The **carbocyanines** are prepared by condensing two molecules of a quinaldine ethiodide with formaldehyde, chloroform, or an orthoformate.

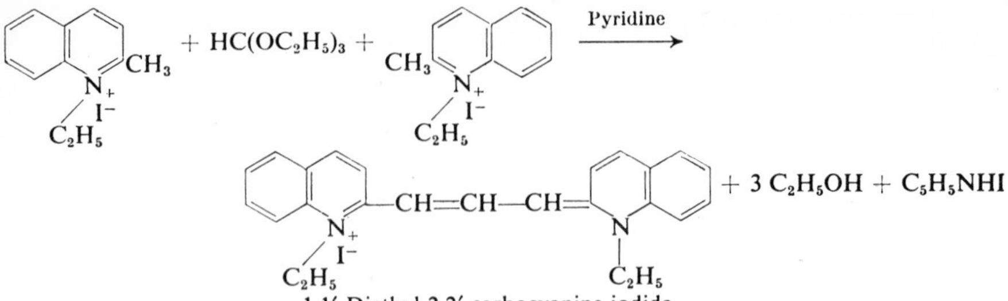

1,1'-Diethyl-2,2'-carbocyanine iodide

For each vinylene (CH=CH) group introduced between the two nuclei, the absorption and sensitizing action are shifted about 100 mμ to the red. Di-, tri-, tetra-, and pentacarbocyanines having two, three, four, and five vinylene groups in the conjugated system have been prepared, resulting in the sensitization of the photographic emulsion up to 1400 mμ in the infrared.

Since a methyl group in the 4 position of quinoline also is reactive (p. 629), cyanines have been prepared from lepidine derivatives as well as from quinaldines. Although the quinoline nucleus was the first to be used in the preparation of cyanine sensitizers, any nucleus having a reactive methyl group can be used. Thus derivatives of 2-methylbenzothiazoles (p. 636) have yielded some of the most important photographic sensitizers, the **thiacarbocyanines.** Derivatives of benzoxazole and benzoselenazole also have been prepared. The **azacyanines** have one or more methylidyne groups replaced by a nitrogen atom.

Some of the **merocyanines** are important sensitizers. They are not salts like the cyanines but are nonionic compounds containing a polymethylidyne chain. They can be made by condensing a quaternary salt with a nonionic compound containing a methylene group adjacent to a carbonyl group.

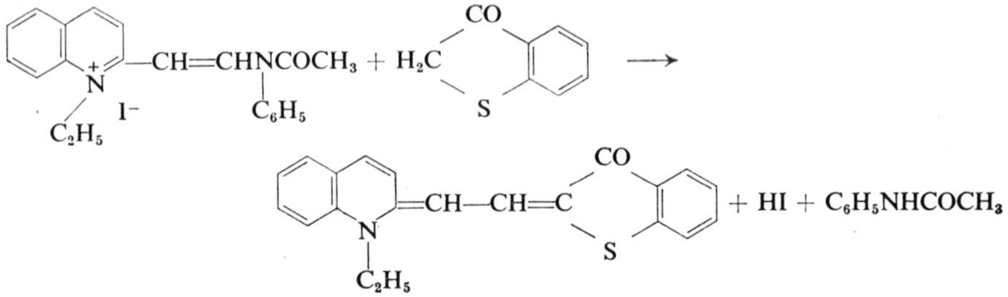

Celliton Fast Yellow 7G and **Genacryl Pink FG** (*Astrazon Pink FG*) are examples of methylidyne dyes for cellulose acetate.

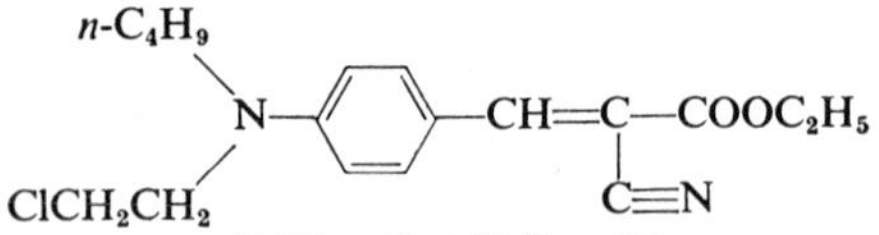

Celliton Fast Yellow 7G

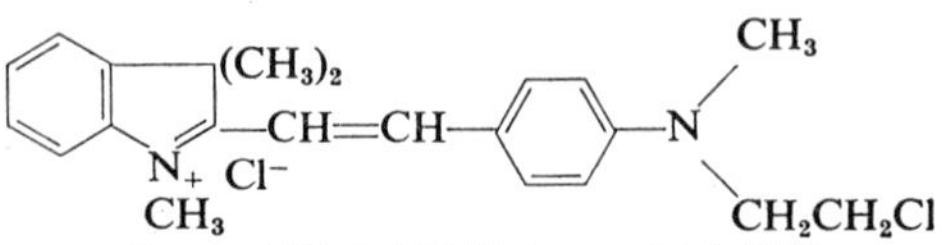

Genacryl Pink FG (Astrazon Pink FG)

Acridine Dyes

Dyes of this class are yellow or brown. They are of interest primarily as another class of colored compounds although two are good antiseptics. **Proflavine** appears to be superior to sulfa drugs as a wound antiseptic under certain conditions. **Acriflavine** has a strong trypanocidal action and has been

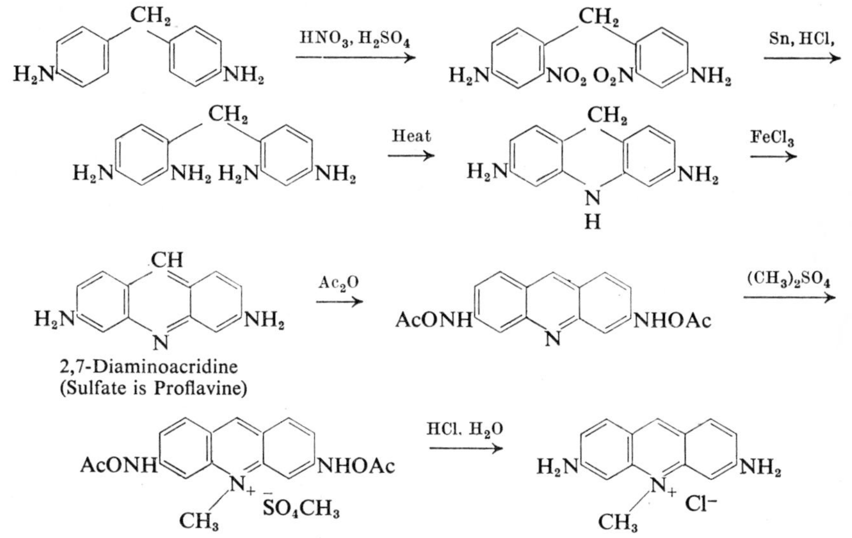

2,7-Diaminoacridine
(Sulfate is Proflavine)

Acriflavine or Trypaflavine

used in the treatment of sleeping sickness. The dye **Phosphine** is a co-product of the magenta melt and is used in dyeing leather.

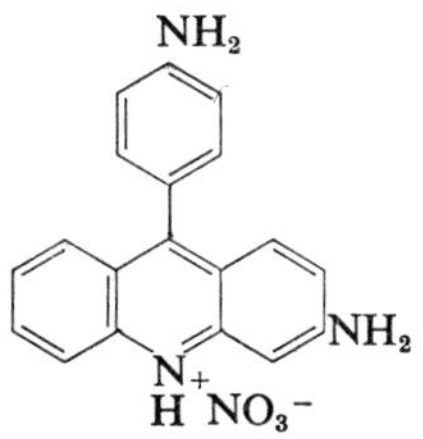

Phosphine

Azine Dyes

These dyes are oxidized amino derivatives of phenoxazine, phenothiazine, and dihydrophenazine, and are known as oxazines, thiazines, and phenazines. They can be reduced to colorless compounds and the color can be regenerated by oxidation.

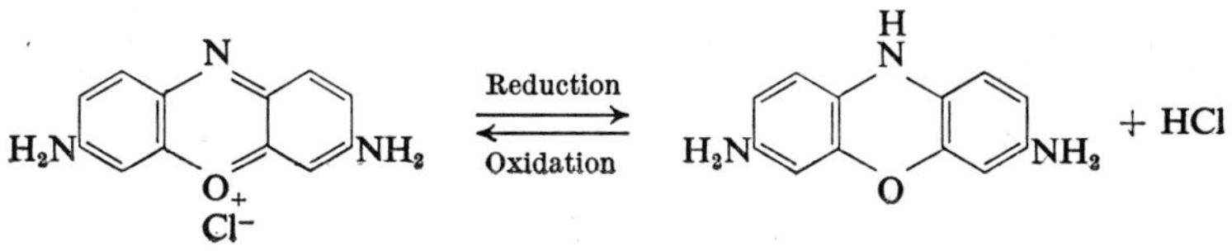

Methylene Blue, which has been used extensively in biological oxidation-reduction experiments, is a thiazine, and the commercial dye **Safranine-T** is a phenazine. It is of interest that Perkin's **mauve** has been shown to be a phenazine derivative.

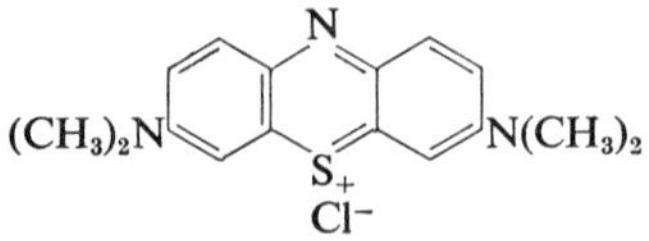

Methylene Blue

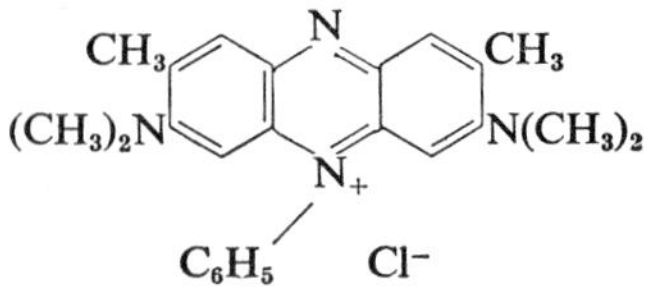

Safranine-T

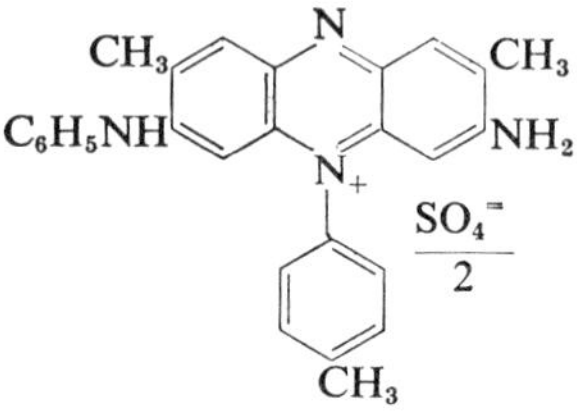

Mauve

One of the most important black dyes is a phenazine derivative called **Aniline Black.** It does not appear in statistics on dyes because it never is isolated as such. It is produced directly on cotton fiber by the oxidation of aniline salts with oxidizing agents such as potassium chlorate, sodium dichromate, or ferric chloride in the presence of vanadium, copper, or iron salts as catalysts. The first Aniline Black was produced by Lightfoot in 1863. The early Aniline Blacks turned green with age. They are believed to have the structure assigned to **Nigraniline.** Later an "ungreenable" Aniline Black was developed which is called **Pernigraniline** and is believed to be a polyphenazine derivative.

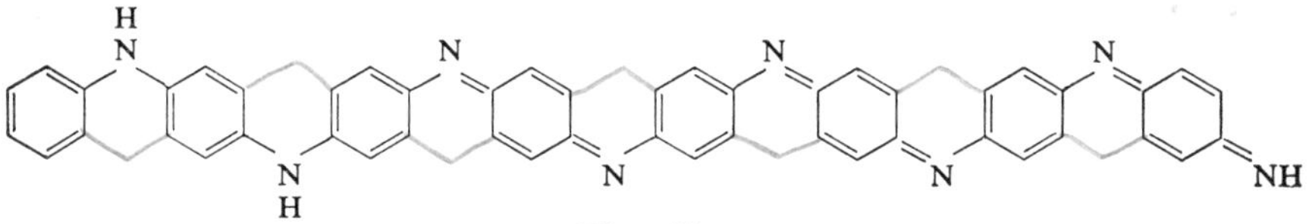

Nigraniline

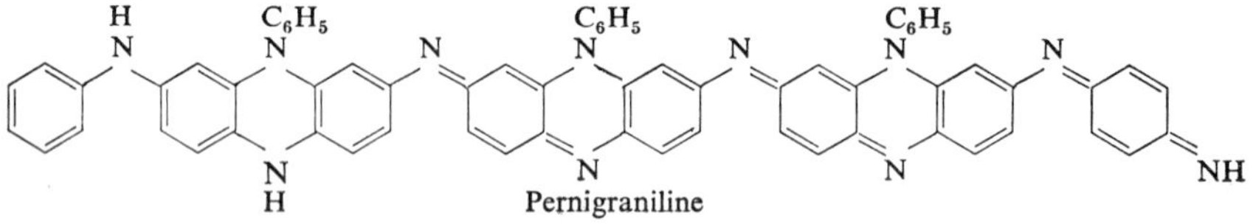

Pernigraniline

Hydrolysis and further oxidation of the Aniline Blacks yields quinone (p. 521).

Nigrosine is a cheap black dye made by oxidizing aniline and aniline hydrochloride with nitrobenzene or nitrophenol in the presence of ferric chloride at 180°. The free base is soluble in oils and waxes, the hydrochloride in alcohol, and the sulfonated product in water. Around 3 million pounds per year is made for dyeing shoe polish, printing inks, leather and paper.

Thiazole Dyes

When *p*-toluidine is heated with sulfur, hydrogen sulfide is evolved and a product known as *Primuline Base* is obtained. Sulfonation gives the yellow dye **Primuline.** These products are believed to be benzothiazole (p. 636) derivatives.

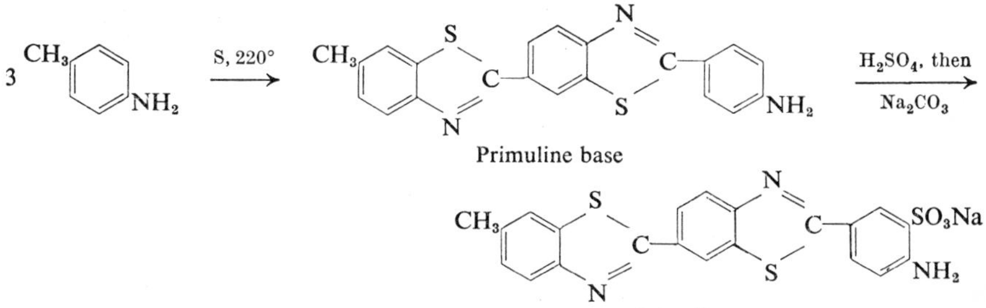

Primuline base

Primuline

Although made like the sulfur dyes, Primuline is not classed with them, because sulfonation permits it to be dyed from a water solution. Primuline is substantive to cotton but is not very fast. It can be diazotized on the fiber, however, and coupled with secondary components to give fast developed shades of red. The most interesting characteristic is that the diazonium group of diazotized Primuline is decomposed readily by exposure to strong light.

This behavior is shown by other diazotized amines also, and important commercial photographic processes are based upon it. For example paper coated with the diazotized amine can be exposed to light through a negative and then passed through a solution of the secondary component. Coupling takes place where the diazonium salt was not decomposed and a dye image results. In current processes the paper is coated with a mixture of a stabilized light-sensitive diazonium salt and a secondary component that will not couple with it except under alkaline conditions. After exposure to light the paper is developed with ammonia which permits coupling at the unexposed portions. The amines most generally used are *p*-aminodimethylaniline, *p*-aminomethylaniline, and *p*-aminohydroxyethylaniline. This process, which is called the *diazotype process* (*Ozalid process*), is used for all types of photographic reproduction, especially line drawings, letters, and other business records.

The thiacarbocyanines mentioned under the polymethylidyne group as important photographic sensitizers (p. 693) are thiazole derivatives.

Flavones and Flavylium Salts

These compounds are benzopyrans and are distributed widely as the coloring matter of flowers.

Flavones. 2-Benzo-4-oxopyran, which is known as *chromone*, is colorless. So is 2-phenylchromone, which is called *flavone*. The presence of a hydroxyl group at the 3 position, however, leads to colored compounds (L. *flavus*, yellow).

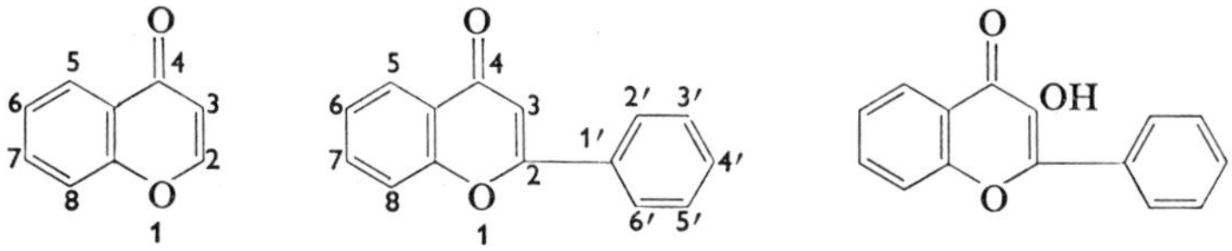

Chromone
(colorless)

Flavone
(colorless)

Flavonol
(yellow)

✔ **Quercitrin** is a rhamnoside (at position 3) present in many plants, but was obtained first from the bark of the black oak, *Quercus tinctoria*. Hydrolysis gives **quercitin** which has been used since the earliest times as a mordant dye.

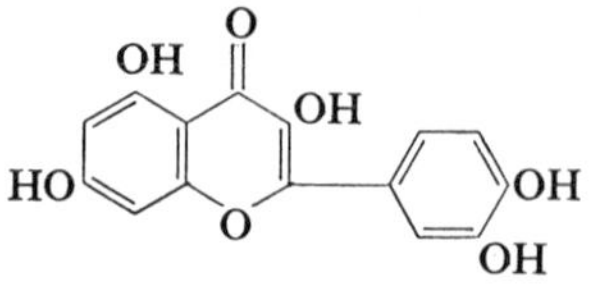

Quercitin

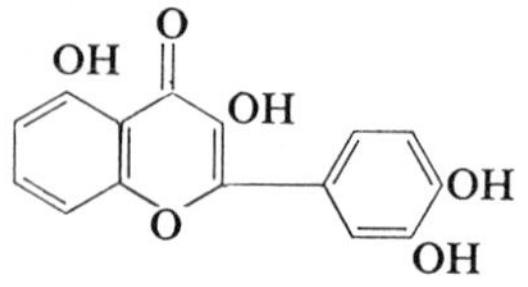

Morin

✓ **Rutin,** the 3-rutinoside of quercitin, has been produced from the buckwheat plant, and is used in the treatment of capillary bleeding. It is present in many other plants and is the yellow coloring matter on the stems and leaves of the tomato plant. **Morin** is a sensitive reagent for aluminum. The **condensed tannins** (cf. p. 561), to which group most of the natural tannins used commercially belong, are believed to be derivatives of flavone. Acid hydrolysis gives red polymeric products known as *tanner's red* or *phlobaphenes*.

Flavylium Salts. Reaction of an *o*-hydroxy aromatic aldehyde with an aldehyde or ketone in the presence of acid yields a benzopyran derivative known as a *benzopyrylium salt*. A probable intermediate in the reaction is the cyclic hemiacetal, which is a pseudo base like that in equilibrium with *N*-methylpyridinium hydroxide (p. 623).

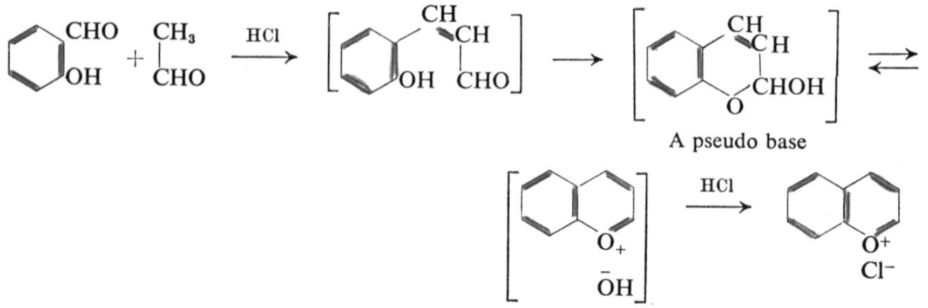

A pseudo base

Benzopyrylium chloride

Most of the red and blue pigments of flowers are derivatives of 2-phenyl-benzopyrylium salts, which are known as *flavylium salts*. They occur in the plants as glucosides known as **anthocyanins,** the aglycone being called an **anthocyanidin.** The anthocyanidins derived from natural anthocyanins belong to three groups. All have hydroxyl groups in the 3, 5, and 7 positions. **Pelargonidin chloride** (scarlet pelargonium, orange dahlia) contains an additional hydroxyl group in the 4' position; **cyanidin chloride** (red rose, blue cornflower, red dahlia, black cherry, plum) has two hydroxyl groups in the 3' and 4' positions; **delphinidin chloride** (delphinium, violet pansy, purple grape) contains three hydroxyl groups in the 3', 4', and 5' positions.

The anthocyanidins have been synthesized by the general method for the synthesis of benzopyrylium salts using the properly substituted aldehydes and ketones as intermediates.

The reaction scheme at the top of the page shows:

A compound with OCH_3, CHO, and CH_3O, OH substituents plus a compound with CH_2OCH_3, OCH_3 groups, reacting with **HCl in HOAc** to give a chromene structure (OCH_3, OH, CH_3O, OCH_3), then with **HCl, heat** →

Pelargonidin chloride

The color of the anthocyanins, which usually are 3,5-diglucosides, depends not only on their components but also on the acidity of the flower. Thus the rose is red because the anthocyanin occurs as the free phenol, but the cornflower is blue because the anthocyanin occurs as the potassium salt.

INDICATOR ACTION

Many compounds have different colors at different hydrogen ion concentrations. These color changes occur because the compounds themselves are acids or bases which enter into proton transfer reactions, and the acid form has a different color than the base form. The hydrogen ion concentration at which the color change takes place depends on the strength of the compound as an acid or a base.

Methyl Orange in solutions that are more basic than pH 4.4 exists almost entirely as the yellow negative ion. In solutions more acidic than pH 3.1 it combines almost completely with a proton and forms the red dipolar ion.

$$Na^+ \; {}^-O_3S \text{—} \langle \rangle \text{—} N{=}N \text{—} \langle \rangle \text{—} N(CH_3)_2$$

Yellow

HCl ↕ NaOH

$$Na^+\left\{ {}^-O_3S\text{—}\langle\rangle\text{—}\overset{+}{\underset{H}{N}}{=}N\text{—}\langle\rangle\text{—}N(CH_3)_2 \longleftrightarrow {}^-O_3S\text{—}\langle\rangle\text{—}\overset{}{\underset{H}{N}}\text{—}N{=}\langle\rangle{=}\overset{+}{N}(CH_3)_2 \right\}$$

Red

The interaction of the unsaturation electrons over a considerable distance is easier in the dipolar ion than in the negative ion, and hence the dipolar ion absorbs at longer wavelength ($\lambda_{max.} = 520 \text{ m}\mu$, Fig. 99). This type of resonance hybridization is less important in the negative ion ($\lambda_{max.} = 460 \text{ m}\mu$) because the quinonoid structure would require a separation of charge in the ion.

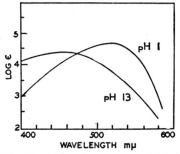

Fig. 99. Absorption spectra of Methyl Orange in alkaline and in acid solution.

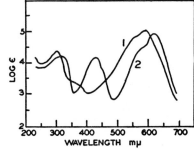

Fig. 100. Absorption spectra of (*1*) Crystal Violet, and (*2*) Malachite Green.

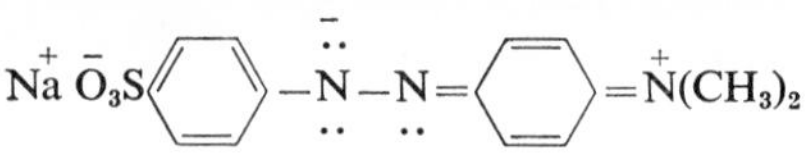

$$\overset{+}{Na}\ \overset{-}{O}_3S\!\!\left\langle\right\rangle\!-\overset{..}{\underset{..}{N}}-N\!\!=\!\!\left\langle\right\rangle\!\!=\!\overset{+}{N}(CH_3)_2$$

Phenolphthalein is colorless in solutions having a pH less than 8.3, where it exists almost entirely as the phenolic lactone. At pH greater than 10 it is in the form of a salt which is red. In very strongly alkaline solutions it is converted slowly to the carbinol which again is colorless.

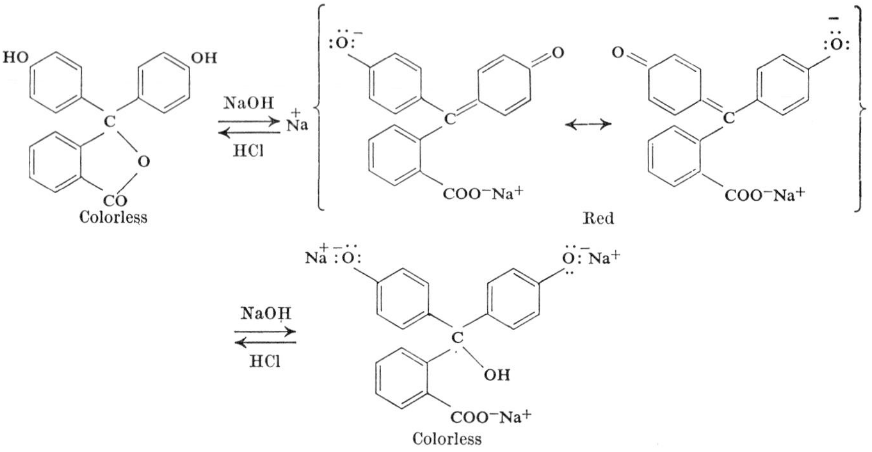

The reason that Methyl Orange changes color on the acid side whereas phenolphthalein changes on the alkaline side is that the salt from Methyl Orange and an acid is a much stronger acid than phenolphthalein, just as an amine hydrochloride is a stronger acid than phenol. The conversion of the red ion of phenolphthalein to the colorless carbinol is characteristic of all triphenylmethane dyes, and merely is the reverse of the formation of the dye from the carbinol base (p. 680).

Some dyes have more than one endpoint; that is, they go through a series of color changes as the acidity is changed. For example, Crystal Violet is deep violet at pH > 6. If the acidity is increased, the color changes between pH 6 and pH 5 to blue-green, which the solution retains until a pH of about 2 is reached. Between pH 2 and pH 0.5 the color changes to yellow. An explanation is possible from the observation that the color between pH 5 and pH 2 is almost identical with that of Malachite Green in solutions having an alkalinity greater than pH 2, and that in strongly acid solutions the colors of Crystal Violet and of Malachite Green are almost identical with the color of the dye from (*p*-dimethylaminophenyl)diphenylcarbinol.

In Crystal Violet at pH > 6 electronic interaction takes place over all three rings. At pH 5 to 2, resonance with one of the rings is prevented because the unshared pair of electrons on one of the dimethylamino groups is bound to hydrogen, and a condition exists analogous to that in Malachite Green at pH > 2. At pH < 0.5 the proton has added to the unshared pairs on both nitrogen atoms of Crystal Violet and on the one nitrogen atom in Malachite Green. Therefore resonance cannot take place with these rings any more than it can with the two phenyl groups in the dye from (*p*-dimethylaminophenyl)-diphenylcarbinol.

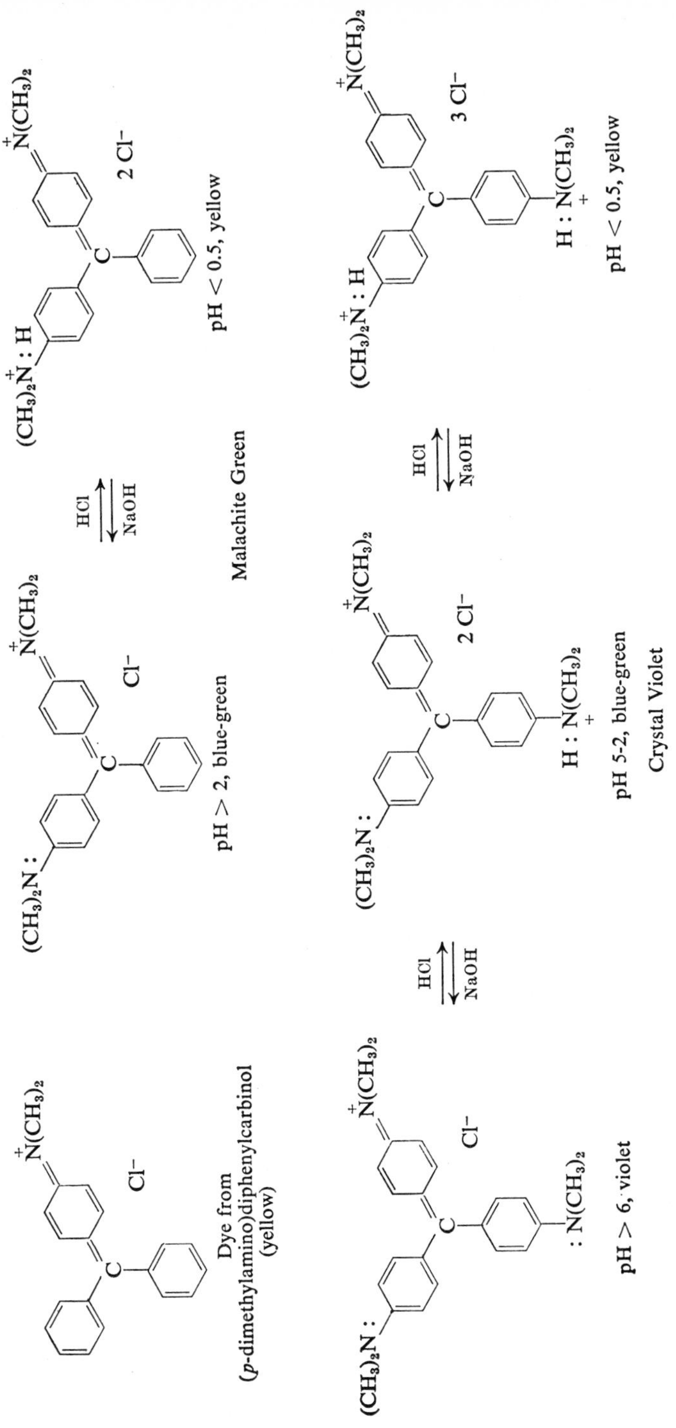
Dye from
(p-dimethylamino)diphenylcarbinol
(yellow)
pH > 2, blue-green
HCl
NaOH
pH < 0.5, yellow
Malachite Green
pH > 6, violet
HCl
NaOH
pH 5-2, blue-green
HCl
NaOH
pH < 0.5, yellow
Crystal Violet

From the simple concept of resonance between valence structures, Crystal Violet should absorb at a longer wavelength than Malachite Green. Actually the long wavelength absorption of Crystal Violet is slightly shorter ($\lambda_{max.}$ = 590 mμ) than that of Malachite Green ($\lambda_{max.}$ = 616 mμ). Moreover both show an absorption band at about the same place in the ultraviolet ($\lambda_{max.}$ = 300 mμ). The spectrum of Malachite Green differs in having a third band at $\lambda_{max.}$ = 423 mμ (Fig. 100, p. 699). The absorption of light is highly directional. According to the molecular orbital view, absorption takes place when an electron can be transferred to a new orbital with an extra nodal plane perpendicular to the electric vector of the light wave. The 423 band of Malachite Green is due to absorption of light waves polarized across the short axis of the resonating system. The 625 band is due to the absorption of light waves polarized across the long axis of the resonating system. Since Crystal Violet is symmetrical and the distance across the resonating system is approximately the same as that of the long axis of the system in Malachite Green, Crystal Violet has only a single band in the visible at approximately the same place as the long wave absorption of Malachite Green.

ORGANIC PIGMENTS

Technically, a pigment (L. *pigmentum*, from *pingere*, to paint) may be defined as any opaque insoluble powder which is used to color another material. Pigments are used chiefly in protective and decorative coatings, printing inks, plastics, and rubber. Frequently pigments are inorganic materials such as clays and the oxides of metals, but often the coloring matter used in pigments is a synthetic organic chemical. The material used as a pigment should be insoluble or practically so in the vehicle or solvent. The physical properties of the product, especially the particle size, are as important as the color and the fastness to light.

Organic pigments are classified as *toners* and *lakes*. **Toners** or **full-strength colors** are essentially pure compounds, being either insoluble organic compounds, metallic salts of organic compounds, or coordination complexes of organic compounds with metals. **Lakes** are diluted products prepared either by adsorbing a dye on a metallic hydroxide such as hydrated alumina, by precipitating a metallic salt in the presence of hydrated alumina, or by diluting a toner with hydrated alumina or with gloss white, a mixture of alumina and barium sulfate. The term *lake* comes from the Persian *lak* applied to the ancient pigment made from clay and a dye from the lac insect (*Lucifer lacca*).

Any mordant dye will form insoluble coordination complexes with metallic salts such as aluminum chloride. Thus three molecules of Orange II react with one of aluminum chloride to give the toner known as **Persian Orange.**

Orange II   Persian Orange

In the preparation of Persian Orange lake, a solution of the dye is mixed with a suspension of alumina, and aluminum chloride is added.

Some of the toners such as the **lithols** appear to be salts of the dye. The lithols are prepared by coupling diazotized Tobias acid (p. 590) with β-naphthol and converting the product to a water-insoluble salt.

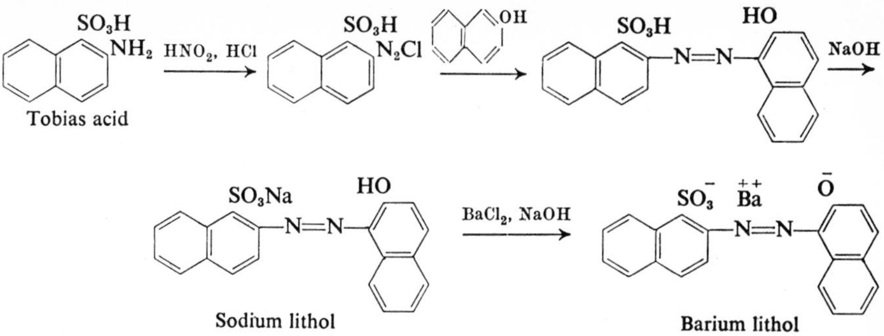

Tobias acid

Sodium lithol   Barium lithol

Sodium lithol is a light orange, and barium lithol is red (5.5 million pounds, 1955).

The basic dyes of the triphenylmethane series (p. 679) are not fast to light, but their phosphotungstates, phosphomolybdates, and phosphotungstomolybdates are considerably more stable and are valuable pigments for printing inks. They usually are regarded as simple salts of the complex phosphotungstic acid, $H_3PW_{12}O_4$, or phosphomolybdic acid, $H_3PMo_{12}O_4$, with three molecules of a triphenylmethane dye such as Methyl Violet or Malachite Green.

Numerous water-insoluble colored organic compounds are used directly as pigments, particularly the water-insoluble azo compounds such as Para Red and the Naphtols (p. 677). The **Hansa Yellows** are important yellow pigments. They are prepared by coupling diazotized aromatic amines with anilides of acetoacetic acid (acetoacetanilides). The latter compounds are enols and couple as the phenols do (p. 498).

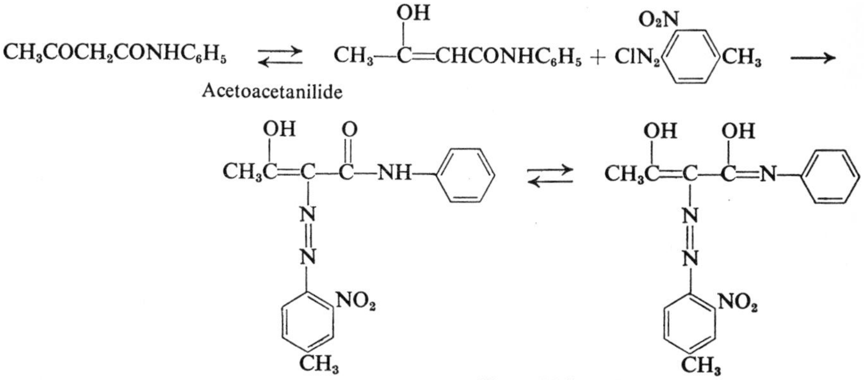

Acetoacetanilide

Hansa Yellow G

The **benzidine yellows** (2.6 million pounds, 1955) are analogous compounds derived from acetoacetanilides and diazotized benzidine.

The **phthalocyanines** form an important group of pigments reported in 1934. Attention was directed to this class first in 1928 with the isolation of a blue material which sometimes formed during the commercial preparation of phthalimide (p. 553) in which ammonia is passed through molten phthalic anhydride in iron vessels. The impurity was shown to be the iron complex of a compound having a 16-membered ring analogous to the porphin nucleus (p. 614) but containing four nitrogen atoms in place of the four methylidyne

(CH) groups. Subsequent work showed that these compounds could be prepared by a strongly exothermic reaction between phthalonitrile and a metal or metallic salt.

Copper phthalocyanine
(Monastral Blue)

Copper phthalocyanine (2.5 million pounds, 1955) is made more cheaply by heating phthalic anhydride with urea in the presence of a copper salt and small amounts of a catalyst such as vanadium oxide, aluminum oxide, or molybdenum oxide. Copper phthalocyanine actually had been prepared in 1927 by the action of cuprous cyanide on *o*-dibromobenzene in pyridine, but it was assigned an incorrect structure and was not further investigated. It is a brilliant blue with high tinctorial properties and is very stable to light, chemical action, and heat. It sublimes at 500° without appreciable decomposition.

The metal-free phthalocyanine, which had been prepared in 1907 but not investigated further, also has considerable utility. The only other phthalocyanine pigments that have found important use are the chlorinated copper phthalocyanines. As the number of chlorine atoms substituted in the benzene nuclei increases, the color becomes greener. The hexadecachloro compound now is made commercially from tetrachlorophthalic anhydride using zirconium or titanium tetrachloride as an additional condensing agent. Some phthalocyanine dyes, useful for dyeing textiles, have been prepared by introducing water-solubilizing or vattable groups.

REVIEW QUESTIONS

1. (*a*) How do direct azo dyes for cotton differ in structure from direct azo dyes for wool and silk? (*b*) Discuss the application of mordant dyes, ice-colors, developed dyes, and vat dyes. Why are vat dyes suitable only for cotton? (*c*) What, in principle, is the difference between the dyeing of acetate rayon and other textiles?
2. (*a*) Define the term *chromophore group* and give three common examples. (*b*) Explain the function of auxochrome groups in producing and modifying the color of dyes.
3. Describe and illustrate by a formula the type of chemical reaction that takes place between a metallic hydroxide mordant and a dye.
4. (*a*) Explain the color change of Methyl Orange with change of pH. (*b*) Phenolphthalein is colorless in acid solution, red in weakly alkaline solutions, but decolorizes again in strongly alkaline solutions; explain. (*c*) On adding increasing amounts of acid to an aqueous solution of Crystal Violet, the color changes from violet to blue-green to yellow, whereas Malachite Green changes from blue-green to yellow; explain.
5. What are the anthocyanins? What is the general structure of the anthocyanidins?

PROBLEMS

6. Starting with compounds obtainable from coal tar, give a series of reactions for the following syntheses: (*a*) Orange II; (*b*) Fast Scarlet R; (*c*) Celliton Fast Yellow G; (*d*) Blankophor R; (*e*) Benzopurpurin 4B; (*f*) Malachite Green; (*g*) Indophenol Blue.

7. Starting with anthracene, give the reactions that Bohn was attempting to complete which led to the discovery of Indanthrene Blue.

8. A dye was decolorized when boiled with tin and hydrochloric acid. From the colorless solution two products were isolated, both of which contained nitrogen, but only one of which contained sulfur. Fusion of the sulfur-containing compound with sodium hydroxide gave a product identical with the compound that was free of sulfur. Oxidation of the latter with ferric chloride gave β-naphthoquinone. Give a likely structure for the dye.

9. Give a series of reactions for the synthesis of Pyrocatechol Violet starting with compounds obtainable from coal tar or wood tar.

10. A red compound, *A*, has the molecular formula $C_{28}H_{18}N_2O_4$. It is insoluble in dilute acid or alkali, but dissolves when warmed with alkaline sodium hydrosulfite solution. *A* is saponified when boiled with alcoholic potassium hydroxide. Removal of most of the alcohol and dilution with water gives a precipitate, *B*, $C_{14}H_{10}N_2O_2$. *B* is soluble in dilute sulfuric acid, and when sodium nitrite is added to the cold acid solution no nitrogen is evolved. When the solution is warmed, nitrogen is produced and compound *C* is obtained. When *C* is distilled with zinc dust, anthracene sublimes.

When the alkaline solution from which compound *B* was removed is acidified, compound *D* is obtained, which has a neutralization equivalent of 122. When *D* is heated with soda-lime, benzene distills. Give a likely structural formula for *A* and equations for the reactions that take place.

11. A yellow, water-soluble compound, *A*, has the molecular formula $C_{14}H_{14}ClN_3$. When *A* is strongly heated, a gas is evolved and the residue, after purification, yields compound *B*, $C_{13}H_{11}N_3$, which is insoluble in water but soluble in dilute acids. Compound *B* can be diazotized, and when the diazonium salt solution is added to an alkaline solution of formaldehyde, compound *C*, $C_{13}H_9N$, is obtained, which is identical with the product formed by heating *bis*(2-aminophenyl)methane followed by oxidation with ferric chloride. Give a structural formula for *A* and equations for the reactions that take place.

Chapter 32

DIENES. RUBBER AND SYNTHETIC RUBBERS

DIENES only

The chemical properties of dienes differ according to the relative positions of the double bonds. If the double bonds are isolated, that is, separated by two or more single bonds, each double bond reacts independently, and the reactions are no different from those when only a single double bond is present. If both double bonds are attached to a single carbon atom, they are known as *cumulative* or *twin double* bonds and readily undergo rearrangement. Hydrocarbons having a pair of twin double bonds are known as *allenes* after the name of the first member of the series, $CH_2=C=CH_2$. Compounds having more than two double bonds joining adjacent carbon atoms are called *cumulenes*. If double bonds alternate with single bonds, they are said to be *conjugated* and exhibit a still different type of chemical behavior.

Allenes

Allene or **propadiene** is the simplest hydrocarbon containing two double bonds and can be made by a series of reactions from glycerol.

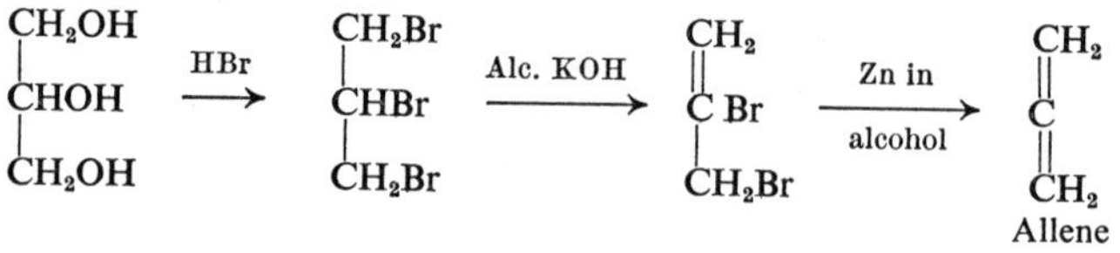

$$
\begin{array}{ccccccc}
CH_2OH & & CH_2Br & & CH_2 & & CH_2 \\
| & \xrightarrow{HBr} & | & \xrightarrow{Alc.\ KOH} & \| & \xrightarrow[alcohol]{Zn\ in} & \| \\
CHOH & & CHBr & & C\ Br & & C \\
| & & | & & | & & \| \\
CH_2OH & & CH_2Br & & CH_2Br & & CH_2 \\
& & & & & & Allene
\end{array}
$$

Its most characteristic behavior is reaction with sodium to give sodium methylacetylide.

$$ CH_2=C=CH_2 \xrightarrow[ether]{Na\ in} CH_3C\equiv CNa $$

The greater stability of the acetylenic linkage over the allene structure is indicated by the fact that dihalides having the halogen atoms on adjacent carbon atoms yield chiefly acetylenes on reaction with alcoholic alkali (p. 129). For example, the gas obtained by the reaction of propylene bromide with hot alcoholic potassium hydroxide solution is about 95 per cent methylacetylene and 5 per cent allene. **Butatriene,** $CH_2=C=C=CH_2$, is the simplest cumulene.

The planes of the two double bonds in the allenes are perpendicular to each other. Hence if the two groups attached to each carbon atom at the ends of the allene system are different, the molecule is dissymmetric and two enantiomorphic forms are possible (Fig. 101). van't Hoff

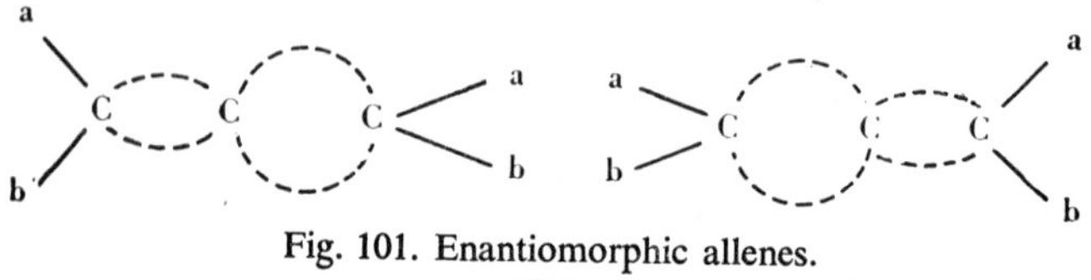

Fig. 101. Enantiomorphic allenes.

706

predicted in 1874 that it should be possible to obtain such optically active isomers. His prediction was not realized until 1935 when 1,3-diphenyl-1,3-di-α-naphthylallene was obtained in the highly active ($[\alpha]_{546}$ 437°) dextro and levo forms. In 1952 a natural product was isolated, which was optically active because of an allene structure (p. 790). An odd number of cumulative double bonds can lead to *cis-trans* geometrical isomers, an example of which was reported in 1954.

Conjugated Dienes

The most important conjugated diene is **1,3-butadiene.** Because of its technical use in the manufacture of synthetic rubbers, the methods of preparation are deferred to page 716. A characteristic chemical behavior of conjugated dienes is 1,4 addition. Thus Thiele (p. 51) found that if one mole of bromine is added to 1,3-butadiene, the chief product is 1,4-dibromo-2-butene.

$$CH_2=CH-CH=CH_2 + Br_2 \longrightarrow CH_2-CH=CH-CH_2 \text{ and } CH_2=CH-CH-CH_2$$
$$ \overset{|}{Br} \overset{|}{Br} \overset{|}{Br} \overset{|}{Br}$$
$$ 80 \text{ per cent} 20 \text{ per cent}$$

This behavior is in accord with the stepwise mechanism postulated for halogen addition (p. 54).

$$CH_2=CH-CH=CH_2 \overset{Br_2}{\underset{[Br^-]}{\rightleftarrows}} \left(CH_2=CH-CH-CH_2Br \longleftrightarrow CH_2-CH=CH-CH_2Br \right) \overset{Br_2}{\longrightarrow}$$
$$ \overset{+}{} \overset{+}{}$$
$$CH_2=CHCHBrCH_2Br \text{ and } BrCH_2-CH=CH-CH_2Br + [Br^+]$$

Conjugated dienes also add 1,4 to the double bond of maleic anhydride (p. 805), a reaction that can be used for their quantitative estimation.

The most important reaction of conjugated dienes is their polymerization by 1,4 addition to rubber-like products under the influence of catalysts of the free-radical type (p. 717).

$$x\ CH_2=CH-CH=CH_2 \xrightarrow[\text{catalyst}]{\text{Free-radical}} (-CH_2-CH=CH-CH_2-)_x$$

Conjugated dienes can be detected easily by their high intensity absorption band at 220–250 mμ (p. 664). If two double bonds are conjugated in a single ring the absorption band lies at 250–290 mμ.

Conjugation of double bonds is nothing more than the formation of polycentric molecular orbitals (pp. 154, 419). Thus in 1,3-butadiene use of sp^2 hybrid bonding orbitals leaves one *p* orbital containing one electron on each carbon atom. Overlapping of the *p* orbitals (Fig. 92*a*, p. 663) permits the formation of two molecular orbitals each encompassing all four carbon nuclei. The π orbital of lowest energy has a single nodal plane (Fig. 92*b*) whereas the second has two nodal planes (Fig. 92*c*) and has a higher energy. However the total energy of the electrons in these polycentric orbitals is less than the total energy would be if they were located in the dicentric orbitals of two isolated double bonds. If an additional single bond separates the two double bonds as in 1,4-pentadiene, the *p* orbitals of the 2 and 4 carbon atoms cannot overlap and no conjugation results.

RUBBER

Sources

Rubber was introduced to Europe shortly after the discovery of America. Early Spanish explorers found that South and Central American natives used the substance to waterproof household utensils and to make balls for their games. The name *rubber* was given to it by Joseph Priestley, who used it to rub out pencil marks.

Rubber is distributed extensively in the plant kingdom. It usually occurs as a colloidal solution in a white fluid known as *latex*. If the milky fluid from goldenrod or dandelion is rubbed between the fingers, a small ball of rubber soon is formed. Many such sources have been investigated, but the principal commercial production is from the rubber tree, *Hevea braziliensis*, which accounts for over 98 per cent of the world production. The tree is a native of the Amazon valley, and rubber production at one time was a Brazilian monopoly. In 1876, 70,000 seeds were brought to England, and nearly 3000 were germinated successfully in Kew Gardens. The young trees were shipped to various English colonies in the Far East and successfully grown on plantations in Ceylon and the Straits Settlements. Four thousand acres had been planted by 1899, in which year four tons of rubber was exported. By 1910, because of the increasing use of the automobile, plantation production had reached 11,000 tons and wild rubber production 83,000 tons. In 1922 world production was 400,000 tons, 93 per cent of which was plantation grown. In 1940, 1.4 million tons was produced of which 97 per cent was grown on plantations, 1 per cent was from wild *Hevea*, and 2 per cent was from other sources. After recovery from the disruption of World War II, production reached 2 million tons in 1955.

The price of rubber has fluctuated greatly. It reached $3.12 per pound in 1910 and dropped to $0.12 in 1921. It rose to $1.21 in 1925 because of British controls and dropped to $0.03 in 1932. In 1940 it sold for $0.19, but the opinion prevailed at that time that it could be sold profitably at the plantation for $0.03 and delivered in New York for $0.07 per pound. With the development of the synthetic rubber industry during World War II, nations were freed of dependence on natural rubber. Consequently the price in the future under normal conditions should not exceed greatly the cost of the synthetic product, which has been about $0.25 per pound.

Production

In 1940 over 9 million acres were planted to rubber, and the yield averaged about 400 pounds per acre. This average will tend to increase because the yield from new plantations using budded stock reaches 2000 pounds per acre. As a comparison, goldenrod will yield 60 to 90 pounds per acre and the Russian dandelion, kok-saghyz, 30 to 60 pounds per acre.

Latex is not the sap of the rubber tree. It occurs in microscopic tubules distributed throughout the plant and is obtained from those in the cortex layer between the bark and the cambium layer. A sloping V-shaped incision is made one third of the way around the trunk starting 3 feet above the ground, and the latex is drained into a cup attached to the trunk at the end of the incision. Since there is no flow in the tubules, a thin slice must be removed every other day to expose a fresh surface, the cut being lowered about 1 inch per month.

From 15 to 30 cc. of latex containing 35 per cent rubber is obtained per tapping. A single worker can tap 350 to 400 trees per day.

The latex is diluted to 15 per cent rubber and coagulated by the addition of salt and acetic acid. The precipitate is rolled into sheets, washed, and smoked to preserve it against mold. This product is dark brown. In the preparation of the light-colored crepe rubber, bisulfite is added before precipitation to prevent oxidation, and the product is washed more thoroughly to remove the serum and prevent spoilage.

Increasing quantities of rubber are shipped as latex, which is stabilized by the addition of ammonia and concentrated to 60 to 75 per cent solids in one of three ways: (*1*) by centrifuging, (*2*) by *creaming* in which the addition of a small amount of a hydrated colloid such as Irish moss or gum tragacanth causes a more concentrated layer to separate, or (*3*) by evaporation.

Small amounts of rubber are produced from the guayule shrub, *Parthenium argentatum*, a native of northern Mexico and southwestern United States. The rubber occurs as particles throughout the plant and is separated by grinding the whole plant, allowing it to ret in water, and skimming off the rubber particles which float to the top. In recent years extensive breeding experiments have been undertaken and attempts made to grow it economically in the United States, but these attempts have been largely abandoned. Guayule has a much higher resin content (18 to 25 per cent) than plantation rubber (1 to 4 per cent), but for certain purposes a higher resin content than that present in plantation rubber is desirable. Hence guayule always has been in demand for blending purposes.

Constitution

Crude plantation rubber contains 2 to 4 per cent protein and 1 to 4 per cent resins, the latter being the substances soluble in acetone. The remainder is the *rubber hydrocarbon*, which has the empirical formula C_5H_8 as established by Faraday in 1826. Many attempts have been made to determine its molecular weight. One investigation indicates that the molecular weight ranges from 50,000 to 3,000,000, with 60 per cent of the molecules having molecular weights greater than 1,300,000.

Destructive distillation of rubber yields among other products a hydrocarbon called **isoprene,** which has the molecular formula C_5H_8 and is 2-methyl-1,3-butadiene, $CH_2=C(CH_3)CH=CH_2$. The fact that isoprene reverts gradually to a rubber-like product led to the view that rubber is a polymerization product of isoprene. Rubber is unsaturated, adding one mole of hydrogen catalytically, one mole of bromine, or one mole of hydrogen chloride for each five carbon atoms. Hence one double bond is present for each isoprene unit. Harries [1] in 1904 prepared the ozonide of rubber and isolated from the hydrolysis products levulinic aldehyde and levulinic acid. A painstaking quantitative investigation of the products of ozonolysis reported in 1936 accounted for 95 per cent of the carbon content of the rubber molecule, and 90 per cent of the products isolated can be considered as derived from levulinic aldehyde. These results

---

[1] Carl Dietrich Harries (1866–1923), professor at the University of Kiel. He is known for his extensive work on the ozonation of unsaturated organic compounds.

leave little doubt that the rubber hydrocarbon is a linear polymer of isoprene having the structure first postulated by Pickles in 1910. The nature of the end groups has not been determined.

$$\left[-CH_2C\!=\!CHCH_2(CH_2C\!=\!CHCH_2)_xCH_2C\!=\!CHCH_2-\right] \xrightarrow{\text{Ozonolysis}} (x+2) \quad O\!=\!CHCH_2CH_2C\!=\!O$$

$$\underset{CH_3}{\qquad} \underset{CH_3}{\qquad} \underset{CH_3}{\qquad} \qquad \underset{CH_3}{\qquad}$$

Rubber hydrocarbon   Levulinic aldehyde

Vulcanization

Because there is little if any cross linkage of the chains of the molecules, rubber is thermoplastic and becomes soft and sticky on heating. When cooled to low temperatures it becomes hard and brittle. These properties were undesirable even in the early use of rubber, which was chiefly for the waterproofing of textiles. In 1834 Charles Goodyear[2] began experiments attempting to overcome this disadvantage. Mixtures with sulfur had been experimented with previously, and in 1839, while attempting to improve these mixtures, Goodyear accidentally dropped one of his preparations on a hot stove, thus discovering the process which he called **vulcanization.** Development of the process led to the production of a material with much greater toughness and elasticity than natural rubber, and one which withstood relatively high temperatures without softening and which retained its elasticity and flexibility at low temperatures.

Vulcanization is a chemical reaction of the rubber hydrocarbon with sulfur in which sulfur adds to the double bonds. Addition takes place in such a way that the chains of rubber molecules are tied together giving a large cross-linked molecule.

$$[-CH_2C(CH_3)\!=\!CHCH_2-]_x \qquad \left[-CH_2\overset{|}{C}(CH_3)CHCH_2-\right]_x$$

$$+\,2\,S \quad\longrightarrow\quad S$$

$$[-CH_2C(CH_3)\!=\!CHCH_2-]_x \qquad \left[-CH_2C(CH_3)\overset{|}{C}HCH_2-\right]_x$$

$$S-$$

If only a few cross links are present, the molecules can be aligned and elongated to a considerable extent by stretching but cannot slip past one another. When the tension is removed, thermal agitation returns the molecules to their original random orientation (Fig. 102).

The exact types of sulfur linkages in vulcanized rubber are not known. It is reasonably certain that some of the combined sulfur adds to the double bonds without causing cross linking and that polysulfide as well as sulfide bridges are possible.

As little as 0.3 per cent of sulfur or 1 per cent of that necessary to saturate the double bonds effects a cure. Commercial rubber is either low in sulfur (1 to 3 per cent) for soft rubber, or high in sulfur (23 to 35 per cent) for hard

---

[2] Charles Goodyear (1800–1860) was a New England inventor. His first patent was granted in 1844 and was followed in subsequent years by over sixty more. Many honors were bestowed on Goodyear, but he was kept in poverty because of litigations arising from infringements of his patents.

rubber or ebonite. Rubbers containing intermediate amounts are intractable and of no value. Since the amount of sulfur necessary to saturate the double bonds is 32 per cent, hard rubber has the maximum amount of cross linking.

Vulcanizing agents other than sulfur or sulfur-containing compounds are known. When thin sheets of rubber are exposed to light, sufficient cross linking

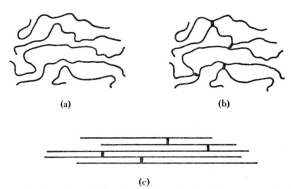

(a)   (b)

(c)

Fig. 102. Rubber molecules: (*a*) unvulcanized; (*b*) vulcanized but unstretched; (*c*) vulcanized and stretched.

takes place to produce the same effect as vulcanization. Rubber vulcanized with certain aromatic nitro compounds is used as an insulating coating for copper wire. It has the advantage that it does not cause discoloration of the copper. Peroxides such as cumyl peroxide also may be used as vulcanizing agents.

Accelerators and Other Additives

Many types of compounds, both inorganic and organic, increase the rate of vulcanization, and permit vulcanization to be carried out rapidly at a lower temperature with less sulfur. These compounds are known as **accelerators.** Some of the more important accelerators in current use are zinc diethyl- and dibutyldithiocarbamates (p. 325), 2-mercaptobenzothiazole and the corresponding disulfide (p. 636), and tetramethylthiuramdisulfide (*Tuads*, p. 325). More recently compounds prepared by the oxidative condensation of 2-mercaptobenzothiazole and aliphatic amines have been developed which are especially useful for milled rubber goods and synthetic rubbers.

$$\text{2-Mercaptobenzothiazole} + H_2NC_6H_{11} \xrightarrow{\text{NaOCl}} \text{CSNHC}_6H_{11} + NaCl + H_2O$$

2-Mercapto-   Cyclo-
benzothiazole   hexylamine

Most organic accelerators work best in the presence of **accelerator activators,** the most commonly used being zinc oxide.

One of the outstanding developments in the rubber industry has been the use of **antioxidants** (p. 886) to prolong the life of rubber articles. The ageing of rubber is due to the reaction of the double bonds with oxygen, with subsequent scission of the double bond and reduction in the molecular weight. This reaction is autocatalytic and can be prevented by the addition of secondary aromatic amines such as phenyl-β-naphthylamine. The aldehyde-aromatic amine condensation products, such as the mixture of condensation products from acetaldehyde or *n*-butyraldehyde and aniline (p. 481), not only are antioxidants but also have an accelerating action.

Reinforcing agents increase the stiffness, tensile strength, and resistance to abrasion. *Carbon black* (p. 70) is used most for this purpose (750,000 tons, 1954). Recently a superfine silica powder has been introduced called *carbon white*, which is said to be more effective in increasing tear and abrasion resistance, and which does not interfere with translucence or added color. **Fillers** such as barium sulfate, calcium carbonate, and diatomaceous earth decrease the strength and are used to reduce the cost of articles where strength is not important. **Softeners** such as fatty acids or pine oil also may be added.

Manufacturing Operations

Rubber is compounded by incorporating the various ingredients on mixing rolls, an operation known as *milling*. The rubber is squeezed through two large metal rolls rotating slowly in opposite directions at different speeds. The rubber mass is so handled that it encircles one of the rolls and is passed continuously between them. The rubber thus is subjected to a shearing action, which causes it to become warm. Air oxidation takes place, the chain length of the rubber molecules is reduced, and the mass becomes sticky and plastic. The rubber is said to be *broken down* or *masticated* by this operation. In this condition the various solids and liquids that are to be added to the rubber can be worked in on the rolls. The thoroughly mixed compounded rubber is cut from the roll and rolled into sheets. The sheets are used to line a mold which then is subjected to heat and pressure to form the finished product.

Latex can be compounded with the various finely powdered ingredients of the rubber mix by simple mixing. Articles are shaped by gelation on a mold and then vulcanized. The mix also can be deposited by electrodeposition. Latex can be spun into a coagulating bath to give thread. The use of latex is increasing, because expensive heavy machinery and high power consumption are not required in the manufacturing operations. Moreover the products are stronger because the rubber is not broken down in a milling operation.

Reclaimed Rubber

Vulcanized rubber is reclaimed on a large scale, especially from discarded automobile tires. The tire is shredded and heated with 4 to 8 per cent sodium hydroxide solution at 180°–200° to plasticize the rubber and to disintegrate the fabric, which then can be washed out. A fermentation process also has been developed for removing the cotton. After plasticizing with pine oil and straining, the mixture is sheeted. No sulfur is removed during the process, but since the initial sulfur content was low, there still are sufficient double bonds present for revulcanization. The price usually is one fourth to one third that of natural rubber, and a certain amount of reclaim is used in most rubber articles. Production in the United States in 1954 was 287,000 tons.

Rubber Derivatives

Oxygenated rubber is a sticky product prepared by air oxidation in the presence of cobalt linoleate. It is useful in certain types of paints and as a self-sticking adhesive on tapes and envelopes.

Hydrorubber is prepared by catalytic hydrogenation. It varies from a soft paraffin-like material to a heavy oil. It is very stable and is a good transformer oil.

Chlorinated rubber (Parlon, Duroprene, Tornesite) is prepared by passing chlorine into a carbon tetrachloride solution of rubber until the chlorine content reaches 60 to 65 per cent. The product is a white powder that is soluble in aromatic and chlorinated hydrocarbons, is thermoplastic, nonflammable, and resistant to aqueous acids, alkalies, and oxidizing agents. It is useful in formulating corrosion resistant paints for wood and metal.

Isomerized rubber is made by heating rubber with phenolsulfonic acid or with stannic chloride. The properties vary from those of gutta-percha to shellac. The tough products dissolved in a solvent make good adhesives for attaching rubber to metal (Vulcalock process), and the resin-like products are compounded to give molding powders under the name Plioform.

Gutta-percha and Balata

Gutta-percha and balata are materials from the latex cells of numerous members of the family *Sapotaceae*. Gutta-percha now is obtained almost exclusively from the leaves of hybrids of *Palaquium* grown on plantations in the Malay States and in the East Indies. Balata is similar to gutta-percha but is obtained from *Mimusops globosa*, which is native to Panama and the northern part of South America.

The hydrocarbon of gutta-percha is identical with that of balata and has the same composition as rubber hydrocarbon. In contrast to rubber, gutta-percha and balata are horny. They soften to a plastic condition below 100° and are used principally as a covering for submarine cable and for golf balls. In chemical properties the gutta-percha and balata hydrocarbon resembles rubber hydrocarbon, although the former is somewhat less reactive. On catalytic hydrogenation a product is obtained that cannot be distinguished from hydrogenated rubber. Accordingly the two hydrocarbons are believed to be stereoisomeric.

Stretched rubber gives an X-ray diffraction pattern like that of crystals, and the identity period is 8.2 Å. This distance can be accounted for only by a *cis* configuration at the double bonds with a certain amount of buckling with the result that the carbon atoms of the chain do not lie in a plane. Gutta-percha exists in two modifications, called α and β, the transition temperature being 68°. The α form has an identity period of 8.7 Å which is exactly that expected for a *trans* configuration with all of the carbon atoms of the chain lying in a plane. The β modification has an identity period of 4.8 Å which corresponds to a *trans* configuration, but with the carbon atoms of the chain being nonplanar as in the rubber molecule.

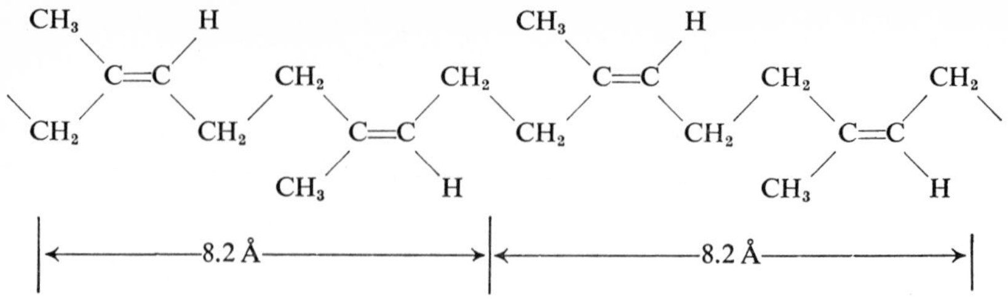

$$CH_3 \quad H \qquad\qquad CH_3 \quad H$$
$$C=C \qquad CH_2 \qquad CH_2 \qquad C=C \qquad CH_2 \qquad CH_2$$
$$CH_2 \qquad CH_2 \qquad C=C \qquad CH_2 \qquad CH_2 \qquad C=C$$
$$CH_3 \qquad H \qquad\qquad\qquad CH_3 \qquad H$$

|←————8.2 Å————→|←————8.2 Å————→|

Rubber

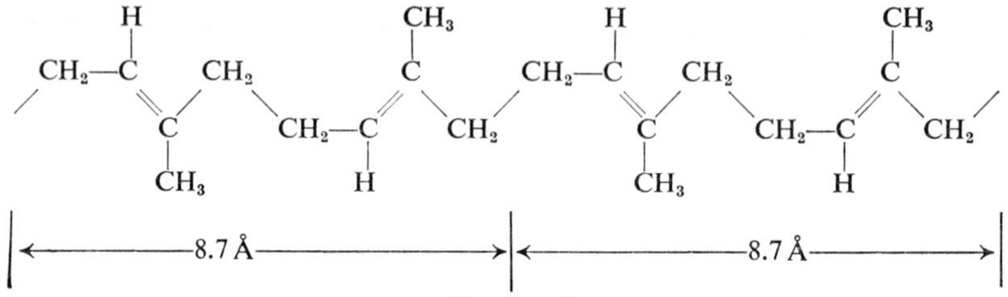

$$H \qquad\qquad CH_3 \qquad\qquad H \qquad\qquad CH_3$$
$$CH_2-C \quad CH_2 \qquad C \qquad CH_2-C \quad CH_2 \qquad C$$
$$C \qquad CH_2-C \quad CH_2 \qquad C \qquad CH_2-C \quad CH_2$$
$$CH_3 \qquad H \qquad\qquad CH_3 \qquad H$$

|←————8.7 Å————→|←————8.7 Å————→|

α-Gutta-percha

$$CH_3 \qquad CH_3 \qquad CH_3 \qquad CH_3$$
$$CH_2 \quad C \quad CH_2 \quad C \quad CH_2 \quad C \quad CH_2 \quad C$$
$$C \quad CH_2 \quad C \quad CH_2 \quad C \quad CH_2 \quad C \quad CH_2$$
$$H \qquad H \qquad H \qquad H$$

|←——4.8 Å——→|←——4.8 Å——→|←——4.8 Å——→|←——4.8 Å——→|

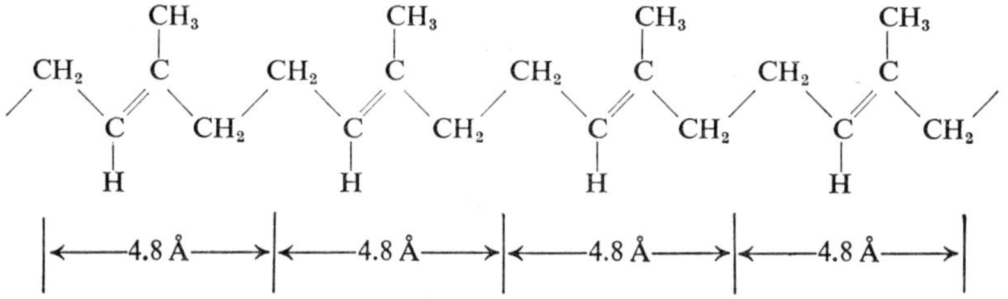

β-Gutta-percha

Chicle is a resin obtained by concentrating the latex of the sapodilla tree (*Sapota achras*) which grows only on the Yucatan peninsula. It is a mixture containing about 5 per cent *cis* polyisoprenes and 12 per cent *trans* polyisoprenes. The balance is resin, carbohydrates and inorganic compounds. The chief use is in the manufacture of chewing gum.

SYNTHETIC RUBBERS

Historical

Isoprene was obtained first by the distillation of rubber by Gregory in 1835. In 1879 Bourchardt reported the polymerization of isoprene to an elastic product which again gave isoprene on distillation. Continuously since then attempts have been made to develop a commercial process for the synthesis of rubber. For years some of the most able English and German chemists, both industrial and academic, vied with each other in their efforts to solve the problem. In 1910 Harries discovered the catalytic effect of sodium on the polymerization of isoprene and found that homologs of isoprene such as butadiene and 2,3-dimethylbutadiene also polymerized to rubber-like products. Although the synthetic rubber industry usually is thought to be a recent development, and in some ways rightly so, it is of interest that Matthews and Perkin, Jr., had worked out a process based on sodium polymerization in 1910, and the Badische Company exhibited a pair of automobile tires made of synthetic rubber at the Eighth International Congress of Pure and Applied Chemistry held in New York in 1912.

There are two principal reasons for the slow technical development of synthetic rubber. First, it was practically impossible to compete with a product whose price ranged from $0.03 to $3.00 per pound, and second, the synthetic product was not so satisfactory as the natural product for most uses. Hence in the past, synthetic rubbers have been used only when a nation has been excluded from world markets either by war or by a controlled economy. By the end of World War I Germany was producing 165 tons per month of *methyl rubber* from dimethylbutadiene starting with acetone, but the product was not good for general purposes. Research was continued after the war and better products known as *Buna* rubbers (contraction of *butadiene* and *natrium*) were developed. Under the controlled economies of Germany and Russia, they were manufactured on a large scale. The German Minister of Economy boasted in 1936 that the cost was only 60 to 80 per cent higher than the market price of natural rubber, and the Russians claimed that their product was cheaper in terms of man-hours of labor. The first synthetic product to compete with natural rubber in a free economy was *neoprene*, a purely American development. It did not result from direct attempts to produce a synthetic rubber but from Nieuwland's purely academic investigations of acetylene.[3] This product was competitive solely because of its superior properties for certain purposes, the introductory price in 1932 being $1.00 per pound, when rubber was selling for $0.15 per pound.

With the loss of the East Indies and the Malay Peninsula as a source of rubber during World War II, American chemists and chemical engineers were faced with the problem of creating a synthetic rubber industry within two years to replace the total output of 9 million acres of plantations employing over 2 million people and resulting from 60 years of development. Fortunately far-sighted industries had built experimental pilot plants before the war, and the remarkable feat was accomplished. By 1945 total synthetic rubber production was at the rate of 700,000 tons per year and reached 1,130,000 tons in 1955. The synthetic industry now is firmly established and although natural rubber has regained most of its original market, it never again will dominate the market and eventually may become of minor importance.

Manufacture

Actually there is no synthetic product identical with natural rubber, which has a regular head to tail arrangement of isoprene units with entirely *cis* configuration at the double bonds. Most so-called synthetic rubbers are not polymers of isoprene, do not have a regular arrangement of monomer units, and the double bonds have both *cis* and *trans* configurations. In 1955 processes were announced for making polymers of isoprene which resemble natural rubber very closely but still are not identical with it (p. 720). An attempt has been made to introduce the term *elastomers* for all substances having rubber-like

---

[3] Julius Arthur Nieuwland (1879–1936), American professor of chemistry at the University of Notre Dame. Besides being well known for his investigations of the chemistry of acetylene, he was a distinguished botanist.

properties, but the term *synthetic rubbers* is used most frequently. Although a synthetic true rubber is unknown, many different synthetic products are made, each of which has its own desirable characteristics that frequently are superior to those of rubber.

Butadiene Syntheses. The synthetic rubbers produced in largest amounts are based on butadiene, and a number of technical processes for its manufacture have been developed.

1. FROM ALCOHOL. This process was developed in Russia by Ostromislensky and in an improved form was used to produce much of the synthetic rubber made in the United States during World War II. Alcohol first was dehydrogenated to acetaldehyde (p. 194) and then allowed to react with another mole of alcohol over a silica catalyst containing 2 per cent of tantalum or zirconium oxide.

$$C_2H_5OH + CH_3CHO \xrightarrow{SiO_2-TaO_2\ (375°)} CH_2=CH-CH=CH_2 + 2\ H_2O$$

An alcohol-aldehyde ratio of 2.5 to 1 was used and the unreacted material recycled. The yield of butadiene was 64 per cent. At least 25 co-products are formed. The C_4 fraction is 98 per cent butadiene.

2. FROM PETROLEUM. In the thermal cracking of naphtha or light oil at 700°–760° about 0.5 to 0.8 per cent is converted to butadiene. Better yields are obtained by dehydrogenating butane or butene.

$$CH_3CH_2CH_2CH_3 \xrightarrow[600°,\ 1\ at.]{Al_2O_3-Cr_2O_3} CH_3CH=CHCH_3 \xrightarrow[650°,\ 0.1\ at.]{Ca_8Ni(PO_4)_6-Cr_2O_3} CH_2=CHCH=CH_2$$

The reduced partial pressure is achieved by admixture with steam. The conversion of butenes to butadiene in 85 per cent yield reaches 30 per cent per pass. The chief problem is the purification of the product. Selective solubility in furfural or in ammoniacal cuprous acetate solutions, and azeotropic distillation with ammonia have been used.

During World War II it was necessary to produce alcohol from grain, and at a cost of $0.60 per gallon for alcohol, production of butadiene from petroleum was much cheaper. However at the time that the first plants were built, technical knowledge for the alcohol process was farther advanced than for the petroleum process. Moreover the butane fractions were required for the synthesis of high octane gasoline (p. 77). Since the war, butadiene has been produced chiefly from butane and butenes. With improved processes and lower costs for the production of ethyl alcohol from ethylene, it is possible that alcohol may become competitive with butane and butenes as raw material.

3. FROM ACETYLENE. Germany, deficient in both petroleum and carbohydrates, based her syntheses on acetylene (p. 133). The process most used consisted of a series of conventional reactions (pp. 131, 205).

$$HC≡CH \xrightarrow[HgSO_4]{H_2O,\ H_2SO_4,} CH_3CHO \xrightarrow{Dil.\ NaOH} CH_3CHOHCH_2CHO \xrightarrow{H_2,\ Ni}$$

$$CH_3CHOHCH_2CH_2OH \xrightarrow[heat]{NaH_2PO_4,} CH_2=CHCH=CH_2$$

1,3-Butanediol (under first formula), Aldol (under second formula)

By the end of the war the Reppe process was being used. A mixture of acetylene, steam, and 30 per cent formaldehyde was passed at 110° and 45 pounds pressure over silica coated with cuprous acetylide. The acetylene added to the formaldehyde to give 1,4-dihydroxy-2-butyne. A sufficient excess of acetylene was used to convert all of the formaldehyde to the diol. The aqueous solution of diol was hydrogenated to 1,4-butanediol, which was dehydrated first to tetrahydrofuran and then to butadiene.

$$HC\equiv CH + 2\ HCHO \xrightarrow[110°,\ 45\ lbs.]{Cu_2C_2\ on\ SiO_2,} HOCH_2C\equiv CCH_2OH \xrightarrow{H_2,\ Ni}$$

1,4-Dihydroxy-2-butyne

$$HO(CH_2)_4OH \xrightarrow[270°]{H_3PO_4} \underset{\underset{O}{\overset{|}{}}}{\overset{CH_2\text{——}CH_2}{\underset{CH_2\qquad CH_2}{}}} \xrightarrow{H_2SO_4} CH_2{=}CH{-}CH{=}CH_2$$

1,4-Butanediol

Tetrahydrofuran

The chief danger of the process is the handling of exothermic acetylene under pressure. Contrary to previous views it is not sensitive to impurities, but all contact with copper or copper alloys must be avoided. Pipe lines must be kept short and all free space reduced to a minimum. No pipes should be larger than 35 mm. diameter, all larger pipes being filled with small pipes. Under these conditions local explosions may take place but no detonation occurs. The nonexplosive pressure that can be attained increases with the amount of diluent, such as steam or nitrogen, that is present.

Buna S or GRS, GRS-10, and Cold Rubber. The useful butadiene rubbers are copolymers with other compounds. The synthetic rubber made in the largest quantity is a copolymer of three parts by weight of butadiene and one part of styrene (p. 573). Polymerization is carried out in aqueous emulsion. The butadiene and styrene are emulsified with soap, and a peroxide catalyst (hydrogen peroxide, ammonium or potassium persulfate, or sodium perborate) is added, together with a modifier such as dodecyl mercaptan. A latex of the polymer is formed which is precipitated by the addition of salt and acetic acid.

When soap is used as an emulsifier, the product lacks *building tack*, the ability of layers of unvulcanized rubber mix to cohere and retain cohesion after vulcanization. This property is extremely important in the manufacture of rubber articles. A great improvement in this respect results if the sodium salt of disproportionated abietic acid (p. 861) is used as an emulsifying agent instead of soap. The resulting product is called **GRS-10**. More recently it has been found that peroxide-catalyzed polymerizations proceed much faster in the presence of oxidation-reduction systems. Using cumene hydroperoxide or *p*-menthane hydroperoxide (p. 874) as the catalyst, fructose as a reducing agent, and ferric pyrophosphate as an activator, it is possible to bring about the production of GRS at a practical rate at 5° compared with the previously used 50°. The product, known as *cold rubber*, has improved tensile strength, elongation, and processibility. Production of all types of GRS rubber in 1955 was around 850,000 tons.

Butadiene adds by both 1,4 and 1,2 addition. Hence the units present in GRS are $-CH_2CH{=}CHCH_2-$, $CH_2{=}CHCHCH_2-$, and $-CH_2CH-$. About 20

$$\overset{|}{C_6H_5}$$

per cent of the butadiene units result from 1,2 addition, and the various units appear to be randomly distributed. About one fifth of the double bonds remaining after 1,4 addition have the *cis* configuration and about four fifths are *trans*. Some branching and cross linking of molecules also takes place. The average molecular weight is about 100,000, but individual molecules range from 10,000 to 1,650,000.

Emulsion polymerization takes place by a free-radical mechanism. In the oxidation-reduction system, the primary step is the transfer of an electron from the reduced form of the metal ion to the peroxide to give a free radical which attacks a molecule of monomer to initiate the polymerization.

$$Fe^{++} + RO : OH \longrightarrow Fe^{+++} + : OH^- + RO \cdot$$

$$RO \cdot + CH_2{=}\underset{\underset{Z}{|}}{CH} \longrightarrow RO : CH_2\underset{\underset{Z}{|}}{CH} \cdot \quad (or\ RO \cdot + CH_2{=}CHCH{=}CH_2 \longrightarrow RO : CH_2CH{=}CHCH_2 \cdot)$$

In the propagation steps further reaction with monomer takes place extremely rapidly, as often as 1000 times in 0.01 second, because the activation energy is very low (approximately 5 kcal. per mole).

$$ROCH_2\underset{\underset{Z}{|}}{CH} \cdot + x\,CH_2{=}\underset{\underset{Z}{|}}{CH} \longrightarrow RO(CH_2\underset{\underset{Z}{|}}{CH})_x\,CH_2\underset{\underset{Z}{|}}{CH} \cdot$$

The modifier in the form of the mercaptan regulates the chain length by transferring a hydrogen atom and terminating the chain. At the same time it gives rise to a free radical which can initiate another chain reaction.

$$RO(CH_2\underset{\underset{Z}{|}}{CH})_x\,CH_2\underset{\underset{Z}{|}}{CH} \cdot + RSH \longrightarrow RO(CH_2\underset{\underset{Z}{|}}{CH})_x\,CH_2\underset{\underset{Z}{|}}{CH}_2 + RS \cdot$$

$$RS \cdot + CH_2{=}\underset{\underset{Z}{|}}{CH} \longrightarrow RS : CH_2\underset{\underset{Z}{|}}{CH} \cdot$$

The function of the reducing agent is to reduce the metallic ion and make it again available for initiating polymerization.

$$Fe^{+++} + sugar \longrightarrow Fe^{++} + oxidized\ sugar$$

The efficient utilization of the peroxide requires that the concentration of ferrous ions be kept extremely low and accounts for the use of pyrophosphate as a sequestering agent. The low concentration of ferrous ions also prevents the precipitation of the soaps used as emulsifiers.

Tire treads made from cold rubber wear better than those made from natural rubber. GRS rubbers, however, are not as easily processed, but this difficulty is being overcome by adding up to 35 parts of special petroleum oils to each 100 parts of GRS. The oil is added as an emulsion to the polymerized rubber emulsion before coagulation. The extender not only increases workability but at one sixth the price of GRS considerably decreases cost. Synthetic rubbers generate more heat on flexing than natural rubber. Hence the latter is preferred for the casings of heavy duty truck tires, but GRS is used in the tread.

Buna N or GRN. This product is a copolymer of butadiene and acrylonitrile, $CH_2{=}CHCN$ (p. 787). It is hard to mill and its light resistance is poor, but it has good resistance to oil.

Butyl Rubber or GRI. The polymerization of isobutylene (p. 62) gives a viscous to rubber-like product that is completely saturated and hence cannot be vulcanized. If it is copolymerized with a small amount of a diene such as isoprene one double bond remains for each molecule of the diene used. By using about 3 per cent of the diene, sufficient double bonds are present to give on vulcanization a rubber-like product that is practically saturated and hence has good resistance to chemicals and oxidation. The isoprene is produced by the cracking of gas oils and naphthas. Polymerization is carried out at $-100°$ in methyl chloride using aluminum chloride as a catalyst and liquid ethylene as a refrigerant. Because butyl rubber is very impermeable to gases, its chief use has been for the manufacture of inner tubes for automobile tires. New developments in the processing of butyl rubber have improved its other physical properties, and it shows promise of becoming a general purpose rubber. Production in 1955 was 62,000 tons.

Neoprene or GRM. During his investigations of the chemistry of acetylene, Nieuwland discovered the formation of a dimer, **vinylacetylene,** by the action of cuprous salts. Carothers[4] found that the dimer adds hydrogen chloride to yield 2-chloro-1,3-butadiene, known as **chloroprene.** The initial 1,4 addition product rapidly undergoes an allylic rearrangement (p. 728) in the presence of acid.

$$2\ HC\!\equiv\!CH \xrightarrow[\text{NH}_4\text{Cl}]{\text{Cu}_2\text{Cl}_2} \underset{\text{Vinylacetylene}}{H_2C\!=\!CH\!-\!C\!\equiv\!CH}$$

$$H_2C\!=\!CH\!-\!C\!\equiv\!CH \xrightarrow{HCl} [ClCH_2\!-\!CH\!=\!C\!=\!CH_2] \longrightarrow \underset{\underset{\underset{\text{Chloroprene}}{Cl}}{|}}{H_2C\!=\!CH\!-\!C\!=\!CH_2}$$

Polymerization of chloroprene takes place rapidly, being complete in 10 days even in the absence of a catalyst. This product is known as **neoprene.** Without vulcanization it resembles soft vulcanized rubber, being nonplastic and unworkable on the mill. If polymerization is allowed to proceed only partially, an elastic product is obtained which can be stabilized by the addition of phenyl-β-naphthylamine as an antioxidant. This material can be worked on rolls for the addition of other substances. The properties are enhanced by the addition of metallic oxides, but carbon black does not greatly increase its strength. The action of metallic oxides appears to be due to the formation of ether cross links that result from reaction with the small amount of active halogen which arises from some 1,2-addition during polymerization. The plastic mix is molded into the desired article, and the polymerization completed by heating. Neoprene latex can be made by allowing chloroprene emulsions to polymerize.

Neoprene is a good general purpose rubber, but its high cost of manufacture has limited its use to those applications that require its unique properties, such as resistance to oils, chemicals, air, light, heat, and flame. The price in 1955 was $0.42 per pound, compared to $0.30 for natural rubber, $0.25 for GRS rubber, and $0.22 for butyl rubber.

Thiokols. Thiokols are made by condensing a polychloro compound with sodium polysulfide. **Thiokol A** is made from ethylene chloride.

$$(x+1)\ ClCH_2CH_2Cl + x\ Na_2S_4 \longrightarrow Cl(CH_2CH_2SSSS)_x\,CH_2CH_2Cl \xrightarrow{H_2O}$$

$$\underset{\text{Thiokol A}}{HO(CH_2CH_2SSSS)_x CH_2CH_2OH}$$

---

[4] Wallace Hume Carothers (1896–1937), American-trained chemist and director of a laboratory for fundamental research in organic chemistry at the du Pont Experimental Station. In addition to his work on neoprene he conducted an investigation of the reactions of polyfunctional molecules which led to the discovery of nylon (p. 798), and to the production of many-membered ring compounds (p. 848).

Thiokol ST results from the reaction of sodium disulfide with chloroethyl formal (p. 743).

$$(x + 1)\ ClCH_2CH_2OCH_2OCH_2CH_2Cl \xrightarrow{Na_2S_2,\ H_2O}$$

$$HO(CH_2CH_2OCH_2OCH_2CH_2SS)_xCH_2CH_2OCH_2OCH_2CH_2OH$$
Thiokol ST

Cross linking can be brought about by adding up to 2 per cent of 1,2,3-trichloropropane. **Thiokol FA** is a copolymer from ethylene chloride and chloroethyl formal.

The thiokols show the best resistance of any synthetic rubbers to oils, but their physical properties are poor. They were used to line underground concrete storage tanks for liquid fuels during the war but find their principal peacetime use as gasket material.

Polyisoprene Rubber. Early attempts to prepare satisfactory synthetic rubbers from isoprene were unsuccessful. In 1955 processes were announced for preparing polymers with properties very close to those of natural rubber and suitable for heavy-duty truck tires. High purity isoprene is treated with finely dispersed lithium at 35° with rigorous exclusion of oxygen and moisture. The product is reported to have entirely the *cis* configuration and to differ from natural rubber only in that a small amount of 3,4 addition has taken place.

Latex Paint Vehicles. The so-called rubber-base latex paints are water emulsions of a pigment and a resin made by copolymerizing one part of butadiene with three parts of styrene. They are fast-drying, nonflammable, and lack the usual paint odor.

Miscellaneous Elastomers. Numerous other products have rubber-like properties. One of the oldest is **art gum** used for erasers and made by the vulcanization of vegetable drying oils. When polyethylene (p. 61) is treated with chlorine and sulfur dioxide, about 25 per cent by weight of chlorine is introduced together with a small number of chlorosulfonyl groups.

$$RH + Cl_2 \longrightarrow RCl + HCl$$

$$RH + SO_2 + Cl_2 \longrightarrow RSO_2Cl + HCl$$

The product is known as **Hypalon.** The chlorine atoms keep the chains apart and prevent them from aligning as in polyethylene. Vulcanization to an elastic material can be brought about by heating with water to form sulfonic acid groups and then with magnesium oxide to give a salt which causes cross linking of the chains. The product is saturated and exceptionally resistant to ozone and strong oxidizing agents. The ozone resistance of other rubbers is increased by compounding them with Hypalon. **Urethan rubbers** are discussed on p. 799 and **silicone rubbers** on p. 914.

Many other rubber-like products result from plasticizing nonrubber-like substances. For example, polyvinyl chloride (p. 726) can be plasticized with cresyl phosphate (p. 515) or 2-ethylhexyl phthalate (p. 552) (**Koroseal, Geon, Tygon**).

REVIEW QUESTIONS

1. How do the reactions of conjugated dienes differ from those of nonconjugated dienes? What physical property is important for the detection and estimation of conjugated dienes?
2. What is the principal source of natural rubber? How is it obtained and prepared for market?

3. Give the arguments for the accepted structure of the rubber hydrocarbon. How does it differ from the hydrocarbon of gutta-percha and balata?
4. Discuss the chemistry of vulcanization. What is meant by the term accelerator; antioxidant; reinforcing agent; milling?
5. What procedures have been used for the production of butadiene?
6. What are the chief differences in constitution between GRS, neoprene, butyl rubber, Buna N and Thiokol A?
7. Discuss the mechanism of emulsion polymerization as it applies to the production of GRS rubber.

Chapter 33

CHLORINATED AND FLUORINATED ALIPHATIC HYDROCARBONS

CHLORINATED HYDROCARBONS

Around 3.5 million tons of chlorine was produced in the United States in 1955, and 60 per cent was used for the preparation of organic compounds. The total production of noncyclic halogenated hydrocarbons alone amounted to over 1.7 million tons and was valued at over $190,000,000. Both substitution and addition reactions are used in their preparation.

The **chlorination of methane** at one time was investigated extensively for the production of methyl chloride to be used as a source of methyl alcohol, but these investigations were discontinued with the advent of the synthesis of methyl alcohol from carbon monoxide and hydrogen (p. 90). More recently, chlorination has been applied to the synthesis of methyl chloride, methylene chloride, chloroform, and carbon tetrachloride. The reaction is strongly exothermic, and the chief problem is to bring the gases to the reacting temperature (250°–400°) without the deposition of carbon. In one procedure the mixture of chlorine and methane is blown through a molten bath kept at the desired temperature, and in another the gases are preheated separately, and the chlorine added through jets to a high-velocity stream of methane. The velocity of the gases exceeds that of the rate of propagation of the flame, and no explosion results. In still another process the gases react between room temperature and 100°, the reaction being catalyzed by light from mercury vapor arc lamps.

Methyl chloride is produced chiefly from methanol and hydrogen chloride (p. 118). **Methylene chloride,** CH_2Cl_2, b.p. 40°, is a nonflammable fat solvent that frequently is used instead of ether for extractions. It is used also as a solvent for cellulose triacetate in the manufacture of film and fiber (p. 403). **Chloroform,** $CHCl_3$, b.p. 61°, also is a useful solvent, particularly for the extraction of penicillin. It formerly was made by the reaction of ethanol or acetone with calcium hypochlorite but acetaldehyde is a more economical starting point (p. 214). It has been made also by the iron and water reduction of carbon tetrachloride. Both methylene chloride and chloroform are made by the chlorination of methyl chloride from methyl alcohol as well as by the chlorination of methane. **Carbon tetrachloride,** b.p. 77°, is used in fire extinguishers, although it has the disadvantage that it is partially oxidized to phosgene, which may reach dangerous concentrations in closed spaces. It has been displaced for this purpose largely by liquid carbon dioxide. The most important use is in degreasing compounds and nonflammable dry cleaning solvents, but its toxicity is a hazard. Large quantities are used to prepare the chlorofluoromethanes (p. 733). In addition to its preparation from methane, carbon tetrachloride is made by the reaction of chlorine with carbon disulfide (p. 324).

$$CS_2 + 3\,Cl_2 \longrightarrow CCl_4 + S_2Cl_2$$
$$2\,S_2Cl_2 + CS_2 \longrightarrow CCl_4 + 6\,S$$

722

The sulfur is reconverted into carbon disulfide. Some carbon tetrachloride also is obtained by chlorinolysis of compounds containing several carbon atoms.

$$CH_3CHClCH_2Cl + 6\ Cl_2 \xrightarrow{250°-425°} Cl_2C=CCl_2 + CCl_4 + 6\ HCl$$

Propylene chloride   Tetrachloro-
                                                    ethylene

Ethyl chloride is made from ethyl alcohol or ethylene and hydrogen chloride or by the chlorination of ethane (p. 118). **Ethylene chloride, 1,2-dichloroethane,** b.p. 84°, may be made by passing ethylene and chlorine over anhydrous calcium chloride, copper or iron at 80°–100°. Chlorine addition can be brought about in the liquid phase at 40° using ethylene chloride or some other chlorinated hydrocarbon as a solvent. Some induced substitution, that is, substitution that takes place in the presence but not in the absence of olefin, accompanies addition. The amount of substitution is reduced considerably if small amounts of ferric chloride are present. Ethylene chloride also is a co-product of the action of hypochlorous acid on ethylene (p. 743). It is used as a solvent, in dry-cleaning fluids, and for the preparation of vinyl chloride (p. 725), Thiokol A (p. 719), and ethylenediamine (p. 754).

Numerous polyhalogenated compounds are produced from acetylene. Addition of two moles of hydrogen chloride gives **ethylidene chloride, CH_3CHCl_2,** b.p. 58°, which can be chlorinated to **methylchloroform (1,1,1-trichloroethane),** b.p. 74°.

$$HC \equiv CH + 2\ HCl \xrightarrow{AlCl_3} CH_3CHCl_2$$

$$CH_3CHCl_2 + Cl_2 \longrightarrow CH_3CCl_3 + HCl$$

Methylchloroform can be prepared also by the addition of hydrogen chloride to vinylidene chloride (p. 726).

$$CH_2=CCl_2 + HCl \longrightarrow CH_3CCl_3$$

The addition of chlorine to acetylene with the formation of **1,1,2,2-tetrachloroethane** takes place explosively, and antimony pentachloride has been used as the chlorinating agent. Acetylene and chlorine are introduced alternately into the liquid. Some penta- and hexachloroethane also are formed.

$$HC \equiv CH + 2\ SbCl_5 \longrightarrow HCl_2CHCl_2 + 2\ SbCl_3$$

1,1,2,2-Tetrachloroethane
(acetylene tetrachloride)

$$2\ SbCl_3 + 2\ Cl_2 \longrightarrow 2\ SbCl_5$$

Tetrachloroethane can be prepared also by mixing solutions of acetylene and chlorine in tetrachloroethane at 70°–95° using ferric chloride as a catalyst. To prevent explosions the tetrachloroethane is circulated downwards, acetylene mixed with it, and the chlorine bubbled in at a point below, where it reacts with a dilute solution of the acetylene in tetrachloroethane. Tetrachloroethane, b.p. 146°, is an excellent solvent, but it is highly toxic and corrodes metals in the presence of moisture. Most of it is used for the production of **trichloroethylene** by the action of an aqueous slurry of lime or by pyrolysis.

$$CHCl_2CHCl_2 \xrightarrow{475°} CHCl=CCl_2 + HCl$$

Trichloroethylene

This product boils at 87° and is one of the most important of the chlorinated solvents. It is stable and noncorrosive and is about as toxic as carbon tetrachloride. It is used chiefly for degreasing metal parts. The cold metal part is passed through the hot vapors which condense on the metal and wash away the oil and dirt.

Reaction of tetrachloroethane with iron or reduction of trichloroethylene with iron and water gives a mixture of the *cis-* and *trans-***1,2-dichloroethylenes** (*cis*, b.p. 48°, *trans*, b.p. 60°).

$$CHCl_2CHCl_2 \xrightarrow{\;Fe\;}$$
$$\xrightarrow{\;Fe,\ H_2O\;} CHCl{=}CHCl$$
$$CHCl{=}CCl_2 \;\; \text{1,2-Dichloro-ethylenes}$$

Addition of chlorine to trichloroethylene gives **pentachloroethane**, b.p. 162°, which can be converted to **tetrachloroethylene** (perchloroethylene),[1] b.p. 118°, by the action of lime. Further addition of chlorine yields **hexachloroethane**.

$$CHCl{=}CCl_2 \xrightarrow{Cl_2} CHCl_2CCl_3 \xrightarrow{Ca(OH)_2} CCl_2{=}CCl_2 \xrightarrow{Cl_2} CCl_3CCl_3$$

| Penta-chloroethane | | Tetra-chloroethylene | | Hexa-chloroethane |

Pyrolysis of pentachloroethane is more economical because the anhydrous hydrogen chloride formed can be used for the manufacture of ethyl chloride or vinyl chloride.

$$CHCl_2CCl_3 \xrightarrow[250°]{Act.C,\ BaCl_2} CCl_2{=}CCl_2 + HCl$$

Both hexachloroethane and tetrachloroethylene are obtained by the thermal decomposition of carbon tetrachloride.

$$2\,CCl_4 \xrightarrow{600°} Cl_2 + CCl_3CCl_3 \xrightarrow{800°-900°} Cl_2 + CCl_2{=}CCl_2$$

Tetrachloroethylene also is one of the products of chlorinolysis of propylene chloride (p. 723). Tetrachloroethylene is an important solvent for the drycleaning industry. It is preferred to trichloroethylene because it does not extract acetate dyes. Hexachloroethane is used in the production of naval smoke screens. A mixture with zinc powder, when ignited, reacts vigorously to give zinc chloride vapor, which causes moisture to condense from the air and form a heavy smoke.

The relative importance of some of these halogen compounds is indicated by the following rounded figures for production in the United States in 1955 in millions of pounds: ethyl chloride, 542; ethylene chloride, 510; trichloroethylene, 316; carbon tetrachloride, 287; perchloroethylene, 178; methylene chloride, 74; chloroform, 40; methyl chloride, 36. The prices ranged from $0.07 per pound for carbon tetrachloride to $0.13 per pound for chloroform.

Polyhalogenated methanes containing at least one bromine atom add readily to olefins in the presence of peroxide catalysts.

---

[1] The prefix *per* (L. *per*, through) is used to indicate not only a high state of oxidation, but also the maximum amount of substitution or addition.

$$RCH{=}CH_2 + BrCCl_3 \xrightarrow{Ac_2O_2} RCHBrCH_2CCl_3$$

$$BrCHBr_2 \longrightarrow RCHBrCH_2CHBr_2$$

If the halogen is less reactive, as in carbon tetrachloride or chloroform, more than one mole of olefin reacts to give a mixture of polymeric compounds in which the parts of the halogen compound have added to the ends of the chain.

$$x\,CH_2{=}CH_2 + CCl_4 \longrightarrow Cl(CH_2CH_2)_x\,CCl_3$$

Usually x is much smaller than in ordinary polymers, so much so that the ends of the chain are chemically significant. To distinguish these products from polymers of high molecular weight, they have been called **telomers** (Gr. *telos*, end; *meros*, part) and the process is called **telomerization**. By varying the ratio of olefin to polyhalogen compound, x can be varied from less than ten to fifty or more. Telomers may be useful intermediates for the synthesis of other compounds. For example, the hydrolysis of the α-chloro-ω-trichloromethylalkanes yields ω-chlorocarboxylic acids.

$$Cl(CH_2CH_2)_x\,CCl_3 \xrightarrow{H_2O,\ H_2SO_4} Cl(CH_2CH_2)_x\,COOH$$

The addition of polyhalogen compounds to olefins is a free-radical chain reaction.

$$(CH_3CO)_2O_2 \longrightarrow 2\,CH_3CO_2 \cdot \longrightarrow 2\,CH_3 \cdot + 2\,CO_2$$

$$CH_3 \cdot + XCX_3 \longrightarrow CH_3X + \cdot CX_3$$

$$RCH{=}CH_2 + \cdot CX_3 \longrightarrow RCH{-}CH_2CX_3$$
$$\overset{\cdot}{}$$

$$RCHCH_2CX_3 + XCX_3 \longrightarrow RCHXCH_2CX_3 + \cdot CX_3$$

Telomerization does not differ essentially from any other polymerization catalyzed by free radicals. It arises merely because enough of a sufficiently reactive compound is present to act as a chain transfer reagent, but the concentration and reactivity are not high enough to give rise chiefly to 1,2 addition.

$$X_3C \cdot + CH_2{=}CH_2 \longrightarrow X_3CCH_2CH_2 \cdot$$

$$X_3CCH_2CH_2 \cdot + x\,CH_2{=}CH_2 \longrightarrow X_3C(CH_2CH_2)_xCH_2CH_2 \cdot$$

$$X_3C(CH_2CH_2)_xCH_2CH_2 \cdot + XCX_3 \longrightarrow X_3C(CH_2CH_2)_xCH_2CH_2X + \cdot CX_3$$

Vinyl chloride (chloroethylene) can be produced by the dehydrohalogenation of ethylene chloride. The usual laboratory reagent for this type of reaction is methyl alcoholic sodium hydroxide, but the reaction can be brought about thermally at relatively low temperatures in the presence of 0.5 to 1 per cent of chlorine.

$$CH_2ClCH_2Cl \xrightarrow[(Cl_2)]{310°} CH_2{=}CHCl + HCl$$
Vinyl chloride

Vinyl chloride is made also by the catalytic addition of hydrogen chloride to acetylene and by the chlorination of ethylene.

$$HC{\equiv}CH + HCl \xrightarrow[+\ Hg_2Cl_2]{Act.\ carbon} CH_2{=}CHCl$$

$$CH_2{=}CH_2 + Cl_2 \xrightarrow{500°} CH_2{=}CHCl + HCl$$

Vinyl chloride polymerizes readily in the presence of peroxides to a hard brittle resin in which the units are linked regularly in a head to tail fashion.

$$3x\ CH_2\!=\!CHCl \longrightarrow [-CH_2CHCl\vdots CH_2CHCl\vdots CH_2CHCl-]_x$$

Addition of plasticizers such as cresyl phosphate (p. 515) or 2-ethylhexyl phthalate (p. 552) gives tough, long-wearing, leather- or rubber-like materials (p. 720). Many other commercial plastics, such as Vinylite (p. 736) and Dynel (p. 788), are copolymers with vinyl chloride.

The halogen atom in vinyl chloride is about as unreactive as that in chlorobenzene (p. 435). This reduced reactivity is characteristic of halogen on a doubly-bonded carbon atom, and is ascribed to the interaction of the unshared electrons in a p orbital of the halogen atom with the electrons in the π orbital of the double bond, which leads to greater bond strength and decreased bond length and reactivity.

$$\left\{ CH_2\!=\!\overset{..}{\underset{..}{C}}HCl: \quad \longleftrightarrow \quad \overset{-}{C}H_2CH\!=\!\overset{+}{\underset{..}{C}}l: \right\}$$

The decrease in the C—Cl bond distance is observable, the interatomic distance for ethyl chloride being 1.77 Å and for vinyl chloride 1.69 Å.

Vinylidene chloride, 1,1-dichloroethylene, may be made by the action of lime on 1,1,2-trichloroethane, which may be prepared directly from ethylene or through vinyl chloride.

$$CH_2\!=\!CH_2 \xrightarrow{2\ Cl_2}$$
$$CH_2\!=\!CHCl \xrightarrow{Cl_2} CH_2ClCHCl_2 \xrightarrow[90^\circ]{Ca(OH)_2} CH_2\!=\!CCl_2$$

Vinylidene chloride

Vinylidene chloride can be prepared also by the reaction of acetylene with chlorine at 135° in the presence of ferric chloride, a reaction that may involve substitution and addition of hydrogen halide.

$$HC\!\equiv\!CH + Cl_2 \xrightarrow[135^\circ]{FeCl_3} CH_2\!=\!CCl_2$$

Vinylidene chloride polymerizes to a material that is characterized by chemical inertness, high tensile strength, and resistance to abrasion. The commercial products, known as Sarans, usually are copolymers with a small amount of vinyl chloride or acrylonitrile to improve their working properties. Emulsions of vinylidene chloride polymers have the unusual property of forming tough coherent sheets when spread on a smooth surface and allowed to dry.

Both vinyl chloride and vinylidene chloride and their polymers have been known for over a hundred years. Their rapid development since 1927 has resulted from a reduction in the cost of raw materials, and from the accumulation of knowledge concerning the nature of polymerization reactions that has permitted the production of materials having useful properties.

Allyl chloride, $CH_2\!=\!CHCH_2Cl$, is made by the chlorination of propylene at a high temperature.

$$CH_2\!=\!CHCH_3 + Cl_2 \xrightarrow{500^\circ-600^\circ} CH_2\!=\!CHCH_2Cl + HCl$$

Although secondary base olefins (those yielding secondary alkyl derivatives on the addition of unsymmetrical addenda) add halogen readily in the liquid phase, they do not do so in the vapor phase, and at sufficiently high temperatures rapid substitution takes place without addition. Thus propylene gives 85–90 per cent of allyl chloride. The principal use for allyl chloride is as a starting point for the preparation of allyl alcohol (p. 738), glycerol (p. 748), and epichlorohydrin (p. 750). Addition of hydrogen bromide in the absence of antioxidants gives 1-chloro-3-bromopropane (trimethylene chlorobromide) used for the manufacture of cyclopropane (p. 834).

$$CH_2{=}CHCH_2Cl + HBr \xrightarrow{\text{Peroxides}} BrCH_2CH_2CH_2Cl$$

Substitution of a second chlorine atom into allyl chloride by high temperature chlorination produces a mixture of 10 per cent 3,3-dichloropropene and 90 per cent 1,3-dichloropropene.

$$CH_2{=}CHCH_2Cl \xrightarrow[\text{(500°–600°)}]{Cl_2} \underset{\text{10 per cent}}{CH_2{=}CHCHCl_2} \text{ and } \underset{\text{90 per cent}}{ClCH{=}CHCH_2Cl}$$

The mixed **dichloropropenes** are valuable as a soil fumigant for the destruction of nematodes.

With tertiary base olefins (those that can give tertiary alkyl derivatives) the ratio of substitution to addition is not affected by temperature, and substitution is extremely rapid in the liquid phase or at higher temperatures in the vapor phase in contact with porous materials. By taking proper precautions to minimize side reactions, it is possible to obtain up to 87 per cent **methallyl chloride** from isobutylene. Some isocrotyl chloride also is formed.

$$(CH_3)_2C{=}CH_2 + Cl_2 \xrightarrow[\substack{\text{contact time}\\\text{1 sec.}}]{300°,} \underset{\substack{\text{Methallyl}\\\text{chloride}}}{\underset{\underset{CH_3}{|}}{CH_2{=}CCH_2Cl}} \text{ and } \underset{\substack{\text{Isocrotyl}\\\text{chloride}}}{(CH_3)_2C{=}CHCl} + HCl$$

This reaction was discovered by Sheshukov in 1884, but has been operated commercially only since 1939. Methallyl chloride may be used as a raw material for the preparation of methyl methacrylate (p. 788).

The chlorination of propylene and that of isobutylene take place by different mechanisms. The latter reacts by an ionic mechanism which involves loss of proton to give the substitution product.

$$Cl_2 + \underset{\underset{CH_3}{|}}{CH_2{=}CCH_3} \longrightarrow [Cl^-] + \left[\underset{\underset{CH_3}{|}}{ClCH_2\overset{+}{C}{-}CH_3} \right] \longrightarrow \underset{\underset{CH_3}{|}}{ClCH_2C{=}CH_2} + [H^+]$$

The migration of the double bond in this type of reaction is evident from the behavior of isocrotyl chloride.

$$Cl_2 + \underset{\underset{CH_3}{|}}{ClCH{=}C{-}CH_3} \longrightarrow [Cl^-] + \left[\underset{\underset{CH_3}{|}}{Cl_2CH\overset{+}{C}CH_3} \right] \longrightarrow \underset{\underset{CH_3}{|}}{Cl_2CHC{=}CH_2} + [H^+]$$

Propylene adds chlorine by an ionic mechanism.

$$Cl_2 + CH_2{=}CHCH_3 \longrightarrow [Cl^-] + [ClCH_2\overset{+}{C}HCH_3] \xrightarrow{[Cl^-]} \underset{\underset{Cl}{|}}{ClCH_2CHCH_3}$$

At sufficiently high temperatures, substitution takes place by a free-radical chain mechanism.

$$Cl_2 \longrightarrow 2\,[Cl \cdot]$$

$$[Cl \cdot] + HCH_2CH{=}CH_2 \longrightarrow ClH + \left| \cdot CH_2CH{=}CH_2 \longleftrightarrow CH_2{=}CHCH_2 \cdot \right| \xrightarrow{Cl_2} CH_2{=}CHCH_2Cl + [Cl \cdot]$$

The system C=C—C is known as the **allylic system**. It confers high reactivity on halogen atoms attached to the carbon atom which is not doubly bound (cf. p. 437). The allylic system also is very prone to rearrangement. Thus heating either pure 1-bromo-2-butene or 3-bromo-1-butene gives an equilibrium mixture.

$$CH_3CH{=}CHCH_2Br \overset{\text{Heat}}{\rightleftarrows} \underset{\underset{Br}{|}}{CH_3CHCH{=}CH_2}$$

Moreover when either of the corresponding alcohols reacts with hydrogen bromide, the equilibrium mixture of the bromides is obtained. Similarly the reaction of either bromide with magnesium gives an equilibrium mixture of both Grignard reagents. This behavior is known as the **allylic rearrangement.**

Both the high reactivity and the rearrangement of allyl halides appear to result from resonance of the carbonium ion.

$$\left| CH_2{=}CHCH_2{}^+ \longleftrightarrow \overset{+}{C}H_2CH{=}CH_2 \right|$$

The resonance stabilizes the carbonium ion, and makes it easier for halogen to leave the molecule as a halide ion. When the carbonium ion combines with a negative ion, the latter may fix itself to either end of the allylic system. With the symmetrically constituted ions, only one product results, but if the intermediate is unsymmetrical, two isomers are formed and the composition depends on their relative thermodynamic stability.

FLUORINATED HYDROCARBONS

The extensive contributions to the chemistry of fluorine compounds in recent years tend to obscure the fact that the fundamental chemistry of these compounds has been known for a long time. The pioneering work of Moissan[2] was completed about 1900 and that of Swarts[3] by about 1925. The discovery of commercial uses for organic fluorine compounds, however, has led to the entrance of a large number of workers into the field, particularly chemists connected with industrial research laboratories. The commercial production of liquid hydrogen fluoride and fluorine, the development of methods for handling them safely, and the ready availability of commercially manufactured chlorinated organic compounds have led to a rapid extension of the work of the early investigators.

---

[2] Ferdinand Frederic Henri Moissan (1852–1907), professor of chemistry at the University of Paris. He was the first to isolate fluorine in 1886, and in 1892 he prepared calcium carbide by heating lime and carbon in the electric arc furnace. He investigated many other reactions at high temperatures and was awarded the Nobel Prize in Chemistry in 1906.
[3] Frederic-Jean Edmond Swarts (1866–1940), professor of chemistry at the University of Ghent. He developed methods for the synthesis of many organic fluorine compounds, particularly the reaction of antimony fluoride and mercurous fluoride on chloro derivatives, and studied extensively the thermochemistry and refractometry of fluorine compounds. He also prepared many organic chlorine compounds for purposes of comparison.

Chemical and Physical Properties

Fluorine compounds are characterized by extremes and opposites. Some are the most reactive of organic compounds and others are the most inert. Some are extremely toxic and others are as nontoxic as nitrogen or water. The introduction of fluorine may raise or lower the boiling point, and the progressive introduction of fluorine not only reduces the solubility in water but also in other organic solvents. Thus completely fluorinated hydrocarbons, known as *fluorocarbons*, are soluble in ether and in chlorofluorocarbons but are insoluble in most other solvents.

Compounds containing a single fluorine atom attached to a carbon atom differ markedly in their properties from those having two or more fluorine atoms attached to the same carbon atom. Whereas the alkyl fluorides hydrolyze readily to the alcohol and, with the exception of methyl fluoride, are very unstable and lose hydrogen fluoride spontaneously at ordinary temperatures, the *gem*-difluorides[4] are extremely inert to all chemical reactions. Fluorocarbons are surpassed in stability only by the inert gases. They are decomposed only at a red heat, the products being carbon and carbon tetrafluoride. They react with sodium or potassium at 300°–400° and with sodium in liquid ammonia. Above 400° they react with silica to form silicon tetrafluoride. It is the reactions with sodium and silica that must be used for analytical purposes.

Two fluorine atoms also reduce the reactivity of other halogen atoms attached to the same carbon atom. Thus the reactivity of the chlorine atoms in CCl_2F_2 is less than that in CH_2Cl_2 or CCl_4. Even the usual course of a reaction may be changed. For example, methyl iodide is hydrolyzed easily to methyl alcohol, but trifluoromethyl iodide gives fluoroform and hypoiodite.

$$CF_3I + KOH \longrightarrow CF_3H + KOI$$

Attempts to replace iodine by the amino, cyano, or nitro group using the ordinary reagents have failed. Grignard reagents can be prepared only under special conditions, preferably in the presence of the carbonyl compound with which they are to react. Whereas monofluorides are toxic compounds, *gem*-difluorides usually are nontoxic. Even CCl_2F_2 lacks the toxicity and anesthetic action of CH_2Cl_2 or CCl_4. Exceptions to this rule are some extremely toxic polyfluorocyclopropanes.

The unexpected chemical behavior of organic fluorine compounds extends also to their physical properties. The progressive replacement of hydrogen by chlorine causes a continual increase in the boiling point, but progressive replacement by fluorine causes an initial rise, which then is followed by a decrease. Thus the boiling points of methane, methyl fluoride, methylene fluoride, fluoroform, and carbon tetrafluoride are respectively −161°, −78°, −52°, −83°, and −128°. Similarly the boiling points of chloro-, chlorofluoro-, chlorodifluoro-, and chlorotrifluoromethane are −24°, −9°, −41°, and −81°. When the nuclear hydrogen atoms of aromatic compounds are replaced by fluorine, little change in boiling point takes place. Thus benzene, fluorobenzene, *o*-, *m*-, and *p*-difluorobenzene, trifluorobenzene, and hexafluorobenzene all boil within the range 80°–91°.

---

[4] The prefix *gem*- (L. *geminus*, twin) refers to two like atoms or groups attached to the same carbon atom.

A striking difference between mono- and polyfluoro compounds is observed in the interatomic distances. Although there is no detectable difference in the C—Cl bond distances in the chlorinated methanes, the C—F distance in methyl fluoride is 1.42 Å, whereas that in *gem*-difluoro compounds is 1.36 Å. Moreover the bond distances to other atoms attached to the same carbon atom are detectably decreased. Thus the C—Cl distance of 1.76 Å in carbon tetrachloride is decreased to 1.70 Å in dichlorodifluoromethane, and the C—C distance of 1.54 Å in ethane is decreased to 1.48 Å in 1,1,1-trifluoroethane.

The high reactivity of monofluoro derivatives compared to monochloro derivatives may be ascribed to the much greater electron-attracting power of the fluorine atom which causes the C—F bond to be much more polar than the C—Cl bond. At the same time the carbon atom is made more strongly electron-attracting, and the bond to a second atom becomes much stronger. The result is decreased bond distances and decreased reactivity.

Preparation

1. **Fluorination.** The amount of energy liberated when fluorine reacts with a hydrocarbon to give a fluoro derivative and hydrogen fluoride is 103 kcal. per mole, and when fluorine adds to a double bond, 107 kcal. per mole. The corresponding values for chlorine substitution and addition are 23 and 33 kcal. per mole. Since the energy necessary to dissociate a carbon-carbon bond is about 85 kcal. per mole, it is not surprising that the uncontrolled reaction of fluorine with organic molecules is violent and that the only product identifiable in quantity is carbon tetrafluoride.

Several methods have been devised for moderating this reaction. In one procedure the reactants are diluted with nitrogen and passed over a large heat-conducting surface such as metal gauze or turnings. One of the most satisfactory reactor packings is silver-plated copper turnings. By this procedure heptane gives a 62 per cent yield of **perfluoroheptane**, C_7F_{16}, and benzene gives a 58 per cent yield of **perfluorocyclohexane**, C_6F_{12}.

A second method of fluorination consists of using a less reactive fluorinating agent than fluorine itself. Certain metallic fluorides such as CoF_3, AgF, CeF_4, and MnF_3 are suitable for this purpose. Cobaltic fluoride is used most often. The heat of reaction is only about half that when fluorine is used, the other half being evolved during the formation of the cobaltic fluoride. The reaction is carried out as a cycle. The cobaltic fluoride is prepared by passing fluorine over cobaltous fluoride at 250°, the excess fluorine is flushed out with nitrogen, and the hydrocarbon vapor passed over the cobaltic fluoride. The operations then are repeated.

Neither of the above processes can be used to prepare high molecular weight fluorocarbons, which are of interest as lubricating oils. These products are prepared by using fluorocarbons boiling in the range 150°–200° as a diluent for the reaction between lubricating oil and cobalt trifluoride. Unfortunately these products have a poor viscosity index (p. 82).

Direct fluorination causes rearrangement, degradation, and polymerization, as well as substitution. For example fluorination of heptane with cobaltic fluoride gives a 69 per cent yield of perfluoroheptane, but the completely fluorinated derivatives of ethylcyclopentane (8 per cent), dimethylcyclopentane (3 per cent), hexane (1 per cent), and polymeric fluorocarbons (1 per cent) also have been isolated. Similarly fluorination of methane yields some hexafluoro-ethane and octafluoropropane. Such products are to be expected if the reaction takes place by a free-radical mechanism.

2. **Addition to Unsaturated Compounds.** Hydrogen fluoride adds to carbon-carbon double bonds, the mode of addition following the Markovnikov rule. The position of equilibrium is unfavorable at ordinary temperature for the simple olefins (p. 59), but if a halogen atom already is present on a doubly-linked carbon atom, a stable product results.

$$CH_3CCl{=}CH_2 + HF \longrightarrow CH_3CClFCH_3$$

Acetylenes also yield stable products.

$$CH{\equiv}CH \xrightarrow{HF} CH_2{=}CHF \xrightarrow{HF} CH_3CHF_2$$

$$CH_3C{\equiv}CH \xrightarrow{HF} CH_3CF{=}CH_2 \xrightarrow{HF} CH_3CF_2CH_3$$

Lead tetrafluoride, prepared from lead dioxide and hydrogen fluoride, adds fluorine to the double bond.

$$CCl_2{=}CCl_2 + PbF_4 \ (PbO_2 + HF) \longrightarrow CCl_2FCCl_2F + PbF_2$$

Trifluoroiodomethane adds to acetylene when irradiated with ultraviolet light.

$$CF_3I + HC{\equiv}CH \xrightarrow[280 \ m\mu]{Light} CF_3CH{=}CHI$$

Tetrafluoroethylene under these conditions undergoes telomerization (p. 725) to give perfluoro homologs of trifluoroiodomethane.

$$x \, CF_2{=}CF_2 + CF_3I \xrightarrow[280 \ m\mu]{Light} CF_3(CF_2CF_2)_xI$$

3. **Replacement of Halogen.** Exchange reactions take place between many organic halides and inorganic fluorides. This behavior is known as the *Swarts reaction* and has been the most fruitful method for the preparation of organic fluoro compounds. Usually chlorine is exchanged for fluorine. Fluorides of silver, mercury, antimony, arsenic, and cobalt, and hydrogen fluoride have been used. Simple alkyl halides are converted to fluorides best with mercurous fluoride.

$$2 \, CH_3Br + Hg_2F_2 \longrightarrow 2 \, CH_3F + Hg_2Br_2$$

Alkyl fluorides can be made also by heating alkyl bromides or chlorides, or alkyl *p*-toluenesulfonates with finely powdered potassium fluoride at 100° to 250°, usually in ethylene glycol or diethylene glycol. Hydrogen fluoride replaces chlorine with fluorine if all of the chlorine is on a single carbon atom.

$$CH_3CCl_3 + 3 \, HF \longrightarrow CH_3CF_3 + 3 \, HCl$$

$$CH_3CCl_2CH_3 + 2 \, HF \longrightarrow CH_3CF_2CH_3 + 2 \, HCl$$

Antimony trifluoride containing some pentavalent antimony halide is used on polychloro compounds.

$$3 \ CCl_4 + SbF_3 \longrightarrow 3 \ CCl_3F + SbCl_3$$

$$3 \ CCl_3F + SbF_3 \longrightarrow 3 \ CCl_2F_2 + SbCl_3$$

$$CHCl_3 \xrightarrow{SbF_3} CHCl_2F \xrightarrow{SbF_3} CHClF_2$$

$$CH_2Cl_2 \xrightarrow{SbF_3} CH_2ClF \xrightarrow{SbF_3} CH_2F_2$$

The small amount of pentavalent antimony halide added to the trifluoride undoubtedly is the active agent and is regenerated by exchange with the antimony trifluoride.

$$CH_2Cl_2 + SbF_5 \longrightarrow CH_2ClF + SbF_4Cl$$

$$SbF_4Cl + SbF_3 \longrightarrow SbF_5 + SbF_2Cl$$

The antimony trifluoride is regenerated, usually continuously, by reaction with hydrogen fluoride.

$$SbF_2Cl + HF \longrightarrow SbF_3 + HCl$$

The replacement reactions stop when two fluorine atoms have been introduced at a single carbon atom because their presence decreases the reactivity of the remaining chlorine atoms. If the halogen is activated by a double bond (allyl halides), three atoms can be replaced.

$$CCl_2{=}CClCCl_3 + SbF_3 \longrightarrow CCl_2{=}CClCF_3 + SbCl_3$$

The unreactive vinyl type halogen atoms are not replaced, nor is antimony fluoride able to react with a primary halide such as methyl chloride.

Iodine pentafluoride converts carbon tetraiodide to **trifluoroiodomethane.**

$$5 \ CI_4 + 3 \ IF_5 \longrightarrow 5 \ CF_3I + 9 \ I_2$$

It can be prepared more readily, however, from trifluoroacetic acid (p. 778) by the Hunsdiecker reaction (p. 157).

$$F_3CCOOAg + I_2 \longrightarrow F_3CI + AgI + CO_2$$

4. **Electrochemical Process.** Solutions of organic oxygen or nitrogen compounds in liquid hydrogen fluoride conduct the electric current. If a current is passed through the solution using a potential of 5 to 6 volts, the organic compound is converted without the evolution of fluorine to a perfluorohydrocarbon or a perfluoro derivative, depending on the conditions. Acetic acid, for example, can give chiefly carbon tetrafluoride or trifluoroacetyl fluoride. Sometimes rearranged products are obtained. The actual product or products formed must be determined by experiment. The perfluorinated products are insoluble in liquid hydrogen fluoride and are removed from the top of the cell as gases or from the bottom of the cell as liquids.

Commercially Important Products

Interest in fluorine compounds in recent years arises from a few technical applications. The most important compound is **dichlorodifluoromethane** (*Freon-12*), which is used as a refrigerant for commercial refrigerators and air-conditioning equipment, and as a solvent-propellant for aerosol-type spray preparations. It is entirely noncorrosive, nontoxic, and nonflammable. Its cheap production depends on the reconversion of antimony trichloride to antimony trifluoride by reaction with anhydrous hydrogen fluoride, on the relatively high boiling point of hydrogen fluoride, on the decrease in boiling point of 40°–50° for each replacement of chlorine by fluorine, and on the fact that the reaction will not proceed beyond the desired stage. The reactions are

$$CCl_4 \xrightarrow{SbF_3} CCl_3F \xrightarrow{SbF_3} CCl_2F_2 + 2\,SbF_2Cl$$

$$2\,SbF_2Cl + 2\,HF \longrightarrow 2\,SbF_3 + 2\,HCl$$

The boiling points of the reactants and products in decreasing order are carbon tetrachloride, 76°; **trichlorofluoromethane**(*Freon-11*), 25°; hydrogen fluoride, 20°; dichlorodifluoromethane, −29°; and hydrogen chloride, −85°. Hence hydrogen fluoride and carbon tetrachloride can be added continuously to a reactor, and hydrogen chloride and dichlorodifluoromethane removed through a column and condenser, the hydrogen chloride being absorbed in water. **Chlorodifluoromethane** (*Freon-22*), b.p. 41°, can be made by a similar process from chloroform. It is the intermediate for the production of tetrafluoroethylene. Both Freon-11 and Freon-22 are used as diluents for Freon-12 in aerosol sprays to reduce the pressure in the container. **Bromotrifluoromethane** and **dibromodifluoromethane** are very efficient in extinguishing fires and because of their low toxicity are useful in closed areas such as aircraft, submarines and automobiles.

1,1-Difluoroethane (*Genetron-100*), b.p. −25°, is made by the addition of hydrogen fluoride to acetylene. Subsequent chlorination gives **1-chloro-1,1-difluoroethane** (*Genetron-101*), b.p. −10°.

1,1,2-Trichloro-1,2,2-trifluoroethane (*Freon-113*), b.p. 48°, and **1,2-dichloro-1,1,2,2-tetrafluoroethane** (*Freon-114*), b.p. 3.8°, are made from hexachloroethane and antimony fluoride. The reaction always takes place to produce a symmetrical product and stops when four chlorine atoms have been replaced.

$$CCl_3CCl_3 \xrightarrow{SbF_3} CCl_3CCl_2F \longrightarrow CCl_2FCCl_2F \longrightarrow CCl_2FCClF_2 \longrightarrow CClF_2CClF_2$$

Freon-114 is the common refrigerant for household refrigerators.

Pyrolysis of chlorodifluoromethane gives **tetrafluoroethylene**. It is a surprisingly

$$2\,CHClF_2 \xrightarrow[\text{1 sec.}]{700°\text{ for}} F_2C{=}CF_2 + 2\,HCl$$

reactive compound, easily adding halogen, including iodine, and the halogen acids. At 200° in the absence of catalysts it gives the cyclic dimer, perfluorocyclobutane.

$$2\,CF_2{=}CF_2 \longrightarrow \begin{array}{c} F_2C{-}CF_2 \\ | \quad\ | \\ F_2C{-}CF_2 \end{array}$$

Polymerization at 700 p.s.i. in the presence of peroxide catalysts gives a product of molecular weight 500,000 to 2,000,000 known as **Teflon**.

$$x\,CF_2{=}CF_2 \longrightarrow (—CF_2CF_2—)_x$$

This polymer is characterized by extreme chemical inertness, withstanding the attack of all reagents except molten alkali metals. Aqueous alkalies, concentrated acids, oxidizing agents, and organic solvents have no effect on it. It can be used in the temperature range $-70°$ to $250°$. It softens above $250°$, changes to a rubbery state at $325°$, and depolymerizes at $600°-800°$ without charring. Although it thus is thermoplastic, it is much more difficult to work than most plastics. A property useful in the laboratory is the ability of small pieces to prevent bumping in boiling operations.

Chlorotrifluoroethylene can be made by the action of zinc dust in methanol on 1,1,2-trichloro-1,2,2-trifluoroethane, a product of the action of antimony fluoride on hexachloroethane (p. 733).

$$CCl_2FCClF_2 \xrightarrow[CH_3OH]{Zn,} CClF{=}CF_2$$

Polymerization gives the product called **Kel-F** or **fluorothene** which, like Teflon, is chemically inert but softens at $230°$. Thus Kel-F cannot be used at as high a temperature as Teflon but can be molded or extruded more readily. Polymers of lower molecular weight are oils and greases known as **Fluorolubes.**

Perfluorobutadiene has been made by several processes, for example from chlorotrifluoroethylene.

$$CF_2{=}CFCl \xrightarrow{ICl} ClF_2CCFClI \xrightarrow{Zn,\ Ac_2O}$$

$$ClF_2CCFClCFClCF_2Cl \xrightarrow{Zn,\ alc.} F_2C{=}CFCF{=}CF_2$$

It polymerizes readily, but the products obtained have been greases and resins. Copolymers with vinyl ethers are elastomers that are completely resistant to ozone and do not swell or soften in solvents even at elevated temperatures.

In the development during World War II of the separation of uranium isotopes by the gaseous diffusion of uranium hexafluorides, the need arose for nonvolatile liquids that could be used as seals and lubricants for pumps, and for a volatile liquid which would not be attacked by the highly reactive uranium hexafluoride. The volatile liquid used was **perfluoro-1,3-dimethylcyclohexane,** b.p. $100°$. It was prepared by chlorinating *m*-xylene to *m*-bis(trichloromethyl)-benzene, converting to the hexafluoro compound, and then fluorinating to the perfluoro derivative.

The nonvolatile fluorocarbons were prepared by direct fluorination of non-volatile hydrocarbons (p. 730).

Effect of the Trifluoromethyl Group on Other Functions

The strong electron-withdrawing effect of the trifluoromethyl group markedly alters the behavior of other functional groups, particularly by increasing their acidity and decreasing their basicity. Thus 2,2,2-trifluoroethanol forms a salt with aqueous sodium hydroxide, and the acidity of 1,1,1,3,3,3-hexafluoro-2-propanol ($K_a = 2 \times 10^{-7}$) is about like that of carbonic acid. Perfluoromethyl ether does not dissolve boron fluoride, and it does not react with 40 per cent hydrogen iodide at $100°$. Tris(trifluoromethyl)amine does not form salts even with strong acids. Trifluoromethyl phenyl ketone is soluble in 10 per cent sodium hydroxide. Immediate acidification regenerates the ketone. On standing, however, the usual haloform decomposition takes place.

$$C_6H_5COCF_3 \xrightarrow{\text{NaOH}} C_6H_5\overset{\displaystyle O^{-+}Na}{\underset{\displaystyle OH}{\overset{\displaystyle |}{\underset{\displaystyle |}{C}}}}CF_3 \longrightarrow C_6H_5COO^{-+}Na + CHF_3$$

REVIEW QUESTIONS

1. Discuss the reactions of propylene and of isobutylene with chlorine.
2. What is meant by the term allylic rearrangement?
3. Discuss the effect of the presence of more than one fluorine atom at a single carbon atom on the physical and chemical properties of a compound.
4. Compare the effects of the methyl group and the trifluoromethyl group on the chemical properties of the functional group with which they are combined.

PROBLEMS

5. Construct a chart indicating the steps for the preparation of the following compounds starting with acetylene, including necessary reagents, catalysts, and conditions: acetylene tetrachloride, vinyl chloride, vinylidene chloride, ethylidene chloride, vinyl fluoride, 1,1-difluoroethane, 1-chloro-1,1-difluoroethane, trichloroethylene, methylchloroform, pentachloroethane, hexachloroethane, 1,2-dichloroethylene, and perchloroethylene.
6. What halogenated hydrocarbons containing one and two carbon atoms can be made starting with methane?
7. Indicate four different practical paths for the synthesis of vinyl chloride.
8. Give reactions for the conversion of propylene into 1,2-dichloropropane, perchloroethylene, carbon tetrachloride, hexachloroethane, allyl chloride, 1-bromo-3-chloropropane, 1,2-dibromo-3-chloropropane, 2,3-dibromopropylene, and allene.
9. Give reactions for the following syntheses: (*a*) chlorotrifluoroethylene from methane; (*b*) tetrafluoroethylene from acetaldehyde; (*c*) *p*-fluorotrifluoromethylbenzene from toluene; (*d*) 1,2-dichloro-2-fluoropropane from allyl chloride; (*e*) trifluoroiodomethane from acetic acid; (*f*) tribromofluoromethane from acetone.
10. Compound *A* has the molecular formula $C_7H_{13}Cl$. It readily decolorizes a solution of bromine in carbon tetrachloride. Ozonolysis gives two products, each of which gives a color with Schiff reagent, but only one gives a positive iodoform test. After *A* is boiled with water, the aqueous layer gives a precipitate with silver nitrate. When *A* is heated, two products are obtained which can be separated by careful fractional distillation. One is identical with *A*, but the other, *B*, is isomeric with *A*. *B* likewise decolorizes bromine but hydrolyzes somewhat more slowly than *A*. Ozonolysis of *B* also gives two products, one of which gives a color with Schiff reagent but a negative iodoform test, whereas the other gives a negative test with Schiff reagent and a positive iodoform test. Give a formula for *A* and equations for the reactions that take place.

Chapter 34

UNSATURATED ALCOHOLS, POLYHYDRIC ALCOHOLS, AND THEIR DERIVATIVES. AMINO ALCOHOLS AND POLYAMINES

UNSATURATED ALCOHOLS

The first member of this series, **vinyl alcohol,** is unknown in the monomeric state because the carbonyl form is more stable.

$$[CH_2=CHOH] \longrightarrow CH_3CHO$$
Vinyl   Acetalde-
alcohol   hyde

Vinyl acetate can be made by the catalyzed addition of acetic acid to acetylene either in the liquid or the vapor phase, by reaction of ethylene chloride and sodium acetate, or by the reaction of acetaldehyde with acetic anhydride.

$$HC\equiv CH + HOCOCH_3 \xrightarrow[\substack{\text{or Zn (OAc)}_2 \text{ at} \\ 210°-250°}]{\text{HgSO}_4 \text{ at } 75°-80°} H_2C=CHOCOCH_3$$
Vinyl acetate

$$ClCH_2CH_2Cl + 2\,NaOCOCH_3 \longrightarrow H_2C=CHOCOCH_3 + 2\,NaCl + CH_3COOH$$

$$CH_3CHO \rightleftharpoons [CH_2=CHOH] \xrightarrow{Ac_2O} CH_2=CHOCOCH_3 + CH_3COOH$$

It boils at 72° and can be polymerized readily using peroxide catalysts to give a tough, thermoplastic resin, soluble in aromatic hydrocarbons.

$$2x\,CH_2=CHOCOCH_3 \longrightarrow \left[\begin{array}{c} -CH_2CH-CH_2-CH- \\ \qquad | \qquad\qquad | \\ \quad OCOCH_3 \quad OCOCH_3 \end{array}\right]_x$$
Polyvinyl acetate

Polyvinyl acetate emulsions are used as adhesives and in latex paints. Copolymerization of vinyl acetate and vinyl chloride in various proportions and to varying degrees of polymerization gives products known as *Vinylite* resins, which have a wide range of properties. They are very inert to chemical agents and weathering, and can be used to produce rigid sheets, flexible sheeting and films, textile fibers (*Vinyon*), molded and extruded articles, and surface coatings that are long-wearing and scuff and stain resistant. Floor coverings, upholstering materials, and shoe soles are made from it.

Saponification of polyvinyl acetate gives **polyvinyl alcohol.** Its physical

$$\left[\begin{array}{c} -CH_2CH-CH_2-CH- \\ \qquad | \qquad\qquad | \\ \quad OCOCH_3 \quad OCOCH_3 \end{array}\right]_x \xrightarrow{NaOH} \left[\begin{array}{c} -CH_2CHCH_2CH- \\ \qquad | \qquad | \\ \quad OH \quad OH \end{array}\right]_x$$
Polyvinyl alcohol

properties are similar to those of starch, and it finds use where a coating soluble in water but insoluble in organic solvents is desired.

736

Although polyvinyl alcohol is chiefly a linear polymer with a head to tail arrangement, about 0.4 per cent of the oxygen is present as carbonyl groups. Moreover a small amount of tail to tail addition during polymerization results in a few of the hydroxyl groups occupying 1,2 instead of 1,3 positions.

Because most of the hydroxyl groups of polyvinyl alcohol occupy 1,3 positions, it reacts readily with aldehydes to give cyclic acetals having six-membered

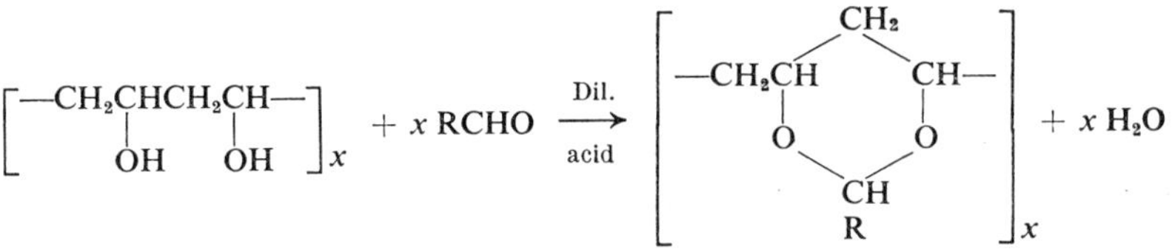

$$
\left[\begin{array}{c} -CH_2CHCH_2CH- \\ \ \ \ | \ \ \ \ \ \ \ \ \ | \\ \ \ OH \ \ \ \ OH \end{array}\right]_x + x\ RCHO \ \xrightarrow[\text{acid}]{\text{Dil.}} \ \left[\begin{array}{c} CH_2 \\ -CH_2CH \quad CH- \\ | \quad\quad | \\ O \quad\quad O \\ \diagdown \quad \diagup \\ CH \\ R \end{array}\right]_x + x\ H_2O
$$

rings (p. 741). The reaction product with *n*-butyraldehyde is known as **polyvinyl butyral** and is used as the filling to make a very strong safety glass.

1-Methylvinyl acetate (*isopropenyl acetate*), $CH_2=\underset{\underset{CH_3}{|}}{C}OCOCH_3$, is made by passing ketene into acetone containing a trace of sulfuric acid (p. 761).

$$
CH_3COCH_3 \ \underset{}{\overset{[H^+]}{\rightleftharpoons}} \ \left[CH_2=\underset{\underset{CH_3}{|}}{C}-OH\right] \ \xrightarrow{CH_2=C=O} \ CH_2=\underset{\underset{CH_3}{|}}{C}-OCOCH_3
$$

Alcohols add to acetylene in the presence of potassium hydroxide at elevated temperatures to give *vinyl alkyl ethers* which can be polymerized.

$$
HC{\equiv}CH + HOR \ \xrightarrow[150°-180°]{KOH} \ H_2C{=}CHOR \ \longrightarrow \ \left[\begin{array}{c} -CH_2CH- \\ | \\ OR \end{array}\right]_x
$$

Polyvinyl methyl ether may be obtained as a sticky thick liquid or as a soft solid. It is soluble in organic solvents and in cold water but is precipitated from aqueous solutions by heating to 35°. It is used as an adhesive coagulant in aqueous media.

Hydrolysis of the vinyl ethers yields the alcohol and acetaldehyde.

$$
H_2C{=}CHOR + H_2O \ \xrightarrow{[H^+]} \ ROH + [H_2C{=}CHOH] \ \longrightarrow \ CH_3CHO
$$

Like vinyl alcohols, **ethynyl alcohol** exists only in the form of its derivatives, the stable form being ketene (p. 760).

$$
\underset{\text{Ethynyl alcohol}}{[HC{\equiv}COH]} \ \longrightarrow \ \underset{\text{Ketene}}{H_2C{=}C{=}O}
$$

Ethers are made best from chloroacetals.

$$
ClCH_2CH(OR)_2 \ \xrightarrow[\text{in } NH_3]{NaNH_2} \ NaC{\equiv}COR \ \xrightarrow{H_2O} \ HC{\equiv}COR
$$

They are useful intermediates for the synthesis of α,β-unsaturated aldehydes (p. 762).

$$
HC{\equiv}COC_2H_5 \ \xrightarrow{CH_3MgBr} \ BrMgC{\equiv}COC_2H_5 \ \xrightarrow{RCHO} \ RCHOHC{\equiv}COC_2H_5 \ \xrightarrow{H_2,Pd}
$$

$$
RCHOHCH{=}CHOC_2H_5 \ \xrightarrow{H_2O,\ [H^+]} \ RCH{=}CHCHO
$$

Allyl alcohol may be prepared by the reductive dehydration of glycerol by heating with formic or oxalic acid.

$$HOCH_2CHOHCH_2OCHO \xrightarrow{Heat} HOCH_2CH{=}CH_2 + CO_2 + H_2O$$
$$\text{α-Glyceryl formate} \qquad\qquad \text{Allyl alcohol}$$

It now is made on a large scale commercially by the hydrolysis of allyl chloride (p. 726) at pH 8 to 11.

$$CH_2{=}CHCH_2Cl \xrightarrow[\text{NaOH}]{Na_2CO_3,} CH_2{=}CHCH_2OH$$
$$\text{Allyl chloride} \qquad\qquad \text{Allyl alcohol}$$

It can be prepared also, along with propionaldehyde, by passing propylene oxide (p. 746) over hot chromia.

$$CH_3CH{-}CH_2 \underset{O}{\diagdown\diagup} \xrightarrow[350°]{Cr_2O_3} CH_2{=}CHCH_2OH \text{ and } CH_3CH_2CHO$$
$$\qquad\qquad\qquad\qquad\qquad 2 \qquad\qquad . \qquad 1$$

Although simple allyl compounds do not polymerize readily, some of their esters such as allyl phthalate do and the polymers have found use, particularly as laminating resins. Other more complex esters give hard transparent resins. Since 1948 allyl alcohol has been used as an intermediate in the production of synthetic glycerol (p. 748). **Crotyl alcohol** is made by the Meerwein-Ponndorf reduction (p. 199) of crotonic aldehyde, and **methallyl alcohol** (*2-methylallyl alcohol*) by the hydrolysis of methallyl chloride (p. 727).

$$CH_3CH{=}CHCHO + (CH_3)_2CHOH \xrightarrow{Al(OC_3H_7)_3} CH_3CH{=}CHCH_2OH + CH_3COCH_3$$
$$\text{Crotonic aldehyde} \qquad\qquad\qquad\qquad \text{Crotyl alcohol}$$

$$CH_2{=}C(CH_3)CH_2Cl \xrightarrow{NaOH} CH_2{=}C(CH_3)CH_2OH$$
$$\text{Methallyl chloride} \qquad\qquad \text{Methallyl alcohol}$$

Allylic rearrangement (p. 728) of crotyl alcohol gives the equilibrium mixture with **1-methylallyl alcohol.**

$$CH_3CH{=}CHCH_2OH \underset{\longleftarrow}{\overset{[H^+]}{\rightleftharpoons}} CH_3CHOHCH{=}CH_2$$
$$\text{30 per cent} \qquad\qquad \text{70 per cent}$$

Allylic rearrangement of allyl alcohol and of 2-methylallyl alcohol is not detectable unless isotopically labeled compounds are used, because no change in structure results from the rearrangement.

Unsaturated alcohols may be one of the products of the Prins reaction (p. 575). Starting with aliphatic olefins, the double bond in the product is adjacent to its position in the olefin.

$$CH_3\underset{\underset{CH_3}{|}}{C}{=}\underset{\underset{CH_3}{|}}{C}CH_3 + HCHO \xrightarrow{H_2SO_4} CH_2{=}\underset{\underset{CH_3}{|}}{C}{-}\overset{\overset{CH_3}{|}}{\underset{\underset{CH_3}{|}}{C}}CH_2OH$$

Use has been made of this reaction for the synthesis of **lavandulol,** a terpene alcohol present in small amount in oil of lavender (*Lavandula vera*).

$$(CH_3)_2\overset{\underset{\displaystyle OCOCH_3}{|}}{C}CH_2CH_2CH{=}C(CH_3)_2 \xrightarrow[\text{[H}^+]]{\text{HCHO, HOAc}} (CH_3)_2\overset{\underset{\displaystyle OCOCH_3}{|}}{C}CH_2CH_2\overset{\underset{\displaystyle CH_2OCOCH_3}{|}}{C}H\overset{\overset{\displaystyle CH_3}{|}}{C}{=}CH_2$$

$$\xrightarrow[\text{hydrolysis}]{\text{Pyrolysis,}} CH_2{=}\overset{\underset{\displaystyle CH_3}{|}}{C}CH_2CH_2\overset{\underset{\displaystyle CH_2OH}{|}}{C}H\overset{\overset{\displaystyle CH_3}{|}}{C}{=}CH_2$$

Lavandulol

The *cis* form of **1-hydroxy-3-hexene** (*leaf alcohol*), $CH_3CH_2CH{=}CHCH_2CH_2OH$, is responsible for the characteristic odor of green grass and leaves.

A general method for the synthesis of **acetylenic alcohols** is the reaction of acetylenic Grignard reagents (p. 132) or sodium or potassium acetylides with aldehydes or ketones.

$$RC{\equiv}CMgX \xrightarrow{R'CHO} RC{\equiv}C\overset{\underset{\displaystyle OMgX}{|}}{C}HR' \xrightarrow{HX} RC{\equiv}C\overset{\underset{\displaystyle OH}{|}}{C}HR' + MgX_2$$

Propargyl alcohol is obtained commercially along with 1,4-dihydroxy-2-butyne by the condensation of acetylene with formaldehyde (p. 205).

$$HC{\equiv}CH \xrightarrow[\text{Cu}_2\text{C}_2]{\text{HCHO,}} HC{\equiv}CCH_2OH \text{ and } HOCH_2C{\equiv}CCH_2OH$$

Propargyl alcohol   1,4-Dihydroxy-2-butyne

It can be prepared also by the action of sodium amide in liquid ammonia on epichlorohydrin (p. 750).

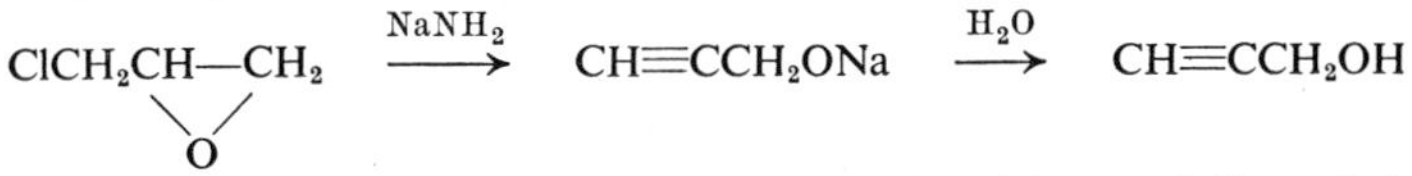

$$ClCH_2CH{-}CH_2 \xrightarrow{\text{NaNH}_2} CH{\equiv}CCH_2ONa \xrightarrow{\text{H}_2\text{O}} CH{\equiv}CCH_2OH$$
$$\underset{O}{\diagdown\diagup}$$

Under the same conditions tetrahydrofurfuryl chloride (p. 618) and 2-chloro-methyltetrahydropyran (p. 632) give **5-hydroxy-1-pentyne** and **6-hydroxy-1-hexyne**.

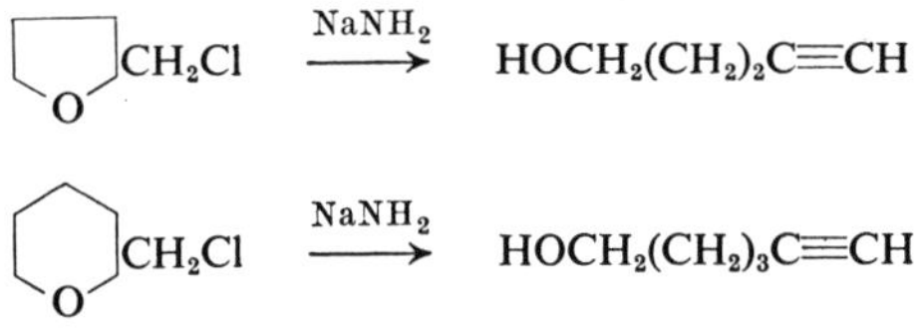

$$\xrightarrow{\text{NaNH}_2} HOCH_2(CH_2)_2C{\equiv}CH$$

$$\xrightarrow{\text{NaNH}_2} HOCH_2(CH_2)_3C{\equiv}CH$$

POLYHYDRIC ALCOHOLS

Aldehyde Hydrates

Compounds having two hydroxyl groups on the same carbon atom usually are unstable and lose water to form the carbonyl derivative. Methanediol, the hydrate of formaldehyde, appears to exist only in aqueous solution (p. 202). The presence of electron-attracting groups, however, increases the stability of the hydrate. Thus dichloroacetaldehyde forms a hygroscopic monohydrate melting at 55°. **Chloral** (trichloroacetaldehyde) is a water-insoluble liquid prepared by the reaction of ethyl alcohol with chlorine.

$$C_2H_5OH + 4\,Cl_2 \longrightarrow Cl_3CCHO + 5\,HCl$$
$$\text{Chloral}$$

On shaking chloral with water, heat is evolved and the crystalline hydrate separates. In order to produce anhydrous chloral again, it is mixed with concentrated sulfuric acid. Whereas chloral gives a color with Schiff reagent, **chloral hydrate** does not. Hence the water has reacted with the aldehyde.

$$Cl_3CCHO + H_2O \longrightarrow Cl_3CCH(OH)_2$$
Chloral hydrate

Chloral hydrate is a quickly acting soporific commonly known as *knock-out drops*.

Derivatives of 1,1-alkanediols such as the hemiacetals (p. 203) also are unstable, but the acetals (p. 203) and acylals (p. 204) are stable compounds.

1,2-Glycols

Preparation. Several general methods for the preparation of 1,2-glycols commonly are used.

1. OXIDATION OF UNSATURATED COMPOUNDS. Suitable oxidizing agents for the hydroxylation of the double bond are dilute aqueous permanganate (p. 57), and hydrogen peroxide in the presence of osmium tetroxide or tungstic oxide.

$$RCH{=}CHR + H_2O_2 \xrightarrow{OsO_4} RCHOHCHOHR$$

These reagents give so-called *cis* glycols; that is, if the R groups are identical and not hydrogen, the *cis* olefin gives the *meso* form whereas the *trans* olefin gives the racemic form (p. 339).

2. HYDROLYSIS OF 1,2-EPOXIDES. The hydrolysis of 1,2-epoxides (ethylene oxides, p. 744) to 1,2-glycols is catalyzed by either acids or bases.

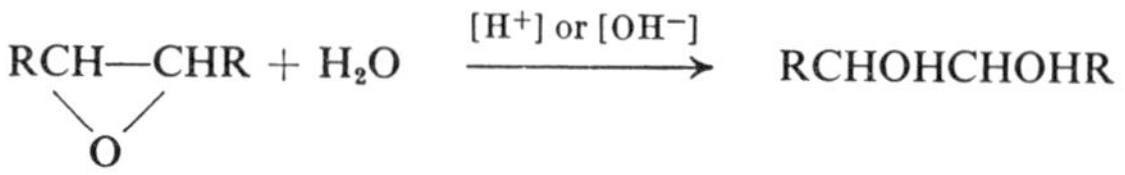

$$RCH{-}CHR + H_2O \xrightarrow{[H^+] \text{ or } [OH^-]} RCHOHCHOHR$$

Here the products are *trans* glycols; that is, *cis* epoxides give racemic glycols, whereas *trans* epoxides give *meso* glycols.

The formation of *trans* glycols involves a Walden inversion at one of the carbon atoms. The inversion is caused by the attack from the back side by a water molecule or a hydroxide ion.

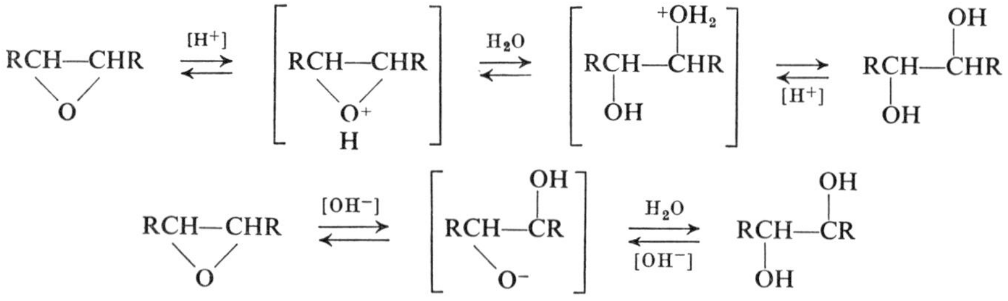

$$RCH{-}CHR \;\underset{}{\overset{[H^+]}{\rightleftarrows}}\; \left[RCH{-}CHR \right] \;\overset{H_2O}{\rightleftarrows}\; \left[RCH{-}CHR \right] \;\underset{[H^+]}{\rightleftarrows}\; RCH{-}CHR$$

$$RCH{-}CHR \;\underset{}{\overset{[OH^-]}{\rightleftarrows}}\; \left[RCH{-}CR \right] \;\underset{[OH^-]}{\overset{H_2O}{\rightleftarrows}}\; RCH{-}CR$$

3. HYDROLYSIS OF 1,2-DIHALIDES OR HALOHYDRINS. Dihalides are converted to the glycols best by way of the diacetates.

$$RCHCHR \xrightarrow{NaOOCCH_3} RCH{-}CHR \xrightarrow{NaOH} RCH{-}CHR$$
$$\underset{X\ \ X}{} \qquad \underset{OCOCH_3\ \ OCOCH_3}{} \qquad \underset{OH\ \ OH}{}$$

The halohydrins, obtained by the reaction of olefins with halogen in the presence of water, hydrolyze very easily to the glycols.

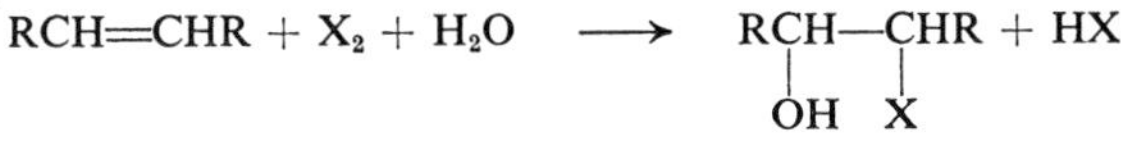

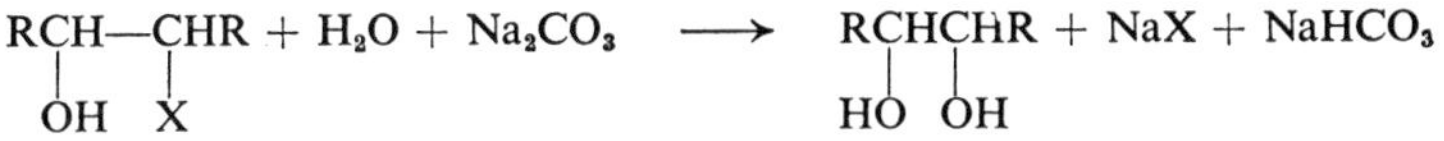

$$RCH{=}CHR + X_2 + H_2O \longrightarrow \underset{\underset{OH \quad X}{|\qquad|}}{RCH{-}CHR} + HX$$

$$\underset{\underset{OH \quad X}{|\qquad|}}{RCH{-}CHR} + H_2O + Na_2CO_3 \longrightarrow \underset{\underset{HO \quad OH}{|\qquad|}}{RCHCHR} + NaX + NaHCO_3$$

The formation of halohydrins by the reaction of olefins with halogen in aqueous solution frequently is spoken of as the addition of hypohalous acid. It has been shown, however, that halohydrins result from an initial attack on the double bond by free halogen. Reaction of the intermediate carbonium ion (p. 54) with water and loss of a proton gives the halohydrin.

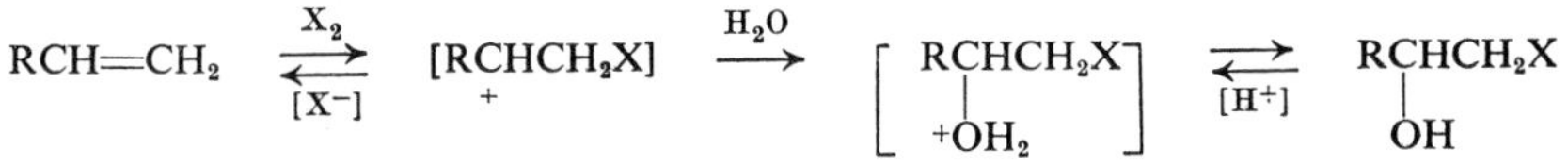

$$RCH{=}CH_2 \underset{[X^-]}{\overset{X_2}{\rightleftarrows}} \underset{+}{[RCHCH_2X]} \overset{H_2O}{\longrightarrow} \left[\underset{+OH_2}{RCHCH_2X} \right] \underset{[H^+]}{\rightleftarrows} \underset{OH}{RCHCH_2X}$$

If halogenation is carried out in methanol, the methoxy halide is formed.

1,2-Glycols result also from the pinacol reduction of ketones (p. 217) and from the reduction of acyloins (p. 173).

Reactions. 1,2-Glycols exhibit several characteristic reactions not given by simple alcohols.

1. FORMATION OF CYCLIC COMPOUNDS. Because of the 1,2 position of the hydroxyl groups, reactions leading to the formation of 5-membered rings are common. Thus reaction with aldehydes or ketones yields **cyclic acetals.**

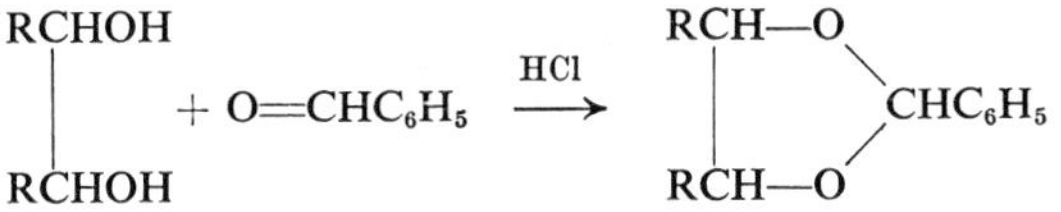

$$\underset{\underset{RCHOH}{|}}{RCHOH} + O{=}CHC_6H_5 \overset{HCl}{\longrightarrow} \underset{\underset{RCH{-}O}{|}}{RCH{-}O} \diagdown CHC_6H_5$$

Benzylidene derivative

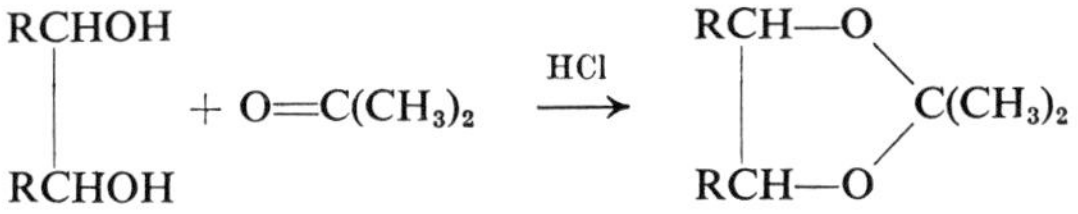

$$\underset{\underset{RCHOH}{|}}{RCHOH} + O{=}C(CH_3)_2 \overset{HCl}{\longrightarrow} \underset{\underset{RCH{-}O}{|}}{RCH{-}O} \diagdown C(CH_3)_2$$

Isopropylidene derivative

Phosgene gives **cyclic carbonates.**

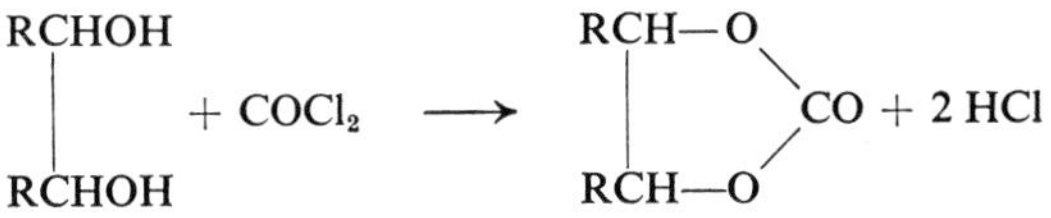

$$\underset{\underset{RCHOH}{|}}{RCHOH} + COCl_2 \longrightarrow \underset{\underset{RCH{-}O}{|}}{RCH{-}O} \diagdown CO + 2\,HCl$$

Cyclic carbonate

1,2-Glycols increase the conductivity of boric acid solutions because, after formation of the borate, the unshared pair of electrons of the fourth hydroxyl group fills the empty orbital of the boron atom, permitting ionization of a proton.

$$\begin{matrix} \text{RCHOH} \\ | \\ \text{RCHOH} \end{matrix} + \text{B(OH)}_3 + \begin{matrix} \text{HOCHR} \\ | \\ \text{HOCHR} \end{matrix} \longrightarrow 3\,\text{H}_2\text{O} + \left[\begin{matrix} \text{RCH—O} & & \text{O—CHR} \\ | & \diagdown\;\diagup & | \\ & \text{B} & \\ | & \diagup\quad\;\; \ddots & | \\ \text{RCH—O} & : \text{O—CHR} \\ & | \\ & \text{H} \end{matrix}\right] \longrightarrow$$

$$\left[\begin{matrix} \text{RCH—O} & & \text{O—CHR} \\ | & \diagdown\;\diagup & | \\ & \text{B} & \\ | & \diagup\;\diagdown & | \\ \text{RCH—O} & & \text{O—CHR} \end{matrix}\right]^{-} \text{H}^{+}$$

Cyclic compounds in which the ring is closed by coordination with an unshared pair of electrons are known as **chelate compounds** (Gr. *chele*, claw), the ring closure being thought of as a pincer-like action. The process is called **chelation**.

2. PINACOL-PINACOLONE REARRANGEMENT. In the acid-catalyzed rearrangement of 1,2-glycols (p. 217), hydrogen migrates in preference to a hydrocarbon group.

$$\text{RCHOHCH}_2\text{OH} \xrightarrow{[\text{H}^+]} \text{RCH}_2\text{CHO} + \text{H}_2\text{O}$$

$$\text{RCHOHCHOHR} \longrightarrow \text{RCH}_2\text{COR}$$

$$\text{R}_2\text{COHCOHR}_2 \longrightarrow \text{R}_3\text{CCOR}$$

The easy preparation of isobutyraldehyde by hydrolysis of methallyl chloride, and of methyl isopropyl ketone by hydrolysis of 2,3-dichloro-2-methylbutane is the result of a pinacol-pinacolone rearrangement.

$$\text{CH}_2{=}\text{C(CH}_3)\text{CH}_2\text{Cl} \xrightarrow[\text{heat}]{\text{H}_2\text{O—H}_2\text{SO}_4} [(\text{CH}_3)_2\text{COHCH}_2\text{Cl}] \longrightarrow$$

$$[(\text{CH}_3)_2\text{COHCH}_2\text{OH}] \longrightarrow (\text{CH}_3)_2\text{CHCHO}$$

$$(\text{CH}_3)_2\text{CClCHClCH}_3 \xrightarrow[\text{heat}]{\text{H}_2\text{O—H}_2\text{SO}_4} [(\text{CH}_3)_2\text{COHCHOHCH}_3] \longrightarrow (\text{CH}_3)_2\text{CHCOCH}_3$$

3. OXIDATIVE SCISSION. The bond between the two hydroxylated carbon atoms can be split readily by oxidation. If reagents such as permanganate or acid dichromate are used, two moles of acid are formed (p. 144). By choosing the proper reagents, the oxidation stops at the aldehyde stage. Lead tetraacetate is the preferred reagent for this purpose in anhydrous solvents (*Criegee reaction*), and periodic acid is the preferred reagent in aqueous solutions (*Malaprade reaction*).

$$\text{RCHOHCHOHR} + \text{Pb(OCOCH}_3)_4 \longrightarrow 2\,\text{RCHO} + \text{Pb(OCOCH}_3)_2 + 2\,\text{HOCOCH}_3$$

$$\text{RCHOHCHOHR} + \text{HIO}_4 \longrightarrow 2\,\text{RCHO} + \text{HIO}_3 + \text{H}_2\text{O}$$

Since both lead tetraacetate and periodic acid can be estimated readily by iodimetric methods, the reactions can be used for the quantitative determination of 1,2-glycols.

Important 1,2-Glycols. After deciding that the structural formula for glycerol is 1,2,3-propanetriol, Wurtz reasoned that an analogous 1,2-ethanediol should be possible. In 1859 he reported its synthesis by the saponification of the acetate which he prepared by the action of silver acetate on ethylene iodide. Because the product resembled glycerol in its properties, it was called *glycol.*

Since 1925 **ethylene glycol,** $\text{HOCH}_2\text{CH}_2\text{OH}$, has been technically important and it was one of the first organic chemicals to be produced commercially from petroleum. Its development was not planned, but resulted from a research program. One of the first industrial fellowships to be established at Mellon Institute was that by the Prest-O-Lite company for the development of a cheaper process for the manufacture of acetylene. A process was developed for the thermal cracking of natural gas or petroleum to acetylene, but large amounts of ethylene also were obtained. Attempts to utilize the ethylene led to the production of ethylene glycol. When glycol first became available in quantity in 1922 there were no important uses for it. Its 1955 production of 888 million pounds placed it fifth in quantity among synthetic organic chemicals.

At present three processes of manufacture are used. In one ethylene is passed into a solution of chlorine in water at 0°. Distillation gives a constant-boiling mixture of **ethylene chlorohydrin** and water. Some ethylene chloride and β-chloroethyl ether are obtained as co-products. The ethylene chlorohydrin is converted to **ethylene oxide**, b.p. 14°, by heating with sodium hydroxide or lime. Hydrolysis with water at 200° or with dilute sulfuric acid at 60° gives the glycol (b.p. 197°), which is freed of water by distillation.

$$CH_2{=}CH_2 \xrightarrow{Cl_2,\ H_2O} HOCH_2CH_2Cl \xrightarrow[Ca(OH)_2]{NaOH\ or} CH_2{-}CH_2 \xrightarrow[200°]{H_2O} HOCH_2CH_2OH$$
$$\underset{O}{\diagdown\diagup}$$

The second process differs in that the ethylene oxide is made by direct oxidation of ethylene with air in the presence of a silver catalyst.

$$CH_2{=}CH_2 + O_2\ (air) \xrightarrow[250°]{Ag\ cat.,} CH_2{-}CH_2$$
$$\underset{O}{\diagdown\diagup}$$

In the third process formaldehyde, carbon monoxide, and water are combined catalytically at high pressure to glycolic acid, which is converted to the methyl ester and reduced to glycol.

$$HCHO + CO + H_2O \xrightarrow{[H^+]} \underset{Glycolic\ acid}{HOCH_2COOH} \longrightarrow HOCH_2COOCH_3 \longrightarrow HOCH_2CH_2OH$$

The chief use for ethylene glycol is as a nonvolatile antifreeze for automobile radiators, and as a coolant for airplane motors. Like glycerol it is hygroscopic and can replace glycerol for many technical uses. Ethylene glycol should not be used in foods or cosmetics, however, because it is relatively toxic. A large part is oxidized to oxalic acid by the body, and calcium oxalate (p. 791) deposits in the renal tubules causing anuria. Besides its use for the preparation of ethylene oxide, ethylene chlorohydrin is converted into **β-chloroethyl formal** (cf. p. 203) for use in making Thiokol ST (p. 720).

$$2\ ClCH_2CH_2OH + HCHO \longrightarrow \underset{\beta\text{-Chloroethyl formal}}{ClCH_2CH_2OCH_2OCH_2CH_2Cl + H_2O}$$

Much ethylene glycol is used for the synthesis of polyethylene terephthalate (p. 555), of polyester resins (p. 807), of urethan rubber (p. 799), and of numerous other derivatives. The **dinitrate** is an explosive and is used to lower the freezing point of nitroglycerin (p. 749). When the glycol is distilled with 4 per cent aqueous sulfuric acid it gives **1,4-dioxane**.

$$2 \text{ HOCH}_2\text{CH}_2\text{OH} \xrightarrow[\text{heat}]{\text{Dil. H}_2\text{SO}_4,} \begin{array}{c} \text{O} \\ \text{H}_2\text{C} \diagup \diagdown \text{CH}_2 \\ | \qquad | \\ \text{H}_2\text{C} \diagdown \diagup \text{CH}_2 \\ \text{O} \end{array} + 2 \text{ H}_2\text{O}$$

1,4-Dioxane

Dioxane is a valuable solvent and paint remover but should be used with good ventilation because it is fairly toxic.

When ethylene oxide reacts with an alcohol or a phenol, a monoalkyl or monoaryl ether of ethylene glycol is formed.

$$(\text{CH}_2)_2\text{O} + \text{ROH} \longrightarrow \text{HOCH}_2\text{CH}_2\text{OR}$$

$$(\text{CH}_2)_2\text{O} + \text{ArOH} \longrightarrow \text{HOCH}_2\text{CH}_2\text{OAr}$$

The **monoethyl ether** was called *Cellosolve* because it is a solvent for cellulose nitrate. It is used in the formulation of lacquers. Other glycol ethers and their acetates also are useful for this purpose.

Ethylene glycol reacts with successive molecules of ethylene oxide to give **diethylene glycol, triethylene glycol,** higher condensation products, and finally high molecular weight **polyethylene glycols.**

$$\text{HOCH}_2\text{CH}_2\text{OH} \xrightarrow{(\text{CH}_2)_2\text{O}} \underset{\text{Diethylene glycol}}{\text{HOCH}_2\text{CH}_2\text{OCH}_2\text{CH}_2\text{OH}} \xrightarrow{(\text{CH}_2)_2\text{O}}$$

$$\underset{\text{Triethylene glycol}}{\text{HOCH}_2\text{CH}_2\text{OCH}_2\text{CH}_2\text{OCH}_2\text{CH}_2\text{OH}} \xrightarrow{(\text{CH}_2)_2\text{O}} \underset{\text{Polyethylene glycols}}{\text{HO}(\text{CH}_2\text{CH}_2\text{O})_x\text{CH}_2\text{CH}_2\text{OH}}$$

The polyethylene glycols vary in properties from sticky viscous liquids to wax-like solids (*Carbowaxes*) and all are soluble in water.

Reaction of monoalkyl ethers of ethylene glycol with ethylene oxide gives the **monoalkyl ethers of diethylene glycols** which are known as *Carbitols* and are used in lacquer formulation. When alkylated phenols react with an excess of ethylene oxide, the alkylaryl ethers of polyethylene glycol are formed.

$$\text{RC}_6\text{H}_4\text{OH} + (x + 1)(\text{CH}_2)_2\text{O} \longrightarrow \text{RC}_6\text{H}_4\text{O}(\text{CH}_2\text{CH}_2\text{O})_x\text{CH}_2\text{CH}_2\text{OH}$$

Products of this type in which the alkyl group has 8 to 10 carbon atoms and x is 8 to 12 are good **nonionic detergents.** The reaction of ethylene oxide with fat acids such as those from tall oil (p. 400) gives esters of polyethylene glycol which also are used as nonionic detergents in the formulation of low-sudsing products for automatic washers.

$$\text{RCOOH} + (x + 1)(\text{CH}_2)_2\text{O} \longrightarrow \text{RCOO}(\text{CH}_2\text{CH}_2\text{O})_x\text{CH}_2\text{CH}_2\text{OH}$$

1,2-Oxides are called **epoxides** or **epoxy derivatives.** Thus ethylene oxide may be called *epoxyethane.* The preparation from 1,2-halohydrins and alkali (p. 743) is a general reaction. Epoxides can be prepared also from unsaturated compounds and peroxy acids. Formerly peroxybenzoic acid (p. 551) and monoperoxyphthalic acids were used but for large scale operations they have been replaced by peroxyacetic acid (pp. 153, 875).

$$\text{RCH}{=}\text{CHR} + \text{CH}_3\text{COO}{-}\text{OH} \longrightarrow \begin{array}{c} \text{RCH}{-}\text{CHR} \\ \diagdown \diagup \\ \text{O} \end{array} + \text{CH}_3\text{COOH}$$

The three-membered ring is more reactive than higher-membered **rings**, and ethylene oxides react with all compounds containing active hydrogen to **give** open chain products. The reactions with alcohols give β-hydroxy ethers (p. 744); with mercaptans, β-hydroxy sulfides; with amines, β-hydroxy amines; **and with** carboxylic acids, β-hydroxy esters. Grignard reagents react to give alcohols. The ring of monosubstituted ethylene oxides usually opens to give a **secondary** hydroxyl group.

$$RCH\!-\!CH_2 + \quad HSR' \quad \longrightarrow \quad RCHOHCH_2SR'$$
$$\underset{O}{\diagdown\!\diagup}$$

$$+ \quad HNHR' \quad \longrightarrow \quad RCHOHCH_2NHR'$$

$$+ \quad HOCOR' \quad \longrightarrow \quad RCHOHCH_2OCOR'$$

$$+ \quad R'MgX \quad \longrightarrow \quad RCHOHCH_2R'$$

The reaction of Grignard reagents with ethylene oxide is very useful in organic synthesis, since it permits building up a carbon chain, two atoms at a time.

$$RMgX + (CH_2)_2O \quad \longrightarrow \quad RCH_2CH_2OMgX \quad \xrightarrow{\;H\,X\;} \quad RCH_2CH_2OH + MgX_2$$

The chief factors which determine the relative rates of opening of the two oxygen bonds in the unsymmetrically substituted epoxides are the nature of the reagent or catalyst, the nature of the substituents, and the relative steric hindrance at the two carbon atoms. In the above examples the attacking reagent probably supplies an unshared pair of electrons to the point of low electron density, which would be the methylene group, provided R is electron-donating such as an alkyl group. Moreover the methylene group offers the smaller hindrance to the approaching reagent. Hence the products are the secondary alcohols. The same mode of addition takes place in the base-catalyzed addition of alcohols.

$$RCH\!-\!CH_2 \quad \xrightarrow{[:\overset{..}{O}R']} \quad \left[\begin{array}{c} R\!-\!CHCH_2OR' \\ \mid \\ O^- \end{array}\right] \quad \underset{[R'\overset{..}{O}:]}{\overset{R'OH}{\rightleftarrows}} \quad \underset{OH}{RCHCH_2OR'}$$
$$\underset{O}{\diagdown\!\diagup}$$

In the acid-catalyzed addition, however, the initial attack is on the oxygen and the ease with which the oxygen atom can leave with the bonding pair of electrons appears to be the deciding factor, because the chief product is the primary alcohol.

$$RCH\!-\!CH_2 \xrightarrow{[H^+]} \left[\begin{array}{c} RCH\!-\!CH_2 \\ \mid \\ {}_+OH \end{array}\right] \underset{}{\overset{R'OH}{\rightleftarrows}} \left[\begin{array}{c} H\overset{+}{O}R' \\ \mid \\ RCHCH_2 \\ \mid \\ OH \end{array}\right] \underset{[H^+]}{\rightleftarrows} \begin{array}{c} OR' \\ \mid \\ RCHCH_2 \\ \mid \\ OH \end{array}$$
$$\underset{O}{\diagdown\!\diagup}$$

If R is a strongly electron-attracting group the mode of addition should be reversed. Mixtures or predominantly one or the other isomer may be obtained depending on the relative importance of the various factors.

Epoxides can undergo a pinacol-pinacolone type of rearrangement in the presence of electron-deficient catalysts. Monosubstituted ethylene oxides give aldehydes, and 1,2-disubstituted oxides usually give ketones.

$$RCH\!-\!CH_2 \quad \xrightarrow{\;MgBr_2\;} \quad RCH_2CHO$$
$$\underset{O}{\diagdown\!\diagup}$$

Using boron fluoride as a catalyst, *cis*-2,3-epoxybutane gives only 2-butanone, whereas *trans*-2,3-epoxybutane gives a mixture of 2-butanone and isobutyraldehyde.

$$\begin{array}{c} CH_3 \quad H \\ | \qquad | \\ C - - - C \\ | \diagdown \diagup | \\ H \quad O \quad CH_3 \end{array} \xrightarrow{BF_3} CH_3CH_2COCH_3 \text{ and } (CH_3)_2CHCHO$$

Propylene glycol is made by a series of reactions analogous to that for the preparation of ethylene glycol.

$$CH_3CH{=}CH_2 \xrightarrow[H_2O]{Cl_2,} \left\{ \begin{array}{c} CH_3CHOHCH_2Cl \\ \text{90 per cent} \\ CH_3CHClCH_2OH \\ \text{10 per cent} \end{array} \right\} \xrightarrow{Ca(OH)_2} \underset{\text{Propylene oxide}}{CH_3CH{-}CH_2 \atop \diagdown O \diagup} \xrightarrow{H_2O} \underset{\substack{\text{1,2-Propanediol} \\ \text{(propylene glycol)}}}{CH_3CHOHCH_2OH}$$

Propylene glycol has properties similar to those of ethylene glycol. Unlike ethylene glycol, however, it is nontoxic and can be used to replace glycerol in food products and cosmetics. It is toxic to lower forms of life and aerosols of it have been used in hospitals and schools to reduce the incidence of air-borne infections. Mixed with ethylene glycol it is used as radiator antifreeze. Production in 1955 amounted to 70 million pounds.

2,3-Butanediol (β-butylene glycol) is the principal product of the fermentation of starch by *Aerobacillus polymyxa*. Ethyl alcohol, acetone, acetic acid, diacetyl, aldehydes, and higher alcohols also are formed during the fermentation.

1,3-Glycols

Trimethylene glycol is formed by boiling trimethylene bromide with water. The 1,3-dibromide results almost exclusively by the addition of hydrogen bromide to allyl bromide in the absence of antioxidants.

$$CH_2{=}CHCH_2Br + HBr \longrightarrow Br(CH_2)_3Br$$

Trimethylene glycol also is formed in the reductive fermentation of glycerol by bacteria and frequently is available as a by-product of soap manufacture.

Many 1,3-glycols can be prepared by reduction of β-hydroxy ketones or esters. The latter compounds are the product of aldol additions (p. 205) or Claisen ester condensations (p. 814). Thus **1,3-butanediol** is prepared by reduction of aldol (p. 205). **2,2-Dimethyl-1,3-propanediol** (technical name *neopentyl glycol*) results from the aldol addition of isobutyraldehyde to formaldehyde followed by a crossed Cannizzaro reaction (p. 534).

$$(CH_3)_2CHCHO \xrightarrow{HCHO} \underset{\substack{| \\ CH_2OH}}{(CH_3)_2CCHO} \xrightarrow[Ca(OH)_2]{HCHO} (CH_3)_2C(CH_2OH)_2 + \tfrac{1}{2}Ca(OCHO)_2$$

2-Methyl-2,4-pentanediol (technical name *hexylene glycol*) is formed by the reduction of diacetone alcohol (p. 206).

$$\underset{\text{Diacetone alcohol}}{(CH_3)_2COHCH_2COCH_3} \xrightarrow{H_2{-}Ni} \underset{\text{2-Methyl-2,4-pentanediol}}{(CH_3)_2COHCH_2CHOHCH_3}$$

Aldol addition of *n*-butyraldehyde, followed by reduction, gives **2-ethyl-1,3-hexanediol.**

$$n\text{-}C_3H_7CHO + \underset{\underset{C_2H_5}{|}}{CH_2CHO} \xrightarrow{\text{Dil. NaOH}} \underset{\underset{C_2H_5}{|}}{C_3H_7CHOHCHCHO} \xrightarrow{\text{H}_2\text{—Ni}} \underset{\underset{C_2H_5}{|}}{C_3H_7CHOHCHCH_2OH}$$

$$\text{2-Ethyl-1,3-hexanediol}$$

It is an effective insect repellent, marketed as "6–12."

The Prins reaction (pp. 575, 738) frequently yields 1,3-glycols, presumably by addition of water to the unsaturated alcohol.

α,ω-Glycols

Glycols in general may be made by the hydrolysis of the corresponding dihalide. Frequently the reaction of the dihalide with sodium acetate in acetic acid solution to produce the diacetate proceeds better, and the ester can be hydrolyzed to the glycol.

$$Br(CH_2)_xBr + 2\,NaOCOCH_3 \longrightarrow CH_3COO(CH_2)_xOCOCH_3 \xrightarrow{\text{NaOH}} HO(CH_2)_xOH$$

If the proper dicarboxylic acids are available, the glycol can be prepared by the reduction of the diester.

$$CH_3OOC(CH_2)_xCOOCH_3 \xrightarrow[\text{Na—ROH}]{\text{H}_2\text{—Ni, or}} HOCH_2(CH_2)_xCH_2OH$$

Tetramethylene glycol can be made from acetylene (p. 717) or from tetrahydrofuran (p. 619). Tetramethylene halohydrins are useful intermediates in laboratory syntheses and tetramethylene chloride is used technically for the synthesis of hexamethylenediamine (p. 756). Since these halogen derivatives can be obtained directly from tetrahydrofuran by reaction with halogen acids, tetramethylene glycol itself has little use. **2,5-Dimethyl-2,5-hexanediol** results from the reduction of the addition product of two moles of acetone with one mole of acetylene.

$$2\,(CH_3)_2CO + HC\equiv CH \longrightarrow \underset{\underset{OH}{|}}{(CH_3)_2CC}\equiv\underset{\underset{OH}{|}}{CC(CH_3)_3} \xrightarrow{\text{H}_2,\text{Ni}} \underset{\underset{OH}{|}}{(CH_3)_2CCH_2CH_2}\underset{\underset{OH}{|}}{C(CH_3)_2}$$

1,5-Pentanediol is obtained readily by the hydrolysis of tetrahydropyran (p. 632). **1,18-Octadecanediol,** isolated from Spanish-broom (*Spartium junceum*), is the first long-chain α,ω-glycol to be found in nature.

Acetylenic Glycols

Acetylenic glycols have been used as intermediates in the synthesis of polyacetylenic and polyethylenic compounds. **1,4-Dihydroxy-2-butyne** is made commercially from acetylene and formaldehyde (p. 717). The hydroxyl groups can be replaced by chlorine using thionyl chloride and pyridine. Dehydrohalogenation of the dichlorobutyne with sodium amide in liquid ammonia gives the sodium salt of butadiyne which can react with formaldehyde to give **1,6-dihydroxy-2,4-hexadiyne.**

$$HOCH_2C\equiv CCH_2OH \xrightarrow[\text{pyr.}]{SOCl_2,} ClCH_2CC\equiv CCH_2Cl \xrightarrow[NH_3]{NaNH_2,}$$

$$NaC\equiv CC\equiv CNa \xrightarrow{HCHO} HOCH_2C\equiv CC\equiv CCH_2OH$$

A repetition of this series of reactions yields **1,8-dihydroxy-2,4,6-octatriyne,** $HOCH_2C\equiv CC\equiv CC\equiv CCH_2OH.$

Reaction of the sodium salt of butadiyne with one mole of an aldehyde followed by oxidation with air in the presence of cuprous salts (*oxidative coupling*) gives a dihydroxy tetrayne.

$$RCHO + NaC\equiv CC\equiv CNa \longrightarrow RCHOHC\equiv CC\equiv CH \xrightarrow[CuCl-NH_4Cl]{O_2 \text{ (air)}}$$

$$RCHOHC\equiv CC\equiv CC\equiv CC\equiv CCHOHR$$

Oxidative coupling is a useful general reaction of monosubstituted acetylenes.

Tri- to Hexahydric Alcohols

The trihydric alcohol of most importance is **glycerol.** It was isolated first by Scheele in 1779 as a saponification product of fats (p. 183). He called it *oelsuess* because of its sweet taste. It was named *glycerin* (Gr. *glykeros,* sweet) by Chevreul (p. 179). Berthelot (p. 93) showed it to be a trihydric alcohol in 1854, and its structural formula was assigned to it by Wurtz in 1855. Until 1948 it was obtained almost exclusively as a co-product of the manufacture of soap, and its price varied greatly. In 1939 it sold for $0.12 and in 1946 for as high as $0.75 per pound.

A small amount of glycerol is formed during alcoholic fermentation, and the amount can be increased by the addition of sodium sulfite or by keeping the fermenting liquors slightly alkaline. Isolation is difficult, however, and the process cannot compete under normal conditions with glycerol from fats.

Many synthetic processes for glycerol manufacture have been developed, but it was not until 1948 that a plant was built utilizing a process announced in 1938. In this process propylene is chlorinated to allyl chloride and the latter hydrolyzed to allyl alcohol (p. 738). The allyl alcohol is converted with aqueous chlorine to glycerol α-chlorohydrin, a product that can be hydrolyzed easily to glycerol.

$$CH_2\!\!=\!\!CHCH_2OH \xrightarrow{Cl_2, H_2O} ClCH_2CHOHCH_2OH \xrightarrow[NaOH]{Na_2CO_3,} HOCH_2CHOHCH_2OH$$

A contract was made for the entire output of the first plant for the synthesis of glycerol at the reputed price of $0.19 per pound when natural glycerol was selling for $0.33 per pound. In 1955 a new process was announced in which acrolein (p. 764) is hydroxylated by hydrogen peroxide and the product reduced to glycerol.

$$CH_2\!\!=\!\!CHCHO \xrightarrow{H_2O_2} HOCH_2CHOHCHO \xrightarrow{H_2, Ni} HOCH_2CHOHCH_2OH$$

Production of glycerol amounted to 228 million pounds in 1955 of which over one third was synthetic. About 30 per cent was used for the manufacture of alkyd resins (p. 553) and ester gums (p. 862), 12 per cent as a humectant for tobacco, 12 per cent for the manufacture of nitroglycerin for explosives, and 11 per cent as a softening agent for cellophane (p. 406). The remaining 35 per cent was used in cosmetics, pharmaceutical preparations, printing inks, textile processing, food products, and in the manufacture of emulsifying agents (p. 192) and other chemicals.

Glyceryl nitrate, commonly called *nitroglycerin*, is an important explosive made by the reaction of glycerol with nitric acid in the presence of sulfuric acid.

$$\begin{array}{c}
CH_2OH \\
| \\
CHOH \\
| \\
CH_2OH
\end{array}
+ 3\,HNO_3
\xrightarrow{(H_2SO_4)}
\begin{array}{c}
CH_2ONO_2 \\
| \\
CHONO_2 \\
| \\
CH_2ONO_2
\end{array}
+ 3\,H_2O$$

Glyceryl
nitrate
(nitroglycerin)

It is an oil which freezes at 13°. Formerly it was the chief explosive ingredient of **dynamite,** being mixed in amounts up to 40 per cent with a combustible mixture such as powdered wood pulp and sodium nitrate in the ratio of about 1 to 3. At present dynamites contain up to 55 per cent ammonium nitrate mixed with about 15 per cent each of sodium nitrate, wood pulp, and *explosive oil.* The last is a mixture of glycol nitrate and glyceryl nitrate which is added merely as a sensitizer for the ammonium nitrate. **Gelatin dynamite** is a mixture of wood pulp, sodium nitrate, and nitroglycerin gelatinized with 2 to 6 per cent of cellulose nitrate. It is plastic and can be loaded solidly into bore holes. It has a high water-resistance, a requirement for work in wet places. Dynamite has many useful applications such as in mining, road building, and agriculture. Over 600 million pounds per year is used in the United States. Double-base military smokeless powders such as *Ballistite* and *Cordite* consist of about 60 per cent cellulose nitrate gelatinized with 40 per cent nitroglycerin. Similar compositions are used as solid rocket fuels.

Reaction of glycerol with hydrogen chloride gives **glycerol α-monochlorohydrin** (3-chloro-1,2-propanediol) and **glycerol α,γ-dichlorohydrin** (1,3-dichloro-2-propanol), with very little of the 2-chloro derivatives.

$$\begin{array}{c}
CH_2OH \\
| \\
CHOH \\
| \\
CH_2OH
\end{array}
\xrightarrow{HCl}
\begin{array}{c}
CH_2Cl \\
| \\
CHOH \\
| \\
CH_2OH
\end{array}
\xrightarrow{HCl}
\begin{array}{c}
CH_2Cl \\
| \\
CHOH \\
| \\
CH_2Cl
\end{array}$$

          Glycerol   Glycerol
          α-mono-   α,γ-di-
        chlorohydrin   chlorohydrin

These chlorohydrins can be made also by the reaction of aqueous chlorine with allyl alcohol or allyl chloride respectively.

$$CH_2{=}CHCH_2OH \xrightarrow{Cl_2,\ H_2O} ClCH_2CHOHCH_2OH$$

$$CH_2{=}CHCH_2Cl \xrightarrow{Cl_2,\ H_2O} ClCH_2CHOHCH_2Cl$$

The two chlorohydrins when heated with alkali give the epoxy derivatives, which have the common names **glycidol** and **epichlorohydrin** respectively.

$$ClCH_2CHOHCH_2OH + NaOH \xrightarrow{\text{Heat}} CH_2-CHCH_2OH + NaCl + H_2O$$
$$\underset{O}{\diagdown\diagup}$$

Glycidol

$$ClCH_2CHOHCH_2Cl + NaOH \xrightarrow{\text{Heat}} CH_2-CHCH_2Cl + NaCl + H_2O$$
$$\underset{O}{\diagdown\diagup}$$

Epichlorohydrin

Epichlorohydrin is one of the two important raw materials for the manufacture of **epoxy resins,** the other being bisphenol-A (p. 514). The base-catalyzed condensation of the two reactants in the presence of base is believed to take place through the opening and formation of the oxide ring rather than by displacement of halogen by the phenoxide ion.

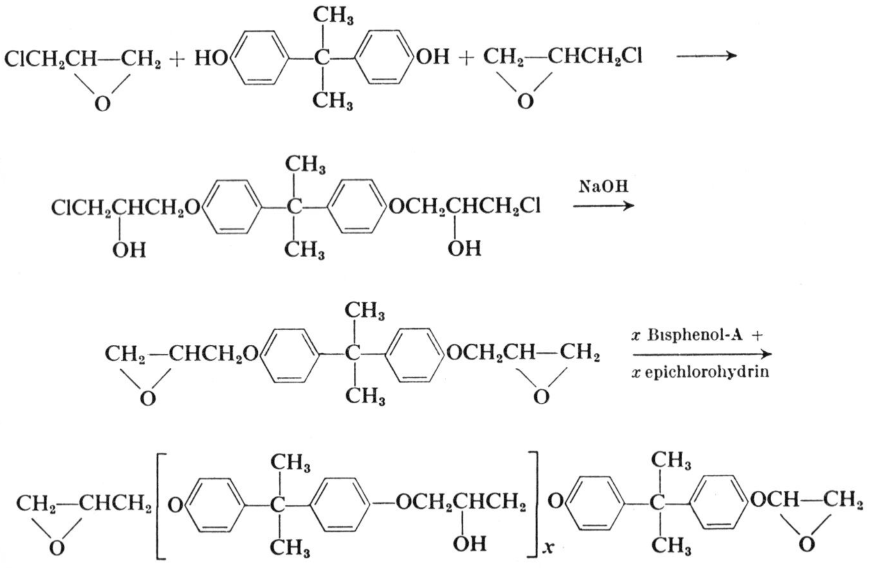

The use of an excess of epichlorohydrin leads to terminal epoxy groups, and the amount of the excess governs the molecular weight. Commercial resins vary from thin liquids of low average molecular weight used as casting resins, through viscous adhesives, to solids used as surface coatings where the average value of x is as high as 25. The linear polymer can be modified by using other polyhydroxy compounds to replace all or part of the bisphenol-A and other epoxides such as those obtained by the epoxidation of unsaturated fatty acids.

The linear polymers are converted to the final products of high molecular weight by adding a curing agent, which may be any compound having reactive hydrogen or a basic group.

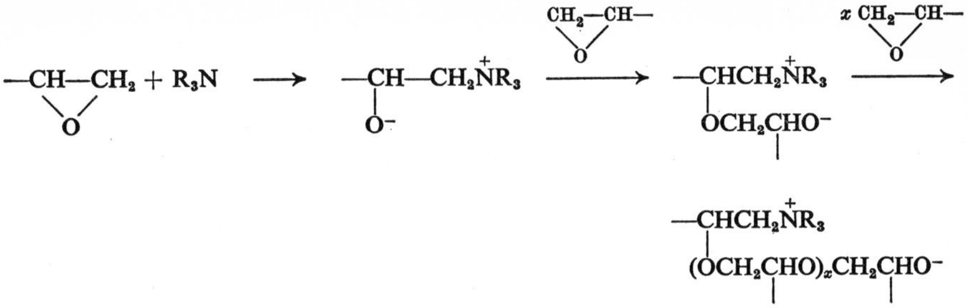

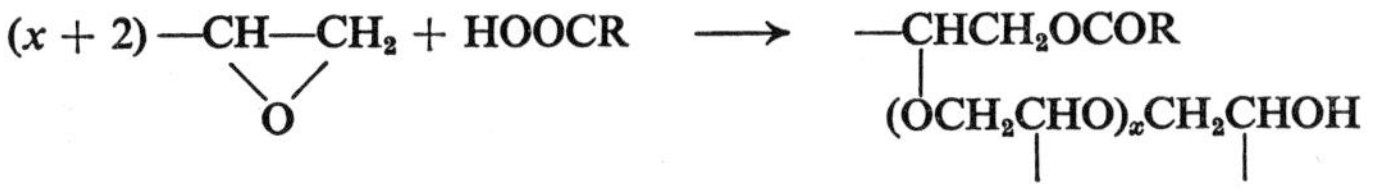

$$\underset{O}{-CH-CH_2} + R_3N \longrightarrow \underset{O^-}{-CH-CH_2\overset{+}{N}R_3} \xrightarrow{\;\overset{\displaystyle CH_2-CH-}{\overset{\diagdown\!\diagup}{O}}\;} \underset{\underset{OCH_2CHO^-}{|}}{-CHCH_2\overset{+}{N}R_3} \xrightarrow{\;x\,\overset{\displaystyle CH_2-CH-}{\overset{\diagdown\!\diagup}{O}}\;}$$

$$\underset{(\underset{|}{O}CH_2CHO)_x\underset{|}{C}H_2CHO^-}{-CHCH_2\overset{+}{N}R_3}$$

$$(x+2)\ \underset{O}{-CH-CH_2} + HOOCR \longrightarrow \underset{(OCH_2CHO)_xCH_2CHOH}{-CHCH_2OCOR}$$

Catalysts containing more than one active hydrogen such as primary or secondary amines, polyamines, and polybasic acids can cause other types of branching in the molecules. Anhydrides of dibasic acids do not have reactive hydrogen and first attack the hydroxyl group. The carboxyl group formed then can react with the epoxy groups, thus cross linking the central portions of the linear polymers with the ends of the chains.

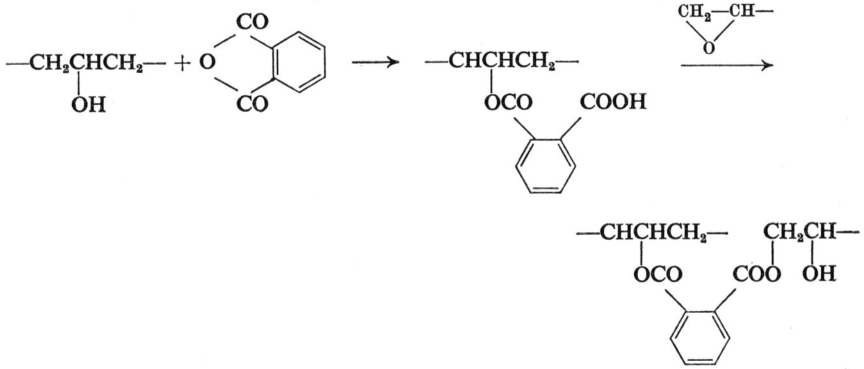

$$-CH_2\underset{\underset{OH}{|}}{C}HCH_2- + O\overset{\displaystyle CO}{\underset{\displaystyle CO}{\diagdown \text{(ring)} \diagup}} \longrightarrow -CH\underset{\underset{OCO}{|}}{C}HCH_2- \quad COOH \xrightarrow{\;\overset{\displaystyle CH_2-CH-}{\overset{\diagdown\!\diagup}{O}}\;}$$

$$-CH\underset{\underset{OCO}{|}}{C}HCH_2- \quad CH_2\underset{\underset{COO}{|} \ \underset{OH}{|}}{C}H-$$

Some of the curing agents commonly used are pyridine, piperidine, ethylenediamine and the higher polyethylene polyamines (p. 755), and succinic, maleic, phthalic and pyromellitic anhydrides. Some agents, like the polyamines, cure rapidly at room temperature, and others require elevated temperatures. The neutral aliphatic amine salts of fatty acids can be added to the linear polymer to give a mixture that is indefinitely stable at room temperature but cures rapidly on warming. Cross linking can be effected also by other polymers containing reactive hydrogen such as the Thiokols (p. 719), the polyamide resins (p. 755) and the phenolic (p. 511), urea (p. 313), and melamine (p. 321) resins to give block polymers and graft polymers that may combine the characteristics of the individual polymers.

The epoxy resins have outstanding adhesive properties and are used for bonding to metal, glass, and ceramics. They also are used as casting resins in electrical assemblies. Their chief use in 1955 was in protective coatings because of their good adhesion, inertness, hardness, and unusual flexibility.

1,2-Dithioglycerol (2,3-dimercapto-1-propanol), known as **BAL** (British Anti-Lewisite), is made from allyl alcohol.

$$CH_2{=}CHCH_2OH \xrightarrow{Br_2} BrCH_2CHBrCH_2OH \xrightarrow{NaSH} HSCH_2CH(SH)CH_2OH$$

It was developed during World War II as an antidote for arsenical war gases such as Lewisite (p. 902). The toxicity of the trivalent arsenic compounds is believed to be due to the inhibition of enzyme action by the combination of arsenic with thiol groups in enzymes. 1,2-Alkanethiols form a more stable cyclic reaction product with the arsenic and prevent combination of the arsenic with the enzyme. The glucoside of BAL has found general use as an antidote for poisoning by heavy metals. **1,2,6-Hexanetriol** is made by the hydrolysis of 2-(hydroxymethyl)tetrahydropyran (p. 632).

Pentaerythritol is the most important tetrahydric alcohol. It is prepared by the reaction of an aqueous solution of acetaldehyde with an excess of para-formaldehyde in the presence of lime. The reaction consists of an aldol addition followed by a crossed Cannizzaro reaction (p. 534).

$$3\ HCHO + CH_3CHO \xrightarrow{Ca(OH)_2} (HOCH_2)_3CCHO \xrightarrow{HCHO-Ca(OH)_2} (HOCH_2)_4C + \tfrac{1}{2} Ca(OCHO)_2$$

Pentaery-thritol   Calcium formate

The highly symmetrical structure accounts for the high melting point of 262°. Over 60 million pounds was produced in 1955, most of which was used for the preparation of alkyd and other polyester resins and for the up-grading of drying oils. By esterification with unsaturated fat acids an ester is produced that has a higher molecular weight than the glycerides of natural fats. Hence a lower degree of polymerization is needed to produce films having the necessary toughness and hardness. Thus soybean oil is not a very good drying oil (p. 187). If the soybean oil is hydrolyzed and the fat acids are reesterified with pentaery-thritol, the product "dries" more rapidly. Another use for pentaerythritol is for the preparation of the nitrate known as **PETN**. Mixed with 30 per cent TNT it is used as a high explosive charge for bombs, torpedoes, and mines, and for demolition purposes. Some is used in peacetime in blasting caps and pulverulent dynamite.

The straight-chain tetra-, penta-, and hexahydric alcohols (p. 412) are readily available by the reduction of sugars (p. 366).

AMINO ALCOHOLS AND POLYAMINES

Like the aldehyde hydrates, the **1-hydroxy-1-amino compounds** (aldehyde ammonias) and **1,1-diamino compounds** usually are unstable, undergoing dehydration or deamination, and polymerization (p. 210).

1-Hydroxy-2-amino compounds can be prepared by the general methods, but those compounds most readily available are prepared by the reaction of ethylene oxides with ammonia or primary or secondary amines, or by the reduction of nitro alcohols. Reaction of ethylene oxide with ammonia gives 2-aminoethanol or 2-hydroxyethylamine, commonly called **ethanolamine**. A second molecule of ethylene oxide gives bis(2-hydroxyethyl)amine or **diethanolamine**, and a third yields tris(2-hydroxyethyl)amine or **triethanolamine**.

$$\underset{O}{CH_2{-}CH_2} \xrightarrow{NH_3} \underset{\text{Ethanolamine}}{HOCH_2CH_2NH_2} \xrightarrow{(CH_2)_2O} \underset{\text{Diethanolamine}}{(HOCH_2CH_2)_2NH} \xrightarrow{(CH_2)_2O} \underset{\text{Triethanolamine}}{(HOCH_2CH_2)_3N}$$

Salts of the ethanolamines with fat acids are soluble in both water and hydrocarbons and are good emulsifying agents. Thus kerosene or paraffin oil containing a small amount of triethanolamine oleate can be mixed with water to give stable emulsions useful as agricultural sprays, or as lubricating coolants during high speed metal-cutting operations. Ethanolamine and diethanolamine are used for the recovery of acidic gases such as carbon dioxide and hydrogen sulfide. The gases are absorbed by the cold amine and are liberated by heating the solution.

Ethanolamine and its trimethylammonium salts, the cholines (p. 243), constitute a portion of an important class of biological substances known as the *phospholipids*. Thus the **lecithins** are mixed esters of glycerol and choline with fat acids and phosphoric acid. The **cephalins** (or kephalins) are esters of ethanolamine or serine (p. 296) instead of choline. **Sphingomyelin** contains the unsaturated dihydroxy amine *sphingosine* instead of glycerol.

$$\begin{array}{ll}
\text{CH}_2\text{OCOR} & \text{CH}_3(\text{CH}_2)_{12}\text{CH}{=}\text{CHCHOH} \\
| & | \\
\text{CHOCOR}' & \text{CHNHCOR} \\
| \quad \text{O}^- & | \quad \text{O}^- \\
| \quad |{+} & | \quad |{+} \\
\text{CH}_2\text{O}{-}\text{P}{-}\text{OCH}_2\text{CH}_2\text{N(CH}_3)_3 & \text{CH}_2\text{O}{-}\text{P}{-}\text{OCH}_2\text{CH}_2\text{N(CH}_3)_3 \\
| \quad \quad \quad \quad \quad + & | \quad \quad \quad \quad \quad + \\
\text{O}^- & \text{O}^- \\
\quad \text{Lecithins} & \quad \text{Sphingomyelin}
\end{array}$$

The phospholipids are components of all animal and vegetable cells and are abundant in the brain, spinal cord, eggs, and soybeans. They possibly function as emulsifying agents for fats and are important in the metabolism of fats. *Soybean lecithin* is used in large quantities for the stabilization of emulsified food fats such as oleomargarine and mayonnaise. The importance of choline and acetylcholine salts has been discussed (p. 243).

Concentrated nitric acid in the presence of acetic anhydride and a small amount of hydrogen chloride converts diethanolamine to **N-nitrodiethanolamine nitrate** (*DINA*), a powerful explosive. Basic amino groups cannot be nitrated but chloroamines can. The hydrogen chloride is converted to chlorine acetate which then acts catalytically for the introduction of the nitro group.

$$\begin{array}{lcl}
(\text{HOCH}_2)_2\text{NH} + 2\,\text{HNO}_3 & \longrightarrow & (\text{O}_2\text{NOCH}_2\text{CH}_2)_2\text{NH} + 2\,\text{H}_2\text{O} \\
2\,\text{HCl} + 2\,\text{HNO}_3 + 3\,(\text{CH}_3\text{CO})_2\text{O} & \longrightarrow & 2\,\text{ClOCOCH}_3 + \text{N}_2\text{O}_3 + 4\,\text{CH}_3\text{COOH} \\
(\text{O}_2\text{NOCH}_2\text{CH}_2)_2\text{NH} + \text{ClOCOCH}_3 & \longrightarrow & (\text{O}_2\text{NOCH}_2\text{CH}_2)_2\text{NCl} + \text{CH}_3\text{COOH} \\
(\text{O}_2\text{NOCH}_2\text{CH}_2)_2\text{NCl} + \text{HONO}_2 & \longrightarrow & (\text{O}_2\text{NOCH}_2\text{CH}_2)_2\text{NNO}_2 + \text{HOCl} \\
\text{HOCl} + (\text{CH}_3\text{CO})_2\text{O} & \longrightarrow & \text{CH}_3\text{COOCl} + \text{CH}_3\text{COOH}
\end{array}$$

DINA is as powerful as RDX (p. 221) or PETN, and its low melting point of 52° permits it to mix better with TNT and to plasticize cellulose nitrate.

Reaction of methyldiethanolamine hydrochloride with thionyl chloride or phosphorus trichloride gives **methylbis(2-chloroethyl)amine hydrochloride.**

$$(\text{HOCH}_2\text{CH}_2)_2\text{NHCH}_3{}^{+-}\text{Cl} + 2\,\text{SOCl}_2 \longrightarrow (\text{ClCH}_2\text{CH}_2)_2\text{NHCH}_3{}^{+-}\text{Cl} + 2\,\text{HCl} + 2\,\text{SO}_2$$

The free base is a nitrogen analog of mustard gas (p. 289) and belongs to the class of compounds known as **nitrogen mustards.** Many nitrogen mustards were prepared and investigated as toxic agents during World War II. They have a local vesicant action similar to that of mustard gas and in addition penetrate the skin and exert a generalized systemic action on living cells similar to the action of X-rays. Exposure to very low concentrations may cause opacity of the cornea.

Reaction of ethanolamine with sulfuric acid yields **2-aminoethyl hydrogen sulfate**, which is an inner salt.

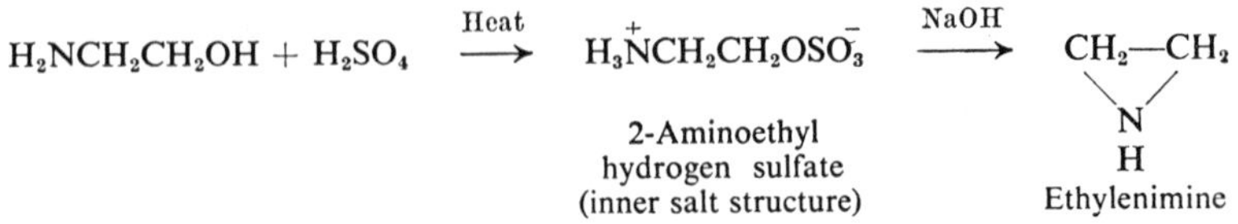

$$H_2NCH_2CH_2OH + H_2SO_4 \xrightarrow{\text{Heat}} H_3\overset{+}{N}CH_2CH_2O\overset{-}{S}O_3 \xrightarrow{\text{NaOH}} \underset{\underset{H}{N}}{CH_2 - CH_2}$$

2-Aminoethyl
hydrogen sulfate   Ethylenimine
(inner salt structure)

When distilled with aqueous sodium hydroxide it gives **ethylenimine**, b.p. 55°. This reaction is an intramolecular alkylation analogous to the ethylation of an amine by ethyl sulfate. Ethylenimine is toxic, but it is a useful reagent since it reacts like ethylene oxide with substances containing active hydrogen. Aqueous sulfur dioxide gives **taurine** (2-aminoethanesulfonic acid).

$$(CH_2)_2NH + H_2SO_3 \longrightarrow H_3\overset{+}{N}CH_2CH_2\overset{-}{S}O_3$$
Taurine

Ethylenimine polymerizes readily in the presence of acids to **polyethylenimine**.

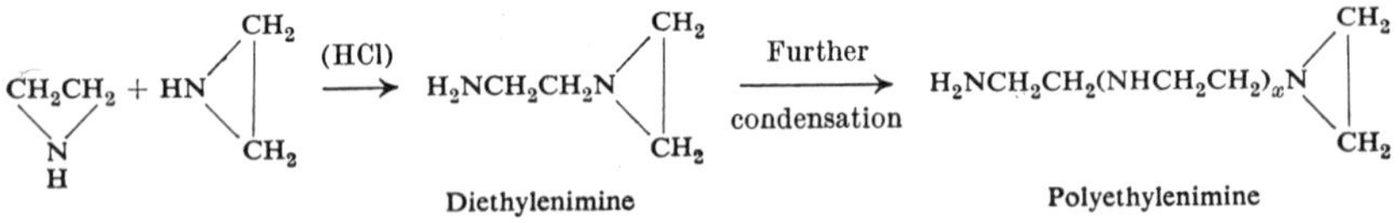

$$\underset{\underset{H}{N}}{CH_2CH_2} + HN\overset{CH_2}{\underset{CH_2}{\Big|}} \xrightarrow{\text{(HCl)}} H_2NCH_2CH_2N\overset{CH_2}{\underset{CH_2}{\Big|}} \xrightarrow[\text{condensation}]{\text{Further}} H_2NCH_2CH_2(NHCH_2CH_2)_xN\overset{CH_2}{\underset{CH_2}{\Big|}}$$

Diethylenimine   Polyethylenimine

Ethylenimine and polyethylenimine react with the hydroxyl groups of cellulose and are used to impart wet strength and abrasion resistance to paper and to decrease the tendency of rayon and cotton fibers to swell in water.

In the reaction of propylene oxide with ammonia the point of attack is the 1 position giving rise to **1-amino-2-propanol**.

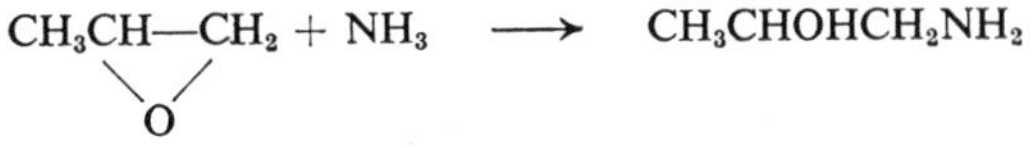

$$CH_3CH - CH_2 + NH_3 \longrightarrow CH_3CHOHCH_2NH_2$$
$$\underset{O}{\diagdown \diagup}$$

2-Amino-1-hydroxy compounds are available by reduction of the corresponding nitro alcohols obtained by the addition of aliphatic nitro compounds to aldehydes (p. 262).

$$(CH_3)_2\underset{NO_2}{\overset{|}{C}}CH_2OH \xrightarrow{H_2-Ni} (CH_3)_2\underset{NH_2}{\overset{|}{C}}CH_2OH$$

Diamino compounds can be prepared by the usual methods for preparing amines. Thus they are formed by the reaction of ammonia with primary or secondary dihalides, by the reduction of dinitriles, or by the Hofmann degradation of diamides. **Ethylenediamine** is obtained by the reaction of ethylene chloride with ammonia.

$$ClCH_2CH_2Cl + 4 NH_3 \longrightarrow H_2NCH_2CH_2NH_2 + 2 NH_4Cl$$

Further reaction with ethylene chloride and ammonia gives the co-products **diethylenetriamine,** $H_2NCH_2CH_2NHCH_2CH_2NH_2$, **triethylenetetramine,** H_2N-$(CH_2CH_2NH)_2CH_2CH_2NH_2$, and **tetraethylenepentamine,** $H_2N(CH_2CH_2NH)_3$-$CH_2CH_2NH_2$. All of these compounds are manufactured on a large scale commercially and are used in the synthesis of pharmaceuticals, textile finishing agents, emulsifying agents and fungicides. **Ethylenediammonium tartrate** crystals are piezo-electric and thin plates cut from them are used instead of quartz plates for the control of high frequency electric currents in telephony, radio, radar, and television. Ethylenediamine is used also in the preparation of basic ion exchange resins by copolymerizing it with formaldehyde and *m*-phenylene-diamine (p. 475) or urea (p. 313). The reaction of ethylenediamine with carbon disulfide and sodium hydroxide gives **sodium ethylenebisdithiocarbamate,** $Na^+{}^-SCSNHCH_2CH_2NHCSS^-{}^+Na$. It is a useful fungicide sold under the trade name *Dithane*. Ethylenediamine and diethylenetriamine are used to cross link polymerized unsaturated fat acids in the manufacture of **polyamide resins.**

A Strecker-type reaction (p. 303) of ethylenediamine with formaldehyde and sodium cyanide in alkaline solution yields the sodium salt of **ethylenediamine-tetraacetic acid** (*EDTA, Sequestrene, Versene*).

$$H_2NCH_2CH_2NH_2 + 4\ HCHO + 4\ NaCN + 4\ H_2O \xrightarrow[80°]{NaOH}$$

$$(NaOOCCH_2)_2NCH_2CH_2N(CH_2COONa)_2 + 4\ NH_3$$

It can be made also from ethylenediamine and sodium chloroacetate. It is a strong chelating (or complexing) agent for alkaline earth and heavy metal ions, the relative position of the unshared pairs of electrons on the four carboxylate ions and the two nitrogen atoms being such that it can form stable five-membered chelate rings with the metal ions. With six unshared pairs of electrons available, one would expect a metal having a coordination number of six to complex completely with EDTA. Usually, however, only four rings form, presumably for steric reasons, and the sixth pair of electrons is supplied by a water molecule.

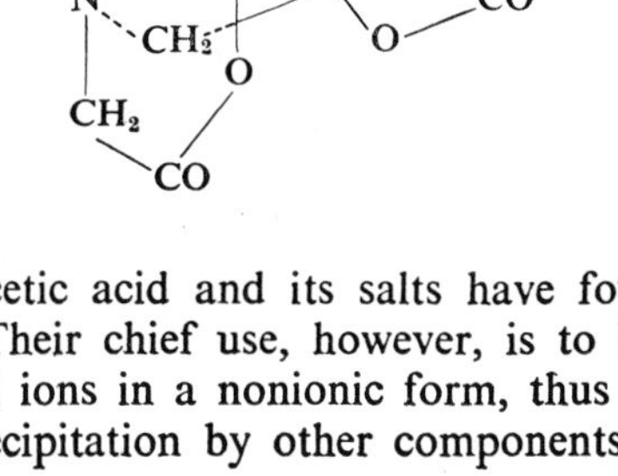

Ethylenediaminetetraacetic acid and its salts have found important uses in analytical chemistry. Their chief use, however, is to bind traces of alkaline earth and heavy metal ions in a nonionic form, thus preventing undesirable catalytic effects or precipitation by other components of aqueous solutions.

Although first introduced in the United States after World War II, production in 1955 was over 5 million pounds.

The ability of 1,2-diamines to form a five-membered ring by coordination of the two unshared pairs of electrons with metallic ions makes these complexes much more stable than those produced from other amines. Cobaltic chloride, for example, gives a very stable complex with three molecules of ethylenediamine.

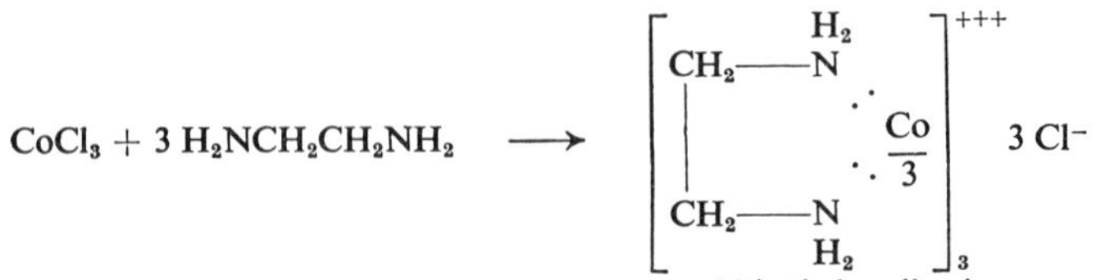

$$CoCl_3 + 3\ H_2NCH_2CH_2NH_2 \longrightarrow \left[\begin{array}{c} CH_2\text{---}N \\ | \\ | \\ CH_2\text{---}N \\ H_2 \end{array} \begin{array}{c} H_2 \\ \ddots \\ \overline{\ \cdot\cdot\ } \\ \end{array} \begin{array}{c} Co \\ 3 \end{array} \right]^{+++}_{3} 3\ Cl^-$$

Trisethylenediamine
cobaltic chloride

Compounds of this type have been important in developing the theory of stereochemistry, particularly in establishing the spatial arrangement of bonds in covalent metallic compounds (p. 352).

Trimethylenediamines can be prepared by the addition of ammonia or amines to acrylonitrile (p. 788) followed by reduction.

$$RNH_2 + CH_2\!\!=\!\!CHC\!\!\equiv\!\!N \longrightarrow RNHCH_2CH_2C\!\!\equiv\!\!N \xrightarrow{H_2,\ Ni} RNHCH_2CH_2CH_2NH_2$$

The fatty acid salts of diamines in which R is a 16 or 18 carbon *n*-alkyl group are used as additives in petroleum lubricants for metal cutting and drawing operations. **Tetramethylenediamine,** known as *putrescine*, and **pentamethylenediamine,** known as *cadaverine*, occur among the bacterial decomposition products of proteins. They arise from the decarboxylation of ornithine and lysine, respectively.

$$H_2N(CH_2)_3CHNH_2COOH \xrightarrow{Bacteria} H_2N(CH_2)_4NH_2 + CO_2$$
Ornithine   Putrescine

$$H_2N(CH_2)_4CHNH_2COOH \xrightarrow{Bacteria} H_2N(CH_2)_5NH_2 + CO_2$$
Lysine   Cadaverine

Spermine, $H_2N(CH_2)_3NH(CH_2)_4NH(CH_2)_3NH_2$, is widely distributed in the organs of mammals and has been isolated also from yeast.

Hexamethylenediamine is an intermediate for the synthesis of *nylon* 66 (p. 798) and is made commercially by the catalytic reduction of tetramethylene cyanide (adiponitrile, p. 799) in the presence of ammonia to prevent the formation of imino derivatives.

$$NC(CH_2)_4CN + 4\ H_2 \xrightarrow{Ni\ (NH_3)} H_2N(CH_2)_6NH_2$$
Adiponitrile   Hexamethylene-
                                                diamine

1,2-, 1,4-, and **1,5-Diamine hydrochlorides** on thermal decomposition lose ammonium chloride to form the salts of five- and six-membered cyclic bases. Thus the hydrochlorides of ethylenediamine, putrescine, and cadaverine give the hydrochlorides of piperazine (p. 641), pyrrolidine (p. 613), and piperidine (p. 621).

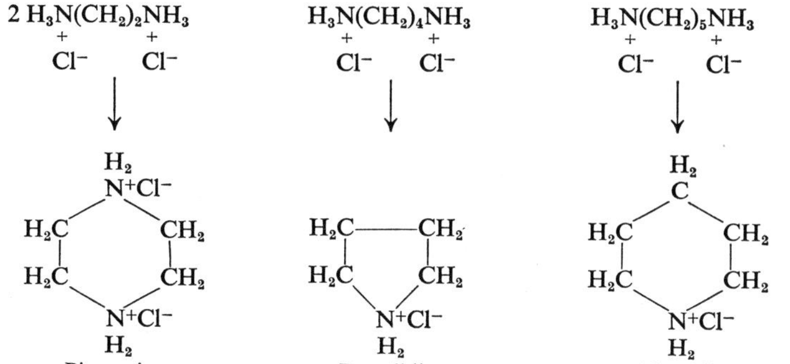

$$2\ H_3N(CH_2)_2NH_3 \qquad H_3N(CH_2)_4NH_3 \qquad H_3N(CH_2)_5NH_3$$

Cl⁻ Cl⁻ ... (reaction schemes showing Piperazine hydrochloride, Pyrrolidine hydrochloride, and Piperidine hydrochloride)

Piperazine hydrochloride   Pyrrolidine hydrochloride   Piperidine hydrochloride

Piperazines can be prepared also from N-substituted bis-2-chloroethylamines and ammonia or primary amines.

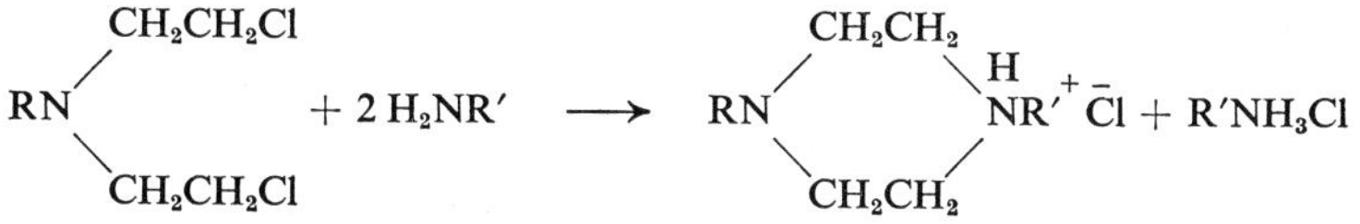

$$RN\Big\langle{}^{CH_2CH_2Cl}_{CH_2CH_2Cl} + 2\ H_2NR' \longrightarrow RN\Big\langle{}^{CH_2CH_2}_{CH_2CH_2}\Big\rangle NR' \overset{H}{\underset{}{}}\overset{+}{Cl}{}^{-} + R'NH_3Cl$$

REVIEW QUESTIONS

1. What are chelate compounds? How does the formation of a chelate compound explain the fact that boric acid becomes a stronger acid in the presence of 1,2-glycols?
2. What is the best source of trimethylene glycol; tetramethylene glycol? Give two general methods for the synthesis of α,ω-glycols.
3. What is the formula and source of each of the following compounds: glycerol; pentaerythritol; mannitol; sorbitol?
4. Discuss the preparation and properties of vinyl alcohol and vinyl acetate; polyvinyl alcohol and polyvinyl acetate.
5. Give reactions for the conversion of glycerol into allyl alcohol; allyl chloride into glycerol. How is allyl chloride made commercially?
6. α-Methylallyl alcohol (methallyl alcohol) on distillation with dilute sulfuric acid is converted into isobutyraldehyde. Explain.

PROBLEMS

7. Give reactions for the following syntheses: (*a*) ethoxyacetylene starting with ethyl alcohol as the only organic raw material; (*b*) crotyl alcohol from acetaldehyde; (*c*) 1-hydroxy-3-hexene from allyl chloride; (*d*) 1-hydroxy-3-hexene from acetylene; (*e*) 2-hydroxy-3-hexene from acetylene; (*f*) 1-hydroxy-2-hexene from acetylene; (*g*) propargyl alcohol from allyl chloride; (*h*) 5-hydroxy-1-pentyne from furfural; (*i*) 6-hydroxy-1-hexyne from acrolein.
8. Construct a chart indicating the reactions, reagents, and conditions for preparing the following compounds starting with ethylene: ethylene glycol, morpholine, ethylene chlorohydrin, ethylene cyanohydrin, ethanolamine, dioxane, glycol nitrate, diethylene glycol, diethanolamine, ethylenimine, Cellosolve, 2-diethylaminoethanol, triethanolamine, β-chloroethyl formal, ethylene oxide, and β-chloroethyl ether.
9. Give reactions for the following conversions: (*a*) propylene to propylene glycol diacetate; (*b*) styrene to phenylacetaldehyde; (*c*) *n*-butyl alcohol to *n*-hexyl alcohol; (*d*) *n*-butyl alcohol to 2,2-bis-(hydroxymethyl)-1-butanol; (*e*) tetrahydrofurfuryl alcohol to 1,5-pentanediol; (*f*) acetaldehyde to 1,3-butanediol; (*g*) allyl alcohol to glycidol; (*h*) ethylene oxide to mustard gas.

10. Construct a chart illustrating the reactions, reagents, and conditions for converting acetylene into the following compounds: propargyl alcohol, tetrahydrofuran, 1,4-dihydroxy-2-butyne, ethyl alcohol, 1,3-butadiyne, tetramethylene glycol, acetaldehyde, *N*-vinyl-carbazole, 3-hydroxy-3-methyl-1-butyne, and vinyl methyl ether.

11. Give reactions for the preparation of: (*a*) pyrrolidine from tetramethylene glycol; (*b*) spermine from trimethylene and tetramethylene glycols; (*c*) hexamethylenediamine from tetramethylene chloride; (*d*) trimethylenediamine from ethylene cyanohydrin; (*e*) 2-amino-2-methyl-1,3-propanediol from 1-nitroethane; (*f*) 1-amino-2-propanol from propylene; and (*g*) 1,4-dimethylpiperazine from ethylene chloride.

12. How can one distinguish readily by chemical reactions between the members of the following pairs of compounds: (*a*) glycerol and ethylene glycol; (*b*) propylene glycol and 1-amino-2-propanol; (*c*) 1,4-butanediol and 2,3-butanediol; (*d*) pentaerythritol nitrate and 2,4,6-trinitrotoluene; (*e*) Cellosolve and ethylene glycol; (*f*) β-chloroethyl ether and β-chloroethyl formal.

13. During the preparation of a batch of 2-methyl-2,4-pentanediol, the Raney nickel was not completely removed before purification by distillation. During the distillation through a column, only acetone distilled. Give an explanation for this behavior.

14. How could one identify, by means of chemical reactions, the following explosives: cellulose nitrate; nitroglycerin; glycol dinitrate; PETN; DINA; RDX; TNT; tetryl.

15. Xylose boiled with 12 per cent hydrochloric acid gives *A*, which can be hydrogenated in the presence of Raney nickel to *B*. Treatment of *B* at low temperature with phosphorus tribromide gives *C*. When *C* is heated with sodium amide, *D* is obtained, which evolves two moles of methane with excess methylmagnesium bromide. The product, after pouring on solid carbon dioxide and acidifying, gives *E*. When *E* is heated at reduced pressure, water is eliminated and a polymeric product is formed. Give equations for the reactions that take place.

16. Three hydrocarbons have the empirical formula CH. Two are liquids and one is a solid. One of the liquids decolorizes bromine, but the other does not. A solution of the solid in benzene does not decolorize bromine. When the reactive liquid is allowed to stand with a chloroform solution of peroxybenzoic acid, a new product is obtained. When this product is warmed with aqueous sodium bisulfite and then acidified with hydrochloric acid, another compound is isolated which gives a color with Schiff reagent. When either this product, the reactive liquid hydrocarbon, or the solid hydrocarbon is vigorously oxidized, the same acid is obtained. When this acid is heated with soda-lime, a hydrocarbon is formed which is identical with the unreactive liquid hydrocarbon. What are the three hydrocarbons and what are the reactions that take place?

17. A compound has the molecular formula $C_7H_{12}O_5$. It is neutral to moist litmus, is hydrolyzed by alkali, and gives a saponification equivalent of 88. When the alkaline solution after saponification is distilled, no organic compound can be detected in the distillate. Acidification with sulfuric acid and distillation gives a volatile acid which has a Duclaux constant of 7. Neutralization of the sulfuric acid solution remaining in the flask after the distillation and evaporation gave a sticky mass of salts. When this residue was mixed with sodium bisulfate and heated strongly, a volatile substance with a sharp odor was formed. Collection of the volatile compound in a small amount of water and addition of Schiff reagent gave a red color. Give a possible structural formula for the original compound and equations for the reactions that take place.

Chapter 35

HYDROXY, UNSATURATED, HALOGENATED, AND AMINO CARBONYL COMPOUNDS. DICARBONYL COMPOUNDS

HYDROXY CARBONYL COMPOUNDS

Glycolic aldehyde, $HOCH_2CHO$, can be made by the oxidation of ethylene glycol with cold nitric acid. It exists in the monomeric form in dilute aqueous solution, but attempts to isolate it have yielded only a crystalline dimeric compound. In aqueous solution, the dimer gradually dissociates to the monomer, indicating that it probably is the cyclic bishemiacetal.

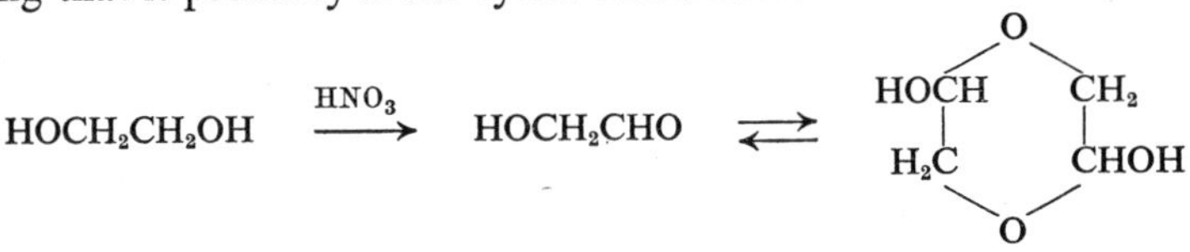

$$HOCH_2CH_2OH \xrightarrow{HNO_3} HOCH_2CHO \rightleftharpoons$$

Glyceraldehyde and **dihydroxyacetone** are degradation products of the sugars (p. 369), which are polyhydroxy aldehydes or polyhydroxy ketones. **D-Glyceraldehyde** is obtained readily by cleavage of 1,2,5,6-diisopropylidene-D-mannitol with lead tetraacetate, followed by removal of the isopropylidene group.

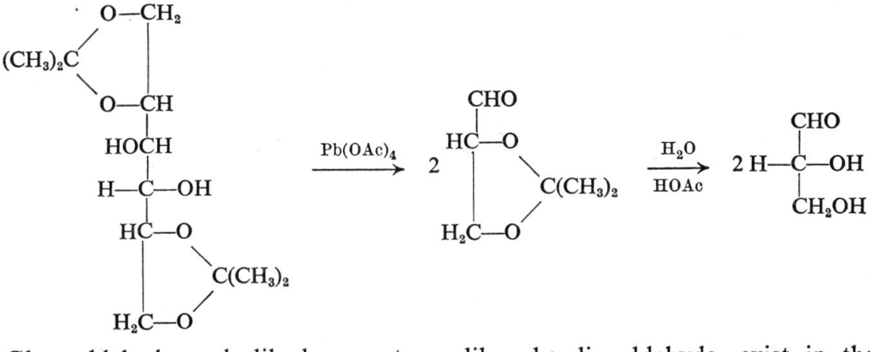

Glyceraldehyde and dihydroxyacetone, like glycolic aldehyde, exist in the monomeric form only in aqueous solution.

The α-hydroxy ketones frequently are called *α-ketols*. Those having a secondary hydroxyl group are known as *acyloins* in the aliphatic series and *benzoins* in the aromatic series. Their methods of preparation and reactions are discussed on pages 173 and 536. The following series of reactions starting with a cyanohydrin and dihydropyran (p. 631) indicates a general method for the synthesis of α-ketols having a tertiary hydroxyl group.

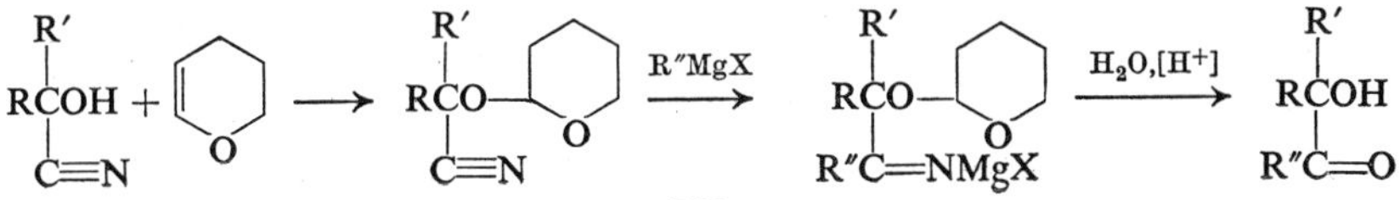

When the sodium salts of acyloins react with alkyl halides, carbon alkylation takes place rather than formation of an enediol ether.

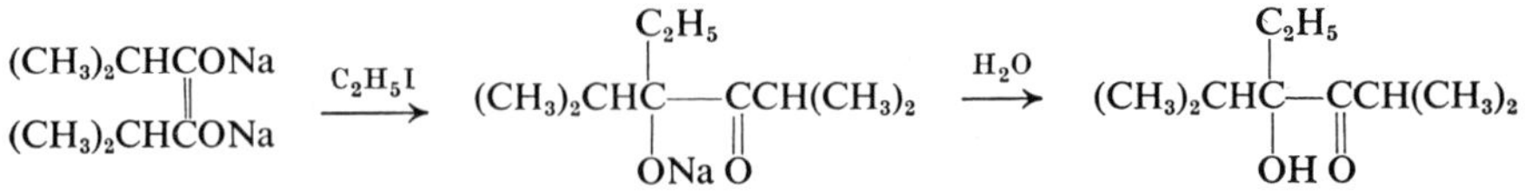

$$\begin{array}{c}(CH_3)_2CHCONa \\ (CH_3)_2CHCONa\end{array} \xrightarrow{C_2H_5I} \begin{array}{c}C_2H_5 \\ | \\ (CH_3)_2CHC—CCH(CH_3)_2 \\ | \quad\ \| \\ ONa\ O\end{array} \xrightarrow{H_2O} \begin{array}{c}C_2H_5 \\ | \\ (CH_3)_2CHC—CCH(CH_3)_2 \\ | \quad\ \| \\ OH\ O\end{array}$$

β-Hydroxy carbonyl compounds are the products of aldol addition of aldehydes and ketones (p. 205). **δ-Hydroxyvaleraldehyde,** which is obtained easily by the hydrolysis of dihydropyran (p. 632), is the starting point for a commercial synthesis of DL-lysine.

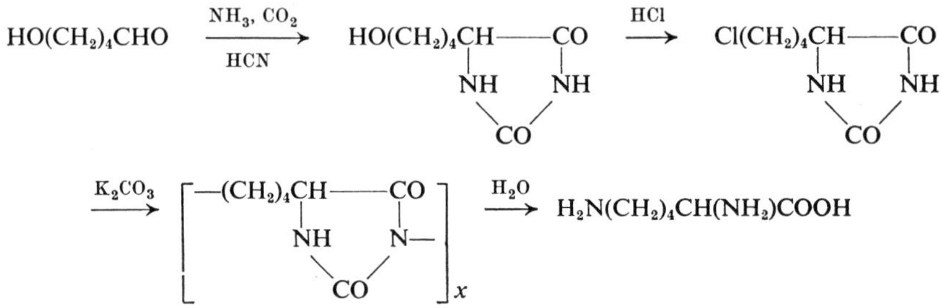

$$HO(CH_2)_4CHO \xrightarrow[HCN]{NH_3,\ CO_2} \begin{array}{c}HO(CH_2)_4CH—CO \\ | \quad\quad | \\ NH \quad\ NH \\ \diagdown\ \diagup \\ CO\end{array} \xrightarrow{HCl} \begin{array}{c}Cl(CH_2)_4CH—CO \\ | \quad\quad | \\ NH \quad\ NH \\ \diagdown\ \diagup \\ CO\end{array}$$

$$\xrightarrow{K_2CO_3} \left[\begin{array}{c}—(CH_2)_4CH—CO \\ | \quad\quad | \\ NH \quad\ N— \\ \diagdown\ \diagup \\ CO\end{array} \right]_x \xrightarrow{H_2O} H_2N(CH_2)_4CH(NH_2)COOH$$

UNSATURATED CARBONYL COMPOUNDS

Ketenes

Compounds containing carbon linked by one double bond to an oxygen atom and by another double bond to a carbon atom are called *ketenes.* General methods of preparation are (*1*) the removal of halogen acid from an aliphatic acyl halide, (*2*) the removal of halogen from α-halogenated acid halides (p. 162), and (*3*) the thermal decomposition of dialkyl- or diarylacetylphthalimides (p. 553).

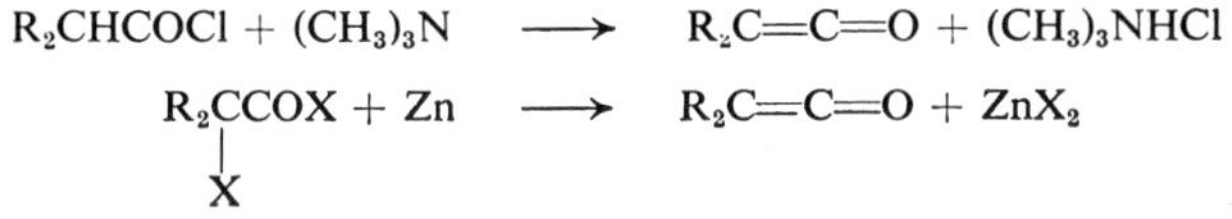

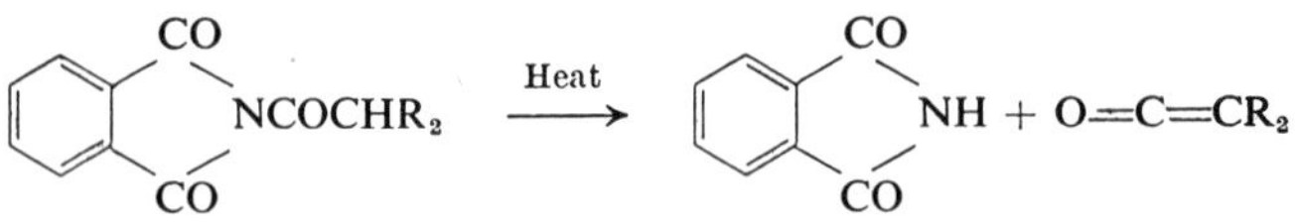

$$R_2CHCOCl + (CH_3)_3N \longrightarrow R_2C\!\!=\!\!C\!\!=\!\!O + (CH_3)_3NHCl$$

$$\begin{array}{c}R_2CCOX + Zn \longrightarrow R_2C\!\!=\!\!C\!\!=\!\!O + ZnX_2 \\ | \\ X\end{array}$$

All of these reactions give satisfactory yields of disubstituted ketenes. The first reaction is best if one of the R groups is hydrogen. **Ketene** itself is obtained by pyrolysis of acetone, acetic acid, or acetic anhydride (p. 164).

$$CH_3COCH_3 \xrightarrow[\substack{\text{Iron-free}\\ \text{copper tube}}]{700°} CH_2\!\!=\!\!C\!\!=\!\!O + CH_4$$

$$CH_3COOH \longrightarrow CH_2\!\!=\!\!C\!\!=\!\!O + H_2O$$

$$(CH_3CO)_2O \longrightarrow 2\ CH_2\!\!=\!\!C\!\!=\!\!O + H_2O$$

A convenient laboratory procedure is the depolymerization of commercial diketene (p. 824) if it is available.

$$(CH_2{=}C{=}O)_2 \xrightarrow[\text{wire}]{\text{Hot Pt}} 2\ CH_2{=}C{=}O$$

Diphenylketene can be prepared by a special method from benzil.

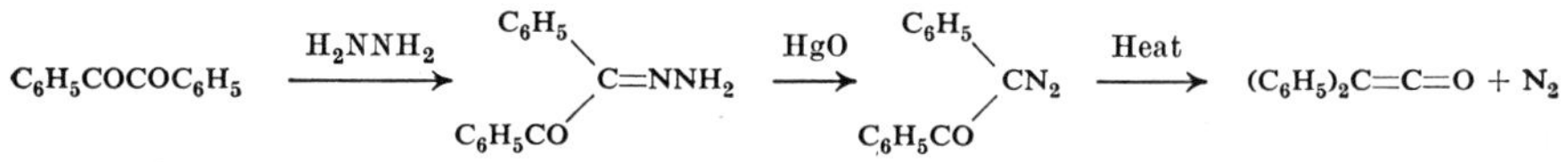

$$C_6H_5COCOC_6H_5 \xrightarrow{H_2NNH_2} \underset{\underset{\text{Benzil}}{\overset{C_6H_5CO}{}}}{\overset{C_6H_5}{\diagdown}}C{=}NNH_2 \xrightarrow{HgO} \underset{\underset{\text{monohydrazone}}{}}{\overset{C_6H_5}{\diagdown}}CN_2 \xrightarrow{\text{Heat}} (C_6H_5)_2C{=}C{=}O + N_2$$

| Benzil | Benzil monohydrazone | Azibenzil (phenylbenzoyl-diazomethane) | Diphenyl-ketene |

Ketenes do not undergo the usual carbonyl reactions. Like all compounds having cumulative or twin double bonds, for example the isocyanates, $RN{=}C{=}O$ (p. 317), the molecule is very reactive and in the presence of acid or basic catalysts adds any compound having a reactive hydrogen atom.

$$R_2C{=}C{=}O + \begin{cases} HOH \longrightarrow R_2CHCOOH \\ R'OH \longrightarrow R_2CHCOOR' \\ H_2S \longrightarrow R_2CHCOSH \\ R'COOH \longrightarrow R_2CHCOOCOR' \\ HX \longrightarrow R_2CHCOX \\ HCN \longrightarrow R_2CHCOCN \\ HNH_2 \longrightarrow R_2CHCONH_2 \\ X_2 \longrightarrow R_2\underset{\underset{X}{|}}{C}COX \end{cases}$$

Ketene reacts with aldehydes and ketones to give β-lactones.

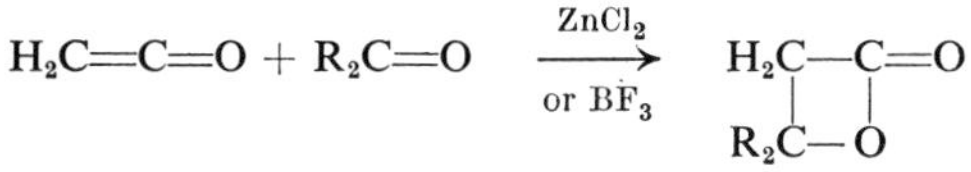

$$H_2C{=}C{=}O + R_2C{=}O \xrightarrow[\text{or BF}_3]{\text{ZnCl}_2} \begin{matrix} H_2C{-}C{=}O \\ | \quad\quad | \\ R_2C{-}O \end{matrix}$$

Before the discovery of this reaction in 1944, β-lactones were difficult to prepare and were laboratory curiosities. In the presence of small amounts of acids, carbonyl compounds having enolizable hydrogen react with ketene to give the enol acetate.

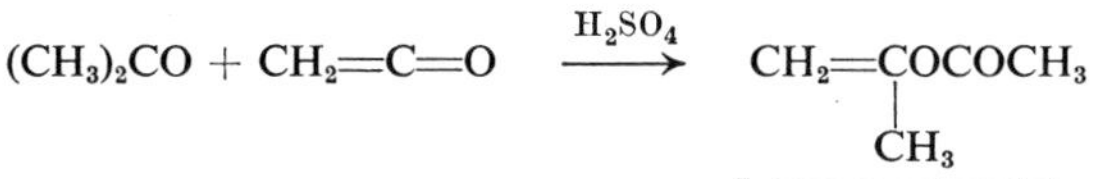

$$(CH_3)_2CO + CH_2{=}C{=}O \xrightarrow{H_2SO_4} \underset{\underset{CH_3}{|}}{CH_2{=}COCOCH_3}$$

Isopropenyl acetate

Isopropenyl acetate is a superior reagent for preparing other enol acetates. An equilibrium is established which can be shifted by distillation of the acetone.

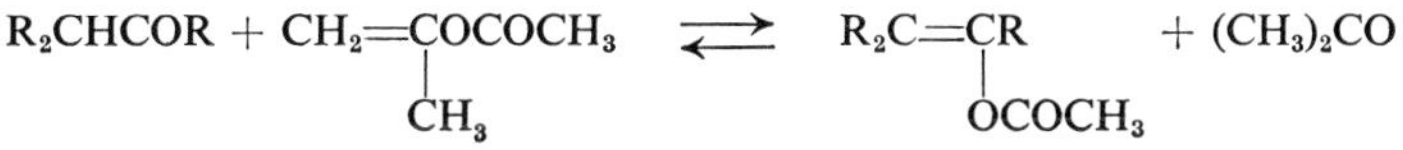

$$R_2CHCOR + \underset{\underset{CH_3}{|}}{CH_2{=}COCOCH_3} \rightleftarrows \underset{\underset{OCOCH_3}{|}}{R_2C{=}CR} + (CH_3)_2CO$$

Ketene adds acetals and ortho esters, in methyl ether solution using boron fluoride as a catalyst, to give β-alkoxy esters.

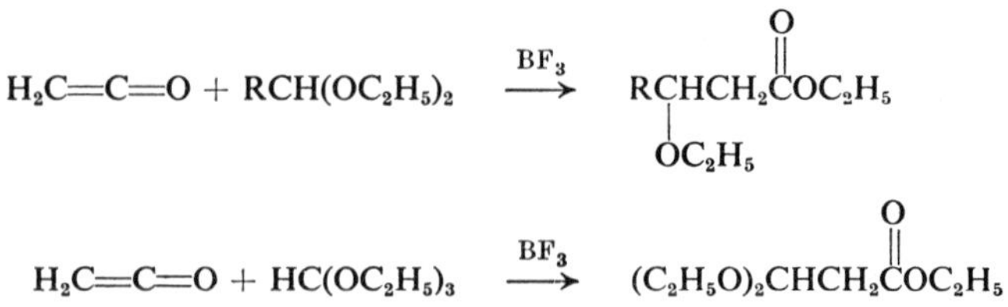

$$H_2C{=}C{=}O + RCH(OC_2H_5)_2 \xrightarrow{BF_3} \underset{\underset{OC_2H_5}{|}}{RCHCH_2}\overset{\overset{O}{\|}}{C}OC_2H_5$$

$$H_2C{=}C{=}O + HC(OC_2H_5)_3 \xrightarrow{BF_3} (C_2H_5O)_2CHCH_2\overset{\overset{O}{\|}}{C}OC_2H_5$$

Ketenes polymerize to dimers, the rate depending on the structure of the ketene. Thus dibenzylketene polymerizes very rapidly whereas diphenylketene is stable at room temperature. The dimers from disubstituted ketenes appear to be derivatives of 1,3-cyclobutanedione, but the dimers of unsubstituted and monosubstituted ketenes are β-unsaturated β-lactones.

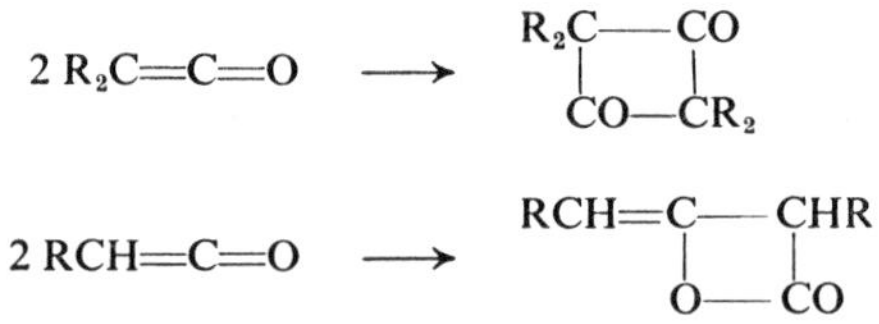

$$2\,R_2C{=}C{=}O \longrightarrow \begin{array}{cc} R_2C & CO \\ | & | \\ CO & CR_2 \end{array}$$

$$2\,RCH{=}C{=}O \longrightarrow \begin{array}{cc} RCH{=}C & CHR \\ | & | \\ O & CO \end{array}$$

The dimer of **methyl ketene** exists in a liquid and a solid form. The liquid form has the β-lactone structure, whereas the solid form has the butanedione structure.

α,β-Unsaturated Carbonyl Compounds

Compounds containing a double bond conjugated with a carbonyl group are of special interest. They are formed by the dehydration of β-hydroxy aldehydes and ketones. The aldols formed by the addition of aliphatic aldehydes to aromatic aldehydes usually cannot be isolated, dehydration taking place spontaneously (p. 536). The hydroxyl group of primary or secondary allyl alcohols may be oxidized selectively to give α,β-unsaturated aldehydes or ketones in good yields by stirring a solution of the compound in a suitable solvent with a suspension of manganese dioxide

$$RCH{=}CHCH_2OH \xrightarrow{MnO_2} RCH{=}CHCHO$$

The behavior of the double bond in α,β-unsaturated carbonyl compounds differs in many respects from isolated double bonds. It can be detected by means of the ultraviolet absorption spectrum of the compound (Fig. 94, p. 664). Strong absorption (log ϵ = *ca.* 4) occurs with $\lambda_{max.}$ between 220 mμ and 250 mμ, in addition to the weaker absorption (log ϵ = *ca.* 2) of the carbonyl group with $\lambda_{max.}$ around 280 mμ (p. 665).

Equilibrium frequently exists between the α,β and β,γ isomers. Thus mesityl oxide contains about 91 per cent of the conjugated compound and 9 per cent of the nonconjugated isomer. The term *mesityl oxide* usually refers to the commercial mixture, although it is used also to designate the pure conjugated isomer, whereas the nonconjugated isomer has been called *isomesityl oxide*. It is preferable, however, to use systematic names for the pure isomers.

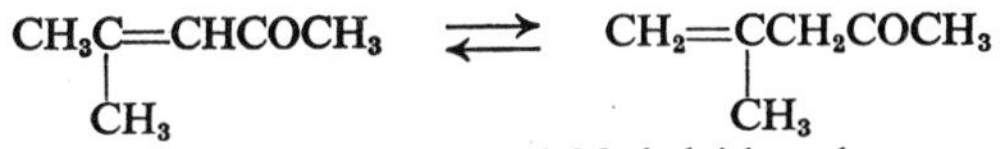

$$CH_3C{=}CHCOCH_3 \; \rightleftarrows \; CH_2{=}CCH_2COCH_3$$

$$\underset{CH_3}{|} \qquad\qquad\qquad \underset{CH_3}{|}$$

.2-Methyl-4-keto-2-pentene   2-Methyl-4-keto-1-pentene
91 per cent   9 per cent

Although catalytic reduction of the conjugated carbon-carbon double bond does not take place as readily as reduction of an isolated double bond, the conjugated double bond can be reduced by chemical reducing agents, such as sodium and alcohol, which do not reduce an isolated carbon-carbon double bond. Since the carbonyl group also is capable of reduction, the final product is the saturated alcohol. The reduction presumably takes place by 1,4 addition to the conjugated system and is followed by 1,2 addition to the carbonyl group.

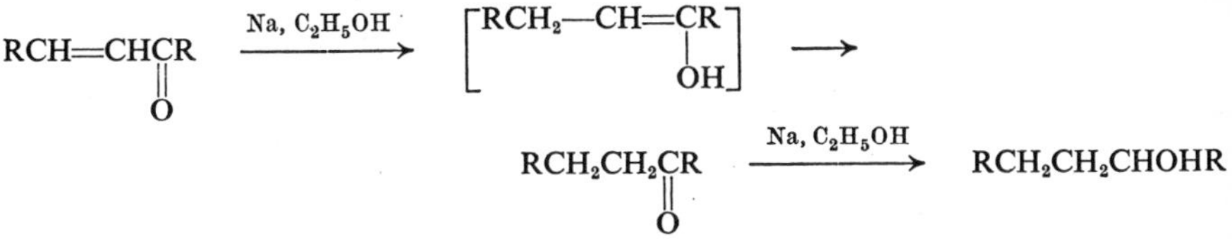

$$RCH{=}CHCR \xrightarrow{\text{Na, } C_2H_5OH} \left[RCH_2{-}CH{=}CR \atop \underset{OH}{|} \right] \longrightarrow$$

$$\underset{\underset{O}{\|}}{RCH_2CH_2CR} \xrightarrow{\text{Na, } C_2H_5OH} RCH_2CH_2CHOHR$$

The reaction can be stopped at the saturated ketone stage using sodium amalgam as the reducing agent.

The double bond in the conjugated system does not react with peroxy acids to give oxides, but hydrogen peroxide adds in the presence of osmium tetroxide to give the dihydroxy compound.

$$R_2C{=}CHCOR \xrightarrow{H_2O_2,\ OsO_4} R_2COHCHOHCOR$$

The carbonyl group is not as reactive to 1,2 addition as that in the simple ketones. Thus the α,β-unsaturated ketones frequently do not form simple oximes with hydroxylamine under the usual conditions. When reaction does occur, it is preceded by 1,4 addition. Hence addition takes place at the double bond as well as at the carbonyl group.

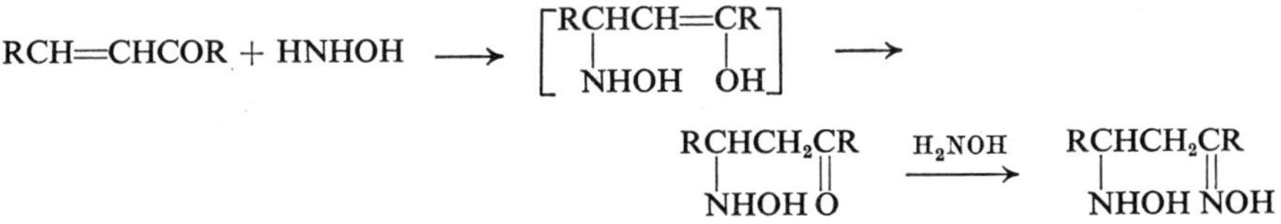

$$RCH{=}CHCOR + HNHOH \longrightarrow \left[RCHCH{=}CR \atop \underset{NHOH}{|} \ \underset{OH}{|} \right] \longrightarrow$$

$$\underset{NHOH\ O}{\underset{|\ \ \|}{RCHCH_2CR}} \xrightarrow{H_2NOH} \underset{NHOH\ NOH}{\underset{|\ \ \ |}{RCHCH_2CR}}$$

Similarly bisulfite adds both to the double bond and to the carbonyl group.

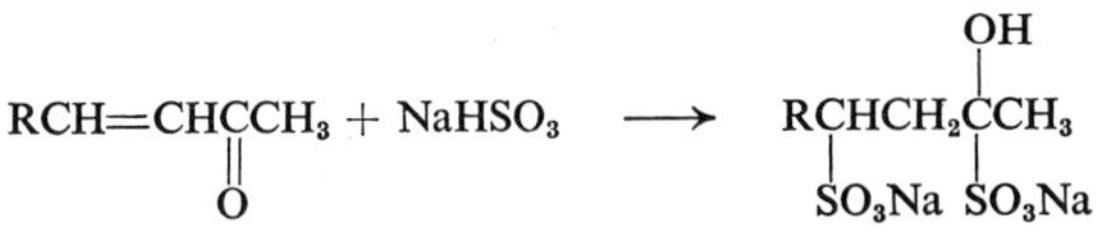

$$\underset{\underset{O}{\|}}{RCH{=}CHCCH_3} + NaHSO_3 \longrightarrow \overset{OH}{\overset{|}{RCHCH_2CCH_3}}$$

$$\qquad\qquad\qquad\qquad\qquad\qquad \underset{SO_3Na\ SO_3Na}{}$$

Since only the bisulfite that adds to the carbonyl group can be removed by acids or alkali (p. 201), the bisulfite addition products cannot be used for purification of α,β-unsaturated aldehydes and ketones.

Ammonia, which does not form stable addition products with the carbonyl group, gives β-amino ketones. The addition product of ammonia and mesityl oxide is called **diacetonamine.**

$$(CH_3)_2C{=}CHCOCH_3 \xrightarrow{NH_3} (CH_3)_2\underset{\underset{NH_2}{|}}{C}CH_2COCH_3$$

Diacetonamine

Phorone (p. 208) adds two moles of ammonia to give **triacetonediamine,** which on heating cyclizes to **triacetonamine.**

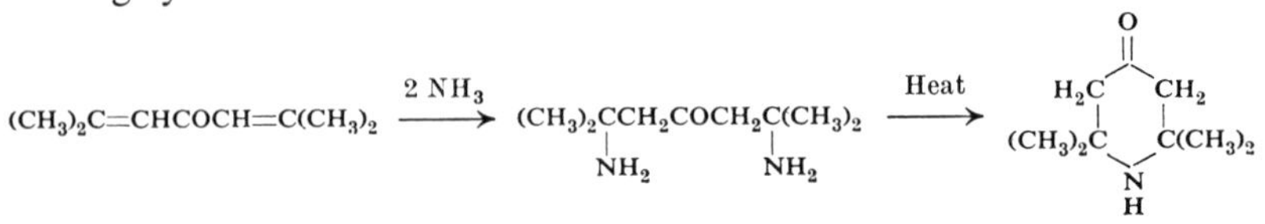

$$(CH_3)_2C{=}CHCOCH{=}C(CH_3)_2 \xrightarrow{2\,NH_3} (CH_3)_2\underset{\underset{NH_2}{|}}{C}CH_2COCH_2\underset{\underset{NH_2}{|}}{C}(CH_3)_2 \xrightarrow{Heat}$$

Phorone   Triacetonediamine   Triacetonamine

Hydrogen cyanide ordinarily adds to carbonyl groups only under anhydrous conditions. Addition of hydrogen cyanide to α,β-unsaturated ketones takes place from aqueous solutions.

$$(CH_3)_2C{=}CHCOCH_3 \xrightarrow[\text{heat}]{HCN} (CH_3)_2\underset{\underset{CN}{|}}{C}CH_2COCH_3$$

Halogen acids give β-halogenated ketones.

$$RCH{=}CHCOR + HX \longrightarrow RCHXCH_2COR$$

α,β-Unsaturated carbonyl compounds undergo also the Michael condensation (p. 803).

Acrolein, $CH_2{=}CHCHO$, the simplest α,β-unsaturated aldehyde, is the most reactive and is the starting point for the manufacture of a large number of technically important compounds. From the time of its discovery in 1843 until 1936, the best method of preparation was the dehydration of glycerol.

$$HOCH_2CHOHCH_2OH \xrightarrow[\text{heat}]{KHSO_4,} [HOCH_2CH{=}CHOH] \longrightarrow [HOCH_2CH_2CHO] \longrightarrow CH_2{=}CHCHO$$

Acrolein

Maximum yields are around 50 per cent, and the procedure does not lend itself to large scale production. Between 1936 and 1949 three commercially feasible processes were developed:

(*1*) Condensation of formaldehyde with acetaldehyde;

$$HCHO + CH_3CHO \xrightarrow[300°]{SiO_2-Na_2SiO_3} [HOCH_2CH_2CHO] \longrightarrow CH_2{=}CHCHO + H_2O$$

(*2*) Pyrolysis of diallyl ether, a co-product in the manufacture of allyl alcohol (p. 738);

$$(CH_2{=}CHCH_2)_2O \xrightarrow{500°} CH_2{=}CHCHO + CH_3CH{=}CH_2$$

(*3*) Catalytic air oxidation of propylene.

$$CH_2{=}CHCH_3 + O_2 \xrightarrow[370°]{Cu_2O} CH_2{=}CHCHO + H_2O$$

Acrolein is a toxic, strongly lachrymatory, volatile liquid, b.p. 53°. It is responsible for the disagreeable nature of the fumes from overheated fats. It can be detected physiologically at a concentration of one part per million and concentrations that would be harmful are unbearable. Acrolein readily undergoes all the usual addition reactions of α,β-unsaturated aldehydes. For example, addition of methyl mercaptan followed by the Strecker synthesis (p. 303) gives DL-methionine.

$$CH_2{=}CHCHO \xrightarrow{CH_3SH} CH_3SCH_2CH_2CHO \xrightarrow{HCN,\ NH_3}$$

$$CH_3SCH_2CH_2CH(NH_2)CN \xrightarrow{H_2O,[H^+]} CH_3SCH_2CH_2CH(NH_2)COOH$$

Acrolein polymerizes readily to resins of high molecular weight, and the monomer is stabilized with hydroquinone (p. 517). If the pure monomer is heated in the absence of air and water, it slowly dimerizes by a Diels-Alder type of addition to give 2-aldehydo-2,3-dihydro-γ-pyran (p. 632). Acrolein can undergo the Diels-Alder reaction acting as the diene with other dienophiles (p. 806), for example the vinyl ethers,

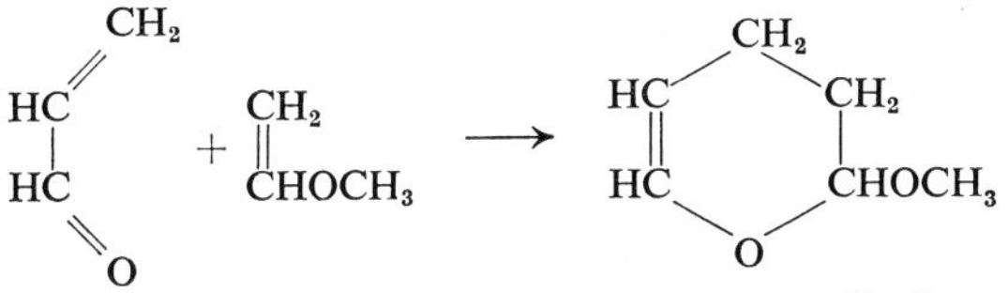

2-Methoxy-2,3-dihydro-γ-pyran

or as the dienophile with other dienes.

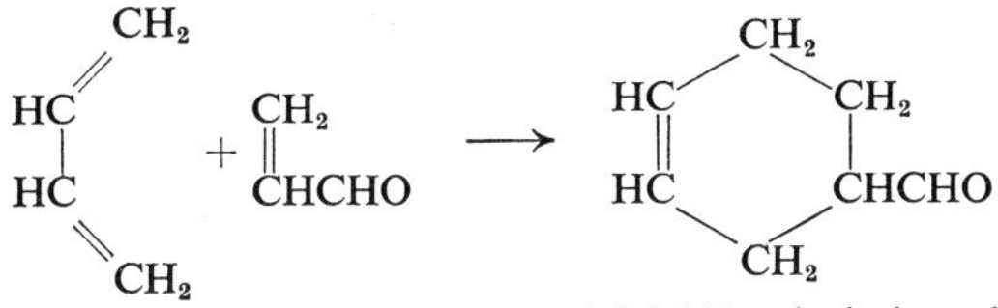

1,2,3,6-Tetrahydrobenzaldehyde

Methyl vinyl ketone, an intermediate in the synthesis of vitamin A (p. 860), cannot be obtained in good yields from formaldehyde and acetone, but is made by the hydration of vinylacetylene (p. 719).

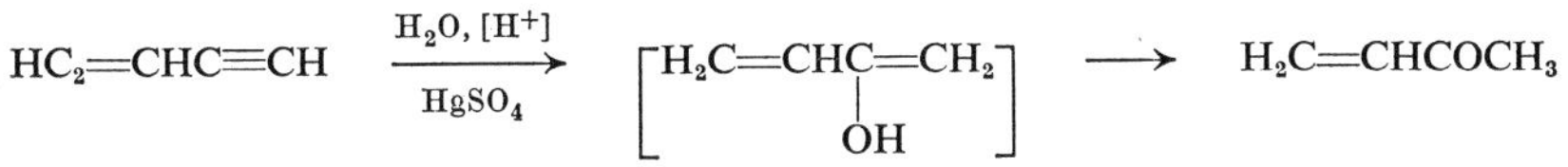

$$HC_2{=}CHC{\equiv}CH \xrightarrow[HgSO_4]{H_2O,\ [H^+]} \left[H_2C{=}CHC{=}CH_2 \atop \qquad\qquad OH\right] \longrightarrow H_2C{=}CHCOCH_3$$

HALOGENATED CARBONYL COMPOUNDS

α-**Halogenated aldehydes** and **ketones** may be prepared by direct halogenation (p. 214). Chloromethyl ketones result from the reaction of acid chlorides and diazomethane, provided the diazomethane is added to the acid chloride, thus insuring that the latter always is in excess (p. 267).

α-Halogenated ketones such as **chloroacetone** and **bromoacetone** are strong lachrymators. It is of interest that 1,3-dichloroacetone is extremely lachrymatory, whereas 1,1-dichloroacetone is not, another example of the *gem*-dihalide effect noted for fluoro compounds (p. 729).

α-Halogenated ketones in general undergo displacement of halogen with great rapidity, the effect of the carbon-oxygen double bond being much greater than that of the carbon-carbon double bond in allyl chloride (p. 728) or benzyl chloride (p. 437). Bases frequently yield acids or esters, a behavior known as the *Favorski rearrangement*.

$$RCH_2COCHR' \xrightarrow{NaOR''} RCH_2CHCOOR'' \text{ and } R'CH_2CHCOOR'' + NaCl$$

(with Cl on first, R' and R substituents shown below)

2,4-Dinitrophenylhydrazine appears to be a specific reagent for the removal of halogen acid to give the hydrazone of the α,β-unsaturated ketone.

$$RCH_2CHCOR + H_2NNHC_6H_3(NO_2)_2 \longrightarrow RCH=CHCR + HCl$$

(with Cl, and =NNHC_6H_3(NO_2)_2)

β-Halogenated ketones can be made by the addition of halogen acid to α,β-unsaturated ketones (p. 764). They are prepared also by the reaction of β-chloroacyl chlorides with alkylzinc halides (p. 893).

$$XCH_2CH_2COX + RZnX \longrightarrow XCH_2CH_2COR + ZnX_2$$

Loss of halogen acid takes place easily to give the α,β-unsaturated ketone.

$$RCHXCH_2COR + (C_2H_5)_2NH \longrightarrow RCH=CHCOR + (C_2H_5)_2NH_2X$$

The addition of an acyl chloride to a double bond in the presence of stannic chloride and subsequent loss of halogen acid resembles the Friedel-Crafts reaction of aromatic hydrocarbons.

$$RCH=CHR + ClCOR' \xrightarrow{SnCl_4} RCHCHR \longrightarrow RCH=CR + HCl$$

(with Cl, COR' substituents and COR')

Acetylene and vinyl chloride yield **β-chloro-α,β-unsaturated ketones.**

$$HC\equiv CH + ClCOR \xrightarrow{AlCl_3} ClCH=CHCOR$$

$$ClCH=CH_2 + ClCOR \xrightarrow{AlCl_3} [Cl_2CHCH_2COR] \longrightarrow ClCH=CHCOR + HCl$$

AMINO KETONES

α-Amino ketones can be prepared from α-halogenated ketones by Gabriel's phthalimide reaction (p. 553).

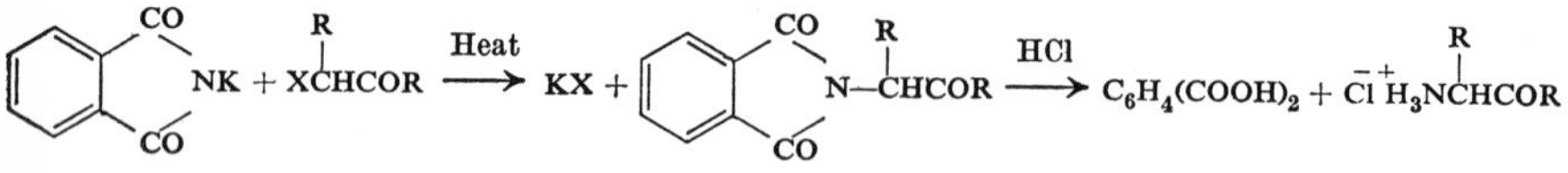

$$\text{(phthalimide)}NK + XCHCOR \xrightarrow{Heat} KX + \text{(phthalimide)}N-CHCOR \xrightarrow{HCl} C_6H_4(COOH)_2 + Cl^- H_3NCHCOR$$

(with R substituents)

They may be prepared also by the reduction of isonitroso derivatives of ketones.

$$RCH_2COR + HONO \longrightarrow \begin{bmatrix} RCHCOR \\ NO \end{bmatrix} \longrightarrow RCCOR \xrightarrow[\text{or Na—Hg}]{Zn—HOAc} RCHCOR$$

(with NOH and NH_2)

α-Amino ketones are stable only as their salts with mineral acids, or as the acetals. The free amino ketones rapidly undergo dehydration and oxidation to pyrazines (p. 641).

The **β-amino ketones** are sufficiently stable to be isolated in the free state. They may be prepared by the addition of ammonia or primary or secondary amines to α,β-unsaturated ketones (p. 764).

Substituted β-amino ketones can be prepared by the Mannich reaction (p. 508). Thus dialkyl- and alkylarylamino ketones result from the condensation of secondary amines with formaldehyde and ketones.

$$RCOCH_2R' + HCHO + HNR_2 \longrightarrow RCOCHR' + H_2O$$
$$\overset{|}{CH_2NR_2}$$

The amine usually is used in the form of the hydrochloride or the reaction may be carried out in glacial acetic acid. Aromatic aldehydes may be used instead of formaldehyde, to give aryl substituted products. If a primary amine is used instead of a secondary amine and the ketone contains a hydrogen atom on both α carbon atoms, a cyclic compound results.

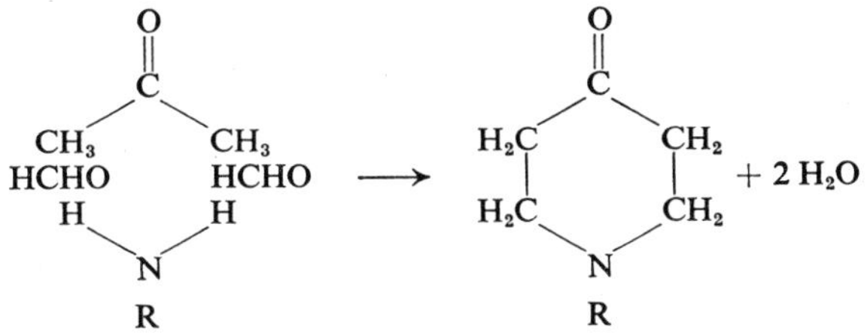

The hydrochlorides of γ- and δ-amino ketones can be prepared from γ- and δ-halogenated ketones, but the free bases cyclize spontaneously to pyrrolines and tetrahydropyridines.

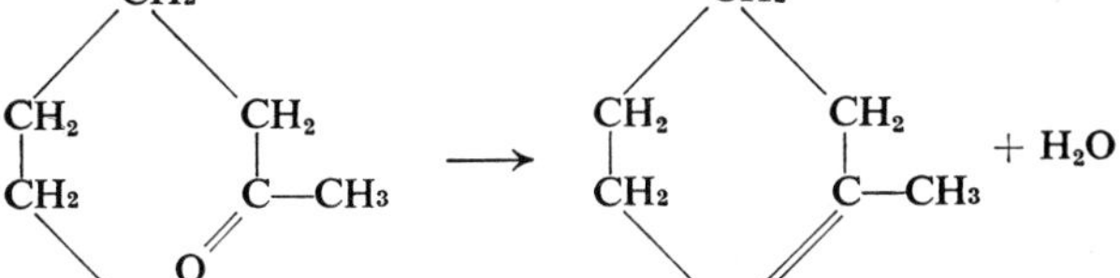

α-Methylpyrroline

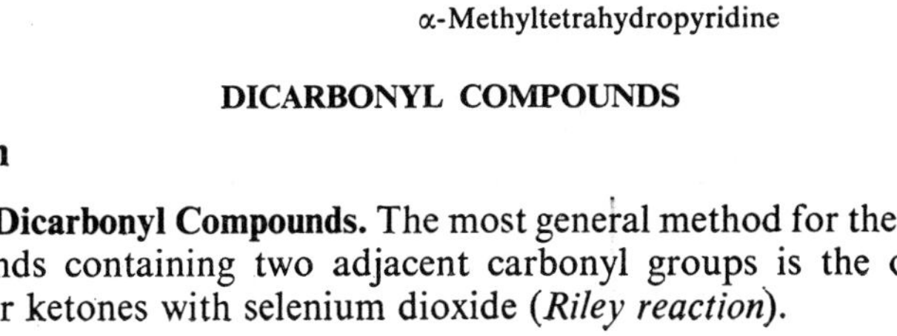

α-Methyltetrahydropyridine

DICARBONYL COMPOUNDS

Preparation

α- or 1,2-Dicarbonyl Compounds. The most general method for the preparation of compounds containing two adjacent carbonyl groups is the oxidation of aldehydes or ketones with selenium dioxide (*Riley reaction*).

$$CH_3CHO + SeO_2 \longrightarrow OCHCHO + H_2O + Se$$
$$\text{Glyoxal}$$

$$CH_3COCH_3 + SeO_2 \longrightarrow CH_3COCHO + H_2O + Se$$
$$\text{Pyruvic}$$
$$\text{aldehyde}$$

$$RCOCH_2R + SeO_2 \longrightarrow RCOCOR + H_2O + Se$$

Another general method is the hydrolysis of the monoximes formed by the nitrosation of ketones.

$$RCOCH_2R + HONO \longrightarrow \begin{bmatrix} RCOCHR \\ | \\ NO \end{bmatrix} \longrightarrow \underset{\underset{NOH}{\parallel}}{RCOCR} \xrightarrow{H_2O-HCl} RCOCOR + HONH_3{}^+Cl^-$$

Pyruvic aldehyde can be made in small amounts by the ozonolysis of benzylideneacetone.

$$C_6H_5CH{=}CHCOCH_3 \xrightarrow{\text{Ozonolysis}} C_6H_5CHO + OCHCOCH_3$$
$$\text{Pyruvic}$$
$$\text{aldehyde}$$

Acyloins and benzoins are oxidized to 1,2-diketones by Fehling solution or by copper sulfate in pyridine (p. 541).

$$RCOCHOHR + 2\ Cu(OH)_2\ \text{(Fehling soln.)} \longrightarrow RCOCOR + Cu_2O + 3\ H_2O$$

An aqueous solution of glyoxal can be obtained by oxidizing ethylene glycol with dilute nitric acid containing some nitrous acid. It is prepared commercially by the vapor phase oxidation of ethylene glycol in the presence of a silver or copper catalyst.

$$HOCH_2CH_2OH + O_2 \xrightarrow[300°]{Ag,\ Cu} OCHCHO + 2\ H_2O$$

β- or 1,3-Dicarbonyl Compounds. The simplest member of this group, **malonic aldehyde,** probably has been obtained in aqueous solution by a complex series of reactions but has not been isolated in a pure state. **1,3-Keto aldehydes** can be prepared by the formylation of ketones using diphenylformamide (cf. p. 533).

$$RCOCH_3 + HCON(C_6H_5)_2 \xrightarrow{NaOC_2H_5} RCOCH_2CHO + (C_6H_5)_2NH$$

1,3-Diketones usually are prepared by the Claisen condensation of esters with ketones (cf. p. 814).

$$RCOCH_3 + C_2H_5OCOR' \xrightarrow[NaNH_2]{NaOC_2H_5\ or} RCOCH_2COR' + C_2H_5OH$$

Acetylation may be brought about also by acetic anhydride and boron fluoride.

$$RCOCH_3 + (CH_3CO)_2O \xrightarrow{BF_3} RCOCH_2COCH_3 + CH_3COOH$$

If both a methyl group and a methylene group are available for acylation, as in methyl ethyl ketone, the ester condensation with alkaline catalysts usually takes place at the methyl group, whereas the boron fluoride catalyzed acylation takes place at the methylene group.

γ- or 1,4-, and δ- or 1,5-Diketones. Higher Diketones. Triketones. The 1,4- and 1,5-diketones are prepared best from β-keto esters (pp. 821, 819). **Glutaric aldehyde** is prepared readily by the hydrolysis of 2-methoxy-2,3-dihydro-γ-pyran (p. 765).

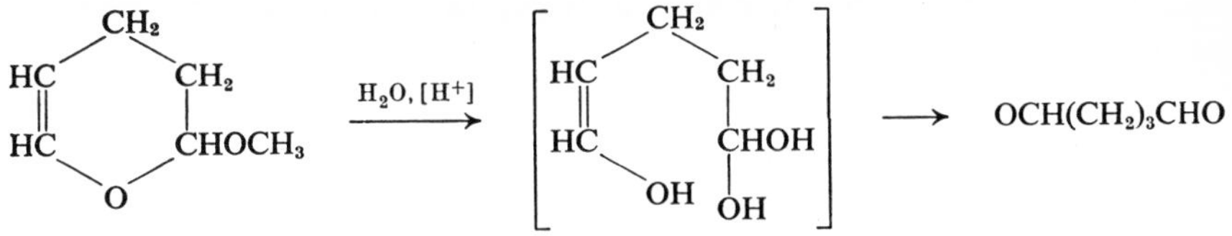

Similarly acrolein dimer (p. 632) yields **α-hydroxyadipic aldehyde.**

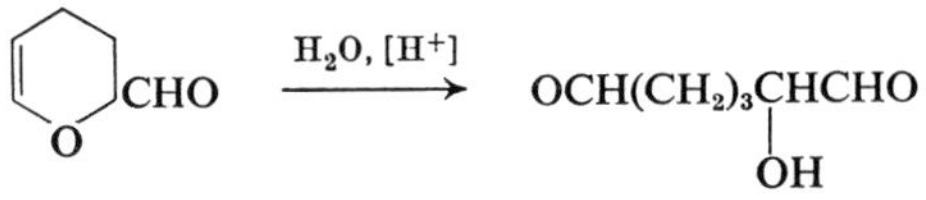

Dialdehydes are used to increase the wet strength of paper and crease resistance of cotton. They cross link the cellulose molecules by forming cyclic acetals with 1,2-hydroxyl groups (p. 741). Dicarbonyl compounds having more than three carbon atoms separating the carbonyl groups can be prepared by the ozonolysis of diolefins, by the Stephen reduction (p. 532) of dinitriles, or by the reaction of diacyl halides with reactive organometallic compounds such as Grignard reagents, alkylzincs or alkylcadmiums.

A few triketones can be prepared readily. Thus reaction of 1,3-diketones with *p*-nitrosodimethylaniline followed by hydrolysis yields **1,2,3-triketones.**

$$\mathrm{RCOCH_2COR + ONC_6H_4N(CH_3)_2 \longrightarrow RCOC(=NC_6H_4N(CH_3)_2)COR \xrightarrow{H_2O-HCl} RCOCOCOR + [H_3\overset{+}{N}C_6H_4\overset{+}{N}H(CH_3)_2]\,2\,Cl^-}$$

Triacylmethanes result from the condensation of acyl halides with the sodium salts (p. 773) of 1,3-diketones.

$$\mathrm{RCOCH_2COR \xrightarrow{NaOC_2H_5} RCO\overset{-}{C}HCOR\ \ \overset{+}{Na} \xrightarrow{R'COCl} RCOCH(COR')COR + NaCl}$$

Properties and Reactions

Besides the usual carbonyl reactions, the polycarbonyl compounds undergo a number of special reactions that depend on the relative position of the functional groups.

α- or 1,2-Dicarbonyl Compounds. Members of this group usually are greenish yellow. They possess a broad absorption band extending from the near ultraviolet into the visible (p. 665).

The position of the maximum depends on the conformation (p. 31) of the molecule. When the two carbon-oxygen bonds are parallel, resonance stabilization due to overlapping of the *p* orbitals is at a maximum and the absorption is at shorter wavelengths than when the carbon-oxygen bonds are at right angles to each other.

The most characteristic property of 1,2-dicarbonyl compounds is their reaction with *o*-phenylenediamine to give quinoxalines.

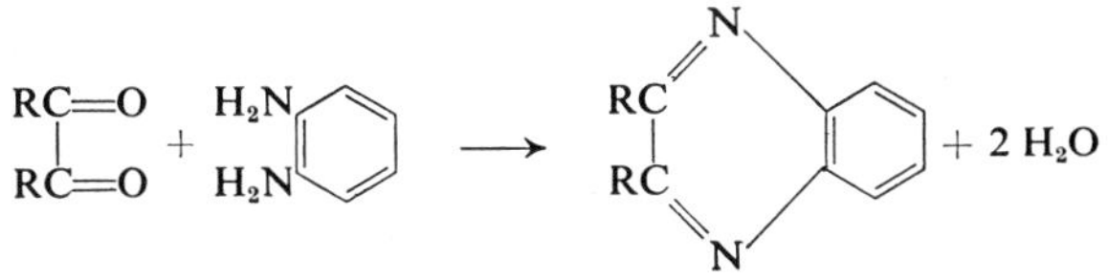

They also are oxidized by alkaline hydrogen peroxide to yield two moles of carboxylic acids.

$$RCOCOR + H_2O_2 \xrightarrow{[OH^-]} 2\,RCOOH$$

Aromatic 1,2-diketones and certain other compounds having adjacent carbonyl groups and lacking α hydrogen atoms undergo the benzilic acid rearrangement (p. 541). Benzil also condenses with ketones having two α methylene groups to give cyclopentadienones.

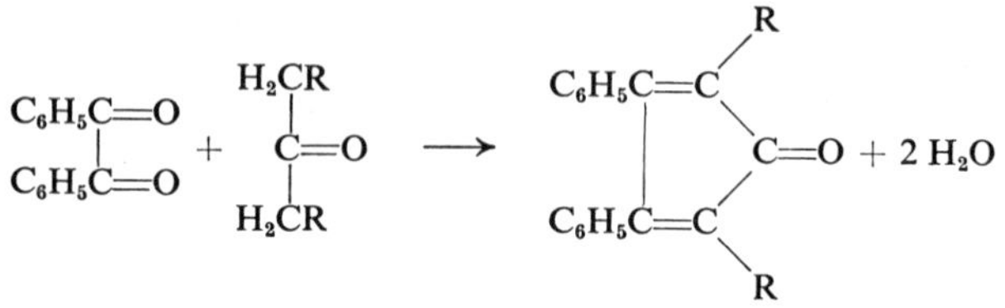

The reaction of 1,2-diketones with an excess of hydroxylamine gives dioximes which form water-insoluble colored chelate compounds (p. 742) with nickel salts. They are used for the qualitative detection and quantitative estimation of nickel.

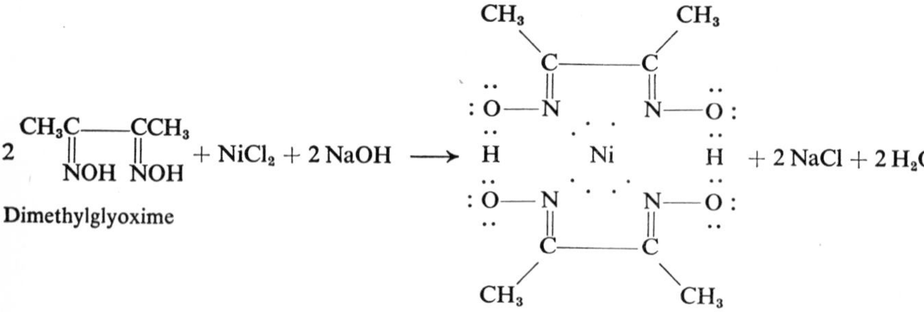

In these nickel complexes all of the atoms of the molecule lie in a plane, the four bonds to the nickel being directed to the corners of a square. As would be expected for a square planar structure, *cis* and *trans* forms of nickel benzylmethylglyoxime have been isolated.

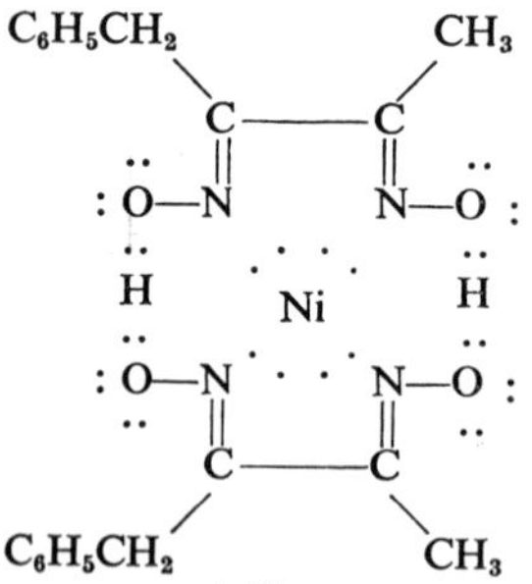

cis Form 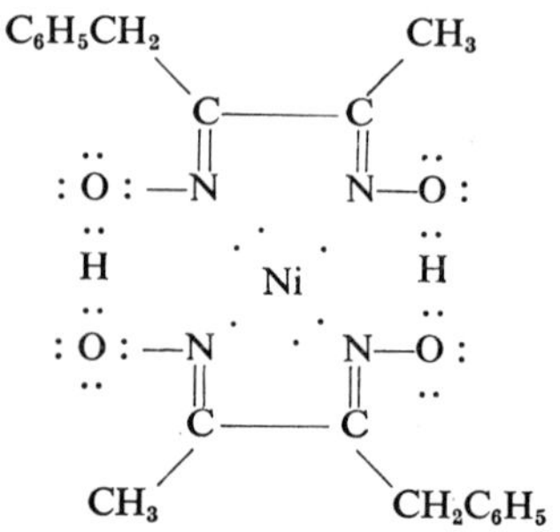   *trans* Form

If the valences of the nickel atom had a tetrahedral distribution, the molecule would be asymmetric giving rise to two optical isomers but not two inactive forms. The square planar distribution of the bonds of nickel is the result of the hybridization of one *3d*, the *4s*, and two *4p* orbitals. Tetracovalent palladium and platinum also have the square planar configuration resulting from dsp^2 hybridization (p. 357).

The yellow phenylosazones of 1,2-dicarbonyl compounds are oxidized by ferric chloride to red **dihydrotetrazines** (osotetrazines).

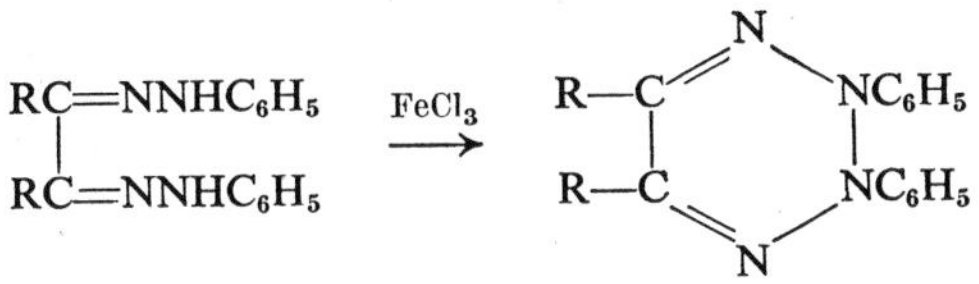

$$RC{=}NNHC_6H_5 \quad \xrightarrow{FeCl_3} \quad$$

An osotetrazine (red)

Glyoxal is manufactured commercially on a large scale. The anhydrous monomeric compound polymerizes rapidly even at a low temperature, but its aqueous solutions and the bisulfite addition compound are fairly stable. An aqueous solution of glyoxal is colorless indicating that it is present as the hydrate, $OCHCH(OH)_2$ or $(HO)_2CHCH(OH)_2$. It is used as a reducing agent in the spray process for silvering mirrors, but its most important use is for shrink-proofing rayon fabrics. This property probably results from the ability to cross link the cellulose chains by forming cyclic acetals.

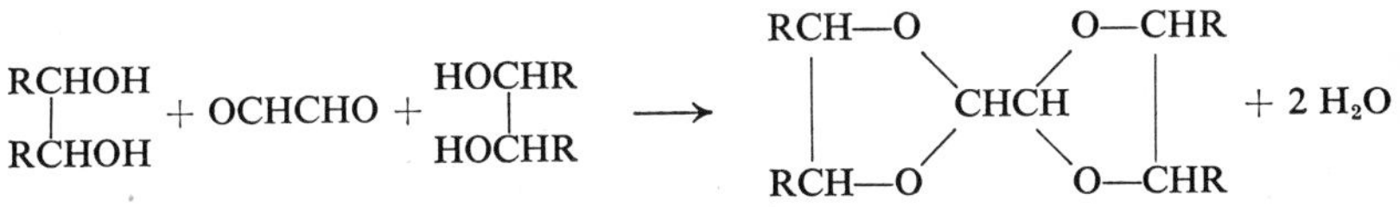

Glyoxal also increases the wet strength and absorbency of paper and can be used to render starch and proteins insoluble. Reaction of glyoxal with alkali brings about an internal Cannizzaro reaction with the formation of **sodium glycolate**.

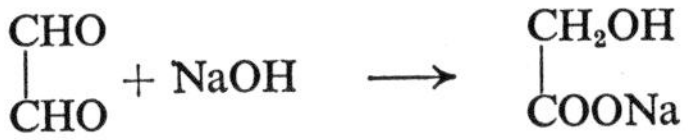

Reductone, $HOCH_2COCHO$, is isolated from alkaline glucose solution (p. 369) as the lead salt. It appears to exist largely in the enediol form, and in alkaline solution is a strong reducing agent. **Diacetyl**, $CH_3COCOCH_3$, is present in small amounts in butter and along with the acyloin, **acetylmethylcarbinol**, $CH_3COCHOHCH_3$, is responsible for the characteristic flavor of butter. They are used as flavoring agents for oleomargarine.

β- or 1,3-Dicarbonyl Compounds. A methylene group united to two carbonyl groups is said to be *active*. The difference between the reactions of an active methylene group and of a methylene group joined to a single carbonyl group merely is one of degree, two activating groups being more effective than one. Just as hydrogen on a carbon atom α to a carbonyl group in aldehydes and ketones is more acidic than that in a hydrocarbon, so the hydrogen in an active methylene group is more acidic than the α hydrogen atoms in aldehydes and ketones. Thus whereas most simple ketones add methylmagnesium bromide to the carbonyl group, 1,3-diketones evolve one mole of methane. Simple ketones are stronger acids than ammonia but weaker than alcohol, since they form salts with sodium amide but not with sodium ethoxide. 1,3-Diketones are stronger acids than alcohol since sodium ethoxide converts them into sodium salts.

The **enol form of the 1,3-diketones** is more stable than that of the simple ketones. Hence appreciable quantities of both enol and keto forms of 1,3-diketones can exist in equilibrium with each other. In fact acetylacetone is present in the enol form to the extent of 20 per cent in aqueous solutions and 92 per cent in hexane solution.

$$CH_3COCH_2COCH_3 \rightleftarrows CH_3COCH=COHCH_3$$

This behavior is understandable since in the enol form the carbon-carbon double bond is in conjugation with the second carbonyl group. Because of the presence of the enol form, the 1,3-diketones give a red color with ferric chloride solutions, a reaction analogous to that of the phenols.

With metallic ions having room in their valence shell for more than one pair of electrons, the location of the second carbonyl group is such that after salt formation with the enolic hydroxyl, the second carbonyl group can coordinate with the metallic atom to give a stable five-membered chelate ring (p. 742). Thus a characteristic reaction is the formation of blue copper compounds having two chelate rings.

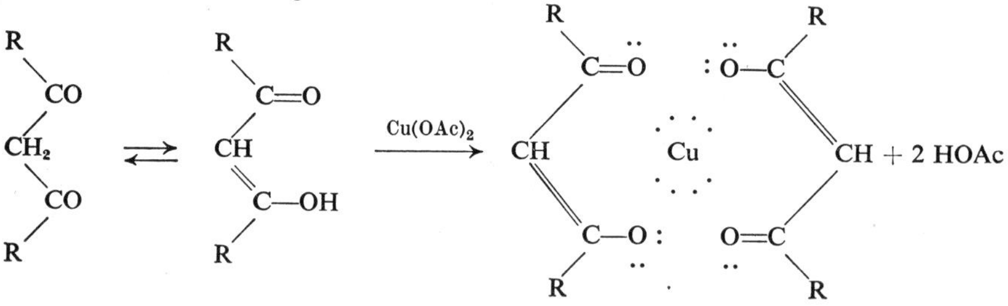

These metallic complexes do not have the properties of salts but behave like covalent compounds. Thus they are soluble in organic solvents, have sharp melting points, and can be distilled without decomposition. The beryllium complex of acetylacetone, $Be(C_5H_7O_2)_2$, melts at $108°$ and boils at $270°$, and the aluminum complex, $Al(C_5H_7O_2)_3$, melts at $193°$ and boils at $214°$. The cupric complexes are planar with the metal bonds directed to the corners of a square, whereas in the beryllium complexes, the bonds are directed to the corners of a tetrahedron. If the metal is hexacovalent as in the aluminum complex, the bonds are directed to the corners of an octahedron (p. 352).

In reactions with one mole of carbonyl reagents, five- or six-membered heterocyclic compounds frequently are formed, the initial condensation product cyclizing with loss of water. Thus phenylhydrazine gives *N*-phenylpyrazoles (p. 634).

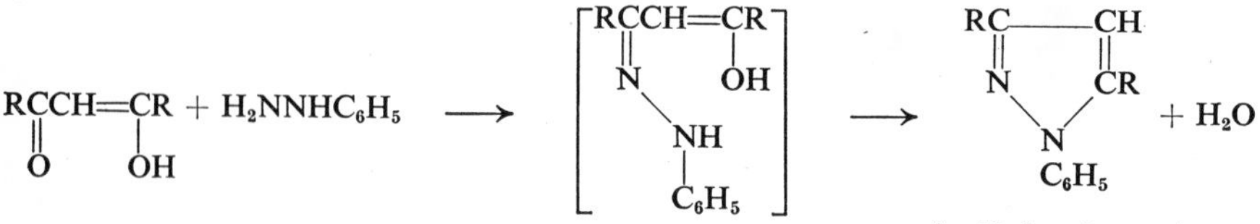

An *N*-phenylpyrazole

Hydroxylamine gives isoxazoles (p. 635).

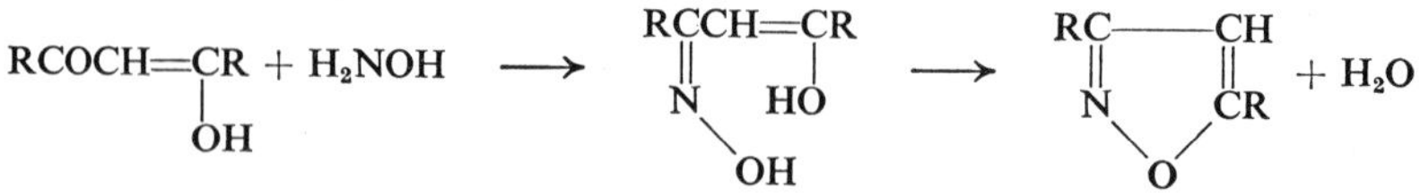

An isoxazole

Aromatic amines give quinolines (p. 628).

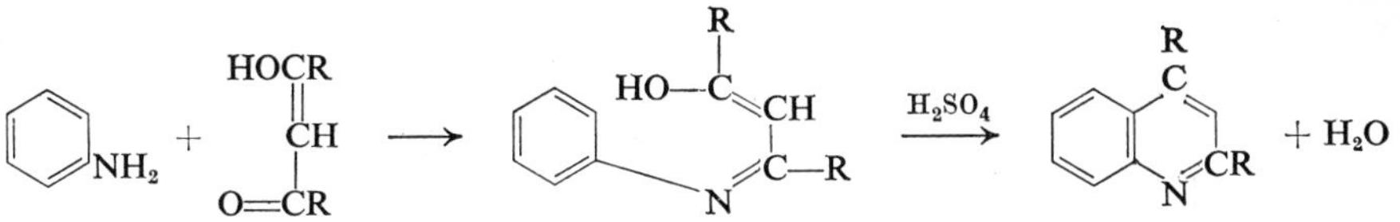

A quinoline

β-Diketones add to aldehydes to give ketols which frequently lose water and form α,β-unsaturated diketones. Secondary amines such as diethylamine or piperidine, together with a small amount of a carboxylic acid usually present as an impurity in the aldehyde, are the preferred catalysts for these condensations.

$$R'CHO + H_2C(COR)_2 \xrightarrow[\substack{C_5H_{10}NH \\ + RCOOH}]{(C_2H_5)_2NH \text{ or}} \left[\begin{array}{c} R'CHCH(COR)_2 \\ | \\ OH \end{array} \right] \longrightarrow R'CH{=}C(COR)_2 + H_2O$$

These reactions merely reflect the ease with which a proton can be removed from active methylene groups. However the condensation of active methylene compounds with aldehydes and ketones in the presence of secondary amines is sufficiently characteristic to be known as the Knoevenagel[1] reaction after its chief investigator.

One of the characteristic reactions of compounds containing an active methylene group is *carbon alkylation*. This reaction usually is brought about by forming the sodium salt of the diketone with sodium ethoxide in absolute alcohol solution, and adding an alkyl halide.

$$RCOCH_2COR \xrightarrow{NaOC_2H_5} [RCO\bar{C}HCOR]\,Na^+ \xrightarrow{R'X} \underset{\underset{R'}{|}}{RCOCHCOR} + NaX$$

The second hydrogen also may be alkylated.

$$\underset{\underset{R'}{|}}{RCOCHCOR} \xrightarrow{NaOC_2H_5} [RCO\bar{C}R'COR]\,Na^+ \xrightarrow{R''X} \underset{\underset{R''}{|}}{RCOCR'COR} + NaX$$

Acetonylacetone reacts with alkyl halides merely by warming in alcohol solution in the presence of potassium carbonate. These reactions are useful for the synthesis of the more complex 1,3-diketones.

The metallic salt of a 1,3-diketone is an ionic compound, and the anion is a resonance hybrid of two extreme structures.

$$\left\{ \begin{array}{ccc} \underset{\underset{:\ddot{O}:^-}{|}}{RCOCH{=}CR} & \longleftrightarrow & \underset{\underset{\ddot{O}}{\|}}{RCO\overset{..}{\ddot{C}}H{-}CR} \end{array} \right\}$$

Whether carbon alkylation or oxygen alkylation takes place depends on the relative effectiveness of attack at the carbon or oxygen end of the resonance hybrid. With alkyl halides attack at the

---

[1] Heinrich Emil Albert Knoevenagel (1865–1921), professor at Heidelberg. He is known chiefly for his work on the condensation reactions of aldehydes and ketones.

carbon end is most effective. When ethyl chloroformate reacts with the sodium salt of acetyl-acetone, however, the chief product is the ethyl carbonate of the enol form together with a small amount of the carbethoxy derivative of the diketone.

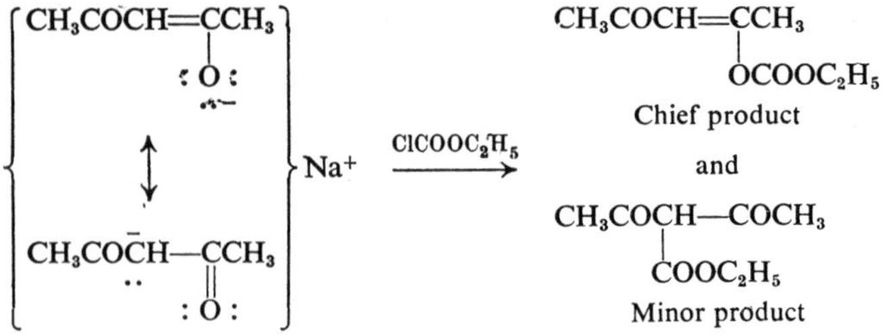

$$\left\{ \begin{array}{c} CH_3COCH=CCH_3 \\ :\overset{..}{O}: \\ \\ \updownarrow \\ \\ CH_3CO\overset{H}{C}H-CCH_3 \\ \overset{..}{\underset{..}{:O:}} \end{array} \right\} Na^+ \quad \xrightarrow{ClCOOC_2H_5} \quad$$

$$CH_3COCH=CCH_3$$
$$\overset{|}{O}COOC_2H_5$$
Chief product

and

$$CH_3COCH-COCH_3$$
$$\overset{|}{C}OOC_2H_5$$
Minor product

When the metallic derivatives are more nearly covalent compounds as are the silver salts, O-alkylation is the chief reaction even with alkyl halides.

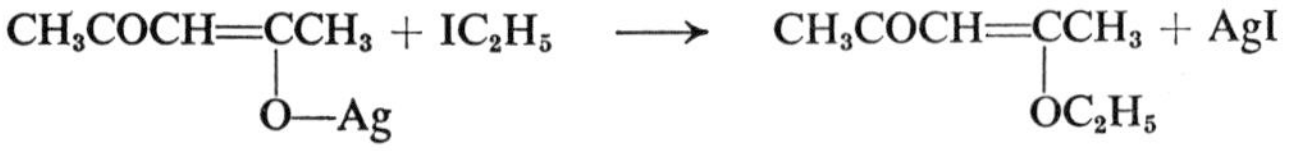

$$CH_3COCH=CCH_3 + IC_2H_5 \longrightarrow CH_3COCH=CCH_3 + AgI$$
$$\overset{|}{O}-Ag \qquad\qquad\qquad \overset{|}{O}C_2H_5$$

The condensation reactions of β-diketones are for the most part dependent on the active hydrogen present in the diketone and do not take place with disubstituted diketones of the type $RCOCR_2COR$. All β-diketones, however, undergo ready scission of a carbon-carbon bond by concentrated aqueous alkali to give one molecule of the salt of a carboxylic acid and one molecule of a simple ketone. If the two acyl groups are different, the smaller or less highly branched R' group appears in the carboxylic acid.

$$R'COCR_2COR'' + NaOH \longrightarrow R'COONa + R_2CHCOR''$$

The mechanism of this reaction is analogous to that for the alkaline saponification of an ester (p. 171). The hydroxide ion attacks a carbonyl carbon and displaces an acetonyl anion.

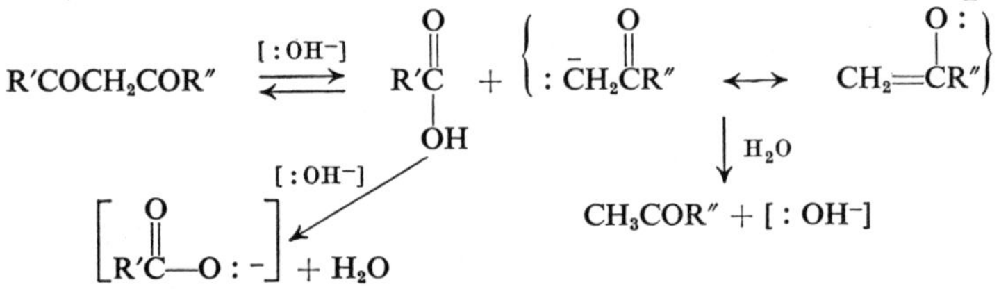

$$R'COCH_2COR'' \underset{[:OH^-]}{\overset{[:OH^-]}{\rightleftharpoons}} R'\overset{O}{\overset{||}{C}} + \left\{ :\overset{O}{\overset{||}{CH_2CR''}} \longleftrightarrow CH_2=\overset{\overset{..}{O}:^-}{CR''} \right\}$$
$$\overset{|}{OH}$$

$$\left[R'\overset{O}{\overset{||}{C}}-O:^- \right] + H_2O \qquad\qquad \downarrow H_2O$$

$$CH_3COR'' + [:OH^-]$$

The easy displacement of the acetonyl anion may be ascribed to the electron-attracting power of the second carbonyl group and to the stabilization of the ion by resonance. The reaction is the reverse of the formation of a 1,3-diketone from an ester and a ketone.

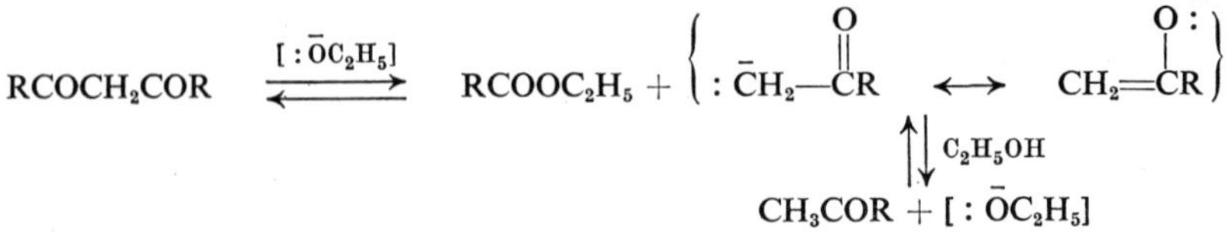

$$RCOCH_2COR \underset{[:\overset{..}{O}C_2H_5]}{\overset{[:\overset{..}{O}C_2H_5]}{\rightleftharpoons}} RCOOC_2H_5 + \left\{ :\overset{O}{\overset{||}{CH_2-CR}} \longleftrightarrow CH_2=\overset{\overset{..}{O}:^-}{CR} \right\}$$
$$\updownarrow C_2H_5OH$$
$$CH_3COR + [:\overset{..}{O}C_2H_5]$$

Whereas the latter reaction is reversible, that with water and alkali is not, since the formation of the sodium salt takes place irreversibly.

γ- or 1,4-Dicarbonyl Compounds. The characteristic behavior of γ-dicarbonyl compounds is their ready conversion into furans (p. 620), thiophenes (p. 607), and pyrrols (p. 610). These reactions may be considered as taking place through the enol forms, although unlike the β-dicarbonyl compounds, no detectable amount of the enol form is present.

$$
\begin{array}{ccc}
\text{H}_2\text{C}\!-\!\text{CH}_2 \\
\text{RC} \quad\quad \text{CR} \\
\parallel \quad\quad\quad \parallel \\
\text{O} \quad\quad\quad \text{O}
\end{array}
\;\rightleftarrows\;
\begin{array}{c}
\text{H}_2\text{C}\!-\!\text{CH} \\
\text{RC} \quad\quad \text{CR} \\
\parallel \quad\quad\quad \diagdown \\
\text{O} \quad\quad \text{O} \\
\quad\quad\quad\quad \text{H}
\end{array}
\;\xrightarrow[\text{HCl}]{\text{Conc.}}\;
\begin{array}{c}
\text{H}_2\text{C}\!-\!\text{CH} \\
\text{HO}\diagdown\!\!\text{C} \quad \text{CR} \\
\text{R}\diagup \quad\quad \diagup \\
\quad\quad \text{O}
\end{array}
\;\rightarrow\;
\begin{array}{c}
\text{HC}\!-\!\text{CH} \\
\text{RC} \quad\quad \text{CR} \\
\diagdown \quad\quad \diagup \\
\quad\quad \text{O}
\end{array}
+ \text{H}_2\text{O}
$$

(via P₂S₅, heat →)

$$
\begin{array}{c}
\text{H}_2\text{C}\!-\!\text{CH} \\
\text{RC} \quad\quad \text{CR} \\
\parallel \quad\quad\quad \diagdown \\
\text{O} \quad\quad \text{S} \\
\quad\quad\quad \text{H}
\end{array}
\;\rightarrow\;
\begin{array}{c}
\text{H}_2\text{C}\!-\!\text{CH} \\
\text{HO}\diagdown\!\!\text{C} \quad \text{CR} \\
\text{R}\diagup \quad\quad \diagup \\
\quad\quad \text{S}
\end{array}
\;\rightarrow\;
\begin{array}{c}
\text{HC}\!-\!\text{CH} \\
\text{RC} \quad\quad \text{CR} \\
\diagdown \quad\quad \diagup \\
\quad\quad \text{S}
\end{array}
+ 2\,\text{HPOS}_2
$$

(via NH₃, heat (sealed tube) →)

$$
\begin{array}{c}
\text{H}_2\text{C}\!-\!\text{CH}_2 \\
\text{RC} \quad\quad \text{CR} \\
\parallel \quad\quad\quad \diagup \\
\text{O} \quad\quad \text{N} \quad \text{OH} \\
\quad\quad\quad \text{H}_2
\end{array}
\;\rightarrow\;
\begin{array}{c}
\text{H}_2\text{C}\!-\!\text{CH} \\
\text{RC} \quad\quad \text{CR} \\
\parallel \quad\quad\quad \diagup \\
\text{O} \quad\quad \text{N} \\
\quad\quad\quad \text{H}_2
\end{array}
\;\rightarrow\;
\begin{array}{c}
\text{H}_2\text{C}\!-\!\text{CH} \\
\text{HO}\diagdown\!\!\text{C} \quad \text{CR} \\
\text{R}\diagup \quad\quad \diagup \\
\quad\quad \text{N} \\
\quad\quad \text{H}
\end{array}
\;\rightarrow\;
\begin{array}{c}
\text{HC}\!-\!\text{CH} \\
\text{RC} \quad\quad \text{CR} \\
\diagdown \quad\quad \diagup \\
\quad\quad \text{N} \\
\quad\quad \text{H}
\end{array}
+ 2\,\text{H}_2\text{O}
$$

The formation of pyrroles has been used as a test for 1,4-diketones, since the pyrrole can be detected easily by the pine splint test (p. 610).

δ- or 1,5-Dicarbonyl Compounds. If a methylene group is adjacent to one of the carbonyl groups on the side more distant from the second carbonyl group in a 1,5-diketone, intramolecular aldol addition and loss of water takes place so readily with the formation of a six-membered ring that the diketone is unknown.

$$
\begin{array}{c}
\quad\quad \text{CH}_3 \\
\text{CH}_2\!-\!\text{C} \\
\text{CH}_2 \quad\quad\quad \text{O} \\
\quad\quad \text{CH}_3 \\
\text{CH}_2\!-\!\text{C} \\
\quad\quad \parallel \\
\quad\quad \text{O}
\end{array}
\;\rightarrow\;
\begin{array}{c}
\quad\quad \text{CH}_3 \\
\text{CH}_2\!-\!\text{C} \\
\text{CH}_2 \quad\quad\quad \text{CH} \\
\text{CH}_2\!-\!\text{C} \\
\quad\quad \parallel \\
\quad\quad \text{O}
\end{array}
+ \text{H}_2\text{O}
$$

If a reaction that should lead to a 1,5-diketone is carried out in the presence of ammonia, dihydropyridines are formed.

$$
\left[
\begin{array}{c}
\quad\quad\quad \text{R} \\
\text{CH}_2\!-\!\text{C} \\
\text{CH}_2 \quad\quad\quad \text{O} \\
\text{CH}_2\!-\!\text{C} \\
\quad\quad\quad \text{O} \\
\quad\quad\quad \text{R}
\end{array}
\right]
\;\rightleftharpoons\;
\left[
\begin{array}{c}
\quad\quad\quad \text{R} \\
\text{CH}\!=\!\text{C} \\
\text{CH}_2 \quad\quad\quad \text{OH} \\
\text{CH}\!=\!\text{C} \\
\quad\quad\quad \text{OH} \\
\quad\quad\quad \text{R}
\end{array}
\right]
\;\xrightarrow{\text{NH}_3}\;
\begin{array}{c}
\quad\quad\quad \text{R} \\
\text{CH}\!=\!\text{C} \\
\text{CH}_2 \quad\quad\quad \text{NH} \\
\text{CH}\!=\!\text{C} \\
\quad\quad\quad \text{R}
\end{array}
$$

Hydroxylamine yields a pyridine derivative.

$$
\left[
\begin{array}{c}
\text{CH=C}^{R}\\
\text{CH}_2 \quad\quad \text{OH}\\
\text{OH}\\
\text{CH=C}\\
R
\end{array}
\right]
\xrightarrow{\text{H}_2\text{NOH}}
\left[
\begin{array}{c}
\text{CH=C}^{R}\\
\text{CH}_2 \quad\quad \text{NOH}\\
\text{CH=C}\\
R
\end{array}
\right]
\longrightarrow
\begin{array}{c}
\text{CH=C}^{R}\\
\text{CH} \quad\quad \text{N} + \text{H}_2\text{O}\\
\text{CH—C}\\
R
\end{array}
$$

ε- or 1,6-Dicarbonyl Compounds. These compounds are more stable than the δ-compounds and can be isolated. Those having a methylene group adjacent to a carbonyl group on the side near the second carbonyl group undergo internal cyclization to a five-membered ring.

$$
\begin{array}{c}
\text{CH}_2\text{—CR}\\
\text{CH}_2 \quad\ \ \text{O}\\
\text{CH}_2\text{—CH}_2\text{COR}
\end{array}
\longrightarrow
\begin{array}{c}
\text{CH}_2\text{—CR}\\
\text{CH}_2\\
\text{CH}_2\text{—CCOR}
\end{array}
+ \text{H}_2\text{O}
$$

REVIEW QUESTIONS

1. Compare the properties of α,β-unsaturated ketones with the properties of simple ketones and simple unsaturated compounds.
2. What reactions may be used to distinguish between α-, β-, and γ-diketones?
3. Discuss the space arrangements of the bonds in the metallic complexes of the 1,2-dioximes and the 1,3-diketones.
4. Why does a 1,5-dicarbonyl compound frequently undergo cyclization to a six-membered ring compound, whereas a 1,6-dicarbonyl compound under similar conditions gives rise to a five-membered ring?
5. Why does o-phenylenediamine give quinoxalines readily with 1,2-dicarbonyl compounds but m- and p-phenylenediamine do not?

PROBLEMS

6. List the names of the compounds that can be formed by the addition to ketene of simple inorganic compounds or organic compounds having one or two carbon atoms.
7. Give reactions for the following syntheses: (a) a mixture of D-threose and D-erythrose starting with D-mannitol; (b) 2-methyl-2-hydroxy-3-pentanone starting with acetone; (c) β-bromocaproic acid starting with n-butyraldehyde; (d) 2,2,6,6-tetramethyl-4-piperidone starting with acetone; (e) α-phenyl-γ-ketovaleric acid starting with benzaldehyde; (f) dimethylketene starting with i-butyraldehyde.
8. Give reactions for the following conversions: (a) propionic acid to ethyl vinyl ketone; (b) acetophenone to α-aminoacetophenone; (c) ethyl ketone to 1,3,5-trimethyl-4-piperidone; (d) tetramethylene chlorohydrin to 5-chloro-2-pentanone; (e) acetylene to crotonic aldehyde; (f) toluene to cinnamic aldehyde; (g) benzene to β-dimethylaminopropiophenone.
9. Construct a chart showing the steps, including other necessary reagents and conditions, for the conversion of acrolein into the following compounds: S-methyl-β-mercaptopropionaldehyde, 2-formyl-2,3-dihydropyran, 2,3-dihydroxypropional, 2-tetrahydropyranylcarbinol, glycerol, 2-methoxy-2,3-dihydropyran, methionine, 3-cyanopropional, glutaric aldehyde, 4-amino-1-butanol, and α-hydroxyadipic aldehyde.
10. Give a series of reactions by which sebacic acid could be converted into: (a) 1,8-octanedial, (b) 1,10-decanediol; (c) 1,12-dodecanedial; and (d) 2,11-dodecanedione.
11. Making use of a dicarbonyl compound, give reactions for the following syntheses: (a) 3, 4-diphenylcyclopentadienone from benzaldehyde; (b) 2,3-dimethylquinoxaline from ethyl

acetate and benzene; (c) dimethylglyoxime from methyl ethyl ketone; (d) 2,4-dimethyl-quinoline from acetone; (e) ethyldibenzoylmethane from acetophenone; (f) 2,5-dimethyl-thiophene from 2,5-dimethylfuran; (g) 5-phenylisoxazole from acetophenone.

12. How could one distinguish readily between the members of the following groups of compounds: (a) acetoin, diacetyl, and acetylacetone; (b) acetylacetone, acetonylacetone, and acetophenone; (c) dibenzoylmethane, benzophenone, and diphenylmethane?

13. Give reactions for the following syntheses: (a) 2′-methyl-2′-hydroxybutyrophenone from methyl ethyl ketone; (b) 4-hydroxy-4-methyl-1-hexen-5-one from ethyl acetate; (c) 2-methylvinyl phenyl ketone from benzene; (d) 2,5-diethyl-3,6-dimethylpyrazine from diethyl ketone; 2,6-dimethylpyridine from ethyl acetate.

14. Compound A has the molecular formula $C_{17}H_{32}O_4$. It is not affected by boiling with alkali, does not absorb in the ultraviolet, and does not evolve methane with methylmagnesium bromide. Boiling with dilute sulfuric acid gives two products, B and C. B has the molecular formula $C_5H_8O_2$. It reacts with hydroxylamine, but the product, D, is stable to hydrolysis and cannot be oxidized. D is basic but does not react with benzenesulfonyl chloride in the presence of sodium hydroxide. It is reduced by sodium and alcohol to compound E, which reacts with benzoyl chloride to give a benzoyl derivative. B takes up two moles of hydrogen on catalytic reduction, and the product reacts with phosphorus tribromide to give the compound $C_5H_{10}Br_2$. When this compound is heated with aqueous ammonia, evaporated to dryness, and the residue strongly heated, a product distills that is identical with E.

Compound C has the molecular formula $C_6H_{12}O$. It forms an oxime and reacts with sodium hypochlorite to give chloroform. Acidification gives an acid identical with that obtained by the carbonation of the Grignard reagent from t-butyl chloride. Give a structural formula for A and equations for the reactions that take place.

Chapter 36

HALOGENATED, HYDROXY, AMINO, AND UNSATURATED ACIDS

It is convenient to group the halogenated, hydroxy, amino, and unsaturated acids together, because they frequently are interconvertible, and their reactions often yield the same type of product.

HALOGENATED ACIDS

Preparation

α-Chloro and bromo acids are prepared by the Hell-Volhard-Zelinsky reaction, which involves a direct halogenation in the presence of a small amount of phosphorus trihalide (p. 162).

$$RCH_2COOH \xrightarrow[\text{(PX}_3\text{)}]{X_2} RCHXCOOH + HX$$

The rate of halogenation of acids, unlike the halogenation of aldehydes and ketones, is dependent on the concentration of the halogen, is not subject to general acid catalysis, and is increased greatly by the presence of a small amount of acyl halide. Hence it is believed that the halogenation takes place through the acyl halide. Because of the equilibrium between the acid and the acyl halide, a small amount of the latter suffices to permit the reaction to take place at a practical rate.

$$RCH_2COX + X_2 \longrightarrow RCHXCOX + HX$$

$$RCHXCOX + RCH_2COOH \rightleftharpoons RCHXCOOH + RCH_2COX$$

Monoiodo acids result from the reaction of the chloro acid with sodium iodide (p. 113). **Fluoroacetic acid** has been prepared by the hydrolysis of its methyl ester. The latter was obtained by the reaction of the iodo ester with mercurous fluoride (p. 731). Fluoroacetic acid is made commercially by the direct combination of carbon monoxide, formaldehyde and hydrogen fluoride.

$$CO + HCHO + HF \xrightarrow[\text{750 at.}]{160°,} FCH_2COOH$$

Trifluoroacetic acid results in 50 per cent yield from the vigorous oxidation of benzotrifluoride.

$$C_6H_5CF_3 \xrightarrow[\text{boil 2 weeks}]{Na_2Cr_2O_7—H_2SO_4,} HOOCCF_3 + 5 CO_2 + 2 H_2O$$

This method demonstrates the remarkable stability of the trifluoromethyl group. Commercially, trifluoroacetic acid is made from acetic acid by the electrochemical process (p. 732).

Distillation of trifluoroacetic acid from phosphorus pentoxide gives the **anhydride** which is a useful reagent for bringing about acylation and sulfonation by carboxylic and sulfonic acids.

$$ROH + R'COOH + (CF_3CO)_2O \longrightarrow ROCOR' + 2 CF_3COOH$$

778

Reaction apparently takes place by way of the mixed anhydride but no trifluoroacetylation occurs.

β-Chloro or **bromo acids** are made by the addition of halogen acids to α,β-unsaturated acids or by the reaction of β-hydroxy acids with halogen acids.

Hydrogen halide always adds to the β carbon atom of an α-β-unsaturated acid regardless of the prediction of the Markovnikov rule, because of 1,4 addition.

$$RCH{=}\overset{\overset{\displaystyle O:}{\|}}{\underset{\underset{\displaystyle R}{|}}{C}}OH \xrightarrow[{[:X^-]}]{HX} \left[RCH{=}\overset{\overset{\displaystyle +OH}{\|}}{\underset{\underset{\displaystyle R}{|}}{C}}OH \longleftrightarrow R\overset{+}{C}H\overset{\overset{\displaystyle OH}{|}}{\underset{\underset{\displaystyle R}{|}}{C}}{=}C{-}OH \right] \underset{\longleftarrow}{\overset{[:X^-]}{\rightleftharpoons}}$$

$$\left[RCH{=}\overset{\overset{\displaystyle OH}{|}}{\underset{\underset{\displaystyle X\;R}{|\;\;|}}{C}}{-}OH \right] \longrightarrow R\overset{|}{\underset{\underset{\displaystyle X\;\;R}{}}{C}}HCHCOOH$$

γ-Halogen acids result from the reaction of γ-hydroxy acids or γ-lactones with halogen acid. **ω-Halogen acids** are obtained from α, ω-dihalides by reaction with one mole of sodium cyanide and hydrolysis of the nitrile.

$$Br(CH_2)_xBr + NaCN \longrightarrow Br(CH_2)_xCN \xrightarrow{HBr{-}H_2O} Br(CH_2)_xCOOH + NH_4Br$$

Properties and Reactions

Increasing substitution by halogen on the α carbon atom increases the acidity of carboxylic acids. The dissociation constants for acetic, chloro-, dichloro-, and trichloroacetic acids are respectively 1.7×10^{-5}, 1.4×10^{-3}, 5×10^{-2}, and 1.3×10^{-1}. Thus trichloroacetic acid is almost as strong as sulfuric acid. Trifluoroacetic acid is considerably stronger than trichloroacetic acid. Only halogen in the α position has an appreciable effect on the acidity of the carboxyl group.

The sodium salts of the perfluoro higher fatty acids are much more effective than other wetting agents in lowering the surface tension of aqueous solutions. They act as emulsifying agents, however, only for other fluorinated liquids or solids because the fluorocarbon chain is not soluble in nonfluorinated compounds.

Chloroacetic acid is toxic to microorganisms at very low concentrations and is an excellent sterilizing agent. Its use as a food preservative is prohibited in the United States. Fluoroacetic acid is much more toxic to mammals than chloroacetic acid, and its sodium salt, known as *1080*, is used as a poison for rodents and other wild animal pests. In contrast sodium di- and trifluoroacetates are reported to be harmless (cf. p. 729). It is of interest that fluoroacetic acid is the toxic principle of the poisonous South African plant *Dichapetalum cymosum*. Apparently fluoroacetate ion is not toxic in itself, but it is converted by the organism into fluorocitric acid which blocks the citric acid portion of the cycle involved in the metabolism of carbohydrates.

Trichloroacetic acid decomposes thermally into chloroform and carbon dioxide (cf. haloform reaction, p. 214).

$$Cl_3CCOOH \xrightarrow{Heat} Cl_3CH + CO_2$$

This reaction takes place slowly even on boiling aqueous solutions and proceeds rapidly in alkaline solutions. Trifluoroacetic acid on the other hand is considerably more stable.

The thermal decarboxylation of trichloroacetic acid, like that of nitroacetic, 2,4,6-trinitrobenzoic (p. 464), and cinnamic acids, is a unimolecular decomposition of the anion, the undissociated acid being stable. The electron-attracting groups on the α carbon atom and the negative charge on the carboxyl group facilitate ionic scission of the carbon-carbon bond.

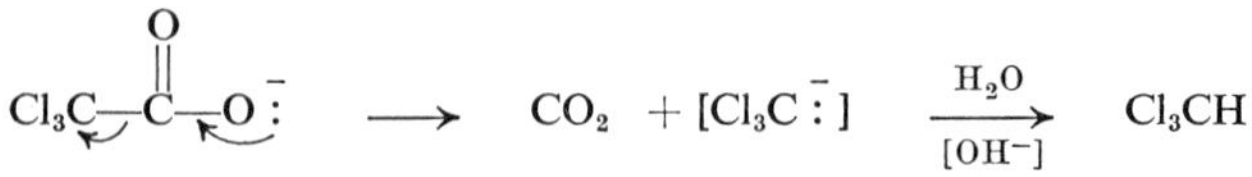

$$Cl_3C{-}\overset{\overset{\displaystyle O}{\|}}{C}{-}O\!:^- \longrightarrow CO_2 + [Cl_3C\!:]^- \xrightarrow[\text{[OH}^-\text{]}]{H_2O} Cl_3CH$$

Although the inductive effect of the trifluoromethyl group is strongly electron-attracting, it has the seemingly anomalous property of shortening (i.e., strengthening) the bond to other atoms (p. 730).

The halogen in halogenated saturated acids behaves like that in alkyl halides and can be replaced by other functional groups by means of the usual reagents. The α-, β-, γ-, and δ-halogenated acids show characteristic differences in their reactions with aqueous or alcoholic alkali. The α-halogenated acids hydrolyze most readily to the α-hydroxy acids, boiling with water or dilute alkali being sufficient. β-Halogenated acids under the same conditions lose halogen acid to give the α,β-unsaturated acid, frequently mixed with the β,γ-unsaturated acid. Boiling with aqueous carbonate solution may lead to decarboxylation as well as loss of halogen acid.

$$CH_3CHBrCHCOONa + Na_2CO_3 + H_2O \xrightarrow{\text{Heat}} CH_3CH{=}CHCH_3 + 2\,NaHCO_3 + NaBr$$
$$|$$
$$CH_3$$

γ- and δ-Halogenated acids when boiled with water or aqueous carbonate solution give five- or six-membered cyclic esters known as *lactones*.

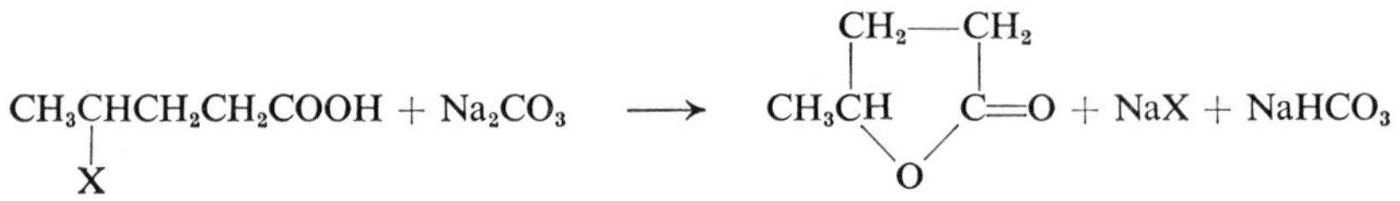

$$CH_3CHCH_2CH_2COOH + Na_2CO_3 \longrightarrow \underset{\substack{| \\ X}}{} \quad CH_3CH\underset{O}{\overset{CH_2{-}CH_2}{\diagdown\diagup}}C{=}O + NaX + NaHCO_3$$

γ-Valerolactone

$$CH_2CH_2CH_2CH_2COOH + Na_2CO_3 \longrightarrow \quad + NaX + NaHCO_3$$
$$|$$
$$X$$

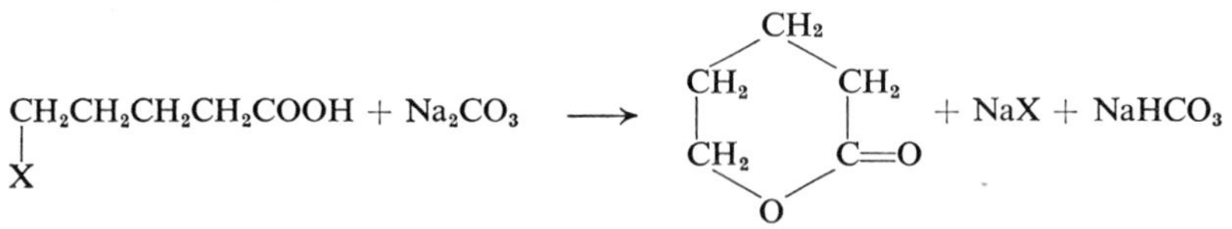

δ-Valerolactone

α-Halogenated acid esters in the presence of base undergo an aldol type addition to ketones with simultaneous cyclization to an epoxide known as a **glycidic ester** (*Darzens reaction*).

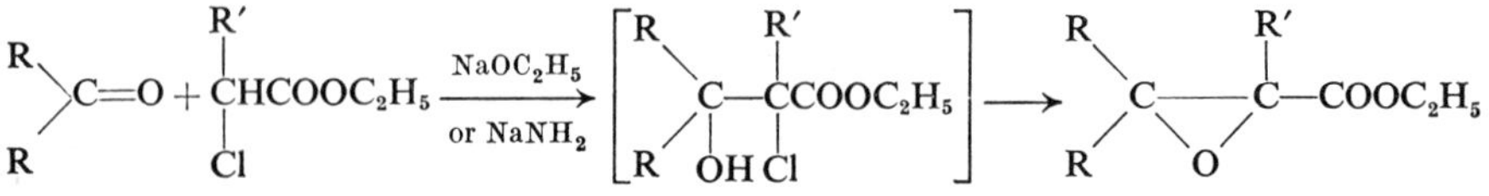

$$\underset{R}{\overset{R}{\diagdown}}C{=}O + \underset{\substack{| \\ Cl}}{\overset{\substack{R' \\ |}}{C}}HCOOC_2H_5 \xrightarrow[\text{or NaNH}_2]{NaOC_2H_5} \left[\underset{\substack{\diagup \ \ | \\ R \ \ OH \ Cl}}{\overset{\substack{R \ \ R' \\ \diagdown \ \ |}}{C{-}C}}COOC_2H_5\right] \longrightarrow \underset{\substack{\diagup \diagdown \diagup \\ R \ \ O}}{\overset{\substack{R \ \ \ \ R' \\ \diagdown \ \ \ \ |}}{C{-}{-}C}}{-}COOC_2H_5$$

Saponification of glycidic esters, followed by acidification, leads to loss of carbon dioxide and rearrangement to an aldehyde (R'=H) or a ketone.

$$\underset{R}{\overset{R}{\diagdown}}\underset{O}{\overset{R'}{\diagup}}C\underset{}{\overset{R'}{\underset{|}{C}}}COOC_2H_5 \xrightarrow{\text{NaOH}} \underset{R}{\overset{R}{\diagdown}}\underset{O}{\overset{R'}{\diagup}}C\underset{}{\overset{R'}{\underset{|}{C}}}COONa \xrightarrow{\text{HCl}} \underset{R}{\overset{R}{\diagdown}}CH\overset{R'}{\underset{}{C}}=O + CO_2$$
$$+ \text{NaCl}$$

Chloroacetic acid is the most important halogenated acid from a commercial standpoint. Large amounts are used in the manufacture of the herbicide, 2,4-D (p. 514), of carboxymethylcellulose (p. 404), and of indigo (p. 685). It is an intermediate for the synthesis of ethyl malonate (p. 792) and hence of many other important organic compounds. In addition to chlorination of acetic acid, it can be made by the hydrolysis of trichloroethylene with dilute acids.

$$ClCH=CCl_2 \xrightarrow{H_2O,\ H_2SO_4} \left[ClCH_2\underset{\underset{Cl}{|}}{\overset{\overset{Cl}{|}}{C}}OH \right] \longrightarrow HCl + ClCH_2\overset{\overset{O}{\|}}{C}Cl \xrightarrow{H_2O} ClCH_2COOH + HCl$$

HYDROXY ACIDS

Preparation

α-**Hydroxy acids** may be prepared by the hydrolysis of α-halogen acids, or by the hydrolysis of the cyanohydrins of aldehydes or ketones.

$$RCHO \xrightarrow{HCN} RCH\overset{\overset{OH}{\diagup}}{\underset{\diagdown CN}{}} \xrightarrow{H_2O-HCl} RCHOHCOOH + NH_4Cl$$

β-**Hydroxy acids** may be made by the catalytic reduction of β-keto esters followed by hydrolysis. The β-hydroxy esters are obtained also by the **Reformatsky reaction.** This reaction is brought about by the addition of zinc to a mixture of an α-halogen ester, usually the α-bromo ester, with an aldehyde or ketone in ether or aromatic hydrocarbon solution.

$$RCHO + BrCH_2COOC_2H_5 + Zn \longrightarrow RCH\underset{\underset{OZnBr}{|}}{}CH_2COOC_2H_5 \xrightarrow{HCl} RCHOHCH_2COOC_2H_5$$

Chloro esters react if a zinc-copper couple is used in place of zinc. Because of the ease of dehydration of β-hydroxy acids, the product may be accompanied by varying amounts of α,β- and β,γ-unsaturated ester.

The Reformatsky reaction is closely related to the Grignard reaction. The initial product undoubtedly is the organozinc compound, $XZnCH_2COOC_2H_5$, which then adds to the carbonyl group. The organomagnesium compounds are more reactive and lead to self condensation with the ester group and with the reactive halogen. For the same reason the organozinc compound must be prepared in the presence of the aldehyde or ketone, with which it reacts more rapidly than with the ester group or halogen.

Compounds containing the hydroxyl group further removed from the carboxyl group than the β position are prepared by hydrolysis of the halogenated acid or by reduction of the keto acid.

Reactions

α-Hydroxy acids undergo bimolecular esterification with the formation of a six-membered ring. Such cyclic esters are known as *lactides.*

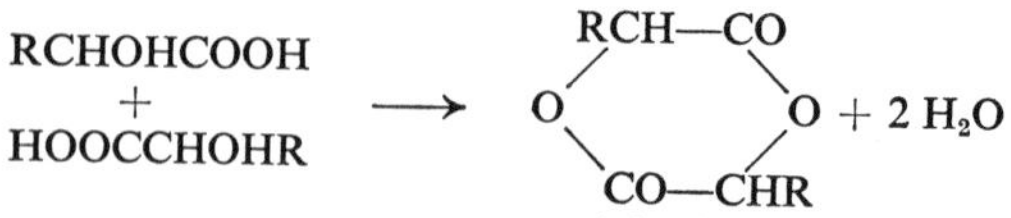

$$\begin{array}{c} \text{RCHOHCOOH} \\ + \\ \text{HOOCCHOHR} \end{array} \longrightarrow \begin{array}{c} \text{RCH---CO} \\ O \qquad\qquad O \\ \text{CO---CHR} \end{array} + 2\,H_2O$$

A lactide

This reaction takes place so readily that it is not possible to keep α-hydroxy acids in their monomolecular state except in the form of their sodium salts.

When α-hydroxy acids are boiled with dilute sulfuric acid, carbon monoxide and water are lost with the formation of an aldehyde.

$$\text{RCHOHCOOH} \xrightarrow[\text{heat}]{H_2SO_4 - H_2O} \text{RCHO} + CO + H_2O$$

This reaction is valuable for the synthesis of higher aldehydes from acids through the α-bromo acid. Since one carbon atom is lost in the process, the series of reactions may be used for the stepwise degradation of a carbon chain.

β-Hydroxy acids lose water easily to give α,β-unsaturated acids, frequently mixed with β,γ-unsaturated acids. β-Hydroxy acids do not form β-lactones readily because of the difficulty in closing four-membered rings. The simplest β-lactone, **β-propiolactone,** was prepared first in 1915 from silver β-iodopropionate. Since 1944, however, it has been available by the reaction of ketene with formaldehyde in the presence of zinc salts or boron fluoride complexes (p. 761).

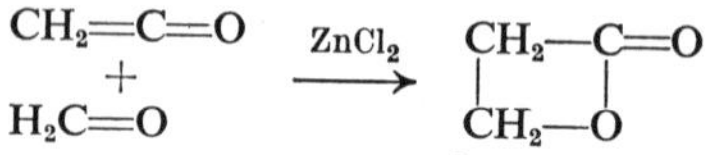

$$\begin{array}{c} CH_2{=}C{=}O \\ + \\ H_2C{=}O \end{array} \xrightarrow{ZnCl_2} \begin{array}{c} CH_2{-}C{=}O \\ | \qquad | \\ CH_2{-}O \end{array}$$

· β-Propiolactone

Ketene reacts similarly with other simple aldehydes and ketones. The four-membered ring of the β-lactones is opened by a variety of reagents to give β-substituted propionic acids. Polymerization of β-propiolactone to a linear polymeric ester takes place with explosive violence in the presence of strong acid or base catalysts. Reagents containing active hydrogen usually are used in the form of aqueous solutions of their sodium salts, resulting in the formation of the sodium salt of the product.

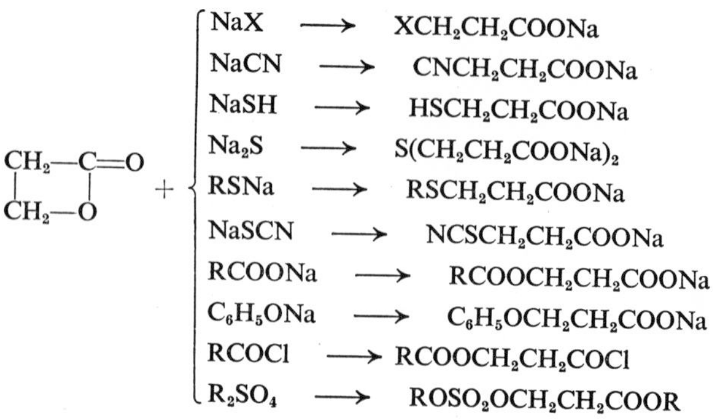

$$\begin{array}{c} CH_2{-}C{=}O \\ | \qquad | \\ CH_2{-}O \end{array} + \left\{ \begin{array}{lll} NaX & \longrightarrow & XCH_2CH_2COONa \\ NaCN & \longrightarrow & CNCH_2CH_2COONa \\ NaSH & \longrightarrow & HSCH_2CH_2COONa \\ Na_2S & \longrightarrow & S(CH_2CH_2COONa)_2 \\ RSNa & \longrightarrow & RSCH_2CH_2COONa \\ NaSCN & \longrightarrow & NCSCH_2CH_2COONa \\ RCOONa & \longrightarrow & RCOOCH_2CH_2COONa \\ C_6H_5ONa & \longrightarrow & C_6H_5OCH_2CH_2COONa \\ RCOCl & \longrightarrow & RCOOCH_2CH_2COCl \\ R_2SO_4 & \longrightarrow & ROSO_2OCH_2CH_2COOR \end{array} \right.$$

Amines yield β-hydroxy or α,β-unsaturated amides or β-amino acids, and alcohols yield β-hydroxy, β-alkoxy, or α,β-unsaturated acids or esters depending on the conditions of the reaction. The diversity of these reactions indicates that β-propiolactone is a promising intermediate for organic synthesis.

γ- and δ-Hydroxy acids are stable only in the form of their salts. The free acids spontaneously cyclize to lactones.

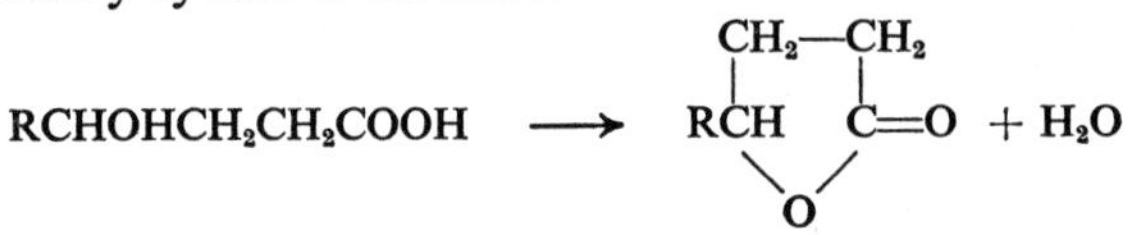

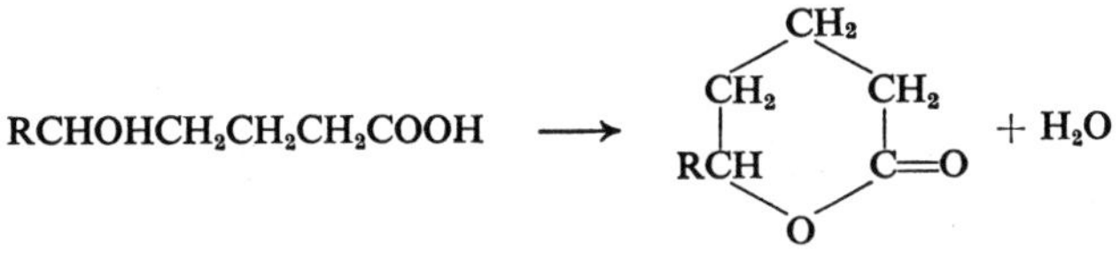

$$RCHOHCH_2CH_2COOH \longrightarrow \underset{\underset{O}{\diagdown \diagup}}{RCH \quad C=O} + H_2O$$

$$RCHOHCH_2CH_2CH_2COOH \longrightarrow \underset{RCH \quad \quad \quad C=O}{\overset{CH_2}{\underset{O}{\diagdown}}} + H_2O$$

An industrial process for the preparation of **γ-butyrolactone** is the catalytic dehydrogenation of tetramethylene glycol (p. 747).

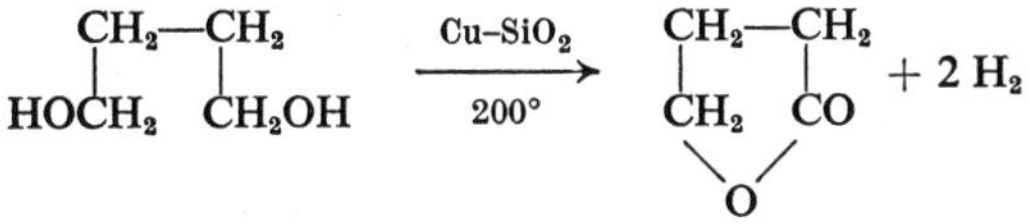

$$\underset{HOCH_2 \quad CH_2OH}{CH_2-CH_2} \xrightarrow[200°]{Cu-SiO_2} \underset{\underset{O}{\diagdown \diagup}}{\overset{CH_2-CH_2}{CH_2 \quad CO}} + 2\,H_2$$

Glycolic acid, $HOCH_2COOH$, can be made by the hydrolysis of chloroacetic acid or by the oxidation of ethylene glycol with dilute acid. The commercial product, used by tanners and dyers, is made by the reaction of formaldehyde with carbon monoxide (p. 743). **Thioglycolic acid** is made from sodium chloroacetate and sodium hydrosulfide.

$$HSNa + ClCOONa \longrightarrow HSCH_2COONa$$

The ammonium salt is the active agent in the preparations used for the cold permanent-waving of hair (p. 299).

Lactic acid, $CH_3CHOHCOOH$, the acid formed when milk turns sour because of the action of *Lactobacillus* on the lactose, was isolated from sour milk by Scheele in 1780. It is manufactured by the fermentation of lactose from whey, of molasses, or of starch hydrolysates, in the presence of an excess of calcium carbonate. It can be synthesized by the hydrolysis of acetaldehyde cyanohydrin. About 5 million pounds was manufactured in the United States in 1948 and over half of this was edible grade. Esters of lactic acid are valuable high-boiling solvents for the formulation of lacquers, and can be used for the manufacture of acrylic esters (p. 788).

Lactic acid contains an asymmetric carbon atom, and the lactic acid formed on muscular contraction is dextrorotatory. It is known as **sarcolactic acid** (Gr. *sarx*, flesh). Fermentation lactic acid may be dextro- or levorotatory or inactive depending on the organisms involved. The lactide of lactic acid has a higher rotation of opposite sign from that of the acid. Hence the rotation of an active lactic acid on standing first will decrease to zero and then increase again in the opposite sense as more lactide is formed, until the equilibrium mixture of lactide, water, and lactic acid is reached.

AMINO ACIDS

Preparation

The synthesis of the natural α-amino acids is discussed on pages 303 and 802. Acids having an amino group in other positions can be prepared from the corresponding halogenated acid, or by reduction of the oxime of the keto acid. β-Amino acids can be made by the addition of ammonia to α,β-unsaturated acids.

$$RCH\!\!=\!\!CHCOOH + NH_3 \longrightarrow \underset{\underset{NH_2}{|}}{RCHCH_2COOH}$$

Reactions

Amino acids in general exist as dipolar ions and are less likely to undergo the types of reactions noted for the hydroxy acids. Nevertheless comparable reactions take place under more drastic conditions. Thus α-amino acids, when heated in glycerol solution to 170°, lose water and form cyclic amides known as *2,5-diketopiperazines.*

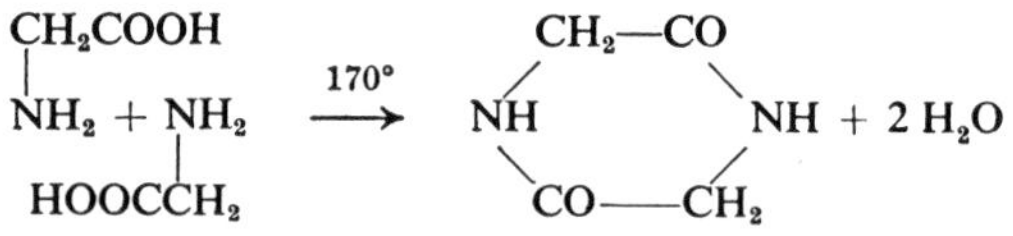

$$\underset{\underset{HOOCCH_2}{|}}{\overset{\overset{CH_2COOH}{|}}{NH_2 + NH_2}} \xrightarrow{170°} \underset{\underset{\diagdown}{\diagup}}{\overset{CH_2\!\!-\!\!CO}{NH}}\underset{CO\!\!-\!\!-\!\!CH_2}{\overset{\diagdown}{NH}} + 2\ H_2O$$

2,5-Diketopiperazine

When the salts of β-amino acids are heated to decomposition, α,β-unsaturated acids are formed.

$$\underset{\underset{NH_3^+\text{-}PO_4H_2}{|}}{RCHCH_2COOH} \xrightarrow{\text{Heat}} RCH\!\!=\!\!CHCOOH + (NH_4)H_2PO_4$$

γ- and δ-Amino acids on heating yield cyclic amides, which are known as *lactams.*

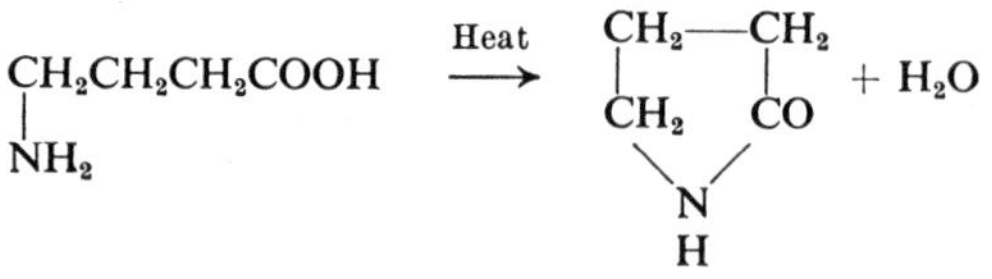

$$\underset{\underset{NH_2}{|}}{CH_2CH_2CH_2COOH} \xrightarrow{\text{Heat}} \underset{\underset{N}{\overset{\diagdown\diagup}{}}}{\overset{\overset{CH_2\!\!-\!\!-\!\!CH_2}{|\quad\quad|}}{CH_2\quad CO}} + H_2O$$

γ-Butyrolactam (pyrrolidone)

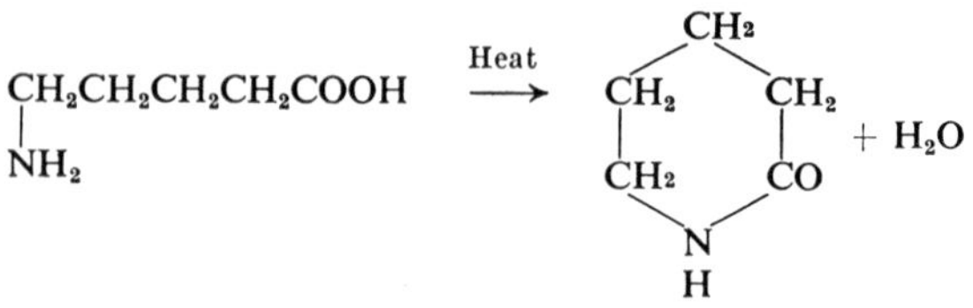

$$\underset{\underset{NH_2}{|}}{CH_2CH_2CH_2CH_2COOH} \xrightarrow{\text{Heat}} \overset{CH_2}{\underset{\underset{N}{\overset{|\quad\quad|}{CH_2\quad CO}}}{\overset{\diagup\diagdown}{CH_2\quad CH_2}}} + H_2O$$

δ-Valerolactam (piperidone)

Pyrrolidone is manufactured commercially from γ-butyrolactone (p. 783) and ammonia. In the presence of an alkaline catalyst, it gives a linear polymer called *nylon 4* (cf. p. 799).

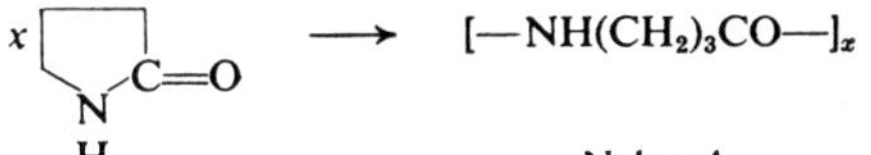

Nylon 4

Condensation of pyrrolidone with acetylene gives **N-vinylpyrrolidone** which polymerizes to **polyvinylpyrrolidone**. The latter gives colloidal solutions in water and has been used as a blood plasma substitute under the name *Periston*. It now is the most widely used film-forming ingredient of hair sprays.

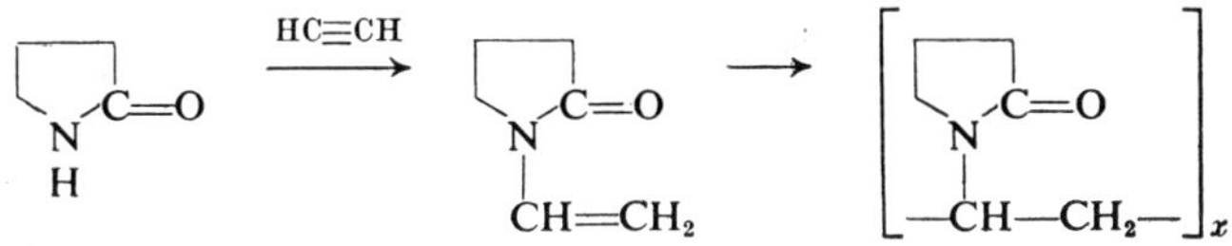

Pyrrolidone   Vinylpyrrolidone   Polyvinylpyrrolidone

Sarcosine is *N*-methylglycine, CH_3NHCH_2COOH. It is present in muscle and hence in meat extract. It can be synthesized from chloroacetic acid and methylamine. The sodium salt of **N-lauroyl sarcosine**, $CH_3(CH_2)_{10}CON(CH_3)$-CH_2COONa, inhibits the action of enzymes and is used in toothpastes to prevent bacterial fermentation of carbohydrates and the formation of acids in the mouth.

The internal quaternary ammonium salts of amino acids are known as *betaines* after betaine itself, which is the simplest representative. **Betaine,** $(CH_3)_3\overset{+}{N}CH_2COO^-$, is present in the juice of beets (*Beta vulgaris*), and the residue from the manufacture of beet sugar is an abundant source. A quaternary ammonium derivative of aminoacetic acid that has proven to be very valuable is the **Girard T-reagent**. It is the hydrazide of carboxymethyltrimethylammonium chloride. It is made by the reaction of ethyl chloroacetate with trimethylamine, followed by reaction with hydrazine.

$$(CH_3)_3N + ClCH_2COOC_2H_5 \longrightarrow [(CH_3)_3\overset{+}{N}CH_2COOC_2H_5]\overset{-}{Cl} \xrightarrow{H_2NNH_2}$$

$$[(CH_3)_3\overset{+}{N}CH_2CONHNH_2]\overset{-}{Cl} + C_2H_5OH$$

Girard T-reagent

Water-insoluble ketones give water-soluble hydrazones with this reagent because of the presence of the quaternary ammonium group, thus enabling the separation from other nonketonic water-insoluble compounds. The ketone is regenerated easily by hydrolysis. The reagent has been invaluable for the separation of ketonic from nonketonic steroidal hormones (p. 870).

β-Alanine is of special interest since it comprises a portion of **pantetheine** which in turn makes up a portion of coenzyme A (p. 645). **Pantothenic acid,**

first isolated from liver extracts and considered to be a member of the vitamin B complex, can be derived from pantetheine.

Pantoic acid portion	β-Alanine portion	Thioethanolamine portion

$$\overbrace{HOCH_2C(CH_3)_2CHOHCONHCH_2CH_2CONHCH_2CH_2SH}$$

Pantothenic acid portion

Pantetheine

UNSATURATED ACIDS

Preparation

Usually only α,β-unsaturated acids are readily available. The methods for the preparation of these compounds are numerous. They can be formed by the oxidation of α,β-unsaturated aldehydes, which are available through the aldol condensation of an aldehyde with acetaldehyde (p. 762). They result also from the dehydrohalogenation of β-halogen acids (p. 780), from the dehydration of β-hydroxy acids (p. 782), and from the deamination of β-amino acids (p. 784). A very practical method is the reaction of an aldehyde and malonic acid (p. 795).

$$RCHO + H_2C(COOH)_2 \xrightarrow{Pyridine} H_2O + RCH{=}C(COOH)_2 \xrightarrow{Heat} RCH{=}CHCOOH + CO_2$$

The β-aryl-substituted α,β-unsaturated acids may be obtained by the Perkin reaction (p. 536).

If the proper unsaturated halide is available, unsaturated acids having the double bond in more remote positions can be synthesized through the cyanide (p. 144) or by the use of ethyl malonate (p. 800). In other cases more complicated syntheses must be used.

Reactions

α,β- and β,γ-Unsaturated acids yield equilibrium mixtures of both types when heated with alkali. The position of equilibrium depends on the structure of the acid. Thus vinylacetic acid isomerizes completely to crotonic acid, γ-methylvinylacetic acid gives 75 per cent of the conjugated acid, β,γ-dimethylvinylacetic acid gives 25 per cent of the conjugated acid, and γ,γ-dimethylvinylacetic acid gives 5 per cent of the conjugated acid.

$$CH_2{=}CHCH_2COOH \rightleftarrows CH_3CH{=}CHCOOH$$
0 per cent   100 per cent

$$CH_3CH{=}CHCH_2COOH \rightleftarrows CH_3CH_2CH{=}CHCOOH$$
25 per cent   75 per cent

$$CH_3CH{=}C(CH_3)CH_2COOH \rightleftarrows CH_3CH_2C(CH_3){=}CHCOOH$$
75 per cent   25 per cent

$$(CH_3)_2C{=}CHCH_2COOH \rightleftarrows (CH_3)_2CHCH{=}CHCOOH$$
95 per cent   5 per cent

Both α,β- and β,γ-unsaturated acids undergo thermal decomposition more readily than saturated carboxylic acids to give olefin and carbon dioxide.

$$RCH_2CH{=}CHCOOH \rightleftarrows RCH{=}CHCH_2COOH \longrightarrow RCH_2CH{=}CH_2 + CO_2$$

The mechanism of decomposition of unsaturated aliphatic acids differs from that of the cinnamic acids (p. 780). α,β-Unsaturated acids when heated decarboxylate more readily than saturated acids, and β,γ- more readily than α,β-unsaturated acids. It appears that decarboxylation of α,β-unsaturated acids takes place by means of a cyclic unimolecular mechanism by way of the undissociated β,γ-unsaturated acid.

$$RCH_2CH=CHCOOH \quad \rightleftharpoons \quad RCH\overset{\displaystyle CH}{\underset{\displaystyle H-O-C=O}{\diagup\diagdown}}CH_2 \quad \longrightarrow \quad RCH_2CH=CH_2 + CO_2$$

The same reagents that add to α,β-unsaturated carbonyl compounds (p. 763) add to the double bond of α,β-unsaturated acids, but the reactions usually are not complicated by participation of the carboxyl group Thus halogen acid, hydrogen cyanide, hydrogen sulfide, and ammonia give β-halogen, β-cyano, β-mercapto, and β-amino acids. Mercaptans and amines give the corresponding sulfides and substituted amino derivatives, and alcohols and phenols give β-alkoxy and β-phenoxy acids. Sodium bisulfite gives the sodium β-sulfonate. Esters and nitriles of the α,β-unsaturated acids behave towards these reagents like the free acids. Frequently the reactions take place with greater ease, especially when base-catalyzed

The effect of basic catalysis on the addition of compounds containing active hydrogen may be very striking. For example a mixture of α,β-unsaturated ester and mercaptan may show no sign of reaction at room temperature, but the addition of a small amount of pyridine will induce a vigorous reaction. Undoubtedly the reaction occurs by the attack of a negative ion at the β position.

$$RSH \underset{\xrightarrow{\hspace{1cm}}}{\overset{C_5H_5N}{\xrightarrow{\hspace{1cm}}}} [C_5H_5\overset{+}{N}H] + [R\overset{-}{S}:] \underset{\xrightarrow{\hspace{1cm}}}{\overset{CH_2=CH\overset{O}{\overset{\|}{C}}OR}{\xrightarrow{\hspace{1cm}}}} \left[RS-CH_2-\overset{O}{\overset{\|}{C}}H\overset{-}{C}OR\right] \overset{[C_5H_5\overset{+}{N}H]}{\xrightarrow{\hspace{1cm}}} RSCH_2CH_2\overset{O}{\overset{\|}{C}}OR$$

The free acids in the presence of a base form the salt of the acid, and the resulting negative charge on the carboxylate ion decreases the polarization of the double bond by the carboxyl group and reduces the tendency of the β carbon atom to combine with electron-donating reagents

Individual Unsaturated Acids

Acrylonitrile, methyl acrylate, and methyl methacrylate are the most important α,β-unsaturated compounds from a technical viewpoint. **Acrylonitrile** may be made from either ethylene or acetylene.

$$CH_2=CH_2 \xrightarrow[\text{Ag cat}]{O_2} CH_2-CH_2 \xrightarrow{HCN} HOCH_2CH_2CN \xrightarrow[\text{heat}]{NaHSO_4} CH_2=CHCN + H_2O$$

$$HC\equiv CH + HCN \xrightarrow[90°]{CuCl,\ NH_4Cl,\ HCl} H_2C=CHCN$$

Acrylonitrile long has been used as a co-monomer in the synthesis of synthetic rubbers (p. 718) and plastics (p. 726). When polymerized alone, it gives a solid resin which is infusible and insoluble in the common organic solvents

$$x\ CH_2=CHCN \xrightarrow{\text{Peroxides}} \left[\begin{array}{c} -CH_2CH- \\ | \\ CN \end{array}\right]_x$$

Polyacrylonitrile

The discovery of solvents in which it could be dissolved and from which it could be spun into threads led to the production of the so-called **acrylic fibers.** The solvents most commonly used for spinning are *N,N*-dimethylformamide and *N,N*-dimethylacetamide, although it can be wet spun from concentrated solutions of salts such as zinc chloride or calcium thiocyanate. The acrylic fibers such as *Orlon* and *Acrilan* usually are copolymers with about 10 per cent of vinylpyridine (p. 627). The introduction of basic groups enables dyes to be adsorbed more readily. Fibers formed by cospinning polyacrylonitrile with cellulose acetate also are dyed readily. *Dynel* is a copolymer of acrylonitrile with around 50 per cent vinyl chloride and can be spun from a solution in acetone.

Hydrolysis of polyacrylonitrile gives **polyacrylic acid** which resembles the polyuronides (p. 408) in that it is a long-chain compound with numerous carboxyl groups along the chain. The discovery that polyuronides derived from the oxidative decomposition of cellulose appear to be responsible for the beneficial effects of humus in the soil has led to the use of polyacrylic acid and similar compounds as soil conditioners.

Acrylonitrile undergoes base-catalyzed addition reactions with all compounds containing reactive hydrogen, such as alcohols, mercaptans, hydrogen cyanide, acids and amines, and even with ketones. Thus the carbon-carbon double bond in acrylonitrile has about the same reactivity as the carbon-oxygen double bond in formaldehyde.

$$CH_2{=}CHCN + HZ \xrightarrow{\text{Base}} ZCH_2CH_2CN$$

A particularly useful catalyst for these reactions is a quaternary ammonium base such as trimethylbenzylammonium hydroxide (*Triton-B*). Because a cyanoethyl group appears in the product, the process has been called *cyanoethylation.*

The esters of acrylic acid and α-methylacrylic acid polymerize in the presence of peroxide catalysts to give the *acrylic* or *acryloid resins.* **Methyl acrylate** can be made by the dehydration of methyl lactate (p. 783), by the methanolysis of acrylonitrile, or by the carbonylation of acetylene in the presence of methanol.

$$CH_3CHOHCOOCH_3 \longrightarrow CH_2{=}CHCOOCH_3 + H_2O$$

$$CH_2{=}CHCN + CH_3OH \xrightarrow{H_2SO_4} CH_2{=}CHCOOCH_3$$

$$HC{\equiv}CH + CO + CH_3OH \xrightarrow[\text{HCl}]{Ni(CO)_4,} H_2C{=}CHCOOCH_3$$

Methyl α-methylacrylate, commonly called **methyl methacrylate,** is made from acetone, although other processes are possible.

$$(CH_3)_2CO \xrightarrow{HCN} (CH_3)_2COHCN \xrightarrow[\text{heat}]{KHSO_4} CH_2{=}\underset{\underset{\textstyle CH_3}{|}}{C}CN \xrightarrow[\text{H}_2SO_4]{CH_3OH,} CH_2{=}\underset{\underset{\textstyle CH_3}{|}}{C}COOCH_3$$

Methyl
methacrylate

Polymerization of methyl methacrylate using peroxide catalysts gives a strong thermoplastic solid that is highly transparent and has a high refractive index. It is sold under the names *Lucite, Crystallite, Plexiglas,* or *Perspex* and is used in place of glass and for molding transparent objects. Numerous other esters also are manufactured commercially for the production of polymers and copolymers for a variety of uses. The monomeric esters are stabilized by the addition of 0.005 to 0.25 per cent of hydroquinone.

Crotonic acid is made by the oxidation of crotonic aldehyde (p. 207). Its esters do not polymerize as easily as those of acrylic acid or of α-methylacrylic acid. **Angelic acid** (from *Angelica archangelica*) and **tiglic acid** (from *Croton tiglium*) are the *cis* and *trans* forms respectively of α-methylcrotonic acid.

$$CH_3 \quad H \qquad\qquad H \quad CH_3$$
$$\diagdown \diagup \qquad\qquad \diagdown \diagup$$
$$C \qquad\qquad\qquad C$$
$$\| \qquad\qquad\qquad \|$$
$$C \qquad\qquad\qquad C$$
$$\diagup \diagdown \qquad\qquad \diagup \diagdown$$
$$CH_3 \quad COOH \qquad CH_3 \quad COOH$$
$$\text{Angelic acid} \qquad\qquad \text{Tiglic acid}$$

10-Undecenoic acid, commonly known as **undecylenic acid,** is one of the products of the destructive distillation of castor oil, the other principal product being heptaldehyde.

$$CH_3(CH_2)_5CHOHCH_2CH{=}CH(CH_2)_7COOH \xrightarrow{\text{Heat}} CH_3(CH_2)_5CHO + CH_2{=}CH(CH_2)_8COOH$$
$$\text{Ricinoleic acid} \qquad\qquad\qquad \text{Heptaldehyde} \qquad \text{Undecylenic acid}$$

Sorbic acid, $CH_3CH{=}CHCH{=}CHCOOH$, was obtained first by Hofmann. He distilled with dilute sulfuric acid the residue remaining after the removal of malic acid from the juice of the fruit of the European mountain ash (*Sorbus aucuparia*). Sorbic acid now is available commercially, being synthesized from acetaldehyde through crotonaldehyde and sorbaldehyde. Reduction of sorbic acid with sodium amalgam takes place by 1,6 addition to give 3-hexenoic acid (hydrosorbic acid).

$$CH_3CH{=}CHCH{=}CHCOOH \xrightarrow{\text{Na—Hg}} \left[CH_3CH_2CH{=}CH{-}CH{=}C{\overset{\displaystyle OH}{\underset{\displaystyle OH}{\diagup}}} \right] \longrightarrow$$
$$CH_3CH_2CH{=}CHCH_2COOH$$

Numerous long-chain unsaturated acids such as oleic, isooleic, petroselenic, linoleic, linolenic, eleostearic, and erucic acid can be obtained by the saponification of natural fats (p. 179). The acetylenic acid, **stearolic acid,** has been obtained by synthesis from oleic acid.

$$CH_3(CH_2)_7CH{=}CH(CH_2)_7COOH \xrightarrow{Br_2} CH_3(CH_2)_7CHBrCHBr(CH_2)_7COOH \xrightarrow{\text{KOH, alc.}}$$
$$CH_3(CH_2)_7C{\equiv}C(CH_2)_7COOH$$

More recently polyunsaturated acids containing triple bonds and both double and triple bonds have been isolated from essential oils of the *Compositae,* from microorganisms, and from fats. The formulas of several examples are given and their sources indicated

$CH_3CH{=}CHC{\equiv}CC{\equiv}CCH_2CH_2COOH$ ⎫
Dihydromatricaric acid   ⎬   *Matricaria inodora*
$CH_3CH{=}CHC{\equiv}CC{\equiv}CCH{=}CHCOOH$ ⎪
Matricaric acid   ⎭

CH₃CH=CHC≡CC≡CC≡CCOOH   *Artemesia vulgaris*
Dehydromatricaric acid

CH₃CH₂CH₂C≡CC≡CCH=CHCOOH   *Lachnophyllum gossypinum*
Lachnophyllic acid

HC≡CC≡CCH=C=CHCH=CHCH=CHCH₂COOH   *Nocardia acidophilus*
Mycomycin

CH₂=CH(CH₂)₄C≡CC≡C(CH₂)₇COOH   *Ongokea klaineana*
Erythrogenic acid (*isanic acid*)

Mycomycin has antibiotic properties. Its structure has a combination of features that make it one of the most surprising compounds of either natural or synthetic origin. The system contains the 1,3-diene, the allene, and the 1,3-diyne systems. Moreover the natural product is optically active because of the molecular asymmetry resulting from the allene structure (p. 706).

REVIEW QUESTIONS

1. What is the Hell-Volhard-Zelinsky reaction? Why is the phosphorus trichloride necessary?
2. What reactions lead to β-halogen acids?
3. Compare the behavior of α-, β-, γ-, and δ-halogen acids on heating in the presence of one mole of aqueous potassium hydroxide.
4. Discuss the action of alkali on α,β-unsaturated acids.
5. Give two general procedures for the synthesis of α-hydroxy acids.
6. Give two general procedures for the synthesis of β-hydroxy acids. What name is associated with one of the methods?
7. Compare the dehydration of α-, β-, γ-, and δ-hydroxy acids. What is the action of sulfuric acid on α-hydroxy acids?
8. How do the reactions of α-, β-, γ-, and δ-amino acids differ from each other?

PROBLEMS

9. What can be said concerning the structure of each of the following compounds: (*a*) When an aqueous solution of the sodium salt of a hydroxy acid was acidified, a neutral compound was obtained; (*b*) an amino acid hydrochloride when heated gave an unsaturated acid; (*c*) a bromo acid when treated with aqueous alkali gave the salt of a hydroxy acid, and with alcoholic alkali, the salt of an ethoxy acid; (*d*) an unsaturated acid reacted with hydrogen sulfide to give a mercapto acid.
10. Give reactions for the following preparations: (*a*) tridecanol from myristic acid; (*b*) phenylalanine from benzaldehyde; (*c*) 3,4-methylenedioxycinnamic acid from piperonal; (*d*) 5-chloropentanoic acid from tetrahydrofuran; (*e*) β-hydroxypropionic acid from ethylene; (*f*) β-mercaptobutyric acid from acetaldehyde; (*g*) β-bromo-β-methylvaleric acid from methyl ethyl ketone; (*h*) sorbic acid from aldol; (*i*) leucine from *i*-valeraldehyde; (*j*) β-alanine from ketene; (*k*) γ-bromovaleric acid from levulinic acid; (*l*) N-lauroylsarcosine from lauric acid and acetic acid; (*m*) 13-aminotridecanoic acid from erucic acid.
11. Devise a reasonable synthesis of pantoic acid from readily available materials.
12. Construct a chart indicating the reactions, including reagents and conditions, for the synthesis of the following compounds starting with acrylonitrile: methyl acrylate, ethylene cyanide, tetramethylenediamine, β,β-diacetylbutyronitrile, γ-nitrobutyronitrile, δ-oxohexanoic acid, β-mercaptoethyl cyanide, α-chloro-β-phenylpropionitrile, β-cyanopropionaldehyde, pyrrolidine, β-aminopropionitrile, α-amino-β-phenylpropionitrile, β-mercaptopropionic acid, β-alanine, β-phenoxyethyl cyanide, γ-butyrolactam, phenylalanine, and trimethylenediamine.
13. How many stereoisomers are possible theoretically for: (*a*) dihydromatricaric acid; (*b*) matricaric acid; (*c*) lachnophyllic acid; (*d*) mycomycin; (*e*) erythrogenic acid? Which of the above compounds should be optically active?

Chapter 37

POLYCARBOXYLIC ACIDS

Of the polycarboxylic acids, the dicarboxylic acids are encountered most frequently, and some are of considerable importance. Thus the ethyl ester of malonic acid is a valuable intermediate for organic syntheses. Adipic acid and the unsaturated maleic acid are technically important intermediates. Some of the hydroxy polycarboxylic acids, such as malic, tartaric, and citric acids, occur in fruit juices

Nomenclature

The unsubstituted polycarboxylic acids have common names which are in general use and serve as family names for the substituted acids. The names of the normal dibasic acids having 2 to 10 carbon atoms are oxalic, malonic, succinic, glutaric, adipic, pimelic, suberic, azelaic, and sebacic acids.

Dicarboxylic Acids

Preparation. Several general methods of preparation are available.

1. OXIDATION OF α,ω-GLYCOLS.

$$(CH_2)_x(CH_2OH)_2 \xrightarrow[\text{or } H_2Cr_2O_7]{HNO_3, \ KMnO_4} (CH_2)_x(COOH)_2$$

2. HYDROLYSIS OF DINITRILES.

$$(CH_2)_x(CN)_2 \xrightarrow{H_2O-HCl} (CH_2)_x(COOH)_2 + 2 \ NH_4Cl$$

3. ELECTROLYSIS OF THE ACID ESTERS OF LOWER DICARBOXYLIC ACIDS (**Kolbe synthesis,** p. 156).

$$2 \ CH_3OOC(CH_2)_x COONa \xrightarrow{\text{Electrolysis}} CH_3OOC(CH_2)_x(CH_2)_xCOOCH_3 +$$
$$2 \ CO_2(+ \ NaOH \ and \ H_2 \ at \ cathode)$$

Frequently special methods are used for the preparation of individual dicarboxylic acids. **Oxalic acid** was known at an early date. The presence of its potassium acid salt in the sorrels (various species of *Rumex* and *Oxalis*; Gr *oxys*, sharp or acid) was observed at the beginning of the seventeenth century. It is present in many other plants such as spinach, rhubarb, sweet potatoes, cabbage, grapes, and tomatoes. When these fruits and vegetables are eaten, microscopic star-shaped crystals of the insoluble calcium oxalate may appear in the urine.

Nitric acid oxidation of any α,β-oxygenated or aminated substance such as the carbohydrates or the amino acids will produce oxalic acid. It can be obtained in good yield by the nitric acid oxidation of sucrose in the presence of vanadium pentoxide. Commercially it is manufactured by heating sodium formate and liberating the free acid from the sodium salt with sulfuric acid.

$$2\ HCOONa \xrightarrow{\text{Heat}} H_2 + NaOOCCOONa \xrightarrow{H_2SO_4} HOOCCOOH$$

Malonic acid is so named because it first was obtained in 1858 as an oxidation product of malic acid (p. 808). It ordinarily is prepared by a series of reactions from sodium chloroacetate. The intermediate cyanoacetate may be hydrolyzed to the acid or alcoholyzed to the ester.

$$NaOOCCH_2Cl \xrightarrow{NaCN} NaOOCCH_2CN$$

Sodium cyanoacetate

$$\xrightarrow{H_2O-H_2SO_4} HOOCCH_2COOH$$
Malonic acid

$$\xrightarrow[H_2SO_4]{C_2H_5OH-} C_2H_5OOCCH_2COOC_2H_5$$
Ethyl malonate

The preparation of substituted malonic acids is described under the reactions of the ester (p. 800). **Malononitrile** can be made by the dehydration of cyanoacetamide.

$$NCCH_2CONH_2 + PCl_5 \longrightarrow NCCH_2CN + POCl_3 + 2\ HCl$$

It is reported to trimerize explosively in the presence of traces of alkali, although metallic salts have been prepared.

Succinic acid was known in the sixteenth century as a distillation product of amber, a fossil resin (*L. succinum*, amber). It can be obtained by the hydrolysis of ethylene cyanide, but is manufactured now by the catalytic reduction of maleic acid or the electrolytic reduction of fumaric acid (p. 805).

$$HOOCCH=CHCOOH + 2\ [H] \xrightarrow[\substack{\text{electrolytic} \\ \text{reduction}}]{\text{Cat. or}} HOOCCH_2CH_2COOH$$

Maleic or fumaric acid — Succinic acid

Derivatives of succinic acid can be made by the hydrolysis of β-cyano esters formed by the addition of hydrogen cyanide to α,β-unsaturated esters (p. 787).

$$RCH=CHCOOC_2H_5 \xrightarrow{HCN} \underset{CN}{RCHCH_2COOC_2H_5} \xrightarrow{H_2O-HCl} \underset{COOH}{RCHCH_2COOH}$$

Numerous other synthetic methods also are available. **Succinonitrile**, NCCH₂- CH₂CN, can be made from ethylene bromide and sodium cyanide, but it is made commercially by the addition of hydrogen cyanide to acrylonitrile (p. 788). Substituted succinonitriles result from the decomposition of azobisnitriles (p. 265).

Glutaric acid was prepared first from the readily obtainable glutamic acid (p. 304) by converting the latter into α-hydroxyglutaric acid and reducing with hydrogen iodide. It is not a commercial product but is made in the laboratory by the hydrolysis of trimethylene cyanide, from malonic ester (p. 804), by the oxidation of glutaric aldehyde (p. 768), or by the nitric acid oxidation of cyclopentanone (p. 798).

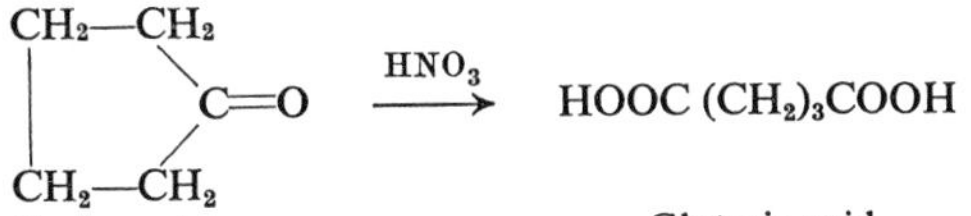

$$\text{Cyclopentanone} \xrightarrow{\text{HNO}_3} \text{HOOC (CH}_2)_3\text{COOH}$$

Cyclopentanone   Glutaric acid

Adipic acid (L. *adeps*, fat) is one of the compounds formed when many unsaturated fats or fat acids are oxidized. It is the chief product from the oxidation of cyclohexanol (p. 834) or cyclohexanone with nitric acid.

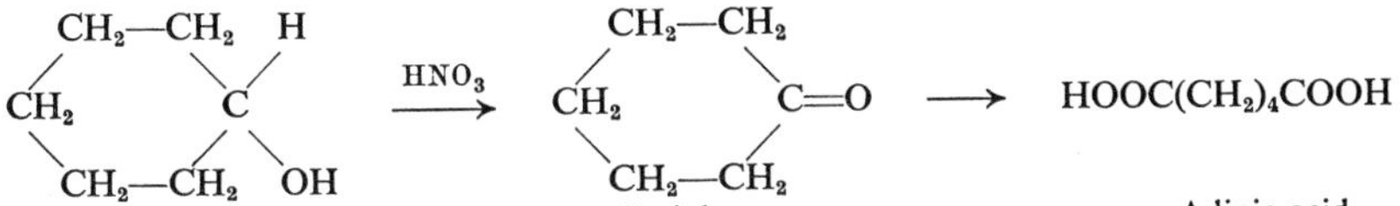

$$\text{Cyclohexanol} \xrightarrow{\text{HNO}_3} \text{Cyclohexanone} \longrightarrow \text{HOOC(CH}_2)_4\text{COOH}$$

Cyclohexanol   Cyclohexanone   Adipic acid

It formerly was made from cyclohexanol (p. 841) but now is produced by the catalytic air oxidation of cyclohexane (p. 830) in the liquid phase and by the carbonylation of tetrahydrofuran (p. 619).

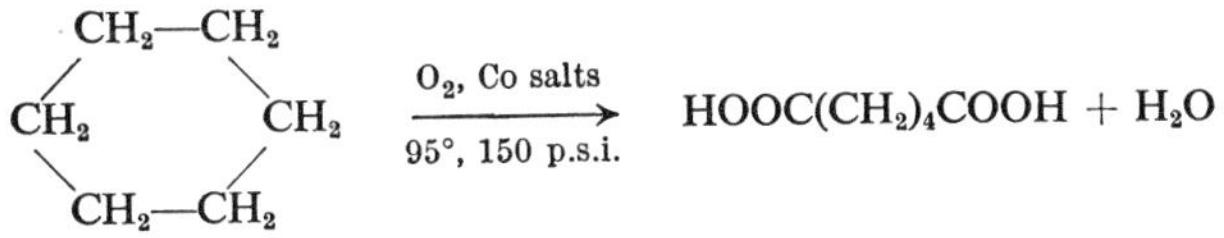

$$\text{Cyclohexane} \xrightarrow[95°, 150 \text{ p.s.i.}]{\text{O}_2, \text{ Co salts}} \text{HOOC(CH}_2)_4\text{COOH} + \text{H}_2\text{O}$$

Cyclohexane

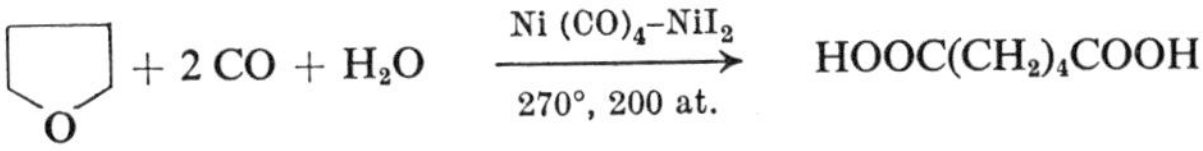

$$\square_\text{O} + 2\,\text{CO} + \text{H}_2\text{O} \xrightarrow[270°, 200 \text{ at.}]{\text{Ni (CO)}_4\text{–NiI}_2} \text{HOOC(CH}_2)_4\text{COOH}$$

Cyclohexanol and cyclohexanone are intermediates in the reaction. Adipic acid can be obtained also by the hydrolysis of adiponitrile (p. 799).

Pimelic acid (Gr. *pimele*, fat) also is an oxidation product of unsaturated fats. It is not available commercially, but it can be synthesized by the hydrolysis of pentamethylene cyanide or by several other procedures.

$$\text{CN(CH}_2)_5\text{CN} \xrightarrow{\text{H}_2\text{O—HCl}} \text{HOOC(CH}_2)_5\text{COOH}$$

Penta-methylene cyanide   Pimelic acid

Suberic acid (L. *suber*, cork oak), $\text{HOOC(CH}_2)_6\text{COOH}$, is obtained in small amounts by the oxidation of cork with nitric acid. It usually is prepared by the nitric acid oxidation of castor oil, although the yield still is low. It has been postulated that suberic acid arises by oxidation of trihydroxystearic acid, but it is conceivable that a methylene group α to the double bond is the initial point of attack (p. 881).

Azelaic acid is the chief product of the oxidation of unsaturated fat acids with nitric acid (F. *azote*, nitrogen, and Gr. *elaion*, olive oil) or with potassium permanganate.

$$\text{CH}_3(\text{CH}_2)_7\text{CH}{=}\text{CH(CH}_2)_7\text{COOH} \xrightarrow{\text{Ox.}} \text{CH}_3(\text{CH}_2)_7\text{COOH} + \text{HOOC(CH}_2)_7\text{COOH}$$

Oleic acid   Nonylic acid   Azelaic acid

Oxidation of the ozonide of oleic acid with dichromic acid gives better yields.

Sebacic acid (L. *sebum*, tallow) is a waxy solid. The sodium salt is one of the products of the destructive distillation of the sodium soap from castor oil with excess alkali. The other chief product is 2-octanol **(capryl alcohol).**

$$CH_3(CH_2)_5CHOHCH_2CH=CH(CH_2)_7COONa + NaOH + H_2O \xrightarrow{\text{Heat}}$$

Sodium ricinoleate

$$CH_3(CH_2)_5CHOHCH_3 + NaOOC(CH_2)_8COONa + H_2$$

2-Octanol   Sodium sebacate

Technical "**isosebacic acid**" is a mixture of approximately 75 per cent 2-ethylsuberic acid, 15 per cent 2,2'-diethyladipic acid, and 10 per cent sebacic acid. It is made from butadiene and sodium, the reactions probably involving dimerization, carbonation of the disodium derivative, and catalytic reduction. The sebacic acids are used in the formulation of alkyd resins, and their esters are used as plasticizers, hydraulic fluids, and synthetic lubricants.

Brassylic acid can be obtained easily by the oxidation of erucic acid (p. 180) or the geometrical isomer (p. 354), brassidic acid.

$$CH_3(CH_2)_7CH=CH(CH_2)_{11}COOH \xrightarrow{HNO_3} CH_3(CH_2)_7COOH + HOOC(CH_2)_{11}COOH$$

Erucic or brassidic acid   Nonylic acid   Brassylic acid

The C_9, C_{20}, and C_{21} dibasic acids have been reported as saponification products of Japan wax (from *Rhus succedaneum*).

Long chain **α,ω-dicarboxylic acids** in the molecular weight range 600 to 3000 have been prepared. Dehydrohalogenation of the diacyl chloride from a dicarboxylic acid gives a polymeric ketene which can be hydrolyzed to a poly-β-keto acid. Loss of carbon dioxide and Clemmensen reduction yields the long-chain dibasic acid.

$$ClCOCH_2(CH_2)_xCH_2COCl \xrightarrow{(CH_3)_3N} O=C=CH(CH_2)_xCH=C=O \longrightarrow$$

$$O=C=CH(CH_2)_x \left[\begin{matrix} CO-O \\ | \quad | \\ CH-C=CH(CH_2)_x \end{matrix} \right]_y CH=C=O \xrightarrow[\text{heat}]{H_2O}$$

$$HOOCCH_2(CH_2)_x[CH_2COCH_2(CH_2)_x]_yCH_2COOH \xrightarrow[\text{HCl}]{Zn-Hg} HOOC(CH_2)_zCOOH$$

Reactions. The dicarboxylic acids, like all polyfunctional compounds, have certain characteristic behaviors depending on the relative positions of the functional groups. Being an electron-attracting group, the presence of one carboxyl close to another increases the ease of ionization of the first hydrogen ion. This effect rapidly decreases as the carboxyl groups become more separated. Thus oxalic acid is somewhat stronger than phosphoric acid, the first dissociation constants being 3.8×10^{-2} and 1.1×10^{-2} respectively. For malonic acid $K_A = 1.6 \times 10^{-3}$, but when two or more methylene groups intervene, the two carboxyl groups have little effect on each other. Thus succinic acid, $K_A = 6.4 \times 10^{-5}$, is only slightly stronger than acetic acid, $K_A = 1.8 \times 10^{-5}$.

The dicarboxylic acids differ in their *behavior on heating with or without dehydrating agents.* When **oxalic acid** is heated slowly to 150° it sublimes unchanged, but rapid heating to a higher temperature decomposes it into carbon dioxide and formic acid, and the latter decomposes further into carbon monoxide and water.

$$\text{HOOCCOOH} \xrightarrow{\text{Heat}} CO_2 + HCOOH \longrightarrow CO + H_2O$$

These reactions are brought about better by warming with concentrated sulfuric acid.

Malonic acid and substituted malonic acids, when heated above the melting point, lose carbon dioxide to give the monocarboxylic acid.

$$\text{HOOCCH}_2\text{COOH} \xrightarrow{\text{Heat}} CO_2 + CH_3COOH$$

$$\text{RCH(COOH)}_2 \xrightarrow{\text{Heat}} CO_2 + RCH_2COOH$$

$$\text{R}_2\text{C(COOH)}_2 \xrightarrow{\text{Heat}} CO_2 + R_2CHCOOH$$

The easy decarboxylation of malonic acids may be explained by a concerted action in which proton transfer takes place simultaneously with the elimination of carbon dioxide from the internally proton bonded dibasic acid.

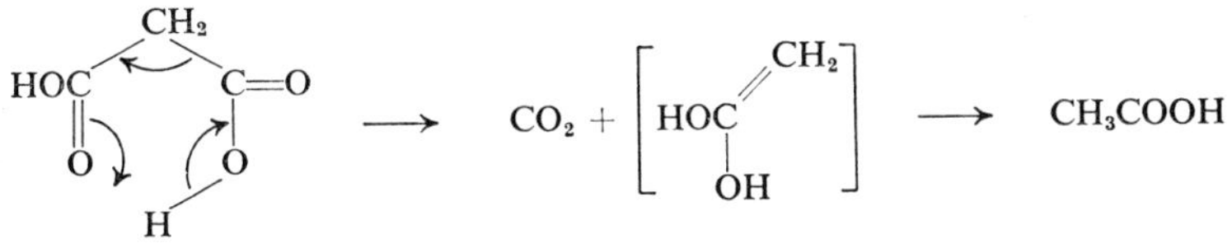

This view is supported by the observation that the dianion does not decompose, that the monoanion decomposes less rapidly than the undissociated acid, and that the replacement of methylene hydrogen by electron-attracting groups increases the ease of decomposition. An increase in electron density would be expected to strengthen the carbon-carbon bond, whereas a decrease in electron density should weaken it in the postulated mechanism.

Unsubstituted malonic acid with its active methylene group condenses with aldehydes to give α,β-unsaturated malonic acids, which lose carbon dioxide on heating to give α,β-unsaturated acids.

$$\text{RCHO} + \text{H}_2\text{C(COOH)}_2 \xrightarrow{\text{Pyridine}} H_2O + RCH{=}C(COOH)_2 \xrightarrow{\text{Heat}}$$
$$RCH{=}CHCOOH + CO_2$$

Bases stronger than pyridine may give an $\alpha,\beta:\beta,\gamma$-mixture (p. 786). A modification of this reaction permits the synthesis of α,β-unsaturated aldehydes. An aldehyde is condensed with the carbazole half amide of malonic acid. Decarboxylation and reduction of the product with lithium aluminum hydride gives an aldehyde-ammonia which loses carbazole to give the unsaturated aldehyde.

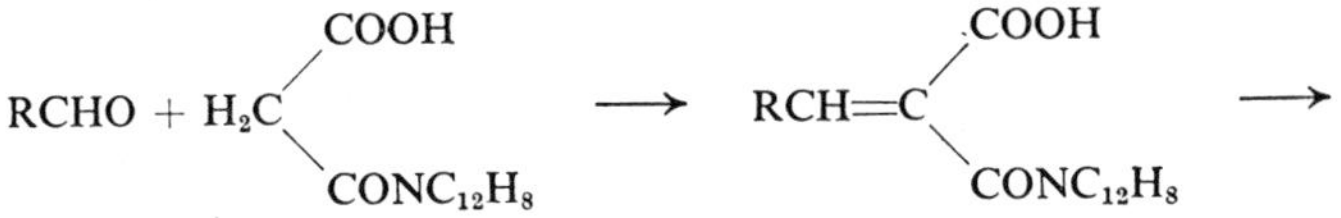

$$\text{RCH}{=}\text{CHCONC}_{12}\text{H}_8 \xrightarrow{\text{LiAlH}_4} [\text{RCH}{=}\text{CHCHOHNC}_{12}\text{H}_8] \longrightarrow$$
$$\text{RCH}{=}\text{CHCHO} + \text{HNC}_{12}\text{H}_8$$

The cyclic anhydride of malonic acid is unknown, but distillation of a mixture of malonic acid and phosphorus pentoxide gives a gas (b.p. 7°) having a bisketene structure. It is known as **carbon suboxide** from the molecular formula C_3O_2.

$$HOOCCH_2COOH + 2 P_2O_5 \longrightarrow O{=}C{=}C{=}C{=}O + 4 HPO_3$$

Succinic and **glutaric** acids and their substitution products lose water on heating to give the stable five- and six-membered cyclic anhydrides.

$$\begin{array}{ccc}
CH_2COOH & & CH_2{-}CO \\
| & \xrightarrow{\text{Heat}} & | \qquad\quad \diagdown \\
| & & | \qquad\qquad O + H_2O \\
CH_2COOH & & CH_2{-}CO \diagup
\end{array}$$

Succinic anhydride

$$\begin{array}{ccc}
CH_2COOH & & CH_2{-}CO \\
\diagup & \xrightarrow{\text{Heat}} & \diagup \qquad\quad \diagdown \\
CH_2 & & CH_2 \qquad\qquad O + H_2O \\
\diagdown & & \diagdown \qquad\quad \diagup \\
CH_2COOH & & CH_2{-}CO
\end{array}$$

Glutaric anhydride

These reactions take place at much lower temperatures in the presence of dehydrating agents. Thus simple refluxing of succinic acid with acetyl chloride and allowing to cool gives good yields of succinic anhydride.

Succinic esters react with aldehydes or ketones in the presence of alkoxides to give unsaturated dibasic acids (*Stobbe condensation*). Potassium *t*-butoxide is the preferred condensing agent.

$$R_2CO + \begin{array}{c} CH_2COOC_2H_5 \\ | \\ CH_2COOC_2H_5 \end{array} + KOC_4H_9\text{-}t \longrightarrow \begin{array}{c} R_2C{=}CCOOC_2H_5 \\ | \\ CH_2COOK \end{array} + C_4H_9OH$$

The usual course of the reaction of esters with aldehydes or ketones having an α hydrogen atom is the Claisen ester condensation (p. 814). It has been postulated that the Stobbe condensation proceeds by way of an intermediate γ-lactone (*paraconic ester*), the last step of the series being irreversible.

$$\begin{array}{c} CH_2COOC_2H_5 \\ | \\ CH_2COOC_2H_5 \end{array} \xrightarrow[\text{HOR}]{[^-OR]} \begin{array}{c} \overset{-}{:}CHCOOC_2H_5 \\ | \\ CH_2COOC_2H_5 \end{array} \xrightarrow{R_2CO} \begin{array}{c} CHCOOC_2H_5 \\ R_2C \diagup \qquad \diagdown CH_2 \\ | \qquad\quad _- \quad | \\ O \overset{..}{:} \underset{\curvearrowleft}{\diagdown}COOC_2H_5 \end{array} \xrightarrow{[^-OC_2H_5]}$$

$$\begin{array}{c} CHCOOC_2H_5 \\ R_2C \diagup \qquad \diagdown CH_2 \\ | \qquad\qquad | \\ O{-}{-}{-}CO \end{array} \xrightarrow[\text{HOC}_2\text{H}_5]{[^-OC_2H_5]} \begin{array}{c} \overset{..}{(:}CCOOC_2H_5 \\ R_2C \diagup \qquad \diagdown CH_2 \\ \curvearrowleft O{-}{-}{-}CO \end{array} \longrightarrow \begin{array}{c} COOC_2H_5 \\ | \\ R_2C{=}CCH_2COO^- \end{array}$$

Succinic anhydride resembles phthalic anhydride (p. 552) in its reactions. Phosphorus pentachloride gives **succinyl chloride.** The latter, like phthalyl chloride (p. 554), appears to be an equilibrium mixture of the cyclic and open chain forms. Thus reaction with benzene in the presence of aluminum chloride gives a mixture of the lactone and the diketone.

$$\begin{array}{c}\text{CH}_2\text{—CO} \\ | \qquad\qquad \diagdown \\ | \qquad\qquad\qquad \text{O} \\ | \qquad\qquad \diagup \\ \text{CH}_2\text{—CO} \end{array} \xrightarrow{\text{PCl}_5} \begin{array}{c}\text{CH}_2\text{—CCl}_2 \\ | \qquad\qquad \diagdown \\ | \qquad\qquad\qquad \text{O} \\ | \qquad\qquad \diagup \\ \text{CH}_2\text{—CO} \end{array} \rightleftarrows \begin{array}{c}\text{CH}_2\text{COCl} \\ | \\ \text{CH}_2\text{COCl} \end{array}$$

$$\downarrow \text{C}_6\text{H}_6\text{—AlCl}_3$$

$$\begin{array}{c}\text{CH}_2\text{—C(C}_6\text{H}_5)_2 \\ | \qquad\qquad\qquad \diagdown \\ | \qquad\qquad\qquad\qquad \text{O} \\ | \qquad\qquad\qquad \diagup \\ \text{CH}_2\text{—CO} \end{array} \quad\text{and}\quad \begin{array}{c}\text{CH}_2\text{COC}_6\text{H}_5 \\ | \\ \text{CH}_2\text{COC}_6\text{H}_5 \end{array}$$

Heating succinic anhydride with ammonia gives **succinimide.**

$$\begin{array}{c}\text{CH}_2\text{—CO} \\ | \qquad\qquad \diagdown \\ | \qquad\qquad\qquad \text{O} + \text{NH}_3 \\ | \qquad\qquad \diagup \\ \text{CH}_2\text{—CO} \end{array} \xrightarrow{\text{Heat}} \begin{array}{c}\text{CH}_2\text{—CO} \\ | \qquad\qquad \diagdown \\ | \qquad\qquad\qquad \text{NH} \\ | \qquad\qquad \diagup \\ \text{CH}_2\text{—CO} \end{array}$$
$$\text{Succinimide}$$

When succinimide is treated with bromine and alkali under the usual conditions of the Hofmann reaction, the product is β-alanine.

$$\begin{array}{c}\text{CH}_2\text{—CO} \\ | \qquad\qquad \diagdown \\ | \qquad\qquad\qquad \text{NH} \\ | \qquad\qquad \diagup \\ \text{CH}_2\text{—CO} \end{array} \xrightarrow{\text{H}_2\text{O}} \begin{array}{c}\text{CH}_2\text{COOH} \\ | \\ \text{CH}_2\text{CONH}_2 \end{array} \xrightarrow{\text{Br}_2,\ \text{NaOH}} \begin{array}{c}\text{CH}_2\text{COOH} \\ | \\ \text{CH}_2\text{NH}_2 \end{array}$$
$$\beta\text{-Alanine}$$

If, however, bromine is added to an ice-cold alkaline solution of succinimide, **N-bromosuccinimide** precipitates in almost quantitative yield.

$$(\text{CH}_2\text{CO})_2\text{NH} + \text{Br}_2 + \text{NaOH} \xrightarrow{0°} (\text{CH}_2\text{CO})_2\text{NBr} + \text{NaBr} + \text{H}_2\text{O}$$
$$\begin{array}{c}\textit{N}\text{-Bromo-} \\ \text{succinimide}\end{array}$$

This valuable reagent has the property of being able, in boiling carbon tetrachloride solutions, to brominate unsaturated or aromatic compounds α to the double bond or the ring to give allyl or benzyl bromides. An α-methylene group brominates more rapidly than an α-methyl group

$$\text{RCH}_2\text{CH}=\text{CHCH}_3 + (\text{CH}_2\text{CO})_2\text{NBr} \longrightarrow \text{RCHBrCH}=\text{CHCH}_3 + (\text{CH}_2\text{CO})_2\text{NH}$$

$$\text{ArCH}_2\text{R} + (\text{CH}_2\text{CO})_2\text{NBr} \longrightarrow \text{ArCHBrR} + (\text{CH}_2\text{CO})_2\text{NH}$$

Conjugated dienes do not react with this reagent and compounds containing hydroxyl and carboxyl groups decompose the reagent to give hypobromous acid. Esters of α,β-unsaturated acids, however, behave normally.

$$\text{RCH}_2\text{CH}=\text{CHCOOCH}_3 + (\text{CH}_2\text{CO})_2\text{NBr} \longrightarrow$$
$$\text{RCHBrCH}=\text{CHCOOCH}_3 + (\text{CH}_2\text{CO})_2\text{NH}$$

1,3-Dibromo-5,5-dimethylhydantoin (p. 635) may be used instead of N-bromosuccinimide. It is more stable and soluble in organic solvents and has a higher content of active bromine. N-Bromophthalimide gives poorer yields than

N-bromosuccinimide, and other *N*-bromo compounds are entirely unsuitable. *N*-Chlorosuccinimide is not a suitable chlorinating agent. *p*-Chloro- or *p*-nitro-*N*-chloroacetanilides react satisfactorily but their high molecular weight makes them relatively inefficient.

Catalysis of the bromination by light and peroxides indicates that it takes place by a free-radical mechanism.

$$ZNBr \rightleftarrows ZN \cdot + Br \cdot$$

$$RH + \cdot NZ \rightleftarrows R \cdot + HNZ$$

$$R \cdot + BrNZ \rightleftarrows RBr + \cdot NZ$$

Adipic acids and acids having the carboxyl groups more widely separated do not give cyclic anhydrides. On heating with dehydrating agents they give linear polymeric anhydrides.

$$(x + 1) \text{ HOOC(CH}_2)_4\text{COOH} + x \text{ (CH}_3\text{CO})_2\text{O} \xrightarrow{\text{Heat}}$$
$$\text{HOOC(CH}_2)_4[\text{COOCO(CH}_2)_4]_x\text{COOH} + 2x \text{ CH}_3\text{COOH}$$
Polyadipic anhydride

When adipic acids are heated, especially in the presence of a small amount of barium hydroxide, five-membered cyclic ketones are formed.

$$\begin{array}{c} \text{CH}_2\text{CH}_2\text{COOH} \\ | \\ \text{CH}_2\text{CH}_2\text{COOH} \end{array} \xrightarrow{\text{Ba(OH)}_2,\ \text{heat}} \begin{array}{c} \text{CH}_2\text{---CH}_2 \\ | \qquad\quad \diagdown \\ \qquad\qquad \text{CO} + \text{H}_2\text{O} + \text{CO}_2 \\ | \qquad\quad \diagup \\ \text{CH}_2\text{---CH}_2 \end{array}$$
Cyclopentanone

Pimelic acids on similar treatment yield six-membered cyclic ketones.

$$\begin{array}{c} \diagup \text{CH}_2\text{CH}_2\text{COOH} \\ \text{CH}_2 \\ \diagdown \text{CH}_2\text{CH}_2\text{COOH} \end{array} \xrightarrow{\text{Ba(OH)}_2,\ \text{heat}} \begin{array}{c} \text{CH}_2\text{---CH}_2 \\ \diagup \qquad\qquad \diagdown \\ \text{CH}_2 \qquad\qquad \text{CO} + \text{H}_2\text{O} + \text{CO}_2 \\ \diagdown \qquad\qquad \diagup \\ \text{CH}_2\text{---CH}_2 \end{array}$$

The generalization that succinic and glutaric acids give cyclic anhydrides, whereas adipic and pimelic acids yield cyclic ketones, is known as the **Blanc rule.** It has been of considerable value in determining whether oxygenated or unsaturated rings in compounds of unknown constitution are five- or six-membered. Thus a five-membered ring on oxidation gives a glutaric acid which cyclizes to an anhydride, whereas a six-membered ring on oxidation gives an adipic acid which cyclizes to a ketone. The rule is not infallible, however, since at least one example is known in which a nonterminal six-membered ring in a polycyclic compound gives on oxidation an adipic acid that forms a seven-membered cyclic anhydride.

Adipic acid is the most important of the dicarboxylic acids commercially. It is an intermediate for the synthesis of **nylon 66,** which is a polyamide formed by heating the hexamethylenediamine (p. 756) salt of adipic acid. The number 66 indicates that this particular nylon has two six-carbon constituents.

$$(x + 1)^-\text{OOC(CH}_2)_4\text{COO}^-\overset{+}{\text{H}_3}\text{N(CH}_2)_6\text{NH}_3^+ \xrightarrow[200°-300°]{\text{Heat}}$$
Nylon salt

$$^-\text{OOC(CH}_2)_4\text{CO[NH(CH}_2)_6\text{NHCO(CH}_2)_4\text{CO]}_x\text{NH(CH}_2)_6\text{NH}_3^+ + 2(x + 1)\text{ H}_2\text{O}$$
Nylon 66

The molecular weight of nylon 66 is about 10,000 and the melting point around 260°. It is insoluble in water and most organic solvents with the exception of formic acid and phenols. It can be extruded from a melt into monofilaments used for brush bristles, or spun from a solution in formic acid or phenol. The filaments are cold-drawn to four times their original length to orient the molecules along the axis of the fiber. The resulting fibers are elastic and lustrous and either dry or wet have a higher tensile strength than silk. Disadvantages are the low melting point and the difficulty in dyeing the fibers. Similar polyamides can be made from any dibasic acid and any diamine or from an ω-amino acid and the generic term *nylon* has been coined for all of them. Numerals following nylon, for example nylon 4 (p. 785) and nylon 6 (p. 841), indicate the number of carbon atoms in the polymeric unit.

Hexamethylenediamine is made by the reduction of **adiponitrile** (p. 756), which before 1948 was made from adipic acid by passing the vapors with an excess of ammonia over a catalyst such as boron phosphate at 350°.

$$(CH_2)_4(COONH_4)_2 \longrightarrow 2\ H_2O + (CH_2)_4(CONH_2)_2 \longrightarrow 2\ H_2O + (CH_2)_4(CN)_2$$
Ammonium adipate　　　　　　　　　　Adipamide　　　　　　　　　　Adiponitrile

With the growing scarcity of benzene, a process has been developed for preparing adiponitrile from furfural by way of tetrahydrofuran and tetramethylene chloride (Fig. 86, p. 619).

$$(CH_2)_4Cl_2 + 2\ NaCN \longrightarrow (CH_2)_4(CN)_2 + 2\ NaCl$$

Adiponitrile can be made also from acetylene by way of tetrahydrofuran (p. 717) or from 1,3-butadiene (p. 707).

$$CH_2{=}CHCH{=}CH_2 \xrightarrow{\ Cl_2\ } ClCH_2CH{=}CHCH_2Cl \xrightarrow{\ NaCN\ }$$

$$NCCH_2CH{=}CHCH_2CN \xrightarrow{\ H_2{-}Ni\ } NC(CH_2)_4CN$$

These reactions illustrate the diverse raw materials that frequently are available to the manufacturer of organic chemicals.

Another important technical use for adipic acid is in the manufacture of **urethan rubbers.** Initially a polyethylene adipate is made by esterification of adipic acid with ethylene glycol, removing the water by distillation. An excess of ethylene glycol is used to provide alcoholic hydroxyl groups at the ends of the chain.

$$HOOC(CH_2)_4COOH + (x + 1)\ HOCH_2CH_2OH \longrightarrow$$
$$H[OCH_2CH_2OCO(CH_2)_4CO]_xOCH_2CH_2OH + 2x\ H_2O$$

The proportions and time of reaction are chosen to give an average molecular weight of about 1800 ($x = 10$). Reaction of the ends of the chains with a diisocyanate gives a long chain diisocyanate.

$$H[OCH_2CH_2OCO(CH_2)_4CO]_xOCH_2CH_2OH + 2\ O{=}C{=}NArN{=}C{=}O \longrightarrow$$
$$O{=}C{=}NArNHCO[OCH_2CH_2OCO(CH_2)_4CO]_xOCH_2CH_2OCONHArN{=}C{=}O$$

Vulcanization now can be brought about by adding a glycol to join the ends of the chains.

$$-N{=}C{=}O + HOCH_2CH_2OH + O{=}C{=}N- \longrightarrow -NHCOOCH_2CH_2OCONH-$$

If water and an amine catalyst is added, the carbamic acid formed loses carbon dioxide which produces a foamed rubber. The amino group formed links the chains.

$$-N{=}C{=}O + H_2O \longrightarrow -NHCOOH \longrightarrow CO_2 \div -NH_2$$
$$-NH_2 + O{=}C{=}N- \longrightarrow -NHCONH-$$

The ramifications of these reactions are infinite. 2,4-Toluenediisocyanate (p. 479) and 1,5-naphthalenediisocyanate appear to be the preferred chain-extending reagents. However any polyamine can yield a polyisocyanate. Moreover any dibasic acid and any dihydric alcohol, amino alcohol or diamine could undergo reactions similar to those of adipic acid and ethylene glycol. Using polybasic acids, polyhydric alcohols, and polyamines, numerous degrees and types of cross linking could result. The products currently being marketed are characterized by extreme resistance to abrasion, tear, oil and solvents, and atmospheric oxidation.

Reactions of Malonic Esters

The reactions of the esters of malonic acid are sufficiently important to require special attention. Usually the ethyl ester is used, and the term *malonic ester* ordinarily means ethyl malonate. The methylene group joined to the two carboethoxy groups is unusually reactive. Bromination takes place with extreme ease, although ethyl malonate does not give a color with ferric chloride and other tests indicate the absence of a detectable amount of an enol form.

The most important reaction of malonic esters is *carbon alkylation*. Reaction of ethyl malonate with sodium ethoxide in absolute alcohol gives a sodium salt which reacts with an alkyl halide to give an alkyl-substituted malonic ester. A second alkyl group may be introduced if desired. Since the esters can be saponified and decarboxylated, the reaction leads to the preparation of substituted acetic acids.

$$CH_2(COOC_2H_5)_2 \xrightarrow{NaOC_2H_5} Na^+\bar{C}H(COOC_2H_5)_2 \xrightarrow{RX}$$
Ethyl sodiomalonate

$$NaX + RCH(COOC_2H_5)_2 \xrightarrow[HCl]{NaOH,\ then} RCH(COOH)_2 \xrightarrow{Heat} RCH_2COOH + CO_2$$
Ethyl alkylmalonate / Alkylmalonic acid / Alkylacetic acid

$$RCH(COOC_2H_5)_2 \xrightarrow{NaOC_2H_5} Na^+R\bar{C}(COOC_2H_5)_2 \xrightarrow{R'X}$$

$$\begin{array}{c}R\\ \diagdown \\ \diagup \\ R'\end{array}C(COOC_2H_5)_2 \xrightarrow[HCl]{NaOH,\ then} \begin{array}{c}R\\ \diagdown \\ \diagup \\ R'\end{array}C(COOH)_2 \xrightarrow{Heat} \begin{array}{c}R\\ \diagdown \\ \diagup \\ R'\end{array}CHCOOH + CO_2$$
Ethyl dialkylmalonate / Dialkylmalonic acid / Dialkylacetic acid

The reaction of esters with ethyl carbonate (p. 802) is reversible and the position of equilibrium is unfavorable for disubstituted malonic esters (cf. p. 815). Hence the products from the carbon alkylation of monosubstituted malonic esters frequently are the substituted monocarboxylic ester and ethyl carbonate instead of or along with the malonic ester.

$$RCH(COOC_2H_5)_2 + R'X \xrightarrow{NaOC_2H_5} RR'C(COOC_2H_5)_2 \underset{\longleftarrow}{\overset{HOC_2H_5}{\longrightarrow}}$$
$$RR'CHCOOC_2H_5 + (C_2H_5O)_2CO$$

Reaction of the sodium salt with iodine causes coupling of two malonic ester units and provides a method for the synthesis of α,β-disubstituted succinic acids.

$$2 I_2 + 2 Na^+ R\bar{C}(COOC_2H_5)_2 \longrightarrow 2 NaI + \begin{array}{c} R-C(COOC_2H_5)_2 \\ | \\ R-C(COOC_2H_5)_2 \end{array} \xrightarrow[\text{HCl}]{\text{NaOH, then}}$$

$$\begin{array}{c} RC(COOH)_2 \\ | \\ RC(COOH)_2 \end{array} \xrightarrow{\text{Heat}} \begin{array}{c} RCHCOOH \\ | \\ RCHCOOH \end{array} + 2 CO_2$$

Methylene halides react with two moles of ethyl sodiomalonate to give tetracarboxylic esters. If it is possible to form a three- to six-membered ring, a cyclic derivative also may be formed.

$$ClCH_2CH_2Cl + 2 Na^+\bar{C}H(COOC_2H_5)_2 \longrightarrow (C_2H_5OOC)_2CHCH_2CH_2CH(COOC_2H_5)_2$$
Ethyl 1,1,4,4-butanetetracarboxylate

$$ClCH_2CH_2Cl + Na^+\bar{C}H(COOC_2H_5)_2 \longrightarrow ClCH_2CH_2CH(COOC_2H_5)_2 \xrightarrow{\text{NaOR}}$$

$$\underset{Na^+}{ClCH_2CH_2\bar{C}(COOC_2H_5)_2} \longrightarrow \begin{array}{c} CH_2 \\ | \quad\diagdown \\ \quad\quad C(COOC_2H_5)_2 + NaCl \\ | \quad\diagup \\ CH_2 \end{array}$$

Ethyl 1,1-cyclo-
propanedicar-
boxylate

Similarly trimethylene, tetramethylene, and pentamethylene bromides give cyclobutane-, cyclopentane-, and cyclohexanedicarboxylic esters. If the halogen atoms are farther apart, only the tetracarboxylic esters are obtained.

The halide may contain other functional groups as long as they are not affected by sodium ethoxide. For example ethyl chloroacetate gives a tricarboxylic ester and acyl chlorides give β-keto dicarboxylic esters.

$$C_2H_5OOCCH_2Cl + Na^+\bar{C}H(COOC_2H_5)_2 \longrightarrow C_2H_5OOCCH_2CH(COOC_2H_5)_2$$
Ethyl 1,1,2-ethanetricarboxylate

$$RCOCl + Na^+\bar{C}H(COOC_2H_5)_2 \longrightarrow RCOCH(COOC_2H_5)_2$$

Ketones cannot be made by the hydrolysis and decarboxylation of ethyl acylmalonates because carbon-carbon cleavage takes place to give the sodium salts of the original acids.

$$RCOCR'(COOC_2H_5)_2 + 3 NaOH \longrightarrow RCOONa + R'CH(COONa)_2 + 2 C_2H_5OH$$

The *t*-butyl ester, however, decomposes on warming with acetic acid into the ketone, 2-butene, and carbon dioxide.

$$RCOCR'(COOC_4H_9\text{-}t)_2 \xrightarrow[\text{warm}]{CH_3COOH} 2 C_4H_8 + RCOCH_2R' + 2 CO_2$$

Another procedure makes use of the 2-tetrahydropyranyl esters, prepared by the addition of malonic acids to tetrahydropyran. The acylated esters also decompose readily on warming with acetic acid.

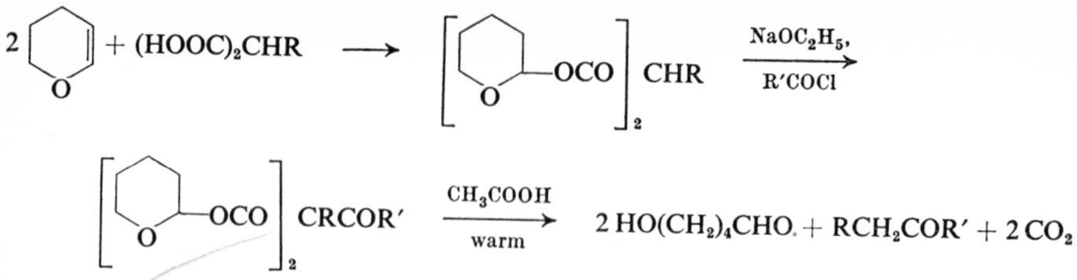

$$2 \; \bigcirc\!\!=\!\!O + (HOOC)_2CHR \longrightarrow \left[\bigcirc\!\!-OCO \right]_2 CHR \xrightarrow[R'COCl]{NaOC_2H_5,}$$

$$\left[\bigcirc\!\!-OCO \right]_2 CRCOR' \xrightarrow[\text{warm}]{CH_3COOH} 2 \, HO(CH_2)_4CHO + RCH_2COR' + 2 \, CO_2$$

It also is possible to obtain the malonic acid by hydrogenolysis of the benzyl ester.

$$RCOCR'(COOCH_2C_6H_5)_2 + 2 \, H_2 \xrightarrow{Ni} 2 \, C_6H_5CH_2OH + RCOCR'(COOH)_2 \xrightarrow{Heat}$$

$$RCOCH_2R' + 2 \, CO_2$$

Arylmalonic esters cannot be made from aryl halides because the halogen is not sufficiently reactive. Frequently they can be made by a Claisen ester condensation (p. 814). For example, ethyl phenylmalonate results from the reaction of ethyl phenylacetate with ethyl carbonate.

$$C_6H_5CH_2COOC_2H_5 + C_2H_5OCOOC_2H_5 \xrightarrow{NaOC_2H_5} \underset{COOC_2H_5}{C_6H_5CHCOOC_2H_5} + C_2H_5OH$$

Aryl malonic esters can be made also by the Arndt-Eistert reaction (p. 267) from aroyl halides and ethyl diazoacetate (p. 267).

$$ArCOCl + N_2CHCOOC_2H_5 \longrightarrow ArCOC(N_2)COOC_2H_5 \xrightarrow[Ag]{C_2H_5OH}$$

$$C_2H_5OCOCHArCOOC_2H_5 + N_2$$

Aryl- and alkylmalonic esters can be obtained by the thermal decomposition of α'-substituted oxosuccinic esters (p. 826).

One method of synthesis of α-amino acids from substituted malonic esters involves bromination, decarboxylation, and reaction with ammonia (p. 303). More recently convenient syntheses involving the use of (acetylamino)malonic ester have been developed. This intermediate is prepared by the following series of reactions.

$$\underset{\substack{\text{Ethyl} \\ \text{malonate}}}{\overset{COOC_2H_5}{\underset{COOC_2H_5}{CH_2}}} \xrightarrow{HNO_2} \underset{\substack{\text{Ethyl nitrosomalonate}}}{\overset{COOC_2H_5}{\underset{COOC_2H_5}{CHNO}}} \rightleftarrows \overset{COOC_2H_5}{\underset{COOC_2H_5}{C\!\!=\!\!NOH}} \underset{H_2(Ni)}{\rightleftarrows} \underset{\substack{\text{Ethyl} \\ \text{aminomalonate}}}{\overset{COOC_2H_5}{\underset{COOC_2H_5}{CHNH_2}}} \xrightarrow{Ac_2O} \underset{\substack{\text{Ethyl} \\ \text{(acetylamino)-} \\ \text{malonate}}}{\overset{COOC_2H_5}{\underset{COOC_2H_5}{CHNHCOCH_3}}}$$

(Acetylamino)malonic ester undergoes carbon alkylation. Saponification and loss of carbon dioxide yields the amino acids.

$$\underset{\underset{COOC_2H_5}{|}}{\overset{\overset{COOC_2H_5}{|}}{RCH_2X + CHNHCOCH_3}} \xrightarrow{NaOC_2H_5} \underset{\underset{COOC_2H_5}{|}}{\overset{\overset{COOC_2H_5}{|}}{RCH_2CNHCOCH_3}} \xrightarrow[\text{then acidity}]{NaOH}$$

$$\underset{\underset{COOH}{|}}{\overset{\overset{COOH}{|}}{RCH_2CNH_2}} \xrightarrow{\text{Heat}} RCH_2CH(NH_2)COOH + CO_2$$

Mannich bases of the type $ArCH_2N(CH_3)_2$ also alkylate malonic esters, and the reaction has been used for the synthesis of tryptophan.

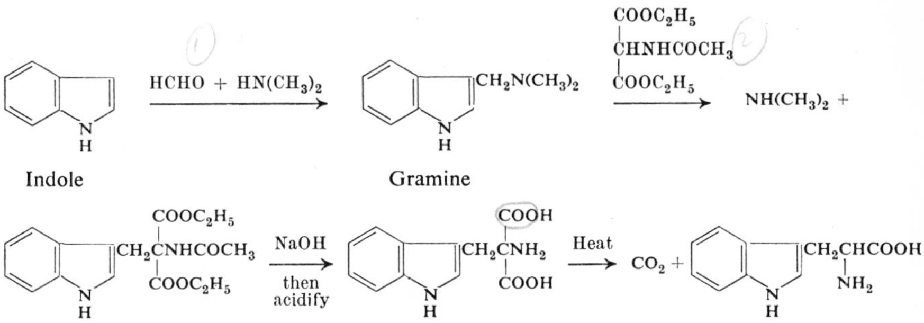

Indole   Gramine

                                                      Tryptophan

Ethyl malonate adds to α,β-unsaturated esters in the presence of a basic catalyst such as sodium ethoxide. The product can be saponified and decarboxylated to give a β-substituted glutaric acid.

$$RCH{=}CHCOOC_2H_5 + H_2C(COOC_2H_5)_2 \xrightarrow{NaOC_2H_5} \underset{\underset{CH(COOC_2H_5)_2}{|}}{RCHCH_2COOC_2H_5} \xrightarrow[\text{then HCl}]{NaOH,}$$

$$\underset{\underset{CH(COOH)_2}{|}}{RCHCH_2COOH} \xrightarrow{\text{Heat}} \underset{\underset{CH_2COOH}{|}}{RCHCH_2COOH} + CO_2$$

Other active methylene compounds such as ethyl cyanoacetate, $NCCH_2$-$COOC_2H_5$, ethyl phenylacetate, $C_6H_5CH_2COOC_2H_5$, benzyl cyanide, C_6H_5-CH_2CN, and ethyl acetoacetate, $CH_3COCH_2COOC_2H_5$, also add to α,β-unsaturated ketones and esters. This behavior is known as the *Michael*[1] *reaction*

As in the alkylation of malonic esters (p 800), the reversibility of the Claisen ester condensation can lead to abnormal products. For example, methylmalonic ester adds normally to ethyl crotonate in the presence of less than one mole of sodium ethoxide, but an excess of sodium ethoxide causes the elimination of ethyl carbonate, which then condenses with the α-methylene group to give the more stable isomer

---

[1] Arthur Michael (1854–1942), professor of chemistry at Harvard University. His work, which was published for the most part in the German chemical literature, was concerned chiefly with the theoretical aspects of addition to the double bond and the behavior of active methylene compounds

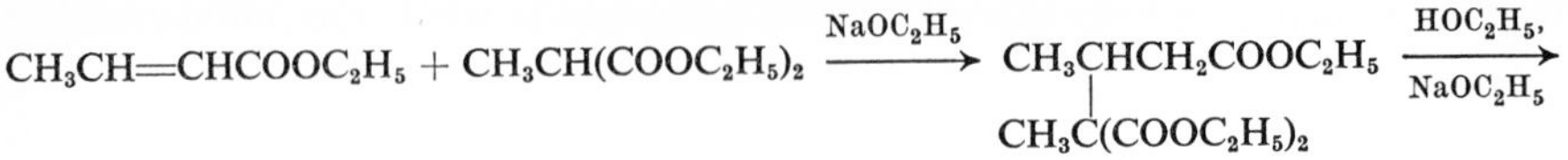

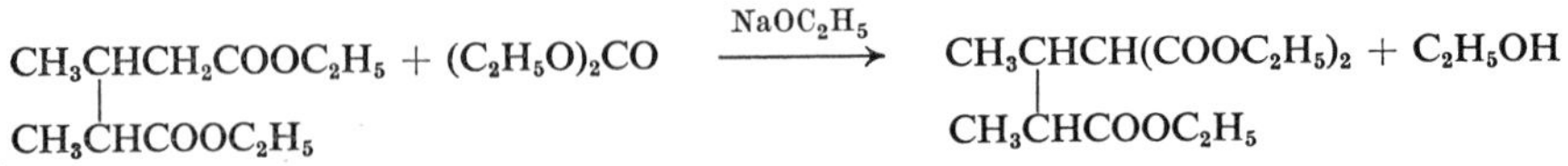

$$\text{CH}_3\text{CH}=\text{CHCOOC}_2\text{H}_5 + \text{CH}_3\text{CH(COOC}_2\text{H}_5)_2 \xrightarrow{\text{NaOC}_2\text{H}_5} \underset{\overset{|}{\text{CH}_3\text{C(COOC}_2\text{H}_5)_2}}{\text{CH}_3\text{CHCH}_2\text{COOC}_2\text{H}_5} \xrightarrow[\text{NaOC}_2\text{H}_5]{\text{HOC}_2\text{H}_5,}$$

$$\underset{\overset{|}{\text{CH}_3\text{CHCOOC}_2\text{H}_5}}{\text{CH}_3\text{CHCH}_2\text{COOC}_2\text{H}_5} + (\text{C}_2\text{H}_5\text{O})_2\text{CO} \xrightarrow{\text{NaOC}_2\text{H}_5} \underset{\overset{|}{\text{CH}_3\text{CHCOOC}_2\text{H}_5}}{\text{CH}_3\text{CHCH(COOC}_2\text{H}_5)_2} + \text{C}_2\text{H}_5\text{OH}$$

Addition to α,β-unsaturated ketones may involve simultaneous ester condensations (p. 814). For example, the reaction of ethyl malonate with mesityl oxide gives ethyl 2,4-diketo-6,6-dimethylcyclohexanecarboxylate.

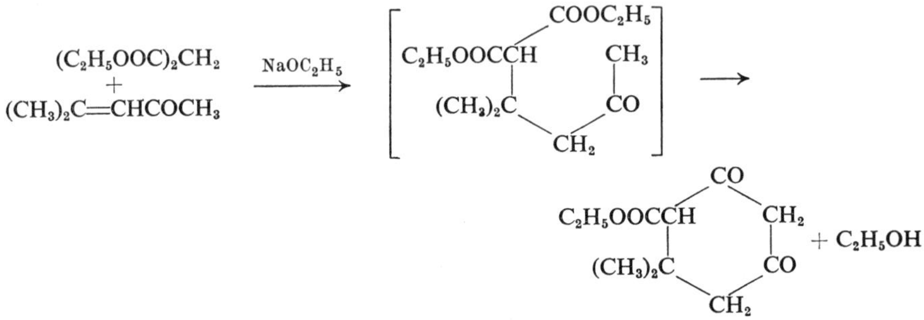

Hydrolysis of the cyclic diketo ester and decarboxylation (p. 813) give 5,5-dimethyl-1,3-cyclohexanedione, commonly known as **methone** or **dimedone**.

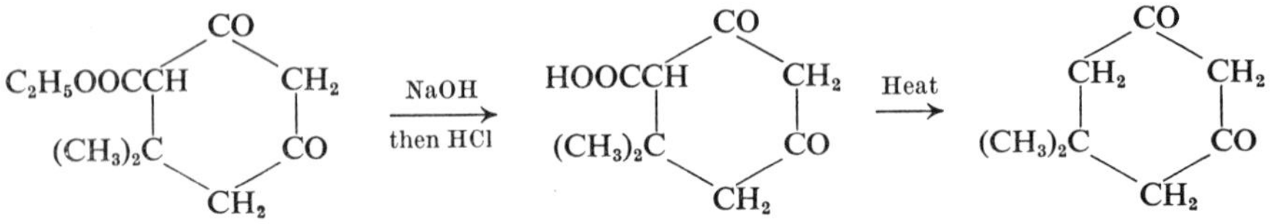

It is a valuable reagent for preparing solid derivatives of aldehydes.

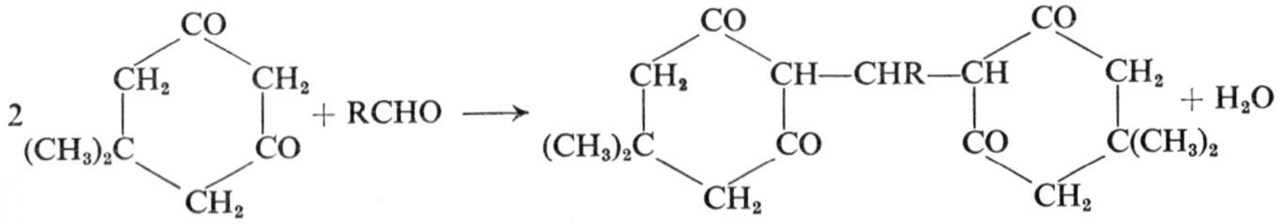

These derivatives are useful particularly for the lower molecular weight aldehydes because of the large increase in the molecular weight. Thus the molecular weight of the derivative of formaldehyde is over nine times that of formaldehyde.

Like the 1,3-diketones and other active methylene compounds, ethyl malonate undergoes the Knoevenagel reaction (p. 773) with aldehydes. Diethylamine or piperidine is the usual catalyst.

$$\text{RCH}=\text{O} + \text{H}_2\text{C(COOC}_2\text{H}_5)_2 \xrightarrow[\text{or C}_5\text{H}_{10}\text{NH}]{(\text{C}_2\text{H}_5)_2\text{NH}} [\text{RCHOHCH(COOC}_2\text{H}_5)_2] \longrightarrow$$

$$\text{RCH}=\text{C(COOC}_2\text{H}_5)_2 + \text{H}_2\text{O}$$

If R is aliphatic and an excess of ethyl malonate is used, the initial reaction usually is followed by a Michael addition to give the tetracarboxylic ester.

$$RCH{=}C(COOC_2H_5)_2 + H_2C(COOC_2H_5)_2 \xrightarrow{R_2NH} RCH[CH(COOC_2H_5)_2]_2$$

Unsaturated Dicarboxylic Acids

A few unsaturated dicarboxylic acids are of special interest. **Maleic and fumaric acids** (*cis*- and *trans*-ethylenedicarboxylic acids) are the classic examples of geometrical isomerism (p. 354). Maleic acid readily yields an anhydride on heating, indicating that the carboxyl groups are on the same side of the double bond. Fumaric acid on the other hand does not yield an anhydride easily. When heated to a sufficiently high temperature (250°–300°), isomerization takes place and maleic anhydride is formed.

Maleic acid → Maleic anhydride

Heat at 100° under reduced pressure

Fumaric acid — Heat at 200° → Sublimes unchanged

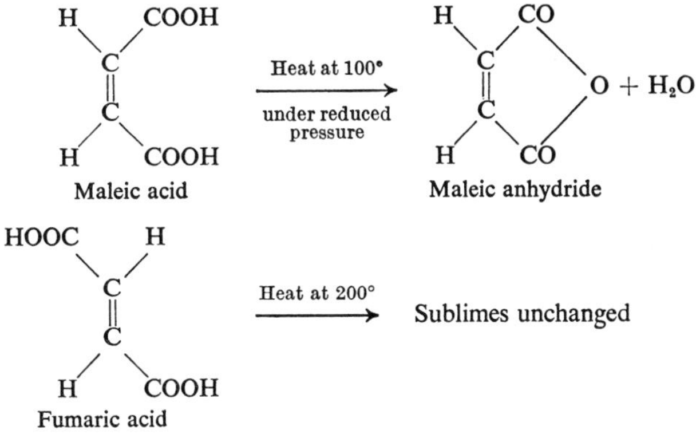

Maleic acid is obtained in the form of its anhydride by the catalytic air oxidation of benzene.

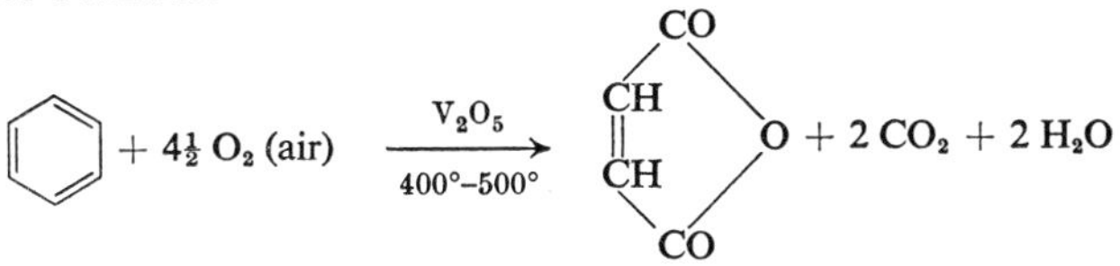

$$\bigcirc + 4\tfrac{1}{2} O_2 \text{ (air)} \xrightarrow[400°-500°]{V_2O_5} \text{(maleic anhydride)} + 2 CO_2 + 2 H_2O$$

Unsaturated compounds such as crotonic aldehyde can be used in this process when benzene is in short supply.

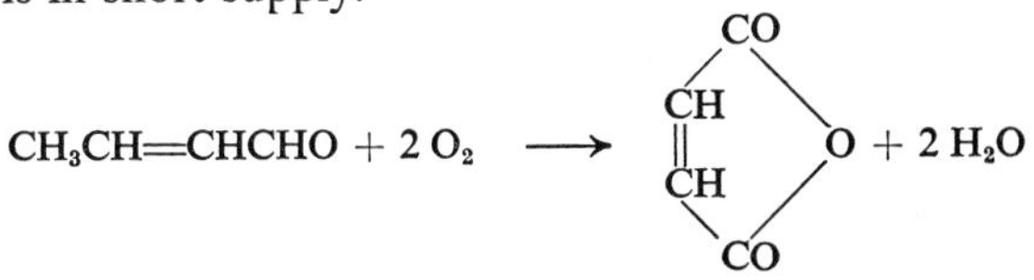

$$CH_3CH{=}CHCHO + 2 O_2 \longrightarrow \text{(maleic anhydride)} + 2 H_2O$$

Maleic anhydride is formed to the extent of 5 to 8 per cent in the production of phthalic anhydride (p. 552) and is separated as a co-product. **Fumaric acid** can be made by the isomerization of maleic acid or by a fermentation process from starch or other carbohydrates using molds of the genus *Rhizopus*.

The most characteristic reaction of maleic anhydride is its 1,4 addition to conjugated dienes (p. 707).

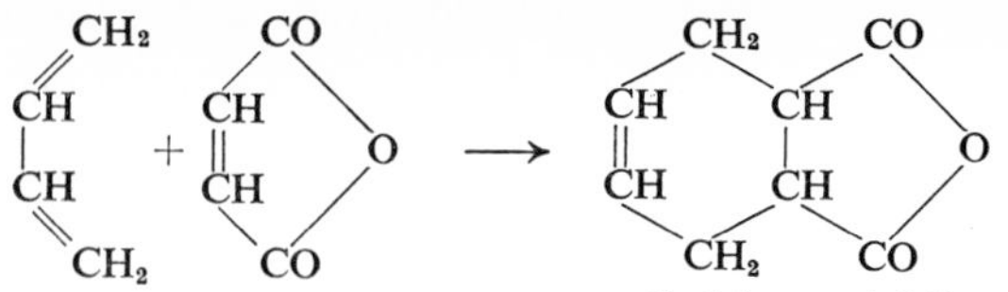

Cyclohexene-4,5-di-
carboxylic anhydride

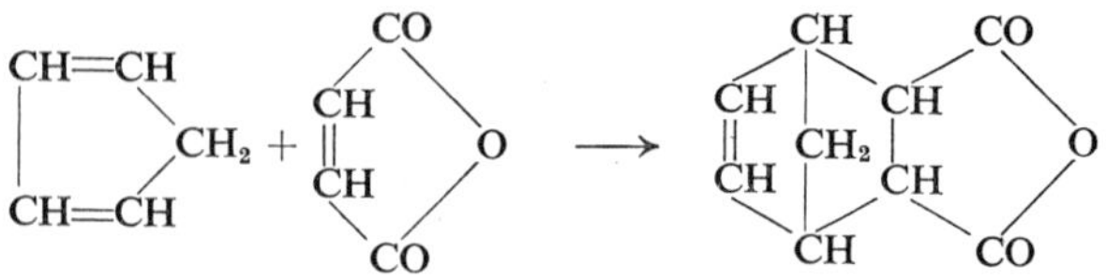

Cyclopentadiene

3,6-Methylenecyclo-
hexene-4,5-dicarboxylic
anhydride

Furan condenses normally and anthracene condenses in the 9,10 position. Thiophene, benzene, and condensed aromatic nuclei other than anthracenes do not react, but vinyl substituted benzenes give exocyclic[2] condensation products.

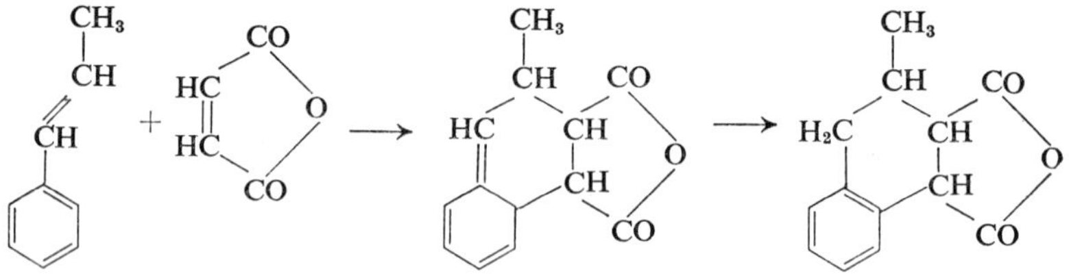

Other compounds containing a double or triple bond conjugated with a carbonyl group or a nitrile group, such as acrolein, crotonic aldehyde, acrylic acid, crotononitrile, acetylenedicarboxylic esters, quinones and vinyl ethers, also add to a system of conjugated carbon-carbon multiple bonds. The first group of compounds are called *dienophiles*, the second are the *dienes*, and the product of the reaction of dienophile with a diene is called the *adduct*. These reactions commonly are known as **Diels-Alder diene syntheses.**[3]

The mechanism of the Diels-Alder reaction is of interest, since it appears to bear some relation to complex formation of polynitro compounds with aromatic hydrocarbons (p. 461). The reaction is preceded by the formation of a transient, yellow molecular compound between the reactants. It has been proposed that the diene, having a low ionization potential, transfers an electron to the dienophile, which has a high electron affinity. The two free-radical ions constitute the initial complex, which then forms the covalent cyclic adduct.

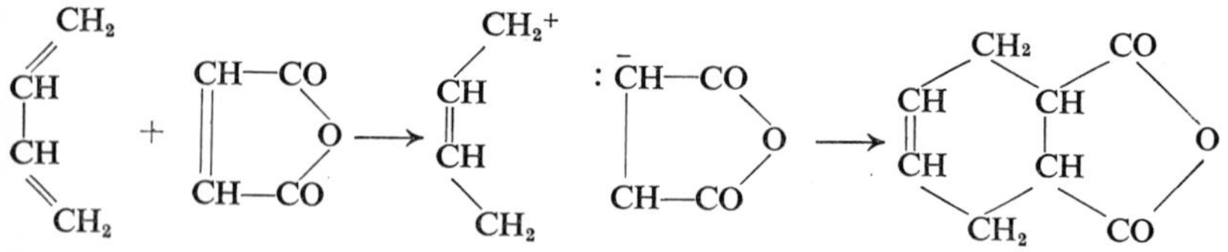

---

[2] The prefixes *exo* and *endo* are used to indicate whether a group is outside or inside of a ring (Gr. *exo*, outside; *endon*, within).

[3] Otto Diels (1876–1954), professor of chemistry at the University of Kiel. He discovered carbon suboxide (p. 796) and was the first to use selenium for the dehydrogenation of natural products, but is best known for the reaction that bears his name. He was awarded the Nobel Prize in Chemistry in 1950.

Commercial production of maleic anhydride began in the United States in 1933 and in 1954 amounted to 40 million pounds. The most important use is in the formulation of **polyester resins.** Alkyd resins (p. 552), polyethylene terephthalate (p. 555), and urethan rubbers (p. 799) also have the ester linkage as the most important type of bonding in the polymer, but technically the term *polyester* or *polyester resin* refers to a solution of an unsaturated linear polymer in a liquid monomer that is capable of copolymerizing with the linear polymer. Most polyester resins consist of a solution of an alkyd resin, prepared for example from propylene glycol, maleic anhydride, and adipic acid, in 30 per cent of its weight of styrene. An inhibitor, such as a quaternary ammonium salt, is added to prevent polymerization before use. Just prior to use a peroxide catalyst such as benzoyl peroxide or *t*-butylhydroperoxide together with a cobalt or manganese salt as a promoter is added. The liquid may be cast or applied to a reinforcing agent such as glass fiber. Copolymerization of the alkyd resin with the monomer takes place at room temperature or higher depending on the formulation. Wide variations in the composition of the alkyd are possible and other liquid monomers, such as diallyl phthalate or mixtures of styrene with vinyl acetate, methyl methacrylate, or vinyl toluene, may be used as solvent.

The **copolymer of vinyl acetate and maleic anhydride,** after hydrolysis, gives a linear polyhydroxypolycarboxylic acid used as a soil conditioner (cf. p. 788).

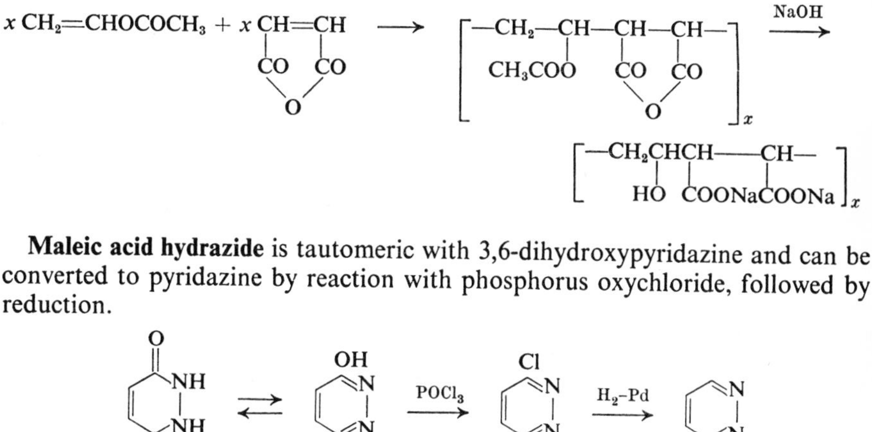

$$x\ CH_2{=}CHOCOCH_3 + x\ CH{=}CH \longrightarrow \left[\begin{array}{c} {-}CH_2{-}CH{-}CH{-}CH{-} \\ CH_3COO\quad CO\ \ CO \\ O \end{array}\right]_x \xrightarrow{NaOH}$$

$$\left[\begin{array}{c} {-}CH_2CHCH{-}\!\!-\!\!CH{-} \\ HO\ \ COONaCOONa \end{array}\right]_x$$

Maleic acid hydrazide is tautomeric with 3,6-dihydroxypyridazine and can be converted to pyridazine by reaction with phosphorus oxychloride, followed by reduction.

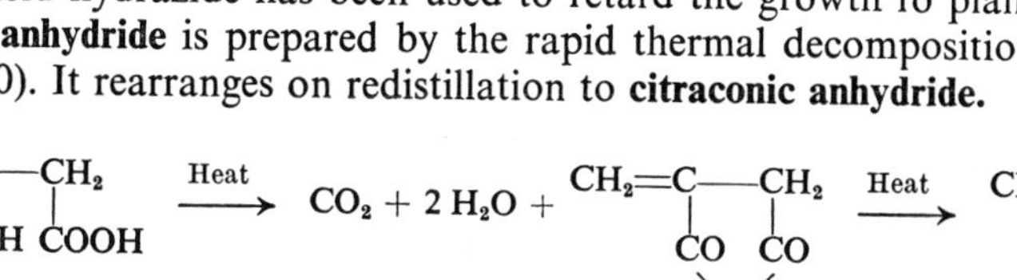

Maleic acid hydrazide has been used to retard the growth fo plants.

Itaconic anhydride is prepared by the rapid thermal decomposition of citric acid (p. 810). It rearranges on redistillation to **citraconic anhydride.**

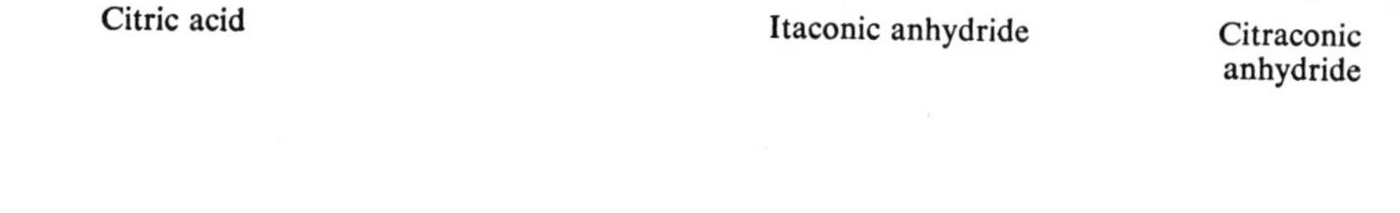

$$\begin{array}{c} CH_2{-}COH{-}CH_2 \\ COOH\ COOH\ COOH \end{array} \xrightarrow{Heat} CO_2 + 2\,H_2O + \begin{array}{c} CH_2{=}C{-}CH_2 \\ CO\ \ CO \\ O \end{array} \xrightarrow{Heat} \begin{array}{c} CH_3C{=}CH \\ CO\ \ CO \\ O \end{array}$$

Citric acid   Itaconic anhydride   Citraconic anhydride

Hydrolysis of the anhydrides gives the acids. Either itaconic or citraconic acid, when heated with oxides of nitrogen, rearranges to the equilibrium mixture with **mesaconic acid,** the geometrical isomer of citraconic acid.

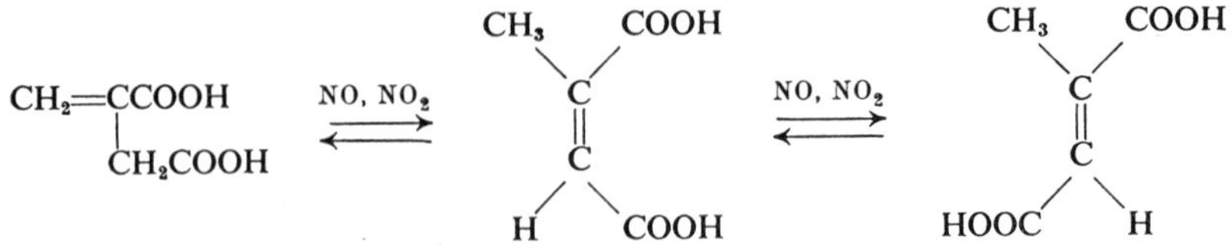

$$CH_2=CCOOH \over CH_2COOH \quad \xrightarrow[\text{NO, NO}_2]{} \quad \begin{matrix} CH_3 & COOH \\ \diagdown & \diagup \\ & C \\ & \| \\ & C \\ \diagup & \diagdown \\ H & COOH \end{matrix} \quad \xrightarrow[\text{NO, NO}_2]{} \quad \begin{matrix} CH_3 & COOH \\ \diagdown & \diagup \\ & C \\ & \| \\ & C \\ \diagup & \diagdown \\ HOOC & H \end{matrix}$$

Itaconic acid	Citraconic acid	Mesaconic acid
17 per cent	16 per cent	67 per cent

Glutaconic acid is made by dehydration of β-hydroxyglutaric acid. The latter can be obtained by reduction of acetonedicarboxylic acid (p. 810).

$$HOOCCH_2COCH_2COOH \xrightarrow{H_2-Pt} HOOCCH_2CHOHCH_2COOH \xrightarrow{H_2SO_4}$$

Acetonedicarboxylic acid β-Hydroxyglutaric acid

$$HOOCCH_2CH=CHCOOH$$
Glutaconic acid

Glutaconic acid gives an anhydride which appears to have an enol structure, since it gives a color with ferric chloride.

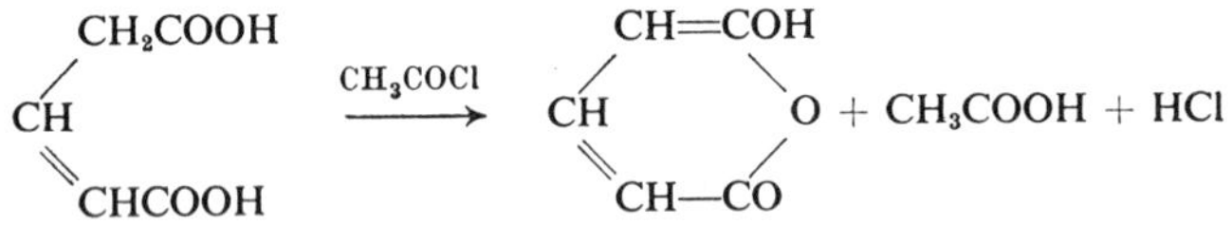

$$\begin{matrix} CH_2COOH \\ \diagup \\ CH \\ \diagdown\diagdown \\ CHCOOH \end{matrix} \quad \xrightarrow{CH_3COCl} \quad \begin{matrix} CH=COH \\ \diagup \quad \diagdown \\ CH \qquad O \\ \diagdown\diagdown \quad \diagup \\ CH-CO \end{matrix} + CH_3COOH + HCl$$

Glutaconic
anhydride

Careful hydrolysis of glutaconic anhydride gives *cis*-glutaconic acid, which is isomerized rapidly in aqueous solution to the stable *trans* form because of the easy allylic shift of the double bond (p. 728).

Ethyl glutaconate like ethyl malonate gives a sodium salt which undergoes carbon alkylation with alkyl halides.

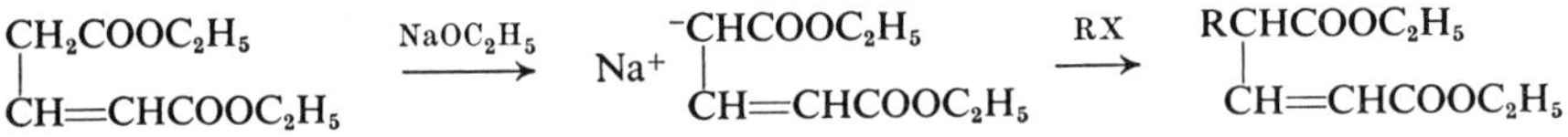

$$\begin{matrix} CH_2COOC_2H_5 \\ | \\ CH=CHCOOC_2H_5 \end{matrix} \xrightarrow{NaOC_2H_5} Na^+ \begin{matrix} ^-CHCOOC_2H_5 \\ | \\ CH=CHCOOC_2H_5 \end{matrix} \xrightarrow{RX} \begin{matrix} RCHCOOC_2H_5 \\ | \\ CH=CHCOOC_2H_5 \end{matrix}$$

This behavior is another example of the transmission of the effect of an activating group through a conjugated double bond. Because of the easy $\alpha,\beta-\beta,\gamma$ shift of the double bond, all three α hydrogen atoms can be alkylated.

Hydroxy Dicarboxylic Acids

Tartronic acid is hydroxymalonic acid, $HOOCCHOHCOOH$. It is made by the hydrolysis of bromomalonic acid or by the reduction of mesoxalic acid, $HOOCCOCOOH$ (p. 826).

Malic acid is hydroxysuccinic acid, $HOOCCH_2CHOHCOOH$. It is present in many fruit juices and was isolated by Scheele in 1785 from unripe apples (L. *malum,* apple). Calcium acid 1-malate separates during the concentration of maple sap and is known as *sugar sand.* Malic acid has the property of attracting plant spermatozoa; that is, they migrate toward the point of highest concentration. Surprisingly D- and L-malic acid are equally effective. Racemic malic acid is manufactured by the hydration of maleic or fumaric acid.

Thiomalic acid is made by the addition of hydrogen sulfide to maleic acid.

$$HOOCCH{=}CHCOOH + H_2S \longrightarrow HOOCCH_2CH(SH)COOH$$

Sodium thiomalate is reported to be more effective and less toxic than BAL as an antidote for heavy metal poisoning (cf. p. 752). Addition of O,O-diethyldithiophosphate to ethyl maleate gives the mixed dithiophosphate known as **malathion.** It is an important insecticide because of its high toxicity to a variety of insects and its low toxicity to mammals.

$$4\,C_2H_5OH + P_2S_5 \longrightarrow 2\,(C_2H_5O)_2PSSH + H_2S$$

$$(C_2H_5O)_2PSSH \; + \; \begin{matrix} CHCOOC_2H_5 \\ \| \\ CHCOOC_2H_5 \end{matrix} \longrightarrow \begin{matrix} (C_2H_5O)_2PSSCHCOOC_2H_5 \\ | \\ CH_2COOC_2H_5 \end{matrix}$$

Malathion

Tartaric acid is dihydroxysuccinic acid, HOOCCHOHCHOHCOOH, and is one of the most widely distributed plant acids. Its potassium acid salt is present in grape juice and is the chief constituent of the lees of wine (p. 334). The crude product is called *argol*. The pure product is called *cream of tartar*. It is used as the acid component in some baking powders. Neutralization of cream of tartar with sodium hydroxide yields sodium potassium tartrate, which is known as *Rochelle salts* (after Rochelle, France) and is used as a purgative. Tartar was known to the ancients, but tartaric acid was isolated first by Scheele in 1769.

Meso or racemic tartaric acid can be made synthetically by the hydroxylation of maleic or fumaric acid with hydrogen peroxide in the presence of tungstic oxide (p. 740). Either form may be converted to its equilibrium mixture with the other by boiling with alkali (p. 345).

Fehling solution (p. 212) is prepared from copper sulfate, sodium hydroxide, and Rochelle salts. The tartrate ion forms a chelate complex (p. 742) which decreases the cupric ion concentration below that necessary for the precipitation of cupric hydroxide. The complex salt is formed by a series of steps analogous to those for the formation of the cupric complex of biuret (p. 316).

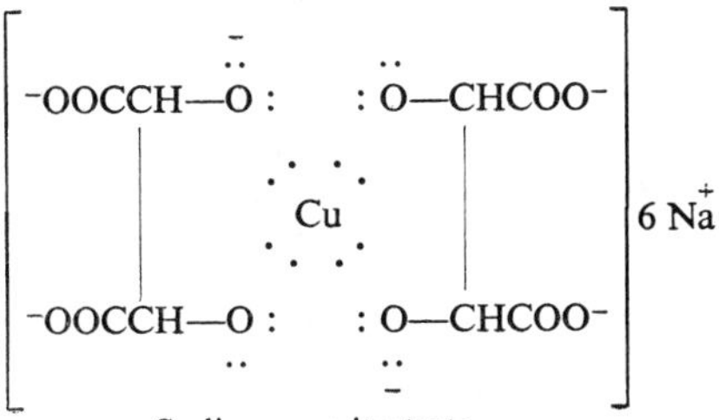

$$\begin{bmatrix} {}^-OOCCH{-}\overset{..}{O}: & :\overset{..}{O}{-}CHCOO^- \\ | & | \\ & Cu \\ | & | \\ {}^-OOCCH{-}\overset{..}{O}: & :\overset{..}{O}{-}CHCOO^- \end{bmatrix} 6\,\overset{+}{Na}$$

Sodium cupritartrate

Phloionic acid, isolated from cork, is 9,10-dihydroxyoctadecanedioic acid, $HOOC(CH_2)_7CHOHCHOH(CH_2)_7COOH.$

Tricarboxylic Acids

Tricarballylic acid (*1,2,3-propanetricarboxylic acid*) is made by the saponification and decarboxylation of the hexacarboxylic ester that results from a Michael addition of ethyl malonate to ethyl fumarate or ethyl maleate (p. 803).

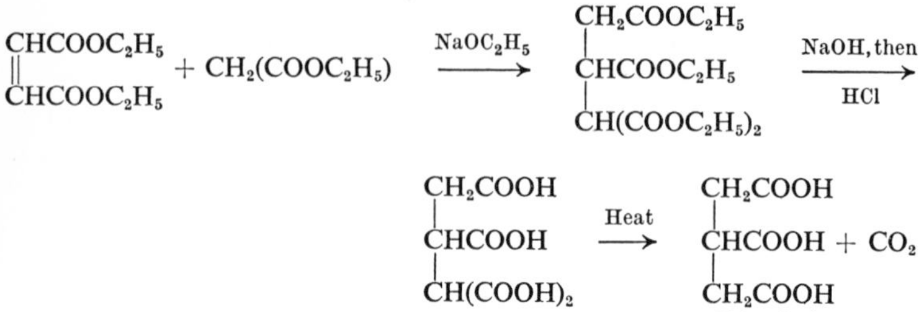

$$\begin{array}{l} CHCOOC_2H_5 \\ \| \\ CHCOOC_2H_5 \end{array} + CH_2(COOC_2H_5) \xrightarrow{NaOC_2H_5} \begin{array}{l} CH_2COOC_2H_5 \\ | \\ CHCOOC_2H_5 \\ | \\ CH(COOC_2H_5)_2 \end{array} \xrightarrow[HCl]{NaOH, then}$$

$$\begin{array}{l} CH_2COOH \\ | \\ CHCOOH \\ | \\ CH(COOH)_2 \end{array} \xrightarrow{Heat} \begin{array}{l} CH_2COOH \\ | \\ CHCOOH \\ | \\ CH_2COOH \end{array} + CO_2$$

Tricarbal-
lylic acid

Citric acid, $HOOCCH_2COHCH_2COOH$, is 2-hydroxy-1,2,3-propanetri-
$\;$|
$\;$COOH
carboxylic acid. It is the chief acid constituent of citrus fruits, amounting to 6 to 7 per cent of lemon juice. It is present also in currants, gooseberries and many other fruits, as well as in the roots and leaves of many plants. It was obtained in a crystalline form from unripe lemons by Scheele in 1784. Commercial manufacture is from cull lemons, or by the fermentation of molasses or starch with *Aspergillus niger* at pH 3.5.

Benedict solution (p. 370) is prepared from copper sulfate, sodium carbonate, and sodium citrate. The structure of the complex is similar to that of the tartrate complex except that a carboxyl group has entered into complex formation instead of a hydroxyl group.

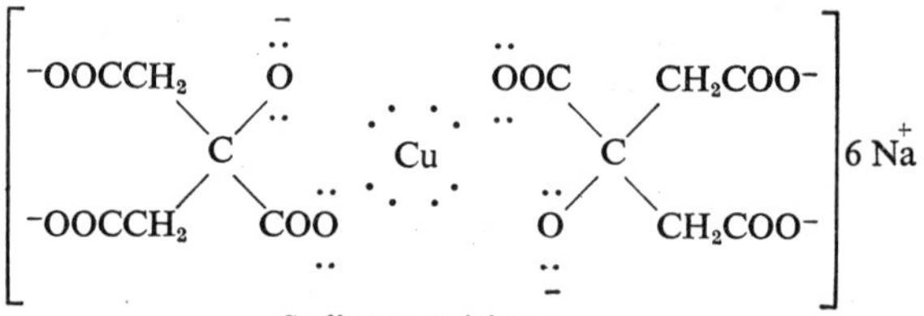

Sodium cupricitrate

As an α-hydroxy acid, citric acid loses carbon monoxide and water when it reacts with fuming sulfuric acid at 0° (p. 782) to give **acetonedicarboxylic acid.** Esterification of the latter gives ethyl acetonedicarboxylate, which is a β-keto ester having two active methylene groups (p. 771) and is a valuable intermediate in organic syntheses.

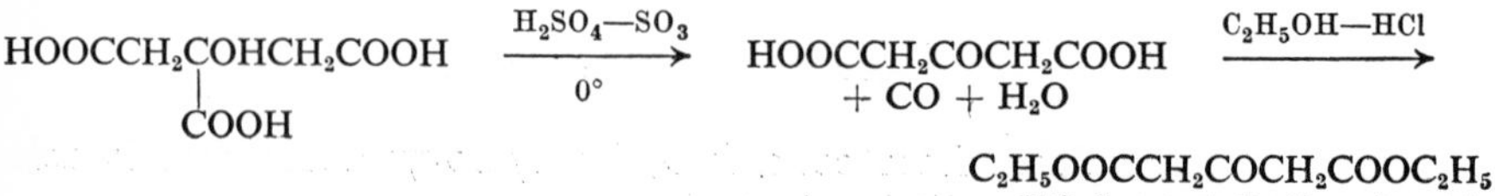

$$HOOCCH_2COHCH_2COOH \xrightarrow[0°]{H_2SO_4-SO_3} HOOCCH_2COCH_2COOH \xrightarrow{C_2H_5OH-HCl}$$
$\;\;\;\;\;\;\;$|
$\;\;\;\;\;\;\;$COOH $\;$ + CO + H_2O

$$C_2H_5OOCCH_2COCH_2COOC_2H_5$$
Ethyl acetonedicarboxylate

When citric acid is refluxed with 65 per cent sulfuric acid, dehydration to **aconitic acid** (1,2,3-propenetricarboxylic acid) takes place.

$$\underset{\substack{|\\ \text{COOH}\\ \text{Citric acid}}}{\text{HOOCCH}_2\text{COHCH}_2\text{COOH}} \xrightarrow{\text{H}_2\text{SO}_4} \underset{\substack{|\\ \text{COOH}\\ \text{Aconitic acid}}}{\text{HOOCCH}_2\text{C}\!=\!\text{CHCOOH}}$$

Aconitic acid is present in many plants and accompanies sugar in the juice of sugar cane, sorghum, and beets. Its name is derived from its presence in plants of the genus *Aconitum*. Catalytic reduction gives tricarballylic acid. It is of interest that succinic, fumaric, malic, citric, and aconitic acids all are involved through the citric acid cycle in the metabolism of carbohydrates, fats, proteins, porphyrins, and probably many other natural products.

REVIEW QUESTIONS

1. Give reactions for three general methods for the preparation of α,ω-dicarboxylic acids.
2. Give the name and the best method of preparation for the normal α,ω-dicarboxylic acids containing from two to ten carbon atoms.
3. How can chemical reactions be used to determine the number of carbon atoms separating the carboxyl groups in a dicarboxylic acid? What is Blanc's rule?
4. Give equations for the reaction of ethyl sodiomalonate (from ethyl malonate and sodium ethoxide) with alkyl halides; with iodine; with urea.
5. Discuss the use of *N*-halogenated imides as brominating agents.
6. What similarities exist between the reactions of malonic esters and those of 1,3-diketones?
7. What are the steps involved in the condensation of an aliphatic aldehyde with two moles of malonic ester to give a tetracarboxylic ester?
8. List the various types of commercially important polymers that contain an ester linkage, and indicate the raw materials used in the manufacture of each and the nature of the reactions involved.

PROBLEMS

9. Give reactions for the synthesis of the following compounds from malonic acid or ethyl malonate: (*a*) cyclobutanecarboxylic acid; (*b*) α,α'-di-*i*-propylsuccinic acid; (*c*) β-phenyl-glutaric acid; (*d*) 2,5-dimethylcaproic acid; (*e*) leucine; (*f*) 4-methyl-2-pentenoic acid; (*g*) tyrosine.
10. Give reactions illustrating three different procedures for the synthesis of *n*-amyl *n*-butyl ketone starting with malonic acid.
11. Write equations for the reactions that probably take place in the production of the various components of technical "isosebacic acid."
12. Give the series of reactions necessary for the following conversions: (*a*) chloroacetic acid to malononitrile; (*b*) acrolein to glutaric acid; (*c*) phenol to glutaric acid; (*d*) chloroacetic acid to glutaric acid; (*e*) benzaldehyde to phenylsuccinic acid; (*f*) malonic acid to 2-nonenal; (*g*) succinic acid to *i*-butylidenesuccinic acid; (*h*) acetylene to adipic acid; (*i*) ethyl diazo-acetate to ethyl *m*-chlorophenylmalonate; (*j*) benzene to malic acid; (*k*) citric acid to β-bromoglutaric acid.
13. Give the formulas for the products of the following Diels-Alder additions: (*a*) furan and maleic anhydride; (*b*) 1,3-butadiene and acrylic acid; (*c*) acrolein and methyl vinyl ether; (*d*) cyclopentadiene and crotonic aldehyde; (*e*) anthracene and maleic anhydride; (*f*) 1,3-butadiene and quinone; (*g*) dimerization of acrolein.

Chapter 38

KETO ACIDS

Keto acids are important intermediates in biological oxidations and reductions. They also are used frequently in organic syntheses and have played a leading role in the interpretation of the phenomenon known as tautomerism.

α-Keto Acids

The simplest compound containing both a carbonyl group and a carboxyl group is **glyoxylic acid,** OCHCOOH. It can be made by logical reactions such as the ozonolysis of maleic or fumaric acid, or the hydrolysis of dichloroacetic acid. It can be prepared also by the electrolytic reduction of oxalic acid. Like chloral, it forms a stable hydrate having the structure $(HO)_2CHCOOH$. Esters of glyoxylic acid can be prepared by the action of lead tetraacetate on esters of tartaric acid (cf. p. 742).

$$ROOCCHOHCHOHCOOR + Pb(OCOCH_3)_4 \longrightarrow$$

$$2\,OCHCOOR + Pb(OCOCH_3)_2 + 2\,CH_3COOH$$

Pyruvic acid (*α-oxopropionic acid*), the first true α-keto acid, is made by the pyrolysis of tartaric acid and hence frequently is called *pyrotartaric acid.*

$$\begin{matrix} HOCHCOOH \\ | \\ HOCHCOOH \end{matrix} \xrightarrow{\text{Heat}} H_2O + \left[\begin{matrix} CHCOOH \\ \| \\ HOCCOOH \end{matrix} \rightleftharpoons \begin{matrix} CH_2COOH \\ | \\ COCOOH \end{matrix} \right] \longrightarrow \begin{matrix} CH_3 \\ | \\ COCOOH \end{matrix} + CO_2$$

Tartaric acid   Pyruvic acid

It plays an important part in the fermentation and metabolism of carbohydrates.

A general method of preparation of α-keto acids is the hydrolysis of acyl cyanides prepared from acyl chlorides.

$$RCOCl + CuCN \longrightarrow RCOCN \xrightarrow{\text{Hydrolysis}} RCOCOOH$$

α-Keto esters containing other functional groups may be made by the Claisen ester condensation (p. 814) of ethyl oxalate with other esters or ketones having an α hydrogen atom.

$$RCH_2COOC_2H_5 + C_2H_5OOCCOOC_2H_5 \xrightarrow{NaOC_2H_5} \begin{matrix} RCHCOOC_2H_5 \\ | \\ COCOOC_2H_5 \end{matrix} + C_2H_5OH$$

The products from esters are also *β*-keto esters and can be hydrolyzed and decarboxylated (p. 813) to α-keto acids.

$$\begin{matrix} RCHCOOC_2H_5 \\ | \\ COCOOC_2H_5 \end{matrix} \xrightarrow{\text{Hydrolysis}} \begin{matrix} RCHCOOH \\ | \\ COCOOH \end{matrix} \xrightarrow{\text{Heat}} \begin{matrix} RCH_2 \\ | \\ COCOOH \end{matrix} + CO_2$$

Another general procedure involves the nitrosation and hydrolysis of substituted malonic or acetoacetic esters (pp. 802, 819).

$$RCH(COOC_2H_5)_2 \xrightarrow{\text{HONO}} \underset{NO}{RC(COOC_2H_5)_2} \xrightarrow[\text{and de-carboxylation}]{\text{Hydrolysis}} \left[\underset{NO}{RCHCOOH} \right] \longrightarrow$$

$$\underset{NOH}{RCCOOH} \xrightarrow{\text{Hydrolysis}} \underset{O}{RCCOOH}$$

$$CH_3COCHRCOOC_2H_5 \xrightarrow{\text{HONO}} \underset{NO}{CH_3COCRCOOC_2H_5} \xrightarrow{\text{NaOH}}$$

$$CH_3COONa + \left[\underset{NO}{HCRCOONa} \right] \longrightarrow \underset{NOH}{RCCOONa} \xrightarrow{\text{Hydrolysis}} \underset{O}{RCCOOH}$$

α-Keto esters result also when the acetals of α-keto aldehydes are brominated with N-bromosuccinimide (p. 797). The acetals are available by the reaction of Grignard reagents on the piperidide of diethoxyacetic acid.

$$\overset{O}{\overset{\|}{C_6H_{10}NCCH(OC_2H_5)_2}} \xrightarrow{\text{RMgX}} \overset{OMgX}{\overset{|}{C_5H_{10}NCRCH(OC_2H_5)_2}} \xrightarrow{H_2O}$$

$$RCOCH(OC_2H_5)_2 \xrightarrow{\text{BrN(COCH}_2)_2} RCOCBr(OC_2H_5)_2 \longrightarrow RCOCOOC_2H_5 + C_2H_5Br$$

α-Keto acids are oxidized easily to carbon dioxide and the monocarboxylic acid having one less carbon atom. Thus pyruvic acid reduces Tollens reagent and is oxidized to carbon dioxide and acetic acid. α-Keto acids are stable to dilute acids and alkalies. When heated to a relatively high temperature (above 170°) or at a lower temperature in the presence of concentrated sulfuric acid, carbon monoxide is lost and the carboxylic acid results.

$$CH_3COCOOH \xrightarrow{170°} CH_3COOH + CO$$

Likewise α-keto esters on heating lose carbon monoxide to give the ester of the carboxylic acid having one less carbon atom.

$$RCOCOOC_2H_5 \xrightarrow{\text{Heat}} RCOOC_2H_5 + CO$$

When the C-2 carbonyl group of ethyl pyruvate is labeled with radioactive C^{14} and decomposed at 130°, the carbon monoxide evolved is not radioactive. Hence the carbonyl group lost is that from the carboethoxy group.

β-Keto Acids

β-Keto acids can be obtained by the saponification of their esters with cold dilute sodium hydroxide solutions. The free acids decompose on heating to carbon dioxide and a ketone.

$$RCOCH_2COOH \xrightarrow{\text{Heat}} RCOCH_3 + CO_2$$

This easy loss of carbon dioxide resembles the behavior of malonic acid (p. 795). The reaction is unimolecular and takes place through the proton-bonded form.

$$RC\overset{CR_2}{\diagdown}C=O \longrightarrow CO_2 + \left[RC\overset{CR_2}{\diagup} \atop OH \right] \longrightarrow RCCHR_2 \atop O$$

In the combustion of fat acids by the animal organism, two carbon atoms are removed at a time, the intermediates being the β-hydroxy and β-keto acids. In the next to the last stage acetoacetic acid is converted to acetic acid. This step requires the simultaneous combustion of carbohydrates which in turn requires the hormone insulin. The diabetic lacking insulin excretes carbohydrates as glucose, and acetoacetic acid accumulates in the blood stream. Decarboxylation of the acetoacetic acid gives rise to acetone.

$$CH_3COCH_2COOH \longrightarrow CH_3COCH_3 + CO_2$$

Both acetoacetic acid and acetone can be detected in the blood and in the urine of uncontrolled diabetics. The toxic effects of the acetoacetic acid (sometimes called *diacetic acid*) and acetone lead to coma and death.

Preparation of β-Keto Esters. The esters of β-keto acids are stable, and since they are prepared easily and contain an active methylene group, they form an important class of organic compounds. In 1863 Geuther, who thought that acetic acid contained two hydrogen atoms replaceable by metals, attempted to prepare a sodium salt of ethyl acetate by reaction with metallic sodium. He observed the evolution of hydrogen, and the formation of sodium ethoxide and a crystalline compound $C_6H_9O_3Na$. The latter compound on acidification gave a liquid which, though neutral to litmus, reacted with bases to form salts. It was shown later that a small amount of alcohol is necessary for the reaction to take place and that the actual catalyst is sodium ethoxide, which brings about condensation with the liberation of ethyl alcohol. The condensation product reacts with the sodium ethoxide to give Geuther's sodium salt. Hence a molar proportion of sodium ethoxide or metallic sodium is needed to complete the reaction.

$$C_2H_5OH + Na \longrightarrow C_2H_5ONa + \tfrac{1}{2} H_2$$

$$CH_3\overset{O}{\overset{\|}{C}}OC_2H_5 + CH_3\overset{O}{\overset{\|}{C}}OC_2H_5 \xrightarrow{NaOC_2H_5} C_2H_5OH + CH_3COCH_2COOC_2H_5 \xrightarrow{NaOC_2H_5}$$

$$C_2H_5OH + [CH_3CO\bar{C}HCOOC_2H_5]Na^+ \xrightarrow{HOAc} CH_3COCH_2COOC_2H_5 + NaOAc$$
Ethyl acetoacetate

Later Claisen[1] and others showed that esters can be condensed by means of sodium ethoxide with a wide variety of compounds having hydrogen α to a carbonyl group. The reaction usually is called the *Claisen ester condensation* and should not be confused with the Claisen reaction (p. 536).

---

[1] Ludwig Claisen (1851–1930), professor at the University of Kiel. He is noted chiefly for his work on the condensation of aromatic aldehydes with ketones, on ester condensations, on the rearrangement of allyl phenyl ethers, and on tautomeric compounds.

The best yields are obtained in the condensation of like molecules of esters having two α hydrogen atoms or in mixed condensations in which one of the esters lacks α hydrogen atoms.

$$RCH_2COOC_2H_5 + RCH_2COOC_2H_5 \xrightarrow{NaOC_2H_5} RCH_2COCHCOOC_2H_5 + C_2H_5OH$$
$$\underset{R}{|}$$

$$\overset{O}{\underset{||}{H C}}OC_2H_5 + CH_3COOC_2H_5 \xrightarrow{NaOC_2H_5} \overset{O}{\underset{||}{H C}}CH_2COOC_2H_5 + C_2H_5OH$$

Ethyl   Ethyl formylacetate
formate   (formylacetic ester)

$$C_2H_5OCOCOOC_2H_5 + CH_3COOC_2H_5 \xrightarrow{NaOC_2H_5} C_2H_5OCOCOCH_2COOC_2H_5 + C_2H_5OH$$

Ethyl oxalate   Ethyl oxalacetate
                                       (oxalacetic ester)

$$C_6H_5COOC_2H_5 + CH_3COOC_2H_5 \xrightarrow{NaOC_2H_5} C_6H_5COCH_2COOC_2H_5 + C_2H_5OH$$

Ethyl   Ethyl benzoylacetate
benzoate   (benzoylacetic ester)

If the ester being acylated contains only one α hydrogen atom, the ethoxide ion is not a sufficiently strong base to catalyze the reaction. However, a stronger base such as the triphenylmethide ion effects the condensation.

$$C_6H_5COOC_2H_5 + (CH_3)_2CHCOOC_2H_5 \xrightarrow{Na^+{}^-C(C_6H_5)_3} C_6H_5COC(CH_3)_2COOC_2H_5 + C_2H_5OH$$

Ethyl
benzoyldimethylacetate

The Claisen ester condensation of ethyl acetate may be represented by the following series of equilibria.

$$CH_3COOC_2H_5 \underset{C_2H_5OH}{\overset{[^-OC_2H_5]}{\rightleftarrows}} [^-CH_2COOC_2H_5] \underset{[^-OC_2H_5]}{\overset{CH_3COOC_2H_5}{\rightleftarrows}}$$

$$CH_3COCH_2COOC_2H_5 \underset{C_2H_5OH}{\overset{[^-OC_2H_5]}{\rightleftarrows}} [CH_3COCHCOOC_2H_5]^-$$

The position of equilibrium for the first stage is determined by the acidity of the ester and the basicity of the catalyst. Any catalyst sufficiently basic to bring about this step will form a salt with the product of the second step, since the β-keto esters are much more acidic than the esters. Hence the reaction will go to completion. The acidity of the α hydrogen atoms of the ester is reduced by the presence of electron-donating alkyl groups on the α carbon atom, and if two are present as in ethyl isobutyrate, the remaining α hydrogen is not sufficiently acidic for ethoxide ion to cause the first stage of the reaction. This stage takes place, however, with a sufficiently strong base such as the triphenylmethide ion, and hence triphenylmethylsodium is used to effect such condensations.

β-Keto esters result also from the Claisen condensation of ketones with ethyl carbonate. The preferred condensing agent is sodium hydride.

$$RCOCH_3 + (C_2H_5O)_2CO \xrightarrow{NaH} RCOCH_2COOC_2H_5 + C_2H_5OH$$

Because the activating effect of the ester group of α,β-unsaturated esters is transmitted through the conjugated system, condensation with this class of compounds takes place on the carbon atom α to the carbon-carbon double bond.

$$\text{HCOOC}_2\text{H}_5 + \text{CH}_3\text{CH}=\text{CHCOOC}_2\text{H}_5 \xrightarrow{\text{NaOC}_2\text{H}_5} \text{HCOCH}_2\text{CH}=\text{CHCOOC}_2\text{H}_5 + \text{C}_2\text{H}_5\text{OH}$$

Ethyl   Ethyl crotonate   Ethyl formylcrotonate
formate

$$\text{C}_2\text{H}_5\text{OCOCOOC}_2\text{H}_5 + \text{CH}_3\text{CH}=\text{CHCH}=\text{CHCOOC}_2\text{H}_5 \xrightarrow{\text{NaOC}_2\text{H}_5}$$

Ethyl oxalate   Ethyl sorbate

$$\text{C}_2\text{H}_5\text{OCOCOCH}_2\text{CH}=\text{CHCH}=\text{CHCOOC}_2\text{H}_5 + \text{C}_2\text{H}_5\text{OH}$$

Ethyl oxalosorbate

If in a dibasic ester the hydrogen α to one ester group is δ or ε to the other, intramolecular condensation may occur with the formation of a five- or six-membered ring. This type of reaction is called a *Dieckmann condensation.*

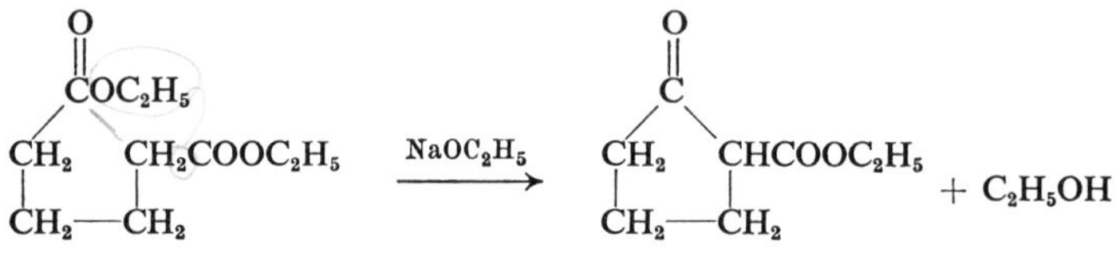

Ethyl adipate   Ethyl 2-oxocyclopentane-
                       carboxylate

Five- and six-membered rings may result also from intermolecular condensations.

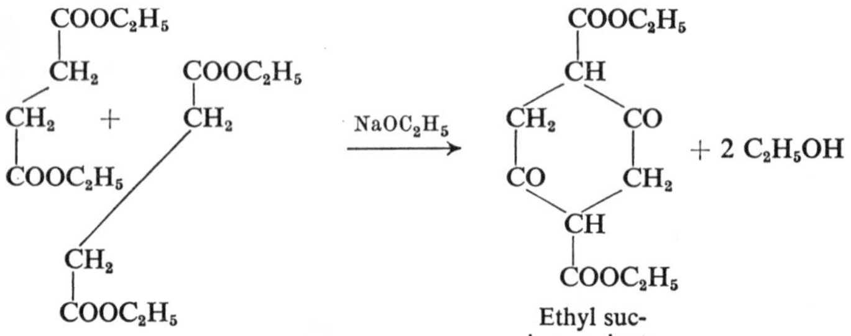

Ethyl succinate   Ethyl suc-
                         cinosuccinate

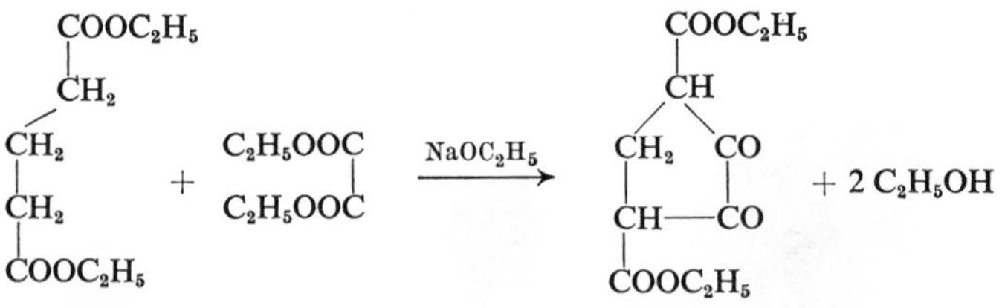

Ethyl   Ethyl   Ethyl 4,5-dioxo-1,3-
glutarate   oxalate   cyclopentane-dicarboxylate

The Claisen condensation is used also for the preparation of 1,3-diketones from esters and ketones (p. 768) and of malonic esters (p. 802).

Because of the importance of β-keto esters and the limitations of the Claisen ester condensation, several other methods have been developed for their synthesis. For example the reaction of acyl chlorides with the ethoxymagnesium salt of *t*-butyl ethyl malonate gives the acyl derivative, which decomposes on heating with an acid catalyst to the β-keto ethyl ester.

$$RCOCl + [C_2H_5OMg^+]\begin{bmatrix} \overset{-}{C}H \overset{COOC_4H_9\text{-}t}{\underset{COOC_2H_5}{}} \end{bmatrix} \longrightarrow RCO\overset{COOC_4H_9\text{-}t}{\underset{COOC_2H_5}{CH}} \xrightarrow[\text{acid}]{\text{Heat}}$$

$$RCOCH_2COOC_2H_5 + CH_2=C(CH_3)_2 + CO_2$$

This reaction is useful for the preparation of small quantities but has the disadvantage that the preparation of *t*-butyl ethyl malonate is somewhat involved. The latter can be made by the carbonation of the sodium derivative of *t*-butyl acetate, but preparation of the sodium salt requires the use of triphenylmethylsodium. A better method uses a series of reactions starting with ethyl malonate.

$$CH_2(COOC_2H_5)_2 \xrightarrow[\text{HCl}]{\text{NaOH, then}} C_2H_5OOCCH_2COOH \xrightarrow[\text{chloride}]{\text{Phthalyl}}$$

$$C_2H_5OOCCH_2COCl \xrightarrow{t\text{-}C_4H_9OH} C_2H_5OOCCH_2COOC_4H_9\text{-}t$$

The over-all yield is about 45 per cent. Frequently β-keto esters can be made in good yield by the reaction of ethyl cyanoacetate with Grignard reagents.

$$RMgX + N{\equiv}CCH_2COOC_2H_5 \longrightarrow R\overset{}{\underset{NMgX}{C}}CH_2COOC_2H_5 \xrightarrow[\text{HX}]{H_2O}$$

$$RCOCH_2COOC_2H_5 + NH_4X + MgX_2$$

They can be made also from aldehydes and ethyl diazoacetate (p. 266).

$$RCHO + N_2CHCOOC_2H_5 \longrightarrow RCOCH_2COOC_2H_5 + N_2$$

Ethyl acetoacetate is made commercially from diketene (p. 825). Other β-keto esters can be made from ethyl acetoacetate (pp. 819, 820, 822).

Reactions of β-Keto Esters. Geuther reported the reaction of his sodium salt of ethyl acetoacetate with ethyl iodide and isolated an ethyl derivative of ethyl acetoacetate in 1863. He showed in 1868 that reaction with sodium ethoxide in alcohol gave ethyl butyrate, but it was not until 1877 that the work of Wislicenus[2] led to an understanding of the reactions involved. The subsequent investigations of Wislicenus, Claisen, and others showed the great value of these reactions for the synthesis of organic compounds and soon led to the discovery of the related reactions of malonic esters (p. 800) and 1,3-diketones (p. 773).

Like the 1,3-diketones an appreciable amount of the enol form of β-keto esters exists in equilibrium with the keto form.

$$CH_3COCH_2COOC_2H_5 \rightleftharpoons CH_3\overset{}{\underset{OH}{C}}=CHCOOC_2H_5$$

---

[2] Johannes Adolph Wislicenus (1835–1902). His father was a Lutheran minister who was forced to leave Germany because of his liberal views and who brought his family to America in 1853. Young Wislicenus obtained a position at Harvard University but returned with the family to Germany in 1855. He completed his studies at Halle and later became professor of chemistry at Wuerzburg and at Leipzig. Among his many chemical interests were the condensation of aldehydes with ammonia, the synthesis of α-hydroxy acids from cyanohydrins, the chemistry of the lactic acids, ester condensations, the alkylation of acetoacetic esters, and stereochemistry.

Hence β-keto esters decolorize bromine readily and give a red color with ferric chloride. They also form covalent metallic chelate compounds (p. 742). Thus the copper complex of ethyl acetoacetate can be recrystallized from benzene and melts at 192°.

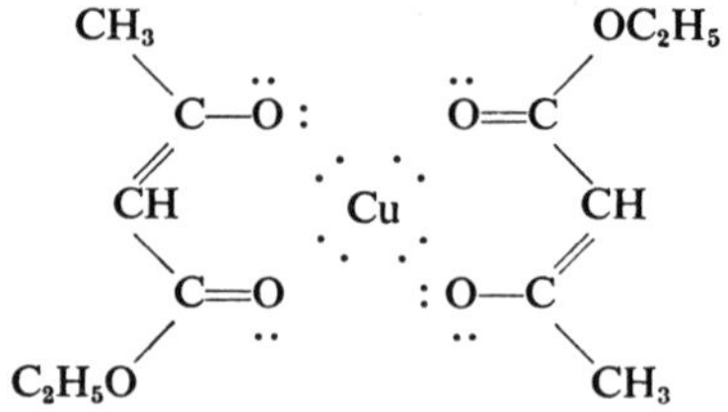

Copper ethyl acetoacetate

Reaction with diazomethane gives the *O*-methyl ether (p. 266).

$$CH_3C\!=\!CHCOOC_2H_5 + CH_2N_2 \longrightarrow CH_3C\!=\!CHCOOC_2H_5 + N_2$$
$$\underset{OH}{|} \qquad\qquad\qquad\qquad \underset{OCH_3}{|}$$

The usual carbonyl reagents react with ethyl acetoacetate. It forms a bisulfite addition compound and a cyanohydrin. Ammonia and primary and secondary amines yield β-aminocrotonic acids.

$$CH_3COCH_2COOC_2H_5 \xrightarrow{NH_3} \left[CH_3\overset{}{\underset{NH_2\ OH}{C}}\!-\!CH_2COOC_2H_5\right] \longrightarrow CH_3C\!=\!CHCOOC_2H_5 + H_2O$$
$$\underset{NH_2}{|}$$

The reaction products with hydroxylamine and phenylhydrazine lose ethyl alcohol and give dihydroisoxazolones and dihydropyrazolones.

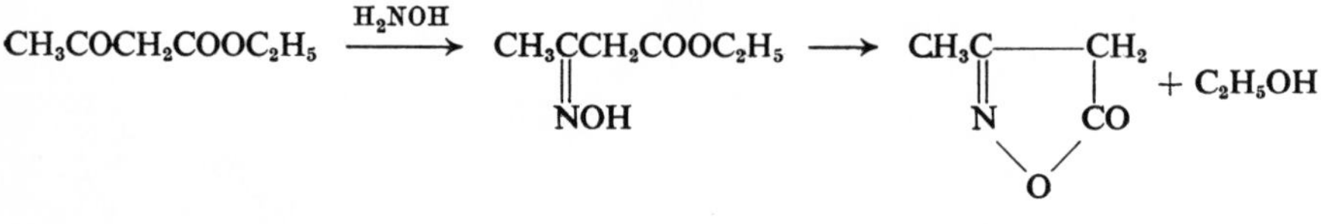

$$CH_3COCH_2COOC_2H_5 \xrightarrow{H_2NOH} CH_3\underset{NOH}{\overset{\|}{C}}CH_2COOC_2H_5 \longrightarrow$$

3-Methyl-4,5-dihydro-
5-isoxazolone

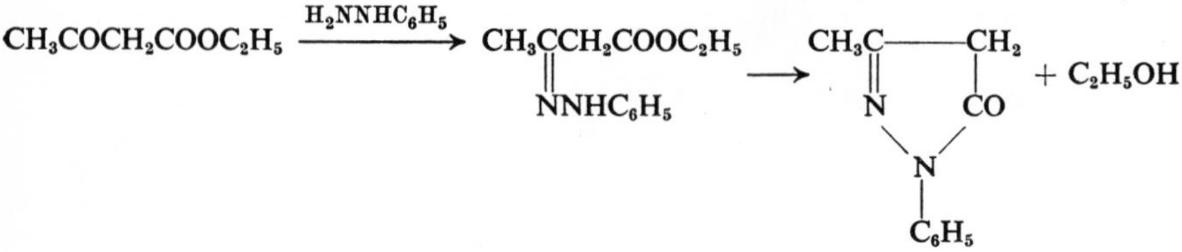

$$CH_3COCH_2COOC_2H_5 \xrightarrow{H_2NNHC_6H_5} CH_3\underset{NNHC_6H_5}{\overset{\|}{C}}CH_2COOC_2H_5 \longrightarrow$$

1-Phenyl-3-methyl-4,5-
dihydro-5-pyrazolone

In the latter reaction the intermediate phenylhydrazone can be isolated and can be converted to the pyrazolone by warming. Nitration of the pyrazolone gives the compound known as **picrolonic acid.** With amines it forms salts, known as *picrolonates*, that have found some use as derivatives.

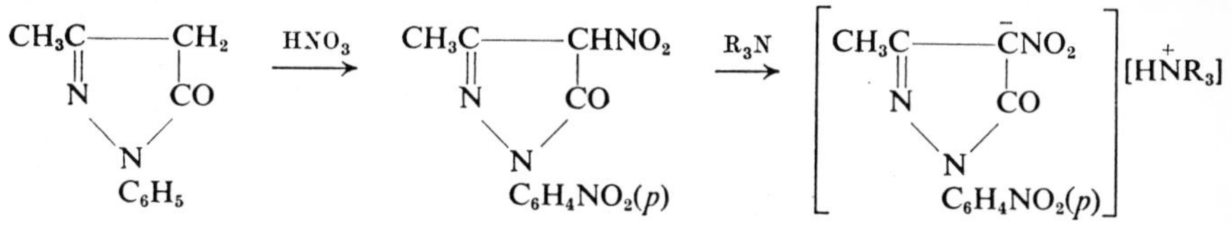

$$
\begin{array}{ccc}
\underset{\substack{N \quad CO \\ \diagdown N \diagup \\ C_6H_5}}{CH_3C\!\!-\!\!-\!\!-\!\!CH_2}
& \xrightarrow{HNO_3} &
\underset{\substack{N \quad CO \\ \diagdown N \diagup \\ C_6H_4NO_2(p)}}{CH_3C\!\!-\!\!-\!\!-\!\!CHNO_2}
& \xrightarrow{R_3N} &
\left[\underset{\substack{N \quad CO \\ \diagdown N \diagup \\ C_6H_4NO_2(p)}}{CH_3C\!\!-\!\!-\!\!-\!\!\bar{C}NO_2}\right][\overset{+}{H}NR_3]
\end{array}
$$

Picrolonic acid   Amine picrolonate

β-Keto esters condense with amidines and ureas to give pyrimidines (p. 639).

Like other active methylene compounds, β-keto esters undergo the Knoevenagel reaction (p. 773), which may be followed by a Michael addition (p. 803).

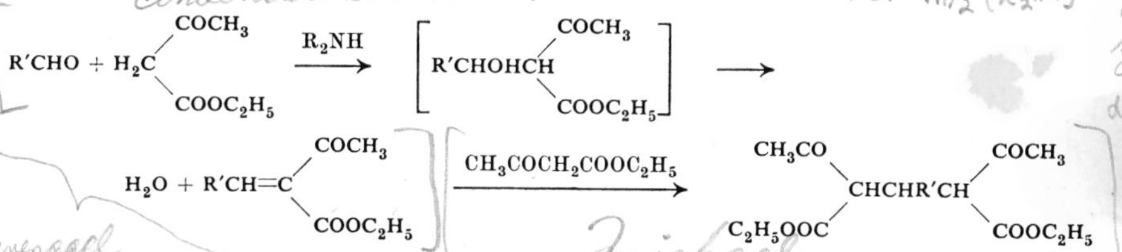

$$
\underset{COOC_2H_5}{R'CHO + H_2C\!\!-\!\!COCH_3} \xrightarrow{R_2NH} \left[\underset{COOC_2H_5}{R'CHOHCH\!\!-\!\!COCH_3}\right] \longrightarrow
$$

$$
\underset{COOC_2H_5}{H_2O + R'CH\!\!=\!\!C\!\!-\!\!COCH_3} \xrightarrow{CH_3COCH_2COOC_2H_5} \underset{\substack{C_2H_5OOC}}{\overset{CH_3CO}{}\diagdown CHCHR'CH \diagup \underset{COOC_2H_5}{\overset{COCH_3}{}}}
$$

Hydrolysis of these products gives rise to β-keto acids which decarboxylate on heating to α,β-unsaturated ketones or 1,5-diketones respectively.

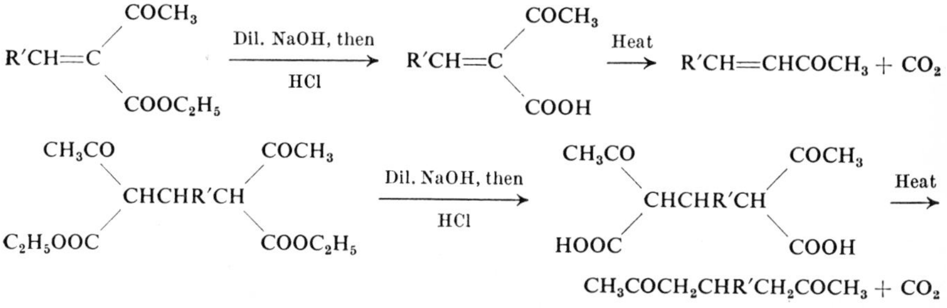

$$
\underset{COOC_2H_5}{\overset{COCH_3}{}R'CH\!\!=\!\!C} \xrightarrow[HCl]{\text{Dil. NaOH, then}} \underset{COOH}{\overset{COCH_3}{}R'CH\!\!=\!\!C} \xrightarrow{\text{Heat}} R'CH\!\!=\!\!CHCOCH_3 + CO_2
$$

$$
\underset{C_2H_5OOC}{\overset{CH_3CO}{}}\diagdown CHCHR'CH\diagup\underset{COOC_2H_5}{\overset{COCH_3}{}} \xrightarrow[HCl]{\text{Dil. NaOH, then}} \underset{HOOC}{\overset{CH_3CO}{}}\diagdown CHCHR'CH\diagup\underset{COOH}{\overset{COCH_3}{}} \xrightarrow{\text{Heat}}
$$

$$
CH_3COCH_2CHR'CH_2COCH_3 + CO_2
$$

Numerous extensions of reactions of this type have been made leading to the synthesis of many other types of compounds. For example, in the *Knorr*[3] synthesis of pyrroles an isonitroso derivative is reduced in the presence of the keto ester.

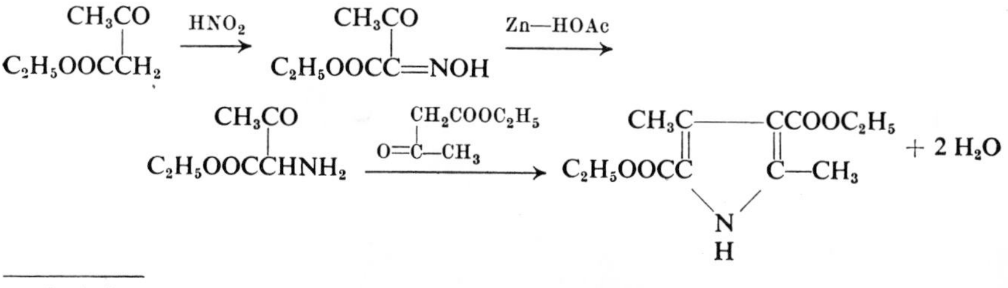

$$
\underset{C_2H_5OOCCH_2}{\overset{CH_3CO}{}} \xrightarrow{HNO_2} \underset{C_2H_5OOCC\!\!=\!\!NOH}{\overset{CH_3CO}{}} \xrightarrow{Zn\!\!-\!\!HOAc}
$$

$$
\underset{C_2H_5OOCCHNH_2}{\overset{CH_3CO}{}} \xrightarrow[O=C-CH_3]{CH_2COOC_2H_5} \underset{\substack{C_2H_5OOCC \qquad C\!\!-\!\!CH_3 \\ \diagdown N \diagup \\ H}}{CH_3C\!\!-\!\!-\!\!-\!\!CCOOC_2H_5} + 2\,H_2O
$$

---

[3] Ludwig Knorr (1859–1921), professor at the University of Jena. He is known chiefly for his syntheses of heterocyclic compounds and for his separation of the tautomers of ethyl acetoacetate (p. 822).

In the *Hantzsch pyridine synthesis* one mole of an aldehyde and two moles of β-keto ester react with ammonia to give a dihydropyridine, which can be oxidized to the pyridine with nitrous acid.

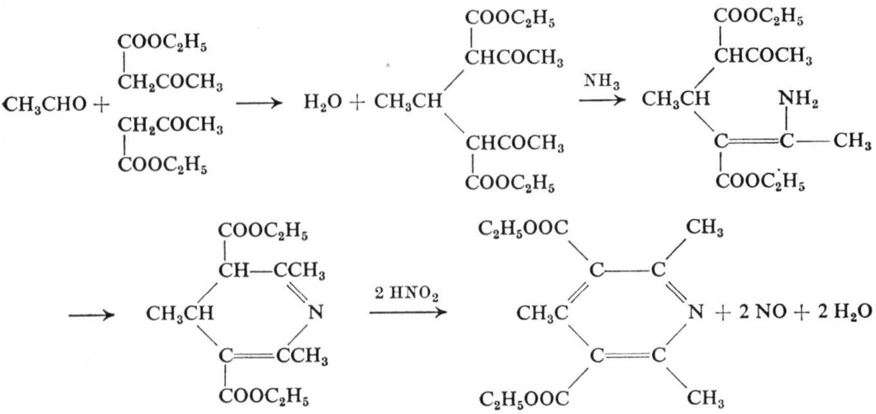

$$CH_3CHO + \begin{array}{c} COOC_2H_5 \\ | \\ CH_2COCH_3 \\ \\ CH_2COCH_3 \\ | \\ COOC_2H_5 \end{array} \longrightarrow H_2O + CH_3CH \begin{array}{c} COOC_2H_5 \\ | \\ CHCOCH_3 \\ \\ CHCOCH_3 \\ | \\ COOC_2H_5 \end{array} \xrightarrow{NH_3} CH_3CH \begin{array}{c} COOC_2H_5 \\ | \\ CHCOCH_3 \\ \\ NH_2 \\ | \\ C{=\!=}C{-\!\!-}CH_3 \\ | \\ COOC_2H_5 \end{array}$$

$$\longrightarrow CH_3CH \begin{array}{c} COOC_2H_5 \\ | \\ CH{-\!\!-}CCH_3 \\ \diagdown \\ N \\ \diagup \\ C{=\!\!=}CCH_3 \\ | \\ COOC_2H_5 \end{array} \xrightarrow{2\ HNO_2} \begin{array}{c} C_2H_5OOC \qquad CH_3 \\ C{-\!\!-}C \\ CH_3C \qquad\qquad N \\ C{=\!\!=}C \\ C_2H_5OOC \qquad CH_3 \end{array} + 2\ NO + 2\ H_2O$$

As with 1,3-diketones and malonic ester (pp. 773, 800), *carbon alkylation* or *acylation* leads to substituted β-keto esters.

$$RCOCH_2COOC_2H_5 \xrightarrow{NaOC_2H_5} [RCO\bar{C}HCOOC_2H_5]Na^+ \xrightarrow{R'X}$$

$$RCOCHR'COOC_2H_5 \xrightarrow{NaOC_2H_5} [RCO\bar{C}R'COOC_2H_5]Na^+ \xrightarrow{R''X} \underset{R''}{RCOCR'COOC_2H_5}$$

Like the anion of the sodium salt of 1,3-diketones (p. 773), that of β-keto esters is a resonance hybrid.

$$\left\{ \underset{O}{RC}{-\!\!-}\bar{C}HCOOC_2H_5 \longleftrightarrow \underset{O^-}{RC}{=\!\!=}CHCOOC_2H_5 \right\}$$

Thus ethyl chloroformate gives *O*-alkylation instead of *C*-alkylation. Acetyl chloride gives both *O*- and *C*-alkylation.

Hydrolysis and decarboxylation of the carbon-alkylated esters give good yields of the substituted ketones. This reaction frequently is referred to as *ketonic cleavage*.

$$RCOCHR'COOC_2H_5 \xrightarrow[\text{then HCl}]{\text{Dil. NaOH,}} RCOCHR'COOH \xrightarrow{\text{Heat}} RCOCH_2R' + CO_2$$

$$\underset{R''}{RCOCR'COOC_2H_5} \xrightarrow[\text{then HCl}]{\text{Dil. NaOH,}} \underset{R''}{RCOCR'COOH} \xrightarrow{\text{Heat}} \underset{R''}{RCOCHR'} + CO_2$$

Hydrolysis and decarboxylation can be brought about simultaneously by boiling the keto ester with dilute acid, but the yields and purity of the product usually are inferior. The alkaline hydrolysis is carried out at room temperature with dilute alkali to avoid carbon-carbon scission (p. 821).

With halogen and with polymethylene halides, the sodium derivatives of the β-keto esters behave like those of malonic esters. Iodine causes condensation of two moles. Hydrolysis and decarboxylation of the product gives a 1,4-diketone.

$$2\,[\text{RCO}\overset{-}{\text{C}}\text{HCOOC}_2\text{H}_5]\text{Na}^+ + \text{I}_2 \longrightarrow 2\,\text{NaI} + \underset{\text{RCOCHCOOC}_2\text{H}_5}{\text{RCOCHCOOC}_2\text{H}_5} \quad \overset{\text{Hyd.}}{\longrightarrow}$$

$$\underset{\text{RCOCHCOOH}}{\text{RCOCHCOOH}} \quad \overset{\text{Heat}}{\longrightarrow} \quad 2\,\text{CO}_2 + \underset{\text{RCOCH}_2}{\text{RCOCH}_2}$$

Polymethylene halides give α,ω-diketones.

$$2\,[\text{RCO}\overset{-}{\text{C}}\text{HCOOC}_2\text{H}_5]\text{Na}^+ + \text{X}_2(\text{CH}_2)_n \longrightarrow$$

$$2\,\text{NaX} + \underset{\underset{\text{RCOCHCOOC}_2\text{H}_5}{(\text{CH}_2)_n}}{\text{RCOCHCOOC}_2\text{H}_5} \quad \overset{\text{Hydrolysis}}{\underset{\text{and heat}}{\longrightarrow}} \quad \text{RCOCH}_2(\text{CH}_2)_n\text{CH}_2\text{COR}$$

β-Keto esters resemble 1,3-diketones in that they undergo carbon-carbon scission with concentrated alkali. Whereas the 1,3-diketones give one mole of ketone and one mole of sodium carboxylate (p. 774), the β-keto esters give two moles of sodium carboxylate. This reaction frequently is referred to as the *acid cleavage* of β-keto esters because acids are formed, but it is brought about by strong alkali.

$$\underset{\overset{|}{\text{R}''}}{\text{RCOCR}'\text{COOC}_2\text{H}_5} + 2\,\text{NaOH} \longrightarrow \text{RCOONa} + \text{R}'\text{R}''\text{CHCOONa} + \text{C}_2\text{H}_5\text{OH}$$

The mechanism of this reaction is essentially the reverse of that for the Claisen ester condensation. However, the reaction is not reversible because the formation of the sodium salt of the carboxylic acid is an irreversible step.

$$\text{RCOCR}_2\text{COOR}' \quad \overset{2\,[\text{OH}^-]}{\longrightarrow} \quad \left[\underset{\overset{|}{\text{OH}} \quad \overset{|}{\text{OH}}}{\text{R}\overset{:\ddot{\text{O}}\,\bar{}}{\text{C}}\text{CR}_2\overset{:\ddot{\text{O}}\,\bar{}}{\text{C}}\text{OR}} \right] \longrightarrow$$

$$\text{RCOOH} + [:\bar{\text{C}}\text{R}_2\text{COOH}] + [:\bar{\text{O}}\text{R}] \longrightarrow [\text{RCOO}^-] + [\text{R}_2\text{CHCOO}^-] + \text{HOR}$$

Sodium ethoxide in alcohol catalyzes the reversal of the Claisen ester condensation. Since the position of equilibrium using this catalyst with dialkylacetic esters is unfavorable for condensation (p. 815), dialkylacetoacetic esters are cleaved to the dialkylacetic esters.

$$\underset{\overset{|}{\text{R}''}}{\text{RCOCR}'\text{COOC}_2\text{H}_5} \quad \overset{\text{C}_2\text{H}_5\text{OH,}}{\underset{\text{NaOC}_2\text{H}_5}{\longrightarrow}} \quad \text{RCOOC}_2\text{H}_5 + \underset{\overset{|}{\text{R}''}}{\text{R}'\text{CHCOOC}_2\text{H}_5}$$

Although these reactions give satisfactory yields, substituted acetic acids usually are prepared from ethyl malonate. However the carbon-carbon scission reaction sometimes is used for the preparation of higher β-keto esters from acylated acetoacetic esters.

$$CH_3COCH_2COOC_2H_5 \xrightarrow[\text{then RCOCl}]{\text{NaOC}_2\text{H}_5,} CH_3COCHCOOC_2H_5 \xrightarrow{\text{NH}_3}$$
$$\underset{\displaystyle COR}{|}$$

$$RCOCH_2COOC_2H_5 + CH_3CONH_2 \text{ (and } RCONH_2 + CH_3COCH_2COOC_2H_5)$$

Since either acyl group may be eliminated, a mixture of the new ester with acetoacetic ester is obtained.

Tautomerism. Ethyl acetoacetate is the classical example of tautomerism, which usually is defined as the ability of a substance to possess or to react as if it possesses more than one structure. This definition is satisfactory except for the implication that the substance concerned is a single compound, the view held by Laar who coined the term tautomerism (Gr. *tauto*, the same) in 1885. Actually tautomerism is the dynamic equilibrium existing between two spontaneously interconvertible isomers. In 1887 Wislicenus reported the isolation of two isomeric ethyl formylphenylacetates, $C_6H_5CHCOOC_2H_5$, a

$$\underset{\displaystyle CHO}{|}$$

liquid which gave a color with ferric chloride and a solid which did not. The solid slowly changed to the liquid on standing. In 1893 Claisen reported two forms of acetyldibenzoylmethane. One melted at 85°–90°, was soluble in dilute carbonate solution, gave in alcoholic solution a red color with ferric chloride, and reacted at once with cupric acetate to give an insoluble blue copper salt. Crystallization from alcohol of the product melting at 85°–90° gave a compound melting at 109°–112°, which at first was completely insoluble in dilute alkali but which slowly dissolved. Alcoholic solutions gave no color immediately on adding ferric chloride, and no blue precipitate on adding cupric acetate, but both reactions slowly took place on standing. In an article published in 1896 Claisen postulated that the lower-melting form had an enol structure and that the higher-melting form was completely ketonic.

$$CH_3C=C(COC_6H_5)_2 \quad \rightleftarrows \quad CH_3COCH(COC_6H_5)_2$$
$$\underset{\displaystyle OH}{|}$$

Enolic form of   Ketonic form of
acetyldibenzoylmethane   acetyldibenzoylmethane

In the same year Hantzsch isolated two forms of phenylnitromethane. The solid form had acidic properties and changed spontaneously to the nonacidic liquid form.

$$C_6H_5CH_2N{\overset{\displaystyle O}{\underset{\displaystyle O}{<}}} \quad \rightleftarrows \quad C_6H_5CH=N{\overset{\displaystyle O}{\underset{\displaystyle OH}{<}}}$$

It was not until 1911 that Knorr succeeded in isolating two forms of ethyl acetoacetate. The ketonic form separated when solutions in alcohol, ether, or petroleum ether were cooled to $-78°$. It did not give a color immediately with ferric chloride, and did not decolorize bromine. When dry hydrogen chloride was passed into a solution of the sodium salt of ethyl acetoacetate at $-78°$, a glassy solid was obtained which reacted instantaneously with ferric chloride and with bromine. On permitting either isomer to reach room temperature, the equilibrium mixture was obtained.

$$CH_3COCH_2COOC_2H_5 \rightleftharpoons CH_3COH{=}CHCOOC_2H_5$$

This interconversion is catalyzed by traces of acids or bases. By using specially treated quartz apparatus, K. H. Meyer in 1920 succeeded in separating the two forms by distillation. Since alcohols boil higher than ketones, it is surprising that the enol form of ethyl acetoacetate boils lower than the keto form. An explanation is that the enol form contains an internal proton bond which prevents intermolecular proton-bonding.

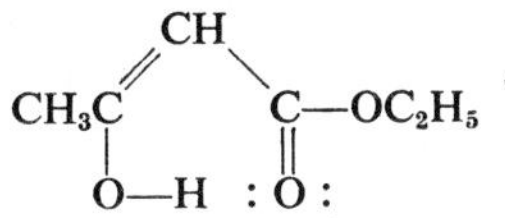

$$CH_3C\overset{CH}{\diagup}\underset{\underset{O{-}H\ :O:}{|}}{\diagdown}C{-}OC_2H_5$$

Knorr determined the refractive index of the keto form to be $n_D^{10} = 1.4225$ and of the enol form $n_D^{10} = 1.4480$. From the refractive index of the equilibrium mixture, $n_D^{10} = 1.4232$, the enol content was estimated to be 3 per cent. Meyer found that the keto form does not isomerize too rapidly to prevent the estimation of the enol content by reaction with bromine if the procedure is carried out quickly. He mixed a solution of the ester with an excess of a solution of bromine at 0° and removed the excess bromine by the addition of a solution of β-naphthol within a period of only fifteen seconds.

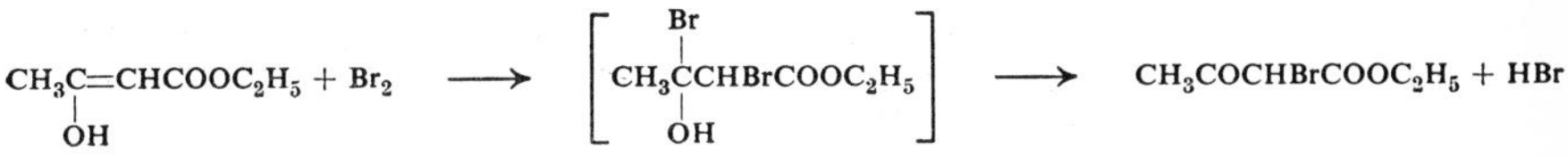

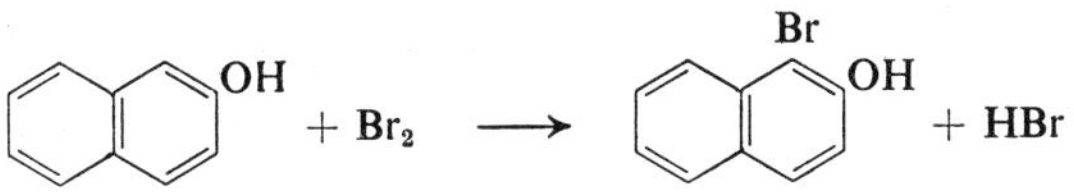

$$CH_3C{=}CHCOOC_2H_5 + Br_2 \longrightarrow \left[\underset{\underset{OH}{|}}{CH_3}CCHBrCOOC_2H_5 \right] \longrightarrow CH_3COCHBrCOOC_2H_5 + HBr$$
$$\underset{OH}{|}$$

Since α-bromo ketones are reduced by hydrogen iodide, they can be estimated by acidifying, adding sodium iodide, and titrating the iodine with standard thiosulfate solution.

$$CH_3COCHBrCOOC_2H_5 + 2 HI \longrightarrow CH_3COCH_2COOC_2H_5 + I_2 + HBr$$

By this procedure the amount of enol form in the pure ester was estimated to be 8 per cent.

The amount of enol form present in solution varies with the solvent and the concentration. At a concentration of presumably a few per cent, Meyer found that the per cent of ethyl acetoacetate in the enol form was 0.4 in water, 6 in acetic acid, 10 in ethyl alcohol, 16 in benzene, 27 in ether, and 46 in hexane. In hexane the amount of enol was 9 per cent when the concentration was 90 per cent, and 59 per cent when the concentration was 0.02 per cent. The poor correlation of the extent of enolization with properties of the solvent such as basicity or dielectric constant indicates that several factors probably are acting simultaneously. Meyer's bromine titration method has been used for estimating the amount of enol form in other equilibrium mixtures, for example the 1,3-diketones (p. 771).

The difference between simple aldehydes and ketones, β-diketones and β-keto esters, and phenols is purely one of degree. For the aldehydes and ketones, the position of equilibrium is far on the keto side. Determinations by a modification of Meyer's procedure indicate that only 2.5×10^{-4} per cent of liquid acetone is in the enol form. For β-diketones and β-keto esters appreciable quantities of both the keto and enol forms are present at equilibrium. With phenols the position of equilibrium is far on the enol side. It also is realized now that the anions of the metallic salts are resonance hybrids and that whether the product of a reaction is a derivative of the enol or keto form depends on the relative rate of attack at the two points.

Diketene. The constitution of diketene, which has been the subject of considerable discussion, probably is best represented as 3-buteno-β-lactone, the lactone of an enol form of acetoacetic acid. Ketene polymerizes to diketene spontaneously, and the latter now is manufactured commercially.

$$
\begin{array}{c}
CH_2{=}C{=}O \\
+ \\
CH_2{=}C{=}O
\end{array}
\longrightarrow
\begin{array}{c}
CH_2{-}C{=}O \\
| \quad | \\
CH_2{=}C{-}\!{-}O
\end{array}
$$

Ketene   Diketene

The reaction is analogous to the formation of β-propiolactone by the addition of formaldehyde to ketene (p. 782).

Diketene is a highly lachrymatory liquid that boils at $127°$ and melts at $-6.5°$. At room temperature it undergoes a further exothermic polymerization which is retarded by storing in the solid state. Since the polymerization may proceed explosively, producers hesitate to ship the material, and hence it is not readily available for laboratory use.

Diketene depolymerizes at $650°$ and is a convenient source of ketene free of methane and carbon monoxide. Catalytic reduction gives β-butyrolactone which hydrolyzes to β-hydroxybutyric acid.

$$
\underset{\underset{O{-}CO}{|\quad|}}{CH_2{=}C{-}CH_2}
\xrightarrow{\text{H}_2{-}\text{Ni}}
\underset{\underset{\bullet{-}C\bullet}{|\quad|}}{CH_3C{-}CH_2}
\xrightarrow{\text{H}_2\text{O}}
CH_3CHOHCH_2COOH
$$

Halogen gives the γ-haloacetoacetyl halide, which on hydrolysis yields the halogenated acetone.

$$
\underset{\underset{O{-}CO}{|\;|}}{CH_2{=}C{-}CH_2}
\xrightarrow{\text{Cl}_2}
ClCH_2COCH_2COCl
\xrightarrow{\text{H}_2\text{O}}
ClCH_2COCH_2COOH
\longrightarrow
ClCH_2COCH_3 + CO_2
$$

Ozonolysis yields formaldehyde and malonic acid, a reaction that furnishes strong proof of structure.

$$
\underset{\underset{O{-}CO}{|\;|}}{CH_2{=}C{-}CH_2}
\xrightarrow{\text{Ozonolysis}}
CH_2O +
\left[
\underset{\underset{O{-}CO}{|\quad|}}{CO{-}CH_2}
\right]
\xrightarrow{\text{H}_2\text{O}}
CH_2(COOH)_2
$$

Water, alcohols, and amines give acetoacetic acid, acetoacetic esters, and acetoacetamides.

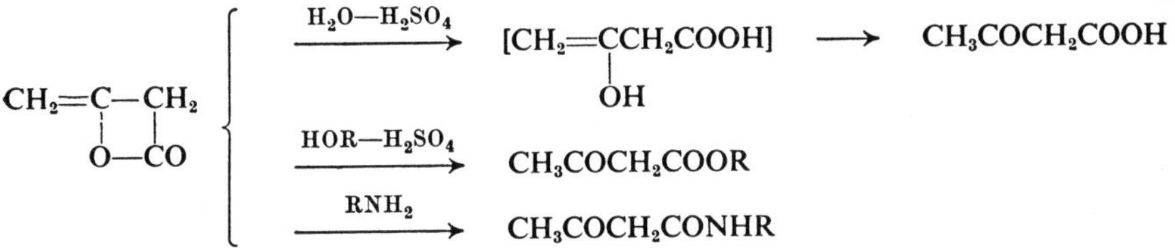

$$CH_2=C-CH_2 \begin{cases} \xrightarrow{\;H_2O-H_2SO_4\;} & [CH_2=CCH_2COOH] \longrightarrow CH_3COCH_2COOH \\ & \qquad\qquad\quad |\!\!\quad OH \\ \xrightarrow{\;HOR-H_2SO_4\;} & CH_3COCH_2COOR \\ \xrightarrow{\;RNH_2\;} & CH_3COCH_2CONHR \end{cases}$$

In many other condensation reactions, diketene gives the same products that would be expected from ethyl acetoacetate. For example urea gives 4-methyl-uracil (cf. p. 639).

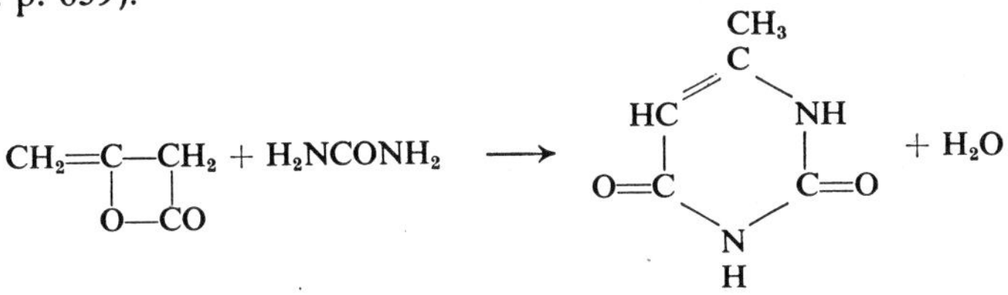

$$CH_2=C-CH_2 + H_2NCONH_2 \longrightarrow \text{4-methyluracil} + H_2O$$

The dimers of long-chain alkyl ketenes such as that derived from stearoyl chloride (p. 760) are used as water repellent sizes for cellulose products. Presumably reaction with the primary hydroxyl group of the cellulose molecules (p. 399) gives a surface coating of the hydrocarbon chains.

$$C_{16}H_{33}CH=C-CHC_{16}H_{33} + HOCH_2R \longrightarrow C_{16}H_{33}CH_2COCHC_{16}H_{33}$$
$$\qquad\qquad\qquad\qquad\qquad\qquad\qquad\qquad\qquad COOCH_2R$$

Other Keto Acids

General methods for the synthesis of **γ-keto acids** are the hydrolysis of acylsuccinic esters made either from β-keto esters or maleic ester, or the reaction of cyclic anhydrides with one mole of a Grignard reagent.

(*1*) $RCOCH_2COOC_2H_5 \xrightarrow{\;NaOC_2H_5\;} RCOCHCOOC_2H_5 \xrightarrow{\;ClCH_2COOC_2H_5\;}$
$$\qquad\qquad\qquad\qquad\qquad\qquad Na^+$$

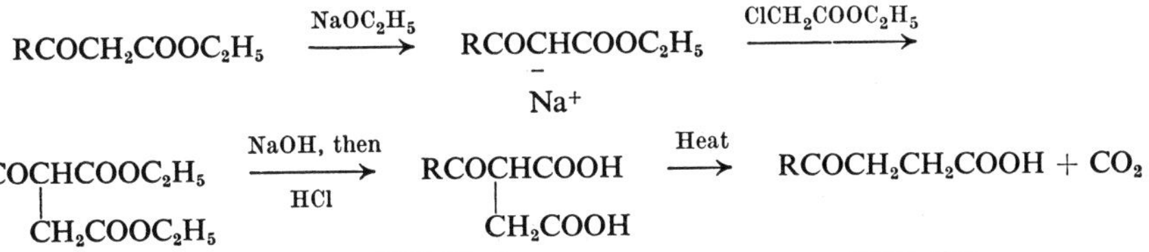

$RCOCHCOOC_2H_5 \xrightarrow[\;HCl\;]{\;NaOH, then\;} RCOCHCOOH \xrightarrow{\;Heat\;} RCOCH_2CH_2COOH + CO_2$
$|\quad$
$CH_2COOC_2H_5 \qquad\qquad\qquad CH_2COOH$

(2) $RCHO + HCCOOC_2H_5 \xrightarrow{\;(C_6H_5CO)_2O_2\;} RCOCHCOOC_2H_5 \xrightarrow[\;HCl\;]{\;NaOH, then\;}$
$\qquad\qquad ||$
$\qquad\qquad HCCOOC_2H_5 \qquad\qquad\qquad CH_2COOC_2H_5$

$\qquad\qquad RCOCHCOOH \xrightarrow{\;Heat\;} RCOCH_2CH_2COOH + CO_2$
$\qquad\qquad |$
$\qquad\qquad CH_2COOH$

(3) R_2C-CO
$\qquad |\qquad\; O + R'MgX \longrightarrow R_2CCOR' \xrightarrow{\;HX\;} R_2CCOR'$
$R_2C-CO \qquad\qquad\qquad R_2CCOOMgX \qquad R_2CCOOH$

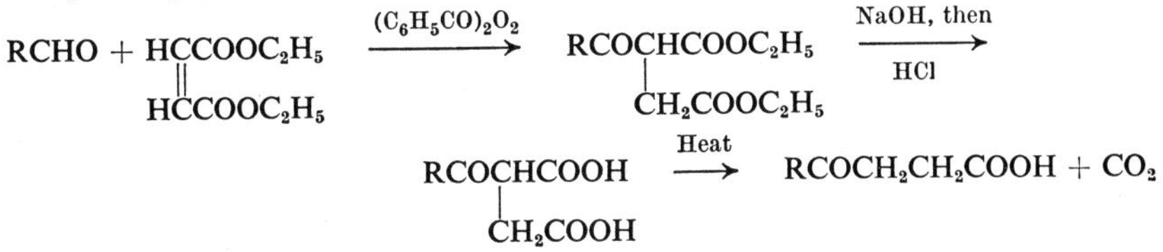

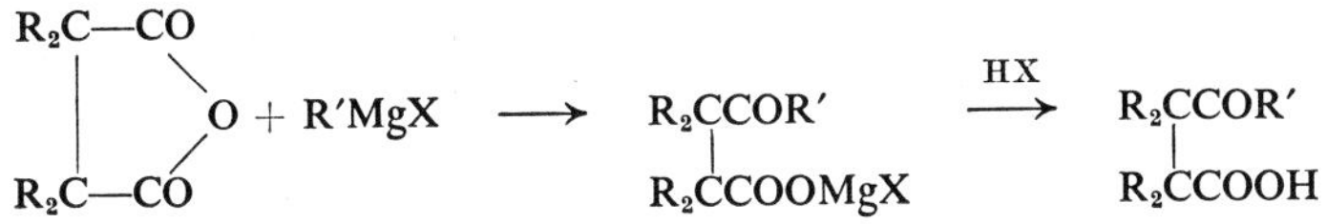

The only γ-keto acid readily available is **levulinic acid** which is formed by the hydrolysis of hexoses with strong acids (p. 379).

$$C_6H_{12}O_6 \xrightarrow{\text{Conc. HCl}} HCOOH + \underset{\text{Levulinic acid}}{CH_3COCH_2CH_2COOH} + H_2O$$

ϵ-Keto acids are available by the oxidation of 2-alkylcyclohexanols obtainable by the catalytic hydrogenation of 2-alkylphenols

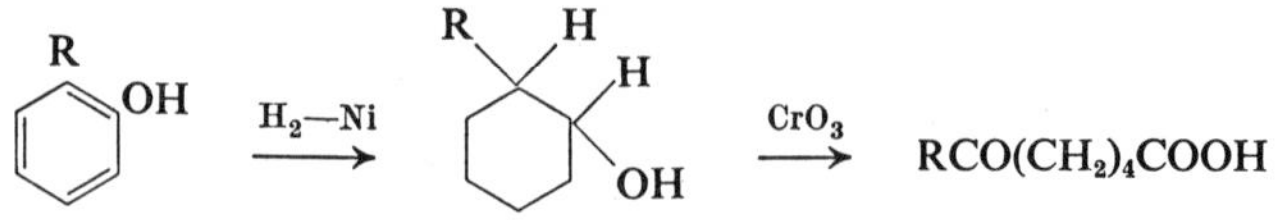

Higher keto esters can be made by the reaction of alkylzinc halides with the acyl halide from the half ester of a dibasic acid.

$$RZnCl + ClCO(CH_2)_nCOOC_2H_5 \longrightarrow RCO(CH_2)_nCOOC_2H_5 + ZnCl_2$$

Licanic acid, $CH_3(CH_2)_3CH{=}CHCH{=}CHCH{=}CH(CH_2)_2CO(CH_2)_4COOH$, makes up 70 to 80 per cent of the fat acids from *oiticica oil*, the seed fat of *Licania rigida* (p. 183).

When γ- or δ-keto acids are heated, they slowly lose water with the formation of γ- or δ-unsaturated lactones.

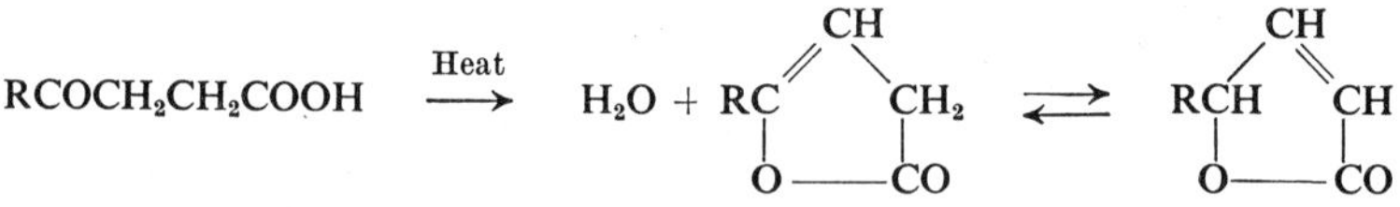

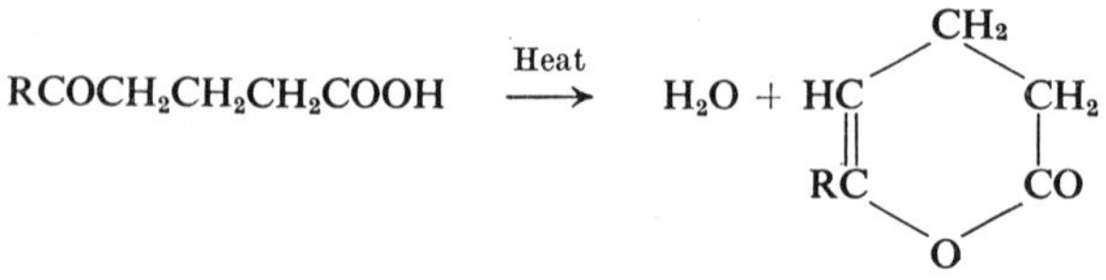

Mesoxalic acid is oxomalonic acid. Its ethyl ester is prepared by the oxidation of ethyl malonate with oxides of nitrogen.

$$H_2C(COOC_2H_5)_2 + 2\,N_2O_3 \longrightarrow O{=}C(COOC_2H_5)_2 + 4\,NO + H_2O$$

The acid and its esters form relatively stable hydrates which, like the hydrate of chloral (p. 739), are believed to contain two hydroxyl groups united to a single carbon atom.

$$(C_2H_5OOC)_2C{=}O + H_2O \longrightarrow (C_2H_5OOC)_2C(OH)_2$$

α-Oxosuccinic esters are obtained by the condensation of an ester with ethyl oxalate. Like other α-keto esters, they lose carbon monoxide when distilled and yield alkyl- or arylmalonic esters.

$$RCH_2COOC_2H_5 + C_2H_5OCOCOOC_2H_5 \xrightarrow{NaOC_2H_5}$$

$$\begin{matrix} RCHCOOC_2H_5 \\ | \\ COCOOC_2H_5 \end{matrix} \xrightarrow{\text{Heat}} \begin{matrix} RCHCOOC_2H_5 \\ | \\ COOC_2H_5 \end{matrix} + CO$$

Acetonedicarboxylic acid is β-ketoglutaric acid (p. 810). The methyl or ethyl ester is a useful intermediate for organic syntheses.

REVIEW QUESTIONS

1. What general methods are available for the preparation of α-keto acids? What happens in the thermal decomposition of α-keto acids and esters?
2. How are β-keto acids prepared and what is their most characteristic reaction? What other type of compound behaves in a similar fashion?
3. What is the Claisen ester condensation? What is the Dieckmann condensation?
4. Ethyl acetoacetate forms an oxime, a phenylhydrazone, an *O*-methyl ether, a sodium salt, readily decolorizes bromine, and gives a color with ferric chloride. Explain. Define the term *tautomerism*.
5. Give two procedures for the separation of the keto and enol forms of ethyl acetoacetate. Why does the enol form have the lower boiling point? How may the per cent of enol form in an equilibrium mixture be estimated?
6. Discuss the behavior of β-keto esters to cold dilute alkali, hot dilute acid, and hot concentrated alkali.
7. Why does methyl acetoacetate fail to give the iodoform test?

PROBLEMS

8. Give reactions for the following syntheses: (*a*) 2-oxo-3-methylbutanoic acid from ethyl malonate; (*b*) α-oxo-γ-phenylbutyric acid from cinnamic acid: (*c*) α-oxopimelic acid from ethyl adipate; (*d*) diethoxyacetpiperidide from pyridine and acetic acid; (*e*) ethyl α-oxo-*i*-valerate from diethoxyacetpiperidide.
9. Give reactions for three different methods for the synthesis of ethyl phenylmalonate.
10. Starting with ethyl acetoacetate, give reactions for the preparation of the following compounds: (*a*) methyl *i*-hexyl ketone; (*b*) α,β-dimethylbutyric acid; (*c*) α-methyladipic acid; (*d*) ethyl ester of 2,5-dimethyl-3,4-pyrroledicarboxylic acid; (*e*) 3,4-dimethyl-4,5-dihydro-5-isoxazolone; (*f*) 2-hydroxy-4-methylquinoline; (*g*) 4-*i*-propyl-2,6-heptanedione; (*h*) 1-methyl-3-oxocyclohexene; (*i*) 1-methyl-2-acetylcyclohexene; (*j*) ethyl β-oxomyristate; (*k*) δ-oxocaproic acid.
11. Give reactions for the following preparations: (*a*) 2-amino-4-hydroxypyrimidine starting with ethyl acetate; (*b*) 1-oxo-1,3-diphenylpropane from ethyl benzoate; (*c*) ethyl ester of 2,4-diphenyl-3,5-pyrroledicarboxylic acid by a Knorr synthesis; (*d*) α-methyladipic acid using a Dieckmann condensation; (*e*) 2,6-dimethylpyridine by the Hantzsch synthesis; (*f*) γ-oxoheptoic acid from ethyl maleate; (*g*) 5,5-dimethyl-4-oxohexanoic acid from succinic acid; (*h*) 2-acetylcyclopentanone from *o*-cresol.
12. Tell how one may distinguish by means of chemical reactions each of the following compounds from the other members of the group: levulinic acid, methylmalonic acid, oxosuccinic acid, 2-oxobutanoic acid, isobutyric acid, and α-ethylacetoacetic acid.
13. Compound *A* has the molecular formula $C_9H_{14}O_5$. It is neutral to moist litmus and is insoluble in water but goes into solution when boiled with aqueous potassium hydroxide. The saponification equivalent is 67. The compound gives a negative test with Schiff reagent but reacts with hydroxylamine to give compound *B*, $C_7H_9NO_4$. When *A* is saponified and distilled, the distillate gives a yellow precipitate with sodium hypoiodite. Acidification of the still residue with sulfuric acid and distillation gives a distillate in which only acetic acid can be detected. After acetic acid no longer comes over, no organic material remains in the sulfuric acid solution. Give a possible structural formula for *A* and equations for the reactions that take place.

Chapter 39

ALICYCLIC COMPOUNDS. TERPENES AND STEROIDS

ALICYCLIC COMPOUNDS

Alicyclic compounds are cyclic compounds having aliphatic properties. In a strict sense the term should apply to both carbocyclic and heterocyclic compounds, but in practice it usually is limited to carbocyclic compounds. The saturated alicyclic hydrocarbons frequently are called *cycloparaffins* or *cyclanes* although petroleum technologists usually call them *naphthenes* because cyclopentane (pentamethylene) and cyclohexane (hexamethylene) and their homologs have been isolated from the naphtha fraction of petroleum. Those compounds obtainable by the hydrogenation of aromatic rings frequently are called *hydroaromatic* compounds.

General Theory Regarding Cyclic Compounds

Previous to 1879 only five- and six-membered ring compounds were known. They could be accounted for without too much difficulty, since the internal angles of a regular pentagon are 108 degrees and of a regular hexagon 120 degrees. The synthesis of a four-membered ring compound by Markovnikov in 1879 and of three-membered ring compounds by Freund in 1882 and Perkin Jr.[1] in 1883, and the chemical properties of these compounds led Baeyer in 1885 to propose his **strain theory.** Baeyer postulated that the ease of formation of a ring depends on the amount which the bond must deviate from its normal tetrahedral angle of $109°28'$ in order to form the bond. The amount of deviation was designated as the *strain* in the ring. The greater the amount of strain, the easier it should be to open the ring, that is, the more reactive the compound should be. Thus in the formation of the highly reactive double bond, which in older theory consisted of two identical single bonds, each bond must be bent through one-half of the tetrahedral angle or $54°44'$; for a cyclopropane ring, $\frac{1}{2}(109°28' - 60°) = 24°44'$; for cyclobutane, $\frac{1}{2}(109°28' - 90°) = 9°44'$; for cyclopentane, $\frac{1}{2}(109°28' - 108°) = 0°44'$; and for cyclohexane, $\frac{1}{2}(109°28' - 120°) = -5°44'$. Since rings having more than seven atoms were unknown, Baeyer assumed that all of the atoms must be in a plane, which would require increasing negative strain for larger rings. This assumption was questioned at once by Werner, and other discrepancies were obvious. For example, although olefins are highly reactive, they are obtained easily in excellent yield. Moreover although in certain reactions cyclopentanes are formed in better yields than cyclohexanes, all evidence indicated that once formed the two ring systems are of equal stability.

---

[1] William Henry Perkin, Jr. (1860–1929), student of Wislicenus and Baeyer, and professor of chemistry at the University of Oxford. He is noted for his synthetic and degradative work in the field of natural products, particularly the terpenes and alkaloids.

The reality of planar alicyclic rings above C_5 was questioned from time to time, but it was not until the period 1921–1926 that sufficient evidence accumulated to cause this feature of Baeyer's theory to be abandoned. The most convincing of this evidence was the synthesis of rings containing from seven to over thirty carbon atoms, all of which appeared to be as stable as cyclopentane or cyclohexane. Currently it is assumed that the ease of formation of cyclic compounds, that is, the tendency for intramolecular reaction, depends on the proximity of the atoms being joined in the reaction. This tendency is high for the formation of a double bond, where the two atoms are adjacent to each other. Moreover it no longer is assumed that the double bond is a two-membered ring. Instead it is believed that one pair of electrons occupies a π orbital which involves no strain in the original sense, and the high reactivity is accounted for by the higher energy level of the π orbital (p. 49).

If the atoms were forced to remain in an extended chain, the chance for intramolecular reaction would decrease as more and more carbon atoms separated the reacting groups. However rotation about the single bonds permits the assumption of a spiral structure as indicated in Fig. 103. If in this figure the

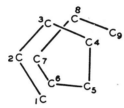

Fig. 103. Spiral arrangement of a carbon chain.

distance between C-1 and C-2 = 1.54 Å, then C-1 to C-3 = 2.51 Å, C-1 to C-4 = 2.52 Å, and C-1 to C-5 = 1.67 Å. Hence the double bond and the five-membered ring can be formed readily, but it is more difficult to form three- and four-membered rings. Because of the flexibility of the molecule, C-1 and C-6 can approach each other to any desired distance. Therefore once the bond is formed the ring is entirely strainless. The same situation exists for longer chains, but above five carbon atoms other atoms in the chain begin to get in the way of the reacting groups, and a greater amount of maneuvering of the chain is necessary to bring the reacting groups into the proper space relationship for reaction to take place. As a result intermolecular reaction to give polymeric products becomes predominant, and the yields of cyclic compounds are very low. In confirmation of this theory, large ring compounds can be obtained in excellent yields if the reaction is carried out at extremely high dilution where the chance of intramolecular reaction is again greater than the chance of intermolecular reaction.

The question of the relative stability of cyclopentane and cyclohexane has acquired renewed interest in recent years. Precise work on the heats of combustion of cyclopentane, cyclohexane, and cycloheptane indicates that cyclohexane is more stable by about 1 kcal. per mole than either cyclopentane or cycloheptane. In other words cyclohexane is less strained than cyclopentane or cycloheptane even though all of these compounds should have tetrahedral valence angles. An explanation can be given from a consideration of the fact that the conformation of the ethane molecule in which the methyl groups are rotated 60 degrees with respect to each other and the hydrogen atoms are staggered is more stable by about 3 kcal. per mole than the conformation in which the hydrogen atoms are opposite each other (p. 31). In the chair form of cyclohexane (Fig. 106, p. 843), the hydrogen atoms are completely staggered and hence cyclohexane is the most stable of the cycloparaffins. In the larger rings some of the hydrogen atoms can be staggered but not all. In cyclopentane no hydrogen atoms are staggered if the carbon atoms are all in a plane, and it is believed that the carbon atoms actually are forced into a nonplanar conformation to permit some staggering of the hydrogen atoms.

Preparation of Alicyclic Compounds; General Methods

1. From Dihalides.

$$(CH_2)_nX_2 + Zn \longrightarrow (CH_2)_n + ZnX_2$$

2. From Dicarboxylic Acids (p. 798).

$$(CH_2)_n(COOH)_2 \xrightarrow[\text{Th salt}]{\text{Heat, Ca or}} (CH_2)_nCO + CO_2 + H_2O$$

3. From Polymethylene Halides and Ethyl Malonate (p. 801).

$$X(CH_2)_nX + CH_2(COOC_2H_5)_2 \xrightarrow{\text{NaOC}_2\text{H}_5} X(CH_2)_nCH(COOC_2H_5)_2 \xrightarrow{\text{NaOC}_2\text{H}_5}$$

$$(CH_2)_nC(COOC_2H_5)_2 \xrightarrow[\text{HCl and heat}]{\text{NaOH, then}} (CH_2)_nCHCOOH$$

4. From Polymethylenebismalonic Esters (p. 801).

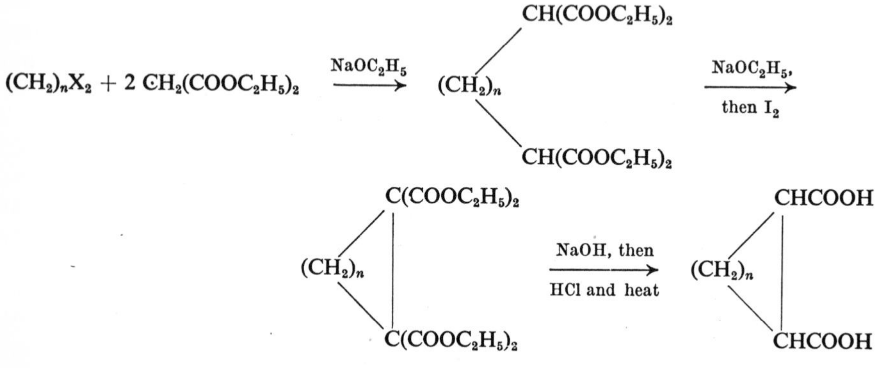

$$(CH_2)_nX_2 + 2\ CH_2(COOC_2H_5)_2 \xrightarrow{\text{NaOC}_2\text{H}_5} (CH_2)_n \begin{array}{c} CH(COOC_2H_5)_2 \\ \diagup \\ \diagdown \\ CH(COOC_2H_5)_2 \end{array} \xrightarrow[\text{then I}_2]{\text{NaOC}_2\text{H}_5,}$$

$$(CH_2)_n \begin{array}{c} C(COOC_2H_5)_2 \\ \diagup\ | \\ \diagdown\ | \\ C(COOC_2H_5)_2 \end{array} \xrightarrow[\text{HCl and heat}]{\text{NaOH, then}} (CH_2)_n \begin{array}{c} CHCOOH \\ \diagup\ | \\ \diagdown\ | \\ CHCOOH \end{array}$$

5. By Reduction of Aromatic Compounds.

$$C_6H_6 + 3\ H_2 \xrightarrow[200°]{\text{Ni,}} C_6H_{12}$$

Cyclohexane
(hexahydrobenzene,
hexamethylene)

The reaction is reversible and benzene, toluene, and the xylenes now are made from the cyclohexanes present in petroleum (p. 429). Reduction of aromatic compounds by metals in liquid ammonia gives 1,4-dihydro derivatives. The best results are obtained using lithium followed by decomposition of the lithium adduct with alcohol.

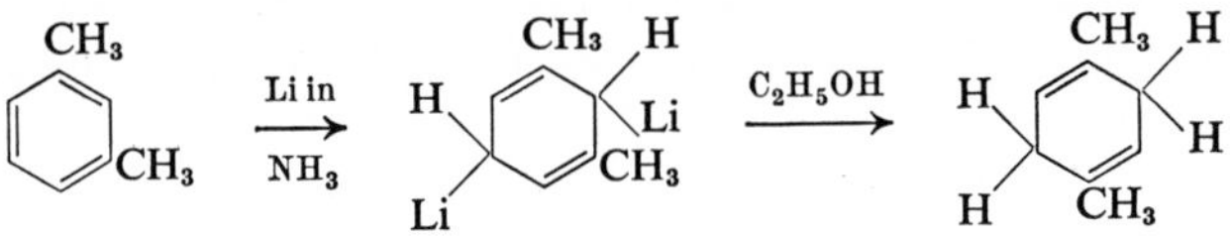

Lithium and ethylamine give cyclohexenes.

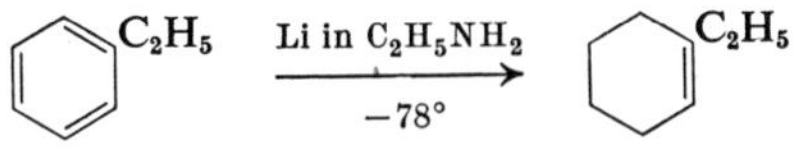

6. **By Ring Enlargement of Cyclic Ketones.** Reaction of ketones with diazomethane gives a homolog of the ketone (p. 266).

$$RCOR + CH_2N_2 \longrightarrow RCOCH_2R + N_2$$

Similarly a cyclic ketone gives a ketone having one more methylene group in the ring.

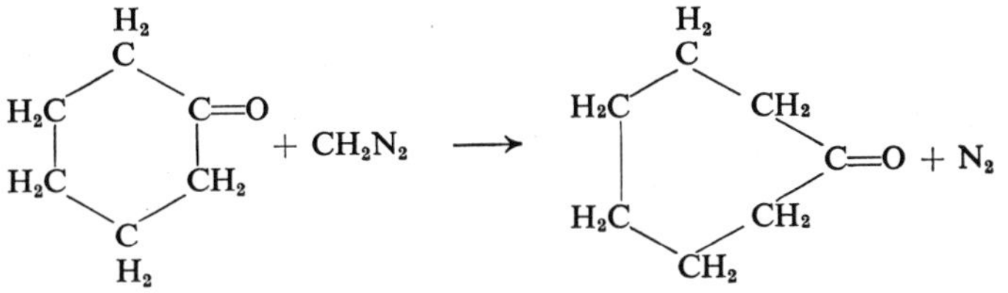

Cyclohexanone   Cycloheptanone

The best yields are obtained when the diazomethane is generated in the presence of the ketone by adding potassium carbonate to an alcohol solution of nitrosomethylurethan (p. 319) and the cyclic ketone. Under these conditions the effective concentration of the diazomethane is high.

7. **By Other Methods.** Any chemical reaction that leads to the formation of a carbon-carbon bond should be capable of forming ring compounds, for example, the Friedel-Crafts reaction (p. 598) and the Dieckmann reaction (p. 816). In addition many intermolecular reactions such as the Diels-Alder reaction (p. 806) and the bimolecular ester condensations (pp. 804, 816) also lead to cyclic compounds.

General Reactions of Alicyclic Compounds

In general the reactions of alicyclic compounds are identical with those of aliphatic compounds except that the three- and four-membered rings are less stable. Thus cyclopropane and most of its derivatives react with the same reagents as olefins to give open-chain compounds.

$$(CH_2)_3 + H_2SO_4 \longrightarrow CH_3CH_2CH_2OSO_3H$$

$$(CH_2)_3 + HBr \longrightarrow CH_3CH_2CH_2Br$$

$$(CH_2)_3 + Br_2 \longrightarrow BrCH_2CH_2CH_2Br$$

$$(CH_2)_3 + H_2 \xrightarrow[80°]{Pt} CH_3CH_2CH_3$$

The rates of reactions of cyclopropanes may differ greatly from those of olefins. For example, cyclopropane reacts more rapidly than propylene with sulfuric acid but more slowly with bromine. Catalytic reduction of cyclopropane requires a somewhat higher temperature than reduction of propylene. Unlike propylene, cyclopropane does not react with alkaline permanganate solution. Moreover in reactions with unsymmetrical reagents such as sulfuric acid or hydrogen bromide, cyclopropane yields *n*-propyl derivatives and not *i*-propyl derivatives.

Cyclobutane does not react with sulfuric acid, hydrobromic acid, or bromine. However it can be reduced catalytically at 120°, whereas cyclopentane and higher cyclanes are not reduced at temperatures up to 200°.

Many instances have been recorded in which reactions of alicyclic compounds take place with simultaneous ring expansion or contraction. The reaction of nitrous acid with either cyclobutylamine or (cyclopropylmethyl)amine gives a mixture of cyclobutanol and cyclopropylcarbinol (*Desmejanov reaction*).

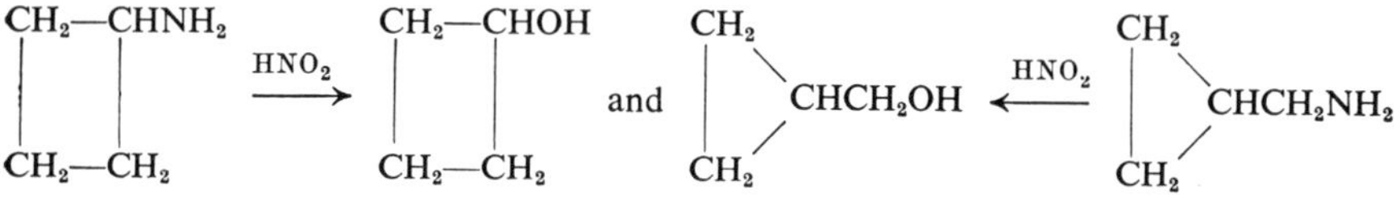

$$CH_2{-}CHNH_2 \quad \xrightarrow{HNO_2} \quad CH_2{-}CHOH \quad \text{and} \quad CH_2\!\!\diagdown_{CHCH_2OH} \quad \xleftarrow{HNO_2} \quad CH_2\!\!\diagdown_{CHCH_2NH_2}$$

| Cyclo-butylamine | Cyclo-butanol | Cyclopropyl-carbinol | (Cyclopropyl-methyl)amine |

When (cyclopropylmethyl)amine labeled with C^{14} in the side chain was treated with nitrous acid, the C^{14} became distributed among the four carbon atoms of both the cyclopropylcarbinol and the cyclobutanol. It has been suggested that an intermediate pyramidal carbonium ion is formed having the positive charge distributed about the four carbon atoms.

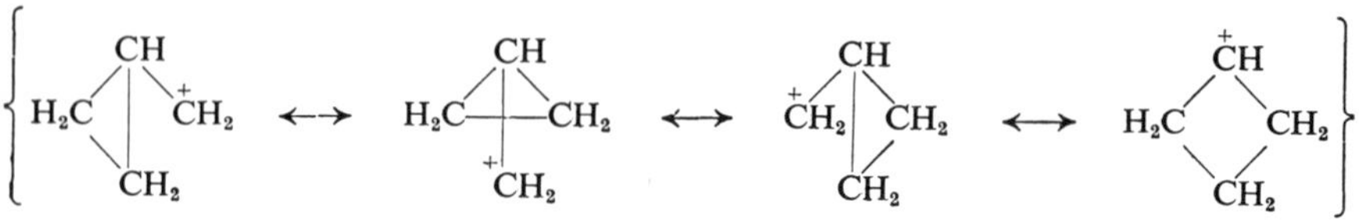

$$\left\{ \begin{array}{cccc} & CH & & CH \\ H_2\overset{+}{C}\diagup \diagdown CH_2 & \longleftrightarrow & H_2C{-}\!\!\diagup \diagdown\!\!{-}CH_2 & \longleftrightarrow \cdots \\ & CH_2 & & \overset{+}{C}H_2 \end{array} \right\}$$

Dehydration of cyclobutylcarbinol gives a mixture of methylenecyclobutane and cyclopentene.

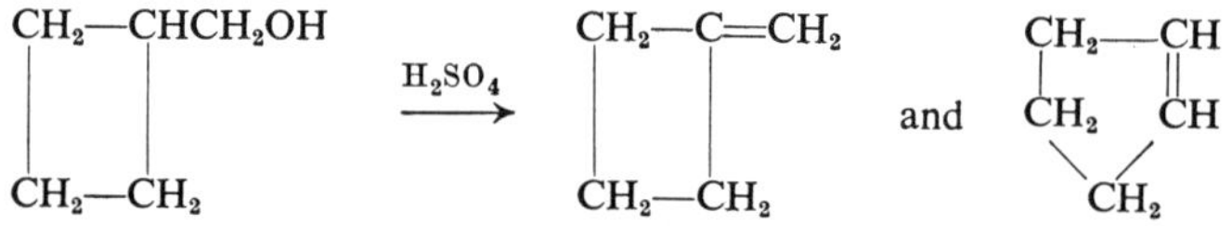

$$CH_2{-}CHCH_2OH \quad \xrightarrow{H_2SO_4} \quad CH_2{-}C{=}CH_2 \quad \text{and} \quad \begin{array}{c} CH_2{-}CH \\ CH_2 \quad CH \\ CH_2 \end{array}$$

| Cyclobutyl-carbinol | Methylene-cyclobutane | Cyclopentene |

Pinacol rearrangements may involve ring contraction and ring expansion.

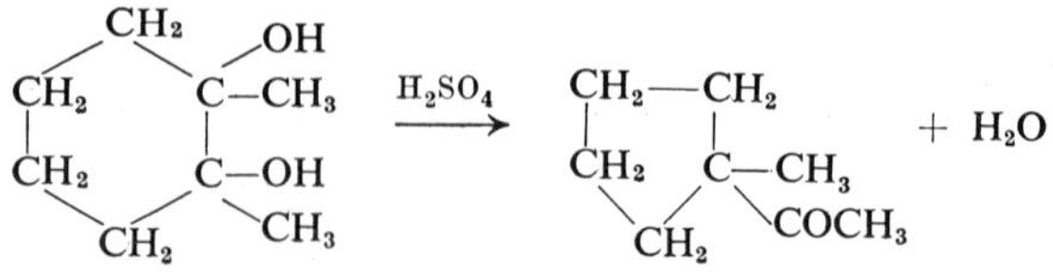

$$\begin{array}{c} CH_2 \quad OH \\ CH_2 \quad C{-}CH_3 \\ CH_2 \quad C{-}OH \\ CH_2 \quad CH_3 \end{array} \quad \xrightarrow{H_2SO_4} \quad \begin{array}{c} CH_2{-}CH_2 \\ CH_2 \quad C{-}CH_3 \\ CH_2 \quad COCH_3 \end{array} \quad + H_2O$$

| 1,2-Dimethyl-1,2-cyclo-hexanediol | 1-Methylcyclo-pentyl methyl ketone |

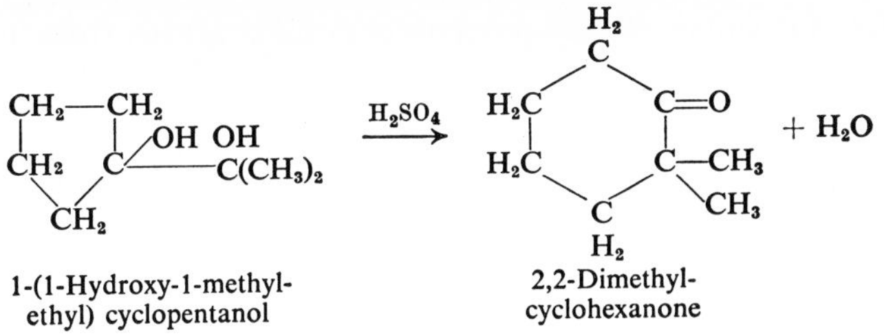

1-(1-Hydroxy-1-methyl-
ethyl) cyclopentanol

2,2-Dimethyl-
cyclohexanone

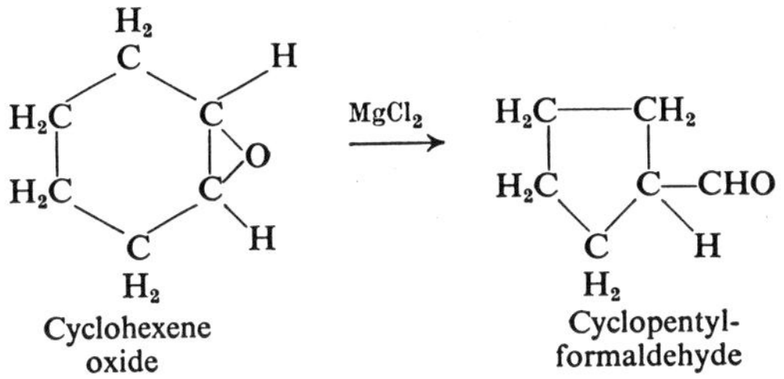

Cyclohexene
oxide

Cyclopentyl-
formaldehyde

Even hydrocarbons undergo rearrangements in the presence of catalysts such as aluminum chloride. Thus 1,2-dimethylcyclopentane gives a mixture containing 97 per cent of methylcyclohexane, and cyclohexane gives a mixture containing around 20 per cent of methylcyclopentane.

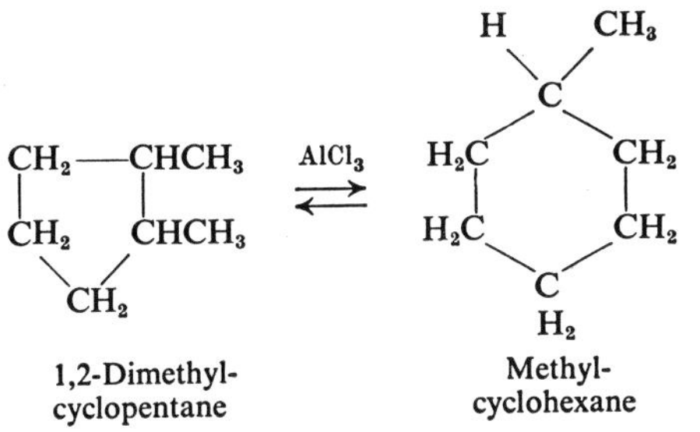

1,2-Dimethyl-
cyclopentane

Methyl-
cyclohexane

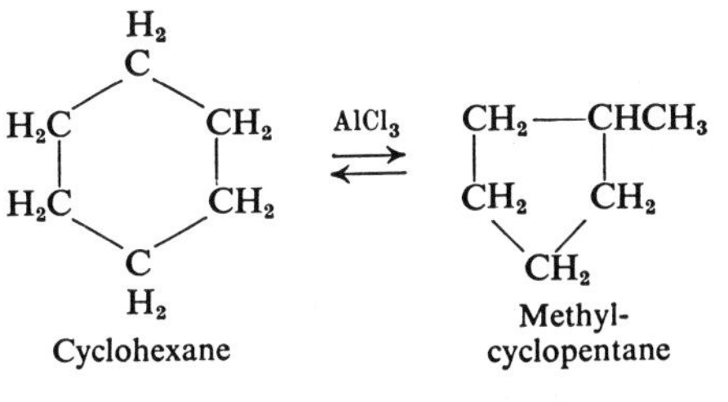

Cyclohexane

Methyl-
cyclopentane

The hydroaromatic compounds show none of the properties of the aromatic compounds. Thus cyclohexane, under the conditions used for benzene, does not undergo direct nitration, sulfonation, or the Friedel-Crafts reaction. Cyclohexanol is not soluble in alkali and reacts like a secondary alcohol.

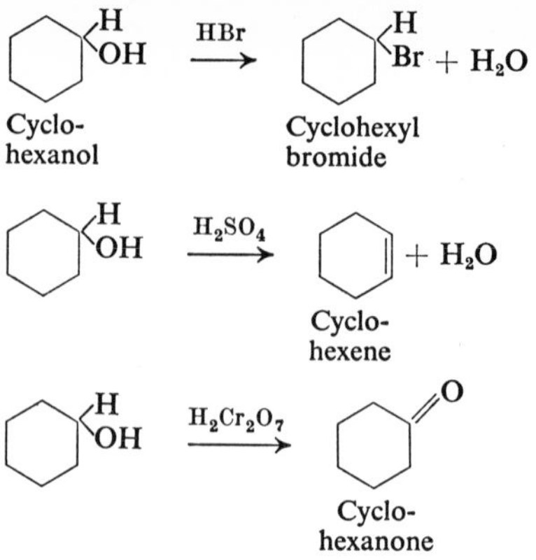

Cyclo-
hexanol

Cyclohexyl
bromide

Cyclo-
hexene

Cyclo-
hexanone

Cyclohexyl bromide reacts with silver hydroxide to give cyclohexanol, with alcoholic potassium hydroxide to give cyclohexene, and with sodium cyanide to give cyclohexyl cyanide. Cyclohexene decolorizes permanganate to give first the diol and then adipic acid, and decolorizes bromine to form cyclohexene bromide (1,2-dibromocyclohexane). Cyclohexylamine is as basic as aliphatic amines ($K_B = 4.4 \times 10^{-4}$), and no diazonium salt can be obtained by reaction with nitrous acid. The unsaturated and oxygenated rings are opened readily by oxidation. Thus cyclohexene and cyclohexanone give good yields of adipic acid (p. 793).

Cyclopropanes

Cyclopropane is prepared by the reaction of zinc dust with trimethylene chlorobromide (p. 727). It is a gas, b.p. $-34°$, used frequently instead of ether as a general anesthetic.

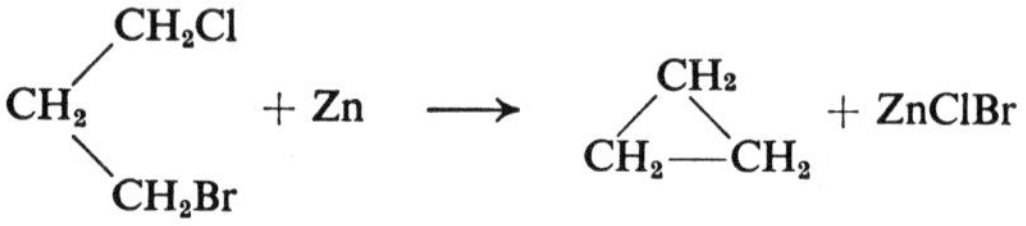

Cyclopropane

The addition of a methylene group to a carbon-carbon double bond would form a cyclopropane ring. This reaction frequently can be brought about by means of aliphatic diazo compounds (p. 266).

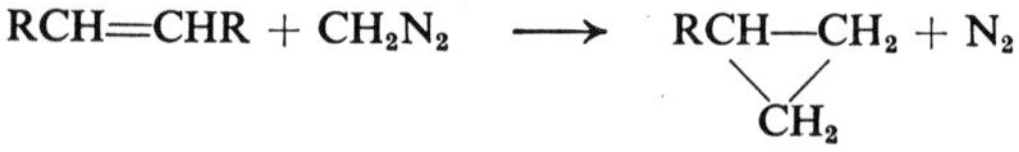

Aromatic compounds also give cyclopropane derivatives which rearrange on heating to a mixture of a substituted benzene and a cycloheptatriene.

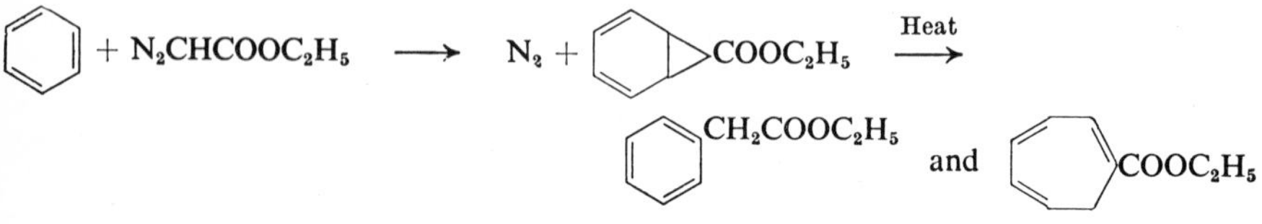

In the reaction of cyclohexene with chloroform and potassium hydroxide, a dichloromethylene group adds to the double bond (cf. p. 237).

$$\text{(cyclohexene)} + CHCl_3 + KOH \longrightarrow \text{(bicyclic)} CCl_2 + KCl + H_2O$$

The reaction of the double bond with aliphatic diazo compounds appears to take place through the intermediate formation of a dipolar ion which can lose nitrogen to give the cyclopropane or an unsaturated isomer, or cyclize to a pyrazoline. The pyrazolines generally decompose when heated to give nitrogen and the cyclopropane.

$$\begin{array}{c} RCH \\ \| \\ RCH \end{array} + : \overset{-}{C}H_2-\overset{+}{N}\equiv N: \longrightarrow \begin{array}{c} RCHCH_2-\overset{+}{N}\equiv N: \\ R\overset{-}{C}: \\ H \end{array} \longrightarrow \begin{array}{c} RCH-CH_2 \\ | \quad | \\ RCH \quad N \\ \diagdown \diagup \\ N \end{array} \xrightarrow{\text{Heat}} \begin{array}{c} RCH \\ \diagdown \\ \quad CH_2 + N_2 \\ \diagup \\ RCH \end{array}$$

$$\begin{array}{c} RCCH_3 \\ \| \\ R-CH \end{array}, \begin{array}{c} CHCH_2R \\ \| \\ RCH \end{array} \text{ and } \begin{array}{c} RCH \\ \diagdown \\ \quad CH_2 + N_2 \\ \diagup \\ RCH \end{array}$$

The reaction with chloroform and potassium hydroxide may proceed by way of the dichloromethylene group (cf. pp. 175, 532).

Cyclopropene has been prepared by the pyrolysis of trimethylcyclopropyl-ammonium hydroxide made from cyclopropylamine.

$$\begin{array}{c} CH_2 \\ \diagdown \\ \quad CHNH_2 \\ \diagup \\ CH_2 \end{array} \xrightarrow[\text{AgOH}]{CH_3I,} \left[\begin{array}{c} CH_2 \\ \diagdown \\ \quad CH\overset{+}{N}(CH_3)_3 \\ \diagup \\ CH_2 \end{array}\right] [^-OH] \xrightarrow{\text{Heat}} \begin{array}{c} CH=CH + (CH_3)_3N + H_2O \\ \diagdown \diagup \\ CH_2 \end{array}$$
Cyclopropylamine   Cyclopropene

Despite the strain that must exist in the cyclopropane and cyclopropene rings, examples of these structures have been found in **lactobacillic acid,** which is present to the extent of 30 per cent and 19 per cent respectively in the fat acids from *Lactobacillus arabinosus* and *Lactobacillus casei,* and in **sterculic acid** from the kernel oil of *Sterculia foetida.* 1-Aminocyclopropanecarboxylic acid has been reported to be present in pears and apples. The cyclopropane ring is present also in the active principles of pyrethrum (p. 839).

$$\begin{array}{c} CH_3(CH_2)_5CH-CH(CH_2)_9COOH \\ \diagdown \diagup \\ CH_2 \end{array} \qquad \begin{array}{c} CH_3(CH_2)_7C=C(CH_2)_7COOH \\ \diagdown \diagup \\ CH_2 \end{array}$$
Lactobacillic acid   Sterculic acid

Cyclobutanes

Cyclobutane and its derivatives have been of considerable theoretical interest. Cyclobutane has been synthesized in poor yield by several standard procedures but has not been obtained by the dimerization of ethylene. However, tetra-fluoroethylene readily undergoes cyclo addition (p. 733). When 1,1-dichloro-2,2-difluoroethylene is heated at 200°, **1,1,2,2-tetrachloro-3,3,4,4-tetrafluoro-cyclobutane** is formed.

$$\begin{array}{c} CF_2 \\ \| \\ CCl_2 \end{array} + \begin{array}{c} CF_2 \\ \| \\ CCl_2 \end{array} \longrightarrow \begin{array}{c} F_2C-CF_2 \\ | \quad\quad | \\ Cl_2C-CCl_2 \end{array}$$

Neither cyclobutene nor cyclobutadiene is known but derivatives have been prepared. Phenylacetylene adds to chlorotrifluoroethylene to give **1-phenyl-3,3,4-trifluoro-4-chlorocyclobutene** which can be hydrolyzed to **1-phenyl-3,4-dioxo-cyclobutene** (*phenylcyclobutadienoquinone*).

$$C_6H_5C{\equiv}CH + CFCl{=}CF_2 \xrightarrow{120°} C_6H_5\underset{FCl}{\overset{F_2}{\rule{}{}}} \xrightarrow[H_2SO_4]{H_2O} C_6H_5\underset{=O}{\overset{O}{\rule{}{}}}$$

The reaction of pentaerythrityl bromide with zinc leads to the formation of **methylenecyclobutane** rather than spiropentane.

$$\begin{array}{c} BrCH_2 \quad CH_2Br \\ \diagdown \quad \diagup \\ C \\ \diagup \quad \diagdown \\ BrCH_2 \quad CH_2Br \end{array} \xrightarrow{2\ Zn} \begin{array}{c} H_2C{-}C{=}CH_2 \\ | \qquad | \\ H_2C{-}CH_2 \end{array}$$

The dimers of disubstituted ketenes are **1,3-cyclobutanediones** (p. 762).

The **truxinic** and **truxillic acids** are derivatives of cyclobutane that are formed by the dimerization of cinnamic acid when exposed to sunlight.

$$2\ C_6H_5CH{=}CHCOOH \longrightarrow \begin{array}{c} C_6H_5CH{-}CHCOOH \\ | \qquad\qquad | \\ C_6H_5CH{-}CHCOOH \end{array} \text{ and } \begin{array}{c} C_6H_5CH{-}CHCOOH \\ | \qquad\qquad | \\ HOOCCH{-}CHC_6H_5 \end{array}$$

Truxinic acids   Truxillic acids

Both truxinic and truxillic acid can exist in several stereoisomeric forms. Thus the five truxillic acids are represented by the structures shown in Fig. 104. The

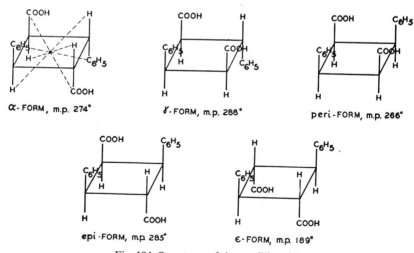

Fig. 104. Structures of the truxillic acids.

α form is of particular interest because it does not contain a plane of symmetry and yet mirror images of this molecule are superposable. The reason for the superposability is the presence of a center of symmetry (p. 336) indicated by the dotted lines.

Cyclopentanes

Cyclopentadiene, b.p. 41°, is a component of coal gas and is a co-product in the manufacture of isoprene by the cracking of petroleum fractions (p. 719). It polymerizes spontaneously by a Diels-Alder addition (p. 806) to dicyclopentadiene, m.p. 33°, which depolymerizes at its boiling point (170°) to the monomer.

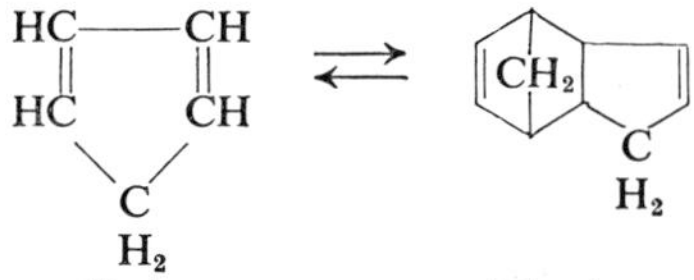

Cyclo-
pentadiene

Dicyclo-
pentadiene

Vapor-phase chlorination of cyclopentadiene gives **hexachlorocyclopentadiene.** The Diels-Alder addition product of hexachlorocyclopentadiene and cyclopentadiene adds chlorine in carbon tetrachloride solution to give the important insecticide **chlordan.**

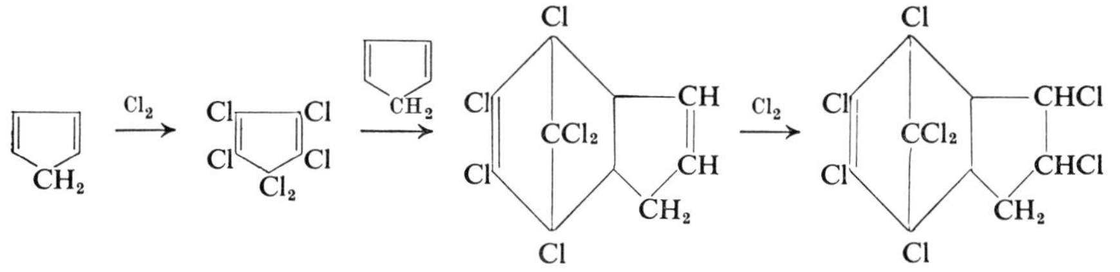

Hexachloro-
cyclopentadiene

Chlordan

Diels-Alder addition of acetylene to cyclopentadiene gives **1,4-endomethylene-cyclohexadiene** which adds to hexachlorocyclopentadiene to give the insecticide **Aldrin.** When aldrin is converted to the epoxide with peroxyacetic acid, still another insecticide known as **Dieldrin** is formed.

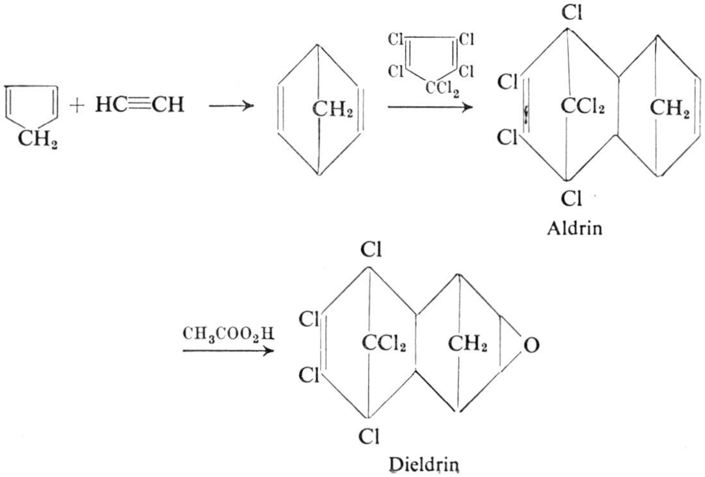

Aldrin

Dieldrin

The hydrogen of the methylene group of cyclopentadiene is sufficiently acidic to react with potassium in benzene solution and to evolve methane from methylmagnesium bromide.

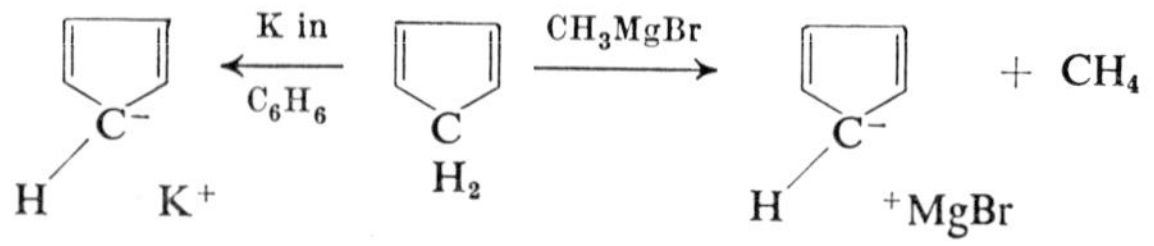

Either salt reacts with carbon dioxide to give **cyclopentadienecarboxylic acid.** Cyclopentadiene also undergoes aldol addition and dehydration to give colored compounds known as **fulvenes.** The products from formaldehyde and acetone are yellow and orange oils respectively that resinify and oxidize readily, but those from benzaldehyde or benzophenone are red crystalline solids.

Phenylfulvene

The acidity of the methylene hydrogen may be ascribed to the stabilization of the cyclopentadienyl anion by resonance (cf. p. 154).

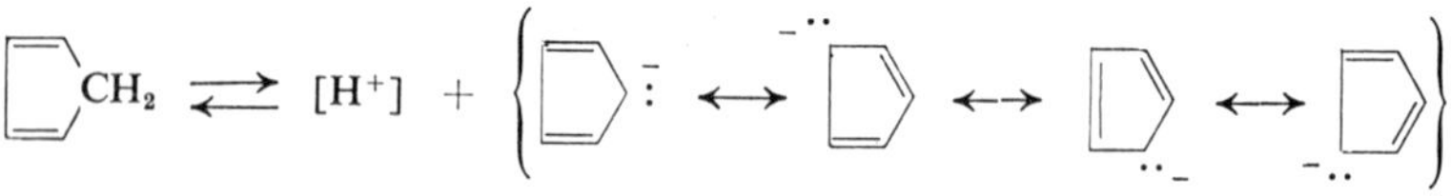

One of the most interesting properties of cyclopentadiene is a reaction with metals and their salts. When cyclopentadiene vapor is passed over activated iron at 300°, a stable orange compound sublimes having the molecular formula $FeC_{10}H_{10}$. It is formed also by the reaction of the sodium or halomagnesium salt of cyclopentadiene with ferrous chloride.

$$2 C_5H_6 + Fe \longrightarrow Fe(C_5H_5)_2 + H_2$$

$$2 C_5H_5Na + FeCl_2 \longrightarrow Fe(C_5H_5)_2 + 2 NaCl$$

It boils at 249°, is insoluble in water and soluble in organic solvents, and is not affected by boiling acid or alkali. The compound is not unsaturated and undergoes Friedel-Crafts acylations like an aromatic compound.

$$FeC_{10}H_{10} + (CH_3CO)_2O \xrightarrow{HF} FeC_{10}H_9COCH_3 + CH_3COOH$$

Because of the aromatic character of the cyclopentadienyl rings, the compound was called **ferrocene.** Reagents with oxidizing properties such as the halogens and nitric or sulfuric acid cause oxidation rather than substitution. Since the discovery of ferrocene in 1951, analogous compounds have been obtained with numerous metals from all groups of the periodic table except I and VII.

Ferrocene and its analogs have been called *sandwich molecules.* The metal atom lies between the two cyclopentadienyl rings which are staggered to give an antiprismatic structure (Fig. 105).

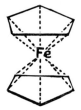

Fig. 105. Ferrocene.

There is no evidence for free rotation of the rings with respect to each other. The structure can be explained best by the molecular orbital theory. The three pair of electrons in each ring occupy molecular orbitals which can overlap hybrid atomic orbitals of the metal atom sufficiently to give a stable molecule.

The term **naphthenic acids** is applied to the mixture of carboxylic acids obtained from the alkali washes of petroleum fractions. Judging from the pure compounds that have been isolated, they are complex mixtures of normal and branched aliphatic acids, alkyl derivatives of cyclopentane and cyclohexane-carboxylic acids, and cyclopentyl and cyclohexyl derivatives of aliphatic acids. The crude naphthenic acids are available in large amounts and are used chiefly in the form of metallic salts, which are soluble in oils and organic solvents. The copper salts are used in wood preservatives and the lead, manganese, zinc, and iron salts as driers (oxidation catalysts) for paints and varnishes (p. 187). **Chaulmoogric** and **hydnocarpic acids,** the characteristic fat acids of chaulmoogra oil, long used in the treatment of leprosy, contain a terminal cyclopentene ring.

$$\boxed{}(CH_2)_{10}COOH \qquad\qquad \boxed{}(CH_2)_{12}COOH$$

Hydnocarpic acid   Chaulmoogric acid

The active principles of **pyrethrum,** the commercially important insecticide derived from the flower heads of *Chrysanthemum cinerariaefolium,* and a few other varieties, are four esters of cyclopropanecarboxylic acids with cyclopentyl alcohols, called *pyrethrin I, pyrethrin II, cinerin I,* and *cinerin II.* The relative toxicity to houseflies is 100 : 23 : 71 : 18.

Pyrethrin I

Pyrethrin II

Cinerin I

Cinerin II

The acid formed by hydrolysis of pyrethrin I and cinerin I is called *chrysanthemum monocarboxylic* or *chrysanthemic acid*, and that from pyrethrin II and cinerin II is called *chrysanthemum dicarboxylic acid* or *pyrethric acid*. The alcohol from pyrethrin I and pyrethrin II is called *pyrethrolone* and that from cinerin I and cinerin II is called *cinerolone*. A commercial synthetic analog of pyrethrin I, called **allethrin,** has an allyl side chain instead of the pentadienyl side chain.

Indene and **fluorene** occur in coal tar. Their structures are represented by condensed nuclear systems containing a cyclopentadiene ring and one and two benzene rings respectively. Oxidation of colorless fluorene gives yellow fluorenone. 2,4,7-Trinitrofluorenone forms addition complexes with polynuclear aromatic hydrocarbons and their derivatives that are useful for the purpose of identification (p. 460).

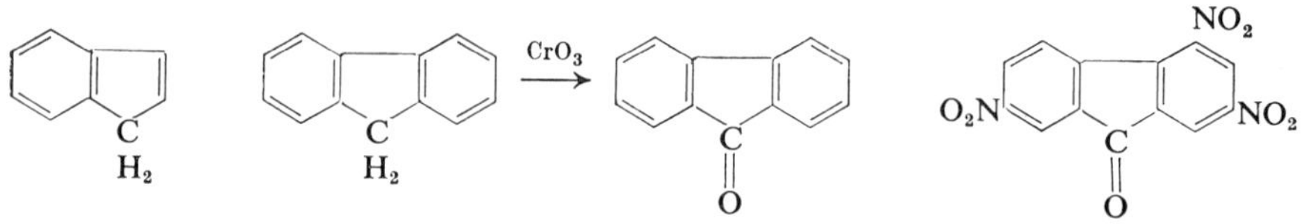

Indene   Fluorene   Fluorenone   2,4,7-Trinitrofluorenone

2,3-Dihydroindene is **indane** or **hydrindene.** 1,2,3-Triketohydrindene forms a stable hydrate known as **ninhydrin.** It is a valuable reagent for the colorimetric detection and estimation of α-amino acids (p. 306). In this reaction the Schiff base initially formed decomposes and hydrolyzes to give 2-amino-1,3-diketohydrindene, an aldehyde, and carbon dioxide. Reaction of the amino diketone with hydrindene gives a deep blue product.

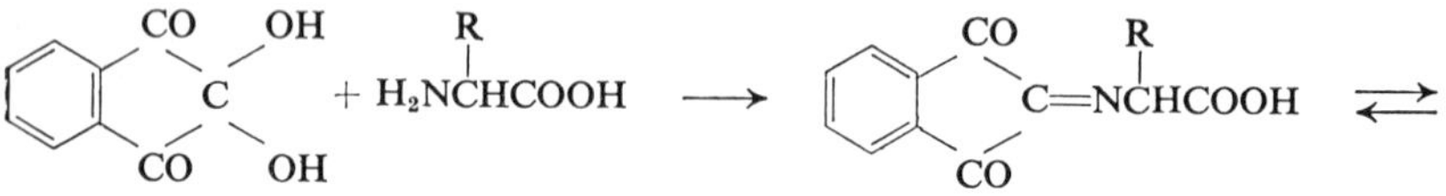

Triketohydrindene
hydrate (ninhydrin)

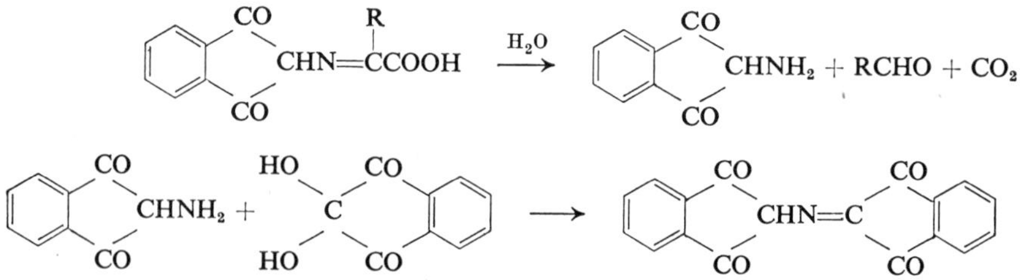

(Blue)

Ammonium salts, dilute ammonia solutions, and certain amines also give a blue color under certain conditions, apparently because of an intermolecular oxidation and reduction of the ninhydrin in the presence of ammonia.

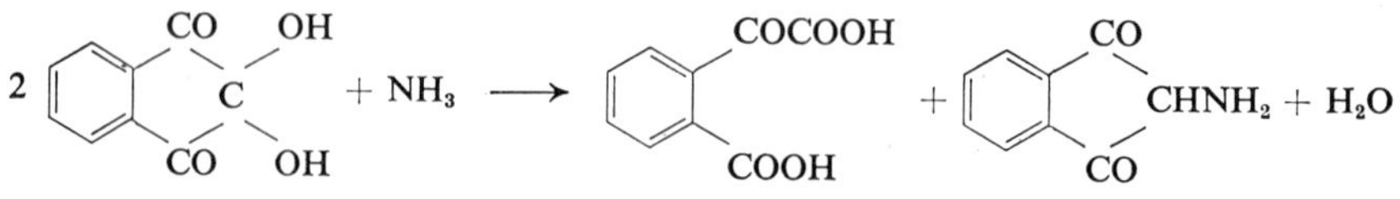

The ninhydrin reaction is a special case of the more general *Strecker degradation* in which any compound containing an aldehydo or keto group in conjugation with another carbonyl group or a nitro group reacts with an α-amino acid to give an aldehyde and carbon dioxide. The ready loss of carbon dioxide is dependent on the ability of the second carbonyl group or the nitro group to accommodate the pair of electrons that binds the carboxyl group.

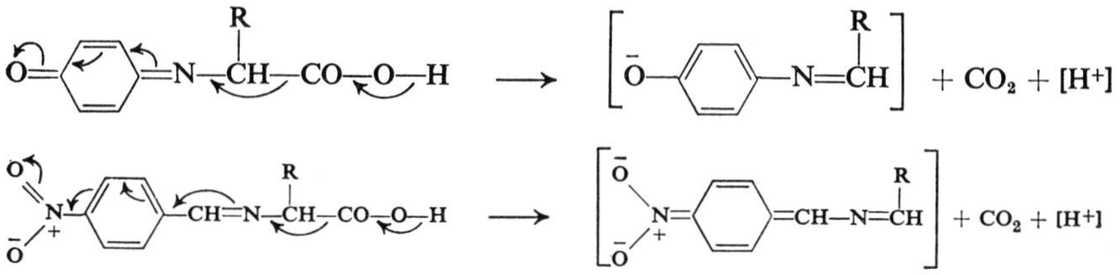

Measurement of the amount of carbon dioxide evolved in these reactions may be used for the quantitative estimation of α-amino acids.

Cyclohexanes

Cyclohexane, **methylcyclohexane, cyclohexanol** (*hexalin*), **cyclohexylamine, tetrahydro-** and **decahydronaphthalene** (*tetralin* and *decalin*) are commercial products made by the catalytic hydrogenation of the corresponding aromatic compounds. **Dihydroresorcinol** (*1,3-cyclohexanedione*) results from the reduction of resorcinol with sodium amalgam or with hydrogen and nickel in alkaline solution.

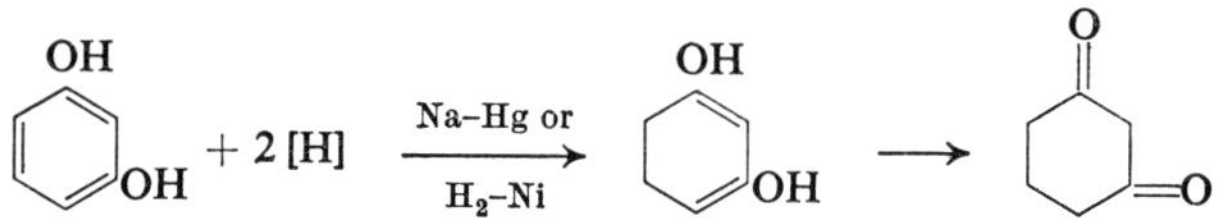

As a β-diketone it is a useful intermediate for synthesizing other compounds (p. 772 ff).

Vapor phase nitration of cyclohexane gives **nitrocyclohexane** which can be converted to **cyclohexanone oxime** by direct reduction or preferably by carrying out a Nef reaction (p. 262) in the presence of hydroxylamine.

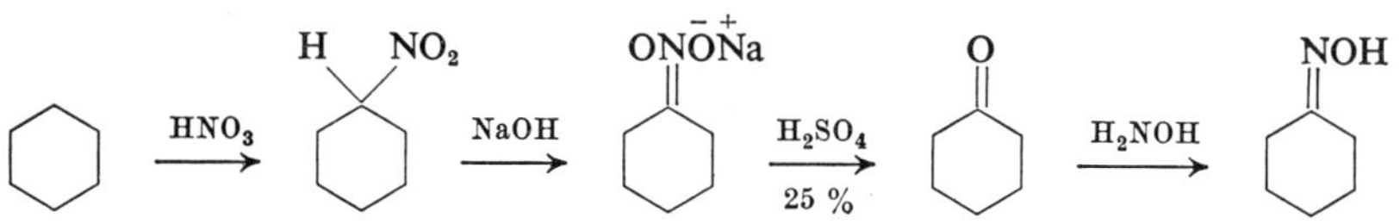

Beckmann rearrangement (p. 544) of cyclohexanone oxime gives the **lactam** of **ε-aminocaproic acid** from which the amino acid can be obtained by hydrolysis.

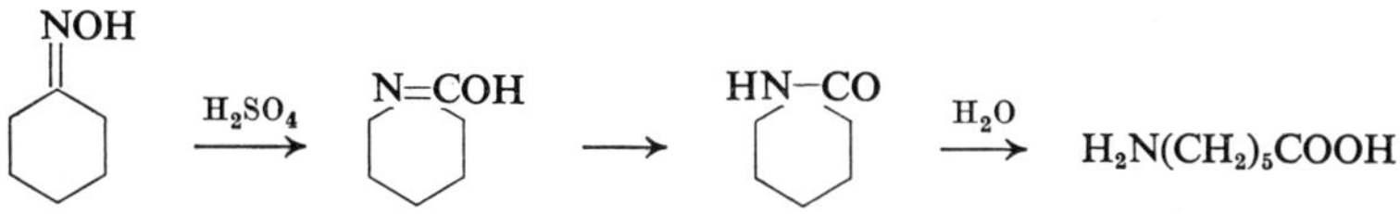

When ε-caprolactam is heated to 250° with an acidic or basic catalyst, it is converted into the linear polymeric amide $[-NH(CH_2)_5CO-]_n$ which can be spun into fibers known as **nylon 6** (cf. p. 799).

Cyclohexenones are converted readily to phenols by dehydrogenation or to aromatic hydrocarbons by dehydration.

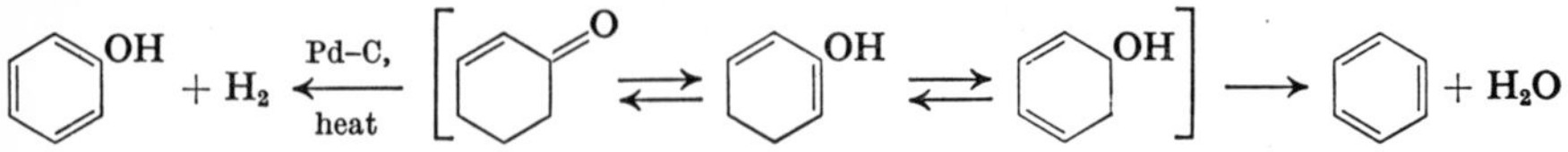

Properly substituted cyclohexenones may yield aromatic compounds that are difficult to obtain by other methods. **Cyclohexadienones** containing quaternary carbon atoms rearrange to phenol acetates when heated with acetic anhydride in the presence of sulfuric acid (*dienone-phenol rearrangement*).

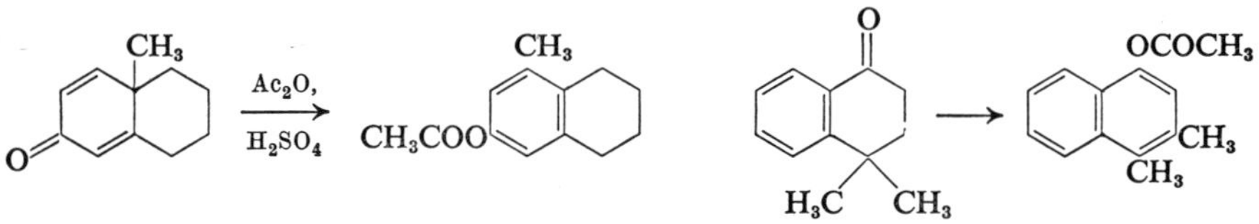

Numerous **polyhydroxycyclohexanes** occur naturally and have been discussed along with the related sugar alcohols (p. 413). Two polyhydroxycyclohexane-carboxylic acids are of importance because they appear to be the intermediates in the formation of several naturally occurring aromatic compounds from carbohydrates. **Quinic acid** was obtained first from cinchona bark in 1790 but has since been found in many plants. **Shikimic acid** was isolated from Japanese star anise, *shikimi-no-ki* (*Illicium religiosum*) in 1885. Both are readily converted into benzene derivatives.

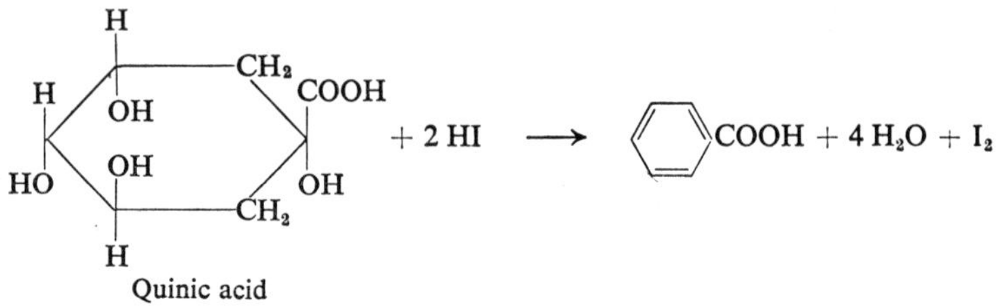

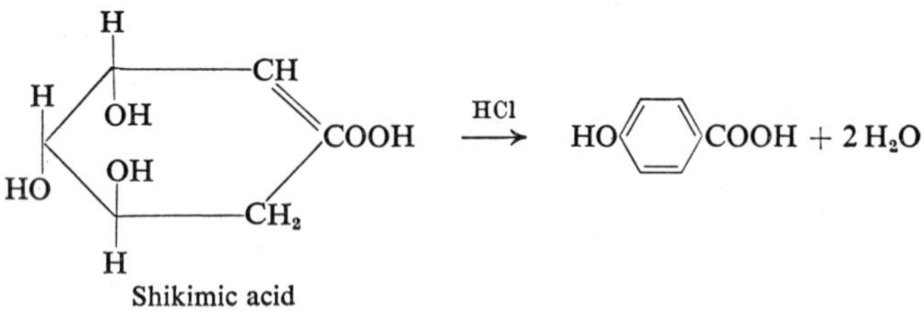

Quinic acid

Shikimic acid

By the use of mutant strains of *Neurospora*, shikimic acid has been shown to be, for this organism, a precursor of anthranilic acid, indole, tryptophan, phenylalanine, tyrosine, and *p*-aminobenzoic acid. It appears to be a precursor also of the aromatic rings in lignin (p. 527).

The sodium salt of cyclohexylsulfamic acid is about 30 times sweeter than cane sugar and is used as a noncarbohydrate sweetening agent under the name of *cyclamate* or *Sucaryl*. **Dicyclohexylamine nitrite** under the name VPI (*vapor-phase inhibitor*) is used to impregnate bags and wrapping materials for machine parts to prevent rusting. **Captan,** a powerful fungicide, contains a cyclohexene ring.

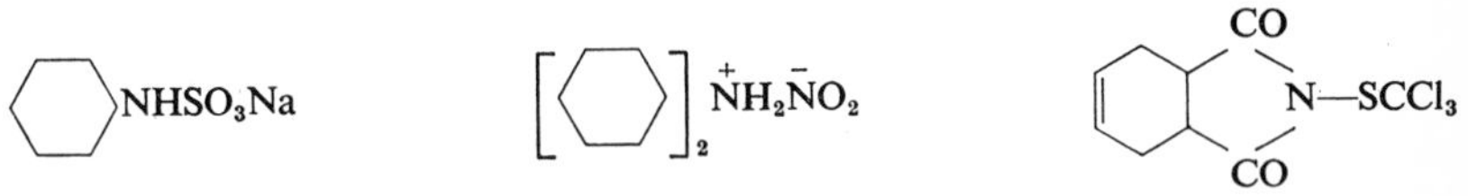

Sodium cyclohexylsulfamate
(cyclamate)

Dicyclohexylamine nitrite
(VPI)

Captan

Decalin exists in two isomeric forms which differ in the space relationship of the 9 and 10 hydrogen atoms. These two forms were postulated as possible

cis-Decalin

trans-Decalin

by Mohr in 1918 but were not isolated until 1927. Since these two isomers could not exist if the carbon atoms of the rings were planar, because of the amount of strain that would be involved, the isolation of the two forms was a proof that carbocyclic rings need not be planar (p. 828).

As early as 1890 Sachse had pointed out that if the carbon atoms of cyclohexane are permitted to assume nonplanar positions, two isomers of cyclohexane should exist. In one form, called the *boat* form, two carbon atoms lie on one side of the plane of the other four. In the *chair* form, the carbon atoms lie in two parallel planes, three alternate carbon atoms in each plane (Fig. 106). An examination of models indicates that the two forms probably are interconvertible

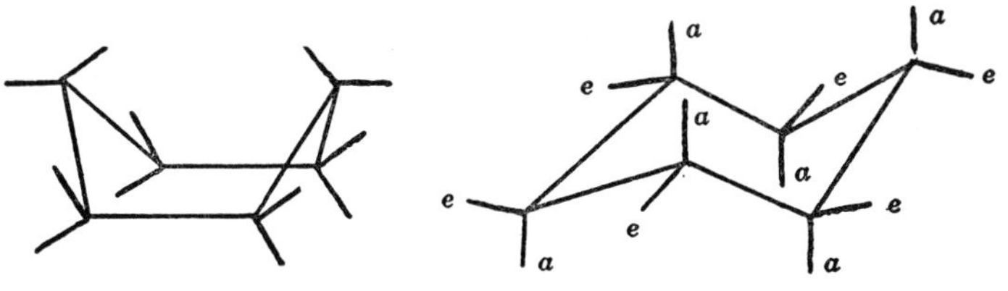

Boat Form

Chair Form

Fig. 106. Stereochemical conformations.

without the breaking of chemical bonds, and thus far no example of isomerism of this type is known; that is, the boat and chair forms merely are different *conformations* (p. 31) of the same molecule.

Thermodynamic calculations indicate that the chair form of cyclohexane is more stable than the boat form by almost 6 kcal. per mole, and electron-diffraction measurements indicate that cyclohexane and its derivatives have predominantly the chair conformation. In this conformation the hydrogen atoms are of two types. If the plane passing through the center of the molecule and parallel to the planes of the carbon atoms is designated as the plane of the ring, six of the carbon-hydrogen bonds are perpendicular to this plane with three hydrogen atoms above and three below the plane. These hydrogen atoms are called *axial* (*a*). The other six hydrogen atoms lie more or less in the plane of the ring and around its circumference and are called *equatorial* (*e*). Actually these hydrogen atoms alternate slightly above and below the plane of the ring, the carbon-hydrogen bonds making angles of 19.5° (109.5° minus 90°) with this plane (Fig. 106).

If now one of the hydrogen atoms is replaced by a larger group, the substituent may occupy either an axial or an equatorial position. In the axial position more crowding with the hydrogen atoms results than in the equatorial position. Electron-diffraction measurements show that, where a choice of positions is possible, the substituents invariably are in the equatorial position. If two substituents are present on different carbon atoms, stable *cis-trans* isomers can exist, and in one isomer one of the substituents must occupy an axial position. With more substituents, more of them are required to occupy axial positions. Thus far, however, no compound is known which has three substituents larger than hydrogen in the axial position on the same side of the plane of the ring. Thus of the nine possible inositols (p. 413), all are known but the all-*cis* compound. Furthermore, none of the naturally occurring inositols has two hydroxyl groups in the axial 1,3-positions. These considerations also apply to the sugars, in the ring structure of which an oxygen atom replaces a methylene group of cyclohexane. None of the naturally occurring aldohexoses or aldopentoses in either the α or β form of the pyranose ring structure has two hydroxyl groups in the axial 1,3-positions except the α-pyranose structure of ribose, and this sugar is the only one which exists chiefly in the furanose ring form.

Since groups in the equatorial position are less subject to steric hindrance than those in the axial positions, it is to be expected that reactions involving addition intermediates will be faster when the group is in the equatorial position. Thus hydroxyl and carboxyl groups are more easily esterified and ester groups are more easily hydrolyzed when in the equatorial than when in the axial position. Secondary alcohols are more easily oxidized to ketones when the hydroxyl group is in the axial position, presumably because the rate determining step is the breaking of the carbon-hydrogen bond which then is equatorial. On the other hand, the simple displacement reaction cannot operate on groups in the equatorial position because the approach from the back side is blocked by the groups in the axial positions. Before reaction can take place, the group must be forced into the energetically less favorable axial position. In this position, however, it is *trans* to hydrogen on an adjacent carbon atom, a situation that is favorable to elimination of hydrogen along with the functional group with the formation of a double bond. Considerations such as these have been very useful in arriving at constitution and configuration, particularly in condensed ring systems such as those present in the terpenes and sterols.

Larger Rings

Cycloheptanone (p. 831) is the usual starting point for the synthesis of the simpler compounds containing a seven-carbon ring. The chief interest in these compounds has been in the unsaturated derivatives such as **tropone, tropolone,** and **cycloheptatrienyl bromide** (*tropylium bromide*).

Tropone   Tropolone   Tropylium bromide

Neither tropone nor tropolone shows the usual reactions of the carbonyl group and both form crystalline hydrochlorides. Tropolone is a stronger acid than enols or phenols and approaches the acidity of carbonic acid. Tropylium bromide has all the properties of a salt, being high-melting, soluble in water and insoluble in nonhydroxylic solvents.

These properties are consistent with the view that the classical structural formulas do not adequately represent these compounds. For each compound, removal of a pair of electrons from a ring carbon atom permits resonance of the type present in benzene and in the cyclopentadienyl anion (pp. 419, 838). Hence tropone and tropolone are more stable as the dipolar ions and tropylium bromide as the carbonium salt. The location of the positive charge on all seven atoms of the ring can be represented by the general symbol of a seven-membered ring with the positive charge in the center.

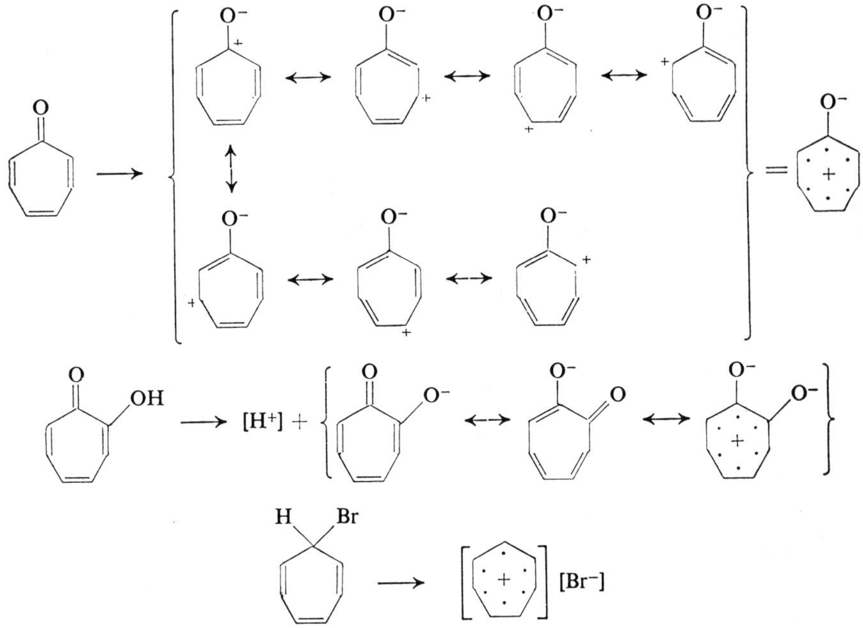

Numerous natural products contain seven-membered carbon rings and several contain the tropolone system. **Stipitatic acid,** the first compound for which a tropolone structure was proposed, was isolated from the mold *Penicillium stipitatum.* The α-, β-, and γ-**thujaplicins** are the three isopropyl tropolones. They are present in the heartwood of western red cedar (*Thuja plicata*), and their high fungicidal activity is responsible for the resistance of red cedar to decay. **Purpurogallin** is a red crystalline compound formed by the oxidation of pyrogallol. It occurs naturally as a diglucoside in oak galls.

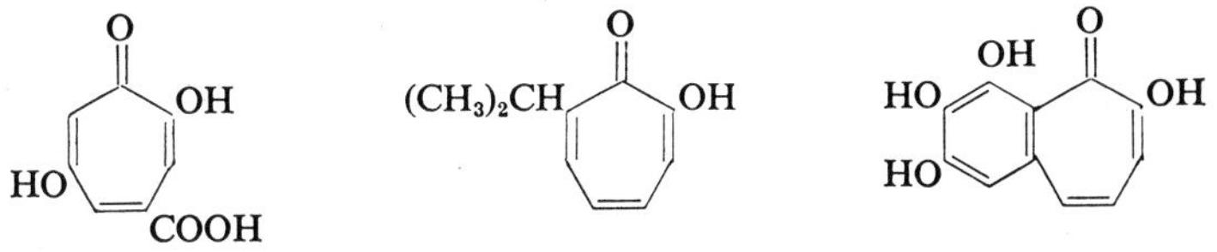

| Stipitatic acid | α-Thujaplicin | Purpurogallin |

Cyclooctatetraene has been of considerable interest. It was prepared first by Willstaetter [2] by a rational synthesis from the alkaloid pseudopelletierine.

---

[2] Richard Willstaetter (1872–1942), successor to Baeyer at the University of Munich. He was one of the outstanding investigators of the constitution of natural products such as alkaloids, anthocyanins, carotenes, and chlorophyll. He was awarded the Nobel Prize in Chemistry in 1915.

More recently it has been prepared in quantity by the polymerization of acetylene.

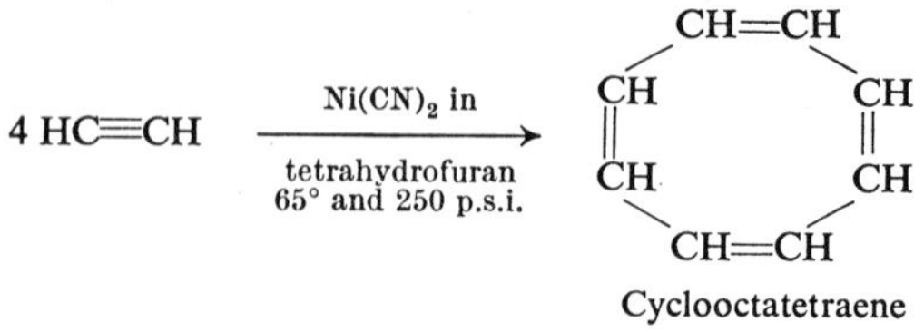

$$4 \text{ HC} \equiv \text{CH} \xrightarrow[\substack{\text{tetrahydrofuran} \\ 65° \text{ and } 250 \text{ p.s.i.}}]{\text{Ni(CN)}_2 \text{ in}}$$

Cyclooctatetraene

Originally cyclooctatetraene was prepared to determine whether its chemical properties would resemble those of benzene (cyclohexatriene). They do not, since the compound readily adds four moles of halogen or four moles of halogen acid, and is oxidized by cold permanganate. It is much less stable than benzene as shown by its ready and complete rearrangement to styrene.

The nonaromatic character of cyclooctatetraene no longer is surprising since resonance of the type characteristic of benzene would require that the carbon atoms be planar. The amount of energy required to produce coplanarity would reduce the resonance energy considerably. Quantum mechanical calculations indicate that only those cyclic conjugated systems will have aromatic properties in which the number of unsaturation electrons is equal to $4n + 2$ where n is an integer. Thus far no monocyclic compound is known where n is greater than 1, the value it has in benzene, cyclopentadienyl anion, and tropylium ion and their derivatives.

The conformation and space relationship in an alicyclic compound having eight or more members in the ring frequently are such that reactions which normally involve adjoining atoms take place at sites separated by one, two, or three ring atoms. These reactions have been thought of as taking place across the ring and have been called *transannular reactions*. The reaction of 1,2-epoxycyclopentane, -cyclohexane, and -cycloheptane with formic acid (solvolysis) leads exclusively to the formate of the *trans*-1,2-diol with inversion of the configuration of one carbon atom and retention of configuration of the other.

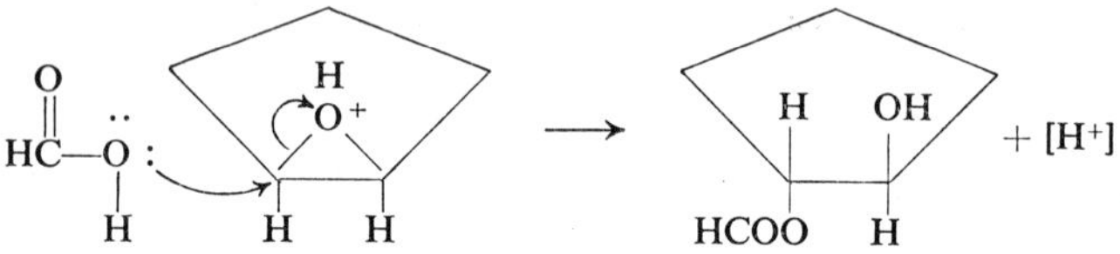

1,2-Epoxycyclooctane, however, gives the formate of 1,4-cyclooctanediol in addition to that of the 1,2-diol. The nonplanar conformation of the ring produces sufficient blocking of the approach of a formic acid molecule to either of the epoxide carbon atoms, and a sufficiently close approach of a hydrogen atom on carbon atom 4, to permit a competing reaction to take place in which simultaneous or concerted attack of the carbon atom 4 by a formic acid molecule and transfer of a hydrogen atom with its pair of electrons (hydride ion shift) to carbon atom 2 gives the ester of the *cis*-1,4-diol.

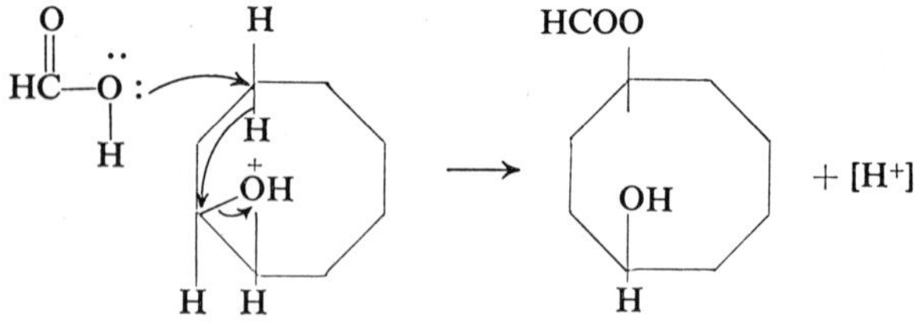

Reaction of *cis*-cyclodecene with performic acid gives exclusively *cis*-1,6-cyclodecanediol and *trans*-cyclodecene gives exclusively *trans*-1,6-diol with none of the 1,2-diols. Transannular reactions are not uncommon and arise for the same reason essentially that intramolecular reactions, such as the Dieckmann condensation (p. 816), take place rather than intermolecular condensation.

The reason for Baeyer's postulation that large rings are planar was that large-ring compounds were unknown. In 1918 a ten-membered ring containing nitrogen and bridging the *meta* positions of a benzene ring was prepared by v. Braun (p. 239), and in 1926 it was shown that **muscone** from the secretion of the musk deer and **civetone** from the secretion of the civet cat are fifteen- and seventeen-membered ring compounds respectively.

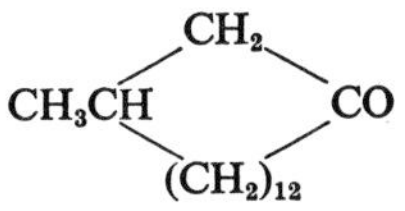

Muscone

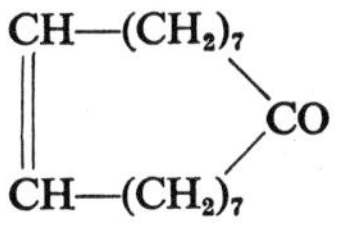

Civetone

In the following year the plant musks from angelica root and ambrette seed were found to be lactones containing sixteen- and seventeen-membered rings.

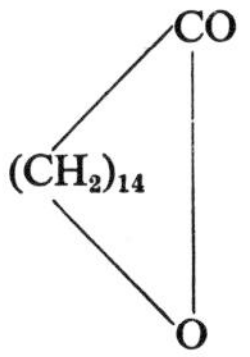

Penta-
decanolide

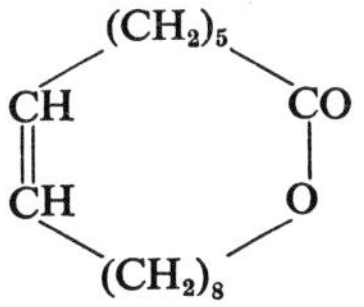

Ambrettolide

Since 1956 several antibiotics isolated from various species of *Streptomyces* have been shown to contain highly oxygenated large lactone rings. Thus **methymycin,** **erythromycin,** and **carbomycin** contain 12-, 14-, and 17-membered rings respectively. This class of natural products has been designated as **macrolides.**

Over a period of years several types of compounds containing seven to thirty-four atoms in a ring were synthesized. It is of interest that all cyclic ketones, lactones, carbonates, imines, and formals having fourteen to seventeen atoms in a ring have a musk odor. **Cyclopentadecanone,** known as **Exaltone,** is manufactured commercially for use in perfumery in place of the natural musks. It is used in the laboratory as solvent for molecular weight determinations, since it has a high cryoscopic constant and melts lower than camphor (Table 3, p. 22). Cyclopentadecanone was prepared first by the decomposition of the thorium salt of 1,14-tetradecanedicarboxylic acid. The yield is less than 1 per cent.

$$[(CH_2)_{14}(CO\bar{O})_2]_2 \; Th^{++++} \xrightarrow{\text{Heat}} 2 \, (CH_2)_{14}CO + 2 \, CO_2 + ThO_2$$

Cyclopenta-
decanone
(Exaltone)

Better yields of large-ring ketones have been obtained by carrying out an intramolecular Thorpe[3] condensation at high dilution. Hydrolysis gives a

---

[3] Jocelyn Field Thorpe (1872–1940), professor of organic chemistry at the Imperial College of Science and Technology in London. He was noted particularly for his investigations of the tautomerism of the glutaconic acids (p. 808) and for the effect of substitution on ring formation.

β-keto acid which loses carbon dioxide on heating. Later intramolecular

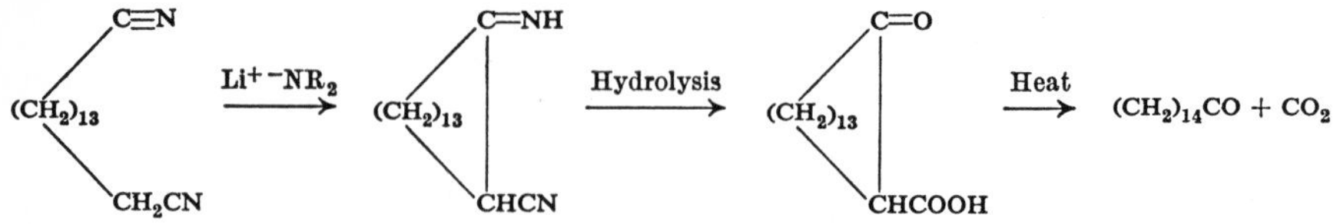

$$(CH_2)_{13} \begin{cases} C{\equiv}N \\ CH_2CN \end{cases} \xrightarrow{Li^+ {}^-NR_2} (CH_2)_{13} \begin{cases} C{=}NH \\ CHCN \end{cases} \xrightarrow{Hydrolysis} (CH_2)_{13} \begin{cases} C{=}O \\ CHCOOH \end{cases} \xrightarrow{Heat} (CH_2)_{14}CO + CO_2$$

dimerization of two ketene groups was used to synthesize large-ring ketones and other derivatives (p. 762).

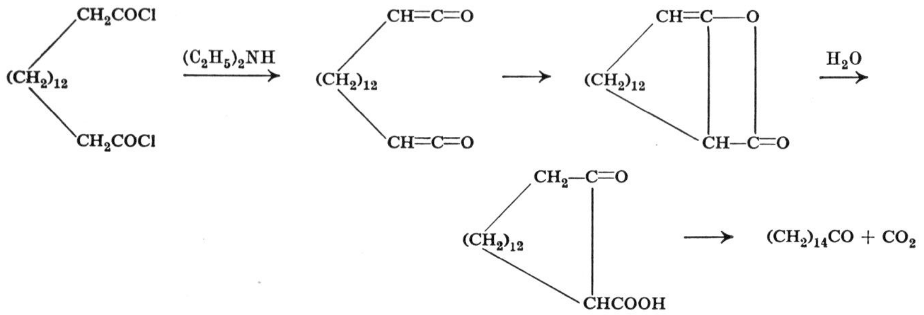

$$(CH_2)_{12} \begin{cases} CH_2COCl \\ CH_2COCl \end{cases} \xrightarrow{(C_2H_5)_2NH} (CH_2)_{12} \begin{cases} CH{=}C{=}O \\ CH{=}C{=}O \end{cases} \longrightarrow (CH_2)_{12} \begin{cases} CH{=}C{-}O \\ \quad | \quad | \\ CH{-}C{=}O \end{cases} \xrightarrow{H_2O}$$

$$(CH_2)_{12} \begin{cases} CH_2{-}C{=}O \\ CHCOOH \end{cases} \longrightarrow (CH_2)_{14}CO + CO_2$$

Carothers (p. 719) used reversible reactions to synthesize large-ring compounds by taking advantage of the fact that the monomeric cyclic compounds boil lower than the linear polymers. Thus ω-hydroxy acids on heating yield polymeric esters. High vacuum distillation yields the cyclic lactone.

$$(x + 1)\, HO(CH_2)_{14}COOH \longrightarrow HO(CH_2)_{14}[COO(CH_2)_{14}]_x COOH + x\, H_2O$$

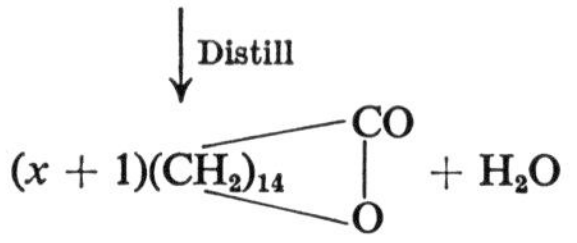

$$\downarrow \text{Distill}$$

$$(x + 1)(CH_2)_{14} \begin{cases} CO \\ \quad | \\ O \end{cases} + H_2O$$

Pentadecanolide

The most generally satisfactory method for synthesizing large-ring compounds is acyloin formation (p. 173) from α,ω-dicarboxylic esters. These esters are readily available, and the yields of cyclic acyloins range from 50 to 90 per cent.

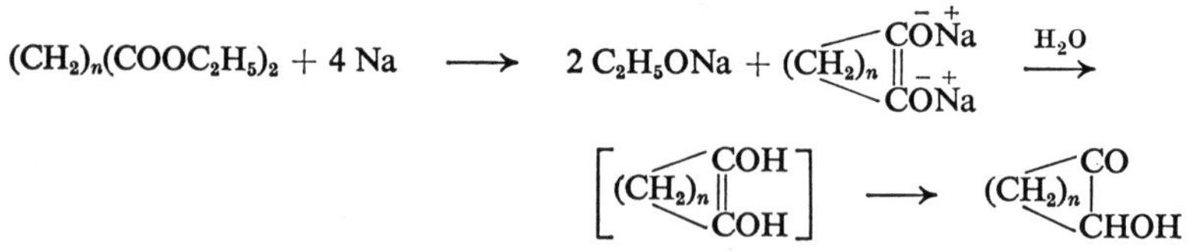

$$(CH_2)_n(COOC_2H_5)_2 + 4\, Na \longrightarrow 2\, C_2H_5ONa + (CH_2)_n \begin{cases} CONa \\ \quad \| \\ CONa \end{cases} \xrightarrow{H_2O}$$

$$\left[(CH_2)_n \begin{cases} COH \\ \quad \| \\ COH \end{cases} \right] \longrightarrow (CH_2)_n \begin{cases} CO \\ \quad | \\ CHOH \end{cases}$$

The acyloins can be converted to diols, diketones, alcohols, ketones, hydrocarbons, and heterocyclic amides and amines by the usual reactions.

Bridged Benzene Rings

Since the carbon-hydrogen bonds of benzene lie in the plane of the ring, small external rings can be formed only across the *ortho* positions. Thus only *o*-phthalic acid forms a cyclic anhydride.

With large enough alicyclic rings, however, it is possible to include the *meta* and *para* positions in a cycle as well as the *ortho* positions.

Such structures have been called *ansa* compounds (L. *ansa*, handle).

Hetero atoms, carbonyl, and other groups may replace one or more methylene groups, and the size of the ring required depends on its structure. For entirely methylene groups it appears that *n* must be at least 6 in *meta* rings to retain the characteristic aromatic properties of the benzene ring. For example, *p*-nitrophenol with a *meta* ring containing six methylene groups can exist in the form of the phenol (*a*), but with five methylene groups the strain is sufficient to force the benzene ring into the nonaromatic keto form (*b*).

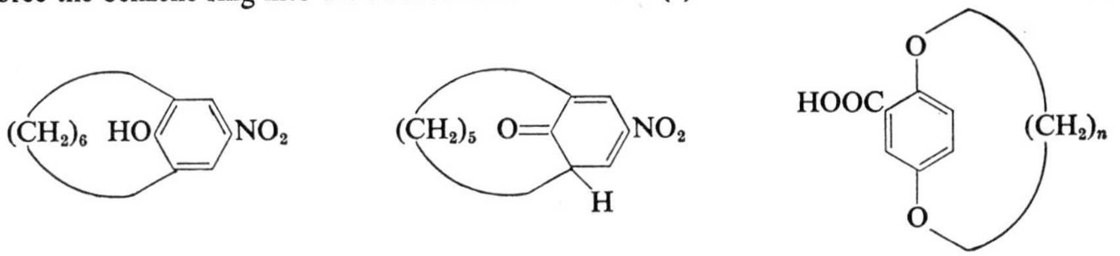

(*a*)   (*b*)   (*c*)

In the series of compounds represented by formula (*c*), resolution into active forms should be possible if *n* is small enough to prevent the benzene ring from rotating about the axis through the *para* positions. Resolution has been accomplished when $n = 8$ but not when $n = 10$. If a bromine atom is *para* to the carboxyl group, rotation is blocked even when $n = 10$.

Structures incorporating two benzene rings likewise are of interest. In the *para* series, known as *paracyclophanes*, X-ray diffraction measurements show that when $n = 2$ the strain is sufficient

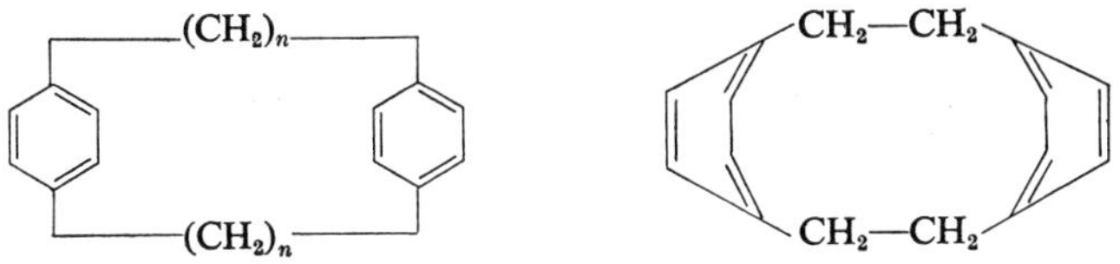

to bend the benzene rings into boat shapes. Since they no longer are planar, they do not show the characteristic ultraviolet absorption of the benzene rings. When $n = 4$ the compound has the normal ultraviolet absorption spectrum. However, Friedel-Crafts acylation introduces only a single acetyl group indicating a transannular deactivating effect of the acetyl group on the second benzene ring. When $n = 6$, the two benzene rings act independently and each ring is acylated to give a diacetyl derivative.

TERPENES

The odorous components of plants are volatile with steam and usually are separated from the plant material by steam distillation. They are known as the **volatile** or **essential oils.** They consist of hydrocarbons, alcohols, ethers, aldehydes, and ketones. Some of these substances such as anethole, eugenol, safrole, and cinnamaldehyde belong to the aromatic series (pp. 515, 516, 537). In the exudations of conifers and in the oils from the citrus fruits and from eucalyptus trees, alicyclic hydrocarbons of the composition $C_{10}H_{16}$ are especially abundant, and it is to these compounds that the term *terpene* (Gr. *terebinthos*, turpentine tree) was applied in the restricted sense. However, closely related open chain hydrocarbons having ten carbon atoms also were included under this term. The oxygenated terpenes were known as *camphors*. It soon became evident, however, that compounds containing 15, 20, 30, and 40 carbon atoms also are closely related to the terpenes. The one common characteristic of all of these compounds is that their carbon skeletons are evenly divisible into iso-C_5 units (frequently referred to as isoprene or isopentane units). The term *terpene* in its broadest sense now includes all such compounds, whether hydrocarbons or not. Terpene in the limited sense still refers to compounds containing two iso-C_5 units. Hence the broad class of terpenes is divided into hemiterpenes, C_5; terpenes, C_{10}; sesquiterpenes, C_{15}; diterpenes, C_{20}; triterpenes, C_{30}; tetraterpenes, C_{40}; and polyterpenes, C_{5x}.

Hemiterpenes

To be consistent this group should include isopentane, the 2-methylbutenes, isopropylacetylene, isoprene, methylcyclobutane, methylenecyclobutane, and the methylcyclobutenes. In practice, only isoprene is considered to be a hemiterpene. It is a product of the pyrolysis of rubber, turpentine, and other terpenes, and of the dehydrogenation of isopentane. It can be synthesized from acetone in an over-all yield of 65 per cent by the following series of reactions.

$$(CH_3)_2CO + HC\!\equiv\!CH \xrightarrow{\text{KOH}} (CH_3)_2C(OH)C\!\equiv\!CH \xrightarrow{\text{Pd}\!-\!H_2}$$

$$(CH_3)_2C(OH)CH\!=\!CH_2 \xrightarrow[\text{heat}]{\text{Al}_2O_3} CH_2\!=\!\underset{\underset{\textstyle CH_3}{|}}{C}\!-\!CH\!=\!CH_2$$

Isoprene

Technically it is manufactured by the thermal cracking of petroleum fractions (p. 719).

Terpenes

Acyclic Terpenes. Citral a (geranial) and **citral b (neral)** are the most important members of this group. They comprise 80 per cent of East Indian lemon-grass oil, which is the essential oil of the grass *Cymbopogon flexuosus*. Both have the composition $C_{10}H_{16}O$ and contain two double bonds and an aldehyde group. Ozonolysis gives acetone, levulinic acid, and oxalic acid. Hence the structure must be I, II, or III.

$$(CH_3)_2C\!=\!CHCH_2\underset{\underset{\textstyle CH_3}{|}}{CH_2C}\!=\!CHCHO \qquad (CH_3)_2C\!=\!\underset{\underset{\textstyle CH_3}{|}}{C}CH_2CH_2CH\!=\!CHCHO$$

I II

$$(CH_3)_2C\!=\!CHCH\!=\!CCH_2CH_2CHO$$

CH_3

III

Chromic acid oxidation gives a methyl ketone having two less carbon atoms. Hence structure I is indicated. The dotted line indicates the presence of two iso-C_5 units. This structure has been confirmed by synthesis from isoprene.

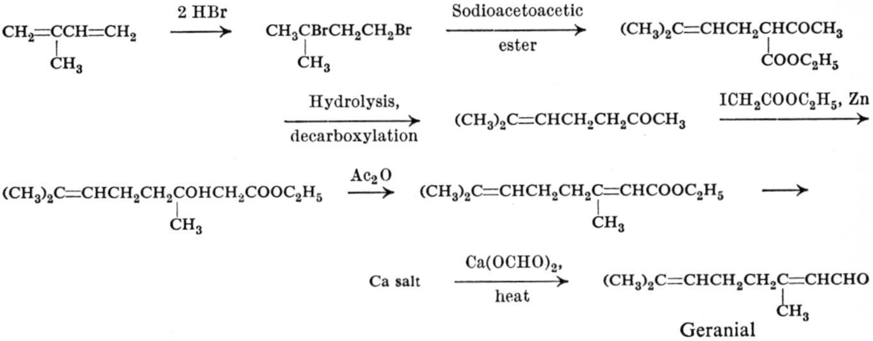

$$CH_2=CCH=CH_2 \quad \xrightarrow{2\ HBr} \quad CH_3CBrCH_2CH_2Br \quad \xrightarrow[\text{ester}]{\text{Sodioacetoacetic}} \quad (CH_3)_2C=CHCH_2CHCOCH_3$$

with CH_3 branches shown on the first two structures and $COOC_2H_5$ on the third.

$$\xrightarrow[\text{decarboxylation}]{\text{Hydrolysis,}} \quad (CH_3)_2C=CHCH_2CH_2COCH_3 \quad \xrightarrow{ICH_2COOC_2H_5,\ Zn}$$

$$(CH_3)_2C=CHCH_2CH_2COHCH_2COOC_2H_5 \quad \xrightarrow{Ac_2O} \quad (CH_3)_2C=CHCH_2CH_2C=CHCOOC_2H_5 \quad \longrightarrow$$

with CH_3 branches.

$$\text{Ca salt} \quad \xrightarrow[\text{heat}]{Ca(OCHO)_2,} \quad (CH_3)_2C=CHCH_2CH_2C=CHCHO$$

with CH_3 branch — **Geranial**

Citral is important as the starting point for the synthesis of vitamin A. A commercial synthesis of citral has been developed, using acetone, acetylene, and diketene as the raw materials.

Since geranial and neral give the same products on oxidation and are reduced to the same saturated alcohol, they must be geometrical isomers. In geranial the methyl and aldehyde groups are *cis* and in neral they are *trans*. Later work has shown that a small amount of formaldehyde is produced on ozonolysis. The infrared spectrum (p. 658), however, does not indicate the presence of a terminal methylene group, and the current view is that it is formed by isomerization.

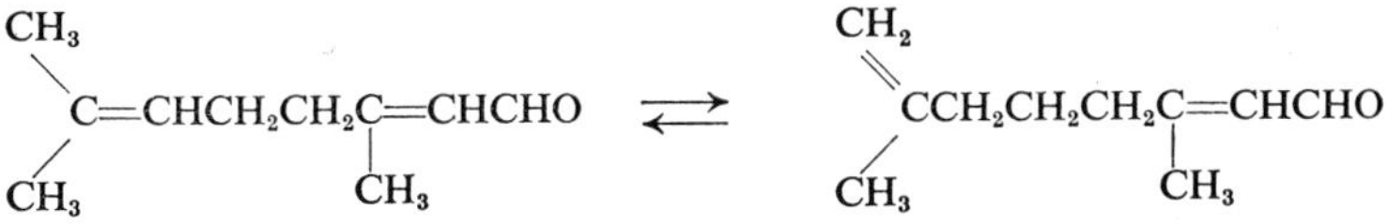

$$\begin{array}{c} CH_3 \\ \diagdown \\ \diagup \\ CH_3 \end{array} C=CHCH_2CH_2C=CHCHO \quad \rightleftharpoons \quad \begin{array}{c} CH_2 \\ \diagdown \\ \diagup \\ CH_3 \end{array} CCH_2CH_2CH_2C=CHCHO$$

with CH_3 branches.

This type of equilibrium exists also for mesityl oxide (p. 763) and diisobutylene (p. 62), and is characteristic of compounds containing this terminal structure.

The acyclic terpenes frequently undergo easy cyclization to yield derivatives either of 1-methyl-4-isopropylcyclohexane (*p*-menthane) or 1,1,3-trimethylcyclohexane. Citral, in the presence of strong acids, gives chiefly *p*-cymene by cyclization and dehydration.

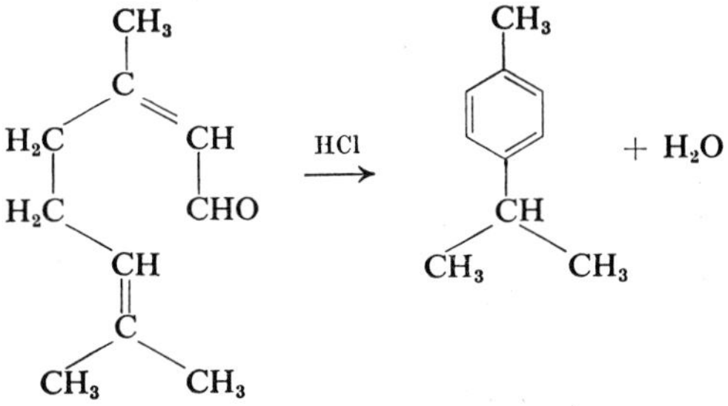

α- and **β-Cyclocitral** also are formed in small amounts.

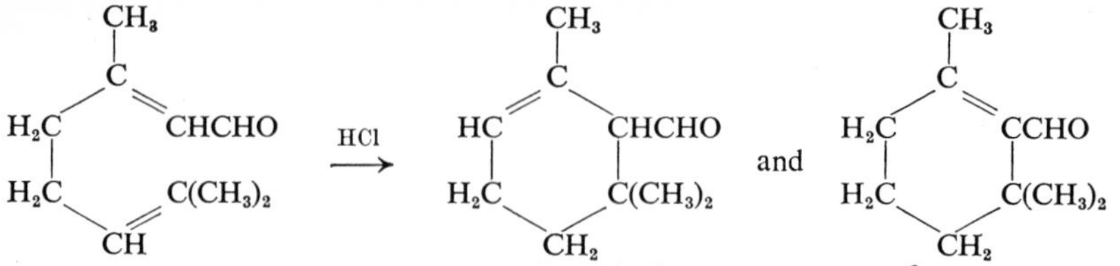

α-Cyclocitral   β-Cyclocitral

Acid-catalyzed cyclizations are important reactions of many terpenes. The formation of a six-membered ring can be initiated by the attack of a proton on either the oxygen function at one end of the chain to give 1-methyl-4-isopropylcyclohexane derivatives or on the double bond at the other end of the chain to give 1,3,3-trimethylcyclohexane derivatives.

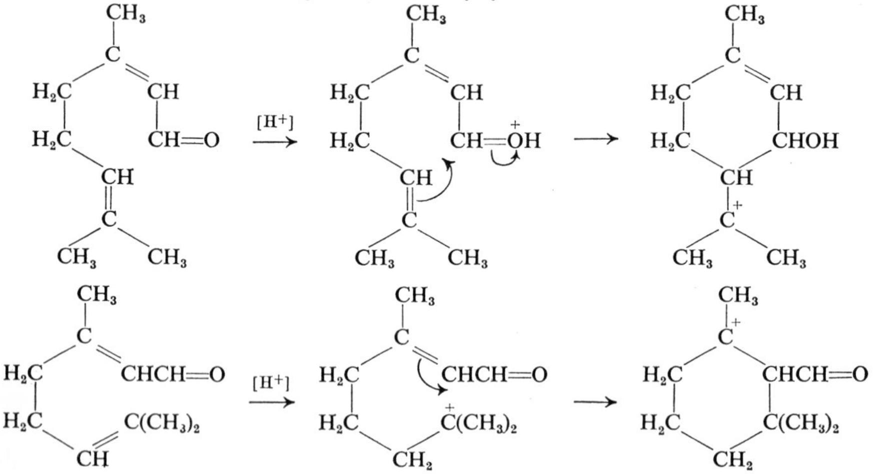

Either intermediate can be stabilized by loss of a proton which may be preceded by hydride ion shifts or rearrangement. The predominant point of attack undoubtedly is determined by the relative basicity of the unsaturated atoms.

Condensation of citral with acetone gives **pseudoionone,** which is cyclized by acids to a mixture of **α-** and **β-ionone.**

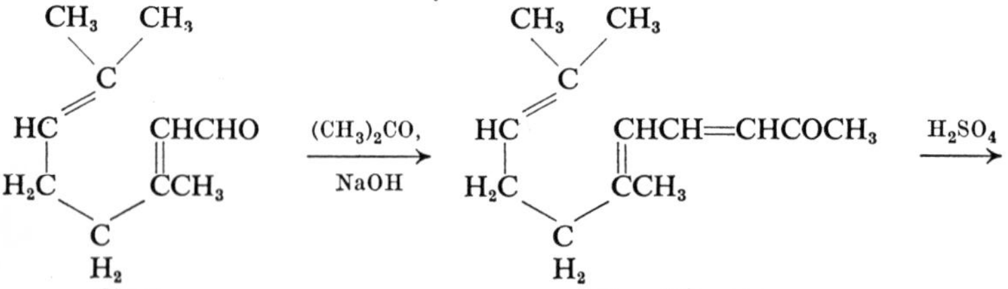

Citral   Pseudoionone

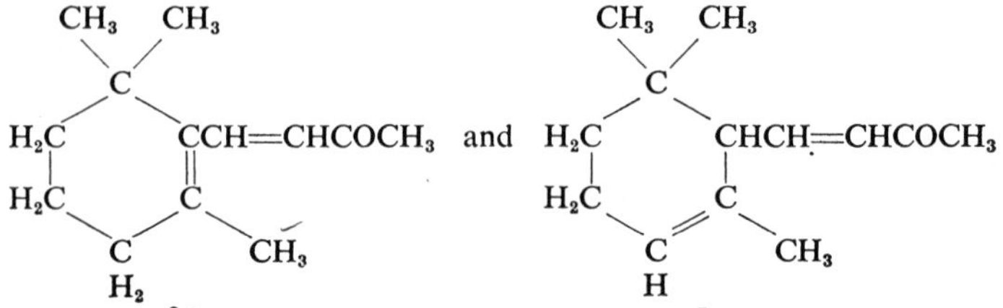

β-Ionone   α-Ionone

The ionones have an odor resembling that of violets and are used in inexpensive perfumes. β-Ionone is an intermediate in the synthesis of vitamin A (p. 860).

Geraniol, the alcohol corresponding to geranial, is present in many plants and is the chief constituent of palmarosa oil from gingergrass (*Cymbopogon martini*). **Nerol,** the alcohol corresponding to neral, is a component of orange blossom oil (*neroli*).

Citronellal is the chief component of oil of citronella, one of the lemon-grass oils (*Cymbopogon nardus*). It differs from citral only in that it lacks one of the double bonds, namely the one conjugated with the aldehyde group. It is used in a synthesis of menthol (p. 854). **Citronellol,** the corresponding alcohol, occurs in rose oil, which is produced chiefly in Bulgaria from hybrids of *Rosa damascena* and *Rosa centifolia*, the wild roses being odorless. It is the water-insoluble layer obtained by steam distillation of the flowers. The aqueous layer constitutes rose water. About 4000 kg. of flowers is needed to produce 1 kg. of rose oil.

Linalool is a tertiary alcohol isomeric with geraniol and nerol. It is a constituent of oil of linaloa, a Mexican wood, and of the flowers of ylang-ylang (*Canangium odoratum*), a tree native to the Philippines.

$$(CH_3)_2C=CHCH_2CH_2\underset{\underset{CH_3}{|}}{C}OH-CH=CH_2$$

Linalool

Monocyclic Terpenes. Most of the monocyclic terpenes are derivatives of 1-methyl-4-isopropylcyclohexane. In order to simplify the writing of structural formulas of cyclic terpenes, the convention is adopted that carbon and hydrogen atoms are not indicated but only the bonds between the carbon atoms. Hence in these formulas a carbon atom is present at each intersection of two or more lines and at the end of each line. Other elements and double bonds are indicated

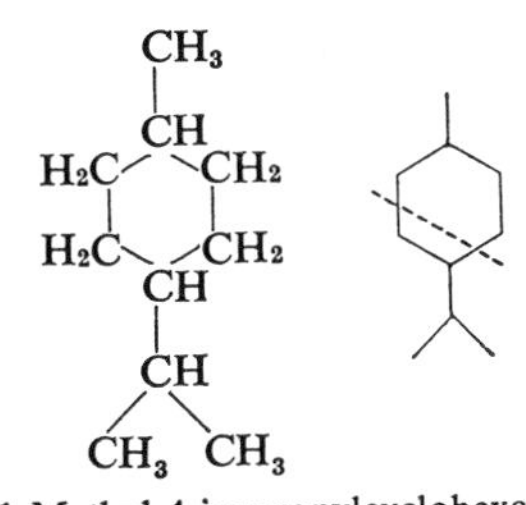

1-Methyl-4-isopropylcyclohexane 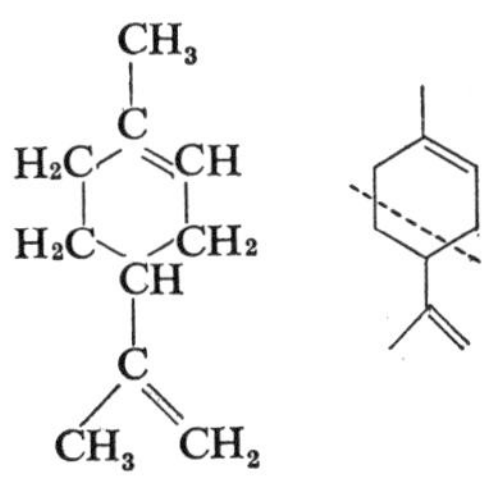   Limonene

and each carbon atom is attached to a sufficient number of hydrogen atoms to satisfy the remaining valences.

Limonene, $C_{10}H_{16}$, is the main terpene constituent of lemon, orange, caraway, dill, bergamot, and many other oils. With the possible exception of α-pinene, no terpene is present in more varieties of plants. It contains an asymmetric carbon atom and both *d* and *l* forms occur naturally. The racemic mixture is known as **dipentene.** The determination of the structure of limonene was involved and uncertain, but the currently accepted structure was confirmed by synthesis in 1904. Of the fourteen possible isomers having the limonene skeleton but differing in the position of the double bonds, six have been found in natural products. The other five are **terpinolene, α-** and **γ-terpinene,** and **α-** and **β-phellandrene.**

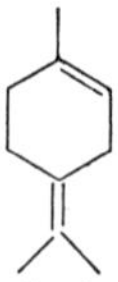

Terpinolene 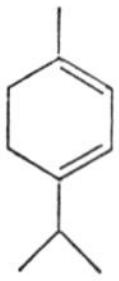 α-Terpinene 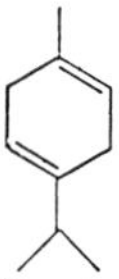 γ-Terpinene

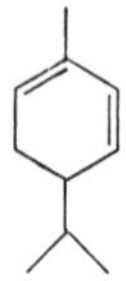

α-Phellandrene 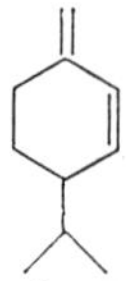 β-Phellandrene 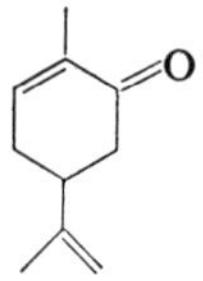 Carvone 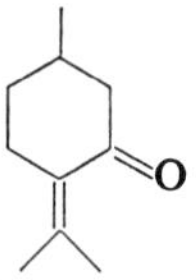 Pulegone

Among the oxygenated derivatives may be mentioned **l-carvone,** the chief component of spearmint oil, **d-pulegone,** a component of oil of pennyroyal, and **l-menthol,** a component of the mint oils, especially Japanese peppermint oil. Menthol is synthesized from citronellal by way of isopulegol, or from thymol (p. 515).

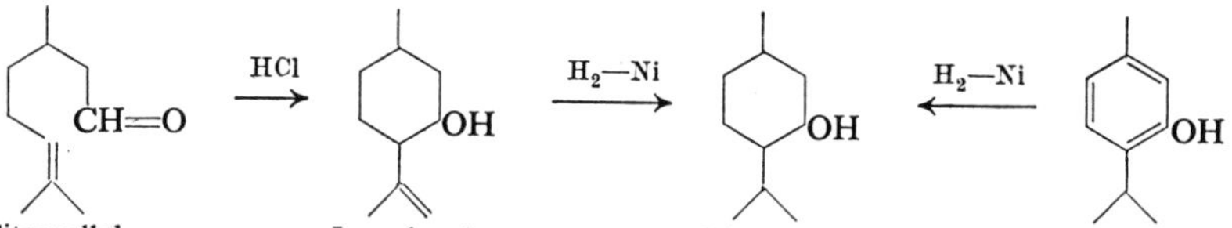

Citronellal Isopulegol Menthols Thymol

Since menthol contains three asymmetric carbon atoms, eight active isomers are known. They are d- and l-menthol, d- and l-isomenthol, d- and l-neomenthol, and d- and l-isoneomenthol. Hence the technical production even of dl-menthol is an involved process. The mixture of isomers, however, is suitable for most purposes.

When pulegone is heated with either acids or bases, it is converted to 3-methylcyclohexanone and acetone. This reaction is the reverse of an aldol addition and accounts for the fact that pulegone gives a positive iodoform test.

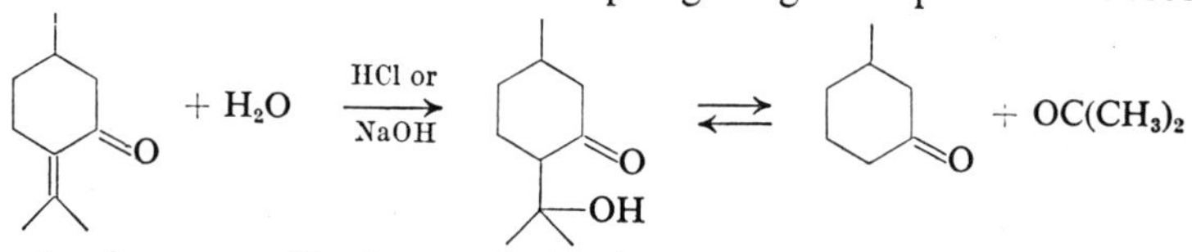

The **terpins** are dihydroxy derivatives of 1-methyl-4-isopropylmethane. **Cineole,** an oxide, is present in many essential oils. **Ascaridole** is a peroxide which is the active constituent of chenopodium oil formerly used as an anthelmintic (Gr. *askaris*, an intestinal worm).

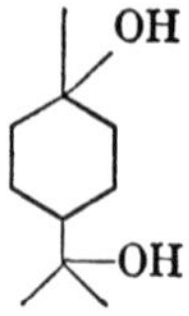

α-Terpin 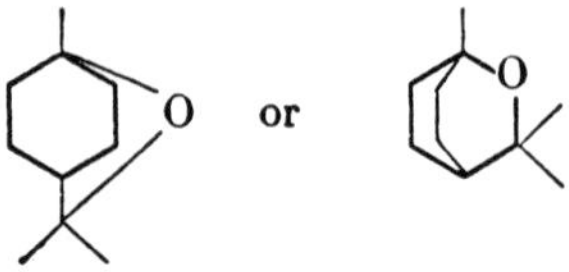 Cineole  Ascaridole

Dicyclic Terpenes. Derivatives of the following saturated dicyclic hydrocarbons are known.

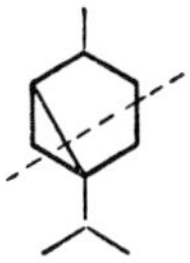

Thujane    Carane 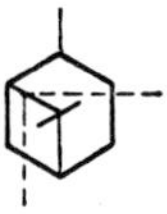   Pinane 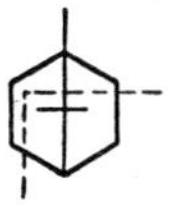   Camphane

Isobornylane    Isocamphane    Fenchane

α-Pinene is the principal component of oil of turpentine, which is important as a paint thinner (p. 187). Turpentine is believed to have been prepared first in Persia because *termentin* or *turmentin* is a Persian word. It was mentioned in the European literature in the thirteenth century. The first analysis was made by Lavoisier, but the correct composition, C_5H_8, was assigned by Labillardière in 1818. Biot had observed in 1815 that it possessed optical activity even in the vapor state, and Dumas determined its molecular weight in 1833 and found that it corresponded to $C_{10}H_{16}$.

The problem of the structure of α-pinene was connected intimately with that of limonene, and the most important advances in the chemistry of these terpenes were made by Wallach,[4] who in 1887 stated the isoprene rule, namely that the structures of the terpenes are divisible into isoprene or isopentane units. It was Wagner, however, who in 1894 proposed the correct formula for α-pinene, along with that for limonene, and showed how it could explain the known reactions, a few of which are indicated.

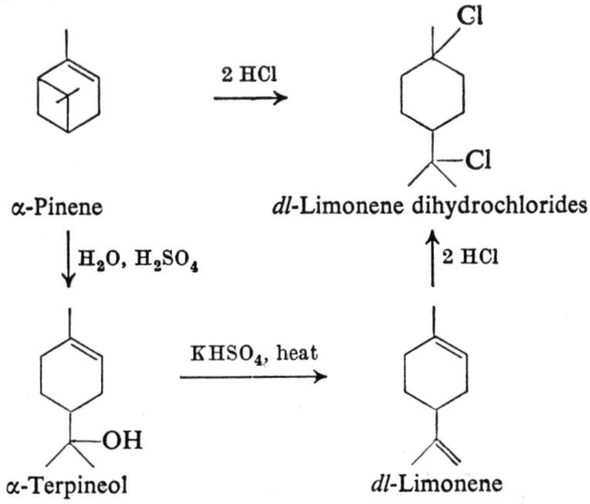

α-Pinene   *dl*-Limonene dihydrochlorides

H₂O, H₂SO₄   2 HCl

α-Terpineol   KHSO₄, heat   *dl*-Limonene

---

[4] Otto Wallach (1847–1931), successor to Victor Meyer as professor of chemistry at Goettingen. He entered the field of terpenes in 1879 by being required to teach pharmacy at the University of Bonn. Wallach, unlike E. Fischer and Baeyer, was primarily an analyst and it was largely through his efforts that the confusion existing in the field of the terpenes was resolved. He announced his famous isoprene rule in 1887. He was awarded the Nobel Prize in Chemistry in 1910.

Direct proof of the presence of the cyclobutane ring came from Baeyer, who reported in 1896 the isolation of 2,2-dimethyl-1,3-cyclobutanedicarboxylic acid as the end product of a series of oxidations.

The dehydration of α-terpineol to give limonene is contrary to the Saytzev rule (p. 104). A double bond exocyclic to a cyclohexane ring generally produces a less stable conformation (p. 843) than two single bonds.

Camphor is a dicyclic ketone, the dextro form of which occurs in the wood of the camphor tree, *Cinnamonum camphora*. The tree is native to the Chinese coast from Cochin-China to Shanghai, and to the coastal islands from Hainan to Southern Japan.

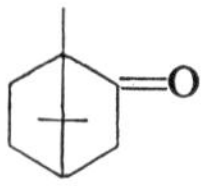

Camphor	Camphoric acid	10-Camphorsulfonic acid

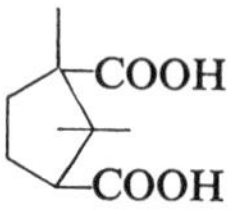

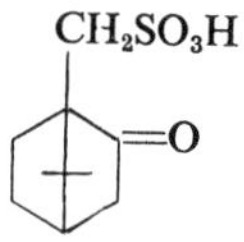

Although camphor contains two asymmetric carbon atoms, only one pair of enantiomorphs is known. An examination of models shows that the second pair of isomers cannot exist because of the extreme distortion of bond angles that would be required. Oxidation of camphor with nitric acid gives **camphoric acid,** and sulfonation with sulfuric acid in acetic anhydride gives **10-camphorsulfonic acid.** Both acids are optically active if prepared from natural camphor, and are useful for the resolution of racemic amines (p. 344).

Camphor has been known and valued for medicinal purposes since earliest times, although modern medicine has found it to have no therapeutic value. It is not recorded in the Greek and Roman literature and probably was introduced into western Europe by the Arabians under the name *kafar*. Its chief industrial importance has been as a plasticizer for the manufacture of celluloid and photographic film base (p. 402). Camphor formerly was produced chiefly in China, but with the acquisition of Formosa by Japan, its production became a monopoly of the Japanese government. Exorbitant prices forced its production in Germany and the United States by synthesis from pinene. Since celluloid largely has been replaced by other plastics and since nitrate film base no longer is manufactured in the United States (p. 403), the commercial importance of camphor has greatly decreased.

Reduction of camphor with sodium and alcohol gives a mixture of the epimeric alcohols, **borneol** and **isoborneol.** Borneol has the hydroxyl group on the side of the six-membered ring opposite to the bridge, whereas isoborneol has the hydroxyl on the same side. Both the (+) and (−) forms of borneol occur naturally, the (+) form being known as *Borneo camphor* and the (−) form as *Ngai camphor*. When either borneol or isoborneol is dehydrated the product is camphene instead of bornylene.

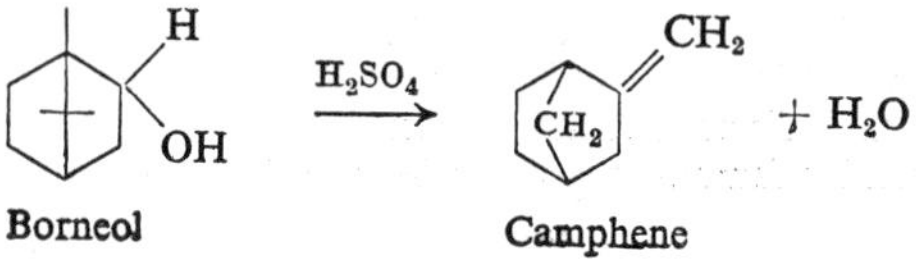

Borneol	Camphene

Rearrangements of this type occur frequently with the dicyclic terpenes and are called *Wagner-Meerwin rearrangements*. Loss of water from the protonated alcohol is accompanied by migration of a ring carbon and loss of proton from the methyl group. Isoborneol dehydrates more readily than borneol because it permits *trans* elimination.

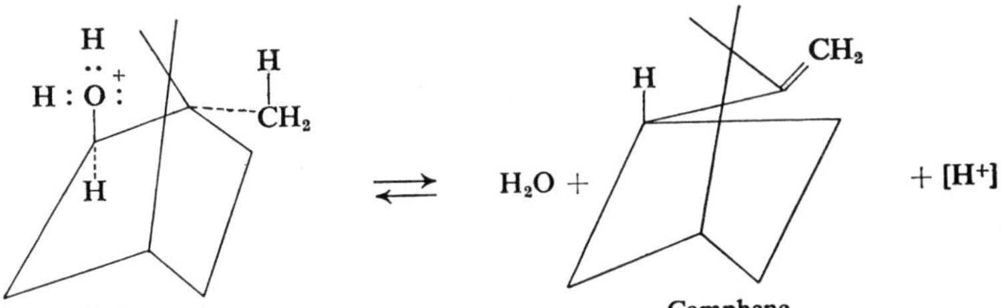

Isoborneol $\rightleftharpoons$ H_2O +   Camphene $+ [H^+]$

These rearrangements take place without racemization and hence do not involve free carbonium ions or cyclopropane rings as intermediates. Undoubtedly the same type of mechanism operates in simpler rearrangements such as the dehydration of methyl-*t*-butylcarbinol (p. 105) which yields 31 per cent of 2,3-dimethyl-1-butene, 61 per cent of 2,3-dimethyl-2-butene, and 3 per cent of the unrearranged 3,3-dimethyl-1-butene.

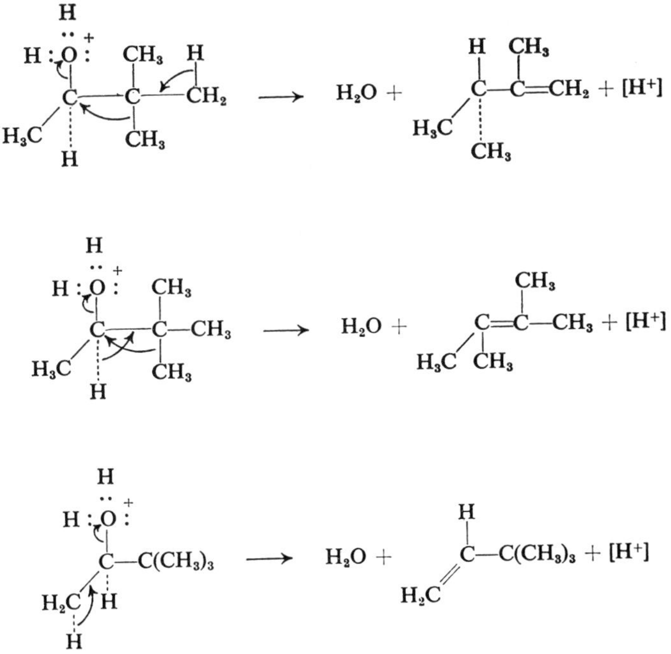

Here the relative amount of each product is determined by its thermodynamic stability, the compound having the most highly substituted double bond being the most stable (p. 105). In the dehydration of borneol, an additional factor enters. The second type of dehydration, available to the acyclic alcohol, cannot take place with borneol because it would lead to a double bond at the bridge head. The excessive deformation of bond angles in such structures prevents their formation (*Bredt rule*).

Sesquiterpenes

Acyclic Sesquiterpenes. Farnesol, $C_{15}H_{26}O$, is the best known example of the acyclic sesquiterpenes. It is present in many essential oils such as those from ambrette seeds, citronella, palmarosa, rose, and neroli.

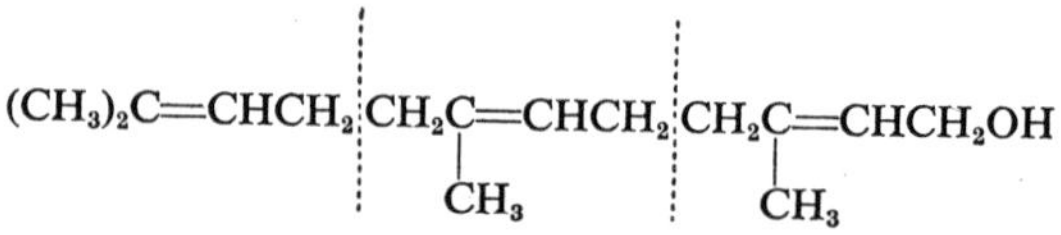

$$(CH_3)_2C=CHCH_2 \vdots CH_2C=CHCH_2 \vdots CH_2C=CHCH_2OH$$
$$CH_3 \qquad CH_3$$

Farnesol

Nerolidol is the tertiary alcohol that bears the same relation to farnesol as linalool does to geraniol. Both farnesol and nerolidol have been synthesized.

Monocyclic Sesquiterpenes. Bisabolene is a hydrocarbon that occurs in many plants. It has been made by the dehydration of farnesol.

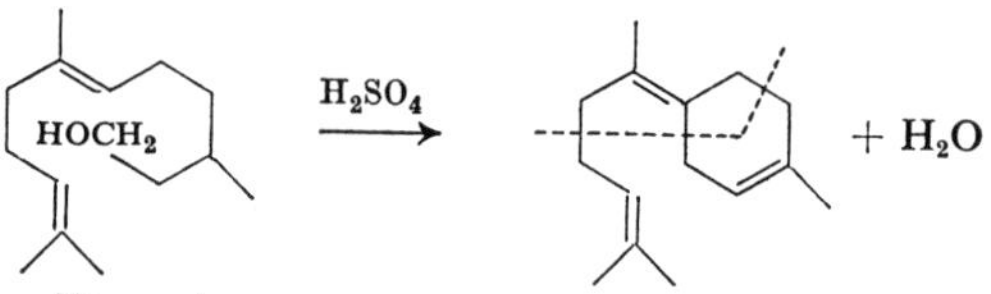

Farnesol   Bisabolene

Dicyclic Sesquiterpenes. Several types of dicyclic sesquiterpenes are known. One type is represented by **cadinene** which is present in oil of cade (from *Juniperus oxycedrus*) and in oil of cubebs (from *Piper cubeba*). The ring structure was arrived at by dehydrogenation with sulfur (p. 602), which gives 1,6-dimethyl-4-isopropylnaphthalene (*cadalene*). Other work has indicated the probable position of the double bonds.

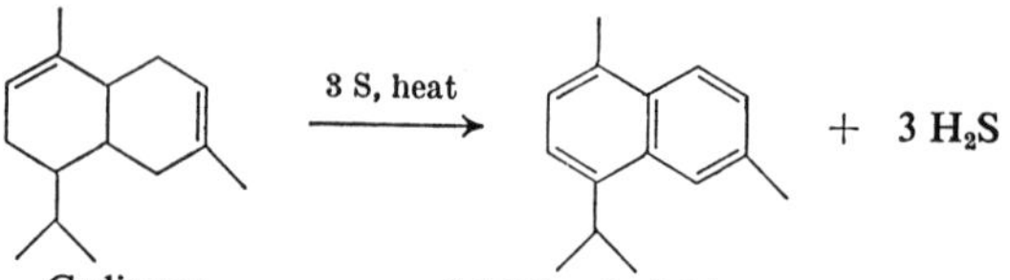

Cadinene   1,6-Dimethyl-4-isopropyl-
naphthalene (cadalene)

A second type is represented by **β-selinene** from oil of celery, and **eudesmol** from eucalyptus oils. Both yield 1-methyl-7-isopropylnaphthalene (*eudalene*) on dehydrogenation.

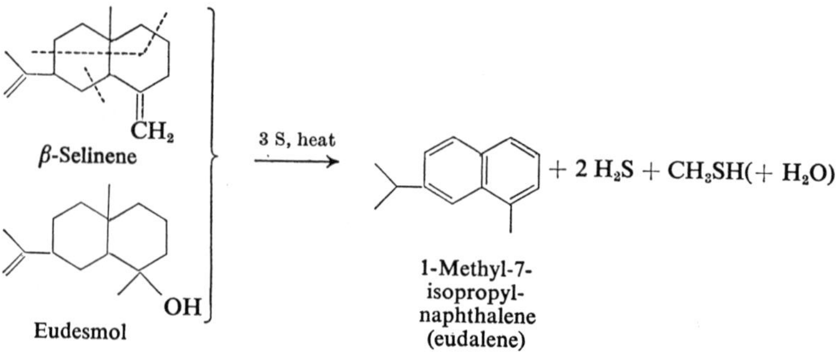

β-Selinene

Eudesmol

1-Methyl-7-
isopropyl-
naphthalene
(eudalene)

Members of a third type of dicyclic sesquiterpenes are known as **azulenes** from the fact that they give rise to blue-violet oils on dehydrogenation. The blue color of camomile oil was noted as early as the fifteenth century, and it since has been found that a fifth of the essential oils investigated contain or give rise to azulenes. Structures having a five-membered ring fused to a seven-membered ring have been assigned to **guaiol** from guaiacum wood and to **β-vetivone** from vetiver oil. On dehydrogenation they give rise to **guaiazulene** and **vetivazulene** which have been synthesized.

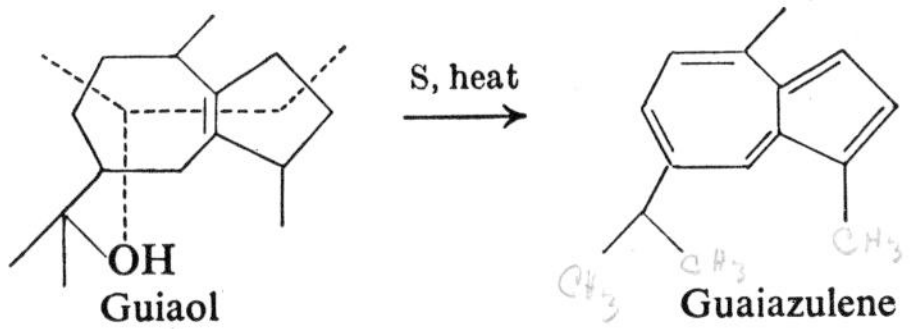

Guiaol   Guaiazulene

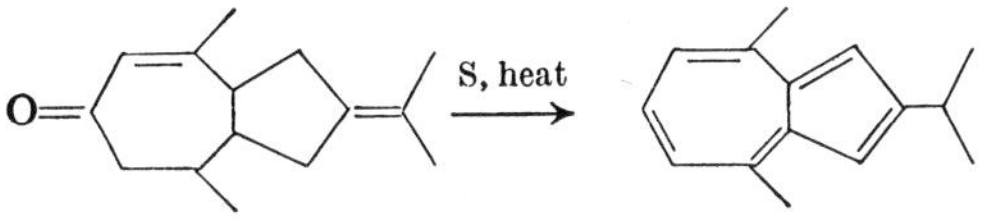

Vetivone   Vetivazulene

Guaiazulene occurs naturally in geranium oil, and vetivazulene in vetiver oil.

Caryophyllene (*β-caryophyllene*) and **humulene** (*α-carophyllene*) are present in oil of clove (*Eugenia caryophyllata*) and first were investigated in 1834. Humulene also is a major component of oil of hops. Their structures were not completely determined until 1953. Both are rather unusual in that caryophyllene has a cyclobutane ring fused to a nine-membered ring, and humulene has an eleven-membered ring.

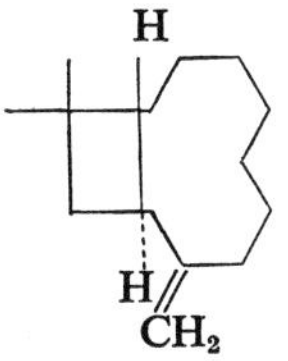

Caryophyllene 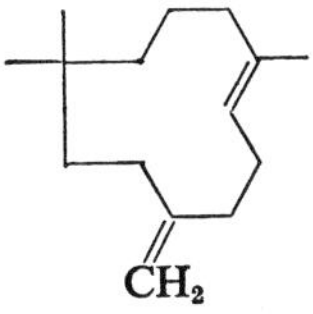   Humulene

Tricyclic Sesquiterpenes. Several types of tricyclic sesquiterpene structures are represented by **copaene** from copaiba balsam, **α-cedrene** from red cedar oil, and **longifolene** from pine oils.

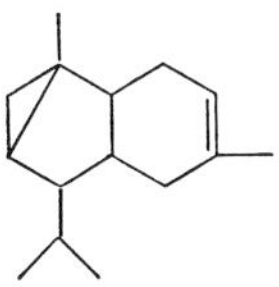

Copaene 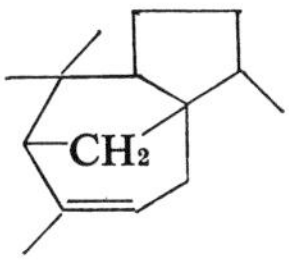   Cedrene 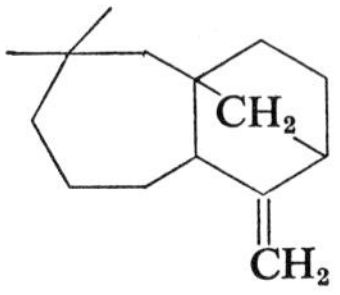   Longifolene

Diterpenes

Acyclic Diterpenes. Phytol, $C_{20}H_{39}OH$, constitutes about one third of the chlorophyll molecule (p. 614), from which it is obtained by saponification. The same alcohol has been isolated from the chlorophyll of over 200 species of plants. It has been synthesized starting with pseudoionone (p. 852).

$$(CH_3)_2CHCH_2CH_2(CH_2CHCH_2CH_2)_2CHC=CHCH_2OH$$
$$\underset{CH_3}{|} \qquad \underset{CH_3}{|}$$

Phytol

Although phytol has two asymmetric carbon atoms, the natural product has no observable rotation. Dehydration, however, gives an optically active diene, showing that the natural product is not a racemic mixture but that the enantiomorphs have a very low or zero rotation.

Monocyclic Diterpenes. Vitamin A_1 is the fat-soluble vitamin which is necessary for the growth of rats, which plays a part in the resistance of the animal organism to infection, and which is required for the production of visual purple, a pigment necessary for sight. Its structure has been determined by degradation reactions, and several syntheses starting with β-ionone (p. 852) have been reported since 1946. A synthesis starting with cyclohexanone also has been developed.

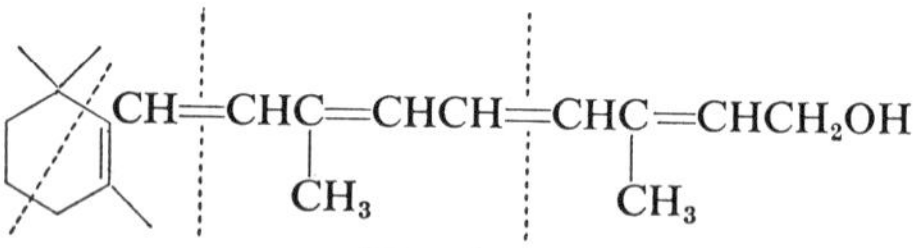

Vitamin A_1

The pure alcohol melts at 64° and has a biological potency of 4.3×10^6 U.S.P. units per gram or 3.3×10^6 International units per gram. Before commercial production of the acetate by synthesis, which began in 1950, the chief source was the fish liver oils which vary greatly in potency. Thus cod liver oil contains 3000 to 5000 units per gram, halibut liver oil 10,000 to 15,000, and soupfin shark liver oil 15,000 to 500,000 (average 350,000) units per gram.

Vitamin A_2 from the liver oil of fresh-water fish has an additional double bond in the ring in conjugation with the other double bonds. **Visual purple** (*rhodopsin*) is a protein complex, the prosthetic group of which is **retinene₁**, the aldehyde corresponding to vitamin A_1. **Retinene₂** is the aldehyde corresponding to vitamin A_2.

Dicyclic Diterpenes. Agathic acid, $C_{20}H_{30}O_4$, is a dicarboxylic acid that occurs in the natural resins Manila copal (from *Agathis alba*) and Kauri copal, a fossil resin from New Zealand. Dehydrogenation with selenium yields 1,2,5-trimethylnaphthalene (*agathalene*).

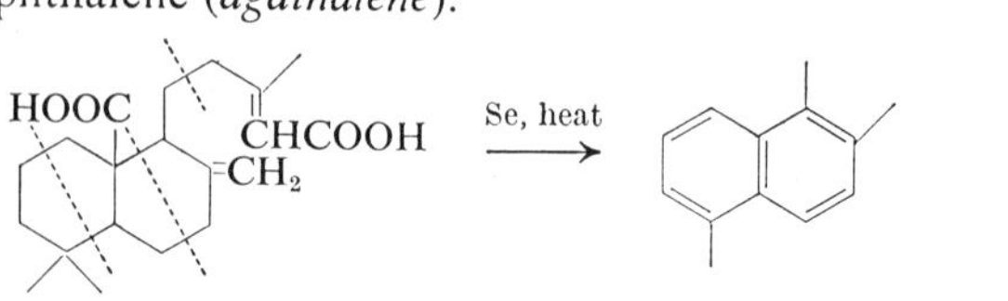

Agathic acid

1,2,5-Trimethyl-
naphthalene (agathalene)

Tricyclic Diterpenes. The most important diterpene commercially is **abietic acid,** $C_{20}H_{30}O_2$, the chief constituent of rosin or colophony, the resin obtained from various species of pine (L. *abies*, fir). Abietic acid is an original component of the tree secretions, and is formed also by the isomerization of other acids during the distillation of the turpentine.

Abietic acid was one of the first resin acids to be investigated, and the chief features of its carbon skeleton have been known since 1910 when retene, the product obtained by Vesterberg in 1903 by dehydrogenation with sulfur, was shown to be 1-methyl-7-isopropylphenanthrene (p. 602). Determination of the location of the remaining carbon atoms and the position of the two double bonds was considerably more difficult, and the verification of the currently accepted structure was not made until 1941.

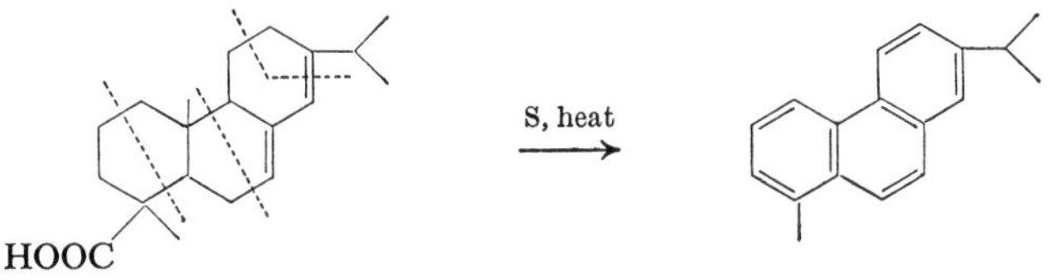

Abietic acid $\xrightarrow{\text{S, heat}}$ Retene

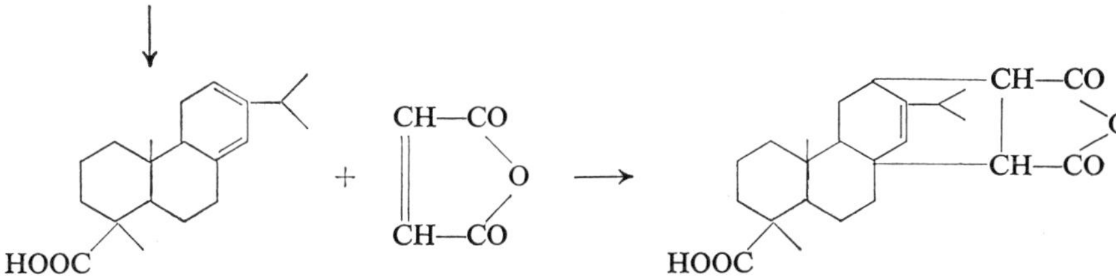

l-Sapietic acid
(*l*-pimaric acid)   +   Maleic anhydride adduct

Maleic anhydride reacts with abietic acid at 100°, but the adduct is identical with that obtained at room temperature from another resin acid, *l*-sapietic acid (formerly called *l*-pimaric acid). Although the two double bonds of abietic acid are conjugated, they are present in two different rings, and it is impossible to form a maleic anhydride adduct from this structure because of the strain involved. At the higher temperature rearrangement to conjugation in a single ring takes place, and the adduct is formed.

When rosin is heated with palladium on activated carbon or on alumina at 150°–250°, disproportionation takes place; that is, some molecules are dehydrogenated with rearrangement of the double bonds to give an aromatic ring and other molecules are hydrogenated to give dihydro- and tetrahydroabietic acids.

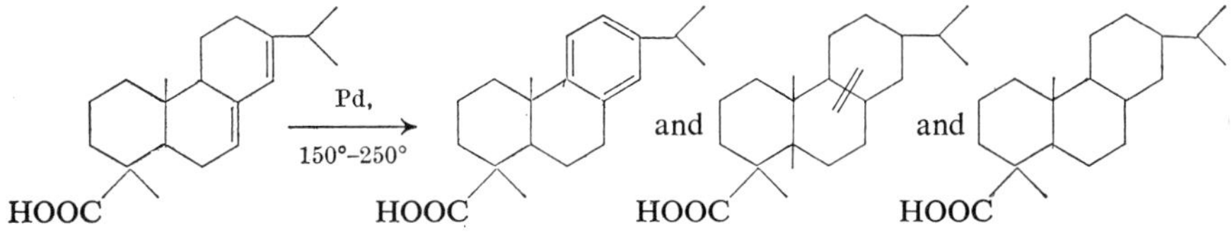

Abietic acid $\xrightarrow{\text{Pd,}\ 150°-250°}$ Dehydroabietic acid   and   Dihydroabietic acids   and   Tetrahydroabietic acid

Rosin is an important article of commerce. Production in the United States amounts to around 1 billion pounds per year. It is the most abundant and cheapest organic acid. The crude sodium salt is used to size paper and to increase the lathering property of laundry soap. The sodium salt of disproportionated rosin is used as an emulsifier in the production of synthetic rubber (p. 717). Rosin is used as a component of varnish. Its glyceryl ester, known as *ester gum*, is superior for this purpose. The maleic anhydride adduct obtained from rosin is used in the production of alkyd type synthetic resins (p. 553). Uses of lesser importance are too numerous to mention.

An interesting natural product related to abietic acid is the glucoside ester, **stevioside**, isolated from the leaves of a South American shrub, *Stevia rebaudiana*. It is reported to be 300 times sweeter than sucrose.

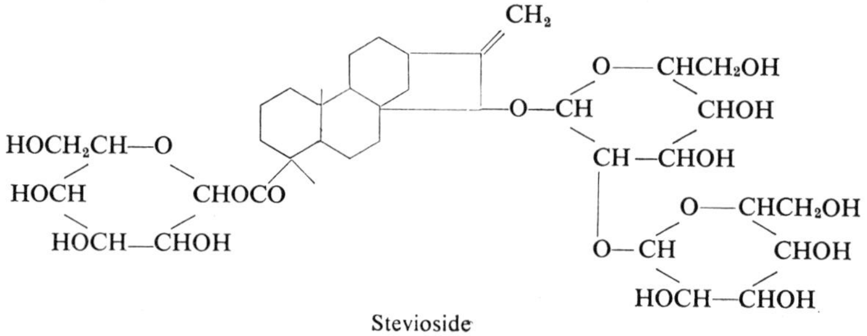

Stevioside

Triterpenes

Acyclic Triterpenes. Although hydrocarbons usually have not been considered to play an important part in animal metabolism, **squalene**, $C_{30}H_{50}$, makes up as high as 90 per cent of the liver oil of certain species of sharks of the family *Squalidae*. It has six double bonds and hence is acyclic. When heated with formic acid, a tetracyclic isomer is formed which gives agathalene on dehydrogenation with sulfur. These reactions can be explained by assuming that squalene consists of two farnesyl chains joined end to end.

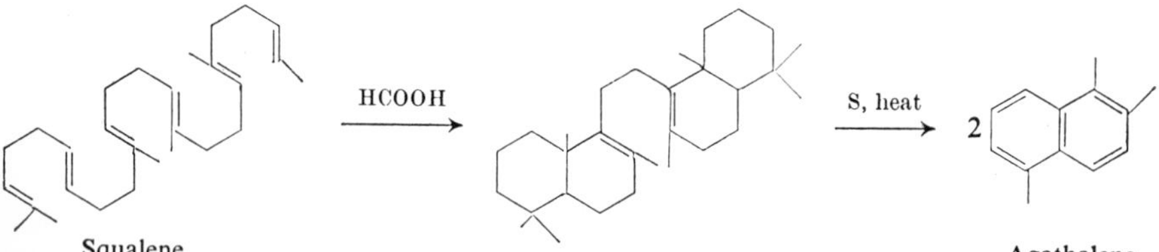

Squalene   HCOOH   S, heat   Agathalene

This structure has been confirmed by synthesis by the action of magnesium on two moles of farnesyl chloride (p. 858), a Wurtz type of reaction. It now is known that squalene is an intermediate in the biological synthesis of cholesterol (p. 867) and probably is present in all animals.

Mono-, Di-, Tri-, and Tetracyclic Triterpenes. Thus far no mono- or dicyclic triterpenes are known. **Ambrein**, $C_{30}H_{52}O$, an alcohol from ambergris, is believed to be tricyclic. Numerous tetracyclic triterpenes are known, the most important of which is **lanosterol**, $C_{30}H_{50}O$, which occurs along with other triterpenes and the steroid cholesterol (p. 867) in wool grease (*lanolin*), and is an intermediate in the biological conversion of squalene to cholesterol (p. 868). Selenium dehydrogenation of lanosterol gives 1,2,8-trimethylphenanthrene, which is regarded as typical of tetracyclic triterpenes.

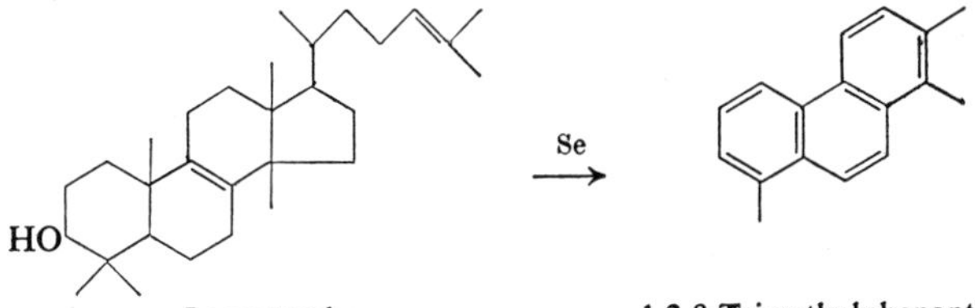

Lanosterol   1,2,8-Trimethylphenanthrene

Pentacyclic Triterpenes. Pentacyclic triterpenes are found in many plants and may occur in any part of the plant, either free or combined with sugars. Their glycosides constitute one group of the **saponins,** and the aglycones formed on hydrolysis frequently are called triterpene **sapogenins.** The saponins are characterized by their toxicity to fish and by their ability to lower the surface tension of water. They are the active principles of the numerous soap roots, soap nuts, and soap barks.

Among the many pentacyclic triterpenes that have been isolated and characterized may be mentioned the α- and β-amyrins, $C_{30}H_{50}O$, from Manila elemi; **betulin,** $C_{30}H_{50}O_2$, the white pigment of birch bark (*Betula alba*); **gypsogenin,** $C_{30}H_{46}O_4$, which occurs as a saponin in white soap root (*Gypsophila*); **hederagenin,** $C_{30}H_{48}O_4$, from ivy leaves (*Hedera helix*) and soap nuts (*Sapindus* species); **oleanolic acid,** $C_{30}H_{48}O_3$, which occurs as a saponin in guaiac bark, sugar beet, and calendula flowers, and free in olive leaves, clove buds, mistletoe, and grape skins; and **ursolic acid,** $C_{30}H_{48}O_3$, which is present in the wax-like coatings of leaves and fruits such as the apple, cherry, bearberry, and cranberry.

The carbon skeleton of oleanolic acid is characteristic of the many pentacyclic triterpenes related to *β*-amyrin.

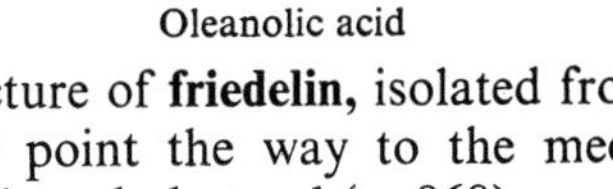

Oleanolic acid 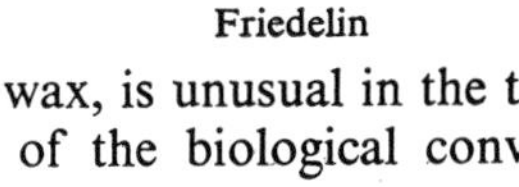   Friedelin

The structure of **friedelin,** isolated from cork wax, is unusual in the triterpenes and may point the way to the mechanism of the biological conversion of lanosterol to cholesterol (p. 868).

Tetraterpenes

Most members of the large group of compounds known as *carotenoids* may be classed as tetraterpenes. They constitute the yellow to red fat-soluble pigments of plants. Usually several pigments occur together. Because of the small amounts present and the close similarities in structure, isolation and purification by the usual crystallization procedures have been difficult. Rapid progress in the chemistry of the carotenoids began with the use of chromatographic adsorption

(p. 16) on alumina, magnesia, or calcium carbonate. It was in the separation of carotenoids that this technique first was highly developed.

Acyclic Tetraterpenes. Lycopene, $C_{40}H_{56}$, is the red pigment in the ripe fruit of the tomato (*Lycopersicum esculentum*) and of the watermelon (*Cucumis citrullus*). On catalytic hydrogenation 13 moles of hydrogen are absorbed to give the saturated hydrocarbon *perhydrolycopene*, $C_{40}H_{82}$. Perhydrolycopene has been synthesized by a Wurtz reaction from two moles of dihydrophytyl bromide (cf. p. 860), thus establishing the carbon skeleton. Ozonolysis of lycopene yields almost two moles of acetone, together with levulinic aldehyde, thus locating the positions of the double bonds.

$$\left[(CH_3)_2C{=}CHCH_2CH_2\underset{\underset{CH_3}{|}}{C}{=}CHCH{=}CH\underset{\underset{CH_3}{|}}{C}{=}CHCH{=}CH\underset{\underset{CH_3}{|}}{C}{=}CHCH{=}\right]_2$$

Lycopene

Monocyclic and Dicyclic Tetraterpenes. 1. HYDROCARBONS. The tetraterpenes that have been of greatest interest are the **carotenes**, because they are converted by the animal organism into vitamin A_1. The name *carotene* was given to the yellow pigment of the carrot (*Daucus carota*) from which it first was isolated in 1831. It was assigned the formula of a hydrocarbon, C_5H_8, in 1847. Between 1885 and 1887 it was isolated from green leaves and assigned the formula $C_{26}H_{38}$. In 1907 the correct formula, $C_{40}H_{56}$, was determined.

The application of the methods of chromatographic adsorption has shown that the early carotene is a mixture of isomers. Six carotenes have been identified so far and have been named α-, β-, γ-, δ-, ε-, and ζ-**carotene.** The last three have been characterized chiefly by their absorption spectra, and the structures of only the first three are known.

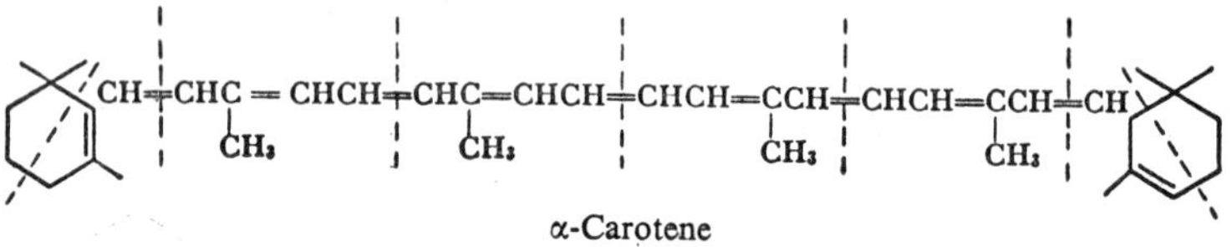

α-Carotene

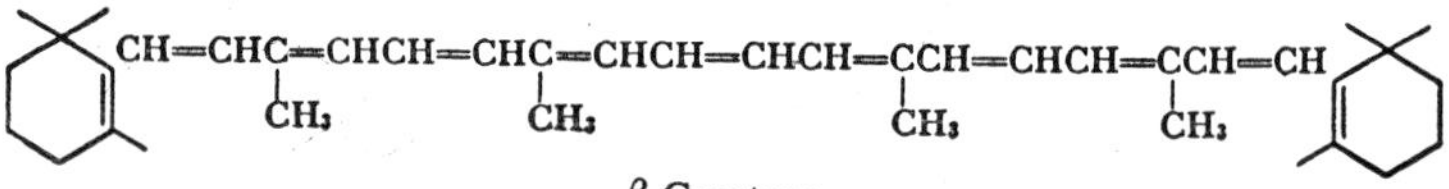

β-Carotene

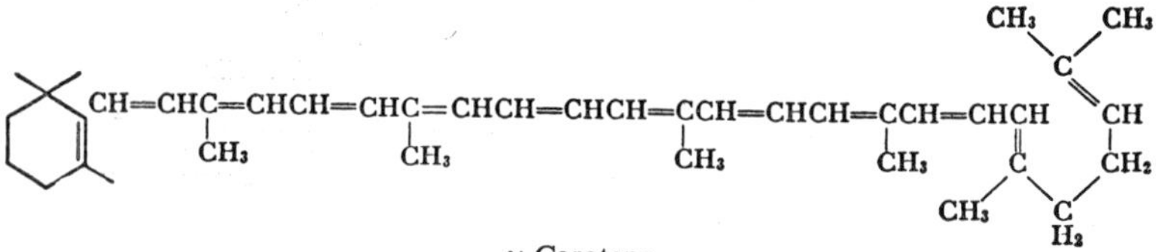

γ-Carotene

If β-carotene could react at the center of the molecule with two molecules of water in such a way that scission takes place and the two central carbon atoms become primary alcohol groups, two molecules of vitamin A_1 would result. The intestines and liver of the animal organism have the power to do this, and β-carotene has vitamin A activity. α-Carotene has only one β-ionone ring, the other ring being of the α-ionone type (p. 852). In γ-carotene half of the molecule is like β-carotene but the other half is like half of the lycopene molecule. The animal organism does not have the ability to isomerize the α-ionone to the β-ionone structure, nor can it cyclize the end of the lycopene chain to a β-ionone ring. Hence the activity of α- or γ-carotene is less than the activity of β-carotene, and lycopene is entirely inactive.

The total and relative amounts of α-, β-, and γ-carotene present in plants vary with the source. Leaves contain approximately 0.01 per cent of mixed carotenes on a dry weight basis. β-Carotene is the chief component of this mixture. The amount of α-carotene varies from 0 to 35 per cent of the total carotenes and the amount of γ-carotene usually is much less.

Lycopene, β-carotene, α-carotene, and γ-carotene all have been synthesized starting respectively with pseudoionone, β-ionone, a mixture of α- and β-ionone, and a mixture of pseudoionone and β-ionone. The commercial synthesis of β-carotene makes available a coloring matter for foods that can replace the carcinogenic azo dyes.

2. OXYGENATED COMPOUNDS. Leaves contain, in addition to the carotenes, yellow pigments known as **xanthophylls** (leaf yellow) or **xanthins** that contain oxygen. It is these pigments, along with the carotenes, that are responsible for the autumn color of leaves, since they persist after the destruction of the green chlorophyll. Yellow to red tetraterpenes containing oxygen have been isolated from other sources also. The oxygen may be present as one or more hydroxyl groups, one or more carbonyl groups, or as both hydroxyl and carbonyl groups. The hydroxyl groups may be free or esterified. Oxygen may be present also as 1,2 or 1,4 oxide rings.

Lutein (leaf xanthophyll), $C_{40}H_{56}O_2$, is present in green and yellow leaves and in yellow flowers. Together with zeaxanthin it constitutes the pigment of egg yolk. It has been shown to be a dihydroxy derivative of α-carotene. Since all of the tetraterpenes contain the same central structure, this portion of the

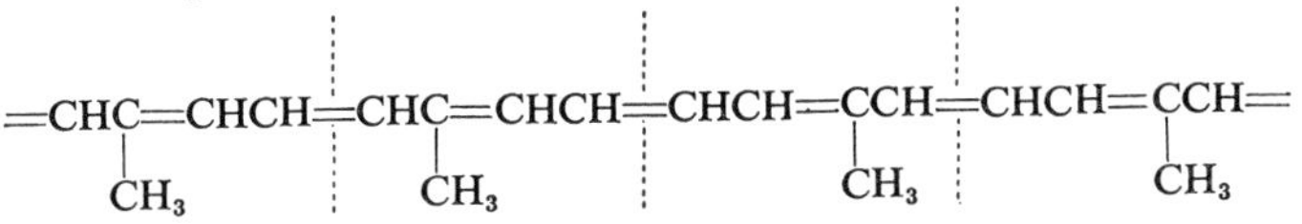

=CHC=CHCH=CHC=CHCH=CHCH=CCH=CHCH=CCH=
CH3
CH3
CH3
CH3

molecule will be represented hereafter by four dashes, one for each of the four isopentane units.

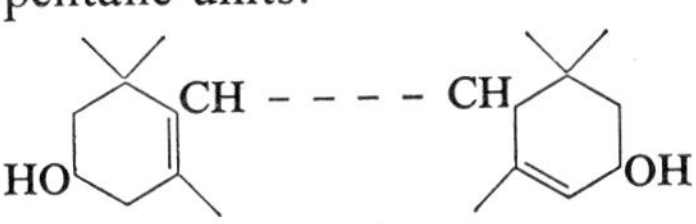

CH - - - - CH
HO
OH

Lutein

CH - - - - CH
HO
OH

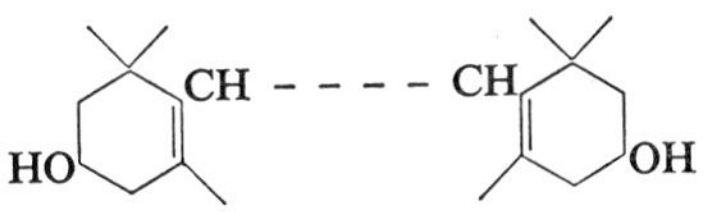

Zeaxanthin

Zeaxanthin, $C_{40}H_{56}O_2$, is a dihydroxy derivative of β-carotene. It is the chief pigment of yellow corn (*Zea mays*) and is present in varying amount in egg yolk. **Physalein,** the pigment of the pods of *Physalis*, is the dipalmitate of zeaxanthin and is the best source.

Cryptoxanthin, $C_{40}H_{56}O$, is a monohydroxy derivative of β-carotene. It is found free and esterified in yellow corn, physalis pods, and paprika, and is the

CH - - - - CH
HO

Cryptoxanthin

=CH - - - - CH=
O
O

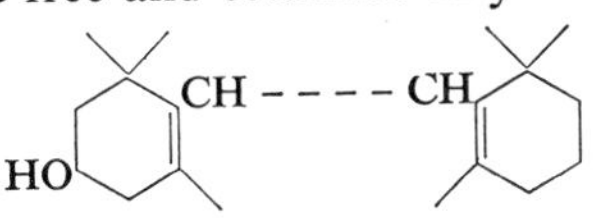

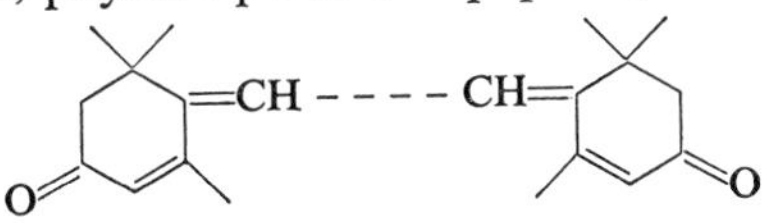

Rhodoxanthin

main pigment of the mandarin orange. Neither lutein nor zeaxanthin has vitamin A activity but cryptoxanthin has half the activity of vitamin A.

Rhodoxanthin, $C_{40}H_{50}O_2$, is of interest as an example of ketonic carotenoids. Because all of its double bonds are conjugated including those of its carbonyl groups, its absorption bands lie farther to the red than those of any other carotenoid. It was isolated first from the red berries of the Irish yew (*Taxus baccata*).

Examples of pigments containing oxide rings are **violaxanthin** and **auroxanthin** isolated from pansy flowers (*Viola tricolor*). The 1,2-oxides are very easily isomerized to 1,4-oxides by traces of acid.

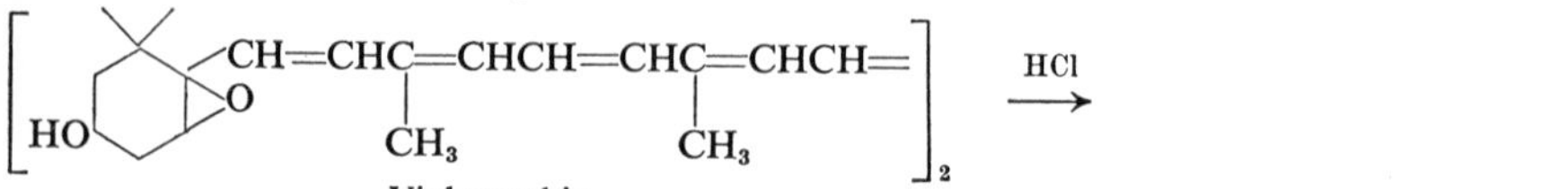

$$\left[\underset{HO}{\text{}} \overset{}{\underset{O}{\diamond}} \text{CH}=\text{CHC}=\text{CHCH}=\text{CHC}=\text{CHCH}= \right]_2 \quad \xrightarrow{\text{HCl}}$$

Violaxanthin

$$\left[\underset{HO}{\text{}} \overset{=\text{CH}}{\underset{O}{\diamond}} \text{C}=\text{CH}-\text{CH}=\text{CHC}=\text{CHCH}= \right]_2$$

Auroxanthin

Products Related to Tetraterpenes. Terpenes by definition are those compounds whose structures are divisible into isopentane units of five carbon atoms each. Yet naturally occurring compounds are known whose carbon skeletons without question are related to the terpenes but which do not contain an even multiple of isopentane units. Among these may be mentioned **torularhodin** from red yeast (*Torula rubra*), $C_{37}H_{50}O_2$; **azafrin** from azafran (*Escobedia*), $C_{27}H_{38}O_4$; and **bixin,** a monomethyl ester of the dibasic acid, $C_{24}H_{28}O_4$, from annatto (*Bixa orellana*).

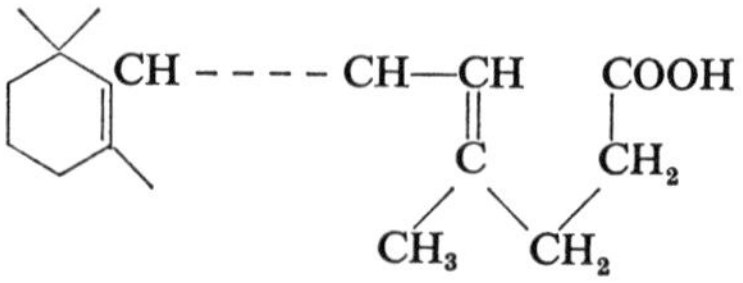

$$\text{CH}----\text{CH}-\text{CH} \quad \text{COOH}$$

Torularhodin

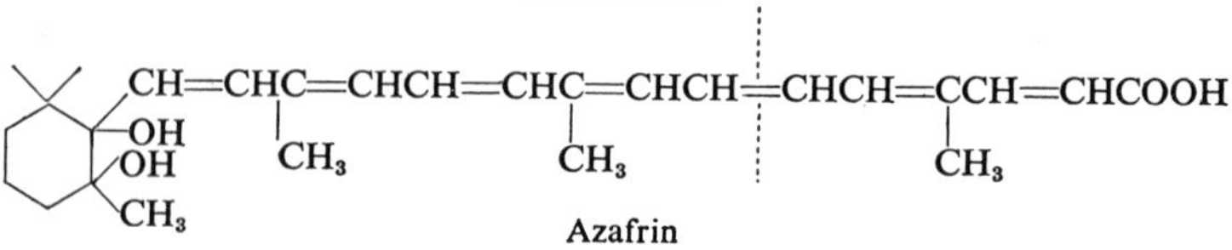

$$\text{CH}=\text{CHC}=\text{CHCH}=\text{CHC}=\text{CHCH}=\text{CHCH}=\text{CCH}=\text{CHCOOH}$$

Azafrin

$$\text{CH}_3\text{OOCCH}=\text{CHC}=\text{CHCH}=\text{CHC}=\text{CHCH}=\text{CHCH}=\text{CCH}=\text{CHCH}=\text{CCH}=\text{CHCOOH}$$

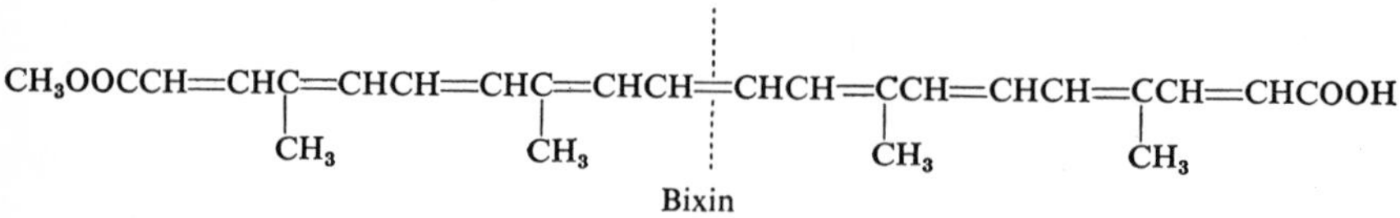

Bixin

From the proposed structures for these compounds it appears likely that they are derived from tetraterpenes by degradation.

Crocetin, $C_{20}H_{24}O_4$, is the yellow pigment of saffron, the dried stigma and styles of the autumn crocus (*Crocus sativas*), and **β-citraurin,** $C_{30}H_{40}O_2$, is the pigment of the orange. From the number of carbon atoms in these compounds, it might be thought that they belong to the diterpenes and triterpenes respectively. However, the structure contains a point of inversion of the arrangement of the isopentane units, and hence they more likely are degradation products of tetraterpenes.

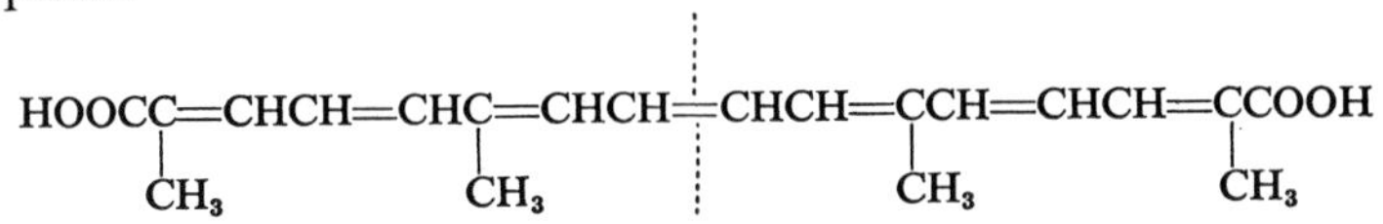
HOOCC=CHCH=CHC=CHCH=CHCH=CCH=CHCH=CCOOH
CH3
CH3
CH3
CH3
Crocetin

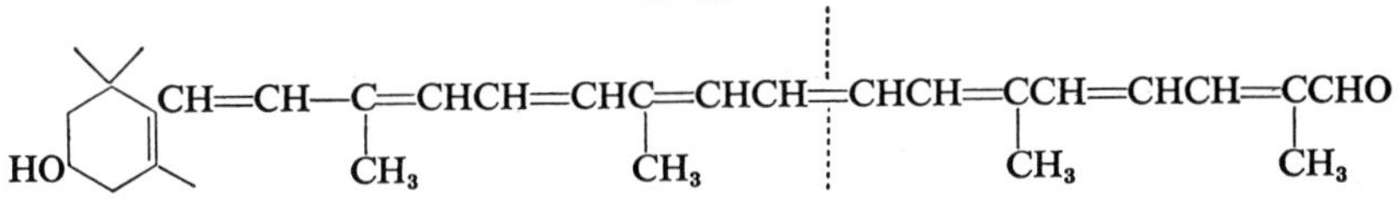
HO
CH=CH—C=CHCH=CHC=CHCH=CHCH=CCH=CHCH=CCHO
CH3
CH3
CH3
CH3
β-Citraurin

Crocetin is of considerable biological interest, since its glycoside **crocin,** $C_{44}H_{64}O_{26}$, in minute quantities causes the inactive gametes of the various strains of the green algae, *Chlamydomonas eugametos,* to develop cilia and become motile. It has been estimated that only one molecule of crocin per gamete is necessary to produce activity. Moreover, a definite ratio of the *cis* and *trans* forms is necessary to activate the gametes for reproduction. Crocin is capable of rendering the gametes motile at a dilution of one part in 250 trillion (1 in 2.5×10^{14}), and this test has been employed to show the presence of crocin in the sexual organs of lilies and other flowers, indicating that it may play a part in the fertilization process of higher plants.

Polyterpenes

Rubber, gutta percha, and balata are polyterpenes. Their structure and properties are discussed on pages 709 and 713.

STEROIDS

Steroids may be defined as those compounds which contain a ring system like that present in cholesterol. They are characterized by the fact that they yield methylcyclopentenophenanthrene (Diels hydrocarbon) on dehydrogenation with selenium.

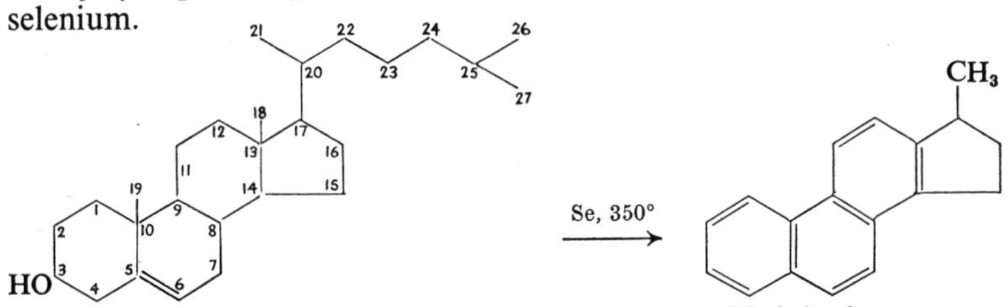
21
22
24
26
20
23
25
27
18
12
17
13
16
11
14
15
19
1
9
2
10
8
3
5
7
HO
4
6
Se, 350°
CH3
Cholesterol

Methylcyclopenteno-phenanthrene (Diels hydrocarbon)

To this group belong the sterols, the bile acids, the cardiac aglycones, the sex hormones, the adrenal steroids, the toad poisons, and the steroid sapogenins. In view of the complexity of the chemistry and the large number of compounds in the group, the formulas of only a few representatives of the various subgroups are given.

Zoosterols

Cholesterol, $C_{27}H_{46}O$, is present in the blood of animals and hence in all parts of the body. It is concentrated in the spinal cord, the brain, skin secretions, and gallstones. It was isolated first from gallstones by Conradi in 1775 and was named cholesterine (Gr. *chole*, bile; *stereos*, solid) in 1816 by Chevreul (p. 179) who showed that unlike the fats it was not saponifiable. Berthelot (p. 93) recognized that it was an alcohol in 1859, but the correct molecular formula, $C_{27}H_{46}O$, was not proposed until 1888 by Reinitzer. The currently accepted structure was not arrived at until 1932 after over eighty years of active chemical investigation. With eight asymmetric carbon atoms, 256 active isomers are possible. Not only has the configuration of each asymmetric carbon atom been established, but the last steps in the total synthesis of cholesterol having the exact configuration of the natural product were completed in 1951. It also has been established by means of isotopically labeled compounds that cholesterol is synthesized by the animal organism from acetate ion, and that squalene and lanosterol (p. 863) are intermediates in the synthesis.

Coprosterol, a stereoisomer of dihydrocholesterol, occurs in feces. **7-Dehydrocholesterol** has been isolated from fish liver oils.

Phytosterols

Cholesterol occurs only in animals, no trace ever having been found in plants. However, plants contain a large number of closely related compounds known as the phytosterols. **Stigmasterol,** $C_{29}H_{48}O$, for example, can be obtained from the unsaponifiable portion of soybean oil, and **β-sitosterol,** $C_{29}H_{50}O$, is one of at least six sterols present in wheat germ oil.

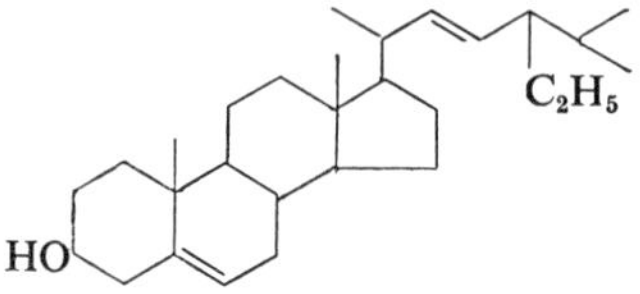

Stigmasterol 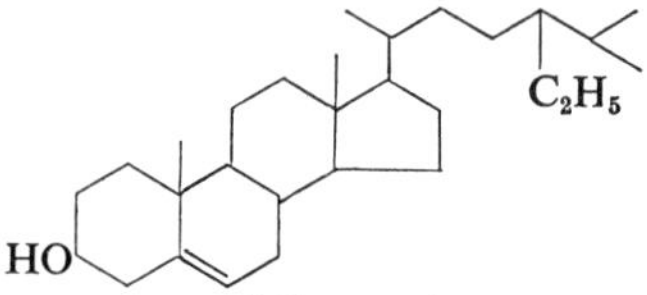   β-Sitosterol

Ergosterol, $C_{28}H_{44}O$, was isolated first from ergot, but is obtained more readily from yeast. Irradiation by ultraviolet light transforms it into a number of products, one of which is **calciferol** or **vitamin D₂.**

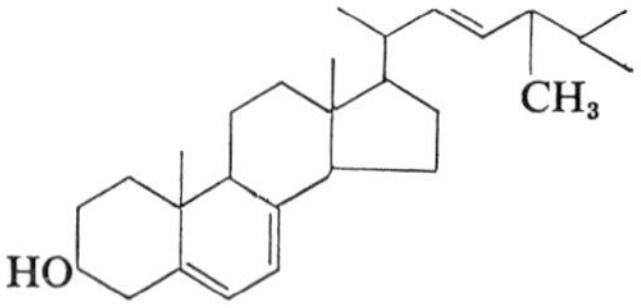

Ergosterol $\xrightarrow[\text{light}]{\text{Ultraviolet}}$ Lumisterol $\longrightarrow$ Tachysterol $\longrightarrow$

Precalciferol $\longrightarrow$ Calciferol (vitamin D₂) $\xrightarrow[\text{irradiation}]{\text{Further}}$ { Suprasterol I, Suprasterol II, Toxisterol }

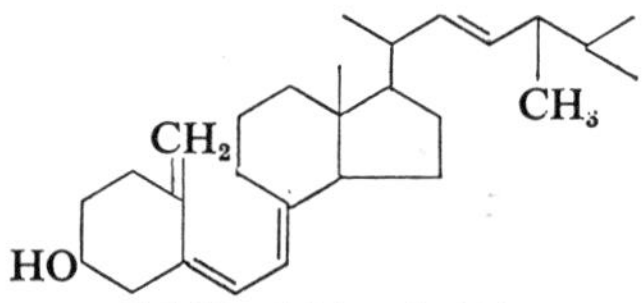

The nature of the side chain does not appear to be important and several compounds have vitamin D activity. Thus irradiation of 7-dehydrocholesterol gives vitamin D_3 which is much more active than vitamin D_2. The vitamins D control the amount and ratio of calcium and phosphorus in the blood. In the absence of vitamin D these elements fall below normal, the bones soften and bend, and the joints swell. The condition is known as rickets.

Bile Acids

The bile acids are obtained by the alkaline hydrolysis of bile salts which are present in the bile of various animals. In the bile salts, the bile acids are combined by an amide linkage between their carboxyl group and the amino group of glycine, H_2NCH_2COOH, or taurine, $H_2NCH_2CH_2SO_3H$. Thus **glycocholic acid** on hydrolysis gives cholic acid and glycine, whereas **taurocholic acid** gives cholic acid and taurine. The function of the bile salts is to act as emulsifying agents for fats and hence to promote the hydrolysis and absorption of fats from the intestinal tract. The four bile acids occurring in human and ox bile are **cholic acid, deoxycholic acid, chenodeoxycholic acid,** and **lithocholic acid.** The first two are the more abundant.

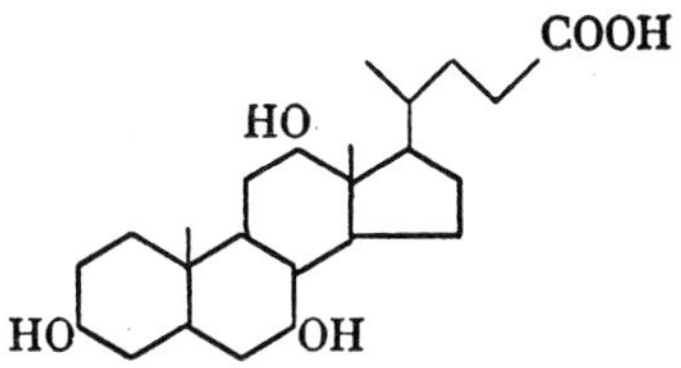

Cholic acid

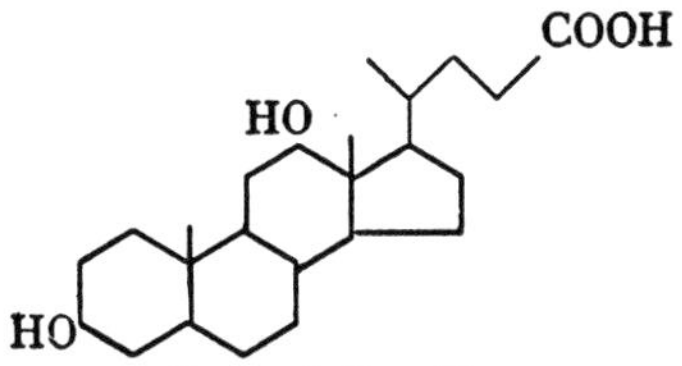

Deoxycholic acid

Steroid Sapogenins

Many saponins on hydrolysis yield steroid sapogenins rather than triterpenes (p. 863). The steroid sapogenins are characterized by a dicyclic acetal side chain. **Diosgenin** has been obtained from certain species of yams (*Dioscorea*), and **tigogenin** from *Digitalis* species and from *Chlorogalum pomeridianum*. They have been used as starting points for the synthesis of sex hormones (p. 870).

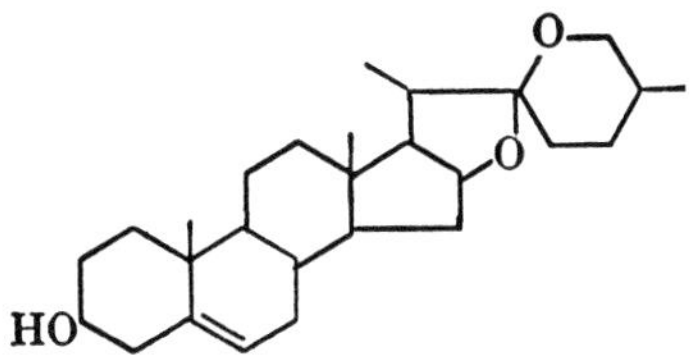

Diosgenin

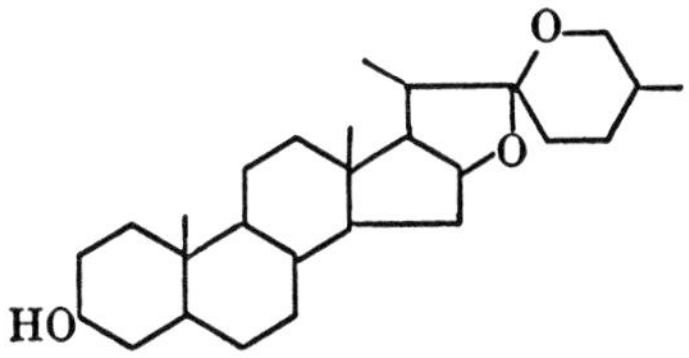

Tigogenin

Digitonin, a saponin from the foxglove (*Digitalis purpurea*), is a valuable reagent because it forms insoluble molecular complexes with steroids having a hydroxyl group at C-3 and having a configuration such that the hydroxyl group and the methyl group at C-10 occupy *cis* positions (β configuration). Occasionally compounds having other structures also give insoluble complexes.

Cardiac Glycosides and Toad Poisons

The cardiac glycosides have a highly specific and powerful action on heart muscles. Thus 0.07 mg. of strophanthin, the active principle of African arrow poisons from *Strophanthus* seeds, stops the heart of a 20 g. mouse. The glycosides from *Digitalis purpurea* and *Digitalis lanata* are used in small doses to stimulate contraction of the heart and constitute the most valuable remedial agents in the treatment of heart ailments. The glycosides from squill (*Urginea maritima*) and the toad poisons have a similar action. The aglycones of these substances are characterized by an unsaturated lactone ring at C-17. This ring is five-membered and contains one double bond in **digitoxigenin** and **strophanthidin,** and is six-membered with two double bonds in **scillaren-A** from squill and in **bufotalin** from the skin glands of toads.

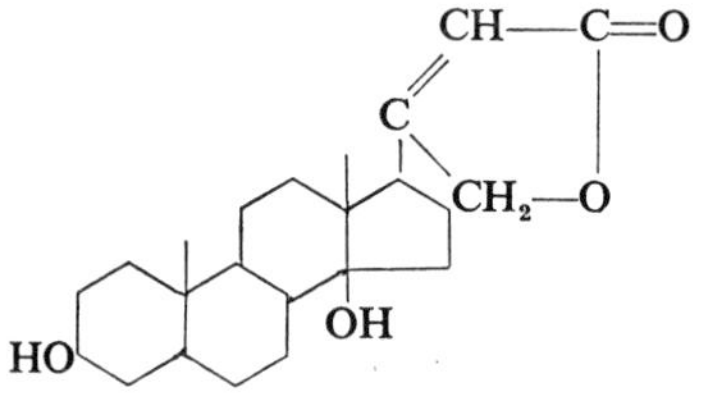

Digitoxigenin 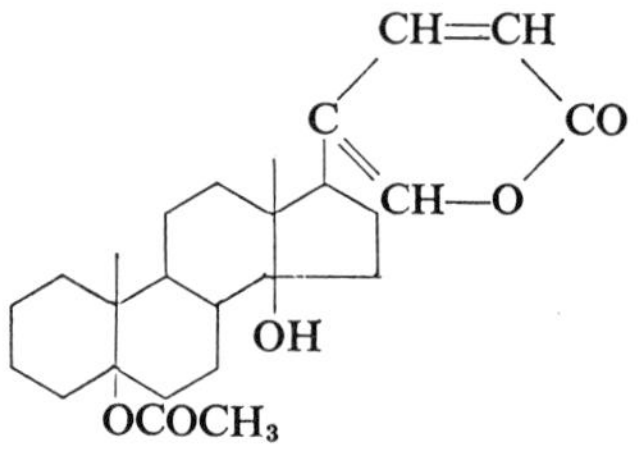   Bufotalin

Sex Hormones

The sex hormones are substances responsible for the sex characteristics and the sexual processes of the animal organism. They are formed in the testes and ovaries, which are stimulated by other hormones, the gonadotropic hormones secreted by the anterior lobe of the pituitary gland. **Testosterone** is secreted by the testes and controls the development of the genital tract, accessory male organs, and secondary male characteristics such as the comb and wattles of a rooster. **Estradiol** is produced in the ovaries, probably in the ripening follicles.

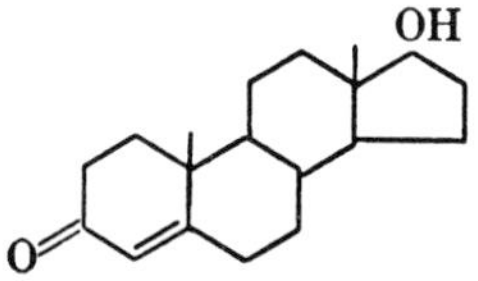

Testosterone 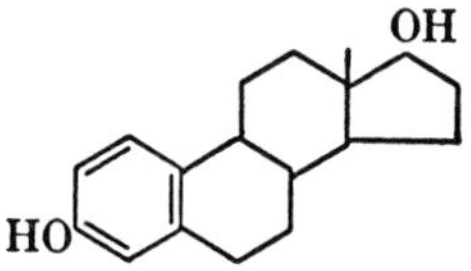   Estradiol

It controls the development of female characteristics and initiates the first phase in the menstrual cycle, namely the proliferation of cells in the uterus. The estrogenic effect is not very specific and a synthetic compound, **stilbestrol** (*diethylstilbestrol*), is used more commonly than natural estradiol to alleviate trouble arising from a deficiency of the hormone and to arrest prostatic cancer. Large amounts are used as a growth stimulant for cattle. **Hexestrol** is the corresponding compound in which the ethylene double bond is hydrogenated. Tri-*p*-anisylchloroethylene (*TACE*) is a more recently introduced estrogen.

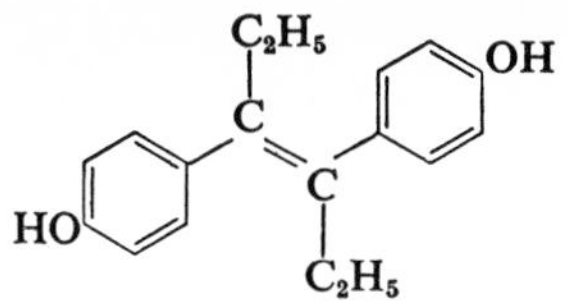

Stilbestrol 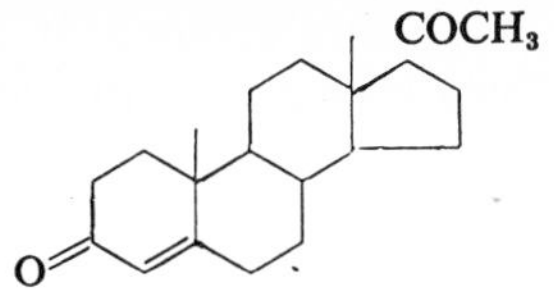   Progesterone

Progesterone is secreted by the corpus luteum (yellow body) formed after the expulsion of the ovum. This hormone prepares the bed of the uterus for the implantation of the fertilized ovum. It is used clinically to prevent abortion.

Adrenal Steroids

The adrenals are two small glands, one above each kidney, that have two important functions, namely the secretion of epinephrine and norepinephrine (p. 529) and the secretion of cortin. Both secretions are essential to life, but the secretion of cortin is the more important, because it is secreted only by the adrenals whereas epinephrine and norepinephrine are secreted by other organs as well. A deficit of cortin leads to a bronzing of the skin, muscular weakness, and an increase in blood urea (Addison's disease). An excess in children produces precocious sex development.

Cortin activity resides in the steroidal fraction present in the adrenal cortex. Thirty different compounds of the androstane and pregnane series have been isolated from this fraction and their structure identified. Seven of these have cortin activity. The structures of a few of the compounds are indicated.

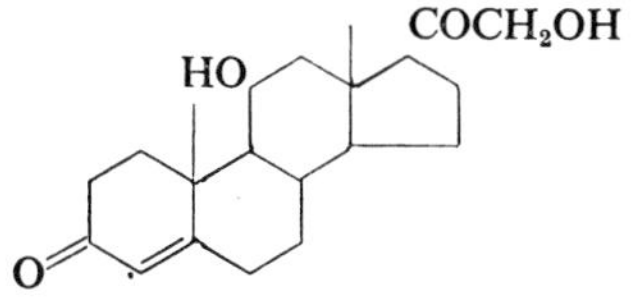

Corticosterone 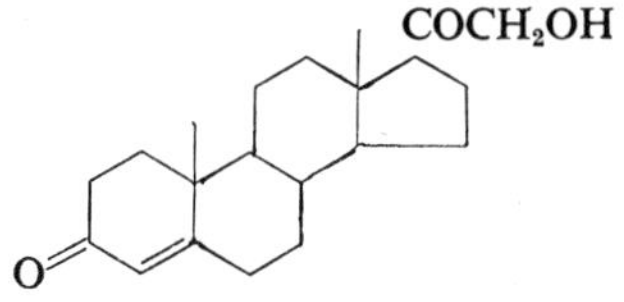   Deoxycorticosterone

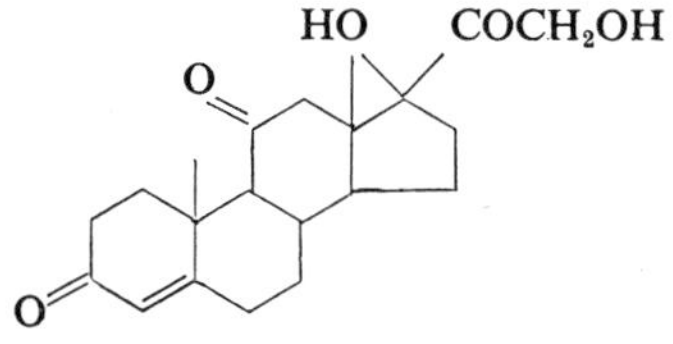

Cortisone 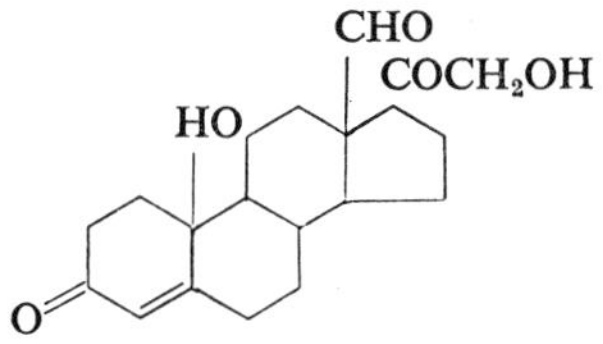   Aldosterone

It is of interest that deoxycorticosterone was synthesized from stigmasterol before it was isolated from the adrenal cortex. Since 1948 considerable interest has centered on a component called **cortisone,** because of its beneficial effects in the treatment of various maladies, especially rheumatoid arthritis. Numerous modifications in the structure of cortisone have been made with the object of enhancing its desirable properties or reducing undesirable action. Some of the more effective compounds contain a double bond at the 1,2-position, halogen at the 9-position, or a methyl group at the 2-position. It is surprising that reduction of the double bond of deoxycorticosterone followed by conversion to the acid succinate gives a product that is useful as an anesthetic.

REVIEW QUESTIONS

1. What are alicyclic compounds? What other names are applied to the parent hydrocarbons?
2. Discuss the synthesis of alicyclic hydrocarbons, ketones, and dibasic acids by ring closure.
3. Compare the ease of formation and stability of carbocyclic rings. What was Baeyer's strain theory and how has it been modified?
4. What are the most readily available alicyclic compounds and how are they prepared? Compare their chemical properties with those of the corresponding aromatic compounds.
5. What feature do benzene, the cyclopentadienyl anion, and the tropylium cation have in common?
6. What are the terpenes and camphors?
7. Write structural formulas for and indicate the source of limonene, pulegone, menthol, pinene, and camphor.
8. Give the structures of representative members of cyclic terpenes having 7-, 9-, and 11-membered rings.
9. To what class of terpenes do the following groups of compounds belong: vitamins A; acid sapogenins; xanthophylls; rosin acids; carotenes?
10. What is meant by the following terms: cyclophane; transannular reaction; equatorial bond; center of symmetry; Strecker degradation; Wagner-Meerwein rearrangement?
11. What are the more important classes of steroids, and what structural feature is characteristic of each?
12. What is the biological connection between squalene, lanosterol, and cholesterol?

PROBLEMS

13. Starting with ethylene bromide, construct a chart, including reagents and conditions, for the preparation of the following compounds: 1,1-cyclopropanedicarboxylic acid, cyclopropylcarbinol, cyclopropyldimethylamine, ethyl cyclopropanecarboxylate, cyclopropanecarboxylic acid, cyclopropylamine, cyclopropene, cyclopropanecarboxamide, and cyclopropyltrimethylammonium hydroxide.
14. Give equations illustrating the preparation of cyclopropanecarboxylic acid and of cyclopropyl methyl ketone starting with ethyl acetoacetate.
15. Construct a chart, including reagents and conditions, for preparing the following compounds starting with adipic acid: cyclopentanone, cyclopentylcarbinol, cyclopentyl bromide, cyclopentylamine, cyclopentanol, ethyl β-oxo-β-cyclopentylpropionate, cyclopentanone oxime, cyclopentanecarboxylic acid, 2-cyclopentylethanol, cyclopentyl methyl ketone, δ-valerolactam, and ethyl cyclopentanecarboxylate.
16. Construct a chart, including reagents and conditions, for synthesizing the following compounds starting with ethyl adipate: ethyl 2-oxocyclopentanecarboxylate, 1-ethyl-2-phenylcyclopentene, 2-ethylcyclopentanone, 2-ethyl-1-phenylcyclopentanol, 2-ethyl-5-(hydroxymethyl)cyclopentanone, 1-ethyl-2-phenylcyclopentane, 2-benzylidene-5-ethylcyclopentanone, and ethyl 1-ethyl-2-oxocyclopentanecarboxylate.
17. 1-Ethynylcyclohexyl carbamate is a short-acting soporific. Devise a synthesis starting with cyclohexanone.
18. Devise a synthesis for the fungicide Captan starting with 1,3-butadiene (cf. pp. 806, 553, 289).
19. Write perspective formulas indicating the most stable conformation of (a) α-D-glucose, (b) β-D-mannose, (c) α-L-arabinose, (d) α-D-fructopyranose, and (e) α-D-ribopyranose.
20. Predict the configuration of the chief isomer formed on the reduction of *m*-hydroxybenzoic acid with sodium and alcohol to hexahydro-*m*-hydroxybenzoic acid.
21. When either the *cis* or *trans* isomer of 1,3-cyclohexanediol is treated with hydrogen bromide only a single 1,3-dibromocyclohexane is obtained. Similarly only a single 1,4-dibromocyclohexane is obtained from either *cis* or *trans* 1,4-cyclohexanediol. Predict the configuration of the 1,3- and the 1,4-dibromocyclohexanes.
22. Starting with erucic acid, give equations for the synthesis of 2-hydroxycyclotetracosanone and for its conversion into the diol, the diketone, the ketone, the halide, the hydrocarbon, the alcohol, and the amine.

Chapter 40

ORGANIC PEROXIDES. AUTOXIDATION AND ANTIOXIDANTS

The use of organic peroxides as catalysts and their formation by autoxidation have become increasingly important in recent years. This chapter summarizes the synthesis of the various classes of peroxides by conventional methods, the formation of peroxides by autoxidation, and the mechanism of autoxidation and its inhibition by antioxidants.

ORGANIC PEROXIDES

Organic peroxides may be considered as derivatives of hydrogen peroxide, HO—OH, in which the hydrogen atoms are replaced by organic groups. The more common types are tabulated below.

R—O—OH	Alkyl hydroperoxide
R—O—O—R	Alkyl peroxide
$\overset{\text{O}}{\overset{\|}{R C}}$—O—OH	Acyl hydroperoxide (peroxy acid or per acid)
$\overset{\text{O}}{\overset{\|}{R C}}$—O—O—$\overset{\text{O}}{\overset{\|}{C R}}$	Acyl peroxide
$\overset{\text{O}}{\overset{\|}{R C}}$—O—O—R	Acyl alkyl peroxide (peroxy ester or per ester)

Other peroxides analogous in structure to aldehyde hydrates, hemiacetals, and cyclic acetals also are known.

RCH—O—OH | OH	α-Hydroxyalkyl hydroperoxide
RCH—O—O—CHR | | OH OH	α-Hydroxyalkyl peroxide
RCH—O—O—R | OH	α-Hydroxyalkyl alkyl peroxide

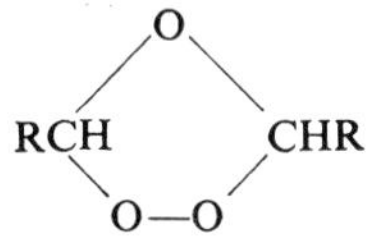

Ozonide 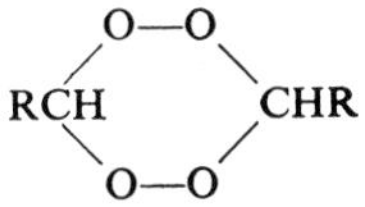   Alkylidene peroxide

The constitution of many of the peroxides obtained by autoxidation is uncertain or entirely unknown. The purification and determination of the constitution of organic peroxides have been particularly difficult because of the ease with which they decompose, often with explosive violence.

873

Alkyl Hydroperoxides and Alkyl Peroxides

Alkyl hydroperoxides are made by the monoalkylation of hydrogen peroxide. Further alkylation yields the **alkyl peroxides.** Primary and secondary alkyl sulfates and alkyl methanesulfonates have been used in the presence of aqueous or aqueous-methanolic alkali. Alkyl methanesulfonates are prepared more readily than alkyl sulfates and give better yields.

$$H_2O_2 + CH_3SO_2OR + NaOH \longrightarrow ROOH + CH_3SO_3Na + H_2O$$

$$RO{-}OH + CH_3SO_2OR + NaOH \longrightarrow RO{-}OR + CH_3SO_3Na + H_2O$$

Tertiary as well as primary or secondary alkyl hydroperoxides may be prepared by the reaction of alkyl hydrogen sulfates, prepared from the alcohol or olefin and concentrated sulfuric acid, with 30 to 90 per cent hydrogen peroxide at 0°.

$$H_2O_2 + ROSO_3H \longrightarrow RO{-}OH + H_2SO_4$$

$$RO{-}OH + ROSO_3H \longrightarrow RO{-}OR + H_2SO_4$$

They have been obtained also by the oxidation of Grignard reagents with oxygen at −70°.

$$RMgX + O_2 \longrightarrow RO{-}OMgX \xrightarrow{H_2O} RO{-}OH$$

Tertiary alkyl hydroperoxides can be formed by the reaction of hydrocarbons containing a tertiary hydrogen with molecular oxygen in either the gaseous or liquid phase. Thus *t*-butyl hydroperoxide results from the reaction of isobutane and air at 155° using hydrogen bromide as a catalyst. Explosion is prevented by coating the surfaces of the reactor with boric acid.

$$(CH_3)_3CH + O_2 \xrightarrow[155°]{HBr} (CH_3)_3C{-}O{-}OH$$

The oxidation of liquid alkylcyclopentanes or alkylcyclohexanes with air at 135° is catalyzed by ultraviolet light or by the addition of peroxides.

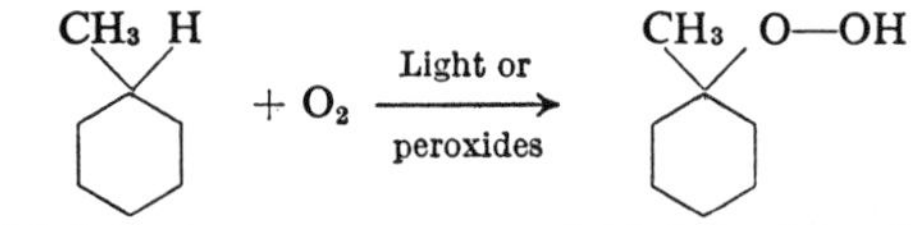

Methylcyclo-   1-Methylcyclohexyl
hexane   hydroperoxide

The hydroperoxides of cumene, *p*-menthane, and diisopropylbenzene are made by the air oxidation of the hydrocarbon in basic emulsion.

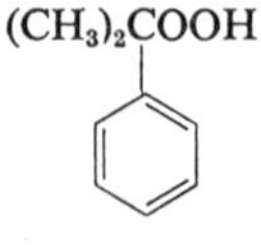

Cumene   *p*-Menthane   Diisopropylbenzene
hydroperoxide   hydroperoxide   dihydroperoxide

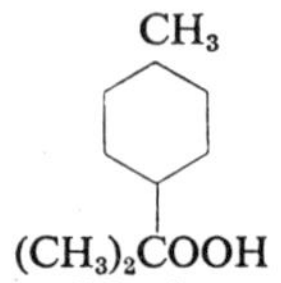

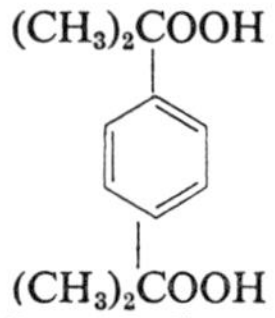

These oxidations take place by a free-radical chain mechanism. Thus the function of the hydrogen bromide in the preparation of *t*-butyl hydroperoxide is to produce bromine atoms.

$$HBr + O_2 \longrightarrow [HO—O \cdot] + [Br \cdot]$$

The bromine atoms then bring about the following chain reaction.

$$(CH_3)_3CH + [Br \cdot] \longrightarrow [(CH_3)_3C \cdot] + HBr$$

$$[(CH_3)_3C \cdot] + O_2 \longrightarrow [(CH_3)_3C—O—O \cdot]$$

$$[(CH_3)_3C—O—O \cdot] + HBr \longrightarrow (CH_3)_3C—O—OH + [Br \cdot]$$

The hydroperoxides and peroxides that have been prepared are stable below 60° in the absence of acids or bases, and the lower members are liquids that can be distilled at reduced pressure. Methyl and ethyl hydroperoxides explode violently when heated more strongly or when subjected to shock. The hydroperoxides and peroxides of higher molecular weight decompose smoothly at 80° to 100°. Complex mixtures of products are obtained, the components of which depend on the particular compound and the conditions of decomposition, such as temperature, whether in the gas phase, liquid phase, or in solvent, and whether noncatalyzed or catalyzed by acids, bases, or metal ions.

The alkyl hydroperoxides are more acidic than alcohols and form salts with aqueous solutions of strong alkalies. Both the alkyl hydroperoxides and peroxides are less readily reduced than hydrogen peroxide. Methyl and ethyl hydroperoxide liberate iodine from hydrogen iodide, but the reaction is not quantitative. *t*-Butyl hydroperoxide reacts quantitatively. The alkyl peroxides liberate very little iodine. *t*-Butyl peroxide does not react even with concentrated hydrogen iodide. Ethyl peroxide does not react with metallic sodium, but *t*-butyl peroxide gives sodium *t*-butoxide.

$$(CH_3)_3C—O—O—C(CH_3)_3 + 2\,Na \longrightarrow 2\,NaOC(CH_3)_3$$

All of the alkyl peroxides are reduced by zinc and acetic acid to the alcohols.

$$R—O—O—R + Zn + 2\,CH_3COOH \longrightarrow 2\,ROH + Zn(OCOCH_3)_2$$

t-Butyl hydroperoxide, like hydrogen peroxide (p. 740), converts olefins into glycols in the presence of osmium tetroxide, vanadium pentoxide, or chromium trioxide.

$$RCH{=}CHR + (CH_3)_3COOH + H_2O \xrightarrow{\text{OsO}_4} RCHOHCHOHR + (CH_3)_3COH$$

Acyl Hydroperoxides (Peroxy Acids or Per Acids), Acyl Peroxides, and Acyl Alkyl Peroxides (Peroxy Esters or Per Esters)

Solutions of **acyl hydroperoxides** can be obtained by allowing aliphatic acids to react with 30 to 90 per cent hydrogen peroxide solutions in the presence of sulfuric acid.

$$CH_3COOH + H_2O_2 \underset{\xleftarrow{\hspace{1cm}}}{\overset{H_2SO_4}{\xrightarrow{\hspace{1cm}}}} \overset{\overset{\textstyle O}{\|}}{CH_3C}—O—OH + H_2O$$

Peroxyacetic acid
(peracetic acid)

This reaction is reversible and peroxy acids slowly hydrolyze in aqueous solution to the carboxylic acid and hydrogen peroxide. Peroxyacetic acid is made commercially also by the autoxidation of acetaldehyde (p. 159). The sodium salts result when acid anhydrides react with an excess of aqueous alkaline solutions of hydrogen peroxide.

$$(CH_3CO)_2O + Na_2O_2 \longrightarrow CH_3\overset{\overset{\displaystyle O}{\|}}{C}-O-ONa + CH_3COONa$$

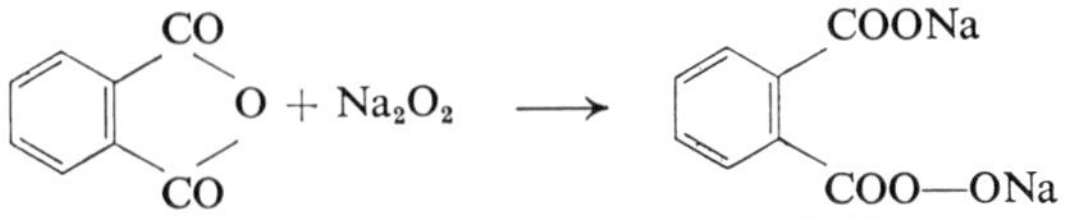

Sodium
monoperoxyphthalate

Acidification and extraction with an organic solvent gives a solution of the peroxy acid. Peroxy acids can be prepared also from acyl peroxides (p. 877).

The most important reaction of the peroxy acids is the formation of epoxides from unsaturated compounds (*epoxidation*, pp. 153, 551, 744).

$$RCH{=}CHR + RCOO_2H \longrightarrow RCH\overset{\diagdown\diagup}{\underset{O}{\quad}}CHR + RCOOH$$

In the presence of a strong acid, the monoacylated glycol is formed.

$$RCH\underset{O}{\diagdown\diagup} + RCOOH \xrightarrow{[H^+]} RCH\underset{OCOR}{\overset{|}{C}}HOHR$$

Another important reaction is the conversion of ketones into esters. In general the smaller group of the ketone remains attached to the carbonyl group.

$$RCOR' + R''COO_2H \longrightarrow RCOOR' + R''COOH$$

α,β-Unsaturated ketones give vinyl esters (enol esters).

$$C_6H_5CH{=}CHCOCH_3 + RCOO_2H \longrightarrow C_6H_5CH{=}CHOCOCH_3 + RCOOH$$

Cyclic ketones yield lactones, and 1,2-diketones in nonhydroxylic solvents give anhydrides.

$$RCOCOR + R'COO_2H \longrightarrow (RCO)_2O + R'COOH$$

Peroxy acids also oxidize sulfides to sulfoxides and sulfones, tertiary amines to amine oxides, aromatic iodides to iodoso and iodoxy compounds, and aromatic amines to nitro compounds (p. 481). **Peroxytrifluoroacetic acid** gives especially good yields in these reactions. Thermal decomposition of the peroxy acids resembles that of *t*-butyl hydroperoxide in that oxygen is one of the products.

$$2\,R\overset{\overset{\displaystyle O}{\|}}{C}-O-OH \xrightarrow{\text{Heat}} 2\,RCOOH + O_2$$

Acyl peroxides are obtained by the reaction of an excess of acid anhydride or acyl chloride with alkaline solutions of hydrogen peroxide.

$$2\,(CH_3CO)_2O + Na_2O_2 \longrightarrow CH_3\overset{\displaystyle O}{\overset{\|}{C}}-O-O-\overset{\displaystyle O}{\overset{\|}{C}}CH_3 + 2\,NaOCOCH_3$$
$$\text{Acetyl peroxide}$$

$$2\,C_6H_5COCl + Na_2O_2 \longrightarrow C_6H_5\overset{\displaystyle O}{\overset{\|}{C}}-O-O-\overset{\displaystyle O}{\overset{\|}{C}}C_6H_5 + 2\,NaCl$$
$$\text{Benzoyl peroxide}$$

Violent explosions of acetyl peroxide have been reported and extreme care should be taken when it is prepared or used. Benzoyl peroxide is considerably more stable.

The acyl hydroperoxides and peroxides liberate iodine quantitatively, and hence they can be estimated iodimetrically. The acyl peroxides react with sodium alkoxides to give the sodium salt of the peracid and the alkyl ester

$$C_6H_5\overset{\displaystyle O}{\overset{\|}{C}}-O-O-\overset{\displaystyle O}{\overset{\|}{C}}C_6H_5 \xrightarrow{\text{NaOCH}_3} C_6H_5\overset{\displaystyle O}{\overset{\|}{C}}-O-ONa + CH_3OCOC_6H_5$$

This reaction is the one most frequently used in the laboratory for the preparation of perbenzoic acid, which is liberated from the sodium salt by acidification and extracted with chloroform. The chief use for the acyl peroxides is as catalysts for polymerization reactions and as bleaching agents for flour, oils, fats, and waxes.

The primary-alkyl **peroxy esters** have been prepared by the reaction of the barium salts of hydroperoxides with acyl chlorides. They cannot be prepared by the esterification of peroxy acids with alcohols.

$$2\,RCOCl + Ba(O-OR')_2 \longrightarrow 2\,R\overset{\displaystyle O}{\overset{\|}{C}}-O-OR' + BaCl_2$$

The tertiary-alkyl peroxy esters result from the simultaneous addition of aqueous alkali and acyl chloride to the hydroperoxide.

$$(CH_3)_3C-O-OH + C_6H_5COCl \xrightarrow{\text{NaOH}} (CH_3)_3C-O-O-\overset{\displaystyle O}{\overset{\|}{C}}C_6H_5 + NaCl$$
$$\textit{t}\text{-Butyl peroxybenzoate}$$

Saponification of the peroxy esters yields the acid and the hydroperoxide rather than the peroxy acid and the alcohol.

$$R\overset{\displaystyle O}{\overset{\|}{C}}-O-OR' + NaOH \longrightarrow RCOONa + HO-OR'$$

$$+\,NaOCH_3 \longrightarrow RCOOCH_3 + Na\overset{+\ -}{O}-OR$$

Thus both the method of preparation and the mode of hydrolysis indicate that the peroxy esters are acyl derivatives of hydroperoxides rather than alkyl derivatives of peroxy acids, which is in keeping with the fact that peroxy acids are not acids in the same sense as carboxylic acids but are acyl derivatives of hydrogen peroxide.

Acyl derivatives of tertiary-alkyl hydroperoxides when heated with pyridine rearrange to give the ester of a hemiacetal.

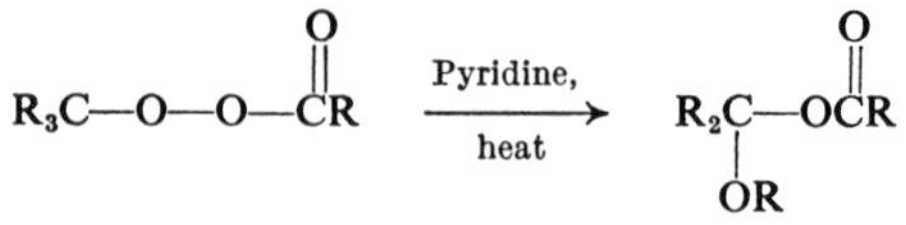

$$R_3C-O-O-\overset{\overset{\textstyle O}{\|}}{C}R \xrightarrow[\text{heat}]{\text{Pyridine,}} R_2\overset{\overset{\textstyle }{|}}{\underset{\underset{\textstyle OR}{|}}{C}}-O\overset{\overset{\textstyle O}{\|}}{C}R$$

α-Hydroxyalkyl Hydroperoxides and Peroxides

Just as certain aldehydes form hydrates and hemiacetals by the addition of water or alcohol to the carbonyl group, so do they form **α-hydroxyalkyl hydroperoxides** and **α-hydroxyalkyl peroxides** by the addition of hydrogen peroxide or alkyl hydroperoxides. The peroxide addition compounds are considerably more stable than most of the hydrates and hemiacetals of aldehydes. Thus when one mole each of an aldehyde and hydrogen peroxide are mixed in ether solution, the hydroxyalkyl hydroperoxide is formed.

$$RCHO + H_2O_2 \longrightarrow R\underset{\underset{\textstyle OH}{|}}{C}H-O-OH$$

These compounds are not explosive but decompose on heating in aqueous solution to give the hydroxyalkyl peroxide.

$$2\,R\underset{\underset{\textstyle OH}{|}}{C}H-O-OH \xrightarrow[\text{H}_2\text{O}]{\text{Heat in}} R\underset{\underset{\textstyle OH}{|}}{C}H-O-O-\underset{\underset{\textstyle OH}{|}}{C}HR + H_2O_2$$

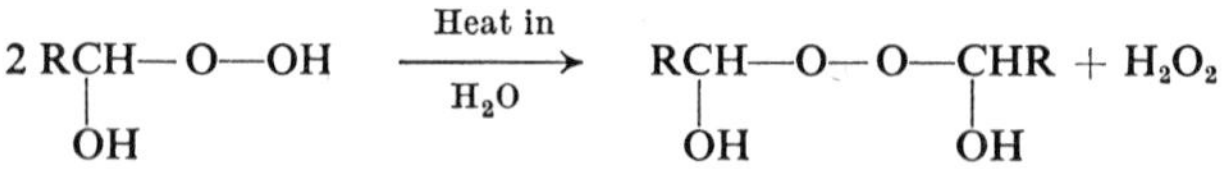

The same compound is formed when the hydroperoxide reacts with a second mole of aldehyde.

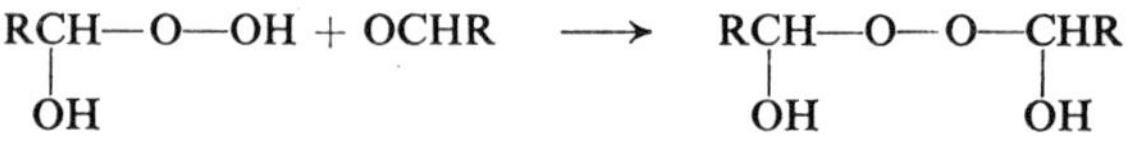

$$R\underset{\underset{\textstyle OH}{|}}{C}H-O-OH + OCHR \longrightarrow R\underset{\underset{\textstyle OH}{|}}{C}H-O-O-\underset{\underset{\textstyle OH}{|}}{C}HR$$

When the hydroxyalkyl hydroperoxide is heated alone or with acetic acid, or when an ether solution is treated with phosphorus pentoxide, the acid is formed.

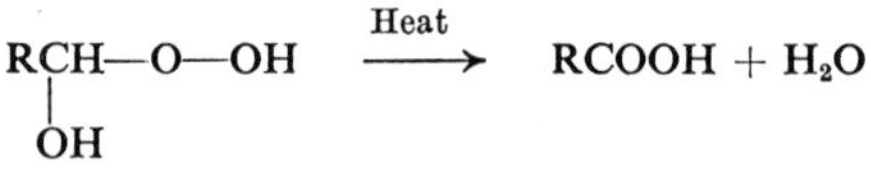

$$R\underset{\underset{\textstyle OH}{|}}{C}H-O-OH \xrightarrow{\text{Heat}} RCOOH + H_2O$$

Reducing agents such as hydrogen iodide do not react quantitatively, presumably because of this decomposition to the acid.

Of the hydroxyalkyl peroxides, hydroxymethyl peroxide is the best known. It is one of the products formed when a mixture of ether vapor and air is exposed to a hot metal surface, and was identified as an individual compound in 1881. It is obtained readily from hydrogen peroxide and an excess of formaldehyde.

$$2\,HCHO + H_2O_2 \longrightarrow HOCH_2-O-O-CH_2OH$$
Hydroxymethyl peroxide

It is highly explosive and oxidizes hydrogen iodide. It is decomposed by aqueous alkali into two moles of formic acid and one of hydrogen.

$$HOCH_2\!-\!O\!-\!O\!-\!CH_2OH + 2\,NaOH \longrightarrow 2\,HCOONa + H_2 + 2\,H_2O$$

This reaction and the previous one between formaldehyde and hydrogen peroxide form the basis of a method for the quantitative estimation of formaldehyde. Alkaline hydrogen peroxide is added to the sample, and the volume of hydrogen evolved is measured.

The homologous hydroxyalkyl peroxides are prepared easily from the higher aldehydes or ketones and hydrogen peroxide, and some have been isolated as decomposition products of ozonides. They are less explosive than hydroxymethyl peroxide, and decomposition in aqueous solution even in the presence of alkali does not give hydrogen but one molecule of aldehyde, one of carboxylic acid, and one of water, or two molecules of aldehyde and one of hydrogen peroxide.

$$
\begin{array}{ll}
\text{RCH}\!-\!\text{O}\!-\!\text{O}\!-\!\text{CHR} & \nearrow \text{RCHO} + \text{HOOCR} + H_2O \\
\;\;|\qquad\qquad\;\; | \\
\;\;\text{OH}\qquad\quad\text{OH} & \searrow 2\,\text{RCHO} + H_2O_2
\end{array}
$$

When molecular amounts of alkyl hydroperoxide and an aldehyde are allowed to stand in ether solution, the **hydroxyalkyl alkyl peroxide** is formed.

$$
\text{RCHO} + \text{HOOR}' \longrightarrow \underset{\underset{\text{OH}}{|}}{\text{RCH}}\!-\!\text{O}\!-\!\text{OR}'
$$

The addition products of hydrogen peroxide with ketones are used as poly-merization catalysts. The product from methyl ethyl ketone is sold under the name "methyl ethyl ketone peroxide."

Ozonides

The simplest formula for ozone would be that in which the oxygen atoms form a three-membered ring, each of the oxygen atoms being divalent. If this formula were correct, the infrared absorption spectrum should resemble that of cyclopropane, but instead the spectrum resembles that of nitrosyl chloride in which the atoms occupy the corners of an open triangle. The bond angle is calculated to be 125 degrees. Electron diffraction measurements indicate an angle of 127 degrees $\pm$ 3 degrees. Hence the molecule must be a resonance hybrid of the structures that contain two oxygen atoms linked by a double bond and the third by a coordinate covalency.

$$
\left\{
\begin{array}{ccc}
\overset{\cdot\cdot}{\text{O}}\bar{} & & \overset{\cdot\cdot}{\text{O}} : \\
\diagup\;\overset{\cdot\cdot}{} & & \diagup\!\!\diagup \\
:\text{O}^+ & \longleftrightarrow & :\text{O}^+ \\
\diagdown\!\!\diagdown & & \diagdown\;\overset{\cdot\cdot}{} \\
\text{O} : & & \overset{\cdot\cdot}{\text{O}}\bar{} \\
\cdot\cdot & & \cdot\cdot
\end{array}
\right\}
$$

When ozone adds to a double bond, the initial product probably contains a four-membered ring which rearranges to a five-membered ring with scission of the carbon-carbon bond. The initial product is called the *molozonide*, and the rearranged product the *ozonide*.

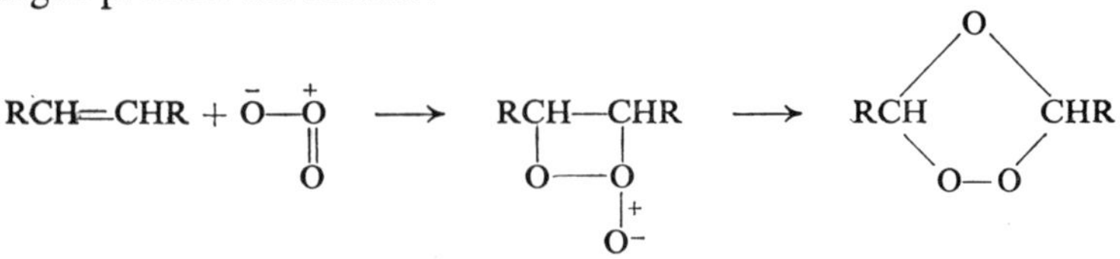

$$\text{RCH=CHR} + \bar{O}\text{—}\overset{+}{O} \longrightarrow \text{RCH—CHR} \longrightarrow \text{RCH} \quad \text{CHR}$$

Molozonide   Ozonide

Probably the best proof of this structure for the ozonide is the synthesis of butylene ozonide by the action of phosphorus pentoxide on hydroxyethyl peroxide.

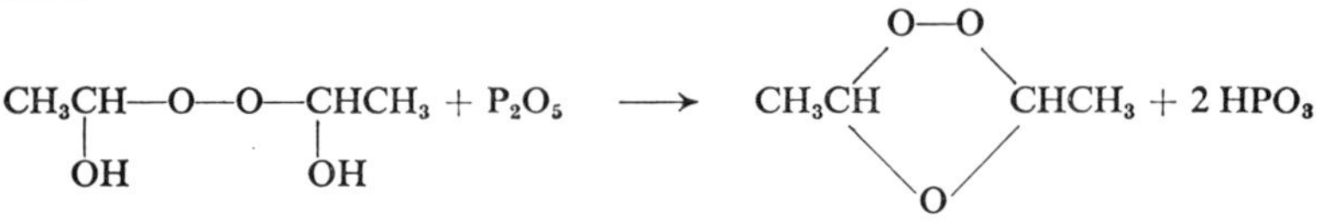

$$\underset{\text{OH}}{\text{CH}_3\text{CH}}\text{—O—O—}\underset{\text{OH}}{\text{CHCH}_3} + \text{P}_2\text{O}_5 \longrightarrow \text{CH}_3\text{CH} \quad \text{CHCH}_3 + 2\,\text{HPO}_3$$

Hydrolysis of the ozonide presumably gives the hydroxyalkyl peroxide as the initial product.

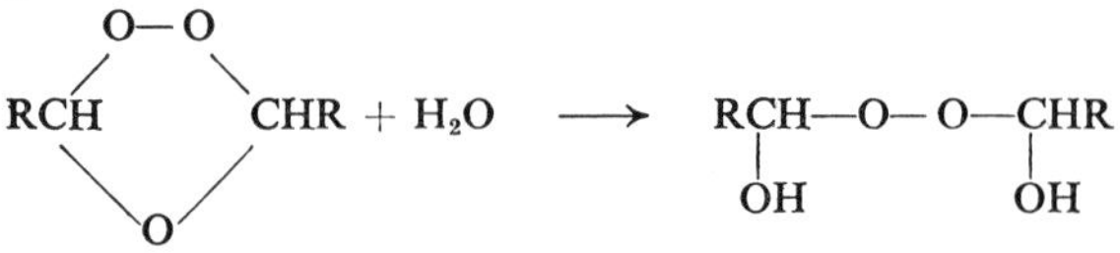

$$\text{RCH} \quad \text{CHR} + \text{H}_2\text{O} \longrightarrow \underset{\text{OH}}{\text{RCH}}\text{—O—O—}\underset{\text{OH}}{\text{CHR}}$$

The hydroxy peroxide decomposes into one mole of acid and one mole of carbonyl compound, or two moles of carbonyl compound and one of hydrogen peroxide (pp. 879, 56). Compounds having structures other than that of the ozonides may be produced on ozonation. 9,10-Octalin, for example, gives a dialkylidene peroxide, and α-phenyl-β-ethylindenone gives a keto anhydride.

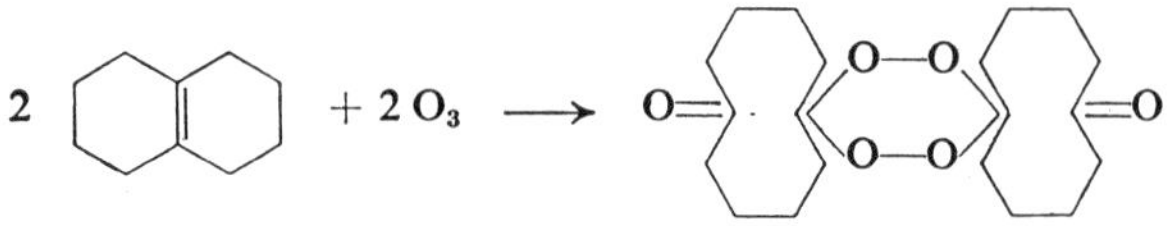

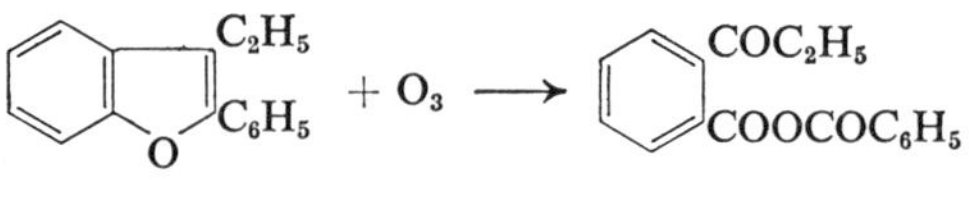

The ozonides of low molecular weight are very unstable. It is reported that a sample of ethylene ozonide exploded when poured from one test tube to another.

Besides the monomeric ozonides, polymeric ozonides also are formed which probably have the structure (—O—OCHR—OCHR—)$_x$. Hydrolysis yields the same products as the monomeric ozonides. Excessive ozonation leads to the formation of products called *oxozonides* which have a higher oxygen content.

AUTOXIDATION

Autoxidation may be defined as the spontaneous reaction of a compound with molecular oxygen at room temperature. The limiting conditions imposed by the terms *spontaneous* and *room temperature* are artificial, since most autoxidations are accelerated by light or by traces of catalysts, or decelerated by antioxidants (substances that inhibit autoxidation), and many oxidations by oxygen at elevated temperatures are no different from those occurring at room temperature.

The reaction of organic compounds with molecular oxygen of the air is more common than generally is recognized. The initial products are peroxides, which can be detected easily in liquids by shaking with a globule of clean mercury. In the presence of peroxides the surface of the mercury is tarnished. If a considerable amount of peroxide is present, the mixture becomes black because of the formation of mercurous oxide. If this test is applied to various solvents that have been exposed to air over a period of time, many of them will be found to contain peroxides. For example among a group of technical solvents taken from the laboratory shelf, cyclohexane, methylcyclohexane, benzene, toluene, chloroform, ethyl ether, isopropyl ether, and dioxane gave a positive test for peroxides. Significantly, carbon tetrachloride and the alcohols gave negative tests (cf. p. 887).

Hydrocarbons

Autoxidation in general probably does not differ from the reaction for the preparation of *t*-alkyl hydroperoxides at elevated temperatures (p. 874) and may be represented by the following equation.

$$RH + O_2 \longrightarrow R{-}O{-}OH$$

The rate of the reaction varies with the nature of R. Tertiary hydrogen is oxidized more easily than secondary hydrogen, and secondary more easily than primary (p. 874). The controlled oxidations of saturated hydrocarbons such as methane, the propanes and butanes, and higher hydrocarbons (p. 220) undoubtedly proceed by way of the peroxide.

The presence of a double bond greatly increases the reactivity of hydrogen on adjacent carbon atoms. Thus cyclohexene reacts with oxygen in the presence of ultraviolet light to give 2-cyclohexenyl hydroperoxide.

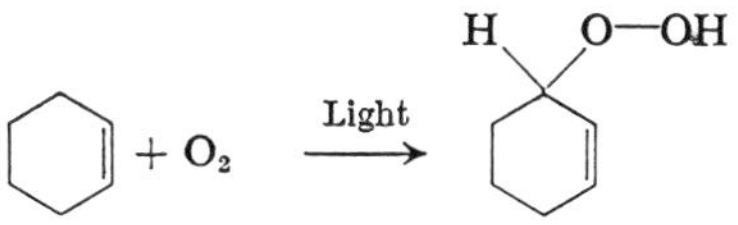

In this reaction the double bond is not attacked. Similarly tetralin reacts in the position α to the aromatic ring.

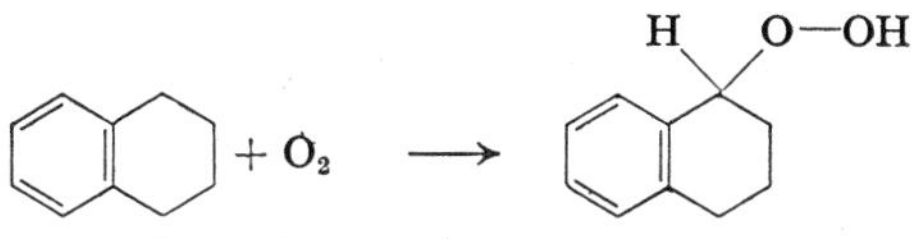

Oxidation takes place fairly rapidly at 75° in the absence of added catalysts, but in the presence of catalysts it is detectable at room temperature. In most of these oxidations further reaction occurs to give more stable oxidation products.

Thus α-tetralone can be prepared conveniently by passing air into tetralin at its boiling point, the initially formed hydroperoxide undergoing decomposition.

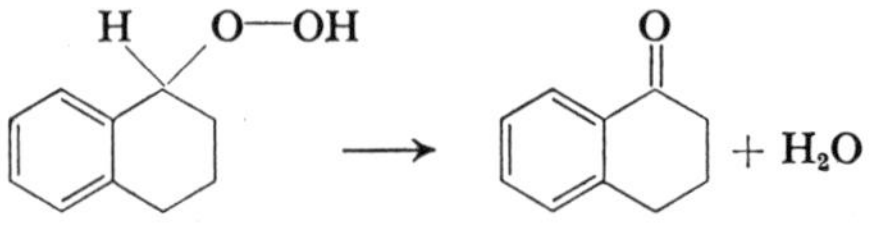

α-Tetralone

It is doubtful whether the autoxidation of tetralin takes place in the absence of catalysts. The absorption of oxygen by purified tetralin is very slow at first but eventually becomes rapid; that is, the reaction is autocatalytic. If substances that produce free radicals are added, such as benzoyl peroxide or lead tetraacetate, oxygen is absorbed rapidly at once.

$$(C_6H_5CO)_2O_2 \longrightarrow 2\,[C_6H_5COO \cdot] \longrightarrow 2\,[C_6H_5 \cdot] + CO_2$$

$$RH + [C_6H_5 \cdot] \longrightarrow [R \cdot] + C_6H_6$$

$$[R \cdot] + O_2 \longrightarrow [R{-}O{-}O \cdot] \Big\} \text{ Chain reaction}$$
$$[R{-}O{-}O \cdot] + RH \longrightarrow [R \cdot] + ROOH$$

Hence it seems likely that even the initial slow reaction in the absence of added catalysts is caused by the presence of free radicals in low concentration and that the decomposition of the hydroperoxide that is formed provides more free radicals which cause an acceleration of the reaction.

The increased ease of oxidation of olefins and of tetralin over saturated hydrocarbons is believed to result from the stabilization of the intermediate free radical by resonance.

$$RCH{=}CHCH_2R \longrightarrow \{RCH{=}CHCHR \longleftrightarrow RCHCH{=}CHR\}$$

Direct evidence in favor of this postulation is the isolation of two products from the autoxidation of 1,2-dimethylcyclohexene.

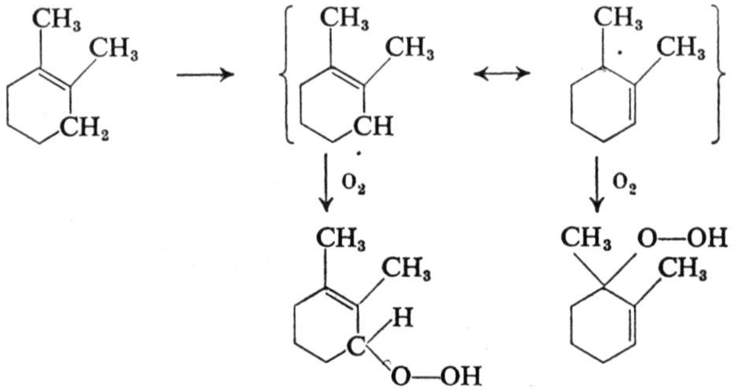

Autoxidation of conjugated polyenes takes place by 1,4 addition to give polymeric peroxides.

$$x\,RCH{=}CHCH{=}CHR + x\,O_2 \longrightarrow (-CH{-}CH{=}CHCH{-}O{-}O{-})_x$$
$$ R R$$

This type of reaction takes place even though methylene groups are α to the conjugated system as in methyl sorbate, $CH_3CH{=}CHCH{=}CHCOOCH_3$, methyl eleostearate, $CH_3(CH_2)_3CH{=}CHCH{=}CHCH{=}CH(CH_2)_7COOCH_3$, and 1,3-cyclohexadiene.

The drying oils containing linoleic and linolenic acid also are noted for their ease of oxidation by air. The structure —CH=CHCH₂CH=CH—, having a methylene group α to two double bonds, is especially susceptible to autoxidation, the initial product being a hydroperoxide.

$$RCH{=}CHCH_2CH{=}CHR + O_2 \longrightarrow RCH{=}CHCHCH{=}CHR$$
$$\underset{O-OH}{|}$$

Here the intermediate free radical is stabilized even more strongly by resonance than in the case of olefins with a single bond, because the resonance involves five carbon atoms.

$$\left[RCH{=}CHCHCH{=}CHR \longleftrightarrow RCH{=}CHCH{=}CHCHR \longleftrightarrow RCHCH{=}CHCH{=}CHR \right]$$

If the R groups are different as with linoleic acid, three different hydroperoxides can be formed. Moreover, the hydroperoxides derived from the second and third of the above structures contain two conjugated double bonds which can form polymeric peroxides. The intermediate free radicals also can undergo carbon-carbon condensation. It is these polymerization reactions that lead to the solidification or drying of the oil.

Ascaridole, which occurs naturally in chenopodium oil (p. 854), is a trans-annular monomeric peroxide. It has been synthesized by the oxidation of α-terpinene with air in the presence of light and chlorophyll. When heated, it is converted to the dioxide.

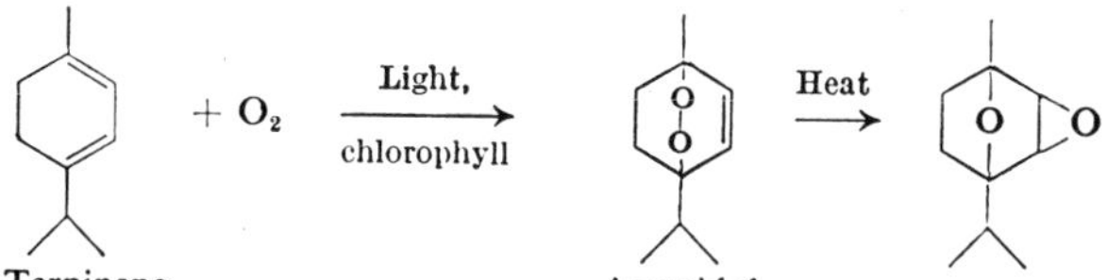

α-Terpinene   Ascaridole

5,6,11,12-Tetraphenylnaphthacene, called **rubrene** because of its ruby color, forms a colorless transannular peroxide on exposure to oxygen in the presence of light. The reaction is reversible, oxygen being given up on heating.

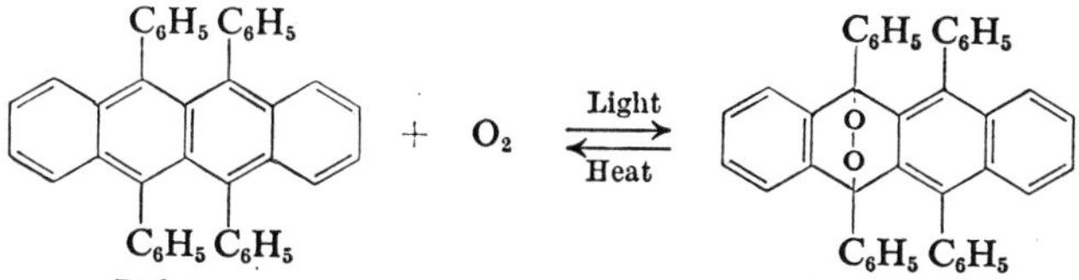

Rubrene   Rubrene peroxide

The ready loss of molecular oxygen on heating may be ascribed to the fact that rubrene possesses a more highly conjugated system of double bonds than the peroxide, whereas other possible oxidation products could be formed only by decreasing the amount of conjugation.

Still another type of reaction takes place when hydrocarbons that dissociate in solution into free radicals (p. 567) are exposed to air. Here a linear peroxide is formed which, when heated, dissociates into alkoxy radicals.

$$(C_6H_5)_3CC(C_6H_5)_3 \rightleftarrows 2[(C_6H_5)_3C\cdot] \xrightarrow{O_2} (C_6H_5)_3C{-}O{-}O{-}C(C_6H_5)_3 \xrightarrow{Heat} 2[C_6H_5)_3CO\cdot]$$

Hexaphenyl-   Triphenyl-   Triphenylmethylperoxide
ethane   methyl

Ethers

The easy autoxidation of ethers is manifested strikingly by the frequency with which violent explosions have been reported when residues from the distillation of ether have become heated above the boiling point of the ether or rubbed with a sharp glass rod. One instance has been reported in which a partially filled can of isopropyl ether detonated on being jarred. Explosions have been reported also during the distillation of dioxane, ethyl acetal, and tetrahydrofuran. Moreover, peroxides in solvents may cause undesirable reactions with the material in solution. Hence compounds of this type should be tested for peroxides before use, preferably with a solution of titanium sulfate in 50 per cent sulfuric acid. The formation of a yellow or orange color indicates the presence of peroxides. The peroxides may be removed by shaking with a variety of reducing agents, such as zinc-copper couple or ferrous sulfate in 50 per cent sulfuric acid, or by adsorption on a column of activated alumina. The purified solvents should be stored in filled dark bottles to exclude air and light, preferably over sodium ribbon. Addition of 1 p.p.m. of hydroquinone or diphenylamine, or 0.05 p.p.m. of sodium diethyldithiocarbamate (p. 325) as antioxidant has been recommended.

Numerous proposals have been made concerning the nature of the peroxides formed from ethyl ether. It seems likely that the initial product is the hydroperoxide.

$$CH_3CH_2OCH_2CH_3 + O_2 \longrightarrow CH_3\underset{\underset{O-OH}{|}}{C}HOCH_2CH_3$$

All investigators have noted the presence of hydrogen peroxide as an autoxidation product, and ethyl vinyl ether has been postulated as another of the oxidation products. These substances conceivably could arise from the hydroperoxide.

$$CH_3\underset{\underset{O-OH}{|}}{C}HOCH_2CH_3 \longrightarrow CH_2{=}CHOCH_2CH_3 + H_2O_2$$

α-Hydroxyethyl peroxide also has been reported as an oxidation product of ether. Presumably it arises by a series of reactions.

$$CH_3\underset{\underset{O-OH}{|}}{C}HOCH_2CH_3 + H_2O \longrightarrow CH_3\underset{\underset{O-OH}{|}}{C}HOH + C_2H_5OH$$

$$CH_3\underset{\underset{O-OH}{|}}{C}HOH \;\rightleftarrows\; CH_3CHO + H_2O_2$$

$$CH_3\underset{\underset{OH}{|}}{C}H-O-OH + OCHCH_3 \longrightarrow CH_3\underset{\underset{OH}{|}}{C}H-O-O-\underset{\underset{OH}{|}}{C}HCH_3$$

However neither hydrogen peroxide, the hydroperoxides, nor the hydroxyalkyl peroxides are as violently explosive as the peroxidic residues from oxidized ether. Only the dimolecular alkylidene peroxides are as explosive, and it has been postulated that such compounds may be formed from the hydroperoxides.

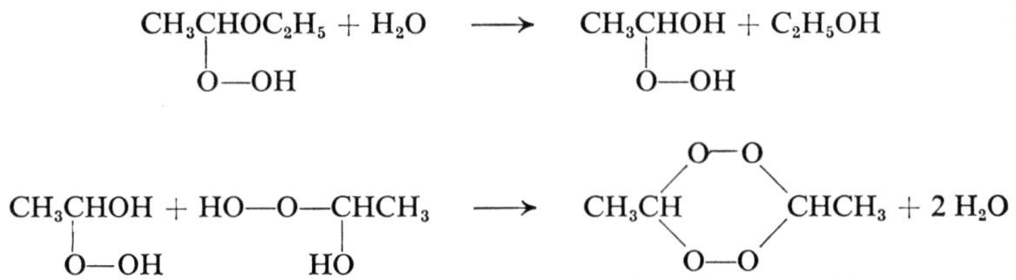

$$CH_3\underset{\underset{O-OH}{|}}{C}HOC_2H_5 + H_2O \longrightarrow CH_3\underset{\underset{O-OH}{|}}{C}HOH + C_2H_5OH$$

$$CH_3\underset{\underset{O-OH}{|}}{C}HOH + HO-O-\underset{\underset{HO}{|}}{C}HCH_3 \longrightarrow CH_3CH\underset{O-O}{\overset{O-O}{\diagdown\diagup}}CHCH_3 + 2\,H_2O$$

Diethylidene peroxide

Both dimeric and trimeric acetone peroxides, along with several other substances, have been isolated from the autoxidation products of isopropyl ether.

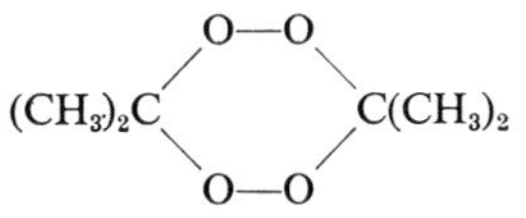

$$(CH_3)_2C\underset{O-O}{\overset{O-O}{\diagdown\diagup}}C(CH_3)_2$$

Diisopropylidene
peroxide

$$(CH_3)_2C\ \begin{matrix} O-C(CH_3)_2 \\ O \qquad\qquad O \\ | \qquad\qquad | \\ O \qquad\qquad O \\ O-C(CH_3)_2 \end{matrix}$$

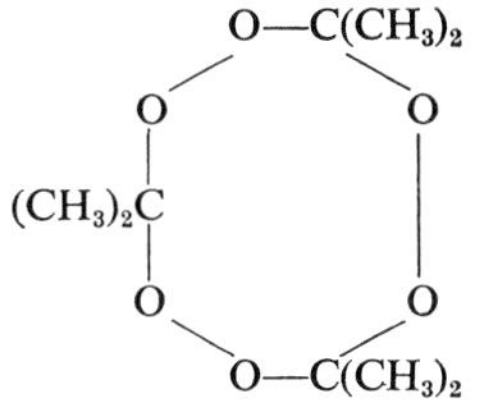

Triisopropylidene
peroxide

The latter product had been made previously by the action of hydrogen peroxide on acetone. The dimeric product, although present in smaller amount, is more explosive and more sensitive to shock than the trimeric form.

Aldehydes

The ease of oxidation of aldehydes by air has been recognized for a long time. Liebig and Woehler showed in 1832 that the conversion of benzaldehyde to benzoic acid by air is accelerated by light, and since then the autoxidation of benzaldehyde and other aldehydes has been studied by many workers. Peroxybenzoic acid can be isolated from the oxidation mixture and has been postulated to be the first stable product of the reaction. It reacts with more benzaldehyde to give benzoic acid.

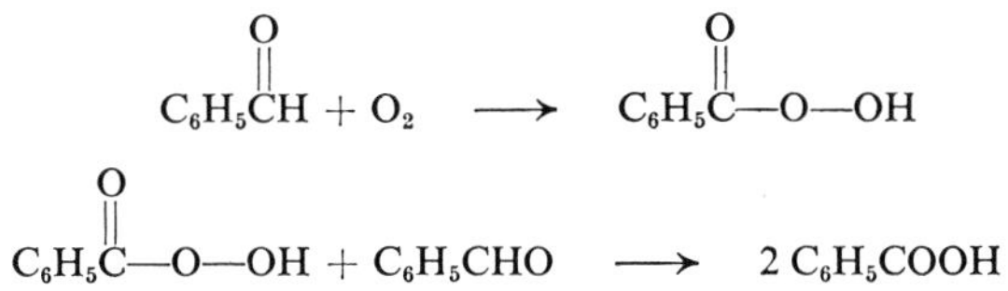

$$C_6H_5\overset{\overset{O}{\|}}{C}H + O_2 \longrightarrow C_6H_5\overset{\overset{O}{\|}}{C}-O-OH$$

$$C_6H_5\overset{\overset{O}{\|}}{C}-O-OH + C_6H_5CHO \longrightarrow 2\,C_6H_5COOH$$

It is believed that the formation of the peroxybenzoic acid results from a chain reaction which is initiated by light or by adventitious free radicals.

$$C_6H_5CHO + [\cdot R] \longrightarrow [C_6H_5\underset{.}{C}O] + RH$$

The activation by light is a more complicated process but may be represented by the over-all reaction

$$C_6H_5CHO + O_2 \overset{Light}{\longrightarrow} [C_6H_5\underset{.}{C}O] + [HO-O\cdot]$$

Since the oxygen molecule has two unpaired electrons and therefore is a free radical (p. 570), it seems likely that the above reaction may take place slowly even in the absence of light. These initiating processes are followed by the chain reactions

$$[C_6H_5\overset{\cdot}{C}O] + O_2 \longrightarrow \left[C_6H_5\overset{O}{\underset{\|}{C}}\!-\!O\!-\!O\cdot \right]$$

$$\left[C_6H_5\overset{O}{\underset{\|}{C}}\!-\!O\!-\!O\cdot \right] + C_6H_5CHO \longrightarrow C_6H_5\overset{O}{\underset{\|}{C}}\!-\!O\!-\!OH + [C_6H_5\overset{\cdot}{C}O]$$

The conversion of the peroxybenzoic acid into benzoic acid also may be a chain process.

$$C_6H_5\overset{O}{\underset{\|}{C}}\!-\!O\!-\!OH + [C_6H_5\overset{\cdot}{C}O] \longrightarrow \left[C_6H_5\overset{O}{\underset{\|}{C}}\!-\!O\cdot \right] + C_6H_5\overset{O}{\underset{\|}{C}}\!-\!OH$$

$$\left[C_6H_5\overset{O}{\underset{\|}{C}}\!-\!O\cdot \right] + C_6H_5CHO \longrightarrow C_6H_5\overset{O}{\underset{\|}{C}}\!-\!OH + [C_6H_5\overset{\cdot}{C}O]$$

In addition to being accelerated by light, the autoxidation of benzaldehyde is catalyzed by traces of salts of metals of variable valence such as those of iron, nickel, manganese, chromium, and copper. Moreover the reaction is autocatalytic; that is, the reaction is catalyzed by some product of the reaction. The autocatalysis may be explained by the decomposition of the peroxybenzoic acid, which leads to twice the number of free radicals that are required to produce it.

$$C_6H_5\overset{O}{\underset{\|}{C}}\!-\!O\!-\!OH \longrightarrow \left[C_6H_5\overset{O}{\underset{\|}{C}}\!-\!O\cdot \right] + [\cdot OH]$$

The metallic ions probably catalyze this decomposition by single electron transfer reactions.

$$Fe^{++} + C_6H_5\overset{O}{\underset{\|}{C}}\!-\!O\!-\!OH \longrightarrow Fe^{+++} + \left[C_6H_5\overset{O}{\underset{\|}{C}}\!-\!O\cdot \right] + :OH^-$$

$$Fe^{+++} + :OH^- \longrightarrow Fe^{++} + [\cdot OH]$$

Fenton reagent (hydrogen peroxide and ferrous sulfate, p. 381) oxidizes by a similar mechanism.

$$Fe^{++} + HO\!-\!OH \longrightarrow Fe^{+++} + [\cdot OH] + :OH^-$$

$$Fe^{+++} + :OH^- \longrightarrow Fe^{++} + [\cdot OH]$$

$$RH + [\cdot OH] \longrightarrow [R\cdot] + H_2O$$

$$[R\cdot] + HO\!-\!OH \longrightarrow ROH + [\cdot OH]$$

ANTIOXIDANTS

Many substances when present in small amount inhibit autoxidation and are known as **antioxidants.** These substances have the common property of being easily oxidized. Thus sulfites, iodides, benzyl alcohol, hydroquinone, or diphenylamine decrease autoxidations to a negligible rate in concentrations as low as 0.001 per cent.

Peroxides are important because of their ability to catalyze polymerization and other reactions catalyzed by free radicals, but antioxidants are important because of their ability to inhibit unwanted oxidation or unwanted reactions catalyzed by free radicals. Thus the tocopherols (p. 632) are used to prevent foods from becoming rancid, diphenylamine is used to stabilize cellulose nitrate, phenyl-α-naphthylamine to prolong the life of rubber articles, α-naphthol or di-s-butyl-p-phenylenediamine to prevent gum formation in cracked gasolines, and hydroquinone to prevent the spontaneous polymerization of readily polymerized monomers. Autoxidation of liquids can be inhibited also by the addition of chelating agents which remove metallic ions that act as catalysts. Thus the addition of 0.001 per cent of disalicylidene-1,2-diaminopropane in gasoline deactivates cupric ions and aids in preventing gum formation.

Just as the positive catalysis of autoxidation can be explained by an increase in the concentration of free radicals necessary for the propagation of a chain reaction, the action of antioxidants can be ascribed to a decrease in the concentration of free radicals. Thus a transfer of a hydrogen atom to a free radical gives a stable molecule.

$$[C_6H_5CO\cdot] + RH \longrightarrow C_6H_5CHO + [R\cdot]$$

Since this process also generates a free radical, only those substances act as inhibitors which give rise to short-lived free radicals, that is, free radicals which are converted rapidly into stable molecules thus breaking the chain. Primary and secondary alcohols inhibit autoxidation because the initial free radical formed from them can transfer a second hydrogen atom and give an aldehyde or ketone.

$$[C_6H_5CO\cdot] + RCH_2OH \longrightarrow C_6H_5CHO + [RCHOH\cdot]$$

$$[RCHOH\cdot] + [C_6H_5CO\cdot] \longrightarrow C_6H_5CHO + RCHO$$

Alternatively the process may involve initial removal of a hydrogen atom from the hydroxyl group.

$$[C_6H_5CO\cdot] + RCH_2OH \longrightarrow C_6H_5CHO + [RCH_2O\cdot]$$

$$[RCH_2O\cdot] + [C_6H_5CO\cdot] \longrightarrow C_6H_5CHO + RCHO$$

Peroxybenzoate radicals likewise can be destroyed by conversion into the more stable peroxybenzoic acid. Tertiary alcohols are ineffective because the tertiary carbon atom does not carry a hydrogen atom, and neither the first step of the first process nor the second step of the second process can take place. Substances like hydroquinone and diphenylamine are more effective than alcohols because they are much more easily oxidized to quinone or an indophenol than are alcohols to aldehydes or ketones. Ease of oxidation alone, however, is not sufficient to cause inhibition of autoxidation. Thus the aldehyde formed as a product of the inhibition by a primary alcohol is more readily oxidized under the proper conditions than the alcohol. However aldehydes are not antioxidants because the radical formed cannot be stabilized without the formation of a new radical. If such were not the case, aldehydes would not undergo rapid autoxidation, since they would act as their own antioxidants. Conversely alcohols do not undergo rapid autoxidation because they do act as their own antioxidants. It has been reported, however, that the photochemical air oxidation of isopropyl alcohol can give up to 0.4 mole of peroxide per liter, and an industrial process for the manufacture of acetone and hydrogen peroxide from isopropyl alcohol is based on air oxidation at $500°$ (p. 224). Iodides and sulfites act as anti-oxidants because of their ready oxidation to iodine and to dithionate ion.

$$[C_6H_5CO] + HI \longrightarrow C_6H_5CHO + [I \cdot]$$

$$2[I \cdot] \longrightarrow I_2$$

$$[C_6H_5CO] + [HSO_3^-] \longrightarrow C_6H_5CHO + [\cdot SO_3^-]$$

$$2[\cdot SO_3^-] \longrightarrow [S_2O_6^=]$$

REVIEW QUESTIONS

1. What are organic peroxides? Give the names and structures for the more important types of organic peroxides. Of what use are peroxides?
2. Summarize the various methods for the preparation of epoxides. Why are epoxides important?
3. Discuss the autoxidation of (a) benzaldehyde; (b) olefins.
4. What are antioxidants, how do they act, and what use is made of them?
5. What is the current view concerning the structure of (a) ozone; (b) ozonides?
6. How can the presence of peroxides in ether be detected? Why should they be removed before the ether is used?

PROBLEMS

7. Give equations for the preparation of the following compounds: (a) *n*-butyl peroxide; (b) cumene hydroperoxide; (c) formyl hydroperoxide; (d) 2,2-dimethylvinyl acetate from mesityl oxide; (e) 2-(3-hydroxypropyl)benzoic acid from α-tetralone; (f) 1-hydroxybutyl peroxide from butanal.
8. Give reactions for the preparation of α-tetralone from (a) benzene and (b) naphthalene.
9. From the given volume of hydrogen (S.T.P.) evolved when 1 g. of aqueous formaldehyde was treated with alkaline hydrogen peroxide, calculate the per cent of formaldehyde in the solution: (A) 80 cc.; (B) 55 cc.; (C) 110 cc.; (D) 35 cc.
10. A weighed sample of an unsaturated compound was dissolved in a measured volume of a solution of peroxybenzoic acid in chloroform and the solution was allowed to stand in the dark for twelve hours. The peroxybenzoic acid solution was standardized before use, and the amount of unreacted peroxybenzoic acid determined at the end of the reaction by iodimetric titration. If Y is the weight of sample in grams, X the volume in cubic centimeters of $0.2N$ thiosulfate solution equivalent to the peroxybenzoic acid consumed, and Z the approximate molecular weight of the compound, calculate the equivalent weight of the compound and the number of double bonds present.

	A	B	C	D
X	30.2	45.6	25.8	18.4
Y	0.2476	0.2827	0.1058	0.2502
Z	90	175	80	140

Chapter 41

ORGANOMETALLIC COMPOUNDS

Organometallic compounds are defined as those compounds in which carbon is linked to a metal. The bonds with different metals may have a wide range of polarity from largely covalent to the ion-pair type. Typical organometallic compounds are the Grignard reagents (p. 120) and the metallic acetylides (p. 131). Metallic derivatives in which the anion is a resonance hybrid as is postulated for ethyl sodiomalonate (p. 800) or ethyl sodioacetoacetate (p. 820) usually are not classed with the organometallic compounds. For convenience the organometallic compounds are discussed in groups according to the position of the metal in the periodic table.

GROUP Ia (Li, Na, K, Rb, Cs)

A few **organolithium** compounds can be made in good yields directly from alkyl or aryl halides using ether, benzene, or cyclohexane as a solvent.

$$n\text{-}C_4H_9Cl + 2\,Li \longrightarrow n\text{-}C_4H_9Li + LiCl$$
$$n\text{-Butyllithium}$$

$$C_6H_5Br + 2\,Li \longrightarrow C_6H_5Li + LiBr$$
$$\text{Phenyllithium}$$

$$p\text{-}(CH_3)_2NC_6H_4Br + 2\,Li \longrightarrow p\text{-}(CH_3)_2NC_6H_4Li + LiBr$$
$$p\text{-Dimethylamino-}$$
$$\text{phenyllithium}$$

Both alkyl and aryl halides react readily with metallic sodium to give organosodium compounds if the sodium is highly dispersed (10–30 μ) in a liquid hydrocarbon. Triphenylmethylsodium is formed directly from triphenylmethyl chloride in ether.

$$(C_6H_5)_3CCl + 2\,Na(Hg) \xrightarrow{\text{Ether}} (C_6H_5)_3CNa + NaCl$$

Since 1 to 3 per cent amalgam must be used, it is not convenient to prepare large quantities. The solution may be used to remove oxygen from inert gases, and as a strongly basic catalyst. Even certain vinyl halides, which usually are unreactive, give the alkenyllithium provided the halide is sufficiently pure.

$$\underset{\text{Cl}}{\bigcirc} + 2\,Li \longrightarrow \underset{\text{Li}}{\bigcirc} + LiCl$$

Metal-halogen exchange frequently can be used to advantage in the preparation of lithium compounds.

$$RLi + R'Br \rightleftarrows RBr + R'Li$$

The position of equilibrium depends on the relative electron-attracting power of the R groups. Thus the reaction of *n*-butyllithium with α-bromonaphthalene

889

gives a 95 per cent yield of α-naphthyllithium, whereas phenyllithium and
p-iodotoluene reach equilibrium at 50 per cent conversion.

A general method is available for the preparation of alkyl derivatives of any
of the alkali metals. It consists of heating the metal with an alkylmercury
(p. 893) in a sealed tube.

$$(C_2H_5)_2Hg + 2\ Na \longrightarrow 2\ C_2H_5Na + Hg$$

  Ethylmercury   Ethylsodium

o-Phenylenelithium has been prepared by the reaction of biphenylenemercury
with lithium.

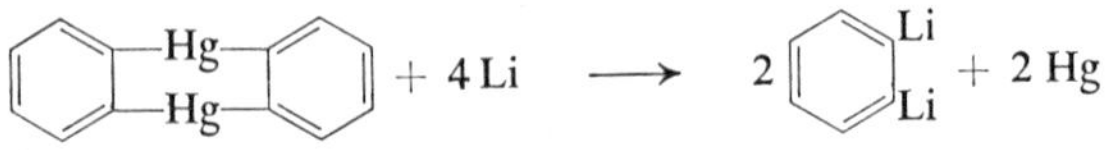

Compounds having sufficiently acidic hydrogen react with the alkali metal
directly.

$$RC{\equiv}CH + Na(molten) \longrightarrow RC{\equiv}CNa + \tfrac{1}{2}\ H_2$$

$$(C_6H_5)_2CH_2 + K \xrightarrow{230°} (C_6H_5)_2CHK + \tfrac{1}{2}\ H_2$$

Cyclopentadiene, indene, and fluorene are sufficiently acidic to react with
sodium amide.

If another compound is more acidic than that from which an organometallic
compound is derived, an ordinary acid-base exchange reaction similar to the
reaction with sodium amide takes place. For example, benzene reacts with
ethylsodium to give ethane and phenylsodium.

$$C_6H_6 + C_2H_5Na \longrightarrow C_6H_5Na + C_2H_6$$

From reactions such as this, hydrocarbons may be listed in the following order
of increasing acidity.

$$C_2H_6 < C_6H_6 < C_6H_5CH_3 < (C_6H_5)_2CH_2 < (C_6H_5)_3CH$$

This exchange reaction has practical value, since it can be used to synthesize
organometallic compounds that may be difficult to synthesize by other methods.
For example, α-picolyllithium is made easily from α-picoline and phenyllithium.

The reactivities of the organometallic compounds also vary in these exchange
reactions, because the more ionic the carbon-metal bond, the stronger in effect
is the substance as a base. Thus RMgX does not react with dibenzofuran, RLi
gives a lithium derivative, and RNa gives a disodium derivative.

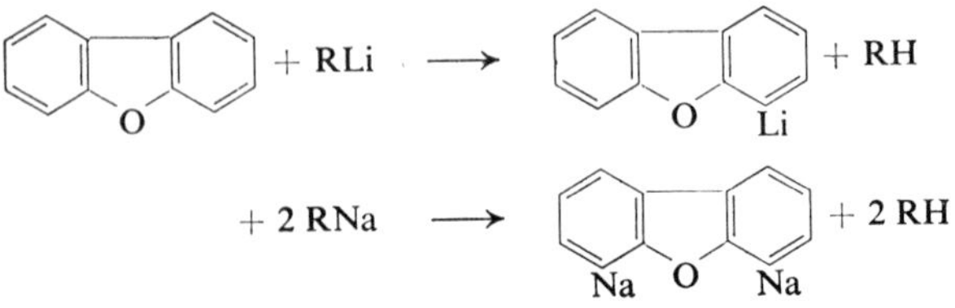

The term *metalation* has been coined for this type of reaction, but it merely is a typical acid-base exchange reaction.

Organosodium compounds are formed also by addition of the metal to conjugated carbon-carbon double bonds in naphthalene (p. 585), anthracene (p. 597), and the phenylsubstituted ethylenes (p. 577). Moreover the polymerization of conjugated dienes by metallic sodium undoubtedly involves the formation of an intermediate organometallic compound (p. 714).

Alkyl- and aryllithiums are sufficiently covalent to be soluble in ether, benzene, and hexane. The extent of homopolarity in some compounds is demonstrated by the isolation of geometrical isomers.

$$
\begin{array}{ccc}
ClC_6H_5 & & Li \\
\diagdown & & \diagup \\
& C{=}C & \\
\diagup & & \diagdown \\
C_6H_5 & & C_6H_5
\end{array}
\qquad\qquad
\begin{array}{ccc}
ClC_6H_5 & & C_6H_5 \\
\diagdown & & \diagup \\
& C{=}C & \\
\diagup & & \diagdown \\
C_6H_5 & & Li
\end{array}
$$

The other alkali metals form colorless nonvolatile derivatives that are insoluble in most organic solvents. With increasing charge on the nucleus the bond to carbon becomes more and more ionic. Thus the molar conductivities in ethylzinc solution of ethyllithium, -sodium, -potassium, and -rubidium are 0.13, 4.01, 6.49, and 9.39. Not only is the basicity of these organometallic compounds in this order, but also their reactivity in the usual Grignard type reactions, the lithium compounds being least reactive.

Of the organoalkali metal compounds, the organolithium compounds are the most useful. For synthetic purposes they supplement the Grignard reagents. Thus they add to sterically hindered carbonyl groups that do not react with Grignard reagents. They also add more readily to nitriles and give better yields of ketones on hydrolysis. Lithium salts of carboxylic acids react to give lithium salts of ketone hydrates which hydrolyze to ketones.

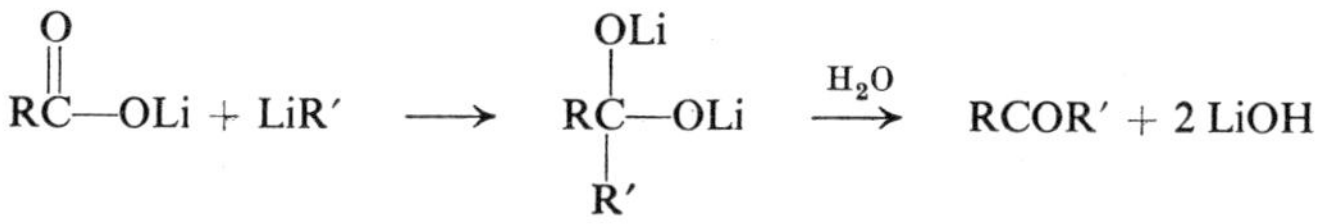

$$
\begin{array}{c}
O \\
\parallel \\
RC{-}OLi + LiR'
\end{array}
\longrightarrow
\begin{array}{c}
OLi \\
\mid \\
RC{-}OLi \\
\mid \\
R'
\end{array}
\xrightarrow{H_2O}
RCOR' + 2\,LiOH
$$

This reaction can be used to synthesize mixed ketones. Moreover, because of it, carbon dioxide reacts with organolithium compounds to give ketones rather than carboxylic acids.

GROUP Ib (Cu, Ag, Au)

Organocopper, -silver, and **-gold** compounds have been made by the reaction of the halides with Grignard reagents.

$$
MX + RMgX \longrightarrow RM + MgX_2
$$

They react normally with organic compounds having the more reactive groups. For example, acyl chlorides yield ketones and phenylisocyanate gives anilides (p. 479). They are relatively unstable and decompose to give the coupled hydrocarbon and the metal.

$$
2\,RM \longrightarrow RR + 2\,M
$$

The coupling action of cupric chloride on Grignard reagents (p. 123) probably proceeds through the organocopper compound.

$$2\,RMgX + CuCl_2 \longrightarrow 2\,MgX_2 + [R_2Cu] \longrightarrow RR + Cu$$

GROUP IIa (Be, Mg, Ca, Sr, Ba, Ra)

Organoberyllium compounds can be prepared from beryllium chloride and Grignard reagents.

$$BeCl_2 \xrightarrow{\ RMgX\ } RBeCl \xrightarrow{\ RMgX\ } R_2Be$$

They resemble the organomagnesium compounds but are less reactive.

Dialkyl compounds of the other alkaline earth metals are made from the metal and an alkylmercury. Reaction of the alkylmetal with the metallic halide gives the alkylmetal halide.

$$R_2Hg + M \longrightarrow R_2M + Hg$$

$$R_2M + MX_2 \longrightarrow 2\,RMX$$

As with compounds of group Ia, the reactivity increases with increasing ionic properties of the bond in the order Be $<$ Mg $<$ Ca $<$ Sr $<$ Ba. The alkyl-calcium compounds resemble the alkylsodium compounds in their properties.

The preparation and reactions of the **alkyl-** and **arylmagnesium halides (Grignard reagents)** are discussed in Chapter 6 and subsequently. The rates of reactions of different Grignard reagents with different types of compounds vary greatly. Thus the time in hours required for complete disappearance of RMgBr in the presence of an excess of benzonitrile under standardized conditions is as follows: R=mesityl, 0.01; p-tolyl, 0.10; phenyl, 0.31; ethyl, 0.85; benzyl, 1.60; n-butyl, 4.57; s-butyl, 11.65; t-butyl, 25.5; phenylethynyl ($C_6H_5C\equiv C$), 77.0. By allowing one mole of a Grignard reagent to react with a mixture of one mole of each of two compounds, and determining the amounts of the products formed, it is possible to determine which compound is the more reactive. By a series of such competitive reactions with phenylmagnesium bromide, the following order of reactivity was obtained.

$$C_6H_5CHO > C_6H_5COCH_3 > C_6H_5NCO > C_6H_5COF > C_6H_5COC_6H_5 > C_6H_5COCl >$$
$$C_6H_5COBr > C_6H_5COOC_2H_5 > C_6H_5CN$$

Although such results are helpful in estimating the relative rate of reaction of a Grignard reagent, they should not be relied on completely, since different series of reactions do not yield wholly concordant results.

Alkylmagnesiums may be made by heating the alkylmercury with magnesium in a sealed tube.

$$R_2Hg + Mg \longrightarrow R_2Mg + Hg$$

They are solids soluble in ether.

In ether solution the alkylmagnesium halides are in equilibrium with alkylmagnesium and magnesium halide.

$$2\,RMgX \rightleftarrows R_2Mg + MgX_2$$

Although the ether complexes of the components of the equilibrium are soluble in ether, the dioxane complex of magnesium halide is not. Hence addition of dioxane precipitates the magnesium halide and shifts the equilibrium giving a solution of alkylmagnesium. Varying amounts of alkylmagnesium halide may be precipitated at the same time, but the solution is substantially free of halogen. The reactions of solutions of alkylmagnesiums are essentially the same as those of alkylmagnesium halides, although there appear to be some minor differences.

GROUP IIb (Zn, Cd, Hg)

The simpler primary and secondary **alkylzincs** and **alkylzinc halides** can be prepared directly from the alkyl halide and a zinc-copper couple.

$$C_2H_5I + Zn(Cu) \longrightarrow C_2H_5ZnI$$

$$2\ C_2H_5ZnI \longrightarrow (C_2H_5)_2Zn + ZnI_2$$

This reaction was discovered by Frankland[1] in 1849 while he was attempting to prepare free ethyl radicals. Higher alkyl halides give largely disproportionation products, and tertiary alkyl halides give olefins and hydrogen. Alkylzincs can be prepared also from the Grignard reagent and zinc halide, or from the alkylmercury and zinc.

$$ZnX_2 \xrightarrow{RMgX} RZnX \xrightarrow{RMgX} R_2Zn$$

$$R_2Hg + Zn \longrightarrow R_2Zn + Hg$$

The alkylzincs react with the same types of compounds as do Grignard reagents, and although methyl- and ethylzinc are spontaneously flammable in air, they were used for syntheses before the discovery of organomagnesium compounds. The alkylzinc halides undergo addition to carbonyl groups less readily than Grignard reagents, and may be used to prepare ketones from acyl chlorides without appreciable formation of tertiary alcohol.

$$RCOCl + R'ZnCl \longrightarrow RCOR' + ZnCl_2$$

In order to carry out a comparable reaction with a Grignard reagent a low temperature ($-60°$ to $-80°$) must be used.

Cadmium compounds are made from Grignard reagents and cadmium chloride. They are still less reactive than the zinc compounds and may be preferable for the preparation of ketones from acyl halides (p. 196).

Among the organometallic compounds, those of **mercury** are next in importance to those of magnesium. They are not so useful in organic syntheses but have considerable use as antiseptics and medicinals. Most of them are highly toxic and special care should be used in handling the volatile alkylmercury compounds.

Aryl- or alkylmercury compounds can be prepared from the halides and sodium amalgam, or from the Grignard reagent and mercuric halide.

$$2\ RX + Na_2Hg \longrightarrow R_2Hg + 2\ NaX$$

$$HgX_2 \xrightarrow{RMgX} RHgX \xrightarrow{RMgX} R_2Hg$$

---

[1] Edward Frankland (1825–1899), successor to Hofmann at the Royal School of Mines (previously the Royal College of Chemistry) at London. He was the originator of the theory of valence as applied to what now are known as covalent compounds, and along with Kolbe and Kekulé was largely responsible for its development.

Ethylmercuric chloride, which is an important fungicide used to prevent sap stain in lumber and to disinfect seeds, is made from mercuric chloride and tetraethyllead.

$$4\ HgCl_2 + Pb(C_2H_5)_4 \longrightarrow 4\ C_2H_5HgCl + PbCl_4$$

Aromatic mercury compounds can be made by the replacement of groups other than halogen. The diazonium group is replaced in the Nesmejanov reaction (p. 495). Sulfinic acid and boric acid groups can be replaced by heating with mercuric chloride.

$$C_6H_5SOOH + HgCl_2 \longrightarrow C_6H_5HgCl + SO_2 + HCl$$

$$C_6H_5B(OH)_2 + HgCl_2 \longrightarrow C_6H_5HgCl + HBO_2 + HCl$$

The preparation of mercury compounds by substitution of hydrogen or addition to a double bond is called *direct mercuration*. Olefins, for example, add mercuric acetate.

$$RCH\!=\!CHR + Hg(OAc)_2 \longrightarrow \underset{\underset{OAc\ \ \ HgOAc}{|\ \ \ \ \ |}}{RCH\!-\!CHR}$$

Since crystallizable solids frequently are obtained from liquid unsaturated compounds, the reaction is used for the isolation and purification of unsaturated compounds such as the unsaturated fat acids. The unsaturated compound is regenerated by heating with hydrochloric acid.

$$\underset{\underset{OAc\ \ \ HgOAc}{|\ \ \ \ \ |}}{RCH\!-\!CHR} + 2\ HCl \longrightarrow RCH\!=\!CHR + HgCl_2 + 2\ HOAc$$

Acetylenes react with mercuric cyanide to give cyanomercuric derivatives.

$$RC\!\equiv\!CH + Hg(CN)_2 \longrightarrow RC\!\equiv\!CHgCN + HCN$$

Readily substituted aromatic compounds react with mercuric acetate in alcohol solution.

$$C_6H_5OH + Hg(OAc)_2 \longrightarrow o\text{- and }p\text{-}HOC_6H_4HgOAc + HOAc$$

The reaction is very mild compared to the usual substitution reactions. Hence compounds like furan which are sensitive to acids and do not give good yields of substitution products on bromination, nitration, or sulfonation because of ring scission and polymerization, can be mercurated readily.

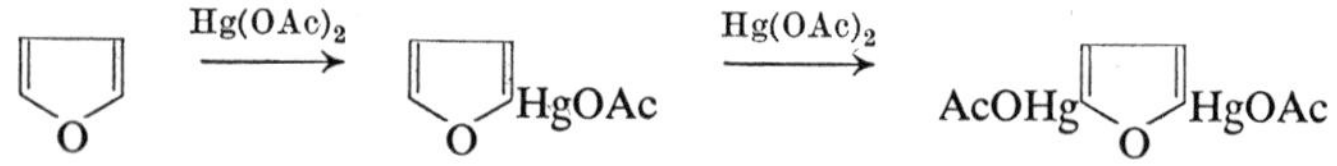

The lower alkylmercury compounds are volatile liquids soluble in organic solvents, indicating that they are covalent compounds. They are the least reactive of any of the organometallic compounds of the first two groups of the periodic table.

The order of reactivity for addition to carbonyl groups of organometallic compounds of the Ia series is Li < Na < K < Rb < Cs, and for the Ib group it is Cu > Ag > Au. Similarly for the IIa group the order is Be < Mg < Ca < Sr < Ba, whereas for the IIb group it is Zn > Cd > Hg. The reversal in the order of reactivity for the *b* series as compared with that of the *a* series is connected with the change in the electronic structures of the atoms. In the *a* series all of the atoms have cores which have electronic structures corresponding to those of the rare gases. Hence there is no interaction of the valence electrons with the core, and the greater the charge on the nucleus, the more nearly ionic is the carbon-metal bond. In the *b* series, however, the cores do not correspond in structure to the rare gases and there is interaction of the valence electrons with the next inner shell of electrons. The heavier the atom the more complex is this interaction and the more nearly covalent does the bond become. Accordingly in those reactions in which the extent of ionic binding governs the order of reactivity, the latter increases with increase in atomic weight for the *a* series but decreases for the *b* series.

Alkylmercury compounds are not hydrolyzed by water but are split by halogen acids or halogens.

$$R_2Hg \xrightarrow{HX} RH + RHgX \xrightarrow{HX} RH + HgX_2$$

$$R_2Hg \xrightarrow{X_2} RX + RHgX \xrightarrow{X_2} RX + HgX_2$$

$$R_2Hg \xrightarrow{(SCN)_2} RSCN + RHgSCN \xrightarrow{(SCN)_2} RSCN + Hg(SCN)_2$$

The last two reactions may be used for the preparation of halogen or thiocyanogen compounds. Thus *o*- and *p*-acetoxymercuriphenol, made by direct mercuration of phenol, react with sodium chloride to give the chloromercuric compounds, which can be separated readily by crystallization. Reaction of either purified compound with one mole of halogen or thiocyanogen gives the halogenated phenol or the hydroxyphenyl thiocyanate. Similarly bromo- and iodofuran can be made from chloromercurifuran.

Several aromatic mercury compounds are used as antiseptics. One of the more widely used is **Mercurochrome** (p. 683), although it has poor penetrating power and is a poor antiseptic. Because of the deep red stain, a potency which it does not possess is attributed to it by the user. Its effectiveness against most organisms is about one-hundredth that of an equal concentration of mercuric chloride. **Metaphen** and **Merthiolate** on the other hand are about ten times more effective than mercuric chloride. None of the mercurials, however, is very effective in killing spores. This deficiency is not surprising, since their high molecular weights and insolubility in fats prevent penetration of cellular tissue.

Mercurochrome　　　　　　　　Metaphen　　　　　　　　Merthiolate

Both Metaphen and Merthiolate are colorless. Hence it was necessary to add a dye to their solutions before the public would accept them.

The alkylmercury compounds are valuable for the synthesis of other organometallic compounds because the mercury can be exchanged for any metal above it in the electromotive series.

$$R_2Hg + 2\,M' \longrightarrow 2\,RM + Hg$$

$$R_2Hg + M'' \longrightarrow R_2M + Hg$$

$$3\,R_2Hg + 2\,M''' \longrightarrow 2\,R_3M + 3\,Hg$$

Alkylmercury compounds react also with the halides of nonmetals.

$$3 R_2Hg + 2 BX_3 \longrightarrow 2 BR_3 + 3 HgX_2$$

$$2 R_2Hg + SiX_4 \longrightarrow SiR_4 + 2 HgX_2$$

GROUP III (B, Al, Ga, In, Tl; Sc, Y, La, Ac)

Boron and **aluminum** compounds can be made from the metal halide and a Grignard reagent or from the metal and an alkylmercury.

$$BF_3 \xrightarrow{\text{RMgX}} RBF_2 \xrightarrow{\text{RMgX}} R_2BF \xrightarrow{\text{RMgX}} R_3B$$

$$3 R_2Hg + 2 Al \longrightarrow 2 R_3Al + 3 Hg$$

Although alkylborons are spontaneously flammable in air, they add only slowly to the carbonyl group. The aryl-boron bond is very stable. Thus the intermediate aryl halogen compounds hydrolyze to the arylboronic and arylborinic acids.

$$C_6H_5BF_2 + 2 H_2O \longrightarrow \underset{\text{Phenylboronic acid}}{C_6H_5B(OH)_2} + 2 HF$$

$$(C_6H_5)_2BF + H_2O \longrightarrow \underset{\text{Diphenylborinic acid}}{(C_6H_5)_2BOH} + HF$$

Phenylboronic acid can be nitrated without cleavage of the carbon-boron bond. The trisubstituted boron compounds lack a pair of electrons in the valence shell of boron and readily form addition complexes with electron-donor molecules such as the amines and ethers.

$$R_3B + :NR_3 \rightleftarrows R_3\overset{-}{B}-\overset{+}{N}R_3$$

The position of equilibrium for the reaction of trimethylboron with trimethylamine, triethylamine and quinuclidine in the gas phase indicates the following order of stability of the complexes.

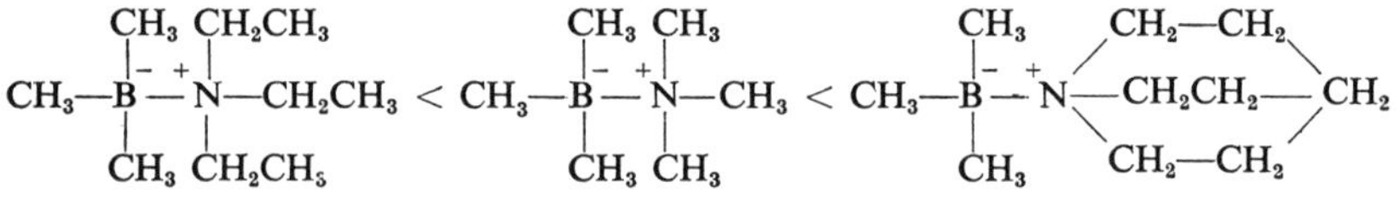

$$\underset{\substack{CH_3 \ CH_2CH_3 \\ | \ | \\ CH_3-B-N-CH_2CH_3 \\ | \ | \\ CH_3 \ CH_2CH_3}}{} < \underset{\substack{CH_3 \ CH_3 \\ | \ | \\ CH_3-B-N-CH_3 \\ | \ | \\ CH_3 \ CH_3}}{} < \underset{\substack{CH_3 \ CH_2-CH_2 \\ | \ / \ \backslash \\ CH_3-B-N-CH_2CH_2-CH_2 \\ | \ \backslash \ / \\ CH_3 \ CH_2-CH_2}}{}$$

Since the electron-donating ability of all three tertiary amines should be almost equal, the relative stability must depend on the amount of steric interference of the groups attached to nitrogen with the methyl groups on boron. Thus steric factors as well as polar factors can influence the basicity of amines. This type of steric interference that leads to the reduced basicity of amines has been called **F strain** (*F* for *front*).

Triphenylboron adds lithiumphenyl in ether solution to give **lithium tetra-phenylboride** (*lithium tetraphenylboron*).

$$(C_6H_5)_3B + C_6H_5Li \longrightarrow (C_6H_5)_4\overset{-}{B}\overset{+}{Li}$$

It is insoluble in hydrocarbons but is soluble in water, and it is not decomposed by boiling water. The sodium salt also is soluble in water but the potassium, rubidium, cesium, ammonium and many amine salts are very insoluble. The **sodium salt,** which is used as a reagent for the quantitative determination of these ions, is made from boron fluoride and an excess of Grignard reagent, followed by decomposition with sodium carbonate.

$$BF_3 + 4\ C_6H_5MgBr \longrightarrow (C_6H_5)_4\overset{-\ +}{B\ \ \ }MgBr + 3\ MgBrF$$

$$(C_6H_5)_4\overset{-\ +}{B\ \ \ }MgBr + Na_2CO_3 \longrightarrow (C_6H_5)_4\overset{-\ +}{B\ \ \ }Na + MgCO_3 + NaBr$$

The alkylaluminums also are spontaneously flammable in air and are hydrolyzed by water. **Trimethylaluminum** can be made readily by the direct reaction of aluminum with methyl iodide.

$$2\ Al + 3\ CH_3I \longrightarrow Al(CH_3)_3 + AlI_3$$

It boils at 130° but is dimeric both in solution and in the vapor phase. Simple valency theory cannot account for this association and special modifications have been proposed. The dimeric compound reacts with electron-donor molecules to give normal products.

$$Al_2(CH_3)_6 + 2\ N(CH_3)_3 \longrightarrow 2\ (CH_3)_3\overset{-\ +}{Al-}N(CH_3)_3$$

$$+ 2\ (C_2H_5)_2O \longrightarrow 2\ (CH_3)_3\overset{-\ +}{Al-}O(C_2H_5)_2$$

Since 1952 a new process for the large-scale preparation of other alkylaluminums has been available, and they have become of technical interest. Isobutylene reacts with hydrogen and clean finely divided aluminum, in the absence of oxygen, at 150° and 200 atmospheres to give **triisobutylaluminum.**

$$6\ (CH_3)_2CH{=}CH_2 + 3\ H_2 + 2\ Al \longrightarrow 2\ Al[CH_2CH(CH_3)_2]_3$$

Triisobutylaluminum undergoes an exchange reaction at 100° with other olefins having a terminal double bond to give other trialkylaluminums.

$$Al(C_4H_9)_3 + 3\ C_2H_4 \longrightarrow Al(C_2H_5)_3 + 3\ C_4H_8$$

$$+ 3\ RCH{=}CH_2 \longrightarrow Al(CH_2CH_2R)_3 + 3\ C_4H_8$$

Triethylaluminum cannot be made directly from ethylene, hydrogen and aluminum because at the temperature required, triethylaluminum adds to ethylene to give a mixture of the higher alkylaluminums.

$$Al(C_2H_5)_3 + 3\ x\ C_2H_4 \longrightarrow Al[CH_2(CH_2)_{2x}CH_3]_3$$

However, a cyclic process can be operated in which triethylaluminum is converted to **diethylaluminum hydride** at 120°, and the latter allowed to react with ethylene at 70°.

$$4\ Al(C_2H_5)_3 + 2\ Al + 3\ H_2 \xrightarrow{120°} 6\ AlH(C_2H_5)_2$$

$$3\ AlH(C_2H_5)_2 + 3\ C_2H_4 \xrightarrow{70°} 3\ Al(C_2H_5)_3$$

The trialkylaluminums are not as generally useful as the alkyllithiums or Grignard reagents because only one alkyl group can be added to a carbonyl group.

$$R_2C{=}O + AlR'_3 \longrightarrow R_2C\underset{\underset{R'}{|}}{-}OAlR'_2$$

However, all three alkyl groups can be oxidized to alkoxyl groups, and hydrolysis of the alkoxides gives alcohols.

$$AlR_3 \xrightarrow{O_2} Al(OR)_3 \xrightarrow{H_2O} Al(OH)_3 + 3\ HOR$$

Bromine gives the primary alkyl bromide.

$$AlR_3 \xrightarrow{Br_2} 3\ RBr + AlBr_3$$

Thus a process is available for converting any olefin with a terminal double bond into a primary alcohol or halide, in contrast to the secondary or tertiary alcohols or halides obtained by the addition of water or halogen acids.

When triisobutylaluminum is heated to 180° it gives **diisobutylaluminum hydride,** a distillable liquid.

$$Al(C_4H_9)_3 \xrightarrow{180°} AlH(C_4H_9)_2 + C_4H_8$$

Diisobutylaluminum hydride can be used instead of lithium aluminum hydride for most reductions.

The complex of one mole of sodium fluoride with two moles of triethyl-aluminum is a liquid with a high electrical conductivity. When it is electrolyzed using a lead anode, pure aluminum deposits at the cathode. The ethyl radicals formed at the anode react with the lead to give **tetraethyllead** which sinks to the bottom of the cell and can be withdrawn.

$$4\ Al(C_2H_5)_3 + 12\ e \longrightarrow 4\ Al + 12\ [C_2H_5\ \overset{..}{:}\ ]$$

$$12\ [C_2H_5\ \overset{..}{:}\ ] + 3\ Pb \longrightarrow 12\ e + 3\ Pb(C_2H_5)_4$$

The addition of ethylene to triethylaluminum at 120° leads to higher trialkyl-aluminums which on hydrolysis give polyethylenes. However, average molecular weights of only about 25,000 are obtained because of the exchange reaction.

$$Al(C_2H_5)_3 + 3\ x\ C_2H_4 \longrightarrow Al[CH_2(CH_2)_{2x}CH_3]_3$$

$$Al[CH_2(CH_2)_{2x}CH_3]_3 + 3\ CH_2{=}CH_2 \longrightarrow Al(C_2H_5)_3 + CH_2{=}CH(CH_2)_{2x-1}CH_3$$

If, however, certain nonreducible metallic halides such as titanium chloride are added, average molecular weights up to 3,000,000 are obtainable. This process has led to the synthesis of commercial polyethylenes and polypropylenes from the olefins at atmospheric pressure (p. 61).

Organogallium compounds resemble the aluminum compounds very closely, although **trimethylgallium** is monomeric. The **indium** and **thallium compounds** do not form complexes with amines or ethers. The etherates of **triethylscandium** and **triethylyttrium** have been described.

GROUP IV (Ge, Sn, Pb; Ti, Zr, Hf, Th)

Alkylgermanium compounds have been prepared by means of the Grignard reaction.

$$GeCl_4 + 4\ RMgX \longrightarrow R_4Ge + 4\ MgX_2$$

They do not add to a carbonyl group but react with acyl chlorides to give ketones.

$$4\ RCOCl + R_4Ge \longrightarrow 4\ RCOR + GeCl_4$$

Hexaphenyldigermane, $(C_6H_5)_3Ge$—$Ge(C_6H_5)_3$, unlike hexaphenylethane (p. 556), does not dissociate into free radicals.

Both divalent and tetravalent **tin** compounds are known and are prepared by the usual procedure.

$$SnCl_2 + 2\,RMgX \longrightarrow R_2Sn + MgX_2$$

$$SnCl_4 \xrightarrow{RMgX} RSnCl_3 \xrightarrow{RMgX} R_2SnCl_2 \xrightarrow{RMgX} R_3SnCl \xrightarrow{RMgX} R_4Sn$$

Dibutyltin dilaurate, prepared from dibutyltin dichloride and sodium laurate, is used as a stabilizer in polyvinyl chloride polymers. The dialkyltin dichlorides can be reduced to dialkyltins.

$$R_2SnX_2 + 2\,Na(Hg) \longrightarrow R_2Sn + 2\,NaX$$

Reaction with sodium in liquid ammonia gives a disodium derivative which, when acidified with ammonium chloride, gives the dialkyldihydrotin.

$$R_2SnCl_2 + 4\,Na(in\,NH_3) \longrightarrow R_2SnNa_2 + 2\,NaCl$$

$$R_2SnNa_2 + 2\,NH_4Cl \longrightarrow R_2SnH_2 + 2\,NH_3 + 2\,NaCl$$

Trialkyltin chlorides react with sodium in liquid ammonia to give hexaalkyl-distannanes.

$$2\,R_3SnCl + 2\,Na(in\,NH_3) \longrightarrow R_3Sn—SnR_3 + 2\,NaCl$$

When lead chloride reacts with the Grignard reagent, the product may be the di- or **tetraalkyl-** or **aryllead,** or the hexaalkyl- or aryldiplumbane, depending on the nature of the hydrocarbon group.

$$PbCl_2 + 2\,RMgX \longrightarrow PbR_2 + 2\,MgX_2$$

$$3\,PbCl_2 + 6\,RMgX \longrightarrow R_3Pb—PbR_3 + Pb + 6\,MgX_2$$

$$2\,PbCl_2 + 4\,RMgX \longrightarrow PbR_4 + Pb + 4\,MgX_2$$

Chlorine reacts with disubstituted or hexasubstituted lead compounds to give the tetravalent chloro derivative, which can react with Grignard reagents to give the tetrasubstituted lead.

$$R_2Pb + Cl_2 \longrightarrow R_2PbCl_2$$

$$(R_3Pb)_2 + Cl_2 \longrightarrow 2\,R_3PbCl$$

$$R_2PbCl_2 + 2\,RMgX \longrightarrow R_4Pb + 2\,MgX_2$$

$$R_3PbCl + RMgX \longrightarrow R_4Pb + MgX_2$$

Tetraethyllead, the most important lead compound (p. 80), is made from ethyl chloride and sodium-lead alloy.

$$4\,C_2H_5Cl + Na_4Pb \longrightarrow (C_2H_5)_4Pb + 4\,NaCl$$

An electrolytic process has been reported (p. 898). Tetraethyllead can be made also by the reaction of lead salts, especially those of organic acids such as lead formate, with reactive organometallic compounds such as triethylaluminum, diethylzinc, or ethylsodium.

$$6\,Pb(OCHO)_2 + 4\,(C_2H_5)_3Al \longrightarrow 3\,Pb(C_2H_5)_4 + 3\,Pb + 4\,Al(OCHO)_3$$

The tetraalkylleads behave much like the alkylmercury compounds. Thus they are stable to hydrolysis but can be cleaved by halogen acid or halogen.

Organometallic compounds of **titanium, zirconium, hafnium,** and **thorium** are practically unknown.

GROUP V (As, Sb, Bi; V, Nb, Ta, Pa)

Arsenic is a borderline element between the metals and the nonmetals. However, the organic derivatives of arsenic differ considerably from those of nitrogen and phosphorus, and it is convenient to consider the organic arsenic compounds here along with those of antimony and bismuth.

The alkyldichloroarsines, dialkylchloroarsines, and trialkylarsines may be prepared by the reaction of arsenic trichloride with an alkylmercury.

$$AsCl_3 \xrightarrow{R_2Hg} RAsCl_2 \xrightarrow{R_2Hg} R_2AsCl \xrightarrow{R_2Hg} R_3As$$

Grignard reagents give the trisubstituted arsines.

$$AsCl_3 + 3\,RMgCl \longrightarrow R_3As + 3\,MgCl_2$$

Reduction of the chloroarsines with amalgamated zinc and hydrochloric acid gives the alkylarsines.

$$RAsCl_2 + 2\,Zn(Hg) + 2\,HCl \longrightarrow RAsH_2 + 2\,ZnCl_2$$

$$R_2AsCl + Zn(Hg) + HCl \longrightarrow R_2AsH + ZnCl_2$$

The arsines are insoluble in water and do not form salts with acids. They react with alkyl iodides to give quaternary salts.

$$R_3As + RI \longrightarrow R_4As^+I^-$$

The more volatile arsines fume in air because of rapid oxidation, and sometimes are spontaneously flammable. The initial oxidation products differ with the type of arsine oxidized.

$$CH_3AsH_2 + O_2 \longrightarrow CH_3As{=}O + H_2O$$
Methylarsine   Methylarsenoxide (arsenosomethane)

$$2\,(CH_3)_2AsH + O_2 \longrightarrow (CH_3)_2As{-}O{-}As(CH_3)_2 + H_2O$$
Dimethylarsine   Dimethylarsenoxide (cacodyl oxide)

$$2\,(CH_3)_3As + O_2 \longrightarrow 2\,(CH_3)_3As^{\pm}O$$
Trimethylarsine   Trimethylarsine oxide

Methylarsenoxide and dimethylarsenoxide are different types of compounds from trimethylarsine oxide in that in the former the oxygen atoms are linked by nonpolar bonds, whereas in the latter the oxygen atom is linked by a semipolar bond (cf. p. 240). The difference is indicated by calling the one type *arsenoxides* and the other *arsine oxides*. The AsO group which formally is analogous to the nitroso group is called the *arsenoso* group, and methylarsenoxide can be called arsenosomethane.

Because of the nauseating odor of the volatile arsenic compounds, Berzelius called them *kakodyls* (Gr. *kakodes*, stinking), the English transliteration being cacodyl. The first of these substances was *Cadet's liquid*, which is chiefly dimethylarsenoxide and was prepared by Cadet in 1760 by heating a mixture of arsenic trioxide and potassium acetate.

$$As_2O_3 + 4\,KOCOCH_3 \longrightarrow (CH_3)_2AsOAs(CH_3)_2 + 2\,K_2CO_3 + 2\,CO_2$$

Bunsen[2] during the years 1837–1843 showed that this liquid could be considered as the oxide of the radical C_2H_6As and that the same radical, which was called *cacodyl*, was present in the products obtained by numerous chemical reactions. Thus cacodyl oxide reacts with hydrochloric acid to give cacodyl chloride, which can be converted to cacodyl cyanide, cacodyl sulfide, and cacodyl disulfide. This work substantiated the earlier work of Gay-Lussac on cyanogen (1815) and of Liebig and Woehler on benzoyl (1832), and helped to establish the fact that a group of atoms can be carried intact through a series of chemical transformations.

In the air oxidation of the primary and secondary arsines, water is formed, and the oxidation may proceed further to give arsonic and arsinic acids.

$$2\ CH_3AsO + 2\ H_2O + O_2 \longrightarrow 2\ CH_3AsO(OH)_2$$
Methylarsonic
acid

$$(CH_3)_2AsOAs(CH_3)_2 + H_2O + O_2 \longrightarrow 2\ (CH_3)_2As(O)OH$$
Dimethylarsinic
acid

The sodium alkylarsonates can be made also by the alkylation of sodium arsenite.

$$Na_3AsO_3 + (CH_3)_2SO_4\ (or\ CH_3Cl) \longrightarrow CH_3AsO(ONa)_2 + NaCH_3SO_4\ (or\ NaCl)$$

Reduction with sulfurous acid gives the arsenoxide.

$$CH_3AsO(ONa)_2 + H_2SO_3 \longrightarrow CH_3AsO + Na_2SO_4 + H_2O$$

Sodium hydroxide converts the arsenoxide to the disodium alkylarsonite, which can be alkylated to the sodium dialkylarsinate.

$$CH_3AsO + 2\ NaOH \longrightarrow H_2O + CH_3As(ONa)_2 \xrightarrow{(CH_3)_2SO_4} (CH_3)_2As(O)ONa$$

Reduction of the sodium dialkylarsinate gives the cacodyl oxide. The oxide reacts with sodium hydroxide to give the sodium dialkylarsinite which can be alkylated to the arsine oxide.

$$2\ (CH_3)_2As(O)ONa \xrightarrow{2\ H_2SO_3} 2\ NaHSO_4 + H_2O + (CH_3)_2AsOAs(CH_3)_2 \xrightarrow{2\ NaOH}$$

$$H_2O + 2\ (CH_3)_2AsONa \xrightarrow{(CH_3)_2SO_4} (CH_3)_3AsO$$

These reduction products can be reduced further to the arsines, or converted to the chloroarsines with hydrochloric acid.

$$CH_3AsO(OH)_2 + 3\ Zn\ (Hg) + 6\ HCl \longrightarrow CH_3AsH_2 + 3\ H_2O + 3\ ZnCl_2$$

$$CH_3AsO + 2\ HCl \longrightarrow CH_3AsCl_2 + H_2O$$

---

[2] Robert Wilhelm Bunsen (1811–1899), professor of chemistry at the University of Heidelberg. He is known popularly for the burner, gas valve, and clamp that bear his name. Except for his early work on cacodyl compounds, most of his contributions dealt with inorganic and physical chemistry. He is noted particularly for his work on spectral analysis which was done in collaboration with the physicist Kirchhoff, and for his explanation of the action of geysers. Among his students were Baeyer, Beilstein, Carius, Curtius, Erlenmeyer, Graebe, Ladenburg, V. Meyer, and Thorpe.

All the arsenic compounds are highly toxic. **Methyl-** and **ethyldichloroarsine** were tried as military gases in World War I but were not so effective as mustard gas. **2-Chlorovinyldichloroarsine** (*primary Lewisite*) is a vesicant that is considerably more toxic than mustard gas but was not prepared on a large scale until the end of World War I. Since no war gas was used extensively in World War II, the effectiveness of Lewisite in combat has not been tested. It is prepared by the reaction of arsenic trichloride and acetylene in the presence of aluminum chloride.

$$HC{\equiv}CH + AsCl_3 \xrightarrow{AlCl_3} ClCH{=}CHAsCl_2, (ClCH{=}CH)_2AsCl, \text{ and } (ClCH{=}CH)_3As$$

| Primary | Secondary | Tertiary |
| Lewisite | Lewisite | Lewisite |

The secondary and tertiary Lewisite which are formed as co-products are less effective and may be converted to the primary Lewisite by reaction with more arsenic trichloride. The development during World War II of BAL as an antidote for arsenic poisoning (p. 752) has decreased the potential effectiveness of Lewisite as a war gas.

Of the *arylarsenic compounds*, the **arsonic acids** are the most important. They can be made by the Bart reaction (p. 495).

$$ArN_2Cl + Na_2HAsO_3 \longrightarrow ArAsO_3HNa + NaCl + N_2$$

Aromatic phenols and amines can be arsonated directly using syrupy arsenic acid.

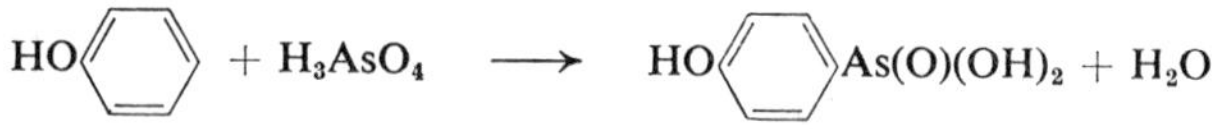

$$HO\text{—}\langle\text{—}\rangle + H_3AsO_4 \longrightarrow HO\text{—}\langle\text{—}\rangle As(O)(OH)_2 + H_2O$$

p-Hydroxyphenyl-
arsonic acid

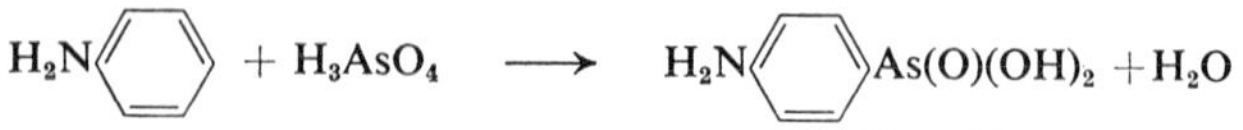

$$H_2N\text{—}\langle\text{—}\rangle + H_3AsO_4 \longrightarrow H_2N\text{—}\langle\text{—}\rangle As(O)(OH)_2 + H_2O$$

Arsanilic acid

Arsenobenzene, the arsenic analog of azobenzene, can be made from phenylarsine and phenylarsenoxide, or by the reduction of phenylarsonic acid with sodium hydrosulfite.

$$C_6H_5AsH_2 + OAsC_6H_5 \longrightarrow C_6H_5As{=}AsC_6H_5 + H_2O$$

$$2\,C_6H_5AsO_3H_2 + 4\,Na_2S_2O_4 + 8\,NaOH \longrightarrow C_6H_5As{=}AsC_6H_5 + 6\,H_2O + 8\,Na_2SO_3$$

Arsenobenzene is less stable than azobenzene. On heating, it decomposes into triphenylarsine and arsenic, and reaction with chlorine, oxygen, or sulfur breaks the arsenic-arsenic bond.

$$3\,C_6H_5As{=}AsC_6H_5 \xrightarrow{Heat} 2\,(C_6H_5)_3As + 4\,As$$

$$C_6H_5As{=}AsC_6H_5 + 2\,Cl_2 \longrightarrow 2\,C_6H_5AsCl_2$$

$$+ O_2 \longrightarrow 2\,C_6H_5AsO$$

The sodium salt of **arsanilic acid** (*p*-aminophenylarsonic acid) was introduced into medicine in 1905 by Thomas, who found it to be more effective than inorganic arsenic compounds for the treatment of sleeping sickness and other diseases caused by trypanosomes. It was called **atoxyl** because it once was thought to be nontoxic, although it now is known to be especially dangerous because of its effect on the optic nerve. A derivative of atoxyl, **tryparsamide,** p-$H_2NCOCH_2NHC_6H_4AsO_3HNa$, is highly trypanocidal and much safer to use. Moreover tryparsamide is particularly valuable in the treatment of late syphilis involving the central nervous system, although it is of no use for early syphilis because it is not highly treponemicidal.

Modern chemotherapy began with the work of Ehrlich.[3] Beginning with the knowledge that certain dyes stain some tissues and not others, he developed azo dyes which were effective in combating trypanosomes in mice. With the publication of the work of Thomas on atoxyl and the discovery in the same year that a member of the Protozoa, *Treponema pallidum*, was the cause of syphilis, Ehrlich prepared and tested arsenic analogs of azo compounds. One of these analogs, called **Salvarsan** or **arsphenamine,** was for many years the most widely used agent for the treatment of syphilis.

Arsphenamine
(Salvarsan)

m-Amino-*p*-
hydroxyphenylarsenoxide
(Mapharsen)

For a short time around 1940 it was replaced by its oxidation product, *m*-**amino-*p*-hydroxyphenylarsenoxide** (*Mapharsen*). Ehrlich had considered the use of the arsenoxide but had rejected it because of its high toxicity. He overlooked, however, the high therapeutic index, that is, the ratio of the maximum tolerated dose to the minimum effective dose. Since the advent of penicillin in 1941, the use of arsenicals for the treatment of syphilis has been discontinued.

The best general method for preparing **antimony** and **bismuth** compounds is from the trichlorides and the Grignard reagent. The Bart reaction can be used for preparing stibonic acids but not for preparing bismuth compounds. Trivalent antimony compounds readily form pentavalent derivatives.

$$R_3Sb + X_2 \longrightarrow R_3SbX_2$$

$$R_3Sb + RX \longrightarrow R_4SbX$$

Trivalent bismuth compounds do not add alkyl halides. Trialkylbismuths are cleaved by halogen, although the triarylbismuths give dihalides.

$$R_3Bi + X_2 \longrightarrow R_2BiX + RX$$

$$Ar_3Bi + X_2 \longrightarrow Ar_3BiX_2$$

Many organic bismuth compounds have been tried as antisyphilitic agents but none has proved so useful as inorganic bismuth preparations, especially those in which the bismuth is present in a negative ion such as the bismuthate ion.

GROUPS VI, VII, AND VIII

A few organochromium and manganese compounds are known. Tetraphenylchromium iodide is of interest in that reduction with lithium aluminum hydride

---

[3] Paul Ehrlich (1854–1915), physiologist and professor of experimental therapy at the University of Frankfurt. He was the first to attempt to synthesize chemical compounds that are more toxic for a pathogenic organism than for the host, a field of investigation to which he gave the name *chemotherapy*. He was awarded the Nobel Prize in Medicine in 1908.

gives two moles of biphenyl. Ethyliron chloride, phenyliron chloride, and trimethylplatinum iodide are known. All of these compounds have been made from the metallic chlorides and Grignard reagents. The dicyclopentadienyl derivatives of metals are discussed on page 838.

METAL CARBONYLS

Carbon monoxide forms coordination compounds with metals, especially with those of the sixth and eighth groups of the periodic table. The simple carbonyls have the molecular formulas $Ni(CO)_4$, $Fe(CO)_5$, $Ru(CO)_5$, $Os(CO)_5$, $Cr(CO)_6$, $Mo(CO)_6$, and $W(CO)_6$. All of these compounds are either volatile liquids or solids and are soluble in organic solvents including the hydrocarbons. All are highly toxic.

Nickel carbonyl was discovered by Mond in 1890, and in the following year he prepared **iron carbonyl.** These metal carbonyls can be prepared by passing carbon monoxide over the metal at atmospheric pressure, usually at a somewhat elevated temperature. Since the reaction takes place with a decrease in volume, it is facilitated by the application of pressure. In fact nickel and iron carbonyls are the only ones that can be formed at atmospheric pressure.

The metal carbonyls decompose to the metal and carbon monoxide at high temperatures. Advantage was taken of this behavior in the development of the Mond process for the separation of nickel from its ores. Since the development of powder metallurgy, a process for molding high-precision metal parts from powdered metals, pure metallic iron powder is being made for this purpose by the thermal decomposition of iron carbonyl. Processes known as *gas plating* have been developed for the plating of nickel, iron, chromium, tungsten, and molybdenum on almost any type of surface, whether metal or nonmetal, by the thermal decomposition of the metal carbonyls. At one time iron carbonyl was used as an antiknock agent for motor fuel but was insufficiently stable for the purpose. Nickel carbonyl and the cobalt carbonyls are important catalysts in several industrial processes for the synthesis of organic compounds (pp. 223, 250, 778).

The structure of the metal carbonyls has received considerable attention in recent years. The electronic structure of carbon monoxide is considered to be that in which the carbon and oxygen are linked by a triple bond, one bond being semipolar, $: \overset{-}{C}\!\!\equiv\!\!\overset{+}{O} :$. In the simple metal carbonyls the number of moles of carbon monoxide combined with the element is half of the number of electrons required to give to the metal the electronic structure of the next higher inert gas. Thus nickel with an atomic number of 28 requires 8 electrons to have the electronic structure of krypton of atomic number 36. The number of moles of carbon monoxide in nickel carbonyl is 4. Iron with atomic number 26 requires 10 electrons and the number of moles of carbon monoxide in iron carbonyl is 5. Chromium of atomic number 24 combines with 6 moles of carbon monoxide. Hence it appears that in the metal carbonyls the carbon monoxide is bound covalently by the unshared pair of electrons on the carbon atom, thus filling the incomplete valence shells of the metal. Cobalt with the odd atomic number 27 does not form a carbonyl with a single atom of metal, but dicobaltoctacarbonyl with two cobalt atoms, $Co_2(CO)_8$, is known. Reaction of cobalt with carbon monoxide in the presence of water gives the volatile cobalt tetracarbonyl hydride, $HCo(CO)_4$, which is a strong acid. Carbonyls containing more than one atom of an element having an even atomic number also are known, for example $Fe_2(CO)_9$. Here the two iron atoms are believed to be joined by one molecule of carbon monoxide in which the unshared pair of electrons on both carbon and oxygen are coordinated with iron atoms.

$$\begin{array}{ccccccc}
O & & O & O & & & O \\
\diagdown\!\!\!\equiv\!\!\!C & C\!\!\!\equiv & & \diagdown C & & C\!\!\!\equiv \\
& Fe\!\!-\!\!C\!\!\equiv\!\!O\!\!-\!\!Fe & & & & \\
C\diagup & C & & C\diagup & & C \\
O & \diagdown O & O & & O
\end{array}$$

The chemical properties of the different types of metal carbonyls vary considerably. Some of the reactions of iron pentacarbonyl are of interest. Halogen reacts with loss of one mole of carbon monoxide.

$$Fe(CO)_5 + X_2 \longrightarrow Fe(CO)_4X_2 + CO$$

With aqueous alkali iron pentacarbonyl gives a yellow liquid dihydride.

$$Fe(CO)_5 + 2\,NaOH \longrightarrow Fe(CO)_4H_2 + Na_2CO_3$$

It is a weak acid. Aqueous solutions of this compound can be boiled without decomposition, but it is oxidized with extreme ease. In alkaline solutions it reduces methylene blue quantitatively.

Reaction of iron pentacarbonyl with nitric oxide gives iron dicarbonyl dinitrosyl.

$$Fe(CO)_5 + 2\,NO \longrightarrow Fe(CO)_2(NO)_2 + 3\,CO$$

Thus the number of groups with which the iron atom bonds still depends on the number of electrons necessary to make its electronic structure that of the next higher inert gas. In the pentacarbonyl the ten electrons are supplied by five unshared pairs on the carbon atoms of the carbonyl groups. In the tetracarbonyl dihydride, eight are supplied by the four carbonyl groups and one by each of the two hydrogen atoms. In the dicarbonyl dinitrosyl, four electrons are supplied by the two carbonyl groups and three by each nitrogen atom of the two nitrosyl groups.

REVIEW QUESTIONS

1. What are organometallic compounds?
2. How are the alkylzincs prepared and what are their properties?
3. How are Grignard reagents prepared and what advantage do they have over alkylzincs? What is the function of the solvent? What side reactions may take place during the preparation of the reagent?
4. Give two examples of the indirect preparation of Grignard reagents.
5. Give equations for the reaction of Grignard reagents with oxygen, carbon dioxide, carbon disulfide, sulfur dioxide, water, alcohols, primary and secondary amines; with halides of zinc, mercury, aluminum, tin, bismuth, and antimony, and halides of phosphorus, boron, and silicon; with formaldehyde, other aldehydes, ketones, esters, acyl chlorides, ethylene oxide, benzonitrile, and phenyl isocyanate.
6. How do the reactions of alkyllithiums differ from those of alkylmagnesium halides?
7. How are alkylmercuric halides and dialkylmercury compounds prepared?
8. What is meant by direct mercuration? Give a specific example.
9. How may alkylmercury compounds be used to prepare other alkylmetals?
10. Compare the physical properties and chemical reactivity of alkyl alkali metals with alkylmercury compounds.
11. What are the structural formulas for primary Lewisite, cacodyl, arsanilic acid, Salvarsan, Mapharsen, and tryparsamide, and of what interest are they? What organic compound has been found to be a specific for arsenic and other heavy-metal poisoning?

12. List the metals that give rise to the more generally useful types of organometallic compound.
13. What organometallic compound is produced in largest amount? Its manufacture led to the large scale production of what element?
14. What is the importance of the metal carbonyls?

PROBLEMS

15. Give reactions for the following preparations: (*a*) 9,10-dihydroanthracene from anthracene; (*b*) 2,9-dimethyldibenzofuran from dibenzofuran; (*c*) α,α,α′,α′-tetraphenyladipic acid from benzophenone; (*d*) α-pyridylacetic acid from α-picoline; (*e*) dicyclopentadienyl from cyclopentadiene.
16. Give reactions for the following conversions: (*a*) furan to 2-iodofuran; (*b*) benzenesulfonyl chloride to phenylmercuric chloride; (*c*) anthranilic acid to Merthiolate; (*d*) phenol to *o*-hydroxyphenyl thiocyanate; (*e*) *p*-bromotoluene to *p*-*p*′-dimethylbiphenyl; (*f*) *i*-butylene to *i*-butyl alcohol by way of an organometallic compound; (*g*) *p*-bromochlorobenzene to *p*-chlorophenylboronic acid.
17. Give reactions for the preparation of the following compounds from readily available materials: (*a*) ethyldichloroarsine; (*b*) triphenylbismuth dichloride; (*c*) tryparsamide; (*d*) *p*-methylstibonic acid; (*e*) tetraethylstibonium bromide.

Chapter 42

PHOSPHORUS AND SILICON COMPOUNDS

PHOSPHORUS COMPOUNDS

The position of phosphorus in the fifth group of the periodic table is between nitrogen and arsenic. Hence the properties of organic phosphorus compounds are intermediate between those of nitrogen and arsenic.

Because of its low boiling point and insolubility in water, phosphine usually is not used for preparing the alkyl phosphines. Instead a mixture of phosphonium iodide, alkyl halide, and zinc oxide is heated in a sealed tube.

$$2\,PH_4I + 2\,RI + ZnO \xrightarrow{150°} 2\,RPH_3I + ZnI_2 + H_2O$$
$$2\,RPH_3I + 2\,RI + ZnO \longrightarrow 2\,R_2PH_2I + ZnI_2 + H_2O$$
$$2\,R_2PH_2I + 2\,RI + ZnO \longrightarrow 2\,R_3PHI + ZnI_2 + H_2O$$
$$2\,R_3PHI + 2\,RI + ZnO \longrightarrow 2\,R_4P^{+-}I + ZnI_2 + H_2O$$

Phosphine is much less basic than ammonia and not until two alkyl groups are present are the salts stable in aqueous solution. Hence on the addition of water to the reaction mixture, the unreacted phosphine and **primary alkylphosphine** are liberated. Addition of alkali then frees the **secondary** and **tertiary phosphines,** leaving the **quaternary salt** in solution.

Phosphines can be prepared also by the reaction of sodium phosphides with alkyl halides.

$$NaPH_2 + RX \longrightarrow RPH_2 + NaX$$

Tertiary phosphines are prepared best from phosphorus trichloride and a Grignard reagent.

$$PCl_3 + 3\,RMgX \longrightarrow PR_3 + 3\,MgX_2$$

There is no tendency for proton bonding in the phosphines. Thus phosphine (mol. wt. 34) boils at $-85°$ which is lower than ammonia ($-78°$, mol. wt. 17) and approximately the same as ethane ($-88°$, mol. wt. 28). Moreover there is no inversion in the boiling point trend in passing from the secondary phosphine to the tertiary phosphine. Similarly the solubility of phosphine in water is only slight, and the alkyl derivatives are practically insoluble.

Like phosphine itself the alkyl derivatives are highly toxic. They oxidize easily in air, the lower members being spontaneously flammable. The oxidation with air or with nitric acid gives products analogous to the final oxidation products of the arsines (p. 901), although the intermediate oxides from the primary and secondary phosphines are not obtained.

$$RPH_2 + 3\,[O] \longrightarrow RP(O)(OH)_2$$
Alkylphosphonic
acid

$$R_2PH + 2\,[O] \longrightarrow R_2P(O)OH$$
Dialkylphosphinic
acid

$$R_3P + [O] \longrightarrow R_3P(O)$$
Trialkylphosphine
oxide

907

The problem of the structure of the oxygen compounds of phosphorus in its highest valence state is the same as that for compounds of sulfur and other elements of the third period (p. 273). Although there is evidence for double-bonding between the phosphorus and one of the oxygen atoms, the chemical properties of the bond are more like those of the semipolar bond in amine oxides than those of the double bond in the carbonyl group. Hence it seems preferable to indicate the bond by the semipolar symbol or the noncommittal (0).

The trialkylphosphine oxides may be prepared also by the reaction of phosphorus oxychloride with Grignard reagents.

$$POCl_3 + 3\ RMgCl \longrightarrow R_3PO + 3\ MgCl_2$$

They are very stable compounds. The oxygen is not removed even by heating with metallic sodium.

The reaction of phosphorus trichloride with dialkyl- or diarylmercury compounds gives the alkyl- or aryldichlorophosphine.

$$PCl_3 + R_2Hg \longrightarrow RPCl_2 + RHgCl$$

Aryldichlorophosphines can be prepared from aromatic compounds and phosphorus trichloride by the Friedel-Crafts reaction.

$$C_6H_6 + PCl_3 \xrightarrow{AlCl_3} C_6H_5PCl_2 + HCl$$

Hydrolysis of the alkyl- or aryldichlorophosphines gives the **phosphonous acid,** which is monobasic and can be oxidized to the **phosphonic acid.**

$$RPCl_2 \xrightarrow{H_2O} [RP(OH)_2] \xrightarrow{Ox.} RP(O)(OH)_2$$

This tendency of phosphorus to exhibit its highest covalent state is characteristic. Thus whereas hydroxylamine is stable in the nitrogen series, phosphine oxide is the stable phosphorus analog.

<table>
<tr><td>H₂NOH</td><td>H₃P(O)</td></tr>
</table>

$$\text{H}_2\text{NOH} \qquad\qquad\qquad \text{H}_3\text{P(O)}$$
Hydroxylamine   Phosphine oxide

Similarly phosphoric, phosphorous, and hypophosphorous acids are tribasic, dibasic, and monobasic, respectively.

$$(HO)_3P(O) \qquad (HO)_2PH(O) \qquad HOPH_2(O)$$
Phosphoric acid   Phosphorous acid   Hypophosphorous acid

The alkylphosphonic acids can be prepared by methods other than the oxidation of the monoalkylphosphines or phosphinic acids, which are not easily available. Thus alkyl phosphites react with alkyl halides at 150° to give alkylphosphonic esters. Similarly sodium alkyl phosphites resulting from the partial hydrolysis of the alkyl phosphites react with alkyl halides in organic solvents.

$$(RO)_3P + R'X \xrightarrow{150°} R'P(O)(OR)_2 + RX$$

$$(RO)_3P \xrightarrow{NaOH} (RO)_2PO^-Na^+ \xrightarrow{R'X} R'P(O)(OR)_2$$

Primary halides give the best yields. The phosphonic esters can be hydrolyzed to the free acids. In another reaction, which is of interest because it is unusual, the phosphonyl chloride is formed when oxygen is bubbled through a mixture of an aliphatic hydrocarbon and phosphorus trichloride. Phosphorus oxychloride is formed simultaneously. The phosphonyl chloride can be separated and converted to the phosphonic acid, esters, or amides by reaction with water, alcohols, or amines.

$$RH + PCl_3 + [O](air) \longrightarrow RPOCl_2 + HCl$$

$$RPO(OH)_2 \xleftarrow{H_2O} \quad \downarrow R'OH \quad \searrow NH_2R'$$

$$RPO(OH)_2 \qquad RPO(OR')_2 \qquad RPO(NHR')_2$$

This reaction has the disadvantage of other aliphatic substitution reactions in that it is not selective and mixtures of isomeric products are obtained. Phosphonyl chlorides can be obtained also by the oxidation of the dichlorophosphines with chlorine in the presence of phosphorus pentoxide.

$$3\ RPCl_2 + P_2O_5 + 3\ Cl_2 \longrightarrow 3\ RPOCl_2 + 2\ POCl_3$$

The alkyl- and aryldichlorophosphines add chlorine, and hydrolysis of the addition products gives phosphonic acids.

$$RPCl_2 \xrightarrow{Cl_2} RPCl_4 \xrightarrow{3\ H_2O} RPO(OH)_2 + 4\ HCl$$

The quaternary salts react with moist silver oxide to give the quaternary phosphonium hydroxides, which are strong bases like the ammonium and sulfonium hydroxides. In contrast to these compounds, however, thermal decomposition does not give olefin, water, and the trialkylphosphine (pp. 242, 283), but instead the saturated hydrocarbon and the phosphine oxide.

$$R_4POH \xrightarrow{Heat} RH + R_3PO$$

The reaction of quaternary phosphonium salts with molten alkali metals, or alkylmetals, gives *ylides* analogous to those obtained from quaternary ammonium salts (p. 243).

$$(CH_3)_4PBr + C_6H_5Li \longrightarrow (CH_3)_3\overset{+}{P}\text{—}\overset{..}{\overset{..}{C}}H_2 + LiBr + C_6H_6$$

The triphenylphosphonium methylide is of interest in that it reacts with benzophenone to give 1,1-diphenylethylene and triphenylphosphine oxide, a reaction whereby a carbonyl oxygen atom is replaced by a methylene group.

$$(C_6H_5)_3\overset{+}{P}\text{—}\overset{..}{C}H_2 + (C_6H_5)_2C{=}O \longrightarrow \left[\begin{matrix} (C_6H_5)_3\overset{+}{P}\text{—}CH_2 \\ | \\ \bar{O}\text{—}C(C_6H_5)_2 \end{matrix} \right] \longrightarrow$$

$$(C_6H_5)_3\overset{+}{P}\text{—}\bar{O} + (C_6H_5)_2C{=}CH_2$$

Other ketones and some aldehydes give analogous products. The corresponding intermediate from trimethylphosphonium methylide is stable and yields with halogen acid the hydroxy quaternary salt.

$$(CH_3)_3\overset{+}{P}CH_2C(C_6H_5)_2 \xrightarrow{HI} \left[(CH_3)_3\overset{+}{P}CH_2C(C_6H_5)_2 \right] I^-$$
$$\qquad\qquad | \qquad\qquad\qquad\qquad\qquad | $$
$$\qquad\qquad O^- \qquad\qquad\qquad\qquad\qquad OH$$

The reaction of phenylphosphonic acid with phenylphosphonyl chloride produces **phosphobenzene**, the phosphorus analog of nitrobenzene.

$$C_6H_5PO(OH)_2 + C_6H_5POCl_2 \longrightarrow 2\ C_6H_5PO_2 + 2\ HCl$$
$$\text{Phosphobenzene}$$

Phenylphosphine and phenyldichlorophosphine form an addition compound which is decomposed by water to give **phosphorobenzene**, a pale yellow solid which is the analog of azobenzene.

$$C_6H_5PH_2 + C_6H_5PCl_2 \longrightarrow C_6H_5P{=}PC_6H_5 + 2\ HCl$$

It is oxidized by air to an oxide which presumably is the analog of azoxybenzene and may be called **phosphoroxybenzene.**

$$C_6H_5P{=}PC_6H_5 + [O]\ \text{(air)} \longrightarrow C_6H_5P{=}PC_6H_5$$
$$\overset{|+}{\underset{\overset{|}{O^-}}{}}$$

Very little practical application of the organophosphorus compounds has been made, the most important compounds of phosphorus being the esters of phosphoric acid (pp. 110, 515). **Tetra(hydroxymethyl)phosphonium chloride,** $(HOCH_2)_4P^+{}^-Cl$, has been used in flameproofing cotton fabrics. The so-called *nerve gases* developed in Germany during World War II are very effective in inhibiting the action of choline esterase (p. 243). The **isopropyl ester** of **methyl-fluorophosphonic acid,** $CH_3PF(O)OC_3H_7\text{-}i$, called *Sarin*, is over ten times more toxic than hydrogen cyanide. **Triphenylphosphine** forms complexes with nickel carbonyl that are very effective catalysts for the cyclopolymerization of acetylenes to aromatic compounds.

$$3\ HC{\equiv}CH \xrightarrow{\ (C_6H_5)_3PNi(CO)_3\ } C_6H_6$$

SILICON COMPOUNDS

The part played by silicon in organic chemistry may be considered from two points of view. First, silicon is just below carbon in the periodic table, and would be expected to resemble carbon in its chemical properties and give rise to a group of silicon analogs of carbon compounds. However, because the valence electrons are farther away from the nucleus and are held less strongly than in carbon, silicon is more electron-donating or metallic in its properties. Hence silicon does not give rise to all of the many types of compounds derived from carbon, and the silicon analogs of carbon compounds that are known exhibit markedly different properties. The second aspect of the place of silicon in organic chemistry lies in the preparation and properties of compounds in which silicon is linked to carbon. Both of these aspects are considered here, sometimes independently and sometimes simultaneously.

When crude magnesium silicide, prepared by heating silica with magnesium, reacts with mineral acids, a mixture of **silicon hydrides** is obtained consisting of 40 per cent silane, SiH_4; 30 per cent disilane, Si_2H_6; 15 per cent trisilane, Si_3H_8; and 10 per cent tetrasilane, Si_4H_{10}. The remaining 5 per cent is a mixture of higher silanes, the highest identified being Si_6H_{14}. **Silane** boils at $-112°$ and decomposes at $400°$ to silicon and hydrogen. The higher silanes decompose to mixtures of lower silanes and silicon at progressively lower temperatures. The silanes are stable to aqueous acids but are hydrolyzed by boiling with bases.

$$SiH_4 + H_2O + 2\ NaOH \longrightarrow Na_2SiO_3 + 4\ H_2$$

Silicon tetrachloride, $SiCl_4$, was discovered by Berzelius in 1823. It is prepared by the reaction of chlorine with silicon, some Si_2Cl_6 and Si_3Cl_8 being formed at the same time.

$$Si + 2\ Cl_2 \longrightarrow SiCl_4\ (\text{and } Si_2Cl_6 \text{ and } Si_3Cl_8)$$

The boiling point is 58°, or 19° lower than carbon tetrachloride. It is hydrolyzed readily by water, although it may be distilled from sodium with which it does not react below 200°.

$$SiCl_4 + 3 H_2O \longrightarrow H_2SiO_3 + 4 HCl$$

Reaction with alcohols gives the orthosilicates (p. 110).

$$SiCl_4 + 4 ROH \longrightarrow (RO)_4Si + 4 HCl$$

Reduction with lithium aluminum hydride gives almost quantitative yields of silane.

$$SiCl_4 + LiAlH_4 \longrightarrow SiH_4 + LiAlCl_4$$

Trichlorosilane (*silicochloroform*), first prepared by Woehler in 1857, results along with silicon tetrachloride from the action of dry hydrogen chloride on silicon.

$$Si + 3 HCl \longrightarrow SiHCl_3 + H_2 \text{ (and } SiCl_4)$$

It boils at 32°, or 29° below chloroform. It fumes in moist air because of its ready hydrolysis.

$$SiHCl_3 + 3 H_2O \longrightarrow H_2SiO_3 + 3 HCl + H_2$$

The first compound containing a carbon-silicon bond was **tetraethylsilane,** b.p. 153°, prepared by Friedel and Crafts in 1863 by the reaction of ethylzinc and silicon tetrachloride.

$$SiCl_4 + 2 Zn(C_2H_5)_2 \xrightarrow{160°} Si(C_2H_5)_4 + 2 ZnCl_2$$

Tetramethylsilane boils at 27°. Although it is fairly stable to most reagents, it reacts with methyl alcohol at 250° to give the monomethoxy derivative.

$$Si(CH_3)_4 + CH_3OH \longrightarrow (CH_3)_3SiOCH_3 + CH_4$$

The first arylsilicon compound was prepared by Ladenburg in 1873 by the reaction of silicon tetrachloride and phenylmercury at 300°.

$$SiCl_4 + Hg(C_6H_5)_2 \longrightarrow C_6H_5SiCl_3 + C_6H_5HgCl$$

Kipping[1] began his study of silicon compounds in 1889 with the object of synthesizing a tetrasubstituted silicon compound and determining whether it could be resolved into optically active isomers. During the next forty-five years he continued the study of silicon compounds and most of our basic knowledge of these substances resulted from his work. He found in 1904 that the Grignard reagents react with the halogenated silicon compounds, and this reaction has been the most fruitful in the synthesis of organosilicon compounds. Silicon

---

[1] Frederick Stanley Kipping (1863–1949), professor of chemistry at the University of Nottingham. He worked under W. H. Perkin, Jr. (p. 828) in Baeyer's laboratory in Munich, and had as a student Arthur Lapworth (p. 201) in the laboratory of H. E. Armstrong (p. 671). Since Perkin and Lapworth later married sisters of Kipping's wife, all three were associated closely throughout most of their lives. "Organic Chemistry" by Perkin and Kipping was the standard text in England for many years.

tetrachloride reacts with Grignard reagents to give a mixture of the compounds having from one to four chlorine atoms replaced by hydrocarbon groups.

$$SiCl_4 \xrightarrow{RMgX} RSiCl_3 \xrightarrow{RMgX} R_2SiCl_2 \xrightarrow{RMgX} R_3SiCl \xrightarrow{RMgX} R_4Si$$

By regulating conditions it is possible to obtain good yields of the desired products.

Trialkylchlorosilanes, R_3SiCl, are silicon analogs of tertiary alkyl chlorides; yet it is not possible to eliminate hydrogen chloride to form an unsaturated compound with a carbon-silicon double bond. Hydrolysis in the presence of ammonia gives the silanol.

$$R_3SiCl + H_2O + NH_3 \longrightarrow R_3SiOH + NH_4Cl$$

These silanols lose water easily and form the oxides.

$$2\,R_3SiOH \longrightarrow R_3SiOSiR_3 + H_2O$$

Often this reaction takes place spontaneously, but the more stable compounds such as triphenylsilanol require the presence of alkali. Reaction of the chlorosilanes with anhydrous ammonia or amines gives the silylamines, but they are hydrolyzed readily to the silanols.

$$R_3SiCl \xrightarrow{NH_3} R_3SiNH_2 \xrightarrow{H_2O} R_3SiOH$$

The silanols do not esterify with acids, but acyl chlorides give the chloro derivatives as occurs with tertiary alcohols.

$$R_3SiOH + CH_3COCl \longrightarrow R_3SiCl + CH_3COOH$$

It is impossible to obtain unsaturated compounds by the loss of water.

Hydrolysis of dialkyldichlorosilanes, R_2SiCl_2, gives diols which are insoluble in water but soluble in aqueous alkali.

$$R_2SiCl_2 + 2\,H_2O \longrightarrow 2\,HCl + R_2Si(OH)_2 \xrightarrow{NaOH} R_2Si(ONa)_2 + 2\,H_2O$$

The diols lose water readily to give compounds which are called **silicones,** a name that was given to them before their structure was known in the belief that they corresponded to ketones. No silicon analog of a ketone is known, however. Apparently silicon is not able to form a double bond with an oxygen atom any more than with a carbon atom. From the dehydration products of diphenylsilanediol, Kipping was able to isolate a number of individual products, some of which were linear polymers and others cyclic polymers.

$$HO[Si(C_6H_5)_2{-}O]_2Si(C_6H_5)_2OH$$

$$HO[Si(C_6H_5)_2{-}O]_3Si(C_6H_5)_2OH$$

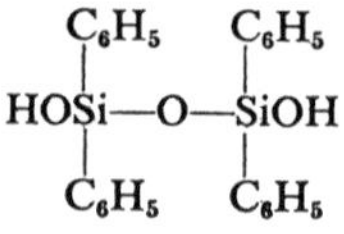

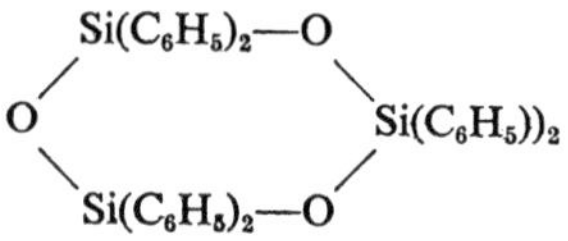

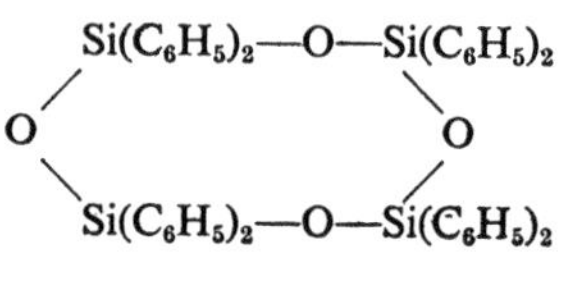

In 1928 he reported the formation of much more complex polymers of high molecular weight. Actually the first such product had been obtained in 1872 by Ladenburg, who hydrolyzed diethyldiethoxysilane, $(C_2H_5)_2Si(OC_2H_5)_2$, and obtained a viscous oil that did not freeze at $-15°$ and decomposed only at a very high temperature. Polymers of this type sometimes are called *siloxanes* although the term silicone is used more frequently.

The products of hydrolysis of alkyltrichlorosilanes, $RSiCl_3$, were believed at first to be analogous to the carboxylic-acids and were assigned the formula $RSiOOH$, but Kipping found them to be complex compounds of high molecular weight. These compounds also now are grouped with the silicones.

The inability of silicon to form an ordinary double bond, that is, one in which the π bond is formed by the overlapping of p orbitals on adjacent atoms, has been ascribed to the larger size of the silicon atom as compared with elements in the second period. This inability to form a double bond also accounts for the fact that whereas electron-donating groups in the *para* positions increase the rate of hydrolysis of triarylmethyl chlorides, they decrease the rate of hydrolysis of triarylchlorosilanes. In the former they can stabilize the planar carbonium ion and increase the ease with which the chlorine can leave as a chloride ion. In the latter the silicon cannot become planar and the increase in electron density on the silicon atom decreases the effectiveness of attack by a negative ion.

Usually the trimethylsilyl group is more electron-donating than the *t*-butyl group because the outer shell of electrons is further away from the nucleus in silicon than in carbon. Thus trimethylsilylacetic acid is a weaker acid than *t*-butylacetic acid and trimethylsilylmethylamine is a stronger base than methylamine. Similarly the trimethylsilyl group, when in the *meta* position, decreases the acidity of phenols and increases the basicity of aromatic amines. On the other hand if it is in the *para* position, it has the opposite effect. Here a resonance effect apparently can operate in which the silicon atom can accept electrons by using d orbitals (cf. p. 273).

$$\left\{ HO-\!\!\left\langle \bigcirc \right\rangle\!\!-Si(CH_3)_3 \quad \longleftrightarrow \quad HO\!=\!\!\left\langle \bigcirc \right\rangle\!\!\overset{+}{=}\overset{-}{Si}(CH_3)_3 \right\}$$

Thus an apparently anomalous situation exists in which silicon is unable to form a p-p π bond but can form a d-p π bond.

In a summary of his work in 1937, Kipping pointed out that the number of types of silicon compounds was small compared to carbon, and because of the limited number of reactions which they undergo, he concluded that "the prospect of any immediate and important advance in this section of organic chemistry does not seem to be very hopeful." At that very time, however, industrial chemists were trying to make use of Kipping's polymeric compounds because of their insolubility, nonreactivity, and stability to heat. A Russian publication in 1939 indicated that polymers from diphenylsilanediol and from benzylsilanetriol were suitable as dielectrics and insulating materials at elevated temperatures. American publications followed in 1941. Commercial production in the United States of the silicones in the form of oils, greases, resins, and elastomers was announced in 1944. In general the silicones are made by hydrolyzing the alkyl- or aryldichloro- or trichlorosilanes. Hydrolysis of the pure dichlorosilanes can give only linear polymers which are oils or greases.

$$x\,R_2SiCl_2 + (x+1)H_2O \longrightarrow HO\left[\begin{array}{c} R \\ | \\ -Si-O \\ | \\ R \end{array}\right]_{x-1}\!\!\!\!\begin{array}{c} R \\ | \\ -Si\,OH + 2x\,HCl \\ | \\ R \end{array}$$

The trichlorosilanes permit cross linking of the chains after hydrolysis and give three-dimensional solid resins.

$$RSiCl_3 \xrightarrow{H_2O}$$

$$
\begin{array}{c}
\quad\;\; R \quad\;\; OH \\
\quad\;\; | \quad\quad | \\
-O-Si-O-Si-O-Si-OH \\
\quad\;\; | \quad\quad | \quad\quad | \\
\quad\;\; OH \quad\; R \quad\;\; R \\
\\
\quad\;\; OH \quad\; R \quad\;\; R \\
\quad\;\; | \quad\quad | \quad\quad | \\
-O-Si-O-Si-O-Si-OH \\
\quad\;\; | \quad\quad | \\
\quad\;\; R \quad\;\; OH
\end{array}
$$

Dehydration →

$$
\begin{array}{c}
\quad\;\; R \quad\;\; O- \\
\quad\;\; | \quad\quad | \\
-O-Si-O-Si-O-Si-O- \\
\quad\;\; | \quad\quad | \quad\quad | \\
\quad\;\; O \quad\;\; R \quad\;\; R \\
\quad\;\; | \\
\quad\;\; O \quad\;\; R \quad\;\; R \\
\quad\;\; | \quad\quad | \quad\quad | \\
-O-Si-O-Si-O-Si-O- \\
\quad\;\; | \quad\quad | \\
\quad\;\; R \quad\;\; O-
\end{array}
$$

By using mixtures of the dichloro- and trichlorosilanes and varying the nature of the R group, it is possible to obtain products with widely varying properties.

All of the silicones have to a marked extent the properties of not being wet by water and of resistance to a relatively high temperature. Films and coatings are used to waterproof materials and machines, and the resins are used to fill the voids and act as a binder for glass fiber insulation of magnet wire, thus permitting motors to operate at a higher temperature than if the usual organic resins were used. The oils have the unique property of remaining fluid at low temperatures. Silicone rubber in contrast to other rubbers is not attacked by ozone, does not become set under compression at high temperatures, and retains its flexibility at low temperatures. It is cured or vulcanized by cross linking, using a peroxide catalyst at 125°.

The organochlorosilanes at first were manufactured by the Grignard reaction, but less expensive methods soon were developed. The alkyl derivatives can be made by passing the alkyl chlorides over heated silicon and metallic copper. The predominant reaction yields dialkyldichlorosilanes, although other products such as the alkyltrichlorosilanes, the trialkylchlorosilanes, silicon tetrachloride, and hydrocarbons also are formed.

$$2\,RCl + Si(Cu) \xrightarrow{300°} R_2SiCl_2$$

$$4\,RCl + 2\,Si(Cu) \longrightarrow RSiCl_3 + R_3SiCl$$

In the reaction with methyl chloride, it appears that methylcopper is an intermediate product. The best yields of phenylchlorosilanes are obtained by reaction of chlorobenzene with a silver-silicon alloy at 400°. Ethyl and higher alkyltrichlorosilanes are made by the addition of trichlorosilane to olefins.

$$CH_2{=}CH_2 + HSiCl_3 \xrightarrow[\text{heat}]{\text{Peroxides,}} CH_3CH_2SiCl_3$$

Between 1947 and 1954 more than a thousand organosilicon compounds having functional groups in the hydrocarbon portions of the molecule were prepared. For example, the addition of trichlorosilane to acetylene in the presence of platinum gives **vinyl trichlorosilane.**

$$HC{\equiv}CH + HSiCl_3 \xrightarrow[\text{heat}]{\text{Pt,}} H_2C{=}CHSiCl_3$$

Reaction of silicon tetrachloride with diazomethane gives **chloromethyltrichlorosilane.**

$$CH_2N_2 + SiCl_4 \longrightarrow ClCH_2SiCl_3 + N_2$$

Halogen derivatives can be made also by direct halogenation.

$$(CH_3)_3SiCl + Cl_2 \longrightarrow CHCl_2(CH_3)_2SiCl + HCl$$

$$C_6H_5SiCl_3 + 4\,Cl_2 \xrightarrow[\text{in } CCl_4]{AlCl_3} C_6HCl_4SiCl_3 + 4\,HCl$$

Halogen in alkyl groups undergoes the usual displacement reactions. It also gives Grignard reagents from which other derivatives may be made.

$$(CH_3)_3SiCH_2Cl \xrightarrow{Mg} (CH_3)_3SiCH_2MgCl \xrightarrow{CO_2} (CH_3)_3SiCH_2COOH$$

Hexaaryldisilanes are cleaved by alkali metals using the dimethyl ether of ethylene glycol as solvent to give triarylsilylmetals which show some of the properties of organometallic compounds.

$$(C_6H_5)_3SiSi(C_6H_5)_3 + 2\,K \longrightarrow 2\,(C_6H_5)_3SiK$$

Some of these newer compounds already are finding technical application. The incorporation of polychlorinated aryl derivatives into the oils greatly improves their lubricating properties without changing the viscosity index. Vinyl groups in the linear polymers permit easier curing by peroxide catalysts such as di-*t*-butyl peroxide to give superior silicone rubbers.

REVIEW QUESTIONS

1. Compare the chemical properties of the phosphines with those of the amines and the arsines.
2. Give the various reactions by which alkylphosphonic acids may be prepared.
3. Compare the usual methods for the preparation of azobenzene, phosphorobenzene, and arsenobenzene.
4. What is the best method for the preparation of silane? How does the number of known hydrides of silicon compare with the number of hydrides of carbon?
5. Compare the chemical properties of carbon tetrachloride with those of silicon tetrachloride; of 1,1-alkanediols with those of 1,1-silanediols.
6. What are the silicones? Why is this term a misnomer? What are some of the advantages of silicones in certain technical applications over other high molecular weight polymers?

PROBLEMS

7. Give reactions for the following preparations: (*a*) phenylphosphonic acid from benzene; (*b*) ethyl *n*-butylphosphonate from ethyl phosphite; (*c*) ethyl cyclohexylphosphonate from cyclohexane; (*d*) triphenylphosphonium methylide from benzene; (*e*) tetra(hydroxymethyl)-phosphonium chloride from formaldehyde.
8. Starting with silicon, construct a chart, including reagents and conditions, for the preparation of the following compounds: dimethyldichlorosilane, chloromethyltrimethylsilane, silicochloroform, trimethylchlorosilane, chloromethyltrichlorosilane, ethyltrichlorosilane, trimethylsilylacetic acid, trimethylhydroxysilane, tetramethylsilane, trimethylsilyl oxide, vinyltrichlorosilane, methyltrichlorosilane, and dimethyldihydroxysilane.

INDEX

Abietic acid, 861
  retene from, 602
Abnormal Michael reaction, 803
Absolute alcohol, 94
Absolute configuration, 347
Absolute ether, 141
Absorbance, 661
Absorption and visual color, 670
Absorption spectra, 657
  aniline, 666
  anilinium ion, 666
  anthracene, 667
  azobenzene, 665
  azomethane, 665
  benzene, 665, 667
  1, 3-butadiene, 663
  carbonyl compounds, 665
  conjugated dienes, 663, 707
  conjugated polyenes, 664
  coronene, 667
  Crystal Violet, 699
  diacetyl, 665
  electronic, 661–668
  electron paramagnetic resonance, 669
  electron-spin resonance, 669
  ethylene, 663
  formaldehyde, 665
  hydrogen atom, 662
  hydrogen molecule, 662
  infrared, 658–661
  ketones, 665
  Malachite Green, 699
  mesityl oxide, 664
  Methyl Orange, 699
  microwave, 657
  naphthacene, 667
  naphthalene, 667
  nitrobenzene, 665
  p-nitrophenol, 666
  nuclear magnetic resonance, 668
  nuclear-spin resonance, 668
  pentacene, 667
  phenanthrene, 667
  trans-stilbene, 665
  ultraviolet, 661–668
  α,β-unsaturated carbonyl compounds,
    665, 762
  vibrational, 658–661
  visible, 661–668

α carbon atom, 148
Accelerators, rubber, 711
Acenaphthene, 428, 595
Acetal, 203
Acetaldehyde, 222
  acetic acid from, 159
  from alcoholic fermentation, 91
Acetaldehyde cyanohydrin, 200
Acetaldol, 205
Acetaldoxime, 210
Acetals, 203
  cyclic, from dihydropyran, 632
  from 1,2-glycols, 637, 741
  hydrolysis, 196
Acetanilide, 479, 487
Acetate free radicals, 163, 568
Acetate rayon, 406
Acetic acid, 147, 158
  from acetaldehyde, 159
  anhydride from, 164
  from butane, 159
  from ethyl alcohol, 158
  by fermentation, 158
  ketene from, 164
  from pyroligneous liquor, 158
  salts of, 159
  synthetic, 159
Acetic anhydride, 163
Acetoacetamides, 825
Acetoacetanilides, 703
Acetoacetic acid, 814
Acetoacetic ester, see Ethyl acetoacetate,
    814
Acetoacetic esters, 825
Acetobacter, 158
Acetobromoglucose, 378
Acetoin, see Methylacetylcarbinol, 186
Acetone, 224
  conversion to ketene, 164
  reaction with sugars, 379
Acetone cyanohydrin, 200
Acetonedicarboxylic acid, 808, 810
Acetone peroxides, 885
Acetonitrile, 249
Acetonylacetone, 620
Acetophenetidine, 520
Acetophenone, 541
2-Acetothiophene, see 2-Thienyl methyl ke-
    tone, 608

Aceto-*p*-toluidide, 479
Acetoxime, 210
Acetylacetone, 771
Acetylaminomalonic ester, 802
Acetyl chloride, 161
Acetylcholine ion, 243
  esterase inhibitors, 520
Acetyldibenzoylmethane, tautomerism, 822
Acetylene, 133
  acidity, 132
  acrylonitrile from, 787
  alkynediols from, 205, 717, 747
  alkynols from, 205
  addition of hydrogen fluoride, 731
  benzene from, 910
  butadiene from, 716
  chlorinated hydrocarbons from, 723, 725
  cyclooctatetraene from, 845
  methyl acrylate from, 788
  reaction with acetic acid, 164
  uses, 133
Acetylene dichlorides, *see* 1,2-Dichloroeth-
    ylenes, 724
Acetylenes, *see* Alkynes
Acetylene tetrachloride, 723
Acetylenic acids, 789
N-acetyl-2-glucosamine, 409, 411
Acetylides, 131
Acetylmethylcarbinol, 771
Acetyl peroxide, 163, 876
  free radicals from, 568
Acetylsalicylic acid, 560
2-Acetylthiophene, 608
Acetyl value, 184
1,2,4-Acid, 592
Acid Alizarin Blue B, 688
Acid anhydrides, *see* Anhydrides, 162–165
Acid azides, *see* Azides, 268
Acid-base reactions, 235
Acid cleavage of β-keto esters, 821
Acid dissociation constants, *see* Acidity
Acid dyes, 674
Acid exchange with amides, 245
Acid halides, *see* Halides, acyl
Acidity, acetylene, 132
  amides, 246
  barbituric acids, 640
  boric acid complexes with glycols, 376,
    742
  carboxylic acids, aliphatic, 150, 794
    aromatic, 548
  cyclopentadiene, 838
  1,3-dicarbonyl compounds, 771
  dicarboxylic acids, 794
  enols, 822
  halogenated acids, 779
  hydrocarbons, relative, 890
  hydroperoxides, 875
  imides, 246, 312, 640

Acidity—(*Continued*)
  ketones, 771
  mercaptans, 277
  methylene groups, reactive, 771
  nitroalkanes, 260
  phenols, 503
  pyrrole, 611
  sulfonamides, 288, 471
  sulfonic acids, 468
  theophylline, 647
  tropolone, 844
  trimethylsilylacetic acid, 913
  ureids, 313
Acids and bases, general concepts, 235
Acids, *see type, e.g.,* Carboxylic acids
Aci form, 261
Aconitic acid, 811
Acridine, 631
Acridine dyes, 695
Acriflavine, 695
Acrilan, 788
Acrolein, 764
  dimer, 632
  glycerol from, 748
Acrose, 386
Acrylic acid, 788
Acrylic fibers, 788
  dyeing, 680
Acrylic resins, 788
Acryloid resins, 788
Acrylonitrile, 787
  infrared absorption, 660
  synthetic rubber, 718
β-ACTH, 301
Activated alumina, 104
Activated charcoal, 16
Activated complex, *see* Transition state, 42
Activating group, aromatic substitution, 442
Activation, benzene nucleus, cause, 449
Activation energy, 42
Active amyl alcohol, 91
Active components, 335
Active forms, 335
Active hydrogen, *see* Reactive hydrogen,
    121
Active methylene group, acetoacetic esters,
    817
  addition to α, β-unsaturated carbonyl
    compounds, 803
  alkylation, 773, 800, 820
  coupling with diazonium salts, 499
  1, 3-diketones, 771
  β-keto esters, 817
  malonic esters, 800
Acyclic compounds, 24
Acyl, *see main function, e.g.,* Halides
Acylals, 204
Acylation, amines, aliphatic, 237
  aromatic, 479

Acylation—(*Continued*)
by azides, 305
esters, 814
β-keto esters, 820
ketones, 768
malonic esters, 801
phenolic hydroxyl, 504
Acyloins, cyclic, 848
from esters, 173, 759
Acyl-oxygen fission, esters, 169
peroxy esters, 877
Addition, acetylene to aldehydes and ketones, 205
acid anhydrides to aldehydes and ketones, 204
active methylene compounds to α, β-unsaturated carbonyl compounds, 803
alcohols to aldehydes and ketones, 203
alcohols to alkenes, 138
alkali metals to arylalkenes, 577
ammonia to aldehydes and ketones, 209
ammonia to α, β-unsaturated carbonyl compounds, 764
anhydrides to aldehydes and ketones, 204
bromine to arylalkenes, 577
carbon tetrachloride to alkenes, 725
1, 4 to conjugated dienes, 707
Grignard reagents to aldehydes and ketones, 199
Grignard reagents to carbon dioxide, 123, 143
halogen to alkenes, 53
halogen to alkynes, 131, 723
halogen to benzene, 432
halogen acid to alkenes, 59, 731
halogen acid to alkynes, 131, 731
hydrogen to aldehydes and ketones, 198
hydrogen to alkenes, 54
hydrogen to alkynes, 130
hydrogen cyanide to aldehydes and ketones, 200
hydrogen cyanide to α, β-unsaturated carbonyl compounds, 764, 787
hydrogen peroxide to aldehydes, 878
hydroperoxides to aldehydes, 879
hydroxylamine to α, β-unsaturated carbonyl compounds, 763, 787
hypohalous acid to alkenes, 741
nitroalkanes to aldehydes, 262
ozone to alkenes, 56
sodium bisulfite to aldehydes and ketones, 201
sodium bisulfite to α, β-unsaturated carbonyl compounds, 763, 787
sulfuric acid to alkenes, 58
water to aldehydes and ketones, 202
water to alkynes, 131
1,4 to α, β-unsaturated carbonyl compounds, 763, 779

Addition complexes of ethers, 139
Addition polymers, 61
Addition reactions, alkenes, 53
α, β-unsaturated carbonyl compounds, 763, 787
Adducts, Diels-Alder, 806
Adenine, 643
Adenosine, 644
Adenosine phosphates, 644
Adenylic acids, 644
Adipamide, 799
Adipic acid, preparation, 793
reactions, 798
Adipic anhydride, *see* Polyadipic anhydride, 798
Adiponitrile, 799
Adjective dyes, 674
Adjuvants, ether anesthesia, 243, 652
ADP, *see* Adenosine diphosphate, 644
Adrenal hormones, 529, 871
Adrenalin, 529
Adrenocorticotropic hormone, 301
Adsorption, 16
Aerosols, 290
After-chroming, 674
Agar, 410
Agathalene, 860
Agathic acid, 860
Agenized flour, 304
Alanine, 296
β-Alanine in pantothenic acid, 785
from succinimide, 797
Albuminoids, 294
Albumins, 294
Alcoholates, *see* Alkoxides, 99, and Coordination complexes, 97
Alcoholic fermentation, 90
Alcohols, aliphatic, nomenclature, 84
physical properties, 86
preparation, 89–97
from acids, 172
from acyl halides, 162
from aldehydes and ketones, 198
from esters, 172
from ethers, 140
from Grignard reagents, 173, 199
reactions, 97–108
addition to aldehydes and ketones, 203
dehydration, mechanism, 104
dehydrogenation, 105, 194
esterification, 166–169
ether formation, 137
with Grignard reagents, 121
with halogen acids, mechanism, 103
oxidation to acids, 144
to aldehydes and ketones, 105, 194
Zerevitinov determination, 122
Alcohols, aromatic, 525, 575
unsaturated, 736

Alcoholysis, acyl halides, 161
  anhydrides, 163
  cyanides, 254
  esters, 170
Aldehyde-ammonia, 210
Aldehyde-collidine, 627
Aldehyde cyanohydrins, 200
Aldehyde hydrates, 202, 739
Aldehyde resins, 207
Aldehydes, aliphatic, nomenclature, 196
  physical properties, 197
  preparation, 194–196
    from amides, 248
    from α-hydroxy acids, 782
    from nitroalkanes, 262
    from sulfoxides, 283
  reactions, 198–220
    with aromatic amines, 481
    autoxidation, 885
    with hydrogen peroxide, 878
    with hydrogen sulfide, 281
    with hydroperoxides, 879
    with nitroalkanes, 262
    with phenols, 508
    with sugars, 379
Aldehydes, aromatic, 530–539
Aldehydine, 627
Aldehydo derivatives of sugars, 382
2-Aldehydo-2,3-dihydro-γ-pyran, 632
Aldimines, 210, 252
Aldol addition, 205
Aldol condensation, *see* Aldol addition, 205
Aldols, 205
  dehydration, 207
Aldonic acids, 360
Aldoses, 360–384
Aldosterone, 871
Aldoximes, aliphatic, 210
  dehydration to cyanides, 250
Aldoximes, aromatic, stereochemistry, 542
Alginic acid, 408
Alicyclic compounds, general theory, 828
  preparation, 830
  reactions, 831
Aliphatic compounds, 25
Alizarin, 599, 687
Alizarin Cyanine Green, 688
Alkali cellulose, 404
Alkali metal compounds, 889
Alkaloids, 648
Alkanes, nomenclature, 33–38
  number of isomers, 38
  physical properties, 38
  preparation, 126, 156
  reactions, aromatization, 66
    autoxidation, 881
    chlorination, 119, 722
    combustion, 42
    dehydrogenation, 79

Alkanes—(*Continued*)
  reactions—(*Continued*)
    fluorination, 730, 732
    halogenation, 119, 722
    isomerization, 46, 78
    nitration, 259
    oxidation by air, controlled, 159, 220
    oxidation to carboxylic acids, 160
    phosphonic acids from, 909
    pyrolysis, 59, 44
    sulfonation, 287
  sources, 40
  structure, 28
Alkenes, nomenclature, 51
  physical properties, 53
  preparation, 127
    from alkynes, 130
    from esters, 173
    from quaternary ammonium hydroxides, 242
    from sulfonium hydroxides, 283
  purification through dihalides, 128
  reactions, addition of alcohols, 138
    of aldehydes, 209
    to alkyl cyanides, 254
    of carbon tetrachloride, 725
    of disulfides, 281
    of halogen, 53
    of halogen acid, 59
    of hydrogen, 54
    of hydrogen cyanide, 250
    of hydrogen fluoride, 731
    of hydrogen sulfide, 274
    of hypohalous acid, 741
    of mercury salts, 894
    of nitrogen dioxide, 260
    of ozone, 56, 879
    of sulfur dioxide, 285
    of sulfuric acid, 58
  autoxidation, 881
  mechanism of addition of halogen, 54
    of halogen acid, 60
  mechanism of formation from
      alcohols, 104
    from alkyl halides, 118
    by pyrolysis of alkanes, 44
  oxidation to acids, 144
    to glycols, 57, 740
  polymerization, 61
  test for double bond, 54, 57, 263
  structure, 49
Alkoxides, 99
Alkoxycarbonyl group, 169
Alkoxyl groups, estimation, 140
  free radicals, 883
Alkyd resins, 553, 807
Alkyl, *see function, e.g.,* Cyanides, Halides, Sulfides, etc.
Alkylated benzenes, interconversion, 429, 449

Alkylation, active methylene compounds, 773, 800, 820
  acyloins, 760
  aliphatic amines, 237
  alkenes, 77
  ammonia, 229, 230
  aromatic amines, 478
  benzene, 429
  carbohydrates, 373, 390
  cyanides, 254
  1,3-diketones, 773
  hydrazine, 264
  β-keto esters, 820
  malonic esters, 800, 803
  nitroalkanes, 263
  phenols, 504, 507
  phloroglucinol, 518
  quinones, 594
  by sulfonic esters, 288, 470
  thiophene, 608
Alkyl groups, 34, 35
Alkyl-oxygen scission of esters, 169
Alkynediols, 205
Alkynes, 128–134
  acidity, 131
  addition of water, 195
  aldehydes and ketones from, 195
Alkynols, 205
Allantoin, 645
Allenes, 706
Allethrin, 840
Allicin, 290
Allophanates, 315
Allose, 366
Alloxan, 640, 641
Allyl alcohol, 738
  glycerol from, 748
Allyl chloride, 726, 738
Allyl disulfide, 290
Allyl ether, pyrolysis, 764
Allylic rearrangement, 728
  of crotyl alcohol, 738
  of glutaconic acid, 808
Allylic system, 728
Allyl isothiocyanate, 326
Allyl phthalate polymers, 738, 807
Aloes, cathartic principle, 599
α carbon atom, 148
Alternating axis of symmetry, 336
Alternation in melting points, of alkanes, 40
  of carboxylic acids, 149
*Altro*heptulose, 388
Altrose, 366
Aluminum acetate, 159
Aluminum alkoxides, 100
Aluminum compounds, 896
Aluminum halides, in Friedel-Crafts reactions, 429, 559

Aluminum halides—(*Continued*)
  reaction with Grignard reagents, 123
Amber, succinic acid from, 792
Ambergris, 862
Ambrein, 862
Ambrettolide, 847
Amides, 244–248
  from cyanides, 253, 254
  dehydration to cyanides, 250
  Hofmann rearrangement, 231
  N-substituted, 245
  of sulfonic acids, 288, 471
Amidines, 248
Amido Naphthol Brown G, 676
Amidone, 652
Amination, of pyridines, 622
Amine nitrites, 239
Amine oxides, 240
  optically active, 351
Amine picrolonates, 818
Amines, aliphatic, nomenclature, 228
  physical properties, 233
  preparation, 229–233
    from alkylanilines, 481
    from cyanamide, 232
    from cyanides, 230, 232, 254
    from dialkylanilines, 481
    from isocyanates, 317
    from isocyanides, 257, 258
    from nitroalkanes, 262
    from phthalimide, 553
    from Schiff bases, 536
  reactions, 234–240
  t-alkyl, 255, 259
Amines, aralkyl, 527–530
Amines, aromatic, physical properties, 476
  physiological action, 476
  preparation, 476
  reactions, 477–485
Amines, Hinsberg reaction, 471
Amino acids, 293, 296, 784
  configuration of natural, 349
  essential, 302
  estimation, 306, 841
  isoelectric point, 300
  metabolism, 301
  ninhydrin reaction, 840
  from proteins, 296–297
  special reactions, 306
  Strecker degradation, 841
  syntheses, from aldehydes, 303
    from azlactones, 635
    from halogenated acids, 303
    from ketones, 303
    from malonic ester, 802
    from rhodanine, 636
  test for, 306
Amino alcohols, 752
Aminoanthraquinones, 599
p-Aminoazobenzene, 498

o-Aminobenzaldehyde, 628
p-Aminobenzaldehyde, 530
Aminobenzenesulfonic acids, 485, 486
p-Aminobenzoic acid, 558
ε-Aminocaproic acid, 841
2-Amino-2-deoxyglucose, 409
2-Aminoethanol, 752
2-Aminoethyl hydrogen sulfate, 754
Amino groups, estimation, 306, 841
2-Amino-6-hydroxypurine, 643
Amino ketones, 766
Aminomalonic ester, 802
2-Amino-2-methyl-1-propanol, 754
Aminonaphthalenesulfonic acids, 589–591
Aminonaphthols, 591
Aminonaphtholsulfonic acids, 591
Aminophenols, 519
p-Aminophenylarsonic acid, 902
p-Aminophenyl sulfone, 489
1-Amino-2-propanol, 754
Aminopterin, 647
6-Aminopurine, 643
Aminopyridines, 622, 624
2-Aminopyrimidine, 639
p-Aminosalicylic acid, 560
Amino sugars, 409, 411, 414
2-Aminothiophene, 609
Ammonium carbamate, 311
Ammonium cyanate, conversion to urea, 311
Ammonium salts, optically active, 350
    pyrolysis, 245
Ammonium thioglycolate, 299
Ammonolysis, acid anhydrides, 163
    acyl halides, 161
    alkyl halides, 229
    aryl halides, 477
    esters, 171
    naphthols, 588
    phenols, 505
AMP, *see* Adenosine monophosphate, 644
Amphetamine, *see* Benzedrine, 529
Amphi-, prefix, 592
Amygdalin, 255, 537
i-Amyl acetate, 174
(+)Amyl alcohol, *see* Active amyl alcohol, 91
i-Amyl alcohol, 91
s-Amyl alcohol, 97
t-Amyl alcohol, 97
Amyl alcohols, from amylenes, 97
    from amyl chlorides, 119
    in fusel oil, 91
Amyl amines, 241
Amylases, 397, 398
Amyl chlorides, 119
Amylenes, 52
    conversion to amyl alcohols, 97
i-Amyl ether, 141

Amyl mercaptans, 119
i-Amyl nitrite, 110
Amylopectin, 397
Amylose, 396
Amyl sulfides, 119
i-Amyl valerate, 174
Amyrins, 863
Amytal, 640
Analgesic action of salicylates, 559
Analysis of organic compounds, accuracy, 24
    for the elements, 17
Analyzer, 332
Anesthesin, 558
Anesthetics, general, 141, 640, 834
    local, 558, 650
Anethole, 515, 537
Aneurin, 641
Angelic acid, 789
Anhydrides, 162–165
    addition to aldehydes, 204
    cyclic, from dicarboxylic acids, 796
        from 1,2-diketones, 876
    of sulfonic acids, 289
Anhydro sugars, 388
Aniline, absorption spectrum, 665
    nuclear-spin resonance spectrum, 669
    origin of name, 684
    oxidation, 481, 482
    syntheses, 486
Aniline acetate test for furfural, 617
Aniline Black, 696
Anilinium ion, absorption spectrum, 666
Anilinoquinone, 522
Anils, 482, 535
Animal fats and oils, 181
Anion exchange resins, 513, 575
Anionoid reagents, 117
Anisaldehyde, 537
Anise oil, 515
Anisic aldehyde, 537
Anisidines, 520
Anisole, 504
Annatto pigment, 866
Anomeric carbon atom, 372
Anomers, 372
Ansa compounds, 849
Antabuse, 325
Anthocyanidins, 698
Anthocyanins, 698
Anthracene, 596
    absorption spectrum, 667
    Diels-Alder reaction, 806
    isolation, 427
Anthracene oil, 427, 596
Anthracite, 426
Anthranilic acid, 558
    origin of name, 684
Anthranol, 601

Anthraquinone, 597
Anthraquinone dyes, 687
  plant pigments, 599
Anthraquinonesulfonic acids, 598
Anthraquinone Vat Blues, 689
Anthraquinone Vat Dark Blue BO, 691
Anthraquinone Vat Golden Orange G, 690
Anthraquinones, acylamino-, 689
Anthrone, 600
Anti-, prefix, 500, 542
Antibiotics, aureomycin, 604
  carbomycin, 847
  chloramphenicol, 530
  chloromycetin, 530
  erythromycin, 847
  Magnamycin, 847
  methymycin, 847
  mycomycin, 790
  penicillins, 636
  streptomycin, 414
  Terramycin, 604
  tetracycline, 604
Anticonvulsants, 634, 640
Antifebrine, 487
Antihemorrhagic factors, 593
Antihistaminics, 634
Antiknock agents, *see* Knock inhibitors, 80,
    904
Antimalarials, 653
Antimetabolites, 558
  aminopterin, 647
Antimony compounds, 903
Antioxidants, 886
  as gum inhibitors for gasoline, 77, 488,
      887
  for rubber, 712, 887
Antipyretics, 487, 559
Antispasmodics, 651
Apiose, 361
Arabans, 407
Arabic acid, 411
Arabinose, 361
Arabitol, 412
*Arabo*hexulose, 384
Arachidic acid, 147, 181
Arago, biography, 331
Aralen, 654
Aralkylamines, 527–530
Aralkyl halides, preparation, 434
  reactions, 437
Arginine, 297
  in nitrogen metabolism, 301
Argol, 809
Armstrong, biography, 671
Arndt-Eistert reaction, 267, 802
Arochlors, 578
Aromatic compounds, 416 ff., *see also in-
    dividual type, e.g.,* Nitro compounds

and Condensed nuclear hydrocar-
    bons
Aromatic hydrocarbons, nomenclature, 420
  reactions, 422
  sources, 426
  structure, 417
Aromatic rings, 846
Aromatization, alicyclic compounds, 66
  alkanes, 66
Aroyl chlorides, 549
Arrow poisons, 652, 870
Arsanilic acid, 902
Arsenic compounds, 900
Arsenites, 108
Arsenobenzene, 902
Arsenosomethane, 900
Arsenoso group, 900
Arsenoxides, 900
Arsine oxides, 900
Arsines, 900
Arsinic acids, 901
Arsonic acids, 495, 901, 902
Arsphenamine, 903
Arterenol, 529
Art gum, 720
Artificial leather, 402
Arylalkanes, 565
Arylalkenes, 573–577
Arylalkynes, 577
Arylation of aromatic amines, 478
Aryl cyanides from diazonium salts, 495
  from sulfonic acids, 469
Aryl ethers of polyethylene glycols, 744
Aryl groups, 421
Aryl halides, preparation, 433
    from diazonium salts, 494
    from phenols, 504
  reactions, 435
    ammonolysis, 477
Arylmalonic esters, 802
Ascaridole, 854, 883
Ascorbic acid, 387
Asparagine, 295
Aspartic acid, 297
Aspergillus oryzae, alcoholic fermentation,
    91
Asphalt, 82
Aspirin, 560
Association, alcohols, 87
  carboxylic acids, 148
  proton bonding, 87
A-stage resin, 512
Astrazon Pink FG, 694
Asymmetric atoms, 335, 350
Asymmetric decomposition, 344
Asymmetric synthesis, 342
Asymmetry, 335
Atabrine, 653

Ataraxic drugs, chlorpromazine, 643
  Equanil, 315
  meprobamate, 315
  Miltown, 315
  reserpine, 654
  Serpasil, 654
Atomic orbitals, 5
Atoxyl, 902
ATP, *see* Adenosine triphosphate, 644
Atropine, 650
Aubepine, 537
Aureomycin, 604
Aurins, 682
Auroxanthin, 866
Autoxidation, 880–886
  aldehydes, 885
  ethers, 884
  hydrocarbons, 881
Auxins, 595
Auxochromes, 671
Avocado, heptulose in, 388
Axial groups in cyclohexanes, 843
Azacyanine dyes, 694
Azafrin, 866
Azelaic acid, 793
Azeoptrope, *see* Constant-boiling mixture, 93
Azibenzil, 761
Azides, acyl, 268
  alkyl, 267
Azine dyes, 695
Azlactones, 635
Azobenzene, absorption spectrum, 665
  cis-trans isomers, 500
  preparation, 459
α,α′-Azobisisobutyronitrile, 265
Azo compounds, aliphatic, 265
  aromatic, 498, 676
Azo dyes, 676
Azoic dyes, 674, 677
Azomethane, 265
  absorption spectrum, 665
  free radicals from, 265, 568
Azophenin, 522
Azoxybenzene, 458
Azulenes, 859

Babassu oil, 180
Bacillus acetobutylicus, see *Clostridium,* 96
Baeyer, biography, 615
Baeyer strain theory, 828
Baeyer test for unsaturation, 57
Bakelite, 511
Baking process, sulfonation, 485, 589
BAL, 752
Balancing oxidation-reduction equations, 145
Balata, 713
Ballistite, 401, 749
Banana oil, *see* i-Amylacetate, 174

Band spectra, 662
Barbier, biography, 120
Barbital, 640
Barbiturates, 640
Barbituric acid, 639
Barium lithol, 703
Barrel process for vinegar, 158
Barrier to free rotation, ethane, 31
  nitroethane, 258
Bartholinus, biography, 330
Bart reaction, 495
Bases and acids, general concepts, 235
Basic dissociation constants, *see* Basicity
Basic dyes, 674
  azo, 677
  disazo, 678
  triphenylmethane, 679
Basicity, 98, 235
  acetamide, 312
  acetoxime, 211
  alcohols, 98, 252
  aldimines, 252
  alkylated benzenes, 449
  amides, 235, 246, 249
  amidines, 249
  amine oxides, 240
  amines, alicyclic, 834
    aliphatic, 234, 235
    aromatic, 462, 477
  cyanides, 252
  F strain, 896
  hydrazines, 264, 453
  hydroxylamines, 252, 453
  guanidine, 322
  ketones, 252
  oximes, 211, 252
  piperidine, 621
  pyridine, 621
  pyrrole, 611
  steric effect, 896
  trimethylsilylamine, 913
  urea, 312
    N-alkyl, 319
    o-alkyl, 319
Beckmann, biography, 544
Beckmann rearrangement, 544, 841
Beeswax, 178
Beet sugar, 393
Behenic acid, 147
Belladonna, 650
Benadryl, 526
Benedict solution, constitution, 810
  oxidation of aldehydes, 212
Benzal-, *see also* Benzylidene-
Benzaldehyde, 537
  autoxidation, 885
  cyanohydrin, 537
  reaction with picolines, 626
Benzaldoximes, stereochemistry, 542

Benzal halides, 434
Benzanilide, 544
Benzanthracenes, 603
Benzanthrone, 601, 691
Benzedrine, 529
Benzene, 416–426
  absorption spectrum, 665
  from acetylene, 910
  fluorination, 730
  homologs, 429
  m- and *p*-bridges, 848
  removal of thiophene, 608
Benzenediazonium chloride, 492
m-Benzenedisulfonic acid, 467
Benzene hexachloride, 432
Benzenesulfinic acid, 473
Benzenesulfonamides, 471
Benzenesulfonic acid, 466
Benzenesulfonyl chloride, 470
1,3,5-Benzenetrisulfonic acid, 467
Benzhydrol, 525
Benzhydryl ether, 525
Benzidam, 486
Benzidine, 578
Benzidine Blue, 579
Benzidine rearrangement, 578
Benzidine Yellows, 703
Benzil, 541
Benzilic acid rearrangement, 541
Benzoate radicals, 568, 882, 886
Benzofuran, 620
Benzoic acid, 550
Benzoin, 536
Benzoin condensation, 536
Benzol, *see* Benzene, 416
Benzonitrile, 469
Benzophenanthrenes, 603
Benzophenone, 541
Benzophenone oxime, 544
Benzopurpurin 4B, 678
Benzopyrans, 632
Benzopyrazines, 642
Benzopyridines, 628, 630
Benzopyrroles, 615
Benzopyrylium salts, 698
Benzoquinones, 520
Benzothiophenes, 609
Benzotrichloride, benzoic acid from, 547
Benzotrihalides, 434
Benzoylacetic ester, 815
Benzoylation, *see* Schotten-Baumann reaction, 549
o-Benzoylbenzoic acid, 596
Benzoyl chloride, 534, 550
Benzoyl peroxide, 550, 876
  free benzoate radicals from, 568
Benzoyl radicals, 885–888
Benzpinacol, 540
Benzyl acetate, 525

Benzyl alcohol, 525
Benzylamine, 527
Benzyl benzoate, 525
Benzyl chloride, 434
Benzyl chloroformate, 305
Benzyl cyanide, 803
Benzyl group, removal by catalytic reduction, 305, 526
Benzyl halides, reactivity, 463
Benzylideneacetone, 536
Benzylideneacetophenone, 541
Benzylideneaniline, 535
Benzylidene halides, 434
Benzylidenepicolines, 626
Benzylidyne halides, 434
Benzylisoquinolines, 651
Benzylmagnesium halides, abnormal reactions, 437
Benzylmethylglyoxime, 770
4-Benzyloxypyridine-*N*-oxide, 624
S-Benzylthiourea, 327
S-Benzyl thiuronium salts, 327
Bergius process, 83
Bergman, biography, 3
Bergmann, biography, 305
Berthelot, biography, 93
Beryllium compounds, 892
Berzelius, biography, 3
Betaines, 785
Betulin, 863
Bhang, 633
BHC, 432
Biguanide, 321
Bile acids, 869
Bile pigments, 615
Bile salts, 869
Bilirubin, 615
Bimolecular mechanism, displacement reactions, 116
Binary mixtures, 94
Bios I, 414
Biot, biography, 332
Biotin, 648
Biphenyls, 496, 578
2,2'-Biphenyldicarboxylic acid, 602
Biphenylenemercury, 890
Biradicals, 570, 669
Birch bark pigment, 863
Bisabolene, 858
Bischler-Napieralski synthesis, 630
1,1-Bis-*p*-chlorophenyl-2,2,2-trichloroethane, 566
Bis(diphenylmethyl)biphenyls, 570
Bis(2-hydroxyethyl)amine, 752
Bismarck Browns, 678
1,1-Bis-*p*-methoxyphenyl-2,2,2-trichloroethane, 566
Bismuth compounds, 903
Bisphenol-A, 514, 750

Bisulfite addition compounds, 201, 763
Bisulfonium ion, 448
Bitter almond oil, 463, 537
Bituminous coal, 426
Biuret, 316
Biuret reaction, 306, 316
Bixin, 866
Black pepper, 649
Blackstrap molasses, 92, 394
Blanc rule, 798
Blankophors, 675, 679
Blood pigments, 613
Blood plasma extenders, dextran, 407
    polyvinylpyrrolidone, 785
Blowing agents, 473, 555
Boat form, cyclohexane, 843
Boiling point apparatus, 23
Boiling points, 14, *see also* Physical properties
    of alkanes, alkyl halides, and alcohols, 114
    of *n*-alkyl derivatives of water, ammonia, and hydrogen sulfide, 276
    and dipole moments, 251
    effect of branching, 38
    effect of proton bonding, 87
    and van der Waals forces, 38, 86, 197
Boiling point diagrams of binary mixtures, 94
BON acid, 594, 677
Bond angles, 9
    benzene, 419
    cobalt complexes, 352
    ethylene, 355
    nickel complexes, 770
Bond distances, *see* Interatomic distances
Bond energies, 45
Bond moments, 198
Bond orbitals, 9
Bonds, direction of, 9
    benzene, 419
    cobalt complexes, 352
    nickel complexes, 770
Bond strengths, 45
Bond types, 5
Bone oil, 610
Borates, 108
Boric acid, conductivity change with glycols, 376, 741
Borinic acids, 896
Borneo camphor, 856
Borneol, 856
Boron compounds, 896
Boronic acids, 896
Boron trifluoride, polymerization catalyst, 62
Bottled gas, 72
Branched chains, 30

Branching of chain, effect on boiling and melting points, 38
Brassidic acid, 794
Brassylic acid, 794
von Braun, biography, 239
von Braun reaction, 239
Bredt rule, 857
Bridged benzene rings, 848
Briegleb models, *see* Stuart models, 30
British Anti-Lewisite, 752
Bromides, *see* Halides
Bromination, *see* Halogenation
Bromindigo Blue 2BD, 686
p-Bromoacetanilide, 484
Bromoacetone, 765
ω-Bromoacetophenone, 541
Bromo acids, 778, 779
Bromobenzene, 435
p-Bromobenzenesulfonyl chloride, 471
Bromobutenes, 728
Bromocyanogen, *see* Cyanogen bromide, 239, 280, 319
Bromoform, 215
2-Bromofuran, 895
p-Bromomandelic acid, 562
Bromonaphthalenes, 588
Bromonium ion, 54
Bromophenols, 505
4-Bromopyridine-*N*-oxide, 624
Bromopyridines, 622
ω-Bromostyrene, 576
N-Bromosuccinimide, 797, 813
Bromotoluenes, 434
Bromotrifluoromethane, 733
3-Bromotyrosine, 297
Brønsted, biography, 236
Brønsted theory of acids and bases, 236
Brosylation, 471
Brosyl chloride, 471
Brown sugar, 394
Bubble cap column, 15
Bucherer reaction, 588
Bufotalin, 870
Buna *N*, 718
Buna rubbers, 715
Buna *S*, 717
Bunsen, biography, 901
Burton, biography, 73
Butacite, *see* Polyvinylbutyral, 737
1,3-Butadiene, absorption spectrum, 663
    preparation, 79, 716
    reactions, 707
    synthetic rubbers, 717
1,3-Butanediol, 746
1,4-Butanediol, 717
2,3-Butanediol, 746
Butanes, equilibrium composition of isomeric, 78
    structure, 29
Butanetetracarboxylic esters, 801

Butanols, *see* Butyl alcohols
Butatriene, 706
Butenes, conversion to butadiene, 716
 to butyl alcohols, 97
 to gasoline, 76, 77
 to polymers, 62, 76
 to synthetic rubber, 718
2-Butenes, configuration, 355
Butesin, 558
Butlerov, biography, 220
Butter, 180
 flavor, 186
n-Butyl acetate, 173
i-Butyl alcohol, abnormal behavior, 102
 from fusel oil, 91
n-Butyl alcohol, from acetaldehyde, 222
 by fermentation, 96
s-Butyl alcohol, 97
t-Butyl alcohol, 97
n-Butylamines, 241
n-Butyl-*p*-aminobenzoate, 558
p-*t*-Butylbenzoic acid, 551
Butyl bromides, *see* Halides, alkyl
n-Butyl *n*-Butyrate, 174
t-Butyl chloride, dipole moment, 453
t-Butyl cyanide, 250
β-Butylene glycol, 746
Butylenes, *see* Butenes
n-Butyl ether, 141
t-Butyl ethyl malonate, acylation, 817
i-Butyl halides, reactivity, 116, 117
t-Butyl hydroperoxide, 874
t-Butyl hypochlorite, 109
n-Butyllithium, 889
t-Butyl malonate, 801
n-Butyl mercaptan, 289
n-Butyl nitrite, 110
t-Butyl peroxide, 875
t-Butyl peroxybenzoate, 877
t-Butylphenol, 513
n-Butyl phthalate, 552
i-Butyl propionate, 174
Butyl rubber, 718
t-Butylthiophenes, 608
Butyn, 559
Butynediol, 205
i-Butyraldehyde, 223, 742
n-Butyraldehyde, 223, 747
n-Butyric acid, 147, 159
γ-Butyrolactam, 784
β-Butyrolactone, 824
γ-Butyrolactone, 783

C^{14}, radioactive tracer, 813, 832
Cacodyl oxide, 900
Cacodyls, 901
Cadalene, 858
Cadaverine, 756
Cadet liquid, 900

Cadinene, 858
Cadmium compounds, 196, 893
Caffeine, 646
Calciferol, 868
Calcium carbide, 133
 conversion to cyanamide, 320
Calcium cyanamide, 320
Calcium propionate, 159
Caledon Jade Green, 691
C-alkylation, *see* Carbon alkylation
Camomile oil, 859
Camphane, 855
Camphene, 856
Camphor, 856
Camphoric acid, 856
Camphor oil, 516
10-Camphorsulfonic acid, 856
Cane sugar, 393
Cannizzaro, biography, 3
 and molecular weights, 3, 21
Cannizzaro reaction, aliphatic aldehydes, 219
 aromatic aldehydes, 534
 crossed, 534
 glyoxal, 771
 mechanism, 535
Capric acid, 147, 181
Caproic acid, 147, 181
ε-Caprolactam, 841
Capryl alcohol, 794
Caprylic acid, 147, 181
Capsaicin, 649
Captan, 843
Captax, 636
Carane, 855
Carbamates, 315, 317
Carbamic acid, 311
Carbamide, 310
Carbamidine, *see* Guanidine, 321
Carbamyl chlorides, 317
Carbanions, 42, 573
Carbazole, 616
 dyes, 689
 isolation, 428
Carbene, *see* Methylene group
Carbethoxy group, *see* Ethoxycarbonyl group, 169
Carbides, 131
Carbinol base, 680
Carbinols, 84
Carbitols, 744
Carboalkoxy group, *see* Alkoxycarbonyl group, 169
Carbobenzoxy chloride, *see* Benzyl chloroformate, 305
Carbobenzoxy group, *see* Benzyloxycarbonyl group, 305
Carbocyanines, 693
Carbocyclic compounds, 25, 606

Carbodiimides, 322
Carbohydrates, *see also individual compound, e.g.,* Glucose
acetates, 377, 382
acetone sugars, 379
action of alkali, 368
action of strong acids, 378
aldehydo derivatives, 380
aldonic acids, 360
aldoses, 360
amino sugars, 409, 411
anhydro sugars, 388
anomers, 372
benzoates, 378
boric acid complexes, 376
carbonates, 378
classification, 359
configuration, 361–367, 384
conversion to next higher sugar, 380
cyanohydrin reaction, 362, 380
cyclic acetal formation, 379
definition, 359
degradation by alkali, 368
degradation to lower sugars, 381
deoxy sugars, 367
dextrans, 407
disaccharides, 389
end group method, 398
enediol forms, 368
epimerization, 381
ester formation, 377
families, D and L, 365
fermentation, 90
furanoses, 386
gamma(γ)-sugars, 386
glycaric acids, 362
glyconic acids, 360, 362
glyconolactones, 380
glycosans, 388
glycoside formation, 371
glycuronic acids, 408
gums, 411
Haworth formulas, 383
heteropolysaccharides, 410
hexosans, 407
hexoses, 360
homopolysaccharides, 396
hydrazones, 371, 382
immunopolysaccharides, 411
isomerization, 368
isopropylidene derivatives, 379
ketoses, 384
Kiliani reaction, 362, 380
lactones, 380
Lobry de Bruyn-Alberda van Ekenstein transformation, 368
mercaptals, 382
mesyl derivatives, 378
metabolism, 398

Carbohydrates—(*Continued*)
methylation, 373, 390
methylpentoses, 367
monosaccharides, 360
mucilages, 411
mutarotation, 374
nitrates, 378
nomenclature, 359
nonreducing disaccharides, 393
oligosaccharides, 389
osazone formation, 363, 370
osazones, solubility, 392
oxidation by Fehling solution, 370
by Fenton reagent, 381
to glycaric acids, 362
by periodic acid, 373
pectins, 407
pentosans, 407
pentoses, 361
phosphates, 378
polysaccharides, 396
pyranoses, 386
reaction with Schiff reagent, 375
reducing disaccharides, 389
ring structures, 373, 376, 383
of oximes and hydrazones, 382
saccharic acids, 362
sugar acetones, 379
sugar alcohols, 411
sugar anhydrides, 388
sulfonates, 378
sweetness, 385
synthesis from lower sugars, 380
of monosaccharides, 386
of sucrose, 395
tosyl derivatives, 378
trisaccharides, 395
uronic acids, 408
Carbolic acid, 503
Carbolic oil, 427
Carbomethoxy group, *see* Methoxycarbonyl group, 169
Carbomycin, 847
Carbon, analysis for, 17, 18
radioactive, as tracer element, 813, 832
test for, 17
tetravalency, 14
Carbon alkylation of acyloins, 760
of cyanides, 254
of 1,3-diketones, 773
of glutaconic ester, 808
of β-keto esters, 820
of malonic esters, 800, 803
of nitroalkanes, 263
of quinones, 594
of sulfones, 286
Carbonates, 310
cyclic, 741
Carbonation of Grignard reagents, 123, 143
Carbon black, 70

Carbon dioxide, reaction with Grignard reagents, 123, 143
Carbon disulfide, 324
  chlorination, 722
  for viscose rayon, 405
Carbonic acid derivatives, 308 ff.
Carbonium ions, 42, 572
Carbonium-ion intermediates, acid-catalyzed polymerizations, 62
  addition reactions, 60
  dehydration of alcohols, 104
  hydrolysis of alkyl halides, 116
  reactions of alcohols with halogen acids, 102
  removal of halogen acids from alkyl halides, 118
Carbonization of coal, 426
Carbon monoxide, from natural gas, 70
  synthesis of aldehydes, 223, 531
    of ethylene glycol, 743
    of glycollic acid, 743
    of hydrocarbons, 83
    of ketones, 223
    of methyl alcohol, 90
    of sodium formate, 157
Carbon oxysulfide, 324
Carbon skeleton, 32
Carbon suboxide, 796
Carbon tetrachloride, 722
  addition to olefins, 725
  as derivative of orthocarbonic acid, 310
  thermal decomposition, 724
Carbonylation, tetrahydrofuran, 793
Carbonyl chloride, *see* Phosgene, 310
Carbonyl compounds, *see also* Aldehydes *and* Ketones
  absorption spectra, 665
  amino, 766
  halogenated, 765
  hydroxylated, 759
  unsaturated, 760
Carbonyl group, polarization of, 123
  reduction to methylene, 216
Carbostyril, 629
Carbowaxes, 744
Carboxylate ion, resonance, 153
Carboxylic acids, aliphatic, nomenclature, 147
  physical properties, 148
    Duclaux values, 150
  preparation, 143–145
    from cyanides, 253
    from β-keto esters, 821
    from malonic esters, 800
    from nitroalkanes, 262
  reactions, 150–157
    of salts, 156
    Schmidt reaction, 232
Carboxylic acids, aromatic, 547, 548

Carboxymethylcellulose, 404
Carbylamine test, 237
Carcinogenic hydrocarbons, 604
Cardanol, 516
Cardiac glycosides, 810
Carius method, 20
Carnauba wax, 178
Carob bean flour, 411
Caro reagent, 436
Carotenes, 864
Carotenoids, 863
Carothers, biography, 719
Carrot pigments, 864
Carvacrol, 515
Carvone, 854
Caryophyllenes, 859
Cascara, 599
Casein, 295, 299
Cassava, 255
Cassia oil, 537
Castor oil, 181, 182
  dehydration, 187
  pyrolysis, 789, 794
  sulfation, 191
Catalases, 615
Catalytic dehydrogenation of alcohols, 194
Catalytic hydrogenation, *see* Hydrogenation
Catalytic reduction, *see* Hydrogenation
Catalysts, 42
Catechol, *see* Pyrocatechol, 516
Cation-exchange resins, 513, 575
Cationic detergents, 243
Cationoid reagents, 117
Cayenne pepper, 649
Cedar oil, 859
α-Cedrene, 859
Celery oil, 858
Celliton Fast Blue FFR, 688
Celliton Fast Pink, 688
Celliton Fast Yellow G, 677
Celliton Fast Yellow 7G, 694
Cellobiose, 391
Cellophane, 406
Cellosolve, 744
Celluloid, 402
Cellulose, 398
  acetates, 403
  acetatebutyrates, 404
  acetatepropionates, 404
  esters, 400
  ethers, 404
  nitrates, 401
  oxidized, 405
  xanthate, 405
α-Cellulose, 401
Cellulose acetate dyeing, 675
  anthraquinone dyes, 688
  azo dyes, 677
  methylidyne dyes, 694
  nitro dyes, 676

Celogen, 473
Center of symmetry, 336
  in α-truxillic acid, 836
Cephalins, 753
Cerotic acid, 147
Cetane, 81
Cetane number, 81
Cetyl alcohol, 172
Cetyl palmitate, 178
Cetylsulfonic acid, 287
Cetyltrimethylammonium chloride, 243
Chain reaction, 46
Chair form, cyclohexane, 843
Chalcones, 541
Chardonnet process, 406
Charge distribution of electron, 9
Chaulmoogra oil, 839
Chaulmoogric acid, 839
Chelate compounds, Benedict solution, 810
  biuret reaction, 306, 316
  from carbohydrates and boric acid, 276
  of 1,3-diketones, 772
  ethylenediamines, 756
  ethylenediaminetetraacetic acid, 755
  Fehling solution, 810
  from 1,2-glycols and boric acid, 742
  8-hydroxyquinoline, 630
  of β-keto esters, 818
  in mordant dyeing, 674
  oximes of 1,2-diketones, 770
  o-phenanthroline, 631
  phthalocyanines, 704
  porphyrins, 614
Chelation, 742
Chelidonic acid, 632
Chemical Foundation, 673
Chemotherapy, 903
Chenodeoxycholic acid, 869
Chenopodium oil, 854
Chevreul, biography, 179
Chichibabin, biography, 622
Chichibabin hydrocarbon, 570, 669
Chichibabin reaction, 622
Chicle, 714
China wood oil, 183
Chitin, 409
Chitosamine, *see* 2-Amino-2-deoxyglucose, 409
Chloral, 739
Chloral hydrate, 740
Chloramine-B, 472
Chloramine-T, 472
Chloramphenicol, 530
Chloranil, 522
Chlordan, 837
Chlorex, 141
  in refining lubricating oils, 81
Chlorides, *see* Halides

Chlorinated hydrocarbons, aliphatic, 722–728
  aromatic, 432, 438
Chlorinated rubber, 713
Chlorination, *see* Halogenation
Chloroacetic acid, 779, 781
Chloroacetone, 765
ω-Chloroacetophenone, 541
Chloro acids, 778, 779
Chloroamines, reaction with Grignard reagents, 233
1-Chloro-4-aminobutane, pyrolysis, 613
m-Chloroaniline, 484
N-Chloroaniline, 458
Chloroanthraquinones, 599
Chlorobenzene, 433
2-Chloro-1,3-butadiene, 719
Chlorocarbonates, 310
Chlorocarbonic acid, 308
Chlorocyanogen, *see* Cyanogen chloride, 319
1-Chloro-1,1-difluoroethane, 733
Chlorodifluoromethane, 733
Chloroethylene, 725
β-Chloroethyl ether, 141
  in refining of lubricating oils, 81
β-Chloroethyl formal, 743
β-Chloroethyl sulfide, 289
Chlorofluoromethane, 732
2-Chloro-2-fluoropropane, 731
Chloroform, 215, 722
Chloroformates, 310
Chloroformic acid, 308
Chlorohydrins, 743
2-Chloromercurithiophene, 608
Chloromethylation benzene, 435
  naphthalene, 595
  thiophene, 608
Chloromethyl ketones, 267
2-Chloromethyltetrahydropyran, 739
2-Chloromethylthiophene, 608
(Chloromethyl)trichlorosilane, 914
(Chloromethyl)trimethylsilane, 915
Chloromycetin, 530
Chloronaphthalenes, 585, 588
Chloronitrobenzenes, 440
Chlorophylls, 614
Chloropicrin, 264, 515
  use in preparation of orthocarbonates, 310
Chloroplatinates of amines, 234
Chloroprene, 719
3-Chloro-1,2-propanediol, 749
Chloropyridine-N-oxide, 624
Chloropyridines, 612, 624
Chloroquine, 654
N-Chlorosulfonamides, 472
Chlorosulfonates, alkyl, 108

Chlorosulfonation of aromatic compounds, 470
8-Chlorotheophylline, 647
2-Chlorothiophene, 608
Chlorotoluenes, 434
N-Chloro-*p*-toluenesulfonamide sodium salt, 472
2-Chlorovinyldichlorarsine, 902
Chlorpromazine, 643
Cholesterol, 867, 868
Cholic acid, 869
Choline chloride, 243
Chondroitin sulfuric acid, 411
Chromatographic adsorption, 17, 863
Chrome Blue Black R, 677
Chrome dyes, 674
Chromium compounds, 903
Chromium trioxide, as oxidizing agent, 144
Chromone, 697
Chromophores, 671
Chromoproteins, 295
Chrysanthemic acid, 840
Chrysanthemum carboxylic acids, 840
Chrysene, 603
Chrysoidine Y, 677
Chugaev, biography, 121
Chymotrypsins, 301
Cinchomeronic acids, 630
Cinchona alkaloids, 653
Cinchona bark, 652
Cinchonicine, 653
Cinchonidine, 653
Cinchonine, 653
Cinchoninic acid, 630
Cineole, 854
Cinerins, 839
Cinerolone, 840
Cine substitution, 456
Cinnamaldehyde, 536, 537
Cinnamic acid, 562
    decarboxylation to styrene, 562
Cinnamic aldehyde, 536, 537
Cinnamon oil, 537
Cinnamyl alcohol, 527
Circular dichroism, 344
Circularly-polarized light, 344, 352
cis isomers, 355
cis-trans isomerism, *see* Geometrical isomerism, 354
cis-trans isomerization by light, 663
Citraconic acid, 808
Citraconic anhydride, 807
Citrals, 850
β-Citraurin, 866
Citric acid, 807, 810
Citric acid cycle, 811
Citronellal, 853
Citronella oil, 853

Citronellol, 853
Citrovorum factor, 647
Citrulline, 298
Civetone, 847
Claisen, biography, 814
Claisen ester condensations, 802, 814
    with ketones, 768
    with sulfones, 286
Claisen reaction, 536
Clarke-Othmer process, 159
Clathrate compounds, 97; *see also* Inclusion compounds, 311
Clemmensen reduction of ketones, 216, 219
Cleve acids, 589
Clostridium acetobutylicum, 96
Clove oil, 516, 859
CMC, 404
C-Methyl determination, 144
Coal, 426
Coal gas, 426
Coal tar, 427
Coal tar dyes, historical, 672
Cobaltammines with ethylenediamine, 756
Cobalt carbonyl, 904
Cobalt complex ions, optically active, 352
Coca bush, 650
Cocaine, 650
Cocarboxylase, 641
Cocoa, 646
Coconut oil, 180, 181
Codeine, 651
Cod-liver oil, 860
Coenzyme A, 645
Coenzymes I and II, 625
Coffee, 646
    aroma, 620
Coke, from coal, 426
    from petroleum, 82
Cola nuts, 646
Cold rubber, 717
Collagen, 294
Collidines, 627
Collodion cotton, 401
Colophony, 861
Color, 670
    and chemical structure, 671
    of flowers, 698
    of polynitro molecular complexes, 460
Color base, 680
Color photography, 692
Columbian spirits, 89
Colza oil, 183
Combustion apparatus, 17
Common names, 33
Composition, 21, 329
Compression ratio, Diesel engines, 81
    gasoline engines, 73
Condensation polymers, 314

Condensation reactions, 205
Condensed nuclear hydrocarbons, 582
Condensed rings, 582
Condensed tannins, 698
Configuration, 329
  absolute, 347
  amino acids, 349
  geometrical isomers, 355
  monosaccharides, 361–367, 384
  relative, 349
  various compounds, 347
Conformation, cyclohexanes, 843
  definition, 31, 329
  effect on ultraviolet, absorption of 1,2-
    diketones, 769
  ethane, 31
  long-chain hydrocarbons, 31, 32
Congo Red, 678
Coniferin, 527
Coniferyl alcohol, 527
Coniine, 648
Conjugate acids and bases, 235
Conjugated dienes, 707
  absorption spectra, 663, 707
  1,4-addition, 707
  addition of maleic anhydride, 806, 861
  of sulfur dioxide, 285
Conjugated polyenes, absorption spectra,
    664
  autoxidation, 882
Conjugated proteins, 294
Conjugation, 707
Constant-boiling mixtures, 93
Constitution, 30, 329
Coordinate covalence, 238
Coordination complexes, alcohols and me-
    tallic salts, 97
Copaene, 859
Copals, 860
Copolymerization, 717
Copper compounds, 891
Copper ethyl acetoacetate, 818
Copper phthalocyanine, 704
Coprosterol, 868
Cordite, 401, 749
Cori ester, 378
Corn oil, 181, 182, 396
Corn starch, 396
Corn steep water, 396
Corn syrup, 398
Coronene, 604
  absorption spectrum, 667
Corticosterone, 871
Cortin, 871
Cortisone, 871
Cotton, 400
  direct dyes, 678
Cotton effect, 344
Cottonseed oil, 181, 182

Coumarin, 562
Coumarone, 620
Coumarone resins, 620
Couper, biography, 14
Couple, metallic, 216
  reduction by, 216
Coupling reaction of diazonium salts, 498
  with naphthols and naphthylamines, 676
Covalence, 7
Covalent bonds, 7, 9
Cracking, alkanes, 44
  basic equipment, 74
  Burton process, 73
  catalytic, 75
  Dubbs' process, 74
  Fluid Catalyst process, 75
  hydrocarbons to acetylene, 133
  petroleum, 74, 75
  thermal, 74
  Thermofor process, 75
Crafts, biography, 423
Cranberry wax, 863
Cream of tartar, 809
Creatine, 322
Creatinine, 322
Creosote oil, 427, 515
Crepe rubber, 709
Cresols, 428, 502, 515
Cresylic acid, 502
  in refining lubricating oils, 81
Cresyl phosphate, 515
Criegee reaction, 742
Critical complex, *see* Transition state, 42
Crocetin, 866
Crocin, 867
Cronar, 555
Crossed Cannizzaro reaction, 534
Crotonaldehyde, 207
Crotonic acid, 789
Crotonic aldehyde, 207
Crotyl alcohol, 738
Cryoscopic molecular weight determination,
    21, 22
Cryptophenols, 515
Cryptoxanthin, 865
Crystallite, 788
Crystallization, 16
Crystal Violet, 681
  absorption spectrum, 699
  indicator action, 700
Cube root, 633
Cumar resin, 427
Cumene, 420, 430
  phenol from, 511
Cumene hydroperoxde, 874
Cumulative double bonds, 314, 706
Cumulenes, 706
Cupferron, 458
Cuprammonium process for rayon, 406

Cuprammonium solution, 399
Cupriethylenediamine solution, 399
Cuprous acetylide, 132
Cuprous carbide, 132
Curare, 652
Curtius, biography, 268
Curtius rearrangement, 268
Cyamelide, 314
Cyanamide, 320
  secondary amines from, 232
Cyanates, 316
Cyanic acid, 314
Cyanides, alkyl, nomenclature, 249
  physical properties, 250
  physiological action, 252
  preparation, 249
    from isocyanides, 257
    from primary amines, 231
  reactions, 252–255
    amidines from, 249
    with Grignard reagents, 196
    imido esters from, 248
    ortho esters from, 175
Cyanides, aryl, from diazonium salts, 495
  from sulfonic acids, 469
  reaction with Grignard reagents, 540
Cyanidin chloride, 698
Cyanine dyes, 693
Cyanoacetic acid, 792
o-Cyanobenzoic acid, 554
β-Cyano esters, 792
Cyanoethylation, 788
Cyanogen bromide, 319
  reaction with amines, 239
    with sulfides, 279
Cyanogen chloride, 319
Cyanogenetic glycosides, 255, 537
Cyanogen iodide, 319
Cyanohydrins, 200
3-Cyanopyridine, 623
Cyanurates, 317
Cyanuric acid, 314
Cyanuric chloride, 320
Cyclamate, 843
Cyclanes, 828
Cyclic acetals, from dihydropyran, 632
  from 1,2-glycols, 741
  from sugars, 379
Cyclic anhydrides from dicarboxylic acids, 796
Cyclic carbonates, 637, 741
Cyclic hydrocarbons, *see* Alicyclic hydro-
  carbons *and* Aromatic hydrocarbons
Cyclization, carboxylic acids, 598
  diketones, 775, 776
  ester condensations, 816
  ethyl adipate, 816
  terpenes, 851, 858
1,3-Cyclobutanediones, 762

Cyclobutanes, 835
  reactions, 832
Cyclobutanol, 832
Cyclobutenes, 836
Cyclobutylamine, 832
Cyclobutylcarbinol, 832
Cyclocitrals, 852
Cycloheptanes, 829, 844
Cycloheptanone, 844
Cycloheptatrienyl bromide, 844
Cyclohexadienones, 842
Cyclohexane, 830
  isomerization, 833
  oxidation to adipic acid, 793
  stability, 829
Cyclohexanecarboxylic acid, 550
1,3-Cyclohexanedione, 841
Cyclohexanes, 841
  conformation, 843
  polyhydroxy, 842
  stereoisomerism, 843
Cyclohexanol, 841
  oxidation to adipic acid, 793
  reactions, 834
Cyclohexanone, 793, 798
  oxidation to adipic acid, 793
Cyclohexanone oxime, 841
Cyclohexene, 834
  autoxidation, 881
4,5-Cyclohexenedicarboxylic anhydride,
  806
Cyclohexene oxide, 833
Cyclohexenes, 831
Cyclohexenones, 842
  from 1,5-dicarbonyl compounds, 775
2-Cyclohexenyl hydroperoxide, 881
1-Cyclohexenyllithium, 889
Cyclohexylamine, 834, 841
Cyclohexyl bromide, 834
Cyclohexylsulfamic acid, 843
Cyclonite, 221
Cyclooctatetraene, 845
Cycloparaffins, 828
Cyclopentadecanone, 847
Cyclopentadiene, 837
  addition of maleic anhydride, 806
Cyclopentadienecarboxylic acid, 838
Cyclopentadienones, 770
Cyclopentadienyl anion, 838
Cyclopentanes, 829, 837
Cyclopentanone, 798
  oxidation to glutaric acid, 793
Cyclopentene, 832
Cyclopentylformaldehyde, 833
Cyclophanes, 849
Cyclopropanedicarboxylic esters, 801
Cyclopropanes, 834
  reactions, 831, 832
Cyclopropene, 835

Cyclopropylamine, 835
Cyclopropylcarbinol, 832
(Cyclopropylmethyl)amine, 832
p-Cymene, 420, 431
  from citral, 851
  p-cresol from, 515
Cysteic acid, 301
Cysteine, 296
Cystine, 296
Cytidylic acids, 644
Cytochromes, 615
Cytosine, 638

2,4-D, 514
Dacron, 555
  dyeing, 675
  dyes, 688
Damson gum, 411
Dandelion rubber, 708
Daraprim, 654
Darzens reaction, 780
Dative bond, definition, 238
d atomic orbitals, 5, 273
DDD, 566
DDT, 566
Deactivating groups in aromatic substitution, 442
Deactivation of benzene nucleus, cause, 449
Dead oil, 427
Deadly nightshade, 650
Debenzylation, 305, 526
Debye unit, 198
Decahydronaphthalenes, 584, 843
Decalins, 584, 843
Decanes, 33
Decarbonylation, 813
Decarboxylation, aromatic acids, 549
  cinnamic acid, 562
  gallic acid, 517
  β-keto acids, 814
  malonic acids, 795
  phenolcarboxylic acids, 518
  pyridineacetic acids, 628
  pyridinecarboxylic acids, 627
  pyrrolecarboxylic acids, 613
  trichloroacetic acid, 779
  2,4,6-trinitrobenzoic acid, 464
  unsaturated acids, 786, 787
Decolorizing carbon, 16
Defecation of cane juice, 393
Deformation vibrations, 659
Degras, 178
Dehydration, alcohols, 104
  aldols, 207
  aldoximes, 250
  amides, 250
  borneol, 856

Dehydroabietic acid, 861
7-Dehydrocholesterol, 868
Dehydrogenation, alcohols, 105, 194
  alicyclic hydrocarbons, 66
  alkanes, 79
  with selenium, 602, 863, 867
  with sulfur, 602, 858–862
Dehydromatricaric acid, 790
Delepine reaction, 232
Delocalization energy, 153
Delphinidin chloride, 698
Demerol, 651
Denatured alcohol, 95
Denier, 406
Density, see Physical properties
Deoxyaldoses, 367, 381
Deoxycholic acid, 869
Deoxycorticosterone, 871
6-Deoxy-L-galactose, 367
6-Deoxy-L-mannose, 367
2-Deoxy-D-ribose, 368
Deoxy sugars, 367
Depolymerization, 208, 837
Depsides, 561
Derris root, 633
Desmejanov reaction, 832
Desoxy, see Deoxy
Destructive distillation, coal, 426
  wood, 89
Destructive hydrogenation of carbonaceous material, 79
Desulfuration with Raney nickel, 285
Detergents, alkylated aromatic sulfonic acids, 469
  Aerosols, 290
  cationic, 243
  nonionic, 744
  soaps, 187
  sulfated alcohols, 191
  synthetic, 191
Deuterium, as tracer element, 214, 369, 446
Deuterium exchange, aldehydes and ketones, 202
  aromatic nucleus, 446
  monosaccharides, 369
1-Deuterobutyl acetate, resolution, 344
Developed Black BH, 678
Developed dyeing, 674, 678
Dewaxing lubricating oils, 81
Dexedrine, 529
Dextrans, 407
Dextrins, 398
Dextrorotation, 332
Dextrose, 360
D family, 348
  sugars, 365
Diacetic acid, 814
Diacetonamine, 764

Diacetone alcohol, 206, 208
  reduction to glycol, 746
Diacetyl, 771
  absorption spectrum, 665
  butter flavor, 186
Diacetyl peroxide, *see* Acetyl peroxide
Dialkylhydrazines, 264
Diamagnetism, 567
Diamines, 754
2,7-Diaminoacridine, 695
Diaminoanthraquinones, 600
1,1-Diamino compounds, 752
Diaminodiphenyl sulfone, 489
Di-*i*-amyl ether, *see i*-Amyl ether, 141
Dianisidine, 578
Diastase, 91
Diastereoisomers, 337
Diazines, 638
Diazoacetic ester, 267
Diazoaminobenzene, 498
Diazoates, 499
Diazo compounds, aliphatic, 266
  addition to double bonds, 834
  aromatic, 499
Diazo cyanides, 499
Diazo hydrates, 499
Diazo hydroxides, 499
Diazoic acids, 499
Diazomethane, 266
  reaction with enols, 818
    with ketones, 831
    with nitroalkanes, 263
    with silicon tetrachloride, 914
  ring enlargement, 831
  synthesis, 318, 473
Diazomethyl ketones, 267
Diazonium salts, 492
  preparation, 493
  reactions with elimination of nitrogen, 494
    without elimination of nitrogen, 497
    with quinones, 522
Diazotates, 499
Diazotization, 493
Diazotype process, 697
Dibenzalacetone, 536
Dibenzanthracenes, 604
Dibenzopyrazine, 642
Dibenzopyridine, 631
Dibenzopyrone, 633
2,4-Dibenzopyrrole, 616
Dibenzothiophene, 609
Dibenzoyl peroxide, *see* Benzoyl peroxide, 550, 876
Dibenzylamine, 527
Dibenzylideneacetone, 536
Dibromodifluoromethane, 733
1,3-Dibromo-5,5-dimethylhydantoin, 635
3,5-Dibromopyridine, 622

2,6-Dibromoquinone chloroimide, 523
3,5-Dibromotyrosine, 297
Dibutyl, *see also* Butyl
Di-*i*-butylaluminum hydride, 898
2,6-Di-*t*-butyl-4-methylphenol, 515
N,N'-Di-*s*-butyl-*p*-phenylenediamine, 488
Dicarbonyl compounds, preparation, 767–769
  reactions, 769–776
Dicarboxylic acids, hydroxy, 808–811
Dicarboxylic acids, saturated, preparation, 791–794
  reactions, 794–800
Dicarboxylic acids, unsaturated, 805–808
Dichloramine T, 472
Dichloroacetaldehyde, 739
Dichloroacetic acid, 779
9,10-Dichloroanthracene, 597
Dichlorobenzenes, 433
1,4-Dichloro-2-butyne, 748
Dichlorocarbene, *see* Dichloromethylene
1,1-Dichloro-2,2-difluoroethylene, dimerization, 835
Dichlorodifluoromethane, 732
Dichlorodiphenyltrichloroethane, *see* DDT, 566
1,2-Dichloroethane, 723
1,1-Dichloroethylene, 726
1,2-Dichloroethylenes, 724
  configuration, 355
Di-*β*-chloroethyl ether, *see β*-Chloroethyl ether, 141
Dichlorofluoromethane, 732
Dichloromethane, *see* Methylene chloride, 722
Dichloromethylene, addition to double bond, 835
  intermediate in reactions of chloroform, 175, 237, 532, 612
Dichloronaphthalenes, 584
2,4-Dichlorophenoxyacetic acid, *see* 2,4-D, 514
Dichlorophosphines, 908
1,3-Dichloro-2-propanol, 749
Dichloropropenes, 727
2,6-Dichloroquinone chloroimide, 523
1,2-Dichloro-1,1,2,2-tetrafluoroethane, 733
N,N-Dichloro-*p*-toluenesulfonamide, 472
Dichroism, 331, 344
Dicoumarin, 563
Dicumarol, 563
Dicyandiamide, 320
Dicyandiamidine, 321
Dicyclohexylammonium nitrite, 843
Dicyclopentadiene, 837
Dicyclopentadienyliron, 838
2,6-Dideoxy-D-allose, 368
Dieckmann condensation, 816
Dielectric constant, 12

Dieldrin, 837
Diels-Alder diene syntheses, 765, 806
Diels, biography, 806
Diels hydrocarbon, 867
Dienes, 706, *see also* Conjugated dienes
Dienone-phenol rearrangement, 842
Dienophiles, 806
Diesel engines, 81
Diesel oil, 80
Diethanolamine, 752
Diethyl, *see also* Ethyl
2,2'-Diethyladipic acid, 794
Diethylaluminum hydride, 897
p-Diethylaminoaniline, 490
1,1'-Diethyl-2-2'-carbocyanine iodide, 694
1,1'-Diethyl-2,2'-cyanine iodide, 693
Diethyldiethoxysilane, 912
Diethylene glycol, 744
Diethylenetriamine, 755
Diethylenimine, 754
Diethylidene peroxide, 885
Diethylstilbestrol, 870
1,1-Difluoroethane, 733
Difluoromethane, 732
2,2-Difluoropropane, 731
Difurfurylideneacetone, 618
Digallic acid, 561
Digestion, fats and oils, 186, 814
    proteins, 301
    starch, 398
Digitalis glycosides, 869, 870
Digitonin, 869
Digitoxigenin, 870
Digitoxose, 368
Digonal hybridization, 12
1,2-Dihalides, hydrolysis, 740
Dihydroabietic acids, 861
9,10-Dihydroanthracene, 597
Dihydroanthraquinone, 600
Dihydroisoxazolones from β-keto esters, 818
Dihydromatricaric acid, 789
Dihydronaphthalenes, 584
Dihydropyran, 631
    α-ketols from, 759
Dihydropyrazolones from β-keto esters, 818
Dihydropyridines from 1,5-dicarbonyl compounds, 775
2,5-Dihydropyrrole, 613
1,2-Dihydroquinoline, 629
Dihydroresorcinol, 841
Dihydrotetrazines, 771
Dihydroxyacetone, 759
9,10-Dihydroxyanthracene, 600
Dihydroxyanthraquinones, 599
Dihydroxybenzenes, 516
1,4-Dihydroxy-2-butyne, 205, 717, 747
1,6-Dihydroxy-2,4-hexadiyne, 748

1,8-Dihydroxy-2,4,5-octatriyne, 748
2,6-Dihydroxypurine, 643
3,6-Dihydroxypyridazine, 807
Dihydroxysuccinic acid, 809
3,5-Diiodotyrosine, 297
Diisobutylenes, 62
    synthesis of 3,5,5-trimethylhexanal, 223
Diisocyanates, 479, 799
Diisopropylidenegalactose, 379
Diisopropylideneglucose, 380
Diisopropylidene peroxide, 885
Diketene, 824
Diketones, preparation, 767–769
    from β-keto esters, 819, 821
    reactions, 769–776
1,4-Diketones, pyridazines from, 638
2,5-Diketopiperazines, 642, 784
Dilantin sodium, 634
Dimedone, 804
Dimer, definition, 61
2,3-Dimercapto-1-propanol, 752
Dimethyl, *see also* Methyl
N,N-Dimethylacetanilide, 247
Dimethylamine, 240
p-Dimethylaminoaniline, 490
p-Dimethylaminoazobenzene, 498
p,p'-Dimethylaminobenzophenone, *see*
    Michler ketone, 541
N,N-Dimethylaniline, 488
Dimethylarsenoxide, 900
Dimethylarsine, 900
Dimethylarsinic acid, 901
Dimethylbenzenes, *see* Xylenes, 420, 429
2,3-Dimethyl-1,3-butadiene, 715
2,5-Dimethyl-1,3-cyclobutanedicarboxylic
    acid, 856
5,5-Dimethyl-1,3-cyclohexanedione, 804
1,2-Dimethylcyclohexene, autoxidation, 882
1,2-Dimethylcyclopentane, 833
Dimethyldihydroresorcinol, *see*
    5,5-Dimethyl-1,3-cyclohexanedione,
    804
N,N-Dimethyl-N,N'-dinitrosoterephthala-
    mide, 555
N,N-Dimethylformamide, 247
2,5-Dimethylfuran, 620
2,3-Dimethyl-O-glucose, 398
Dimethylglyoxime, 770
2,5-Dimethyl-2,5-hexanediol, 747
2,5-Dimethyl-2,5-hexynediol, 747
2,3-Dimethyl-1,4-naphthoquinone, 594
Dimethylolurea, 314
2,3-Dimethyl-1,3-propanediol, 746
Dimethylpyridines, 627
DINA, 753
Dinaphthocoronene, 604
2,4-Dinitroaniline, 462
m-Dinitrobenzene, 439
    reduction to m-nitroaniline, 487

3,5-Dinitrobenzoic acid, 551
3,5-Dinitrobenzoyl chloride, 551
2,2'-Dinitrobiphenyl-6,6'-dicarboxylic acid, 580
2,4-Dinitrochlorobenzene, 462, 514
2,4-Dinitrofluorobenzene, 462
  as reagent, 300
Dinitrogen tetroxide, 260
  as nitrating agent, 448
  reaction with amides, 247
    with alkenes, 260
Dinitronaphthalenes, 587
2,4-Dinitrophenol, 462
2,4-Dinitrophenyldisulfide, 462
2,4-Dinitrophenyl fluoride, *see* 2,4-Dinitrofluorobenzene, 462
2,4-Dinitrophenylhydrazine, 462
2,4-Dinitrophenylsulfenyl chloride, 473
2,4-Dinitrophenyl sulfide, 462
2,5-Dinitrothiophene, 608
2,4-Dinitrothiophenol, 462
2,4-Dinitrotoluene, 439
N,N'-Di-2-octyl-p-phenylenediamine, 488
Diosgenin, 869
1,4-Dioxane, 642, 743
Dioxindole, 684
Dipentene, 853
Diphenic acid, 602
Diphenyl, *see* Biphenyl, 578
Diphenyl, *see also* Phenyl
Diphenylacetylene, 576
Diphenylamine, 478, 488
  blue oxidation product, 572
Diphenylbenzenes, 569, 578
Diphenylboric acid, *see* Diphenylborinic acid, 896
Diphenylborinic acid, 896
Diphenylcarbinol, 525
1,1-Diphenylethane, 566
Diphenylethylenes, 576
Diphenylformamide, 768
Diphenylguanidine, 475
Diphenylketene, 761
Diphenylmethane, 565
Diphenylnitrogen, 571
Diphenyl oxide, *see* Phenyl ether, 510
Diphenylsilanediol, 912
Diphenylthiourea, 482
Dipolar ions, 299
Dipole, definition, 13
  permanent, 197
  transient, 39
Dipole association, 197
Dipole moment, 197
  acetone, 198
  amines, 476
  benzene derivatives, 451
  boiling point and, 251
  t-butyl chloride, 453

Dipole moment—(*Continued*)
  1,2-dihaloethylenes, 356
  p-dinitrobenzene, 450
  direction, 450, 451
  ethyl cyanide, 252
  ethyl isocyanide, 252
  geometrical isomers, 355
  hydroquinone, 450
  methyl ethyl ether, 198
  p-nitrochlorobenzene, 451
  p-nitrotoluene, 451
  p-phenylenediamine, 450
Dippel oil, 610
Di-i-propylammonium nitrite, 239
Di-i-propylbenzene dihydroperoxide, 874
Di-i-propyl ether, *see* i-Propyl ether, 141
Direct Black EW, 678
Direct Blue 2B, 678
Direct dyes, 673
Directive influence of substituents in benzene, 451
  in naphthalene, 586
  theory, 451
Direct whites, 675, 679
Disaccharides, 389–395
  nonreducing, 393
  osazones, 392
  reducing, 389
Disalicylidene-1,2-diaminopropane, 887
Disazo dyes, 678
Disilane, 910
9,10-Disodioanthracene, 597
Disperse dyes, 675
  anthraquinone, 688
  azo, 677
  nitro, 676
Dispersion, rotatory, 333
Displacement reactions, alkyl halides, 114
  aromatic nitro groups, 456
  mechanism, 116
Disproportionation of abietic acid, 861
  of iodosobenzene, 436
Dissociation constants of acids, *see* Acidity
  of bases, *see* Basicity
Dissymmetry, 335
Distillation, 14–16
  types of binary mixtures, 93
Disulfides, 280
  by oxidation of mercaptans, 277
  reaction with chlorine, 284
    with olefins, 281
  reduction to mercaptans, 275
  sulfonyl chlorides from, 288
Disulfones, 285
Diterpenes, 860
Dithane, 755
Dithiocarbamates, 325
  mercaptans from, 275
Dithiocarbonates, 324

Dithiocarboxylic acids, 282
Dithio esters, 282
1,2-Dithioglycerol, 752
Divinylbenzene, 574
DMP, 552
DNP derivatives of amino acids, 300
Docosanes, 33
Doctor process, 277
Dodecanes, 33
n-Dodecylmercaptan, 289
Doebner-Miller synthesis of quinaldine, 629
d orbitals, 5, 273
Double bond, 273
  estimation with perbenzoic acid, 551
  oxygen-sulfur, 273
  restricted rotation, 355
  tests for, 54, 57, 263
Double refraction, ordinary light, 330
  plane-polarized light, 352
Dow process for phenol, 510
Dramamine, 647
Drying oils, 181, 186
  autoxidation, 883
  up-grading, 187, 752
dsp^2 hybridization, 357
d^2sp^3 hybridization, 352
Dubbs process, 74
Duclaux values of carboxylic acids, 150
Dulcin, 482
Dulcite, *see* Dulcitol, 412
Dulcitol, 412
Dumas, biography, 3
  and substitution, 119
Dumas molecular weight determination, 21
Dumas nitrogen determination, 19
Durene, 420
Duroprene, 713
Dyeing, 672–675
Dyes, *see also individual type or name, e.g.,* Azo, Methyl Orange, Mordant, *etc.*
  application, 673–675
  chemical classes, 675–699
  color and chemical structure, 671
  historical, 672
  indicator action, 699–702
  pigments, 702–704
Dynamite, 749
Dynamite cotton, 401
Dynel, 788

E, extinction, 661
E1 and E2 mechanisms, 118
ε, molecular extinction coefficient, 661
Ebonite, 711
Ebullioscopic molecular weight determination, 21, 22
Edeleanu process, 80
EDTA, 755
Egg yolk pigments, 865

Ehrlich, biography, 903
Eicosanes, 33
Elaidic acid, geometrical isomerism, 356
Elaidinization, 186
Elastins, 294
Elastomers, 715
Electrical dipole, permanent, 197
  transient, 39
Electric moment, *see* Dipole moment, 197
Electrodotic reagents, 117
Electrolysis of acid esters, 791
  of salts, 156
Electromagnetic radiation, absorption by organic molecules, 657
Electromeric effect in aromatic substitution, 453
Electron-acceptors, 237
Electron-affinity, 6, 117
Electron cloud, 9
Electron distribution, 6, 9
Electronegative groups, 6, 117
Electronic spectra, 661
Electronic theory of structure, 5
Electron interaction, 7
Electron-pair bond, 7
Electron paramagnetic resonance, 669
Electrons, distribution in orbitals, 5
Electron-spin resonance, 669
  detection of free radicals, 568
Electrophilic reagents, 117
  substitution, aromatic, 444
Electrophoresis, 295
Electropositive groups, 117
Electrostatic effect, 153
Electrovalence, 7
Elemi, 863
Eleostearic acid, 179
Elimination reactions, 104, 118
Ellagic acid, 581
Ellagic tannins, 581
Elon, 519
Emodin, 599
Empirical formulas, 20
Emulsifying agents, 187, 191, 753
Emulsin, 389
Emulsion polymerization, 718
Enamine form, aromatic amines, 475
Enanthaldehyde, *see* n-Heptaldehyde, 224, 789
Enanthic acid, 147
Enantiomers, 335
Enantiomorphic crystals, 344
Enantiomorphs, 332, 335
End group method, 398
Endo-, prefix, 806
1,4-Endomethylenecyclohexadiene, 837
Endothermic reaction, 167
Enediol forms of sugars, 368
Energy barrier, 31
Enol acetates, 214, 761

Enolate ion, structure, 213
Enol esters, 214, 761, 876
Enol form, aldehydes, and ketones, 207
  1,3-diketones, 771
  estimation, 823
Enolization, aldehydes and ketones, 207, 213
  1,3-diketones, 771
  β-keto esters, 817
  mechanism, 214
Enolization and racemization, 345
Enols, *see also* Tautomerism
  ferric chloride test, 504
Enteric coating for pills, 559
Entrainers for removal of water, 95
Enzymes, 90
Eosin, 683
Ephedrine, 529
Epichlorohydrin, 750
Epimerization, 346, 381
Epimers, 346
Epinephrine, 529
Epiquinidine, 653
Epiquinine, 653
Epoxidation, 153, 876
Epoxides, 740, 744
Epoxy derivatives, 744
Epoxy resins, 750
EPR spectra, 669
ε, molecular extinction coefficient, 661
Equations, oxidation-reduction, balancing, 145
Equatorial groups, cyclohexanes, 844
Equilibrium constant, effect of temperature, 167
  esterification, 166
Ergonovine, 654
Ergosterol, 868
Ergot alkaloids, 654
Erlenmeyer, biography, 582
Error, absolute and relative, 24
Erucic acid, 180, 794
Erythrogenic acid, 180, 790
Erythromycin, 847
*Erythro*pentulose, 384, 387
Erythrose, 366
Erythrosin, 683
Erythrulose, 384
Eschweiler-Clarke reaction, 231
ESR spectra, 669
Essential amino acids, 302
Essential oils, 849
Ester condensations, 814
  cyclic, 804, 816
  with ketones, 768
  malonic esters by, 802
Ester gum, 862
Esterification, 165–169
  aromatic acids, 549
  neopentyl alcohol, 169

Esterification law of Victor Meyer, 549
Esters of carboxylic acids, preparation, 165–169
  from cyanides, 254
  from ketones, 876
  from quaternary salts, 242
  reactions, 169–174
  with amines, 244
Esters of inorganic acids, 108
  of phenols, 504
  of sulfonic acids, 288, 470, 471
  of thiols, 278
Estradiol, 870
Estrogenic hormones, 870
Ethane, barrier to free rotation, 31
  conformation, 31
  structure, 28
1,2-Ethanediol, 742
Ethanol, *see* Ethyl alcohol, 90–96
Ethanolamine, 752
Ethavan, 538
Ethene, *see* Ethylene
Ether, *see* Ethyl ether, 140
Etherates, 139
Ethers, 136–141
  aromatic, 504
  autoxidation, 884
  from esters of sulfonic acids, 288, 470
  from Grignard reagents, 203
  peroxides in, 140, 884
Ethionic acid, 58
Ethoxyl determination, 140
p-Ethoxyphenylurea, 482
Ethyl acetate, 173
  from acetaldehyde, 220
  ester condensation, 814
Ethyl acetoacetate, 814
  from diketene, 825
  tautomerism, 822
Ethyl acetonedicarboxylate, 810
Ethyl (acetylamino)malonate, 802
Ethyl adipate, cyclization, 816
Ethyl alcohol, 90–96
  butadiene from, 716
  nuclear-spin resonance spectrum, 668
Ethyl *p*-aminobenzoate, 558
Ethyl aminomalonate, 802
2-Ethylanthranol, 601
2-Ethylanthraquinone, 601
Ethylbenzene, 430
  styrene from, 574
Ethyl benzoate, 526
Ethyl benzoylacetate, 815
Ethyl benzoyldimethylacetate, 815
Ethyl bromide, *see* Halides, alkyl
Ethyl carbonate, 310
  β-keto esters from, 815
  malonic esters from, 802
Ethylcellulose, 404

Ethyl chloride, 118
Ethyl chlorocarbonate, *see* Ethyl chloroformate, 310
Ethyl chloroformate, 310
Ethyl crotonate, ester condensations, 816
Ethyl cyanoacetate, 803
  β-keto esters from, 817
Ethyl 1,1-cyclopropanedicarboxylate, 801
Ethyl diazoacetate, 267
Ethyldichloroarsine, 902
Ethylene, absorption spectrum, 663
  bond angles, 49, 355
  ethyl alcohol from, 93
  molecular orbital picture of, 50
  polymerization, 61, 898
  structure, 49
Ethylenebisdithiocarbamic acid, sodium salt, 755
Ethylene bromide, use in Ethyl Fluid, 80
Ethylene chloride, 723
  use in Ethyl Fluid, 80
Ethylene chlorohydrin, 743
Ethylene cyanohydrin, 787
Ethylenediamine, 754
Ethylenediaminetetraacetic acid, 755
Ethylenediammonium tartrate, 755
Ethylene dibromide, *see* Ethylene bromide, 80
Ethylene dichloride, *see* Ethylene chloride, 723
Ethylene glycol, 742
  monoethyl ether, 744
  nitrate, 743
Ethylene hydrocarbons, *see* Alkenes
Ethylene oxide, 743
  acrylonitrile from, 787
Ethylenimine, 754
Ethyl ether, 140
  autoxidation, 884
  oxidation of vapor, 878
Ethyl Fluid, components, 80
Ethyl formate, 174
  ester condensation, 815
Ethyl formylacetate, 815
Ethyl formylcrotonate, 816
Ethyl formylphenylacetates, tautomerism, 822
Ethyl glutaconate, 808
Ethyl glutarate, cyclic ester condensation, 816
2-Ethyl-1,3-hexanediol, 747
2-Ethyl-1-hexanol, 96, 223
2-Ethylhexyl phthalate, 552
Ethyl hydrogen sulfate, 93, 139
Ethyl hydroperoxide, 875
Ethylidene acetate, 164, 204
Ethylidene chloride, 723
Ethyl imidoacetate hydrochloride, 175
Ethyl iodide, *see* Halides, alkyl

Ethyl malonate, reactions, 800–805
  synthesis, 792
Ethylmercuric chloride, 894
Ethylmercury, 890
Ethyl N-methylcarbamate, 319
Ethyl nitrate, 109
Ethyl nitrite, 110
Ethyl nitrosomalonate, 802
Ethyl orthoacetate, 175
Ethyl orthocarbonate, 310
Ethyl orthoformate, 175
Ethyl oxalacetate, 815
Ethyl oxalate, ester condensations, 812, 815, 816
Ethyl oxalosorbate, 816
Ethyl perchlorate, 109
Ethyl peroxide, 875
Ethyl phenylacetate, 802, 803
Ethyl phenylmalonate, 802
Ethyl phosphate, 110
Ethyl phthalate, 552
Ethyl pyridines, 623
Ethyl pyrophosphate, 110
Ethyl silicate, 110
Ethyl sodiomalonate, 800
Ethylsodium, 890
Ethyl sorbate, ester condensations, 816
2-Ethylsuberic acid, 794
Ethyl succinate, intermolecular cyclization, 816
Ethyl succinosuccinate, 816
Ethyl sulfate, 108
Ethylsulfuric acid, *see* Ethyl hydrogen sulfate, 93, 139
Ethyltrichlorosilane, 914
Ethyl vanillate, 561
Ethyl vinyl ether, 884
Ethynyl alcohol, 737
Ethynyl alkyl ethers, 737
Ethynylation, 205
Ethynyl group, 205
Eucalyptus oils, 858
Eudalene, 858
Eudesmol, 858
Eugenol, 516
Exaltone, 847
Exhaustive methylation, 621
Exo-, prefix, 806
Exothermic reaction, 167
Explosion limits, 44
Explosive oil, 749
Explosives, ballistite, 401, 749
  cellulose nitrate, 401
  cordite, 401, 749
  cyclonite, 222
  DINA, 753
  dynamite, 743
  ethylene glycol nitrate, 743
  flashless, 322

Explosives—(*Continued*)
  gelatin dynamite, 749
  glyceryl nitrate, 749
  glycol dinitrate, 743
  guncotton, 401
  hexogen, 222
  mercury fulminate, 318
  nitrocellulose, 401
  N-nitrodiethanolamine nitrate, 753
  nitroglycerin, 749
  nitroguanidine, 322
  nitrostarch, 398
  pentaerythritol nitrate, 752
  PETN, 752
  RDX, 222
  smokeless, 401, 749
  starch nitrate, 398
  tetracene, 637
  tetryl, 490
  TNT, 464
  trimethylenetrinitramine, 222
  trinitrotoluene, 464
Extinction, 661
Extinction coefficient, 661
Extraction, 16
Extraordinary ray, 331
Extreme pressure lubricants, 82

Families of stereoisomers, 348
  of sugars, 365
Family of compounds, 24
Faraday, biography, 92
Farnesol, 858
Fast bases, 677
Fast salts, 677
Fast Scarlet R, 677
Fat acids, 147, 179, 181
  separation, 185
  uses, 192
Fat metabolism, 186, 814
Fats and oils, 179–192
Fatty acids, 147
Favorski rearrangement, 766
Febrifuges, 487, 520, 559
Fehling solution, constitution, 809
  oxidation of aldehydes, 212
  of carbohydrates, 370, 385
  of α-keto alcohols, 541
Fenchane, 855
Fenton reagent, 381, 886
Fermate, 325
Fermentation, acetic acid, 158
  acetone, 96
  alcoholic, 90
  butyl alcohol, 96
  butyric acid, 159
  fumaric acid, 805
  lactic acid, 783
  propionic acid, 159

Ferrocene, 838
Fibers, natural, 299, 400
  synthetic, acetate rayon, 406
    Acrilan, 788
    acrylic, 788
    cellulose acetate, 406
    Dacron, 555
    Dynel, 788
    nylon 4, 785
    nylon 6, 841
    nylon 66, 798
    Orlon, 788
    rayon, 405
    Saran, 726
    synthetic wool, 299
    Terylene, 555
    viscose rayon, 405
Fibroin, 299
Fibrous proteins, 299
Finckelstein reaction, 113
Fire damp, 41
Fischer, E., biography, 305
Fischer indole synthesis, 615
Fischer-Tropsch synthesis, 83
Fisher-Hirschfelder Models, *see* Hirsch-
  felder models, 30
Fish liver oils, 860
Fish oils, 183
Fish poisons, 633, 863, 869
Fittig, biography, 435
Flammability, 44
Flashless explosives, 322
Flash point, 44
Flavianic acid, 675
Flavones, 697
Flavonol, 697
Flavoproteins, 647
Flavor of butter, 186
  of esters, 174
  of fruits, 174
Flavylium salts, 698
Flax, 400
Flaxseed mucilage, 411
Flower pigments, 698, 866
Fluid Catalyst process, 75
Fluorene, 840
  in coal tar, 428
Fluorenone, 840
Fluorescein, 683
Fluorescence, 667
Fluorescent dyes, 683
Fluorides, *see* Halides
Fluorinated hydrocarbons, aliphatic, 728
Fluorination, 730, 732
Fluoroacetic acid, 778, 779
Fluorocarbons, 729
Fluoro compounds, 728–735
Fluorolubes, 734
Fluorthene, 734

Foaming agents, α,α'-azobisisobutyronitrile, 265
Celogen, 473
N,N'-dimethyl-N,N'-dinitrosoterephthalamide, 555
NTA, 555
sulfonhydrazides, 473
Folic acids, 647
Formal charge, 155
Formaldehyde, 220
  absorption spectrum, 665
  estimation with hydrogen peroxide, 879
  test for, 222
Formaldehyde hydrate, 739
Formaldehyde methylhydrazone, 265
Formaldehyde-urea resins, 313, 314
Formalin, 220
Formamide, 245
Formazans, 637
Formic acid, 147, 157
Formose, 222, 386
Formylacetic ester, 815
Formylation of ketones, 768
Formyl chloride, 531
Foxglove, glycosides, 869
Fractional distillation, 14
Fractionating columns, 15
Frankland, biography, 893
Free groups, 567
Free-radical catalysis of isomerization, 356
Free-radical mechanisms, 42
Free radicals, 42, 567–572; *see also individual radical, e.g.,* Methyl radical
  from acetyl peroxide, 163
  from azomethane, 265, 568
Free rotation, barrier to, in ethane, 31
  in nitromethane, 258
  restriction by double bonds, 50, 354
Freezing point apparatus, 23
Freons, 732, 733
Fresnel, biography, 353
Friedel, biography, 423
Friedel-Crafts reaction, 423
  ketones by, 539
  mechanism, 447
  naphthalene, 586
  phosphorus trichloride, 908
  thiophene, 608
Friedelin, 863
Friedlaender synthesis of quinolines, 628
Fries reaction, 540
Fructose, 385
  fermentation, 92
Fruit flavors and odors, 174
F strain, 896
Fuchsin, 681
Fucose, 367
Fuel oil, 80
Full-strength colors, 702
Fulminic acid, 317

Fulvenes, 838
Fumaric acid, 805
  reduction to succinic acid, 792
Function, definition, 63
Functional groups, 63
Functional isomers, 329
Furacin, 620
Furan, 619
  Diels-Alder reaction, 806
  mercuration, 894
Furanoses, 386
Furanosides, 395, 410
Furans from 1,4-dicarbonyl compounds, 775
Furfural, 617, 620
  from pentoses, 378
  refining lubricating oils, 81
Furfuryl alcohol, 618
Furfurylideneacetone, 618
α-Furfuryl mercaptan, 620
Furil, 619
Furilic acid, 619
Furoic acid, 619
Furoin, 619
Furylacrylic acid, 618
Fused rings, 582
Fusel oil, 91

Gabriel phthalimide synthesis, 553
G-acid, 590
γ-acid, 591
Galactaric acid, 362
Galactitol, 412
Galactomannans, 411
Galactose, 361
  phenylhydrazone, structure, 383
α-Galactosidase, 395
D-Galacturonic acid, 408
Gallic acid, 561
  decarboxylation, 517
Gallium compounds, 898
Gallotannin, 561
m-Galloylgallic acid, 561
Gall stones, 868
Gamma acid, 591
Gamma sugars, 386
Gammexane, 432
Gardenia odor, 525
Garlic oil, 290
Gas from petroleum, 81
Gas black, *see* Carbon black, 70
Gases, poison, *see* Poison gases
Gas-fading of dyes, 675
Gas-liquid partition chromatography, 17
Gas oil, 80
Gasoline, 73
  additives, 77, 80
  by alkylation, 77
  octane number, 74

Gasoline—(*Continued*)
  by polymerization, 76
  reforming, 76
  straight run, 73
Gasoline engine, 73
Gas turbines, 81
Gattermann, biography, 531
Gattermann carbon monoxide synthesis, 531
  hydrogen cyanide synthesis, 531
  reaction of diazonium salts, 494
Gattermann-Koch reaction, 531
Gelatin, 295
Gelatin dynamite, 749
gem-, prefix, 729
*gem-*dihalide effect, 729, 765
Genacryl Pink FG, 694
General anesthetics, 141
  adjuvants, 243, 652
  cyclopropane, 834
  ethyl ether, 141
  Pentothal, 640
  thiopental, 640
Genetrons, 733
Geneva system of nomenclature, 36, *see also* Nomenclature
Gentianose, 396
Gentian Violet, 681
Gentiobiose, 392
Geometrical isomerism, 354–357
  cumulenes, 707
  decalins, 843
  lithium compounds, 891
  nickel complexes, 770
  platinous complex ions, 357
Geon, 720
Geranial, 850
Geraniol, 853
Germanium compounds, 898
  optical activity, 350
Gingergrass oil, 853
Girard T-reagent, 785
Globulins, 294
Glucagon, 301
D-Glucitol, 412
Gluconic acid, 360
Gluconolactones, *see* Glyconolactones, 380
Glucosamine, *see* 2-Amino-2-deoxyglucose, 409
β-Glucosan, 388
Glucosazone, *see* Glucose phenylosazone, 371
Glucose, action of alkali, 368
  from cellulose, 400
  configuration, 361
  constitution, 360
  degradation by alkali, 368
  fermentation, 91
  α and β forms, 376
  glycoside formation, 372

Glucose—(*Continued*)
  isomerization, 368
  methylation, 373
  mutarotation, 375
  osazone formation, 370
  oxidation by Fehling solution, 370
  oxidation to saccharic acid, 363
  pentaacetates, 377, 382
  phosphates, 378
  ring structure, 373, 376
  from starch, 397
Glucose phenylhydrazone, ring structure, 382
Glucose phenylosazone, 371
Glucose phosphates, 378
α- and β-Glucosidase, 389
Glucosides, *see* Glycosides, 372
Glucuronic acids, *see* Glycuronic acids, 408
Glutaconic acid, 808
Glutaconic anhydride, 808
Glutamic acid, 297, 304
Glutamine, 298
Glutaric acid, preparation, 792
  reactions, 796
Glutaric acids, β-substituted, 803
Glutaric aldehyde, 768
Glutaric anhydride, 796
Glutathione, 302
Glutelins, 294
Glycaric acids, 362
  conversion to pyrrole, 610
(+)Glyceraldehyde, 348, 759
(−)Glyceric acid, configuration, 349
Glycerides, 179
Glycerin, 748
Glycerol, 748
  acrolein from, 764
  allyl alcohol from, 738
Glycerol dichlorohydrins, 749
Glycerol monochlorohydrins, 749
*Glycero*tetrulose, 384
Glyceryl monostearate, 191
Glyceryl nitrate, 749
Glycidic esters, 780
Glycidol, 750
Glycine, 296
  photographer's, 519
Glyco, prefix, 359
Glycocholic acid, 869
Glycocoll, *see* Glycine, 296
Glycogen, 398
Glycol, *see* Ethylene glycol, 742
  dinitrate, 743
Glycolic acid, 743, 783
  synthesis and conversion to ethylene glycol, 743
Glycolic aldehyde, 759
1,2-Glycols, 217, 740, 875
1,3-Glycols, 746

α,ω-Glycols, 747
Glyconic acids, 360, 362
Glyconolactones, 380
Glycoproteins, 294, 411
Glycosans, 388
Glycoses, 359
Glycosides, 372
    cyanogenetic, 255, 537
Glycosones, 371
Glycuronic acids, 408
Glyoxal, 768, 771
Glyoxalic acid, *see* Glyoxylic acid, 812
Glyoxylic acid, 812
Glyptal resins, 552
Gmelin, biography, 4
Gold compounds, 891
Goldenrod rubber, 708
Gomberg, biography, 566
Gomberg reaction, 496
Gonadotropic hormones, 870
Goodyear, biography, 710
Graebe, biography, 582
Grain alcohol, 90
Gramicidin-S, 302
Gramine, 803
Grape odor and flavor, 558
Graphic formulas, 30
Graphite, structure, 556
Gray acetate of lime, 158
Greases, lubricating, 82, 191
Green oil, 427, 596
GRI, 718
Griess, biography, 492
Grignard, biography, 120
Grignard reagents, 120–124, 892
    abnormal reactions, 437
    acetylenic, 132
    condensing action, 200
    coupling reaction, 121, 123
    enolizing action, 196, 200
    mechanism of addition to carbon-oxygen
        double bond, 123
    preparation, 120
        from acetylenes, 132
        from pyrroles, 611
    reactions, acetylene, 132
        acyl halides, 196
        aldehydes and ketones, 199
        alkylsulfonates, 289
        amide, 248
        carbon dioxide, 123, 143
        carbon disulfide, 282
        carboxylic esters, 173
        chloroamines, 233
        cyanides, 196, 540, 892
        epoxides, 745
        esters, 173
        halogen, 122
        α-halogen ethers, 203
        inorganic halides, 123

Grignard reagents—(*Continued*)
    reactions—(*Continued*)
        isocyanates, 479
        ketones, 199
        ortho esters, 175, 196
        oxygen, 122
        pyrrole, 611
        reactive hydrogen, 121
        silicon tetrachloride, 912
        sulfite, 283
        sulfonic esters, 288, 471
        sulfur dioxide, 284
        thionyl chloride, 283
    reducing action, 200
    relative reactivity, 892
    role of ether as solvent, 123
    side reactions in preparation, 121
Grignard syntheses, acetals, 175, 196
    acetylenic compounds, 132
    alcohols, 122, 173, 199
    amides, 479
    arsines, 900
    carboxylic acids, 123, 143
    dithiocarboxylic acids, 282
    ethers, 203
    hydrocarbons, 126, 289, 471
    ketones, 196, 540
    organometallic compounds, 123, 891–900
    phosphines, 907
    pyrrole derivatives, 611
    silicon compounds, 912
    sulfinic acids, 284
GRM, 719
GRN, 718
Ground state, 661
Group, definition, 35
GRS and GRS-10, 717
γ sugars, 386
Guaiacol, 516
Guaiacol carbonate, 516
Guaiac resin, 516
Guaiazulene, 859
Guaiol, 859
Guanidine, 321
Guanine, 643
Guano, 645
Guanylic acids, 644
Guanylurea, 321
Guar flour, 411
Guayule rubber, 708
Guerbet reaction, 96
Gulose, 366
Gum arabic, 411
    benzoin, 416, 550
    catechu, 516
    tragacanth, 411
Gum inhibitors, 77
Gums, 411, *see also type, e.g.,* Damson
    gum

Guncotton, 401
Gutta-percha, 713
Gypsogenin, 863

H-acid, 591
Hair, 299
Halazone, 557
Half second cotton, 402
Halides, acyl, preparation, 160
  reactions, 161–162
   with amines, 244
   with Grignard reagents, 196
Halides, alkyl, preparation, 113
  from alkenes, 59, 731
  from carboxylic acids, 157
  from hydrocarbons, 118, 722
  reactions, 114–118
   ammonia, 229
   dehydrohalogenation, 115, 128
   nitrites, 258
   reduction, 126
   sodium cyanide, 249
   sodium disulfide, 280
   sodium hydrosulfide, 274
   sodium sulfide, 278
   sodium sulfite, 286
Halides, aromatic, 432–438
  from diazonium salts, 494
Halochromic salts, 573
Haloform reaction, 214
Halogen, addition to alkenes, 53
  to alkynes, 131, 723
  to aromatic compounds, 432
  determination, 20
  mechanism of addition to double bond, 54
  reaction with aromatic compounds, 433
   with Grignard reagents, 122
  test for, 17
Halogen acids, addition to alkenes, 59, 731
  to alkynes, 131, 731
  mechanism of addition to double bond, 60
  of reaction with alcohols, 102
  of removal from alkyl halides, 118
α-Halogen acids, 162, 778
Halogenated acids, 778
Halogenated carbonyl compounds, 765
Halogenated hydrocarbons, aliphatic, 722–734
  aromatic, 432–438
Halogenation, 118, 119
  acyl halides, 162
  aldehydes, 214
  alkanes, 119
  alkenes, 726, 727
  aromatic compounds, 433
   mechanism, 447
  aromatic aldehydes to acyl halides, 534
  aromatic amines, 482

Halogenation—(*Continued*)
  with *N*-bromosuccinimide, 797
  carboxylic acids, 162, 778
  ketones, 214
  naphthalene, 585
  nitroalkanes, 261
  phenols, 505
  pyridine, 622
  pyrrole, 612
  thiophene, 608
Halogen compounds, aliphatic, 722–735
  aromatic, 432–438
   effect of *m*-directing groups on reactivity, 461
  from mercury compounds, 895
α-Halogen ethers, 203
Halohydrins, hydrolysis, 741
Hammett equation, 549
Hansa Yellows, 703
Hantzsch, biography, 500
Hantzsch pyridine synthesis, 820
Hanus solution, 184
Hard coal, 426
Hard rubber, 711
Harries, biography, 708
Hashish, 633
Haworth, biography, 374
Haworth formulas for sugars, 383
Hawthorn odor, 537
Häuy, biography, 332
Heat of combustion of alkanes, 43
Heavy hydrogen as tracer element, 214, 369, 446
Heavy oil, 428
Heavy oxygen as tracer element, 169, 171, 202
Hederagenin, 863
Helidon Pink R, 687
Heliotropin, 538
Hell-Volhard-Zelinsky reaction, 162, 778
Heme, 614
Hemiacetal esters, 878
Hemiacetals, 203
Hemicelluloses, 400, 401
Hemihedral facets, 334
Hemin, 613
Hemiterpenes, 850
Hemlock, 648
Hemocyanins, 295, 296
Hemoglobins, 295, 296
Hemp fiber, 400
  flowers, 633
  seed oil, 182
Henbane, 650
Heneicosanes, 33
Heneicosanoic acid, 147
Henna, 593
Hennel, biography, 92
Hentriacontanes, 33
n-Heptaldehyde, 224, **789**

n-Heptane, as standard fuel, 74
  sources, 41
Heroin, 651
Herschel, biography, 334
Heterocyclic compounds, 606
Heterolytic fission, 41
Heteropolysaccharides, 410
Hexachlorocyclopentadiene, 837
Hexachloroethane, 724
Hexachlorophene, 565
Hexadecane, 81
1,1,1,3,3,3-Hexafluoro-2-propanol, 734
Hexahydrobenzene, 830
Hexahydrobenzoic acid, 550
Hexalin, 841
Hexamethonium, 243
Hexamethylene, 830
Hexamethylenediamine, 756
  from adiponitrile, 799
Hexamethylenetetramine, 221, 232
1,2,6-Hexanetriol, 752
Hexaphenyldigermane, 899
Hexaphenyldisilane, 915
Hexaphenylethane, 566
3-Hexenoic acid, 789
Hexestrol, 870
Hexogen, 221
Hexosans, 407
Hexoses, 360
Hexylene glycol, 746
n-Hexylresorcinol, 517
Hinsberg reaction, 471
Hippuric acid, 550
Hiptagin, 264
Hirschfelder models, 30
Histamine, 634
Histidine, 297, 634
Histones, 294
van't Hoff, biography, 335
Hofmann, biography, 229
Hofmann decomposition of quaternary am-
  monium hydroxides, 242, 621
  exhaustive methylation procedure, 242,
    621
  method for preparing amines, 230
  rearrangement of amides, 231, 247
  of phthalimide, 558
  of urea, 312
  rule, 242
Hofmeister, biography, 304
Homologous series, 28
Homologs, 28
Homolytic fission, 41
Homophthalic acid, 556
Homopolysaccharides, 396
Honey, 360, 385
Honeystone, 556
Hop oil, 859
Hormones, adrenal, 529, 871
  sex, 870

Hudson, biography, 377
Humulene, 859
Hund rule, 5
Hunsdiecker reaction, 157
Huygens, biography, 330
Hyalouronic acid, 411
Hybrid bond orbitals, 11
dsp^2 Hybridization of nickel, platinum and
  palladium, 357, 770
d^2*sp*^{3} Hybridization of cobalt, 352
Hydantoic acid, 634
Hydantoins, 634
Hydnocarpic acid, 839
Hydrated ions, 13
Hydrates of metallic salts, types, 97
Hydration of aldehydes, 202
Hydrazines, 264
  from diazonium salts, 497
  reaction with aldehydes and ketones, 211
Hydrazobenzene, 459
Hydrazones, 211
o-Hydrazotoluene, 578
Hydrindene, 840
Hydroaromatic compounds, 828
Hydroazines, 689
Hydrobenzamide, 535
Hydrobenzoin, 537
Hydrocarbons, *see* Alicyclic hydrocarbons,
    Alkanes, Alkenes, Alkynes, Aro-
    matic hydrocarbons, Condensed nu-
    clear hydrocarbons
Hydrocyanic acid, 255
Hydrofurfuramide, 618
Hydrogen, absorption spectrum, 662
  detection in organic compounds, 17
  determination, 18
  from natural gas, 70
  ortho-para interconversion by free radi-
    cals, 567
  reactivity in compounds, 100
  from reforming operations, 76
Hydrogenated oils, 184
Hydrogenated rubber, 713
Hydrogenation, catalytic, of acids, 172
    mechanism, 55
    of aldehydes and ketones, 198
    of alkenes, 54
    of alkynes, 130
    of aromatic hydrocarbons, 830
    of benzyl derivatives, 526
    of coal, 83, 428
    of cyanides, 230
    of esters, 172
    of ketones, 198
    of oils, 184
Hydrogen atom, absorption spectrum, 662
Hydrogen bonding, *see* Proton bonding, 87
Hydrogen bromide, abnormal addition to
    double bond, 60, 61

Hydrogen cyanide, 255
  addition to aldehydes and ketones, 200
    to alkenes, 250
    to α,β-unsaturated carbonyl compounds, 764, 787
Hydrogen exchange, aldehydes and ketones, 214
  benzene, 446
  monosaccharides, 369
Hydrogen molecule, absorption spectrum, 662
Hydrogenolysis of benzyl derivatives, 526
Hydrogen peroxide, nonelectrolytic preparation, 601
  reaction with acid anhydrides, 876
    with aldehydes, 878
    with aldoses, 381
    with alkyl sulfates, 874
    with alkyl sulfonates, 874
    with carboxylic acids, 875
    with ketones, 879
    with sulfides, 279
    with sulfoxides, 283
    with tertiary amines, 240
    with unsaturated compounds, 740, 763
Hydrolysis, acetals, 196
  acid anhydrides, 163
  acyl halides, 161
  alkyl cyanides, 144, 252, 253
  alkyl halides, mechanism, 116
  amides, 246
  aromatic amines, 481, 588, 590
  aryl cyanides, 547
  aryl halides, 502
  dihalides, 531
  dithiocarbamates, 275
  esters, 170, 549
  fats and oils, 183, 186
  inorganic esters, 109
  isocyanides, 258
  nitroalkanes, 262
  ortho esters, 175
  ozonides, 195
  peroxy esters, 877
  steric hindrance, 170, 549
  sulfonic acids, 468
  urea, 312
Hydroperoxides, 874
Hydroquinone, 517
Hydrorubber, 713
Hydrosorbic acid, 789
Hydroxamic acids, 262
Hydroxy acids, 781
α-Hydroxyadipic aldehyde, 769
Hydroxyalkyl alkyl peroxides, 879
Hydroxalkyl hydroperoxides, 878
Hydroxyalkyl peroxides, 878
2-Hydroxy-4-aminobenzoic acid, 560
Hydroxy amino compounds, 752
Hydroxyanthraquinones, 599

p-Hydroxyazobenzene, 498
o-Hydroxybenzaldehyde, 532, 562
Hydroxybenzoic acids, 559
Hydroxybenzyl alcohols, 508
Hydroxy carbonyl compounds, 759
Hydroxy dicarboxylic acids, 808
2-Hydroxyethylamine, 752
Hydroxyethylcellulose, 404
Hydroxyethyl peroxide, 884
Hydroxyethylpyridines, 626
Hydroxyethyl sulfide, 289
β-Hydroxyglutaric acid, 808
1-Hydroxy-3-hexene, 739
6-Hydroxy-1-hexyne, 739
α-Hydroxy ketones, 173, 759
Hydroxylamine, from nitroalkanes, 262
  reaction with aldehydes and ketones, 210
    with α,β-unsaturated carbonyl compounds, 763
Hydroxyl group, 84
  test for, 97
  Zerevitinov determination, 122
Hydroxylysine, 297
Hydroxymalonic acid, 808
5-Hydroxymethyl furfural, 379
3-Hydroxy-3-methyl-1-pentyne, 205
Hydroxymethyl peroxide, 878
3-Hydroxy-2-naphthoic acid, 594
5-Hydroxy-1-pentyne, 739
p-Hydroxyphenylarsonic acid, 902
p-Hydroxyphenylglycine, 519
Hydroxyphenylmercuric acetate, 894
Hydroxyproline, 297, 613
6-Hydroxypurine, 643
Hydroxypyridines, 623, 624
Hydroxyquinolines, 629
Hydroxytricarboxylic acid, 810
δ-Hydroxyvaleraldehyde, 632, 760
l-Hyoscyamine, 650
Hypalon, 720
Hyperconjugation, 669
Hypochlorites, alkyl, 109
Hypohalous acid, addition to alkenes, 741
Hypoxanthine, 643

Ice colors, 674
Idose, 366
Igepons, 291
Ignition temperature, 44
Imidazoles, 634
Imides, 244, 313
  cyclic, 553, 639, 797
Imido esters, 175, 248
Imido ethers, *see* Imido esters, 175, 248
Imino esters, *see* Imido esters, 175, 248
Imino form of aromatic amines, 475
Immunopolysaccharides, 411
Impregnite, 557
Inclusion compounds, 97, 311
  resolution by, 344

Indane, 840
Indanthrene Blue R, 689
  Brilliant Violet RK, 689
  Brown BR, 690
  Brown RRD, 687
  Khaki, 690
  Red 5GK, 689
  Yellow, FFRK, 690
1,2,3-Indantrione, *see* 1,2,3-Triketohydrindene, 840
Indene, 840
Indian snake root, 654
Indican, 683
Indicator action, 699
Indigo, 683
Indigoid dyes, 683
Indigo white, 685
Indispensable amino acids, 302
Indium compounds, 898
Indoaniline, 483
Indole, 615, 684
β-Indoleacetic acid, 616
β-Indolealdehyde, 616
Indophenin reaction, 606
Indophenins, 687
Indophenol Blue, 692
Indoxyl, 684
Indoxylic acid, 685
Inductive effect, 153
  acidity of aromatic acids, 548
  alkyl groups, 153
  aromatic substitution, 452
  of trimethylsilyl group, 913
Industrial alcohol, 92
Inflammability, *see* Flammability, 44
Infrared spectra, 657
Ingrain dyes, *see* Azoic dyes, 674, 677
Ink, blue-black, 561
  red, 683
Inorganic acid halides, reaction with alcohols, 100
Inorganic halides, reaction with Grignard reagents, 123
Inositols, 413
Insecticides, allethrin, 840
  cinerins, 839
  diphenylethane derivatives, 566
  Lethanes, 325
  malathion, 809
  pyrethrins, 839
  tetraethyl pyrophosphate, 110
Insect repellents, 552, 747
Insulin, role in metabolism, 814
  structure, 301
Interatomic distance and resonance, 156, 419, 453
Interatomic distances, C—C in alkanes, 51
  C—C in benzene, 418
  C=C in alkenes, 51
  C≡C in alkynes, 418

Interatomic distances—(*Continued*)
  C—Cl in *t*-butyl chloride, 453
    in chlorobenzene, 453
    in vinyl chloride, 726
  C—F in fluorine compounds, 730
  C—O in carboxylate ion, 155
    in carboxyl group, 156
    in ethers, 155
  C=O in aldehydes and ketones, 155
    in carboxyl group, 156
Interconversion method of orientation, 425
International Union of Chemistry, system of nomenclature, 36, *see also* Nomenclature
Inulin, 410
Inversion of sucrose, 394
Invertase, *see* Sucrase, 92, 394
Invert soaps, 243
Invert sugar, 394
Iodides, *see* Halides
Iodination, aromatic compounds, 434
Iodine, adsorption complex with starch, 397
  catalyst for dehydration, 207
  color of solutions, 449
Iodine compounds, polyvalent, 436
Iodine value, 181, 184
Iodo acids, 778
p-Iodoaniline, 484
Iodobenzene, 434, 436
Iodobenzene dichloride, 436
Iodocyanogen, *see* Cyanogen iodide, 319
Iodoform, 215
Iodofuran, 895
Iodogorgoic acid, 297
Iodohippuric acid, 551
Iodonium salts, 436
Iodoso acetates, 436
Iodosobenzene, 436
Iodosobenzene acetate, 436
  oxidation of aromatic amines, 481
Iodotyrosine, 297
Iodoxybenzene, 436
Ion-exchange resins, 513, 575
Ionic bonds, 7
Ionic catalysis of isomerization, 47, 78, 356
Ionic mechanisms, 42
Ionization constants of acids, *see* Acidity of bases, Basicity
Ionones, 852
Ions, hydration, 13
Iron carbonyl, 904
Irvine, biography, 374
Isanic acid, 180, 790
Isatin, 684
Iso-, prefix, 33, *see also* compound, *e.g.,* *i*-Propyl alcohol
Isoborneol, 856
Isobornylane, 855
Isocamphane, 855

Isocrotyl chloride, 727
Isocyanates, alkyl, 317
   in Curtius rearrangement, 268
   from isocyanides, 257
   aryl, 479
Isocyanic acid, 314
Isocyanide test for primary amines, 237
Isocyanides, 256, 257, 482
   structure, 238
Isoelectric point, 300
Isoeugenol, 538
Isoleucine, 296
Isomaltose, 390
Isomenthols, 854
Isomer distribution in nitration, 441
Isomerism, 29
   geometrical, 354–357
   optical, 333
   structural, 329
   types, 329
Isomerization, 46
   alicyclic compounds, 833
   alkanes, 47, 78
   alkylated benzenes, 429, 449
   catalysis by light, 663
   geometrical isomers, 356
   sugars, 368
Isomerized rubber, 713
Isomers, 29
   kinds, 329
Isomesityl oxide, 762
Isoneomenthols, 854
Isonicotinic acid, 625
Isonicotinic acid hydrazide, 626
   N-methyl-*p*-toluenesulfonate, 626
Isonitriles, *see* Isocyanides
"Isooctane," *see* 2,2,4-Trimethyl pentane, 74, 78
Isophorone, 208
Isophthalic acid, 555
Isoprene, from petroleum, 719
   from rubber, 709
   synthesis, 850
Isoprene rubber, 720
Isoprene rule, 855
Isopropenyl acetate, 737, 761
Isopropylidene derivatives of sugars, 379
Isopulegol, 854
Isoquinoline, 630
"Isosebacic acid," 794
(+)Isoserine, configuration, 349
Isothiazole, 635
Isothiocyanates, 257, 325
Isothioureas, 288, 327
Isothiuronium salts, *see* Thiuronium salts
Isotopes as tracers, C^{14}, 813, 832
   H^2, 214, 369, 446
   O^{18}, 169, 171, 202
Isoxazole, 635
Isoxazoles from 1,3-diketones, 772

Itaconic acid, 808
Itaconic anhydride, 807
I.U.C. system of nomenclature, 36
I.U.P.A.C. system of nomenclature, 36
Ivanov reagent, 562

J acid, 591
Jade Green, 691
Japan wax, 794
Jasmine odor, 525
Jet engine fuel, 80
Juglone, 593
Jute, 400

Kakodyls, 900
Kauri copal, 860
Kekulé, biography, 4
Kel-F, 734
Kephalins, 753
Keratins, 294
Kerosene, 80
Ketals, 204
Ketene, 164, 224, 760
Ketene dimers, 762
Ketenes, 760
Ketimines, 228
Keto, *see also* Oxo
α-Keto acids, 812
β-Keto acids, 813
γ-Keto acids, 825
ε-Keto acids, 826
Keto-enol tautomerism, *see* Tautomerism
β-Keto esters, preparation, 814–817
   reactions, 817–824
      dihydroisoxazolones from, 818
      dihydropyrazolones from, 818
Ketol acetates, 267
α-Ketols, 759
Ketones, nomenclature, 197
   physical properties, 197
   preparation, 194–196, 539
      from acyl halides, 196
      from acylmalonic esters, 801
      from aldehydes and diazomethane, 226
      from amides, 248
      from *t*-butyl malonate, 801
      from carboxylic acids, 152
      from β-keto esters, 820
      from nitroalkanes, 262
      from sulfoxides, 283
   reactions, 198–220
      formylation, 768
      with hydrogen sulfide, 281
      Leuckart reaction, 231, 528
      with nitroalkanes, 262
      nitrosation, 768
      with phenols, 508
      with thiols, 278
Ketonic cleavage of β-keto esters, 820
Ketoses, 381, 384

Ketoximes, 210
  stereochemistry, 542
Ketyls, 570
Kiliani, biography, 362
Kiliani reaction, 362, 380
Kipping, biography, 911
Kjeldahl method for nitrogen, 19
Knocking characteristics of fuels, 74
Knocking in gasoline engines, 73
Knock inhibitors, 80, 904
Knock-out drops, 740
Knoevenagel, biography, 773
Knoevenagel reaction, 1,3-diketones, 773
  β-keto esters, 819
  malonic esters, 804
  sulfones, 286
Knorr, biography, 819
Knorr pyrrole synthesis, 819
Koch acid, 591
Koerner, biography, 424
Koerner's absolute method of orientation, 424
Kojic acid, 632
Kolbe hydrocarbon synthesis, 156
  synthesis of dicarboxylic esters, 791
  of hydroxybenzoic acids, 559
Kopp, biography, 40
Koroseal, 720
Kraft pulp, 400
Krystallin, 486
Kyanol, 486

Lachnophyllic acid, 790
Lacquers, 402
Lactalbumin, 294
Lactams, 784
Lactic acid, 783
(−)Lactic acid, configuration, 349
Lactides, 782
Lactobacillic acid, 835
β-Lactones, 782
  β-unsaturated, 824
γ- and δ-Lactones, from halogenated acids, 780
  from hydroxy acids, 783
  from keto acids, 826
  unsaturated, 826, 870
ε-Lactones from cyclic ketones, 876
Lactose, 392
Ladenburg, biography, 623
Ladenburg rearrangement, 623
Lakes, 702
Lamp black, *see* Carbon black, 70
Lanolin, 178, 863
Lanosterol, 862
Lanum, 178
Lapworth, biography, 201
Lard, 181, 182
Lard oil, 181, 182
Large rings, 844

Latex, 708, 709, 712
  paint vehicles, 720, 736
Laudanine, 651
Laurent, biography, 535
Laurent acid, 589
Lauric acid, 147, 179
N-Lauroylsarcosine, 785
Lauryl alcohol, 172
Laurylsulfonic acid, 287
Lavandulol, 738
Lavender oil, 738
Lavoisier, biography, 2
Lawsone, 593
Lead acetate, 159
Lead compounds, 899
  optically active, 350
Lead susceptibility, 80
Lead tetraacetate, alkylating agent, 594
  oxidizing agent, 742
Lead tetraethyl, *see* Tetraethyllead, 898, 899
Leaf alcohol, 739
Leaf pigments, carotenoids, 865
  chlorophylls, 614
Leaf xanthophyll, 865
Leaf yellow, 865
Le Bel, biography, 335
Lecithins, 753
Lederer-Manasse reaction, 508
Lees of wine, 809
Lemon grass oils, 850
Lemon juice, 810
Lemon oil, 853
Lepidine, 629
Lethanes, 325
Leucine, 296
Leuckart reaction, 231, 528
Leuco base, 680
Leucopterin, 647
Levoglucosan, 388
Levorotation, 332
Levulinic acid, 826
  from carbohydrates, 379
Levulinic aldehyde, 710, 864
Levulose, *see* Fructose, 385
Lewis, biography, 236
Lewis acids, 236
Lewisites, 902
Lewis theory of acids and bases, 236
L family, 348
Licanic acid, 180, 826
Liebermann, biography, 506
Liebermann's nitroso reaction, 506
Liebig, biography, 3
Light, catalysis of halogenation, 119
  of isomerization, 356, 663
  modes of propagation, 330
Light oil, 427
Lignin, 400, 527
Lignite, 426

Lignoceric acid, *see* Tetracosanoic acid, 147, 181
Ligroins, 82
Liming-out process, 467
Limit dextrin, 398
Limonene, 853, 855
Limonene dihydrochloride, 855
Linalool, 453
Lindane, 432
Line spectra, 662
Linoleic acid, 179
Linolenic acid, 179
Linoleum, 187
Linolic acid, 179
Linseed oil, 181, 182
    in paint, 187
Lipoic acid, 635
Liquefied petroleum gas, 72
Lithium aluminum hydride, reduction of acids, 172, 550
    of acyl halides, 162
    of aldehydes and ketones, 199
    of esters, 172
Lithium compounds, 889
Lithium derivatives of picolines, 626
Lithium tetraphenylboride, 896
Lithocholic acid, 869
Lithols, 702
Lobry de Bruyn-Alberda van Ekenstein transformation, 368
Local anesthetics, p-aminobenzoates, 558
    cocaine, 650
    xylocaine, 487
Locust bean flour, 411
London forces, 39
Longifolene, 859
Loschmidt, biography, 416
Lowitz, biography, 2
Lowry, biography, 236
L P gas, *see* Liquified petroleum gas, 72
Lubricating greases, 191
Lubricating oils, 81
Lubrication, 81
Lucas test, 102
Lucite, 788
Luminal, 640
Lumisterol, 868
Lutein, 865
Lutidines, 627
Lycopene, 864
Lysergic acid, 654
Lysine, 297, 304
    synthesis, 760
L-Lyxitol, 412
*Lyxo*hexulose, 384
Lyxose, 366

Macroanalysis, 20
Macrolides, 847
Madder, 687

Madelung synthesis, 615
Magenta, 681
Magnamycin, 847
Magnesious iodide as reducing agent, 540
Magnesium compounds, 892
Magnesium methoxide, 100
Ma Huang, 529
Malachite Green, 680
    absorption spectrum, 699
    indicator action, 700
Malaprade reaction, 742
Malathion, 809
Maleic acid, 805
    hydrazide, 807
    reduction to succinic acid, 792
Maleic anhydride, 805
    vinyl acetate copolymer, 807
Malic acids, 808
(−)Malic acid, configuration, 349
Malonaldehyde, 768
Malonic acid, preparation, 792
    reactions, 795
Malonic aldehyde, 768
Malonic anhydride, 796
Malonic ester, preparation, 792
    reactions, 800–805
Malononitrile, 792
Malt, 91
Maltase, hydrolysis of maltose, 91, 389
Maltobionic acid, *see* Maltonic acid, 390
Maltol, 632
Maltonic acid, 390
Maltose, 389
Malus, biography, 331
Mandarin orange pigment, 866
Mandelic acid, 562
Mandelonitrile, 562
Manihot, 255
Manila copal, 860
Manila elemi, 863
Manioc, 255
Mannans, 407
Mannaric acids, 362
Mannich bases, alkylation of malonic esters, 803
Mannich reaction, indole, 803
    ketones, 767
    nitroalkanes, 263
    phenols, 508, 514
    thiophene, 608
Mannite, *see* Mannitol, 412, 413
D-Mannitol, 412, 413
Mannogalactans, *see* Galactomannans, 411
*Manno*heptulose, 388
Mannosaccharic acid, 362
Mannose, 361
Mannose phenylhydrazone, 371
D-Mannuronic acid, 409
Mapharsen, 903
Maple sugar, 394

Marfanil, 489
Margaric acid, 147
Marijuana, 633
Markovnikov, biography, 58
Markovnikov rule, 58
Marsh gas, 41
Masking of odors, 538
Mass spectrometry, 657
Maté, 646
Matricaric acid, 789
Mauve, 672, 696
Mauveine, *see* Mauve, 672, 696
Mechanism of organic reactions, 41
  abnormal addition of hydrogen bromide, 61
  abnormal Grignard reactions, 437
  abnormal Michael reaction, 803
  acetal formation, 204
  acid cleavage, β-keto esters, 821
  activation of benezene nucleus, 449
  addition, aldehydes to alkenes, 209
    diazomethane to double bonds, 835
    halogen, 54
    halogen acid, 60
    hydrogen, 55
    hydrogen bromide, 61
    hydrogen cyanide to carbonyl groups, 201
    hydrogen sulfide to alkene, 275
    water to aldehydes and ketones, 202
  1,4-addition, 707
  aldol addition, 206
  alkylation of alkenes, 77
    of quinones, 594
    of urea, 319
  ammonolysis of esters, 171
  antioxidant action, 887
  aromatic halogenation, 447
  aromatic nitration, 447
  aromatic substitution, 444
  aromatic sulfonation, 447
  autoxidation, aldehydes, 885
    hydrocarbons, 882, 883
  base-catalyzed addition to α,β-unsaturated acids, 787
  Beckmann rearrangement, 545
  benzidine rearrangement, 578
  benzilic acid rearrangement, 542
  benzoin condensation, 537
  benzyl halide reactivity, 463
  bimolecular mechanisms, 116
  Bucherer reaction, 588
  Cannizzaro reaction, 535
  catalytic reduction, 55
  chlorination of olefins, 727
  Claisen ester condensation, 815
  Clemmensen reduction, 219
  complex formation with polynitro compounds, 461

Mechanism of organic reactions—(*Cont.*)
  coupling of diazonium salts, 498
  cyclization of carboxylic acids, 598
    of terpenes, 852
  deactivation of benzene nucleus, 449
  decarboxylation, hydroxybenzoic acids, 518
    β-keto acids, 814
    malonic acids, 795
    pyridine carboxylic acids, 627
    pyridylacetic acids, 628
    trichloroacetic acid, 780
    2,4,6-trinitrobenzoic acid, 464
    unsaturated acids, 787
  decomposition, carboxylic acids to ketones, 152
  diazonium salts, 497
  peroxides, 511
  quaternary ammonium salts, 242
  dehydration, of alcohols, 104
    by carbodiimides, 323
    catalysis by iodine, 207
    of isoborneol, 857
    of methyl-*t*-butylcarbinol, 857
  dehydrohalogenation, 118
  Diels-Alder reaction, 806
  directive influence of substituents, 451
  displacement of aromatic halogen, 463
  displacement reaction, 116
  electromeric effect, 453
  electrophilic substitution, 444
  elimination reactions, 104, 118
  emulsion polymerization, 718
  enolization, 213
  ester condensations, 815
  esterification, carboxylic acids, 168
    halogen acids, 102
    inorganic oxygen acids, 102
    tertiary alcohols, 169
  ether formation, 138
  formose from formaldehyde, 385
  free-radical mechanisms, 42
  Friedel-Crafts reactions, 447
  halogenation, acyl halides, 216
    aldehydes and ketones, 215
    alkenes, 727, 728
    aromatic compounds, 447
  halohydrin formation, 741
  hemiacetal formation, 203
  Hunsdiecker reaction, 157
  hydrazone formation, 211
  hydrogenation, catalytic, 55
  hydrolysis, acyl halides, 161
    alkyl halides, 116
    amides, 246
    aromatic amines, 481
    cyanides, 253
    epoxides, 740
    esters, 171

Mechanism of organic reactions—(*Cont.*)
hydroperoxides from hydrocarbons, 875
inductive effect, 452
ionic mechanisms, 42
isocyanides from alkyl halides, 257
from primary amines, 237
isomerization, alkylated benzenes, 449
geometrical isomers, 663
β-keto ester cleavage, 821
Lobry de Bruyn-Alberda van Ekenstein
transformation, 368
Meerwein-Ponndorf reduction, 199
mesomeric effect, 453
methylation with methyl radicals, 594
molecular complex formation, polynitro
compounds, 461
ninhydrin reaction, 841
nitration of aromatic compounds, 447
of phenols, 507
nucleophilic substitution, 454
osazone formation, 371
oxidation, alcohols, 106
aldehydes and ketones, 212, 533
by Fenton reagent, 886
sulfides by hydrogen peroxide, 279
tertiary amines by hydrogen peroxide,
240
oxide ring opening, 745
oxime formation, 211
pinacol-pinacolone rearrangement, 217
pinacol reduction, 218
polymerization, addition, 61, 62
aldehydes, 209
alkenes, acid catalyzed, 62
free-radical catalyzed, 61
1,3-dienes, free-radical catalyzed, 718
pyrroles, 611
pyrolysis, of hydrocarbons, 45
reactions of acyl halides, 161
of alcohols with halogen acids, 102
carbonyl compounds and diazomethane, 267
of chloroform, 175, 237
cyanides from alkyl halides, 250
cyanides and hydrogen peroxide, 253
halides and inorganic nitrites, 259
ortho esters from chloroform, 175
phenol from cumene hydroperoxide,
511
2-pyrrolealdehyde from pyrrole, 612
reactivity of benzyl halides, 463
reduction, bimolecular, of aromatic nitro
groups, 460
catalytic, 55
Clemmensen, 219
Meerwein-Ponndorf, 199
by metals, 217
Reimer-Tiemann reaction, 532
resonance effect, 453

Mechanism of organic reactions—(*Cont.*)
scission of β-keto esters, 821
of 1,3-diketones, 774
S_N1 and S_N2 reactions, 116, 117
Stobbe condensation, 796
Strecker degradation, 841
substitution in aromatic nucleus, by
electron-donating (nucleophilic) reagents, 454
by electron-seeking (electrophilic) reagents, 444
substitution in naphthalene, 587
in pyridine, 622
in pyrroles, 616
sulfonation of aromatic compounds, 447
aromatic amines, 485
tautomeric effect, 453
teleomerization, 725
unimolecular mechanisms, 117
vulcanization, 710
Wagner-Meerwein rearrangement, 857
Meerwein-Ponndorf reduction of aldehydes
and ketones, 199
Meerwein reaction, 496
Meisenheimer, biography, 543
MEK, *see* Methyl ethyl ketone, 225
Melamine, 321
Melamine resins, 321
Melibiose, 392
Mellite, 556
Mellitic acid, 556
Mellitic anhydride, 556
Melting point apparatus, 23
Melting points, alternation for alkanes, 39
alternation for carboxylic acids, 149
see also Physical properties
Menhaden oil, 182
p-Menthane hydroperoxide, 874
Meprobamate, 315
Mercaptals of sugars, 382
Mercaptans, nomenclature, 276
physical properties, 276
preparation, 274–276
reactions, 277, 284, 286
2-Mercaptobenzothiazole, 636
Mercapto group, 276
Mercerized cotton, 400
Mercuration, 894
of thiophene, 608
Mercuric halides, reaction with Grignard
reagents, 123
Mercurochrome, 683, 895
Mercury compounds, 893
from diazonium salts, 495
Mercury fulminate, 318
Meriquinones, *see* Semiquinones, 571, 669
Merocyanine dyes, 694
Merthiolate, 895
Mesaconic acid, 808
Mescaline, 530

Mesitylene from acetone, 208, 430
Mesityl oxide, 207, 208
  absorption spectrum, 665
  addition of ammonia, 764
  addition of hydrogen cyanide, 764
  condensation with ethyl malonate, 804
  from diacetone alcohol, 207
  isomerization, 762
meso forms, 339
meso inositol, 413
Mesoionic compounds, 637
Mesomeric effect in aromatic substitution, 453
Mesomerism, 453
Mesoxalic acid, 826
Mesquite gum, 411
Mesyl chloride, 291
Mesyl derivatives of sugars, 378
meta, prefix, 417, 420
Metabolism, amino acids, 301
  fats, 186, 814
  nitrogen, 293, 301
  proteins, 301
  starch, 398
Meta-chroming, 674
meta-directing groups, 441
Metadiazine, *see* 1,3-Diazine, 638
Metalation, 891
Metal carbonyls, 904
Metaldehyde, 223
Metal-halogen exchange, 889
Metal ion deactivators, 755, 887
Metal ketyls, 570
Metallic halides, reaction with Grignard reagent, 123
Metalloorganic compounds, *see* Organometallic compounds
Metals, reaction with alcohols, 99
Metanilic acid, 486
Metaphen, 895
meta rings,   849
Methacrylonitrile, 788
Methadone, 652
Methallyl alcohol, 738
Methallyl chloride, 727
Methane, chlorination, 722
  fluorination, 731
  sources, 40
  structure, 28, 30, 32
Methanediol, 739
Methane series, *see* Alkanes
Methanesulfonates of sugars, 378
Methanesulfonic acid, 288
Methanesulfonyl chloride, 291
Methanesulfonyl derivatives of sugars, 378
Methanol, *see* Methyl alcohol, 89
Methenamine, 222
Methine group, 680

Methionine, 296, 304
  sulfoximine, 304
  synthesis, 765
Methone, 804
Methoxycarbonyl group, 169
Methoxychlor, 566
2-Methoxy-2,3-dihydro-γ-pyran, 765
Methoxyl determination, 140
N-Methylacetanilide, 479
"Methyl acetone," 89
Methylacetylcarbinol, butter flavor, 186
Methyl acrylate, 788
α-Methylacrylonitrile, 788
Methylal, 203
Methyl alcohol, 89
  structural formula, 84
Methylallyl alcohols, 738
2-Methylallyl chloride, 727
Methylamine, 240
p-(Methylamino)phenol, 519
N-Methylaniline, 480
Methyl anthranilate, 558
Methylarsenoxide, 900
Methylarsine, 900
Methylarsonic acid, 901
Methylation of carbohydrates, 373, 390
  free radical, 594
  of phenols, 504
Methyl azide, 268
2-Methylbenzothiazole, 636
α-Methylbenzylamine, 528
α-Methylbenzyl ether, 525
Methylbis(2-chloroethyl)amine, 753
Methyl bromide, 118
Methyl *i*-butyl ketone, 225
Methyl-*t*-butylcarbinol, dehydration, 857
Methyl carbamates from amides, 231
Methylcellulose, 404
Methyl chloride, 118, 722
  from methane, 722
  from trimethylamine, 241
Methylchloroform, 723
Methylchlorosilanes, 914
Methylcholanthrene, 604
Methyl cyanide, *see* Acetonitrile, 249
Methylcyclohexane, 833, 841
  toluene from, 66
1-Methylcyclohexyl hydroperoxide, 874
Methylcyclopentane, 64, 833
Methylcyclopentenophenanthrene, 867
Methylcytosine, 638
Methyldichloroarsine, 902
Methylene Blue, 696
Methylene chloride, 722
Methylenecyclobutane, 832, 836
3,6-Methylene cyclohexene-4,5-dicarboxylic anhydride, 806
Methylene group, definition, 51
  reactive, 771

Methyl esters from diazomethane, 266
Methyl ether, 140
Methyl ethyl ketone, 159, 225
"Methyl ethyl ketone peroxide," 879
2-Methyl-5-ethylpyridine, 627
Methyl fluoride, 731
5-Methylfurfural, 378
Methyl glycosides, 373
Methyl groups, determination, 144
Methyl hydrogen terephthalate, 555
Methyl hydroperoxide, 875
Methylidyne dyes, 694
Methylidyne group, 680, 693, 703
3-Methylindole, 615
Methyl iodide, *see* Halides, alkyl
Methyl ketone, *see* Acetone, 224
Methyl ketones from aldehydes, 266
2-Methyl-4-keto-1-pentene, 763
2-Methyl-4-keto-2-pentene, 763
Methyl mercaptan, 289
Methyl methacrylate, 788
    infrared absorption, 660
    polyester resins, 807
Methylnaphthalenes, 588
    in coal tar, 428
2-Methyl-1,4-naphthoquinone, 594
Methyl naphthyl ketones, 586
N-Methyl-N-nitroso-p-toluenesulfonamide, 473
Methylolacetamide, 313
Methylolurea, 313
Methyl Orange, indicator action, 699
2-Methyl-2,4-pentanediol, 746
2-Methyl-1-pentanol, 96
Methylpentoses, 367
Methylpentynol, 205
Methylphenylcarbinol, 525
α-Methylphenylhydrazine as reagent for fructose, 385
Methyl phthalate, 552
1-Methyl-4-i-propylbenzene, 420, 431
Methyl propyl ether, 141
Methyl i-propyl ketone, 742
1-Methyl-7-i-propylphenanthrene, 602
Methylpyridines, 625
N-Methylpyridone, 623
α-Methylpyrroline, 767
Methylquinolines, 629
Methyl radicals, from acetyl peroxide, 568
    from azomethane, 265
    from lead tetraacetate, 594
    from tetraethyllead, 568
Methyl rubber, 715
Methyl salicylate, 560
Methylstyrenes, 575
Methyl sulfate, 108, 110
Methyl sulfide, 289
Methyl sulfoxide, 284
Methyl terephthalate, 555

α-Methyltetrahydropyridine, 767
Methyl-2-thienyl ketone, 608
Methyl toluates, 555
Methyl trimethylsilyl ether, 911
4-Methyluracil, 825
N-Methylurea, 318
O-Methylurea, 319
1-Methylvinyl acetate, 737, 761
Methyl vinyl ether, 737
Methyl vinyl ketone, 765
Methyl Violet, 681
Methymycin, 847
Metol, 519
Metopryl, 141
Meyer, V., biography, 21
MIBK, 225
Michael, biography, 803
Michael reaction of β-keto esters, 819
    of malonic esters, 803
    of sulfones, 286
Michler ketone, 541
Microanalysis, 20
Microcrystalline wax, 82
Microwave spectroscopy, 657
Middle oil, 427
Milk sugar, 392
Miltown, 315
Mineral oils, 82
Mirror images, 335
Miticide, benzyl benzoate, 525
Mitscherlich, biography, 416
Mixed ethers, 136, 137
    from α-halogen ethers, 203
mμ, abbreviation for millimicron, 658
Mobile electrons, 153
Moissan, biography, 728
Molasses, blackstrap, 92, 394
Molding powders, 512
Molecular asymmetry, allenes, 706
    without asymmetric atoms, 335
    asymmetric atoms other than carbon, 350
    asymmetric carbon atoms, 335
    biphenyl derivatives, 580
    dimethylbenzo(c)phenanthrenes, 604
    mycomycin, 790
Molecular complexes, *see also* Coordination complexes
    of polynitrocompounds, 460
Molecular dissymmetry, 335
Molecular extinction coefficient, 661
Molecular formula, 21
Molecular orbitals, 9
    π-type in acetylene, 129
    in benzene, 419
    in carboxylate ion, 154
    in 1,3-dienes, 663
    in ethylene, 50
    in thiophene, 609
    σ-type, 10

Molecular rearrangement, alcohols, 105, 857
alicyclic compounds, 832
alkanes, 46
alkenes, 105
alkylbenzenes, 449
N-alkylpyridinium iodides, 623
allylic, 728
Beckmann, 544, 841
benzidine, 578
benzilic acid, 541
Curtius, 268
dienone-phenol, 842
epoxides, 745
Favorski, 766
Hofmann, 231, 247
isocyanides to cyanides, 257
pinacol-pinacolone, 217, 742
semidine, 578
Wagner-Meerwein, 857
Molecular rotation, 333
Molecular weight determination, 21–24
Molozonides, 880
Monastral Blue, 704
Monoazo dyes, 677
Monoglycerides, emulsifying agents, 191
Monomer, definition, 61
Monoperphthalic acid, *see* Monoperoxy-phthalic acid, 555, 875
Monosaccharides, 360
Monosodium glutamate, 304
Monothiocarbonic acid, 309
Mordant dyes, 674
anthraquinone, 687
azo, 677
Mordants, 674
Morin, 698
Morphine, 651
Morpholine, 642
Mother of vinegar, 158
MQ developer, 519
Mucic acid, 362, 619
Mucilages, 411
Mucins, 294
Mucoids, 294
Muscle adenylic acid, 644
Muscone, 847
Musk ambrette, 464
Musk ketone, 464
Musks, natural, 847
synthetic, 464
Musk tibetine, 464
Musk xylene, 464
Mustard gas, 289
Mustard oils, 325, 482
Mutarotation, 375
aldehydo derivatives of sugars, 380
Mycomycin, 790
Mydriatics, 528, 650

Mylar, 555
Myristic acid, 147
Myristyl alcohol, 172

Naphtha, coal tar, 427
petroleum, 82
Naphthacene, 603
absorption spectrum, 667
Naphthalene, 582
absorption spectrum, 667
derivatives, 588–596
isolation, 427
reactions 583–588
Naphthalene diisocyanate, 800
Naphthalenedisulfonic acids, 587
Naphthalenesulfonic acids, 586
Naphthalene tetrachloride, 585
Naphthalic acid, 595
Naphthalic anhydride, 595
Naphthalimide, 595
Naphthazarin, 687
Naphthenes, 64, 828
Naphthenic acids, 839
Naphthionic acid, 589
Naphthoic acids, 594
α- and β-Naphthol, 588
Naphtholdisulfonic acids, 590
Naphthol Green B, 676
α- and β-Naphthol Orange, 591, 677
Naphtholsulfonic acids, 589
Naphthol Yellows S, 675
Naphthoquinones, 592
α-Naphthylacetic acid, 595
α-Naphthylamine oxidation, 583
Naphthylamines, 588
Naphthylaminesulfonic acids, 589
Naphtol AS, 595, 677
Narcotine, 651
Natural gas, 69, 70
acetylene from, 133
oxygenated compounds from, 159, 220
NBS, *see* N-Bromosuccinimide, 797
Neat's foot oil, 182
Neat soap, 189
Nef, biography, 262
Nef reaction, 262
Nembutal, 640
Neo-, prefix, 33
Neohetramine, 641
Neomenthols, 854
Neopentane, structure, 32
Neopentyl alcohol, dehydration, 105
esterification, 169
reaction with hydrogen bromide, 102
Neopentyl glycol, 746
Neoprene, 719
Neo-Synephrine, 529
Neral, 850
Nerol, 853

Neroli, 853
Nerolidol, 858
Nerve gases, 910
  antidote, 626
Nesmejanov reaction, 495
Neutralization equivalent, 151
Nevile-Winther acid, 590
Ngai comphor, 856
Niacin, 625
Niamide, 625
Nickel carbonyl, 904
Nickel coordination complexes, 770
Nicol, biography, 330
Nicol prism, 330
Nicotinamide, 625
Nicotine, 649
  oxidation, 625
Nicotinic acid, 625
Nieuwland, biography, 715
Nightshade, 650
Nigraniline, 696
Nigre, 189
Nigrosine, 696
Ninhydrin, 306, 840
Ninhydrin reaction, 306, 840
Nitrate process for rayon, 406
Nitrates, 108
Nitration, alkanes, 259
  aromatic amines, 484
  aromatic compounds, 439
  cyclohexane, 841
  displacement of other groups, 441
  isomer distribution, 441
  mechanism for aromatic compounds, 448
  naphthalene, 585, 587
  phenols, 507
  pyridine, 622
  pyrrole, 612
  relative rates, 442
  thiophene, 608
Nitrile rubber, *see* GRN, 718
Nitriles, *see* Cyanides
Nitrites, 108, 258
Nitroacetanilides, 485
Nitroalcohols, reduction to amino alcohols, 754
Nitroalkanes, 258–264
  coupling with diazonium salts, 499
p-Nitroalkylacetanilides, 481
(Nitroalkyl)amines, 263
Nitroanilines, 484, 487
  basicity, 477
α-Nitroanthraquinone, 598
Nitrobenzene, 439, 463
  absorption spectrum, 665
  reduction products, 459
Nitrobenzenesulfonic acids, 468
Nitrobenzid, 463
Nitrocellulose, 401

Nitrochlorobenzenes, 440
Nitro compounds, aliphatic, 258–264
  aromatic, 439, 463
    from diazonium salts, 495
    displacement reactions, 456
    molecular complexes, 460
    physical properties, 455
    physiological action, 455
    reduction products, 456–460
Nitrocyclohexane, 841
N-Nitrodiethanolamine nitrate, 753
Nitro dyes, 675
Nitroethane, 259
Nitro form, 261
Nitrofurazone, 620
Nitrofurfural diacetate, 620
Nitrogen compounds, optical activity, 350
Nitrogen cycle, 293
Nitrogen determination, 19
Nitrogen dioxide, addition to alkenes, 260
  see also Dinitrogen tetroxide, 247
Nitrogen free radicals, 570
Nitrogen metabolism, 293, 301
Nitrogen mustards, 753
Nitrogen rings, opening by exhaustive methylation, 621
Nitrogen tetroxide, *see* Dinitrogen tetroxide, 247
Nitroglycerin, 749
Nitro group, aromatic, effect on reactivity of other substituents, 461
Nitroguanidine, 322
Nitrolic acids, 261
Nitromethane, 259, 381
Nitromethylnaphthalenes, 587
Nitro musks, 464
α-Nitronaphthalene, oxidation, 583
Nitronaphthalenes, 585
Nitronaphthalenesulfonic acids, 589
Nitronic esters, 263
Nitronium ion in aromatic nitrations, 448
Nitroparaffins, *see* Nitroalkanes, 258–264
p-Nitrophenacyl bromide, 541
p-Nitrophenacyl esters, 541
p-Nitrophenol, absorption spectrum, 666
Nitrophenols, 503, 507
Nitrophenylamine dyes, 676
3-Nitrophthalic acid, 583
Nitropropanes, 259
β-Nitropropionic acid, 264
3-Nitropyridine, 622
4-Nitropyridine-N-oxide, 624
3-Nitropyrrole, 612
Nitrosation, acetoacetic esters, 813
  ketones, 768
  malonic esters, 802, 813
  nitroalkanes, 261
  phenols, 506
  secondary amines, 239, 480

Nitrosation—(*Continued*)
　tertiary aromatic amines, 480
　ureas, 318
Nitrosoamines, 239, 480
Nitrosobenzene, by oxidation of *N*-phenyl-
　hydroxylamine, 458
p-Nitrosodialkylanilines, 480, 481
p-Nitrosodimethylaniline, 480, 489
Nitroso dyes, 675
Nitrosomalonic ester, 802
N-Nitroso-*N*-methylaniline, 480
Nitrosomethylurea, 318
Nitrosomethylurethan, 319
Nitrosonitroalkanes, 261
Nitrosonium ion, 448
p-Nitrosophenol, 506
Nitrostarch, 398
2-Nitrothiophene, 608
Nitrotoluenes, 439
Nitrourea, 318
Nitrous acid, reactions, aliphatic amines,
　238
　　amides, 247
　　aromatic amines, 479, 480
　　nitroalkanes, 261
　　phenols, 506
　　ureas, 318
NMR spectra, 668
Nodal plane, 10
Nomenclature, acid anhydrides, 163
　acyl halides, 161
　alcohols, 84
　aldehydes, 196
　alkanes, 33, 36
　alkenes, 51
　alkyl groups, 34
　alkynes, 129
　amides, 245
　amines, aliphatic, 228
　　aromatic, 475
　aromatic compounds, 420
　carbohydrates, 359
　carboxylic acids, 147
　disulfides, 280
　esters, 169
　ethers, 136
　Geneva system, 36
　heterocyclic compounds, 648
　I.U.C. system, 36
　I.U.P.A.C. system, 36
　ketones, 197
　mercaptans, 276
　oxa-aza system, 648
　sulfides, 278
　sulfones, 286
　sulfonic acids, 287, 466
　sulfoxides, 284
Nonadecanoic acid, 147
Nonionic detergents, 744
Nonreducing disaccharides, 393

"Nonylaldehyde," *see* 3,5,5-Trimethyl-
　hexanal, 224
Nonylic acid, from oleic acid, 793
Norepinephrine, 529
Normal, definition, 30
Novocain, 558
NSR spectra, 668
NTA, 555
Nuclear magnetic resonance, 668
Nuclear-spin resonance, 668
Nucleic acids, 644
Nucleophilic reagents, 117
Nucleophilic substitution, 454
Nucleoproteins, 294
Nucleosides, 644
Nucleotides, 644
Nylon 4, 785
Nylon 6, 841
Nylon 66, 798
Nylon dyeing, 675
　anthraquinone dyes, 688
　nitro dyes, 676
Nylon salt, 798

O^{18}, as tracer element, 169, 171, 202
O-alkylation, *see* Oxygen alkylation
Occlusion compounds, *see* Inclusion com-
　pounds, 311
Octaacetylsucrose, *see* Sucrose octaacetate,
　394
1,18-Octadecanediol, 747
Octahedral configuration of cobalt com-
　pounds, 352
Octane number, 74
2-Octanol, 794
Odor of fruits, 174
Odors, masking of, 538
Oe-, *see* E-
Oil cloth, 187
Oil gas, 81
Oil of, *see also source, e.g.,* Orange oil
Oil of bitter almonds, artificial, 463
Oil of mirbane, 463
Oil Orange, 677
Oils, *see also individual oil, e.g.,* Olive oil
　acetyl value, 184
　animal, 181
　consumption, 183
　digestion, 186
　drying, 181, 186
　essential, 849
　fish, 181
　hydrogenation, 184
　hydrolysis, 183, 190
　iodine value, 181, 184
　lubricating, 81
　nondrying, 181
　rancidity, 184
　reactions, 183
　saponification, 183

Oils—(*Continued*)
  saponification value, 181, 183
  semidrying, 181
  sulfated, 191
  thiocyanogen value, 184
  uses, 186–192
  vegetable, 181
  volatile, 849
Oil-soluble dyes, 675, 677
Oiticica oil, 181, 183
Oleanolic acid, 863
Olefiant gas, 53
Olefins, *see* Alkenes
Oleic acid, 179, 793
  geometrical isomerism, 356
Oleomargarine, 186
Oligosaccharides, 389
Olive oil, 181, 182
One-two-four Acid (1,2,4-Acid), 592
Onion, volatile oil, 289
Opium, 650
Oppenauer oxidation, 199
Optical activity, 331
  cause, 352
Optical antipodes, 335
Optical bleaches, 675, 679
Optical density, 661
Optical isomerism, 329–354
  allenes, 706
  biphenyl derivatives, 580
  dimethylbenzo(*c*)phenanthrenes, 604
Optical isomers, 333
  number, 337
  representation, 338, 339, 340
Optically active compounds, origin, 344
Optical rotation, 332
  of anomers, 377
Orange I, 591
Orange II, 591, 677
Orange blossom oil, 853
Orange oil, 853
Orange pigment, 866
Orbital, atomic, 5
  molecular, 10
Orcinol, 517
Ordinary ray, 331
Organic chemistry, definition, 4
  fundamental principles, 14
  historical, 1
Organic compounds, classification, 24
  isolation and purification, 14
  number, 4, 13, 24
Organic pigments, 702
Organomagnesium compounds, *see* Grignard reagents
Organometallic compounds, 120, 889, *see also individual metal, e.g.*, Sodium compounds
  relative reactivity, 892, 894
Orientation of aromatic compounds, 424

Orinase, 489
Orlon, 788
Ornithine, 298
Orthanilic acid, 486
ortho, prefix, 417, 420
Orthocarbonates, 310
Orthocarbonic acid, 308
Orthodiazine, *see* 1,2-Diazine, 638
Ortho esters, 174
  reactions with Grignard reagents, 175, 196
  with ketones, 204
Orthoformic acid, 174
ortho, para-directing groups, 441
ortho and *para* hydrogen interconversion by free radicals, 567
Orthothiocarbonic acid, 309
Osazone formation, 370
Osazones, of 1,2-dicarbonyl compounds, 771
  of disaccharides, solubility, 392
  ring structure, 382
Osmium tetroxide, catalyst for hydrogen peroxide addition, 763
Osones, 371
Osotetrazines, 771
Ouricuri wax, 178
Ovalbumin, 294
Overlapping of bond orbitals, 10
Ovomucoid, 411
Oxa-aza nomenclature, 648
1,2,3-Oxadiazoles, 637
Oxalacetic esters, 815
Oxalic acid, reactions, 794
  synthesis, 791
Oxazines, 695
Oxazole, 635
Oxidation, *see also* Autoxidation *and individual oxidizing agent, e.g.*, Selenium dioxide
  alcohols, 105, 144, 194
  aldehydes, 212, 533
  alkanes, 42, 159, 220, 874
  alkenes, 56, 57, 144, 740, 876
  amines, 240, 259
  aniline, 481, 482
  anthracene, 597
  anthraquinone vats, 600
  aromatic amines, 481, 482
  aromatic side chains, 424, 530, 547
  benzene to maleic anhydride, 805
  carbohydrates, 362, 370, 373, 381
  crotonic aldehyde to maleic anhydride, 805
  disulfides, 281
  1,2-glycols, 742
  Grignard reagents, 122
  indigo white, 686
  isocyanides, 257
  isoquinoline, 630

Oxidation—(*Continued*)
  ketones, 212
  leuco bases, 680
  mercaptans, 277, 278
  naphthalene, 552
  α-naphthylamine, 583
  nicotine, 625
  1-nitronaphthalene, 583
  oximes, 259
  phenanthrene, 602
  phenols, 505, 520
  picolines, 625
  quinoline, 628
  saturated hydrocarbons, 42, 159, 220, 874
  sulfides, 279
  tertiary-alkyl amines, 259
  tertiary amines, 240
  unsaturated acids, 185
  o-xylene, 552
Oxidation number, 145
Oxidation-reduction equations, balancing, 145
Oxidative coupling of acetylenes, 748
Oxidative scission of 1,2-glycols, 742
Oxides, *see* Alkoxides, Amine oxides, Sulfoxides, Epoxides, *and* Ethers
Oxides of carbon, malonic anhydride, 796
  mellitic anhydride, 556
Oxidized cellulose, 405
Oximes, 210
  Beckmann rearrangement, 544, 841

  dehydration to cyanides, 250
  reduction to primary amines, 232
  stereochemistry, 542
Oxindole, 684
β-Oxoglutaric acid, *see* Acetonedicarboxylic acid, 810
Oxomalonic acid, 826
Oxonium ions, intermediates, in ether formation, 138
  in reactions of alcohols with acids, 102, 103, 104
Oxonium salts, alcohols, 98
  ethers, 139
  pyrylium salts, 631, 698
Oxo process, 223
α-Oxopropionic acid, 812
Oxosuccinic esters, 826
α-Oxosulfones, 285
Oxozonides, 880
Oxyacetylene flame, 134
Oxygen, autoxidation by, 880–886
  catalyst for polymerization, 61
  as free biradical, 62, 570
  free radicals, 570
  reaction with Grignard reagents, 122

Oxygen alkylation, 1,3-diketones, 774
  β-keto esters, 818
  nitroalkanes, 263
Oxygenated rubber, 713
Oxygen exchange in acetone, 202
Oxytocin, 303
Ozalid process, 697
Ozonation, alkenes, 56
Ozone, addition to alkenes, 56
  structure, 879
Ozonides, 56, 195, 879
  anomalous structures, 880
Ozonization, *see* Ozonation
Ozonolysis, 57, 195

Paint, 187
  thinners, 82
  vehicles, 187, 720, 736
Palmarosa oil, 853
Palmitic acid, 147, 179
  use, 192
Palmitoleic acid, 180
Palm oil, 180, 181
Palm sugar, 394
Paludrine, 654
Pamaquine, 653
Pantetheine, 785
Pantocaine, *see* Pontocaine, 559
Pantothenic acid, 785
P.A.P., 519
Papaverine, 651
Paprika, pigment, 865
  pungent principle, 649
para, prefix, 417, 420
Para acid, 679
para-bridged benzenes, 849
Paraconic ester, 796
Paracyclophanes, 849
Paradiazine, *see* 1,4-Diazine, 638
Paradichlor, *see* Dichlorobenzenes, 433
Paraffin hydrocarbons, *see* Alkanes
Paraffin oils, 82
Paraffin wax, 82
Paraformaldehyde, 220
Paraldehyde, 223
Paraldol, 206
Paramagnetism, free radicals, 567, 669
  quinhydrone, 571
  triphenylmethyl, 567
Para Red, 677
para rings, 849
Pararosaniline, 680
Parchment paper, 400
Parinaric acid, 180
Paris green, 159
Parlon, 713
Partial valence theory, 51
PAS, 560
Pasteur, biography, 91

p atomic orbitals, 5
  direction, 10
Pauli exclusion principle, 5, 419, 664
π bonds, 51, *see also* Molecular orbitals,
  π-type
Peanut hulls, 407
Peanut oil, 181, 182
Peat, 426
Pectic acids, 407
Pectinic acids, 407
Pectins, 407
Pelargonic acid, 147
Pelargonidin chloride, 698
π complexes, 60, 445
π electrons, 51
Penicillins, 636
Pennyroyal oil, 854
Pentaacetylglucoses, 377
Pentacene, 604
  absorption spectrum, 667
Pentachloroethane, 724
Pentachlorofluoroethane, 733
Pentachlorophenol, 514
Pentacosanoic acid, 147
Pentadecanoic acid, 147
Pentadecanolide, 847
Pentadigalloylglucose, 561
Pentaerythritol, 752
  nitrate, 752
Pentaerythrityl bromide, 836
Pentamethylene cyanide, 793
Pentamethylenediamine, 621, 756
1,5-Pentanediol, 631, 747
Pentanes, equilibrium composition of iso-
  meric, 78
  structure, 32
Pentanols, *see* Amyl alcohols
Pentasol, 119
Pentenes, *see* Amylenes, 52, 97
Pentobarbital, 640
Pentosans, 407
Pentoses, 361
  color reactions, 379
  furfural from, 378
Pentothal sodium, 640
Pepper, 649
Peppermint oil, 854
Pepsin, 301
Peptidases, 301
Peptide linkage, 299
Peptides, 302, 304
Per-, prefix, 724
Per acids, *see* Peroxy acids, 153, 875
Perchloroethylene, 724
Perchloromethyl mercaptan, 289
Per esters, *see* Peroxy esters, 877
Perfluoro-1,3-butadiene, 734
Perfluorocyclobutane, 733
Perfluorocyclohexane, 730

Perfluoro-1,3-dimethylcyclohexane, 734
Perfluoroheptane, 730
Perfluoromethyl ether, 734
Perfumes, *see individual odor, e.g.,* Jas-
  mine odor
Peri acid, 589
Periodic acid as oxidizing agent, 373, 742
Periodic table, *inside back cover*
  electron distribution of first three peri-
  ods, 6
Periston, 785
Perkin, biography, 672
Perkin, Jr., biography, 828
Perkin synthesis, 536
Permanent dipoles, 197
Permanent waving of hair, 299
Pernigraniline, 696
Peroxide-catalyzed addition of hydrogen
  bromide, mechanism, 60, 61
Peroxides, 873–879
  detection, 140, 884
Peroxyacetic acid, 153, 159, 875
Peroxy acids, 153, 875
Peroxybenzoic acid, 551
Peroxy esters, 877
Peroxytrifluoroacetic acid, 259, 481, 876
Persian Orange, 702
Perspective formulas, 338, 383
Perspex, 788
Perylene, 604
Pethidine, 651
PETN, 752
Petrolatum, 82
Petroleum, 69–83
Petroleum ether, 82
Petroleum jelly, 82
Petroselenic acid, 180
Pfitzinger synthesis, 630
Phellandrenes, 854
Phenacetin, 520
Phenacyl bromide, 541
Phenacyl chloride, 541
Phenacyl esters, 541
Phenanthraquinone, 602
Phenanthrene, 602
  absorption spectrum, 667
  alkaloids, 651
  isolation, 428
Phenanthridine, 631
o-Phenanthroline, 631
Phenazine, 642
Phenazines, 695
Phene, 535
Phenethyl alcohol, 527
Phenethylamine, 528
Phenetidines, 520
Phenobarbital, 640
Phenol, from coal tar, 427
  commercial syntheses, 509

Phenol—(*Continued*)
  infrared spectrum, 660
  mercuration, 894
Phenol coefficient, 509
Phenol ethers from diazonium salts, 494
  from phenols, 504
Phenol-formaldehyde resins, 512
Phenolic resins, 511
Phenolindophenol, 506
Phenolphthalein, 682
  indicator action, 700
Phenols, occurrence, 502
  physical properties, 503
  physiological action, 509, 516, 517
  preparation, 502
  reactions, 502
  test for, 523
Phenolsulfonic acids, 505
Phenolsulfonphthalein, 682
Phenoquinone, 505
Phenothiazine, 643
Phenyl, 421
Phenyl acetate, 504
Phenylacetic acid, 561
Phenylacetylene, 576, 836
Phenylalanine, 296
Phenylarsine, 902
Phenylarsenoxide, 902
Phenylarsonic acid, 902
Phenylazopyrrole, 612
Phenylboric acid, *see* Phenylboronic acid, 896
Phenylboronic acid, 896
γ-Phenylbutyric acid, 598
N-Phenylcarbamyl chloride, 479
Phenylchlorosilanes, 914
Phenyl cyanide, 469
Phenyldichlorophosphine, 910
Phenylenediamines, 475, 487
Phenylene group, 421
o-Phenylenelithium, 890
Phenyl ether, 510
β-Phenylethyl alcohol, 527
Phenylethylamines, 528
Phenylethylene, 573
  substitution reactions, 454
Phenylfulvene, 838
Phenylglucosazone, *see* Glucose phenylosazone, 371
N-Phenylglycine, 685
N-Phenylglycine-o-carboxylic acid, 685
Phenylhydrazine, reaction with aldehydes and ketones, 211
  synthesis, 497
Phenylhydrazones, 211
N-Phenylhydroxylamine, 458, 519
Phenyl isocyanate, 317, 479
Phenyl isothiocyanate, 326, 482
Phenyllithium, 889

Phenylmalonic ester, 802
Phenyl methyl ether, *see* Anisole, 504
Phenyl mustard oil, 482
Phenylnitromethane, tautomerism, 822
Phenylosazones, 363, 370
Phenylphenols, 510
Phenyl phosphate, 515
Phenylphosphine, 910
Phenylphosphonic acid, 909
Phenylphosphonyl chloride, 909
Phenylpropiolic acid, 563
N-Phenylpyrazoles from 1,3-diketones, 772
Phenyl radicals, 497, 568, 882
Phenyl salicylate, 559
Phenylsilicon trichloride, 911
N-Phenylsulfamic acid, 485
Phenyl sulfone, 467, 473
Phenylthiourea, 482
Phenyl tolyl ketoximes, 542
Phenyltrichlorosilane, 911
Phlobaphenes, 698
Phloionic acid, 809
Phloroglucinol, 517
  reaction with furfural, 617
Phorone, 208
  addition of ammonia, 764
Phosgene, 310
Phosphagen, 322
Phosphates, alkyl, 108
  aryl, 515
Phosphatides, *see* Phospholipids, 753
Phosphine (dye), 695
Phosphine oxides, 908
Phosphines, 907
Phosphinic acids, 907
Phosphites, alkyl, 108
Phosphobenzene, 909
Phospholipids, 753
Phosphonamides, 909
Phosphonic acids, 907
Phosphonic esters, 908
Phosphonium salts, 907
Phosphonous acids, 908
Phosphonyl chlorides, 909
Phosphoproteins, 295
Phosphor N, *see* Azobisisobutyronitrile, 265
Phosphorobenzene, 910
Phosphorous acid, structure, 908
Phosphoroxybenzene, 910
Phosphorus compounds, 907
Phosphorus, determination in organic compounds, 20
Phosphorus trihalides, reaction with acids, 151
  with alcohols, 100
  with alkanes, 909
  with Grignard reagents, 123

Photographic developers, 519
  film base, 402, 403
  image development, 519
  processes, black and white, 519
    color, 692
    diazotype, 697
    Ozalid, 697
    sensitizers, 693
Phototropism, 500
Phthaleins, 682
Phthalhydrazide, 553
Phthalic acid, 551
Phthalic anhydride, 551
Phthalid, 554
Phthalimide, 553
Phthalocyanines, 703
Phthalyl chloride, 554
Phthiocol, 593
Physalein, 865
Physcion, 599
Physical properties, acid anhydrides, 163
  acyl halides, 161
  alcohols, 86–88
  aldehydes, 197
  alkanes, 38–40
  alkenes, 53
  alkyl halides, 113
  alkynes, 129
  amides, 245
  amines, 233, 475
  benzene, 421
  carboxylic acids, 148–150
  cellulose derivatives, 404
  covalent and electrovalent compounds, 4, 8, 12
  cyanides, 250
  diastereoisomers, 337
  diazonium salts, 492
  enantiomorphs, 337
  esters, 169
  ethers, 136
  fluorinated hydrocarbons, 729
  geometrical isomers, 354
  hydrogen cyanide, 256
  isocyanides, 257
  ketones, 197
  mercaptans, 276
  nitro compounds, 260, 455
  nitrophenols, 507
  phenols, 502
  pyridine, 621
  pyrrole, 610
  sulfones, 286
  sulfonic acids, 287, 466
  sulfoxides, 283
Physiological properties
  acetanilide, 487
  adrenal steroids, 871
  alkyl cyanides, 252

Physiological properties—(*Continued*)
  aromatic amines, 476
  aromatic nitro compounds, 455
  arsenic compounds, 902
  benzene, 422
  cardiac glycosides, 870
  cinchona alkaloids, 653
  curare alkaloids, 652
  cyanides, 252
  diazomethane, 266
  Dulcin, 482
  ergot alkaloids, 654
  fluorine compounds, 729, 779
  halogen compounds, 722, 723
  Indian snake root, 654
  isocyanides, 257
  mercaptans, 277
  mercury compounds, 893
  metal carbonyls, 904
  opium alkaloids, 651
  phenols, 509, 516, 517
  β-phenylethylamines, 528
  phenylthiourea, 482
  Rauwolfia alkaloids, 654
  salicylates, 560
  sex hormones, 870
  tropane alkaloids, 650
  vitamin A, 860
Phytic acid, 413
Phytin, 413
Phytol, 860
Phytosterols, 868
Pi bonds, *see* π bonds
Picene, 604
Picolines, 625
Picolinic acids, 625
α-Picolyllithium, 890
Pi complexes, 60, 445
Picramide, 477
Picrates, 460
Picric acid, 514
  molecular complexes, 460
Picrolonates, 818
Picrolonic acid, 818
Picryl chloride, 477
Pi (π) electrons, 51
Pigments, synthetic organic, 702, *see also* Plant pigments
Pilchard oil, 182
l-Pimaric acid, 861
Pimelic acid, preparation, 793
  reaction, 798
Pi molecular orbitals, *see* π bonds
Pinacol, 217, 537
Pinacolone, 217
Pinacol-pinacolone, rearrangement, 217, 742, 832
Pinacol reduction, 217
  mechanism, 218

Pinacols, from aromatic aldehydes, 537
  by reduction of ketones, 217, 540
Pinane, 855
Pineapple, volatile oils, 174
α-Pinene, 855
Pine oil, 859
Pine splint test for pyrrole, 610
Pinitol, 414
Piperazine hydrochloride, 757
Piperazines, 641
Piperic acid, 649
Piperidine, 621
Piperidine hydrochloride, 757
Piperidones, 767, 784
Piperine, 649
Piperonal, 538
Pitch, petroleum, 82
Pi-type molecular orbitals, see Molecular
  orbitals, π type
Pivalonitrile, 250
Plane configuration of platinous complexes,
  357
  of nickel complexes, 770
Plane of symmetry, 336
Plane-polarized light, 330
Plantation rubber, 708
Plant fibers, 400
  gums, 411
  mucilages, 411
  pigments, anthocyanins, 698
    anthraquinone, 599
    carotenoid, 863
    chlorophylls, 614
    flavones, 697
    naphthoquinones, 593
Plasmochin, 653
Plastic, melamine, 321
  phenol-formaldehyde, 512
  polyethylene, 61, 898
  polymethyl methacrylate, 788
  polystyrene, 574
  polytetrafluoroethylene, 733
  polyvinyl, 617, 726, 736
  urea-formaldehyde, 313, 314
Platinous complexes, isomerism, 357
Plexiglas, 788
Plioform, 713
π molecular orbitals, see π bonds
Poison gases, chloroarsines, 902
  Lewisite, 902
  mustard gas, 289
  nerve gases, 910
  nitrogen mustards, 753
  phosgene, 310
  sarin, 910
Poison hemlock, 648
Poison ivy, 516
Poison oak, 516
Polarimeter, 332
Polarimeter tube, 332

Polariscope, 332
Polarizability of molecules, 39, 197
Polarization, of light, 329
  of molecules, 39, 197
  direction in substituted benzenes, 450
Polarized light, 329
Polarizer, 332
Polar molecules, 197
Polar number, 145
Polarographic analysis, 375
Polaroid, 331
Polyacrylates, 788
Polyacrylic acid, 788
Polyacrylonitrile, 787
Polyadenylic acid, 644
Polyadipic anhydride, 798
Polyamide resins, 755
Polyamines, 755
Polycarboxylic acids, 791
Polyenes, absorption spectra, 664
  autoxidation, 882
Polyester resins, 807
Polyesters, 552, 555, 799, 807
Polyethylenes, 61, 898
Polyethylene glycols, 744
Polyethylenimine, 754
Polygenetic dyes, 688
Polyhydric alcohols, 739
Polyhydric phenols, 516
Polyhydroxycyclohexanes, 309, 842
Polyisobutylene, 62
  to improve viscosity index, 82
Polyisoprene rubbers, 720
Polymer, definition, 61
Polymerization, acid-catalyzed, 62
  acrolein, 765
  addition, 61
  aldehydes, 208, 220
  alkenes, 61
  condensation, 314
  cracked gases to liquid fuels, 76
  1,3-dienes, 707
  free-radical catalyzed, 61, 718
  methyl methacrylate, 788
  pyrroles, 610
  styrene, 574
  tetrafluoroethylene, 733
  vinyl compounds, 617, 726, 736
Polymethylidyne dyes, 693
Polymethyl methacrylate, 788
Polynitro compounds, molecular complexes, 460
Polynuclear hydrocarbons, see Biphenyl,
  578, and Condensed nuclear hydrocarbons, 582
Polynucleotides, 644
Polyoxymethylene, 220
Polypeptides, 304
Polypropylene, 62
Polysaccharides, 396–412

Polystyrene, 574
Polysulfides, 281
Polyterpenes, 709, 713
Polytetrafluoroethylene, 733
Polythene, *see* Polyethylene, 61
Polyuronic acids, 408
Polyuronides, 408
Polyvinyl acetate, 736
Polyvinyl alcohol, 736
Polyvinyl butyral, 737
Polyvinylcarbazole, 617
Polyvinyl chloride, 726
Polyvinyl methyl ether, 737
Polyvinylpyrrolidone, 785
Ponndorf reduction, *see* Meerwein-Ponn-
      dorf reduction, 199
Pontocaine, 559
Pope, biography, 351
Poppy alkaloids, 650
p orbitals, 10
Porphins, 613
Porphyrins, 613
Position isomers, 329
Potassium compounds, 890
Potassium triphenylmethide, 565
Potassium triphenylsilane, 915
Potato starch, 397
Poutet reagent, 186
Powdered sugar, 394
Precalciferol, 868
Prechromed dyes, 674
Pressor activity of β-phenylethylamines,
      528
Primaquine, 654
Primary alcohols, 85
   amines, 228
   carbon atoms, 85
Primary component in coupling reactions,
      676
Primuline, 697
Prins reaction, 575
   for 1,3-glycols, 747
   for unsaturated alcohols, 738
Procaine, 558
Profile region, 659
Proflavine, 695
Progesterone, 871
Projection formulas, 336
Prolamines, 294
Proline, 297, 613
Prontosil, 488
"Proof" of alcohol, 95
Propadiene, 706
Propadrine, 528
Propane, pyrolysis, 45
   structure, 29, 30
1,2-Propanediol, 746
1,2,3-Propanetricarboxylic acid, 810
Propanols, *see* Propyl alcohols
Propargyl alcohol, 739

β-Propiolactone, 782
Propionic acid, 147, 159
i-Propyl alcohol, synthesis, 97
n-Propyl alcohol, 96
i-Propylbenzene, 420, 430
Propyl bromides, *see* Halides, alkyl
Propylene, 53
   chlorination, 726
   oxidation to acrolein, 764
Propylene chlorohydrins, 746
Propylene glycol, 746
Propylene oxide, 738, 746
i-Propyl ether, 141
Propyl mercaptan, 289
i-Propyl methylfluorophosphonate, 910
α-n-Propylpiperidine, 648
Prosthetic groups, 294
Prostigmin, 520
Protamines, 294
Protective coatings, lacquer, 402
   paint, 187
   synthetic enamel, 553
   varnish, 187
Proteins, amino acids from, 296
   carbohydrates associated with, 411
   composition, 293
   half-life in organism, 302
   metabolism, 301
   molecular weights, 295
   structure, 295
Protocatechuic acid, 561
Proton-bonding, 87
   alcohols, 87
   amines, 233
   carboxylic acids, 148
   ethyl acetoacetate, 823
   nitrophenols, 507
Protonoid reagents, 237
Proton transfer reactions, 99
Protopectins, 407
Protoporphyrin, 613
Prussic acid, 255
Pseudoasymmetric carbon atom, 340
Pseudoasymmetry, 340
Pseudo bases, 623, 698
Pseudoionone, 852
Pseudouric acid, 646
Psicose, 384
Pteridine, 647
Pterins, 647
Pteroic acid, 647
Pteroylglutamic acids, 647
π-type molecular orbitals, *see* Molecular
      orbitals, π-type
Pulegone, 854
Pungent principles, 649
Purdie, biography, 374
Purines, 643
Purity, criteria, 18
Purpurogallin, 845

Putrescine, 756
PVA, *see* Polyvinyl alcohol, 736
Pyranoses, 386
Pyranosides, 389–393
Pyrans, 631
2,3-Pyrazinedicarboxylic acid, 642
Pyrazines, 641
Pyrazole, 634
Pyrazoles, *N*-phenyl, from 1,3-diketones, 772
Pyrazolone dyes, 679
Pyrene, 603
Pyrethric acid, 840
Pyrethrins, 839
Pyrethrolone, 840
Pyrethrum, 839
Pyribenzamine, 628
Pyridazines, 638, 807
Pyridine, 620
　isolation, 428
Pyridinealdehydes, 626
2-Pyridinealdoxime methiodide, 626
Pyridinecarboxylic acids, 625, 627
2,3-Pyridinedicarboxylic acid, 628
2,5-Pyridinedicarboxylic acid, 627
3,4-Pyridinedicarboxylic acid, 630
Pyridine-*N*-oxide, 624
Pyridines, 620
　from 1,5-dihydrodicarbonyl compounds, 775
　Hantzsch synthesis, 820
3-Pyridinesulfonic acid, 622
Pyridinium bromide perbromide, 622
Pyridones, 623
Pyridoxal, 628
Pyridoxamine, 628
Pyridoxine, 628
Pyridylacetic acids, 626, 628
Pyrimidines, 638, 818
Pyrocatechol, 516
Pyrocatechol Violet, 682
Pyrocatechuic acid, *see* Catechol, 516
Pyrogallic acid, 517
Pyrogallol, 517
Pyroligenous acid, 89, 158
Pyrolysis, 44
　carboxylic acids, 195, *see also* Decarboxylation
　esters, 173
　hydrocarbons, 44
　mechanism, 45
Pyromellitic acid, 556
Pyromellitic anhydride, 556
Pyromucic acid, 619
γ-Pyrones, 632
Pyrotartaric acid, 812
Pyroxylins, 401
Pyrrole, 610
2-Pyrrolealdehyde, 612

Pyrrolecarboxylic acids, 611, 613
Pyrroles, from 1,4-dicarbonyl compounds, 775
　from β-keto esters, 819
　Knorr synthesis, 819
Pyrrolidine, 613
Pyrrolidine hydrochloride, 757
Pyrrolidones, 613, 784
Pyrroline, 613
Pyrrolines from γ-amino ketones, 767
2-Pyrrylmethanol, 612
2-Pyrryl methyl ketone, 612
2-Pyrryl ketones, 612
Pyruvic acid, 812
Pyruvic aldehyde, 768
Pyrylium salts, 631

Quantitative analysis, 17
Quartz, optical activity, 331, 332, 334
Quaternary ammonium compounds, 241
　resolution, 350
Quaternary phosphonium hydroxides, 909
Quaterphenyls, 569, 578
Quebrachitol, 414
Quercitin, 698
Quercitol, 414
Quercitrin, 698
Quick process for vinegar, 158
Quinacrine, 653
Quinaldine, 629
　cyanine dyes from, 693
Quinaldinic acid, 630
Quinhydrone, 523
Quinhydrones, structure, 571
Quinic acid, 842
Quinidine, 653
Quinine, 653
Quinizarin, 599
Quinoline, 628
Quinolinecarboxylic acid, 630
Quinoline dyes, *see* Methylidyne dyes, 693
Quinolines from 1,3-diketones, 773
Quinolinic acid, 628
α-Quinolone, 629
Quinone, 521
Quinone chloroimide, 483
Quinone chloroimides, 523
Quinonediimines, 521
Quinonemonoxime, 506
Quinones, 520, 592, 597
Quinonimine dyes, 692
Quinonimines, 521
Quinoxalines, 642
　from 1,2-dicarbonyl compounds, 769

Racemic acid, 334
Racemic forms, 339
Racemization, 345
R-acid, 590

Radicals, *see* Free radicals
Radioactive carbon as tracer, 813, 832
Raffinose, 395
Rancidity of fats and oils, 184
Raney nickel, desulfuration of sulfones, 285
Rapeseed oil, 182
Raschig process for phenol, 510
Rast camphor method, 23
Rayon acetate, 406
    viscose, 405
RDX, 221
Reactive hydrogen, Zerevitinov determination, 122
Reactive methylene groups, 771
Reactivity, alcohols with halogen acids, 102
    alcohols with inorganic acid halides, 100
    alkenes, 58, 59
    alkyl halides, 115, 116
    allyl halides, 728
    aryl halides, 435, 462
    effect of other substituents, 461
    benzyl halides, 437, 463
    carboxylic acids, 165, 549
    dehydration of alcohols, 104
    Grignard reagents, 892
    hydrogen, 890
    organometallic compounds, 892, 894
    vinyl halides, 726
Rearrangements, *see* Molecular rearrangements
Reclaimed rubber, 712
Red ink, 683
Red oil, 191
Red pepper, 649
Reducing disaccharides, 389
Reduction, acids, 172, 550
    aldehydes, 198, 216, 217
    alkenes, 127
    alkynes, 130
    anthracene, 597
    aromatic acids, 550
    aromatic esters, 550
    aromatic nitro compounds, 456
    aromatic ring, 550
    carboxylic acids, 172
    cyanides, 230, 232, 532
    diazonium salts, 494, 497
    disulfides, 275, 280
    esters, 172, 550
    halides, acyl, 162
        alkyl, 126
    isocyanides, 257
    ketones, 198, 216, 217
    mechanism, by active metals, 217
        catalytic, 55
    naphthalene, 584
    nitroalkanes, 262
    oximes, 232

Reduction—(*Continued*)
    phenols, 504
    pyrrole, 613
    Schiff bases, 536
    α,β-unsaturated carbonyl compounds, 763
Reductone, 369, 771
Red, white, and blue reaction, 262
Red yeast pigment, 866
Reformatsky reaction, 781
Reforming of gasoline, 76
Reimer-Tiemann reaction, 532
Reissert compounds, 630
Relative configuration, 347
Remsen, biography, 556
R-enzyme, 398
Reserpine, 654
Resin acids, 860, 861
Resins, acrylic or acryloid, 788
    alkyd, 553, 807
    epoxy, 750
    glyptal, 552
    ion-exchange, 513, 575
    melamine, 321
    methylmethacrylate, 788
    natural, 860, 861
    phenol-formaldehyde, 512
    polyethylene, 61, 898
    polystyrene, 574
    urea-formaldehyde, 313
Resole, 512
Resolution of racemic mixtures, 341
Resonance, acidity of aromatic acids, 548
    acidity of carboxylic acids, 153
    acidity of phenols, 503
    allyl carbonium ion, 728
    amidine salts, 249
    aniline, 477
    anthracene, 597
    and aromatic substitution, 453
    and autoxidation, 882
    azides, 268
    barbiturates, 640
    benzene, 419
    Benzidine Blue, 579
    carbanions, 573
    carbonium ions, 572
    carboxylate ion, 153
    carboxyl group, 155
    chlorobenzene, 453
    Crystal Violet, 702
    cyclopentadienyl anion, 838
    cyclopropylmethyl carbonium ion, 832
    definition, 153
    diazomethane, 266
    energy, 154
    enolate ion, 213
        1,3-diketones, 773
        of β-keto esters, 820

Resonance—(*Continued*)
 free radical intermediates in autoxidation, 882, 883
 free radicals, 569, 571
 guanidinium ion, 322
 hybrid, 154
 indophenols, 507
 inhibition, *see* steric inhibition
 and interatomic distance, 154
 and light absorption, 702
 Malachite Green, 702
 mesoionic compounds, 637
 Methyl Orange, 699
 naphthalene, 583
 nitroalkane salts, 261
 nitro group, 258, 450
 p-nitrosodimethylaniline salts, 480
 phenanthrene, 602
 phenolphthalein, 700
 phenoxide ion, 454
 pyrrole, 611
 stabilization of free radicals, 569, 882
 steric inhibition, aromatic amines, 480
  aromatic ketones, 539
  biphenyl derivatives, 580
  meta-bridged benzene rings, 849
 sydnones, 637
 thiophene, 609
 triphenylmethide ion, 573
 triphenylmethonium ion, 572
 triphenylmethyl, 569
 tropolone anion, 845
 tropone anion, 845
 tropylium ion, 845
 urea salts, 312
 vinyl chloride, 726
 Wurster salts, 572
Resonance effect, 453
 of trimethylsilyl group, 913
Resorcinol, 517
Resorcylaldehyde, 531
Restricted rotation, about double bonds,
  50, 355
 in ethane, 31
 in *o*-substituted biphenyls, 580
Retene, 602
Retinenes, 860
Retrogradation of amylose, 397
Rhamnose, 367
Rheum, 599
Rhodanine, 635
Rhodopsin, 860
Rhodoxanthin, 866
Rhubarb, cathartic principle, 599
Riboflavin, 647
*Ribo*hexulose, 384
Ribonucleic acid, 644
Ribose, 361
Ribulose, 384, 387
Ricinoleic acid, 180, 793, 794

Riley reaction, 767
Ring enlargement and contraction, 631,
  831, 832
Ring opening of nitrogen heterocycles, 621
Ring structures, carbohydrates, 373, 375
  383
 perspective formulas, 383
 sugar oximes and hydrazones, 382
Robison ester, 378
Rochelle salts, 809
Rosaniline dyes, 680
Rosenmund reduction, 162
Rose oil, 527, 853
Rose water, 853
Rosin, 861
 disproportionated, 861
Rosolic acid, 682
Rotation, optical, 332
 cause, 352
Rotatory dispersion, 333
Rotenone, 633
Royal purple, 686
Rubber, natural, 708–714
 synthetic, 714–720
Rubber accelerators, 711
Rubrene, 833
 peroxide, 833
Runge, biography, 672
Rust inhibitors, 239, 843
Rutin, 698
Rutinose, 392

Sabatier, biography, 55
Saccharic acid, 363
Saccharic acids, 362
Saccharides, *see* Carbohydrates
Saccharin, 557
Saccharinic acids, 369
Saccharomyces, 91
Saffron pigment, 866
Safranine-T, 696
Safrole, 516
Salicin, 525
Salicylaldehyde, 532, 562
Salicylates, 559
Salicylic acid, 559
Saligenin, 508, 525
Salol, 559
Salt colors, 674
Salting-out, 467
Salts of carboxylic acids, reactions, 156,
  162
 of sulfonic acids, reactions, 468
Salvarsan, 903
Sandmeyer reaction, 494
Sandwich molecules, 839
l-Sapietic acid, 861
Sapogenins, 863, 869
Saponification, esters, 170
 fats and oils, 183

Saponification—(*Continued*)
  peroxy esters, 877
  steric effect with aromatic acids, 549
Saponification equivalent, 170
Saponification value, 183
  fats and oils, 181
Saponins, 863, 869
Sarans, 726
Sarcolactic acid, 783
Sarcosine, 785
Sarin, 910
Sassafras oil, 516
s atomic orbitals, 5
  direction, 9
Saturated hydrocarbons, *see* Alkanes
Saytzev rule, 104, 242
  exception, 856
Scandium compounds, 898
Schaeffer acid, 590
Scheele, biography, 2
Schiff bases, 481, 482, 535
Schiff reagent, 213, 375
  structure, 681
Schmidt reaction, 232
Schotten-Baumann reaction, 549
Schweitzer reagent, 399
Scillaren-A, 870
Scleroproteins, 294
σ complexes in aromatic substitution, 445
Scyllitol, 414
Sebacic acid, 794
Seconal, 640
Secondary, definition, 35
Secondary alcohols, 85
  alkyl groups, 35
  amines, 228
  carbon atoms, 35, 85
Secondary component in coupling reactions, 498, 676
Second order Beckmann rearrangement, 545
Sedoheptulose, 387
Selenides, 285
Selenium dehydrogenation, 602, 863, 867
Selenium dioxide, oxidizing agent, 768
Selenonium salts, 283, 351
β-Selinene, 858
Semicarbazide, 318
  reaction with aldehydes and ketones, 211
Semicarbazine, *see* Semicarbazide
Semicarbazones, 211
Semidine rearrangement, 578
Semimicroanalyses, 20
Semipolar bonds, 238
  amine oxides, 240
  isocyanides, 238
  nitro group, 258
  phosphorus compounds, 908
  sulfur compounds, 273, 352

Semiquinones, 571, 669
Senderens, biography, 55
Senna, cathartic principle, 599
Sensitizers, photographic, 693
Sequestering agents, 755, 887
Sequestrene, 755
Serine, 296
Serotonin, 616
Serpasil, 654
Serum albumins, 294, 296
Serum globulins, 294
Sesame oil, 182
Sesquiterpenes, 858
Sex hormones, 870
Shark liver oils, 860, 862
Shikimic acid, 842
Side chain, aromatic, halogenation, 434
  oxidation, 424
Sidgwick, biography, 237
Sigma complexes in aromatic substitution, 445
Sigma-type orbitals, 10
Signer method for molecular weight determination, 23
Silane, 910
Silanols, 912
Silicane, *see* Silane, 910
Silicates, alkyl, 108
Silicochloroform, 911
Silicoethane, *see* Disilane, 910
Silicon chloride, reaction with Grignard reagents, 912
Silicon compounds, 910
  optical activity, 350
Silicone oils, 914
Silicone rubbers, 914
Silicones, 912
Silicon hydrides, 910
Silicon tetrachloride, 910
Silk, 299
Siloxanes, *see* Silicones, 912
Silver acetylides, 132
Silver carbide, 132
Silver compounds, 891
Silver salt, 598
Silylamines, 912
Simple proteins, 294
β-Sitosterol, 868
6–12 (six-twelve), 747
666 (six-six-six), 432
Skatole, 615
Skeletal isomers, 329
Skraup synthesis of quinolines, 628
Skunk secretion, 289
Slippery elm mucilage, 411
Smokeless powder, 749
Smoke screens, 724
S_N1 and S_N2 reactions, 116, 117
Soap plants, 863

Soaps, 188
    invert, 243
Soda pulp, 400
Sodioacetoacetic ester, 814
Sodiomalonic ester, 800
Sodium acetate, 159
Sodium acetylide, 131
Sodium alcoholates, *see* Sodium alkoxides, 99
Sodium alkoxides, 99
Sodium alkylarylsulfonates, 469
Sodium alkyl sulfates, 58, 191
Sodium ammonium tartrates, 334
Sodium azide, 267
Sodium benzenesulfonate, 467
Sodium benzoate, 550
Sodium bisulfite, addition to aldehydes and ketones, 201
    addition to double bonds, 286
Sodium borohydride, reducing agent, 199
Sodium carbide, 131
Sodium chloride, electronic structure, 7
    hydration of ions, 13
Sodium compounds, 889
Sodium cupricitrate, 810
Sodium cupritartrate, 809
Sodium cyanide, 255
Sodium ethoxide, 100
Sodium ethyl xanthate, 324
Sodium formate, 157
Sodium lithol, 703
Sodium methoxide, 99
Sodium oxalate, 158
Sodium reductions, mechanism, 217
Sodium salicylate, 559
Sodium tetraphenylboride, 896
Sodium tetraphenylboron, 896
Sodium thiopental, 640
Soft coal, 426
Soil conditioners, 788, 807
Solubility, *see also* Physical properties
    effect of bond type, 12
Solvents, 89
Solvolysis, 846
Sommlet reaction, 532
Sorbic acid, 789
s orbitals, 5, 9
σ orbitals, 10
Sorbitol, 412
Sorbose, 387
Sorghum, 394
Soybean oil, 181, 182
Spans, 413
$s-p$ bond, 10
Specific rotation, 333
Spectra, 657–669
Spermaceti, 178
Spermine, 756
Sperm oil, 183
Sphingomyelin, 753

Sphingosine, 753
sp hybrid orbitals, 12
sp^2 hybrid orbitals, 12
sp^3 hybrid orbitals, 12
Spirit-soluble dyes, 675
Spontaneous combustion, 184
Spruce turpentine, *see p*-Cymene, 431
Spun rayon, 406
Squalene, 862
Square configurations, 357
Squill glycosides, 870
$s-s$ bond, 10
Stannic chloride, reaction with Grignard reagents, 123
Staple fiber, 406
Star anise, 842
Starch, 396
    metabolism, 398
Starch nitrates, 398
Steam distillation, 16
Steapsin, 186
Stearic acid, 147, 179, 192
Stearolic acid, 789
Stearyl alcohol, 172
Stephen reaction, 532
Sterculic acid, 835
Stereoisomerism, 329–357
    allenes, 706
    azobenzenes, 500
    biphenyls, 580
    cobalt coordination complexes, 352
    cumulenes, 707
    diazo compounds, 500
    1,12-dimethylbenzo (*c*) phenanthrenes, 605
    geometrical, 354–357
    nickel coordination complexes, 770
    optical, 329–354
    oximes, 542
    platinum coordination complexes, 357
    trithymotide, 344, 560
Stereoisomers, 329
Steric effect, alkyl groups, 117
    esterification, 165, 549
Steric hindrance, 117
    effect on reactivity of alkyl halides, 117
    esterification, 165, 549
Steric inhibition of resonance, *see* Resonance, steric inhibition
Steroids, 867–872
Sterols, 868
Stevioside, 862
Stibonic acids, 903
Stigmasterol, 868
cis- and *trans*-Stilbene, 576
trans-Stilbene, absorption spectrum, 665
Stilbene dyes, 679
Stilbestrol, 870
Stipitatic acid, 845
Stobbe condensation, 796

Storax, 573
Straight-chain, definition, 30
Strain theory, 828
Straw oil, 427
Strecker degradation, 841
Strecker synthesis, 303
Streptamine, 414
Streptomycin, 414
Streptone, 414
Stretching vibrations, 659
Strophanthidin, 870
Strophanthin, 870
Structural formulas, 28–32
Structural isomers, 329
Structure,   effect on color, 671
    electronic theory, 5
Stuart models, 30
σ-type orbitals, 10
Styphnic acid, 517
Styrene, 573, 807
    from cyclooctatetraene, 846
Styrene oxide, 575
Suberic acid, 793
Substantive dyes, 673
Substitution reactions, 119
    aromatic compounds, 422, 423
    halogenation, 118, 433, 722
    indole, 616
    mechanism, 444, 454
    naphthalene, 585
    nitration, 259, 439
    pyridine, 622
    sulfonation, 287, 467
    thiophene, 608
Sucaryl, 843
Succinic acid, preparation, 792
    reactions, 796
Succinic acids, α,β-disubstituted, 801
Succinic anhydride, 796
Succinimide, 797
Succinonitrile, 792
Succinyl chloride, 796
Succinylcholine, 243
Sucrase, hydrolysis of sucrose, 92, 394
Sucrose, 393
Sucrose octaacetate, 394
Sudan I, 677
Sugar acetates, 377, 382
Sugar acetones, 379
Sugar alcohols, 412
Sugar anhydrides, 388
Sugar benzoates, 378
Sugar lactones, 380
Sugar of lead, 159
Sugar sand, 808
Sugars, *see* Carbohydrates
Suida process, 158
Sulfadiazine, 489
Sulfa drugs, 488, 558
Sulfamerazine, 489

Sulfamethazine, 489
Sulfamic acid, 318
Sulfanilamide, 488
Sulfanilic acid, 485, 488
Sulfated fats and oils, 191
Sulfate pulp, 400
Sulfates, alkyl, disulfides from, 280
    ethers from, 137, 373, 504
    preparation, 59, 103, 108
    sulfides from, 274, 278
Sulfates, alkyl hydrogen, from alcohols, 103
    from alkenes, 59
Sulfenic acids, 473
Sulfenyl chlorides, 280, 473
Sulfhydryl group, 276
Sulfide dyes, 674, 691
Sulfides, 278, 283
Sulfinic acid esters, optically active, 352
Sulfinic acids, 284, 473, 894
Sulfinyl chlorides, 284
Sulfinyl group, 284
Sulfisoxazole, 489
Sulfite liquors, fermentation, 92
Sulfite pulp, 400
Sulfites, alkyl, 108, 204
Sulfonal, 290
Sulfonamides, 288, 471
Sulfonated fats and oils, 191
Sulfonates, 288, 470, 471
Sulfonation, alkenes, 287
    anthraquinone, 598
    aromatic amines, 485
    aromatic compounds, 466
    benzene, 466
    mechanism, 448
    naphthalene, 586
    phenols, 505
    pyridine, 622
    thiophene, 608
Sulfones, 285, 473
Sulfonic acid anhydrides, 289
Sulfonic acid esters, 288, 470, 471
Sulfonic acids, 286, 466
Sulfonium hydroxides, 283
Sulfonium salts, 283
    from disulfides, 281
    optically active, 351
    from sulfides, 279
Sulfonphthaleins, 682
Sulfonyl chlorides, 287, 470
    reduction to mercaptans, 284, 473
Sulfonyl group, 286
Sulforaphene, 352
Sulfoxides, 283
    optically active, 352
Sulfur, covalency, 273
    detection in organic compounds, 17
    determination, 20
Sulfur Black, 692

Sulfur compounds, aliphatic, 272–291
  optically active, 352
Sulfur dehydrogenations, 602, 858–862
Sulfur dioxide, addition to alkenes, 285
  refining kerosene, 80
  refining lubricating oils, 81
Sulfur dyes, 674, 691
Sulfuric acid, addition to alkenes, 58
Sulfur-oxygen double bonds, 273
Sulfur, test for, 17
Sulfur trioxide as sulfonating agent, 448
Sultams, 643
Sultones, 643
Sunflower seed oil, 182
Superposability, 335
Suprarenine, *see* Epinephrine, 529
Suprasterols, 868
Surface-active agents, *see* Detergents
Swarts, biography, 728
Swarts reaction, 731
Sweetness, saccharin, 557
  sugars, 385
Sydnones, 637
sym-, prefix, 51
Symmetry and optical activity, 335
Sympathins, 529
Sympathomimetic amines, 528
Syn-, prefix, 500, 542
Syndets, *see* Synthetic detergents
Synthetic detergents, *see* Detergents
  fibers, *see* Fibers, synthetic
  fuels, 83
  musks, 464
  resins, *see* Resins
  rubbers, 718–720, 799, 914
  wool, 299
Syringenin, 527
Syringic aldehyde, 527
Syringin, 527

2,4,5-T, 514
Tabasco, 649
TACE, 870
Tachysterol, 868
Tagatose, 384
Tall oil, 400
Tallow, 181, 182
Talose, 366
Tanner's red, 698
Tannic acid, 561
Tannins, 561, 581, 698
Tar acids, 427, 502
Tar bases, 427
Tariric acid, 180
Tartar, 809
Tartaric acid, 809
(—)Tartaric acid, configuration, 367
Tartaric acids, optical isomerism, 333, 339

Tartrazine, 679
Tartronic acid, 808
Taurine, 754, 869
Taurocholic acid, 869
Tautomeric effect in aromatic substitution, 453
Tautomerism, 207, 822
  β-keto esters, 822
  nitroalkanes, 261
  phloroglucinol, 518
  quinones, 593
  thioacids and thioamides, 282
TCP, 515
TDE, 566
Tea, 646
Teepol, 191
Teflon, 733
TEL, *see* Tetraethyllead, 898, 899
Telomerization, 725
1080 (ten-eighty), 779
TEPP, *see* Ethyl pyrophosphate, 110
Terephthalic acid, 555
Terminal methyl determination, 144
Terpenes, 849, 850
  acyclic, 850
  dicyclic, 855
  monocyclic, 853
Terphenyls, 569, 578
Terpinenes, 854
α-Terpineol, 855
Terpin hydrate, 854
Terpinolene, 854
Terpins, 854
Terramycin, 604
α-Terthienyl, 607
Tertiary, definition, 35
Tertiary alcohols, 86
  alkyl groups, 35
  amines, 228
  carbon atoms, 35, 86
Terylene, 555
Testosterone, 870
Tetraacetylglucosyl bromide, 378
Tetrabromofluorescein, 683
Tetracaine, 559
Tetracarboxylic esters, 801
Tetracene, 637
1,2,4,5-Tetrachlorobenzene, 514
Tetrachloro-*p*-benzoquinone, *see* Chloranil, 522
2,2′-6,6′-Tetrachlorobiphenyl, resonance inhibition, 580
Tetrachloro-1,2-difluoroethane, 733
1,1,2,2-Tetrachloroethane, 723
Tetrachloroethylene, 723, 724
Tetrachlorophenyltrichlorosilane, 915
Tetrachloroquinone, *see* Chloranil, 522
Tetracontanes, 33
Tetracycline, 604

Tetradecanes, 33
Tetraethylammonium bromide, 243
Tetraethylenepentamine, 755
Tetraethyllead, 898, 899
  as knock inhibitor, 80
Tetraethylpyrophosphate, *see* Ethyl
  pyrophosphate, 110
Tetraethylsilane, 911
Tetraethylthiuram disulfide, 325
Tetrafluoroethylene, 733
Tetragonal hybridization, 12
Tetrahedral configuration of carbon com-
  pounds, 335
Tetrahedral hybridization, 12
Tetrahydroabietic acid, 861
1,2,3,6-Tetrahydrobenzaldehyde, 765
Tetrahydrocannabinols, 633
Tetrahydrofuran, 619, 620, 717
Tetrahydrofurfuryl alcohol, 618, 631
Tetrahydrofurfuryl chloride, 739
Tetrahydronaphthalene, 584
Tetrahydropyran, 631
Tetrahydropyridines from δ-amino ketones,
  767
Tetrahydropyrrole, 613
Tetra(hydroxymethyl) phosphonium
  chloride, 910
Tetraiodophenolphthalein, 682
Tetraiodopyrrole, 612
3,5,3',5'Tetraiodothyronine, 297
Tetralin, 584
  autoxidation, 881
Tetralin hydroperoxide, 881
α-Tetralone, 598, 882
Tetramethylammonium hydroxide, 242
Tetramethylammonium salts, decomposi-
  tion, 241
1,2,4,5-Tetramethylbenzene, 420
Tetramethylene chloride, 619
Tetramethylene chlorohydrin, 619
Tetramethylenediamine, 756
Tetramethylene glycol, 619, 747
  dehydrogenation, 783
1,3,4,6-Tetramethylfructose, 394
2,3,4,6-Tetramethylglucose, 390
Tetramethyllead, free radicals from, 568
Tetramethylsilane, 911
Tetramethylsuccinonitrile, 265
Tetramethylthiuram disulfide, 325, 711
Tetranitromethane, 263
Tetraphenylchromium iodide, 903
Tetraphenylethylene, 577
Tetraphenylhydrazine, 571
Tetraphenylmethane, 566
Tetraphenylnaphthacene, 883
Tetrasilane, 910
Tetraterpenes, 863
Tetrazole, 637
Tetrazolium Blue, 638

Tetrazolium salts, 637
Tetronal, 290
Tetryl, 490
Thallium compounds, 898
Thebaine, 651
2-Thenylammonium chloride, 608
2-Thenyl chloride, 608
Thenyl sulfone, 608
Theobromine, 646
Theophylline, 646
Therapeutic index, 903
Thermal decomposition, *see* Pyrolysis
Thermofor process, 75
Thiacarbocyanines, 694
Thials, 281
Thiamine, 641
Thianaphthene, 609
Thiazines, 695
Thiazole dyes, 697
Thiazoles, 635
Thiele, biography, 51
2-Thienyl chloride, 608
2-Thienylmercuric chloride, 608
2-Thienyl methyl ketone, 608
Thioacetals, 278, 382
Thioacetamide, 290
Thio-alcohols, *see* Mercaptans
Thioaldehydes, 281
Thioamides, 282
Thiobarbiturates, 640
Thiocarbamates, 326
  N- and S-alkyl, 325
Thiocarbamic acid, 309
Thiocarbanilide, 482
Thiocarbonic acid derivatives, 324–327
Thiocarboxylic acids, 282
Thioctic acid, 635
Thiocyanates, 325, 895
  sulfonyl chlorides from, 288
Thiocyanogen, 184, 326
Thiocyanogen value, 184
Thiodiphenylamine, 643
Thioesters, 282
  from mercaptans, 278
Thioglycolic acid, 783
Thioindigos, 687
Thioindoxyl, 687
Thioketones, 281
Thiokols, 719
Thiols, *see* Mercaptans
Thiomalic acid, 809
Thionation, 691
Thiones, 281
Thionyl chloride, reaction with acids, 160
  with alcohols, 101
Thiopental sodium, 640
Thiophene, 606
Thiophenecarboxylic acid, 607, 608

Thiophenes, 607–610
  from 1,4-dicarbonyl compounds, 775
  sulfones, 608, 610
2-Thiophenesulfonic acid, 608
Thiophenols, 473, 495
Thiopyruvic acids, 636
Thiosulfonates, 281
Thioureas, 276, 326, 327
Thiourethans, 326
Thiouronium salts, 327
Thiuram disulfides, 325
Thiuronium salts, 327
Thorpe, biography, 847
Thorpe condensation, 847
Threonine, 296
*Threo*pentulose, 384
Threose, 366
Thujane, 855
Thujaplicins, 845
Thyme oil, 515
Thymine, 638
Thymol, 515
Thymosalicylic acid, 560
Thyronine, 297
Thyroxine, 297
Tiglic acid, 789
Tigogenin, 869
Timbo root, 633
Tin compounds, 899
  optically active, 350
Tishchenko reaction, 220, 535
Titanates, 108
TNT, 464
Toad poisons, 870
Tobacco, 648
Tobacco mosaic virus, 296
Tobias acid, 590
Tocopherols, 632
Tolan, 576
Tolbutamide, *see* Orinase, 489
o-Tolidine,   578
Tollens reagent, oxidation of aldehydes,
  212
  of α-keto acids, 813
p-Tolualdehyde, 531
Tolu balsam, 416
Toluene, 66, 428
Toluene diisocyanate, 479
o-Toluenesulfonamide, 557
p-Toluenesulfonates of sugars, 378
p-Toluenesulfonic acid, 470
Toluenesulfonyl chlorides, 470, 557
Toluic acids, 551, 555
Toluidines, 479, 487, 488
Toluol, *see* Toluene, 420
Tolyl group, 421
Tomato pigment, 864
Toners, 702
Tonka bean, 562

Tornesite, 713
Torularhodin, 866
Tosylation, 471
Tosyl chloride, 471
Tosyl derivatives of sugars, 378
Tourmaline, 331
Toxicity, aromatic amines, 476
  aromatic nitro compounds, 455
  arsenic compounds, 902
  benzene, 422
  cyanides, 252
  diazomethane, 266
  fluorine compounds, 729, 779
  halogen compounds, 722, 723
  isocyanides, 257
  mercaptans, 277
  mercury compounds, 893
  metal carbonyls, 904
  phenols, 509, 517
Toxisterol, 868
Tragacanth gum, 411
Tranquilizing drugs, chlorpromazine, 643
  Equanil, 315
  meprobamate, 315
  Miltown, 315
  reserpine, 654
  Serpasil, 654
Transannular reactions, 846
Transesterification, up-grading of drying
  oils, 185
trans isomers, 354
Transition complex, *see* Transition state, 42
Transition dipole, 662
Transition state, 42
Trehalose, 393
Triacetonamine, 764
Triacetonediamine, 764
Triacontanes, 33
Triacylmethanes, 769
2,4,6-Triaminobenzoic acid, 518
Tri-*p*-anisylchloroethylene, 870
Tribenzylamine, 527
2,4,6-Tribromoaniline, 483
1,3,5-Tribromobenzene, 494
2,4,6-Tribromophenol, 506
Tri-*i*-butylaluminum, 897
2,4,6-Tri-*t*-butyloxygen, 571
Tricarballylic acid, 810
Tricarboxylic acids, 810
Tricarboxylic esters, 801
Trichloroacetaldehyde, 739
Trichloroacetic acid, 779
2,4,6-Trichloroaniline, 483
1,2,4-Trichlorobenzene, 433
1,1,1-Trichloroethane, 723
1,1,2-Trichloroethane, 726
Trichloroethylene, 723
Trichlorofluoromethane, 732, 733
Trichloromethanesulfenyl chloride, 289

Trichloromethyl radicals, 725
Trichloronitromethane, 515
2,4,5-Trichlorophenol, 514
2,4,5-Trichlorophenoxyacetic acid, 514
2,4,6-Trichloropyrimidine, 639
Trichlorosilane, 911
1,1,2-Trichlorotrifluoroethane, 733
1,1,2-Trichloro-3,3,3-trifluoropropene, 732
Tricosanes, 33
Tricosanoic acid, 147
Tricresyl phosphate, 515
Tridecanes, 33
Tridecanoic acid, 147
Tridecylic acid, 147
Triethanolamine, 752
Triethylaluminum, 897
Triethylene glycol, 744
Triethylenetetramine, 755
Triethyl phosphate, *see* Ethyl phosphate, 110
Trifluoroacetic acid, 778
Trifluoroacetic anhydride, 778
1,1,1-Trifluoroethane, 731
2,2,2-Trifluoroethanol, 734
Trifluoroiodomethane, 732
Trifluoromethyl ether, 734
Trifluoromethyl group, effect on other functions, 734
Trifluoromethyl phenyl ketone, 734
Triglycerides, *see* Glycerides, 179
Trigonal hybridization, 12
Trihydric alcohols, 748
1,2,3-Trihydroxybenzene, *see* Pyrogallol, 517
1,3,5-Trihydroxybenzene, *see* Phloroglucinol, 517
1,4,5-Trihydroxynaphthalene, 593
2,6,8-Trihydroxypurine, 645
3,5,3'-Triiodothyronine, 297
Triisopropylidene peroxide, 885
1,2,3-Triketohydrindene, 840
Triketohydrindene hydrate, 306, 840
Triketones, 769
Trimer, definition, 61
Trimerization of aldehydes, 208
Trimesic acid, 556
Trimethylaluminum, 897
Trimethylamine, 240
Trimethylamine oxide, 240
Trimethylammonium methylide, 243
Trimethylarsine, 900
Trimethylarsine oxide, 900
1,3,5-Trimethylbenzene, 430
Trimethylbenzylammonium hydroxide, 788
Trimethyl-*s*-butylammonium hydroxide, decomposition, 242
Trimethylcetylammonium chloride, 243
Trimethylene bromide, 746
Trimethylenechlorobromide, 727

Trimethylenediamine, 756
Trimethylene glycol, 746
Trimethylenetrinitramine, 221
Trimethylethylammonium hydroxide, decomposition, 242
Trimethylgallium, 898
2,3,6-Trimethylglucose, 391
3,5,5-Trimethylhexanal, 224
Trimethylmethoxysilane, 911
2,2,4-Trimethylpentane, as a standard fuel, 74, 78
  synthesis, 77
Trimethylphosphonium methylide, 909
Trimethylpyridines, 627
(Trimethylsilyl)acetic acid, 915
Trimethylsilyl group, inductive and resonance effects, 913
p-Trimethylsilylphenol, 913
2,4,6-Trinitroaniline, 477
1,3,5-Trinitrobenzenates, 460
1,3,5-Trinitrobenzene, 464
  molecular complexes, 460
2,4,6-Trinitrobenzoic acid, 464, 518
2,4,6-Trinitrochlorobenzene, 477
2,4,7-Trinitrofluorenone, molecular complexes, 840
2,4,6-Trinitrophenol, 514
Tri-*p*-nitrophenylmethane, 565
2,4,6-Trinitroresorcinol, 517
  molecular complexes, 460
2,4,6-Trinitrotoluene, 464
  molecular complexes, 460
Trional, 290
1,3,5-Trioxane, 221
Trioxymethylene, *see* 1,3,5-Trioxane, 221
Triphenylamine, 478
Triphenylbenzenes, 569, 578
Triphenylboron, 896
Triphenylcarbinol, 526
Triphenylchloromethane, 526
Triphenylene, 603
Triphenylethylene, 577
Triphenylmethane, 565
Triphenylmethane dyes, 679
Triphenylmethide ion, 573
Triphenylmethonium ion, 572
Triphenylmethoxide radicals, 883
Triphenylmethyl, 567, 569
  electron-spin resonance, 669
Triphenylmethyl chloride, 526
Triphenylmethyl peroxide, 883
Triphenylmethylpotassium, 565, 573
Triphenylmethylsodium, 573, 889
Triphenyl phosphate, 515
Triphenylphosphine, 910
Triphenylphosphonium methylide, 909
Triphenyls, *see* Terphenyls, 569, 578
Triphenylsilanol, 912
Triphenyltetrazolium chloride, 638

Triple bond, molecular orbital representation, 129
Tri-*i*-propylidene peroxide, 885
Triptane, as high-octane fuel, 74
Triptycene, 573
Trisaccharides, 395
Trisazo dyes, 678
Tris(2-hydroxyethyl)amine, 752
Trisilane, 910
Tris(trifluoromethyl)amine, 734
Triterpenes, 862
Trithymotide, 344, 560
Triton-β, 788
Tritylation, 526
Trityl chloride, 526
Trivalent carbon, *see* Free radicals
Trivial names, 33
Troeger's base, preparation, 482
  resolution, 350
Tropane alkaloids, 650
Tropolone, 844
Tropone, 844
Tropylium bromide, 844
Truxillic acids, 836
Truxinic acids, 836
Trypaflavine, 695
Tryparsamide, 903
Trypsin, 301
Tryptophan, 297, 304, 616
  synthesis, 803
Tschischenko, *see* Tishchenko reaction, 220, 535
Tschugaev, *see* Chugaev, 121
Tuads, 325
Tuberculostatic drugs, *p*-aminosalicylic acid, 560
  isonicotinic acid hydrazide, 626
  streptomycin, 414
Tuberculostearic acid, 160
d-Tubocurarine chloride, 652
Tung oil, 181, 183
  in paint, 187
Turkey Red, 688
Turkey Red oil, 191
Turpentine, 855
Tweens, 413
Twin double bonds, 314, 706
Twitchell process, 190
Two,four-D (2,4-D), 514
Two,four,five-T (2,4,5-T), 514
Tygon, 720
Tyramine, 530
Tyrian Purple, 686
Tyrosine, 296

Ullman reaction, 435, 579
Ultraviolet absorption spectra, *see* Absorption spectra

Undecanes, 33
Undecanoic acid, 147
10-Undecenoic acid, 789
Undecylenic acid, 789
Unimolecular mechanism, displacement reactions, 117
Unsaturated acids, 786–790
α,β-Unsaturated acids, from malonic acid, 795
Unsaturated alcohols, 736
α,β-Unsaturated aldehydes, from ethynyl alkyl ethers, 737
  from malonic acid, 795
α,β-Unsaturated compounds, addition of diazonium salts, 496
α,β-Unsaturated carbonyl compounds, 762–765
  absorption spectra, 665, 762
Unsaturated dicarboxylic acids, 805
α,β-Unsaturated diketones, from 1,3-diketones, 773
α,β-Unsaturated esters, 803, 815
Unsaturated fat acids, 179, 180
  autoxidation, 883
Unsaturated hydrocarbons, *see* Alkenes *and* Alkynes
α,β-Unsaturated ketones, 804, 819
Unsaturated lactones, 824, 826, 870
Unsaturation electrons, 51
Unsaturation, estimation, 54, 551
Unsaturation, test, 54, 57, 263
unsym-, prefix, 51
Up-grading of drying oils, 187, 752
Uracil, 638
Uramil, 646
Uranine, 683
Urea, estimation, 312, 634
  inclusion compounds, 311
  reactions, 311–314
  as resolving agent, 344
  synthesis, 310
Urea-formaldehyde resins, 313, 314
Urea nitrate, 312
Ureas, *N*-substituted, 315, 319
  O-substituted, 319
Urease, 312
Ureids, 313
Urethan rubbers, 799
Urethans, 315
  from isocyanates, 317
Uric acid, 645
Uridylic acids, 644
Urinary calculi, 645
Uronic acids, 408
Urotropin, 222
Ursolic acid, 863
Urushiol, 516
U. S. proof, definition, 95

Vaccenic acid, 180
Vacuum distillation, 16
Valeric acid, 147
δ-Valerolactam, 784
Valerolactones, 780
Valine, 296
van der Waals forces, 38, 86, 197
Vanilla beans, 538
Vanilla flavor, 538
Vanillic acid, 561
Vanillin, 527, 538
Vanillyl alcohol, 538
Vanillylamine, 650
Van Slyke method for amino nitrogen, 306
van't Hoff, biography, 335
Vapor-phase rust inhibitors, 239, 843
Varnish, 187
Vaseline, 82
Vat dyes, 675
    anthraquinone, 689
    carbazole derivatives, 689
    complex carbocyclics, 690
    hydroazines, 689
    indigoid, 683
    indophenols, 692
    sulfur, 691
Vat Orange R, 687
Vat Red B, 687
Vegetable fats and oils, 181
Veratral, 538
Veratric acid, 561
Veratrole, 516
Verdigris, 159
Veronal, 640
Versene, 755
Vetivazulene, 859
β-Vetivone, 859
Vibrational spectra, 657
Victor Meyer apparatus for molecular weight determination, 21
Victor Meyer esterification law, 549
Vieboeck and Schwappach modification of Zeisel determination, 140
Vinegar, 158
Vinyl acetate, 736
    in polyester resins, 807
Vinylacetic acid, 786
Vinylacetylene, 719, 765
Vinyl alcohol, 736
Vinyl alkyl ethers, 737
Vinylbenzene, *see* Styrene, 573
N-Vinylcarbazole, 617
Vinyl chloride, 725
Vinyl esters from α,β-unsaturated ketones, 876
Vinyl group, directive influence, 454
Vinylidene chloride, 726
Vinylite resins, 736
Vinyl methyl ether, 737

Vinyl plastics, 726, 736
Vinylpyridines, 626
N-Vinylpyrrolidone, 785
Vinyltoluenes, 575
Vinyltrichlorosilane, 914
Vinyon, 736
Violaxanthin, 866
Violet odor, 853
Violuric acid, 646
Virus, tobacco mosaic, 296
Viscose rayon, 405
Viscosity of alkanes, 40
Viscosity index of lubricating oils, 81
Visible light, 670
Visible spectra, 661
Visual color and absorption, 670
Visual purple, 860
Vitalistic theory, 3
Vitamins, A, 860
    B complex, 414
    B$_1$, 641
    B$_2$, 647
    B$_6$, 628
    B$_{12}$, 615
    C, 387
    D, 868, 869
    E, 632
    K, 593
Vitellin, 295
Volatile oils, 849
VPI, 239, 843
Vulcalok process, 713
Vulcanization, 710

van der Waals forces, 38, 86, 197
Wagner-Meerwein rearrangement, 857
Walden, biography, 347
Walden inversion, 116, 346
Wallach, biography, 855
Walnut stain, 593
Warfarin, 563
War gases, *see* Poison gases
Water, addition to aldehydes and ketones, 202
Watermelon pigment, 864
Wavenumber, 659
Waxes, animal, 178
    paraffin, 82
    synthetic, 61, 744
    vegetable, 41, 178
Weizmann, biography, 224
Werner, biography, 340
Wetting agents, 187
Whale oil, 181, 182
White light, 670
White oils, 82
Wijs solution, 184
Willgerodt reaction, 540
Williamson, biography, 137

Williamson synthesis, 137
Willow bark, 525
Willstaetter, biography, 845
Wintergreen oil, 560
Wislicenus, biography, 817
Woad, 683, 686
Woehler, biography, 3
   synthesis of urea, 311, 315
Wolff-Kishner reduction, 216
Wood, 400
Wood alcohol, 89
Wood distillation, 89
Wood pulp, 400
Wood tar, 89
   pyrocatechol from, 516
Wool, 299
   synthetic, 299
Wool grease, 178, 863
Wort, 91
Wurster salts, 572
Wurtz, biography, 126
Wurtz-Fittig reaction, 435
Wurtz reaction, 126

Xanthates, 324
Xanthene dyes, 683
Xanthic acid, 324
Xanthine, 643
Xanthins, 865
Xanthone, 633
Xanthophylls, 865
Xanthoproteic reaction, 306
Xanthopterin, 647

Xanthydrol, 634
Xylans, 407
Xylenes, 420, 429
Xylenols, 502
   in coal tar, 428
Xylidines, 487
Xylocaine, 487
*Xylo*hexulose, 384
Xylose, 361
Xylulose, 384
Xylyl groups, 421

Yellow enzymes, 647
Yellow pigments, 697, 865
Yield, definition, 59
Ylang-ylang oil, 853
Ylides, 243, 909
Yttrium compounds, 898

Zeaxanthin, 865
Zein, 299
Zeisel determination of methoxyl and
   ethoxyl, 140
Z-enzyme, 397
Zerevitinov determination of reactive hy-
   drogen, 122
Zerlate, 325
Zinc compounds, 893
Zinc dust distillations, 504, 684
Zinc reductions, mechanism, 219
Zinc stearate, 192
Zoosterols, 868
Zwitter ions, 299
Zymase, fermentation by, 91

PERIODIC TABLE OF THE ELEMENTS

Period \ Group	I a	I b	II a	II b	III a	III b	IV a	IV b	V a	V b	VI a	VI b	VII a	VII b	VIII	0
1	1 H															2 He
2	3 Li		4 Be			5 B		6 C		7 N		8 O		9 F		10 Ne
3	11 Na		12 Mg			13 Al		14 Si		15 P		16 S		17 Cl		18 A
4	19 K	29 Cu	20 Ca	30 Zn	21 Sc	31 Ga	22 Ti	32 Ge	23 V	33 As	24 Cr	34 Se	25 Mn	35 Br	26 Fe 27 Co 28 Ni	36 Kr
5	37 Rb	47 Ag	38 Sr	48 Cd	39 Y	49 In	40 Zr	50 Sn	41 Nb	51 Sb	42 Mo	52 Te	43 Tc	53 I	44 Ru 45 Rh 46 Pd	54 Xe
6	55 Cs	79 Au	56 Ba	80 Hg	57 La 58-71 rare earths	81 Tl	72 Hf	82 Pb	73 Ta	83 Bi	74 W	84 Po	75 Re	85 At	76 Os 77 Ir 78 Pt	86 Rn